CW00429290

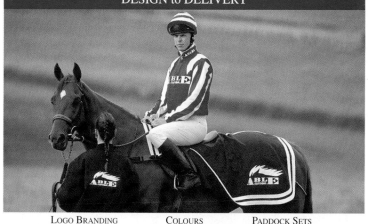

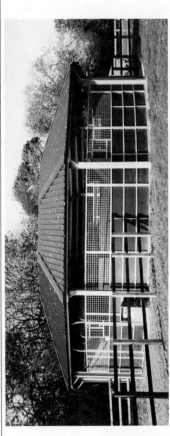

105th
YEAR OF PUBLICATION

Raceform

HORSES

in Training 1998

ISBN 1 901100 70 7

INDEX TO GENERAL CONTENTS

Editor; Len Bell; Orbit House, Albert Street, Eccles, Manchester, M30 0BL.
Tel: 0161 789 3237
Fax 0161 788 9152

Production Editor; Alan Mosley; Eclipse Pedigrees, Weatherbys, Sanders Road, Wellingborough, NN8 4BX.

Orders; Raceform Ltd., Compton, Newbury, Berkshire, RG20 6NL. Tel: 01635 578080
Fax: 01635 578101 E-mail: orders@raceform.co.uk

Advertisements; Tanya Liddiard; Compton, Newbury, Berkshire, RG20 6NL.
Tel: 01635 578128, Fax: 01635 578101

Printed by Woolnough Bookbinding Ltd., Irthlingborough, Northamptonshire, NN9 5SE.
Distributed to the Newstrade by MMC, Octagon House, White Hart Meadows, Ripley, Woking, Surrey, GU23 6HR. Tel: 01483 211222

www.raceform.co.uk.

INDEX TO ADVERTISERS

1998

RACING FIXTURES AND SALE DATES

Flat fixtures are in **Black Type**; Jump in Light Type; Irish in *Italic*; French in ***Italic***; asterisk (☆) indicates an evening meeting;
† indicates an All Weather meeting. Sale dates are at foot of fixtures.

Fixtures and sales dates are subject to alteration.

Owners names are shown against their horses where this information is available. In the case of Partnerships and Syndicates, the nominated owner is given alongside the horse with other owners listed below the team.

Foaling dates are shown for two-year-olds where these are provided.

JANUARY

Sun	Mon	Tues	Wed	Thur	Fri	Sat
				1 Catterick Cheltenham Exeter Leicester **Lingfield†** Windsor *Fairyhouse* *Tramore*	**2** Ayr Newbury **Southwell†**	**3** **Lingfield†** Musselburgh Newbury Uttoxeter *Naas*
4	**5** Folkestone **Southwell†**	**6** **Lingfield†** Ludlow *Thurles*	**7** Lingfield Musselburgh **Wolverhampton†** *Downpatrick*	**8** Catterick **Lingfield†** Market Rasen	**9** Exeter **Southwell†** Towcester	**10** Haydock **Lingfield†** Sandown Warwick **Wolverhampton †☆** *Leopardstown*
11 *Navan*	**12** Plumpton **Southwell†** Keeneland Sales	**13** Leicester **Lingfield†** Keeneland Sales	**14** Folkestone Sedgefield **Wolverhampton†** Keeneland Sales	**15** **Lingfield†** Wetherby Wincanton *Tramore* Keeneland Sales	**16** Kempton Musselburgh **Southwell†** Keeneland Sales	**17** Ascot **Lingfield†** Newcastle Warwick *Naas*
18 *Fairyhouse*	**19** Fontwell **Southwell†**	**20** Carlisle **Lingfield†**	**21** Huntingdon Windsor **Wolverhampton†** *Down Royal*	**22** **Lingfield†** Ludlow Taunton	**23** Ascot Kelso **Southwell†**	**24** Catterick Haydock Kempton **Lingfield†** **Wolverhampton †☆** *Thurles*
25 *Leopardstown*	**26** **Southwell†** Windsor	**27** Leicester **Lingfield†** Doncaster Sales	**28** Lingfield Sedgefield **Wolverhampton†** Doncaster Sales	**29** Huntingdon **Lingfield†** Wincanton *Gowran Park* Doncaster Sales	**30** Doncaster Folkestone **Southwell†**	**31** Ayr Cheltenham Doncaster **Lingfield†** *Fairyhouse*

FEBRUARY

Sun	Mon	Tues	Wed	Thur	Fri	Sat
1 *Naas* Fasig-Tipton Sales	**2** Plumpton **Southwell†**	**3** **Lingfield†** Musselburgh Malvern Sales	**4** Leicester Windsor **Wolverhampton†**	**5** Kelso **Lingfield†** Towcester *Clonmel*	**6** Catterick Lingfield **Southwell†**	**7** **Lingfield†** Sandown Uttoxeter Wetherby **Wolverhampton †☆** *Naas*
8 *Leopardstown* Fasig-Tipton Sales	**9** Fontwell Newcastle **Southwell†** Goffs Sales	**10** Carlisle **Lingfield†** Warwick Goffs Sales	**11** Ascot Ludlow **Wolverhampton†** *Navan*	**12** Huntingdon **Lingfield†** Wincanton Deauville Sales	**13** Bangor-on-Dee Newbury **Southwell†**	**14** Ayr Catterick **Lingfield†** Market Rasen Newbury *Thurles*
15 *Fairyhouse*	**16** Hereford Plumpton **Southwell†**	**17** Leicester **Lingfield†** Sedgefield	**18** Lingfield Musselburgh **Wolverhampton†**	**19** **Lingfield†** Sandown Taunton *Clonmel*	**20** Fakenham Sandown **Southwell†**	**21** Chepstow **Lingfield†** Newcastle Warwick Windsor **Wolverhampton †☆** *Gowran Park*
22 *Navan*	**23** Fontwell **Southwell†** Fasig-Tipton Sales	**24** Doncaster **Lingfield†** Fasig-Tipton Ascot Sales	**25** Folkestone Sedgefield **Wolverhampton†** ***M-Laffitte***	**26** Huntingdon **Lingfield†** Wincanton *Thurles*	**27** Haydock Kempton **Southwell†** ***Saint-Cloud***	**28** Haydock Kempton **Lingfield†** Musselburgh ***Naas***

MARCH

Sun	Mon	Tues	Wed	Thur	Fri	Sat
1 *Fairyhouse*	**2** Newcastle Plumpton **Southwell†**	**3** Catterick Leicester **Lingfield†** ***M-Laffitte***	**4** Chepstow Wetherby **Wolverhampton†** *Downpatrick*	**5** Lingfield Ludlow Taunton ***Saint-Cloud*** Tattersalls (IRE) Sales	**6** Doncaster Kelso Newbury ***M-Laffitte*** Tattersalls (IRE) Sales	**7** Doncaster Huntingdon Newbury Warwick **Wolverhampton †☆** *Listowel* ***Saint-Cloud***
8 *Leopardstown*	**9** Newton Abbot **Southwell†**	**10** Exeter Leicester Sedgefield ***M-Laffitte***	**11** Bangor-on-Dee Catterick **Southwell†**	**12** Carlisle Towcester Wincanton *Tramore* ***Saint-Cloud***	**13** Ayr Market Rasen Sandown ***M-Laffitte***	**14** Ayr Chepstow Sandown **Wolverhampton†** *Navan* ***Saint-Cloud***
15 *Naas*	**16** Plumpton Stratford Taunton	**17** Cheltenham Sedgefield **Southwell†** *Down Royal* *Limerick* Fasig-Tipton Sales	**18** Cheltenham Huntingdon Newton Abbot	**19** Cheltenham Hexham **Lingfield†** ***M-Laffitte***	**20** Fakenham Folkestone **Southwell†**	**21** Hereford Lingfield Newcastle Uttoxeter **Wolverhampton †☆** *Gowran Park*
22 *Leopardstown* *Limerick*	**23** Newcastle **Southwell†** Russell Baldwin & Bright Breeze-Up Sales (at Wolverhampton)	**24** Chepstow Fontwell Uttoxeter ***M-Laffitte*** Ascot Sales	**25** Exeter Ludlow Towcester *Downpatrick*	**26** **Doncaster** Plumpton Wincanton *Wexford* ***Saint-Cloud*** Doncaster Sales	**27** **Doncaster** Kelso Newbury ***M-Laffitte*** Doncaster Sales	**28** Bangor-on-Dee **Doncaster** Newbury **Warwick** (mixed) **Wolverhampton †☆** *Clonmel* Doncaster Sales
29 *Curragh*	**30** **Hamilton** Hexham **Lingfield†** Doncaster Sales	**31** **Newcastle** (mixed) **Nottingham** Sandown ***Saint-Cloud***				

APRIL

Sun	Mon	Tues	Wed	Thur	Fri	Sat
			1	**2**	**3**	**4**
			Ascot **Catterick** **Folkestone** ***M-Laffitte***	Aintree **Leicester** Taunton *Tipperary* ***Longchamp***	Aintree **Lingfield†** Sedgefield Goffs France Sales	Aintree **Hamilton** Hereford **Wolverhampton †☆** Goffs France Sales
5	**6**	**7**	**8**	**9**	**10**	**11**
Curragh ***Longchamp***	Fontwell Kelso **Southwell†** ***M-Laffitte***	**Folkestone** **Nottingham** **Wolverhampton†** *Gowran Park*	Ascot Ludlow **Ripon** ***Saint-Cloud***	**Leicester** **Lingfield†** **Musselburgh** ***M-Laffitte***		Carlisle **Haydock** **Kempton** Newton Abbot Plumpton Towcester **Wolverhampton †☆** *Down Royal* *Naas*
12	**13**	**14**	**15**	**16**	**17**	**18**
Cork Carlisle Chepstow Fakenham Hereford Huntingdon **Kempton** Market Rasen **Newcastle** (mixed)	**Nottingham** Plumpton Towcester Uttoxeter **Warwick** Wetherby Wincanton *Cork* *Fairyhouse* ***Longchamp***	Exeter **Newmarket** Uttoxeter Wetherby *Fairyhouse* ***Saint-Cloud*** Keeneland Goffs France Sales	Cheltenham **Newmarket** **Pontefract** *Fairyhouse* Keeneland Tattersalls Sales	Cheltenham **Newmarket** **Ripon** *Ballinrobe* ***Longchamp*** Tattersalls Sales	Ayr **Newbury** **Thirsk**	Ayr Bangor-on-Dee **Newbury** Stratford **Thirsk** **Wolverhampton †☆** *Listowel*
19	**20**	**21**	**22**	**23**	**24**	**25**
Leopardstown *Listowel* ***Longchamp***	**Brighton** Hexham **Nottingham** ***Chantilly***	Chepstow **Folkestone** **Pontefract**	**Epsom** Perth **Redcar** Towcester ***M-Laffitte***	**Beverley** Fontwell Perth *Clonmel* ***Longchamp***	**Carlisle** Ludlow☆ Perth **Sandown** Taunton☆ Warwick☆ ***Chantilly***	**Leicester** Market Rasen **Ripon** **Sandown** (mixed) Sedgefield☆ **Wolverhampton †☆** Worcester☆ *Navan*
26	**27**	**28**	**29**	**30**		
Cork ***Longchamp***	**Pontefract** **Southwell†** *Sligo☆* ***Saint-Cloud*** Fasig-Tipton Sales	Ascot☆ **Bath** Huntingdon☆ **Nottingham** *Punchestown*	**Ascot** Cheltenham☆ Exeter Kelso☆ Plumpton *Punchestown* ***Chantilly***	**Brighton** **Redcar** **Wolverhampton†** *Punchestown* ***Longchamp***		

Scotts
OF THRAPSTON

MAY

Sun	Mon	Tues	Wed	Thur	Fri	Sat
31 *Sligo* *Tralee* ***Chantilly***					**1** Bangor-on-Dee☆ **Musselburgh** **Newmarket** Newton Abbot Sedgefield☆ ***Saint-Cloud*** Ascot Sales	**2** **Haydock** (mixed) Hereford Hexham **Newmarket** **Thirsk** Uttoxeter *Curragh*
3 **Hamilton** **Newmarket** **Salisbury** *Gowran Park* ***Chantilly*** *Navan*	**4** **Doncaster** Fontwell **Kempton** Ludlow **Newcastle** Southwell Towcester **Warwick** *Down Royal* *Limerick*	**5** **Brighton** **Chester** Exeter ***Longchamp*** Fasig-Tipton Sales	**6** Chepstow **Chester** **Musselburgh** Uttoxeter☆ Wetherby☆ ***Saint-Cloud***	**7** **Chester** **Hamilton** **Southwell†** *Tipperary☆*	**8** **Carlisle** **Lingfield** **Nottingham** Stratford☆ Wincanton☆ *Dundalk☆*	**9** **Beverley** Hexham **Lingfield** Worcester *Fairyhouse*
10 **Bath** **Beverley** **Haydock** *Killarney* *Leopardstown* ***Longchamp***	**11** **Redcar** **Southwell†** Towcester☆ **Windsor☆** *Killarney☆* Doncaster Sales	**12** Hereford **York** *Killarney☆* ***Saint-Cloud*** Doncaster Sales	**13** Chepstow Folkestone☆ Huntingdon☆ **Lingfield†** Perth☆ **York** *Navan☆* ***Chantilly*** Doncaster Sales	**14** Perth **Salisbury** **York** *Clonmel☆* ***Longchamp*** Doncaster Sales	**15** Aintree☆ **Hamilton☆** **Newbury** **Newmarket** Stratford☆ **Thirsk** *Downpatrick☆* ***Saint-Cloud***	**16** Bangor-on-Dee **Newbury** **Nottingham** **Thirsk** *Cork* *Downpatrick*
17 Fakenham **Kempton** **Ripon** *Naas* ***Longchamp***	**18** **Bath** **Musselburgh☆** **Southwell†** **Windsor☆** *Roscommon☆* ***Chantilly*** Baden-Baden Fasig-Tipton Sales	**19** **Beverley** **Goodwood** ***Saint-Cloud*** Fasig-Tipton Sales	**20** **Goodwood** Kelso Newton Abbot☆ Uttoxeter☆ Worcester *Leopardstown☆*	**21** Exeter **Goodwood** **Newcastle** *Tipperary☆* ***Longchamp***	**22** **Brighton** **Haydock** **Nottingham** **Pontefract☆** Towcester☆ *Dundalk☆* ***Saint-Cloud***	**23** Cartmel **Doncaster** **Haydock** Hexham **Kempton** **Lingfield☆** **Warwick☆** *Curragh*
24 *Curragh* Cartmel	**25** **Chepstow** Fontwell Hereford Huntingdon **Leicester** **Redcar** **Sandown** Uttoxeter Wetherby *Kilbeggan☆*	**26** Hexham☆ **Leicester** **Redcar** **Sandown☆** ***Longchamp*** Malvern Sales	**27** Cartmel **Folkestone** **Newbury☆** **Ripon☆** **Yarmouth** *Fairyhouse☆* ***Saint-Cloud*** Goffs France Sales	**28** **Ayr** **Brighton** Uttoxeter *Clonmel☆*	**29** **Ayr** **Bath☆** **Catterick** Stratford☆ **Wolverhampton†** *Down Royal☆* *Wexford☆* ***Saint-Cloud***	**30** **Catterick** **Kempton☆** **Lingfield** Market Rasen☆ **Musselburgh☆** **Newmarket** Stratford *Gowran Park* ***Chantilly***

JUNE

Sun	Mon	Tues	Wed	Thur	Fri	Sat
31	1	2	3	4	5	6
	Hamilton Hereford☆ **Leicester** **Thirsk☆** **Windsor☆** *Leopardstown* *Tralee*	**Brighton** **Pontefract** ***Saint-Cloud*** Ascot Sales	**Beverley☆** **Chester☆** **Folkestone☆** **Goodwood** **Newcastle** **Warwick**	**Haydock** Perth **Yarmouth** *Tipperary☆* ***Chantilly***	**Catterick** **Epsom** **Goodwood☆** **Haydock☆** Perth☆ **Southwell†** *Curragh☆*	**Doncaster** **Epsom** **Haydock** **Newmarket☆** Newton Abbot☆ **Wolverhampton** **†☆** Worcester *Cork* ***M-Laffitte***
7	8	9	10	11	12	13
Roscommon ***Chantilly***	**Nottingham** **Pontefract** **Warwick☆** **Windsor☆** *Roscommon☆*	**Redcar** **Salisbury** *Laytown☆* ***Saint-Cloud*** Goffs Sales	**Beverley** **Hamilton☆** **Kempton☆** **Salisbury** Uttoxeter☆ *Leopardstown☆*	**Carlisle** **Newbury** **Yarmouth** ***Chantilly***	**Chepstow☆** **Goodwood☆** Market Rasen☆ **Sandown** **Southwell†** **York** *Wexford☆* ***M-Laffitte***	**Bath** Hexham☆ **Leicester☆** **Lingfield☆** Market Rasen **Sandown** **York** *Cork* *Navan*
14	15	16	17	18	19	20
Gowran Park	**Brighton** **Musselburgh** **Pontefract☆** **Windsor☆** *Kilbeggan☆* ***Chantilly***	**Royal Ascot** **Thirsk** ***M-Laffitte***	**Royal Ascot** **Hamilton** **Nottingham☆** **Ripon☆** **Wolverhampton†** Worcester☆ *Naas☆*	**Royal Ascot** **Ripon** **Southwell†** *Ballinrobe☆* ***Longchamp***	**Royal Ascot** **Ayr** **Goodwood☆** Hexham☆ **Newmarket☆** **Redcar** *Tipperary☆* ***Chantilly***	**Ascot** **Ayr** **Lingfield☆** Newton Abbot **Redcar** Southwell☆ **Wolverhampton** **†☆** *Thurles*
21	22	23	24	25	26	27
Clonmel ***Longchamp***	**Musselburgh** **Nottingham** **Windsor☆** **Yarmouth☆** *Sligo☆* ***Chantilly***	**Beverley** **Lingfield**	**Carlisle** **Chester☆** **Epsom☆** **Hamilton☆** **Salisbury** **Warwick** *Dundalk☆*	**Carlisle** **Newcastle** **Salisbury** *Tipperary☆* Tattersalls (Ire) Sales	**Folkestone** **Goodwood☆** **Newcastle☆** **Newmarket** Stratford☆ **Wolverhampton†** *Curragh☆* ***M-Laffitte*** Tattersalls (Ire) Sales	**Bath** **Doncaster☆** **Lingfield☆** **Newcastle** **Newmarket** Newton Abbot☆ Worcester *Curragh* ***Longchamp***
28	29	30				
Doncaster **Goodwood** Uttoxeter *Curragh* ***Saint-Cloud***	**Musselburgh☆** **Pontefract** **Southwell†** **Windsor☆** Doncaster Sales	**Chepstow** **Hamilton** *Cork☆* ***M-Laffitte*** Ascot Sales				

JULY

Sun	Mon	Tues	Wed	Thur	Fri	Sat
			1 **Brighton** **Kempton☆** **Redcar** **Yarmouth☆** *Bellewstown☆* ***Chantilly***	**2** **Catterick** **Haydock** **Yarmouth** *Bellewstown☆* Goffs France Sales	**3** **Beverley☆** **Hamilton☆** **Haydock☆** Market Rasen **Sandown** **Warwick** *Bellewstown☆*	**4** **Beverley** **Carlisle☆** **Chepstow** **Haydock** **Nottingham☆** **Sandown** Wolverhampton☆ *Leopardstown* ***Deauville***
5 *Naas*	**6** **Bath** **Musselburgh** Newton Abbot☆ **Ripon☆** **Windsor☆** *Roscommon☆* ***Chantilly***	**7** **Newmarket** **Pontefract** Tattersalls Malvern Sales	**8** **Folkestone** **Kempton☆** **Newmarket** Worcester☆ *Wexford☆* ***M-Laffitte*** Tattersalls Sales	**9** **Lingfield** **Newmarket** **Southwell†** *Tipperary☆* Tattersalls Sales	**10** **Chepstow☆** **Chester☆** **Hamilton☆** **Lingfield** **Wolverhampton†** **York** *Gowran Park☆* ***Deauville***	**11** **Chester** **Lingfield** **Salisbury** Sedgefield☆ **Southwell†☆** **Warwick☆** **York** *Limerick*
12 **Haydock** **Newbury** Stratford *Curragh* ***Deauville***	**13** **Ayr** **Brighton** **Windsor☆** Wolverhampton☆ *Dundalk☆* *Killarney☆* ***Deauville***	**14** **Beverley** **Brighton** *Down Royal* *Killarney* ***Deauville***	**15** **Catterick** **Doncaster☆** **Folkestone** **Sandown☆** Worcester☆ **Yarmouth** *Down Royal☆* *Killarney* ***M-Laffitte***	**16** **Bath** **Doncaster** **Leicester** *Killarney*	**17** **Carlisle** **Newbury** **Newmarket☆** **Pontefract☆** **Salisbury☆** **Southwell†** *Kilbeggan☆* ***Chantilly***	**18** **Ayr☆** **Newbury** **Newmarket** **Nottingham** **Redcar☆** **Ripon** **Warwick☆** *Leopardstown*
19 *Tipperary* ***M-Laffitte***	**20** **Ayr** **Beverley☆** **Windsor☆** **Wolverhampton†** *Ballinrobe☆* Keeneland Sales	**21** **Bath** **Yarmouth** *Ballinrobe☆* ***Chantilly*** Keeneland Sales	**22** **Catterick** **Leicester☆** **Sandown☆** Worcester *Naas☆* ***M-Laffitte*** Keeneland Fasig-Tipton Sales	**23** **Brighton** **Sandown** Sedgefield	**24** **Ascot** **Chepstow☆** **Newmarket☆** **Nottingham☆** **Thirsk** **Wolverhampton†** *Wexford☆*	**25** **Ascot** **Lingfield☆** Market Rasen **Newcastle** **Redcar☆** **Southwell†☆** Stratford *Curragh* ***M-Laffitte***
26	**27** **Folkestone** **Newcastle** **Windsor☆** **Yarmouth☆** *Galway☆*	**28** **Beverley** **Goodwood** *Galway☆* Ascot Sales	**29** **Doncaster☆** **Epsom☆** **Goodwood** Sedgefield *Galway*	**30** **Doncaster** **Goodwood** Newton Abbot *Galway*	**31** Bangor-on-Dee **Goodwood** **Newmarket☆** **Salisbury☆** **Thirsk** *Galway☆*	

AUGUST

Sun	Mon	Tues	Wed	Thur	Fri	Sat
30 *Wexford* ***Deauville*** Cartmel **Chepstow** **Epsom** Fontwell	**31** Huntingdon **Newcastle** Newton Abbot **Ripon** Southwell **Warwick** *Downpatrick* Fasig-Tipton Sales					**1** **Goodwood** **Hamilton**☆ **Lingfield**☆ Market Rasen☆ **Newmarket** **Thirsk** Worcester *Galway* ***Deauville***
2 **Chester** **Newcastle** **Sandown** *Cork* ***Deauville***	**3** **Carlisle**☆ Newton Abbot **Ripon** **Windsor**☆ *Cork* *Leopardstown*	**4** **Bath** **Catterick** *Roscommon*☆ ***Deauville***	**5** **Brighton** **Kempton**☆ **Leicester**☆ **Newcastle** **Pontefract** **Yarmouth**☆ *Sligo*☆	**6** **Folkestone** **Haydock** *Sligo*☆ ***Deauville***	**7** **Ascot** **Haydock**☆ **Newmarket**☆ **Salisbury** **Wolverhampton**† Worcester☆ *Kilbeggan*☆	**8** **Ascot** **Haydock** **Newmarket** **Redcar** *Wexford* ***Deauville***
9 **Epsom** **Redcar** **Yarmouth** *Leopardstown* ***Deauville***	**10** **Leicester**☆ **Thirsk**☆ **Windsor** Worcester *Cork*☆ Doncaster Sales	**11** **Ayr** **Bath** *Gowran Park*☆ ***Deauville*** Doncaster Fasig-Tipton Sales	**12** **Beverley** **Brighton** **Hamilton**☆ **Nottingham**☆ **Salisbury** **Sandown**☆ *Gowran Park*☆ ***Deauville*** Fasig-Tipton Sales	**13** **Beverley** **Chepstow** *Tramore*☆ Fasig-Tipton Tattersalls (Ire) Sales	**14** **Catterick**☆ **Folkestone** **Newbury** **Southwell**† **Warwick**☆ *Tramore*☆ Tattersalls (Ire) Sales	**15** Bangor-on-Dee **Newbury** **Ripon** Stratford *Curragh* *Tramore* ***Deauville***
16 **Lingfield** Newton Abbot **Pontefract** *Dundalk* *Tramore* ***Deauville*** Fasig-Tipton Sales	**17** **Hamilton** **Windsor** *Roscommon*☆	**18** **Brighton** **York** Fasig-Tipton Goffs Sales	**19** **Kempton**☆ **Leicester**☆ **Musselburgh** **York** *Dundalk*☆ ***Deauville*** Goffs Sales	**20** **Salisbury** **Yarmouth** **York** *Tipperary*☆	**21** **Chester** Perth **Sandown** *Kilbeggan*☆	**22** **Chester** **Lingfield**☆ Market Rasen☆ Perth **Ripon** **Sandown** **Wolverhampton** †☆ *Fairyhouse* ***Deauville*** Deauville Sales
23 *Leopardstown* ***Deauville*** Deauville Sales	**24** **Beverley** **Brighton** *Tralee*☆ Deauville Sales	**25** **Lingfield** **Pontefract** *Tralee* ***Deauville*** Deauville Sales	**26** **Carlisle** **Lingfield** Worcester *Tralee* Deauville Sales	**27** Cartmel☆ **Folkestone** **Musselburgh** *Tralee* Deauville Sales	**28** **Goodwood** **Newmarket** **Thirsk** *Tralee* **Beverley** Cartmel	**29** **Goodwood** **Newmarket** **Nottingham**☆ **Redcar**☆ **Windsor**☆ *Curragh* *Tralee* ***Deauville*** Baden-Baden Sales

SEPTEMBER

Sun	Mon	Tues	Wed	Thur	Fri	Sat
		1 **Ripon** Uttoxeter *Sligo☆* ***Longchamp*** Fasig-Tipton Ascot Sales	**2** **Brighton** Newton Abbot **York** *Dundalk* ***Chantilly***	**3** Fontwell **Salisbury** **York** *Clonmel*	**4** **Epsom** **Haydock** Sedgefield *Kilbeggan*	**5** **Epsom** **Haydock** Stratford **Thirsk** **Wolverhampton †☆** *Cork* Baden-Baden Sales
6 *Ballinrobe* *Curragh* ***Longchamp***	**7** **Bath** **Hamilton** *Galway*	**8** **Leicester** **Lingfield** **Newcastle** *Galway* ***Longchamp*** Doncaster Sales	**9** **Doncaster** **Kempton** *Galway* ***Chantilly*** Doncaster Sales	**10** **Chepstow** **Doncaster** Newton Abbot Doncaster Sales	**11** **Doncaster** **Goodwood** Worcester *Downpatrick* Doncaster Sales	**12** Bangor-on-Dee **Doncaster** **Goodwood** Worcester *Leopardstown* Doncaster Sales
13 ***Longchamp***	**14** **Musselburgh** **Nottingham** Plumpton *Roscommon* ***Chantilly*** Keeneland Sales	**15** **Sandown** Sedgefield **Yarmouth** ***Saint-Cloud*** Keeneland Sales	**16** **Beverley** **Sandown** **Yarmouth** *Fairyhouse* Keeneland Sales	**17** **Ayr** **Newbury** **Yarmouth** *Gowran Park* ***Longchamp*** Keeneland Sales	**18** **Ayr** Huntingdon **Newbury** ***Chantilly*** Keeneland Sales	**19** **Ayr** Carlisle **Catterick** Market Rasen **Newbury** **Wolverhampton †☆** *Curragh* *Down Royal* ***Longchamp*** Keeneland Sales
20 *Curragh* Keeneland Sales	**21** Hereford **Kempton** **Leicester** *Listowel* Keeneland Sales	**22** **Beverley** Fontwell **Warwick** *Listowel* ***Chantilly*** Keeneland Tattersalls (Ire) Sales	**23** **Chester** **Goodwood** Perth *Listowel* ***M-Laffitte*** Keeneland Tattersalls (Ire) Sales	**24** **Goodwood** Perth **Pontefract** *Listowel* Keeneland Doncaster Sales	**25** **Folkestone** **Haydock** **Redcar** *Listowel* ***Saint-Cloud*** Doncaster Sales	**26** **Ascot** **Haydock** **Nottingham** Worcester *Listowel*
27 **Ascot** Huntingdon **Musselburgh**	**28** **Bath** **Hamilton**	**29** **Newmarket** Sedgefield **Southwell†** ***M-Laffitte*** Ascot Tattersalls Sales	**30** **Brighton** **Newcastle** **Salisbury** ***Saint-Cloud*** Tattersalls Goffs France Sales			

OCTOBER

Sun	Mon	Tues	Wed	Thur	Fri	Sat
				1 Hereford **Newmarket** Taunton *Punchestown* Tattersalls Sales	**2** Hexham **Lingfield** **Newmarket** ***M-Laffitte***	**3** **Catterick** Chepstow **Newmarket** Uttoxeter **Wolverhampton** †☆ *Curragh* *Down Royal* ***Longchamp*** Goffs France Sales
4 Kelso Market Rasen **Warwick** *Tipperary* ***Longchamp***	**5** **Brighton** **Pontefract** Southwell Fasig-Tipton Sales	**6** Fontwell **Nottingham** **Redcar** Fasig-Tipton Goffs Sales	**7** Exeter Towcester **York** *Fairyhouse* ***Saint-Cloud*** Goffs Sales	**8** Ludlow Plumpton Wincanton **York** *Thurles* ***Longchamp*** Goffs Sales	**9** **Ascot** Carlisle Huntingdon *Downpatrick* ***M-Laffitte***	**10** **Ascot** Bangor-on-Dee Hexham Worcester **York** *Cork*
11 *Naas* ***Longchamp***	**12** **Ayr** **Leicester** Newton Abbot *Roscommon* Tattersalls Sales	**13** **Ayr** **Leicester** Sedgefield ***M-Laffitte*** Tattersalls Sales	**14** **Haydock** **Nottingham** Wetherby *Gowran Park* Tattersalls Sales	**15** **Catterick** **Newmarket** Taunton ***Longchamp*** Tattersalls Sales	**16** **Catterick** Hereford **Newmarket** ***Saint-Cloud*** Tattersalls Sales	**17** Kelso Kempton **Newmarket** **Redcar** Stratford **Wolverhampton**†☆ *Curragh* *Down Royal* Fasig-Tipton Tattersalls Sales
18 *Limerick* ***Longchamp*** Fasig-Tipton Sales	**19** Plumpton **Pontefract** **Southwell**† ***Deauville*** Deauville Sales	**20** Exeter **Folkestone** **Yarmouth** ***Deauville*** Deauville Sales	**21** Chepstow **Newcastle** **Nottingham** *Navan* ***Deauville*** Deauville Doncaster Sales	**22** **Brighton** Ludlow **Nottingham** *Punchestown* ***Longchamp*** Doncaster Sales	**23** **Doncaster** Fakenham **Newbury** Doncaster Sales	**24** Carlisle **Doncaster** Market Rasen **Newbury** Worcester *Leopardstown* *Tipperary*
25 **Leicester** Wetherby Wincanton *Galway* *Wexford* ***Longchamp***	**26** Bangor-on-Dee **Leicester** **Lingfield** *Galway* *Leopardstown* Fasig-Tipton Tattersalls Sales	**27** **Bath** Cheltenham **Redcar** ***Saint-Cloud*** Fasig-Tipton Tattersalls Sales	**28** Cheltenham Fontwell **Yarmouth** Tattersalls Sales	**29** **Nottingham** Sedgefield Stratford ***Longchamp*** Tattersalls Sales	**30** **Newcastle** **Newmarket** Towcester Wetherby ***M-Laffitte*** Tattersalls Malvern Goffs Sales	**31** Ascot Kelso **Newmarket** Wetherby **Wolverhampton** †☆ *Navan* ***Saint-Cloud*** Baden-Baden Sales

NOVEMBER

Sun	Mon	Tues	Wed	Thur	Fri	Sat
1	**2**	**3**	**4**	**5**	**6**	**7**
Cork *Punchestown*	**Nottingham** Plumpton **Redcar** Tattersalls (Ire) Sales	**Catterick** Exeter Warwick ***M-Laffitte*** Tattersalls (Ire) Ascot Sales	Kempton **Musselburgh** Newton Abbot *Fairyhouse* Tattersalls (Ire) Sales	**Brighton** Haydock Towcester *Clonmel* Tattersalls (Ire) Goffs France Fasig-Tipton . Sales	**Doncaster** Hexham Uttoxeter *Curragh* ***M-Laffitte*** Tattersalls (Ire) Fasig-Tipton Sales	Chepstow **Doncaster** Sandown Uttoxeter Wincanton ***Naas*** ***Saint-Cloud*** Tattersalls (Ire) Sales
8	**9**	**10**	**11**	**12**	**13**	**14**
Clonmel *Leopardstown* Tattersalls (Ire) Fasig-Tipton Keeneland Sales	Carlisle Fontwell **Lingfield†** ***M-Laffitte*** Tattersalls (Ire) Fasig-Tipton Keeneland Sales	Huntingdon Newbury Sedgefield ***Saint-Cloud*** Tattersalls (Ire) Keeneland Sales	Kelso Newbury Worcester *Downpatrick* Tattersalls (Ire) Keeneland Sales	**Lingfield†** Ludlow Taunton *Thurles* Tattersalls (Ire) Keeneland Sales	Cheltenham Newcastle **Southwell†** Tattersalls (Ire) Keeneland Sales	Ayr Cheltenham Market Rasen Windsor **Wolverhampton** **†☆** *Punchestown* Keeneland Sales
15	**16**	**17**	**18**	**19**	**20**	**21**
Ayr Cheltenham Towcester *Navan* Keeneland Sales	Leicester Plumpton **Wolverhampton†** ***Saint-Cloud*** Keeneland Sales	**Lingfield†** Newton Abbot Wetherby ***M-Laffitte*** Keeneland Sales	Haydock Hereford Kempton ***Saint-Cloud*** Keeneland Malvern Sales	Sedgefield Warwick Wincanton *Tipperary*	Ascot Exeter **Southwell†**	Aintree Ascot Catterick Huntingdon *Naas*
22	**23**	**24**	**25**	**26**	**27**	**28**
Clonmel	Ludlow **Southwell†** Windsor ***M-Laffitte*** Doncaster Sales	Cheltenham **Lingfield†** Market Rasen Doncaster Fasig-Tipton Sales	Chepstow Hexham **Lingfield†** *Gowran Park* ***Saint-Cloud*** Doncaster Sales	Carlisle Taunton Uttoxeter Doncaster Goffs Sales	Bangor-on-Dee **Lingfield†** Newbury ***M-Laffitte*** Goffs Ascot Sales	Haydock Newbury Newcastle Warwick **Wolverhampton** **†☆** *Fairyhouse* ***Saint-Cloud*** Goffs Sales
29	**30**					
Fairyhouse Goffs Sales	Folkestone Kelso Worcester ***M-Laffitte*** Tattersalls Sales					

DECEMBER

Sun	Mon	Tues	Wed	Thur	Fri	Sat
		1 Newcastle Newton Abbot **Southwell†** ***Saint-Cloud*** Tattersalls Sales	**2** Catterick Fontwell **Wolverhampton†** Tattersalls Sales	**3** Leicester Wincanton Windsor Tattersalls Sales	**4** Exeter Hereford Sandown Tattersalls Sales	**5** Chepstow Sandown Towcester Wetherby **Wolverhampton†** *Cork* Tattersalls Sales
6 *Punchestown* Fasig-Tipton Sales	**7** Ayr Fakenham **Lingfield†** Tattersalls Fasig-Tipton Sales	**8** Huntingdon Plumpton Sedgefield *Clonmel* Tattersalls Sales	**9** Hexham Leicester **Lingfield†** Tattersalls Sales	**10** Ludlow Market Rasen Taunton Tattersalls Sales	**11** Cheltenham Doncaster **Lingfield†** Tattersalls Sales	**12** Cheltenham Doncaster Haydock Lingfield **Wolverhampton †☆** *Navan* Deauville Sales
13 *Thurles* Deauville Tattersalls (Ire) Sales	**14** Newcastle Newton Abbot Deauville Tattersalls (Ire) Sales	**15** Folkestone Hereford Musselburgh Goffs Sales	**16** Bangor-on-Dee Catterick **Wolverhampton†** Goffs Sales	**17** Catterick Exeter Towcester Goffs Sales	**18** Lingfield **Southwell†** Uttoxeter Goffs Sales	**19** Ascot **Lingfield†** Uttoxeter Warwick *Navan* Goffs Sales
20	**21** Kelso **Lingfield†** Ascot Sales	**22** Ludlow **Southwell†**	**23**	**24**	**25**	**26** Kempton Market Rasen Newton Abbot Sedgefield Wetherby Wincanton **Wolverhampton†** *Down Royal* *Leopardstown* *Limerick* Ayr Hereford Huntingdon
27 *Leopardstown* *Limerick*	**28** Chepstow Kempton Leicester Wetherby *Leopardstown* *Limerick*	**29** Haydock **Lingfield†** Musselburgh Taunton *Leopardstown* *Limerick*	**30** Carlisle Plumpton Stratford	**31** Catterick Fontwell Warwick *Punchestown*		

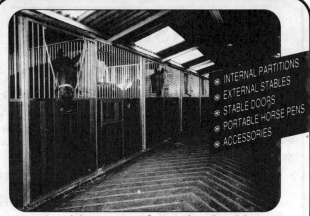

Front cover— John Dunlop's team at exercise in the picturesque setting of the Arundel estate on the South Downs in Sussex.

Photographs by Alan Johnson.

INDEX TO TRAINERS

† denotes Permit to train under N.H. Rules only

Name	Team No.
BELL, MR S. B.	043
BELMONT, MR FRANCOIS	044
†BENNETT, MR C. J.	045
BENNETT, MR J. A.	046
BENSTEAD, MR C. J.	047
BERRY, MR J.	048
BERRY, MR J. C. DE P	049
BERRY, MR N.	050
BEST, MR J. R.	051
BETHELL, MR J. D.	052
†BETHELL, MR W. A.	053
†BEVAN, MR E. G.	054
BEVAN, MR P. J.	055
†BICKERTON, MRS P. F.	056
†BILLINGE, MR J. N. R.	057
BIRKETT, MR J. J.	058
BISHOP, MR K.	059
†BLACK, MRS C. J.	060
†BLACKMORE, MR A. G.	061
BLANSHARD, MR M. T. W.	062
BOLGER, MR J. S.	063
BOLTON, MR M. J.	064
BOOTH, MR CHARLES B.	065
BOSLEY, MR M. R.	066
†BOUSFIELD, MR B.	067
BOWER, MISS L. J.	068
BOWLBY, MRS A. J.	069
BOWRING, MR S. R.	070
BRADBURNE, MRS S. C.	071
BRADLEY, MR J. M.	072
†BRADLEY, MR P.	073
BRADSTOCK, MR M. F.	074
BRAMALL, MRS S. A.	075
BRAVERY, MR G. C.	076
BRAZINGTON, MR R. G.	077
BRENNAN, MR OWEN	078
†BREWIS, MISS RHONA	079

Name	Team No.
BRIDGER, MR J. J.	080
BRIDGWATER, MR K. S.	081
BRISBOURNE, MR W. M.	082
BRITTAIN, MR C. E.	083
BRITTAIN, MR M. A.	084
BROMHEAD, MR H. DE	085
BROOKS, MR C. P. E.	086
BROOKSHAW, MR S. A.	087
BROTHERTON, MR R.	088
†BROWN, MR I. R.	089
BROWN, MRS J.	090
†BROWN, MR J. L.	091
†BROYD, MISS A. E.	092
BUCKLER, MR R. H.	093
†BUCKLEY, MRS J. R.	094
BUCKLEY, MR MARK	095
BURCHELL, MR DAVID	096
BURKE, MR K. R.	097
BUTLER, MR GERARD	098
BUTLER, MR P.	099
BYCROFT, MR N.	100

C

Name	Team No.
CALDWELL, MR T. H.	101
CALLAGHAN, MR N. A.	102
CALVER, MR P.	103
CAMACHO, MISS J. A.	104
CAMBIDGE, MR B. R.	105
CAMPBELL, MR I.	106
CAMPION, MR A. M.	107
CANDY, MR HENRY D. N.	108
†CAREY, MR D. N.	109
†CARO, MR D. J.	110
CARR, MR T. J.	111
CARROLL, MR A. W.	112
CARROLL, MR DECLAN	113

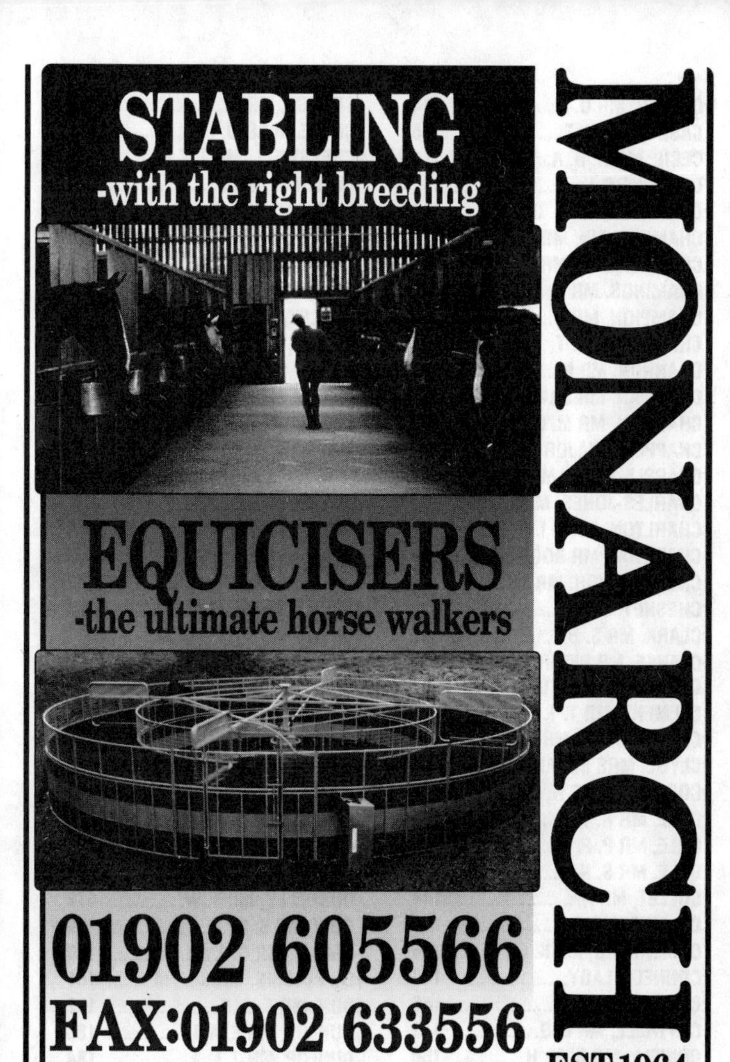
STABLING
-with the right breeding
EQUICISERS
-the ultimate horse walkers
01902 605566
FAX:01902 633556
MONARCH
EST.1964

Name	Team No.
†CARTER, MR O. J.	114
CASEY, MR W. T.	115
CECIL, MR H. R. A.	116
CECIL, MRS J	117
†CHADWICK, MR S. G.	118
CHAMBERLAIN, MR A. J.	119
CHAMBERLAIN, MR N.	120
CHAMINGS, MR P. R.	121
CHAMPION, MR R.	122
CHANCE, MR N. T.	123
CHANNON, MR M.	124
CHAPMAN, MR DAVID W.	125
CHAPMAN, MR M. C.	126
CHAPPELL, MAJOR D. N.	127
CHAPPLE-HYAM, MR P. W.	128
CHARLES-JONES, MR G. F. H.	129
CHARLTON, MR J. I. A.	130
CHARLTON, MR ROGER J.	131
CHEESBROUGH, MR P.	132
†CHESNEY, DR D.	133
†CLARK, MR S. B.	134
CLARKE, MR PETER C.	135
CLEMENT, MR NICOLAS	136
CLEMENT, MR T. T.	137
†CLUTTERBUCK, MR K. F.	138
†CLYDE, MRS SUSAN	139
†COCKBURN, MR R. G.	140
†COLE, MR H. T.	141
COLE, MR P. F. I.	142
COLE, MR S. N.	143
COLLET, MR R.	144
COLLINS, MR C.	145
COMERFORD, MR K. C.	146
†CONNELL, LADY	147
†COTON, MR F.	148
COTTRELL, MR L. G.	149
COWELL, MR R. M. H.	150

Name	Team No.
CRAGGS, MR R.	151
CRAZE, MISS J. F.	152
†CRESSWELL, MR J. K. S.	153
CULLINAN, MR J.	154
CUMANI, MR L. M.	155
CUNDELL, MR P. D.	156
CUNNINGHAM, MR M.	157
CUNNINGHAM-BROWN, MR K.	158
CURLEY, MR B. J.	159
†CURTIS, MR J. W. P.	160
CURTIS, MR R.	161
CUTHBERT, MR T. A. K.	162
CYZER, MR CHARLES	163

D

Name	Team No.
DACE, MR L. A.	164
†DALTON, MR J. N.	165
DALTON, MR P. T.	166
†DAVIES, MR G. W. J.	167
†DAVIS, MISS L. V.	168
DAVISON, MISS Z. C.	169
DE HAAN, MR B.	170
†DEAN, MR RICHARD	171
†DENNIS, MR W. W.	172
DICKEN, MR A. R.	173
DICKIN, MR R.	174
†DIXON, MR J. E.	175
DODDS, MR JOHN P.	176
DODS, MR M. J. K.	177
DONNELLY, MR T. W.	178
DOW, MR S. L.	179
DREWE, MR C. J.	180
†DU PLESSIS, MISS J. M.	181
†DUN, MR T. D. C.	182
DUNLOP, MR E. A. L.	183
DUNLOP, MR J. L.	184

Name	Team No.
†DUNN, MR A. J. K.	185
DUTFIELD, MR P. N	186
DWYER, MR C. A.	187

E

Name	Team No.
EARLE, MR S. A.	188
EASTERBY, MR M. W.	189
EASTERBY, MR T. D.	190
ECCLES, MR P.	191
†ECKLEY, MR B. J.	192
ECKLEY, MR MALCOLM W.	193
†EDWARDS, MR G. F.	194
EDWARDS, MISS S.	195
EGERTON, MR C. R.	196
†ELLIOTT, MR E. A.	197
ELLISON, MR BRIAN	198
ELSWORTH, MR D. R. C.	199
†ENGLAND, MISS E. M. V.	200
ENRIGHT, MR G. P.	201
ETHERINGTON, MR T. J.	202
EUSTACE, MR J. M. P.	203
†EVANS, MR J. T.	204
†EVANS, MRS M.	205
EVANS, MR P. D.	206
EYRE, MR J. L.	207

F

Name	Team No.
FABRE, MR A.	208
FAHEY, MR R. A.	209
FAIRHURST, MR C. W.	210
FANSHAWE, MR J. R.	211
FARRELL, MR P.	212
FELGATE, MR P. S.	213
FETHERSTON-GODLEY, MR M. J.	214
FFRENCH DAVIS, MR D. J. S.	215
FITZGERALD, MR J. G.	216
FLOOD, MR F.	217
FLOWER, MR R. M.	218
†FORBES, MR A. L.	219
†FORSTER, MR D. M.	220
FORSTER, CAPT T. A.	221
FOSTER, MR A. G.	222
FOWLER, MR J. R. H.	223
FOX, MR J. C.	224
FROST, MR R. G.	225

G

Name	Team No.
GANDOLFO, MR D. R.	226
GASELEE, MR N. A.	227
†GEE, MR B.	228
GEORGE, MR T. R.	229
GIBSON, MR RICHARD	230
GIFFORD, MR J. T.	231
GILLIGAN, MR PATRICK L.	232
GLOVER, MR J. A.	233
†GOESS-SAURAU, COUNTESS	234
GOLDIE, MR J. S.	235
GOLDIE, MR ROBERT H.	236
GOLLINGS, MR S.	237
†GOODFELLOW, MRS A. C. D.	238
GOSDEN, MR J. H. M.	239
†GRAHAM, MRS H. O.	240
GRAHAM, MR N. A.	241
GRANT, MR C.	242
GRASSICK, MR L. P.	243
GRASSICK, MR M. J.	244
†GRAY, MR FREDERICK	245
†GREATHEAD, MR T. R.	246
GREDLEY, MR W. J.	247
†GREENWAY, MR V. G.	248
†GRIFFITHS, MR S. G.	249

Name	Team No.
GRISSELL, MR D. M.	250
GUBBY, MR BRIAN	251
GUEST, MR R.	252

H

Name	Team No.
HAGGAS, MR W. J.	253
HAINE, MRS D.	254
HALDANE, MR J. S.	255
HALL, MR L. M.	256
HALL, MISS S. E.	257
HAM, MR G. A.	258
HAMMOND, MR M. D.	259
HANNON, MR R.	260
HARRINGTON, MRS JESSICA	261
HARRIS, MR J. L.	262
HARRIS, MR PETER W.	263
HARVEY, MR A. H.	264
HASLAM, MR PATRICK	265
HAWKE, MR N. J.	266
HAYDEN, MR JOHN C	267
HAYDN JONES, MR D.	268
HAYNES, MR H. E.	269
†HAYNES, MR J. C.	270
HAYNES, MR M. J.	271
HAYWARD, MR P. A.	272
HEAD, MRS C.	273
HEATON-ELLIS, MR M. J. B.	274
HEDGER, MR P. R.	275
HEMSLEY, MR C. J.	276
HENDERSON, MR N. J.	277
HENDERSON, MRS R. G.	278
HERRIES, LADY	279
HETHERTON, MR J.	280
HIATT, MR P. W.	281
HICKS, MRS C. M.	282
HILLS, MR B. W.	283
HILLS, MR J. W.	284
HOAD, MR R. P. C.	285
HOBBS, MR A. G.	286
HOBBS, MR P. J.	287
HODGES, MR R. J.	288
HOGAN, MR T.	289
†HOLLINGSWORTH, MR A. F.	290
HOLLINSHEAD, MR R.	291
HORGAN, MR CON	292
†HORNER-HARKER, MRS S. L.	293
HOWE, MR H. S.	294
HOWLING, MR P.	295
HUBBARD, MR G. A.	296
†HUBBUCK, MR J. S.	297
HUGHES, MR D. T.	298
HUGHES, MR JOHN R.	299
HUNTINGDON, LORD	300

I

Name	Team No.
INCISA, DON E.	301
INGRAM, MR R.	302

J

Name	Team No.
JACKSON, MR C. F. C.	303
†JACKSON, MR F. S.	304
JAMES, MR E. L. J. D.	305
JARVIS, MR A. P.	306
JARVIS, MR M. A.	307
JARVIS, MR W.	308
JEFFERSON, MR J. M.	309
JENKINS, MR J. R. W.	310
JENKS, MR W. P.	311
†JESSOP, MR A. E. M.	312
†JESTIN, MR F.	313
JEWELL, MRS L. C.	314

Name	Team No.
JOHNSEY, MISS C.	315
JOHNSON, MRS A. E.	316
JOHNSON, MR J. H.	317
†JOHNSON, MR P. R.	318
JOHNSON, MR ROBERT W.	319
†JOHNSON, MRS S. M.	320
JOHNSON HOUGHTON, MR G. F.	321
JOHNSON HOUGHTON, MR R. F.	322
JOHNSTON, MR M. S.	323
JONES, MR A. P.	324
JONES, MR BOB	325
JONES, MR C. H.	326
†JONES, MR G. ELWYN	327
JONES, MRS M. A.	328
†JONES, MR P. J.	329
JONES, MR T. M.	330
JORDAN, MR F. T. J.	331
JORDAN, MRS J.	332
†JOSEPH, MR J.	333
JUCKES, MR R. T.	334

K

Name	Team No.
†KAVANAGH, MR H. M.	335
KEDDY, MR T.	336
KELLEWAY, MR A.	337
KELLEWAY, MISS G. M.	338
KELLY, MR G. P.	339
KEMP, MR W. T.	340
KETTLEWELL, MR S. E.	341
KING, MR J. S.	342
†KINSEY, MR T. R.	343
†KIRBY, MR F.	344
†KIRBY, MR J.	345
KNIGHT, MISS H. C.	346
KNIGHT, MR S. G.	347

L

Name	Team No.
LAFFON-PARIAS, MR C.	348
LAMB, MR D. A.	349
†LAMB, MRS K. M.	350
LAMYMAN, MRS S.	351
LE BROCQ, MRS J. L.	352
LE PENNEC, MR ROBIN	353
LEADBETTER, MR S. J.	354
LEAHY, MR AUGUSTINE	355
†LEDGER, MR R. R.	356
LEE, MR RICHARD	357
LEIGH, MR J. P.	358
LEWIS, MR G.	359
LITTMODEN, MR N. P.	360
†LIVERMORE, MR R. E. A.	361
LLEWELLYN, MR B. J.	362
†LLOYD, MR F.	363
LLOYD-JAMES, MR L. R.	364
LOCKWOOD, MR ALAN	365
LODER, MR D. R.	366
LONG, MR J. E.	367
LUNGO, MR L.	368
LYONS, MR GER	369

M

Name	Team No.
MACAULEY, MRS N. J.	370
MACKIE, MR W. J. W.	371
MACTAGGART, MR A. B.	372
MADGWICK, MR M. J.	373
MAHDI, MR K.	374
MAKIN, MR P. J.	375
MANGAN, MR JAMES J.	376
MANN, MR C. J.	377
MARGARSON, MR G. G.	378
MARKS, MR D.	379

Name	Team No.
†MARSHALL, MRS L. A.	380
MARVIN, MR R. F.	381
†MASON, MR N. B.	382
MCAULIFFE, MR K.	383
MCCAIN, MR D.	384
MCCONNOCHIE, MR J. C.	385
MCCOURT, MR G. M.	386
MCGHIN, MR RAY	387
MCGOVERN, MR T. P.	388
†MCINNES SKINNER, MRS C.	389
MCKELLAR, MR R.	390
†MCKENZIE-COLES, MR W. G.	391
MCKEOWN, MR W. J.	392
MCKIE, MRS V.	393
MCMAHON, MR B. A.	394
MCMATH, MR B. J.	395
†MCMILLAN, MR M. D.	396
MEADE, MR MARTYN	397
MEADE, MR N.	398
MEAGHER, MR M. G.	399
MEEHAN, MR B. J.	400
MELLOR, MR S.	401
MILLIGAN, MISS M. K.	402
MILLMAN, MR B. R.	403
MILLS, MR T. G.	404
†MITCHELL, MR C. W.	405
MITCHELL, MR N. R.	406
MITCHELL, MR PAT	407
MITCHELL, MR PHILIP	408
†MOBLEY, MRS HELEN	409
MOFFATT, MR D.	410
MONTEITH, MR PETER	411
MOORE, MR A. L.	412
MOORE, MR G. L.	413
MOORE, MR G. M.	414
MOORE, MR J. S.	415
MORGAN, MR B. C.	416

Name	Team No.
MORGAN, MR K. A.	417
MORLOCK, MR C. P. H.	418
MORRIS, MR DAVID	419
MORRIS, MR DERRICK	420
MORRIS, MR M.	421
MORRISON, MR H.	422
†MOSCROP, MRS E.	423
MUGGERIDGE, MR M. P.	424
MUIR, MR WILLIAM R.	425
MULHOLLAND, MR A. B.	426
MULLINEAUX, MR M.	427
MULLINS, MR J. W.	428
MURPHY, MR F.	429
MURPHY, MR P. G.	430
MURRAY SMITH, MR D. J. G.	431
MURTAGH, MR F. P.	432
MUSSON, MR W. J.	433

N

Name	Team No.
NAUGHTON, MRS A. M.	434
NAUGHTON, MR T. J.	435
NEVILLE, MR JAMES	436
NICHOLLS, MR D.	437
NICHOLLS, MR P. F.	438
NICHOLSON, MR DAVID	439
†NIXON, MR G. R. S.	440
†NOCK, MRS S.	441
NOLAN, MR D. A.	442
NORTON, MR JOHN	443
NOSEDA, MR J. J.	444

O

Name	Team No.
O'BRIEN, MR CHARLES	445
O'BRIEN, MR D. C.	446
O'GRADY, MR E. J.	447

Name	Team No.
O'NEILL, MR J. J.	448
O'NEILL, MR O.	449
O'REILLY, MR J. F. P.	450
O'SHEA, MR J. G. M.	451
O'SULLIVAN, MR EUGENE M.	452
†ODELL, MRS S. M.	453
OLD, MR J. A. B.	454
OLDROYD, MR G. R.	455
OLIVER, MR J. K. M.	456
†ORDE-POWLETT, MR H.	457
†OWEN, MR E. H.	458
OXX, MR JOHN M.	459
P	
PALLING, MR BRYN	460
†PARK, MR I.	461
PARKER, MR C.	462
PARKES, MR J. E.	463
†PAYNE, MR J. R.	464
PAYNE, MR J. W.	465
PEACOCK, MR R. E.	466
PEARCE, MR B. A.	467
PEARCE, MR J.	468
PEASE, MR J. E.	469
PEILL, MR M. A.	470
PERRATT, MISS L. A.	471
PERRETT, MRS A. J.	472
PHILLIPS, MR R. T.	473
†PILKINGTON, MRS T. D.	474
PIPE, MR MARTIN	475
PITMAN, MRS J.	476
PITMAN, MR M. A.	477
†PITTENDRIGH, MR S. I.	478
†PLATER, MS L. C.	479
†POCOCK, MR ROBERT E.	480
POLGLASE, MR M. J.	481
POPHAM, MR C. L.	482
POULTON, MR J. C.	483

Name	Team No.
POULTON, MR J. R.	484
PREECE, MR W. G.	485
PRENDERGAST, MR P.	486
PRESCOTT BT, SIR MARK	487
†PRICE, MR C. J.	488
PRICE, MR RICHARD J.	489
PRITCHARD, MR P. A.	490
†PRITCHARD, DR P. L. J.	491
PURDY, MR P. D.	492
Q	
QUINN, MR J. J.	493
QUINN, MR MICK	494
R	
RAMSDEN, MRS J. R.	495
†RATCLIFFE, MR C. I.	496
†RAW, MR W.	497
REED, MR W. G.	498
REVELEY, MRS G. R.	499
RICH, MR P. M.	500
RICHARDS, MR G. W.	501
†RICHARDS, MR GRAHAM	502
RICHARDS, MRS LYDIA	503
†RICHARDSON, MRS S. L.	504
RITCHENS, MR P. C.	505
†ROBESON, MRS P.	506
ROE, MR C. G.	507
ROPER, MR W. M.	508
ROTHWELL, MR B. S.	509
ROUALLE, MR J. DE	510
ROUGET, MR J. C.	511
ROWE, MR R.	512
ROWLAND, MISS M. E.	513
ROYER-DUPRE, MR A. DE	514
RUSSELL, MISS L. V.	515
†RYALL, MR B. J. M.	516
RYAN, MR M. J.	517

Name	Team No.
S	
SANDERS, MISS B.	518
SAUNDERS, MR M. S	519
SCARGILL, DR J. D.	520
†SCRIVEN, MR B.	521
†SCRIVENS, MRS J.	522
SHAW, MR D.	523
SHEEHAN, MR J. J.	524
SHEEHY, MR FINBARR	525
SHEPPARD, MR M. I.	526
SHERWOOD, MR O. M. C.	527
SIDDALL, MISS L. C	528
SIMPSON, MR RODNEY	529
†SLACK, MRS D. E.	530
SLY, MRS P. M.	531
SMAGA, MR D.	532
SMART, MR B.	533
†SMITH, MR A. D.	534
SMITH, MR ALFRED	535
SMITH, MR C.	536
SMITH, MR DENYS	537
SMITH, MR J. P.	538
SMITH, MR JULIAN S.	539
SMITH, MR N. A.	540
SMITH, MR RALPH JOHN	541
SMITH, MRS S. J.	542
SMYTH-OSBOURNE, MR J. G.	543
†SNOOK, MR L. A.	544
SOANE, MR V. ST JOHN	545
SOWERSBY, MR M. E.	546
SPEARING, MR J. L.	547
SPICER, MR R. C.	548
STACK, MR T.	549
†STEPHENS, MISS V. A.	550
STEWART, MR A. C.	551
STOKELL, MISS ANN	552
†STOREY, MR F. S.	553
STOREY, MRS J. M.	554
STOREY, MR W.	555
STOUTE, MR M.	556
STREETER, MR A. P.	557
STUBBS, MRS L.	558
†SUPPLE, MR K. R.	559
SWAN, CAPT. D.	560
SWINBANK, MRS A.	561
†SWINDLEHURST, MR D. G.	562
T	
TATE, MR T. P	563
†TAYLOR, MRS L. C.	564
THOM, MR D. T.	565
†THOMAS, MRS D.	566
THOMPSON, MR RONALD	567
†THOMSON, MR A. M.	568
THOMSON, MRS DOROTHY	569
THOMSON, MR N. B.	570
†THOMSON, MR R. W.	571
THORNER, MR G. E.	572
THORNTON, MR C. W.	573
†TINNING, MR W. H.	574
TODHUNTER, MR D. M.	575
TOLLER, MR J. A. R.	576
TOMPKINS, MR M. H.	577
TOWNSLEY, MRS P. LAXTON	578
TREGONING, MR M. P.	579
TUCK, MR J. C.	580
†TUCKER, MR F. G.	581
TURNELL, MR ANDREW	582
†TURNER, MR D. C.	583
TURNER, MR W. G. M.	584
TWISTON-DAVIES, MR N. A.	585
U	
UPSON, MR J. R.	586
USHER, MR M. D. I.	587

Name	Team No.
V	
†VINCENT, MR K.	588
W	
†WADHAM, MRS L. A. M.	589
†WAGGOTT, MR N.	590
WAINWRIGHT, MR J. S.	591
†WALEY-COHEN, MR ROBERT B.	592
WALL, MR C. F.	593
WALL, MR T. R.	594
WALTON, MRS H. L.	595
WALWYN, MR P. T.	596
WANE, MR M.	597
WARD, MRS V. C.	598
WARING, MRS BARBARA	599
†WARING, MR L.	600
WARING, MR MIKE	601
†WATERMAN, MISS S.	602
WATSON, MR T. R.	603
†WEBB, MR H. J. M.	604
WEBBER, MR P. R.	605
WEEDEN, MR M. J.	606
WEEDON, MR C. V.	607
†WEGMANN, MR P.	608
WELD, MR D. K.	609
WELLS, MR L.	610
WEYMES, MR E.	611
WHARTON, MR J. R. H.	612
WHEELER, MR E. A.	613
WHILLANS, MR A. C.	614
WHITAKER, MR R. M.	615
WHITTLE, MISS P. M.	616
†WHYTE, MR J. W.	617
WILKINSON, MR M. J.	618
WILLIAMS, MR D. L.	619
WILLIAMS, MR IAN	620
†WILLIAMS, MR L. J.	621
WILLIAMS, MR R. J. R.	622
WILLIAMS, MR S. C.	623
WILLIAMS, MRS S. D.	624
WILLIAMS, MISS V. M.	625
WILSON, MR A. J.	626
WILSON, CAPT J. H.	627
WILTON, MISS S. J.	628
WINKWORTH, MR P. L.	629
†WOOD, MR R. S.	630
WOODHOUSE, MR R. D. E.	631
WOODMAN, MR S.	632
†WOODROW, MRS A. M.	633
WOODS, MR S. P. C.	634
WOODWARD, MR G.	635
†WORMALL, MISS J.	636
WRAGG, MR GEOFFREY	637
Y	
YARDLEY, MR G. H.	638
†YOUNG, MR W. G.	639

ADDITIONAL TEAMS

Name	Team No.
BOLLACK-BADEL, MRS M.	640
DAY, MISS H.	641
HUGHES, MR P.	642
KERSEY, MR T.	643
KETTLE, MR MICHAEL	644
WHITE, MRS F. E.	645

1

PROPERTY OF HER MAJESTY

The Queen

Colours: Purple, gold braid, scarlet sleeves, black cap with gold fringe

Trained by **Lord Huntingdon,** West Ilsley Stables, Newbury

1 **ARABIAN STORY,** 5, gr h Sharrood (USA)—Once Upon A Time
2 **DUST,** 4, b f Green Desert (USA)—Storm Warning
3 **HEBRIDES,** 4, ch f Gone West (USA)—Sleeping Beauty
4 **RUTLAND CHANTRY (USA),** 4, b c Dixieland Band (USA)—Christchurch (FR)
5 **SHAFT OF LIGHT,** 6, gr g Sharrood (USA)—Reflection
6 **SPANISH KNOT (USA),** 4, b f El Gran Senor (USA)—Ingenuity
7 **TEMPTING PROSPECT,** 4, b f Shirley Heights—Trying For Gold (USA)
8 **THREADNEEDLE (USA),** 5, b g Danzig Connection (USA)—Sleeping Beauty
9 **WHITECHAPEL (USA),** 10, b g Arctic Tern (USA)—Christchurch (FR)

THREE-YEAR-OLDS

10 **BLUEPRINT (IRE),** b c Generous (IRE)—Highbrow
11 **CELTIC CROSS,** b f Selkirk (USA)—Abbey Strand (USA)
12 **COOL PERFORMANCE (USA),** b c Lear Fan (USA)—Christchurch (FR)
13 **FEEL FREE (IRE),** b f Generous (IRE)—As You Desire Me
14 **ISLAND STORY,** b f Shirley Heights—Once Upon A Time
15 **MAGIC TOUCH,** b f Fairy King (USA)—Gentle Persuasion
16 **STAGE WHISPER,** b c Alzao (USA)—Starlet

TWO-YEAR-OLDS

17 **DAYTIME,** b c 22/3 Danehill (USA)—Zenith (Shirley Heights)
18 **FICTITIOUS,** ch f 9/3 Machiavellian (USA)—Trying For Gold (USA) (Northern Baby (CAN))
19 **GLOW,** b f 20/2 Alzao (USA)—Shimmer (Bustino)
20 **GRACIOUS GIFT,** ch f 18/4 Cadeaux Genereux—Gentle Persuasion (Bustino)
21 **LEGEND,** b f 18/3 Belmez (USA)—Once Upon A Time (Teenoso (USA))
22 **OZZIE,** b f 9/1 Ezzoud (IRE)—Australia Fair (AUS) (Without Fear (FR))

Trained by **Mr I. A. Balding,** Park House, Kingsclere

THREE-YEAR-OLDS

23 **CELEBRATION,** br f Selkirk (USA)—No Restraint
24 **DOUBLET,** ch g Bustino—Pas de Deux
25 **FILIGREE,** ch f Salse (USA)—Trying For Gold (USA)

TWO-YEAR-OLDS

26 **CHEER,** b f 20/2 Efisio—Chancel (USA) (Al Nasr (FR))
27 **NIGHTINGALE,** ro f 6/1 Night Shift (USA)—Grey Angel (Kenmare (FR))

PROPERTY OF HER MAJESTY

The Queen

Trained by **Mr Roger J. Charlton,** Beckhampton

28 GHILLIES BALL, 4, ch g Groom Dancer (USA)—Highbrow

THREE-YEAR-OLD

29 DAY DREAMING, b f Efisio—Fade

TWO-YEAR-OLDS

30 FAIRY GODMOTHER, b f 1/4 Fairy King (USA)—Highbrow (Shirley Heights)
31 HOLLY BLUE, ch f 26/3 Bluebird (USA)—Nettle (Kris)
32 TEMPLE WAY, b c 26/4 Shirley Heights—Abbey Strand (USA) (Shadeed (USA))

2

THE PROPERTY OF
H.M. QUEEN ELIZABETH THE QUEEN MOTHER

Colours: Blue, buff stripes, blue sleeves, black cap with gold tassel

Trained by **Mr N. J. Henderson**, Seven Barrows, Lambourn

1 AMBER GLEAM, 4, ch g Bustino—First Romance
2 BLAZER, 5, b g Lighter—Australia Fair (AUS)
3 BOLD ROMEO, 6, b g Bold Owl—First Romance
4 CLOSE HARMONY, 6, ch m Bustino—Highland Lyric
5 EASTER ROSS, 5, ch g Ardross—Caserta
6 FATHER HENRY (IRE), 7, b g The Parson—Little Sloop
7 KEEL ROW, 8, b m Relkino—Caserta
8 KINGS RHAPSODY, 5, ch g Rakaposhi King—First Romance

Trained by **Mr I. A. Balding**, Park House, Kingsclere

THREE-YEAR-OLDS

9 DOUBLE BRANDY, ch c Elmaamul (USA)—Brand
10 HOT SPOT, ch g Bustino—Royal Seal

TWO-YEAR-OLD

11 CHERRY BRANDY ch c 24/2 Elmaamul (USA)—Brand (Shareef Dancer (USA))

Trained by **Mr F. Doumen**, Lamorlaye, France

12 FIRE BALL (FR), 5, b g Perrault—Scala IV (FR)

3 MR JAMES R. ADAM, Gordon

Postal: **Morven, Westruther, Gordon, Berwickshire, TD3 6NF.**
Phone: **(01578) 740229 FAX (01578) 740320**

1 **BOLD CLASSIC (IRE)**, 5, b g Persian Bold—Bay Street **Mr James R. Adam**
2 **BOUNTY HUNTER (IRE)**, 5, br g Mandalus—The Foalicule **Mr James R. Adam**
3 **CHEVALIER BAYARD (IRE)**, 5, br g Strong Gale—Flying Pegus **Mr James R. Adam**
4 **CHEVALIER ERRANT (IRE)**, 5, b br g Strong Gale—Luminous Run **Mr James R. Adam**
5 **FILS DE CRESSON (IRE)**, 8, b g Torus—Hellfire Hostess **Mr James R. Adam**
6 **JUDICIOUS CHARLIE (IRE)**, 6, b br g Strong Gale—Miss Spike **Mr James R. Adam**
7 **JUDICIOUS NORMAN (IRE)**, 7, br g Strong Gale—Smart Fashion **Mr James R. Adam**
8 **MONNAIE FORTE (IRE)**, 8, b g Strong Gale—Money Run **Mr James R. Adam**
9 **MONSIEUR DARCY (IRE)**, 7, b g Phardante (FR)—Ballycurnane Lady **Mr James R. Adam**

Jockey (NH): B Powell (w.a).

4 MR H. AKBARY, Newmarket

Postal: **Egerton Stud, Cambridge Road, Newmarket, Suffolk, CB8 OTJ.**
Phone: **(01638) 661178 or (0467) 407804**

1 **LOXLEY'S GIRL (IRE)**, 4, b f Lahib (USA)—Samnaun (USA) **Mr S. R. Hudson**
2 **MAC'S DELIGHT**, 4, b g Machiavellian (USA)—Bashoosh (USA) **Mr S. R. Hudson**

THREE-YEAR-OLDS

3 B br f Mr Prospector (USA)—Embellished (USA) **Count Federico Zichy-Thyssen**
4 **QISMAT**, b f Selkirk (USA)—Plaything **Mr S. R. Hudson**
5 **TAIPEI**, b c Perpendicluar—Gitee (FR)
6 B f Dixieland Band (USA)—Turkstand (USA) **Count Federico Zichy-Thyssen**

TWO-YEAR-OLDS

7 B f Makbul—Boxit (General Ironside)
8 B c Bigstone (IRE)—In High Spirits (Head For Heights)
9 B c Timeless Times (USA)—La Pepper (Workboy)
10 B c Fayruz—Loma Breeze (Cure The Blues (USA))
11 B c Komaite (USA)—Luaga (Tyrnavos)
12 **NINO BONITO (IRE)**, b c Second Set (IRE)—Netsuke (Tachypous)
13 B c Lugana Beach—Rosy Diamond (Jalmood (USA))
14 B f Safawan—Seaward (Slip Anchor)
15 B c Never So Bold—Treeline (High Top)

Apprentice: Angela Barsby (7-6).

5 MR JONATHAN AKEHURST, Epsom

Postal: **South Hatch Stables, 44 Burgh Heath Road, Epsom, Surrey, KT17 4LX.**
Phone: **(01372) 745880 FAX (01372) 744231**

1 **ACADEMY HOUSE (IRE)**, 5, b h Sadler's Wells (USA)—Shady Leaf (IRE) **A. D. Spence**
2 **BOWCLIFFE COURT (IRE)**, 6, b g Slip Anchor—Res Nova (USA) **A. D. Spence**
3 **BRISKA (IRE)**, 4, b f River Falls—Calash **Mr R. Schafer**
4 **CROFT SANDS**, 5, ch g Crofthall—Sannavally **Miss V. Pratt**

MR JONATHAN AKEHURST—continued

5 **DARK AGE (IRE)**, 5, b h Darshaan—Sarela (USA) **A. D. Spence**
6 **DARTER (IRE)**, 6, b g Darshaan—Mamouna (USA) **A. D. Spence**
7 **DOMULLA**, 8, br h Dominion—Ulla Laing **A. W. Boon**
8 **FAHS (USA)**, 6, br g Riverman (USA)—Tanwi **City Industrial Supplies**
9 **FIONN DE COOL (IRE)**, 7, b g Mazaad—Pink Fondant **Canisbay Bloodstock Ltd**
10 **FORZA FIGLIO**, 5, b h Warning—Wish You Well **Grid Thoroughbred Racing**
11 **HIGH ON LIFE**, 4, b g Mazilier (USA)—Tina Rosa **Canisbay Bloodstock Ltd**
12 **KRAYYAN DAWN**, 8, ch g Krayyan—Tana Mist **Mr R. E. Greatorex**
13 **MARENGO**, 4, b c Never So Bold—Born To Dance **Mr J. B. Sharp**
14 **MARSAD (IRE)**, 4, ch c Fayruz—Broad Haven (IRE) **Canisbay Bloodstock Ltd**
15 **MIHRIZ (IRE)**, 6, b g Machiavellian (USA)—Ghzaalh (USA) **Normandy Developments (London)**
16 **MR WILD (USA)**, 5, b g Wild Again—Minstress (USA) **A. D. Spence**
17 **NEUWEST (USA)**, 6, b h Gone West (USA)—White Mischief **Mr Paul Green**
18 **NEWLANDS CORNER**, 5, b m Forzando—Nice Lady **The Jolly Skolars**
19 **NEWPORT KNIGHT**, 7, ch g Bairn (USA)—Clara Barton **Mr Thorburn Muirhead & Mr Lomax**
20 **NORSONG**, 6, b g Northern State (USA)—Winsong Melody **The Golfers Partnership**
21 4, B f Fools Holme (USA)—Pas du Tout **Mr D. Hefin Jones**
22 **PODDINGTON**, 7, b g Crofthall—Bold Gift **Miss V. Pratt**
23 **PROTON**, 8, b g Sure Blade (USA)—Banket **Persian War Racing**
24 **ROSEBERRY AVENUE (IRE)**, 5, b h Sadler's Wells (USA)—Lady's Bridge (USA) **P. D. Savill**
25 **SHADIRWAN (IRE)**, 7, b h Kahyasi—Shademah **C. Batt**
26 **SHII-TAKE**, 4, b c Deploy—Super Sally **C. Batt**
27 **THREEPLAY (IRE)**, 4, b c Mac's Imp (USA)—Houwara (IRE) **The For Fore Four Partnership**
28 **TISSUE OF LIES (USA)**, 5, br g Ascot Knight (CAN)—Choral Group (CAN) **The No Hassle Partnership**
29 **TRY ME AND SEE**, 4, ch c Rock City—Al Raja **The Ashbourne Levy Partnership**
30 **WILDFIRE (SWI)**, 7, b g Beldale Flutter (USA)—Little White Star **Canisbay Bloodstock Ltd**
31 **WILLIE CONQUER**, 6, ch g Master Willie—Maryland Cookie (USA) **R. Tooth**

THREE-YEAR-OLDS

32 **ADVANCEALOT**, ch f Deploy—Copper Burn **Advance Ltd**
33 **BRAVE ACADEMY**, b c Rock City—Astolat **Chris & Jackie Mulally**
34 **CAPE HOPE**, b c Risk Me (FR)—Bernstein Belle **Mr K. Sturgis**
35 **CITY EXPRESS**, b c Rock City—Caroles Express **Peter Crane**
36 **OK BABE**, b f Bold Arrangement—Celtic Bird **OK Partnership**
37 **OK JOHN (IRE)**, b c Mac's Imp (USA)—Ching A Ling **OK Partnership**
38 **PRINCESS CARABOO (IRE)**, b f Alzao (USA)—Commanche Belle **Colin C. Clarke**
39 **ROBANNA**, b f Robellino (USA)—Pounelta **P. Valentine**
40 **RUSH OFF**, b c Robellino (USA)—Arusha (IRE) **R. Tooth**

TWO-YEAR-OLDS

41 Br f 27/4 Petardia—Ballerina Anna (IRE)
42 B c 24/3 Deploy—Kumzar **Mr D. Hefin Jones**
43 B c 7/4 Then Again—Zahiah **Mr D. Hefin Jones**

Other Owners: Mrs John Akehurst, Amity Finance Ltd, Mr Bill Bigmore, Mr Julian Bradford, Mrs Susan Crane, Mr D. F. Francis, Mr Paul V. Jackson, Mr P. Karanjia, Mr Richard Levy, Mr M. A. Mauro, Mrs S. K. McLean, Mr Peter Newman, Rags Racing Club, Mr Malcolm Ritz, Mr D. L. Syberg, Mr A. R. Travers, Mr John Trickett, Mr Randal Van Twisk.

Jockeys (Flat): T Quinn (w.a.), S Sanders (w.a.).

Amateur: Miss Jane Allison.

6 MR D. S. ALDER, Belford

Postal: **Lucker Mill, Lucker, Belford, Northumberland, NE70 7JH.**
Phone: **(01668) 213 883**

1 **CAMPTOSAURUS (IRE)**, 9, br g Strong Gale—Baybush **Mrs D. S. Alder**
2 **CHERRY POKEY**, 11, b g Uncle Pokey—Cherry Brig **Mr D. S. Alder**
3 **CRANNON BEAUTY (IRE)**, 8, gr g Castle Keep—Crannon Girl **Mr D. S. Alder**
4 **GLACIAL GIRL (IRE)**, 6, b m Glacial Storm (USA)—Zimuletta **Mr D. S. Alder**
5 **ROYAL RANK (USA)**, 8, ch g Miswaki (USA)—Westminster Palace **Mr D. S. Alder**
6 **SAFETY FACTOR (IRE)**, 10, gr g Strong Gale—Myra Grey **Mr D. S. Alder**

7 MR A. R. ALLAN, Cornhill-on-Tweed

Postal: **Pallinsburn Stables, Cornhill-on-Tweed, Northd, TD12 4SG.**
Phone: **CROOKHAM (01890) 820581 MOBILE (0468) 850014**

1 **ADAMATIC (IRE)**, 7, b g Henbit (USA)—Arpal Magic **Mr Geoff Adam**
2 **AMERICAN HERO**, 10, ch g Persian Bold—American Winter (USA) **Mrs R. P. Aggio**
3 **ASTRALEON (IRE)**, 10, b g Caerleon (USA)—Noah's Acky Astra (USA) **Mr A. H. Dunlop**
4 **BIG TARGET (IRE)**, 4, b g Sauve Dancer (USA)—Prima Domina (FR) **Mr Ian S. M. Dalgleish**
5 **BIT O MAGIC (IRE)**, 6, ch g Henbit (USA)—Arpal Magic **Mr Geoff Adam**
6 **BORIS BROOK**, 7, ch g Meadowbrook—Crella **Mrs V. Scott Watson**
7 **BRIAR'S DELIGHT**, 10, b g Idiot's Delight—Briar Park **Mr A. Clark**
8 **DOUBLING DICE**, 7, b g Jalmood (USA)—Much Too Risky **Mr R. Allan**
9 **FASTER RON (IRE)**, 7, b g Rontino—Ambitious Lady **Mrs V. Scott Watson**
10 **KING OF SHOW (IRE)**, 7, b g Green Desert (USA)—Don't Rush (USA) **Mr Ian R. Flannigan**
11 **LATVIAN**, 11, gr g Rousillon (USA)—Lorelene (FR) **Mr I. Bell**
12 **MASTER HYDE (USA)**, 9, gr g Trempolino (USA)—Sandspur (USA) **Mr D. Callaghan**
13 **MAYYAADA (IRE)**, 6, b g Nabeel Dancer (USA)—Badiya (USA) **Mr R. Allan**
14 **MONACO (IRE)**, 4, b g Classic Music (USA)—Larosterna **Mr Ian R. Flannigan**
15 **MOUNTAIN DREAM**, 5, b h Batshoof—Echoing **Mrs Liz Adam**
16 **SABRE DANCER**, 4, b g Rambo Dancer (CAN)—My Candy **Mr R. Allan**
17 **TEACHER (IRE)**, 8, b g Caerleon (USA)—Clunk Click **Mr R. Allan**
18 **THUNDERHEART**, 7, b g Celestial Storm (USA)—Lorelene (FR) **Mr Ian G. M. Dalgleish**
19 **VICTOR LASZLO**, 6, b g Ilium—Report 'em (USA) **Mr Ian G. M. Dalgleish**

Other Owners: Mr S. Aitken, Mr T. W. Beaty, Mr I. R. Clements, Miss Louise Davis, Mr L. Grant, Mr R. M. C. Jeffreys, Mrs W. M. Morton, Mr I. Rodden, R. P. Adam Ltd, Mr J. Stephenson.

Jockeys (Flat): J Fortune (w.a.), J Weaver (w.a.).

Jockey (NH): B Storey (10-0, w.a.).

Conditional: Stephen Melrose (9-7).

Amateur: Andrew Robson (10-7).

8 MR C. N. ALLEN, Newmarket

Postal: **Shadowfax Stables, Hamilton Road, Newmarket, Suffolk, CB8 0NQ.**
Phone: **(01638) 667870 FAX (01638) 668005**

1 **CARATI,** 4, b f Sellkirk (USA)—Clytie (USA) **Mr Peter Gleeson**
2 **ENCHANTING EVE,** 4, ch f Risk Me (FR)—Red Sails **Newmarket Connections Ltd**
3 **LAKOTA BRAVE,** 4, ch c Anshan—Pushkinia (FR) **Newmarket Connections Ltd**
4 **LANDCRUISER,** 6, b g Warning—Marseillaise **Mr T. G. Burke**
5 **LE BAM BAM,** 6, ch h Emarati (USA)—Lady Lustre **John Peters Le Bam Bam Syndicate**
6 **MARKAPEN (IRE),** 4, b f Classic Music (USA)—Dahsala **Mr B. Walker**
7 **RANZEL,** 8, b g Shirley Heights—Kanz (USA) **Eclipse Management (Newmarket) Ltd**
8 **WINDBORN,** 4, b f Superpower—Chablisse **Shadowfax Racing**

THREE-YEAR-OLDS

9 **DEVA LADY,** b f Prince Sabo—Known Line **Mr Cliff Woof**
10 **GUEST ENVOY (IRE),** b f Paris House—Peace Mission **Newmarket Connections Ltd**
11 Br c Kasakov—Kind Lady **Mr John Peters**
12 **PIROSHKA,** b f Soviet Star (USA)—Sophisticated Lady (FR) **Mrs C. Tribe**
13 **ROBEENA,** b f Robellino (USA)—Raheena (USA) **Village Green Racing**
14 **SABO'S JOY,** b f Prince Sabo—Port Na Blath **Conrad's Angels**
15 **SPRING BEACON,** ch f Pharly (FR)—Vernair (USA) **Newmarket Connections Ltd**

TWO-YEAR-OLDS

16 **ANNELIINA,** b f 18/3 Cadeaux Genereux—Blasted Heath **Mrs Kaarina Hyytiainen**
17 **BASHER JACK,** b c 26/5 Suave Dancer (USA)—Possessive Lady **J. T. B. Racing**
18 B f 22/2 Batshoof—Petite Louie **Mr B. Garner**

Other Owners: Mrs C. N. Allen, Mr C. N. Allen, Mr A. Ashjian, Lisa Brady, Mrs M. Brown, Bryants Pride, Mr F. Carr, Jaqueline Clarke, Mr Clarke, Mr G. Coles, Mr P. Collins, Mrs P. Collinson, Mr P. Collinson, Ms A. L. Cullinane, Miss J. Lee Cunningham, Mrs S. Darby, Mr N. Derbyshire, Mr P. B. Doyle, Mr M. Dwyer, Eclipse Management (Newmarket) Ltd, Mr J. Feely, Mr E. Fisher, Mrs M. Flowers, Mr J. Fodden, Mr A. Foden, Mr R. Fuff, Mr J. Gallacher, Mrs E. Garner, Mr J. Harris, Mrs Maria Harrison, Mrs D. Hodgekinson, Mr J. Hodgekinson, Susan Jaklin, Ms M. Kennedy, Baron Bergsma Of Longford, Mr B. Malin, Mrs B. Matthews, Mr P. McGonnell, Mr McSkimming, Mr R. Moffat, Mr S. Morris Watts, Mr B. Moulton, Mrs M. Moulton, Mrs J. May, Multipulse Ltd, Mrs J. K. Payne, Mrs Katherine Peters, Mrs Jan Phillips, Dave Prosser, Mr K. Reeves, Miss A. Robertson, David Rusher, L. J. Sharman, J. Simmons, Mr F. Snell, Mr R. Spittles, Mrs J. Thompson, Mr M. Upton, Mr H. Wake, Mrs Linda Walker, Mrs R. Ware, Miss K. Webb, Mr R. Wightman, Mrs J. Williams, Mr Cliff Woof.

Jockeys (Flat): L Dettori (8-4, w.a.), M J Dwyer (7-10).

Apprentice: M Hammond (8-5).

9 MR J. S. ALLEN, Alcester

Postal: **Alne Park, Park Lane, Great Alne, Alcester, Warwickshire, B49 6HU.**
Phone: **STABLES (01789) 488469 OFFICE (01789) 299492 FAX (01789) 415330**

1 **FIJON (IRE),** 5, b m Doyoun—Tasskeen (FR) **Mr W. H. Allen**
2 **GRATE BRITISH (IRE),** 6, b g Astronef—Stapelea (FR) **Mr J. Allen**
3 **NICANJON,** 7, ch g Nicholas Bill—Rosalina **Mr J. Allen**
4 **WELSH DAISY,** 6, b m Welsh Captain—Singing Hills **Mr J. Allen**

Other Owners: Mrs Carol Allen, Mr Neil Allen.

Jockeys (NH): X. Aizpuru (9-7), Gary Lyons (10-0).

10 MR R. H. ALNER, Blandford

Postal: **Locketts Farm, Droop, Blandford, Dorset, DT11 0EZ.**
Phone: **(01258) 817271 MOBILE (0467) 436375**

1 **ALL CLEAR (IRE)**, 7, b g Castle Keep—Hustle Bustle **J. P. M. & J. W. Cook**
2 **ALLER MOOR (IRE)**, 7, b g Dry Dock—Boggy Peak **Mr G. Keirle**
3 **APATURA HATI**, 9, br m Senang Hati—Apatura Iris **Mrs R. O. Hutchings**
4 **ARTISTIC PLAN (IRE)**, 6, b g Creative Plan (USA)—North Rose VII **Forum Racing**
5 **BEAUREPAIRE (IRE)**, 10, b g Beau Charmeur (FR)—Running Stream **Pell-mell Partners**
6 **BOLDER STILL**, 5, ch g Never So Bold—Glenfinlass **Mrs Jenny Willment**
7 **BRAMSHAW WOOD (IRE)**, 6, b g Brush Aside (USA)—Lovely Sanara **Mrs U. Wainwright**
8 **CALLEVA STAR (IRE)**, 7, b g Over The River (FR)—Ask The Madam **Mr James Burley**
9 **CLASSICAL JOKER**, 5, b m Old Jocus—Classy Miss **Thai Racing**
10 **COOL DAWN (IRE)**, 10, br g Over The River (FR)—Aran Tour **The Hon Miss D. Harding**
11 **COOLTEEN HERO (IRE)**, 8, b g King Luthier—Running Stream **J. P. M. & J. W. Cook**
12 **DEXTRA DOVE**, 11, gr g Julio Mariner—Grey Dove **Dextra Lighting Systems**
13 **ELLEN GAIL (IRE)**, 6, br m Strong Gale—Kemchee **Mr H. V. Perry**
14 **FLYER'S NAP**, 12, b g Rolfe (USA)—English Flyer **Mr R. J. Tory**
15 **FOR JUSTIN**, 11, gr g Celio Rufo—Wind Over Spain **Mr Tony Thomas & Mr Stewart McDonald**
16 **GALACIA (IRE)**, 6, br m Gallic League—Little Wild Duck **Mr Richard Hedditch**
17 **GILLAN COVE (IRE)**, 9, b g The Parson—Shanban **Forum Racing**
18 **HARWELL LAD (IRE)**, 9, b g Over The River (FR)—Gayles Approach **Mr H. Wellstead**
19 **I'MINONIT**, 8, b g Rolfe (USA)—Lorrensino **Iminonit Partnership**
20 **LETS RUMBLE (IRE)**, 9, b g Buckskin (FR)—Cherry Branch **Mr H. V. Perry**
21 **LONICERA**, 8, br m Sulaafah (USA)—Cygne **Mrs Susie Old**
22 **MALWOOD CASTLE (IRE)**, 8, b g Bustineto—Boreen Nua **Mrs U. Wainwright**
23 **MAMMY'S CHOICE (IRE)**, 8, br m Mandalus—Liffey's Choice **Mr David Young**
24 **MARKET GOSSIP**, 8, b g Rolfe (USA)—Buckbe **Mr R. J. Tory**
25 **MASTER BOMBER (IRE)**, 7, b g Lancastrian—London Anne **Mr D. R. Fear**
26 **MASTER MARIO**, 10, b g Julio Mariner—Mrs Stephens **Mrs M. A. T. Potter**
27 **MENESONIC (IRE)**, 8, b g Meneval (USA)—Kandy Kate **Mrs W. H. Walter**
28 **MILLCROFT REGATTA (IRE)**, 6, br g Miner's Lamp—Stradbally Bay **Mr John Carter**
29 **MILLCROFT RIVIERA (IRE)**, 7, b g Henbit (USA)—Rathtrim **Mr John Carter**
30 **MINERS GLOW (IRE)**, 6, b m Miner's Lamp—Gilt Course **Mr H. V. Perry**
31 **MOYFENRATH LAD**, 11, b br g Frigid Aire—Clara Novello **Mrs Jenny Willment**
32 **NIGELLO**, 6, b g El Conquistador—Saffron Poser **Mr John Bugg**
33 **NOBLELY (USA)**, 11, b g Lyphard (USA)—Nonoalca (FR) **Mrs Cynthia Walker**
34 **NODDIS DILEMMA (IRE)**, 8, b g Roselier (FR)—Noddi Fliw **Mr P. M. De Wilde**
35 **NORTH TYNE (IRE)**, 4, ch g Good Thyne (USA)—Northern Gift **Lady Talbot of Malahide**
36 **OSCAR WILDE**, 6, b g Arctic Lord—Topsy Bee **Mr P. Green**
37 **OVER THE WATER (IRE)**, 6, gr g Over The River (FR)—Shanacloon Lass **The Droop Partners**
38 **PHILATELIC (IRE)**, 7, br g Buckskin (FR)—Sami (FR) **Mr P. M. De Wilde**
39 **PLAN-A (IRE)**, 8, br g Creative Plan (USA)—Faravaun Rose **Mr R. J. Bullock**
40 **PURBECK CAVALIER**, 9, ch g Sula Bula—Party Miss **Mrs E. M. Curtis**
41 **ROLLCALL (IRE)**, 8, br g Callernish—Coolbawn Lady **Pell-mell Partners**
42 **SECRET BID (IRE)**, 8, ch g Seclude (USA)—Trial Bid **The Droop Partners**
43 **SHAMARPHIL**, 12, b m Sunyboy—Chaffcombe **Miss S. Barraclough**
44 **SOLOISM**, 5, br m Sulaafah (USA)—Solo Waltz **Mr and Mrs M. C. Yeo**
45 **SUPER TACTICS (IRE)**, 10, b g Furry Glen—Hilarys Pet **Mr H. V. Perry**
46 **THE COCKERTOO**, 7, b g Rakaposhi King—More Rheola **Mr G. Porter**
47 **THE JOLLY BARMAID (IRE)**, 5, b m Don't Forget Me—Gay Broad **Mr J. L. Woolford**
48 **VICOSA (IRE)**, 9, gr g General View—Mesena **Diamond Racing Ltd**
49 **WHO AM I (IRE)**, 8, b g Supreme Leader—Bonny Joe **Mr H. Wellstead**

Other Owners: Mr R. Alner, Mr M. J. Bolwell, Mr David Briers, Mr H. S. Butt, Mr T. J. Carroll, Mr T. H. Chadney, Mr V. K. Champion, Mr J. Chromiak, Ms Janet Creber, Mr B. Curtis, Mr D. R. Curtis, Mr B. Dennett, Mr N. R. Freak, Mr Richard Gilder, Mrs G. M. Habershon-Butcher, Mr J. T. Habershon-Butcher, Mr P. Henley, Mr H. John Irish, Mr Michael A. Johnson, Kavanagh Roofing Southern Limited, Mr C. Kendall, Mrs Audrey Kley, Mr M. T. Lockyer, Mr P. S. Macrae,

MR R. H. ALNER—continued

Mr Dwight Makins, Mrs Penelope Makins, Mrs J. E. Purdie, Mr Anthony Pye-Jeary, Mrs Richard Stanley, Mrs Barbara Tarlo, Mr Laurence Tarlo, Mr G. G. H. Tory, Mrs Monica Tory, Mr Norman Tory, Mrs V. A. Tory, Mr Stephen T. Vass, Mr J. R. Webber, Mr T. Wilson.

Jockey (NH): A Thornton (10-0).

Conditional: N Willmington (9-9).

Amateur: Mr J D Moore (10-0).

Lady Riders: Miss S Barraclough (9-7), Hon Miss D Harding (9-7).

11 MR E. J. ALSTON, Preston

Postal: **Edges Farm Stables, Chapel Lane, Longton, Preston, Lancashire, PR4 5NA.**
Phone: **(01772) 612120 FAX (01772) 612120 MOBILE (0831) 680131**

1 **AMBIDEXTROUS (IRE),** 6, b h Shareef Dancer (USA)—Amber Fizz (USA) **Mrs Carol P. McPhail**
2 **BOWCLIFFE,** 7, b g Petoski—Gwiffina **Mr Philip Davies**
3 **CHINOUR (IRE),** 10, b g Dalsaan—Chishtiya **Edges Farm Racing Stables**
4 **DANTES AMOUR (IRE),** 7, b g Phardante (FR)—Love of Paris **Wetherby Racing Bureau Ltd**
5 **DUKHAN (USA),** 4, b c Silver Hawk (USA)—Azayim **Ms Jan Fletcher O.B.E.**
6 **FLOATING LINE,** 10, ch g Bairn (USA)—County Line **Mr G. Lowe**
7 **GULF SHAADI,** 6, b g Shaadi (USA)—Ela Meem (USA) **The Bibby Halliday Partnership**
8 **HILTONS EXECUTIVE (IRE),** 4, b f Petorius—Theatral **Mr Derek Hilton**
9 **JULMAT JOHN (IRE),** 6, b g Conquering Hero (USA)—Ramich John **Lords Of The Manor**
10 **MADRIGAL CAVALIER,** 5, b m Teenoso (USA)—Springfield Match **Cavalier Carpets Limited**
11 **MARCOMIR (USA),** 5, br h Dayjur (USA)—Mariella (USA) **Mrs Carol P. McPhail**
12 **MURCHAN TYNE (IRE),** 5, ch m Good Thyne (USA)—Ardnamurchan **Harrington Worrall**
13 **NOMORE MR NICEGUY,** 4, b c Rambo Dancer (CAN)—Lariston Gale **Mrs Carol P. McPhail**
14 **ORDAINED,** 5, b m Mtoto—In The Habit (USA) **Peter Ebdon Racing**
15 **POW WOW,** 4, b c Efisio—Mill Hill (USA) **Valley Paddocks Racing Limited**
16 **RYMER'S RASCAL,** 6, b g Rymer—City Sound **Mr Brian Chambers**
17 **SUEZ TORNADO (IRE),** 5, ch g Mujtahid (USA)—So Stylish **Mr Chris Thomas**
18 **SUGA HAWK (IRE),** 6, b g Pennine Walk—Ishtar Abu **Mr John Patrick Barry**
19 **TEDBURROW,** 6, b g Dowsing (USA)—Gwiffina **Mr Philip Davies**
20 **UNSHAKEN,** 4, b c Environment Friend—Reel Foyle (USA) **G.G.Sanderson & M.Twentyman & A.J.Picton**
21 **ZIGGY'S DANCER (USA),** 7, b h Ziggy's Boy (USA)—My Shy Dancer (USA) **Mr John Patrick Barry**

THREE-YEAR-OLDS

22 **POETRY IN MOTION (IRE),** gr f Ballad Rock—Nasseem (FR) **Peter Ebdon Racing**

TWO-YEAR-OLDS

23 **DAMALIS (IRE),** b f 3/4 Mukaddamah (USA)—Art Age (Artaius (USA)) **Mr Liam Ferguson**
24 **DILETTO (IRE),** b f 25/4 Mujadil (USA)—Avidal Park (Horage) **Mr Liam Ferguson**
25 **RECORD TIME,** ch f 27/2 Clantime—On The Record (Record Token) **Mr Peter Onslow**
26 **SHARP EDGE BOY,** gr c 20/4 Mystiko (USA)—Leap Castle (Never So Bold) **Mr A. P. Shandley, Mr N. S. Gilbert**
27 B c 22/5 College Chapel—Tweedling (USA) (Sir Ivor) **Mrs Carol P. McPhail**

Other Owners: Mrs S. Y. Alston, Mr Andrew Bates, Mr S. Bibby, Mr W. Brereton, Mr D. Dowey, Mrs D. K. Ebdon, Mr P. D. Ebdon, Mr M. J. Halliday, Mr R. Halliday, Mr J. F. Harrington, Miss Kim E. Jones, Mr Michael Shaun Kelly, Mr Frank McKevitt, Mr D. C. Pooley, Mr A. M. Proos, Dr J. G. Randall, Miss Cherry Tagart, Mr C. Weir, Mr G. Worrall.

Jockey (Flat): K Fallon (8-1, w.a.).

Apprentice: Melanie Worden (7-10).

12 MR D. W. P. ARBUTHNOT, Compton

Postal: **Hamilton Stables, Compton, Newbury, Berkshire, RG20 6QJ.**
Phone: **COMPTON (01635) 578427 FAX (01635) 578427 MOBILE (0836) 276464**

1 **BEWITCHING LADY,** 4, ch f Primo Dominie—Spirit of India **Mr Noel Cronin**
2 **BRAND NEW DANCE,** 4, b g Gildoran—Starawak **Mr J. S. Gutkin**
3 **DANDE FLYER,** 5, b g Clantime—Lyndseylee **Dandelion Distribution Ltd**
4 **FILMORE WEST,** 5, b g In The Wings—Sistabelle **Mr Christopher Wright**
5 **GINGER ROGERS,** 4, ch f Gildoran—Axe Valley **Mr W. H. Ponsonby**
6 **LAMORNA,** 4, ch f Shavian—Malibasta **Mr W. H. Ponsonby**
7 **MELASUS (IRE),** 6, ch g Nashamaa—Sweet Camden **Mrs S. Watts**
8 **PREMIER GENERATION (IRE),** 5, b g Cadeaux Genereux—Bristle **Mrs W. A. Oram**
9 **PRINCE OF DENIAL,** 4, b c Soviet Star (USA)—Gleaming Water **Mr J. S. Gutkin**
10 **QUEEN'S INSIGNIA (USA),** 5, b m Gold Crest (USA)—Years (USA) **Mr W. H. Ponsonby**
11 **ROBELLION,** 7, b g Robellino (USA)—Tickled Trout **Mr George S. Thompson**
12 **STORM COMMAND,** 4, b g Gildoran—Summer Sky **Henry Ponsonby & Partners (2)**
13 **STRAT'S QUEST,** 4, b f Nicholas (USA)—Eagle's Quest **Mr Jack Blumenow**
14 **TOI TOI (IRE),** 4, b f In The Wings—Walliser **Mr Noel Cronin**

THREE-YEAR-OLDS

15 **CHRYSALIS,** b f Soviet Star (USA)—Vivienda **Mr Christopher Wright**
16 **COURAGE UNDER FIRE,** b g Risk Me (FR)—Dreamtime Quest **Mrs Adrian Ireland**
17 **CUT DIAMOND,** ch c Keen—Diamond Princess **Mr Stephen Crown**
18 B f Lyphento (USA)—La Comedienne **Mr J. Rarrant & Partners**
19 **MERCURY FALLING,** ch f Magic Ring (IRE)—Try The Duchess **Mr Philip Banfield**
20 **SURE QUEST,** b f Sure Blade (USA)—Eagle's Quest **Miss P. E. Decker**

TWO-YEAR-OLDS

21 **CHARLIE'S QUEST,** b c 4/6 Kylian (USA)—Pleasure Quest (Efisio) **Miss P. Decker**
22 Gr f 11/4 Petong—Dark Eyed Lady (IRE) (Exhibitioner) **Mrs M. Gutkin**
23 **FIERY WATERS,** b c 12/4 Rudimentary (USA)—Idle Waters (Mill Reef (USA)) **Mr R. Crutchley, Mrs R. E. Crutchley**
24 B f 27/4 Mujadil (USA)—Kentucky Wildcat (Be My Guest (USA))
25 **MONABIER,** ch c 18/4 Shalford (IRE)—La Pirouette (USA) (Kennedy Road (CAN)) **Mr D. C. Broomfield**
26 **MONKSTON POINT (IRE),** b c 24/4 Fayruz—Doon Belle (Ardoon) **Mr D. C. Broomfield**
27 **PRICE OF PASSION,** b f 19/4 Dolphin Street (FR)—Food of Love (Music Boy) **Mr Noel Cronin**
28 **QUEENS SIGNET,** ch f 11/5 King's Signet (USA)—Axe Valley (Royben) **Mr W. H. Ponsonby**
29 **ZUCCHERO (IRE),** br c 12/4 Dilum (USA)—Legal Sound (Legal Eagle) **Mr Philip Banfield**

Other Owners: Mrs Sue Addington-Smith, Mrs V. Bampton, Mr R. J. Bolam, Mrs B. Cressey, Mr Alan R. Hall, Mrs A. Haynes, Mrs A. Hopkins, Mr Peter F. Jordan, Mrs G. Kindersley, Miss E. A. Lake, Mr D. N. Larke, Mrs B. J. Lee, Lady Judy Martin, Mr D. S. Mossman, Mrs Tessa Mulligan, Mr T. S. Redman, Miss Nicola Ridley, Mrs F. C. Saint Jean, Mr Roddy Shand, Mr S. A. Smith, Lady Whent, Mrs David Woodd, Mr Alan A. Wright, Mrs P. M. Yeomans.

Jockeys (Flat): T Quinn (w.a.), S Whitworth (w.a.).

13 MR R. J. ARMSON, Melbourne

Postal: **Scotlands Farm, Burney Lane, Staunton-Harold, Melbourne, Derbyshire, DE73 1BH.**
Phone: **Home: (01332) 865383 Office: (01332) 865293 Mobile(0468) 996072**

1 **BALLINDOO,** 9, ch g Buzzards Bay—Model Lady **Mr R. J. Armson**
2 **CAN YOU JUST (IRE),** 10, b g Tumble Wind (USA)—Double Figures (FR) **Mr R. J. Armson**
3 **ERIK THE VIKING,** 7, b g Leading Star—Gay Viking **Mr R. J. Armson**
4 **ROYAL HAND,** 8, b g Nearly A Hand—Royal Rushes **Mr R. J. Armson**

Amateur: Mr R J Armson (10-7).

14 MR R. W. ARMSTRONG, Newmarket

Postal: **St Gatien, Newmarket, Suffolk, CB8 8HJ.**
Phone: **(01638) 663333 FAX 662412 MOBILE (0385) 396616**

1 **ABLE LASS (IRE)**, 4, ch f Classic Music (USA)—Miami Life **Dr Cornel Li**
2 **GRAND LAD (IRE)**, 4, ch c Mujtahid (USA)—Supportive (IRE) **Mr Hugh Hart**
3 **KAILEY GODDESS (USA)**, 5, b h Nureyev (USA)—Gay Senorita (USA) **Mr Po Shing Woo**
4 **KAILEY SENOR (USA)**, 5, ch h Woodman (USA)—Sex Appeal (USA) **Mr Po Shing Woo**
5 **NATURAL EIGHT (IRE)**, 4, b c In The Wings—Fenny Rough **Mrs Melody Siu**
6 **SHEER DANZIG (IRE)**, 6, b h Roi Danzig (USA)—Sheer Audacity **Mr R. J. Arculli**
7 **SHEER WARNING (IRE)**, 4, b g Warning—Native Magic **Mr R. J. Arculli**
8 **SILVER KRISTAL**, 4, gr f Kris—Reine d'Beaute **Sir Eric Parker**
9 **TAOISTE**, 5, ch h Kris—Tenue de Soiree (USA) **Mr Po Shing Woo**

THREE-YEAR-OLDS

10 **ABUSAMRAH (USA)**, b c Riverman (USA)—Azayim **Mr Hamdan Al Maktoum**
11 **AFTER EIGHT**, b c Presidium—Vickenda **Mr Michael Siu**
12 **BEWARE**, br c Warning—Dancing Spirit (IRE) **Wyck Hall Stud**
13 **DIVVINAYSHAN (IRE)**, b c Darshaan—Sharaniya (USA) **Mr Ravi Tikkoo**
14 **ETISALAT (IRE)**, b c Lahib (USA)—Sweet Repose **Mr Hamdan Al Maktoum**
15 **FA BELLA FIGURA (USA)**, b c El Gran Senor (USA)—Miss Lilian **Dr G. W. W. Tsoi**
16 **GOLD MIST**, b f Darshaan—Lake Mist **Mrs S. J. McKeever**
17 **HAJAL (IRE)**, b br f Mujtahid (USA)—Three For Fantasy (IRE) **Mr Hamdan Al Maktoum**
18 **HAKEEM (IRE)**, ch c Kefaah (USA)—Masarrah **Mr Ahmed Al Shafar**
19 **HIGHLAND TRACKER (IRE)**, ch c Indian Ridge—Track Twenty Nine (IRE) **Mr Hugh Hart**
20 **IKHTEYAAR (USA)**, br f Mr Prospector (USA)—Linda's Magic (USA) **Mr Hamdan Al Maktoum**
21 **JALAAB (IRE)**, b c Green Desert (USA)—Stay Sharpe (USA) **Mr Hamdan Al Maktoum**
22 **JILA (IRE)**, ch c Kris—Enaya **Mr Hamdan Al Maktoum**
23 **KING LION**, b c Lion Cavern (USA)—Alo Ez **Mr R. J. Arculli**
24 **KIRILOV (IRE)**, b c Roi Danzig (USA)—Ever So **Mr R. N. Bracher**
25 **MUNAZA (USA)**, b br c Trempolino (USA)—Known Feminist (USA) **Mr Hamdan Al Maktoum**
26 **PRIORS MOOR**, br c Petong—Jaziyah (IRE) **Mrs L. Alexander**
27 **RACHAELS NORTH (IRE)**, gr c Night Shift (USA)—Anne de Beaujeu **Mr P. J. Vela**
28 **RAYIK**, br c Marju (IRE)—Matua (IRE) **Mr Hamdan Al Maktoum**
29 **SHADOW CREEK (IRE)**, b c Fairy King (USA)—Daniela Samuel (USA) **Mr R. R. McAnulty**
30 **TAVERNER SOCIETY (IRE)**, b c Imp Society (USA)—Straw Boater **Pink & Blue Ribbon Racing Syndicate**
31 **WARS (IRE)**, b f Green Desert (USA)—Ardassine **Mr Hamdan Al Maktoum**
32 **ZAHA (IRE)**, b c Lahib (USA)—Mayaasa (USA) **Mr Hamdan Al Maktoum**

TWO-YEAR-OLDS

33 **ABLE MILLENIUM (IRE)**, ch c 13/3 Be My Guest (USA)—Miami Life (Miami Springs) **Dr Cornel Li**
34 **ADMIRALS PLACE (IRE)**, ch c 21/4 Perugino (USA)—Royal Daughter (High Top) **Mr C. G. Donovan**
35 **AHDAAB (USA)**, ch f 13/5 Rahy (USA)—Dish Dash (Bustino) **Mr Hamdan Al Maktoum**
36 **ALAAMA (IRE)**, ch f 6/5 Elmaamul (USA)—Rahik (Wassl) **Mr Hamdan Al Maktoum**
37 Ch c 13/3 Thatching—Calaloo Sioux (USA) (Our Native (USA))
38 B c 4/3 Pips Pride—Classic Ring (IRE) (Auction Ring (USA))
39 **HADLEIGH (IRE)**, b c 2/2 Perugino (USA)—Risacco (ITY) (Sir Gaylord) **Mr C. G. Donovan**
40 **HAIFAA (IRE)**, b br f 22/5 Doyoun—Mayaasa (USA) (Lyphard (USA)) **Mr Hamdan Al Maktoum**
41 **INTETHAR**, b c 24/2 Shirley Heights—Mileeha (USA) (Blushing Groom (FR)) **Mr Hamdan Al MaktoumM**
42 **KHUCHN (IRE)**, b c 31/1 Unfuwain (USA)—Stay Sharpe (USA) (Sharpen Up) **Mr Hamden Al Maktoum**
43 **KINAN (USA)**, b c 31/1 Dixieland Band (USA)—Alsharta (USA) (Mr Prospector (USA)) **Mr Hamdan Al Maktoum**
44 B c 15/5 Fayruz—La Gravotte (FR) (Habitat) **Mr Horst Geicke**
45 **MAKNAAS**, ch c 23/1 Wolfhound (USA)—White-Wash (Final Straw) **Mr Hamdan Al Maktoum**
46 **MALAAH (IRE)**, gr c 9/2 Pips Pride—Lingdale Lass (Petong) **Mr Hamdan Al Maktoum**
47 Ch c 16/1 In The Wings—Monus (IRE) (Thatching) **Mr Ahmed Al Shafar**
48 B c 11/3 Lion Cavern (USA)—One Quick Bid (USA) (Commemorate (USA)) **Mr R. J. Arculli**
49 **RED LAD (IRE)**, ch g 27/3 Mujtahid (USA)—Gustavia (IRE) (Red Sunset) **Mrs J. Armstrong**
50 **SULALAT**, br f 30/3 Hamas (IRE)—Enaya (Caerleon (USA)) **Mr Hamdan Al Maktoum**
51 **ZIENAT (USA)**, ch f 25/4 Woodman (USA)—Icy Folly (USA) (Icecapade (USA)) **Mr Hamdan Al Maktoum**

Other Owners: Mr Farhad Azima, Mr Barry Root, Mrs Joan Root, Dr Meou Tsen Geoffrey Yeh.

Jockeys (Flat): Richard Hills, Russell Price.

15 MR J. R. ARNOLD, Upper Lambourn

Postal: **Cedar Lodge, Upper Lambourn, Hungerford, Berkshire, RG17 8QT.**
Phone: **(01488) 73808 FAX (01488) 73826 E-mail: r-arnold@easynet.co.uk.**

1 **BAKERS DAUGHTER**, 6, ch m Bairn (USA)—Tawnais **Mrs Sue A. Baker**
2 **CLAN CHIEF**, 5, b g Clantime—Mrs Meyrick **Mr P. G. Lowe**
3 **CRYHAVOC**, 4, b c Polar Falcon (USA)—Sarabah (IRE) **Mr A. H. Robinson**
4 **SUN O'TIROL (IRE)**, 4, b g Tirol—Nous **Mrs Annette Barwick**

THREE-YEAR-OLDS

5 **APPLE SAUCE**, b f Prince Sabo—Mrs Bacon **Mrs B. Skinner**
6 **BOREAS HILL (IRE)**, b g Petardia—Salonniere (FR) **Mr P. G. Lowe**
7 **JATO DANCER (IRE)**, b f Mukaddamah (USA)—Que Tranquila **Norman Hill**
8 **MARI-ELA (IRE)**, ch f River Falls—Best Swinger (IRE) **Mr J. K. Gale**
9 **MEASURELESS**, ch c Lion Cavern (USA)—Magnetic Point (USA) **Mr A. H. Robinson**
10 **PETANE (IRE)**, b g Petardia—Senane **Mr A. H. Robinson**
11 B g Elmaamul—Ural Dancer **Lady Whent**

TWO-YEAR-OLDS

12 **BRAVE VISION**, b c 23/3 Clantime—Kinlet Vision (IRE) (Vision (USA)) **Mr J. K. Gale**
13 **FAIRYTIME**, b f 23/3 Efisio—Fairy Flax (IRE) (Dancing Brave (USA)) **Mr A. H. Robinson**
14 **LUCY MARIELLA**, b f 5/4 Mystiko (USA)—Deanta In Eirinn (Red Sunset) **Mr T. Barwick**
15 **MERANIE GIRL**, b f 8/4 Mujadil (USA)—Christoph's Girl (Efisio) **Mr George Darling**
16 **ROYAL TARRAGON**, b f 23/4 Aragon—Lady Philippa (IRE) (Taufan (USA)) **Mr A. N. Brooke Rankin**
17 Ch c 29/4 Casteddu—Tawnais (Artaius (USA)) **Mr J. Tahany**

Other Owners: Mr J. R. Arnold, Mr J. T. Arnold, Mr M. T. Else, Dr C. D. Green, Mr A. F. Rae Smith, Mr D. D. Rae Smith, Mrs M. A. Rae Smith, Mrs A. F. Shepherd, Mrs B. Skinner, Mr S. T. Young.

16 MRS P. M. A. AVISON, York

Postal: **Little Manor Farm, Highfield Lane, Nawton, York, York, YO6 5TU.**
Phone: **(01439) 771672**

1 **PRAH SANDS**, 5, b g Henbit (USA)—Minor Furlong **Mr M. Avison**
2 **PRINCE SKYBURD**, 7, b g Domynsky—Burntwood Lady **Mrs P. M. A. Avison**
3 **TABRIZ**, 5, b m Persian Heights—Faisalah **Mr George Coates**

17 MR N. G. AYLIFFE, Minehead

Postal: **Glebe Stables, Little Ham, Winsford, Minehead, Somerset, TA24 7JH.**
Phone: **WINSFORD (0164385) 265**

1 **DANTE'S RUBICON (IRE)**, 7, ch g Common Grounds—Dromorehill **Mr R. A. Bimson**
2 **GRIFFIN'S GIRL**, 6, ch m Bairn (USA)—All That Crack **Mr N. G. Ayliffe**
3 **MILESTONE**, 6, b g Presidium—Light de Light (USA) **Mr R. Allatt**
4 **PROUD IMAGE**, 6, b g Zalazl (USA)—Fleur de Foret (USA) **Mr D. T. Hooper**
5 **ROUTING**, 10, b g Rousillon (USA)—Tura **Mr Derek Jones**
6 **SPARKLING BUCK**, 6, gr m Buckley—Sparkling Time (USA) **Mr J. R. Wootten**
7 **THEOS (IRE)**, 4, b g Darshaan—Salabella **Mr Derek Jones**
8 8, B m Sergeant Drummer (USA)—Twenty Minutes **Mr R. Hayes**

THREE-YEAR-OLDS

9 Ch f No Evil—Classical Chimes **Mr D. T. Hooper**

Other Owners: Mrs S. L. Hooper.

18 MR J. W. F. AYNSLEY, Morpeth

Postal: **Rye Hill Farm, Thropton, Morpeth, Northd, NE65 7NG.**
Phone: **(01669) 620271**

1 **CHAIN LINE,** 8, br g Relkino—Housemistress **Mr J. W. F. Aynsley**
2 **RYE RUM (IRE),** 7, br g Strong Gale—Eimers Pet **Mr J. W. F. Aynsley**

Jockeys (NH): R Hodge, P Niven, B Storey.

19 MR A. BAILEY, Tarporley

Postal: **Sandybrow Stables, Little Budworth, Tarporley, Cheshire, CW6 9EG.**
Phone: **(01829) 760762 FAX (01829) 760370**

1 **AIRBORNE HARRIS (IRE),** 5, ch g Persian Heights—Excuse Slip (USA) **Hammer And Pincers Partnership**
2 **AMYLOU,** 5, b m Dunbeath (USA)—La Chiquita **Mr I. Bell**
3 **ANDY CLYDE,** 5, b g Rambo Dancer (CAN)—Leprechaun Lady **Sandybrow Stables Ltd**
4 **BEA'S RUBY (IRE),** 4, b f Fairy King (USA)—Beautiful Secret (USA) **Mr M. Tabor & Mrs John Magnier**
5 **BODFARI WREN,** 4, b f Handsome Sailor—My Valentine Card (USA) **Bodfari Stud Ltd**
6 **CALLFOURSEASONS (IRE),** 6, b g Euphemism—Home And Dry **Mr J. E. Stockton**
7 **EVERSET (FR),** 10, b g Green Desert (USA)—Eversince (USA) **Sandybrow Stables Ltd**
8 **GADGE,** 7, br g Nomination—Queenstyle **Mr J. B. Wilcox**
9 **HIGHLY RESPECTED (IRE),** 4, b f High Estate—Respectfully (USA) **Mr Gordon Mytton**
10 **HYPE SUPERIOR (IRE),** 4, ch g Mac's Imp (USA)—Katysue **Mr Robert Cox**
11 **IKRAM BOY (USA),** 4, b g Salem Drive (USA)—Vast Domain (CAN) **Mr Ahmed Farook**
12 5, B g Glacial Storm (USA)—Impressive Reward (USA) **Mr G. White**
13 **JOB RAGE (IRE),** 4, b br g Yashgan—Snatchingly **Sandybrow Stables Ltd**
14 **KOMREYEV DANCER,** 6, b g Komaite (USA)—L'Ancressaan **Mr Denis Gallagher**
15 **LORD SKY,** 7, b g Emarati (USA)—Summer Sky **Mr Ray Bailey**
16 **MARJORIE ROSE (IRE),** 5, b m Magical Strike (USA)—Arrapata **Sandybrow Stables Ltd**
17 **MARTINE,** 4, ch f Clantime—Marcroft **Mr C. Clayton**
18 **REBEL COUNTY (IRE),** 5, b m Maelstrom Lake—Haven Bridge **Showtime Ice Cream Concessionaire**
19 **ROYALE ROSE (FR),** 4, ch f Bering—Rose Blanche (USA) **Bodfari Stud Ltd**
20 **SAFIO,** 5, ch g Efisio—Marcroft **Mrs M. A. Clayton**
21 **SILENCE IN COURT (IRE),** 7, b g Law Society (USA)—Fair Flutter **Mr Peter G. Freeman**
22 **SO KEEN,** 5, ch g Keen—Diana's Bow **Mr Ray Bailey**
23 **TAEL OF SILVER,** 6, b m Today And Tomorrow—Schula **Mr Peter G. Freeman**
24 **WENTBRIDGE LAD (IRE),** 8, b g Coquelin (USA)—Cathryn's Song **Mr John Pugh**

THREE-YEAR-OLDS

25 **ASHLEIGH BAKER (IRE),** b br f Don't Forget Me—Gayla Orchestra **The David James Partnership**
26 **BODFARIDISTINCTION (IRE),** b f Distinctly North (USA)—Brave Louise **Bodfari Stud Ltd**
27 **BODFARI PRIDE (IRE),** b g Pips Pride—Renata's Ring (IRE) **Bodfari Stud Ltd**
28 **CAROLINE'S PET (IRE),** b f Contract Law (USA)—Princess Roxanne **Mr G. White**
29 **CHASKA,** b f Reprimand—Royal Passion **Mr J. B. Wilcox**
30 **LADY IMZA,** b f Polar Falcon (USA)—Blade of Grass **Mr Ahmed Farook**
31 **LAMBRINI LAD (IRE),** b g Shalford (IRE)—Swift Reply **Halewood International Ltd**
32 **MAMBLE'S PENSION (IRE),** ch f Elmaamul (USA)—Chance All (FR) **Simple Technology UK Ltd**
33 **MR MIYAGI,** b g Full Extent (USA)—All The Girls (IRE) **Sandybrow Stables Ltd**
34 **PHANTOM RING,** ch f Magic Ring (IRE)—Follow The Stars **Mr Ray Bailey**
35 **SIAN'S GIRL,** gr f Mystiko (USA)—Embroglio (USA) **Cormell Bros**
36 **SOAP STONE,** b f Gunner B—Tzarina (USA) **Mr G. V. Gann**
37 **SUPER SNIP,** ch c Superpower—Marcroft **Mrs M. A. Clayton**

TWO-YEAR-OLDS

38 **DIAMOND ROUGE,** b f 12/3 Puissance—Maravilla (Mandrake Major) **Diamond Racing**
39 Ch f 15/5 Clantime—Lyndseylee (Swing Easy (USA)) **Sandybrow Stables Ltd**
40 Ch f 9/3 Risk Me (FR)—Miss Serlby (Runnett) **Sandybrow Stables Ltd**

MR A. BAILEY—continued

41 **MYTTON'S MOMENT (IRE),** b c 20/4 Waajib—Late Swallow (My Swallow) **Mr Gordon Mytton**
42 **PRIDEWAY (IRE),** b f 23/3 Pips Pride—Up The Gates (Captain James) **Mr N. C. Jones**
43 Ch f 30/1 Clantime—Tendency (Ballad Rock) **Sandybrow Stables Ltd**

Other Owners: Mrs J. Bailey, Mr Ken Baker, Mr C. P. Bayliss, Mr Rob Beardmore, Mr A. H. Bennett, Mr K. Benson, Mr P. Cosgrove, Mr S. A. Ewart, Mr R. Farrington, Mr E. J. Gilbertson, Mrs P. Hewitt, Mr Bob Heywood, Mrs S. P. Jones, Mr T. J. Kelly, Mr R. Kinsey, Mr P. J. Lawton, Miss V. C. Lawton, Mr Darren C. Mercer, Mr R. Mills, Mr J. M. Newbould, Mr J. Parry, Mr D. O. Pickering, Reach Recruitment Limited, Miss B. E. Roberts, Mr A. Thomson, Mrs C. A. Wallace, Mr T. S. Wallace, Mrs Fiona Williams, Mr Bill Woodward.

Apprentices: Anthony Bond, James Bosley.

Amateurs: Miss Bridget Gatehouse, Mr David Bernard Shaw.

Ladv Rider: Miss E Gatehouse.

20 MR K. C. BAILEY, Upper Lambourn

Postal: **The Old Manor, Upper Lambourn, Hungerford, Berkshire, RG17 8RG.**
Phone: **LAMBOURN (01488) 71483 FAX LAMBOURN (01488) 72978**

1 **ALLEGRIA,** 6, b g Derrylin—Goldaw **Mrs Sharon C. Nelson**
2 **ANDRE LAVAL (IRE),** 9, ch g Over The River (FR)—French Academy **Mrs Christopher Wright**
3 **ANNIE BUCKERS (IRE),** 7, br m Yashgan—Glenkins **Mr A. M. Grazebrook**
4 **ARTIC BAY,** 6, b g Arctic Lord—Galley Bay **Mrs Jacqueline Conroy**
5 **AWARD (IRE),** 7, b g Executive Perk—Stage Debut **Mrs Philippa Cooper**
6 **BADGE OF FAME (IRE),** 4, gr g Caerleon (USA)—Infamy **Mr John Law**
7 **BADGER'S LANE,** 7, b g Don't Forget Me—Rose Parade **Sir Gordon Brunton**
8 **BENVENUTO,** 7, b g Neltino—Rydewells Daughter **Mrs Lucia Farmer**
9 **BERTONE (IRE),** 9, b g Montelimar (USA)—Lady of Eilat **Mrs Harry J. Duffey**
10 **BIBURY COURT (IRE),** 6, b g Henbit (USA)—Hard Lady **Mr Huw Davies**
11 5, Gr g Roselier (FR)—Brau Ble Lane **Mrs J. M. Corbett**
12 **CARIBOO GOLD (USA),** 9, b g Slew O' Gold (USA)—Selket's Treasure (USA) **Mrs Sharon C. Nelson**
13 5, B g Yashgan—Carrigart **Mrs E. Kellar**
14 **CARRINGTON HOUSE,** 5, b g Teenoso (USA)—Erica Superba **Mr I. F. W. Buchan**
15 **CELTIC PARK,** 8, b g Celtic Cone—Once Bitten **Mr Urs E. Schwarzenbach**
16 **CHEVAL DE GUERRE (IRE),** 7, b g Satco (FR)—Treasured Gift **Mr John Stanley**
17 **CLINTON (IRE),** 7, b g Lord Americo—Diana's Flyer **Mr E. N. Thomas**
18 **CONCHOBOR (IRE),** 6, b br g Supreme Leader—Nights Crack **Scott Hardy Partnership**
19 **COSA FUAIR (IRE),** 8, b g Roselier (FR)—Bold And True **Mr Martyn Booth**
20 **CROOKEDSTONE (IRE),** 6, br g Brush Aside (USA)—Pops Princess (IRE) **Major-Gen. R. L. T. Burges**
21 **CYRUS THE GREAT (IRE),** 6, ch g Persian Heights—Smart As Paint (USA) **Mr P. J. Vogt**
22 **DANCING LAIRD,** 6, ch g Scottish Reel—Well Connected **This Horse Is For Sale Partnership**
23 **DANDE DOVE,** 7, gr g Baron Blakeney—Ryans Dove **Dandelion Distribution Ltd**
24 **DOASYOULIKE (IRE),** 6, b br g Hollow Hand—Maeve's Choice **Leeds Plywood and Doors Ltd**
25 **DRUID'S BROOK,** 9, b g Meadowbrook—Struide **Major A. M. Everett**
26 **DRUMCULLEN (IRE),** 9, gr g Celio Rufo—Lawless Secret **Mr Martyn Booth**
27 **DUN COADY (IRE),** 9, b g Duky—Vesper Time **Top Brass Partnership**
28 **FEEL THE POWER (IRE),** 10, b g Torus—Donadea **Mr Martyn Booth**
29 **FRENO (IRE),** 7, ch g Henbit (USA)—Sapphire Red **Mr P. A. Matthews**
30 **FULL OF FIRE,** 11, ch g Monksfield—Sheila's Flame **Mr J. M. Gillow**
31 **FUTURE KING,** 11, b g Dynastic—Forthcoming **Mr Martyn Booth**
32 5, B g Executive Perk—Golden Chestnut **Mr K. C. Bailey**
33 **GRANHAM PRIDE (IRE),** 8, ch g The Parson—Stand In **I. M. S. Racing**
34 **HAVEN'T AN OCEAN (IRE),** 7, ch g Over The River (FR)—Money For Honey **Mrs Philippa Cooper**
35 **HERBERT LODGE (IRE),** 9, b g Montelimar (USA)—Mindyourbusiness **Mrs Harry J. Duffey**

MR K. C. BAILEY—continued

36 **HOMME DE FER,** 6, b g Arctic Lord—Florence May **Miss M. Vencatagadoo**
37 **KAMIKAZE,** 8, gr g Kris—Infamy **Major B. Gatensbury**
38 **KITTY SUPREME (IRE),** 6, b m Supreme Leader—Kitty Cullen **Mr D. A. Mayes**
39 **LAUGHING FONTAINE (IRE),** 8, b g Lafontaine (USA)—Graig Island **The Laughing Stock**
40 **LOBSTER COTTAGE,** 10, b g Southern Music—Seal Flower **Major-Gen. R. L. T. Burges**
41 **LUCIA FORTE,** 7, b m Neltino—Celtic Well **Mrs Lucia Farmer**
42 **MANNEKEN PIS (IRE),** 5, b g Royal Fountain—Cree's Figurine **Mr G. W. Cleaver**
43 **MAORI WISDOM,** 6, b g Be My Native (USA)—Kakapo **Willsford Racing Incorporated**
44 **MESA VERDE (IRE),** 7, b br g Yashgan—Random Princess **Mrs Philippa Cooper**
45 **MONTEL'S FRIEND (IRE),** 5, b m Montelimar (USA)—Gaye Diane **Mrs Jacqueline Conroy**
46 **MYSTERE (IRE),** 5, b m Montelimar (USA)—Fine Gale **Mrs Christine Davies**
47 **ODELL (IRE),** 8, br g Torus—Indian Isle **Mrs Christine Davies**
48 **PARTY ANIMAL (IRE),** 6, b g Buckskin (FR)—More Chat **Mr David G. W. Curtis**
49 **PERRYMAN (IRE),** 7, ch g Good Thyne (USA)—Poetic Lady **Mrs S. C. Ellen**
50 **PERSIAN VIEW (IRE),** 8, ch g Persian Bold—Recapture **Racing Club KCB**
51 **POLAR LORD (IRE),** 6, b g Lord Americo—Polar Princess **The No-One Nose Partnership**
52 **POLYDAMAS,** 6, b h Last Tycoon—Graecia Magna (USA) **Mr Martin Boase**
53 **PRICE'S HILL,** 11, gr g Furry Glen—Clever Milly **Mr G. D. W. Swire**
54 **PRUSSIAN EAGLE (IRE),** 6, b m Strong Gale—Court Session **Quicksilver Racing Partnership**
55 **QUITE LIVELY (IRE),** 6, b g Roselier (FR)—Restless Saint **May We Never Be Found Out Partnership**
56 **REGAL SPRING (IRE),** 6, b g Royal Fountain—Ride The Rapids **Mr John Grist**
57 **ROYAL PHILOSOPHER,** 6, b g Faustus (USA)—Princess Lucy **Mr A. Miller**
58 **SHERWOOD BOY,** 9, ch g Seclude (USA)—Madame Persian **Mr Peter Granger**
59 **SIMPLE ARITHMETIC,** 10, ch g Southern Music—Graphics Eska **Mrs M. Motley**
60 **SPARKLING SPRING (IRE),** 7, b g Strong Gale—Cherry Jubilee **Mr E. Benfield**
61 **SPRUNG RHYTHM (IRE),** 8, ch g Remainder Man—Creation Lady **The Sporting Has Beens**
62 **STEEL BLADE (IRE),** 5, gr g Lafontaine (USA)—Steal On **Mrs Philippa Cooper**
63 **STRONG BREW (IRE),** 6, br g Strong Gale—Teapot Hall **Lady St Clair-Ford, J.Perriss S.Marshall**
64 **STRONG MEDICINE,** 11, b g Strong Gale—In The Forest **Dr D. B. A. Silk**
65 **STRONG VISION (IRE),** 7, b g Strong Gale—Deep Vision **Mr I. F. W. Buchan**
66 **SUPREME CHARM (IRE),** 6, b g Sovereign Water (FR)—Welsh Charmer **Mr P. J. Vogt**
67 **TALLIS (IRE),** 6, br g Orchestra—Deep Slaney **Mr E. N. Thomas**
68 **THE LADY SCORES (IRE),** 6, br m Orchestra—Lysanders Lady **Mr A. F. Lousada**
69 **THE WHOLE HOG (IRE),** 9, b g Cataldi—Beeston **Mrs Harry J. Duffey**
70 **TIDEBROOK,** 8, ch h Callernish—Hayley **Mr Richard Williams**
71 **TIM FRENCH (IRE),** 6, ch g John French—Annalough Rose **Mr P. Henley**
72 **TRICKY TREVOR (IRE),** 5, b br g Arctic Lord—Chancer's Last **Mr W. J. Ives**
73 **TROUBLE AHEAD (IRE),** 7, b g Cataldi—Why 'o' Why **Mrs Sharon C. Nelson**
74 **UP THE SLANEY (IRE),** 6, b m Over The River (FR)—Twice As Fluffy **Mr G. P. D. Milne**
75 **VICAR'S VASE,** 5, b m Montelimar (USA)—Church Leap **Mr G. P. D. Milne**
76 **WINDLE BROOK,** 6, b g Gildoran—Minigale **Mr Peter Granger**

Other Owners: Sarah Lady Allendale, Mr D. F. Allport, Capt. F. Barker, Mr Alastair Beck, Mr C. R. Black, Mr A. J. Brettell, Mr W. J. Brown, Mr Ian Bullerwell, Mr Philip Buscombe, Mr M. C. Byrne, Dr S. R. Cannon, Mr D. M. Clancy, Mr Kevin T. Clancy, Miss M. P. Clancy, Mr J. Conroy, Mr Noel Cronin, Mr P. A. Deal, Mr D. R. Du Croz, Mr S. T. Ellen, Mr P. Fowler, Mrs Laura Goedhuis, Mrs Peter Granger, Mr H. C. Hardy, Mr D. W. R. Harland, Mr Patrick Hayes, Major Basil Heaton, Mrs Jennifer Heaton, Mr A. J. Heyes, Mr D. A. Hibbert, Mr D. F. Hill, Mr A Hunter, Mr D. J. Jarvis, Mrs Ann L. Jones, Mr Richard I. G. Jones, Mr B. J. Kelly, Mr Michael Kerr-Dineen, Mr M. W. Kwiatkowski, Mr A. G. Lay, Mr Marco Lehmann, The Hon C. Leigh, Mrs E. A. Lerpiniere, Mrs D. Lousada, Mrs Jayne Mackintosh, Mr David R. Martin, Mrs Julie Martin, Mr D. Masters, Major G. H. W. Oakford, Mr Craig Pearman, Mrs K. Peyton, Mr E. Pick, Mr R. K. Purkis, Mr Preston Rabl, Mr Keith Robinson, Mr A. Scott, Mr M. A. Sherwood, Mr D. Sieff, Mr D. M. Simpson, Mr A. N. Solomons, Mrs I. M. Steinman, Mr J. D. Steinman, Mr T. N. Stopford Sackville, Mr T. R. Thomas, Mrs David Thompson, Mrs D. Todd, Mr David Todd, Mr Robert Warden, Mr M. Whelan, Mr Peter Wiegand, Miss Sarah Wills, Miss J. Winch, Mr Christopher Wright, Ms Nancy Yearsley.

Jockeys (NH): A Thornton (10-0), N Williamson.

Conditional: W Walsh.

Amateurs: Mr E Byrne, Mr R Forristal (9-7), Mr R Wakley.

21 MR R. J. BAKER, Tiverton

Postal: **Steart House Racing Stables, Stoodleigh, Tiverton, Devon, EX16 9QA.**
Phone: **(01398) 351317**

1 **ANOTHER HUBBLICK,** 7, ch g Nearly A Hand—Sue Lark **Mr T. Hubbard**
2 **BLACK VELVET,** 6, b g Arctic Lord—Rose Window **Mr G. K. Hullett**
3 **BOWDEN SURPRISE,** 8, ch g Morgans Choice—Bankers Surprise **Mr R. J. Baker**
4 **COEUR BATTANT (FR),** 8, ch g General Holme (USA)—Feerie Boreale (FR) **Mr B. P. Jones**
5 **COOCHIE,** 9, b m King of Spain—York Street (USA) **Mr S. M. McCausland**
6 **DTOTO,** 6, b g Mtoto—Deposit **Mr B. P. Jones**
7 5, B m Joligeneration—Fast Market **Mr S. Cornew**
8 **GUSHY,** 12, ch g Hard Fought—Be Gustful **Mr B. P. Jones**
9 **HAPPY HOUR,** 4, b g Joligeneration—La Belle Vie **Mr V. R. Lawson**
10 **KEVASINGO,** 6, b g Superpower—Katharina **Horses Away Racing Club**
11 **MOGUL,** 4, b g Formidable (USA)—Madiyla **Mr R. J. Baker**
12 **MUSIC CLASS (IRE),** 7, ch g Orchestra—Tacova **Horses Away Racing Club**
13 **MU-TADIL,** 6, gr g Be My Chief (USA)—Inveraven **Mrs V. W. Jones**
14 **MUTAWALI (IRE),** 8, ch g Exactly Sharp (USA)—Ludovica **Mr John Warren**
15 **NORFOLK GLORY,** 6, ch g Weldnaas (USA)—Caviar Blini **Oak Ford Horse Transport**
16 **OFFICE HOURS,** 6, b g Danehill (USA)—Charmina (FR) **Oak Ford Horse Transport**
17 **OLD MASTER (IRE),** 7, b g Tate Gallery (USA)—Nancy Drew **Mr S. M. McCausland**
18 **OPERA FESTIVAL (IRE),** 8, ch g Buckskin (FR)—Glencairn Belle **Mr B. P. Jones**
19 **ORANGE JUICE (IRE),** 8, b g Orange Reef—Vital Spirit **Mr R. J. Baker**
20 **PEARLA DUBH (IRE),** 9, b g Over The River (FR)—Canverb **Mr E. Madden**
21 **RAPID LINER,** 5, b g Skyliner—Stellaris **Mrs V. W. Jones**
22 **RICH LIFE (IRE),** 8, b g Dance of Life (USA)—Ringawoody **Mr B. P. Jones**
23 **ROAD TO AU BON (USA),** 10, b g Strawberry Road (AUS)—Village Lady (USA) **Mr M. H. Holland**
24 **SAAFI (IRE),** 7, b g Primo Dominie—Baby's Smile **Mr H. J. W. Davies**
25 **STAR PLAYER,** 12, ch g Simply Great (FR)—Star Girl **Mr P. K. Smith**
26 **TANGO'S DELIGHT,** 10, b g Idiot's Delight—Lucky Tango **Mr B. P. Jones**
27 **TAP SHOES (IRE),** 8, b g Nordance (USA)—Dance Fan **Mr R. J. Baker**
28 **TIOTAO (IRE),** 8, b g Burslem—Linbel **Mr R. J. Baker**
29 **WESTERN PLAYBOY,** 6, b g Law Society (USA)—Reine d'Beaute **Mr B. P. Jones**

Other Owners: Mr D. F. Bassett, Mr H. J. W. Davies, Mr M. H. Holland, Horses Away Racing Club, Mr T. Hubbard, Mr G. K. Hullett, Mr B. P. Jones, Mrs V. W. Jones, Mr Robin Lawson, Mr E. Madden, Mr S. M. McCausland, Trefusis Farm, Mr John Warren, Mr A. White.

Jockey (Flat): V Slattery (8-6).

Jockey (NH): V Slattery (10-0).

22 MR G. B. BALDING, Andover

Postal: **Fyfield Stables, Fyfield, Andover, Hampshire, SP11 8EW.**
Phone: **TEL (01264) 772278 FAX (01264) 771221**

1 **ARGUABLY,** 6, ch g Sharp Deal—Dusty Run **Mrs Colin Murray**
2 **BALLYMICHAEL (IRE),** 6, br g Riberetto—Shuil Le Dia **Mr J. H. C. Harris**
3 **BAVARDIER (IRE),** 7, ch g Le Bavard (FR)—Clairellen **Bavardier Partnership**
4 **BELLATOR,** 5, b g Simply Great (FR)—Jupiter's Message **Mr P. Richardson**
5 **BLAIR CASTLE (IRE),** 7, b g Waajib—Caimanite **Highflyers**
6 **BOOTS N ALL (IRE),** 8, bl g Strong Statement (USA)—Sallstown **Mrs Toni S. Tipper**
7 **BRAVE TORNADO,** 7, ch g Dominion—Accuracy **Miss B. Swire**
8 **BULLSHOT (IRE),** 5, ch g Torus—Barnmeen Lass (IRE) **Strauss Partnership**
9 **CA'D'ORO,** 5, ch g Cadeaux Genereux—Palace Street (USA) **Miss B. Swire**

MR G. B. BALDING—continued

10 **CALANDRELLA,** 5, b m Sizzling Melody—Maravilla **Mr M. Clemence**
11 **CAMPECHE BAY (IRE),** 9, b g Sandalay—Golden Goose **Mr J. M. Kinnear**
12 **CHARMER'S WELL (IRE),** 10, b g Beau Charmeur (FR)—Palmers Well **Mr G. B. Balding**
13 **CHASING THE MOON (IRE),** 6, b g Yashgan—Super Cailin **Renking**
14 **CONTI D'ESTRUVAL (FR),** 8, b g Synefos (USA)—Barbara Conti (ITY) **Mr Bernard Keay**
15 **CUGINA,** 4, b f Distant Relative—Indubitable **Miss B. Swire**
16 **DANCING POSER (IRE),** 6, b g Posen (USA)—Naughty Lass **Baldings (Training) Ltd**
17 **DUKESTOWN (IRE),** 6, b g Duky—Small Iron **The Rumble Racing Club**
18 **FOOLS ERRAND (IRE),** 8, b g Fools Holme (USA)—Zalazula **Mrs David Russell**
19 **GOLDENSWIFT (IRE),** 8, ch m Meneval (USA)—Golden Seekers **Mrs S. Watts**
20 **GREY TROOPER (IRE),** 5, gr h Celio Rufo—Mrs Sauga **Mrs D. Claessen-Brierton**
21 **HARRISTOWN LADY,** 11, b m Muscatite—Harristown Rose **Mr Roger J. Spencer**
22 **HIBERNICA (IRE),** 4, b br f Law Society (USA)—Brave Ivy **Mr Theo Waddington**
23 **HUNGARIAN QUEEN,** 7, ch m Sunley Builds—May Lady **Mrs Anthony Andrews**
24 **HURDANTE (IRE),** 8, ch g Phardante (FR)—Hurry **TJA Consultants Ltd**
25 **JIMMY'S CROSS (IRE),** 8, ch g Phardante (FR)—Foredefine **Leslie Garratt Racing**
26 **KEYNOTE (IRE),** 6, ch g Orchestra—St Moritz **Michael Jackson Bloodstock Ltd**
27 **KINNAHALLA (IRE),** 6, b m Lancastrian—Eadestown **Mr Roger J. Spencer**
28 **KORALOONA (IRE),** 5, b g Archway (IRE)—Polynesian Charm (USA) **Mr Bernard Keay**
29 **LORD BUSTER,** 5, gr g Bustino—Crispahan **Strauss Partnership**
30 **LOSLOMOS (IRE),** 6, b g The Bart (USA)—Katebeaujolais **Russell Publishing Ltd**
31 **MASTER PILGRIM,** 6, b g Supreme Leader—Patterdon **Mr J. M. Kinnear**
32 **MAYDAY DANCER (IRE),** 5, b m Strong Gale—Paperchain **Miss B. Swire**
33 **ORIENTAL STYLE (IRE),** 4, ro g Indian Ridge—Bazaar Promise **Style Partners**
34 **PA D'OR (USA),** 8, ch g Slew O' Gold (USA)—Padelia **Scott Trotter Partnership**
35 **PALAEMON,** 4, b g Slip Anchor—Palace Street (USA) **Miss B. Swire**
36 **PEVERIL PENDRAGON,** 4, b g Emarati (USA)—Princess Siham **Mrs E. A. Haycock**
37 **PHAR FROM FUNNY,** 7, ch g Phardante (FR)—Joca **Mrs E. A. Haycock**
38 **PHONETIC,** 5, b g Shavian—So True **Miss B. Swire**
39 **PIPER'S ROCK (IRE),** 7, ch g Zaffaran (USA)—Misclaire **Baldings (Training) Ltd**
40 **POLDEN PRIDE,** 10, b g Vital Season—Bybrook **D. F. Lockyer,C. A. Parry,G. B. Balding**
41 **PROUD TOBY (IRE),** 8, b br g Lancastrian—Lady Conkers **Mr J. M. Kinnear**
42 **RAMBLING SAM (IRE),** 6, b g Detroit Sam (FR)—Rambling Moss **Mr Q. J. Jones**
43 **RASHSKIN (IRE),** 7, br g Rashar (USA)—Mary Buckskin **Mr Bernard Keay**
44 **REITERATE,** 5, b m Then Again—Indubitable **Miss B. Swire**
45 **ROBSAND (IRE),** 9, b g Sandalay—Remindful **Sir Brian McGrath**
46 **SAVUTI (IRE),** 9, ch g Amoristic (USA)—Aprils Choice **Mrs Toni S. Tipper**
47 **SEA FREEDOM,** 7, b h Slip Anchor—Rostova **Miss B. Swire**
48 **SECRET LOCH,** 6, b g Lochnager—Be Serious (USA) **Mr Q. J. Jones**
49 **SIR PRIZE (IRE),** 5, b g Prince Rupert (FR)—Banasiya **Michael Jackson Bloodstock Ltd**
50 **SOUTHAMPTON,** 8, b g Ballacashtal (CAN)—Petingo Gold **Highflyers**
51 **SOUTHERN SURVIVOR (IRE),** 6, b m Gildoran—Joca **Baldings (Trainings) Ltd**
52 **STAR PRECISION,** 4, ch f Shavian—Accuracy **Miss B. Swire**
53 **SUPER SERENADE,** 9, b g Beldale Flutter (USA)—Super Melody **Baldings (Training) Ltd**
54 **SWIFT VENTURE (IRE),** 6, b g Meneval (USA)—Golden Seekers **The On The Run Partnership**
55 **TAUFAN BOY,** 5, b h Taufan (USA)—Lydia Maria **Supreme Team**
56 **THE FLYING DOCTOR (IRE),** 8, b g Camden Town—Sparkling Opera **Mr David M. Williams**
57 **THE ISLANDER,** 5, b g Derrylin—Lindisfarne Rose **Mr A. G. F. Leather**
58 **THE REVEREND BERT (IRE),** 10, b g Decent Fellow—Best of Kin **The Bollie Club**
59 **THE RURAL DEAN (IRE),** 7, ch g Good Thyne (USA)—Best of Kin **Baldings (Training) Ltd**
60 **TIMOTHY GEORGE (IRE),** 4, b g Don't Forget Me—Ward of Court (IRE) **Mr Theo Waddington**
61 **TOM PINCH (IRE),** 9, b g Mandalus—Spanish Royale **Baldings (Training) Ltd**
62 **TRACEYTOWN (IRE),** 6, ch m Lancastrian—Knockarone Star **Mr J. G. Thatcher**
63 **TUG OF PEACE,** 11, b g Tug of War—Ardglass Pride **Mr P. Richardson**
64 **VICTORY TEAM (IRE),** 6, b g Danehill (USA)—Hogan's Sister (USA) **Mr R. J. Lavelle**

THREE-YEAR-OLDS

65 **BOMB ALASKA,** br g Polar Falcon (USA)—So True **Miss B. Swire**
66 **BRONZINO,** ch g Midyan (USA)—Indubitable **Miss B. Swire**

MR G. B. BALDING—continued

67 CHIEF CASHIER, b g Persian Bold—Kentfield **Surgical Spirits**
68 DELPHIC WAY, b f Warning—Palace Street (USA) **Miss B. Swire**
69 LORD WARFORD, b g Bustino—Jupiter's Message **Mr P. Richardson**
70 LUCKY LOVER (IRE), br c Ballad Rock—Petticoat Lane **Mrs J. Doveton**
71 MAGIC POWERS, ch g Magical Wonder (USA)—Kissin' Cousin **Highflyers**
72 ROSY SCINTILLA (IRE), b f Thatching—Regal Scintilla **Mr Theo Waddington**
73 WATER FORCE, b g River Falls—Quelle Chemise **Mr B. T. Attenborough**

TWO-YEAR-OLDS

74 CITY GUILD, b g 4/5 Saddlers' Hall (IRE)—Indubitable (Sharpo) **Miss B. Swire**
75 Br c 27/3 Unblest—Jumana (Windjammer (USA))
76 Br f 7/3 Tirol—La Duse (Junius (USA))
77 LITTLE PIPPIN, ch f 12/2 Rudimentary (USA)—Accuracy (Gunner B) **Miss B. Swire**
78 Ch g 7/2 Superlative—Louisianalightning (Music Boy)
79 L V GIRL, ch f 15/3 Mukaddamah (USA)—Penny Fan (Nomination) **Mrs C. Richardson**
80 RIVER'S SPARKLE, b f 15/5 River Falls—El Zaana (Priamos (GER)) **Mrs K. L. Perrin**
81 B f 12/4 Magical Wonder (USA)—Shamanka (IRE) (Shernazar)
82 Br c 18/4 Rock Hopper—Strike Home (Be My Guest (USA)) **Mr David M. Williams**
83 B f 27/4 Robellino (USA)—Top Treat (USA) (Topsider (USA))
84 B g 10/5 Then Again—Whitchurch Silk (IRE) (Runnett) **Mr G. B. Balding**

Other Owners: Mr P. J. G. Aldous, Atlantic Foods Ltd, Mrs B. T. Attenborough, Mrs G. B. Balding, Mr T. R. Bull, Mr Chris Burrell, Mr W. Craig, Mr David Erwin, Mr L. J. Garrett, Mrs Margaret Geake, Mr Tony Geake, Mrs P. D. Gulliver, Mr P. J. Hartnett, Mr M. F. Jackson, Mr R. A. Keen, Kendall White & Co Ltd, Wing Cmdr J. H. King, Miss M. Lane, Dr J. M. Leigh, Mr Steve Miller, Mr Jim Milward, Mr Stephen W. Molloy, Mrs Margaret Renshaw, Mr C. T. Scott, Mr L. Shack, Mrs S. Shack, Mr G. P. Spanner, Mrs Derek Strauss, Mr Derek Strauss, Major G. D. B. Thatcher, Mr T. H. S. Trotter, Mr N. F. Weir, Michael Wood-Power.

Jockey (Flat): S Drowne (8-0, w.a.).

Jockeys (NH): B Clifford (10-0), B Fenton (10-0), S Fox (10-0), A P McCoy (10-0).

Apprentices: R Lake (8-0), F Tynan (8-7).

Conditional: F Keniry (9-7).

Amateurs: Mr E Babington (9-7), Mr A Balding (10-7).

Lady Rider: Miss S Newby-Vincent (9-7).

23 MR I. A. BALDING, Kingsclere

Postal: **Park House, Kingsclere, Newbury, Berkshire, RG20 5PY.**
Phone: **KINGSCLERE (01635) OFFICE 298210 HOME 298274 FAX 298305**

1 AL AZHAR, 4, b c Alzao (USA)—Upend **Al Muallim Partnership**
2 BOLD BUSTER, 5, b g Bustino—Truly Bold **Mr Robert Hitchins**
3 BRANDON JACK, 4, ch g Cadeaux Genereux—Waitingformargaret **Mr R. P. B. Michaelson**
4 CAPTAIN WILLIAM (IRE), 4, b g Shernazar—Our Galadrial **Mr D. Watson**
5 DASHING BLUE, 5, ch g Dashing Blade—Blubella **Mrs Duncan Allen**

MR I. A. BALDING—continued

6 **DEAD AIM (IRE)**, 4, b g Sadler's Wells (USA)—Dead Certain **Al Muallim Partnership**
7 **FITZWILLIAM (USA)**, 5, b g Rahy (USA)—Early Lunch (USA) **Mr Paul Mellon**
8 **GRAND MUSICA**, 5, b g Puissance—Vera Musica (USA) **Mach 3 Racing**
9 **GREY SHOT**, 6, gr g Sharrood (USA)—Optaria **Mr J. C. Smith**
10 **HANDLEY CROSS (USA)**, 4, b br g Houston (USA)—Imaginary Lady (USA) **Mr Paul Mellon**
11 **HIDDEN MEADOW**, 4, b c Selkirk (USA)—Spurned (USA) **Mr George Strawbridge**
12 **JAYANNPEE**, 7, ch g Doulab (USA)—Amina **Mr I. A. Balding**
13 **JORROCKS (USA)**, 4, b g Rubiano (USA)—Perla Fina (USA) **Mr Paul Mellon**
14 **JUNCTION CITY (USA)**, 4, b g Forty Niner (USA)—Key Witness (USA) **Mr Paul Mellon**
15 **LOCHANGEL**, 4, ch f Night Shift (USA)—Peckitts Well **Mr J. C. Smith**
16 **MISTY POINT**, 4, ch f Sharpo—Clouded Vision **Mr & Mrs C. M. Judd, Mr M. E. Wates**
17 **MR SPONGE (USA)**, 4, ch c Summer Squall (USA)—Dinner Surprise (USA) **Mr Paul Mellon**
18 **PAPUA**, 4, ch g Green Dancer (USA)—Fairy Tern **Mr Robert Hitchins**
19 **PAY HOMAGE**, 10, ch g Primo Dominie—Embraceable Slew (USA) **Miss A. V. Hill**
20 **ROKEBY BOWL**, 6, b g Salse (USA)—Rose Bowl (USA) **Mr Paul Mellon**
21 **SAUSALITO BAY**, 4, b c Salse (USA)—Cantico **Mr J. C. Smith**
22 **SPINNING**, 11, b g Glint of Gold—Strathspey **Mr I. A. Balding**
23 **STAR TALENT (USA)**, 7, b g Local Talent (USA)—Sedra **Mr R. P. B. Michaelson**
24 **STURM UND DRANG**, 4, ch g Selkirk (USA)—Historiette **Mr I. A. Balding**
25 **SUDEST (IRE)**, 4, b g Taufan (USA)—Frill **Mr Robert Hitchins**
26 **SUNLIT BOY**, 6, ch g Ardross—Sunlit River **Mr D. F. Pitcher**
27 **TIKOPIA**, 4, b g Saddlers' Hall (IRE)—Shesadelight **Mr Robert Hitchins**
28 **VOLA VIA (USA)**, 5, b br g Known Fact (USA)—Pinking Shears (USA) **Mr G. M. Smart**

THREE-YEAR-OLDS

29 **AMABEL (USA)**, b f Silver Hawk (USA)—Routilante **Mr George Strawbridge**
30 **BIG BUYER (USA)**, b f Quest For Fame—Royal Procession (USA) **Mr Robin F. Scully**
31 **BORANI**, b c Shirley Heights—Ower (IRE) **Dr J. Hobby**
32 **BORDER ARROW**, ch c Selkirk (USA)—Nibbs Point (IRE) **R. P. B. Michaelson & Wafic Said**
33 **DACLAN (USA)**, br f Diesis—Barb's Lass **G. D. Hawkins & J. J. McEntee**
34 **DANCING DERVISH**, b g Shareef Dancer (USA)—Taj Victory **Miss A. V. Hill**
35 **EASTER OGIL (IRE)**, ch g Pips Pride—Piney Pass **Mr G. M. Smart**
36 **ELFINAUNT**, ch f Magic Ring (IRE)—Aunt Judy **Mr M. E. Wates**
37 **ELLWAY PRINCE**, b g Prince Sabo—Star Arrangement **Ellway Racing**
38 **FIELDS OF OMAGH (USA)**, b g Pleasant Tap (USA)—Brave And True (USA) **Mr Paul Mellon**
39 **GAILY MILL**, b f Keen—Island Mill **Mr D. D. Rae Smith & Mr N. H. Harris**
40 **GRANGEVILLE (USA)**, b g Gulch (USA)—Cor Anglais (USA) **Mr George Strawbridge**
41 **HALMAHERA (IRE)**, b c Petardia—Champagne Girl **Mr Robert Hitchins**
42 **LOCH SABRE**, ch c Sharpo—Peckitts Well **Mr J. C. Smith**
43 **LUCY GLITTERS (USA)**, b f Cryptoclearance (USA)—Way of The World (USA) **Mr Paul Mellon**
44 **MERLIN'S RING**, br c Magic Ring (IRE)—Dramatic Mood **Mrs Richard Plummer & Partners**
45 **MOON AT NIGHT**, gr g Pursuit of Love—La Nureyeva (USA) **Mrs D. Joly**
46 **NIGHT SHOT**, br g Night Shift (USA)—Optaria **Mr J. C. Smith**
47 **PANTAR (IRE)**, b c Shirley Heights—Spring Daffodil **Mr Robert Hitchins**
48 **PRIDE OF MY HEART**, b f Lion Cavern (USA)—Hearten **Mr N. H. Harris**
49 **PRIME TIME GIRL**, b f Primo Dominie—Timely Raise (USA) **Mr J. C. Smith**
50 **PUTUNA**, b f Generous (IRE)—Ivoronica **Mr Robert Hitchins**
51 **ROYAL ARROW (IRE)**, b f Royal Academy (USA)—Fighting Run **R. P. B. Michaelson & Wafic Said**
52 **SCORNED (GER)**, b c Selkirk (USA)—Spurned (USA) **Mr George Strawbridge**
53 **SHARP FELLOW**, ch g Keen—Clarandal **Park House Partnership**
54 **SILVER SEA (USA)**, gr f Java Gold (USA)—Gray And Red (USA) **Mr Paul Mellon**
55 **SOLLY'S PAL**, gr g Petong—Petriece **Mrs Paul Levinson**
56 **TRANS ISLAND**, b c Selkirk (USA)—Khubza **Al Muallim Partnership**

TWO-YEAR-OLDS

57 **BLUES BROTHER**, b c 23/3 Bluebird (USA)—Manx Millenium (Habitat (USA)) **Mr J. C. Smith**
58 **BORDER PRINCE**, ch c 2/4 Selkirk (USA)—
Princess Oberon (IRE) (Fairy King (USA)) **Mr R. P. B. Michaelson, Mr D. F. Allport**
59 **BREAD WINNER**, b c 20/3 Reprimand—Khubza (Green Desert (USA)) **Al Muallim Partnership**
60 **CARMARTHEN**, ch c 4/3 Hamas (IRE)—Solar Attraction (IRE) (Salt Dome (USA)) **Elite Racing Club**

MR I. A. BALDING—continued

61 COCO GIRL, ch f 1/3 Mystiko (USA)—Cantico (Green Dancer (USA)) **Mr J. C. Smith**
62 DAYRAVEN, ch c 14/4 Midyan (USA)—Aunt Judy (Great Nephew) **Mr T. Mason**
63 DILLINGER, br c 31/3 Dilum (USA)—Sharp Chief (Chief Singer) **Mr J. C. Smith**
64 ELLWAY DANCER, b f 8/4 Mujadil (USA)—Moonlight Partner (IRE) (Red Sunset)
65 B f 18/3 Efisio—Floralia (Auction Ring (USA)) **Miss A. V. Hill**
66 FORT SUMTER (USA), b c 16/2 Sea Hero (USA)—Gray And Red (USA) (Wolf Power (SAF)) **Mr Paul Mellon**
67 GRIP FAST, b c 4/4 Saddler's Hall (IRE)—Comic Talent (Pharly (FR)) **Lady Rothes & Mr & Mrs D. Clee**
68 HARD LINES (USA), b c 27/3 Silver Hawk (USA)—Arctic Eclipse (USA) (Northern Dancer) **Mr Robin F. Scully**
69 HOH HOH SEVEN, b c 10/5 College Chapel—Fighting Run (Runnett) **Mr D. F. Allport & HOH Supply Ltd**
70 HUSTLER, b c 23/5 Dashing Blade—Spurned (USA) (Robellino (USA)) **Mr I. A. Balding**
71 Ch f 5/4 Inchinor—Indian Jubilee (Indian King (USA)) **Lord Lloyd-Webber**
72 LOCH MAGIC, b c 5/5 Arazi (USA)—Peckitts Well (Lochnager) **Mr J. C. Smith**
73 LORINER'S LASS, b f 13/4 Saddlers' Hall (IRE)—Sixslip (USA) (Diesis) **Summmertree Stud**
74 MAKE WAY (USA), b c 27/3 Red Ransom (USA)—Way of The World (USA) (Dance of Life (USA)) **Mr Paul Mellon**
75 Ch f 8/3 Selkirk (USA)—Miss Blitz (Formidable (USA)) **Mr George Strawbridge**
76 B c 24/2 Mazilier (USA)—Moore Stylish (Moorestyle) **Miss A. V. Hill**
77 MR PECKSNIFF, b c 14/4 Cyrano de Bergerac—Light Bidder (Auction Ring (USA)) **Mr A. Hogarth**
78 PALAWAN, br c 24/2 Polar Falcon (USA)—Krameria (Kris) **Mr Robert Hitchins**
79 PEAK PERFORMANCE, b c 5/2 Shirley Heights—Sharp Castan (Sharpen Up) **Mr J. C. Smith**
80 POKER DICE, b f 25/3 Primo Dominie—Poker Chip (Bluebird (USA)) **Mr J. C. Smith**
81 RADA'S DAUGHTER, br f 21/3 Robellino (USA)—Drama School (Young Generation (USA)) **Mrs Richard Plummer**
82 READING RHONDA (USA), b f 26/2 Eastern Echo (USA)—Higher Learning (USA) (Fappiano (USA)) **Mr Paul Mellon**
83 REALMS OF GOLD (USA), ch f 5/2 Gulch (USA)—Royal Pageant (USA) (Majestic Light (USA)) **Mr Paul Mellon**
84 RIMATARA, ch c 20/3 Selkirk (USA)—Humble Pie (Known Fact (USA)) **Mr Robert Hitchins**
85 B f 17/5 Woodman (USA)—Routilante (Rousillon (USA)) **Mr George Strawbridge**
86 SANKATY LIGHT (USA), b f 5/4 Summer Squall (USA)—Brave And True (USA) (Fappiano (USA)) **Mr Paul Mellon**
87 SARANGANI, b c 7/2 Polish Precedent—Height of Folly (Shirley Heights) **Mr Robert Hitchins**
88 SHAKIRA (IRE), b f 5/5 Lycius (USA)—Shakanda (IRE) (Shernazar) **Mrs P. Reditt & Catridge Farm**
89 B c 17/4 Salse (USA)—Sheer Luck (Shergar) **Mr I. A. Balding**
90 SOLE SINGER (GER), b c 4/2 Slip Anchor—Singer On The Roof (Chief Singer) **Mr J. C. Smith**
91 SULU (IRE), b c 14/2 Elbio—Foxy Fairy (IRE) (Fairy King (USA)) **Mr Robert Hitchins**
92 B c 22/3 Thatching—Susie Sunshine (IRE) (Waajib) **Axom Ltd**
93 TALAUD (IRE), ch c 18/4 Salse (USA)—Furry Friend (USA) (Bold Bidder) **Mr Robert Hitchins**
94 TARAWAN, ch c 2/4 Nashwan (USA)—Soluce (Junius (USA)) **Mr Robert Hitchins**
95 UZY, ch c 28/4 Common Grounds—Loch Clair (IRE) (Lomond (USA)) **Stamford Bridge Partnership**
96 VIE INDIENNE, ch f 5/3 Indian Ridge—La Strada (Niniski (USA)) **Miss K. Rausing**
97 WAIT FOR THE WILL (USA), ch c 20/4 Seeking The Gold—You'd Be Surprised (USA) (Blushing Groom (FR)) **Mr Paul Mellon**
98 B f 18/2 Danehill (USA)—Wizardry (Shirley Heights) **Mr G. Coull**

Other Owners: The Queen, Queen Elizabeth, Mr Nagy Azar, Mrs I. A. Balding, Mr C. H. Bothway, Mr Peter Box, Mr David Burton, Mrs Gavin Casey, Mr M. Djojomartono, Mr S. T. Ellen, D. Gay, Lord Lane Of Horsell, Mrs Anne Ireland, Mr R. Leah, Sir Nevil Macready, Mr G. Middlebrook, Baron F. C. Oppenheim, Mrs M. A. Rae Smith, Mr J. Y. Smart, Mrs E. M. Wechsler, Mr Jerrard Williamson.

Jockeys (Flat): L Dettori (8-6, w.a.), Martin Dwyer (7-7).

Jockey (NH): J Osborne (10-0, w.a.).

Apprentice: Leanne Masterton (8-7).

Amateur: Mr Andrew Balding (11-0).

24 MR J. BALDING, Doncaster

Postal: **Mayflower Stables, Saracens Lane, Scrooby, Doncaster, South Yorkshire, DN10 6AS.**
Phone: **HOME (01302) 710096**

1 **DYCE,** 4, b f Green Ruby (USA)—Miss Display **Mrs Gillian A. R. Jones**
2 **GENERAL EQUATION,** 5, b g Governor General—Logarithm **Make Our Day**
3 **MADAM ZANDO,** 5, ch m Forzando—Madam Trilby **Mrs Gillian A. R. Jones**
4 **TINKER'S SURPRISE (IRE),** 4, b g Cyrano de Bergerac—Lils Fairy **Classic Racing**

THREE-YEAR-OLDS

5 **DEKELSMARY,** b f Komaite (USA)—Final Call **Mr Derrick Moss**
6 **MUFTUFFENUF,** ch f Elmaamul (USA)—Tower Glades **Coghlan-Everitt**
7 **SUPACALIFRAGILISTK,** b f Sabrehill—Lucky Thing **Mr Josef Fusenich and Whitegate Travel**
8 **TOM TUN,** b c Bold Arrangement—B Grade **Mrs O. Tunstall**

TWO-YEAR-OLDS

9 **ARDO,** b f 28/5 Handsome Sailor—Grubby (Green Ruby (USA)) **Coghlan-Everitt**
10 B f 11/3 Lugana Beach—B Grade (Lucky Wednesday) **Mrs O. Tunstall**
11 **CELTIC SEAL,** b f 8/3 Lugana Beach—Celtic Bird (Celtic Cone) **Mrs Paula Haigh**
12 B c 4/5 River Falls—Northern Amber (Shack (USA)) **Mr S. Massarella**

Other Owners: Miss C. Balding, Mr Peter Balding, Mr J. D. Cooke, Mrs Catherine Lane, Mr Alan Smith.

Jockey (Flat): Jason Edmunds (8-0).

25 MR J. E. BANKS, Newmarket

Postal: **Jamesfield Place, Hamilton Road, Newmarket, Suffolk, CB8 7JQ.**
Phone: **HOME (01638) 661472 YARD (01638) 667997**

1 **ALBAHA (USA),** 5, br g Woodman (USA)—Linda's Magic (USA) **UK Packaging Supplies Ltd**
2 **BEAUMONT (IRE),** 8, br g Be My Native (USA)—Say Yes **Mr P. Cunningham**
3 **DELEGATE,** 5, ch g Polish Precedent (USA)—Dangora (USA) **M. J. & P. A. Reditt**
4 **ERINRINCA (IRE),** 4, ch f Waajib—Rivulet (USA) **Mr J. A. Bianchi**
5 **PRINCE BABAR,** 7, b g Fairy King (USA)—Bell Toll **Mr Giles W. Pritchard-Gordon**

THREE-YEAR-OLDS

6 **FRIENDLY WARNING,** b f Warning—Dedara **The Allez France Partnership**
7 **GOLD PARK,** b g Wing Park—Little Park **Roger Shilton**
8 **LUTINE BELL,** b g Fairy King (USA)—Bell Toll **Mr Giles W. Pritchard-Gordon**
9 **MARK OF PROPHET (IRE),** b c Scenic—Sure Flyer (IRE) **Mr P. Cunningham**
10 **SOCIETY KING (IRE),** b c Fairy King (USA)—Volga (USA) **Mr R. Sabey**
11 **SUPERCHIEF,** b g Precocious—Rome Express **Sir Freddie Laker**
12 **U K MAGIC (IRE),** b g Alzao (USA)—Lightino **UK Packaging Supplies Ltd**

TWO-YEAR-OLDS

13 B f 27/2 Deploy—Carn Maire (Northern Prospect (USA)) **Giles W. Pritchard-Gordon**
14 B f 12/3 Namaqualand (USA)—Casla (Lomond (USA)) **Giles W. Pritchard-Gordon**
15 B f 20/2 Common Grounds—Credit Crunch (IRE) (Caerleon (USA))
16 B f 10/3 Phountzi—Devils Dirge (Song) **Giles W. Pritchard-Gordon**
17 **LION CUB (IRE),** b c 26/4 Catrail (USA)—
Lightly Dancing (FR) (Groom Dancer (USA)) **The Allez France Partnership**
18 B f 15/3 Thatching—No Reservations (IRE) (Commanche Run) **Giles W. Pritchard-Gordon**
19 B f 16/3 Dolphin Street (FR)—Royaltess (Royal And Regal (USA)) **E. Carter**
20 B f 21/3 Brief Truce (USA)—Sharp Deposit (Sharpo)
21 Ch f 21/3 Keen—Touch of White (Song) **L. Ellines**

Other Owners: Mr J. E. Banks, Mrs A. M. Byrne, Mr Colin Marlow, Mr K. J. Mercer, Mrs S. Mercer, Mr A. E. T. Mines, Mrs Barbara Morris, Mr Tony Nichols, Mr Stan Ovenden, Mrs P. Reditt, Mr T. S. Redman, Mr Charles C. Walker.

Amateur: Mr J. G. Townson (10-10).

26 MRS A. BARCLAY, Moreton-in-Marsh

Postal: **Fotherop, Oddington, Moreton-in-Marsh, Gloucestershire.**
Phone: **(01451) 830680 FAX (01451) 870572**

1 **FOLDING,** 7, b g Rymer—Dealers Dream **Mrs Althea Barclay**
2 **PERUDO,** 5, b g Broadsword (USA)—Dealers Dream **Mrs Althea Barclay**
3 5, B g Pitpan—Two Shares **Mrs Althea Barclay**

27 MR J. BARCLAY, Leslie

Postal: **Kinneston, Leslie, Fife, KY6 3JJ.**
Phone: **(01592) 840331 FAX (01592) 840866**

1 **BELLS HILL LAD,** 11, ch g Buckskin (FR)—Laiton Peni **Kinneston Racing**
2 **BUSTER BEN (IRE),** 9, b g Bulldozer—Busted Angel **Mr Lewis Grant**
3 **CARDENDEN (IRE),** 10, b g Bustomi—Nana **Kinneston Farmers**
4 **COMMON SOUND (IRE),** 7, b g Common Grounds—Northern Wind **Kinneston Racing**
5 **NORTH TIPP (IRE),** 9, b g Lafontaine (USA)—Jury Box **Mrs Miff Hall**
6 **OLLIES BOY (IRE),** 7, br g Electric—Kilcor Rose **Kinneston Racing**
7 **SEEKING GOLD (IRE),** 9, b m Lancastrian—Platinum Gold **Gilry**
8 **SOLSGIRTH,** 7, br g Ardross—Lillies Brig **Kinneston Farmers**
9 **SUPER GUY,** 6, b g Exodal (USA)—Custard Pie **Miss L. Wood**

Other Owners: Mr Jamie Alexander, Mr Nicholas Alexander, Mr Edward Baxter, Mrs Kathryn Collins, Mr John Drysdale, Mr Andrew Hamilton, Mr J. N. Llewellen Palmer.

28 MR D. W. BARKER, Richmond

Postal: **Greenbury Grange, Scorton, Richmond, Yorkshire, DL10 6EP.**
Phone: **(01748) 811371 (01325) 378266 FAX (01748) 818910**

1 4, B g Be My Native (USA)—Bissie's Jayla **Mr D. W. Barker**
2 **CAIRN DHU,** 4, ch g Presidium—My Precious Daisy **Mrs S. J. Barker**
3 **FLOWER MILLER,** 5, b g Formidable (USA)—Sunflower Seed **Mr D. W. Barker**
4 **HOH EXPLORER (IRE),** 4, ch c Shahrastani (USA)—Heart's Harmony **Saltire Racing Syndicate**
5 **MY HANDY MAN,** 7, ch g Out of Hand—My Home **Mrs P. A. Barker**
6 **PRIDDY FAIR,** 5, b m North Briton—Rainbow Ring **The Ebor Partnership**
7 **PROPELLANT,** 4, b g Formidable (USA)—Kirsheda **Mr D. W. Barker**
8 **SUMMERHILL SPECIAL (IRE),** 7, b m Roi Danzig (USA)—Special Thanks **Alba Racing Syndicate**
9 **TANCRED MISCHIEF,** 7, b m Northern State (USA)—Mischievous Miss **Mr D. W. Barker**

THREE-YEAR-OLDS

10 Gr g Petong—Go Tally-Ho **Mr D. W. Barker**
11 **PIGEON,** b f Casteddu—Wigeon **Mr D. W. Barker**
12 **TANCRED TIMES,** ch f Clantime—Mischievous Miss **The Ebor Partnership**

Other Owners: Mr P. Asquith, Mr D. G. Atkinson, Mr A. Campbell, Mr J. P. Fisher, Mr I. McLeod, Mr Tony Stephens, Mr G. A. Swinbank, Ms Diane Tunstall.

29 SIR JOHN K. BARLOW, BT, Nantwich

Postal: **Ash House, Brindley, Nantwich, Cheshire, CW5 8HX.**
Phone: **Tel: (Office) (01270) 524339 Fax: (01270) 524047**

1 **KHALIKHOUM (IRE),** 5, b g Darshaan—Khalisiyn **Sir John Barlow Bt**
2 **SEVEN POTATO MORE (IRE),** 8, b g Salluceva—Why Don't Ye **Sir John Barlow Bt**
3 **SPANISH LIGHT (IRE),** 9, b g Spanish Place (USA)—Arconist **Sir John Barlow Bt**

30 MR M. A. BARNES, Penrith

Postal: **Bank House, Little Salkeld, Penrith, Cumbria, CA10 1NN.**
Phone: **(01768) 881257**

1 **CAULKER,** 5, ch g Noblissimo (FR)—Cape Farewell **Mr T. A. Barnes**
2 **CINDER KOPJE,** 5, ch m Mirror Boy—Meall Mhor **Miss A. P. Lee**
3 **GONE ASHORE (IRE),** 7, b g Dry Dock—Fandango Girl **Barnes/Greenwell/Smithson**
4 **HELM WIND,** 5, b m North Col—Shy Hiker **Mr J. G. Graham**
5 **IFAFA BEACH (IRE),** 6, b g Le Moss—Greenpeace **Mr K. Hunter**
6 **MR BRUNO,** 5, ch g Primitive Rising (USA)—Thelmas Secret **Mr S. C. Brown**
7 **NIJWAY,** 8, b g Nijin (USA)—Runaway Girl (FR) **Mr T. A. Barnes**
8 **NORTH PRIDE (USA),** 13, ch g Northjet—Necie's Pride (USA) **Mr J. Wills**
9 **ONE STOP,** 5, b m Silly Prices—Allerdale **Mr Michael Brennan**
10 **PLAYMAKER,** 5, b g Primo Dominie—Salacious **Mr Robin Johnson**
11 **REBEL KING,** 8, b g Doc Marten—Cape Farewell **Mr M. Barnes**
12 **SKIDDAW KNIGHT (IRE),** 7, br g Carmelite House (USA)—Mrs Baggins **Mr J. Wills**
13 **SUITAFELLA,** 6, b m Sharkskin Suit (USA)—Getta Fella **Mr Maurice Wharton**
14 **TOPUP,** 5, b g Weldnaas (USA)—Daisy Topper **Mr M. Barnes**

Other Owners: Ms Anne Barnes, Mr K. Greenwell, Mrs C. Johnston, Mr T. Metcalfe, Mr A. Smithson, Mr J. G. White.

Jockeys (NH): B Storey (w.a.), A Thornton (w.a.).

Conditional: Scott Taylor (9-9).

31 MR R. E. BARR, Middlesbrough

Postal: **Carr House Farm, Seamer, Stokesley, Middlesbrough, Cleveland, TS9 5LL.**
Phone: **STOKESLEY (01642) 710687**

1 **CATCH THE PIGEON,** 9, b m Wonderful Surprise—Cheeky Pigeon **Mrs R. E. Barr**
2 **GEMOLLY (IRE),** 5, b m Be My Native (USA)—Hayhurst **Mr R. E. Barr**
3 **JIMMY SPRITE,** 7, b g Silly Prices—Little Mittens **Mr J. C. Garbutt**
4 **MAGGIE SIMPSON,** 5, ch m Say Primula—Little Mittens **Mr R. E. Barr**
5 **NITE SPRITE,** 8, b m Silly Prices—Little Mittens **Mr R. E. Barr**
6 **PENNY PEPPERMINT,** 6, b br m Move Off—Cheeky Pigeon **Mrs R. E. Barr**
7 **STOLEN MUSIC (IRE),** 5, b m Taufan (USA)—Causa Sua **Mr P. Cartmell**
8 **THATCHED (IRE),** 8, b g Thatching—Shadia (USA) **Mr C. W. Marwood**
9 **TOEJAM,** 5, ch g Move Off—Cheeky Pigeon **Mrs R. E. Barr**

THREE-YEAR-OLDS

10 B g Marching On—Cheeky Pigeon **Mrs R. E. Barr**
11 **ROYAL REPRIMAND (IRE),** br g Reprimand—Lake Ormond **Mr R. E. Barr**

TWO-YEAR-OLDS

12 Ch f 10/5 Minster Son—Little Mittens **Mr R. Barr**

Other Owners: Mr J. O. Barr, Mr D. Thomson.

Apprentices: P Fessey, K Sked.

Conditional: Scott Taylor.

Amateur: Mr S Swiers.

32 MR L. J. BARRATT, Oswestry

Postal: **Bromwich Park, Oswestry, Shropshire, SY11 4JQ.**
Phone: **(01691) 610209**

1 **COUNTESS MILLIE,** 6, ch m Rakaposhi King—Countess Carlotti **Mr L. J. Barratt**
2 **DOUBLE INDEMNITY (IRE),** 5, b g Doubletour (USA)—Splendid Pleasure **Mr L. J. Barratt**
3 **EPWORTH,** 4, b f Unfuwain (USA)—Positive Attitude **Mr L. J. Barratt**
4 **FLOOD'S FANCY,** 5, ro m Then Again—Port Na Blath **Mr P. L. Loake**
5 **I SAY DANCER (IRE),** 5, b m Distinctly North (USA)—Lady Marigot **Mr Doug Brereton**
6 **JUST NUISANCE,** 5, b m Hadeer—Pacific Gull (USA) **Mr L. J. Barratt**
7 **LADY RAMBO,** 5, b m Rambo Dancer (CAN)—Albaciyna **Mr L. J. Barratt**
8 **MR LOWRY,** 6, b g Rambo Dancer (CAN)—Be Royal **Mr L. J. Barratt**
9 **MY TRACEY,** 4, ch f Risk Me (FR)—Tricky Tracey **Mr L. J. Barratt**
10 **OCCAM (IRE),** 4, ch g Sharp Victor (USA)—Monterana **Mr L. J. Barratt**
11 **REGAL RAMBLER (CAN),** 7, ch g Regal Classic (CAN)—Rushing Rachel (USA) **Mr P. L. Loake**
12 **SHARP SUSY,** 4, b f Beveled (USA)—Sharp Anne **Mr Ray Bailey**

THREE-YEAR-OLDS

13 **PRINCE AURUM,** ch c Mystiko (USA)—Jarin Rose (IRE) **Miss Sheila Smith**

TWO-YEAR-OLDS

14 **DARK HUNTER,** ch g 15/5 Mon Tresor—Beaver Skin Hunter **Mr L. J. Barratt**
15 **HEAD LADY,** ch f 15/2 Headin' Up—Lady Gail **Mr L. J. Barratt**

Lady Rider: Miss Diana Jones.

33 MR T. D. BARRON, Thirsk

Postal: **Maunby House, Maunby, Thirsk, North Yorkshire, YO7 4HD.**
Phone: **(01845) 587435**

1 **ALLINSON'S MATE (IRE),** 10, b g Fayruz—Piney Pass **Mrs Christine Barron**
2 **ASHOVER,** 8, gr g Petong—Shiny Kay **Mr Timothy Cox**
3 **COASTAL BLUFF,** 6, gr g Standaan (FR)—Combattente **Mrs D. E. Sharp**
4 **DAMARIS,** 6, ch m Dancing High—Lekuti **Mr J. Hall**
5 **DEPRECIATE,** 5, ch h Beveled (USA)—Shiny Penny **Mr W. I. Armitage**
6 **DOVEBRACE,** 5, b g Dowsing (USA)—Naufrage **Mr David A. Jones**
7 **FOR THE PRESENT,** 8, b g Then Again—Axe Valley **Mrs J. Hazell**
8 **KRYSTAL MAX (IRE),** 5, b g Classic Music (USA)—Lake Isle (IRE) **Oakfield Nurseries Partnership**
9 **LA SCALA,** 5, b m Scallywag—Dark City **Mr J. Baggott**
10 **MALLIA,** 5, b g Statoblest—Pronetta (USA) **Mr H. T. Duddin**
11 **MIDDLE EAST,** 5, b g Beveled (USA)—Godara **Mrs J. Hazell**
12 **OVER TO YOU (USA),** 4, ch c Rubiano (USA)—Overnight (USA) **Mr D. Scott**
13 **PROMPTED,** 4, b g Then Again—Tarazando **Mr J. A. Welsh**
14 **REBEL SON,** 4, b g Minster Son—Rebrona **Mrs F. T. Walton**
15 **ROSE BURTON,** 4, b f Lucky Wednesday—Holly Burton **Mrs R. M. West**

THREE-YEAR-OLDS

16 **SEA FIG,** gr f Robellino (USA)—Aimee Jane (USA) **Mr J. Baggott**
17 **SINCH,** ch f Inchinor—Swinging Gold **Mr Geoffrey Martin**
18 **TAYLOR'S PRIDE,** b f Nordico (USA)—Jendor **H. Taylor & Sons**
19 **THISTLE PARK,** ch g Selkirk (USA)—Kimberley Park **Mrs J. Hazell**
20 **THREE STAR RATED (IRE),** b f Pips Pride—Preponderance (IRE) **Miss J. Salt**
21 **TORRENT,** ch g Prince Sabo—Maiden Pool **Mrs J. Hazell**

TWO-YEAR-OLDS

22 **ASHOVER AMBER,** b f 2/1 Green Desert (USA)—Zafaaf (Kris) **Mr Timothy Cox**
23 **BECKON,** ch f 19/3 Beveled (USA)—Carolynchristensen (Sweet Revenge) **Lady Burnham**

MR T. D. BARRON—continued

24 CAPE CHARLOTTE, ch f 22/3 Mon Tresor—Laena (Roman Warrior) **Mr R. West**
25 CARRIE POOTER, b f 30/4 Tragic Role (USA)—Ginny Binny (Ahonoora) **Mr S. Woodall**
26 CHALCEDONY, ch c 6/3 Highest Honor (FR)—Sweet Holland (USA) (Alydar (USA)) **Mr J. Baggott**
27 B c 25/2 Petong—Madam Bold (Never So Bold) **Mr P. D. Savill**
28 B c 30/3 Deploy—Shamaka (Kris) **Mr T. D. Barron**
29 Ch f 23/3 Aragon—So So (Then Again) **Mr Geoffrey Martin**
30 SUPREME SALUTATION, ch c 22/3 Most Welcome—Cardinal Press (Sharrood (USA)) **Mr J. Baggott**
31 B g 28/3 Then Again—Tawny (Grey Ghost) **Mr T. D. Barron**
32 B c 17/4 Distinctly North—Trilby's Dream (IRE) (Mansooj) **Mr Timothy Cox**
33 VENIKA VITESSE, b c 2/5 Puissance—Vilanika (FR) (Top Ville) **Mr K. Shaw**
34 B f 30/3 Fayruz—Whittingham Girl (Primo Dominie) **Mr D. Scott**

Other Owners: Mrs M. E. Armitage, Mrs M. Baggott, Miss N. J. Barron, Mrs I. M. Boyle, Mr J. G. Brown, Mr E. Buck, Mr Robbie Cameron, Mr B. Church, Mr Austin Copping, Mr S. R. Counsell, Mr M. Dalby, Lady Eyre, Mr Peter Jones, Mr John Knotts, Mr P. Leng, Mrs S. Sturman, Mrs P. J. Taylor-Garthwaite, Mr Ken Topham.

Apprentices: Victoria Appleby (7-13), Kimberley Hart (7-8).

Amateur: Maneula Keuthen (9-0).

34 MR A. K. BARROW, Bridgwater

Postal: **Marsh Mills Farm, Over Stowey, Bridgwater, Somerset, TA5 1HG.**
Phone: **(01278) 732522 MOBILE (0860) 879115**

1 DICKYVEARNCOMBE, 6, ch g Persian Heights—Royal Celerity (USA) **Duckhaven Stud**
2 FLYING ANGEL, 4, br f Almoojid—Silvie **Duckhaven Stud**
3 GRANSTOWN LAKE (IRE), 7, b g Clearly Bust—More Hassel **Mr M. R. Churches**
4 GROSVENOR HEATH (NZ), 10, b br g Grosvenor (NZ)—Sellou (NZ) **Mr Tim Collins**
5 JHAL FREZI, 10, b g Netherkelly—Warham Trout **Mrs R. T. H. Heeley**
6 KALMOOJID, 4, b g Almoojid—Skerryvore **Duckhaven Stud**
7 LISAHANE OATS, 8, b g Oats—Pinchapenny **Mr J. J. Whelan**
8 L'UOMO PIU, 14, b g Paddy's Stream—Easter Vigil **Mr C. J. Spencer**
9 NATTIE, 4, b g Almoojid—Defy Me **Duckhaven Stud**
10 PRIMERO (IRE), 4, b g Lycius (USA)—Pipitina **Mr Alan Harrington**
11 SOMETHING CATCHY (IRE), 8, b m Toravich (USA)—Spring Flower II **Avalon Surfacing Ltd**
12 THEFIELDSOFATHENRY (IRE), 8, b g King Persian—Clodianus **Unity Farm Holiday Centre Ltd**
13 YES WE ARE, 12, br m Strong Gale—Are You Sure **Mr A. Barrow**

Other Owners: Mrs Maureen Emery, Mr J. E. Fear, Mr M. J. Hayes, Mr Don Hazzard, Mr Jack Miller, Mr A. D. Smith, Mr A. P. Smith, Mrs J. M. Smith.

Jockey (Flat): N Adams (7-8).

Jockey (NH): B Powell (10-0).

Conditional: S Mitchell.

Amateur: Mr O McPhail.

35 MR R. A. BARTLETT, Airdrie

Postal: **'Meikle Ben', Yetts Hole Road, Glenmavis, Airdrie, Lanarkshire, ML6 0PS.**
Phone: **Home: (01236) 875279 Work: (01236) 762831 Fax: (01236) 751791**

1 4, B g General Ironside—Bucks Princess **Mr R. A. Bartlett**
2 **DRAKEWRATH (IRE)**, 8, b g Good Thyne (USA)—Velpol **Mr R. A. Bartlett**
3 **IT COULD BE YOU (IRE)**, 5, b g Big Sink Hope (USA)—Kemazan **Mr R. A. Bartlett**
4 **NOLUCKMATE (IRE)**, 6, b g Satco (FR)—Bellteen **Mr R. A. Bartlett**
5 **NOTHINGTOTELLME (IRE)**, 7, gr g Roselier (FR)—Tower Road **Mr R. A. Bartlett**
6 **NOT LONG NOW (IRE)**, 6, ch g Nestor—Tim's Brief **Mr R. A. Bartlett**
7 **SECRET SCEPTRE**, 11, ch g Kambalda—Secret Suspicion **Mr R. A. Bartlett**
8 **WHAT BECOMES (IRE)**, 5, b g Broken Hearted—Another Partner **Mr R. A. Bartlett**

Other Owners: Albert Bartlett & Sons (Airdrie) Ltd.

36 MR C. R. BARWELL, Tiverton

Postal: **Ashfields, Stoodleigh, Tiverton, Devon, EX16 9QF.**
Phone: **OAKFORD (01398) 351333 MOBILE (0836) 599699**

1 **ANDSOME BOY**, 5, ch g Out of Hand—My Home **The Select Partnership**
2 **BOURNEL**, 10, ch m Sunley Builds—Golden Granite **Mr Nicholas Bowden**
3 **COOLE CHERRY**, 8, b g Buckley—Cherry Opal **Mrs L. Field**
4 **CURTIS THE SECOND**, 5, b m Thowra (FR)—Bay Jade **The Curtis Partnership**
5 **DID YOU KNOW (IRE)**, 5, ch m Balinger—Dim Drums **Mr Robin Barwell**
6 **DRAGON KING**, 6, b g Rakaposhi King—Dunsilly Bell **Dragon Industrial Services D. J. Evans**
7 **FU'S BABY**, 4, b g Shahrastani (USA)—Fu's Lady **Mrs Angie Malde**
8 **JOLSON**, 7, ch g Black Minstrel—Pearly Lady **Mr Robin Barwell**
9 **MARITSA-B**, 5, b m Teamster—Sheer Gold **Mrs L. Field**
10 5, B g Supreme Leader—Modelligo Wood (IRE) **Mr Robin Barwell**
11 **POLLYS SISTER**, 6, b m Green Adventure (USA)—Fly Blackie **Mrs P. L. Aldersey**
12 **QUICKSWOOD (IRE)**, 5, b g Yashgan—Up To Trix **Mr Harvey Spack**
13 **RAGTIME BOY**, 10, b g Sunyboy—Ragtime Dance **Mrs Jo Clarke**
14 **REGAL GEM (IRE)**, 7, ch m Torus—Queen's Prize **Mr D. W. E. Coombs**
15 **RUM CUSTOMER**, 7, b g Morgans Choice—Man Maid **Mrs Diana Nicholson**
16 **SECRET SERVICE (IRE)**, 6, b g Classic Secret (USA)—Mystery Bid **The Hole In The Wall Gang**
17 **SPECIAL ACCOUNT**, 12, b g Le Moss—Liffey's Choice **Mr Tony Fiorillo**
18 **STEEL MOSS (IRE)**, 9, ch g Le Moss—Iron Star **Mr Tony Fiorillo**
19 **TIME PROJECT (IRE)**, 4, b f Project Manager—Bright Era **Lady Maria Coventry**
20 **TOP SCHOLAR**, 6, b m Derrylin—Herald The Dawn **Mrs P. L. Aldersey**

THREE-YEAR-OLDS

21 Ch f Out of Hand—My Home **Burrow Racing Two**

TWO-YEAR-OLDS

22 B f 12/4 Teamster—Highly Inflammable (USA) (Wind And Wuthering (USA)) **Mr Robin Barwell**

Other Owners: Mr R. C. Allen, Mr Brian Dochery, Mr Paul Edwards, Mr David J. Evans, Mr Patrick Fuller, Mr R. T. Grant, Mr A. R. Hutter, Mr Simon Jamieson, Mr Paul Laird, Mrs Pam Mulle, Mr Paul Mulle, Mrs L. Roberts, Mr Danny Schaffer.

Jockeys (NH): Barry Fenton (10-0), Tony McCoy (10-0, w.a.).

Amateur: Mr Richard White (10-10).

37 MR P. BARY, Chantilly

Postal: **5 Chemin des Aigles, 60500 Chantilly, France.**
Phone: **03 44 57 14 03 FAX 03 44 58 56 12**

1 **DRAGONADA (USA),** 4, b f Nureyev—Don't Sulk **Niarchos Family**
2 **GALLIPOLI,** 4, b g Efisio—Gemmologie **Mme D. Jacob**
3 **LAURENTINE (USA),** 4, b f Private Account—La Sky **Scuderia Pieffegi**
4 **MORINI,** 4, ch f Unfuwain—Possessive Lady **J. L. Bouchard**
5 **OA BALDIXE (FR),** 4, gr c Linamix—Bal d'Oa **F. Prat**
6 **ORFORD NESS,** 4, b f Selkirk—Nesaah **K. Abdulla**

THREE-YEAR-OLDS

7 **AIGRETTE (USA),** b f Gone West—Absurde **Mme A. O'Reilly**
8 **AQUA DUCE (USA),** b f St Jovite—Paulistana **Wattlefield Hall Stud**
9 **ARMILINA (FR),** gr f Linamix—Armarama **J. L. Lagardere**
10 **AWARE,** gr c Kenmare—Nesaah **K. Abdulla**
11 **AZELNA (FR),** ch f Tropular—La Miserable **J. Biraben**
12 **BEG MEIL (FR),** br f Tel Quel—Stop Fiddling **Mme H. Devin**
13 **BUSHMAN'S RIVER (USA),** ch c Irish River—Tertiary **K. Abdulla**
14 **CRAZY CANARD (USA),** b f Woodman—Catopetl **W. Said**
15 **CREME ANGLAISE,** b f Caerleon—Ameridienne **W. Said**
16 **CROCO ROUGE (IRE),** b c Rainbow Quest—Alligatrix **W. Said**
17 **DREAM WELL (FR),** b c Sadler's Wells—Soul Dream **J. L. Bouchard**
18 **ECLAIR (USA),** b c Storm Bird—Secretly **Overbrook Farm**
19 **ENIPEUS (FR),** ch c Acatenango—Eidothea **E. Wanke**
20 **EURYBIE (FR),** br f Kendor—Enodia **Succ. E. Wanke**
21 **FLAVINIA,** b f Cadeaux Genereux—Floralia **Wattlefield Hall Stud**
22 **GEOLOGUE (FR),** b c Priolo—Gemmologie **K. Abdulla**
23 **GOLDEN GLIMMER (FR),** gr f Kendor—Marie Glitters **Scuderia Pieffegi**
24 **GREAT CARE (USA),** b f El Gran Senor—Never A Care **K. Abdulla**
25 **HAPPY (FR),** b f Hero's Honor—Serie Bleu Nuit **Mr N. S. Yong**
26 **HELIETTE (FR),** ch f Tropular—Fraulein **J. L. Bouchard**
27 **HERBUS (FR),** ch f Kendor—Hekabe **Succ. E. Wanke**
28 **IMBABALA,** ch f Zafonic—Interval **K. Abdulla**
29 **JOVARO (USA),** ch f St Jovite—Smugly **Ed Seltzer**
30 **LA PETITE DANSEUSE (USA),** b f Woodman—La Tritona **Mme A. O'Reilly**
31 **LAURA FAIR (USA),** ch f Blushing John—Arbitrage Lady **J. Steiner**
32 **LESGOR (USA),** ch f Irish River—Let's Sgor **Scuderia Pieffegi**
33 **MEATBALL (FR),** ch c Nashamaa—Northern Bank **J. Steiner**
34 **MILLER (FR),** b c Subotica—Jezebel Monroe **Niarchos Family**
35 **MINORITY,** ch f Generous—Minskip **K. Abdulla**
36 **MISCAST,** gr f Kenmare—Mistreat **Mme A. O'Reilly**
37 **NEEM (USA),** ch g Nabeel Dancer—Anytimeatall **Mme A. Plesch**
38 **NOW NANETTE (FR),** b f Exit To Nowhere—Neomeris **Mme D. Jacob**
39 **OISELINA (FR),** gr f Linamix—Oiseau de Feu **J. L. Lagardere**
40 **OLYDORA (GER),** ch f Acatenango—Opeia **Succ. E. Wanke**
41 **PHEBUS (FR),** b c Last Tycoon—Consolation **J. L. Bouchard**
42 **POLLY'S BIRD (FR),** ch g Arctic Tern—Polly's Mira **Mr N. S. Yong**
43 **QUIANLONG (USA),** b c Zilzal—Iva Reputation **S. Fradkoff**
44 **RESTING (FR),** b c Bering—Restrained **J. C. Seroul**
45 **RISARSHANA (FR),** b f Darshaan—Risantaya **J. L. Lagardere**
46 **ROSEMONDE (IRE),** ch f Royal Academy—Simply Great **A. D. S. Mangnall**
47 **SAND FALCON,** ch g Polar Falcon—Sand Grouse **K. Abdulla**
48 **SAYARSHAN (FR),** br c Darshaan—Sayyara **J. L. Lagardere**
49 **SECRET MUSIC (USA),** b f Dixieland Band—Secret Form **Mme A. O'Reilly**
50 **SECURE,** b g Forzando—Secret Dancer **Dr H. P. Kurth**
51 **SERALIA,** ch f Royal Academy—Serafica **Mme A. O'Reilly**
52 **SIBILANT,** ch f Selkirk—Daki **K. Abdulla**
53 **SILIC (FR),** b c Sillery—Balletomane **Mme D. Jacob**

MR P. BARY—continued

54 **TAKESON (FR)**, gr c Take Risks—Sonning **Ste D'Entrmt P. Bary**
55 **TANABATA (FR)**, b f Shining Steel—Horphaly **Mme Seydoux de Clausonne**
56 **TREMENDO (IRE)**, ch c Thatching—Twin Island **Mme V. Riva**
57 **TRUE (FR)**, b f Common Grounds—Tirana **Skymarc Farm**
58 **TRUE VISION (USA)**, b f Lear Fan—Oeilladine **J. Biraben**
59 **UNA FIJA (FR)**, b f Fijar Tango—Rivariana **P. Mussat**
60 **VALIXA (FR)**, gr f Linamix—Valira **J. L. Lagardere**
61 **WENGE (USA)**, b f Housebuster—Hooriah **M. Zerolo**
62 **WEST SIDE (FR)**, br f Tel Quel—Arkova **Mme H. Devin**
63 **ZIGTRICK (FR)**, b c Phone Trick—Zigaura **J. L. Lagardere**

TWO-YEAR-OLDS

64 **AIRLIFT (FR)**, b f 6/2 Barathea—Air Reveuse **Skymarc Farm**
65 B c Nureyev—Ancient Regime **W. Said**
66 B c Dayjur—Angela Serra **Skymarc Farm**
67 B f Generous—Aquamarine **K. Abdulla**
68 **ATTRAPE (USA)**, ch f 7/3 Woodman—Absurde **Mme A. O'Reilly**
69 B f 16/4 Sanglamore—Beaute Dangereuse **Niarchos Family**
70 B c Kingmambo—Beautiful Legend **G. Biszantz**
71 B f Polish Precedent—Besotted **K. Abdulla**
72 B f Slew O' Gold—Bold Ballerina **K. Abdulla**
73 **BRIGHT LIGHTS (IRE)**, b f 18/3 Priolo—Briesta **Skymarc Farm**
74 B c Generous—Cattermole **K. Abdulla**
75 **CHAUVIRE**, ch f 30/4 Elmaamul—Kamalia **Scuderia Pieffegi**
76 Ch c Holy Bull—Cheyenne Dream **K. Abdulla**
77 B c Grand Lodge—Docklands **K. Abdulla**
78 **FALCON FLIGHT (FR)**, br c 12/5 Persian Bold—Flying Circus **J. L. Bouchard**
79 B c 28/3 Common Grounds—Fextal **Niarchos Family**
80 **FLYING SPINAKER (FR)**, b c 9/5 Saint Estephe—Lorelta **Mme Y. Houyvet**
81 **GLASS**, b f 16/3 Bering—Gemmologie **Skymarc Farm**
82 **HARAWACK (FR)**, b c 15/5 Unfuwain—Sequoya Forest **K. Yano**
83 **I AM A STAR (FR)**, b f 13/2 Tel Quel—Carmissa **Ste D'Entrmt P. Bary**
84 **ILDIKO (FR)**, ch f 10/2 Beaudelaire—Fraulein **J. L. Bouchard**
85 B c Rainbow Quest—Jamaican Punch **W. Said**
86 **KAPOCK (FR)**, b c 30/4 Kaldoun—Karannja **Mme D. Jacob**
87 **KOBOLD (FR)**, b c 11/2 Tropular—Keen's Like **J. L. Bouchard**
88 **LA BECHEUSE (IRE)**, ch f 21/3 Pistolet Bleu—Myrobella **Elie Aoun**
89 **LA JOIE (USA)**, b f Kingmambo—La Tritona **Mme A. O'Reilly**
90 **LANDLOCKED (USA)**, b f Unbridled—Land Shark **Mme A. O'Reilly**
91 **LUNE ROUGE (IRE)**, b f 22/1 Unfuwain—Luvia **Mme A. O'Reilly**
92 Ch f 17/2 Carson City—Mais Oui **Eric Puerari**
93 **MARIA DE LA LUZ**, b f 8/3 Machiavellian—Light of Hope **Mme R. G. Ehrnrooth**
94 **MEADOWMIST (IRE)**, ch c 1/3 Priolo—Meadowsweet **J. L. Bouchard**
95 B f Sanglamore—Minskip **K. Abdulla**
96 B c Kingmambo—Miss Summer **K. Abdulla**
97 **MYTHICAL MYSTERY (USA)**, ch f 14/5 Rahy—Mythomania **Overbrook Farm**
98 **NADRASHAAN (FR)**, b f 14/2 Darshaan—Nadra **J. L. Bouchard**
99 B c Kris—Nesaah **K. Abdulla**
100 B c Caerleon—Noble Chick **W. Said**
101 **PAGE DANS MA VIE (FR)**, ch f 12/2 Generous—Page Bleue **Mme R. G. Ehrnrooth**
102 **PARTY ZANE**, b f 24/4 Zafonic—Party Doll **J. L. Bouchard**
103 **PINK RISKS (FR)**, ch f 24/4 Take Risks—Gold Script **D. Tsui**
104 B f 26/2 Indian Ridge—Piper's Pool **G. Larrieu**
105 **RAINBOWAIN (FR)**, b c 19/4 Unfuwain—Rainbow Reliance **J. C. Seroul**
106 B c Leo Castelli—Rajana **G. Biszantz**
107 Br c 8/3 Woodman—Salchow **Niarchos Family**
108 Ch f 22/3 Caerleon—Search For Spring **M. de Chambure**
109 **SERAFICAT (FR)**, ch c 1/5 Catrail—Serafica **Mme A. O'Reilly**
110 **SEVENTY NINE (FR)**, ch c 1/3 Kendor—Princess Waya **Dr H. P. Kurth**

MR P. BARY—continued

111 B f Cozzene—Shining Bright **K. Abdulla**
112 SIOBHAN, b f 1/2 Generous—Shamiad **Scuderia Pieffegi**
113 STELLA BERINE (FR), ch f 1/2 Bering—Beaujolaise **Mme D. Jacob**
114 B f Barathea—Twixt **K. Abdulla**
115 B f 17/4 Exit To Nowhere—Unopposed **Skymarc Farm**
116 VALIRAMIX (FR), gr c 18/4 Linamix—Valira **J. L. Lagardere**
117 WATERSTONE, b c 12/4 Riverman—Lovealoch **Grundy Bloodstock Ltd**
118 WINTER ICE (USA), br f 3/5 Kingmambo—Spring Colors **Overbrook Farm**
119 XENA (FR), br f 16/4 Highest Honor—Clear Hero **Mr N. S. Yong**

Jockeys (Flat): F Grenet (8-7), S Guillot.

Apprentice: S Lobel.

38 MR R. BASTIMAN, Wetherby

Postal: **Goosemoor Farm, Warfield Lane, Cowthorpe, Wetherby, Yorkshire, LS22 5EU.**
Phone: **(01423) 359397**

1 BLACK ICE BOY (IRE), 7, b g Law Society (USA)—Hogan's Sister (USA) **Mrs Judith Marshall**
2 DALERIVER, 7, ch g Never So Bold—Omnia **Mr I. B. Barker**
3 DANCING DESTINY, 6, b m Dancing Brave (USA)—Tender Loving Care **Mr Charles Castle**
4 DARLING CLOVER, 6, ch m Minster Son—Lady Clementine **Mr P. A. Brigham**
5 EAT YOUR PEAR, 4, ch f Dunbeath (USA)—Track Angel **Victor Chandler (Equus) Ltd**
6 ES GO, 5, ch g Dunbeath (USA)—Track Angel **Victor Chandler (Equus) Ltd**
7 FOOLISH FLUTTER (IRE), 4, b br f Fools Holme (USA)—Thornbeam **The Foolish Six**
8 HILLZAH (USA), 10, ch g Blushing Groom (FR)—Glamour Girl (ARG) **Mrs P. Churm**
9 KHABAR, 5, b g Forzando—Ella Mon Amour **Mrs N. Skelton**
10 LADY CAROLINE LAMB (IRE), 5, b m Contract Law (USA)—Tuft Hill **Mr Charles Castle**
11 8, B m Gambler's Cup (USA)—Lady Carousel **Mrs J. Swiers**
12 MARTINDALE (IRE), 5, b g Fairy King (USA)—Whist Awhile **Mrs M. Smith, Whisk Swan Partnership**
13 MYBOTYE, 5, br g Rambo Dancer (CAN)—Sigh **Mr Anthony Moroney**
14 SUPER ROCKY, 9, b g Clantime—Starproof **Mr I. B. Barker**
15 TOM PLADDEY, 4, ch c Clantime—Croft Original **Mr A. D. Bastiman**
16 TURGENEV (IRE), 9, b g Sadler's Wells (USA)—Tilia (ITY) **Mrs Bridget Tranmer**

THREE-YEAR-OLDS

17 B c Presidium—Countess of Honour (USA) **Mr J. F. Wright, Mr Dukes**
18 ITCH, b c Puissance—Panienka (POL) **Mr Charles Castle**
19 WERE NOT STOPPIN, b g Mystiko (USA)—Power Take Off **Mr Robin Bastiman**

Other Owners: Mrs P. Bastiman, Mr Dukes, Foolish Six, Mr R. L. Maynard, Mr B. Rubble, Mr Tom Segrue, Mrs M. Smith, Mr James Swailes, Mr Trevor Swailes.

Jockey (Flat): D McKeown (w.a.).

Jockey (NH): M Dwyer (w.a.).

Apprentice: H J Bastiman (8-11).

Conditional: H J Bastiman (9-7).

Lady Rider: Miss Rebecca Bastiman (9-7).

39 MR A. G. BATES, Maisons-Laffitte

Postal: **1 Avenue Champaubert, 78600 Maisons-Laffitte, France.**
Phone: **01 39 62 77 77 PHONE 01 39 62 03 14 FAX**

1 **DJA DANCER,** 5, b h Groom Dancer—Djaka Belle **Ecurie Bader**
2 **LAURIS SOVEREIGN,** 5, b h Round Sovereign—Lauris **Alain Bates**
3 **LUX HONOR,** 5, gr h Highest Honor—Luxurious **Robert Fournier Sarloveze**
4 **PAMVER,** 8, b br g Pampabird—Viverba **Mrs Alain Bates**
5 **SEA PLANE,** 9, gr g Nishapour—Pirogue **Robert Fournier Sarloveze**

THREE-YEAR-OLDS

6 **LES LANDES,** gr g Turgeon—Bellaparthe **J. C. Cheuvreux**
7 **LIGHT WAVE,** ch f Marignan—Liberty Nell **Ecurie A.B.U.**

TWO-YEAR-OLDS

8 **ALMIRENA,** b f 2/4 Subotica—Kenyatta (Kenmare) **Robert Fournier Sarloveze**
9 **IBIS DE LA ROQUE,** b br c 6/6 Fijar Tango—Last Love (Platonic Love) **Alain Bates**

Jockey (NH): X Hondier.

Lady Rider: Mrs Chantal Bates.

40 MR B. P. J. BAUGH, Audley

Postal: **Brooklands, Park Lane, Audley, Stoke on Trent, SG7 8RH.**
Phone: **STABLES (01782) 723524 HOME (01782) 723144 MOBILE (0589) 703420**

1 **AMERTON HEATH,** 5, b m Henbit (USA)—Rodeo Fun **Mr G. A. Greaves**
2 **BASHFUL BRAVE,** 7, ch g Indian Ridge—Shy Dolly **Mr W. P. Burnell**
3 **BETABETCORBETT,** 7, b g Prince Sabo—Leprechaun Lady **Mrs J. Gill**
4 **BILLYCAN (IRE),** 4, b c Mac's Imp (USA)—Sassalin **Mr Frank Dobby**
5 **BOFFY (IRE),** 5, ch h Mac's Imp (USA)—No Dowry **Mr Iain A. Gillies**
6 **FLORISMART,** 6, b g Never So Bold—Spoilt Again **Messrs Chrimes, Winn & Wilson**
7 **GABLESEA,** 4, b g Beveled (USA)—Me Spede **Messrs Chrimes, Winn & Wilson**
8 **JOYFUL JOY,** 4, b f River God (USA)—Joyfulness (FR) **Mr E. Bennion**
9 **MACARI,** 4, gr g Arzanni—View Halloa **Mr Iain A. Gillies**
10 **MARGARETROSE ANNA,** 6, b m Handsome Sailor—Be Bold **Mr Frank Dobby**
11 **MAYSMAXIMUS,** 6, b g Silver Season—Minster Scally **Mrs Joan M. Chrimes**
12 **MERCURY (IRE),** 5, b g Contract Law (USA)—Monrovia (FR) **Mr M. J. Lyons**
13 **MISSED MAY,** 4, br f Petong—Altara (GER) **Esprit de Corps Racing**
14 **PORTOLANO (FR),** 7, b g Reference Point—Kottna (USA) **Mr T. A. Peake**
15 **SINGLE MAN (IRE),** 5, b g Mansooj—Sniggy **Miss Susan Rodman**
16 **SPONDULICKS (IRE),** 4, b g Silver Kite (USA)—Greek Music **Mrs Joan M. Chrimes**
17 **TEXAS SCRAMBLE,** 9, b g Norwick (USA)—Orange Parade **Messrs Chrimes, Winn & Wilson**
18 **TTYFRAN,** 8, b g Petong—So It Goes **Mrs J. Gill**

THREE-YEAR-OLDS

19 **COMPANYS GAMBLE,** b f Barrys Gamble—Pleasant Company **Mrs P. Stevens**
20 **STRAVSEA,** b f Handsome Sailor—La Stravaganza **Mr E. Bennion**
21 **WINDSPEED,** ch g Sheerwind—Speed Baby (USA) **Mrs L. Sargent**

TWO-YEAR-OLDS

22 **COMPANYS ISLAND,** ch g 27/1 Jupiter Island—Pleasant Company (Alzao (USA)) **Mrs P. Stevens**
23 Ch f 19/4 Weld—Joyfulness (FR) (Cure The Blues (USA)) **Mr E. Bennion**

Other Owners: Mrs Diane Baugh, Mr Mel Buckley, Mr J. Chester, Mr G. A. Greaves, Mr A. Kirkham, Mr R. Marklew, Mr John W. Meredith, Miss C. A. Smithson, Mrs C. A. Wallace, Mr T. S. Wallace, Mr K. G. Williams.

Jockey (NH): Gary Lyons (10-0).

Lady Rider: Miss S Potts (10-4).

41 MR P. BEAUMONT, Brandsby

Postal: **Foulrice Farm, Brandsby, York, YO6 4SB.**
Phone: **BRANDSBY (01347) 888208 FAX (01347) 888208**

1 **ARCHIE-T,** 5, b g Totem (USA)—Nicola Mandy **Mrs J. M. Plummer**
2 **ASKRIGG VENTURE (IRE),** 5, br m Jurado (USA)—Brave Polly **T. Weatherald Ltd**
3 **BEGGARS BANQUET (IRE),** 8, b g Callernish—Mo Storeen **Mr E. H. Ruddock**
4 **BRANDSBY MINSTER,** 7, gr g Minster Son—Courting Day **Mrs P. A. H. Hartley**
5 **CHERRY DEE,** 7, ch m Ardross—Merry Cherry **Mr George Dilger**
6 **CHORUS LINE (IRE),** 9, b m Torus—Right Chimes **Mrs A. P. Stead**
7 **DRUMDONNA (IRE),** 8, b m Drumalis—Decoy Duck **Mrs M. R. Beaumont**
8 **FLICKERING LIGHT,** 7, b m Baron Blakeney—Palmerston Girl **Mrs D. L. Holloway**
9 **FROSTY LIGHT,** 5, ch m Glacial Storm (USA)—Always Shining **Miss R. Search**
10 **GALE FORCE (IRE),** 7, b g Strong Gale—Stay As You Are **Mr George Dilger**
11 **GOOD MAN,** 5, b g Good Times (ITY)—Mantina **Mr W. R. Lofthouse**
12 **GRATE DEEL (IRE),** 8, ch g The Parson—Cahernane Girl **Mrs M. Ashby**
13 **GREAT POTENTIAL,** 6, br g Ovac (ITY)—Annamanda **Mrs J. M. Plummer**
14 **HEAD FOR THE HILLS,** 5, ch g Scottish Reel—Merry Cherry **Mr D. S. Bowring**
15 **HUDSON BAY TRADER (USA),** 11, b g Sir Ivor—Yukon Baby (USA) **Mr P. C. N. Curtis**
16 **ISLAND CHIEF (IRE),** 9, b g Carlingford Castle—Run Piggy Run **Mr George Dilger**
17 **JAY'M,** 8, b g Primitive Rising (USA)—Brox Treasure **Mr L. V. Marshall**
18 **JUST CLYDE,** 6, gr g Ovac (ITY)—Georgie's Crusade VII **Mrs M. R. Beaumont**
19 **KERRISDALE,** 6, b m Arctic Lord—Good Way **Brandsby Racing**
20 **KING PIN,** 6, b g King's Ride—Bowling Fort **Mr J. R. Hinchliffe**
21 **KINGS SERMON (IRE),** 9, br g King's Ride—Sunday Sermon **Mrs P. A. H. Hartley**
22 **MADEMIST SAM,** 6, b g Lord Bud—Mademist Susie **Mrs C. M. Clarke**
23 **NETHERBY SAID,** 8, b g Say Primula—Netherby Maid **Mrs S. Sunter**
24 **NIKI DEE (IRE),** 8, b g Phardante (FR)—Curragh Breeze **Mr George Dilger**
25 **PENDLETON,** 5, b g Belfort (FR)—Spanish Beauty **Mr N. W. A. Bannister**
26 **PETRICO,** 6, b g Petong—Balearica **Mr W. R. Lofthouse**
27 **RAMA DE ORO,** 4, ch f Lord Bud—Naturally Autumn **Mr A. R. Boocock**
28 **SPORTING JO,** 5, ch m Primitive Rising (USA)—Joes Baby **Miss J. Hey**
29 **THIRKLEBY SKEENA,** 7, b m Marching On—Thirkleby Kate VII **Mrs M. R. Beaumont**
30 **THREE FRIENDS (IRE),** 8, b m The Parson—Four Friends **Hogarth Racing**
31 **TIMEFORANOTHER,** 5, b m Cruise Missile—New Cherry **Ampleforth Racing**
32 **TOPOTHENORTHRACING (IRE),** 8, b m Tremblant—Waving Penant **The Foulrice Twenty**
33 **TWEEDSWOOD (IRE),** 8, b g Strong Gale—Paulas Fancy **Mr J. N. Yeadon**
34 **WESTWELL BOY,** 12, b g Kambalda—Lady Ashton **Mr D. N. Yeadon**
35 **WINNING BID,** 5, ch m Opening Run (USA)—Better Try Again **Mr A. R. Boocock**
36 **YOUNG KENNY,** 7, b g Ardross—Deirdres Dream **Mr J. G. Read**

Other Owners: Mrs J. Allinson, Mr N. W. A. Bannister, Mr J. Barker, Mr G. D. Benson, Mr R. J. Blenkinsop, Mr Peter Burnside, Mrs C. M. G. Cawte, Mr Paul Clarkson, Mr P. Clews, Mr G. L. Comer, Mr J. Davison, Mrs Maureen Dilger, Mrs E. Dixon, Mr Ian Gibbons, Mr R. Goad, Mr D. Hall, Mrs D. W. Hill, Mr M. J. Hill, Mr J. H. Hinchcliffe, Mr H. P. Hogarth, Mr J. Hogarth, Mr J. L. Hogarth, Mr P. H. Hogarth, Mr C. Jackson, Mr M. Leake, Mrs M. E. Leake, Mrs J. M. Marshall, Mrs Anthea L. Morshead, Mr Ian Mosey, Mr J. Peckitt, Mr H. Phipps, Mrs Brigitte Pollard, Mr G. Ratcliffe, Mr P. Sawyer, Mr W. L. Smith, Mr M. P. Sutton, Mr A. Swindale, Mr D. W. Thompson, Mr John Veitch, Mr S. Vowles, Mr C. N. Wilmot-Smith, Mrs Joe Wilson, Wise Owl Discount Drug Stores Ltd.

Jockey (NH): R Supple.

Conditional: B D Gratton (9-7).

42 MR M. L. W. BELL, Newmarket

Postal: **Fitzroy House, Newmarket, Suffolk, CB8 0JT.**
Phone: **(01638) 666567 FAX (01638) 668000 MOBILE (0802) 264514**

1 **ARANTXA,** 4, b f Sharpo—Amalancher (USA) **Mrs Anne Yearley**
2 **BLOCKADE (USA),** 9, b g Imperial Falcon (CAN)—Stolen Date (USA) **Mr A. M. Warrender**
3 **DANCING QUEEN (IRE),** 4, b f Sadler's Wells (USA)—Bay Shade (USA) **Mrs E. A. Harris**
4 **DINA LINE (USA),** 4, ch f Diesis—Lajna **Mr T. F. Harris**
5 **IVAN LUIS (FR),** 4, b c Lycius (USA)—Zivania (IRE) **Mr Luciano Gaucci**
6 **JOHN EMMS (IRE),** 4, ch g Shalford (IRE)—Miss Lee Ann **Richard Green (Fine Paintings)**
7 **KEEN ALERT,** 4, b g Keen—Miss Coco **Ms Dawn A. Stagg**
8 **MIDYAN CALL,** 4, b c Midyan (USA)—Early Call **Mr Luciano Gaucci**
9 **SHELTEEZ (USA),** 4, b br f St Jovite (USA)—Dictina (FR) **Mr Anthony Rizzo**
10 **SHINING CLOUD,** 5, ch m Indian Ridge—Hardiheroine **Mrs Anne Yearley**
11 **SOLAR STORM,** 4, ch c Polar Falcon (USA)—Sister Sophie (USA) **Mr T. F. Harris**
12 **STAR TURN (IRE),** 4, ch c Night Shift (USA)—Ringtail **Innlaw Racing**

THREE-YEAR-OLDS

13 **ADESTE FIDELES,** b f Groom Dancer (USA)—Decided Air (IRE) **Capt B. W. Bell**
14 **ALDWYCH ARROW (IRE),** ch g Rainbows For Life (CAN)—Shygate **The Aldwych Partnership**
15 **ALL MADE UP (USA),** b c Sheikh Albadou—Mascara Miss (USA) **Mr Nasser Abdullah**
16 **ASPIRANT DANCER,** b g Marju (IRE)—Fairy Ballerina **Mr Peter Coe**
17 **BERNARDO BELLOTTO (IRE),** b g High Estate—Naivity (IRE) **Richard Green (Fine Paintings)**
18 **CAPTAIN'S LOG,** b c Slip Anchor—Cradle of Love (USA) **Mr Christopher Wright**
19 **DONNA GRAZIA,** ch f Sharpo—Little Change **Mr Cyril Humphris**
20 **DRY LIGHTNING,** b f Shareef Dancer (USA)—Valkyrie **Mr A. M. Warrender**
21 **EGO NIGHT (IRE),** b c Night Shift (USA)—Sharp Ego (USA) **Mr Luciano Gaucci**
22 **FEAR NOT (IRE),** b f Alzao (USA)—Fear Naught **Die-Hard Racing Club**
23 **FLUENCY,** b f Formidable (USA)—Habitancy **Mr P. A. Philipps**
24 **GORGEOUS GUSSY (USA),** b br f Quiet American (USA)—Bounding Away (CAN) **Mr Nasser Abdullah**
25 **HOH CHI MIN,** ch f Efisio—Special Guest **Mr D. F. Allport**
26 **HOH NAVIGATOR (IRE),** ch c Common Grounds—Flying Diva **Mr D. F. Allport**
27 **KINGS ARROW (IRE),** b c Mujadil (USA)—Great Leighs **R. P. B. Michaelson & Wafic Said**
28 **LORD LIEUTENANT,** b g Primo Dominie—Danzig Harbour (USA) **Highclere Thoroughbred Racing Ltd**
29 **MAGIC RAINBOW,** b c Magic Ring (IRE)—Blues Indigo **Mr P. T. Fenwick**
30 **MINETTA,** ch f Mujtahid (USA)—Minwah (USA) **Mrs G. Rowland-Clark**
31 **MINIVET,** b g Midyan (USA)—Bronzewing **Sir Thomas Pilkington**
32 **NEXT ROUND (IRE),** b f Common Grounds—Debbie's Next (USA) **Deln Ltd**
33 **PRE CATELAN,** ch f Polar Falcon (USA)—Anneli Rose **Mr M. B. Hawtin**
34 **PRINCE BATSHOOF,** b c Batshoof—Sipsi Fach **Mr Frank A. Farrant**
35 **SCURRILOUS,** ch f Sharpo—Tea And Scandals (USA) **The Hon. Peter Stanley**
36 **SHAANXI ROMANCE (IRE),** b c Darshaan—Easy Romance (USA) **Mr K. Y. Lim**
37 **SILENT TRIBUTE (IRE),** b f Lion Cavern (USA)—Tribal Rite **Mrs E. A. Harris**
38 **SKY RED,** gr f Night Shift (USA)—Noble Haven **Mr Terry Neill**
39 **STATE GALA (IRE),** b f High Estate—Our Galadrial **Mr R. A. Baker**
40 **TIMEKEEPER (USA),** b br c Exbourne (USA)—Falabella **Mr C. M. Watt**
41 **TUSSLE,** b c Salse (USA)—Crime Ofthecentury **Mr T. F. Harris**
42 **WROUGHT IRON (USA),** b br f Dayjur (USA)—Pris de Fer (USA) **Mr Nasser Abdullah**
43 **YOUME THE GATEPOST,** gr f Absalom—Cinderwench **Mr John G. Morley**
44 **YOU RANG SIR (USA),** b f El Gran Senor (USA)—Phone Booth (USA) **Mr K. Y. Lim**

TWO-YEAR-OLDS

45 **AFFIDAVIT,** b f 16/2 Slip Anchor—Lady Barrister (Law Society (USA)) **Cheveley Park Stud**
46 **ALBERTA (IRE),** b c 13/4 Inchinor—Dance A Jig (Dance In Time (CAN)) **Mrs Anne Yearley**
47 **ALPINE RED,** b c 12/2 Tirol—Rohita (IRE) (Waajib) **Mr Terry Neill**
48 **AUTOMATIC,** b c 25/4 Clantime—Gentle Gypsy (Junius (USA)) **Mr Billy Maguire**
49 **BLUE DIAMOND,** b f 8/2 First Trump—Lammastide (Martinmas) **Billion In Mind Partnership**
50 **BRATBY (IRE),** b c 14/4 Distinctly North—Aridje (Mummy's Pet) **Mr C. M. Watt**
51 **CATULLUS,** b c 5/5 Prince Sabo—Rive-Jumelle (IRE) (M Double M (USA)) **Mr Desmond Fitzgerald**
52 **COOGAN (ITY),** ch c 19/4 Caerleon (USA)—Tapage Nocturne (USA) (Irish River (FR)) **Mr Luciano Gaucci**

MR M. L. W. BELL—continued

53 **HARP PLAYER (IRE)**, ch c 28/1 Pips Pride—Angelic Sounds (IRE) (The Noble Player (USA)) **Mr Billy Maguire**
54 **HOH STEAMER (IRE)**, b c 28/4 Perugino (USA)—Dane's Lane (IRE) (Danehill (USA)) **Mr D. F. Allport**
55 **HOT PASSION**, b c 24/4 Keen—Love You Madly (IRE) (Bob Back (USA)) **Mr & Mrs Frank Farrant**
56 **HOUSEMASTER (IRE)**, b c 17/2 Rudimentary (USA)—
Glenarff (USA) (Irish River (FR)) **Highclere Thoroughbred Racing Ltd**
57 B f 30/1 Exbourne (USA)—Meteoric (High Line)
58 **NEST EGG**, ch f 19/2 Prince Sabo—Ministrel's Gift (The Minstrel (CAN)) **Cheveley Park Stud**
59 **NIGHT LIFE (IRE)**, gr f 21/3 Night Shift (USA)—Petula (Petong) **Hon Mrs J. M. Corbett**
60 **OH I SAY**, b f 10/2 Primo Dominie—Isotonic (Absalom) **Mr G. & Mr L. Lederman**
61 B f 23/5 Green Desert (USA)—Old Domesday Book (High Top) **Mr T. F. Harris**
62 **OUR MATE MART**, ch c 11/3 Keen—Princess Moodyshoe (Jalmood (USA)) **Mr & Mrs Frank Farrant**
63 **PENYBONT**, b f 9/3 Unfuwain (USA)—Morgannwg (IRE) (Simply Great (FR)) **Mr & Mrs Kevin Mercer**
64 **PRAIRIE WOLF**, ch c 26/3 Wolfhound (USA)—Bay Queen (Damister (USA)) **Mr Bernard Warren**
65 B f 18/3 Royal Academy (USA)—Quinsigimond (Formidable (USA))
66 B f 19/4 Rudimentary (USA)—Redgrave Design (Nebbiolo)
67 **RED PRAIRIE**, b c 3/2 El Prado (IRE)—Kates Delimma (USA) (Tank's Prospect (USA)) **Mr Terry Neill**
68 **RING OF LOVE**, b f 11/2 Magic Ring (IRE)—Fine Honey (USA) (Drone) **Mr K. Ratcliffe**
69 **ROCK RING**, ch f 16/3 Magic Ring (IRE)—Rock Face (Ballad Rock) **Mr Gerry Byrne**
70 **ROYAL FUSILIER**, b c 4/4 Case Law—Tropical Rain (Rainbow Quest (USA)) **Mr W. H. Ponsonby**
71 **ROYAL PREVIEW (IRE)**, b f 16/2 Prince Sabo—Visible Form (Formidable (USA)) **Sir Peter Davis**
72 **SCHNITZEL (IRE)**, b c 8/2 Tirol—Good Reference (IRE) (Reference Point) **Mrs G. Rowland-Clark**
73 **SHANGHI CRAB (USA)**, b c 4/5 Manila (USA)—Saraa Ree (USA) (Caro) **Mr Christopher Wright**
74 B c 30/3 Up And At 'Em—Sperrin Mist (Camden Town)
75 **SWEET COLLEGE (IRE)**, b f 24/4 College Chapel—Sweet Thatch (IRE) (Thatching) **Mr Luciano Gaucci**
76 **VOLCANIC STAR**, ch f 13/3 Primo Dominie—Lava Star (IRE) (Salse (USA)) **Cheveley Park Stud**
77 B f 6/4 Lycius (USA)—Wassl This Then (IRE) (Wassl) **Miss Susannah Farr**

Other Owners: Mr Paddy Barrett, Mr R. H. Brookes, Mr A. Buxton, Mr Peter Deal, Mr Thomas Dyer, Mr D. Elliott, Mr Timothy Evans, Mr P. Girolami, Mr Alex Gorrie, Mrs Rosalinde Gray, Hoh Supply Limited, Mr Richard Holt, Mr W. J. P. Jackson, Mr M. A. Khan, Mr A. G. Lamerton, Mr Alan Lillingston, Mrs S. M. Lim, Mr T. F. McGee, M. L. W. Bell Racing Ltd, Mr J. G. Moore, Mr John C. Moore, Miss Catherine Newman, The Hon David Oliver, Mr Nicholas Peacock, Mr John Purcell, Mrs Gillian Quinn, Mr J. Ransley, Mr J. M. Ratcliffe, Mr T. S. Redman, Mr J. M. Shaw, Mr Alasdair Simpson, Mr M. C. Talbot-Ponsonby, Mr A. M. Tolhurst, Mr Anthony Trace, Mr R. P. Voelcker, Miss Carolyn Walton, Mr John Wates.

Jockey (Flat): M Fenton (8-2).

Jockey (NH): C Llewellyn (w.a.).

Apprentice: R Mullen (7-7).

43 MR S. B. BELL, Driffield

Postal: **Hall Farm, Burton Fleming, Driffield, North Humberside, YO25 0PT.**
Phone: **(01262) 470519 FAX (01262) 470547**

1 **AQUASEEKER**, 8, b g Dowsing (USA)—Patois **Mr C. H. P. Bell**
2 **CORBLEU (IRE)**, 8, b g Corvaro (USA)—Another Daisy **Mr David Woodcock**
3 **LAW DESIGNER (IRE)**, 6, ch g Architect (USA)—Femme Gendarme (USA) **Mr L. C. Maultby**
4 **PARRY**, 6, b m Ring Bidder—Lucky Joker **Mr David Woodcock**
5 **RED JAM JAR**, 13, ch g Windjammer (USA)—Macaw **Mr C. H. P. Bell**
6 **SIRERIC (IRE)**, 8, b g Asir—Twice Regal **Mr C. H. P. Bell**
7 **THE TIG**, 4, b g Tigani—The Ranee **Mrs Cheryl L. Owen**
8 **TIMMOSS (IRE)**, 7, b g Le Moss—Tangaroa **Mr S. B. Bell**

Jockeys (NH): K Johnson, N Smith.

44 MR FRANCOIS BELMONT, Lamorlaye

Postal: **21b Rue Charles Pratt, 60260 Lamorlaye, France.**
Phone: **44 21 51 24 FAX 44 21 51 68**

1 **BASSANO (USA)**, 4, b c Alwasmi (USA)—Mantena (GER) **G. von Finck**
2 **LIBOR (GER)**, 5, gr h Kings Lake (USA)—Love Affair (GER) **K. Nercessian**

THREE-YEAR-OLDS

3 **ALIMOS (FR)**, b c Highest Honor (FR)—Lady Segev (USA) **Ecurie Kura**
4 **CORVINIUS (GER)**, b c Rainbow Quest (USA)—Crystal Ring (IRE) **K. Nercessian**
5 **FURREAU (GER)**, ch f Ferdinand (USA)—Fluid Dancer (USA) **K. Nercessian**
6 **HASENE (FR)**, b f Akarad (FR)—She's My Lovely **Ecurie Kura**
7 **HOPOPOP (FR)**, b c Bering—Mondialite (FR) **Ecurie Kura**
8 **PYU (GER)**, b f Surumu (GER)—Picturesque (GER) **K. Nercessian**
9 **ROLI ABI (FR)**, b c Bering—All Found (USA) **Ecurie Kura**

TWO-YEAR-OLDS

10 **CARMEL (FR)**, b f Highest Honor (FR)—She's My Lovely **Ecurie Kura**
11 **CHAILAK (FR)**, b c Kendor (FR)—Lady Segev (USA) **Ecurie Kura**
12 **MON COEUR (GER)**, b f Law Society (USA)—Mosella (GER) **K. Nercessian**
13 **PLATINIUM (GER)**, b c Platini (GER)—Picturesque (GER) **K. Nercessian**

45 MR C. J. BENNETT, Dymock

Postal: **Blacklands Farm, Normansland, Dymock, Gloucestershire, GL18 2BE.**

1 **CUT THE CORN**, 10, ch g Oats—Celtic Blade **Mr C. J. Bennett**
2 **FIRST HARVEST**, 11, b g Oats—Celtic Blade **Mr C. J. Bennett**
3 **PLAYING THE FOOL**, 8, b m Idiot's Delight—Celtic Blade **Mr C. J. Bennett**
4 **ROYAL DIVIDE**, 6, b g Lord Americo (IRE)—Divided Loyalties **Mrs E. B. Bennett**

TWO-YEAR-OLDS

5 Gr g 5/5 Arzanni—Swashbuckle (Buckley) **Mr C. J. & Mrs E. B. Bennett**

46 MR J. A. BENNETT, Wantage

Postal: **2 Filley Alley, Letcombe Bassett, Wantage, Oxfordshire, OX12 9LT.**
Phone: **(01235) 762163 MOBILE (0777) 1523076**

1 **ASKING**, 6, b g Skyliner—Ma Famille **Partnership**
2 **BON LUCK (IRE)**, 6, ch g Waajib—Elle Va Bon **Nan Housden Partnership**
3 **CHINA MAIL (IRE)**, 6, b g Slip Anchor—Fenney Mill **The Merlin Syndicate**
4 **GEORDIE LAD**, 4, ch g Tina's Pet—Edraianthus **Miller Place Partnership**
5 **PARISIAN**, 13, b g Shirley Heights—Miss Paris **Miss J. C. Blackwell**
6 **RUBHAHUNISH (IRE)**, 7, b h Darshaan—Captive Island **Lone Star Racing Partnership**
7 **SHARP HOLLY (IRE)**, 6, b m Exactly Sharp (USA)—Children's Hour **Miss J. C. Blackwell**
8 **TINGRITH LAD**, 6, b g Reesh—Bracelet **Mr Jeff Plumb**
9 **TOPANGA**, 6, b g Dancing Brave (USA)—Trampship
10 **WELL ARMED (IRE)**, 7, b g Moscow Society (USA)—Sales Centre **Topanga Partnership**

THREE-YEAR-OLDS

11 **UTHER PENDRAGON (IRE)**, b g Petardia—Mountain Stage (IRE) **Mrs G. S. Blackwell**

MR J. A. BENNETT—continued

Other Owners: Mrs S. Abell, Mr James Bennett, Mrs Sara Clarke, Mrs Jane Geden, Mrs I. A. Hancock, Mr Keith Hatwood, Mr G. M. Heale, Mr B. Hopton, Mr T. Hopton, Mrs I. Housden, Nr B. P. Hoye, Mrs Julia Hucker, Mr G. Jones, Mr F. Keeble, Mrs S. G. King, Mrs L. Leyland, Mr N. Linter, Mr J. McGuigan, Mr R. Ogg, Mrs Maureen Plumb, Mrs J. Rands, Mr J. M. Rands, Mr M. Reynolds, Mr L. G. Ryder, Mr N. P. Sherriff, Mrs K. P. Sherwood, Mr Frederick Smith, Mr R. B. Stubbings, Mr B. G. Thorogood, Mr P. Trounce, Mr P. D. Tugwell, Mr M. Twigg, Mr K. White.

Jockey (NH): L Harvey (w.a.).

47 MR C. J. BENSTEAD, Epsom

Postal: **The Limes, Shepherds Walk, Epsom, Surrey, KT18 6DF.**
Phone: **ASHTEAD (01372) 273152 FAX (01372) 274752**

1 **ARDENT**, 4, b c Aragon—Forest of Arden **Mr R. Lamb**
2 **FLYING COLOURS (IRE)**, 4, b f Fairy King (USA)—Crazed Rainbow (USA) **Mrs R. W. S. Baker**

THREE-YEAR-OLDS

3 **FORGLORI**, b c Formidable (USA)—Glorietta (USA) **Mr R. Lamb**
4 **KAHLA**, b f Green Desert (USA)—Cancan Madame (USA) **Mr Hamdan Al Maktoum**
5 **MISMEWMEW**, b f Weldnaas (USA)—Joan's Gift **Mr R. Lamb**
6 **MOOSRA (IRE)**, b g Elbio—Biddy Mulligan **Mr Hamdan Al Maktoum**
7 **SHAJI (IRE)**, ch c Mukaddamah (USA)—Alkariyh (USA) **Mr Hamdan Al Maktoum**
8 **TAZKIYA**, ch f King's Signet (USA)—Irene's Charter **Mr D. Turner**

TWO-YEAR-OLDS

9 **ALHEYRAH**, b f 27/2 Ezzoud (IRE)—Hamama (USA) (Majestic Light (USA)) **Mr Hamdal Al Maktoum**
10 **MEHMAAS**, b c 5/2 Distant Relative—Guest List (Be My Guest (USA)) **Mr Hamdan Al Maktoum**
11 **TAMMAM (IRE)**, b c 16/2 Priolo (USA)—Bristle (Thatch (USA)) **Mr Hamdan Al Maktoum**
12 **ZAIDAAN**, b c 14/5 Ezzoud (IRE)—River Maiden (USA) (Riverman (USA)) **Mr Hamdan Al Maktoum**

48 MR J. BERRY, Cockerham

Postal: **Moss Side Racing Stable, Crimbles Lane, Cockerham, Lancaster, LA2 0ES.**
Phone: **FORTON (01524) 791179 FAX (01524) 791958 MOBILE (0374) 747718**

1 **ALBERT THE BEAR**, 5, b g Puissance—Florentynna Bay **Chris & Antonia Deuters**
2 **AMLWCH**, 5, b g Weld—Connaughts' Trump **Lord Mostyn**
3 **AMRON**, 11, b g Bold Owl—Sweet Minuet **Mr Roy Peebles**
4 **ANSELLMAN**, 8, gr g Absalom—Grace Poole **Ansells of Watford**
5 **BALLYMOTE**, 4, b g Chilibang—Be My Honey **Manny Bernstein (Racing) Ltd**
6 **BEST OF ALL (IRE)**, 6, b m Try My Best (USA)—Skisette **Mr Robert Aird**
7 **BOLLERO (IRE)**, 4, b f Topanoora—Charo **Mr Ian A. Bolland**
8 **BOLSHOI (IRE)**, 6, br g Royal Academy (USA)—Mainly Dry **Mrs David Brown**
9 **CARLISLE BANDITO'S (IRE)**, 6, b g Exhibitioner—Welsh Rhyme **Mr C. Deuters**
10 **FREDRIK THE FIERCE (IRE)**, 4, b g Puissance—Hollia **Chris & Antonia Deuters**
11 **GARNOCK VALLEY**, 8, b g Dowsing (USA)—Sunley Sinner **Mr Robert Aird**
12 **MILL ORCHID**, 4, b f Henbit (USA)—Milinetta **Mr R. Meredith**
13 **NIFTY NORMAN**, 4, b g Rock City—Nifty Fifty (IRE) **Mrs N. Peebles**
14 **PALACEGATE JACK (IRE)**, 7, gr g Neshad (USA)—Pasadena Lady **Mr William Burns**
15 **PALACEGATE TOUCH**, 8, gr g Petong—Dancing Chimes **Mr Adrian Parr & Partners**
16 **PERSIAN FAYRE**, 6, b g Persian Heights—Dominion Fayre **Mr Murray Grubb**
17 **ROCK ISLAND LINE (IRE)**, 4, b g New Express—Gail's Crystal **Mr J. Berry**
18 **RUNHIM**, 6, b g Runton—Lady Ever-So-Sure **Mrs J. M. Berry**
19 **SELHURSTPARK FLYER (IRE)**, 7, b g Northiam (USA)—Wisdom To Know **Chris & Antonia Deuters**

MR J. BERRY—continued

20 **SMOLENSK (IRE)**, 6, b g Ela-Mana-Mou—Merry Twinkle **Chris & Antonia Deuters**
21 **SUMMER THYME**, 4, b f Henbit (USA)—Hasty Sarah **Mrs Brigitte Pollard**
22 **TUSCAN DAWN**, 8, ch g Clantime—Excavator Lady **Chris & Antonia Deuters**

THREE-YEAR-OLDS

23 **ANTONIA'S DOUBLE**, ch f Primo Dominie—Mainly Sunset **Chris & Antonia Deuters**
24 **ARJAN (IRE)**, gr f Paris House—Forest Berries (IRE) **Mr W. J. Kelly**
25 **BE PRACTICAL**, b f Tragic Role (USA)—Practical **T. G. & M. E. Holdcroft**
26 **BLUEBERRY PARKES**, b f Pursuit of Love—Summerhill Spruce **Mr Joseph Heler**
27 **BOLSHAYA**, gr f Cadeaux Genereux—Mainly Dry **Mr C. Deuters**
28 **CIRCUITEER (IRE)**, ch g Pips Pride—Day Dress **Mr David Fish**
29 **DETROIT CITY (IRE)**, b g Distinctly North (USA)—Moyhora (IRE) **Mr Norman Jackson**
30 **EASTERN LYRIC**, gr f Petong—Songlines **Mr R. Meredith**
31 **ELLENBROOK (IRE)**, b f Petorius—Short Stay **Mr J. K. Brown & Partners**
32 **FIRST VILLAGE (IRE)**, b f Danehill (USA)—L-Way First (IRE) **Dr G. W. W. Tsoi**
33 **FRENCH CONNECTION**, gr c Tirol—Heaven-Liegh-Grey **Mr Peter Dodd**
34 **HENRY THE PROUD (IRE)**, ch g Shalford (IRE)—June Goddess **Chris & Antonia Deuters**
35 **HEY UP MATE (IRE)**, b g River Falls—Damira (FR) **Mr W. R. Astbury**
36 **HOUSE ON FIRE (IRE)**, b g Paris House—La Fille de Feu **Mr Brian Chandler**
37 **IRIS MAY**, b f Brief Truce (USA)—Choire Mhor **John Brown & Megan Dennis**
38 **ITS ALL RELATIVE**, gr f Distant Relative—Sharp Anne **Mr Reg Leah**
39 **JUNIOR MUFFIN (IRE)**, b g Paris House—Clodianus **Mr J. Berry**
40 **JUST ANOTHER TIME**, ch c Mazilier (USA)—Entourage **Miss Lilo Blum & Partners**
41 **LADY FROM LIMERICK (IRE)**, ch f Rainbows For Life (CAN)—Coshlea **Mr Thomas Doherty**
42 **MAMMA'S BOY**, b g Rock City—Henpot (IRE) **Mr G. Tiribocchi**
43 **MARY JANE**, b f Tina's Pet—Fair Attempt (IRE) **Mr W. R. Milner**
44 **MAYTONG**, gr f Petong—Bit O'May **Mr & Mrs Peter Foden**
45 **ONE TO GO (IRE)**, b g Petorius—Caroline's Mark **Mr J. Berry**
46 **ONLY FOR GOLD**, b c Presidium—Calvanne Miss **Mr John Milner & Mr Stephen Milner**
47 **PETER'S IMP (IRE)**, b g Imp Society (USA)—Catherine Clare **Mr & Mrs Peter Foden**
48 **RISKY WHISKY**, b g Risk Me (FR)—Desert Gem **Mr W. J. Kelly**
49 **ROSEATE**, b f Magic Ring (IRE)—Rosy Diamond **Mr J. Berry**
50 **ROYAL DREAM**, b f Ardkinglass—Faraway Grey **Mrs B. A. Matthews**
51 **RYEFIELD STAR**, b g Marju (IRE)—Awayed (USA) **Mr Robert Aird**
52 **SANDSIDE**, b g Mazaad—Deverells Walk (IRE) **Mr J. K. Brown & Partners**
53 **SKIPMANTOO (IRE)**, ch g Pips Pride—Sports Post Lady (IRE) **Mr Paul Williams**
54 **SOMOSIERRA (IRE)**, b g Paris House—Island Heather (IRE) **Chris & Antonia Deuters**
55 **TALAVERA**, gr g Paris House—Gem of Gold **Chris & Antonia Deuters**
56 **TANGERINE FLYER**, ch g Presidium—Factuelle **Pet Express (W&R) Ltd**
57 **THREE TENNERS**, b f Distinctly North—Hollia (USA) **Mr Neville Wilson & Partners**
58 **YANOMAMI (USA)**, ch f Slew O' Gold (USA)—Sunerta (USA) **T. G. & M. E. Holdcroft**

TWO-YEAR-OLDS

59 **ACE OF PARKES**, b c 18/3 Teenoso (USA)—Summerhill Spruce (Windjammer (USA)) **Mr Joseph Heler**
60 **ANGIE BABY**, b f 9/5 Puissance—Hyde Princess (Touch Paper) **The Cooper Group**
61 **ANGUS THE BOLD**, b g 22/3 Puissance—Floral Spark (Forzando) **Chris & Antonia Deuters**
62 **BAYFORD GREEN (IRE)**, b f 3/4 Distinctly North—Paddys Cocktail (IRE) (Tremblant) **Mrs Jean Turner & Mr Jack Hanson**
63 **BEVERLEY MONKEY (IRE)**, b f 17/3 Fayruz—Godly Light (FR) (Vayrann) **The Monkey Partnership**
64 **BON AMI (IRE)**, b c 16/4 Paris House—Felin Special (Lyphard's Special (USA)) **Mr K. T. Ivory & Mr J. Berry**
65 B f 8/3 King's Signet (USA)—Calvanne Miss (Martinmas) **Mr John Milner & Partners**
66 **CARTMEL PARK**, b g 20/5 Skyliner—Oh My Oh My (Ballacashtal (CAN)) **P. G. Airey & R. R. Whitton**
67 **CONWY LODGE (IRE)**, b c 8/3 Lahib (USA)—Alriyaah (Shareef Dancer (USA)) **Lord Mostyn**
68 **CYCLONE FLYER**, br f 14/3 College Chapel—Mainly Dry (The Brianstan) **Mr Reg Leah**
69 **DESERT DARLING**, b f 16/3 Green Desert (USA)—Habibti (Habitat) **The Sussex Stud Ltd**
70 **DONE AND DUSTED (IRE)**, ch f 19/3 Up And At 'Em—Florentink (USA) (The Minstrel (CAN)) **Chris & Antonia Deuters**
71 **FAIR CESTRIAN (IRE)**, b c 30/3 Petardia—Fair Chance (Young Emperor) **J. & J. R. Littler**
72 B c 26/2 Lashkari—Filet Mignon (USA) (Topsider (USA)) **Mr John Milner & Partners**

MR J. BERRY—continued

73 GLANWYDDEN, ch c 9/2 Grand Lodge (USA)—Brush Away (Ahonoora) **Lord Mostyn**
74 HABIBI, b f 12/2 Alhijaz—Balearica (Bustino) **Mr & Mrs W. Kelly, Mr & Mrs J. Berry**
75 B c 28/4 Greensmith—Halka (Daring March) **Red Shirt Brigade Racing Club**
76 Ch c 22/2 Fayruz—Haraabah (USA) (Topsider (USA)) **Lucayan Stud**
77 Gr f 12/4 King Among Kings—Heavenly Pet (Petong)
78 Ch c 22/1 Whittingham (IRE)—Hips'n Haws (IRE) (Thatching) **Mr Tommy Bibby**
79 JANE'S LOFT, b f 26/4 UP And At 'Em—Excitingly (USA) (Val de L'Orne (FR)) **Mr Jack Wilkins**
80 KALAHARI FERRARI, ch c 7/4 Clantime—Royal Agnes (Royal Palace) **Chris & Antonia Deuters**
81 KARISAL (IRE), b f 28/5 Persian Bold—Pasadena Lady (Captain James) **Mrs Joan Hawkins**
82 KASTAWAY, b f 13/2 Distant Relative—Flourishing (IRE) (Trojan Fen) **Mr & Mrs D. Winter, Gerry & Lilo Blum**
83 KEY TO DOOKS (IRE), b c 20/4 Up And At 'Em—
Global Princess (USA) (Transworld (USA)) **Mr Reinhard Fabricuz**
84 B f 2/3 Petong—Klewraye (Lord Gayle (USA))
85 LA SOEUR D'ALBERT, b f 18/1 Puissance—Florentynna Bay (Aragon) **Chris & Antonia Deuters**
86 LAUREL PRINCE, b c 28/1 Reprimand—Laurel Queen (IRE) (Viking (USA)) **Laurel Racing Club**
87 B c 28/4 Magic Ring (IRE)—Lindfield Belle (IRE) (Fairy King (USA)) **Red Shirt Brigade Racing Club**
88 MAMMA'S F-C (IRE), ch f 18/3 Case Law—Wasaif (IRE) (Lomond (USA)) **Mr J. K. Brown & Partners**
89 MARGARET'S FIRST, b f 29/1 Puissance—Margaret's Gift (Beveled (USA)) **The Margaret Partnership**
90 MIDNIGHT ORCHID (IRE), b f 27/3 Petardia—Rosa Van Fleet (Sallust) **T. Herbert-Jackson & T. Holdcroft**
91 MILLISENT, b f 9/2 Primo Dominie—Millaine (Formidable (USA)) **T. G. & M. E. Holdcroft**
92 MISS GRAPETTE (IRE), b f 24/4 Brief Truce (USA)—Grapette (Nebbiola) **Nan Robertson & Mr J. Berry**
93 Gr c 9/4 Magical Strike (USA)—Narrow Band (IRE) (Standaan (FR)) **Mr G. L. Tanner**
94 OLIBERI, b c 15/1 First Trump—Rhiannon (Welsh Pageant) **J. K. M. Oliver & Mrs J. M. Berry**
95 Gr f 14/2 Perugino (USA)—Olivia's Pride (IRE) (Digamist (USA)) **Comerford Bros Ltd**
96 ONE MORE STRIDE, ch c 28/4 Beveled (USA)—Gem of Gold (Jellaby) **Mr & Mrs Deuters & Mr & Mrs J. Berry**
98 PRINCIPALITY, b c 16/3 College Chapel—Desert Palace (Green Desert (USA)) **Coolmore Stud**
99 QUEENSLAND STAR (IRE), b c 6/4 College Chapel—Zenga (Try My Best (USA)) **Mr Alex Ferguson**
100 Ch f 11/4 Perugino (USA)—Reflection Time (IRE) (Fayruz) **Red Shirt Brigade Racing Club**
101 RISK ONE FARTHING, ch f 14/5 Risk Me (FR)—Farinara (Dragonara Palace (USA)) **Mr A. N. Brooke Rankin**
102 ROSSELLI, b c 9/4 Puissance—Miss Rossi (Artaius (USA)) **T. G. Holdcroft & J. Berry**
103 Gr c 22/1 First Trump—Simply Sooty (Absalom) **Mr Jack Hanson**
104 B f 17/3 Elbio—Smart Turn (His Turn) **Pat Conroy**
105 Ch g 23/3 Up And At 'Em—Smashing Pet (Mummy's Pet) **Red Shirt Brigade Racing Club**
106 SMOKIN (IRE), b c 22/4 Magic Ring (IRE)—Casbah Girl (Native Bazaar) **H. Hughes & D. Bloy**
107 STAVANGER (IRE), b c 20/4 Distinctly North—Card Queen (Lord Gayle (USA)) **Chris & Antonia Deuters**
108 Ch c 6/4 Rainbows For Life—Theda (Mummy's Pet) **Red Shirt Brigade Racing Club**
109 B f 12/3 Merdon Melody—Woodland Steps (Bold Owl) **Red Shirt Brigade Racing Club**
110 ZARAGOSSA, gr f 26/3 Paris House—Antonia's Folly (Music Boy) **Slatch Farm Stud**

Additional Horse

INPUT, ch f 1/3 Primo Dominie—Putout (Dowsing (USA)) **Furnace Mill Partnership**

Other Owners: Mr I. Anderson, Mr B. C. Ansell, Mr C. G. Ansell, Mrs M. L. Ansell, Mr Alan Berry, Mr Sam Berry, Mrs M. A. Bibby, Mrs Bridget Blum, Mr David Brown, Mr P. E. T. Chandler, Mrs Sean M. Collins, Mr John A. Conway, Cricketers Syndicate, Mr Martin Cruddace, Mrs S. Dalton, Mr J. A. Forsyth, Mr Scott Gibbons, Mrs Robert Heathcote, Mr J. Henderson, Highgrove Developments Limited, Mrs A. T. Hughes, Mr Rob Hughes, Mr John Hulme, Mr Richard Jinks, Mr J. Laughton, Laurel (Leisure) Limited, Lostford Manor Stud, Mrs John Magnier, Mr John M. Magnier, Mr David R. Martin, Mrs Ann Morris, Miss Teresa O'Hanlon, Mr Neil Pinkstone, Mr Jason Puckey, Mrs A. E. Robertson, Mr William Robertson, Mr John C. Shaw, The Mirror Punters Club, Mr N. Warburton, Mrs Jean Wilson.

Jockeys (Flat): Gary Carter, L Charnock (w.a.), Kevin Darley (w.a.).

Jockey (NH): M Moloney.

Apprentices: Paul Bradley (7-3), Paul Fessey (7-7), Carl Lowther (7-12), Paul Roberts (8-4).

Amateur: R Hale.

Lady Rider: Beverley Kendall (9-7).

49 MR J. C. DE P BERRY, Newmarket

Postal: **Beverley House Stables, Exeter Road, Newmarket, Suffolk, CB8 8LR.**
Phone: **(01638) 660663 FAX (01638) 660663**

1 **CHABROL (CAN),** 5, b h El Gran Senor (USA)—Off The Record (USA) **The Chabrol Partnership**
2 **FURTHER FUTURE (IRE),** 5, br g Doubletour (USA)—Tamara's Reef **Mr A. K. Collins**
3 **IL PRINCIPE (IRE),** 4, b g Ela-Mana-Mou—Seattle Siren (USA) **The 1997 Partnership**
4 **LARGESSE,** 4, b c Cadeaux Genereux—Vilanika (FR) **Mrs Rosemary Moszkowicz**
5 **MARDREW,** 4, b c Rambo Dancer (CAN)—Having Fun **Mr Terry Connors**
6 **STATISTICIAN,** 6, b g Statoblest—Sharp Lady **Mr Richard Sims**
7 **YAVERLAND (IRE),** 6, b h Astronef—Lautreamont **Mrs B. A. Blackwell**

THREE-YEAR-OLDS

8 **HAMERKOP,** br f Damister (USA)—Royal Scene (NZ) **Mr John Berry**
9 **LAKE WOBEGONE (IRE),** ch g Inchinor—Westerlake **Mr John Berry**
10 **QUAKERESS (IRE),** b f Brief Truce (USA)—Deer Emily **Mr H. R. Moszkowicz**
11 **SUPER IMPOSE,** ch g Superpower—Sharp Lady **Mrs V. Bampton**
12 **UNCHAINED MELODY,** ch f Vague Shot—My Sweet Melody **Miss S. Paxton**

TWO-YEAR-OLDS

13 **BOLD CARDOWAN (IRE),** br c 15/5 Persian Bold—Moving Trend (IRE) (Be My Guest (USA)) **Mr J. McCarthy**
14 B c 6/3 Warrshan (USA)—Rise And Fall (Mill Reef (USA)) **The 1997 Partnership**
15 B c 2/5 Thatching—Tatra (Niniski (USA)) **The Deejay Partnership**

Other Owners: Mr C. Benest, Mr W. F. Benter, Mr N. Blake, Mr J. Dumas, Mrs P. Foster, Mr J. Gilbert, Mr G. Grimstone, Mrs C. Haldane, Mr D. Huelin, Miss J. V. May, Miss L. I. McCarthy, Mr F. Rickaby, Mr J. Smith, Mr L. C. Wadey, Mr A. Walker, Mr D. Welch.

Jockeys (Flat): J Egan (8-0, w.a.), K Fallon (8-4, w.a.), M Fenton (8-1, w.a.).

Jockeys (NH): A Maguire (10-0, w.a.), B Powell (10-0, w.a.), G Tormey (10-0, w.a.).

Amateur: Mr C McEntee (9-10).

Lady Rider: Mrs J Le Brocq (8-7).

50 MR N. BERRY, Upper Lambourn

Postal: **Frenchmans House, Upper Lambourn, Hungerford, Berkshire, RG17 8QT.**
Phone: **(01488) 72817 FAX (01488) 72817 MOBILE (0378) 841236**

1 **ABSOLUTE UTOPIA (USA),** 5, b g Mr Prospector (USA)—Magic Gleam (USA) **Mr M. T. Lawrance**
2 **ASHKERNAZY (IRE),** 7, ch m Salt Dome (USA)—Eskaroon **London Bridge II**
3 **BIT ON THE SIDE (IRE),** 9, b m Vision (USA)—Mistress (USA) **Mr B. Beale**
4 **CHASETOWN FLYER (USA),** 4, b c Thorn Dance (USA)—Thought Provoker (USA) **Mr D. W. Smith**
5 **FAIRLY SURE (IRE),** 5, b m Red Sunset—Mirabiliary (USA) **Heavyweight Racing**
6 **OPENING RANGE,** 7, b m Nordico (USA)—Waveguide **The Purple People Racing Partnership**
7 **RAMBOLD,** 7, b m Rambo Dancer (CAN)—Boldie **Mr Ron Collins**
8 **ROCKET RON,** 6, b g Puget (USA)—Aliwood Girl **Mr Ron Collins**
9 **SQUARE MILE MISS (IRE),** 5, b m Last Tycoon—Call Me Miss **Mr P. Rawson**
10 **TAL-Y-LLYN (IRE),** 4, ch c Common Grounds—Welsh Fantasy **BBB Computer Services**
11 **TURF SCORCHER,** 7, ch g Hotfoot—Four Lawns **Mrs Sarah Beale**

MR N. BERRY—continued

THREE-YEAR-OLDS

12 **CAPTAIN MCCLOY (USA),** ch g Lively One (USA)—Fly Me First (USA) **Mr D. W. Smith**
13 **GILDERSLEVE,** ch f Gildoran—Fragrant Hackette **Lancing Racing Club**
14 **GLITTER PRINCESS,** ch f Prince Sabo—Maritime Lady (USA) **Mr Norman Berry**

Other Owners: London Bridge Partnership, Mr J. Bull, Mr A. A. Campbell, Mr G. M. Eales, Mrs Julia Eales, Six Furlongs Racing, Mr A. D. Gipp, Mr B. Hare, Mr Keith Hoffman, Mrs B. E. Keates, Mr P. Kersey, Mr George Patching, Miss Heather Robbie, Mr Chris Romain, Mr L. M. Shepherd, Mrs I. Shine, J. Shine, Mr T. W. Stubbings.

Jockeys (Flat): N Adams (7-7, w.a.), B Doyle (8-1), R Perham (8-4).

Amateur: Miss Emma Folkes (9-0).

51 MR J. R. BEST, Maidstone

Postal: **Scragged Oak Farm, Scragged Oak Road, Hucking, Maidstone, Kent, ME17 1QU.**
Phone: **Tel: (01622) 880276 Fax: (01622) 880904**

1 **BRIGHT SAPPHIRE,** 12, b g Mummy's Pet—Bright Era **Mrs M. H. Pay**
2 **BURNING CASH,** 6, gr m Pitpan—Burning Rhythm **The Classic Link Syndicate**
3 **DON'TCALLMEGEORGE,** 7, b g Lighter—Pennulli **Mr H. J. Jarvis**
4 **GENTLE TUNE (IRE),** 8, b g Paean—Gentle Maggie **Mr H. J. Jarvis**
5 **HEVER GOLF DIAMOND,** 5, b g Nomination—Cadi Ha **The Classic Link Syndicate**
6 **LITTLE NOD,** 9, ch g Domynsky—Vikris **Mr D. Rolfe**
7 **ROLLESTON BLADE,** 11, ch g Broadsword (USA)—Pearl Bride **Mr H. J. Jarvis**
8 **TIPPING THE LINE,** 8, b g Baron Blakeney—Lily Mab (FR) **Mr Malcolm J. Spencer**

THREE-YEAR-OLDS

9 Br f King's Signet (USA)—True Measure **Mr J. C. Window**

Other Owners: Mr N. Larrigan, Ms Tanya Larrigan.

52 MR J. D. BETHELL, Middleham

Postal: **Clarendon House, Middleham, Leyburn, North Yorkshire, DL8 4NP.**
Phone: **WENSLEYDALE (01969) 622962 FAX (01969) 622157**

1 **AL AVA CONSONANT,** 4, b f Reprimand—Dragonist **The Dante Partnership**
2 **BURLESQUE,** 4, b g Old Vic—Late Matinee **The Gordon Partnership**
3 **DOUBLE ECHO (IRE),** 10, br g Glow (USA)—Piculet **Mrs John Lee**
4 **EL BAILADOR (IRE),** 7, b g Dance of Life (USA)—Sharp Ego (USA) **Mrs John Lee**
5 **HUNTERS OF BRORA (IRE),** 8, b m Sharpo—Nihad **Mr Robert Gibbons**
6 **OKRA,** 4, gr f Chilibang—Mollified **Mrs G. Fane**
7 **RETURN OF AMIN,** 4, ch c Salse (USA)—Ghassanah **Sheikh Amin Dahlawi**
8 **SNOWY MANTLE,** 5, b m Siberian Express (USA)—Mollified **Mrs G. Fane**
9 **WINSTON,** 5, b br g Safawan—Lady Leman **Mrs J. E. Vickers**

THREE-YEAR-OLDS

10 **BINT ST JAMES,** b f Shareef Dancer (USA)—St James's Antigua (IRE) **Sheikh Amin Dahlawi**
11 **CAMERON JACK,** b g Elmaamul (USA)—Ile de Reine **Mr M. Territt**
12 **LADY MABEL,** ch f Inchinor—Late Matinee **Mr N. D. Fisher**
13 **LUNCHTIME GIRL,** ch f Cadeaux Genereux—Thewaari (USA) **Mr Robert Gibbons**
14 **RICH CHOICE,** gr f Presidium—Gratclo **Mrs J. E. Vickers**

MR J. D. BETHELL—continued

TWO-YEAR-OLDS

15 CLARENDON (IRE), ch c 28/2 Forest Wind (USA)—Sparkish (IRE) (Persian Bold) **Clarendon Thoroughbred Racing**
16 DISHABILLE, b f 23/2 Dilum (USA)—Swagger Lady (Tate Gallery (USA)) **Mr R. Chethem**
17 FEARBY CROSS, b c 20/3 Unblest—Two Magpies (Doulab (USA)) **Clarendon Thoroughbred Racing**
18 GRIZELDA (IRE), gr f 7/4 Bluebird (USA)—Phazania (Tap On Wood) **Mrs Catherine Corbett**
19 HUNTERS TWEED, b c 3/2 Nashwan (USA)—Zorette (USA) (Zilzal (USA)) **Mr Robert Gibbons**
20 B f 22/1 Marju (IRE)—Ivory Palm (USA) (Sir Ivor)
21 JULIA'S FALCON, b f 20/2 Polar Falcon (USA)—Julia Domna (Dominion) **Mr David Shirley**
22 LITTLE AMIN, b c 27/3 Unfuwain (USA)—Ghassanah (Pas de Seul) **Sheikh Amin Dahlawi**
23 MEDELAI, b f 19/2 Marju (IRE)—No Islands (Lomond (USA)) **Clarendon Thoroughbred Racing**
24 RICH DOMINION, ch c 24/1 First Trump—Tiszta Sharok (Song) **Mrs J. E. Vickers**
25 TRUE FLYER, b f 27/4 Midyan (USA)—Surf Bird (Shareef Dancer (USA)) **Mr T. R. Lock**

Other Owners: Mrs Bernie Allwright, Mr J. D. Bethell, Mrs James Bethell, Mr C. J. Burley, Mrs S. M. Burley, Mr L. B. Holliday, Mr John S. Lee, Mrs Margaret McCrave, Miss Linda C. Parnaby, Mr David G. Sutherland.

53 MR W. A. BETHELL, Hull

Postal: **Arnold Manor, Arnold, Hull, North Humberside, HU11 5HP.**
Phone: **(01964) 562996**

1 CAPTAIN OATES, 5, b g Arctic Lord—Captain's Cottage **Mr W. A. Bethell**
2 5, B br g Phardante (FR)—Clarahill **Mr W. A. Bethell**
3 COTTAGE BAY, 6, b m Arctic Lord—Captain's Cottage **Mr W. A. Bethell**
4 COTTAGE CRAFT, 9, b g Idiot's Delight—Jimmys Cottage **Mr W. A. Bethell**
5 MALAWI, 8, ch g Northern State (USA)—Nyeri **Mr W. A. Bethell**
6 MASTER CORNET, 13, ch g Celtic Cone—Yogurt **Mr W. A. Bethell**
7 QUIET MISTRESS, 8, b m Kind of Hush—Miss Acrow **Mr W. A. Bethell**
8 UBU VAL (FR), 12, b g Kashneb (FR)—Lady Val (FR) **Mr W. A. Bethell**

Jockey (NH): A S Smith (10-0, w.a.).

54 MR E. G. BEVAN, Hereford

Postal: **Pullen Farm, Ullingswick, Herefordshire, HR1 3JQ.**
Phone: **(01432) 820370**

1 LARK'S RISE, 4, b f Niniski (USA)—Line of Cards **Mr E. G. Bevan**
2 LITTLE COURT, 7, b g Little Wolf—Foolish Hooley **Mr E. G. Bevan**

55 MR P. J. BEVAN, Uttoxeter

Postal: **The Stables, Black Pitts Farm, Kingstone, Uttoxeter, Staffordshire, ST14 8QW.**
Phone: **HOME (01889) 500670 STABLES (01889) 500647**

1 COAST ALONG (IRE), 6, b g Satco (FR)—Golden Flats **Peter J. Douglas Engineering**
2 CROMABOO CROWN, 7, b m Crowning Honors (CAN)—La Belle Epoque **Mr John Wardle**
3 HILLS GAMBLE, 8, b g Remezzo—Mayleader **Mr John Hill**
4 HUNTLEY LANE, 5, b m Welsh Captain—L'Aquino **Mr F. A. Jackson**
5 MY HANDSOME PRINCE, 6, b g Handsome Sailor—My Serenade (USA) **Mr D. B. Holmes**
6 SAHHAR, 5, ch h Sayf El Arab (USA)—Native Magic **Mrs P. J. Bevan**
7 TOP SHELF, 4, b f Warning—Troy Moon **Mr U. Loizou**

MR P. J. BEVAN—continued

THREE-YEAR-OLDS

8 **MY FLOOSIE,** b f Unfuwain (USA)—My Chiara **Mr A. Eaton**

Other Owners: Mr L. E. Goddard, Steve Lilley Racing Ltd, Mrs Margaret Underwood.

Jockey (Flat): N Carlisle (w.a.).

Jockey (NH): W Worthington (w.a.).

56 MRS P. F. BICKERTON, Market Drayton

Postal: **3 Pixley Cottages, Hinstock, Market Drayton, Shropshire, TF9 2TN.**
Phone: **(01952) 550384 MOBILE (0966) 441001**

1 **CASHEL QUAY (IRE),** 8, ch g Quayside—Magar's Pride **Mr David Bickerton**
2 **CURRAGH PETER,** 11, b g Orchestra—Slaney Valley **Mr David Bickerton**
3 **LADY RENTON,** 7, ch m Rolfe (USA)—Rentons Gift **Mr David Bickerton**
4 **MAY GIFT,** 6, b m Reesh—Rentons Gift **Mr David Bickerton**

57 MR J. N. R. BILLINGE, Cupar

Postal: **Hilton Farm, Cupar, Fife, Scotland, KY15 4QD.**
Phone: **(01334) 655180**

1 **BO'S ORRAMAN,** 6, b g Belfort (FR)—Princess Scarlett **Mr J. N. R. Billinge**
2 **MASTER KIT (IRE),** 9, b g Lancastrian—Katie Proverb **Mr J. N. R. Billinge**

Amateur: Mr J. N. R. Billinge (11-7).

58 MR J. J. BIRKETT, Workington

Postal: **Garfield House, High Seaton, Workington, Cumbria, CA14 1PD.**
Phone: **(01900) 604189 MOBILE (0378) 483230**

1 **BITACRACK,** 11, ch g Le Bavard (FR)—Gothic Arch **Mr Nick Kyprianou**
2 **CAPTAIN TANCRED (IRE),** 10, b g The Parson—Tudor Lady **Mrs K. P. Birkett**
3 **CHOCOLATE DRUM (IRE),** 7, ch g Orchestra—Precious Petra **The Claret and Blue Partnership**
4 **JAUNTY GIG,** 12, b g Dunphy—Hazel Gig **The Claret and Blue Partnership**
5 **NINE PIPES (IRE),** 7, b g Sure Blade (USA)—Winning Look **Mr G. Gordon**
6 **PRECIPICE RUN,** 13, ch g Deep Run—Lothian Lassie **Mr C. Warwick**
7 **SHEER GIFT,** 9, b m Sheer Grit—Merry Madam **Mrs K. P. Birkett**
8 **WALLS COURT,** 11, ch g Cardinal Flower—Anega **Walls Court Racing**

Other Owners: Mr Sid Alcock, Mr Keith Harding, Mr T. Irving, Mr W. Irving, Mr George McKeown, Mr Tony Stephanou, Mr D. M. Stuart, Mr Keith Thomas, Mr Ian Wilcock.

Jockeys (NH): M Moloney (10-0), L O'Hara (10-0).

59 MR K. BISHOP, Bridgwater

Postal: **Barford Park Stables, Spaxton, Bridgwater, Somerset, TA5 1AF.**
Phone: **SPAXTON (01278671) 437 FAX 01278671437**

1 **ALICE'S MIRROR,** 9, gr m Magic Mirror—Pousdale-Tachytees **A. M. Partnership**
2 **GLACIAL KING (IRE),** 6, br g Glacial Storm (USA)—Doorslammer **Mrs E. K. Ellis**
3 **HILL TRIX,** 12, b g Le Moss—Up To Trix **Mrs E. K. Ellis**
4 **INDIAN TEMPLE,** 7, ch g Minster Son—Indian Flower **Mr Derek Clarke**
5 **JUST JASMINE,** 6, ch m Nicholas Bill—Linguistic **Mrs E. K. Ellis**
6 **PAULTON,** 5, b g Lugana Beach—Runcina **Business Forms Express**
7 **QUABMATIC,** 5, b g Pragmatic—Good Skills **Eric's Friends Racing Partnership**
8 **REDGRAVE WOLF,** 5, ch m Little Wolf—Redgrave Rose **Mr K. Bishop**
9 **SOUTHSEA SCANDALS (IRE),** 7, ch g Phardante (FR)—Wonder Alice **Business Forms Express**
10 **STEEPLE JACK,** 11, b g Pardigras—Mountain Mear **Mr K. Bishop**
11 **WELTON ARSENAL,** 6, b g Statoblest—Miller's Gait **Business Forms Express**

Other Owners: Mrs D. M. Best, Mr S. R. Bowley, Mrs P. J. Butterell, Mr Ken Carr, Mr W. Davies, Mrs Freda Forster, Mrs P. Hooper, Mr H. Kerswell, Mrs Diana C. Kirkman, Mrs Penny Lobb, Mr C. J. Macey, Mr S. J. Norton, Mr C. H. Roberts, Mrs Sandra Smith, Mr D. Tidball, Mr Keith Watkins, Mrs Pamela Westlake.

Jockey (NH): R Greene (10-0).

Conditional: G Supple (9-9).

60 MRS C. J. BLACK, Oswestry

Postal: **Tedsmore Hall, West Felton, Oswestry, Shropshire, SY11 4HD.**
Phone: **(01691) 610208**

1 **EVEN BLUE (IRE),** 10, b g Gianchi—The Blue Pound **Mrs C. J. Black**
2 **MANVULANE (IRE),** 8, b g Mandalus—La Vulane **Mrs C. J. Black**

61 MR A. G. BLACKMORE, Hertford

Postal: **'Chasers', Stockings Lane, Little Berkhamsted, Hertford, SG13 8LW.**
Phone: **(01707) 875060**

1 **HIGHLAND FLAME,** 9, ch g Dunbeath (USA)—Blakesware Saint **Mr A. G. Blackmore**
2 **PHYSICAL FUN,** 7, b g Phardante (FR)—Running Game **Mr A. G. Blackmore**

Conditional: P Henley, G Hogan (9-10).

62 MR M. T. W. BLANSHARD, Upper Lambourn

Postal: **Lethornes Stables, Upper Lambourn, Hungerford, Berkshire, RG17 8QT.**
Phone: **LAMBOURN (01488) 71091 FAX 73497 MOBILE (0385) 370093**

1 **BANDORE (IRE),** 4, ch c Salse (USA)—Key Tothe Minstrel (USA)
2 **BIG BANG,** 4, b g Superlative—Good Time Girl
3 **BRAMBLE BEAR,** 4, b f Beveled (USA)—Supreme Rose
4 **DUELLO,** 7, b g Sure Blade (USA)—Royal Loft
5 **INCLINATION,** 4, b f Beveled (USA)—Pallomere
6 **PADDY'S RICE,** 7, ch g Hadeer—Requiem
7 **POLLY GOLIGHTLY,** 5, ch m Weldnaas (USA)—Polly's Teahouse

MR M. T. W. BLANSHARD—continued

8 **RAMBLING BEAR,** 5, ch h Sharrood (USA)—Supreme Rose
9 **RUNIC SYMBOL,** 7, b g Warning—Pagan Deity
10 **SAFFRON ROSE,** 4, b f Polar Falcon (USA)—Tweedling (USA)
11 **SEA SPOUSE,** 7, ch g Jalmood (USA)—Bambolona
12 **TRAMLINE,** 5, b h Shirley Heights—Trampship

THREE-YEAR-OLDS

13 **BROWN SUGAR,** b f Reprimand—Secret Waters
14 **COASTER (IRE),** ch g Thatching—Modica
15 **COMPRADORE,** b f Mujtahid (USA)—Keswa
16 **FAWNING,** b f Alnasr Alwasheek—Flattering (USA)
17 **FLYING CLOUDS,** b f Batshoof—Fleeting Rainbow
18 **JUST MAGIC,** b f Beveled (USA)—Kissimmee (FR)
19 Ch f Inchinor—Ophrys
20 **THE MAGISTRATE (IRE),** br c Case Law—Bel Ria

TWO-YEAR-OLDS

21 **BARE FACT,** b c 30/1 Wolfhound (USA)—Zeffirella (Known Fact (USA))
22 B f 22/2 Mujtahid (USA)—Duwon (IRE) (Polish Precedent (USA))
23 **GRACE MELBURY,** ch f 19/4 Forzando—Figini (Glint of Gold)
24 **LADY MOORINGS,** b f 3/3 Dolphin Street (FR)—Crimson Ring (Persian Bold)
25 **LOCOMBE HILL,** b c 30/1 Barathea (IRE)—Roberts Pride (Roberto (USA))
26 Ch f 8/3 Chaddleworth (IRE)—Ophrys (Nonoalco (USA))
27 **PAS DE PROBLEME (IRE),** ch c 24/4 Ela-Mana-Mou—Torriglia (USA) (Nijinsky (CAN))
28 Ch c 3/3 Polar Falcon (USA)—Remany (Bellypha)
29 B f 17/4 Then Again—Sheesha (USA) (Shadeed (USA))
30 Ch f 2/4 Beveled (USA)—Swilly Express (Ballacashtal (CAN))

Owners: Mr M. V. S. Aram, Aykroyd & Partners, Mr R. Batty, Mr Nicholas Bird, Mr M. Blanshard, Mr D. J. C. Brown, Mrs Patricia Buckley, Captain Francis Burne, Mr C. R. Buttery, Mrs Heather Chakko, Mr P. F. Chakko, Mr A. K. Collins, Mr P. Doherty, Mrs S. L. Dormeuil, Lady Sam Fairbairn, Mr D. W. J. Garrett, Mrs A. C. Hall, H. C. Promotions Ltd, Mrs Michael Hill, Mr Stanley Hinton, Mr C. McKenna, Mr Tim Mead, Mr J. A. Oliver, Lady Page, Brigadier A. W. Parker Bowles, Mrs M. Payne, Mr Charles Philipson, Mr B. J. Phillips, Miss S. N. Ralphs, Mr D. Sloan, Mr David Sykes, Mr A. R. B. Ward, Mrs C. J. Ward, A. H. Warren (Coombe Farm) Ltd, Mrs James Watkins, Mr James Watkins, Mrs R. G. Wellman, Mr J. W. Wells, Mr Gregory West.

Jockey (Flat): J Quinn (w.a).

Jockey (NH): D Gallagher.

63 MR J. S. BOLGER, Carlow

Postal: **Glebe House, Coolcullen, Carlow, Ireland.**
Phone: **(056) 43150 OR 43158 FAX (056) 43256**

1 **BASANTA (IRE),** 5, b h Sadler's Wells—La Meilleure
2 **CAMBODIAN (USA),** 4, b c Roanoke—September Kaper
3 **CANADIAN VISTA (CAN),** 4, b f St Jovite—Primarily
4 **DEERFIELD FAME (USA),** 4, b f Quest For Fame—Sarced Squaw
5 **GRADUATED (IRE),** 6, b g Royal Academy—Saviour
6 **LIL'S BOY (USA),** 4, b c Danzig—Kentucky Lill

THREE-YEAR-OLDS

7 **ALMERINA (IRE),** b f Erin's Isle—Pennine Music
8 **AMAZINK (IRE),** b c Green Desert—Alysardi
9 **AMRAVATI (IRE),** ch f Project Manager—Smaoineamh

MR J. S. BOLGER—continued

10 APACHE RED (IRE), ch c Indian Ridge—Moonlight Partner
11 AZARINA (IRE), ch f Kenmare—Easy To Please
12 BROGAN'S WELL (IRE), b f Caerleon—Clonsella Lady
13 CHRISTY SENIOR (IRE), b c Erin's Isle—Persian Sparkler
14 DANE RIVER (IRE), b c Danehill—Allegheny River
15 DARINA (IRE), b f Danehill—Sweet Justice
16 DERRY PROJECT (IRE), b c Project Manager—Amparo
17 EMERALD PROJECT (IRE), b f Project Manager—Emerald Pendant
18 HEFFO'S ARMY (IRE), b c Project Manager—Motus
19 INGA (IRE), ch f Project Manager—Heike
20 IRISH SUMMIT (IRE), ch c Erin's Isle—La Meilleure
21 IVORY ISLE (IRE), ch c Erin's Isle—Ivory Home
22 JOVINE (USA), ch f St Jovite—Big E Dream
23 KANANASKIS (IRE), b f Caerleon—Gravieres
24 KEY TO COOLCULLEN (IRE), b f Royal Academy—Guess Again
25 LEAFY ISLE (IRE), b f Erin's Isle—Junijo
26 MADUKA (IRE), ch f Paris House—Topsey's Tipple
27 MAYA (IRE), ch f Brief Truce—Nujoom
28 MEGA PROJECT (IRE), b f Project Manager—Megastart
29 B f Quest For Fame—Miss Jazz
30 MITRA (IRE), gr f Archway—Gravina
31 NORDIC ISLE (IRE), b c Erin's Isle—Nordic Relation
32 REMARKABLE STYLE (USA), b f Danzig—Ophidian
33 RENEWED SPIRIT (IRE), ch f Erin's Isle—Reliable
34 ROSE PETAL (USA), ch f Majestic Light—Gdansk Victory
35 SAANA (IRE), b f Erin's Isle—Nordic Pageant
36 SANTAMANI (IRE), b f Danehill—Noora Abu
37 SARKA (IRE), b f Project Manager—Smaointeach
38 SHELAINE (IRE), b c Erin's Isle—Liberty Bird
39 SILVERY HALO (USA), gr f Silver Ghost—Carolita
40 STYLISH ACADEMY (IRE), b f Royal Academy—Moschino
41 TAISPEAIN (IRE), b f Petorius—Nordic Pride
42 UNDAUNTED (IRE), b c Sadler's Wells—Belle Epoque
43 VAZIMBA (IRE), b f Project Manager—Volnost
44 VIA SPLENDIDA (IRE), b f Project Manager—Closette (FR)
45 WORLD HIBERNIA (IRE), b f Erin's Isle—Just Possible
46 YORBA LINDA (IRE), ch f Night Shift—Allepolina

TWO-YEAR-OLDS

47 Gr f 15/5 Chief's Crown—Add Mint (Vigors)
48 AERAIOCHT (IRE), b f 25/5 Tenby—Direct Lady (Fools Holme)
49 AFRICAN ISLE (IRE), ch f 12/5 Erin's Isle—African Setting (African Sky)
50 ARUNDHATI (IRE), b f 26/4 Royal Academy—Petronelli (Sir Ivor)
51 BARAVELLI (IRE), b c 23/2 Barathea—Savelli (Vision)
52 Ch c 7/4 Grand Lodge—Belle Epoque (Habitat)
53 B c 2/5 Unblest—Caranina (Caro)
54 CATONAHOTTINROOF (IRE), b f 12/4 Catrail—High Glider (High Top)
55 B f 25/4 Fairy King—Clonsella Lady (High Top)
56 DAME EN ROUGE (IRE), ch f 20/4 Imperial Frontier—Zany (Junius)
57 DANCING SEA (USA), b f 18/5 Storm Cat—Coral Dance (Green Dancer)
58 DAZZLING PARK (IRE), br f 22/4 Warning—Park Express (Ahonoora)
59 FARDUS (IRE), b f 11/5 Danehill—Easy To Please (What A Guest)
60 GAELIC PROJECT (IRE), b f 2/3 Project Manager—Gayle Gal (Lord Gayle)
61 B f 13/4 Brief Truce—Garrafita (Zino)
62 GRANDIOSE IDEA (IRE), b f 21/4 Danehill—Gorgeoso (Damascus)
63 GRANITE (IRE), b c 19/3 Project Manager—Marino Waltz (Thatching)
64 HAZEL LAVERY (IRE), ch f 11/1 Grand Lodge—Accell (Magical Wonder)
65 B c 30/5 Erin's Isle—Heike (Glenstal)
66 B f 24/3 Grand Lodge—In Unison (Bellypha)
67 B f 28/5 Sadler's Wells—La Meilleure (Lord Gayle)

MR J. S. BOLGER—continued

68 B f 30/3 Namaqualand—Medicosma (The Minstrel)
69 B f 3/4 Project Manager—My Lady's Key (Key To The Mint)
70 B c 9/5 Project Manager—Nordic Relation (Nordico)
71 **OVAZIONE,** ch f 7/4 Seeking The Gold—O'Slewmova (Seattle Slew)
72 **PASTORELLI (IRE),** b c 18/4 Project Manager—Pennine Music (Pennine Walk)
73 **RIGO (IRE),** b c 27/4 Project Manager—Rigobertha (Nordico)
74 **SANTOVITO (IRE),** b c 29/5 Project Manager—Nordic Pageant (Nordico)
75 **SLANEY ISLE (IRE),** b c 2/4 Erin's Isle—Bold-E-Be (Persian Bold)
76 B c 14/3 Grand Lodge—Special Display (Welsh Pageant)
77 **STEFANOVA (IRE),** b c 17/4 Project Manager—Ivory Home (Home Guard)
78 **SUKEENA (IRE),** b f 13/5 Brief Truce—Smaointeach (Green Desert)
79 **TAISCE (IRE),** b f 17/3 Treasure Kay—Mothers Blessing (Wolver Hollow)
80 **TALLARICO (IRE),** ch f 9/4 Project Manager—Razida (Last Tycoon)
81 **UNION PROJECT (IRE),** ch c 22/4 Project manager—Nordic Union (Nordico)
82 **VANCOUVER ISLE (IRE),** b c 24/2 Erin's Isle—Eileenog (Kahyasi)
83 B c 29/4 Project Manager—Volnost (Lyphard)
84 B f 29/4 Project Manager—Voronova (Sadler's Wells)
85 **WINDY SHORES (IRE),** b c 1/3 Suave Dancer—Allepolina (Trempolino)

Owners: Ballylinch Stud, D. Bernie, Miss Fiona Bolger, Mrs J. S. Bolger, T. F. Brennan, Mrs M. A. Brennan, Mrs N. Brennan, Maurice M. Burns, Mr Seamus Burns, William J. Condren, D. H. W. Dobson, Mrs M. Eivers, John Gaines, Peter J. P. Gleeson, Mrs Mona Halpin, Mrs Gabrielle Rose Kelly, M. H. Keogh, Henryk De Kwiatkowski, Mrs Bridget Lacey, Mrs John Magnier, Mrs Una Manning, Dermot McAuliffe, A. G. Moylan, Mrs Audrey O'Connor, J. P. M. O'Connor, Ms Grace O'Riordan, Mrs S. O'Riordan, Mrs Patricia O'Rourke, Niall Quinn, Capt C. M. Ryan, Mrs J. M. Ryan, F. Salhoub, Anthony Paul Smurfit, Michael W. J. Smurfit, Mrs K. Twomey.

Jockeys (Flat): C Everard (8-11), K J Manning (8-7).

64 MR M. J. BOLTON, Shrewton

Postal: **The Cleeve, Elston Lane, Shrewton, Wilts, SP3 4HL.**
Phone: **(01980) 621059**

1 **ASTRAL WEEKS (IRE),** 7, ch g Astronef—Doon Belle **Mrs S. P. Elphick**
2 4, Ch g Mon Tresor—Dancing Ballerina **Mrs R. A. Murrell**
3 **DARING KING,** 8, b g King of Spain—Annacando **Cleeve Stables**
4 **DAWES OF NELSON,** 13, b br g Krayyan—Killyhevlin **Mr M. J. Bolton**
5 **HALAVADREAM,** 4, b c Mon Tresor—Hala **Mr Geoffrey Seymour**
6 **OSCAR ROSE,** 5, b g Aragon—Mossy Rose **Cleeve Stables**
7 **PETROS GEM,** 5, br m Sulaafah (USA)—Dancing Ballerina **Mrs R. A. Murrell**
8 **SILVER PREY (USA),** 5, b g Silver Hawk (USA)—Truly My Style (USA) **Mr A. R. M. Galbraith**
9 **THE NOBLE OAK (IRE),** 10, ch g The Noble Player (USA)—Sea Palace **Cleeve Stables**
10 **VANBOROUGH LAD,** 9, b g Precocious—Lustrous **Mr A. R. M. Galbraith**

TWO-YEAR-OLDS

11 Ch f 29/5 Past Glories—Welcome Tidings (Record Run) **Cleeve Stables**

Other Owners: Dr J. R. J. Naylor, Mr D. C. Woollard.

Amateur: Dr J R J Naylor (10-7).

65 MR CHARLES B. BOOTH, Flaxton

Postal: **Gravel Pit Farm, Foston, Flaxton, York, YO6 7QD.**
Phone: **(01653) 618586**

1 **BLENHEIM TERRACE,** 5, b g Rambo Dancer (CAN)—Boulevard Girl **Mrs M. Lyons**
2 **LA DOYENNE (IRE),** 4, ch f Masterclass (USA)—Sainthill **Mrs J. B. Robinson**
3 **TARRADALE,** 4, b g Interrex (CAN)—Encore L'Amour (USA) **Ashley Carr Racing**

THREE-YEAR-OLDS

4 **BALI DANCE,** br f Rambo Dancer (CAN)—Baliana **Mr J. A. Porteous**
5 **D'MARTI,** b f Emarati (USA)—Hellene **Mrs M. Rogers**
6 **GINNER MORRIS,** b g Emarati (USA)—Just Run (IRE) **Mrs M. Rogers**

TWO-YEAR-OLDS

7 Ch g 15/2 Second Set (IRE)—Boulevard Girl (Nicholas Bill)
8 Ch f 27/2 College Chapel—Emerald Eagle (Sandy Creek) **Mrs M. Rogers**
9 **FIZZY WHIZZY,** b f 12/2 Rambo Dancer (CAN)—Hi-Hunsley (Swing Easy (USA)) **Mr J. A. Porteous**
10 B f Always Fair (USA)—Karmisymixa (FR) (Linamix (FR))
11 **LA CINECITTA (FR),** ch f 23/3 Dancing Spree (USA)—Cox's Feather (USA) (Cox's Ridge (USA))

Other Owners: Mr Paul Gascoigne, Mrs Diane McKechnie.

Jockeys (Flat): A Culhane (8-0), K Hodgson (8-6).

66 MR M. R. BOSLEY, Wantage

Postal: **Kingston Lisle Farm Stables, Kingston Lisle, Wantage, Oxfordshire, OX12 9QH.**
Phone: **OFFICE/FAX (01367) 820115 MOBILE (0378) 938040**

1 **AIR COMMAND (BAR),** 8, br g Concorde Hero (USA)—Hubbardair **Mr Edwin Phillips**
2 **BAY FAIR,** 6, b m Arctic Lord—Bampton Fair **Mr P. A. Deal**
3 **CATCH THE ACTION,** 5, b m Fearless Action (USA)—Lady Catcher **C. M. C. Partnership**
4 **FOREST BOY,** 5, b g Komaite (USA)—Khadine **C. R. Marks (Banbury)**
5 **HAYDOWN (IRE),** 6, b br g Petorius—Hay Knot **Mr Edwin Phillips**
6 **HERE'S TO HOWIE (USA),** 4, b c Hermitage (USA)—Choice Comment (USA) **Mr M. F. Cartwright/Mr J. P. Carrington**
7 **LADYMALORD,** 6, br m Arctic Lord—Lady Catcher **The Blowingstone Partnership**
8 **PROUD BRIGADIER (IRE),** 10, b g Auction Ring (USA)—Naughty One Gerard **Mr S. J. Edwards**
9 **PROUD MONK,** 5, gr g Aragon—Silent Sister **Mr S. J. Edwards**
10 **PUSEY STREET GIRL,** 5, ch m Gildoran—Pusey Street **C. R. Marks (Banbury)**
11 **RETURN OF THE MAC,** 6, b g Machiavellian (USA)—Home Truth **Mrs R. Brackenbury**
12 **SMART LORD,** 7, br g Arctic Lord—Lady Catcher **The Blowingstone Partnership**
13 **THOMAS CROWN (IRE),** 6, ch g Last Tycoon—Upward Trend **Mr John Hughes**
14 **TWISP,** 7, b g Shirley Heights—Twyla **Mrs J. L. Brindley**
15 **WINDRUSH BOY,** 8, br g Dowsing (USA)—Bridge Street Lady **Miss Cynthia Commons**

THREE-YEAR-OLDS

16 **SWIFT TIME,** b f Timeless Times (USA)—Bustling Around **C. R. Marks (Banbury)**

Other Owners: Mrs S. M. Brotherton, Mr Vernon Commons, Mrs S. Gleeson, Mrs Marinella Johnson, Mrs B. A. Long, Mr J. F. Long, Ms C. Tepper, Mrs K. Whitaker.

Jockey (Flat): C Rutter (w.a.).

Jockeys (NH): R Dunwoody (w.a.), Ian Lawrence.

Conditional: X Aizpuru (w.a.).

Lady Rider: Mrs Sarah Bosley (9-0).

67 MR B. BOUSFIELD, Brough

Postal: **Glaslyn House, Brough, Kirkby Stephen, Cumbria, CA17 4BT.**
Phone: **(017683) 41391**

1 **ARTHUR BEE,** 11, ch g Say Primula—Reigate Head **Mrs D. A. Bousfield**
2 **BROOK HOUSE,** 7, ro m Colway Radial—Move Ahead **Mrs D. A. Bousfield**
3 **WHATDIDYOUSAY,** 10, ch g Say Primula—Reigate Head **Mrs D. A. Bousfield**

68 MISS L. J. BOWER, Alresford

Postal: **'Greendowns', Preshaw Road, Beauworth, Alresford, Hampshire, SO24 0PB.**
Phone: **(01962) 771827 MOBILE (0585) 465408**

1 4, Ch f Current Edition (IRE)—Avenmore Star **Mr M. V. Kirby**
2 **LIGHT O'THE MILL,** 9, b m Electric—Furrette **Mr M. V. Kirby**
3 **MASTER COMEDY,** 14, b g Comedy Star (USA)—Romardia **Miss J. Wilkinson**
4 5, B g Ballacashtal (CAN)—Miss Comedy **Miss J. Wilkinson**
5 **MISS MEZZANINE,** 4, b f Norton Challenger—Forest Fawn (FR) **Mr M. V. Kirby**
6 **ONE MORE MAN (IRE),** 7, b g Remainder Man—Pampered Sally **Mr A. Ilsley**
7 **PAMPERED PILOT,** 5, b g Pitpan—Solent Flyer **Mr D. A. Mayes**

Jockey (Flat): Tyrone Williams.

Jockeys (NH): Luke Harvey, A Maguire, W McFarland, N Williamson.

Amateurs: Mr Chris Bonner (9-7), Mr Rupert Wakely (9-7).

69 MRS A. J. BOWLBY, Wantage

Postal: **Gurnsmead Farm, Kingston Lisle, Wantage, Oxfordshire, OX12 9QT.**
Phone: **(01367) 820888 FAX (01367) 820880 MOBILE (0468) 277833**

1 **BIG ARCHIE,** 8, br g El Conquistador—Royal Declaration **Mr Cliff Basson**
2 **BROOKHAMPTON LANE (IRE),** 7, b g Balinger—Deerpark Rose **Mr R. J. Tompkins**
3 **COCKBURY (IRE),** 4, b g Glacial Storm (USA)—Sales Centre **Mr Robert Hitchins, Mr George Harvey**
4 **LANG WHANG (IRE),** 7, b g Rhoman Rule (USA)—Our Galadrial **Mrs N. Bowlby**
5 4, B g Lighter—Meggies Dene **Mrs Amanda Bowlby**

THREE-YEAR-OLDS

6 **RISQUE,** ch g Risk Me (FR)—Sweet And Sour **Mr P. J. Orme**
7 **ZIGGY STARDUST (IRE),** b g Roi Danzig (USA)—Si Princess **Joe Cool Partnership**

Other Owners: Mr S. P. Clysdale, Mrs Jackie Hurst-Brown.

Jockey (NH): B Powell (9-7, w.a.).

70 MR S. R. BOWRING, Edwinstowe

Postal: **Fir Tree Farm, Edwinstowe, Mansfield, Nottinghamshire, NG21 9JG.**
Phone: **MANSFIELD (01623) 822451**

1 **AL REET (IRE),** 7, b m Alzao (USA)—Reet Petite **The Gemini Partnership 4**
2 **ANTONIAS MELODY,** 5, b m Rambo Dancer (CAN)—Ayodessa **Mr S. R. Bowring**
3 **APICULATE (IRE),** 4, b g Exactly Sharp (USA)—Reine de Chypre (FR) **Ace Employment**

MR S. R. BOWRING—continued

4 **FIRST MAITE,** 5, b g Komaite (USA)—Marina Plata **Mr S. R. Bowring**
5 **GROVEFAIR LAD (IRE),** 4, b g Silver Kite (USA)—Cienaga **Mr David Garner**
6 **KRYSTAL DAVEY (IRE),** 4, b g Classic Music (USA)—Robin Red Breast **Mr Roland M. Wheatley**
7 **KUSTOM KIT KLASSIC,** 4, b c Chilibang—Norvi **Charterhouse Holdings Plc**
8 **KUSTOM KIT XPRES,** 4, gr f Absalom—Miss Serlby **Charterhouse Holdings Plc**
9 **MIRROR FOUR SPORT,** 4, ch f Risk Me (FR)—Madison Girl **Clark Industrial Services Partnership**
10 **MR MORIARTY (IRE),** 7, ch g Tate Gallery (USA)—Bernica (FR) **Mr D. H. Bowring**
11 **PRESENTIMENT,** 4, b g Puissance—Octavia **Anchor Racing**
12 **REDSPET,** 4, ch f Tina's Pet—Manabel **Mr A. H. Ripley**
13 **SAILORMAITE,** 7, ch g Komaite (USA)—Marina Plata **Mr S. R. Bowring**
14 **SANDMOOR DENIM,** 11, b g Red Sunset—Holernzaye **Mr S. R. Bowring**
15 **SCENMOOR,** 4, b c Alhaatmi—Honey Day **Mr G. M. Sheppard**
16 **SEA YA MAITE,** 4, b g Komaite (USA)—Marina Plata **Mr S. R. Bowring**
17 **SUPERAPPAROS,** 4, b g Superpower—Ayodessa **Mr S. R. Bowring**
18 **SWEET MATE,** 6, ch g Komaite (USA)—Be My Sweet **Mr S. R. Bowring**
19 **UP IN FLAMES (IRE),** 7, b g Nashamaa—Bella Lucia **Mr Mark Kilner**

THREE-YEAR-OLDS

20 **BLUE DESERT,** ch g Elmaamul (USA)—Shehana (USA) **Mr Roland M. Wheatley**
21 **COLLACAR,** b g Man Among Men (IRE)—Safety First **Collins Chauffeur Driven Cars**
22 **KUSTOM KIT KATE,** b f Tragic Role (USA)—Wing of Freedom **Charterhouse Holdings Plc**
23 **MAKAHU DON,** ch g Derrylin—Rockalong **Mr J.E Reed & Mr P Sedgewick**
24 **MARINA'S SONG,** b f Savahra Sound—Marina Plata **Mr S. R. Bowring**
25 **SILENT VOTE,** b f Nomination—Whispering Sea **Mr G. M. Sheppard**
26 **SKY MOUNTAIN (IRE),** b c Danehill (USA)—Molvina (ITY) **Mr Ronald M. Wheatley**

TWO-YEAR-OLDS

27 **REX IS OKAY,** ch c 25/3 Mazilier (USA)—Cocked Hat Girl (Ballacashtal (CAN)) **Mr Duncan Belfitt**

Other Owners: Mr M. Belfitt, Mr S. J. Burgan, Mr Jim Clark, Mrs M. Clark, Mr Padraig Flanagan, Mrs B. D. Georgiou, Mrs Zoe Grant, Mr R. D. Marston, Mrs D. L. Salt, Mr G. Stokes, Mr J. Teece, Mr I. A. Wilson.

Apprentice: C. Teague (8-4).

Lady Rider: Mrs M Morris.

71 MRS S. C. BRADBURNE, Cupar

Postal: **Cunnoquhie Cottage, 1 Ladybank, Cupar, Fife, KY15 7RU.**
Phone: **(01337) 810325 FAX (01337) 810486 MOBILE (0468) 705722 (0468) 325117**

1 **ANIKA'S GEM (IRE),** 5, b m Buckskin (FR)—Picton Lass **Mr Timothy Hardie**
2 **ASK ME LATER (IRE),** 9, b g Phardante (FR)—Dancing Bush **Mr Timothy Hardie**
3 **BLUE CHARM (IRE),** 8, b g Duky—Blue Rinse **Mrs M. C. Lindsay**
4 **COTTSTOWN BOY (IRE),** 7, ch g King Luthier—Ballyanihan **The Hon Thomas Cochrane**
5 **FRENCH PROJECT (IRE),** 6, b m Project Manager—Malia **Mr J. G. Bradburne**
6 **JACK DORY (IRE),** 6, b g Lapierre—Gentle Lass **Hardie, Keenan & Gordon**
7 **LITTLE DUKE (IRE),** 6, b g Lord Americo—Paddy's Babs **Mr Douglas Copland**
8 **MONTE CRESTA (IRE),** 5, b br m Montelimar (USA)—Winter Run **Mrs John Etherton**
9 **MY MAVOURNEEN,** 6, b m Ardross—Queen's Darling **Mr Timothy Hardie**
10 **OFF THE BRU,** 13, b g General Ironside—Amelieranne **Mr J. G. Bradburne**
11 **YOUNG STEVEN,** 7, b g Singing Steven—Adoration (FR) **Mr R. Flynn**

Other Owners: Mr D. E. Harman, Mr W. G. Keenan, Mr C. Latilla-Campbell, Mr J. N. Llewellen Palmer, Mr A. S. Lyburn.

Amateur: Mr Mark Bradburne (10-0).

Lady Rider: Miss Lorna Bradburne (9-4).

72 MR J. M. BRADLEY, Chepstow

Postal: **Meads Farm, Sedbury Park, Chepstow, Gwent, NP6 7HN.**
Phone: **(01291) 622486**

1 **ACCOMMODATE YOU,** 5, br m Precocious—Time For Joy **Accomodation UK Ltd**
2 **BOLD ACRE,** 8, ch g Never So Bold—Nicola Wynn **Mrs Marion C. Morgan**
3 **CAN'T SAY (IRE),** 6, br g Gallic League—Mixed Feelings **Mr M. B. Carver**
4 **COMEONUP,** 7, b g Most Welcome—Scarlet Veil **Mr M. B. Carver**
5 **DANZAS,** 4, b g Polish Precedent (USA)—Dancing Rocks **Mr Martyn James**
6 **ELLOPASSOFF,** 6, b m Librate—Elena Patino **Mr E. R. Griffiths**
7 **JASON'S BOY,** 8, b g Librate—Misty Glen **Mr W. E. Jones**
8 **MILLING BROOK,** 6, b g Librate—Indian Stream **Mr Martyn James**
9 **MR CUBE (IRE),** 8, ch h Tate Gallery (USA)—Truly Thankful (CAN) **Mr R. Miles**
10 **NAVAL GAMES,** 5, b g Slip Anchor—Plaything **Mr S. G. Martin**
11 **NUNS BEST FRIEND,** 5, ch g Bedford (USA)—Nunswalk **Mr E. R. Griffiths**
12 **NUNSON,** 9, ch g Celtic Cone—Nunswalk **Mr R. H. Williams**
13 **NUNS TOY BOY,** 6, b g Buckley—Nunswalk **P.O.W.T.C. Ltd/ Speedy Snaps**
14 **PRINCELY AFFAIR,** 5, b g Prince Sabo—Shillay **Mrs Jasmine B. Chesters**
15 **SEVERN MILL,** 7, ch g Librate—Staryllis Girl **Mr E. A. Hayward**
16 **SEVERN REEF,** 7, b g Librate—Opal Lady **Mr Terence A. Hadley**
17 **SOPHIES DREAM,** 7, ch g Librate—Misty Glen **Mr W. E. Jones**
18 **SUBAROO SAM,** 4, gr g Arzanni—Nuns Little One **Mr D. A. Jones**
19 **ZAHRAN (IRE),** 7, b h Groom Dancer (USA)—Welsh Berry (USA) **Mr D. Smith (Saul)**

Other Owners: Mr Robert Bailey, Miss Sue Bennett, Mrs R. Bradley, Mr G. T. Cartwright, Mr N. Cook, Craftbook Ltd, Mr Philip A. Davies, Mrs Gaynor Dickens, Mr Peter Edwards, Mr Gwilym Fry, Mr Nigel Griffiths, Mr C. Grove, Mr Stuart Halliday, Miss Diane Hill, Mr D. Holpin, Mr Clifton Hunt, Mr J. M. Kearney, Mr A. D. Lewis, Mr David S. Lewis, Mr S. J. Merrick, Mr W. D. Morris, Mr T. J. Price, Mr A. J. Protheroe, Mr Alan Purvis, Mr Ken Reece, Mr M. G. Ridley, Mr D. C. Roberts, Mr J. Smith, Mr A. P. Stamp, Mr K. M. Stanworth, Mr N. Tanner, Mr Stephen A. Thomas, Mr C. J. M. Walker, Mr John Wallis.

Jockey (Flat): S Drowne.

Jockey (NH): R Farrant.

Conditional: Guy Lewis.

73 MR P. BRADLEY, Forsbrook

Postal: **New Park, 117 Draycott Old Road, Forsbrook, Stoke-On-Trent, Staffordshire, ST11 9AL.**
Phone: **(01782) 392191 (01782) 324637 FAX (01782) 598427**

1 **BUNGEE JUMPER,** 8, b g Idiot's Delight—Catherine Bridge **Mr Paul Bradley**
2 **CHILL PILL (IRE),** 7, b m Dunbeath (USA)—Golden Flats **Mr Paul Bradley**
3 **DAWN SUMMIT,** 4, ch c Salse (USA)—Bereeka **Mr Paul Bradley**
4 **TEJANO GOLD (USA),** 8, ch g Tejano (USA)—Nelli Forli (USA) **Mr Paul Bradley**
5 **TUDOR FALCON,** 5, b g Midyan (USA)—Tudorealm (USA) **Mr Paul Bradley**

74 MR M. F. BRADSTOCK, Wantage

Postal: **The Old Manor House, Letcombe Bassett, Wantage, Oxfordshire, OX12 9LP.**
Phone: **(01235) 760780 FAX (01235) 760754**

1 **ARCTIC TRIUMPH,** 7, b g Arctic Lord—Borotown **Holman Marketing Ltd**
2 **COLTIBUONO (IRE),** 6, ch g Orchestra—Baby Birch **Mr P. J. D. Pottinger**
3 **DO RIGHTLY (IRE),** 9, ch g Teofane—Lady Hiltop **Mr J. M. Fitzpatrick**

MR M. F. BRADSTOCK—continued

4 EISHKEN (IRE), 6, b g Over The River (FR)—Harlave **Mr P. J. D. Pottinger**
5 FOREST JUMP (IRE), 4, ch g Accordion—Mandy's Last **I. S. Networking Solutions Ltd**
6 LUGS BRANNIGAN (IRE), 9, b g Supreme Leader—Maria Tudor **Mr J. B. Dowler**
7 MONTAGNARD, 14, b g Strong Gale—Louisa Stuart (FR) **Mr Mark Bradstock**
8 MY BLACKBIRD (IRE), 6, br m Mandalus—Cherry Park **The Old Manor Racing Club**
9 PLAID MAID (IRE), 6, b m Executive Perk—Tipperary Tartan **Lord Oaksey**
10 RATAGAN (IRE), 6, b g Strong Gale—Miss Mims **I S Networking Solutions Ltd Partnership**
11 ROYAL TRUMP (IRE), 9, b g King Persian—Four Queens **Mr J. M. Fitzpatrick**
12 SOME DAY SOON, 13, b g Beau Charmeur (FR)—Our Day **Mr C. Elgram**
13 SWEET LORD (IRE), 7, ch g Aristocracy—Sweet And Fleet **I. S. Networking Solutions Ltd**
14 THISTLEKICKER (IRE), 6, b g Mandalus—Miss Ranova **The Thistlekickers**
15 WIXOE WONDER (IRE), 8, ch g Hatim (USA)—Jumana **Mr P. J. D. Pottinger**

Other Owners: Mrs Ann Brett, Mr A. N. Brooke Rankin, Mr G. A. Cowell, Mr N. A. Gill, Mr David Holman, Mrs David Huntington, Miss Sara Lawrence, Mr Alan Waller.

Conditional: Katherine R Hambidge (9-0).

75 MRS S. A. BRAMALL, Wexford

Postal: **Borleagh Manor, Inch, Gorey, Co. Wexford, Ireland.**
Phone: **(0402) 37811 FAX (0402) 37774**

1 7, Ch g Interrex (CAN)—All Fine **Mrs S. A. Bramall**
2 ANTONIN (FR), 10, ch g Italic (FR)—Pin'hup (FR) **G. R. Bailey Ltd, Baileys Horse Feeds**
3 BANGABUNNY, 8, ch g Gunner B—Olympian Princess **Ms Anna Bramall**
4 BLUE IRISH (IRE), 7, gr g Roselier (FR)—Grannie No **Winning Post Racing Syndicate**
5 BORLEAGH PILOT (IRE), 7, ch g Torus—Pilots Row **Mrs S. A. Bramall**
6 CANAILLOU II (FR), 8, b g Le Riverain (FR)—Julie II (FR) **Mr M. Stanners**
7 CAPTAIN CHAOS (IRE), 7, b g Phardante (FR)—Asigh Glen **Miss K. S. Bramall**
8 DRUMCLIFFE (IRE), 7, br g Strong Gale—Kadaga **Mr Richard J. Cohen**
9 ETAT MAJOR (FR), 6, b g Mont Basile (FR)—P'Tite Poi (FR) **Mrs S. Scott-Bell**
10 GALANT DES EPEIRES (FR), 7, ch g Galant Vert (FR)—Marie de Bethisy (FR) **Mrs S. A. Bramall**
11 GALWAY (IRE), 5, b g Jurado (USA)—Solanum **Mrs J. K. Powell**
12 HERITAGE, 4, b c Danehill (USA)—Misty Halo **Mrs S. A. Bramall**
13 KITTYGALE (IRE), 7, br m Strong Gale—Lady's Wager **Mr M. Stanners**
14 PENNYPOT, 6, br m Lord Bud—Karmelanna **Mrs S. A. Bramall**
15 ROCKETTS CASTLE (IRE), 8, ch g Callernish—River Dodo **Winning Post Racing Syndicate**
16 SEGERA RIVER (IRE), 7, ch g Denel (FR)—Royal River **Miss K. S. Bramall**
17 STORM VALLEY (IRE), 6, b g Strong Gale—Windy Run **Mr G. A. Lowe**
18 4, B c Never So Bold—Tosara **Mrs S. A. Bramall**

THREE-YEAR-OLDS

19 HEEMANELA (IRE), b g Classic Secret (USA)—Ela Man Hee **Mrs S. A. Bramall**
20 Ch g Montelimar (USA)—Ladycastle **Mrs S. A. Bramall**
21 MAJOR BALLABY (IRE), b c Balla Cove—Surreal **Mrs S. A. Bramall**
22 STRICTLY RHYTHM, b c Hamas (IRE)—Halimah **Mrs S. A. Bramall**

Jockey (NH): Ken Whelan (9-10).

Amateur: Mr John L Cullen (9-7).

76 MR G. C. BRAVERY, Newmarket

Postal: **Albert House Stables, Moulton Road, Newmarket, Suffolk, CB8 8DU.**
Phone: **STABLES/FAX (01638) 668985 HOME (01638) 730052 MOBILE (0411) 112345**

1 **CITY GAMBLER,** 4, b f Rock City—Sun Street **Mr J. J. May**
2 **EXPLOSIVE POWER,** 7, br h Prince Sabo—Erwarton Seabreeze **Mr G. C. Bravery**
3 **GALLANT HEIGHTS,** 4, b f Anshan—Marie Galante **Mr M. J. Evans**
4 **HIGHLY REPUTABLE (IRE),** 8, ch g Persian Heights—Reputation **Mr Michael C. Whatley**
5 **HUGWITY,** 6, ch g Cadeaux Genereux—Nuit d'Ete (USA)
6 **JUPITER (IRE),** 4, b g Astronef—Native Flower **Mr Michael C. Whatley**
7 **MR SPEAKER (IRE),** 5, ch g Statoblest—Casting Vote (USA) **Mr David Allan**
8 **SWEET LITTLE BRIAR (IRE),** 7, gr m Celio Rufo—Mandias Slave **Mr G. C. Bravery**
9 **SYLVAN DANCER (IRE),** 4, b br f Dancing Dissident (USA)—Unspoiled **Mr J. J. May**

THREE-YEAR-OLDS

10 **DIAMOND WHITE,** b f Robellino (USA)—Diamond Wedding (USA) **Mr P. P. Scott**
11 **FREDDIE MAC (IRE),** b c River Falls—Golden Thread **Bravery Racing**
12 **PEARLY QUEEN,** ch f Superlative—Miss Kimmy **Mr R. Allder**
13 **THE DRUIDESS (IRE),** b f Distinctly North (USA)—Moody Lover **Bravery Racing**
14 **TOY BOX (IRE),** b f Salse (USA)—Belle Enfant **Mr D. B. Clark**

TWO-YEAR-OLDS

15 B f 23/3 Pursuit Of Love—Butosky (Busted)
16 B f 28/2 Distinctly North—Camden Rye (Camden Town)
17 B f 27/1 Northern Park (USA)—Deposit (Thatch (USA))
18 B c 14/4 Common Grounds—Dul Dul (USA) (Shadeed (USA))
19 Ch c 31/1 Sabrehill (USA)—Exotic Forest (Dominion)
20 B f 24/3 Namaqualand (USA)—Fabulous Deed (USA) (Shadeed (USA))
21 Ch c 20/2 Inchinor—Late Matinee (Red Sunset)
22 B f 28/3 Polar Falcon (USA)—No Hard Feelings (IRE) (Alzao (USA))
23 B f 28/2 Then Again—Priors Dean (Monsanto (FR))

Other Owners: Blackfoot Bloodstock, Mrs F. E. Bravery, A. Burke, J. Carrington, L. Cashman, Mrs A. Charlton, E. Charlton, P. Cooper, Mrs S. Dennis, Mr S. A. Griffiths, H. De Burgh, Mrs L. A. Howe, Mr A. D. Mackrill, W. Mason, N. Nugent, J. O'Flynn, Mrs Anthony Penfold, Mrs M. Powell, Mr H. T. Short, D. Veitch, Mr A. G. Venables.

Jockeys (Flat): N Day, M Hills (w.a.).

Amateur: Mr K Santana (9-2).

77 MR R. G. BRAZINGTON, Redmarley

Postal: **Chapel Farm, Redmarley, Gloucestershire, GL19 3JF.**
Phone: **(01452) 840384**

1 **BUCK BOARD,** 8, b g Buckley—Midnight Lily **Mr R. G. Brazington**
2 **BUCKLE ISLAND,** 8, br g Buckley—Ionian Isle (FR) **Mr R. G. Brazington**
3 **CALLYR,** 11, b g Julio Mariner—Midnight Pansy **Mr R. G. Brazington**
4 **CREDIT CALL (IRE),** 10, br g Rhoman Rule (USA)—Maiacourt **Mr R. G. Brazington**
5 **DOTTEREL (IRE),** 10, b g Rhoman Rule (USA)—Miysam **Mr R. G. Brazington**
6 **EMMA'S GEM,** 7, b m Vouchsafe—Hail A Cab **Mr R. G. Brazington**
7 **JIMBALOU,** 15, b g Jimsun—Midnight Pansy **Mr R. G. Brazington**
8 **MARINERS MEMORY,** 10, b g Julio Mariner—Midnight Pansy **Mr R. G. Brazington**
9 7, B h Vouchsafe—Midnight Lily **Mr R. G. Brazington**
10 **SAFE TO ASSUME,** 7, b g Vouchsafe—Assumtion **Mr R. G. Brazington**
11 **TAXI LAD,** 14, ch g Dublin Taxi—Midnight Pansy **Mr R. G. Brazington**
12 **WILL ASSUME,** 6, ch h Buckley—Assumtion **Mr R. G. Brazington**

Conditional: R. Massey (9-11).

78 MR OWEN BRENNAN, Worksop

Postal: **Sloswicks Farm, Broad Lane, Worksop, Nottinghamshire, S80 3NJ.**
Phone: **WORKSOP (01909) 473950**

1 **ERMINE STREET**, 10, ch g Relkino—Nearly Straight **Lady Anne Bentinck**
2 **JOLLY HEART (IRE)**, 8, b g Kambalda—Wrens Lass **Lady Anne Bentinck**
3 **ORGAN RECITAL (IRE)**, 9, b g Orchestra—Brave Polly **Lady Anne Bentinck**
4 **SECOND FIDDLE (IRE)**, 8, ch m Orchestra—Sandyela **Mr O. Brennan**
5 **SPEAKER WEATHERILL (IRE)**, 9, b g Strong Gale—Arctic Verb **Lady Anne Bentinck**
6 **STRATH ROYAL**, 12, b g Furry Glen—Last Princess **Lady Anne Bentinck**
7 **WILLIAM RUFUS**, 7, ch g Nicholas Bill—Llanddona **Lady Anne Bentinck**

Jockey (NH): M J Brennan (9-7).

79 MISS RHONA BREWIS, Belford

Postal: **Chester Hill, Belford, Northumberland, NE70 7EF.**
Phone: **(01668 213) 239/281**

1 **BILLSBROOK**, 8, b g Meadowbrook—Carney **Mr R. Brewis**
2 **CARNAVEN**, 6, b g Le Coq d'Or—Carney **Mrs R. Brewis**
3 **CHANTILLY ROSE**, 6, b m Primitive Rising (USA)—Milly L'Attaque **Miss Rhona Brewis**
4 **KIMOTHY**, 5, br g Primitive Rising (USA)—Kimberley Rose **Miss Rhona Brewis**
5 **NICK ROSS**, 7, b g Ardross—Nicolini **Mr R. Brewis**
6 **RISING MILL**, 7, b g Primitive Rising (USA)—Milly L'Attaque **Miss Rhona Brewis**
7 **SUNNYCLIFF**, 5, b g Dancing High—Nicolini **Mr R. Brewis**

80 MR J. J. BRIDGER, Liphook

Postal: **Upper Hatch Farm, Liphook, Hampshire, GU30 7EL.**
Phone: **LIPHOOK (01428) 722528 FAX (01428) 722528**

1 **ADILOV**, 6, b g Soviet Star (USA)—Volida **Mr Trevor Mitchell**
2 **CLOCK WATCHERS**, 10, b g Sula Bula—Hale Lane **Mr W. R. Shere**
3 **DANCING JACK**, 5, ch h Clantime—Sun Follower **Mrs J. M. Stamp**
4 **DERISBAY (IRE)**, 10, b g Gorytus (USA)—Current Bay **Miss Julie Self**
5 **DIGPAST (IRE)**, 8, ch g Digamist (USA)—Starlit Way **Miss Sarah Jones**
6 **DURABLE GEORGE**, 4, ch g Durandal—Sun Follower **Mrs J. M. Stamp**
7 **HEAVENLY MISS (IRE)**, 4, b f Anita's Prince—Heavenly Blessed **Mr Trevor Mitchell**
8 **JUSTINIANUS (IRE)**, 6, ch h Try My Best (USA)—Justitia **Mr M. R. Pascall**
9 **LOGIE PERT LAD**, 6, b g Green Ruby (USA)—Rhazya **Mr Donald J. Smith**
10 **PLEIN GAZ (FR)**, 5, ch h Lesotho (USA)—Gazzara (USA) **Mr M. R. Pascall**
11 **READYPOWER**, 6, b g Newski (USA)—Bay Runner **Miss Julie Self**
12 **RIVERS MAGIC**, 5, b g Dominion—Rivers Maid **Mr M. R. Pascall**
13 **RUSSIAN RIVER**, 6, b g Sulaafah (USA)—Ninotchka **Miss Julie Self**
14 **SANIWOOD (IRE)**, 5, b m Law Society (USA)—Art Duo **Mr M. R. Pascall**
15 **SCISSOR RIDGE**, 6, ch g Indian Ridge—Golden Scissors **Mr Donald J. Smith**
16 **SEA DANZIG**, 5, ch g Roi Danzig (USA)—Tosara **Mr P. Cook**
17 **SMUGGLER'S POINT (USA)**, 8, b g Lyphard (USA)—Smuggly (USA) **Mrs V. R. Hoare**
18 **SUPERLAO (BEL)**, 6, b m Bacalao (USA)—Princess of Import **Mr J. F. Walls**
19 **THUNDEROUS**, 7, b g Green Desert (USA)—Mixed Applause (USA) **Mr J. J. Bridger**
20 **TONRIN**, 6, b g General Wade—Hot Tramp **Mr J. J. Bridger**
21 **WHIZZ KID**, 4, b f Puissance—Panienka (POL) **Mr J. J. Bridger**

MR J. J. BRIDGER—continued

THREE-YEAR-OLDS

22 **INDIAN FLAG (IRE),** ch f Indian Ridge—Flagpole (IRE) **Mrs H. Sweeting**
23 **SECOND SUN,** ch g Clantime—Sun Follower **Mrs J. M. Stamp**

Other Owners: Mr R. G. Painter, Mr P. Sweeting, Mr Terry Thorn, Mr Brian J. White, Mr W. Wood.

Amateur: Mr David Bridger (10-0).

Lady Rider: Miss Madeleine Bridger (9-0).

81 MR K. S. BRIDGWATER, Lapworth

Postal: **Bear House Farm, Old Warwick Road, Lapworth, Warwickshire, B94 6AZ.**
Phone: **LAPWORTH (01564) 782895 FAX (01564) 782895**

1 **CAPTAIN CHROME,** 11, b g Welsh Captain—Chrome Mag **Mrs Marion Gibbs**
2 **COME ON MAMMA (IRE),** 6, ch m Phardante (FR)—Clairellen **Mrs Hilary Putt**
3 **CROCKNAMOHILL (IRE),** 7, br g Strong Gale—Rusty Iron **Mrs C. Kelly**
4 **DRAKES ADVENTURE,** 6, br m Green Adventure (USA)—Marchiness Drake **Miss E. E. Hill**
5 **IMPENDING DANGER,** 5, ch g Fearless Action (USA)—Crimson Sol **Daltagh Construction Ltd**
6 **MISS KILWORTH (IRE),** 7, b m Lord Americo—Frozen Ground **Kilworth Group**
7 **MR C-I-P (IRE),** 7, ch g Stetchworth (USA)—Auragne (FR) **Coventry Industrial Pipework Limited**
8 **ROMANTIC WARRIOR,** 5, b g Welsh Captain—Romantic Melody
9 **SCHNOZZLE (IRE),** 7, b g Cyrano de Bergerac—Sun Gift **Willsford Racing Incorporated**
10 **SHREWD MAGICIAN,** 4, b g Ardross—Charmed I'm Sure **Mrs L. Donovan**
11 **SIR PAGEANT,** 9, b g Pharly (FR)—National Dress **Mrs Mary Bridgwater**
12 **SPORTING FIXTURE (IRE),** 7, b g Lancastrian—Astrina's Daughter **Mrs Hilary Putt**
13 **STARLIGHT WALTZER,** 5, b g Arzanni—Marchiness Drake **Miss E. E. Hill**
14 **SUCH PRESENCE,** 4, ch g Arzanni—Marchiness Drake **Miss E. E. Hill**

THREE-YEAR-OLDS

15 **THE SWALLOW,** b g Runnett—Minshaar **Mr Aubrey Ellis**

Other Owners: Mr Philip Alexander, Mr Dennis Deacon, Mrs Janet Hicken, Mr Len Jakeman, Paddocks Thoroughbred Racing Ltd, Mr Phil Plowman, Mr Kim D. Pugh, Mr R. Paul Russell, Mr R. B. Sayers.

Jockey (NH): D Bridgwater.

82 MR W. M. BRISBOURNE, Baschurch

Postal: **Ness Strange Stables, Great Ness, Shrewsbury, Shropshire, SY4 2LE.**
Phone: **NESSCLIFFE (01743741) 536 OR 360 MOBILE (0402) 523704**

1 **ABBEYSCOIN,** 4, ch g Andy Rew—Legal Coin **Mr Bob Moseley**
2 **BACKWOODS,** 5, ch g In The Wings—Kates Cabin **Mr P. R. Kirk**
3 **BARGASH,** 6, ch g Sharpo—Anchor Inn **Mr John Pugh**
4 **BARRYBEN,** 9, b br g Seymour Hicks (FR)—Ensigns Kit **Mrs Mary Brisbourne**
5 **BUCKALOON,** 6, b br g Buckley—Bronwyn **Mr A. N. Brooke Rankin**
6 **DANNISTAR,** 6, br m Puissance—Loadplan Lass **Mr John Pugh**
7 4, B g Nalchik (USA)—Delbounty **Mrs Mary Brisbourne & Sons**
8 **DELLA'S PRIDE,** 5, br m Pallards Pride—Delbounty **Mark & Pam Brisbourne**
9 **GODOR SPIRIT,** 8, ch g Plenty Spirit—Godor Alice **Mr Stewart Graves**
10 **HILL FARM BLUES,** 5, b m Mon Tresor—Loadplan Lass **Mr Dennis Newton**

MR W. M. BRISBOURNE—continued

11 **HILL FARM DANCER,** 7, ch m Gunner B—Loadplan Lass **Mr M. E. Hughes**
12 **KENLEYMOUR,** 8, ch m Seymour Hicks (FR)—Friendly Marina **Miss Melissa Brown**
13 **RIVER ENSIGN,** 5, br m River God (USA)—Ensigns Kit **Crispandave Racing Associates**
14 **ROYRACE,** 6, b g Wace (USA)—Royal Tycoon **Mr Andrew Evans**
15 **SWAN ISLAND,** 4, ch f Hubbly Bubbly (USA)—Green's Cassatt (USA) **Mr Keith Baron**
16 **TYCOON TED,** 5, b g Starch Reduced—Royal Tycoon **Mrs Mary Brisbourne**
17 **TYCOON TINA,** 4, b f Tina's Pet—Royal Tycoon **Mr A. N. Brooke Rankin**
18 **WELDUNFRANK,** 5, br g Weld—Damsong **Mrs Julie McCormack**

THREE-YEAR-OLDS

19 **PRINCESS TINA,** br f Tina's Pet—Royal Tycoon **Mr Antony Brisbourne**
20 **RUBY BEAR,** gr f Thethingaboutitis (USA)—Hitravelscene **Mr D. J. Kirkland**

TWO-YEAR-OLDS

21 B f 18/3 Gunner B—Delladear (Sonnen Gold) **Mr Robin Evans**

Other Owners: Mr Christopher Chell, Mr A. Von Dinther, Mr David B. Fretwell, Mr Andrew Letherbarrow, Mrs Bernice Newton, Mr S. Slingsby, Mr Peter A. V. Wright.

Jockeys (Flat): A Garth (7-12), A McCarthy (7-3), R Mullen (7-5).

Jockeys (NH): C Llewellyn (10-0), R Massey (9-10), S Wynne (10-0).

Lady Riders: Miss Melissa Brown (8-12), Miss Diana Jones (9-5).

83 MR C. E. BRITTAIN, Newmarket

Postal: **'Carlburg', 49 Bury Road, Newmarket, Suffolk, CB8 7BY.**
Phone: **OFFICE (01638) 664347 HOME (01638) 663739 FAX (01638) 661744**

1 **ACHARNE,** 5, ch h Pharly (FR)—Sibley **Parrot Racing**
2 **AIR EXPRESS (IRE),** 4, b c Salse (USA)—Ibtisamm (USA) **Mr Mohamed Obaida**
3 **ASSURED GAMBLE,** 4, b g Rock Hopper—Willowbank **Mr Peter A. Head**
4 **ATTITRE (FR),** 4, b f Mtoto—Aquaglow **Mr R. A. Pledger**
5 **AZTEC FLYER (USA),** 5, b g Alwasmi (USA)—Jetta J (USA) **Mr R. Meredith**
6 **DRIVE ASSURED,** 4, gr g Mystiko (USA)—Black Ivor (USA) **Mr Peter A. Head**
7 **ERTLON,** 8, b g Shareef Dancer (USA)—Sharpina **Mr C. E. Brittain**
8 **FIAMETTA,** 4, ch f Primo Dominie—Monaiya **Mr B. H. Voak**
9 **JOUST,** 4, b g Keen—Tudorealm (USA) **Wyck Hall Stud**
10 **LUSO,** 6, b h Salse (USA)—Lucayan Princess **Mr Saeed Manana**
11 **NEEDLE GUN (IRE),** 8, b br h Sure Blade (USA)—Lucayan Princess **Mr Saeed Manana**
12 **PUNISHMENT,** 7, b h Midyan (USA)—In The Shade **Mr A. J. Richards**
13 **PUZZLEMENT,** 4, gr g Mystiko (USA)—Abuzz **Mrs C. E. Brittain**
14 **ROYAL CROWN (IRE),** 4, b g Sadler's Wells (USA)—Rose of Jericho (USA) **Mr Michael H. Watt**
15 **SIREN SONG (IRE),** 7, b g Warning—Nazwa **Mr Michael H. Watt**
16 **ST LAWRENCE (CAN),** 4, gr c With Approval (CAN)—Mingan Isle (USA) **Mr Saeed Manana**
17 **SYLVA PARADISE (IRE),** 5, b g Dancing Dissident (USA)—Brentsville (USA) **Eddy Grimstead Honda**
18 **UNCHANGED,** 6, b m Unfuwain (USA)—Favorable Exchange (USA) **Mr M. J. Simmonds**
19 **UPPER MOUNT CLAIR,** 8, b m Ela-Mana-Mou—Sun Street **Mr C. E. Brittain**
20 **WORLD PREMIER,** 5, b g Shareef Dancer (USA)—Abuzz **Mrs C. E. Brittain**

THREE-YEAR-OLDS

21 **ANNA,** b f Ela-Mana-Mou—Anna Rella (IRE) **Mr C. E. Brittain**
22 **BABANINA,** b f Night Shift (USA)—Babita **Mr Saeed Manana**

MR C. E. BRITTAIN—continued

23 **CERISETTE (IRE),** b f Polar Falcon (USA)—Crimson Conquest (USA) **Sheikh Marwan Al Maktoum**
24 **CIRCUS,** b c Caerleon (USA)—Circo **Mr Saeed Manana**
25 **CLOUD CASTLE,** b f In The Wings—Lucayan Princess **Mr Saeed Manana**
26 **DAHOMEY (USA),** b br c Dayjur (USA)—Dish Dash **Mr Saeed Manana**
27 **ELEGANT FAN (USA),** b br c Lear Fan (USA)—Elegance (USA) **The Thoroughbred Corporation**
28 **FORUM,** b f Lion Cavern (USA)—Top Society **Wyck Hall Stud**
29 **GREENLANDER,** b c Green Desert (USA)—Pipet (USA) **Sheikh Marwan Al Maktoum**
30 **HERE AND NOW (USA),** ch f Green Forest (USA)—All Present (USA) **The Thoroughbred Corporation**
31 **HORIZONTAL,** b f Perpendicular—Silly Games **Mr A. J. Massingberd-Mundy**
32 **LA ROCHELLE (IRE),** b f Salse (USA)—Lagta **Mr Saeed Manana**
33 **LITTLE EMILY,** gr f Zafonic (USA)—Petillante **Mr A. J. Richards**
34 **LONE PIPER,** b c Warning—Shamisen **Mr Saeed Manana**
35 **LUCKY MYST,** b c Mystiko (USA)—Lucky Omen **Mr R. N. Khan**
36 **MEAUX (IRE),** b c Fairy King (USA)—Mo Pheata **Mr B. H. Voak**
37 **MYSTICISM,** ch f Mystiko (USA)—Abuzz **Mrs C. E. Brittain**
38 **NIGHT SPIRIT (IRE),** b f Night Shift (USA)—Brentsville (USA) **Eddy Grimstead Honda**
39 **NIGHT STAR (FR),** b f Village Star (FR)—Racing Home (FR) **Mr A. J. Richards**
40 **PEGNITZ (USA),** b c Lear Fan (USA)—Likely Split (USA) **Mr B. H. Voak**
41 **PERLA DI SASSO (GER),** br f Caerleon (USA)—Pebbles **Sheikh Mohammed**
42 **SALSETTE,** b f Salse (USA)—Amber Fizz (USA) **Mr Saeed Manana**
43 **SEPT CROISETT (IRE),** b c Lahib (USA)—Murooj (USA) **Mr A. Merza**
44 **SIMPLY SUPER,** ch f Superlative—Real Princess **Mr D. Sieff**
45 **THRASHING,** b c Kahyasi—White-Wash **Mr Saeed Manana**
46 **WALTZING MATILDA,** b f Mujtahid (USA)—Where's The Dance **Mrs J. Costelloe**
47 **WENDA (IRE),** ch f Priolo (USA)—Pennine Drive (IRE) **Mr B. H. Voak**

TWO-YEAR-OLDS

48 Gr f 13/3 Petong—Affirmation (Tina's Pet) **Wyck Hall Stud**
49 B f 4/5 Trempolino (USA)—Alimana (Akarad (FR)) **Mr Saeed Manana**
50 Ch c 25/4 Most Welcome—Amber Fizz (USA) (Effervescing (USA)) **Mr Saeed Manana**
51 B c 9/3 Mr Prospector (USA)—Araadh (USA) (Blushing Groom (FR)) **The Thoroughbred Corporation**
52 Ch c 3/4 Bien Bien (USA)—Ardisia (USA) (Affirmed (USA)) **Prince Abdul Aziz Bin Saud**
53 Gr c 26/3 Alzao (USA)—Avice Caro (USA) (Caro) **Mr Saeed Manana**
54 B c 9/3 Darshaan—Avila (Ajdal (USA)) **Mr Saeed Manana**
55 B c 17/3 Green Desert (USA)—Babita (Habitat) **Mr Saeed Manana**
56 B c 5/4 Warning—Badawi (USA) (Diesis) **Sheikh Marwan Al Maktoum**
57 Ch c 29/2 Shalford (IRE)—Candle Hill (Sallust) **Mr Saeed Manana**
58 B f 6/3 College Chapel—Congress Lady (General Assembly (USA)) **Mr Saeed Manana**
59 B f 21/3 Shareef Dancer (USA)—Cormorant Bay (Don't Forget Me) **Mr Saeed Manana**
60 Ch f 10/1 Lycius (USA)—Crimson Conquest (USA) (Diesis) **Sheikh Marwan Al Maktoum**
61 B br f 3/3 Woodman (USA)—Dawn Deal (USA) (Grey Dawn II) **Mr C. E. Brittain**
62 B c 5/2 Danehill (USA)—Donya (Mill Reef (USA)) **Sheikh Mohammed Obaid Al Maktoum**
63 **ENCOUNTER,** br c 24/4 Primo Dominie—Dancing Spirit (IRE) (Ahonoora) **Wyck Hall Stud**
64 B f 4/3 Dayjur (USA)—Fennel (Slew O'Gold (USA)) **Mr Ali Saeed**
65 **GINO'S SPIRITS,** ch f 2/3 Perugino (USA)—Rising Spirits (Cure The Blues (USA)) **Mr R. N. Khan**
66 **GREEN SNAKE,** ch f 20/2 Royal Academy (USA)—Tigwa (Cadeaux Genereux) **Mr Mohamed Obaida**
67 B c 7/5 In The Wings—Hejraan (USA) (Alydar (USA)) **Sheikh Mohammed Obaid Al Maktoum**
68 Ch c 10/5 Mujtahid (USA)—High Tern (High Line) **Sheikh Mohammed Obaid Al Maktoum**
69 B f 1/4 Diesis—Je Comprend (USA) (Caerleon (USA)) **Mr Saeed Manana**
70 B c 2/5 Scenic—La Bella Fontana (Lafontaine (USA)) **Mr Saeed Manana**
71 B c 17/4 Warning—La Dama Bonita (USA) (El Gran Senor (USA)) **Sheikh Marwan Al Maktoum**
72 B c 17/3 Lear Fan (USA)—Ladanum (USA) (Green Dancer (USA)) **The Thoroughbred Corporation**
73 **LADY GEORGIA,** gr f 7/3 Arazi (USA)—Petillante (Petong) **Mr A. J. Richards**
74 B gr f 6/3 Cozzene (USA)—La Llave (USA) (Risen Star (USA)) **Mr Saeed Manana**
75 **L'ORPHELINE (FR),** b f 19/5 Seattle Song (USA)—Buck's Dame (USA) (Damascus (USA)) **Mr Saeed Manana**
76 B c 22/4 Northern Flagship—Love At Dawn (USA) (Grey Dawn II) **Mr Peter A. Head**
77 B c 18/3 Green Desert (USA)—Love of Silver (USA) (Arctic Tern (USA)) **Mr Ali Saeed**
78 B c 20/3 Perugino (USA)—Love With Honey (USA) (Full Pocket (USA)) **Mr C. E. Brittain**
79 Ch c 16/3 Selkirk (USA)—Luana (Shaadi (USA)) **Mr Saeed Manana**

MR C. E. BRITTAIN—continued

80 B c 8/5 Sabrehill (USA)—Lucky Omen (Queen's Hussar) **Mr R. N. Khan**
81 **MAGDA (IRE),** b f 18/2 Turtle Island (IRE)—Pennine Drive (IRE) (Pennine Walk) **Mr B. H. Voak**
82 **MARRY ME,** ch f 15/5 Pursuit Of Love—Perfect Desire (USA) (Green Forest (USA)) **Mr D. Sieff**
83 **MILL AFRIQUE,** b f 16/4 Mtoto—Milinetta (Milford) **Mr R. Meredith**
84 B f 18/5 Nashwan (USA)—Mistle Thrush (USA) (Storm Bird (CAN)) **Mr Saeed Manana**
85 **MISTRESS EWAR (FR),** b f 5/4 Saumarez—Anse Macabou (FR) (Comrade In Arms) **Mr A. J. Richards**
86 B c 5/3 Cadeaux Genereux—On Tiptoes (Shareef Dancer (USA)) **Sheikh Marwan Al Maktoum**
87 B c 18/2 Zafonic (USA)—Overcast (IRE) (Caerleon (USA)) **Mr Ali Saeed**
88 Ch f 15/2 Polish Precedent—Pearl Kite (USA) (Silver Hawk (USA)) **Mr Saeed Manana**
89 **POMME DUCHESSE (USA),** b f 25/4 Alleged (USA)—Quilesse (USA) (Fulmar (USA)) **Mr A. J. Richards**
90 B f 28/1 Sabrehill (USA)—Rani (IRE) (Groom Dancer (USA)) **Sheikh Mohammed Obaid Al Maktoum**
91 **ROYAL DANCE (USA),** b c 1/4 Trempolino (USA)—Rosey Ramble (USA) (Chieftain (USA)) **Mr Jaber Abdullah**
92 **SAILOR JACK (USA),** b c 11/4 Green Dancer (USA)—Chateaubrook (USA) (Alleged (USA)) **Mr R. A. Pledger**
93 **SENA DESERT,** b f 30/1 Green Desert (USA)—Sueboog (IRE) (Darshaan) **Mr Mohamed Obaida**
94 Gr c 8/5 Zilzal (USA)—Silver Glitz (USA) (Grey Dawn II) **Mr C. E. Brittain**
95 **SILVER SNAKE (IRE),** b c 24/2 Salse (USA)—Ibtisamm (USA) (Caucasus (USA)) **Mr Mohamed Obaida**
96 **SLIP STITCH,** b c 29/3 Slip Anchor—Satanic Dance (FR) (Shareef Dancer (USA)) **Mrs Brigitte Pollard**
97 **SYLVA LEGEND (USA),** b c 24/5 Lear Fan (USA)—Likeashot (USA) (Gun Shot (USA)) **Eddy Grimstead Honda**
98 B c 1/2 Warning—Tanz (IRE) (Sadler's Wells (USA)) **Abdullah Saeed bul Hab**
99 **TIME ZONE,** b c 24/2 Shirley Heights—Forthwith (Midyan (USA)) **Wyck Hall Stud**
100 B f 1/6 Selkirk (USA)—Top Society (High Top) **Wyck Hall Stud**
101 Ch c 12/4 Wolfhound (USA)—Virelai (Kris) **Mr Saeed Manana**
102 **WESTMINSTER CITY (USA),** b c 24/4 Alleged (USA)—Promanade Fan (USA) (Timeless Moment (USA)) **Mr A. J. Richards**
103 **WHO CARES WINS,** ch c 27/2 Kris—Anne Bonny (Ajdal (USA)) **Mr Khalifa Dasmal**
104 Ch c 5/2 Lycius (USA)—Zia (USA) (Shareef Dancer (USA)) **Sheikh Marwan Al Maktoum**

Other Owners: Ewar Stud Farms France, Mr C. T. Olley, Mr M. C. Olley.

Apprentice: Kevin Parkin (7-10).

84 MR M. A. BRITTAIN, Warthill

Postal: **Northgate Lodge, Warthill, York, YO3 9XR.**
Phone: **(01759) 371472 FAX (01759) 372915**

1 **AMIARGE,** 8, b g Reference Point—Scotia Rose **Miss Debi J. Woods**
2 **BEDAZZLE,** 7, b g Formidable (USA)—Wasimah **Northgate Lodge Racing Club**
3 **CHINABERRY,** 4, b f Soviet Star (USA)—Crimson Conquest (USA)
4 **DOUBLE-J (IRE),** 4, b g Fayruz—Farriers Slipper **Mr D. H. Armitage**
5 **ERUPT,** 5, b g Beveled (USA)—Sparklingsovereign **Mr Sidney Eaton**
6 **GET A LIFE,** 5, gr m Old Vic—Sandstream **NAJ Racing**
7 **GOLD DESIRE,** 8, b g Grey Desire—Glory Gold **Northgate Lodge Racing Club**
8 **GREY KINGDOM,** 7, gr g Grey Desire—Miss Realm **Mr Mel Brittain**
9 **MONTE CAVO,** 7, b g Bustino—Dance Festival **Mr Mel Brittain**
10 **NOIRIE,** 4, br g Warning—Callipoli (USA) **Miss Debi J. Woods**
11 **OUR WAY,** 4, ch f Forzando—Hanglands **Oasby Racing**
12 **PENDOLINO (IRE),** 7, b g Thatching—Pendulina **Mr Ian Booth**
13 **PORTITE SOPHIE,** 7, b m Doulab (USA)—Impropriety **Ms Maureen Hanlon**
14 **WAGGA MOON (IRE),** 4, b g Mac's Imp (USA)—Faapette

THREE-YEAR-OLDS

15 **CORNISH RING,** ch f King's Signet (USA)—Trelissick **Northgate Lodge Partnerships**
16 **DESIRE'S GOLD,** br g Grey Desire—Glory Gold **Mr Mel Brittain**
17 **EAGER HERO,** ch c Keen—Honour And Glory **Northgate Lodge Partnerships**
18 **HOWIES CHOICE (IRE),** b g Petardia—Better Goods (IRE) **Mr Ronald Howe**
19 **INCHALONG,** b f Inchinor—Reshift **Northgate Lodge Partnerships**
20 **KHATTAFF (IRE),** ch c Hamas (IRE)—Coven
21 **MELODIAN,** b c Grey Desire—Mere Melody **Mr Mel Brittain**
22 **MOY (IRE),** ch f Beveled (USA)—Exceptional Beauty **Mr W. Moore**

MR M. A. BRITTAIN—continued

23 **NOVELTY,** b f Primo Dominie—Nophe (USA) **Mr Mel Brittain**
24 **POKUSSION (IRE),** b f Polski Boy (USA)—Tambourine Girl (USA) **Mr Mel Brittain**
25 **PRINCIPLED,** b c Prince Sabo—Payvashooz **Mr M. J. Paver**
26 **STARLINER (IRE),** ch f Statoblest—Dancing Line **Northgate Lodge Partnerships**
27 **STEPHANGEORGE,** b g La Grange Music—Telegraph Callgirl **Mr Cliff Woof**

TWO-YEAR-OLDS

28 B f 22/4 Forest Wind (USA)—Better Goods (IRE) (Glow (USA))
29 B c 20/1 College Chapel—Genetta (Green Desert (USA))
30 Ch c 27/1 Silver Hawk (USA)—Gharah (USA) (Shadeed (USA))
31 B f 24/2 Presidium—Junuh (Jalmood (USA))
32 B c 12/2 College Chapel—Kaskazi (Dancing Brave (USA))
33 B f 7/3 Prince Sabo—La Reine de France (Queen's Hussar) **Northgate Silver**
34 Ch f 21/3 First Trump—Loving Legacy (Caerleon (USA)) **Mr Mel Brittain**
35 B f 5/3 Magic Ring (IRE)—Lucky Message (USA) (Phone Trick (USA)) **Northgate Bronze**
36 Br f 10/4 College Chapel—Lute And Lyre (IRE) (The Noble Player (USA))
37 Ch f 14/5 First Trump—Musical Sally (USA) (The Minstrel (CAN)) **BJK Partnership**
38 Ch f 4/4 Superlative—Northern Bird (Interrex (CAN)) **Northgate Silver**
39 Ch f 30/4 Never So Bold—Polly Packer (Reform) **Northgate Silver**
40 **PURSUANT,** b c 16/5 Puissance—Payvashooz (Ballacashtal (CAN)) **Mr M. J. Paver**
41 B f 28/4 Then Again—Reshift (Night Shift (USA))
42 Gr c 12/4 Grey Desire—Tanoda (Tyrnavos) **Mr Mel Brittain**
43 B c 8/5 Thatching—Tender Time (Tender King) **Mr Mel Brittain**
44 B c 17/2 Exit To Nowhere (USA)—Venerate (IRE) (Ahonoora)
45 B f 23/3 Inchinor—Walking Saint (Godswalk (USA))

Other Owners: Mr R. Abson, Mr R. Adams, Mrs I. Battla, Mr B. Bedford, Mr E. Bentham, Mr S. Box, Mr G. Canner, Mr L. Chambers, Mrs E. Charlesworth, Mr G. Cowie, Mr J. Croft, Mr C. Durnan, Eclipse Management (Newmarket) Ltd, Mr R. Hebb, Mr R. Hudson, Mr D. Imeson, Mr A. Jane, Mr R. King, Mr C. Knowles, Mr J. Litman, Mr G. N. Marshall, Mr M. Murphy, Mr D. Parker, Mr J. S. Porter, Mr D. C. Rayment, Mr J. Richardson, Mrs S. Shaw, Mr D. Sims, Mr G. K. Taylor, Mr T. Torrance, Mr D. B. White, Mr J. Wilkinson, Mr N. Wilson, Mr S. Winfield.

Apprentices: Richard Farmer, Dean Mernagh.

85 MR H. DE BROMHEAD, Knockeen

Postal: **Knockeen, Waterford, Ireland.**
Phone: **(051) 375726 FAX (051) 352927 MOBILE (086) 603027**

1 **BISHOPS HALL,** 12, br g Pimpernels Tune—Mariner's Dash **Joseph Carroll**
2 **BUCKISH (IRE),** 8, b g Buckskin (FR)—Serbelle **Mr Charles Carroll**
3 **CAULD SIGNAL (IRE),** 5, b m Cataldi—Typhoon Signal **Mr J. E. Thornhill**
4 **CORYMANDEL (IRE),** 9, b g Mandalus—Curry Lunch **M. J. E. Thornhill**
5 **CORYROSE (IRE),** 6, gr m Roselier (FR)—Curry Lunch **M. J. E. Thornhill**
6 **DERRYNAFLAN LAD (IRE),** 6, b g Lord Americo—Madam Exbury **Percy Delany**
7 **DOOLAN'S STAND (IRE),** 7, b g Supreme Leader—Palazon **Rosewood Syndicate**
8 **FEELING GRAND (IRE),** 6, b g Naheez (USA)—Tourney's Girl **I. H. Stewart-Brown**
9 **FIDALUS (IRE),** 5, br g Mandalus—Fifi L'Amour **S. A. Aldridge**
10 **PHAREIGN (IRE),** 7, br g Phardante (FR)—Lena's Reign **K. Casey**
11 **PRIZE OF PEACE (IRE),** 8, ch m Torus—Sheelin Bavard **Mr T. J. Carroll**
12 **ROUGHSHOD (IRE),** 6, b g King's Ride—Golden Cherry (IRE) **M. J. E. Thornhill**
13 **SEVEN AIRS (IRE),** 6, br m Brush Aside (USA)—Dikler Gale (IRE) **Mr T. J. Carroll**

THREE-YEAR-OLDS

14 **PEACE PREVAILS (IRE),** b f Brief Truce (USA)—Orthorising **Mr J. E. Thornhill**

Jockeys (NH): G Bradley, T Horgan, C O'Dwyer, C F Swan.

Amateurs: F Crowley,

86 MR C. P. E. BROOKS, Lambourn

Postal: **Uplands Stables, Lambourn, Hungerford, Berkshire, RG17 8QH.**
Phone: **(01488) 72077 FAX (01488) 71206**

1 **AARDWOLF,** 7, b g Dancing Brave (USA)—Pretoria **Lady Camilla Dempster**
2 **A-EL-CEE (IRE),** 7, ch g Over The River (FR)—November Tide **Uplands Bloodstock**
3 **ANDSUEPHI (IRE),** 6, b g Montelimar (USA)—Butler's Daughter **Mrs J. A. Cohen**
4 **ART PRINCE (IRE),** 8, b g Aristocracy—Come Now **Mr Terry Neill**
5 **BALLYBOLLEN (IRE),** 6, b br g Air Display (USA)—Clair The Lune **Mr Terry Neill and Lady Thompson**
6 **BANN VIEW (IRE),** 7, gr m Ardross—Woodland View **Mr R. D. B. Best**
7 **BARTON,** 5, ch g Port Etienne (FR)—Peanuts (FR) **Mr Stanley W. Clarke**
8 **BERLIN BLUE,** 5, b g Belmez (USA)—Blue Brocade **Mr Alec Tuckerman**
9 **BOLD ORIENTAL (IRE),** 4, b g Tirol—Miss Java **Uplands Bloodstock**
10 5, B g Zaffaran (USA)—Bramble Hatch **Uplands Bloodstock**
11 **CASABLANCA (IRE),** 5, b g Strong Gale—Guess Twice **Uplands Bloodstock**
12 **CHAT IN THE BOX (IRE),** 5, ch m Over The River (FR)—Mahe Reef **Uplands Bloodstock & Mr D. S. Cowie**
13 **CHINA GEM (IRE),** 7, b g Idiot's Delight—Graeme's Gem **Mrs B. Mead**
14 **COULDNT BE BETTER,** 11, br g Oats—Belle Bavard **Mr R. A. B. Whittle**
15 **CROSS THE RUBICON (IRE),** 7, ch g Over The River—One Way Only **Mrs S. Towler**
16 **DARK HORSE (IRE),** 6, br g Kambalda—Laurence Lady **Uplands Bloodstock**
17 **DARK STRANGER (FR),** 7, b g Iveday (FR)—Abeille Royale (USA) **Mr Terry Neill**
18 **DOOR TO DOOR (IRE),** 6, b g Gildoran—Balancing Act **Uplands Bloodstock**
19 **FITZMAURICE (IRE),** 6, ch g Saxon Farm—Milworth **Axom**
20 **FLORID (USA),** 7, ch g The Minstrel (CAN)—Kenanga **Lord Howard de Walden**
21 **FOXTROT ROMEO,** 8, ch g Town And Country—Forest Frolic **Lady Cobham**
22 **GAROLO (FR),** 8, b g Garde Royale—Valgoya (FR) **Lady Lloyd Webber**
23 **GLENALLA STAR (IRE),** 9, b g Fidel—Willowho Pride **Lady Thompson**
24 **GREAT STUFF (IRE),** 7, br g Dromod Hill—Little Loch **Uplands Bloodstock**
25 **HISAR (IRE),** 5, br g Doyoun—Himaya (IRE) **Lady Lloyd Webber**
26 **HOH WARRIOR (IRE),** 7, b g Lord Americo—Princess Isabella **Mr D. F. Allport**
27 **HOLLY'S PRIDE (IRE),** 8, ch g Phardante (FR)—Mawbeg Holly **Mr Anthony Pye-Jeary**
28 **INDIGO TIME,** 6, br g Ela-Mana-Mou—Majestic's Gold **Terry Neill**
29 **KAPCO (IRE),** 6, b g Be My Native (USA)—Shake Up **Willsford Racing Incorporated**
30 **LITTLE MILLER (IRE),** 5, b g Meneval (USA)—Another Miller **Mrs G. Abecassis**
31 5, B g Be My Native (USA)—Madam Owen **Uplands Bloodstock**
32 **MAJOR BLAZE,** 6, b g Royal Vulcan—Loughnavalley **Mrs J. Thornton**
33 **MAN MOOD (FR),** 7, b g Brinkmanship (USA)—Miss Mood **Mr Julian Robbins**
34 6, B g Satco—Mastertown Lucy **Uplands Bloodstock**
35 **MEDIUM WAVE,** 6, b g Domynsky—Alumia
36 **MELSTOCK MEGGIE,** 8, ch m Cardinal Flower—Lake View Lady **Lady Cobham**
37 **MERSHIGINER (IRE),** 5, br g King's Ride—Shelleys Rocky Gem **Glenmore Investments Ltd**
38 **MISTY CLASS (IRE),** 6, gr g Roselier (FR)—Toevarro **Mrs P. Elsbury**
39 **MR MOONLIGHT (IRE),** 6, ch g Orchestra—Midnight Mistress **Mrs J. A. Cohen**
40 **MR PRESIDENT (IRE),** 9, b g Supreme Leader—I've No Idea
41 **OLUMO (IRE),** 7, b g Mandalus—Fleetfoot Lady **Uplands Bloodstock**
42 **PADRE MIO (IRE),** 10, b g The Parson—Mwanamio **Lady Lloyd Webber**
43 **PHAR BETTER (IRE),** 6, b g Phardante (FR)—Markree Castle **Mr R. A. B. Whittle**
44 **RALEAGH NATIVE (IRE),** 5, ch g Be My Native (USA)—Lagan Valley Rose **Michael Jackson Bloodstock Ltd**
45 **RESOURCE (IRE),** 5, ch g Simply Great (FR)—Melarka **Anglia Telecom Centres Plc**
46 **RIVER DAWN (IRE),** 6, ch g Over The River (FR)—Morning Susan **Uplands Bloodstock**
47 **ROUTE ONE (IRE),** 5, b g Welsh Term—Skylin **Uplands Bloodstock**
48 **ROUTE TWO,** 4, b g Welsh Term—Skylin **Uplands Bloodstock**
49 **SCOUT AROUND (IRE),** 6, b g Farhaan—Hard Riche **Lady Thompson and Mr Terry Neill**
50 **SHEKELS (IRE),** 7, ch g Orchestra—Rare Currency **Uplands Bloodstock**
51 **SHOPAHOLIC (IRE),** 5, b g King's Ride—Gift Seeker **Mr A. L. Brodin**
52 **SKIMABIT (IRE),** 7, b g Henbit—Maukas Cross **Mr D. Elsbury**
53 **STANMORE (IRE),** 6, b g Aristocracy—Lady Go Marching (USA) **Uplands Bloodstock**
54 **STROKESAVER (IRE),** 8, ch g Orange Reef—Silver Love **Bow Lane Partnership**
55 **SUNY BAY (IRE),** 9, gr g Roselier (FR)—Suny Salome **Uplands Bloodstock**
56 6, B g The Noble Player (USA)—Suny Salome **Uplands Bloodstock**

MR C. P. E. BROOKS—continued

57 THE FULL MONTY (IRE), 6, b g Montelimar (USA)—Melody Gayle VII **The Nutty Partnership**
58 TIME ENOUGH (IRE), 9, ch g Callernish—Easter Gazette **The Lewis Partnership**
59 UNWANTED (IRE), 6, b g Tremblant—Queens Tricks **Uplands Bloodstock**
60 WILDE MUSIC (IRE), 8, b g Orchestra—Run For Shelter **Mr A. L. Brodin**
61 YANKIE LORD (IRE), 6, b g Lord Americo—Coolstuff
62 YOUBETTERBELIEVEIT (IRE), 9, ch g The Parson—Emperors Twinkle **Uplands Bloodstock**

Other Owners: Mr D. W. H. Bell, Mrs Robert Brooks, Dr P. P. Brown, Mr A. Buller, Mr C. R. Buttery, Mr Nigel Dempster, Mrs Miriam Francome, Mr John Halliday, Mr John Rhys Harris, Mrs Morven Heller, Mr Tony Hill, Mr J. A. Lewis, Mr R. P. B. Michaelson, Mr W. D. Miskin, Mr M. J. Morrison, Mr Martin Myers, Mr William Phillips, Mr W. H. Ponsonby, Mr C. Rubin, Mr S. L. Rubin, Mr P. Shalson, Mrs T. Strowman, Miss M. Talbot, Sir Peter Thompson, Mrs S. Towler, Mrs Victoria Tuckerman.

Jockeys (NH): G Bradley (10-2), D Gallagher (10-0), S McNeill (10-0).

Conditional: M Berry (10-0), G Brace (9-7), C Rafter (9-7).

87 MR S. A. BROOKSHAW, Shrewsbury

Postal: **Preston Farm, Uffington, Shrewsbury, Shropshire, SY4 4TB.**
Phone: **PHONE & FAX (01743) 709227 MOBILE (0973) 959986**

1 BARTON BLACK (NZ), 6, br g Tristrams Heritage (NZ)—Catena Heights (NZ) **Mr Stanley W. Clarke**
2 BARTON CHIC, 6, ch m Sadeem (USA)—Chicory **Mrs H. J. Clarke**
3 BARTON GREEN (NZ), 7, b g Garcia (USA)—Morning Order (NZ) **Mr Stanley W. Clarke**
4 BARTON LIL, 6, ch m Nicholas Bill—Lily Mab (FR) **Mrs H. J. Clarke**
5 BUILDER BOY, 8, ch g Sunley Builds—Geordie Lass **Mr G. J. Jones**
6 CEEYOU AT MIDNIGHT, 7, b g Seymour Hicks (FR)—Midnight Affair **Ms Diana Crewe**
7 5, B g Sadeem (USA)—Chicory **Mr Stanley W. Clarke**
8 CHURCHTOWN GLEN (IRE), 5, b br g Be My Native (USA)—Hill Side Glen **J. & C. Tipton**
9 CORALETTE (IRE), 8, ch g Le Moss—Myralette **Mr S. A. Brookshaw**
10 CUL DE SAC (NZ), 7, ch g Broadway Aly (USA)—Tioga Mellay (NZ) **G. J. Jones & H. Spencer**
11 5, B g Nicholas Bill—Dutch Majesty **Mr Stanley W. Clarke**
12 EMTEC SOMAIREE (NZ), 6, gr g March Hywel (USA)—Southern Ash (NZ) **Mr M. L. Davison**
13 I'M MAGGY (NZ), 8, b m Danseur Etoile (FR)—Twirling Row (NZ) **Mr Stanley W. Clarke**
14 IVOR FILOU (NZ), 7, b g Ivotino (USA)—Amynfilou (NZ) **Mr Stanley W. Clarke**
15 JILL (NZ), 7, br m Tristrams Heritage (NZ)—Judith (NZ) **Harris Associates**
16 5, B g Nicholas Bill—Kamakaze Girl **Mr Stanley W. Clarke**
17 LADY CLARINA (IRE), 8, b m Torus—Coalauct **Mr S. A. Brookshaw**
18 LATE HARVEST (NZ), 6, b g Tarrago (ITY)—Pamira (AUS) **Mrs A. N. Harris**
19 5, Ch g Nicholas Bill—Lily Mab (FR) **Mr Stanley W. Clarke**
20 LISTEN TIMMY (NZ), 9, b g Coral Reef (FR)—Calamity (NZ) **The Sentinel Racing Club**
21 LORD GYLLENE (NZ), 10, b g Ring The Bell (NZ)—Dentelle (NZ) **Mr Stanley W. Clarke**
22 LORD RELIC (NZ), 12, b g Zamazaan (FR)—Morning Order (NZ) **Mrs H. J. Clarke**
23 LORD RICHFIELD (NZ), 7, b g Kirmann—Lady Grange (NZ) **Harris Associates**
24 MAJOR LOOK (NZ), 10, gr g Jiggs Alarm (USA)—War Belle (NZ) **Mrs H. J. Clarke**
25 MANASIS (NZ), 7, b g Tom's Shu (USA)—Ruakiwi Nymph (NZ) **Mr Stanley W. Clarke**
26 PAMALYN, 6, b m Derrylin—Cute Pam **Mr W. R. J. Everall**
27 PENNYAHEI, 7, b m Malaspina—Pennyazena **Mr S. A. Brookshaw**
28 5, B g Henbit (USA)—Pennyazena **Mr S. A. Brookshaw**
29 6, Ch m Nicholas Bill—Pennyazena **Mr S. A. Brookshaw**
30 PRINCESS TOR, 6, b m Sadeem (USA)—Torus Queen **Mr S. A. Brookshaw**
31 SEE MORE FURROWS, 6, b m Seymour Hicks (FR)—Final Furlong **Furrows Ltd**
32 SHACKLEY MERE, 6, ch g Weld—Roscam Lady **Mr Michael Moylan**
33 SOUTHERNDOWN (IRE), 5, ch g Montelimar (USA)—Country Melody (IRE) **Mr C. G. Johnson**

MR S. A. BROOKSHAW—continued

34 **TEAL BAY,** 6, b m Scallywag—Centaura **Mr P. Jones**
35 **THROWER,** 7, b g Thowra (FR)—Atlantic Line **Mr Mark Owen**
36 5, B g Roscoe Blake—Torus Queen **Mr S. A. Brookshaw**
37 **TWELVE BORE,** 7, b g Gunner B—Miss Starworthy **Mr W. R. J. Everall**
38 **VADLAWYS (FR),** 7, b g Always Fair (USA)—Vadlava (FR) **Mr Stanley W. Clarke**
39 5, B m Nicholas Bill—Yamrah **Mr Stanley W. Clarke**

Other Owners: Mrs N. Crow, Mr M. W. Harris, Mr David Hewitt, Mr Brian Ridge, Mr G. B. Rogers, Mrs H. Spencer.

Conditional: Nigel Lynn (9-7).

Amateur: Richard Ford (11-0).

Lady Rider: Heidi Brookshaw (9-6).

88 MR R. BROTHERTON, Pershore

Postal: **Mill End Racing Stables, Netherton Road, Elmley Castle, Pershore, Worcestershire, WR10 3JF.**
Phone: **EVESHAM (01386) 710772 MOBILE (0973) 877280**

1 **ADMIRALTY WAY,** 12, b g Petorius—Captive Flower **Mr M. E. Kirkham**
2 **CAPTAIN MY CAPTAIN (IRE),** 10, ch g Flash of Steel—Amanzi
3 **INDIAN NECTAR,** 5, b m Indian Ridge—Sheer Nectar **Mrs Carol Newman**
4 **KHAZARI (USA),** 10, ch g Shahrastani (USA)—Kozana **Miss M. T. Orson**
5 **KING ACRYLIC (IRE),** 7, b g King of Clubs—Maynooth Belle **Baskerville Racing Club**
6 **LOVELARK,** 9, b m Crested Lark—Emily Love **Mr Harry Bibbey**
7 **MR POPPLETON,** 9, ch g Ballacashtal (CAN)—Greenstead Lady
8 **PERFIK LARK,** 8, ch g Crested Lark—The Dabber **Mr Harry Bibbey**
9 **POLLYKENDU (IRE),** 10, b br g Pollerton—Moykendu **Baskerville Racing Club**
10 **POT BLACKBIRD,** 9, ch m Crested Lark—Blacktop **Mr Harry Bibbey**
11 **ROGER DE MOWBRAY,** 8, b g Grey Desire—Richesse (FR) **Baskerville Racing Club**

THREE-YEAR-OLDS

12 **LAMOURA,** ch f Executive Man—Armalou **Mrs Carol Newman**
13 **RITA'S ROCK APE,** b f Mon Tresor—Failand **Mrs Janet Pearce**

Other Owners: Mr Duncan Beck, Mr Roy Brotherton, Mrs A. Burton, Mr K. T. Carpenter, Mr Chris Yelverton.

Jockeys (Flat): A Mackay (7-8), R Price (7-12).

Jockeys (NH): L J Harvey, C Llewellyn.

89 MR I. R. BROWN, Leominster

Postal: **Highview Farm, Upper Lye, Aymestrey, Leominster, Herefordshire, HR6 9SZ.**
Phone: **Tel: (01568) 770231**

1 4, Ch g Le Moss—Miss Date
2 **RAMILLION,** 6, b m Macmillion—Annie Ra **Mr I. R. Brown**

THREE-YEAR-OLDS

3 B f Relief Pitcher—Bremhill Rosie

TWO-YEAR-OLDS

4 Ch g 1/5 Saxon Farm—Miss Date (Mandamus)

Amateur: Mr A. Brown (9-7).

90 MRS J. BROWN, Malton

Postal: **Bottom Yard, Wold House, Langton Road, Norton, North Yorkshire, YO17 9QG.**

1 **AILSAE,** 5, b m Arctic Lord—Royal Snip **Mr K. Foster**
2 **BOB'S PLOY,** 6, b g Deploy—Santa Magdalena **Mr H. R. Hewitt**
3 **BURES (IRE),** 7, b g Bold Arrangement—Grid (FR) **Mr J. H. Hewitt**
4 **FLOSS THE BOSS,** 5, gr m Weld—Summer Path **Mr I. M. Lynch**
5 **FRYUP SATELLITE,** 7, br g Leading Star—Comedy Imp **Mr John Lees**
6 **JUKE BOX BILLY (IRE),** 10, ch g Kemal (FR)—Friendly Circle **Mr K. Hanson**
7 **MR BOMBASTIQUE (IRE),** 4, b g Classic Music (USA)—Duende **The Howarting's Partnership**
8 **OTTERBURN LAD (IRE),** 5, b g Mandalus—Telemeter Gem **Mr R. Haggas**
9 **TELL MONTY (IRE),** 6, ch g Montelimar (USA)—Time Will Tell **Mr K. Hanson**
10 **UN POCO LOCO,** 6, b g Lord Bud—Trailing Rose **Mr R. Burridge**

Other Owners: Mr Paul Clifton, Mr Tony Fawcett, Mrs J. M. Newitt, Mrs H. Sedgwick, Mr J. B. Slatcher.

Conditional: E Callaghan.

91 MR J. L. BROWN, Llanwrda

Postal: **Yn Yr Haul, Llansadwrn, Llanwrda, Dyfed, SA19 8LH.**
Phone: **(01550) 777050 MOBILE (0421) 854649**

1 **BUSHTON,** 6, b g High Season—Rusty Fern **Mr J. L. Brown**
2 **MIKE'S DREAM,** 6, b g Motivate—Carreg Goch **Mr J. L. Brown**
3 **RACHEL'S BOY,** 5, b g Rustingo—Carreg Goch **Mr J. L. Brown**

92 MISS A. E. BROYD, Crickhowell

Postal: **Penrhiw Farm, Llangenny, Crickhowell, Powys, NP8 1HD.**
Phone: **(01873) 812292**

1 **COUNCILLOR (IRE),** 7, b g Salt Dome (USA)—Virna (USA) **Miss Alison Broyd**
2 **MC CLATCHEY (IRE),** 7, b g Phardante (FR)—Gifted Lady **Miss Alison Broyd**
3 **SYLVESTER (IRE),** 8, ch g Shy Groom (USA)—Single Viking **Miss Alison Broyd**

93 MR R. H. BUCKLER, Bridport

Postal: **Melplash Court Farm, Melplash, Bridport, Dorset, DT6 3UH.**
Phone: **HOME (01308) 488318 FAX 488403 MOBILE (0831) 806360 (0385) 773957**

1 **ANGELO'S DOUBLE (IRE),** 10, b g M Double M (USA)—Bebe Altesse (GER) **Mr J. Henwood**
2 **BALLYEDWARD (IRE),** 8, b g Roselier (FR)—Paico Ana **Mr Nick Elliott**
3 **BEATSON (IRE),** 9, gr g Roselier (FR)—Toevarro **Mrs E. B. Gardiner**
4 **COPPER BOY,** 9, ch g Nearly A Hand—Learctic **Mr C. Raymond**
5 **COPPER COIL,** 8, ch g Undulate (USA)—April Rose **Mr R. A. Lloyd**
6 **COUNTRY CHAT,** 7, b m Derring Rose—Royal Chitchat **Mr J. G. Charlton**
7 **FLAXLEY WOOD,** 7, b br g Kambalda—Coolbawn Run **Mrs D. A. La Trobe**
8 **FLOW,** 9, b m Over The River (FR)—Thrupence **Mrs C. J. Dunn**
9 **FLY IT ALONE,** 8, br g Relkino—Rose Beetle **Mr H. Lott, Mr P. Jones**
10 **GILLY'S CROSS,** 5, ch g River God (USA)—Return To Romance **Mr Nick Elliott**
11 **GROUND NUT (IRE),** 8, ch g Fools Holme (USA)—Corn Seed **Mrs R. L. Haskins**
12 **HE KNOWS THE RULES,** 6, b g Tirol—Falls of Lora **The Hoodwinkers**
13 **HILLHEAD (IRE),** 9, br g Aristocracy—Serpentine Artiste **Miss R. Dobson**

MR R. H. BUCKLER—continued

14 **JOVIE KING (IRE),** 6, ch g Salt Dome (USA)—Jovial Josie (USA) **Mr F. H. M. Reid**
15 **KIRI'S ROSE (IRE),** 8, gr m Roselier (FR)—Kiri's Return **Mr R. H. Buckler**
16 **LA BRIGANTINE (IRE),** 5, br m Montelimar (USA)—Run For Shelter **Mr R. H. Buckler**
17 **LOOK SHARPER (IRE),** 5, ch g Sharp Victor (USA)—Al-Nadda **Against All Odds Partnership**
18 **MISS DISKIN (IRE),** 9, b m Sexton Blake—Knapping **Mr Martyn Forrester**
19 **ON THE CARDS (IRE),** 5, b g Cardinal Flower—Maple Walk **West Dorset Racing**
20 **RHOMAN FUN (IRE),** 9, b g Rhoman Rule (USA)—Fun **The Martyrs To Racing Partnership**
21 **RHYTHM AND BLUES,** 8, b g Myjinski (USA)—Pitskelly Blues **Mrs Peter Gregson**
22 **RISING TROUT,** 5, ch g Primitive Rising (USA)—Rosa Trout **Mr Nick Elliott**
23 **SANDANTE (IRE),** 7, ch m Orchestra—Sandyela **Mr M. West**
24 **SCOTBY (BEL),** 8, gr g Scottish Reel—Two Seasons **Mrs E. B. Gardiner**
25 **SEE ENOUGH,** 10, ch g Sharp Deal—See-O-Duf **Mr J. A. G. Meaden**
26 **ST VILLE,** 12, b g Top Ville—Dame Julian **Melplash Racing**
27 **TOM LOMAX,** 6, ch g Vital Season—Levant Row **Mr Terence Brady**
28 **TOUR LEADER (NZ),** 9, ch g Nassipour (USA)—Colleen (NZ) **Mr J. R. Barr**
29 **VINTAGE CLASSIC (IRE),** 7, br m Orchestra—Vintage Harvest **The Ever Smiling Partnership**

Other Owners: Mrs B. Bishop, Mr Antony D. Brown, Mr Jeffrey Brown, Mrs I. M. Buckler, Mrs P. J. Buckler, Mr Jack Bugler, Mr Mike Burns, Mrs A. Collier, Mrs K. J. Crocker, Mr Paul Davis, Mrs H. T. Edwards, Mrs Mary Graves, Mr C. E. Grover, Mr Frank Habberfield, Mrs Timothy Lewis, Mr S. B. Mitchell, Mr A. M. Morley, Mr K. A. Price, Mrs J. P. Rabbetts, Exors Of The Late Mrs M. Raymond, Mrs S. H. Richards, Mr C. T. Samways, Samways Fish Merchants & Transporters, Mr R. T. C. Searle, Mrs L. M. Stobart, Mr M. A. Styles, Mr J. P. Windsor.

Jockey (NH): B Powell (10-0).

Conditional: Joe McDermott (10-0).

Amateur: Mr K Wheate (9-7).

94 MRS J. R. BUCKLEY, Caistor

Postal: **Cabourne House, Cabourne, Caistor, Lincoln, Lincolnshire, LN7 6HU.**
Phone: **(01472) 852575 MOBILE: (04684) 413961 FAX: (01472) 852853**

1 **CARLY BRRIN,** 13, br g Carlin—Bios Brrin **Mrs J. R. Buckley**
2 **DEEL QUAY (IRE),** 7, b g Tidaro (USA)—Quayside Charm **Mrs J. R. Buckley**
3 **MAN OF WISLEY (IRE),** 8, b g Mandalus—Sabura **Mrs J. R. Buckley**
4 **MINNIES MINSTRAL (IRE),** 6, b g Black Minstrel—Clonbanin Vulvic **Miss S. C. R. Buckley**
5 **SPARROW HALL,** 11, b g Fine Blade (USA)—Churchtown Breeze **Mrs J. R. Buckley**

95 MR MARK BUCKLEY, South Molton

Postal: **West Down Stables, Whitechapel, South Molton, North Devon, EX36 3EQ.**
Phone: **(01769) 550373 FAX (01769) 550839**

1 **DIAGHILEF (IRE),** 6, b g Royal Academy (USA)—Miss Audimar (USA) **Mr C. C. Buckley**

THREE-YEAR-OLDS

2 Br g Be My Native (USA)—Buffs Express **Mr C. C. Buckley**
3 **WATKINS,** ch c King's Signet (USA)—Windbound Lass **Mr R. W. Savery**

TWO-YEAR-OLDS

4 B f 29/3 College Chapel—Arctic Splendour (USA) (Arctic Tern (USA)) **Mrs D. J. Buckley**
5 B c 12/3 Whittingham (IRE)—Miss Derby (USA) (Master Derby (USA))

MR MARK BUCKLEY—continued

6 **MY MOTHERS DREAN,** b f 22/3 Fayruz—With Diamonds (Shirley Heights) **Dulverton Racing**
7 B c 15/2 Tenby—Opening Day (Day Is Done)
8 **ROMAN HOLIDAY (IRE),** ch c 6/4 Lahib (USA)—Beneficiary (Jalmood (USA)) **Mrs N. W. Buckley**
9 B c 5/4 Common Grounds—Whittle Woods Girl (Emarati (USA)) **Mr C. C. Buckley**

96 MR DAVID BURCHELL, Ebbw Vale

Postal: **Drysiog Farm, Briery Hill, Ebbw Vale, Gwent, NP3 6BU.**
Phone: **EBBW VALE (01495) 302551 MOBILE (0831) 601214 FAX (01495) 352464**

1 **BENUAD,** 12, ch g Le Moss—Hogan's Cherry **Mr J. R. W. Hole**
2 **CASTLE SECRET,** 12, b g Castle Keep—Baffle **Mrs Ruth Burchell**
3 **DESERT POWER,** 9, b g Green Desert (USA)—Rivers Maid **Mrs Lynda M. Williams**
4 **FLAHIVE'S FIRST,** 4, ch g Interrex (CAN)—Striking Image (IRE) **Miss N. A. Showers**
5 **MUNTAFI,** 7, b g Unfuwain (USA)—Princess Sucree (USA) **Mr Simon T. Lewis**
6 **PATRICK,** 4, b g Backchat (USA)—Girton Degree **Mr T. R. Pearson**
7 **SOLDIER COVE (USA),** 8, ch g Manila (USA)—Secret Form **Mrs Ruth Burchell**
8 **SUN FAIRY,** 4, ch f Hatim (USA)—Petite Melusine (IRE) **Mr T. G. Brooks**
9 **WADADA,** 7, b br g Adbass (USA)—No Rejection **Mrs Ruth Burchell**
10 **WESLEY'S LAD (IRE),** 4, b br g Classic Secret (USA)—Galouga (FR) **Mr Brian Williams**
11 **WHEN IT RAINS,** 5, br m Gildoran—Flo-Jo (DEN) **Mr T. G. Brooks**

THREE-YEAR-OLDS

12 **PATRICKS SISTER,** ch f Backchat (USA)—Girton Degree **Mr T. R. Pearson**

Other Owners: Bedlinog Racing Club, Caerphilly Building Supplies Ltd, Mr Gerald Demery, Mr G. J. Green, Mrs S. Green, Mr Vivian Guy, Mrs C. G. Heath, Mr Lyn Phillips, Mr Terry Price, Reach Recruitment Limited, Mrs Jane Richards, Mr D. C. Roberts, Mrs Elizabeth J. Stockton, Mr J. L. Thomas, Mr Rhys Thomas Williams, Mrs Sandra Worthington.

Jockey (NH): D J Burchell (10-0).

Conditional: John Prior (10-0).

Amateurs: Mr S Blackwell (10-0), Mr G Richards (9-0).

Lady Rider: Miss Emily Jones (10-0).

97 MR K. R. BURKE, Wantage

Postal: **Ginge Stables, Ginge, Wantage, Oxfordshire, OX12 8QS.**
Phone: **OFFICE (01235) 821455 FAX (01235) 861710**

1 **ALWAYS ALIGHT,** 4, ch g Never So Bold—Fire Sprite **Mr M. Nelmes-Crocker**
2 **BEAU BRUMMIE BOY,** 4, ch g Fearless Action (USA)—Last Shower **Mr J. Williams**
3 **BELLA'S LEGACY,** 5, b m Thowra (FR)—Miss Lawsuit **Vintage Services Limited**
4 **CHALUZ,** 4, b g Night Shift (USA)—Laluche (USA) **Mr Nigel Shields**
5 **CHARLIE BANKER (IRE),** 6, b g Supreme Leader—Hack Along **D.R.A.C. Partnership**
6 **DANCING LAWYER,** 7, b g Thowra (FR)—Miss Lawsuit **Vintage Services Limited**
7 **DARING DESTINY,** 7, b m Daring March—Raunchy Rita **Daring Destiny Partnership**
8 **DIAMOND HALL,** 5, b g Lapierre—Willitwin **Mr R. D. Tudor**
9 **FALLS O'MONESS (IRE),** 4, b f River Falls—Sevens Are Wild **Piquet Opera House Partnership**
10 **FOUR OF SPADES,** 7, ch g Faustus (USA)—Fall To Pieces (USA) **Mrs Anna L. Sanders**

MR K. R. BURKE—continued

11 **JUST LOUI,** 4, gr g Lugana Beach—Absaloui **Mr Nigel Shields**
12 **KIKA,** 5, gr m Niniski (USA)—Goeswell **Mr I. Goldsmith**
13 **LE MEILLE (IRE),** 9, ch g Le Bavard (FR)—Glens Princess **Mrs Elaine M. Burke**
14 **MISKIN HEIGHTS (IRE),** 4, ch f Sharp Victor (USA)—Nurse Jo (USA) **Brooknight Guarding Ltd**
15 **NIGHT CITY,** 7, b g Kris—Night Secret **Mr Nigel Shields**
16 **NOT TO PANIC (IRE),** 8, ch m Torus—Quantas **Mr Barry Hawkins**
17 **PHILISTAR,** 5, ch h Bairn (USA)—Philgwyn **Mr Nigel Shields**
18 **SCATHEBURY,** 5, b g Aragon—Lady Bequick **Mr Nigel Shields**
19 **SLIP JIG (IRE),** 5, b g Marju (IRE)—Taking Steps **Mr Nigel Shields**
20 **SPECIALIZE,** 6, b g Faustus (USA)—Scholastika (GER) **Mrs Diane Smith**
21 **STOCK HILL DANCER,** 4, ch f Interrex (CAN)—Stocktina **Mr W. Sweeting**
22 **SUITE FACTORS,** 4, b g Timeless Times (USA)—Uptown Girl **Mr Nigel Shields**
23 **TARXIEN,** 4, b g Kendor (FR)—Tanz (IRE) **Mr David Whyte**
24 **THE INSTITUTE BOY,** 8, b g Fairy King (USA)—To Oneiro **Mrs J. Addleshaw**
25 **THE WYANDOTTE INN,** 4, ch g Ballacashtal (CAN)—Carolynchristensen **Mrs A. L. Sanders**
26 **WHITE PLAINS (IRE),** 5, b g Nordico (USA)—Flying Diva **Mr Nigel Shields**
27 **ZAHID (USA),** 7, ch g Storm Cat (USA)—Time An' Care (USA) **Mr Keith W. R. Booth**

THREE-YEAR-OLDS

28 **CADMAX (IRE),** b g Second Set (IRE)—Stella Ann **Mrs Elaine M. Burke**
29 **COOLIN RIVER (IRE),** b g River Falls—The Coolin **Kate Booth and Toby Wand**
30 **COUNSEL,** ch g Most Welcome—My Polished Corner **Miss N. Thesiger**
31 **IMPELLING (IRE),** ch g Imp Society (USA)—Real Stunner **Mrs Elaine M. Burke**
32 **LAURENTIAN,** b f Shareef Dancer (USA)—Kiomi **Mr I. Goldsmith**
33 **LITTLE IMP (IRE),** b f Imp Society (USA)—Poka Poka (FR) **Mrs Elaine M. Burke**
34 **PORCELLINO (IRE),** b g Last Tycoon—Supportive (IRE) **Mrs Elaine M. Burke**
35 **ROSEWOOD LADY (IRE),** b f Maledetto (IRE)—Thrill Seeker (IRE) **Mr Maurice Charge**
36 **SLIM PRIOR,** gr g Norton Challenger—Hopeful Katie **Mr Denis McCarthy**
37 **THEATRE OF DREAMS,** b f Tragic Role (USA)—Impala Lass **Mr N. Shields**
38 **ZIZI (IRE),** b f Imp Society (USA)—Timinala **Mr N. Shields**

Other Owners: Mr David S. Adams, Mr R. W. Allen, Astaire & Partners (Holdings) Ltd, Aston House Stud, Mr R. B. Croft, Mr M. Deren, Mr M. Dinneen, Mr Michael Doocey, Mrs Susan Fletcher, Mr David M. Foster, Mr L. Fust, Mr David Garner, Mr Allen Jackson, Mr W. J. P. Jackson, Mr K. L. Larnach, Mr P. A. Matthews, Mr Robert D. Merrigan, Mr N. J. Mitchell, Mr Christopher Neal, Mr H. O'Neill, Mr Ian Parkes, Mr K. Powell, Mr Stuart Prior, Mr David G. Robinson, Mr Robert K. Russell, Mr Raymond Singer, Mr P. Sweeting, Mr R. J. Tompkins, Mr Brendan J. Toner, Vintage Services Limited, Mr Toby Wand, Mr Jonathan Weal, Mrs B. B. Whitehorn, Mr F. H. Williams, Mr G. Wiltshire, Winton Bloodstock Ltd.

Jockeys (Flat): R Hughes, J Quinn (w.a.).

Jockeys (NH): R Dunwoody (w.a.), A Larnach.

Apprentices: Emily Joyce, Richard Painter, Paul Wright.

Conditional: Mark Brown, Richard Painter.

98 MR GERARD BUTLER, Faringdon

Postal: **Fraxinus Operations S.A., Upper Fram, Woolstone, Faringdon, Oxon, SN7 7QL.**
Phone: **(01367) 820650 FAX (01367) 820760**

1 **BEAUCHAMP KING,** 5, gr h Nishapour (FR)—Afariya (FR) **Mr E. Penser**
2 **BEAUCHAMP LION,** 4, ch g Be My Chief (USA)—Beauchamp Cactus **Mr E. Penser**

MR GERARD BUTLER—continued

THREE-YEAR-OLDS

3 **BEAUCHAMP MAGIC,** b g Northern Park (USA)—Beauchamp Buzz **Mr E. Penser**

TWO-YEAR-OLDS

4 **BEAUCHAMP NOBLE,** b c 9/2 Northern Park (USA)—Beauchamp Cactus (Niniski (USA)) **Mr E. Penser**
5 **BEAUCHAMP NYX,** b f 29/2 Northern Park (USA)—Beauchamp Image (Midyan (USA)) **Mr E. Penser**
6 **CAPTAIN CHRIS,** ch c 21/2 Magic Ring (IRE)—Alpine Pass (Head For Heights) **Mr M. Berger**
7 **COMPTON ACE,** ch c 27/3 Pharly (FR)—Mountain Lodge (Blakeney) **Mr E. Penser**
8 **COMPTON ADMIRAL,** b c 11/1 Suave Dancer (USA)—Sumoto (Mtoto) **Mr E. Penser**
9 **COMPTON AJAX (IRE),** gr c 12/5 Paris House—Fear Naught (Connaught) **Mr E. Penser**
10 **COMPTON AKKA (IRE),** b f 2/5 Balla Cove—Adjanada (Nishapour (FR)) **Mr E. Penser**
11 **COMPTON AMBER,** b f 28/2 Puissance—Amber Mill (Doulab (USA)) **Mr E. Penser**
12 **COMPTON AMICA (IRE),** gr f 11/3 High Estate—Nephrite (Godswalk (USA)) **Mr E. Penser**
13 **COMPTON ANGEL (IRE),** b f 11/3 Fairy King (USA)—Embla (Dominion) **Mr E. Penser**
14 **COMPTON ARROW (IRE),** b c 15/3 Petardia—Impressive Lady (Mr Fluorocarbon) **Mr E. Penser**
15 **COMPTON ASTORIA (USA),** ch f 16/5 Lion Cavern (USA)—Perfolia (USA) (Nodouble (USA)) **Mr E. Penser**
16 **COMPTON AVIATOR,** ch c 17/3 First Trump—Rifada (Ela-Mana-Mou) **Mr E. Penser**
17 Ch f 16/3 Up and At 'Em—Cutlers Corner (Sharpen Up) **Mr E. Penser**
18 **MINERS QUEST,** b c 30/4 Miner's Lamp—Interrogate (In Fijar (USA)) **Mr John Jones**

99 MR P. BUTLER, Lewes

Postal: **Homewood Gate Racing Stables, Novington Lane, East Chiltington, Lewes, East Sussex, BN7 3AU.**

Phone: **(01273) 890124/(01273) 477254 MOBILE (0973) 873846 FAX (01273) 890124**

1 **BAROSSA VALLEY (IRE),** 7, b g Alzao (USA)—Night of Wind **Mr Christopher W. Wilson**
2 **CHURCHTOWN PORT (IRE),** 8, gr g Peacock (FR)—Portane Miss **Mr John Plackett**
3 **FAIR SOCIETY (IRE),** 7, ch m Moscow Society (USA)—Fair Freda **Mr Tom Perkins**
4 **FRIAR'S OAK,** 6, b g Absalom—Sunset Ray **Mr Ian Moody**
5 **NOT OUT LAD,** 4, b c Governor General—Sorcha (IRE) **Mr Christopher W. Wilson**
6 **PRECIOUS WONDER,** 9, b g Precocious—B M Wonder **Mr D. J. Butler**
7 **SPENCER'S REVENGE,** 9, ch g Bay Express—Armour of Light **Mrs Janet Coleman**

THREE-YEAR-OLDS

8 **ROONEY PRINCE,** b c Prince Rooney (IRE)—Princess Jessica **Mr P. Butler**
9 **SOUTHDOWN CYRANO (IRE),** b c Cyrano de Bergerac—Value Voucher (IRE) **Mrs Kay Baldry**

Other Owners: Lady Blaker, Mrs J. M. Bonard, Mr Alastair Elliott, Mr Mel Halstead, Mr P. Houlihan, Mr V. James, Mr C. McDonald.

Amateur: Mr J Lawrence.

Lady Rider: Mrs E L Butler (8-7).

100 MR N. BYCROFT, Brandsby

Postal: **Cotman Rise, Brandsby, York, YO6 4RN.**
Phone: **(01347) 888641**

1 **ALISADARA,** 4, b f Nomination—Nishara **Mr G. J. Allison**
2 **BALLYKISSANGEL,** 5, ro g Hadeer—April Wind **Mr G. J. Allison**
3 **BERNIE'S STAR (IRE),** 4, b br g Arcane (USA)—Abaca (USA) **Mr Bernard F. Rayner**
4 **BLUE LUGANA,** 6, b g Lugana Beach—Two Friendly **Mr J. A. Swinburne**

MR N. BYCROFT—continued

5 **CAROL AGAIN,** 6, b m Kind of Hush—Lady Carol **Mr J. G. Lumsden**
6 **CHILL WIND,** 9, gr g Siberian Express (USA)—Springwell **Mr E. H. Daley**
7 **CRAIGIE BOY,** 8, b g Crofthall—Lady Carol **Mr Bernard F. Rayner**
8 **GIFTBOX (USA),** 6, b h Halo (USA)—Arewehavingfunyet (USA) **Mr G. J. Allison**
9 **GLENSTONE BOY,** 4, b g Nomination—Magic Tower **Mr R. Midgley**
10 **PATHAZE,** 5, b m Totem (USA)—Stilvella **Mr Neville L. Warriner**
11 **RICH GLOW,** 7, b g Rich Charlie—Mayglow **Mr M. J. Bateson**
12 **SWANDALE FLYER,** 6, ch g Weldnaas (USA)—Misfire **Mr Andrew Carruthers**

THREE-YEAR-OLDS

13 **ELSA DAWN,** ch f Weldnaas (USA)—Agnes Jane **Mrs Susan Diver**
14 **LICKETYSPLIT,** b f Rock City—Constant Companion **Mrs Susan Diver**
15 **SHOTLEY MARIE (IRE),** b f Scenic—Hana Marie **Mr J. A. Swinburne**

TWO-YEAR-OLDS

16 **BRAVE CHARLIE,** b c 27/2 Rudimentary (USA)—Besito (Wassl) **Mr E. D. Atkinson**
17 **E B PEARL,** ch f 27/4 Timeless Times (USA)—Petite Elite (Anfield) **Mr J. F. Busink**
18 Ch g 29/4 Presidium—Stilvella (Camden Town) **Mr E. Ruddock**

Other Owners: Mr Barrie Abbott, Mr T. Barnes, Mr P. F. Brennan, Mr N. Bycroft, Mrs N. Bycroft, Mr Geoffrey Gallagher, Mr Anthony M. Gant, Mr J. T. Greaves, Mr D. R. Moore, Mr W. G. Moore, Mr D. Pickles, Mr T. Umpleby, Mr D. Wright.

Jockeys (Flat): K Darley (w.a.), J Quinn.

Jockey (NH): R Supple.

Amateur: Mr W Fearon.

101 MR T. H. CALDWELL, Warrington

Postal: **Burley Heyes Cottage, Arley Road, Appleton, Warrington, WA4 4RR.**
Phone: **ARLEY (01565) 777275 FAX (01565) 777275**

1 **ASHGORE,** 8, b g Efisio—Fair Atlanta **Mr Harvey Ashworth**
2 **BEND WAVY (IRE),** 6, ch g Kefaah (USA)—Prosodie (FR) **Mr A. J. McDonald**
3 **BLAZE OF MAJESTY (USA),** 10, b g Majestic Light (USA)—Uncommitted (USA) **Mr T. H. Caldwell**
4 **CHOICE CUT (IRE),** 5, b g Tirol—Lancette **Mr Harvey Ashworth**
5 **DOLIKOS,** 11, b g Camden Town—Wolveriana **Mrs E. A. Smith**
6 **FANION DE NOURRY (FR),** 5, ch g Bad Conduct (USA)—Ottomans (FR) **Mr A. J. McDonald**
7 **HIGH HANDED (IRE),** 7, ch g Roselier (FR)—Slaney Pride **Mr N. T. Gallagher**
8 **KINGS CAY (IRE),** 7, b g Taufan (USA)—Provocation **Mr R. S. G. Jones**
9 **SILK WORD,** 9, gr g Hasty Word—Ramas Silk **Mr T. H. Caldwell**
10 **STYLISH LORD (IRE),** 7, b g Mister Lord (USA)—Marble Cloud **Tony Shannon and George Wilson**

THREE-YEAR-OLDS

11 Gr c High Kicker (USA)—Desert Mist **Mr R. S. G. Jones**
12 **FASHION VICTIM,** b c High Estate—Kirkby Belle **Mr R. S. G. Jones**

TWO-YEAR-OLDS

13 B f 30/3 Casteddu—Amoureuse (IRE) (Petorius) **Mr R. S. G. Jones**
14 Ch f 1/3 Case Law—Nordic Living (IRE) (Nordico (USA)) **Mr R. S. G. Jones**
15 Gr g 6/5 Tina's Pet—Phar Lapa (Grundy) **Mr R. S. G. Jones**
16 B f 14/4 Mukaddamah (USA)—Takhiyra (Vayrann) **Mr R. S. G. Jones**

Other Owners: Mr T. F. Harrington.
Lady Rider: Pat Wharfe (9-7).

102 MR N. A. CALLAGHAN, Newmarket

Postal: **22 Hamilton Road, Newmarket, Suffolk, CB8 0NY.**
Phone: **HOME (01638) 664040 STABLES (01638) 663441 FAX (01638) 668446**

1 **ASSAILABLE,** 4, b c Salse (USA)—Unsuitable **Mr J. P. McManus**
2 **DANETIME (IRE),** 4, b c Danehill (USA)—Allegheny River (USA) **Mr M. Tabor & Mrs John Magnier**
3 **DARCY,** 4, ch c Miswaki (USA)—Princess Accord (USA) **Roldvale Ltd**
4 **DESERT MOUNTAIN (IRE),** 5, b g Alzao (USA)—Curie Point (USA) **Easy Monk Partnership**
5 **GENERAL SIR PETER (IRE),** 6, br g Last Tycoon—Nashya **Mrs Anna L. Sanders**
6 **MISS BERTAINE (IRE),** 9, ch m Denel (FR)—Deepwater Woman **Mr T. Dartnell**
7 **OAKEN WOOD (IRE),** 4, ch g Lycius (USA)—Little Red Rose **Mr Dean Graham Bostock**
8 **PLAISIR D'AMOUR (IRE),** 4, b f Danehill (USA)—Mira Adonde (USA) **Mr M. Tabor & Mrs John Magnier**
9 **POKER SCHOOL (IRE),** 4, b g Night Shift (USA)—Mosaique Bleue **Mr D. Westley**
10 **RIVERDANCE,** 4, b c Rudimentary (USA)—Best Girl Friend **Gallagher Equine Ltd**
11 **SUBTLE INFLUENCE (IRE),** 4, b c Sadler's Wells (USA)—Campestral (USA) **Mr M. Tabor**
12 **TREMPLIN (USA),** 6, gr g Trempolino (USA)—Stresa **Mr M. Tabor**

THREE-YEAR-OLDS

13 **ALPINE LADY (IRE),** b f Tirol—Nonnita **Mr J. Biggane**
14 **BASIC STYLE,** b g Alhijaz—Turbo Rose **Mr Martin Moore**
15 **CERTAIN DANGER (IRE),** br f Warning—Please Believe Me **Paul & Jenny Green**
16 **CHIEFTAIN (IRE),** b c Indian Ridge—Legit (IRE) **Mr M. Tabor & Mrs John Magnier**
17 **DELAYED REACTION,** b g Theatrical Charmer—Pingin **Mr R. E. Sangster**
18 **FALCON CREST,** ch c Polar Falcon (USA)—Glowing With Pride **Mr M. Tabor & Mrs John Magnier**
19 **IRON MOUNTAIN (IRE),** b g Scenic—Merlannah (IRE) **Gallagher Equine Ltd**
20 **LOOKINGFORLOVE DEL (IRE),** ch f Be My Guest (USA)—Debenham **Mr N. A. Callaghan**
21 **MATATA (IRE),** b f In The Wings—Ville Sainte (FR) **Mr Yahya Nasib**
22 **MISS MONEY SPIDER (IRE),** br f Statoblest—Dream of Jenny **Mr Paul Green**
23 **MRS MIDDLE,** b f Puissance—Ibadiyya **Mr Michael Hill**
24 **PAULINE SHRIMPTON (IRE),** b f Tirol—Inner Pearl **Mr Michael Hill**
25 **ROCK SOUNDS,** br g Rock City—Shernborne **Mrs Shirley Anne Miller**
26 **TORNADO PRINCE (IRE),** ch c Caerleon (USA)—Welsh Flame **Mr M. Tabor & Mrs John Magnier**

TWO-YEAR-OLDS

27 **BLACK AMBER (IRE),** b c 26/5 College Chapel—Flying Diva (Chief Singer) **Mrs John Magnier & Mr M. Tabor**
28 **CANYOUHEARME,** b br f 3/5 Sabrehill (USA)—Fiveofive (IRE) (Fairy King (USA)) **Mrs T. A. Foreman**
29 **CASTARA BEACH (IRE),** b f 11/3 Danehill (USA)—Sea Harrier (Grundy) **Mrs John Magnier & Mr M. Tabor**
30 **COMPATRIOT (IRE),** b c 10/3 Bigstone (IRE)—Campestral (USA) (Alleged (USA)) **Mr M. Tabor**
31 **MINNESOTA,** b c 29/3 Danehill (USA)—Santi Sana (Formidable (USA)) **Mrs John Magnier & Mr M. Tabor**

Other Owners: Mr J. R. Bostock, Mr G. A. Dove, Mr John Dunsdon, Mr Don Ilines, Midcourts, Mrs Doreen Tabor, Mr Brian A. Viner.

103 MR P. CALVER, Ripon

Postal: **Whitcliffe Grange Farm, Ripon, North Yorkshire, HG4 3AS.**
Phone: **RIPON (01765) 600313 FAX (01765) 603431**

1 **ARISAIG (IRE),** 4, ch g Ela-Mana-Mou—Glasson Lady (GER) **Mrs Janis MacPherson**
2 **FORGIE (IRE),** 5, b g Don't Forget Me—Damia **Mrs Janis MacPherson**
3 **GILLING DANCER (IRE),** 5, b g Dancing Dissident (USA)—Rahwah **Mrs C. Calver**
4 **INDONESIAN (IRE),** 6, b br g Alzao (USA)—Miss Garuda **Mrs C. Calver**
5 **PERRYSTON VIEW,** 6, b h Primo Dominie—Eastern Ember **Mrs Janis MacPherson**
6 **RICCARTON,** 5, b g Nomination—Legendary Dancer **Mr Kenneth MacPherson**
7 **SOMERTON BOY (IRE),** 8, b h Thatching—Bonnie Bess **Mrs Janis MacPherson**
8 **WAFIR (IRE),** 6, b h Scenic—Taniokey **Mr Kenneth MacPherson**

THREE-YEAR-OLDS

9 **MANTLES PRIDE,** br c Petong—State Romance **Mrs Janis Macpherson**
10 B g Merdon Melody—Silvery Moon **Mr W. B. Imison**

MR P. CALVER—continued

TWO-YEAR-OLDS

11 B f 16/3 Safawan—Aimee Jane (USA) (Our Native (USA)) **Mr W. B. Imison**
12 Ch f 31/3 Chilibang—Broken Silence (Busted) **Mr W. B. Imison**
13 B g 9/3 Ballad Rock—Havana Moon (Ela-Mana-Mou) **Mr W. B. Imison**
14 Ch f 29/3 Never So Bold—Shamasiya (FR) (Vayrann) **Mr D. B. Stanley**
15 Ch f 29/2 Clantime—She's A Breeze (Crofthall) **Mr W. B. Imison**
16 B c 22/3 Presidium—Sister Hannah (Monseigneur (USA)) **Mr W. B. Imison**
17 **STUDLEY PARK,** b f 4/4 Northern Park (USA)—B A Poundstretcher (Laser Light) **The Ripon Ringers**
18 B c 9/4 Be My Guest (USA)—Whist Awhile (Caerleon (USA)) **Mrs Janis MacPherson**

Other Owners: Mr F. Grass, Mr C. M. Sharpe.

104 MISS J. A. CAMACHO, Malton

Postal: **Star Cottage, Welham Road, Norton, Malton, North Yorkshire, YO17 9DU.**
Phone: **(01653) 694901 FAX (01653) 694901 MOBILE (0468) 964895/(0468) 573336**

1 **ALABANG,** 7, ch g Valiyar—Seleter **Elite Racing Club**
2 **AVRO ANSON,** 10, b g Ardross—Tremellick **Axom**
3 **AVRO AVIAN,** 4, b f Ardross—Tremellick **Mr B. P. Skirton**
4 **BACCHUS,** 4, b g Prince Sabo—Bonica **Ashley Carr Racing**
5 **HI NOD,** 8, b h Valiyar—Vikris **Mr Brian Nordan**
6 **LAPU-LAPU,** 5, b m Prince Sabo—Seleter **Mr Dunstan French**
7 **MAKATI,** 4, b g Efisio—Seleter **Exors of the late Mr H. Roberts**
8 **MASTER NOVA,** 8, b g Ra Nova—Maid of The Manor **Matthews Breeding and Racing**
9 **QUEZON CITY,** 4, ch c Keen—Calachuchi **Middleham Park Racing XI**
10 **SARASI,** 6, ch g Midyan (USA)—Early Call **Axom**
11 **SHARLEY COP,** 6, ch m Lord Bud—Buckby Folly **Mrs E. C. York**
12 **TESSAJOE,** 6, ch g Clantime—Busted Love **Riley Partnership**
13 **THE BUD CLUB (IRE),** 10, b g Le Moss—Tipperary Star **Axom**

THREE-YEAR-OLDS

14 **COURTLEDGE,** b g Unfuwain (USA)—Tremellick **Mr B. P. Skirton**
15 **KINGDOM QUEEN (IRE),** b f Night Shift (USA)—Yashina (FR) **G. B. Turnbull Ltd**
16 **KINGDOM RUBY (IRE),** ch f Bluebird (USA)—Tapestry **G. B. Turnbull Ltd**
17 **LAKE TAAL,** ch f Prince Sabo—Calachuchi **Mr M. Gleason**
18 **MIGHTY PERFORMER,** b g Puissance—Hot Performer **Mr B. W. Harland**
19 **STATELY FAVOUR,** ch f Statoblest—Dixie Favor (USA) **Elite Racing Club**

TWO-YEAR-OLDS

20 Br c 2/6 Forzando—Calachuchi (Martinmas) **Mrs S. Camacho**
21 **CORMAN ROSE,** br f 21/2 Be My Chief (USA)—Corman-Style (Ahonoora) **Elite Racing Club**
22 **DIXIE JAZZ,** br f 25/2 Mtoto—Dixie Favor (USA) (Dixieland Band (USA)) **Elite Racing Club**
23 **KINGDOM ROYALE (IRE),** b f 29/3 Royal Academy (USA)—
Foolish Lady (USA) (Foolish Pleasure (USA)) **G. B. Turnbull Ltd**
24 **MAGIC PERFORMER,** b c 12/5 Tragic Role (USA)—Hot Performer (Hotfoot) **Mr B. W. Harland**
25 Ch f 11/3 Deploy—Rainbow Trout (Comedy Star (USA)) **Mr Edmund Smith**
26 B f 1/5 Most Welcome—Salala (Connaught) **Mrs S. Camacho**
27 Ch f 3/5 Sabrehill (USA)—Seleter (Hotfoot) **Mrs S. Camacho**
28 Br c 14/4 Unblest—Sin Sceal Eile (IRE) (Pitskelly) **Mr M. Gleason**
29 **SNUGFIT ROSIE (GER),** ch f 10/3 Kris—Sorceress (FR) (Fabulous Dancer (USA)) **Mr A. G. Greenwood**

Other Owners: Mr Bernard Bloom, Mrs Joan Fay, Mrs J. A. Harland, Mr M. J. Harland, Mr Tony Hill, Miss M. Noden, Mr T. S. Palin, Mr David Riley, Mr Francis Riley, Mr W. Riley, Mr M. K. Slinger, Mr A. N. Stuart.

Jockey (Flat): L Charnock (7-10).

Jockey (NH): P Niven.

105 MR B. R. CAMBIDGE, Bishopswood

Postal: **Park Oak Farm, Tong Road, Bishopswood, Brewood, Stafford, ST19 9AP.**
Phone: **WESTON-UNDER-LIZARD (01952 850) 249**

1 **BEAU QUEST,** 11, b g Rainbow Quest (USA)—Elegant Tern (USA) **Mr B. R. Cambidge**
2 **DIAMOND MARKET,** 6, gr g Absalom—The Victor Girls **Mr G. A. Farndon**
3 **FOXY LASS,** 9, ch m Celtic Cone—Hunters Glen **Mr B. R. Cambidge**
4 **GRACE CARD,** 12, b g Ela-Mana-Mou—Val de Grace (FR) **Mr G. A. Farndon**
5 **KENILWORTH DANCER,** 5, br g Shareef Dancer (USA)—Reltop **Mr G. A. Farndon**
6 **RAMBO TANGO,** 4, b g Rambo Dancer (CAN)—Jumra **Mr A. S. Blackham**
7 **RIMOUSKI,** 10, b h Sure Blade (USA)—Rimosa's Pet **Mr B. R. Cambidge**
8 **SLMAAT,** 7, ch m Sharpo—Wasslaweyeh (USA) **Mr G. A. Farndon**
9 **STEEL CHIMES (IRE),** 9, ch g Burslem—Gaychimes **Mr B. R. Cambidge**

THREE-YEAR-OLDS

10 **SAYBOO,** gr f Thethingaboutitis (USA)—Wayzgoose (USA) **Mr B. R. Cambidge**

Other Owners: Mr D. Craddock, Mrs H. Noonan, Mr R. Pitchford.

Amateur: Mr J R Cambidge (10-0).

106 MR I. CAMPBELL, Newmarket

Postal: **32 Elizabeth Avenue, Newmarket, Suffolk, CB8 0DJ.**
Phone: **NEWMARKET (01638) 660605 MOBILE (0976) 718193**

1 **PLENTY OF SUNSHINE,** 5, ch m Pharly (FR)—Zipperti Do **Mr Maurice Kirby**
2 **PRINCE JORDAN,** 4, ch g Keen—Diami **Mr Maurice Kirby**
3 **REGGAE BEAT,** 13, b g Be My Native (USA)—Invery Lady **Mr Ian Campbell**

THREE-YEAR-OLDS

4 **EMPEROR'S GOLD,** gr g Petong—Tarnside Rosal **Emperor's Gold Partnership**

TWO-YEAR-OLDS

5 Ch c 12/3 Keen—Broken Vow (IRE) (Local Suitor (USA)) **Mr Maurice Kirby**
6 B f 23/2 Saddlers' Hall (IRE)—Fairy Kingdom (Prince Sabo) **Mr Maurice Kirby**
7 Ch c 15/2 Mystiko (USA)—Zipperti Do (Precocious) **Mr Maurice Kirby**

Other Owners: Mr S. Anrude, Mr K. R. Brown, Mr E. Campbell, Mr R. R. Kettles, Mr J. McCaul, Mr J. McManamon, Mr D. Nice.

Jockey (Flat): A Mackay (7-10, w.a.).

107 MR A. M. CAMPION, Tunworth

Postal: **Tunworth Down Stables, Tunworth, Nr Basingstoke, Hampshire, RG25 2LE.**
Phone: **(01256) 463376 FAX (01256) 332968**

1 **EQUINOX,** 7, b g Chauve Souris—Contessa (HUN) **Mrs P. Stroud**
2 **GEMMA'S WAGER (IRE),** 8, b m Phardante (FR)—Lady's Wager **Mr Barry & Dame Sheila Noakes**
3 **GREGORIO,** 8, b g Strong Gale—Cala Conta **The Wellington Partnership**
4 **LADY KAY-LEE,** 8, b m Cruise Missile—Arctic Lee **Mr C. A. Harnett**
5 **LUDO'S ORCHESTRA (IRE),** 7, ch g Orchestra—Madam Milan **Mr Barry & Dame Sheila Noakes**
6 **MANAOLANA,** 10, b m Castle Keep—Ladysave **Mrs Georgina Worsley**
7 **MOON DEVIL (IRE),** 8, br g Strong Gale—Moynalvey Lass **Sir Colin Southgate**

MR A. M. CAMPION—continued

8 **MY WARRIOR,** 10, b g Roman Warrior—My Darling **Mrs Georgina Worsley**
9 **OSCILIGHTS GIFT,** 6, b m Chauve Souris—Oscilight **Mrs P. Stroud**
10 **RAINCHECK,** 7, b g Mtoto—Lashing (USA) **Mrs Georgina Worsley**
11 **SANGRIA,** 4, b f Aragon—Singora **South West Bloodstock Ltd**
12 **TYPHOON (IRE),** 8, br g Strong Gale—Bally Decent **The Cissbury Ring**
13 **WICKED THOUGHTS,** 8, b g Domitor (USA)—Marigold **Mr M. J. Coates**

Other Owners: Mrs L. Alexander, Mrs P. M. Botting, Mr A. M. Campion, Mrs J. Case, Mrs J. Debenham, Mr R. Ewing, Mr P. Gower, Lady Rosemary Hardy, Mrs Michael Hill, Mrs Deenagh Howard-Brown, Mrs J. Howell, Lady Kleinwort, Mr P. Lees, Mr M. Roberts, Mr D. Ryde, Mr J. Sclater, Mr David & Dr Christine Smail, Mrs S. Sorby.

Jockeys (NH): W McFarland (w.a.), B Powell (w.a.), Mark Richards (w.a.).

108 MR HENRY D. N CANDY, Wantage

Postal: **Kingston Warren, Wantage, Oxfordshire, OX12 9QF.**
Phone: **FARINGDON (01367) 820276/514 FAX (01367) 820500 MOBILE (0836) 211264**

1 **BEAUCHAMP KNIGHT,** 5, ch g Chilibang—Beauchamp Cactus **Mr Henry Candy**
2 **BESTEMOR,** 4, b f Selkirk (USA)—Lillemor **Mr M. Berger**
3 **CRYSTAL HEARTED,** 4, b c Broken Hearted—Crystal Fountain **Mrs C. M. Poland**
4 **MARY CULI,** 4, gr f Liboi (USA)—Copper Trader **Mrs David Blackburn**
5 **SEA BUCK,** 12, b g Simply Great (FR)—Heatherside **Mr Henry Candy**
6 **SPEED ON,** 5, b g Sharpo—Pretty Poppy **Mr P. A. Deal**
7 **TOP BANANA,** 7, ch g Pharly (FR)—Oxslip **Mr & Mrs Henry Candy**
8 **WELL DRAWN,** 5, b g Dowsing (USA)—Classic Design **Mrs David Blackburn**
9 **WILLY WILLY,** 5, ch g Master Willie—Monsoon **Mrs G. M. Tricks**
10 **WITH A WILL,** 4, b g Rambo Dancer (CAN)—Henceforth **Mr & Mrs Henry Candy**

THREE-YEAR-OLDS

11 **BATTLE WARNING,** b g Warning—Royal Ballet (IRE) **Mrs C. M. Poland**
12 **FABRICE,** b g Pursuit of Love—Parfum d'Automne (FR) **Girsonfield Ltd**
13 **GENEROUS TERMS,** ch c Generous (IRE)—Time Charter **H.R.H. Prince Fahd Salman**
14 **GORSE,** b c Sharpo—Pervenche **Girsonfield Ltd**
15 **GRACE BROWNING,** b f Forzando—Queen Angel **Mrs Robert Langton**
16 **IN CHARGE,** ch f Be My Chief (USA)—Great Exception **Mr T. A. F. Frost**
17 **INCHTINA,** b f Inchinor—Nikitina **Mr Peter J. Stevenson**
18 **MOTHERS HELP,** b f Relief Pitcher—Laundry Maid **Mr C. J. R. Trotter**
19 **MR MUDDLE (IRE),** b g Mukaddamah (USA)—Festival of Magic (USA) **Mrs David Blackburn**
20 **RITUAL,** ch g Selkirk (USA)—Pure Formality **Exors of the late Commander G. G. Marten**
21 **SHARDELOW,** b f Belmez (USA)—Sliprail (USA) **Major M. G. Wyatt**
22 **SNOW AND ICE,** b f Chilibang—Nisha **Girsonfield Ltd**
23 **STARWORT,** b f Soviet Star (USA)—Collide **Major M. G. Wyatt**
24 **TIME LOSS,** ch c Kenmare (FR)—Not Before Time (IRE) **Mr R. Barnett**

TWO-YEAR-OLDS

25 **BORDERS,** b c 18/2 Selkirk (USA)—Pretty Poppy (Song) **Mrs J. E. L. Wright**
26 **CHALOUPE,** b f 22/1 College Chapel—Shallop (Salse (USA)) **M & S Lidsey**
27 **COLUMNA,** gr f 29/2 Deploy—Copper Trader (Faustus (USA)) **Mrs David Blackburn**
28 B c 19/3 Saumarez—Echoes (FR) (Niniski (USA)) **Mr P. A. Deal**
29 **FLAVIAN,** b f 16/3 Catrail (USA)—Fatah Flare (USA) (Alydar (USA)) **Major M. G. Wyatt**
30 **HIGH BIRD (IRE),** b f 10/2 Polar Falcon (USA)—Lemon Balm (High Top) **Mrs Robert Langton**
31 B f 26/5 Sir Harry Lewis (USA)—Jouvencelle (Rusticaro (FR)) **Mrs H. R. Mould**
32 **LADY FLORA,** b f 8/2 Alflora (IRE)—Lady Marguerrite (Blakeney) **Lord Roborough**
33 **LOVER'S LEAP,** b g 13/3 Pursuit of Love—Anna Karietta (Precocious) **Lord Cadogan**
34 **OVER THE TOP,** b c 24/3 Up And At 'Em—Latin Mass (Music Boy) **Mr S. Broke**
35 **PINK CRISTAL,** b f 15/2 Dilum (USA)—Crystal Fountain (Great Nephew) **Mr David B. Clark**

MR HENRY D. N CANDY—continued

36 **RING FENCE,** b f 11/4 Polar Falcon (USA)—Ring Cycle (Auction Ring (USA)) **Major M. G. Wyatt**
37 **ROLLER,** b c 9/3 Bluebird (USA)—Tight Spin (High Top) **H. R. H. Prince Fahd Salman**
38 B f 9/4 Barathea (IRE)—Scene Galante (FR) (Sicyos (USA)) **Mrs C. M. Poland**
39 **SECRET TREASURE,** b f 28/2 Dilum (USA)—Surprise Surprise (Robellino (USA)) **Mrs A. Dixon**
40 **SIGNET RING,** ch f 12/2 King's Signet (USA)—Geoffreys Bird (Master Willie) **Mr Henry Candy**
41 **STEPSTONE,** b f 19/4 Slip Anchor—Stedham (Jaazeiro (USA)) **Major M. G. Wyatt**
42 **TINA'S ROYALE,** b f 29/4 Prince Sabo—Aventina (Averof) **Wickfield Stud & Hartshill Stud**

Other Owners: Mr & Mrs N. Brookes, Mrs A. L. Deal, Mrs P. Hayward, Mr John Inverdale, Mr & Mrs D. Jenks, Sir Arthur Norman K.B.E. D.F.C., Mr P. Robinson, Mr & Mrs J. Steinman, Mrs C. Sweeting.

Apprentices: S Jackson (7-9), Barry Smith (7-7), N Wright (7-2).

Lady Rider: Mrs C Dunwoody (8-7).

109 MR D. N. CAREY, Raglan

Postal: **Berllanhelyg Cottage, Tregare, Raglan, Monmouthsire, NP5 2BZ.**
Phone: **(01291) 691181 MOBILE (0589) 248578**

1 **MR MONEYMAKER,** 11, b g Reesh—Miss Mint **Mr D. N. Carey**
2 **OYSTER DELIGHT (IRE),** 7, b m Miner's Lamp—Levitstown Lady **Mr D. N. Carey**

Jockey (NH): B Powell.

Amateur: Miss Emily Jones.

110 MR D. J. CARO, Ledbury

Postal: **Lilly Hall Farm, Little Marcle, Ledbury, Herefordshire, HR8 2LD.**
Phone: **Tel:(01531) 631559 (01531) 632892 Fax: (01531) 634049**

1 **CAPE COTTAGE,** 14, ch g Dubassoff (USA)—Cape Thriller **Mr D. J. Caro**
2 **DAWN INVADER (IRE),** 7, b g Fine Blade (USA)—Kova's Daughter **Mr D. J. Caro**
3 **FINE STALKER (IRE),** 10, ch g Stalker—Bellinor **Mr D. J. Caro**
4 **GENERAL KILLINEY (IRE),** 6, ch g General Ironside—Just Killiney **Mr D. J. Caro**
5 **GLACIAL RIVER (IRE),** 5, ch g Glacial Storm (USA)—Lucky Trout **Mr D. J. Caro**
6 **LIGHTENING STEEL,** 7, gr g Sulaafah (USA)—Wotusay **Mr D. J. Caro**
7 **LORD RAPIER,** 5, b g Broadsword (USA)—Doddycross **Mr D. J. Caro**
8 **MONSIEUR MOSSIMAN,** 5, b g Le Moss—Saxon Gift **Mr D. J. Caro**
9 **NATIVE ISLE (IRE),** 6, ch g Be My Native (USA)—Shuil Ard **Mr D. J. Caro**
10 **PUZZLEMAN,** 5, ch g Henbit (USA)—Floreamus **Mr D. J. Caro**

111 MR T. J. CARR, Saltburn-by-Sea

Postal: **Ridge House Stables, Ridge House Farm, Stanghow, Saltburn-by-Sea, Cleveland, TS12 3LD.**
Phone: **(01287) 660506**

1 **CARLINGFORD TYKE (IRE),** 6, b g Carlingford Castle—Athenian Primrose **Josttigo Racing**
2 **CASH BOX (IRE),** 10, ch g Carlingford Castle—Cash Discount **Dr T. A. Wadrop**
3 **DANCING BUD,** 5, ch g Lord Bud—Danny d'Albi **Mr G. Kennedy**
4 **EVEN CLOSE,** 8, b g K-Battery—Stubbs Daughter **Mr R. Dalton**

MR T. J. CARR—continued

5 GORMIRE, 5, ro m Superlative—Lady of The Lodge **Mr P. Barron**
6 4, Gr g Scallywag—Miss Anax **Mr R. Dalton**

Other Owners: Mr Peter Carr, Mr Tim Carr, Mrs V. Chilton, Mr G. Halsall, Mr John Newman (Doncaster), Mrs J. Savage, Mr S. M. Taylor, Mr H. L. Thompson.

Jockey (NH): N Smith.

Amateur: Mr C Mulhall.

112 MR A. W. CARROLL, Worcester

Postal: **Mill House, Kington, Fly Ford, Flavell, Worcestershire, WR7 4DG.**
Phone: **(01386) 793459 FAX (01386) 792303**

1 ALL OVER RED ROVER, 6, b g Newski (USA)—Earth Wood **Mr Gary J. Roberts**
2 AUTUMN BLUNDER, 6, ch g Brotherly (USA)—Thetford Chase **Mrs Olwen Hughes**
3 BURUNDI (IRE), 4, b g Danehill (USA)—Sofala **Mr J. D. Martin**
4 DANDIE IMP, 10, b g Impecunious—Another Dandie **Miss A. Clift**
5 INCH CHAMPION (IRE), 6, b g Down The Hatch—Little Enda **Mr Gordon W. Day**
6 INCH EMPEROR (IRE), 8, b g Torus—Pamrina **Mr T. V. Cullen**
7 KUMARI KING (IRE), 8, ch g Colwyn—Raj Kumari **Mr P. G. Killoughery**
8 MOOR HALL PRINCESS, 4, gr f Chilibang—Forgiving **Mr R. S. Brookhouse**
9 NORTHERN GREY, 6, gr g Puissance—Sharp Anne **Mr A. J. Thomas**
10 OUR SLIMBRIDGE, 10, b br g Top Ville—Bird Point (USA) **Mrs Helen Hogben**
11 PLAY THE TUNE, 5, b g Music Boy—Stepping Gaily **Mr R. S. Brookhouse**
12 PRESIDENTREE, 5, b g Presidium—Snow Tree **Mr R. S. Brookhouse**
13 QUEEN OF SHANNON (IRE), 10, b m Nordico (USA)—Raj Kumari **J. Wigmore Racing Partnership**
14 SHANNON LAD (IRE), 8, ch g Montelimar (USA)—Dusty Busty **The Killoughery Family**
15 TEE TEE TOO (IRE), 6, ch g Hatim (USA)—Scottish Welcome **Mr Stuart Bruce**

Other Owners: Mr A. N. Beale, Mr H. Burford, Mr A. Callow, Miss J. M. Connor, Mr Dennis Deacon, Mrs D. J. Dyson, Mr R. E. Gibbins, Mrs M. R. Jones, Mrs M. T. Killoughery, Mr Ian McLaughlin.

Jockey (Flat): R Studholme (8-0).

Jockeys (NH): W Marston (10-0), B Powell (10-0).

Apprentice: A Hall (7-7).

Amateur: L Brown (10-7).

Lady Rider: Miss C Dyson.

113 MR DECLAN CARROLL, Curragh

Postal: **Cutbush Stables, Brownstown, The Curragh, Co. Kildare, Ireland.**
Phone: **(045) 442004 MOBILE (086) 526487**

1 BANAWAR (USA), 4, b g Green Dancer (USA)—Banque Privee (USA)
2 6, B g Rashar (USA)—Buddie And Duke

MR DECLAN CARROLL—continued

3 **CORRIES HILL (IRE),** 9, ch g Dromod Hill—My Gold
4 **PUNTS TO EURO (IRE),** 5, b g Beau Sher—Chancery Vision
5 **SNAP OUT OF IT (IRE),** 6, b m Strong Gale—Millerstown

THREE-YEAR-OLDS

6 Ch f Priolo (USA)—No Distractions
7 **WELL SMART (IRE),** ch f Durandal—Sharp Goodbye

TWO-YEAR-OLDS

8 B f 12/2 Distinctly North—Bunny Run (Dowsing (USA))
9 B f 19/3 Treasure Kay—Shoot The Dealer (IRE) (Common Grounds)

Other Owners: Mrs M. Behan, Blackhall Stud, T. Coleman, Mrs B. Mannion, Mrs T. M. McCoubrey, S. Murphy, Ms G. O'Farrell, Mrs E. M. Quinn, D. Rafferty, S. Thompson, J. Wallace.

114 MR O. J. CARTER, Ottery St Mary

Postal: **Wild Green, Metcombe, Ottery St Mary, Devon, EX11 1RS.**
Phone: **(01404) 812607**

1 **ABBOTSHAM,** 13, b g Ardross—Lucy Platter (FR) **Mr O. J. Carter**
2 **HEADING NORTH,** 7, ch g North Street—Penny Change **Mr O. J. Carter**
3 **OTTER RIVER,** 9, ch g Celtic Cone—Ottery News **Mr O. J. Carter**
4 **RAKI CRAZY,** 7, ch g Lyphento (USA)—Tom's Nap Hand **Mr O. J. Carter**
5 **TOM'S APACHE,** 9, br g Sula Bula—Tom's Nap Hand **Mr O. J. Carter**
6 **TOM'S GEMINI STAR,** 10, ch g Celtic Cone—Je Dit **Mr O. J. Carter**
7 **TOM'S MRS-T,** 9, b m Pragmatic—Tom's Hideaway **Mr O. J. Carter**

115 MR W. T. CASEY, Dorking

Postal: **Henfold House Cottage, Beare Green, Dorking, Surrey, RH5 4RW.**
Phone: **(01306) 631529 FAX (01306) 631529**

1 **ANNMARINAN (IRE),** 6, br g Satco (FR)—Hy Carol **C. G. H.**
2 **BENJI,** 7, ch g High Kicker (USA)—Snap Tin **Mr A. A. W. Jackson**
3 **CALM DOWN (IRE),** 7, b g Phardante (FR)—Extra Chance **Mrs Andrew Wates**
4 **CHINESE LANTERN (IRE),** 5, gr m Mandalus—Only Flower **Mr G. Galvanoni**
5 **ELTIGRI (FR),** 6, b g Mistigri—Obepine II (FR) **Mr A. T. A. Wates**
6 **EVEN FLOW (IRE),** 9, b g Mandalus—Mariners Chain **Mr A. T. A. Wates**
7 **GRASS ISLAND (IRE),** 9, b g The Parson—Helenium **B. & M. McHugh Ltd Civil Engineering**
8 **I DO THE JOKES (IRE),** 8, b g Buckskin (FR)—Leannan **Mr Colin Frewin**
9 **IRON N GOLD,** 6, b g Heights of Gold—Southern Dynasty **D. C. T. Partnership**
10 **KRATON GARDEN (USA),** 6, b g Sovereign Dancer (USA)—Kenanga **Mr C. M. Wilson**
11 **MAYLIN MAGIC,** 7, b m Minster Son—Miss Felham **Exors of the Late Mr F. Lipscomb**
12 **NATIVE VENTURE (IRE),** 10, b br g Noalto—Aiguiere (FR) **Mr N. M. Corcoran**
13 **PARLIAMENTARIAN (IRE),** 9, br g Idiot's Delight—Elect **Mr J. G. M. Wates**
14 **ROUGH QUEST,** 12, b g Crash Course—Our Quest **Mr A. T. A. Wates**

MR W. T. CASEY—continued

15 **SILVERFORT LAD (IRE),** 9, gr g Roselier (FR)—Sweet Run **Mr A. T. A. Wates**
16 **SPLENDID THYNE,** 6, ch g Good Thyne (USA)—Mrs Jennifer **Mr John Galvanoni**
17 **STREET TRADER (IRE),** 8, ch g Import—Mancha Lady **Mr A. J. S. Palmer**
18 **TOUGH TERMS (IRE),** 6, b g Welsh Term—Glenardina **Mr A. T. A. Wates & Lady Wates**

Other Owners: Mr Nigel Babbage, Mr Nicholas Charles Beecroft, Mrs R. Buck, Ms P. J. Carter, Mr G. E. Copeland, Mr T. G. Coughlan, Mrs Ann Galvanoni, Mr Patrick Hall, Mr David Harrison, Mr P. Hickey, Mr H. R. Hunt, Mr F. R. Jackson, Mr R. Judge, Mr M. A. McEvoy, Mr B. McHugh, Mr J. Morton, Mrs J. Murray, Mrs Laura Pegg, Mr Ashley Tabony, Mr David Wates, Mrs J. Woollatt.

Jockey (Flat): J Reid (w.a.).

Jockeys (NH): M Fitzgerald (w.a.), D Gallagher (w.a.).

116 MR H. R. A. CECIL, Newmarket

Postal: **Warren Place, Newmarket, Suffolk, CB8 8QQ.**
Phone: **(01638) HOUSE 662387 OFFICE 662192 FAX 669005**

1 **AGINOR,** 4, b g Slip Anchor—Fairy Feet **Mrs Irina Tsatsos**
2 **AWESOME WELLS (IRE),** 4, b c Sadler's Wells (USA)—Shadywood **Cliveden Stud**
3 **BESIEGE,** 4, b c Rainbow Quest (USA)—Armeria (USA) **Mr K. Abdulla**
4 **BINA GARDENS,** 4, b f Shirley Heights—Balabina (USA) **Mr K. Abdulla**
5 **CANON CAN (USA),** 5, ch g Green Dancer (USA)—Lady Argyle (USA) **Canon (Anglia) O. A. Ltd**
6 **CARISBROOKE,** 4, b c Kahyasi—Dayanata **Mr Michael Poland**
7 **DARNAWAY,** 4, b c Green Desert (USA)—Reuval **Sir David Wills**
8 **DOKOS (USA),** 4, b c Nureyev (USA)—Pasadoble (USA) **Niarchos Family**
9 **GLEN PARKER (IRE),** 5, ch h Bluebird (USA)—Trina's Girl **Angus Dundee Plc**
10 **HARRY WOLTON,** 4, b c Distant Relative—Tashinsky (USA) **Old Road Securities Plc**
11 **HIGH INTRIGUE (IRE),** 4, b br c Shirley Heights—Mild Intrigue (USA) **Mrs E. A. Harris**
12 **ISMAROS,** 4, ch c Selkirk (USA)—Trikymia **Mr L. Marinopoulos**
13 **LIGHT PROGRAMME,** 4, b c El Gran Senor (USA)—Nashmeel (USA) **Mr K. Abdulla**
14 **MEMORISE (USA),** 4, b c Lyphard (USA)—Shirley Valentine **Mr K. Abdulla**
15 **MONITOR,** 4, ch g Machiavellian (USA)—Instant Desire (USA) **Buckram Oak Holdings**
16 **ROYAL ALIBI,** 4, b c Royal Academy (USA)—Excellent Alibi (USA) **Mr T. F. Harris**
17 **SELFISH,** 4, ch f Bluebird (USA)—Sariza **Mr L. Marinopoulos**
18 **SLEEPYTIME (IRE),** 4, b f Royal Academy (USA)—Alidiva **Greenbay Stables Ltd**
19 **STREET GENERAL,** 4, b c Generous (IRE)—Hotel Street (USA) **Mr Luciano Gaucci**

THREE-YEAR-OLDS

20 **ABI,** ch f Chief's Crown (USA)—Carmelized (CAN) **Old Road Securities Plc**
21 **ALFRESCO,** b f Alzao (USA)—Shadywood **Cliveden Stud**
22 **ANYTIME (IRE),** b c Fairy King (USA)—Alidiva **Greenbay Stables Ltd**
23 **ASSAFIYAH (IRE),** ch f Kris—Fayfa (IRE) **Prince A. A. Faisal**
24 **BAFFIN BAY,** b c Bustino—Surf Bird **Mr L. B. Holliday**
25 **BALTIC STATE (USA),** b c Danzig (USA)—Kingscote **Mr K. Abdulla**
26 **BE GONE,** ch g Be My Chief (USA)—Hence (USA) **Mr Peter Burrell**
27 **BELEAGUER,** ch f Rainbow Quest (USA)—Armeria (USA) **Mr K. Abdulla**
28 **BENIN (USA),** b c Sky Classic (CAN)—Battle Drum (USA) **Baron G. von Ullmann**
29 **BOLD FACT (USA),** b c Known Fact (USA)—Sookera (USA) **Mr K. Abdulla**
30 **BORN WINNER,** b c Rainbow Quest (USA)—Tinaca (USA) **Mr Wafic Said**
31 **BRIMMING,** ch c Generous (IRE)—Rainbow Lake **Mr K. Abdulla**
32 **CAPRI,** ch c Generous (IRE)—Island Jamboree (USA) **H.R.H. Prince Fahd Salman**
33 **CATCHASCATCHCAN,** b f Pursuit of Love—Catawba **Lord Howard de Walden**

MR H. R. A. CECIL—continued

34 **CHESTER HOUSE (USA),** b c Mr Prospector (USA)—Toussaud (USA) **Mr K. Abdulla**
35 **CRAIGSTEEL,** b c Suave Dancer (USA)—Applecross **Sir David Wills**
36 **DABUS,** b c Kris—Licorne **Lord Howard de Walden**
37 **DAGGERS DRAWN (USA),** ch c Diesis—Sun And Shade **Cliveden Stud**
38 **DARK SHADOWS,** b c Machiavellian (USA)—Instant Desire (USA) **Buckram Oak Holdings**
39 **DIDIFON,** b c Zafonic (USA)—Didicoy (USA) **Mr K. Abdulla**
40 **DIGITALIZE (USA),** b br f Dayjur (USA)—Dancer's Candy (USA) **Mr S. Khaled**
41 **DREAM PURSUIT (IRE),** b f Caerleon (USA)—Heaven Only Knows **Mr T. F. Harris**
42 **DR FONG (USA),** ch c Kris S (USA)—Spring Flight (USA) **The Thoroughbred Corporation**
43 **DYNAMISM (FR),** b c Caerleon (USA)—Fextal (USA) **Niarchos Family**
44 **EATON SQUARE (USA),** b c Nureyev (USA)—Jolypha (USA) **Mr K. Abdulla**
45 **EMINENCE GRISE (IRE),** b c Sadler's Wells (USA)—Impatiente (USA) **Mr Wafic Said**
46 **EMPIRE GOLD (USA),** ch c Strike The Gold (USA)—Careless Halo (USA) **Charlton Bloodstock Ltd**
47 **EMPLANE (USA),** b f Irish River (FR)—Peplum (USA) **Mr K. Abdulla**
48 **ENBORNE,** b c Slip Anchor—Pris **Lady Howard de Walden**
49 **EPIDAURUS,** b f Royal Academy (USA)—Trikymia **Mr L. Marinopoulos**
50 **EXIT TO SOMEWHERE (IRE),** b c Exit To Nowhere (USA)—Zivania (IRE) **The Thoroughbred Corporation**
51 **FLEETWOOD (IRE),** ch c Groom Dancer (USA)—Up Anchor (IRE) **H.R.H. Prince Fahd Salman**
52 **FOREST ENDING (USA),** ch c Green Forest (USA)—Perlee (FR) **Buckram Oak Holdings**
53 **GEDY RED (USA),** b c Alleged (USA)—Rose Red (USA) **Mr Luciano Gaucci**
54 **GIVEAWAY,** ch c Generous (IRE)—Radiant Bride (USA) **Mr K. Abdulla**
55 **GOLDEN DICE (USA),** ch c Diesis—Fariedah (USA) **Mr S. Khaled**
56 **GREAT DANE (IRE),** b c Danehill (USA)—Itching (IRE) **Greenbay Stables Ltd**
57 **GRIMSHAW (USA),** ch c St Jovite (USA)—Loa (USA) **H.R.H. Prince Fahd Salman**
58 **HIMSELF (USA),** b c El Gran Senor (USA)—Celtic Loot (USA) **Scrope, Scott Partners**
59 **HITMAN (IRE),** b c Contract Law (USA)—Loveville (USA) **The Paper Boys**
60 **IDMA,** b f Midyan (USA)—Garah **Prince A. A. Faisal**
61 **JIBE (USA),** b f Danzig (USA)—Slightly Dangerous (USA) **Mr K. Abdulla**
62 **KING TANGO (USA),** b c Kingmambo (USA)—Vana Turns (USA) **The Thoroughbred Corporation**
63 **LAMANKA LASS (USA),** ch f Woodman (USA)—Pattimech (USA) **Mr D. Buchanan**
64 **LAURENTIDE (USA),** b c Pleasant Colony (USA)—Northern Sunset **Mrs Virginia Kraft Payson**
65 **LERELE (USA),** b f Chief's Crown (USA)—Ferouz (USA) **Mr F. Hinojosa**
66 **LIFE AND ROSES (USA),** ch f Chief's Crown (USA)—P C J Relaxer (USA) **The Thoroughbred Corporation**
67 **LIGHT STEP (USA),** b f Nureyev (USA)—Nimble Feet (USA) **Mr K. Abdulla**
68 **MAMA CARMEN (IRE),** b f Ela-Mana-Mou—Secretary Bird (IRE) **Mr Wafic Said**
69 **MARCUS MAXIMUS (USA),** ch c Woodman (USA)—Star Pastures **Mr Wafic Said**
70 **MIDNIGHT LINE (USA),** ch f Kris S (USA)—Midnight Air (USA) **H.R.H. Prince Fahd Salman**
71 **MOLAKAI (USA),** b f Nureyev (USA)—Yemanja (USA) **Niarchos Family**
72 **MORATORIUM (USA),** b c El Gran Senor (USA)—Substance (USA) **Mr K. Abdulla**
73 **NEW ABBEY,** b f Sadler's Wells (USA)—Bahamian **Mr K. Abdulla**
74 **NO DOUBT,** b f Sabrehill (USA)—Rockawhile (IRE) **Mr L. Marinopoulos**
75 **NUANCE (IRE),** ch f Rainbow Quest (USA)—Madame Dubois **Cliveden Stud**
76 **OBERON'S MISTRAL,** b f Fairy King (USA)—La Venta (USA) **Lord Lloyd-Webber**
77 **ON THE RIDGE (IRE),** ch c Risk Me (FR)—Star Ridge (USA) **Buckram Oak Holdings**
78 **PAGANINI,** b c Polish Precedent (USA)—Pick of The Pops **Baron G. von Ullmann**
79 **PENDANT,** b c Warning—Emerald (USA) **Mr K. Abdulla**
80 **PONTOON,** br f Zafonic (USA)—Dockage (CAN) **Mr K. Abdulla**
81 **PORTO FORICOS (USA),** b c Mr Prospector (USA)—Gallanta (FR) **Niarchos Family**
82 **POST MODERN (USA),** ch f Nureyev (USA)—Modena (USA) **Mr K. Abdulla**
83 **PROFILER (USA),** b c Capote (USA)—Magnificent Star (USA) **Buckram Oak Holdings**
84 **RAQQASA,** b f Groom Dancer (USA)—Khandjar **Lord Howard de Walden**
85 **ROYAL ANTHEM (USA),** b c Theatrical—In Neon (USA) **The Thoroughbred Corporation**
86 **ROYAL SHOW (IRE),** b f Sadler's Wells (USA)—Regal Beauty (USA) **Mr Michael Poland**
87 **SADIAN,** b c Shirley Heights—Rafha **Prince A. A. Faisal**
88 **SCORPION ORCHID (IRE),** gr f Caerleon (USA)—Negligence **Mrs John Magnier & Mr M. Tabor**
89 **SEA ALMOND (USA),** b f Nureyev (USA)—Dear Dorothy (USA) **Mr M. Tabor & Mrs John Magnier**
90 **SHIVA (JPN),** ch f Hector Protector (USA)—Lingerie **Niarchos Family**
91 **SILVER RHAPSODY (USA),** b f Silver Hawk (USA)—Sister Chrys (USA) **Mr T. F. Harris**
92 **SOUFFLE,** b f Zafonic (USA)—One Way Street **H.R.H. Prince Fahd Salman**

MR H. R. A. CECIL—continued

93 **SPA,** b f Sadler's Wells (USA)—Sandy Island **Lord Howard de Walden**
94 **STAR CRYSTAL (IRE),** b f Brief Truce (USA)—Crystal Spray **Mr Michael Poland**
95 **STERNSINGER (USA),** b c Seeking The Gold (USA)—Song Maker (IRE) **Gestut Schlenderhan**
96 **STORM RIVER (USA),** ch f Riverman (USA)—Storm Dove (USA) **Mr K. Abdulla**
97 **SUCCESS AND GLORY (IRE),** b c Alzao (USA)—More Fizz **The Thoroughbred Corporation**
98 **THE EDITOR,** b c Alzao (USA)—Litani River (USA) **The Thoroughbred Corporation**
99 **TIMBERVATI (USA),** br f Woodman (USA)—Never Scheme (USA) **Mr P. D. Savill**
100 **TRACKING,** ch c Machiavellian (USA)—Black Fighter (USA) **Buckram Oak Holdings**
101 **TRIPLE TREASURE (USA),** b f Gone West (USA)—Lemhi Go (USA) **The Thoroughbred Corporation**
102 **TUNING,** ch f Rainbow Quest (USA)—Discomatic (USA) **Mr K. Abdulla**
103 **TWICKENHAM (USA),** ch c Woodman (USA)—Danse Royale (IRE) **Mr M. Tabor & Mrs John Magnier**
104 **VELLUM,** b f Warning—Avowal **Mr K. Abdulla**
105 **WADI,** b c Green Desert (USA)—Eternal **Mr K. Abdulla**
106 **WATERSHIP DANCE,** b c Sadler's Wells (USA)—Silver Lane (USA) **Lord Lloyd-Webber**
107 **WAYNE LUKAS,** b c Don't Forget Me—Modern Dance (USA) **The Thoroughbred Corporation**
108 **WEMYSS QUEST,** b c Rainbow Quest (USA)—Wemyss Bight **Mr K. Abdulla**
109 **ZAKUSKA,** b f Zafonic (USA)—Connecting Link (USA) **Clark Industrial Services Partnership**
110 **ZANTE,** b f Zafonic (USA)—Danthonia (USA) **Mr K. Abdulla**

TWO-YEAR-OLDS

111 **ADELPHI (IRE),** b c 10/4 Sadler's Wells (USA)—Societe Royale (Milford) **Mr M. Tabor, Mrs J. Magnier, Dr T. Ryan**
112 Ch c 12/2 Trempolino (USA)—Air de Noblesse (USA) (Vaguely Noble) **H. R. H. Prince Fahd Salman**
113 Ch f 31/3 Royal Academy (USA)—Alidiva (Chief Singer) **Greenbay Stables Ltd**
114 Ch f 7/3 Mr Prospector (USA)—All At Sea (USA) (Riverman (USA)) **Mr K. Abdulla**
115 B f 2/6 Royal Academy (USA)—Alligatrix (USA) (Alleged (USA)) **Greenbay Stables Ltd**
116 **ANUSKHA (IRE),** ch f 2/2 Indian Ridge—Shaping Up (USA) (Storm Bird (CAN)) **Clark Industrial Services Partnership**
117 **ARABIS,** ch f 19/2 Arazi (USA)—Mill On The Floss (Mill Reef (USA)) **Cliveden Stud**
118 **AZULA,** b f 26/3 Bluebird (USA)—Dimant Rose (USA) (Tromos) **Dr A. Gillespie & Mr J. Wilson**
119 B c 3/4 Rainbow Quest (USA)—Balleta (USA) (Lyphard (USA)) **Mr K. Abdulla**
120 **BALLET MASTER (USA),** ch c 9/4 Kingmambo (USA)—Danse Royale (IRE) (Caerleon (USA)) **Mr M. Tabor & Partners**
121 Br f 5/3 Zafonic (USA)—Bonash (Rainbow Quest (USA)) **Mr K. Abdulla**
122 **BRIGHTER (USA),** ch f 2/4 Gone West (USA)—Top Trestle (USA) (Nijinsky (CAN)) **H. R. H. Prince Fahd Salman**
123 **BRIGHTEST STAR,** b f 29/4 Unfuwain (USA)—Shirley Superstar (Shirley Heights) **Helena Springfield Ltd**
124 Gr c 18/4 Sabrehill (USA)—Butsova (Formidable (USA)) **H. R. H. Prince Fahd Salman**
125 **COMMANDER,** b c 19/2 Puissance—Tarkhana (IRE) (Dancing Brave (USA)) **H. R. H. Prince Fahd Salman**
126 **CONFIDENTIAL,** ch f 6/2 Generous (IRE)—Just You Wait (Nonoalco (USA)) **H. R. H. Prince Fahd Salman**
127 **COUNTESS PARKER,** ch f 24/3 First Trump—Hoist (IRE) (Bluebird (USA)) **Angus Dundee Plc**
128 B f 14/4 Sadler's Wells (USA)—Cruising Height (Shirley Heights) **Mr K. Abdulla**
129 **DEAL FAIR,** b c 3/2 Grand Lodge (USA)—Darshay (FR) (Darshaan) **Baron G. von Ullmann**
130 **DELTA'S WAY (USA),** b c 14/1 Dayjur (USA)—Lyphard's Delta (USA) (Lyphard (USA)) **Mr S. Khaled**
131 **DUBIETY,** b c 27/1 Machiavellian (USA)—Pevna (USA) (Danzig (USA)) **Lord Howard de Walden**
132 **EASY TO LOVE (USA),** b f 5/2 Diesis—La Sky (IRE) (Law Society (USA)) **Mr T. F. Harris**
133 **ELASSIPOS,** b c 17/2 Warning—Rockawhile (IRE) (Dancing Brave (USA)) **Mr L. Marinopoulos**
134 B c 10/1 Lyphard (USA)—Empress Club (ARG) (Farnesio (ARG)) **Mr Wafic Said**
135 **ENDORSEMENT,** b f 21/5 Warning—Overdrive (Shirley Heights) **Cliveden Stud**
136 **ENEMY ACTION (USA),** b f 6/4 Forty Niner (USA)—Sun And Shade (Ajdal (USA)) **Cliveden Stud**
137 **ENRIQUE,** b c 29/4 Barathea (IRE)—Gwydion (USA) (Raise A Cup (USA)) **Niarchos Family**
138 **ESPERIS (IRE),** br f 15/5 Warning—Trikymia (Final Straw) **Mr L. Marinopoulos**
139 Br c 1/2 Zafonic (USA)—Felucca (Green Desert (USA)) **Mr K. Abdulla**
140 B c 16/2 Barathea (IRE)—Fern (Shirley Heights) **Mr Wafic Said**
141 Ch f 8/2 Miswaki (USA)—Flaming Torch (Rousillon (USA)) **Mr K. Abdulla**
142 B f 26/4 Selkirk (USA)—Flit (USA) (Lyphard (USA)) **Mr K. Abdulla**
143 B c 25/2 Royal Academy (USA)—Funny Hilarious (USA) (Sir Ivor) **Archduke**
144 **GALETTE,** b f 2/5 Caerleon (USA)—Madame Dubois (Legend of France (USA)) **Cliveden Stud**
145 **GINGER SLING (IRE),** ch f 6/3 Kris—Savoy Truffle (FR) (Law Society (USA)) **Mr L. Marinopoulos**
146 B f 26/2 Rainbow Quest (USA)—Guillem (USA) (Nijinsky (CAN)) **Mr K. Abdulla**

MR H. R. A. CECIL—continued

147 Ch f 5/1 Rainbow Quest (USA)—Hatton Gardens (Auction Ring (USA)) **Mr Wafic Said**
148 B c 4/3 West By West (USA)—Immortal Image (USA) (Danzatore (CAN)) **The Thoroughbred Corporation**
149 INITIATIVE, ch c 13/2 Arazi (USA)—Dance Quest (FR) (Green Dancer (USA)) **Lord Howard de Walden**
150 Ch f 7/3 Zafonic (USA)—Interval (Habitat) **Mr K. Abdulla**
151 IPSO FACTO (IRE), b c 29/4 Sunday Silence (USA)—Lingerie (Shirley Heights) **Niarchos Family**
152 B f 29/1 A P Indy (USA)—Jolypha (USA) (Lyphard (USA)) **Mr K. Abdulla**
153 KARLAYA (IRE), b f 6/3 Darshaan—Kalata (Assert) **Mr T. F. Harris**
154 B f 18/4 Rainbow Quest (USA)—Key Flyer (USA) (Nijinsky (CAN)) **H. R. H. Prince Fahd Salman**
155 Ch f 16/2 Lion Cavern (USA)—Mariakova (USA) (The Minstrel (CAN)) **Mr Wafic Said**
156 B c 19/1 Catrail (USA)—Menominee (Soviet Star (USA)) **The Thoroughbred Corporation**
157 MOONLIGHT (IRE), b f 11/4 Night Shift (USA)—
Local Custom (IRE) (Be My Native (USA)) **Dr A. Gillespie & Mr J. Wilson**
158 B f 12/2 Mr Prospector (USA)—Nimble Feet (USA) (Danzig (USA)) **Mr K. Abdulla**
159 Ch c 11/5 Gone West (USA)—Nimble Follly (USA) (Cyane) **Mr K. Abdulla**
160 NO RESERVE (USA), b f 23/1 Gone West (USA)—Milly Ha Ha (Dancing Brave (USA)) **Cliveden Stud**
161 PENNYGOWN, b f 15/3 Rainbow Quest (USA)—Applecross (Glint of Gold) **Dr Catherine Wills**
162 Ch c 24/4 Storm Bird (CAN)—Polemic (USA) (Roberto (USA)) **Mr K. Abdulla**
163 B f 17/3 Gone West (USA)—Prodigious (FR) (Pharly (FR)) **Mr K. Abdulla**
164 B c 8/2 Known Fact (USA)—Proud Lou (USA) (Proud Clarion) **Mr K. Abdulla**
165 PURSE, b f 29/2 Pursuit of Love—Rose Noble (USA) (Vaguely Noble) **Lord Howard de Walden**
166 PYTHIOS (IRE), b c 24/4 Danehill (USA)—Pithara (Never So Bold) **Mrs H. G. Cambanis**
167 Br c 21/1 Zafonic (USA)—Rakli (Warning) **Mr K. Abdulla**
168 RAMRUMA (USA), ch f 17/2 Diesis—Princess of Man (Green God) **H. R. H. Prince Fahd Salman**
169 B c 18/4 Zafonic (USA)—Rappa Tap Tap (FR) (Tap On Wood) **The Thoroughbred Corporation**
170 B c 28/3 Danzig (USA)—Razyana (USA) (His Majesty (USA)) **Mr K. Abdulla**
171 ROYAL HIGHNESS (IRE), b f 14/2 Shirley Heights—
Royal Ballet (IRE) (Sadler's Wells (USA)) **Mr Michael Poland**
172 SAIL AWAY, b f 23/3 Slip Anchor—Meliora (Crowned Prince (USA)) **Lord Howard de Walden**
173 SAMOA, b f 8/3 Rainbow Quest (USA)—Sardegna (Pharly (FR)) **Lady Howard de Walden**
174 SEA OF GOD (USA), b c 24/5 Gone West (USA)—Yemanja (USA) (Alleged (USA)) **Niarchos Family**
175 SHIKASTA (IRE), ch f 14/2 Kris—India Atlanta (Ahonoora) **Mr L. Marinopoulos**
176 B c 19/3 Irish River (FR)—Shirley Valentine (Shirley Heights) **Mr K. Abdulla**
177 B c 2/2 Warning—Sistabelle (Bellypha) **Mr Wafic Said**
178 SIVOTA BAY, b c 6/4 Shirley Heights—Messaria (Ile de Bourbon (USA)) **Mr L. Marinopoulos**
179 B c 6/2 Cryptoclearance (USA)—Something True (USA) (Sir Ivor) **Buckram Oak Holdings**
180 SPICY MANNER (USA), b f 26/4 Cryptoclearance (USA)—Mangala (USA) (Sharpen Up) **Buckram Oak Holdings**
181 SPRY, b f 9/2 Suave Dancer (USA)—Sandy Island (Mill Reef (USA)) **Lord Howard de Walden**
182 SUN HAT, br c 5/4 Warning—Instant Desire (USA) (Northern Dancer) **Buckram Oak Holdings**
183 TAMING (IRE), ch c 13/3 Lycius (USA)—Black Fighter (USA) (Secretariat (USA)) **Buckram Oak Holdings**
184 Br f 13/2 Warning—Tinaca (USA) (Manila (USA)) **Mr Wafic Said**
185 TYRA, b f 22/3 Lion Cavern (USA)—Lara (USA) (Lyphard (USA)) **Buckram Oak Holdings**
186 Br f 2/4 Warning—Valika (Valiyar) **Lord Lloyd-Webber**
187 B c 25/1 Cadeaux Genereux—Victoriana (USA) (Storm Bird (CAN)) **Mr K. Abdulla**
188 B c 20/3 Caerleon (USA)—Wemyss Bight (Dancing Brave (USA)) **Mr K. Abdulla**

Other Owners: Mr Jim Clark, Baroness Karin Von Ullmann, Mr Charles H. Wacker Iii.

Jockeys (Flat): K Fallon, J Lowe (7-10), A McGlone (7-11), W Ryan (8-2).

117 MRS J. CECIL, Newmarket

Postal: **Southgate, Hamilton Road, Newmarket, Suffolk, CB8 0NQ.**
Phone: **OFFICE (01638) 560634 HOUSE 662420 FAX 560636**

1 ADAMTON, 6, b g Domynsky—Berwyn **Mrs J. Cecil**
2 BEVIER, 4, b c Nashwan (USA)—Bevel (USA) **Mrs J. Cecil & Partners**
3 BLOT, 4, b g Warning—Rattle Along **Bernard Gover Bloodstock Trading Ltd**
4 BONANZA PEAK (USA), 5, b h Houston (USA)—Bunnicula (USA) **Gavin Oram and Julie Cecil**

MRS J. CECIL—continued

5 **CYBERTECHNOLOGY,** 4, b c Environment Friend—Verchinina **Mr E. Pick**
6 **DOMAPPEL,** 6, b g Domynsky—Appelania **Mr Michael C. Banks**
7 **ISLE OF CORREGIDOR (USA),** 4, b g Manila (USA)—Comtesse de Loir (FR) **Mrs Pamela Ohrstrom**
8 **KINGFISHER MILL (USA),** 4, ch c Riverman (USA)—Charming Life (NZ) **Lord Howard de Walden**
9 **LIONIZE (USA),** 5, ch h Storm Cat (USA)—Pedestal **Lord Howard de Walden**
10 **MIRY LEADER,** 5, ch m Polar Falcon (USA)—Mrs Leader (USA) **Mrs M. Slater**
11 **MOZAMBIQUE (IRE),** 4, b c Fayruz—Lightning Laser **Mr Martin Myers**
12 **NAMBUCCA,** 4, b f Shirley Heights—Cephira (FR) **Lord Howard de Walden**
13 **RORY,** 7, b g Dowsing (USA)—Crymlyn **Mrs J. Cecil**
14 **TALIB (USA),** 4, b g Silver Hawk (USA)—Dance For Lucy (USA) **Lord Howard de Walden**
15 **WITCHING HOUR (IRE),** 4, b f Alzao (USA)—Itching (IRE) **Greenbay Stables Ltd**
16 **WURLITZER (USA),** 6, ch g Riverman (USA)—Wedge Musical **Mr William Nott**

THREE-YEAR-OLDS

17 **CYBER WORLD (USA),** b br c Robin des Pins (USA)—Strike Alight (USA) **Niarchos Family**
18 **DOUBLE IDENTITY,** b f Rudimentary (USA)—Frivolous Fancy **Mr & Mrs M. A. Roberts**
19 **HARVEY LEADER,** b g Prince Sabo—Mrs Leader (USA) **Mrs M. Slater**
20 **KELANG,** ch f Kris—Ebbing Tide (USA) **Grundy Bloodstock Limited**
21 **LITTLE TRAMP,** b f Trempolino (USA)—Chipaya **Mrs M. Slater**
22 **MOLA (IRE),** b f Robellino (USA)—Epure **Greenbay Stables Ltd**
23 **MY DISCOVERY (IRE),** b f Imperial Frontier (USA)—Llanelli **Mr John Bray**
24 **PLAYGROUP,** ch f Rudimentary (USA)—Miss Paige (AUS) **Lord Howard de Walden**
25 **RAJATI (USA),** b c Chief's Crown (USA)—Charming Life (NZ) **Lord Howard de Walden**
26 **SHAVELING,** ch c Sharpo—Sancta **Lord Howard de Walden**
27 **SOURCE,** b g Rudimentary (USA)—Sakala (NZ) **Lord Howard de Walden**
28 **THE ACCOUNTANT,** ch g Suave Dancer (USA)—Fairy Tern **Mrs M. Slater**

TWO-YEAR-OLDS

29 Ch f 16/5 Rudimentary (USA)—Crymlyn (Welsh Pageant)
30 **CUSIN,** ch c 3/5 Arazi (USA)—Fairy Tern (Mill Reef (USA)) **Mrs M. Slater**
31 **CUTAWAY,** ch f 6/1 Kris—Licorne (Sadler's Wells (USA)) **Lord Howard de Walden**
32 **EBDAA,** ch f 30/3 Nashwan (USA)—Al Theraab (USA) (Roberto (USA)) **Mr Hamdan Al Maktoum**
33 **GEVITY,** b f 5/2 Kris—Cephira (FR) (Abdos) **Lord Howard de Walden**
34 **GRAND SLAM (IRE),** ch c 3/5 Grand Lodge (USA)—Entracte (Henbit (USA)) **Miss Julie Collins**
35 B f 29/2 First Trump—Hotel California (IRE) (Last Tycoon) **Mrs Bobby Cohen**
36 **KIRK,** b f 14/5 Selkirk (USA)—Sancta (So Blessed) **Lord Howard de Walden**
37 Ch c 3/2 Grand Lodge (USA)—Little Change (Grundy) **Mr Michael Sears & Partners**
38 **MY WORD,** b c 8/5 Rudimentary (USA)—Miss Paige (AUS) (Luskin Star (AUS)) **Lord Howard de Walden**
39 **PIPER'S CLAN,** b c 12/4 Aragon—Topwinder (USA) (Topsider (USA)) **Angus Dundee Plc**
40 **SHARH,** ch c 16/2 Elmaamul (USA)—Depeche (FR) (Kings Lake (USA)) **Mr Hamdan Al Maktoum**
41 **TWO CLUBS,** br f 7/3 First Trump—Miss Cindy (Mansingh (USA)) **Mr Stephen R. Hobson**
42 **ZAMAT,** b c 15/3 Slip Anchor—Khandjar (Kris) **Lord Howard de Walden**

Other Owners: Mr A. Boyd-Rochfort, Mr Anthony Cherry-Downes, Mr J. N. W. Dudley, Major Toby Gore, Mr T. Hillman, Mr A. W. N. Lake, Capt. J. Macdonald-Buchanan, Sir Thomas Pilkington B.T., Mr R. W. G. Threlfall, Lady Howard De Walden.

118 MR S. G. CHADWICK, Hayton

Postal: **Eskrigg, Hayton, Aspatria, Carlisle, Cumbria, CA5 2PD.**
Phone: **(016973) 21226**

1 **BISHOPDALE,** 17, ch g Proverb—Garryduff Lady **Mr S. Chadwick**
2 **CHAPEL CROFT,** 5, ch g Gypsy Castle—Young Christine VII **Mr S. Chadwick**
3 **ITS A DEAL,** 12, b g Lochnager—J J Caroline **Mr S. Chadwick**
4 **KARLOVAC,** 12, ch g Stanford—Croatia **Mr S. Chadwick**
5 **SKIPLAM WOOD,** 12, b m Cree Song—Mab **Mr S. Chadwick**

119 MR A. J. CHAMBERLAIN, Swindon

Postal: **North End Farm, Ashton Keynes, Swindon, Wilts, SN6 6QR.**
Phone: **(01285) 861347 MOBILE (0468) 471719**

1 **BILLI BEE,** 6, b g Buckley—Kessie-Bee **Mr G. J. Chamberlain**
2 **BUCKLEMEBLUE,** 4, b g Buckley—Lady Blues Singer **Mrs A. T. Lodge**
3 4, Ch f Handsome Sailor—Countess Carlotti **Mr F. J. Chamberlain**
4 **DOUBLE ACHIEVEMENT (IRE),** 8, gr g Celio Rufo—Jeanarie **Exors of the late Ms Paula Birchall**
5 **GENERAL MARL (IRE),** 6, gr g Over The River (FR)—Fortina's General **Mr G. J. Chamberlain**
6 **HANDCROSS,** 7, b g Handsome Sailor—Standard Breakfast **Mr G. J. Chamberlain**
7 **HULLO MARY DOLL,** 9, br m Lidhame—Princess Story
8 **JAVA SHRINE (USA),** 7, b g Java Gold (USA)—Ivory Idol (USA) **Plough Twenty (Ashton Keynes)**
9 **JIMMY-JADE,** 9, ch g Oats—Newella **Mr G. J. Chamberlain**
10 **KILL THE PLAGUE (USA),** 8, ch g Only Dreamin (USA)—Stephens' Grad (USA) **Mr S. P. Howe**
11 **MISS BLUES SINGER,** 5, b m Sula Bula—Lady Blues Singer **Mrs A. T. Lodge**
12 **RO-JO,** 4, b g Roviris—Joan Addison **Mrs A. Syms**
13 **SIX KINGS (IRE),** 6, b g King's Ride—Six Deep **Exors of the late Ms Paula Birchall**
14 4, B f Broadsword (USA)—Squeaky Cottage **Mr M. J. Ledbury**
15 **THE FOUR ISLES,** 4, b g Never So Bold—Far Claim (USA) **Mr G. J. Chamberlain**
16 **TYROLEAN DANCER (IRE),** 4, b f Tirol—Waffling **Exors of the late Ms Paula Birchall**
17 **VANCOUVER LAD (IRE),** 9, ch g Sheer Grit—Hi Style **Mr A. J. Chamberlain**

Other Owners: Mr M. A. Binnersley, Mr M. Bishop, Mr D. Carroll, Mr A. J. Freeth, Mr C. Gardiner, Mrs Christopher Hanbury, Mr K. R. Howse, Mr H. J. Manners, Mr N. U. Morgan, Mr M. S. Osborne, Mr D. P. Travers-Clark.

Jockey (Flat): R Perham (w.a.).

Jockeys (NH): L Harvey (10-9, w.a.), B Powell (10-0, w.a.).

Amateurs: Mr D Alers-Hankey (10-0), Mr S Howe (9-10), Mr J Juckes (10-0), Miss D Olding (10-4).

120 MR N. CHAMBERLAIN, West Auckland

Postal: **Acrum Lodge, Staindrop Road, West Auckland, Bishop Auckland, Co. Durham, DL14 9PB.**
Phone: **(01388) OFFICE 834636 HOUSE 832465**

1 **BROKEN ENGLISH,** 5, ch m Say Primula—Elitist **Mr R. W. Chamberlain**
2 **CEEJAYELL,** 5, b m Say Primula—Spring Garden **The Northumberland Group Racing Club**
3 **DARK SALLY,** 5, b m Silly Prices—Allez **Mr N. Chamberlain**
4 5, B m Move Off—Gipsy Silk **Mr N. Chamberlain**
5 **GYMCRAK CYRANO (IRE),** 9, b m Cyrano de Bergerac—Sun Gift **Mr N. Chamberlain**
6 **HYA PRIM,** 7, ch g Say Primula—Rilin **Mr N. Chamberlain**
7 **KONINGIN,** 4, b f Minster Son—Elitist **Mr R. W. Chamberlain**
8 **KRALINGEN,** 6, ch m Move Off—Elitist **Mr R. W. Chamberlain**
9 **MARCHWOOD,** 11, ch g Black Minstrel—Lisnagrough **Mr N. Chamberlain**
10 **PAINT YOUR WAGON,** 8, b g Move Off—Gipsy Silk **Mr N. Chamberlain**
11 **PUBLIC WAY (IRE),** 8, b g Common Grounds—Kilpeacon **Mr N. Chamberlain**
12 **SAYONARA,** 5, ch g Say Primula—Rilin **Mr N. Chamberlain**
13 4, Ch f Minster Son—Spring Garden **Mr N. Chamberlain**

Other Owners: Mr K. J. Douglas.

Lady Rider: Miss C Metcalfe (9-7).

121 MR P. R. CHAMINGS, Tadley

Postal: **Inhurst Farm Stables, Baughurst, Tadley, Hampshire, RG26 5JS.**
Phone: **(01189) 814494 FAX (01189) 820454 MOBILE (0831) 360970**

1 **ALL FOR THE CRACK,** 5, gr g Belfort (FR)—Find The Sun **Mr Dave Dixon**
2 **ALZARO (IRE),** 4, b g Alzao (USA)—Merriment (USA) **Mr Peter Oldfield**
3 **BET WILTSHIRE,** 6, b g Arctic Lord—Solhoon **Beat The Book**
4 **BINT ROSIE,** 4, b f Exit To Nowhere (USA)—Butterfly Rose (USA) **Mrs J. Hadden-Wright**
5 6, Gr g Mandalus—Dora Frost **Pell-mell Partners**
6 **EAGLE STORM (IRE),** 5, b g Glacial Storm (USA)—Sapello **Mr Patrick Hartnett**
7 **HOLLAND HOUSE,** 12, b g Sunyboy—Norma Can **Mr Ted Knight**
8 **IDIOTIC,** 10, br g Idiot's Delight—Norma Can **Mr Dave Dixon**
9 5, B g King's Ride—Jenny's Child **Mr Patrick Chamings**
10 **LORD LOVE (IRE),** 6, b g Mister Lord (USA)—Osymandy **Mr John Corbett**
11 **MONMOUTH WAY (IRE),** 6, b g King's Ride—Mimmsie Starr **Mrs V. R. W. Miller**
12 **MORTIMERS CROSS (IRE),** 5, b g Mandalus—Fallen Bloom **Mr Ted Knight**
13 **OVER THE POLE,** 11, b g Cruise Missile—Arctic Lee **Pell-mell Partners**
14 **PRATE BOX (IRE),** 8, b g Ela-Mana-Mou—Prattle On **Mr John Corbett**
15 **PRINCE HIPLEY,** 6, ch g Kinglet—Craig's Queen
16 **SLEIGH RIDE,** 5, b g Broadsword (USA)—Winter Wonder **Heatherwold Stud**
17 **THE BOG MAN (IRE),** 5, b g Brush Aside (USA)—Boderan Bridge (IRE) **Mr Dave Dixon**
18 **THE POLYMATH,** 5, ch g Sharpo—Nisha **Mr M. H. B. Portman**
19 **WHOD OF THOUGHT IT (IRE),** 7, b g Cataldi—Granalice **Inhurst Farm Stables Partnership**
20 **ZELIBA,** 6, br m Doyoun—Zia (USA) **Beat The Book**

TWO-YEAR-OLDS

21 **BOB'S PRINCESS,** b f 17/4 Bob's Return (IRE)—Princess Rosananti (IRE) **Mrs J. E. L. Wright**
22 **KEE RING,** ch c 24/5 Keen—Rose And The Ring **Mrs J. E. L. Wright**

Other Owners: Mr J. Chromiak, Mrs Peter Corbett, Mr Richard Gilder, Mrs Ann Jenkins, Mr John Murphy, Mr Ralph P. Peters, Mr Gary Wiltshire.

Jockeys (NH): T P Jenks (10-0), A R Thornton (10-0).

Amateurs: Mr C Bonner (9-10), Mr C Vigors (10-4).

122 MR R. CHAMPION, Newmarket

Postal: **Cleveland House, Hamilton Road, Newmarket, Suffolk, CB8 7JQ.**
Phone: **(01638) 666546 FAX (01638) 561989**

1 **ALAKDAR (CAN),** 4, ch c Green Dancer (USA)—Population **Mrs Judith Mendonca**
2 **DRUMREAGH LAD (IRE),** 10, b g Torus—Drumreagh **Mr A. P. Stringer**
3 **LAST AMBITION (IRE),** 6, b m Cadeaux Genereux—Fabulous Rina (FR) **Mr R. Champion**
4 **PIRATE MINSTREL (IRE),** 6, bl g Black Minstrel—Ailwee Lady (USA) **Mrs P. S. Hunt**
5 **THE MINISTER (IRE),** 9, br g Black Minstrel—Miss Hi-Land **Mrs P. S. Hunt and Mr C. Wallington**

Other Owners: Mrs T. Cassidy, Mr K. J. Hunt, Mrs P. King, Mr R. W. Kirk, Mr Ian Watkinson, Mr W. White.

Jockeys (NH): A Maguire (w.a.), B Powell.

123 MR N. T. CHANCE, Lambourn

Postal: **Folly House Stables, Upper Lambourn Road, Lambourn, Hungerford, Berkshire, RG17 8QG.**
Phone: **OFFICE (01488) 73436 MOBILE (0385) 300168**

1 **AH SHUSH (IRE)**, 10, ch g Le Moss—Pampered Finch VII **Take A Chance Partnership**
2 **DOWN THE COV (IRE)**, 5, b br g Aristocracy—Small Slam **Michael And Gerry Worcester**
3 **DRESSED IN STYLE (IRE)**, 6, ch m Meneval (USA)—Inundated **Suitwear International**
4 **GENTLE DRIFTER (IRE)**, 4, b f Jackson's Drift (USA)—Gentle Papoose **Mr George Peck**
5 **GO UNIVERSAL (IRE)**, 10, br g Teofane—Lady Dorcet **Universal Conference & Incentive Trv Ltd**
6 **HAUNTING THEME (IRE)**, 5, br g Yashgan—Theme Music **Mr John Dennis**
7 **KILARNEY KING (IRE)**, 5, b g King's Ride—Kylogue's Delight **Mr T. J. Myles**
8 **LARDANTE (IRE)**, 5, b br g Phardante (FR)—Larry's Law (IRE) **Michael And Gerry Worcester**
9 **LAREDO (IRE)**, 5, b h Accordion—Amelita **Michael And Gerry Worcester**
10 **LETS BE FRANK**, 7, b g Malaspina—Letitica **Mrs M. M. Stobart**
11 **LOOKS LIKE TROUBLE (IRE)**, 6, b g Zaffaran (USA)—Lavengaddy **Michael And Gerry Worcester**
12 **MEAD COURT (IRE)**, 8, ch g Torus—Winning Fare **Michael & Gerry Worcester**
13 **MR UNIVERSE (IRE)**, 6, br g Orchestra—Fox Glen **Universal Conference & Incentive Trv Ltd**
14 **ONLY FOR IF (IRE)**, 5, b g Balinger—Dungourney Lady **Michael & Gerry Worcester**
15 **OPTIMISM REIGNS (IRE)**, 7, b g Euphemism—Ellis Town **Michael And Gerry Worcester**
16 **SALLY'S TWINS**, 5, b m Dowsing (USA)—Bird of Love **Michael And Gerry Worcester**
17 **SUNLEY SECURE**, 5, b g Warrshan (USA)—Brown Velvet **Mr Douglas Allum**
18 **THE KERRY LEDGEND (IRE)**, 5, b g Phardante (FR)—I'm Grannie **Mr T. J. Myles**
19 **TOM TOM (IRE)**, 6, b g Dancing Disident (USA)—Ashanti **Mr J. Mullen**
20 5, Ch g Meneval (USA)—Tuney Blade **Middleham Park Racing**
21 **UNIVERSAL MAGIC (IRE)**, 9, ch g Le Bavard (FR)—Autumn Magic **Universal Conference & Incentive Trv Ltd**
22 **VALIANT MEMORY (IRE)**, 5, b m Montelimar (USA)—Derring Lass **Mr C. G. Harriss**
23 **VERMONT NATIVE (IRE)**, 5, br g Be My Native (USA)—Vermont Angel **Michael And Gerry Worcester**

Other Owners: Mr N. Andrew, Mrs M. Chance, Mr P. M. Conway, Mr M. P. Dinneen, Mrs R. F. Greener, Mr D. I. Heathcote, Mr E. R. Hemmings, Mr A. N. M. Longmore, Mr Dave Moss, Mr D. W. Potter, Mr B. R. D. Rudge, Mr E. Sheehan, Mr Martin J. Smith, Mr Nigel Stafford, Mr M. R. Thompson, Mr Stephen Tucker, Mr Thomas Weller.

Jockey (Flat): J F Egan (w.a.).

Jockey (NH): R Johnson (w.a).

Conditional: D Finnegan (9-7), M. N. Scales (9-7).

Amateur: Mr R F Coonan (10-0).

Lady Rider: Miss A McCabe (9-0).

124 MR M. CHANNON, Upper Lambourn

Postal: **Kingsdown, Upper Lambourn, Hungerford, Berkshire, RG17 8QX.**
Phone: **(01488) 71149 FAX (01488) 73235**

1 **ABAJANY**, 4, b g Akarad (FR)—Miss Ivory Coast (USA) **John White and Partners**
2 **BRAVEHEART (IRE)**, 4, br g Mujadil (USA)—Salonniere (FR) **Mr W. H. Ponsonby**
3 **CAUDA EQUINA**, 4, gr g Statoblest—Sea Fret **Mr Michael A. Foy**
4 **CLASSIC FAN (USA)**, 4, b f Lear Fan (USA)—Miss Boniface **Classic Bloodstock Plc**
5 **CLASSIC JENNY (IRE)**, 5, b m Green Desert (USA)—Eileen Jenny (IRE) **Classic Bloodstock Plc**
6 **CORNICHE QUEST (IRE)**, 5, b m Salt Dome (USA)—Angel Divine **Mr M. Bishop**
7 **DANEGOLD (IRE)**, 6, b g Danehill (USA)—Cistus **Circular Distributors Ltd**

MR M. CHANNON—continued

8 FLYING HAROLD, 5, b g Gildoran—Anytime Anywhere **Mr Malcolm P. Allen**
9 FREE AS A BIRD, 4, b f Robellino (USA)—Special Guest **Mr C. Marner**
10 GLEN OGIL, 4, ch g Thatching—Cormorant Bay **Mr W. A. Harrison-Allan**
11 KNOBBLEENEEZE, 8, ch g Aragon—Proud Miss (USA) **Mr Anthony Andrews**
12 LEVELLED, 4, b g Beveled (USA)—Baino Charm (USA) **Maygain Ltd**
13 MALADERIE (IRE), 4, b g Thatching—Native Melody **Mr R. M. Brehaut**
14 MILE HIGH, 4, b g Puissance—Jobiska **Maygain Ltd**
15 MILETRIAN REFURB (IRE), 5, b br g Anita's Prince—Lady of Man **Miletrian Plc**
16 MUCHEA, 4, ch c Shalford (IRE)—Bargouzine **Albion Investments**
17 PEATSWOOD, 10, ch g Rolfe (USA)—Cathy Jane **Mr Peter Taplin**
18 POSEIDON, 4, b c Polar Falcon (USA)—Nastassia (FR) **Allevamento La Nuova Sbarra SRL**
19 PRIDE OF NARVIK, 4, b c Pharly (FR)—Ulla Laing **Mr A. W. Boon**
20 SILANKKA, 4, b f Slip Anchor—Mary Sunley **Mr Simon Legg & Partners**
21 SILVER GROOM (IRE), 8, gr g Shy Groom (USA)—Rustic Lawn **The Silver Darling Partnership**

THREE-YEAR-OLDS

22 AGANON, b c Aragon—Plain Tree **Kingsdown Racing**
23 AJIG DANCER, b f Niniski (USA)—Gloire **Timber Hill Racing**
24 ARCEVIA (IRE), b f Archway (IRE)—Estivalia **Kingsdown Racing**
25 ARCTIC STAR, b g Polar Falcon (USA)—Three Stars **Kingsdown Racing**
26 BABY SPICE, ch f Then Again—Starawak **Mr W. H. Ponsonby**
27 BAY PRINCE (IRE), b c Mujadil (USA)—Kingston Rose **Mr D. W. Shepherd**
28 BRIDE'S ANSWER, ch f Anshan—Ivory Bride **Mrs Jean Keegan**
29 CAROUSE, br g Petong—Merry Rous **Mr John Carey**
30 CUTTING ANSHAKE, gr g Anshan—Golden Scissors **Mrs Jean Keegan**
31 HONEY STORM (IRE), b f Mujadil (USA)—Milk And Honey **Mrs T. Burns**
32 INDIAN SILVER, b f Indian Ridge—Ovideo **Mr Anthony Andrews**
33 LAST KNIGHT (IRE), b g Distinctly North (USA)—Standing Ovation **Mr W. H. Ponsonby**
34 LE SAUVAGE (IRE), b g Tirol—Cistus **Mr R. M. Brehaut**
35 MANSA MUSA (IRE), br c Hamas (IRE)—Marton Maid **Surrey Laminators Ltd**
36 MARLENE, b f Komaite (USA)—Kaiserlinde (GER) **Sheet & Roll Convertors Ltd**
37 MARY LOU (IRE), b f Tirol—Kilcsem Eile (IRE) **Mr M. A. Ryan**
38 MRS MALAPROP, b f Night Shift (USA)—Lightning Legacy (USA) **Mr Michael A. Foy**
39 NARROGIN (USA), ch g Strike The Gold (USA)—Best Regalia **Albion Investments**
40 POPPY TOO (IRE), b f Petardia—My Natalie **Mr Shaun Cunningham**
41 QUEEN OF SCOTLAND (IRE), b f Mujadil (USA)—Hitopah **Mr Noel Wabe**
42 RAFFAELLO (IRE), b c Fairy King (USA)—Silver Dollar **Allevamento La Nuova Sbarra SRL**
43 SATIS (IRE), b f Last Tycoon—Nazwa **Barry Walters Catering**
44 SATWA BOULEVARD, ch f Sabrehill (USA)—Winnie Reckless **Mr A. Merza**
45 SHANILLO, gr g Anshan—Sea Fret **Piccolo Boys**
46 SIENA (GER), ch f Platini (GER)—Smeralda (GER) **Mr M. Channon**
47 SILCA KEY SERVICE, b f Bering—Aquaglow **Aldridge Racing Limited**
48 STATELY PRINCESS, b f Robellino (USA)—Affair of State (USA) **Mr Stephen Crown**
49 STRIDING KING, ch g King's Signet (USA)—Stride Home **Mr Peter Taplin**
50 SUNLEY SEEKER, b f Elmaamul (USA)—Sunley Sinner **Mrs V. Jeyes**
51 TABASCO (IRE), b f Salse (USA)—El Taranda **Mr Martin Myers**
52 TAKE A TURN, br g Forzando—Honeychurch (USA) **Sheet & Roll Convertors Ltd**
53 THE HONORABLE LADY, b f Mystiko (USA)—Mrs Thatcher **Henry Ponsonby & Partners (1)**
54 TROPICAL ZONE, b f Machiavellian (USA)—Tropicaro (FR) **Mrs M. J. Vincent**

TWO-YEAR-OLDS

55 B c 14/4 Komaite (USA)—Brown Velvet (Mansingh (USA)) **Mr J. Sunley**
56 CD DELIVERS, b c 20/2 Forest Wind (USA)—Rose of Summer (IRE) (Taufan (USA)) **Circular Distributors Ltd**
57 CLASSIC AFFAIR (FR), b c 20/1 Always Fair (USA)—Classic Storm (Belfort (FR)) **Derek & Lynne Ayres**
58 B c 18/4 Pursuit of Love—Cominna (Dominion) **Mr Martin St Quinton**
59 B c 3/3 Dolphin Street (FR)—Crazed Rainbow (USA) (Graustark) **Mr S. W. Clarke**
60 B c 30/4 Up And At 'Em—Crimson Crest (Pampapaul) **Miletrian Plc**
61 B c 18/2 Polar Falcon (USA)—Dame Helene (USA) (Sir Ivor) **Kingsdown Racing**
62 DIPLOMAT, b c 25/1 Deploy—Affair of State (IRE) (Tate Gallery (USA)) **Mr Stephen Crown**

MR M. CHANNON—continued

63 B c 25/4 Waajib—Esquire Lady (Be My Guest (USA)) **Mr Tim Corby**
64 FRANCO MINA (IRE), b c 28/2 Lahib (USA)—Play The Queen (IRE) (King of Clubs) **Maygain Ltd**
65 B c 10/2 Grand Lodge (USA)—Frill (Henbit (USA)) **Mr A. Merza**
66 B f 9/5 Hamas (IRE)—Goodnight Girl (IRE) (Alzao (USA))
67 GREYFIELD, b c 15/4 Persian Bold—Noble Dust (USA) (Dust Commander (USA)) **Paulton Bloodstock**
68 B c 10/5 Aragon—Hability (Habitat) **Timberhill Racing Partnership**
69 B c 29/5 Theatrical Charmer—Harmonia (Glint of Gold) **Miss B. Coyle**
70 B c 28/2 Common Grounds—Harmonious (Sharrood (USA)) **Mr P. D. Savill**
71 INYA LAKE, b f 28/2 Whittingham (IRE)—Special One (Aragon) **Mr Barry Minty**
72 KING'S DRAGOON, b c 20/4 College Chapel—Indigo Blue (Bluebird (USA)) **Mr W. H. Ponsonby**
73 LADY BEWARE, b f 4/3 Warning—Thewaari (USA) (Eskimo (USA)) **Mr W. H. Ponsonby**
74 B c 5/3 Turtle Island (IRE)—Lady of Shalott (Kings Lake (USA)) **Mr Martin St Quinton**
75 B f 3/5 Distinctly North—Lady Roberta (USA) (Roberto (USA)) **Mr Tim Corby**
76 B f 4/5 Taufan (USA)—Legend of Spain (USA) (Alleged (USA))
77 B c 10/4 Mujtahid (USA)—Maculatus (USA) (Sharpen Up)
78 B c 2/4 Brief Truce (USA)—Ma Minti (Mummy's Pet) **Mr Ahmed Al Shafar**
79 B f 29/2 Superlative—Matching Lines (Thatching) **Mrs Jean Keegan**
80 MAUREENA, b f 18/3 Grand Lodge (USA)—Inshad (Indian King (USA)) **Mrs Maureen Buckley**
81 B c 2/5 Batshoof—Miller's Gait (Mill Reef (USA)) **Mr John Carey**
82 NATALIE JAY, b f 28/3 Ballacashtal—Falls of Lora (Scottish Rifle) **Mr Peter Jollife**
83 B c 24/2 Midyan (USA)—Panache Arabelle (Nashwan (USA)) **Sheikh Ahmed Al Maktoum**
84 PAULA'S JOY, b f 8/2 Danehill (USA)—Pernilla (IRE) (Tate Gallery (USA)) **Mr John Breslin**
85 B f 1/4 Inchinor—Petastra (Petoski)
86 POLY RULER, b c 8/5 Dancing Dissident—Love Me Tight (Tyrant (USA)) **Sheet & Roll Convertors Ltd**
87 B c 22/2 Darshaan—Pont-Aven (Try My Best (USA)) **Sheikh Ahmed Al Maktoum**
88 B c 13/4 Mtoto—Princess Haifa (USA) (Mr Prospector (USA)) **Sheikh Ahmed Al Maktoum**
89 B c 24/2 Salse (USA)—Rainbow's End (My Swallow) **Allevamento La Nuova Sbarra SRL**
90 B c 17/1 Nashwan (USA)—Raneen Alwatar (Sadler's Wells (USA)) **Sheikh Ahmed Al Maktoum**
91 B f 15/3 Anita's Prince—Regal Charmer (Royal And Regal (USA)) **Timberhill Racing Partnership**
92 REGAL EXIT, b c 1/3 Exit To Nowhere (USA)—Regalante (Gairloch) **Mrs Maureen Buckley**
93 ROBERGERIE, b c 9/4 Robellino (USA)—Daisy Grey (Nordance (USA)) **Mr R. M. Brehaut**
94 ROSIE SMART (IRE), b f 16/4 Hamas (IRE)—Sweet Repose (High Top) **Mr Adrian Greenwood**
95 ROYAL ORIGINE (IRE), b c 23/4 Royal Academy (USA)—Belle Origine (USA) (Exclusive Native (USA)) **Maygain Ltd**
96 B f 10/2 Polish Patriot (USA)—Saint Cynthia (Welsh Saint)
97 B f 10/3 Sadler's Wells (USA)—Salvora (USA) (Spectacular Bid (USA)) **Sheikh Ahmed Al Maktoum**
98 B c 8/5 Ezzoud (IRE)—Sanctuary Cove (Habitat)
99 B f 9/3 Persian Bold—Scotia Rose (Tap On Wood)
100 B f 5/2 Rudimentary (USA)—Show Home (Music Boy) **Mr Martin St Quinton**
101 Ch f 3/3 Inchinor—Silca-Cisa (Hallgate) **Aldridge Racing**
102 B f 19/1 Green Desert (USA)—Society Lady (USA) (Mr Prospector (USA)) **Sheikh Ahmed Al Maktoum**
103 SUNSET FOREST, b f 19/3 Forest Wind (USA)—Superetta (Superlative) **Mr Noel Wabe**
104 TOP STAR (IRE), b c 27/2 Thatching—Decadence Star (IRE) (High Estate) **Mr Stephen Crown**
105 ZIRCON, b c 23/3 Perugino (USA)—Tinktura (Pampapaul) **Mrs M. J. Vincent**
106 ZOLA (IRE), b c 22/4 Indian Ridge—Fluella (Welsh Pageant) **Maygain Ltd**

Other Owners: Mr D. F. Allport, Mr P. R. Anders, Mr Michael Andree, Aston House Stud, Ms K. Baker, Mr P. Baxter, Mr D. C. Broomfield, Mr Robbie Burns, Mrs J. M. Channon, Charles Saunders Ltd, Mr K. F. Chittock, Mr P. Chomiak, Mr John Clark, Mrs N. K. Crook, Mrs S. G. Davies, Mr F. P. Errington, Mr R. A. Fowlston, Mr J. J. Gerrard, Mr A. Gorley, Mr P. Harris, Mr G. C. Howland, Mr J. Hoyer, Mr David Hudd, Indef Limited, Mr Nicholas Irens, Mr R. C. Jack, Mrs J. M. Jeyes, Mr R. J. Johnson, Mrs A. M. Jones, Mr M. R. Jones, Mrs Lorna Keat, Mrs Jonathan Knight, Mr Brook Land, Mr T. Leigh, Mr Alan Leiper, Mr J. R. Littler, Mr Bob Low, Mr C. J. Macey, Mrs Rosie Manning, Mrs F. Marner, Mr F. E. Maslin, Mrs Nichola J. Mathias, Ms C. J. Meynell, Mike Channon Bloodstock Ltd, Mr John W. Mitchell, Mr P. S. Mulligan, Mrs Tessa Mulligan, Mr M. Nixon, Mr F. E. Nowell, Mr Robin Olley, Mr K. Panos, Mr A. J. Parker, Mr D. J. Peers, Mr N. E. Poole, Mrs V. Preece, Mr M. Quinn, Mr T. S. Redman, Dr Brian J. Ridgewell, Mr F. Rowland, Mrs G. Rowland-Clark, Mrs F. C. Saint Jean, Mrs P. D. Savill, Mr Chris Scott, Mr R. R. Shand, Mr P. J. Sheehan, Mr M. B. Small, Mr S. A. Smith, Mr R. J. Sunley Tice, Mr P. Trant, Mr D. J. Turney, Mr J. Wadley, Mr Robin Walsh, Mr Barry Walters, Mr E. J. Ward, Mrs Trish White, Mr Alan Winstanley, Mr R. D. A. Woodall.

Jockey (Flat): Candy Morris (8-1).

Apprentices: Paul Cleary (7-10), A Eddery (7-11).

125 MR DAVID W. CHAPMAN, York

Postal: **Mowbray House Farm, Stillington, York, YO6 1LT.**
Phone: **(01347) 21683 CAR PHONE (0966) 513866 Fax: (01347)821683**

1 **BOWCLIFFE GRANGE (IRE),** 6, b g Dominion Royale—Cala-Vadella **Mr David W. Chapman**
2 **DESERT INVADER (IRE),** 7, br g Lead On Time (USA)—Aljood **Mr David W. Chapman**
3 **EL NIDO,** 10, ch g Adonijah—Seleter **Mr David W. Chapman**
4 **GREAT BEAR,** 6, ch g Dominion—Bay Bay **Mr J. M. Chapman**
5 **KALAR,** 9, b g Kabour—Wind And Reign **Mr J. M. Chapman**
6 **KASS ALHAWA,** 5, b g Shirley Heights—Silver Braid (USA) **Mr J. B. Wilcox**
7 **KID ORY,** 7, ch g Rich Charlie—Woomargama **Mr David W. Chapman**
8 **MUKARRAB (USA),** 4, b br g Dayjur (USA)—Mahassin (NZ) **Mr Ian Armitage**
9 **NOTATION (IRE),** 4, b c Arazi (USA)—Grace Note (FR) **Mr J. M. Chapman**
10 **PALACEGATE JO (IRE),** 7, b m Drumalis—Welsh Rhyme **Mr David W. Chapman**
11 **PETITE DANSEUSE,** 4, b f Aragon—Let Her Dance (USA) **Mr T. S. Redman**
12 **PRAISE BE (FR),** 8, b g Baillamont (USA)—Louange **Mr David W. Chapman**
13 **PURPLE FLING,** 7, ch g Music Boy—Divine Fling **Miss N. F. Thesiger**
14 **REDOUBTABLE (USA),** 7, b h Grey Dawn II—Seattle Rockette (USA) **Mr David W. Chapman**
15 **SHADOW JURY,** 8, ch g Doulab (USA)—Texita **Mrs Jeanne Chapman**
16 **SHUTTLECOCK,** 7, ch g Pharly (FR)—Upper Sister **Mr David W. Chapman**
17 **SOAKED,** 5, b g Dowsing (USA)—Water Well **Mr David W. Chapman**
18 **SQUIRE CORRIE,** 6, b g Distant Relative—Fast Car (FR) **Miss N. F. Thesiger**
19 **TAKHLID (USA),** 7, b h Nureyev (USA)—Savonnerie (USA) **Miss N. F. Thesiger**
20 **TEMPERING,** 12, b g Kris—Mixed Applause (USA) **Mr David W. Chapman**
21 **THAT OLD FEELING (IRE),** 6, b g Waajib—Swift Reply **Mr David W. Chapman**
22 **YOUNG BIGWIG (IRE),** 4, b g Anita's Prince—Humble Mission **Miss N. F. Thesiger**

THREE-YEAR-OLDS

23 **JOCKWEILER (IRE),** b g Night Shift (USA)—Johara (USA) **Mr David W. Chapman**
24 **LINNETSONG,** b f Rambo Dancer (CAN)—Blue Linnet **Mr M. J. Cowie**
25 **VAUDEVILLE,** b g Puissance—Pick A Tune **Mr Bill Waddington**
26 **VOGUE IMPERIAL (IRE),** b g Imperial Frontier (USA)—Classic Choice **Mr David W. Chapman**

Other Owners: Mrs M. E. Armitage, Mr S. B. Clark, Mrs E. A. Cowie, Mr Michael Hill, Mrs M. M. Marshall, Mr K. E. Monaghan, Mr Ian Mosey, Mr J. Stephenson, Mr W. S. Wright.

Lady Rider: Miss Ruth Clark (9-7).

126 MR M. C. CHAPMAN, Market Rasen

Postal: **Woodlands Racing Stables, Woodlands Lane, Willingham Road, Market Rasen, Lincolnshire, LN8 3RE.**
Phone: **(01673) 843663 FAX (01673) 843663 MOBILE (0421) 742755**

1 **ACERBUS DULCIS,** 7, ch g Hadeer—Current Pattie (USA) **Mr George N. Hooke**
2 **AFRICAN SUN (IRE),** 5, b g Mtoto—Nuit d'Ete (USA) **Mr Noel Fletcher**
3 **AWESOME VENTURE,** 8, b g Formidable (USA)—Pine Ridge **Market Rasen Racing Club**
4 **COURT HOUSE,** 4, b g Reprimand—Chalet Girl **Clement Bros**
5 **CRUZ SANTA,** 5, b m Lord Bud—Linpac Mapleleaf **Mr A. S. Newey**
6 **DOWN THE YARD,** 5, b m Batshoof—Sequin Lady **Mr Geoff Whiting**
7 **GUINEAS GALORE (IRE),** 4, b g Classic Secret (USA)—Morning Stroll **G. B. Racing**
8 **LOVE OVER GOLD,** 4, ch f Primo Dominie—Salacious **McCann Limited**
9 **MAID ON THE MILL,** 4, b f Le Solaret (FR)—Maid Mariner **Mrs J. Worthington**
10 **NON VINTAGE (IRE),** 7, ch g Shy Groom (USA)—Great Alexandra **Mr Alan Mann**
11 **ROSE FLYER (IRE),** 8, b m Nordico (USA)—String of Straw **A. M. Packaging Ltd**
12 **RUPPLES,** 11, b g Muscatite—Miss Annie **Mr Tony Satchell**

MR M. C. CHAPMAN—continued

13 **SEA GOD,** 7, ch g Rainbow Quest (USA)—Sea Pageant **McCann Limited**
14 **SHALAAL (USA),** 4, b g Sheikh Albadou—One Fine Day (USA) **Mr Eric Knowles**
15 **SPANISH STRIPPER (USA),** 7, b g El Gran Senor (USA)—Gourmet Dinner (USA) **Mr Tony Satchell**
16 **THIRTY BELOW (IRE),** 9, b g Strong Gale—Arctic Bavard **GB Racing**
17 **UNITUS (IRE),** 5, b h Soviet Star (USA)—Unite **Mr Aiden J. Ryan**
18 **WILLIE WANNABE (IRE),** 8, gr g Roselier (FR)—Quincy Bay **Mr Eric Knowles**

THREE-YEAR-OLDS

19 **JULIES JEWEL (IRE),** ch g Simply Great (FR)—Melungeon **Mrs Julie R. Lamming**
20 **ROSIES MIRACLE,** b g Rambo Dancer (CAN)—Rose Flyer (IRE) **A. M. Packaging Ltd**
21 **WOODLANDS PRIDE (IRE),** ch f Petardia—Valediction **Mr Eric Knowles**

Other Owners: Mr K. D. Blanch, Mr F. W. Brown, Mr E. S. Clement, Mr F. D. Clement, Mr B. S. Derbyshire, Mr T. J. Hayward, Mr G. H. Lamming, Mr Michael Neal, Mr T. Ranshaw, Mr G. D. Seville, Mr K. C. West.

Jockey (NH): W Worthington (10-0).

Amateur: Mr N Chapman (10-0).

127 MAJOR D. N. CHAPPELL, Pulborough

Postal: **Coombelands Stables, Pulborough, West Sussex, RH20 1BP.**
Phone: **(01798) 874795 FAX 874796 CAR (0410) 906655**

1 **GIFT TOKEN,** 4, b f Batshoof—Visible Form **Mrs D. Ellis**
2 **LIVIUS (IRE),** 4, b g Alzao (USA)—Marie de Beaujeu (FR)
3 **PRINTERS QUILL,** 6, b g Squill (USA)—On Impulse **Mrs B. Woodford**
4 **STAR ENTRY,** 4, b f In The Wings—Top Berry **Mr J. H. Widdows**
5 **VOLLEY (IRE),** 5, b m Al Hareb (USA)—Highdrive **Mr R. C. C. Villers**

THREE-YEAR-OLDS

6 **CARVER DOONE,** b g Tragic Role (USA)—Miss Milton **Mr C. Cruden**
7 **INDIAN MISSILE,** ch c Indian Ridge—Haitienne (FR) **Mr R. C. C. Villers**
8 **KATYUSHKA (IRE),** b f Soviet Star (USA)—Welsh Note (USA) **Mrs B. Woodford**
9 **LATEEN,** b f Midyan (USA)—Sail Loft **Major D. N. Chappell**
10 **MANTELLO,** ch c Mon Tresor—Laena **Super Sprinters**
11 **PETRUCHIO (IRE),** b g Petardia—Rising Lady
12 **RIVERS RAINBOW,** b f Primo Dominie—Rivers Maid **Mr Rex L. Mead**
13 **STORM CRY (USA),** b c Hermitage (USA)—Doonesbury Lady (USA) **Rathmore Racing**
14 **THANKSGIVING (IRE),** ch f Indian Ridge—Thank One's Stars **Mrs G. C. Maxwell**

TWO-YEAR-OLDS

15 **FULL MARKS (IRE),** b f 15/3 Perugino (USA)—Centella (IRE) (Thatching) **Super Sprinters**
16 **INDIAN GODDESS (IRE),** b f 3/4 Indian Ridge—Marie de Beaujeu (FR) (Kenmare (FR)) **Mr J. C. Condon**
17 B f 22/4 Mujadil (USA)—Ruby River (Red God) **Mr R. C. C. Villers**
18 Gr f 30/1 Linamix (FR)—Thank One's Stars (Alzao (USA))
19 **WEE MERKIN (IRE),** b f 27/4 Thatching—West of Eden (Crofter (USA)) **Major P. G. Pusinelli**

Other Owners: Mr R. W. Clampett, Mr P. R. Cruden, Mr Donal Douglas, Mr R. Hall, Mr John Lucas, Mr Joe Nally, Mr I. Thompson, Mrs John Tillyard, Mrs C. F. Van Straubenzee, Miss S. E. White.

128 MR P. W. CHAPPLE-HYAM, Marlborough

Postal: **Stone Cottage, Manton House Estate, Manton, Marlborough, Wiltshire, SN8 1PN.**
Phone: **(01672) 514901 OR 515294 FAX (01672) 514907**

1 **CABARET (IRE)**, 5, b m Sadler's Wells (USA)—Chamonis (USA) **Mr Ivan Allan**
2 **CARMINE LAKE (IRE)**, 4, ch f Royal Academy (USA)—Castilian Queen (USA) **Mr R. E. Sangster**
3 **HERON ISLAND (IRE)**, 5, b h Shirley Heights—Dalawara (IRE) **Mr R. E. Sangster & Mrs J. Magnier**
4 **HOWQUA RIVER**, 6, b g Petong—Deep Blue Sea **Mrs Jane Chapple-Hyam**
5 **HURRICANE STATE (USA)**, 4, ch c Miswaki (USA)—Regal State (USA) **Mr R. E. Sangster**
6 **ROMANOV (IRE)**, 4, b c Nureyev (USA)—Morning Devotion (USA) **Mr R. E. Sangster**
7 **SINGLE EMPIRE (IRE)**, 4, ch c Kris—Captive Island **Mr A. K. Collins**
8 **SOVIET STATE (USA)**, 4, b c Nureyev (USA)—Absentia (USA) **Mr R. E. Sangster**
9 **STONE FLOWER (USA)**, 4, b f Storm Bird (CAN)—Lively Living (USA) **Mr R. E. Sangster**

THREE-YEAR-OLDS

10 **BOUNTEOUS (IRE)**, b f Last Tycoon—Fair of The Furze **Mr M. Tabor & Mrs John Magnier**
11 **BRIEF ESCAPADE (IRE)**, ch f Brief Truce (USA)—Repetitious **Mr R. Kaster & Cypress Farms**
12 **CASINO CAPTIVE (USA)**, gr c Kenmare (FR)—Captive Island **Mr R. E. Sangster**
13 **CASINO KING (IRE)**, b c Fairy King (USA)—Justsayno (USA) **Mr R. E. Sangster**
14 **CENTRAL COMMITTEE (IRE)**, ch c Royal Academy (USA)—Idle Chat (USA) **Mr R. E. Sangster**
15 **CHARROUX (IRE)**, b f Darshaan—Durtal **Mr R. E. Sangster**
16 **CHUNITO**, b c Beveled (USA)—Wasimah **In Touch Racing Club**
17 **CLASSIC IMPACT (IRE)**, ch c Generous (IRE)—Vaison La Romaine **Mrs B. V. Sangster**
18 **CONNOISSEUR BAY (USA)**, b c Nureyev (USA)—Feminine Wiles (IRE) **Mr R. E. Sangster**
19 **DARK MOONDANCER**, b c Anshan—Oh So Well (IRE) **Dr Anne J. F. Gillespie & Mr John Wilson**
20 **DESERT MIRAGE**, b c Green Desert (USA)—Anodyne **The Countess of Derby**
21 **DISTANT MIRAGE (IRE)**, b c Caerleon (USA)—Desert Bluebell **Mr R Sangster Mr R Kaster Cypress Farms**
22 **GLORY OF GROSVENOR (IRE)**, ch c Caerleon (USA)—Abury (IRE) **Mr R. E. Sangster**
23 **GROSVENOR SPIRIT (IRE)**, b br f Fairy King (USA)—La Koumia (FR) **Mr R. E. Sangster**
24 **HOLLOW HAZE (USA)**, b br f Woodman (USA)—Libeccio (NZ) **Mr R. E. Sangster**
25 **KING OF THE RIVER (USA)**, b c Kingmambo (USA)—La Favorita (FR) **Mr P. D. Savill**
26 **LAMARQUE (IRE)**, b f Nureyev (USA)—Detroit (FR) **Mr R. E. Sangster**
27 **MANNAKEA (USA)**, b f Fairy King (USA)—Hot Princess **Mr R. E. Sangster**
28 **MONET**, b c Dynaformer (USA)—Ballerina Star (USA) **Mrs Jane Chapple-Hyam**
29 **MUSICAL TWIST (USA)**, ch f Woodman (USA)—Musicale (USA) **Mr R. E. Sangster**
30 **OPENING TITLE (IRE)**, b f Caerleon (USA)—Maiden Concert **Mr R. E. Sangster**
31 **ORMELIE (IRE)**, b c Jade Hunter (USA)—Trolley Song (USA) **Mr K. Doyle**
32 **PAGODA TREE (USA)**, b f Nureyev (USA)—Desert Holly **Mr R. E. Sangster**
33 **SECOND CHORUS (IRE)**, b f Scenic—Never So Fair **Mrs B. V. Sangster**
34 **SEIGNORIAL (USA)**, b c Kingmambo (USA)—Suavite (USA) **Mr J. Gunther**
35 **SOCIAL CHARTER (USA)**, b c Nureyev (USA)—Aunt Pearl (USA) **Mr R. E. Sangster**
36 **SPIRAL DREAM (USA)**, b f El Gran Senor (USA)—Amalise **Mr R. E. Sangster**
37 **STAR OF GROSVENOR (IRE)**, b f Last Tycoon—Castilian Queen (USA) **Mr R. E. Sangster**
38 **VICTORY NOTE (USA)**, b c Fairy King (USA)—Three Piece **Mrs J. Magnier & Mr R. E. Sangster**
39 **VOODOO SAINT (USA)**, ch c St Jovite (USA)—Voo Doo Dance (USA) **Mr R Sangster Mr R Kaster Cypress Farms**

TWO-YEAR-OLDS

40 **ALIZEE (IRE)**, b f 23/2 College Chapel—Richly Deserved (IRE) (Kings Lake (USA)) **Mr B. V. Sangster & Mr R. Cordel**
41 B c 8/4 Danehill (USA)—Always Friendly (High Line) **Mr L. Gaucci**
42 Br c 6/4 Riverman (USA)—Aseltine's Angels (USA) (Fappiano (USA)) **Royal Ascot Racing Club**
43 **ATLANTIC CHARTER (USA)**, b c 22/1 Gone West (USA)—Silk Slippers (USA) (Nureyev (USA)) **Mr R. E. Sangster**
44 B f 8/2 Nureyev (USA)—Aunt Pearl (USA) (Seattle Slew (USA)) **Mr R. E. Sangster**
45 B c 31/3 Dayjur (USA)—Badge of Courage (USA) (Well Decorated (USA)) **Mr L. Gaucci**
46 **BARABASCHI**, b c 16/2 Elmaamul (USA)—Hills' Presidium (Presidium) **Mr P. Calini**
47 **BLANKENBERGE (IRE)**, ch c 14/4 Pips Pride—Renata's Ring (IRE) (Auction Ring (USA)) **Mr R. E. Sangster**
48 B f 12/2 Mukaddamah (USA)—Bourbon Topsy (Ile de Bourbon (USA)) **Mr S. Mulryan**
49 **CASINO QUEEN (IRE)**, ch f 8/3 Royal Academy (USA)—Castilian Queen (USA) (Diesis) **Mr R. E. Sangster**

MR P. W. CHAPPLE-HYAM—continued

50 CIRCLE OF GOLD (IRE), ch f 24/2 Royal Academy (USA)—Never So Fair (Never So Bold) **Mr R. E. Sangster & Mr B. V. Magnier**
51 COMMANDER COLLINS (IRE), b c 8/4 Sadler's Wells (USA)—Kanmary (FR) (Kenmare (FR)) **Mr R. E. Sangster**
52 COURT OF JUSTICE (USA), b c 15/5 Alleged (USA)—Captive Island (Northfields (USA)) **Mr R. E. Sangster**
53 DANCE TRIBUNE (USA), ch f 24/4 Nureyev (USA)—Sam's Diary (USA) (Private Account (USA)) **Mr R. E. Sangster**
54 B f 20/4 Colonel Collins (USA)—Distinctiveness (USA) (Distinctive (USA)) **Mr R. E. Sangster**
55 B f 15/4 Dehere (USA)—Face The Facts (Lomond (USA)) **Mr R. E. Sangster & Mrs J. Magnier**
56 Ch f 3/4 Nureyev (USA)—Feminine Wiles (IRE) (Ahonoora) **Mr R. E. Sangster**
57 FIRST NIGHT (IRE), b f 22/1 Sadler's Wells (USA)—Morning Devotion (USA) (Affirmed (USA)) **Mr R. E. Sangster**
58 FISHERMAN'S SONG (IRE), b c 9/5 Fairy King (USA)—Rose of Jericho (USA) (Alleged (USA)) **Mr R. E. Sangster & Mrs J. Magnier**
59 FOREST SHADOW (IRE), b f 24/4 Sadler's Wells (USA)—Bay Shade (USA) (Sharpen Up) **Mr R. E. Sangster**
60 B c 4/2 Be My Guest (USA)—Green Wings (General Assembly (USA)) **Royal Ascot Racing Club**
61 B c 15/4 Woodman (USA)—Ikebana (IRE) (Sadler's Wells (USA)) **Mr R. E. Sangster**
62 J R STEVENSON (USA), ch c 22/3 Lyphard (USA)—While It Lasts (USA) (Foolish Pleasure (usa)) **Mr R. E. Sangster & Mr B. V. Sangster**
63 KISS ME GOODNIGHT, b f 9/2 First Trump—Flitteriss Park (Beldale Flutter (USA)) **Mr D. Clee**
64 MIDDELKERKE, b c 29/2 College Chapel—Andbell (Trojan Fen) **Mr R. E. Sangster**
65 MIRBECK (USA), ch f 17/5 Gone West (USA)—Oakmead (IRE) (Lomond (USA)) **Mr B. V. Sangster**
66 MONTALCINO (IRE), b c 2/4 Robellino (USA)—Only Gossip (USA) (Trempolino (USA)) **Dr C. Stelling**
67 MOTHER OF PEARL (IRE), b f 14/1 Sadler's Wells (USA)—Sisania (High Top) **Mr R. E. Sangster & Mrs J. Magnier**
68 Ch c 4/2 Gone West (USA)—Musicale (USA) (The Minstrel (CAN)) **Mr R. E. Sangster**
69 MUSICAL TREAT (IRE), ch f 12/2 Royal Academy (USA)—Mountain Ash (Dominion) **Mr R. E. Sangster**
70 Ch c 15/3 Bien Bien (USA)—Nakterjal (Vitiges (FR)) **McCaffrey Toffan Partners**
71 Ch f 7/4 Bien Bien (USA)—Newdaydawning (USA) (Gone West (USA)) **McCaffery Toffan Partners**
72 B f 24/2 Storm Bird (CAN)—Obeah (Cure The Blues (USA)) **Mr R. E. Sangster**
73 OUTER LIMIT (IRE), b c 2/3 Caerleon (USA)—Lady Liberty (NZ) (Noble Bijou (USA)) **Mr R. E. Sangster**
74 SOCIAL SCENE (IRE), ch f 4/4 Grand Lodge (USA)—Ardmelody (Law Society (USA)) **Mr R. E. Sangster & Mr B. V. Sangster**
75 B c 24/5 Pleasant Colony—Star Pastures (Northfields (USA)) **Mr R. E. Sangster**
76 STORMHILL (IRE), b c 18/2 Caerleon (USA)—Jackie Berry (Connaught) **Mr R. E. Sangster**
77 STRING QUARTET (IRE), b f 1/5 Sadler's Wells (USA)—Fleur Royale (Mill Reef (USA)) **Mr R. Sangster**
78 Br c 20/5 Hermitage (USA)—Teresa's Spirit (USA) (Master Derby (USA)) **Mr R. E. Sangster & Mrs J. Magnier**
79 B c 14/2 Forty Niner (USA)—Testy Trestle (USA) (Private Account (USA)) **Mr W. Barnett**
80 Ch f 17/4 Diesis—Timely (Kings Lake (USA)) **Mr R. E. Sangster**
81 TOBRUK (IRE), b c 23/4 Red Ransom (USA)—Memories (USA) (Hail The Pirates (USA)) **Mr R. E. Sangster**
82 VALENCAY (IRE), b f 24/5 Sadler's Wells (USA)—Detroit (FR) (Riverman (USA)) **Mr R. E. Sangster**
83 VANILLE (IRE), b f 1/5 Selkirk (USA)—Stormswept (USA) (Storm Bird (CAN)) **Mr J. Steinmann & Mr P. Deel**
84 WATERFRONT (IRE), b c 7/3 Turtle Island (IRE)—Rising Tide (Red Alert) **Mr R. E. Sangster**
85 WESTBROOK (IRE), b c 9/2 Fairy King (USA)—Abury (IRE) (Law Society (USA)) **Mr R. E. Sangster**
86 WORLD ALERT (IRE), b c 14/4 Alzao (USA)—Steady The Buffs (Balidar) **Mr R. E. Sangster**

Other Owners: Mr W. L. Armitage, Bloomsbury Stud, Cotswold Stud, Mr Ken Ellenberg, Miss Fiona Feeley, Mr Tony Huang, Mr John T. L. Jones, H. R. H. Princess Michael Of Kent, Mr John M. Magnier, Mrs Jacqueline O'Brien, Mr M. V. O'Brien, Mrs Robert Sangster, Mr Richard Santulli, Mr L. Schaffel, Mrs I. M. Steinmann, Mr George Strawbridge, Mr James Wigan, Mr M. Wray.

Jockey (Flat): J Reid (w.a.).

Apprentices: Ryan Cody-Boutcher (7-7), Robert Havlin (7-12).

Lady Rider: Mrs Jane Chapple-Hyam.

129 MR G. F. H. CHARLES-JONES, Wantage

Postal: **The Coach House Stables, Letcombe Regis, Wantage, Oxfordshire, OX12 9LH.**
Phone: **(01235) 767713 CAR (0836) 275292**

1 **ARCH ANGEL (IRE),** 5, ch m Archway (IRE)—Saintly Guest **Mr P. H. Wafford**
2 **BALLYSHEILA,** 6, b m Ayres Rock—Baltana **Mr B. K. Wells**
3 **CADBURY CASTLE,** 4, b f Midyan (USA)—Orange Hill **Mr S. P. Tindall**
4 **CEDAR RUN,** 15, b g Billion (USA)—Sapele **Mrs Jessica Charles-Jones**
5 **COBBLERS COOLER,** 13, b g Posse (USA)—Melaleuca **Mrs Jessica Charles-Jones**
6 **VELVET JONES,** 5, gr g Sharrood (USA)—Cradle of Love (USA) **Mrs Jessica Charles-Jones**
7 **WHIPPERS DELIGHT (IRE),** 10, ch g King Persian—Crashing Juno **Mr S. P. Tindall**

THREE-YEAR-OLDS

8 **LIBERALIS,** ch f Interrex (CAN)—Hello Lady **Mr V. K. Cox**
9 **WAFF'S FOLLY,** b f Handsome Sailor—Shirl **Mr P. H. Wafford**

Jockey (Flat): S Whitworth (w.a.).

Apprentice: Charlotte Cox (7-12).

Conditional: X Aizpuru (9-7, w.a.).

Amateur: Mr A Charles-Jones (10-0).

130 MR J. I. A. CHARLTON, Stocksfield

Postal: **Mickley Grange, Stocksfield, Northd, NE43 7TB.**
Phone: **(01661) 843247 MOBILE (0850) 007415**

1 **BRANCH END,** 6, b g Alias Smith (USA)—Besciamella **Mrs J. J. Straker**
2 **BUCKLEY HOUSE,** 6, b g Buckley—Reperage (USA) **Sydney Ramsey & Partners**
3 **CLAIRABELL (IRE),** 7, b m Buckskin (FR)—Orient Breeze **Mr W. F. Trueman**
4 **FREELANDER (IRE),** 5, b g Satco (FR)—Gueranne **Mr J. I. A. Charlton**
5 **GIVEMEYOURHAND (IRE),** 9, ch g Parliament—Ottavia Abu **Mr F. W. W. Chapman**
6 **KNOCKARA FAIR (IRE),** 5, b g Long Pond—Bonne Fair **Mr J. I. A. Charlton**
7 **LADY MOVE,** 6, b m Move Off—Kelsey Lady **Mr F. W. W. Chapman**
8 **LA RIVIERA (IRE),** 6, ch g Over The River (FR)—La Gloriosa **Mr John Hogg**
9 **LORD DORCET (IRE),** 8, b g Remainder Man—Lady Dorcet **Mr John Hogg**
10 **LORD KNOWS (IRE),** 7, b g Nearly A Nose (USA)—Roaming Free **Mr J. I. A. Charlton**
11 **LUNAR MODULE,** 5, b m Dancing High—Pauper Moon **Mr J. W. Robson**
12 **MR JAKE,** 5, b g Safawan—Miss Tealeaf (USA) **Mr R. A. Ross**
13 **POLITICAL DIAMOND,** 7, b m Politico (USA)—Hejera **Mr J. W. Robson**
14 **RADICAL CHOICE (IRE),** 9, b g Radical—Shule Doe **Mr J. I. A. Charlton**
15 **RADICAL STORM (IRE),** 7, ch g Radical—On The Dry **Mr W. M. Aitchison**

Other Owners: Mrs P. Boynton, Mr A. E. Brown, Mr David Carr, Mr W. R. Middleton, Mr W. R. Page, Mr J. T. Stobbs.

Jockey (Flat): Jane Findlay (8-0).

Jockey (NH): B Storey (10-0, w.a.).

Conditional: D Thomas (9-7).

Amateur: Mr Mark Bradburne (10-2).

131 MR ROGER J. CHARLTON, Beckhampton

Postal: **Beckhampton House, Marlborough, Wilts, SN8 1QR.**
Phone: **OFFICE (01672) 539533 FAX (01672) 539456 HOME (01672) 539330**

1 **BARON FERDINAND,** 8, ch g Ferdinand (USA)—In Perpetuity **Lady Rothschild**
2 **CAP JULUCA (IRE),** 6, b g Mtoto—Tabyan (USA) **Mr Martin Myers**
3 **MYRTLE QUEST,** 6, b g Rainbow Quest (USA)—Wryneck **Miss M. Sheriffe**
4 **PENTAD (USA),** 4, b c Quest For Fame—Nifty Fifty (USA) **Mr K. Abdulla**
5 **SALAMAH,** 4, b g Sadler's Wells (USA)—Ala Mahlik **Mr K. Abdulla**
6 **WIXIM (USA),** 5, ch h Diesis—River Lullaby (USA) **Mr K. Abdulla**
7 **YALTA (IRE),** 5, b g Soviet Star (USA)—Gay Hellene **Lord Weinstock**

THREE-YEAR-OLDS

8 **AMBOSELI,** b g Zafonic (USA)—Aryenne (FR) **Mr K. Abdulla**
9 **AUNT SADIE,** ch f Pursuit of Love—Piney River **Mr J. R. Boughey**
10 **BLUE GENTIAN (USA),** b f Known Fact (USA)—Caithness (USA) **Mr K. Abdulla**
11 **BOATSWAIN,** b g Pursuit of Love—Bay Bay **Lady Rothschild**
12 **BORGIA,** ch f Machiavellian (USA)—Cut Ahead **Lady Rothschild**
13 **BRILLIANCE,** ch f Cadeaux Genereux—Rainbow's End **Lord Carnarvon**
14 **BRILLIANT CORNERS,** b c Royal Academy (USA)—Curie Point (USA) **Mr Michael Pescod**
15 **CHARIVARI,** b f Zafonic (USA)—Star of The Future (USA) **Mr K. Abdulla**
16 **CLOUDS OF GLORY,** b f Lycius (USA)—Dance A Jig **Mr N. Bryce-Smith**
17 **COLD CLIMATE,** b g Pursuit of Love—Sharpthorne (USA) **Mr K. Abdulla**
18 **CONICAL,** b f Zafonic (USA)—De Stael (USA) **Mr K. Abdulla**
19 **DERRYQUIN,** b g Lion Cavern (USA)—Top Berry **Lady Bland**
20 **DESERT LADY (IRE),** b f Danehill (USA)—Hooray Lady **The Thoroughbred Corporation**
21 **EAGLE'S CROSS (USA),** b c Trempolino (USA)—Shining Bright **Mr K. Abdulla**
22 **FAIRER,** gr f Fairy King (USA)—Dimmer **Duke of Roxburghe**
23 **FUEGIAN,** ch g Arazi (USA)—Well Beyond (IRE) **Mr K. Abdulla**
24 **FULL SPATE,** ch c Unfuwain (USA)—Double River (USA) **Mr K. Abdulla**
25 **GALINGAL (USA),** b f Known Fact (USA)—Galega **Mr K. Abdulla**
26 **HARMONIC WAY,** ch c Lion Cavern (USA)—Pineapple **Mrs Alexandra J. Chandris**
27 **HOUSEKEEPER (IRE),** b f Common Grounds—Staff Approved **Anglia Bloodstock Syndicate 1996**
28 **MARATI SPRING,** ch f Emarati (USA)—Chiming Melody **Fieldspring Racing**
29 **MISS PENTON,** ch f Primo Dominie—On The House (FR) **Mr A. E. Oppenheimer**
30 **MONTE LEMOS (IRE),** b g Mukaddamah (USA)—Crimbourne **Mr S. M. De Zoete**
31 **MOON QUEST,** ch c Rainbow Quest (USA)—Mrs Moonlight **Mr K. Abdulla**
32 **MUSTIQUE DREAM,** b f Don't Forget Me—Jamaican Punch (IRE) **Mr Wafic Said**
33 **MYSTIC FLIGHT (USA),** b f Silver Hawk (USA)—Wand (IRE) **Cliveden Stud**
34 **NIGHT CHIME (IRE),** b f Night Shift (USA)—Baydon Belle (USA) **W.V. M.W. & Mrs E.S. Robins**
35 **NIGHT OWL,** b f Night Shift (USA)—Sarah Georgina **Mrs C. F. Van Straubenzee**
36 **PAPER TIGER (USA),** b g Quest For Fame—Absara's Dancer (USA) **Lord De La Warr**
37 **PELAGOS (FR),** gr c Exit To Nowhere (USA)—Southern Maid (USA) **Niarchos Family**
38 **PRECISION,** b c Kris—Sweetly (FR) **Highclere Thoroughbred Racing Ltd**
39 **QUICKSAND (IRE),** ch f Lycius (USA)—Sandbank (USA) **Mr A. E. Oppenheimer**
40 **RED RAMONA,** b c Rudimentary (USA)—Apply **Mr James D. Wolfensohn**
41 **REDWOOD,** b g Salse (USA)—Arboretum (IRE) **Lady Rothschild**
42 **SAPPHIRE RING,** b f Marju (IRE)—Mazarine Blue **The Thoroughbred Corporation**
43 **SPANISH FERN (USA),** b br f El Gran Senor (USA)—Chain Fern (USA) **Mr K. Abdulla**
44 **SPEAKER'S CHAIR,** b c Shirley Heights—Lead Note (USA) **Mr K. Abdulla**
45 **STILL WATERS,** b g Rainbow Quest (USA)—Krill **Mr K. Abdulla**
46 **SULEYMAN,** b c Alhijaz—Aonia **Lady Annabel Goldsmith**
47 **SUMMER MIST (USA),** b f Miswaki (USA)—Miss Summer **Mr K. Abdulla**
48 **TABERNACLE,** ch c Selkirk (USA)—Tabyan (USA) **Mr Martin Myers**
49 **TAMARISK (IRE),** b c Green Desert (USA)—Sine Labe (USA) **Highclere Thoroughbred Racing Ltd**
50 **TERRAZZO (USA),** b c Nureyev (USA)—Diese (USA) **Mr K. Abdulla**
51 **VERVE (IRE),** b f Saddlers' Hall (IRE)—Arousal **Lord Weinstock**
52 **WHITE LIGHT,** br f Zafonic (USA)—White Shadow (IRE) **Mr K. Abdulla**
53 **ZIP,** br f Persian Bold—Lady Zi **Lady Rothschild**

MR ROGER J. CHARLTON—continued

TWO-YEAR-OLDS

54 AMUSEMENT, ch c 15/4 Mystiko (USA)—Jolies Eaux (Shirley Heights)
55 ANALYTICAL, b c 7/4 Pursuit Of Love—Risha Flower (Kris)
56 B c 14/5 Quest For Fame—Another Notch (USA) (Cox's Ridge (USA))
57 B c 5/3 Rainbow Quest (USA)—Armeria (USA) (Northern Dancer)
58 B f 17/3 Sadler's Wells (USA)—Bahamian (Mill Reef (USA))
59 BARRISTER (IRE), ch c 29/1 Barathea (IRE)—Silver Hut (USA) (Silver Hawk (USA))
60 BAYDON BREEZE (IRE), b c 2/5 Common Grounds—Baydon Belle (USA) (Al Nasr (FR))
61 BOMBAY, ch f 30/4 Be My Chief (USA)—Bay Bay (Bay Express)
62 B f 25/3 Diesis—Caithness (USA) (Roberto (USA))
63 Ch c 19/5 El Gran Senor (USA)—Chain Fern (USA) (Blushing Groom (FR))
64 B c 25/4 Tenby—Crown Rose (Dara Monarch)
65 B f 20/3 Shirley Heights—Danilova (FR) (Lyphard (USA))
66 Ch f 1/3 Forty Niner (USA)—Danzante (USA) (Danzig (USA))
67 DARLING COREY, b f 20/4 Caerleon (USA)—Tass (Soviet Star (USA))
68 Ch c 25/4 Nashwan (USA)—De Stael (USA) (Nijinsky (CAN))
69 B c 21/4 Nureyev (USA)—Diese (USA) (Diesis)
70 B f 16/3 Deploy—Double River (USA) (Irish River (FR))
71 DUCK OVER, b f 3/4 Warning—Waterfowl Creek (Be My Guest (USA))
72 B f 13/4 Alzao (USA)—Gold Tear (USA) (Tejano (USA))
73 GREEK MYTH (IRE), b f 29/1 Sadler's Wells (USA)—Greektown (Ela-Mana-Mou)
74 GREEN ACADEMY (IRE), b c 17/3 Royal Academy (USA)—Hellenic (Darshaan)
75 HARPOON, b c 27/3 Kris—Jezebel Monroe (USA) (Lyphard (USA))
76 B c 25/3 Primo Dominie—High Savannah (Rousillon (USA))
77 Ch f 31/1 Generous (IRE)—Kerali (High Line)
78 B f 2/5 Bigstone (IRE)—Lady Chat (CAN) (Shahrastani (USA))
79 LUZ BAY (IRE), b c 1/4 Tenby—Cabcharge Princess (IRE) (Rambo Dancer (CAN))
80 MARTELLO, b c 21/5 Polish Precedent—Round Tower (High Top)
81 MOLY, b f 12/3 Inchinor—Circe's Isle (Be My Guest (USA))
82 OATH (IRE), b c 22/4 Fairy King (USA)—Sheer Audacity (Troy)
83 OCEAN REEF, b f 6/5 Lugana Beach—Princess Athena (Ahonoora)
84 Ch c 16/3 Irish River (FR)—Peplum (USA) (Nijinsky (CAN))
85 PORT MEADOW (IRE), b c 14/3 Common Grounds—Kharimata (IRE) (Kahyasi)
86 REYNOLDS (IRE), b c 15/2 Royal Academy (USA)—In Perpetuity (Great Nephew)
87 Ch c 3/4 Zafonic (USA)—River Lullaby (USA) (Riverman (USA))
88 SALSIFY, b c 10/3 Salse (USA)—Amaranthus (Shirley Heights)
89 SCARLET SCEPTRE (USA), b f 25/3 Red Ransom (USA)—Wand (IRE) (Reference Point)
90 Ch f 24/2 Wolfhound (USA)—Sharpthorne (USA) (Sharpen Up)
91 SHEBA SPRING (IRE), b f 14/2 Brief Truce (USA)—Shebasis (USA) (General Holme (USA))
92 B c 20/4 Lahib (USA)—Sherkova (USA) (State Dinner (USA))
93 Ch f 17/3 Irish River (FR)—Storm Dove (USA) (Storm Bird (CAN))
94 STRIKER (IRE), b c 21/3 Night Shift (USA)—Streak To Glory (USA) (Diesis)
95 B f 18/3 Grand Lodge (USA)—Style of Life (USA) (The Minstrel (CAN))
96 Ch c 30/4 Known Fact (USA)—Sunerta (USA) (Roberto (USA))

Other Owners: The Queen, Anglia Bloodstock Syndicate 1997, Mr M. H. D. Barlow, Beckhampton Stables Ltd, Mrs T. Brudenell, Mr T. M. Brudenell, Mrs M. Bryce-Smith, Mr P. A. Deal, Lord Hopetoun, Mr G. Howard-Spink, Platinum Syndicate Ltd, Miss L. Regis, Mr Ray Richards, Lady Vestey, Mr Patrick Wiener.

Apprentice: Kevin Parsons (7-5).

132 MR P. CHEESBROUGH, Bishop Auckland

Postal: **Crawleas, Leasingthorne, Bishop Auckland, Co. Durham, DL14 8EL.**
Phone: **(01388) 720213**

1 **CRASHBALLOO (IRE)**, 7, ch g Balinger—Crash Approach **Mr J. A. Stephenson**
2 5, B g Meneval (USA)—Fine Artist **Mr J. A. Stephenson**
3 **HOPEFUL LORD (IRE)**, 6, b g Lord Americo—Billie Gibb **Mr P. Piller**
4 **MAJORITY MAJOR (IRE)**, 9, b g Cheval—La Perla **Mr John R. Jones**
5 **MENALDI (IRE)**, 8, b g Meneval (USA)—Top Riggin **Mr J. A. Stephenson**
6 **NOTOOBIG**, 6, b g Lafontaine (USA)—Sugar Owl **Mr J. A. Stephenson**
7 **ROAD BY THE RIVER (IRE)**, 10, ch g Over The River (FR)—Ahadoon **T. P. M. McDonagh Ltd**
8 **STRONGALONG (IRE)**, 8, b g Strong Gale—Cailin Cainnteach **Mr J. A. Stephenson**
9 **STRONG SOUND**, 11, b g Strong Gale—Jazz Music **Mr J. A. Stephenson**
10 **TRUE SCOT (IRE)**, 8, b g Sheer Grit—Highland Worker **Mr J. A. Stephenson**
11 **WHAT THE HECK (IRE)**, 6, b g Mister Lord (USA)—Arianrhod **Mr J. A. Stephenson**

Other Owners: Mr Alan Cairns, Mr I. D. Cheesbrough, Mr P. McDonagh, Mr T. McDonagh, Panther Racing Ltd, Mr G. W. Turner, Miss S. J. Turner, Mr J. Walby, Mr J. Wilson Walker.

133 DR D. CHESNEY, Dorchester

Postal: **Cowden, Charminster, Dorchester, Dorset, DT2 9RN.**
Phone: **(01305) 265450 FAX (01305) 250684**

1 **BILLINGSGATE**, 6, ch g Nicholas Bill—Polly Washdish **Dr D. Chesney**
2 4, B f Ardross—Forty Watts **Dr D. Chesney**
3 5, B g Un Desperado (FR)—Hooch **Dr D. Chesney**
4 **OUR MAN FLIN (IRE)**, 5, br g Mandalus—Flinging **Dr D. Chesney**
5 4, B f Carlingford Castle—Sarah's Venture **Dr D. Chesney**

134 MR S. B. CLARK, Sutton-on-the-Forest

Postal: **Ride Away, Stillington Road, Sutton-on-the-Forest, York, YO6 1EH.**
Phone: **HOME (01347) 810700 CAR (0966) 442579 FAX (01347) 810746**

1 **BAHER (USA)**, 9, b g Damister (USA)—Allatum (USA) **Mr S. B. Clark**
2 **KATOUCHE (IRE)**, 7, b g Cataldi—Jocks Fancy **Mr S. B. Clark**
3 **SUNKALA SHINE**, 10, ch g Kalaglow—Allander Girl **Mr S. B. Clark**

Other Owners: Mrs A. Clark.

Amateur: Mr Richard Clark (10-7).

Lady Rider: Miss Ruth Clark (9-10).

135 MR PETER C. CLARKE, Hailsham

Postal: **Merryweathers Farm Stables, Chilsham Lane, Bodle Street, Hailsham, East Sussex, BN27 4QH.**
Phone: **(01323) 832098 FAX (01323) 833852 MOBILE (0836) 744510**

1 **BEE DEE BOY,** 10, b g Julio Mariner—H And K Gambler **Mrs E. M. R. Ludlow**
2 **CARWYN'S CHOICE,** 5, b m Then Again—Over My Head **Second Chance Racing**
3 **INSURE,** 20, b g Dusky Boy—Shady Tree **Mr Peter C. Clarke**
4 **PEARL DAWN (IRE),** 8, b m Jareer (USA)—Spy Girl **Mrs E. Keep**
5 **P GRAYCO CHOICE,** 5, b m Bold Fox—Unjha **P. Gray Limited**
6 **SAPPHIRE SON (IRE),** 6, ch g Maelstrom Lake—Gluhwein **Mr D. Cobb**
7 **SILENT SOVEREIGN,** 9, ch g Kind of Hush—Regency Brighton **Mr Gareth Dowdell**
8 **STRAIGHT LACED (USA),** 11, b g Alleged (USA)—Swoonmist (USA) **Mrs E. M. R. Ludlow**
9 **TELF,** 18, ch g Le Bavard (FR)—Vulplume **Mr Peter C. Clarke**
10 **VICTORY ANTHEM,** 12, ch g Tug of War—Anvil Chorus **P. Gray Limited**

Other Owners: Miss C. M. Morris.

Jockey (Flat): N Adams.

Jockey (NH): B Powell.

Apprentice: R Ffrench.

Conditional: B Fenton.

Amateur: Mr P C Clarke (10-4).

136 MR NICOLAS CLEMENT, Chantilly

Postal: **37, Avenue de Joinville, 60500 Chantilly, France.**
Phone: **44 57 59 60 FAX 44 57 70 84**

1 **ALLEZ CHANTILLY (FR),** 4, b c Groom Dancer—Comete de Halley
2 **MAKE MY DAY (FR),** 4, b f Akarad—Masada
3 **SACRED FIRE,** 6, b h Saumarez—Miracle of Love
4 **SENSITIVITY (USA),** 4, ch f Blushing John—Andora

THREE-YEAR-OLDS

5 **BE MINE,** b f Wolfhound—Upper Strata
6 **BLUE INDIGO (FR),** b f Pistolet Bleu—Alcove
7 **CENTERFOLD (FR),** gr f Kenmare—Centriste
8 **CHEEKY WEEKY,** b f Cadeaux Genereux—Fadaki Hawaki
9 **ESPERERO (USA),** b c Forty Niner—Hydro Calido
10 **EXIT TO BRASIL (FR),** b g Exit To Nowhere—Belle du Bresil
11 **EXPECT TO SHINE (USA),** ch f Mr Prospector—Frankova
12 **FARINHA (SWI),** b f Wolfhound—Flute
13 **FLIMSY,** b f Mtoto—Flyleaf
14 **GREEN LAAFE,** b c Green Desert—Green Flower
15 **HONOUR BOUND (FR),** ch c Machiavellian—Heavenly Music
16 **JUST WIN (FR),** b f Homme de Loi—Lady of The House
17 **LA MALOMBREE (FR),** b f Sleeping Car—Carmissa
18 **LOOK AND LEARN (FR),** ch c Rock Hopper—Lailati
19 **MALSOON (USA),** b c Hansel—Maysoon

MR NICOLAS CLEMENT—continued

20 **MONTHLERY (FR)**, b g Balleroy—Marjana
21 **MOVING BINN (IRE)**, b f River Falls—All Away
22 **MYSTERY STRIKE (FR)**, b c Alzao—Mysterious Move
23 **NEW TRADITION (FR)**, ch f Wolfhound—Dinner Out
24 **PANFILO**, b c Thatching—Reveuse du Soir
25 **POZARICA (FR)**, b c Rainbow Quest—Anna Matruschka
26 **RAFEEF**, b c Salse—Daisy Grey
27 **SEMANTICA (FR)**, gr f Tel Quel—Une Florentine
28 **SHAATIR**, b c Rainbow Quest—Durrah
29 **SHANJAH**, b f Darshaan—Al Najah
30 **TERROIR (IRE)**, b c Fairy King—Terracotta Hut
31 **TOBAGO (USA)**, b c Gone West—Dry Fly
32 **TRIPLE BLADE (USA)**, b c Mr Prospector—Salchow
33 **VERZASCA (IRE)**, b f Sadler's Wells—Vanishing Prairie
34 **WALEEMA**, ch c Lycius—Nimieza

TWO-YEAR-OLDS

35 **BINN TIN TIN (FR)**, b c 18/4 Irish River—Cordial Lady (The Minstrel)
36 B f 7/2 Time For A Change—Cape (Mr Prospector)
37 Ch f Lyphard—C Sharp (Sharpen Up)
38 **DEBINNAIR (FR)**, ch f 8/2 Wolfhound—Lady Thynn (Crystal Glitters)
39 **FARINEL**, b c 16/5 In The Wings—Dame de L'Oise (Riverman)
40 **FELICITA (IRE)**, gr f 24/4 Catrail—Abergwerle (Absalom)
41 **HORS LA LOI (FR)**, ch c 17/2 Exit To Nowhere—Kernia (Raise A Cup)
42 **LA FROU FROU (IRE)**, b f 5/2 Night Shift—Waffle On (Chief Singer)
43 **LA PASCUA (SWI)**, ch f 7/4 Caerleon—La Venta (Drone)
44 **LA SYLPHIDE (SWI)**, b f 20/2 Barathea—Vanishing Prairie (Alysheba)
45 **LIT (IRE)**, b f 2/2 Danehill—Lisheba (Alysheba)
46 **MARE BALTICUM (FR)**, b f 12/2 Zieten—Marsoumeh (Green Dancer)
47 Ch c 14/2 Machiavellian—Miracle of Love (Nureyev)
48 **NASHAMIX (FR)**, b f 21/5 Linamix—Nashra (Brustolon)
49 **PELLICANO**, ch c 18/2 Arazi—Savoureuse Lady (Caerleon)
50 **ROMANTIQUE (FR)**, b f 23/3 Le Balafre—Red At Night (Ela-Mana-Mou)
51 **SHORTLY (FR)**, gr f 8/3 Linamix—Short Change (Nonoalco)
52 **VALEUREUSE**, ch f 2/3 Nashwan—Valverda (Irish River)

137 MR T. T. CLEMENT, Newmarket

Postal: **Calder Park, Hamilton Road, Newmarket, Suffolk, CB8 0NY.**
Phone: **(01638) 561384 MOBILE (0585) 674474**

1 **ARABIAN FLIGHT**, 6, ch g Sayf El Arab (USA)—Smooth Flight **Mrs C. Clement**
2 **CABCHARGE GLORY**, 4, ch f Executive Man—Clipsall **Mr Glyn Lewis**
3 **CASINO CHIP**, 5, b g Daring March—Important Guest **Mr R. Marks**
4 **COMMANDER TOM**, 9, ch g Jester—Girl Commander (USA) **Mrs C. Clement**
5 **JONBEL**, 10, b g Norwick (USA)—Two Shots **Mr Ian Pattle**
6 **MAGIC LEADER (IRE)**, 6, b g Architect (USA)—Magic Rotation (USA) **Mr Ian Pattle**
7 5, B m Lyphento (USA)—Precociously **Mrs Anne Jackson**
8 **SCORPIUS**, 8, b h Soviet Star (USA)—Sally Brown **Mrs C. Clement**
9 4, Ch f Wing Park—Tarkesha **Mr A. Morley**
10 **TROJAN RED**, 8, ch h Trojan Legend—Equatious **Mr A. Morley**

THREE-YEAR-OLDS

11 **ADRENALIN**, ch g Risk Me (FR)—High Cairn (FR) **Mr C. Holcroft**
12 **DUDLEY ALLEN**, ch c Superlative—Smooth Flight **Miss L. Davies**
13 **PREMIER BARON**, b c Primo Dominie—Anna Karietta **Miss T. J. Fitzgerald**

MR T. T. CLEMENT—continued

TWO-YEAR-OLDS

14 Ch f 20/3 Rock Hopper—Smooth Flight **Mr Glyn Lewis**

Other Owners: Mr Terry Connors, Miss Elizabeth Herbert, Mr W. Heywood, Miss J. Marsden.

Jockey (Flat): John Stack.

Apprentice: Jamie Gotobed.

Amateurs: Mr R Barrett (9-0), Mr V Lukaniuk (9-0).

138 MR K. F. CLUTTERBUCK, Royston

Postal: **The Greenings, Foxfield Farm, Fowlmere Road, Melbourn, Royston, Herts, SG8 6EZ.**
Phone: **(01763) 263143**

1 A GIFT FROM MAGEE (IRE), 6, b m Homo Sapien—Struell Course **Mr K. F. Clutterbuck**
2 BRIDGE END (IRE), 7, ch g Meneval (USA)—Deep Cristina **Mr K. F. Clutterbuck**
3 6, B g Merrymount—Jim's Girl **Mr K. F. Clutterbuck**
4 KNIVENIVEN (IRE), 5, b g Denel (FR)—Loughan-Na-Curry **Mr K. F. Clutterbuck**
5 5, B g King Persian—Shivey **Mr K. F. Clutterbuck**
6 THEYDON PRIDE, 9, ch g Oats—Cavaleuse **Mr K. F. Clutterbuck**

139 MRS SUSAN CLYDE, Antrim

Postal: **Craigs Stud, Ballyclare, Co. Antrim, BT39 9DE, Ireland.**
Phone: **(01960) 322327**

1 ABDULLAH BULBUL, 10, b g Tina's Pet—Shercol **Mrs D. H. Clyde**
2 5, B g Bustomi—Blue Grotto
3 CLOONYQUIN (IRE), 8, b g Bustomi—Mattress
4 COULTERS HILL (IRE), 10, b g Bustomi—Birdcage
5 DEVON CASTLE (IRE), 8, ch g Carlingford Castle—Oula-Ka Fu-Fu
6 GORTNAMONA, 12, ch g Bustomi—Mattress
7 KATHERINE KATH, 7, b m Merdon Melody—Krafty Kate
8 PRINCE YAZA, 11, b g Ya Zaman—Frances Jordan
9 THE DARGLE (IRE), 8, b g Bustomi—Worling-Pearl
10 6, Ch g Bustomi—The Red Mare

Conditional: Adrian O'Shea (8-13).

Lady Rider: Miss E Hyndman (9-0).

140 MR R. G. COCKBURN, Carlisle

Postal: **Stonecroft, High Ireby, Carlisle, Cumbria, CA5 1HF.**

1 ELASTIC, 12, b m Ela-Mana-Mou—Queen of The Dance **Mrs D. Cockburn**
2 JOHNNEYS SPIRIT, 6, b g Kala Shikari—Summerhill Spirit **Mrs D. Cockburn**
3 MY MISSILE, 8, ch m Kabour—Miss Emily **Mrs D. Cockburn**

141 MR H. T. COLE, Taunton

Postal: **Frog Street Farm, Hatch Beauchamp, Taunton, Somerset, TA3 6AF.**
Phone: **(01823) 480430**

1 **CAMILLAS LEGACY**, 7, br m Newski (USA)—Just Certain **Mr Henry T. Cole**
2 **FROG STREET (IRE)**, 4, b f Orchestra—Credora Bay **Mr Henry T. Cole**
3 **SUPREME FLAME (IRE)**, 8, b br g Supreme Leader—Rossacurra **Mr Henry T. Cole**

142 MR P. F. I. COLE, Whatcombe

Postal: **Whatcombe Estate, Whatcombe, Wantage, Oxfordshire, OX12 9NW.**
Phone: **(01488) 638433 FAX (01488) 638609**

1 **BADLESMERE (USA)**, 4, b c Geiger Counter (USA)—Arising (USA) **Exors of the late Lord Sondes**
2 **CRAZY CHIEF**, 5, b h Indian Ridge—Bizarre Lady **Mr David J. Simpson**
3 **CYRIAN (IRE)**, 4, b g Persian Bold—Regina St Cyr (IRE) **Lord Donoughmore**
5 **DARK GREEN (USA)**, 4, ch c Green Dancer (USA)—Ardisia (USA) **H.R.H. Prince Fahd Salman**
6 **FUTURE PERFECT**, 4, b g Efisio—True Ring **R.O.M. Racing**
7 **GRANNY'S PET**, 4, ch g Selkirk (USA)—Patsy Western **Mrs Denise Margot Arbib**
8 **HEART OF ARMOR**, 4, b g Tirol—Hemline **Mr J. S. Gutkin**
9 **KUALA LIPIS (USA)**, 5, b h Lear Fan (USA)—Caerna (USA) **H.R.H. Sultan Ahmad Shah**
10 **MERIT (IRE)**, 6, b h Rainbow Quest (USA)—Fur Hat **H.R.H. Prince Fahd Salman**
11 **MONTFORT (USA)**, 4, b g Manila (USA)—Sable Coated **Sir George Meyrick**
12 **POSIDONAS**, 6, b h Slip Anchor—Tamassos **Mr Athos Christodoulou**
13 **PRESENT ARMS (USA)**, 5, b h Affirmed (USA)—Au Printemps (USA) **H.R.H. Prince Fahd Salman**
14 **PUTRA (USA)**, 4, ch c Dixie Brass (USA)—Olatha (USA) **H.R.H. Sultan Ahmad Shah**
16 **RIYADIAN**, 6, ch h Polish Precedent (USA)—Knight's Baroness **H.R.H. Prince Fahd Salman**
17 **SALMON LADDER (USA)**, 6, b h Bering—Ballerina Princess (USA) **Mr M. Arbib**
18 **SLIP THE NET (IRE)**, 4, b g Slip Anchor—Circus Ring **Mr J. S. Gutkin**
19 **SMART BOY (IRE)**, 4, ch c Polish Patriot (USA)—Bouffant **H.R.H. Sultan Ahmad Shah**
20 **SNOW PARTRIDGE (USA)**, 4, ch c Arctic Tern (USA)—Lady Sharp (FR) **Mr M. Arbib**
21 **STAR MANAGER (USA)**, 8, b g Lyphard (USA)—Angel Clare (FR) **Mr M. Arbib**
22 **STRATEGIC CHOICE (USA)**, 7, b h Alleged (USA)—Danlu (USA) **Mr M. Arbib**
23 **TASIK CHINI (USA)**, 4, b g St Jovite (USA)—Ten Hail Marys (USA) **H.R.H. Sultan Ahmad Shah**
24 **THE WEST (USA)**, 4, ch c Gone West (USA)—Lady For Two (USA) **H.R.H. Prince Fahd Salman**
25 **WINDSOR CASTLE**, 4, b c Generous (IRE)—One Way Street **H.R.H. Prince Fahd Salman**
26 **YORKSHIRE (IRE)**, 4, ch c Generous (IRE)—Ausherra (USA) **H.R.H. Prince Fahd Salman**

THREE-YEAR-OLDS

27 **ACT DEFIANT (USA)**, br c Nureyev (USA)—Alydariel (USA) **E. J. Hudson Jnr & W. S. Kilroy**
28 **AL'S FELLA (IRE)**, br c Alzao (USA)—Crystal Cross (USA) **Mrs Christopher Hanbury**
29 **ALYA (USA)**, br f Deputy Minister (CAN)—Colonial Waters (USA) **H.R.H. Prince Fahd Salman**
30 **ANTIGUA**, ch f Selkirk (USA)—Historiette **Mr Faisal Salman**
32 **BERING GIFTS (IRE)**, b g Bering—Bobbysoxer **GG Partnership**
33 **BODYGUARD**, ch c Zafonic (USA)—White Wisteria **H.R.H. Prince Fahd Salman**
34 **BUSHRA (USA)**, b f Danzig (USA)—Wedding Reception (USA) **H.R.H. Prince Fahd Salman**
35 **CAERNARFON BAY (IRE)**, ch c Royal Academy (USA)—Bay Shade (USA) **Sir George Meyrick**
36 **CARRY THE FLAG**, b c Tenby—Tamassos **Mr Athos Christodoulou**
38 **COPERNICUS**, b c Polish Precedent (USA)—Oxslip **Mr Christopher Wright**
39 **CORNICHE (IRE)**, b br c Marju (IRE)—Far But Near (USA) **H.R.H. Prince Fahd Salman**
40 **COURAGEOUS (IRE)**, ch c Generous (IRE)—Legend of Arabia **H.R.H. Prince Fahd Salman**
41 **COURTEOUS**, b c Generous (IRE)—Dayanata **H.R.H. Prince Fahd Salman**
42 **DECISIVE ACTION (USA)**, br c Alleged (USA)—Maria Balastiere (USA) **Mr Christopher Wright**
43 **DEEP DIVE (USA)**, ch c Manila (USA)—Shamrock Boat (USA) **Mr W. S. Farish III**
44 **DILIGENCE (IRE)**, b c Dilum (USA)—Florinda (CAN) **Axom**
45 **EVANDER (IRE)**, ch c Indian Ridge—Heavenly Hope **Mr Anthony Speelman**
46 **EVENING WORLD (FR)**, ch c Bering—Pivoine (USA) **Mr T. M. Hely-Hutchinson**
47 **EXTRAVAGANZA**, ch c Rainbow Quest (USA)—Affection Affirmed (USA) **H.R.H. Prince Fahd Salman**

MR P. F. I. COLE—continued

48 FATHER KRISMAS, ch c Kris—My Sister Ellen **Mr M. Arbib**
49 FFESTINIOG (IRE), b f Efisio—Penny Fan **Elite Racing Club**
50 GENEROSITY, ch c Generous (IRE)—Pageantry **H.R.H. Prince Fahd Salman**
51 GOLDEN HAWK (USA), ch c Silver Hawk (USA)—Crockadore (USA) **H.R.H. Prince Fahd Salman**
52 GOTHIC ARC (USA), br f Brown Arc (USA)—Crypto Game (USA) **Mr Frank Stella**
53 HIGH TENSION (USA), b c Sadler's Wells (USA)—Very Confidential (USA) **H.R.H. Prince Fahd Salman**
54 ITHADTOBEYOU, b c Prince Sabo—Secret Valentine **Mrs M. McMillan**
55 JAZZ CLUB (USA), b c Dixieland Band (USA)—Hidden Garden (USA) **Mr W. S. Farish III**
56 JOHN FERNELEY, b c Polar Falcon (USA)—I'll Try **Richard Green (Fine Paintings)**
58 LADY IN WAITING, b f Kylian (USA)—High Savannah **Pegasus Racing Ltd**
59 LATIN NEXUS (USA), b f Roman Diplomat (USA)—Miami Game (USA) **Mr Frank Stella**
60 LOVIN SPOONFUL (USA), ch f Dixieland Band (USA)—O My Darling (USA) **Mr Christopher Wright**
61 MOWBRAY (USA), b br c Opening Verse (USA)—Peppy Raja (USA) **Sir George Meyrick**
62 MY WAY (IRE), b f Marju (IRE)—Ausherra (USA) **H.R.H. Prince Fahd Salman**
63 NEW YORKER (USA), ch c Gilded Time (USA)—Doris's Secret (USA) **H.R.H. Prince Fahd Salman**
64 PAY ON RED (USA), br c Red Ransom (USA)—Mo Jo Kate (USA) **Mr Terry Neill**
65 PEMBROKE SQUARE (IRE), b c Tenby—The Poachers Lady (IRE) **Lord Donoughmore**
66 QUINTUS (USA), ch c Sky Classic (CAN)—Superbe Dawn (USA) **Sir George Meyrick**
67 SAHARA, b f Green Desert (USA)—Marie d'Argonne (FR) **Lord Lloyd-Webber**
68 SAUDI, b c Green Desert (USA)—Emaline (FR) **H.R.H. Prince Fahd Salman**
69 SECOND WIND, ch c Kris—Rimosa's Pet **Mr David J. Simpson**
70 SECRECY, b c Polish Precedent (USA)—Blonde Prospect (USA) **H.R.H. Prince Fahd Salman**
71 SHEMA (USA), ch f Silver Hawk (USA)—Capades (USA) **H.R.H. Prince Fahd Salman**
72 SOLDIER (USA), b g Sheikh Albadou—His Ginger (USA) **H.R.H. Prince Fahd Salman**
73 SPIRIT OF THE NILE (FR), b f Generous (IRE)—Egyptale **Mr M. Arbib**
74 SPRING ANCHOR (FR), b c Slip Anchor—Swift Spring (FR) **Mr M. Arbib**
75 STAR FANTASY (USA), ch g Sky Classic (CAN)—Wanda's Dream (USA) **Mr M. Arbib**
76 STARGAZER, b c Magic Ring (IRE)—Buraida **H.R.H. Prince Fahd Salman**
77 STAR OF THE COURSE (USA), b f Theatrical—Water Course (USA) **Mr M. Arbib**
78 STAYINGALIVE (USA), ch f Gone West (USA)—Lady For Two (USA) **H.R.H. Prince Fahd Salman**
79 STYLISH, b f Anshan—Classic Design **H.R.H. Prince Fahd Salman**
80 SUMMER DEAL (USA), b f Summer Squall (USA)—Dariela (USA) **Mr M. Arbib**
82 SURE DANCER (USA), b c Affirmed (USA)—Danlu (USA) **Mr M. Arbib**
83 TOKAY, b f Kylian (USA)—Tokyo **Mrs Jenny Willment**
84 WALES, ch c Caerleon (USA)—Knight's Baroness **H.R.H. Prince Fahd Salman**
86 WINDY GULCH (USA), b f Gulch (USA)—Wyndalia (USA) **Lord Lloyd-Webber**
87 YASMEENA (USA), b f St Jovite (USA)—Lajna **H.R.H. Prince Fahd Salman**

TWO-YEAR-OLDS

88 BOMBARD (USA), ch c 28/2 Lord At War (ARG)—
Mama Hawk (USA) (Silver Hawk (USA)) **H.R.H. Prince Fahd Salman**
89 BORN FREE, ch f 1/2 Caerleon (USA)—
Culture Vulture (USA) (Timeless Moment (USA)) **H.R.H. Prince Fahd Salman**
90 B br f 24/4 Magic Ring (IRE)—Buraida (Balidar) **H.R.H. Prince Fahd Salman**
91 CELEBRATE (IRE), ch f 18/2 Generous (IRE)—
Bright Generation (IRE) (Rainbow Quest (USA)) **H.R.H. Prince Fahd Salman**
92 CHAMBOLLE MUSIGNY (USA), b f 5/2 Majestic Light (USA)—
Bridal Up (USA) (Sharpen Up) **Mr Christopher Wright**
93 CHARLES SPENCELAYH (IRE), b c 4/3 Tenby—Legit (IRE) (Runnett) **Richard Green (Fine Paintings)**
94 CHICAGO BEAR (IRE), ch c 6/5 Night Shift (USA)—
Last Drama (IRE) (Last Tycoon) **Mr Christopher Wright, Mrs J. M. Corbett**
95 COPIOUS (IRE), ch f 5/4 Generous (IRE)—Flood (USA) (Riverman (USA)) **H.R.H. Prince Fahd Salman**
96 B c 3/4 Alleged (USA)—Danlu (USA) (Danzig (USA)) **Mr M. Arbib**
97 B f 26/2 Red Ransom (USA)—Dariela (USA) (Manila (USA)) **Mr M. Arbib**
98 DIAMOND (IRE), b f 7/3 Generous (IRE)—Danishkada (Thatch (USA)) **H.R.H. Prince Fahd Salman**
99 DOLLAR LAW, ch c 29/2 Selkirk (USA)—Western Heights (Shirley Heights) **Mr N. C. Kersey**
100 FOCUS, b c 13/2 First Trump—Glimpse (Night Shift (USA)) **Highclere Throughbred Racing Ltd**
101 B f 7/4 Rahy (USA)—Free Thinker (USA) (Shadeed (USA)) **Lord Lloyd-Webber**
102 FREETOWN (IRE), b c 25/4 Shirley Heights—Pageantry (Welsh Pageant) **H.R.H. Prince Fahd Salman**

MR P. F. I. COLE—continued

103 GREATER (USA), b c 25/3 Dayjur (USA)—Nicer (IRE) (Pennine Walk) **H.R.H. Prince Fahd Salman**
104 HADRA (USA), b f 13/5 Dayjur (USA)—Trampoli (USA) (Trempolino (USA)) **H.R.H. Prince Fahd Salman**
105 IN TIME, ch f 22/4 Generous (IRE)—Affection Affirmed (USA) (Affirmed (USA)) **H.R.H. Prince Fahd Salman**
106 B c 16/4 Primo Dominie—Jalopy (Jalmood (USA))
107 JAQUENETTA, b f 19/3 Manila (USA)—Jadeeda (USA) (Silver Hawk (USA)) **Sir George Meyrick, Lady Sondes**
108 JIG (IRE), b f 25/3 Catrail (USA)—River Jig (USA) (Irish River (FR)) **H.R.H. Prince Fahd Salman**
109 B c 3/2 Barathea (IRE)—Kithanga (IRE) (Darshaan) **Mrs S. Arbib, Lady Harris**
110 LADY BOX, b f 26/3 Pursuit of Love—Island Ruler (Ile de Bourbon (USA)) **Black Run Racing Club**
111 LAILA MANJA (IRE), b f 11/3 Diesis—London Pride (USA) (Lear Fan (USA)) **H.R.H. Prince Fahd Salman**
112 Ch c 30/3 Great Commotion (USA)—L'Americaine (USA) (Verbatim (USA)) **Mrs S. Arbib, Lady Harris**
113 LENNOX, b c 5/2 Bustino—Ivory Gull (USA) (Storm Bird (CAN)) **Sir George Meyrick, J. Wates, P. Cole**
114 LILA, b f 5/2 Zafonic (USA)—Bint Pasha (USA) (Affirmed (USA)) **H.R.H. Prince Fahd Salman**
115 B c 31/3 Red Ransom (USA)—Lilian Bayliss (IRE) (Sadler's Wells (USA)) **Mr J. S. Gutkin**
116 LITTLE ITALY (IRE), b f 5/2 Common Grounds—Broken Romance (IRE) (Ela-Mana-Mou) **Mr Andrea Pecoraro**
117 LS LOWRY (USA), b c 1/2 Thorn Dance (USA)—
Queluz (USA) (Saratoga Six (USA)) **Richard Green (Fine Paintings)**
118 B c 21/2 Danzig (USA)—Lydara (USA) (Alydar (USA)) **Mr M. Arbib**
119 MAGNO (USA), b c 4/5 El Gran Senor (USA)—Nice Noble (USA) (Vaguely Noble) **H.R.H. Prince Fahd Salman**
120 MANCALA, ch f 19/3 Deploy—Alghabrah (Lomond (USA)) **Mr N. C. Kersey**
121 MENTEITH (USA), b c 20/2 Dehere (USA)—Bunka Bunka (USA) (Raja Baba (USA)) **Sir George Meyrick**
122 MR SOLITAIRE (IRE), ch c 21/4 Bigstone (IRE)—
Farewell Song (USA) (The Minstrel (CAN)) **Mrs C. Hanbury, Mrs F. Schwarzenbach**
123 Ch c 24/3 Affirmed (USA)—Norma (USA) (Procida (USA)) **H.R.H. Prince Fahd Salman**
124 B c 24/2 Common Grounds—Overdue Reaction (Be My Guest (USA)) **Mr Frank Stella**
125 PRESENT LAUGHTER, b c 19/4 Cadeaux Genereux—Ever Genial (Brigadier Gerard) **Lord Portman**
126 RED SEA, b c 9/2 Barathea (IRE)—Up Anchor (IRE) (Slip Anchor) **H.R.H. Prince Fahd Salman**
127 Ch c 8/4 Irish River (FR)—Rosyphard (USA) (Lyphard (USA)) **Mrs S. Arbib, Lady Harris**
128 SILVER APPLE (IRE), gr c 3/5 Danehill (USA)—Moon Festival (Be My Guest (USA)) **Mr Anthony Speelman**
129 SO AMOROUS, b f 31/3 Generous (IRE)—Annoconnor (USA) (Nureyev (USA)) **Mr M. Arbib**
130 SUNDAE GIRL (USA), b f 19/5 Green Dancer (USA)—
Charmie Carmie (USA) (Lyphard (USA)) **Mr Christopher Wright**
131 B c 29/2 Snurge—Swift Spring (FR) (Bluebird (USA)) **Mr M. Arbib**
132 B f 16/4 Tenby—Tamassos (Dance In Time (CAN)) **Mr Athos Christodoulou**
133 TOP ORDER (USA), b f 3/5 Dayjur (USA)—
Victoria Cross (USA) (Spectacular Bid (USA)) **H.R.H. Prince Fahd Salman**
134 WORSHIP (USA), ch f 28/3 Irish River (FR)—Pedestal (High Line) **Lord Lloyd-Webber**

ADDITIONS

LADY YAVANNA 3 ch f Lycius — Isotonic **Mr N. Kersey**
2 ch c 7/4 Lycius (USA) — Madame Nureyev (Nureyev (USA)) **Mr N. Cheng**
2 b f Alnasr Alwasheek — Shibui **Mrs J. Williment**
2 b f Common Grounds — Sugar Town **Lord Portman**

NEW 2YO NAMES

No. 96 ex Danlu is named **STRATEGIC COURSE**
No. 97 ex Dariela is named **SCARLET RAIDER**
No. 109 ex Kithanga is named **SINGLE CURRENCY**
No. 131 ex Swift Spring is named **SON OF SNURGE (FR)**

Other Owners: Mr A Balzarini, Mr C Meyrick, Mrs U Schwarzenbach, The Dowager Countess Sondes, Mr C J Wates.

Jockeys (Flat): T R Quinn (8-4), C Rutter (7-10).

Apprentice: David O'Neill (7-10).

Lady Rider: Miss S Higgins (8-12).

143 MR S. N. COLE, Tiverton

Postal: **West Batsworthy Farm, Rackenford, Tiverton, Devon, EX16 8EG.**
Phone: **PHONE & FAX (01884) 881205 MOBILE (0835) 038963**

1 **AGENT,** 5, ch g Anshan—Maria Cappuccini **Mr W. J. Reed**
2 **FIVE LIVE,** 4, b f Pharly (FR)—Manageress **Mr W. J. Reed**
3 **IMPERIAL FORTE,** 8, b m Midyan (USA)—Sunfleet **Mrs G. O. Green**
4 **IMPETUOSITY (IRE),** 4, ch f Imp Society (USA)—Catherine Clare **Mr Roy Smith**
5 **OPEN AFFAIR,** 5, ch m Bold Arrangement—Key To Enchantment **Mr W. J. Reed**
6 **SPORT OF FOOLS (IRE),** 9, b m Trojan Fen—Senouire **Mr W. J. Reed**
7 **THE FLYING FIDDLE,** 6, ch m Northern State (USA)—Miss Flossa (FR) **Mr W. J. Reed**

Other Owners: Mrs A. Cole, Mr R. T. Grant.

Jockeys (NH): R Bellamy, A P McCoy.

Conditional: G Supple (10-0).

Amateur: Mr A Holdsworthy (10-0).

144 MR R. COLLET, Chantilly

Postal: **32, Avenue Marie Amelie, 60500 Chantilly, France.**
Phone: **OFFICE 03 44 57 06 72 HOME 57 59 27 FAX 57 32 25 MOBILE (0608) 789709**

1 **AIMANT (FR),** 4, b c Sillery—Army Life
2 **ANTARCTIQUE (IRE),** 4, b c Sadler's Wells—Arctique Royal
3 **BERANSA (FR),** 4, b f Bering—Dictansa (FR)
4 **BETTYNOUCHE,** 4, b f Midyan—Colourful (FR)
5 **CHAM AL NASSIM (FR),** 4, b c Booming—Crimson Shadows
6 **CRYSTAL GROOM (FR),** 9, b g Crystal Glitters—Green Fee
7 **DANISH MELODY (IRE),** 5, b h Danehill—Cajun Melody
8 **DESERT'S FLOWER (FR),** 4, b f Highest Honor—Never Late
9 **DIVIN DANSEUR (FR),** 4, b g Nureyev—Divine Danse
10 **DODECANESE (USA),** 6, b h Nijinsky—Konafa
11 **FUNNY SPIRIT (FR),** 9, b g Esprit du Nord—Funny Reef
12 **GLORIA CROWN (IRE),** 4, b f Waajib—Kentucky Crown
13 **GRAND CANYON (FR),** 5, b g Lashkari—Le Beau Betouze
14 **HAPPY DANCER (USA),** 4, b f Seattle Dancer—Happy Result
15 **HONNEUR ROYAL (FR),** 5, b g Hero's Honor—Pomme Royale
16 **IL RIVERINO (FR),** 5, b g River Mist—Ideas At Work
17 **KERIDA (FR),** 4, b f Kadrou—La Comparsita
18 **LAS CAJAS (FR),** 10, b g Lashkari—Mi Casa Su Casa
19 **MON COEUR (FR),** 4, b g Saint Andrews—Tell Tale Heart
20 **NIGHT PLAYER (IRE),** 4, b c Night Shift—Racquette
21 **PAVILLON PANAMA (FR),** 4, b c Common Grounds—Corolina
22 **RICHGORL (GER),** 5, b m Neshad—Reklame
23 **STRIKE OIL (FR),** 10, b g Fabulous Dancer—All Found
24 **TYCOON KING (IRE),** 6, b g Last Tycoon—Park Express

THREE-YEAR-OLDS

25 **ALBACORA (IRE),** b f Fairy King—Basilea
26 **ARAN PRINCE (IRE),** b g Arazi—Mill Princess
27 **ASK ME WHY (IRE),** b c Rainbows For Life—Miss Mulaz
28 **BALIDAY (FR),** b f Fijar Tango—Oh Lucky Day
29 **BANQUISE (IRE),** b f Last Tycoon—Arctique Royale

MR R. COLLET—continued

30 BINT AL HAWA (FR), b f River Mist—Badawiya
31 CARALINA (IRE), b f Caerleon—Dinalina
32 DANSE BRETONNE (FR), b f Exit To Nowhere—Safaroa
33 DESERT DRAMA (IRE), b f Green Desert—Tycoon's Drama
34 DINER DE LUNE (IRE), b f Be My Guest—Solo de Lune
35 ESPOIR DU BOCAGE (FR), b c Epervier Bleu—Skay
36 FIELD LEADER (USA), b c Conquistador Cielo—Riverlyph
37 GANDELIA (FR), b f Ganges—Nadelia
38 GO FOR WIN (USA), b c Affirmed—Agretta
39 HAPPY BROOK (USA), b f A P Indy—Villandry
40 HIGH LOVE (FR), b f Highest Honor—Mon Petitnamour
41 HISTOIRE FRANCAISE (FR), b f Ganges—Tell Tale Heart
42 HOTESSE DU WAL (FR), b f Kadrou—Beautywal
43 IN HEAVEN (IRE), b c Rainbows For Life—Nectarine
44 KINGDOM OF TRUCE, b c Brief Truce—Mambo Queen
45 KRISLADY (FR), b f Kris—Gentle Melody
46 LOVE FOR EVER (IRE), b f Darshaan—Fleur d'Oranger
47 MANDOLINE (IRE), b f Suave Dancer—Libertine
48 NAD AL SHEBA (FR), b c General Holme—Erbaya
49 NO LIES (IRE), b c Rainbows For Life—No Disgrace
50 PENTIUM (FR), b c Always Fair—Saquiace
51 PLENTY PROUD (IRE), b f Alzao—Nurah
52 PONTEILLA (FR), b f Arctic Tern—Pontivy
53 PROVIDENTIEL (FR), b c Lesotho—Prolo Dancing
54 RASSULA (FR), b f River Mist—Riwaya
55 RENDORINA (FR), b f Kendor—Rotina
56 SAINTE MARINE (IRE), b f Kenmare—Pont-Aven
57 SATIN CAR (FR), b c Cardoun—Miss Satin
58 SOEUR TI (FR), b f Kaldoun—Habigael
59 SOLINE (FR), b f Linamix—Marie de Solesmes
60 SPLEEN (FR), b f Sillery—Free Hair
61 SWEET SUMMERTIME (IRE), b c Second Set—Taeesha
62 VIRGINIA SPRING (FR), b f Beaudelaire—Magic Spell
63 WENDOR (FR), b c Caerwent—Marianne d'Or
64 YAMADO (FR), b c Noblequest—Yamuna
65 ZELDING (IRE), b f Warning—Zelda

TWO-YEAR-OLDS

66 B f Fijar Tango—Antea (Esprit du Nord)
67 BANANA MOON (IRE), b f Rainbows For Life—Bhama (Habitat)
68 CERULEAN SKY (IRE), b f Darshaan—Solo de Lune (Law Society)
69 CHATON (FR), b c Cardoun—Rapid d'Or (Iron Duke)
70 CITY PROPER (USA), b f Proper Reality—Twin Cities (Nodouble)
71 B f Zafonic—Colconda (Shareef Dancer)
72 B c Saint Cyrien—Europa (Legend of France)
73 FAIRY HOUSE (FR), b c Tel Quel—Ceiling (Thatch)
74 GRIHLINS (FR), b f River Mist—Crimson Shadows (Sharpen Up)
75 JALAL (FR), b g Fill My Hopes—Jolie Mademoiselle (Caro)
76 LA LINOTTE (IRE), b f Priolo—Gale Warning (Last Tycoon)
77 LEKOH (USA), b c Really Awesome—Belle de Reux (Diatome)
78 B c Grand Lodge—Lem's Peace (L'Emigrant)
79 LIZA (IRE), b f Lycius—Taeesha (Mill Reef)
80 MABROUK (FR), b c Zayyani—Music Star (Northjet)
81 B c Warning—Mambo Queen (Sadler's Wells)
82 MATEKA (FR), b c Lesotho—Kenalya (Kenmare)
83 MATURANA (FR), b c Zayyani—Marie de Charmes (Nadjar)
84 B f High Estate—Maura's Guest (Be My Guest)
85 MUCE (FR), b f Pistolet Bleu—Florenly (Pharly)
86 MUMTAZ (FR), b f Kaldoun—Boubskaia (Niniski)
87 B c Exit To Nowhere—Mysterious Plans (Last Tycoon)

MR R. COLLET—continued

88 NICOLAS (FR), b c Ganges—Walter Koenigin (Prince Mab)
89 B f Fairy King—Nunatak (Bering)
90 RAHIB (FR), b c Fijar Tango—Riwaya (Theatrical)
91 SHATOUSH (FR), b f Highest Honor—Baino Bluff (Be My Guest)
92 TENDER IS THE NIGHT (IRE), b f Barathea—Mill Princess (Mill Reef)
93 THE GOOD LIFE (IRE), b f Rainbow Quest—Once In My Life (Lomond)
94 TYCOON'S DOLCE (IRE), b f Rainbows For Life—Tycoon's Drama (Last Tycoon)
95 VENIZE (FR), b f Kaldoun—Canaletto (Iron Duke)
96 ZOOMING (IRE), b f Indian Ridge—Zelda (Caerleon)

145 MR C. COLLINS, The Curragh

Postal: **Conyngham Lodge, The Curragh, Co. Kildare, Ireland.**
Phone: **THE CURRAGH (045) 441239 FAX NO (045) 441605**

1 4, B g Be My Native (USA)—Caffra Mills
2 DEADLY DUDLEY (IRE), 4, gr c Great Commotion (USA)—Renzola
3 GOD FORBID (IRE), 4, ch g Caerleon (USA)—Heaven High
4 IOLANTA (IRE), 4, b f Danehill (USA)—Kifenia (IRE)
5 LIFESFORLIVING, 4, b f Aragon—Dramatic Mood
6 LITTLE SEAN (IRE), 5, br g Broken Hearted—Linanbless
7 LUDGROVE, 5, b br g Royal Academy (USA)—Top of The League
8 PREMARA (IRE), 4, b f Priolo (USA)—Winning Feature
9 4, Ch f Be My Guest (USA)—Raysiya
10 RUM BABA (IRE), 4, b g Tirol—Rum Cay (USA)
11 4, Br c Yashgan—Shabra Princess
12 SIMPANY (IRE), 4, ch g Imp Society (USA)—Volany (IRE)
13 THE BOWER (IRE), 9, br g Don't Forget Me—Nyama (USA)

THREE-YEAR-OLDS

14 ALEXANDER GODDESS (IRE), b f Alzao (USA)—Forli's Treat (USA)
15 ANTRIM COAST, ch c Mujtahid (USA)—Tarsa
16 BAHAMIAN PIRATE (USA), ch c Housebuster (USA)—Shining Through (USA)
17 BEE OFF (IRE), ch f Wolfhound (USA)—Pushoff (USA)
18 BHUTAN (IRE), b c Polish Patriot (USA)—Bustinetta
19 COMMON VERSE (IRE), b f Common Grounds—Prosodie (FR)
20 COUNTRY DAY (IRE), b br f Statoblest—Grass Court
21 COURT PICTURE (IRE), b g Petorius—Cryptic Gold
22 FORGET ABOUT IT (IRE), b f Be My Guest (USA)—You Make Me Real (USA)
23 HEED MY WARNING (IRE), b f Second Set (IRE)—Warning Sound
24 HOLLY HEDGE (IRE), b c Petardia—Holly Bird
25 LADY ALEXANDER (IRE), ch f Night Shift (USA)—Sandhurst Goddess
26 LUCAYAN SPRING, ch c Ela-Mana-Mou—Gorgeous Dancer (IRE)
27 PARIS LINE (IRE), ch g Paris House—Sarahlee
28 PRESIDENT ALBERT (USA), br c Known Fact (USA)—Lower Deck (USA)
29 PRINCE OF ABACO (USA), b c Geiger Counter (USA)—Abala (FR)
30 RAHIKA ROSE, b f Unfuwain (USA)—Rahik
31 SHANKO (IRE), ch c Mukaddamah (USA)—Clanjingle
32 SHEREEVAGH (IRE), ch g Mujtahid (USA)—Lundylux
33 B br c Dynaformer (USA)—Traipsin Lady (USA)
34 VIOLA ROYALE (IRE), b f Royal Academy (USA)—Wood Violet (USA)
35 ZILINA (IRE), b f Pips Pride—Tatra

TWO-YEAR-OLDS

36 B c 18/3 Be My Chief (USA)—Carnbrea Snip
37 B c 20/5 Forest Wind (USA)—Cryptic Gold
38 B c 16/2 Pursuit of Love—Desert Maiden
39 Ch c 4/3 Grand Lodge (USA)—Euridice (IRE)

MR C. COLLINS—continued

40 B c 16/3 Wolfhound (USA)—Euromill
41 Ch f 18/2 Magical Wonder (USA)—Fair Song
42 B f 1/4 Mujadil (USA)—Final Moment
43 B f 14/2 Green Desert (USA)—Gracieuse Majesté (FR)
44 Ch f 23/2 Rainbow Quest (USA)—Green Lucia
45 B f 1/3 Bigstone (IRE)—Kiltimony
46 B br c 15/3 Dolphin Street (FR)—Lavender Beauty
47 **LUCKY LECH (IRE),** br c 13/2 Lucky Guest—Ezilana (IRE)
48 Ch c 10/3 Generous (IRE)—Lupescu
49 Ch c 11/5 Inchinor—Miss Plum
50 **MRS EVANS (IRE),** b f 18/1 College Chapel—Nuit des Temps
51 B c 17/4 Common Grounds—No Distractions
52 B c 14/4 Turtle Island (IRE)—Pinta (IRE)
53 B c 16/4 Perugino (USA)—Regal Society (IRE)
54 **WESTBOUND (IRE),** br f 22/3 Lucky Guest—Five West (USA)
55 B f 28/4 Petorius—Yola (IRE)

Owners: Sheikh Ahmed Al Maktoum, Anamoine Ltd, Mrs J. N. Anthony, H. R. C. Catherwood, Mrs Kathleen Colgan, Mrs C. Collins, Danilo Corridori, Mrs B. J. Eastwood, Prof J. Fennelly, Lord Harrington, The Hon D. F. Howard, Cyril Humphris, John Hurt, G. W. Jennings, Mrs Catherine Lauterpacht, Mallow Cork Syndicate, Mrs H. D. McCalmont, Mr Hugh D. McCalmont, Mrs L. K. McCreery, A. McLean, John McLoughlin, Mrs H. R. Norton, Donal O'Buachalla, Mrs St J. O'Connell, Mr L. V. Pearson, John Perrotta, Mr Gerard Purcell, Mrs K. Quinn, Mrs Sonia Rogers, Peter Savill, Edward St George.

Jockey (Flat): Pat Shanahan.

Apprentices: John Mullins, Mary Williamson.

Lady Rider: Miss Tracey Collins.

146 MR K. C. COMERFORD, Aylesbury

Postal: **Dorton Grange Stables, Brill, Aylesbury, Buckinghamshire, HP18 9UD.**
Phone: **(01844) 238440**

1 **BICTON PARK,** 4, b g Distant Relative—Merton Mill **The Old Style Partnership**
2 **BOXING CLEVER,** 7, ch g Nearly A Hand—April Belle **Dunsmore Racing**
3 **COPPERBEECH (IRE),** 4, ch f Common Grounds—Caimanite **Mr James Owen**
4 **DANKA,** 4, gr g Petong—Angel Drummer **SJV**
5 **IMAD (USA),** 8, b br g Al Nasr (FR)—Blue Grass Field **Mr Alan Brackley**
6 **JUST THE JOB (IRE),** 10, b g Sandalay—Caddy Shack **Mr K. C. Comerford**
7 **LAKE DOMINION,** 9, b g Primo Dominie—Piney Lake **Mrs Betty Bate and Mr Mark Campbell**
8 **LEAD HIM ON (USA),** 5, b h Cahill Road (USA)—Wicked Ways (USA) **Mr S. Comerford**
9 **MISS MOUSE,** 6, br m Arctic Lord—Gypsy's Barn Rat **Mr A. H. Scott**
10 **OPUS WINWOOD (IRE),** 10, ch g Orchestra—Atlantic Hope **Mr Bryan Allen**
11 **REIMEI,** 9, b g Top Ville—Brilliant Reay **Dr A. Kimber**
12 **ROWLANDSONS STUD (IRE),** 5, b br g Distinctly North (USA)—Be My Million **Mr S. Comerford**
13 **SEBASTIAN DUKE (FR),** 6, br g Iron Duke (FR)—Abimaba **Ms Grainne O'Donnell**
14 **SHAHIK (USA),** 8, b g Spectacular Bid (USA)—Sham Street (USA) **Dr A. Kimber**
15 **SHARP EMBRACE,** 5, ch g Broadsword (USA)—Running Kiss **Ms Grainne O'Donnell**
16 **SIDE BAR,** 8, b g Mummy's Game—Joli's Girl **Exell, Bailey And Penwright**
17 **SODA,** 4, gr g Belfort (FR)—Bella Seville **Mr R. E. Baskerville**

MR K. C. COMERFORD—continued

THREE-YEAR-OLDS

18 B g Primitive Rising (USA)—Calder Rose **Mr K. C. Comerford**
19 **CHILTERN EMERALD,** b f Thowra (FR)—Treasure Time (IRE) **Mr Mike Smith & Mrs Brenda Smith**
20 B f Picea—Fisima **Mr John Huckle & Miss Edwina Saunders**
21 **LAURALUCY,** gr f Infantry—Glen Luss **Fiona Lady Arran**
22 Ch g Infantry—Toctic **Mr R. E. Baskerville**

Other Owners: Mr D. S. Bailey, Mr Alan Bosley, Mrs Belinda Brackley, Mr P. J. Cousins, Mr D. Excell, Mr S. J. Kearns, Mr P. Kennedy, Mr T. Morning, Miss N. Parker, Mr D. Penwright, Mrs T. Scott, Mr N. Stewart, Mrs Lesley Wakeling.

Jockey (Flat): W J O'Connor (w.a.).

Jockeys (NH): P Carberry (10-0, w.a.), J F Titley (10-0, w.a.).

Apprentice: James Bosley (7-0).

Conditional: L P Aspell (9-11, w.a.).

Amateurs: P F Cooper (10-0), Dr A Kimber (10-0), Mr J Owen (9-7).

Lady Rider: Mrs S J Comerford (9-0).

147 LADY CONNELL, Brackley

Postal: **Steane Park, Brackley, Northamptonshire, NN13 6DP.**

1 **BROAD STEANE,** 9, b g Broadsword (USA)—Banbury Cake **Sir Michael Connell**
2 **COURT NAP (IRE),** 6, ch g Waajib—Mirhar (FR) **Sir Michael Connell**
3 **SECOND AMENDMENT,** 5, b m Jupiter Island—Banbury Cake **Sir Michael Connell**
4 **TARRY AWHILE,** 12, ch g Crested Lark—Lucky Sandy **Sir Michael Connell**
5 **TOM'S LAD,** 5, gr g Scallywag—Menquilla **Sir Michael Connell**

148 MR F. COTON, Nottingham

Postal: **Chapel Farm, Chapel Lane, Epperstone, Nottingham, NG14 6AE.**
Phone: **(0115) 9663048**

1 **EMERALD VENTURE,** 11, b g Seclude (USA)—No Time For Tears **Mr F. Coton**
2 **LADY BOCO,** 5, b m Roscoe Blake—Bella Banus **Mr F. Coton**
3 **POWER DON,** 5, ch g Superpower—Donalee **Mr F. Coton**

149 MR L. G. COTTRELL, Cullompton

Postal: **Sprinters, Dulford, Cullompton, Devon, EX15 2DX.**
Phone: **KENTISBEARE (01884) 266320**

1 **AGASSI'S ACE,** 5, b g Vital Season—Welsh Flower **Mr A. J. Cottrell**
2 **AKALIM,** 5, b g Petong—Tiszta Sharok **Mr John Boswell**
3 **CAPE PIGEON (USA),** 13, ch g Storm Bird (CAN)—Someway Somehow (USA) **Mr E. Gadsden**
4 **CAPTAIN BIGGLES,** 6, br g My Richard—Kiltipper **Mr F. G. Hollis**
5 **CONSPICUOUS (IRE),** 8, b g Alzao (USA)—Mystery Lady (USA) **Mrs Jenny Hopkins**
6 **DEVON PEASANT,** 6, b m Deploy—Serration **Mrs B. Skinner**
7 **LEGAL PETITION,** 4, b f Petoski—Legal Aid **Mr P. R. Hill**
8 **PINE CREEK,** 4, ch f Bold Arrangement—Sweet Enough **Mr Ray Richards**
9 **RIVERSMEET,** 4, b g Soviet Star (USA)—Zepha **Mr H. C. Seymour**
10 **SOLAZZI (FR),** 6, b m Saint Cyrien (FR)—Sunclad (FR) **Mrs Sarah Faulks**
11 **SOVEREIGNS COURT,** 5, ch g Statoblest—Clare Celeste **Mr E. Gadsden**
12 **TARSKI,** 4, ch g Polish Precedent (USA)—Illusory **Mr E. Gadsden**

THREE-YEAR-OLDS

13 **DESERT VALENTINE,** b g Midyan (USA)—Mo Ceri **Mrs Lucy Halloran**
14 **NICKLES,** b c Lugana Beach—Instinction **Mr Ray Richards**
15 **UPLIFTING,** b f Magic Ring (IRE)—Strapless **Mr Gerry Albertini**

TWO-YEAR-OLDS

16 **ASHBRITTLE LADY,** ch f 28/3 King's Signet (USA)—Lady Longmead (Crimson Beau) **Mrs Jenny Hopkins**

Other Owners: Mr D. J. Cole, Lady Margaret Fortescue, Mrs D. Joly, Mrs Ruth Perry, Mr David Powell, Pride Of Britain Limited, Miss D. Stafford, Mr G. D. W. Swire.

Jockeys (Flat): K. Fallon, M Roberts (w.a.).

Jockey (NH): S McNeill.

Apprentice: A. Daly (7-11).

Amateur: Mr L Jefford (10-0).

150 MR R. M. H. COWELL, Newmarket

Postal: **Bottisham Heath Stud, Six Mile Bottom, Newmarket, Suffolk, CB8 0TT.**
Phone: **Tel: (01638) 570307 Fax: (01638) 570246**

1 **CONSTANT HUSBAND,** 5, gr g Le Solaret (FR)—Miss Mirror **Camilla Horn**
2 **ISABELLA GONZAGA,** 4, b f Rock Hopper—Lawful **Cyril Humphris**
3 **MARY CORNWALLIS,** 4, ch f Primo Dominie—Infanta Real **Bottisham Heath Stud**
4 **MR PARADISE (IRE),** 4, b g Salt Dome (USA)—Glowlamp (IRE) **Platinum Syndicate Ltd.**
5 **SILVERING (FR),** 6, b h Polish Precedent (USA)—Silvermine (FR) **Platinum Syndicate Ltd**

THREE-YEAR-OLDS

6 **JUNE BOUNTY (USA),** b f Red Ransom (USA)—June Bride (USA) **Bottisham Heath Stud**

TWO-YEAR-OLDS

7 **CLEAR AHEAD,** b f 15/2 Primo Dominie—Shoot Clear (Bay Express) **Cheveley Park Stud**
8 **CRUISE AHEAD,** b c 12/4 Arazi (USA)—Cut Clear (Kris) **Bottisham Heath Stud**
9 **MOHICAN PRINCESS,** b f 14/5 Shirley Heights—Mohican Girl (Dancing Brave (USA)) **Compton Hellyer**

MR R. M. H. COWELL—continued

10 **OH SO GRAND,** ch f 27/4 Grand Lodge (USA)—Cutleaf (Kris) **Mr G. W. Byrne**
11 **TWO STEP,** b f 29/3 Mujtahid (USA)—Polka Dancer (Dancing Brave (USA)) **Bottisham Heath Stud**

Other Owners: Mr Chris Akers, Mr Simon Broke, Mr. Anthony Cane, Mr Woody Clark, Viscount Cobham, Robert Cowell, Mr I Macnicol, Mr Charles Maxted, Mr Stuart Richmond-Watson, Mr Gerry Strahan, Mr J. A. Waugh, Mr Stephen Webb.

151 MR R. CRAGGS, Sedgefield

Postal: **East Close Farm, Sedgefield, Stockton-On-Tees, Cleveland, TS21 3HW.**
Phone: **(01740) 620239 FAX (01740) 623476**

1 **HIGHLAND PARK,** 12, ch g Simply Great (FR)—Perchance **Mr Ray Craggs**
2 **KNOTTY HILL,** 6, b g Green Ruby (USA)—Esilam **Mr Ray Craggs**
3 **LIVE PROJECT (IRE),** 6, b g Project Manager—Saturday Live **Mrs Gillian Quinn**
4 **RASIN CHARGE,** 7, b g Governor General—Airlanka **Mr Ray Craggs**
5 **RASIN STANDARDS,** 8, b g Relkino—Growing Wild **Mr Ray Craggs**
6 **SUPERHOO,** 7, b g Superlative—Boo Hoo **Prince Bishop Racing**
7 **THINK AGAIN (IRE),** 4, b g Long Pond—Either Or **Mr Ray Craggs**

THREE-YEAR-OLDS

8 **CHEROKEE CHARLIE,** ch g Interrex (CAN)—Valentine Song **Mr Ray Craggs**

Other Owners: Mr Matthew J. Abel, Mrs M. Dodgson, Mr Dennis Simpson.

152 MISS J. F. CRAZE, York

Postal: **Nook House, Stray Lane, York Road, Elvington, York, YO4 5AX.**
Phone: **(01904) 608458 MOBILE (0585) 683359**

1 **HOLDERNESS GIRL,** 5, b m Lapierre—Isobel's Choice **Mr J. Morris**
2 **LADY SILK,** 7, ch m Prince Sabo—Adduce (USA) **Mr K. West**
3 **LA VOLTA,** 5, b m Komaite (USA)—Khadino **Mr J. Lynam**
4 **NAPOLEON STAR (IRE),** 7, ch g Mulhollande (USA)—Lady Portobello **Miss J. F. Craze**
5 **SOUTHERN DOMINION,** 6, ch g Dominion—Southern Sky **Mrs Angela Wilson**
6 **SUN MARK (IRE),** 7, ch g Red Sunset—Vivungi (USA) **Mr W. Cooper**

THREE-YEAR-OLDS

7 **BINT NADIA,** b f Deploy—Faisalah **Mr T. Marshall**
8 **BURNDEN DAYS (IRE),** ch g Fayruz—Monaco Lady **Mr C. D. Barber-Lomax**
9 **KINGS CHECK,** b c Komaite (USA)—Ski Baby **Mr W. Cooper & Mr N. Cooper**
10 **LADY EMRAL,** br f Handsome Sailor—Precious Jay **Mrs N. Pritchard**
11 **THE FUELOLOGIST,** b g Skyliner—Munequita **Coal Trade Partnership**

TWO-YEAR-OLDS

12 **AVARITIOUS,** b f 9/5 Avarice—Captain Bonnie (Captain James) **Mr R. Holdsworth & Mr R. Hiam**
13 **NINIAN BELL,** ch g 11/4 St Ninian—Ramas Silk (Amber Rama (USA)) **Mr J. Lynam & Mr K. Briggs**
14 **OK MAITE,** ch f 12/2 Komaite (USA)—Gleam of Gold (Crested Lark) **Mr J. Lynam**

Other Owners: Mr Joe Cuby, Mr Mel Jackson, Mr Des Redhead, Dr A. K. Srivastava, Mr S. M. Taylor.

Jockey (Flat): Stuart Webster (8-7).

Jockey (NH): Stuart Webster.

Apprentice: Carolyn Bales (7-13).

Lady Rider: Ms Heather Webster (8-7).

153 MR J. K. S. CRESSWELL, Oakamoor

Postal: **Stoneydale Farm, Oakamoor, Stoke-On-Trent, Staffordshire, ST10 3AH.**
Phone: **HOME (01538) 702362 OFFICE (01782) 324606 FAX (01782) 324410**

1 **CAPTAIN CULPEPPER (IRE),** 7, b g Supreme Leader—Publicola **Mr J. K. S. Cresswell**
2 **DINKY DORA,** 5, ch m Gunner B—Will Be Wanton **Mr J. K. S. Cresswell**
3 5, B m Lord Bud—Immodest Miss **Mr J. K. S. Cresswell**
4 **MOLLIE SILVERS,** 6, b m Derrylin—Will Be Wanton **Mr J. K. S. Cresswell**
5 4, B f Rolfe (USA)—Moment's Pleasure (USA) **Mr J. K. S. Cresswell**
6 **SECONDHAND ROSE,** 5, b m Lord Bud—Moment's Pleasure (USA) **Mr J. K. S. Cresswell**
7 **THE SECRET SEVEN,** 8, ch m Balidar—Will Be Wanton **Mr J. K. S. Cresswell**
8 **WILL SCARLET,** 4, b g Henbit (USA)—Will Be Wanton **Mr J. K. S. Cresswell**
9 **YER 'UMBLE (IRE),** 7, b g Lafontaine (USA)—Miners Girl **Mr J. K. S. Cresswell**

Other Owners: Mrs E. M. Cresswell.

154 MR J. CULLINAN, Aylesbury

Postal: **Ladymead Farm, Quainton, Aylesbury, Buckinghamshire, HP22 4AN.**
Phone: **MOBILE (0468) 661720**

1 **DESERT HARVEST,** 6, b g Green Desert (USA)—Mill On The Floss **Alan Spargo Ltd**
2 **EFHARISTO,** 9, b g Dominion—Excellent Alibi (USA) **Mrs P. A. White**
3 **GRAND CRU,** 7, ch g Kabour—Hydrangea **Alan Spargo Ltd**
4 5, Ch m Dunbeath (USA)—Hydrangea **Alan Spargo Ltd**
5 **MORAN,** 4, b c Bustino—Ower (IRE) **Mrs E. Reid**
6 **SHIKARI'S SON,** 11, br g Kala Shikari—Have Form **Alan Spargo Ltd**
7 **SIS GARDEN,** 5, b m Damister (USA)—Miss Nanna **Alan Spargo Ltd**
8 **TELMAR,** 4, b g Picea—Freeracer **Dodson & Partners**
9 **TELMAR SYSTEMS,** 9, b g Don Enrico (USA)—Russola **Dodson & Partners**

THREE-YEAR-OLDS

10 **ASHJAJON,** b f Lugana Beach—Dondale Rose **Alan Spargo Ltd**
11 B g Buckley—Have Form **Mr W. H. Joyce**
12 **LITTLE TOLERANCE,** ch f Weldnaas (USA)—Beau Dada (IRE) **Alan Spargo Ltd**
13 **PRECISION FINISH,** ch f Safawan—Tricky Tracey **Alan Spargo Ltd**
14 **SAFABEE,** ch f Safawan—Bewails (IRE) **Mr Alan Walder**

TWO-YEAR-OLDS

15 B c 7/2 Kylian (USA)—Beau Dada (IRE) (Pine Circle (USA)) **Alan Spargo Ltd**

Other Owners: Mr Richard Dodson, Mr P. Kennedy, Mr S. C. Scowen, Mr Tony Stephens, Mr R. E. Young.

Amateurs: Miss Emma Garley (9-0), Mr Brian Grant (10-0).

155 MR L. M. CUMANI, Newmarket

Postal: **Bedford House Stables, Bury Road, Newmarket, Suffolk, CB8 7BX.**
Phone: **NEWMARKET (01638) 665432 FAX (01638) 667160**

1 **BRAVE KRIS (IRE),** 4, b f Kris—Famosa **Mr Robert H. Smith**
2 **DR MARTENS (IRE),** 4, b g Mtoto—Suyayeb (USA) **R. Griggs Group Limited**
3 **FLORISTAN (IRE),** 4, b c Fairy King (USA)—Le Melody **Lord Alexander Hope**
4 **GEIMHRIUIL (IRE),** 4, b c Distinctly North (USA)—Ventry **Mr M. J. Dawson**
5 **GRAPESHOT (USA),** 4, b c Hermitage (USA)—Ardy Arnie (USA) **Mrs T. Von Halle & Mr M. Kerr-Dineen**
6 **KALIANA (IRE),** 4, b f Slip Anchor—Kadissya (USA) **H.H. Aga Khan**

MR L. M. CUMANI—continued

7 **KENMIST,** 4, gr f Kenmare (FR)—Mistral's Collette **Dr. U. Saini Fasanotti**
8 **MANDILAK (USA),** 4, b c El Gran Senor (USA)—Madiriya **H.H. Aga Khan**
9 **MIGWAR,** 5, b g Unfuwain (USA)—Pick of The Pops **Umm Qarn Racing**
10 **MONS,** 5, b h Deploy—Morina (USA) **Mrs E. H. Vestey**
11 **ONE SO WONDERFUL,** 4, b f Nashwan (USA)—Someone Special **Helena Springfield Ltd**
12 **POTEEN (USA),** 4, b c Irish River (FR)—Chaleur (CAN) **Lord Vestey**
13 **RIDAIYMA (IRE),** 4, b f Kahyasi—Riyda **H.H. Aga Khan**
14 **SHOUK,** 4, b f Shirley Heights—Souk (IRE) **Fittocks Stud**
15 **WINTER GARDEN,** 4, ch c Old Vic—Winter Queen **Sheikh Mohammed**
16 **XYLEM (USA),** 7, ch h Woodman (USA)—Careful (USA) **Mr Christopher P. Ranson**

THREE-YEAR-OLDS

17 **ALTAWEELAH (IRE),** b f Fairy King (USA)—Donya **Sheikh Ahmed Al Maktoum**
18 **ARKADIAN HERO (USA),** ch c Trempolino (USA)—Careless Kitten (USA) **Mr M. Tabor & Mrs John Magnier**
19 **AVELA (IRE),** b f Doyoun—Avila **Sheikh Mohammed**
20 **BAAJIL,** b c Marju (IRE)—Arctic River (FR) **Sheikh Ahmed Al Maktoum**
21 **BANAAN,** ch c Polish Precedent (USA)—Shadha (USA) **Sheikh Ahmed Al Maktoum**
22 **BOREAS,** b c In The Wings—Reamur **Aston House Stud**
23 **BOUNDLESS SHAPE (IRE),** ch c Petardia—Burren Breeze (IRE) **Mr M. Marchetti**
24 **BOURBON STREET (USA),** b c Dixie Brass (USA)—Riches (USA) **Mrs Timothy Von Halle**
25 **BRIGADE CHARGE (USA),** b c Affirmed (USA)—Fairy Footsteps **Mr Robert H. Smith**
26 **BUZZY BOMB (IRE),** b f Tenby—Buz Kashi **Mr G. Robotti**
27 **CLAPHAM COMMON (IRE),** b c Common Grounds—West of Eden **Anglia Bloodstock Syndicate**
28 **CREON,** b c Saddlers' Hall (IRE)—Creake **Mohammed Al Nabouda**
29 **DIMPLE,** b f Fairy King (USA)—Rapid Repeat (IRE) **Lord Hartington**
30 **DORADO,** b c Royal Academy (USA)—Tolmi **Mr L. Marinopoulos**
31 **DUSHANBE (IRE),** b c Alzao (USA)—Atyaaf (USA) **H.R.H. Prince Fahd Salman**
32 **EMERALD ISLE (IRE),** ch c Second Set (IRE)—Irish Kick **Sheikh Mohammed**
33 **FROND,** b f Alzao (USA)—Fern **Fittocks Stud**
34 **GLANCE (IRE),** b c Ela-Mana-Mou—Cursory Look (USA) **Sheikh Mohammed**
35 **GLOROSIA (FR),** ch f Bering—Golden Sea (FR) **Mr Robert H. Smith**
36 **HARMONY,** b c Shareef Dancer (USA)—Almitra **Sheikh Mohammed**
37 **HIGH NOON,** b c Shirley Heights—Hocus **Mrs E. H. Vestey**
38 **HIGH-RISE (IRE),** b c High Estate—High Tern **Sheikh Mohammed Obaid Al Maktoum**
39 **ICE POINT,** ch f Groom Dancer (USA)—Ice Pool (USA) **Sheikh Mohammed**
40 **IL CAVALIERE,** b g Mtoto—Kalmia **Dr M. Boffa**
41 **INDIA (IRE),** b f Indian Ridge—Athens Belle (IRE) **Fittocks Stud**
42 **INNER LIGHT,** b c Slip Anchor—Radiance (FR) **Prince Abdul Aziz Bin Saud**
43 **INNUENDO (IRE),** b f Caerleon (USA)—Infamy **Mr Gerald Leigh**
44 **KADAKA (IRE),** b f Sadler's Wells (USA)—Kadissya (USA) **H.H. Aga Khan**
45 **KAGOSHIMA (IRE),** b c Shirley Heights—Kashteh (IRE) **Abdullah Saeed Bul Hab**
46 **KAURIS,** br f Acatenango (GER)—Buckwig (USA) **Dr. U. Saini Fasanotti**
47 **KISSOGRAM,** b f Caerleon (USA)—Alligram (USA) **Helena Springfield Ltd**
48 **KUMATOUR,** b c Batshoof—Runelia **Mr Paolo Riccardi**
49 **LEA GRANDE,** ch f Highest Honor (FR)—Lovely Rita (USA) **Allevamento del Torrione**
50 **LOYAL TOAST (USA),** b c Lyphard (USA)—Lisieux (USA) **Lord De La Warr**
51 **MADJAMILA (IRE),** b f Doyoun—Madaniyya (USA) **H.H. Aga Khan**
52 **MALTAYAR (IRE),** ch c Be My Chief (USA)—Malwiya (USA) **H.H. Aga Khan**
53 **MARABELA (IRE),** b f Shernazar—Mariyada (USA) **H.H. Aga Khan**
54 **MARIA ISABELLA (USA),** ch f Kris—Korveya (USA) **Mr Gerald Leigh**
55 **MARIE LOUP (FR),** ch f Wolfhound (USA)—Marie de Fontenoy (FR) **Mr Robert H. Smith**
56 **MARKSMAN (IRE),** b c Marju (IRE)—Warg **Mr G. P. D. Milne**
57 **MIDNIGHT GUEST (IRE),** b c Brief Truce (USA)—Rhoman Ruby (IRE) **Mr I. Helou**
58 **NOUSAYRI (IRE),** b c Slip Anchor—Noufiyla **H.H. Aga Khan**
59 **PAGAN,** b c Last Tycoon—Temple Row **Lord Hartington**
60 **RAJAIYMA (IRE),** b f Kahyasi—Rajaura (IRE) **H.H. Aga Khan**
61 **REFINED (IRE),** b f Statoblest—Annsfield Lady **Sheikh Mohammed**
62 **REGAL OPINION (USA),** b f Gone West (USA)—Queen's View (FR) **Sheikh Mohammed**
63 **ROSE OF SHUAIB (IRE),** ch f Caerleon (USA)—Almuhtarama (IRE) **Sheikh Ahmed Al Maktoum**
64 **SALFORD,** ch g Salse (USA)—Bustellina **Mr Saeed Manana**

MR L. M. CUMANI—continued

65 SHALIMAR GARDEN (IRE), b f Caerleon (USA)—Producer (USA) **Mrs David Nagle & Mrs John Magnier**
66 SHALLEGED (USA), b c Shadeed (USA)—Ann Alleged (USA) **Mr Robert H. Smith**
67 SHAMAWAN (IRE), b c Kris—Shamawna (IRE) **H.H. Aga Khan**
68 SHARERA (IRE), b f Kahyasi—Sharenara (USA) **H.H. Aga Khan**
69 SLIPPER, b f Suave Dancer (USA)—Horseshoe Reef **Lord Halifax**
70 SOTTVUS (IRE), ch c Royal Academy (USA)—Lorne Lady **Scuderia Rencati Srl**
71 SPINDRIFT (IRE), b c Mukaddamah (USA)—Win For Me **Mr M. J. Dawson**
72 SPLENDID ISOLATION (USA), b br c Hermitage (USA)—Hord (USA) **Lord De La Warr**
73 TAFFETY, b f Last Tycoon—Brocade **Mr Gerald Leigh**
74 TALEBAN, b c Alleged (USA)—Triode (USA) **Fittocks Stud**
75 TARAKAN (IRE), b c Doyoun—Tarakana (USA) **H.H. Aga Khan**
76 TENEBRA, br f Warning—Messaria **Mr L. Marinopoulos**
77 TENSILE (IRE), b c Tenby—Bonnie Isle **Mrs V. Shelton**
78 TEQUILA, b c Mystiko (USA)—Black Ivor (USA) **Mr Paul G. S. Silver**
79 WINTER PAGEANT, ch f Polish Precedent (USA)—Winter Queen **Aston House Stud**
80 ZALAL (IRE), b c Darshaan—Zallaka (IRE) **H.H. Aga Khan**
81 ZOMARADAH, b f Deploy—Jawaher (IRE) **Sheikh Mohammed Obaid Al Maktoum**

TWO-YEAR-OLDS

82 AEGEAN DREAM (IRE), b f 26/1 Royal Academy (USA)—L'Ideale (USA) (Alysheba (USA)) **Theobalds Stud**
83 B f 11/2 Polish Precedent—Aquaba (USA) (Damascus (USA)) **Sheikh Mohammed**
84 AVEBURY, b c 5/3 Fairy King (USA)—Circle of Chalk (FR) (Kris) **Sackville Syndicate**
85 BOLD BARON, ch c 9/4 Anshan—Secret Waters (Pharly (FR)) **Platinum Syndicate Limited**
86 CAJOLE (IRE), ch f 14/3 Barathea (IRE)—Frendly Persuasion (General Assembly (USA)) **Sackville Syndicate**
87 Ch c 16/5 Kris—Carotene (CAN) (Great Nephew) **Sheikh Mohammed**
88 CRISIS (IRE), b c 26/4 Second Set (IRE)—Special Offer (IRE) (Shy Groom (USA)) **Mrs Angie Silver**
89 B f 14/2 In The Wings—Crystal Reay (Sovereign Dancer (USA)) **Sheikh Mohammed**
90 DALIAPOUR (IRE), br c 10/3 Sadler's Wells (USA)—Dalara (IRE) (Doyoun) **H. H. Aga Khan**
91 DANCING KING (IRE), b c 24/1 Fairy King (USA)—Zariysha (IRE) (Darshaan) **Mr M. J. Dawson**
92 DARO SOPRAN (GER), b c 18/3 Royal Academy (USA)—Danzica (Rusticaro (FR)) **Sant' Uberto**
93 B c 29/2 Polish Precedent—Decided Air (IRE) (Sure Blade (USA)) **Sheikh Mohammed**
94 B c 25/3 Cadeaux Genereux—Dimmer (Kalaglow) **Umm Qarn Racing**
95 DRIFT OF SANDS, b c 11/5 Exit To Nowhere (USA)—Douceur (USA) (Shadeed (USA)) **Mr M. Marchetti**
96 EDEN, b f 21/3 Polish Precedent—Isle of Flame (Shirley Heights) **Mr L. Marinopoulos**
97 ERMINE, ch f 6/2 Cadeaux Genereux—Nibbs Point (IRE) (Sure Blade (USA)) **Lord Halifax**
98 FAFESTA (IRE), b f 28/4 Rainbow Quest (USA)—Dancing Berry (Sadler's Wells (USA)) **Scuderia Rencati Srl**
99 FIUR (IRE), ch c 22/2 Grand Lodge (USA)—Gift of The Night (USA) (Slewpy (USA)) **Scuderia Rencati Srl**
100 B f 27/3 Gone West (USA)—Frankova (USA) (Nureyev (USA)) **Sheikh Mohammed**
101 FRENZY, b f 15/4 Zafonic (USA)—Free Guest (Be My Guest (USA)) **Fittocks Stud**
102 FRIPPET (IRE), b f 24/4 Ela-Mana-Mou—Happy Tidings (Hello Gorgeous (USA)) **W. V. M. & Mrs E. S. Robins**
103 B f 28/3 Rainbow Quest (USA)—Gayane (Nureyev (USA)) **Sheikh Mohammed**
104 GUN FLINGER (IRE), ch c 19/5 Indian Ridge—Showing Style (Pas de Seul) **Sackville Syndicate**
105 KALANISI, b c 27/3 Doyoun—Kalamba (IRE) (Green Dancer (USA)) **H. H. Aga Khan**
106 B c 5/4 Caerleon (USA)—Kalikala (Darshaan) **Sheikh Mohammed**
107 KUSTER, b c 21/1 Indian Ridge—Ustka (Lomond (USA)) **Lord Vestey**
108 B c 10/5 Unfuwain (USA)—La Masse (High Top) **Sackville Syndicate**
109 LIKING FOR YOU, b c 17/2 College Chapel—Lets Fall In Love (USA) (Northern Baby (CAN)) **Mr M. Marchetti**
110 B f 2/1 Diesis—Line Call (USA) (The Minstrel (CAN)) **Sheikh Mohammed**
111 B c 6/5 Waajib—Maimiti (Goldhill) **Mr M. Tabor & Mrs John Magnier**
112 Ch c 11/3 Polish Patriot (USA)—Malwiya (USA) (Shahrastani (USA)) **H. H. Aga Khan**
113 MARJIN (IRE), b f 20/2 Marju (IRE)—Fiscal Folly (USA) (Foolish Pleasure (USA)) **Fittocks Stud**
114 MARMADUKE (IRE), ch c 24/2 Perugino (USA)—Sympathy (Precocious) **Anglia Bloodstock Syndicate**
115 B c 6/4 Tenby—Mirana (IRE) (Ela-Mana-Mou) **H. H. Aga Khan**
116 Gr f 24/2 Paris House—Missed Opportunity (IRE) (Exhibitioner) **Mr P. A. Leonard**
117 MOVIE STAR (IRE), b f 5/3 Barathea (IRE)—Mary Astor (FR) (Groom Dancer (USA)) **Mr Robert H. Smith**
118 MUKASOL, b c 27/4 Mukaddamah (USA)—So Long Boys (FR) (Beldale Flutter (USA)) **Mr A. Moro**
119 B f 7/5 Wolfhound (USA)—Myth (Troy) **The Speculators**
120 NEUTRALITY (IRE), ch f 19/2 Common Grounds—Azallya (FR) (Habitat) **Mr Robert H. Smith**
121 B c 25/3 Barathea (IRE)—Niamh Cinn Oir (IRE) (King of Clubs) **Sheikh Mohammed**
122 NIGHT QUEST, b f 6/2 Rainbow Quest (USA)—Night At Sea (Night Shift (USA)) **Lady Juliet Tadgell**

MR L. M. CUMANI—continued

123 NINTH WONDER (USA), ch f 6/3 Forty Niner (USA)—Crystal Gazing (USA) (El Gran Senor (USA)) **Sheikh Mohammed**
124 ORO NERO, b c 27/3 Alzao (USA)—Gravette (Kris) **Mr L. Monaldi**
125 PARABLE, b c 28/3 Midyan (USA)—Top Table (Shirley Heights) **Sackville Syndicate**
126 PERUSING, b c 23/4 Perugino (USA)—Sweet Reprieve (Shirley Heights) **Mrs V. Shelton**
127 Ch c 21/3 Arazi (USA)—Pushy (Sharpen Up) **Umm Qarn Racing**
128 QUESTABELLE, ch f 4/3 Rainbow Quest (USA)—Bella Colora (Bellypha) **Helena Springfield Ltd**
129 RATATUIA, b f 23/2 Zafonic (USA)—Refilee (IRE) (Sadler's Wells (USA)) **Scuderia Rencati Srl**
130 B c 3/4 Seeking The Gold—Red Slippers (USA) (Nureyev (USA)) **Sheikh Mohammed**
131 B f 2/2 Bering—Relatively Special (Alzao (USA)) **Helena Springfield Ltd**
132 RING THE RELATIVES, b f 2/2 Bering—Relatively Special (Alzao (USA)) **Helena Springfield Ltd**
133 SALLIGRAM, b f 17/4 Salse (USA)—Alligram (USA) (Alysheba (USA)) **Fittocks Stud**
134 SARPEDON (IRE), ch c 4/3 Be My Chief (USA)—Sariza (Posse (USA)) **Mr L. Marinopoulos**
135 SEEK, br c 5/4 Rainbow Quest (USA)—Souk (IRE) (Ahonoora) **Fittocks Stud**
136 SHAIYRAN (IRE), b c 6/3 Darshaan—Shaiybara (IRE) (Kahyasi) **H. H. Aga Khan**
137 SIGNIFY, b c 4/4 Marju (IRE)—Windmill Princess (Gorytus (USA)) **Mr M. J. Dawson**
138 SINGLE SHOT (USA), b c 21/2 Hermitage (USA)—Bourbon Miss (USA) (Smile (USA)) **Sackville Syndicate**
139 SISIRA, b f 21/2 Shareef Dancer (USA)—Sarama (IRE) (Danehill (USA)) **Mr M. Monaldi**
140 SIVA, ch f 17/4 Cadeaux Genereux—Toast (IRE) (Be My Guest (USA)) **Mr L. Marinopoulos**
141 Ch c 4/3 Hamas (IRE)—Solar Attraction (IRE) (Salt Dome (USA)) **Axom Racing**
142 SOPRAN AGOC (ITY), ch c 27/3 Classic Connection—Ago (ITY) (Bolkonski) **Sant' Uberto**
143 SOPRAN BOLKRIS (IRE), b f 27/3 Kris—Bolivia (GER) (Windwurf (GER)) **Sant' Uberto**
144 ST TRINITY, b f 12/3 Distant Relative—Bint Secreto (USA) (Secreto (USA)) **Mr Paolo Riccardi**
145 Ch c 6/3 Elmaamul (USA)—Sunningwell (IRE) (Sadler's Wells (USA)) **Dr M. Boffa**
146 TENOR BELL (IRE), b br c 8/5 Tenby—Top Bloom (Thatch (USA)) **Mrs E. H. Vestey**
147 TRIPLE TIME, ch f 21/4 Kris—Triple Tipple (USA) (Raise A Cup (USA)) **Fittocks Stud**
148 TURTLE SOUP (IRE), b c 29/5 Turtle Island (IRE)—Lisa's Favourite (Gorytus (USA)) **Sackville Syndicate**
149 Ch c 25/1 Beveled (USA)—Victoria Mill (Free State) **Mrs Luca Cumani**
150 B c 1/5 Silver Hawk (USA)—Wedge Musical (What A Guest) **W. V., M. W. & Mrs E. S. Robins**
151 YORKIE TOO, b c 26/4 Prince Sabo—Petonica (IRE) (Petoski) **Mr M. J. Dawson**
152 ZARFOOT, br c 12/4 Zafonic (USA)—Harefoot (Rainbow Quest (USA)) **Mr D. Hinojosa**

Other Owners: Mr A. M. Abdulla, Mr J. Camuda, Mr J. P. Carroll, Mr Guy Chisenhale-Marsh, Lady Margaret Fortescue, Mr Robert F. Goldhammer, Mr I. Goldsmith, Mr Rupert Hambro, Mr Mohammed Bin Hendi, Sheikh Abdullah Bin Khalifa, Mr Robert Russell, Mr L. Salice, Mr Anthony Speelman, Mr E. H. Vestey, Mr Charles C. Walker, Miss Helena Weinfeld, Mr M. Weinfeld, Ms Jane Withey.

Jockeys (Flat): R Ffrench, O Urbina.

Apprentices: A Polli, G Sparkes, D Young.

156 MR P. D. CUNDELL, Newbury

Postal: **Roden House, Wallingford Road, Compton, Newbury, Berkshire, RG20 6QR.**

Phone: **(01635) 578267 FAX (01635) 578267**

1 AGENT MULDER, 4, b g Kylian (USA)—Precious Caroline (IRE) **Mr P. D. Cundell**
2 HAPPY BRAVE, 6, b g Daring March—Fille de Phaeton **Mr P. D. Cundell**
3 KYLIAN'S DAUGHTER, 4, b f Kylian (USA)—Easter Baby **Mr K. S. Cundell**
4 LEIGH CROFTER, 9, ch g Son of Shaka—Ganadora **Mr P. D. Cundell**
5 LITTLE IBNR, 7, b g Formidable (USA)—Zalatia **Mr P. D. Savill**
6 REPEAT OFFER, 6, b g Then Again—Bloffa **Mr D. M. Brick**
7 SEVEN O SEVEN, 5, b g Skyliner—Fille de Phaeton **Mr John Davies (Stonehill)**

THREE-YEAR-OLDS

8 FLY HOME, br f Skyliner—Fille de Phaeton **Mr P. D. Cundell**
9 KENNET, b g Kylian (USA)—Marwell Mitzi **Miss M. C. Fraser**

Other Owners: Mrs S. M. Booker, Mrs Michael Hill, Mr P. D. Savill, Unity Farm Holiday Centre Ltd.

157 MR M. CUNNINGHAM, Navan

Postal: **Gormanstown Stables, Kildalkey, Navan, Co.Meath, Ireland.**
Phone: **(046) 31672 FAX (046) 31467**

1 6, B g Doubletour (USA)—Amber Gift **Mrs Clair MacCrosain**
2 **APPLEFORT (IRE)**, 8, b g Over The River (FR)—Sweet Apple **Herb M. Stanley**
3 6, B g Strong Gale—Blessed Palm **Pierce Gerard Molony**
4 **BREFFNI STAR (IRE)**, 4, b c Cyrano de Bergerac—Lyphard's Lady **Philip Fleming**
5 **BRIANSANNIE (IRE)**, 6, br m Orchestra—Shule Doe **Friends of Brian Syndicate**
6 **BRIAN'S DELIGHT (IRE)**, 7, b m Celio Rufo—Atlantic Hope **Herb M. Stanley**
7 **CABLE BEACH (IRE)**, 9, ch g Lepanto (GER)—Aliceion **Herb M. Stanley**
8 **CAITRIONA'S CHOICE (IRE)**, 7, b h Carmelite House (USA)—Muligatawny **Herb M. Stanley**
9 **CORRAVOGGY (IRE)**, 9, ch g Buckskin (FR)—Tipperary Star **Mrs B. Lynch**
10 **DANCING CLODAGH (IRE)**, 6, b m Dancing Dissident (USA)—An Tig Gaelige **Sportman's Inn Syndicate**
11 **DERRYMOYLE (IRE)**, 9, b g Callernish—Luminous Lady **Herb M. Stanley**
12 **DIEU A RUN (IRE)**, 5, ch m Commanche Run—Glen Dieu **Noel McGrady**
13 **EOINS LAD (IRE)**, 7, ch h The Noble Player (USA)—Dulcet Dido **Mrs Michael Cunningham**
14 **FAIRY OAK (IRE)**, 4, b f Fairy King (USA)—Miss Ballylea **Mrs Lorli Higgins**
15 **FIDDLERS TUNE**, 8, b g Relkino—Fiddlers Bee **Herb M. Stanley**
16 5, B m Glacial Storm (USA)—Graham Course **Noel McGrady**
17 5, B m Glacial Storm (USA)—Graham Dieu **Noel McGrady**
18 **HI BOY (IRE)**, 6, b g Phardante (FR)—Elite Lady **John McLarnon**
19 **KNOCKALASSA (IRE)**, 4, b g Be My Native (USA)—My Wonder **B. Nangle**
20 **MANUS THE MAN (IRE)**, 7, b g Homo Sapien—Pencil **Mrs Clair MacCrosain**
21 **MEGABYTE (IRE)**, 4, b f Glacial Storm (USA)—Panalpina **Mrs Clair MacCrosain**
22 **MR MUSICMAKER (IRE)**, 4, b g Asir—Ewood Park **B. Kerr**
23 **NOELS DANCER (IRE)**, 8, ch g Nordance (USA)—Royal Desire **Noel McGrady**
24 **NUZUM ROAD MAKERS (IRE)**, 7, b g Lafontaine (USA)—Dark Gold **Edward Nuzum**
25 5, B g Henbit (USA)—Padykin **Mrs Michael Cunningham**
26 **PLAYPRINT**, 5, ch h Persian Heights—Tawnais **Mrs Clair MacCrosain**
27 **STAR MARSHALL (IRE)**, 6, b br g Bustomi—Marshallstown **O. Clarke**
28 **STORM COURSE (IRE)**, 6, b m Glacial Storm (USA)—Graham Course **Noel McGrady**
29 **STORMYROYALE (IRE)**, 6, ch m Glacial Storm (USA)—Royal Desire **Noel McGrady**
30 **VALLEY ERNE (IRE)**, 7, b g King's Ride—Erne Gold VII **S.A.M. Syndicate**

THREE-YEAR-OLDS

31 B f King's Ride—American Lady **Mrs Michael Cunningham**

TWO-YEAR-OLDS

32 B f 6/5 Leading Counsel (USA)—Glen Dieu **Mrs Michael Cunningham**
33 Ch f 5/4 Mac's Imp (USA)—Holly Bird **Mrs Brian Lynch**
34 B c 20/1 Namaqualand (USA)—Lyphard's Lady **Philip Fleming**
35 B c 7/3 Barathea (IRE)—Morning Kiss **Herb M. Stanley**

Conditional: S M McGovern (9-5).

Amateur: Mr P J Burke.

Lady Rider: Miss Tara Cunningham (9-0).

158 MR K. CUNNINGHAM-BROWN, Stockbridge

Postal: **Danebury Place, Stockbridge, Hampshire, SO20 6JX.**
Phone: **(01264) 781061 FAX (01264) 781709/781061**

1 **AIGLE D'ILLYRIA (FR)**, 4, b f Subotica (FR)—Eagle's Nest (FR) **Mr A. J. Richards**
2 **BOLD EFFORT (FR)**, 6, b g Bold Arrangement—Malham Tarn **Mr A. J. Richards**

MR K. CUNNINGHAM-BROWN—continued

3 **CHERRYMENTARY,** 4, b f Rudimentary (USA)—Beaute Fatale **Danebury Racing Stables Limited**
4 **DANCING PADDY,** 10, b g Nordance (USA)—Ninotchka **Bychance Racing**
5 **EL GRANDO,** 8, b g King of Spain—Easterly Wind **Mr M. D. Brunton**
6 **MANGUS (IRE),** 4, b c Mac's Imp (USA)—Holly Bird **Danebury Racing Stables Limited**
7 **MODESTO (USA),** 10, b g Al Nasr (FR)—Modena (USA) **Danebury Racing Stables Limited**
8 **NORLING (IRE),** 8, ch g Nashamaa—Now Then **Mr S. Pedersen**
9 **PRINCE NASHA (IRE),** 8, ch g Norwick (USA)—Merokette **Mr S. Pedersen**
10 **SHELTERED COVE (IRE),** 7, ch g Bold Arrangement—Racing Home (FR) **Mr A. J. Richards**
11 **SHY PADDY (IRE),** 6, b g Shy Groom (USA)—Griqualand **Danebury Racing Stables Limited**
12 **VILLAGE NATIVE (FR),** 5, ch g Village Star (FR)—Zedative (FR) **Mr A. J. Richards**
13 **VILLAGE PUB (FR),** 4, ch c Village Star (FR)—Sloe Berry **Mr A. J. Richards**
14 **WATIM,** 5, ch g Hatim (USA)—Waverley Girl **Mr S. Pedersen**

THREE-YEAR-OLDS

15 **OEUF BACON (IRE),** b g Selkirk (USA)—Sunset Reef **Mr A. J. Richards**
16 **SPREE ROSE,** ch f Dancing Spree (USA)—Pinkie Rose (FR) **Mr D. Bass**

TWO-YEAR-OLDS

17 **COUNTRY BUMPKIN,** ch c 4/2 Village Star (FR)—Malham Tarn (Riverman (USA)) **Mr A. J. Richards**

Other Owners: Mr G. J. Cronin, Mr K. O. Cunningham-Brown, Ewar Stud Farms France, Mr R. Gale, Mr G. H. Galley, Mr M. Green, Mr Frank Ivory, Mrs D. M. Read, Mr Ray Richards, Mr P. S. Wilkinson, Mr M. J. Yates.

Jockeys (Flat): A Clark, T R Quinn, T Sprake, J Weaver.

Jockeys (NH): R Dunwoody, A Maguire, D O'Sullivan.

159 MR B. J. CURLEY, Newmarket

Postal: **104 Centre Drive, Newmarket, Suffolk, CB8 8AP.**
Phone: **(01638) 508251**

1 **BAPTISMAL ROCK (IRE),** 4, ch g Ballad Rock—Flower From Heaven **Mr P. Byrne**
2 **BY JAY (IRE),** 4, b f Last Tycoon—Tomona **Mr P. Byrne**
3 **COHIBA,** 5, b g Old Vic—Circus Ring **Mrs B. J. Curley**
4 **MAGIC COMBINATION (IRE),** 5, b g Scenic—Etage **Mrs B. J. Curley**
5 **MARADI (IRE),** 4, b g Marju (IRE)—Tigora **Mrs B. J. Curley**
6 **MULLINGAR CON (IRE),** 10, gr g Orchestra—Kilross **Mrs B. J. Curley**
7 **MY MAN IN DUNDALK (IRE),** 9, ch g Orchestra—Marla **Mrs B. J. Curley**
8 **MYSTIC RIDGE,** 4, ch g Mystiko (USA)—Vallauris **Mr P. Byrne**
9 **TIP YOUR WAITRESS (IRE),** 5, b br g Topanoora—Zazu **Mr P. Byrne**

Lady Rider: Mrs A Stringer.

160 MR J. W. P. CURTIS, Driffield

Postal: **Manor House, Beeford, Driffield, North Humberside, YO25 8BD.**
Phone: **(01262) 488225**

1 **ALICAT (IRE),** 7, b g Cataldi—Sweet Result **Mr J. W. P. Curtis**
2 **DARK OAK,** 12, br g Kambalda—Dusky Jo **Mrs M. E. Curtis**
3 **EDSTONE (IRE),** 6, b g Mandalus—Smashing Run **Mrs M. E. Curtis**
4 **FRUMERTY,** 6, b g Nicholas Bill—Zulu Dancer **Mr J. W. P. Curtis**
5 **GENERAL ACADEMY (IRE),** 5, b g Royal Academy (USA)—Hastening **Mrs M. E. Curtis**

MR J. W. P. CURTIS—continued

6 **MASTER BUCK (IRE),** 5, b g Buckskin (FR)—Giverahand **Mrs M. E. Curtis**
7 **OLD ALE (IRE),** 8, b g Tale Quale—Golden Mela **Mr J. W. P. Curtis**
8 **OVER THE CORRIB (IRE),** 8, ch g Over The River (FR)—Glencorrin **Mr J. W. P. Curtis**
9 **PERFECT VIEW,** 5, b m Arzanni—View Halloa **Mrs M. E. Curtis**
10 **POINT REYES (IRE),** 6, b g Brush Aside (USA)—Lady's Wager **Mrs M. E. Curtis**

Other Owners: Mr Stephen J. Curtis.

161 MR R. CURTIS, Lambourn

Postal: **Delamere Stables, Baydon Road, Lambourn, Hungerford, Berkshire, RG17 8NT.**
Phone: **(01488) 73007 MOBILE (0836) 320690 FAX (01488) 73909**

1 **AYDISUN,** 6, gr g Aydimour—Briglen **Aydi Racing**
2 **BATH KNIGHT,** 5, b g Full Extent (USA)—Mybella Ann **Heart of the South Racing**
3 **BORRADOR,** 4, b g Full Extent (USA)—Wild Jewel **Dr P Walker,Mrs J Whitehead & Miss Jones**
4 4, Ch g Aydimour—Briglen **Mrs P. Lewis**
5 **BRINDLEY HOUSE,** 11, b g Deep Run—Annick (FR) **Mr S. B. Glazer**
6 **CALL ME CITIZEN,** 12, b g Carlingford Castle—Kelenem **Mr M. L. Shone**
7 **COMPUTERAID LADY,** 8, b br m Shaab—Gypsy Field **Mr M. O'Brien**
8 **DARINGLY,** 9, b g Daring March—Leylandia **Mr Michael Appleby**
9 **DENNYS GOLD (IRE),** 8, b g Stetchworth (USA)—Rose of Cloneen **Mr Denis Harper**
10 **DONTLEAVETHENEST (IRE),** 8, b g Torus—On The Rug **Mr M. L. Shone**
11 **EQUITY PLAYER,** 13, ch g Gala Performance (USA)—Eden Dale **The Mrs S Partnership**
12 **FUNCHEON GALE,** 11, b g Strong Gale—Funcheon Breeze **Kings Of The Road Partnership**
13 **FURRY FOX (IRE),** 10, b g Furry Glen—Pillow Chat **Four Play Racing**
14 **GASMARK (IRE),** 7, br g Rontino—Heatherogan **Mrs G. Fletcher**
15 **HILLWALK,** 12, b g Croghan Hill—Bell Walks Fancy **Mr M. L. Shone**
16 **IL FALCO (FR),** 4, ch g Polar Falcon (USA)—Scimitarlia (USA) **Mrs R. A. Smith**
17 **IRISH DELIGHT,** 6, gr g Pragmatic—Kelly's Delight (IRE) **Mr William P. Dillon**
18 **KREEF,** 6, b g Kris—Pelf (USA) **H. J. S. Racing**
19 **LAHAB NASHWAN,** 4, ch g Nashwan (USA)—Shadha (USA) **Mrs R. A. Smith**
20 **MAYBE LATER,** 6, b m Kinglet—Thorngirl **Mrs K. M. Curtis**
21 **MAZIRAH,** 7, b g Mazilier (USA)—Barbary Court **Mr Michael Appleby**
22 **MIRADOR,** 7, br m Town And Country—Wild Jewel **Mrs J. Whitehead**
23 **MISTER GOODGUY (IRE),** 9, br g Supreme Leader—Mislay **Mr M. O'Brien**
24 **OH SO HANDY,** 10, b g Nearly A Hand—Geordie Lass **Mrs R. A. Smith**
25 **OUROWNFELLOW (IRE),** 9, ch g Arapahos (FR)—Dara's March **Kings Of The Road Partnership**
26 **PETER PERFECT,** 4, gr g Chilibang—Misdevious (USA) **H.J.S. Racing**
27 **PLEASURELAND (IRE),** 5, ch g Don't Forget Me—Elminya (IRE) **Mrs Sylvia E. M. McGarvie**
28 **POPSI'S CLOGGS,** 6, ch g Joli Wasfi (USA)—Popsi's Poppet **The Popsi Partners**
29 **SHARSMAN (IRE),** 8, br g Callernish—Another Dutchess **Len Kruse & Cliff Benford**
30 **SIR GALEFORCE (IRE),** 8, br g Mister Lord (USA)—Forest Gale **To Fill in Time Partnership**
31 **SOOPRIMA (IRE),** 5, ch m Montelimar (USA)—Golden Rapid **Mr Eddie Gloyne**
32 **SQUIRE'S OCCASION (CAN),** 5, b g Black Tie Affair—Tayana (USA) **Chelgate Public Relations Ltd**
33 **STEPASIDEBOY,** 8, b g Idiot's Delight—Waterside **Mr P. M. Warren**
34 **T AND ORANGE,** 6, ch m Gunner B—Musroora **Cavo Vecchio**
35 **THE PROUD POUND,** 7, b g Kinglet—Cut And Thrust **Mr Michael J. Low**
36 **WOODLANDS BOY (IRE),** 10, br g Hawaiian Return—Annie Sue VI **Mr Stan Moore**

Other Owners: Mr Mark Ashwell, Mr D. Auer, Mr Hector H. Brown, Michael Burwell, Mr Anthony Cohen, Mrs Iris E. Evans, Geyer Estates Limited (St Athans Hotel), Mr Roger Graham, Mr G. Grandison, Mr H. Green, Mr Greg Gregory, Mr Roger Harding, Mrs Loretta Harris, Mark Head, Mr Peter Jeffs, John Lee, Miss K. Madden, Mr John Penny, Miss A. G. Penston, Paul Ratman, Dr Charles Raymond, Mr Michael Riley, M. J. Rogers, Mr P. A. Sells, Howard Slone, L. W. Stafford, Ms V. Staveacre, Mr S. D. Swaden, A. Turczyniak, Mr C. J. Wood, Mr David J. C. Wood.

Jockey (NH): Jonathan Leech (10-0).

Conditional: Jason Parkhouse (9-9).

Amateur: Mr Michael Appleby (10-7).

162 MR T. A. K. CUTHBERT, Carlisle

Postal: **26 Eden Grange, Little Corby, Carlisle, Cumbria, CA4 8QW.**
Phone: **(01228) 560822 STABLES (01228) 561317**

1 **JIM'S WISH (IRE),** 10, b g Heraldiste (USA)—Fete Champetre **Mr T. A. K. Cuthbert**
2 **JOE'S BIT OF GOLD,** 6, gr m Gold Song—Katie Grey **Mr W. Hurst**
3 **MARZOCCO,** 10, ch g Formidable (USA)—Top Heights **Mr T. A. K. Cuthbert**
4 **MILS MIJ,** 13, br g Slim Jim—Katie Grey **Mr W. Hurst**
5 **SPIDERS DELIGHT,** 10, ch g Sula Bula—Spiders Web **Mr Nigel Dean**
6 **STAGS FELL,** 13, gr g Step Together (USA)—Honey's Queen **Mrs Joyce Cuthbert**
7 **SWANK GILBERT,** 12, b g Balliol—Song To Singo **Mrs Joyce Cuthbert**
8 **SWIFTLY SUPREME (IRE),** 5, b m Supreme Leader—Malozza Brig **Mr Gordon E. Davidson**
9 **TWO TIMER,** 5, ch g Clantime—Two's Up **Mr T. A. K. Cuthbert**

Other Owners: Miss K. M. A. Clark, Ms Jane Kennedy.

Jockey (NH): Carol Cuthbert (9-7).

Amateur: Miss Helen Cuthbert (9-0).

163 MR CHARLES CYZER, Horsham

Postal: **Elliotts, Maplehurst, Horsham, West Sussex, RH13 6QX.**
Phone: **(01403) 730255 FAX (01403) 730787**

1 **ACROSS THE WATER,** 4, b f Slip Anchor—Stara
2 **ACTION STATIONS,** 4, b g High Estate—Toast (IRE)
3 **BEHIND THE SCENES,** 4, ch g Kris—Free Guest
4 **BOOK AT BEDTIME (IRE),** 4, b f Mtoto—Akila (FR)
5 **BOWLED OVER,** 5, b g Batshoof—Swift Linnet
6 **CASTLES BURNING (USA),** 4, b br g Minshaanshu Amad (USA)—Major Overhaul
7 **CHEEK TO CHEEK,** 4, b f Shavian—Intoxication
8 **DANDY REGENT,** 4, b g Green Desert (USA)—Tahilla
9 **DAYLIGHT DREAMS,** 4, b f Indian Ridge—Singing Nelly
10 **DUNCOMBE HALL,** 5, b g Salse (USA)—Springs Welcome
11 **LOVE AND KISSES,** 5, ch m Salse (USA)—Soba
12 **PRINCESS TOPAZ,** 4, b f Midyan (USA)—Diamond Princess
13 **RASPBERRY SAUCE,** 4, b f Niniski (USA)—Sobranie
14 **RESIST THE FORCE (USA),** 8, br g Shadeed (USA)—Countess Tully
15 **RICH IN LOVE (IRE),** 4, b f Alzao (USA)—Chief's Quest (USA)
16 **RISE 'N SHINE,** 4, ch f Night Shift (USA)—Clunk Click
17 **SIGNED AND SEALED (USA),** 4, b g Rahy (USA)—Heaven's Mine (USA)
18 **SIGNS AND WONDERS,** 4, b f Danehill (USA)—Front Line Romance
19 **SIPOWITZ,** 4, b g Warrshan (USA)—Springs Welcome
20 **SPACE RACE,** 4, b g Rock Hopper—Melanoura
21 **STEAMROLLER STANLY,** 5, b g Shirley Heights—Miss Demure

THREE-YEAR-OLDS

22 **CRYSTAL CRAZE,** b f Warrshan (USA)—Single Gal
23 **FORMAL JOY,** b g Formidable (USA)—Joytime
24 **JONAS NIGHTENGALE,** b g Deploy—Springs Welcome
25 **YABONGA (USA),** b g Storm Bird (CAN)—Only Yours

TWO-YEAR-OLDS

26 **ALMINSTAR,** b f 27/5 Minshaanshu Amad—Joytime (John de Coombe)
27 **BROGAZI (USA),** b c 9/2 Bates Motel (USA)—Classical Way (FR) (Bellypha)

MR CHARLES CYZER—continued

28 **COCONUT,** b c 28/3 Shirley Heights—Magical Retreat (USA) (Sir Ivor)
29 **CORAL WATERS (IRE),** b f 19/3 College Chapel—Premier Leap (IRE) (Salmon Leap (USA))
30 **DOUX DELICE,** b f 22/4 Deploy—Springs Welcome (Blakeney)
31 **FEATHER 'N LACE,** b f 29/3 Green Desert (USA)—Report 'em (USA) (Staff Writer (USA))
32 **FUDGE BROWNIE,** b c 21/3 Deploy—Carte Blanche (Cadeaux Genereux)
33 **LIEUTENANT FANCY,** ch c 16/4 Kris—Noirmant (Dominion)
34 **PALOVERDE,** b c 10/2 Green Desert (USA)—La Tuerta (Hot Spark)
35 **PEARL BUTTON (IRE),** b f 15/4 Seattle Dancer (USA)—Riflelina (Mill Reef (USA))
36 **ROOKIE,** b c 9/3 Magic Ring (IRE)—Shot At Love (IRE) (Last Tycoon)

Owners: Miss J. P. Bentley, Mr Stephen Crown, Mrs E. A. Cyzer, Mr R. M. Cyzer, Mrs G. M. Gooderham, Mrs Barbara Hogan.

164 MR L. A. DACE, Storrington

Postal: **Stooks Farm Stables, Stooks Farm, Hurston Lane, Storrington, West Sussex, RH20 4HF.**
Phone: **(01903) 742004 FAX (01903) 742009**

1 **FOTOEXPRESS,** 10, ch g Librate—Rosefox **Mr C. Sullivan**
2 **GREENSIDE CHAT (IRE),** 8, b g Le Bavard (FR)—Elite Lady **Mr Luke Dace**
3 **HERONSHILL,** 6, b g Tacheron—Dip N Dot **Harry Hawkins Partnership**
4 **LIVE CONNECTION (IRE),** 7, b g Electric—Strong Wings **Barnard Racing Partnership**
5 **MOLLY DREAMER,** 6, b m Rushmere—Dream of Fortune **Harry Hawkins Partnership**
6 **NORTHERN VILLAGE,** 11, ch g Norwick (USA)—Merokette **Mr Luke Dace**
7 **PASSAGE CREEPING (IRE),** 5, b m Persian Bold—Tiptoe **Mr M. A. D. Quinn, Mr L. A. Dace**
8 **SPRING BLADE,** 6, b g Jester—Runfawit Pet **Mr Luke Dace, Mrs Sally Rowe**
9 **SWORDSMAN,** 5, ch g Broadsword (USA)—Easter Princess **Harry Hawkins Partnership**

165 MR J. N. DALTON, Shifnal

Postal: **Sutton House Farm, Sutton Maddock, Shifnal, Shropshire, TF11 9NF.**
Phone: **(01952) 730656 FAX (01952) 730261**

1 **REELISTIC,** 5, b g Scottish Reel—Pernoic **Mr J. N. Dalton**
2 **SHOON WIND,** 15, b g Green Shoon—Gone **Mr J. N. Dalton**

Amateur: Mr A N Dalton (10-12).

166 MR P. T. DALTON, Burton-on-Trent

Postal: **Dovecote Cottage, Bretby Park, Bretby, Burton-on-Trent, Staffordshire, DE15 0RB.**
Phone: **HOME (01283) 221922 OFFICE 221922 FAX 224679 MOBILE (0374) 240753**

1 **APRIL JACKSON,** 4, b f Petong—Raintree Venture **Mr R. N. Fearnall**
2 **ARCHIE TEC (IRE),** 5, b g Architect (USA)—Raga Belle **Mrs Julie Martin**
3 **BIG PERKS (IRE),** 6, ch g Executive Perk—Secret Ocean **Mr R. A. H. Perkins**
4 **GLAMANGLITZ,** 8, ch g Town And Country—Pretty Useful **Mrs Julie Martin**
5 **JOSH THE BOSS (IRE),** 6, b g Strong Gale—Last Sunset **Leicestershire Thoroughbred Racing Ltd**
6 **LOCH GARMAN HOTEL (IRE),** 9, b g Roselier (FR)—Dawn Even **Mr Dan Hall**
7 **LUNAR DANCER,** 6, b g Dancing High—Pauper Moon **Mr R. A. H. Perkins**
8 **PAGAN LEADER (IRE),** 5, b g Supreme Leader—Dawning Glory **Mrs Julie Martin**
9 **SALLY LIGHTFOOT,** 4, ch f Derrylin—Vino Festa **Mrs R. S. Perkins**
10 **SALTZ (IRE),** 6, b g Salt Dome (USA)—Heather Hut **Mrs Julie Martin**
11 **TOPAGLOW (IRE),** 5, ch g Topanoora—River Glow **Mrs Julie Martin**
12 **TRIENTA MIL,** 4, b g Prince Sabo—Burmese Ruby **Mrs Jeffrey Robinson**
13 **TROPPI GUAI,** 4, gr f Thethingaboutitis (USA)—Scrambird **Mrs Lucia Farmer**

MR P. T. DALTON—continued

THREE-YEAR-OLDS

14 CZAR WARS, b c Warrshan (USA)—Dutch Czarina **Mrs Julie Martin**
15 PUIWEE, b f Puissance—Glow Again **Mr J. R. Hall**

Other Owners: Mr David R. Martin, Messinger Stud Limited, Mr J. Oakes, Miss Charlotte A. I. Perkins, Miss Melissa Perkins, Mrs J. Whysall.

Amateur: Miss J Wormall (9-0).

167 MR G. W. J. DAVIES, Abergavenny

Postal: **Home Farm, Llwyndu, Abergavenny, Gwent, NP7 7HU.**
Phone: **(0873) 852292**

1 ROC AGE, 7, ch m Rustingo—La Chica **Mr M. W. Davies**
2 STATION MASTER, 6, ch g Rustingo—Delta Rose **Mrs D. M. Davies**

Conditional: M Brennan (w.a.).

168 MISS L. V. DAVIS, Wolverhampton

Postal: **29 Woodhill Drive, Wombourne, Wolverhampton, WV5 0DT.**
Phone: **(01902) 892232**

1 5, Ch g Rymer—Deity **Miss Louise Davis**
2 ILUSTRE (IRE), 6, ch g Al Hareb (USA)—Time For Pleasure **Miss Louise Davis**
3 KALISKO (FR), 8, b g Cadoudal (FR)—Mista (FR) **Miss Louise Davis**
4 MARROWFAT LADY (IRE), 7, b m Astronef—Lady Topknot **Miss Louise Davis**
5 TWICE THE GROOM (IRE), 8, b g Digamist (USA)—Monaco Lady **Miss Louise Davis**

169 MISS Z. C. DAVISON, Woldingham

Postal: **The Nash, Hillboxes Farm, Marden Park, Woldingham, Surrey, CR3 7JD.**
Phone: **(01883) 331114**

1 DANCING MAN, 5, ch g Executive Man—Lyne Dancer **Mrs J. Irvine**
2 DARK ROMANCE (IRE), 9, b m Sarab—Narnia **Mr A. A. Goldson**
3 DETACHMENT (USA), 5, b g Night Shift (USA)—Mumble Peg **Miss Z. C. Davison**
4 FLAME OF GLORY, 4, ch g Polish Precedent (USA)—Danishkada **Miss Z. C. Davison**
5 INCHYDONEY BOY (IRE), 9, b g Callernish—Inch Tape **Mrs J. Irvine**
6 QUINCE BAY, 6, b g My Treasure Chest—Quince Wine **Miss Audrey Unthank**
7 SAILS LEGEND, 7, b h Hotfoot—Miss Polly Peck **Miss Audrey Unthank**
8 VARNISHING DAY (IRE), 6, b g Royal Academy (USA)—Red Letter Day
9 5, Gr g Decent Fellow—Yet **Miss Z. C. Davison**

THREE-YEAR-OLDS

10 DANCINGFORDOLLARS, b f Tragic Role (USA)—Hala **Mr S. Morrell**

TWO-YEAR-OLDS

11 B c 21/4 Perugino (USA)—Deep In September (IRE) (Common Grounds) **Mr M. Flannery**

Other Owners: Mrs G. Davison, Mrs J. Lungreon, Miss S. Walsh.

Jockeys (NH): D Bridgwater, A P McCoy.

Conditional: Andrew J Irvine (9-10).

170 MR B. DE HAAN, Lambourn

Postal: **Fair View, Long Hedge, Lambourn, Newbury, Berkshire, RG17 8NA.**
Phone: **(01488) 72163 (0831) 104574 MOBILE**

1 **ARTIC MELODY (IRE)**, 5, b g Orchestra—Arctic Brief **The Longhedge Partnership**
2 **BADBURY BOY (NZ)**, 10, gr g Khairpour—Lawanda (NZ) **Mr C. Cowley**
3 **BEACON FLIGHT (IRE)**, 7, br g Phardante (FR)—Flying Pegus **The Heyfleet Partnership**
4 **CHARLIE'S FOLLY**, 7, ch g Capitano—Cavity **Mr Duncan Heath**
5 **COOL NORMAN (NZ)**, 6, b g First Norman (USA)—Ice Flake (NZ) **Mrs D. Vaughan**
6 **FAR EAST (NZ)**, 9, gr g Veloso (NZ)—East (USA) **The Padrino Partnership**
7 **IVORY COASTER (NZ)**, 7, b g Ivory Hunter (USA)—Rajah's Girl (NZ) **Mr Denis Andrews**
8 **JUST BAYARD (IRE)**, 6, b g Kambalda—Whistling Doe **Mr Nicholas Tatman**
9 **KENTAVRUS WAY (IRE)**, 7, b g Thatching—Phantom Row **The Padrino Partnership**
10 **LAURA LYE (IRE)**, 8, b m Carlingford Castle—Pennyala **Mr Duncan Heath**
11 **MY MAN DAN (IRE)**, 5, b g Phardante (FR)—Arctic Tartan **Mr Duncan Heath**
12 **SONG OF THE SOUTH**, 5, b g Southern Music—Gaiety Star **Plough Racing**
13 **SPORT CREST (IRE)**, 6, b g Lafontaine (USA)—Wayside Girl **Sport Crest Partnership**
14 **SPRING SUNRISE**, 8, b m Robellino (USA)—Saniette **Mrs D. Vaughan**

Other Owners: Mr R. S. Allen, Mrs Richard Allen, Mr J. G. K. Borrett, Mr C. W. Foreman, Mrs M. A. Foreman, Mr Joe Gilio, Mr B. R. Jervis, Mrs Joan Marie Jervis, Mrs P. P. Lawrence, Mrs H. W. J. Lowthian, Dr R. D. Pearce, Mr Damian Stalder, Mrs Elizabeth Tatman, Mr J. Walkinshaw, Mrs F. Walwyn, Mr G. Weller.

Jockey (NH): C Llewellyn.

171 MR RICHARD DEAN, Maidstone

Postal: **Judge House Farm, Grafty Green, Maidstone, Kent, ME17 2AY.**
Phone: **(01622) 850230**

1 **JOKER JACK**, 13, ch g Garryowen—Deceptive Day **Mr Richard Dean**
2 **KIROV PROTEGE (IRE)**, 6, b g Dancing Dissident (USA)—Still Water **Mr Richard Dean**

Conditional: T Dascombe (10-0).

172 MR W. W. DENNIS, Bude

Postal: **Thorne Farm, Bude, Cornwall, EX23 0LU.**
Phone: **(01288) 352849**

1 **COOME HILL (IRE)**, 9, b g Riot Helmet—Ballybrack **Mrs Jill Dennis**
2 **MUSIC OF MOURNE (IRE)**, 9, ch m Orchestra—Deladeuce **Mr W. W. Dennis**
3 **SIR FREDERICK (IRE)**, 8, b g Cataldi—Florida Springs **Mrs Jill Dennis**
4 **UPTON GALE (IRE)**, 8, br g Strong Gale—Newtown Colleen **Mrs Jill Dennis**

Amateurs: Mr P Dennis (10-3), Mr T Dennis (10-5).

173 MR A. R. DICKEN, Dunbar

Postal: **Tilton House Stables, West Barns, Dunbar, East Lothian, Scotland.**
Phone: **(01368) 864944 or (0468) 383237**

1 **DUBAI NURSE**, 4, ch f Handsome Sailor—Lady Eccentric (IRE) **Mr J. A. Smith**
2 **LITTLE MISS ROCKER**, 4, b f Rock Hopper—Drama School **Mr & Mrs Raymond Anderson Green**

MR A. R. DICKEN—continued

3 **SCHARNHORST,** 6, b g Tacheron—Stardyn **Mr M. G. Mackenzie**
4 **SIMAFAR (IRE),** 7, b g Kahyasi—Sidama (FR) **Mrs Geraldine Marett**

THREE-YEAR-OLDS

5 **BEAU VIENNA,** b f Superpower—Waltz On Air **The Forth Partnership**
6 **FRENCH PRIDE (IRE),** b f Pips Pride—Reasonably French **Mr A. MacKenzie**

TWO-YEAR-OLDS

7 **HOT POTATO,** b c 9/6 Roman Warrior—My Song of Songs (Norwick (USA)) **Miss S. Brown**
8 **MINALCO,** ch f 10/5 Minster Son—La Millie (Nonoalco (USA)) **Mrs M. Schoenberg**

Other Owners: Mr S. Brown, Mr Paul G. Jacobs, Mr D. Leathem, Mr Chick Moohan, Mr G. Ogg, Mr I. Rennie, Mr R. Smith, Mr J. Wilson.

174 MR R. DICKIN, Stratford-on-Avon

Postal: **Alscot Park Stables, Alscot Park, Atherstone On Stour, Stratford-on-Avon, Warwickshire, CV37 8BL.**

Phone: **TEL: (01789) 450052 FAX 450053 MOBILE (0374) 742430/(0836) 203079**

1 4, Ch f Broken Hearted—A Bit of Honey **Mrs C. Dickin**
2 **ALLEGRO PRINCE,** 8, ch g Regal Steel—Fritillaria **Alscot Park Owners Group**
3 **ALONE TABANKULU (IRE),** 6, ch m Phardante (FR)—Tabankiulu **A. Malone, M. Farrow, & H. J. O'Reilly**
4 5, B g Parliament—Aria **Technicair**
5 **BALLY PARSON,** 12, b g The Parson—Ballyadam Lass **Mr G. Hutsby**
6 **BISQUET-DE-BOUCHE,** 4, ch f Most Welcome—Larive **Mr Martin Brook**
7 **COL MINOR,** 5, b g North Col—Sancal **Warwick Members Racing Club**
8 **COLONEL COLT,** 7, b g Saint Andrews (FR)—Vallee des Sauges (USA) **Mr Pete Holder**
9 **COMMANCHE HERO (IRE),** 5, ch g Cardinal Flower—Fair Bavard **Mr Pete Holder**
10 **DARIEN,** 4, b c Sadler's Wells (USA)—Aryenne (FR) **What The Dickins**
11 **DEERLY,** 5, b m Hadeer—Grafitti Gal (USA) **Mrs Bobbie Mundy**
12 **DR ROCKET,** 13, b g Ragapan—Lady Hansel **The Rocketeers**
13 **ERIN'S LAD,** 7, b g Bold Owl—Vernair (USA) **Mr R. Harris & Micronmetrology**
14 4, Ch g Cardinal Flower—Fair Bavard **Mr H. J. O'Reilly & Partners**
15 **KADASTROF (FR),** 8, ch h Port Etienne (FR)—Kadastra (FR) **Mr A. P. Paton**
16 **KNIGHT'S CREST (IRE),** 8, ch g The Parson—Sno-Cat **Mr G. Hutsby**
17 **LODESTONE LAD (IRE),** 8, b g Norwick (USA)—Gentle Star **Mrs C. M. Weaver**
18 **LO-FLYING MISSILE,** 10, gr g Cruise Missile—Lo-Incost **Mr Brian Clifford**
19 **MACY (IRE),** 5, ch g Sharp Charter—Lumax **Mrs M. Payne**
20 **MILL BAY SAM,** 7, b g Lighter—Emancipated **Mr David John Robbins**
21 **MINE'S A MURPHY'S,** 5, b g North Col—Gardenia Lady **Alscot Park Owners Group**
22 **NOTABLE EXCEPTION,** 9, b g Top Ville—Shorthouse **The Smith Partnership**
23 **PRAIRIE MINSTREL (USA),** 4, b g Regal Intention (CAN)—Prairie Sky (USA) **Mr Martin Brook**
24 **SISSINGHURST FLYER (IRE),** 6, gr m Celio Rufo—Jeanarie **Mr Brian Clifford**
25 **SKRAM,** 5, b g Rambo Dancer (CAN)—Skarberg (FR) **Mr W. P. Evans**
26 **STUDIO THIRTY,** 6, gr g Rock City—Chepstow Vale (USA) **Mr D. & Mrs C. Holder**

THREE-YEAR-OLDS

27 **COURT SHAREEF,** b c Shareef Dancer (USA)—Fairfields Cone **Mr D. & Mrs C. Holder**
28 Ch c Gunner B—Kentucky Calling **Mr Simon Weaver**
29 Ch f True Song—Sancal **Mrs C. Dickin & Mr J. P. Thorne**
30 **SANTA COURT,** b g Be My Native (USA)—Christmas Show **Mr D. & Mrs C. Holder**

TWO-YEAR-OLDS

31 B c 29/2 Lashkari—Bobs (Warpath) **Mr R. Harris**
32 B f 16/4 Batshoof—Fairfield's Breeze (Buckskin (FR)) **Mr D. & Mrs C. Holder**
33 B f 6/6 Batshoof—Fairfields Cone (Celtic Cone) **Mr D. & Mrs C. Holder**

MR R. DICKIN—continued

34 B c 12/3 Petoski—Kadastra (FR) (Stradavinsky) **Mr A. P. Paton & Mr C. Paton**
35 B f 15/3 Rock Hopper—Sea Aura (Roi Soleil) **Mrs C. Dickin**

Other Owners: Mr J. Allen, Mr Allan Bennett, Mr H. Burford, Mr & Mrs J. Cooper, Mr T. W. H. Dancer, Mr N. D. Edden, Mr M. Farrow, Mr Haydn Gott, Dr N. W. Imlah, Wing Comdr J. H. King, Captain B. Lennon-Smith, Mr A. Malone, Mr J. O'Reilly, Mr R. E. Raby, Mr R. Paul Russell, Mr Anthony Smith, Mr B. K. Smith, Mrs M. E. Smith, Mr D. Taylor, Mr Graham Taylor, Mrs M. A. Walters, Mr Chris Whitehead, Mrs C. Williams.

Jockeys (Flat): Dane O'Neill, T Quinn (8-4, w.a.).

Jockeys (NH): Jim Culloty, Richard Dunwoody, B Powell, Andrew Thornton (w.a.).

Apprentice: Paul Mundy.

Conditional: X Aizpuru (9-7).

Lady Rider: Miss Sally Duckett (9-7).

175 MR J. E. DIXON, Carlisle

Postal: **Moor End, Thursby, Carlisle, Cumbria, CA5 6QP.**
Phone: **DALSTON (01228) 710318**

1 **AMBER HOLLY,** 9, ch m Import—Holly Lodge **Mrs E. M. Dixon**
2 **ANOTHER MEADOW,** 10, b g Meadowbrook—Another Joyful **Mrs E. M. Dixon**
3 **CROFTON LAKE,** 10, ch g Alias Smith (USA)—Joyful Star **Mrs E. M. Dixon**
4 **GOLDEN MEADOW,** 6, ch g Ovac (ITY)—Joyful Star **Mrs S. F. Dixon**
5 **HIRT LODGE,** 7, ch g Jumbo Hirt (USA)—Holly Lodge **Mrs S. F. Dixon**
6 **JUMBO'S DREAM,** 7, b g Jumbo Hirt (USA)—Joyful Star **Mrs E. M. Dixon**
7 **JUMBO STAR,** 8, ch g Jumbo Hirt (USA)—Joyful Star **Mrs E. M. Dixon**
8 **YEWCROFT BOY,** 7, ch g Meadowbrook—Another Joyful **Mrs E. M. Dixon**

176 MR JOHN P. DODDS, Alnwick

Postal: **South Hazelrigg, Chatton, Alnwick, Northd, NE66 5RZ.**
Phone: **(01668) 215216 MOBILE (0410) 346076**

1 **CHARLIE D'OR,** 5, ch g Le Coq d'Or—Edwards Victoria (IRE) **Mr E. F. Brown**
2 **CHARLISTIONA,** 7, ch m Good Times (ITY)—Abigails Portrait **Mr J. P. Dodds**
3 **DELWOOD,** 6, br g Dancing High—Lorna's Choice **Mr George F. White**
4 **DISTANT HILLS,** 6, gr m Alias Smith (USA)—Isolationist **Mr R. Nesbitt & Mr David S. Nimmo**
5 6, B m Sizzling Melody—Entourage **Mr David S. Nimmo**
6 **ESTABLISH (IRE),** 10, br m Salluceva—Royal Character **Mr William Harvey**
7 **HOMO DORNEY (IRE),** 5, b m Homo Sapien—Sheer Dorney **Mrs Clare Moore**
8 **JUBRAN (USA),** 12, b g Vaguely Noble—La Vue (USA) **Mrs Elke Scullion**
9 **MEGGIE SCOTT,** 5, ch m Dunbeath (USA)—Abigails Portrait **Mrs Elke Scullion**
10 **MUTASARRIF (IRE),** 5, b h Polish Patriot (USA)—Bouffant **Mr George F. White**

Other Owners: Mr J. A. Riddell, Mr F. V. White.

Jockeys (NH): Richard Guest (w.a.), A Thornton (w.a.).

177 MR M. J. K. DODS, Darlington

Postal: **Denton Hall Farm, Piercebridge, Darlington, Co. Durham, DL2 3TY.**
Phone: **(01325) 374270 FAX (01325) 374020 MOBILE (0860) 411590/(0410) 044763**

1 **ADVANCE EAST,** 6, b g Polish Precedent (USA)—Startino **Mr A. F. Monk**
2 **BIRCHWOOD SUN,** 8, b g Bluebird (USA)—Shapely Test (USA) **Mr A. G. Watson**
3 **ENERGY MAN,** 5, b g Hadeer—Cataclysmic **Mr A. J. Henderson**
4 **EQUERRY,** 7, b g Midyan (USA)—Supreme Kingdom **Mr A. G. Watson**
5 **FRENCH GRIT (IRE),** 6, b g Common Grounds—Charbatte (FR) **Mr C. Michael Wilson**
6 **HENRY THE HAWK,** 7, b g Doulab (USA)—Plum Blossom (USA) **Mr S. Barras**
7 **JEFFREY ANOTHERRED,** 4, b g Emarati (USA)—First Pleasure **Mr A. G. Watson**
8 **MAMICA,** 8, b g Idiot's Delight—Fishermans Lass **Mrs R. Olivier**
9 **MAYDORO,** 5, b m Dominion Royale—Bamdoro **Mr M. J. K. Dods**
10 **MON BRUCE,** 4, ch c Beveled (USA)—Pendona **Mr N. A. Riddell**
11 **MY GODSON,** 8, br g Valiyar—Blessit **Linkchallenge Limited**
12 **SACRED LOCH (USA),** 5, ch g Lomond (USA)—Cypria Sacra (USA) **Mr M. J. K. Dods**
13 **STORYTELLER (IRE),** 4, b g Thatching—Please Believe Me

THREE-YEAR-OLDS

14 **ABERKEEN,** ch c Keen—Miss Aboyne **Mr N. A. Riddell**
15 **MYSTICAL RODGE,** b g Mystiko (USA)—Deux Etoiles **Mr Doug Graham**
16 **SNAPPY TIMES,** ch g Timeless Times (USA)—Hill of Fare **Mr J. A. Wynn-Williams**
17 **WALWORTH WIZARD,** b g Presidium—Mrs Magic **Mr Vernon Spinks**
18 **WISHBONE ALLEY (IRE),** b g Common Grounds—Dul Dul (USA) **Mr Doug Graham**

TWO-YEAR-OLDS

19 Ch f 21/5 Emarati (USA)—Divissima (Music Boy) **Mr M. K. J. Dods**
20 Ch f 27/3 Woods Of Windsor—Go Likecrazy (Dowsing (USA)) **Linkchallenge Limited**
21 B f 12/3 Project Manager—Lovely Ali (IRE) (Dunbeath (USA)) **Linkchallenge Limited**
22 **SAUCY NIGHT,** ch g 13/3 Anshan—Kiss In The Dark (Starry Night) **Mr A. F. Monk**
23 Ch f 26/4 Mukaddamah (USA)—Ski Slope (Niniski (USA)) **Mr M. J. K. Dods**
24 **SMARTIE,** gr g 6/4 Keen—Sweet Whisper (Petong) **Mr A. G. Watson**
25 B g 26/5 Perpendicular—Stellaris (Star Appeal) **Mr J. A. Wynn-Williams**

Other Owners: Mr J. Beadle, Mr K. Chapman, Mr R. Coatsworth, Mrs C. E. Dods, Mr C. Graham, Mr G. E. C. Graham, Mrs L. Jones, Mr Ned Jones, Mr D. Kirsopp, Mr A. Mallen, Mr P. Monk, Mrs Patsy Monk, Mr C. J. Payne, Mrs Karen S. Pratt, Mrs Tracey Profitt, Mr R. Stokell, Mr M. Sweet, Mr Geoffrey Taylor.

Jockey (Flat): Dale Gibson.

Jockey (NH): T Reed (w.a.).

178 MR T. W. DONNELLY, Swadlincote

Postal: **Calke Abbey Racing Stables, Heath Lane, Boundary, Swadlincote, Derbyshire, DE11 7AY.**
Phone: **(01283) 226046 MOBILE (0585) 405497 FAX (01283) 551656**

1 **CHIPALATA,** 5, b g Derrylin—Kirsheda **Mr S. Taberner**
2 **JAMANE,** 8, b g Forzando—Mellow Girl **Mr S. Taberner**
3 **KINTAVI,** 8, b g Efisio—Princess Tavi **Mr S. Taberner**
4 **MR MONTAGUE (IRE),** 6, b g Pennine Walk—Ballyewry **C. I. P. Racing**
5 **ORBITAL LEGACY,** 5, b m Safawan—Orbital Manoeuvers **Mr G. C. Chipman**

Other Owners: Mrs D. E. Andrews, Mr A. C. Birkle, Mrs S. M. Chipman, Mrs Eileen A. Donnelly, Mr T. W. Donnelly, Mr Brian Edwards, Mr E. T. Fitchett, Mr D. Gallagher, Mr K. Halliwell, Mr R. W. Hickman, Mr R. F. Hill, Mrs M. Large, Mrs Barbara Mersh, Mr P. C. Shires, Mr J. Snell.

Jockey (Flat): C Rutter.

Jockey (NH): T Eley.

Amateur: Mr R J Armson.

179 MR S. L. DOW, Epsom

Postal: **Clear Height Stables, Derby Stables Road, Epsom, Surrey, KT18 5LB.**
Phone: **EPSOM (01372) 721490 FAX (01372) 748099 MOBILE (0860) 800109**

1 **CHIEF'S SONG,** 8, b g Chief Singer—Tizzy **Mrs Anne Devine**
2 **CHINGACHGOOK,** 4, b g Superlative—Petomania **G. E. Williams & B. Lawrence**
3 **COH SHO NO,** 5, b m Old Vic—Castle Peak **Rockville Pike Partnership**
4 **CONFRONTER,** 9, ch g Bluebird (USA)—Grace Darling (USA) **Hatfield Limited**
5 **CONTENTMENT (IRE),** 4, b c Fairy King (USA)—Quality of Life **Clear Height Racing**
6 **COSSACK COUNT,** 5, ch h Nashwan (USA)—Russian Countess (USA) **Normandy Developments (London)**
7 **EDAN HEIGHTS,** 6, b g Heights of Gold—Edna **Mr S. Dow**
8 **ED'S FOLLY (IRE),** 5, b g Fayruz—Tabriya **Mr Eddie Davess**
9 **ELA-YIE-MOU (IRE),** 5, ch g Kris—Green Lucia **Hatfield Limited**
10 **FOURDANED (IRE),** 5, b g Danehill (USA)—Pro Patria **Mr John Falvey**
11 **FRENCH MIST,** 4, b f Mystiko (USA)—Flambera (FR) **Mrs A. M. Upsdell**
12 **HIPPIOS,** 4, b br g Formidable (USA)—Miss Doody **Mr S. Dow**
13 **ISMENO,** 7, b g Ela-Mana-Mou—Seattle Siren (USA) **Mrs A. M. Upsdell**
14 **LANCASHIRE LEGEND,** 5, gr g Belfort (FR)—Peters Pet Girl **Bryan Taker & David Wilson**
15 **MAJESTY (IRE),** 4, b g Sadler's Wells (USA)—Princesse Timide (USA) **The Sporting Divots Partnership**
16 **PADDY'S STORM,** 6, b g Celestial Storm (USA)—Hot Tan **Miss Victoria Markowiak**
17 **PALISANDER (IRE),** 4, ch g Conquering Hero (USA)—Classic Choice **Mrs Heather Chakko**
18 **PERFECT POPPY,** 4, b f Shareef Dancer (USA)—Benazir **Mrs I. P. Blance**
19 **PREMIER NIGHT,** 5, b m Old Vic—Warm Welcome **Mr D. G. Churston**
20 **RAINBOW RAIN (USA),** 4, b g Capote (USA)—Grana (USA) **Mr P. McCarthy**
21 **SANDY SADDLER,** 4, ch g Most Welcome—Beryl's Jewel **Mr J. A. Redmond**
22 **SHARBADARID (IRE),** 4, b g Night Shift (USA)—Sharenara (USA) **Mrs Anne Devine**
23 **SHINING DANCER,** 6, b m Rainbow Quest (USA)—Strike Home **The Lalemaha Partnership**
24 **SHOOFK,** 7, ch g Dunbeath (USA)—River Reem (USA) **Mr Sean Devine**
25 **SPARTAN ROYALE,** 4, b c Shareef Dancer (USA)—Cormorant Creek **Mr B. McElhinney**
26 **SUITOR,** 5, b g Groom Dancer (USA)—Meliora **Mrs J. M. A. Churston**
27 **SUPER MONARCH,** 4, ch g Cadeaux Genereux—Miss Fancy That (USA) **Chelgate Public Relations Ltd**
28 **THIRD PARTY,** 4, gr f Terimon—Party Game **Mrs G. R. Smith**
29 **TIGER LAKE,** 5, ch g Nashwan (USA)—Tiger Flower **Mr Brian Solomon and Miss Jo-Ann Wood**
30 **TYPHOON LAD,** 5, ch g Risk Me (FR)—Muninga **Mr P. McCarthy**
31 **ZIBETH,** 4, b f Rainbow Quest (USA)—Tiger Flower **Mr J. E. Mills**

THREE-YEAR-OLDS

32 **ADVANCEALOT,** ch f Deploy—Copper Burn **Advance Reprographic Printers**
33 **ARGUMENTATIVE,** b g Mujadil (USA)—Dusky Nancy **Mr T. R. Mountain**
34 **AURIGNY,** b f Timeless Times (USA)—Dear Glenda **J & S Kelly**
35 **BUMBLE BE,** b g Precocious—Lingering **Mr J. A. Redmond**
36 **CORSECAN,** ch g Phountzi (USA)—Sagareina **Mr Ken Butler**
37 **DESERT SONG,** ch f Desert Dirham (USA)—Affaire de Coeur **Mrs D. R. Hunnisett**
38 **DIXIE CROSSROADS,** b f Efisio—Moments Joy **Mr Eddie Davess**
39 **FACILE TIGRE,** gr c Efisio—Dancing Diana **Mr D. G. Churston & Mr S. Dow**
40 **FIGAWIN,** b g Rudimentary (USA)—Dear Person **Clear Height Racing**
41 **FIRST IDEA,** b f Primo Dominie—Good Thinking (USA) **Mrs A. M. Upsdell**
42 **FLIGHT,** ch g Night Shift (USA)—Caspian Tern (USA) **Clear Height Racing**
43 **GENIUS (IRE),** b c Lycius (USA)—Once In My Life (IRE) **Mr G. Steinberg**
44 **INN ON THE PARK,** b g Northern Park (USA)—Hotel California (IRE) **Mr A. N. Solomons**
45 **MAIL SHOT (IRE),** b g Maladetto (IRE)—Pallachine (FR) **Macdonald Mailing Ltd**
46 **MY MISS,** gr f Mystiko (USA)—Dismiss **Mrs G. R. Smith**
47 **NOBLE DESIRE,** b f Noble Patriarch—North Pine **Mr T. Staplehurst**
48 **ORSINO,** b g Theatrical Charmer—Sonoco **Mrs J. Gittins**
49 **PASSIONATE PURSUIT,** b f Pursuit of Love—Flambera (FR) **Mrs A. M. Upsdell**
50 **PRIMORDIAL (FR),** b g Lesotho (USA)—Prilly (FR) **Mr D. G. Churston**
51 **RED BROOK LAD,** ch g Nomadic Way (USA)—Silently Yours (USA) **Dr B. H. Seal**
52 **ROISIN SPLENDOUR (IRE),** ch f Inchinor—Oriental Splendour **Brighthelm Racing**
53 **RUNAROUND,** b f Northern Park (USA)—Party Game **Mrs G. R. Smith**

MR S. L. DOW—continued

54 **SILVERSMITH (FR)**, b c Always Fair (USA)—Phargette (FR) **Mr D. G. Churston**
55 **THUMBELLINA**, b f Robellino (USA)—Welwyn **Mrs A. M. Upsdell**
56 **TITAN**, b c Lion Cavern (USA)—Sutosky **J & S Kelly**
57 **TOUGH NELL (IRE)**, ch f Archway (IRE)—Mousseux (IRE) **Godorphal Racing Partnership**
58 **TRY AGAIN (IRE)**, b f Mujadil (USA)—Fast Bay **Mr A. F. J. Merritt**
59 **WHITE VALLEY (IRE)**, b br f Tirol—Royal Wolff **Mr Ian Blance**

TWO-YEAR-OLDS

60 **ARZILLO**, b c 2/4 Forzando—Titania's Dance (IRE) **Mr Brian Solomon and Miss Jo-Ann Wood**
61 **AVODIRE**, b f 3/5 Warrshan (USA)—Always A Lady **Mr G. Steinberg**
62 **BROWN'S FLIGHT**, b f 24/2 Jupiter Island—Fearless Princess **Mr Cecil E. Brown**
63 **ECLECTIC**, b f 28/4 Emarati (USA)—Great Aim **Mr Harold Nass**
64 **GIFFOINE**, b f 30/3 Timeless Times (USA)—Dear Glenda **J. & S. Kelly**
65 **GOLD COAST**, b c 7/4 Alhijaz—Odilese **Mr G. Steinberg**
66 **KAZZOUD (IRE)**, b f 5/4 Ezzoud (IRE)—Kates Cabin **Mrs A. M. Upsdell**
67 **MISSING TED**, b f 26/4 Formidable (USA)—Hat Hill **Garvin-Jarvis**
68 **PISCES LAD**, b c 11/3 Cyrano de Bergerac—Tarnside Rosal **Mr J. Falvey & Mr G. Williamson**
69 **QUEEN OF THE KEYS**, b f 7/2 Royal Academy (USA)—Piano Belle (USA) **Mrs A. M. Upsdell**
70 B c 21/4 Merdon Melody—Young Whip **Mr S. Dow**

Other Owners: Mr Duncan M. Cameron, Mr J. S. Court, Mr P. E. Duboff, Mr G. W. Elphick, Sir Clement Freud, Mr B. W. Greaves, Mr S. R. Harman, Mr Michael Hill, Mr Paul G. Jacobs, Mr John A. Kelly, Mrs S. Kelly, Mr G. R. F. Lark, Mr A. Lindsay, Mr Malcolm J. Moss, Mr J. A. Redmond, Mr Roger Sayer, Mr Graham Williamson, Mr C. M. Wilson, Mr A. H. Wright.

Apprentice: P Doe (7-3).

Amateurs: Mr T Cuff (10-0), Mr R Guest (9-0).

180 MR C. J. DREWE, Didcot

Postal: **Lower Cross Farm, Blewbury Road, East Hagbourne, Didcot, Oxfordshire, OX11 9ND.**
Phone: **(01235) 813124**

1 **EXCELLED (IRE)**, 9, gr m Treasure Kay—Excelling Miss (USA) **Mrs J. Strange**
2 **FIRST AVENUE**, 14, b g Tina's Pet—Olympus Girl **Mr C. J. Drewe**
3 **NORTHERN SAGA (IRE)**, 5, b g Distinctly North (USA)—Saga's Humour **Mr C. J. Drewe**
4 **PROPER PRIMITIVE**, 5, gr m Primitive Rising (USA)—Nidd Bridges **The Cosket Partnership**
5 **RED RIVER (IRE)**, 7, ch m Over The River (FR)—Saroan Meed **Mrs Jenny Melbourne**
6 **TIME TO PARLEZ**, 7, b g Amboise—Image of War **Mrs J. Strange**
7 **WILL JAMES**, 12, ch g Raga Navarro (ITY)—Sleekit **Mrs Jenny Melbourne**

Other Owners: Mr P. Benson, Mrs M. J. Drewe, Mrs J. M. Johnstone, Mr R. J. K. Roberts.

181 MISS J. M. DU PLESSIS, Saltash

Postal: **Higher Pill Farm, Saltash, Cornwall, PL12 6LS.**
Phone: **(01752) 842362**

1 **KINGSMILL QUAY**, 9, b m Noble Imp—La Jolie Fille **Miss J. du Plessis**
2 **TAMAR LAD**, 5, gr g Scallywag—Easter Again **Miss J. du Plessis**
3 **TAMAR LILY**, 4, b f Lir—Easter Again **D. G. du Plessis**

182 MR T. D. C. DUN, Heriot

Postal: **Nether Brotherstone, Heriot, Midlothian, EH38 5YS.**
Phone: **(01875) 835225 FAX (01875) 835323**

1 **GALA WATER,** 12, ch m Politico (USA)—Royal Ruby **Mrs T. D. C. Dun**
2 **PLANNING GAIN,** 7, b g Blakeney—Romantiki (USA) **Mrs T. D. C. Dun**

Jockey (NH): T Reed.

Amateur: Mr M Bradburne.

183 MR E. A. L. DUNLOP, Newmarket

Postal: **Gainsborough Stables, Hamilton Road, Newmarket, Suffolk, CB8 OTE.**
Phone: **TEL: (01638) 661998 FAX (01638) 667394**

1 **BOLD WORDS (CAN),** 4, ch c Bold Ruckus (USA)—Trillium Woods (CAN) **Maktoum Al Maktoum**
2 **CADEAUX TRYST,** 6, b h Cadeaux Genereux—Trystero **Maktoum Al Maktoum**
3 **HAJR (IRE),** 4, b g Rainbow Quest (USA)—Dance By Night **Maktoum Al Maktoum**
4 **KUMAIT (USA),** 4, b br g Danzig (USA)—Colour Chart (USA) **Maktoum Al Maktoum**
5 **LATALOMNE (USA),** 4, ch g Zilzal (USA)—Sanctuary **Maktoum Al Maktoum**
6 **MONAASSIB,** 7, ch g Cadeaux Genereux—Pluvial **Maktoum Al Maktoum**
7 **TOP GUIDE (USA),** 7, ch g Diesis—Raahia (CAN) **Maktoum Al Maktoum**
8 **WINTER ROMANCE,** 5, ch h Cadeaux Genereux—Island Wedding (USA) **Maktoum Al Maktoum**

THREE-YEAR-OLDS

9 **ALLGRIT (USA),** b c Shadeed (USA)—Arsaan (USA) **Maktoum Al Maktoum**
10 **ALL ON MY OWN (USA),** ch c Unbridled (USA)—Some For All (USA) **Maktoum Al Maktoum**
11 **ALMAZHAR (IRE),** b c Last Tycoon—Mosaique Bleue **Mr Hamdan Al Maktoum**
12 **ANNADAWI,** b c Sadler's Wells (USA)—Prayers'n Promises (USA) **Maktoum Al Maktoum**
13 **BAY OF DELIGHT,** ch f Cadeaux Genereux—Zawaahy (USA) **Maktoum Al Maktoum**
14 **BLUE DAWN (IRE),** ch f Bluebird (USA)—Spring Carnival (USA) **The Serendipity Partnership**
15 **BRAVE NOBLE (USA),** ch c Woodman (USA)—Badge of Courage (USA) **Maktoum Al Maktoum**
16 **CODED SPIRIT (USA),** ch f Lost Code (USA)—Island Spirit (CAN) **The Coded Spirit Partnership**
17 **COME UP SMILING (USA),** b f Gone West (USA)—Encorelle (FR) **Maktoum Al Maktoum**
18 **COOL SPRAY (USA),** b f Hansel (USA)—Kissogram Girl (USA) **Maktoum Al Maktoum**
19 **COURTLY TIMES,** ch f Machiavellian (USA)—Dancing Moon (IRE) **Maktoum Al Maktoum**
20 **DEEP SPACE (IRE),** br c Green Desert (USA)—Dream Season (USA) **Maktoum Al Maktoum**
21 **DESERT ARROW (USA),** b c Gone West (USA)—Afaff (USA) **Maktoum Al Maktoum**
22 **DIXIE D'OATS,** b f Alhijaz—Helsanon **Downlands Racing**
23 **DUE SOUTH,** b f Darshaan—Island Wedding (USA) **Maktoum Al Maktoum**
24 **ECHELLE MUSICALE,** b f Rainbow Quest (USA)—Water Splash (USA) **Maktoum Al Maktoum**
25 **FOXIE LADY,** ch f Wolfhound (USA)—Final Thought **John Brown & Megan Dennis**
26 **GENEROUS WAYS,** ch c Generous (IRE)—Clara Bow (USA) **Maktoum Al Maktoum**
27 **GLAIZE (USA),** b c Gilded Time (USA)—Courtly Native (USA) **Maktoum Al Maktoum**
28 **HIGHLY PLEASED (USA),** b c Hansel (USA)—Bint Alfalla (USA) **Maktoum Al Maktoum**
29 **IVORY CROWN (IRE),** b f Chief's Crown (USA)—Royal Myth (USA) **The Serendipity Partnership**
30 **KAID (IRE),** b c Alzao (USA)—Very Charming (USA) **Maktoum Al Maktoum**
31 **KHEYRAH (USA),** b br c Dayjur (USA)—Khwlah (USA) **Mr Hamdan Al Maktoum**
32 **KITOPH (IRE),** b f Night Shift (USA)—Soxoph **Mrs Edward Dunlop**
33 **MAN OF COURAGE,** b c Nashwan (USA)—Dafrah (USA) **Maktoum Al Maktoum**
34 **MAWKAB (USA),** b br c Gulch (USA)—Up Sail (USA) **Mr Hamdan Al Maktoum**
35 **MAZBOON (USA),** ch c Diesis—Secretaire (USA) **Mr Hamdan Al Maktoum**
36 **MIGNON,** b f Midyan (USA)—Themeda **Mrs John Dunlop**
37 **MOMENTARILY (USA),** b f Gilded Time (USA)—Saratoga Dame (USA) **Mr Charles Gordon-Watson**
38 **MONSAJEM (USA),** ch c Woodman (USA)—Fairy Dancer (USA) **Maktoum Al Maktoum**
39 **MOULIN ROUGE,** b f Shareef Dancer (USA)—Pride of Paris **Mrs P. Homewood**

MR E. A. L. DUNLOP—continued

40 MUTAFARIJ (USA), ch c Diesis—Madame Secretary (USA) **Mr Hamdan Al Maktoum**
41 MY CAREER, b c Caerleon (USA)—Lady Be Mine (USA) **Dragon's Stud**
42 NATIONAL WISH (USA), ch c Forty Niner (USA)—Regent's Walk (CAN) **Maktoum Al Maktoum**
43 NICE BALANCE (USA), b g Shadeed (USA)—Fellwaati (USA) **Maktoum Al Maktoum**
44 NOBLE CHARGER (IRE), ch c Cadeaux Genereux—Shawgatny (USA) **Maktoum Al Maktoum**
45 OLD TRADITION (IRE), b br f Royal Academy (USA)—Desert Bride (USA) **Maktoum Al Maktoum**
46 OPERA QUEEN (USA), b f Pleasant Colony (USA)—Cadeaux d'Amie (USA) **Maktoum Al Maktoum**
47 PARTICULAR FRIEND, ch f Cadeaux Genereux—Pamela Peach **Maktoum Al Maktoum**
48 PREMIUM RATE (USA), ch c Phone Trick (USA)—Excitable Gal (USA) **Bernard Gover Bloodstock Trading Ltd**
49 PROUD EVENT (USA), ch f Zilzal (USA)—Furajet (USA) **Maktoum Al Maktoum**
50 QUIET ASSURANCE (USA), ch c St Jovite (USA)—Silent Turn (USA) **Maktoum Al Maktoum**
51 SILVER SABRE (USA), b c Silver Hawk (USA)—Explosive Tobin (USA) **Maktoum Al Maktoum**
52 SOCIAL ROUND (FR), ch c Cadeaux Genereux—Dome Lawel (USA) **Maktoum Al Maktoum**
53 STERO HEIGHTS (IRE), b c Shirley Heights—Trystero **Maktoum Al Maktoum**
54 STYLISH FLIGHT (USA), b g Alleged (USA)—Willa Joe (IRE) **Maktoum Al Maktoum**
55 THIHN (IRE), ch c Machiavellian (USA)—Hasana (USA) **Mr Hamdan Al Maktoum**
56 WISE INVESTMENT, b c Rainbow Quest (USA)—Miss Fancy That (USA) **Maktoum Al Maktoum**

TWO-YEAR-OLDS

57 ABLA, b f 11/4 Robellino (USA)—Sans Blaque (USA) (The Minstrel (CAN)) **Mr Hamdan Al Maktoum**
58 AL NABA (USA), ch c 11/2 Mr Prospector (USA)—Forest Flower (USA) (Green Forest (USA)) **Mr Hamdan Al Maktoum**
59 BLACK VELVET BAND, b f 14/2 Sadler's Wells (USA)—Gemaasheh (Habitat) **Mr G. Howard Spink & Miss L. Regis**
60 BRAIDING, b f 15/2 Polish Precedent—Silver Braid (USA) (Miswaki (USA)) **Wyck Hall Stud Ltd**
61 CANDLERIGGS, ch c 8/1 Indian Ridge—Ridge Pool (IRE) (Bluebird (USA)) **Mr A. Ferguson**
62 COLLEGE CHOIR (IRE), b c 10/3 College Chapel—Lypharden (IRE) (Lyphard's Special (USA)) **C. J. & B. V. Pennick**
63 COPS (IRE), ch c 28/2 Grand Lodge (USA)—Gentle Guest (IRE) (Be My Guest (USA)) **Mr Abdullah Ali**
64 DATE, b c 23/2 Cadeaux Genereux—Faribole (IRE) (Esprit du Nord (USA)) **Mr Abdullah Ali**
65 DEVIL'S IMP (IRE), ch f 15/4 Cadeaux Genereux—High Spirited (Shirley Heights) **Maktoum Al Maktoum**
66 DIRECT DEAL, b c 3/3 Rainbow Quest (USA)—Al Najah (USA) (Topsider (USA)) **Maktoum Al Maktoum**
67 EASTERN MYTH (USA), b f 28/2 Housebuster (USA)—Worood (USA) (Vaguely Noble) **Maktoum Al Maktoum**
68 EASTERN TRIBUTE (USA), b c 25/3 Affirmed (USA)—Mia Duchessa (USA) (Nijinsky (CAN)) **Maktoum Al Maktoum**
69 EBINZAYD (IRE), b c 24/3 Tenby—Sharakawa (IRE) (Darshaan) **Mr Hamdan Al Maktoum**
70 ELECTION PROMISE, b c 1/5 Mujtahid (USA)—Trystero (Shareef Dancer (USA)) **Maktoum Al Maktoum**
71 FAIR FLIGHT, b c 11/3 Green Desert (USA)—Barari (USA) (Blushing Groom (FR)) **Maktoum Al Maktoum**
72 FANCY MY CHANCE, b c 7/2 Rainbow Quest (USA)—Yazeanhaa (USA) (Zilzal (USA)) **Maktoum Al Maktoum**
73 FEELING FINE, b f 23/1 Arazi (USA)—Green Flower (USA) (Fappiano (USA)) **Maktoum Al Maktoum**
74 FOLLOW THAT DREAM, b f 27/2 Darshaan—Try To Catch Me (USA) (Shareef Dancer (USA)) **Maktoum Al Maktoum**
75 FRAGRANT OASIS (USA), ch f 2/2 Rahy (USA)—Raahia (CAN) (Vice Regent (CAN)) **Maktoum Al Maktoum**
76 GHAAZI, ch c 7/3 Lahib (USA)—Shurooq (USA) (Affirmed (USA)) **Mr Hamdan Al Maktoum**
77 GOLD ANGEL, ch f 29/2 Machiavellian (USA)—Dafrah (USA) (Danzig (USA)) **Maktoum Al Maktoum**
78 HERO'S LUCK (IRE), ch c 9/5 Lucky Guest—Fancied (Dominion) **Anamoine Limited**
79 HISHMAH, b f 21/4 Nashwan (USA)—Na-Ayim (IRE) (Shirley Heights) **Mr Hamdan Al Maktoum**
80 B c 13/4 Marju (IRE)—Hollybank Lady (USA) (Sir Ivor) **Paul & Jenny Green**
81 IPLEDGEALLEGIANCE (USA), b c 15/4 Alleged (USA)—Yafill (USA) (Nureyev (USA)) **Maktoum Al Maktoum**
82 KHIBRAH (IRE), br f 5/2 Lahib (USA)—Sabayik (IRE) (Unfuwain (USA)) **Mr Hamdan Al Maktoum**
83 MABSHUSH (IRE), b c 4/5 Mujtahid (USA)—Just A Mirage (Green Desert (USA)) **Mr Hamdan Al Maktoum**
84 MANICURE (IRE), b f 26/3 Lucky Guest—Mana (GER) (Windwurf (GER)) **Anamoine Limited**
85 MELLOW MISS, b f 13/3 Danehill (USA)—Like The Sun (USA) (Woodman (USA)) **Maktoum Al Maktoum**
86 Ch c 18/1 Indian Ridge—Mercy Bien (IRE) (Be My Guest (USA))
87 MUTHAAHAB (CAN), b c 20/1 Dixieland Band (USA)—Serene Nobility (USA) (His Majesty (USA)) **Mr Hamdan Al Maktoum**
88 MY ALIBI (USA), b f 7/3 Sheikh Albadou—Fellwaati (USA) (Alydar (USA)) **Maktoum Al Maktoum**
89 MY ENIGMA, b f 4/5 Rainbow Quest (USA)—Zawaahy (USA) (El Gran Senor (USA)) **Maktoum Al Maktoum**
90 PAY THE PIED PIPER (USA), b c 26/4 Red Ransom (USA)—Fife (IRE) (Lomond (USA)) **Maktoum Al Maktoum**
91 B f 22/2 Green Desert (USA)—Pocket Piece (USA) (Diesis) **Mohammed Al Nabouda**

MR E. A. L. DUNLOP—continued

92 B c 7/3 River Falls—Point Of Law (Law Society (USA)) **The Serendipity Partnership**
93 RAIN RAIN GO AWAY (USA), ch c 24/3 Miswaki (USA)—Stormagain (USA) (Storm Cat (USA)) **Maktoum Al Maktoum**
94 RISING LEADER (USA), b c 23/3 Rahy (USA)—Bineyah (IRE) (Sadler's Wells (USA)) **Maktoum Al Maktoum**
95 ROYAL HUSSAR, gr c 2/2 Efisio—Altaia (FR) (Sicyos (USA)) **Mr P. Gwilliam & Mr L. Nester-Smith**
96 SECRET DELL, b c 7/3 Doyoun—Summer Silence (USA) (Stop The Music (USA)) **Mr Ahmed Ali**
97 SEDRAH (USA), ch f 18/4 Dixieland Band (USA)—Madame Secretary (USA) (Secretariat (USA)) **Mr Hamdan Al Maktoum**
98 SIR LEGEND (USA), br c 4/6 El Gran Senor (USA)—Tadkiyra (IRE) (Darshaan) **Maktoum Al Maktoum**
99 SONIC SAPPHIRE, b f 18/5 Royal Academy (USA)—Sit Alkul (USA) (Mr Prospector (USA)) **Maktoum Al Maktoum**
100 SUNSHINE BOY, b c 15/4 Cadeaux Genereux—Sahara Baladee (USA) (Shadeed (USA)) **Maktoum Al Maktoum**
101 SURPRISE ENCOUNTER, ch c 7/2 Cadeaux Genereux—Scandalette (Niniski (USA)) **Mr Ahmed Ali**
102 SWEET EMOTION (IRE), b f 2/3 Bering—Hiwaayati (Shadeed (USA)) **Maktoum Al Maktoum**
103 TICK N PICK, b f 25/4 Reprimand—My Preference (Reference Point) **Mr A. Burrell & Mr P. Burrell**
104 WHISPERING WIND, b c 20/5 Danehill (USA)—Meadow Pipit (CAN) (Meadowlake (USA)) **Maktoum Al Maktoum**
105 ZAAJER (USA), ch c 21/3 Silver Hawk (USA)—Crown Quest (USA) (Chief's Crown (USA)) **Mr Hamdan Al Maktoum**
106 ZERO OPTIONS (USA), b c 24/5 Zilzal (USA)—Bitooh (Seattle Slew (USA)) **Maktoum Al Maktoum**
107 B c 26/3 Diesis—Zonda (Fabulous Dancer (USA)) **Mohammed Al Nabouda**
108 ZULAL (USA), b c 30/1 Zilzal (USA)—My Shafy (Rousillon (USA)) **Mr Hilal Salem**

Other Owners: Mr C. Abbott, Mr P. Afia, Mrs Mark Burrell, Mr R. Chester, Lady Sarah Clutton, Mr T. Coleman, Mr R. Craddock, Mr D. Dobbie, Mr E. A. L. Dunlop, Mrs J. M. Frew, Mr M. Haggas, Mrs S. Hall, Lord Hopetown, Lord Howland, Mr I. Lawrence, Mrs R. Lewin-Smith, Mr J. Macintosh, Mr Simon Marsh, Miss T. Martin, Mr Reiley McDonald, Mr & Mrs J. McKeever, Mr M. Mitchell, Mr M. Newcombe, Mrs J. Odam, Mrs R. Page, Sir Anthony Page-Wood, Mr D. M. Roberts, Mr & Mrs E. Saunders, Mr Skosciuszko, Mr J. Stitt, Mr J. Strauss, Mrs A. M. Sturges, Mr & Mrs E. Voute, Mr Ben P. Walden Jr, Mr E. Warren, Mr J. R. Weatherby, Mr A. Wentworth-Stanley, Mr K. Williams, Mr T. Wishart.

184 MR J. L. DUNLOP, Arundel

Postal: **Castle Stables, Arundel, West Sussex, BN18 9AB.**
Phone: **ARUNDEL (01903) 882194 TELEX-87475 RACDEL FAX (01903) 884173**

1 **BAHHARE (USA),** 4, b c Woodman (USA)—Wasnah (USA) **Mr Hamdan Al Maktoum**
2 **BELOW THE SALT (IRE),** 5, br g Over The River (FR)—Comeallye **Mr J. L. Dunlop**
3 **CELERIC,** 6, b g Mtoto—Hot Spice **Mr C. J. Spence & Mr J. D. Morley**
4 **ELNADIM (USA),** 4, b c Danzig (USA)—Elle Seule (USA) **Mr Hamdan Al Maktoum**
5 **EMBARGO (IRE),** 6, gr g Roselier—Honey Dream **Mr J. L. Dunlop**
6 **EMERGING MARKET,** 6, b g Emarati—Flitteriss Park **Mr P. L. Wroughton**
7 **ESHTIAAL (USA),** 4, br c Riverman (USA)—Lady Cutlass (USA) **Mr Hamdan Al Maktoum**
8 **FIOLINO (FR),** 5, b g Bayolidaan (FR)—Vellea (FR) **Mr J. L. Dunlop**
9 **GARUDA (IRE),** 4, b c Danehill (USA)—Ardmelody **Mr Bob Demuyser**
10 **GROOM'S GORDON (FR),** 4, b g Groom Dancer (USA)—Sonoma (FR) **Mrs H. Focke**
11 **KENNEMARA STAR (IRE),** 4, ch g Kenmare (FR)—Dawn Star **Winf Flower Overseas Holdings Inc**
12 **LORD EUROLINK (IRE),** 4, b c Danehill (USA)—Lady Eurolink **Eurolink Group P.L.C.**
13 **MALABI (USA),** 4, b c Danzig (USA)—Gmaasha (IRE) **Mr Hamdan Al Maktoum**
14 **MAWARED (IRE),** 5, ch h Nashwan (USA)—Harmless Albatross **Mr Hamdan Al Maktoum**
15 **MOON RIVER (IRE),** 4, ch g Mujtahid (USA)—Moonsilk **Mr Benny Andersson**
16 **ORCHESTRA STALL,** 6, b g Old Vic—Blue Brocade **Mr D. Sieff**
17 **PALIO SKY,** 4, b c Niniski (USA)—Live Ammo **Mr J. E. Nash**
18 **RIGHT WING (IRE),** 4, b c In The Wings—Nekhbet **The Earl Cadogan**
19 **SAMRAAN (USA),** 5, br h Green Dancer (USA)—Sedra **Mr K. M. Al-Mudhaf**
20 **SHAGREEN (IRE),** 5, b g Buckskin (FR)—Laiton Peni **Mr J. L. Dunlop**
21 **SHELTERING SKY (IRE),** 4, b c Selkirk (USA)—Shimmering Sea **Mr Victor Behrens (Susan Abbott Racing)**
22 **SILVER PATRIARCH (IRE),** 4, gr c Saddlers' Hall (IRE)—Early Rising (USA) **Mr Peter S. Winfield**
23 **STANTON HARCOURT (USA),** 4, b c Sovereign Dancer (USA)—Island Style (USA) **Mr Cyril Humphris**
24 **TAIPAN (IRE),** 6, b h Last Tycoon—Alidiva **Lord Swaythling**
25 **WAHIBA SANDS,** 5, b g Pharly (FR)—Lovely Noor (USA) **Lord Swaythling**

THREE-YEAR-OLDS

26 **ALCAYDE,** ch c Alhijaz—Lucky Flinders **Lady Cohen**
27 **ALCAZAR (IRE),** b g Alzao (USA)—Sahara Breeze **Mr J. P. Repard**
28 **AL-FATEH (IRE),** b c Caerleon (USA)—Filia Ardross **Mr A. Bahbahani**
29 **ALHARIR (USA),** b f Zafonic (USA)—Thawakib (IRE) **Mr Hamdan Al-Maktoum**
30 **ASHRAAKAT (USA),** b f Danzig (USA)—Elle Seule (USA) **Mr Hamdan Al-Maktoum**
31 **BENEVENTUS,** b c Most Welcome—Dara Dee **Mr R. N. Khan**
32 **BLACK WEASEL (IRE),** br c Lahib (USA)—Glowlamp (IRE) **Tessona Racing Limited**
33 **CALEDONIAN EXPRESS,** b f Northern Park (USA)—New Edition **Mr R. J. McAulay**
34 **CLOSE UP (IRE),** ch c Cadeaux Genereux—Zoom Lens (IRE) **Mr Ian Cameron**
35 **ELHAYQ (IRE),** b c Nashwan (USA)—Mahasin (USA) **Mr Hamdan Al Maktoum**
36 **ELJJANAH (USA),** b c Riverman (USA)—True Celebrity (USA) **Mr Hamdan Al Maktoum**
37 **EUROLINK GIORGIANO,** ch c Selkirk (USA)—Taiga **Eurolink Group P.L.C.**
38 **FAKHR (USA),** br c Riverman (USA)—Roseate Tern **Mr Hamdan Al Maktoum**
39 **FANCY WRAP,** b f Kris—Gift Wrapped **Sussex Stud Ltd**
40 **FANTASY NIGHT (IRE),** b g Night Shift (USA)—Gay Fantasy **Windflower Overseas Holdings Inc**
41 **FIAMMA (IRE),** b f Irish River (FR)—Florie (FR) **Mr Vito Schirone**
42 **FLORAZI,** b c Arazi (USA)—Flo Russell (USA) **Mr Peter S. Winfield**
43 **FLOW BY,** b f Formidable (USA)—Lobinda **Hesmonds Stud Ltd**
44 **FLOWN SOUTH,** b g Robellino (USA)—Belle Danseuse **Mrs S. Lakin**
45 **GHALI (USA),** b c Alleged (USA)—Kareema (USA) **Mr S. Khaled**
46 **GOODWOOD CAVALIER,** b g Efisio—Brassy Nell **Goodwood Racehorse Owners Group (Three)**
47 **GREEN JACKET,** b g Green Desert (USA)—Select Sale **Mr Ian Cameron**
48 **HAAMI (USA),** b c Nashwan (USA)—Oumaldaaya (USA) **Mr Hamdan Al Maktoum**
49 **HARLESTONE LANE,** gr f Chilibang—Harlestone Lake **Mr J. L. Dunlop**
50 **HERMINIUS (IRE),** b c Ballad Rock—Scotia Rose **Mr D. R. Hunnisett**
51 **HONEST BORDERER,** b g Selkirk (USA)—Tell No Lies **Mrs A. Johnstone**
52 **HUJOOM (IRE),** b c Fairy King (USA)—Maellen **Kuwait Racing Syndicate**
53 **IM PROPOSIN (IRE),** b c Posen (USA)—Kitterland **Mr Nicholas Cooper**
54 **INDIMAAJ,** b c Mtoto—Fairy Feet **Kuwait Racing Syndicate**

MR J. L. DUNLOP—continued

55 **IN THE SUN (USA),** b f Alleged (USA)—Pandysia (USA) **Sir P. Payne-Gallwey**
56 **KAHTAN,** b c Nashwan (USA)—Harmless Albatross **Mr Hamdan Al Maktoum**
57 **KARIYH (USA),** b f Shadeed (USA)—Katiba (USA) **Mr Hamdan Al Maktoum**
58 **LEGGERA (IRE),** b f Sadler's Wells (USA)—Lady Ambassador **Mrs H. Focke**
59 **LIKELY STORY (IRE),** b f Night Shift (USA)—Perfect Alibi **Mr M. L. Page**
60 **MAGICAL COLOURS (IRE),** b f Rainbows For Life (CAN)—Immediate Impact **Mrs A. J. C. Pratt**
61 **MAJESTIC HILLS,** b c Shirley Heights—Regent Miss (CAN) **Lady Harrison**
62 **MARCH HARE,** b f Groom Dancer (USA)—Spring **Lord Halifax**
63 **MISS VIOLET,** b f Rainbow Quest (USA)—Youthful (FR) **Aylesfield Farms Stud Ltd**
64 **MOHAWK (IRE),** b c Indian Ridge—Dazzling Fire (IRE) **Mr John Darby**
65 **MONDSCHEIN,** b f Rainbow Quest (USA)—River Spey **Mr Benny Andersson**
66 **MUSHRAAF,** br c Zafonic (USA)—Vice Vixen (CAN) **Mr Hamdan Al Maktoum**
67 **NATAYIG,** b f Fairy King (USA)—Cunning **Mr Hamdan Al Maktoum**
68 **PAIRUMANI STAR (IRE),** ch c Caerleon (USA)—Dawn Star **Windflower Overseas Holdings Inc**
69 **PERSIAN FANTASIA,** b f Alzao (USA)—Persian Fantasy **Windflower Overseas Holdings Inc**
70 **PIPED ABOARD (IRE),** b g Pips Pride—Last Gunboat **Lord Swaythling**
71 **RABAH,** b c Nashwan (USA)—The Perfect Life (IRE) **Mr Hamdan Al Maktoum**
72 **RABEA (USA),** b f Devil's Bag (USA)—Racing Blue **Mrs H. Focke**
73 **REGAL PATRIARCH (IRE),** br c Marju (IRE)—Early Rising (USA) **Mr Peter S. Winfield**
74 **RIBBLESDALE,** b f Northern Park (USA)—Tarib **Mr P. E. Cooper (Susan Abbott Racing)**
75 **ROBORANT,** b g Robellino (USA)—Sunny Davis (USA) **Lord Wakeham**
76 **SALEELA (USA),** b c Nureyev (USA)—Allegretta **Mr Hamdan Al Maktoum**
77 **SAVOURY,** b f Salse (USA)—Metaphysique (FR) **Mr Anthony Burrell**
78 **SHAHER (USA),** ch c Shadeed (USA)—Desirable **Mr Hamdan Al Maktoum**
79 **SHARP HINT,** ch f Sharpo—May Hinton **Sir Thomas Pilkington**
80 **SILVER FAN,** gr f Lear Fan (USA)—Reine de Danse (USA) **Sir Eric Parker**
81 **SOMAYDA (IRE),** b c Last Tycoon—Flame of Tara **Mr Hamdan Al Maktoum**
82 **ST ENODOC (FR),** ch g Sanglamore (USA)—Exemina (USA) **Lord Swaythling**
83 **SURVEYOR,** ch c Lycius (USA)—Atacama **The Earl Cadogan**
84 **SWEET DREAMS,** b f Selkirk (USA)—Ahohoney **Miss K. Rawsing**
85 **SWEET PEA,** b f Persian Bold—Silk Petal **Mr N. M. H. Jones**
86 **TAJASUR (IRE),** ch c Imperial Frontier (USA)—Safiya (USA) **Mr Hamdan Al Maktoum**
87 **THAMUD (IRE),** ch f Lahib (USA)—Taroob (IRE) **Mr Hamdan Al Maktoum**
88 **TRANSYLVANIA,** b f Wolfhound (USA)—Slava (USA) **Capt J. Macdonald-Buchanan**
89 **TRINITY REEF,** b f Bustino—Triple Reef **Hesmonds Stud Ltd**
90 **WAVE ROCK,** b g Tragic Role (USA)—Moonscape **The Earl Cadogan**
91 **WINSA (USA),** b f Riverman (USA)—Wasnah (USA) **Mr Hamdan Al Maktoum**
92 **WOSAITA,** b f Generous (IRE)—Eljazzi **H. R. H. Prince A. A. Faisal**
93 **ZIHAAN (USA),** gr c Dayjur (USA)—Asl (USA) **Mr Hamdan Al Makktoum**

TWO-YEAR-OLDS

94 **ABLE PETE,** b c 19/1 Formidable (USA)—An Empress (USA) (Affirmed (USA)) **Mr P. H. Locke**
95 **ADNAAN (IRE),** ch c 10/3 Nashwan (USA)—Whakilyric (USA) (Miswaki (USA)) **Mr Hamdan Al Maktoum**
96 **ALABAQ (USA),** br f 1/4 Riverman (USA)—Salsabil (Sadler's Wells (USA)) **Mr Hamdan Al Maktoum**
97 **AL SAQIYA (USA),** b f 28/1 Woodman (USA)—
Augusta Springs (USA) (Nijinsky (CAN)) **Mr Hamdan Al Maktoum**
98 **BACKCLOTH (IRE),** b g 30/4 Scenic—Traumerei (GER) (Surumu (GER)) **Mr D. Sieff**
99 **BADAAYER (USA),** br f 7/2 Silver Hawk (USA)—Katiba (USA) (Gulch (USA)) **Mr Hamdan Al Maktoum**
100 **BALSOX,** b c 11/4 Alzao (USA)—Bobbysoxer (Valiyar) **Hesmonds Stud Ltd**
101 **BARN OWL,** ch f 12/2 Sabrehill (USA)—Ever Welcome (Be My Guest (USA)) **Sir Thomas Pilkington**
102 B c 4/4 College Chapel—Bay Supreme (Martinmas)
103 **BEGGARS BELIEF (IRE),** b f 8/4 Common Grounds—Perfect Alibi (Law Society (USA)) **Mrs S. Abbott**
104 **BERYL,** ch f 9/2 Bering—Fayrooz (USA) (Gulch (USA)) **Capt. J. Macdonald-Buchanan**
105 B f 22/2 Doyoun—Bird's Wing (IRE) (Bluebird (USA)) **Mrs H. Focke**
106 **BIRTH OF THE BLUES,** ch c 17/2 Efisio—Great Steps (Vaigly Great) **Mr Bob Lalement**
107 **BONNES NOUVELLES,** b f 24/2 Shirley Heights—La Belle Creole (Rainbow Quest (USA)) **Miss K. Rausing**
108 **CAVERNISTA,** b f 17/3 Lion Cavern (USA)—Princess Genista (Ile de Bourbon (USA)) **Mr I. M. Stewart-Brown**
109 **CHELSEA BARRACKS,** b c 29/3 Deploy—Hymne d'Amour (USA) (Dixieland Band (USA)) **The Earl Cadogan**
110 **CLAXON,** b f 1/4 Caerleon (USA)—Bulaxie (Bustino) **Hesmonds Stud Ltd**

MR J. L. DUNLOP—continued

111 **CREDIT A PLENTY,** ch f 7/3 Generous (IRE)—On Credit (FR) (No Pass No Sale) **Hesmonds Stud Ltd**
112 B f 2/3 Kris S (USA)—Dancing Grass (USA) (Northern Dancer) **Hesmonds Stud Ltd**
113 **DARK ALBATROSS (USA),** b br f 16/1 Sheikh Albadou—Rossard (DEN) (Glacial (DEN)) **Mrs S. Abbott**
114 **DEBAAJ,** ch c 23/4 Indian Ridge—Gold Bracelet (Golden Fleece (USA)) **Kuwait Racing Syndicate**
115 **DIONISIO (USA),** b c 27/3 Polish Precedent—Schwanensee (USA) (Mr Leader (USA)) **Mr Vito Schirone**
116 **EL KARIM (USA),** ch c 1/2 Storm Cat (CAN)—Gmaasha (IRE) (Kris) **Mr Hamdan Al Maktoum**
117 **ELLE QUESTRO,** b f 8/3 Rainbow Quest (USA)—Lady Be Mine (USA) (Sir Ivor) **Mrs M. Burrell**
118 **ELM DUST,** ch f 26/4 Elmaamul (USA)—Galaxie Dust (USA) (Blushing Groom (FR)) **Hesmonds Stud Ltd**
119 **ELTAWAASUL (USA),** ch c 1/3 Nureyev (USA)—Grand Falls (USA) (Ogygian (USA)) **Mr Hamdan Al Maktoum**
120 **ESTERAAD,** ch f 22/2 Cadeaux Genereux—Eclipsing (IRE) (Baillamont (USA)) **Khalil Al Sayegh**
121 **ETIZAAZ (USA),** b f 15/2 Diesis—Alamosa (Alydar (USA)) **Mr Hamdan Al Maktoum**
122 **FANTASY HILL (IRE),** b c 21/2 Danehill (USA)—Gay Fantasy (Troy) **Windflower Overseas Holdings Inc**
123 **GHITA (IRE),** ch f 14/3 Zilzal (USA)—Sabria (USA) (Miswaki (USA)) **Mr R. J. McAulay**
124 **GOODBYE (IRE),** b c 1/4 Thatching—Itqan (IRE) (Sadler's Wells (USA)) **Mr I. D. Cameron**
125 **GOODWOOD JAZZ (IRE),** b f 26/4 Night Shift (USA)—
Wood Violet (USA) (Riverman (USA)) **Goodwood Racehorse Owners Group (Four)**
126 **GRAND MAITRE (USA),** gr ro c 17/4 Gone West (USA)—
La Grande Epoque (USA) (Lyphard (USA)) **Mr Robin F. Scully**
127 **GRINLING GIBBONS,** ch c 12/1 Woodman (USA)—Saddle Bow (Sadler's Wells (USA)) **Lord Swaythling**
128 **HARARAH,** ch f 6/3 Barathea (IRE)—Taroob (IRE) (Roberto (USA)) **Mr Hamdan Al Maktoum**
129 **HAWRIYAH (USA),** b f 4/4 Dayjur (USA)—Lady Cutlass (USA) (Cutlass (USA)) **Mr Hamdan Al Maktoum**
130 **HEIGHT OF FANTASY (IRE),** b f 18/3 Shirley Heights—
Persian Fantasy (Persian Bold) **Windflower Overseas Holdings Inc**
131 B c 12/5 Ela-Mana-Mou—Highland Ball (Bold Lad (IRE)) **Mr M. Watt**
132 Gr f 21/4 Barathea (IRE)—Infamy (Shirley Heights) **Mr G. Pinchen**
133 **INTIZAA (USA),** b f 15/3 Mr Prospector (USA)—Oumaldaaya (USA) (Nureyev (USA)) **Mr Hamdan Al Maktoum**
134 **JOYEUX PLAYER (USA),** b c 15/1 St Jovite (USA)—
Play On And On (USA) (Stop The Music (USA)) **Mr S. Khaled**
135 B c 30/3 Royal Academy (USA)—Lady Ambassador (General Assembly (USA)) **Mrs H. Focke**
136 B c 6/5 Mtoto—Lady Habitat (Habitat)
137 **LAWNETT,** b f 25/1 Runnett—Polar Storm (IRE) (Law Society (USA)) **Miss J. Evans**
138 **LOOP THE LOUP,** b g 17/2 Petit Loup (USA)—Mithi Al Gamar (USA) (Blushing Groom (FR)) **Mr D. Sieff**
139 Ch c 19/4 Elmaamul (USA)—Lovers Light (Grundy) **British Land Co**
140 **LUCKY FEATHER (IRE),** b f 15/3 Lucky Guest—Hens Grove (Alias Smith (USA)) **Anamoine Racing**
141 **LUCKY GITANO (IRE),** b c 19/2 Lucky Guest—April Wind (Windjammer (USA)) **Anamoine Racing**
142 **LUCKY LINDA,** b f 8/4 Bluebird (USA)—Spectacular Dawn (Spectacular Bid (USA)) **Mr Peter S. Winfield**
143 **MAZAYA (IRE),** b f 8/5 Sadler's Wells (USA)—Sharaniya (USA) (Alleged (USA)) **Mr Hamdan Al Maktoum**
144 **MONTE CALVO,** b f 30/4 Shirley Heights—Slava (USA) (Diesis) **Capt. J. Macdonald-Buchanan**
145 **MOONLIT WATER,** b f 16/5 Rainbow Quest (USA)—
Shimmer (FR) (Green Dancer (USA)) **Aylesfield Farms Stud Ltd**
146 **MUJAHID (USA),** b c 31/1 Danzig (USA)—Elrafa Ah (USA) (Storm Cat (USA)) **Mr Hamdan Al Maktoum**
147 **MUKAYED (IRE),** gr c 23/5 Cadeaux Genereux—Al Sylah (Nureyev (USA)) **Mr Hamdan Al Maktoum**
148 **MUQTARIB (USA),** b c 23/4 Gone West (USA)—Shicklah (USA) (The Minstrel (CAN)) **Mr Hamdan Al Maktoum**
149 Ch c 20/4 First Trump—Nagida (Skyliner)
150 **NASHEED (USA),** b f 20/2 Riverman (USA)—Thawakib (IRE) (Sadler's Wells (USA)) **Mr Hamdan Al Maktoum**
151 **NIGHT ADVENTURE (IRE),** ch c 1/2 Night Shift (USA)—Mary Hinge (Dowsing (USA)) **Lord Swaythling**
152 **NIKA NESGODA,** b f 22/2 Suave Dancer (USA)—Highland Ceilidh (IRE) (Scottish Reel) **Mr Cyril Humphris**
153 **OSOOL (USA),** b c 29/3 Danzig (USA)—Histoire (FR) (Riverman (USA)) **Mr Hamdan Al Maktoum**
154 B f 8/3 Caerleon (USA)—Pamplona (GER) (Surumu (GER)) **Mrs H. Focke**
155 **PILOT'S HARBOUR,** b c 24/2 Distant Relative—Lillemor (Connaught) **Mr Magnus Berger**
156 **PIPA,** b f 1/4 Suave Dancer (USA)—Pipitina (Bustino) **Sir Eric Parker**
157 **RAAQI,** b c 7/2 Nashwan (USA)—Mehthaaf (USA) (Nureyev (USA)) **Mr Hamdan Al Maktoum**
158 B c 28/2 Generous (IRE)—Rafha (Kris) **H. R. H. Prince A. A. Faisal**
159 **RAHAYEB,** b f 3/3 Arazi (USA)—Bashayer (USA) (Mr Prospector (USA)) **Mr Hamdan Al Maktoum**
160 **ROSA CANINA,** b f 4/2 Bustino—Moon Spin (Night Shift (USA))
161 **ROYAL PATRON,** b f 5/3 Royal Academy (USA)—Indian Queen (Electric) **Sir Gordon Brunton**
162 **SAABIKAH (USA),** b f 7/4 Dayjur (USA)—Sajjaya (USA) (Blushing Groom (FR)) **Mr Hamdan Al Maktoum**
163 **SAKHA,** ch f 29/3 Wolfhound (USA)—Harmless Albatross (Pas de Seul) **Mr Hamdan Al Maktoum**
164 **SANDERLING (IRE),** b f 2/3 Exit To Nowhere (USA)—
Tartique Twist (USA) (Arctic Tern (USA)) **Sir Thomas Pilkington**

MR J. L. DUNLOP—continued

165 **SANSKRIT,** ch f 31/3 Sabrehill (USA)—Alipura (Anfield) **Midhurst Farm Inc. & Partners**
166 **SARRAIA,** b f 15/4 Formidable (USA)—Lili Cup (FR) (Fabulous Dancer (USA)) **Kuwait Racing Syndicate**
167 **SECOND NATURE,** b c 12/2 Second Set (IRE)—Tittlemouse (Castle Keep) **Hesmonds Stud Ltd**
168 **SHAMEL,** b c 2/2 Unfuwain (USA)—Narjis (USA) (Blushing Groom (FR)) **Mr Hamdan Al Maktoum**
169 **SIGNORINA CATTIVA (USA),** b f 21/4 El Gran Senor (USA)—
Assez Cuite (USA) (Graustark) **S.C.E.A. Haras De Saint Pair Du Mont**
170 **SPANISH LADY (IRE),** b f 23/2 Bering—Belle Arrivee (Bustino) **Windflower Overseas Holdings Inc**
171 **SPUN SILK (IRE),** ch f 2/2 Brief Truce (USA)—Silk Route (USA) (Shahrastani (USA)) **Lord Swaythling**
172 **STARRY NIGHT,** b f 5/2 Sheikh Albadou—My Ballerina (USA) (Sir Ivor) **H. R. H. Prince A. A. Faisal**
173 **TAYIL,** b c 15/3 Caerleon (USA)—Desert Bluebell (Kalaglow) **Mr Hamdan Al Maktoum**
174 **TEYAAR,** b c 22/3 Polar Falcon (USA)—Music In My Life (IRE) (Law Society (USA)) **Kuwait Racing Syndicate**
175 Ch f 12/5 Woodman (USA)—Toujours Elle (USA) (Lyphard (USA)) **Mr Hamdan Al Maktoum**
176 **TRICOLORE,** b f 15/2 Sadler's Wells (USA)—Tricorne (Green Desert (USA)) **Mr M. L. Page**
177 **TRIPLE GREEN,** b f 28/5 Green Desert (USA)—Triple Reef (Mill Reef (USA)) **Hesmonds Stud Ltd**
178 B c 14/3 Exit To Nowhere (USA)—Tromond (Lomond (USA)) **Mr G. Pinchen**
179 **TRUMPET BLUES (USA),** br c 27/1 Dayjur (USA)—Iosifa (Top Ville) **Mr Bob Lalement**
180 **TURTLE VALLEY (IRE),** b c 10/2 Turtle Island (IRE)—Primrose Valley (Mill Reef (USA)) **Hesmonds Stud Ltd**
181 **VISION OF NIGHT,** b c 1/4 Night Shift (USA)—Dreamawhile (Known Fact (USA)) **Hesmonds Stud Ltd**
182 **WINNOWER,** b f 5/2 Robellino (USA)—Corn Circle (IRE) (Thatching) **Aylesfield Farms Stud Ltd**
183 B f 7/4 Robellino (USA)—Working Model (Ile de Bourbon (USA)) **Mr S. S. G. Hayes**

Other Owners: Mr A. Alabdulrazzaq, Mrs Afaf Alessa, Mr M. Al-Qatami, Sheikh Ahmad Yousuf Al Sabah, Mr Hamad A. Alsumait, J. Barber, D. E. Bingley, Miss D. Birks, Mr Peter Burrell, Mr N. C. Clark, Mrs A. Croker-Poole, N. Dallas, Mrs Patrick Darling, Lady Fairbairn, Mr James Flower, A. Grazebrook, A. Grieve, Mrs I. C. C. Hayes, Mr David F. Howard, Mrs Ann Jenkins, Sir Nevil Macready, Mr M. J. Meacock, F. Melrose, Mr P. Mitchell, O. Pawle, L. Reed, Mrs N. Robson, Miss Karin Ruckstuhl, Mrs J. Scott-Barrett, Miss O. Shirley, Mrs Diane Snowden, M. Stokes, Miss A. Struthers, D. Thorpe, P. Townsend, Mr E. S. Tudor-Evans, Mr Tom Wilson.

185 MR A. J. K. DUNN, Minehead

Postal: **The Maltings, Lynch, Allerford, Minehead, Somerset, TA24 8HJ.**
Phone: **(01643) 863124**

1 **GREEN ISLAND (USA),** 12, b g Key To The Mint (USA)—Emerald Reef **Mr A. J. K. Dunn**
2 **GUMAIR (USA),** 5, ch g Summer Squall (USA)—Finisterre (AUS) **Mr A. J. K. Dunn**
3 **HIGH RISK LAD,** 6, b g Risk Me (FR)—Highly Polished **Mr A. J. K. Dunn**
4 **VELLATOR (IRE),** 6, b g Petoski—Impropriety **Mr A. J. K. Dunn**

186 MR P. N. DUTFIELD, Seaton

Postal: **Crabhayne Farm, Axmouth, Seaton, Devon, EX12 4BW.**
Phone: **(01297) 553560**

1 **BOLD HUNTER,** 4, b g Polish Precedent (USA)—Pumpona (USA) **Mrs Nerys Dutfield**
2 **CAUDILLO (IRE),** 5, b m Nordico (USA)—Over Swing (FR) **Mrs Nerys Dutfield**
3 **GEMINI MIST,** 7, b m Ardross—Festive Season **Mrs Nerys Dutfield**
4 **KRAM,** 4, ch g Kris—Balenare **Mrs C. A. Clarke**
5 **MACGILLYCUDDY (IRE),** 9, b br g Petorius—My Bonnie **Mrs Nerys Dutfield**
6 **MRS MCCLUSKY (IRE),** 6, b m Mandalus—Clodagh's Treasure **Mrs Nerys Dutfield**
7 **PROVE THE POINT (IRE),** 5, b m Maelstrom Lake—In Review **Mrs Nerys Dutfield**
8 **ROYAL SEATON,** 9, b g Blakeney—Aldbury Girl **Axminster Carpets Limited**
9 **RUN FOR COVER (IRE),** 6, b m Lafontaine (USA)—Run For Shelter **Mrs Nerys Dutfield**
10 **RUSSIAN RELATION (IRE),** 4, ch g Soviet Star (USA)—Anjaab (USA) **Mrs J. Fuller**
11 **SPRING MARATHON (USA),** 8, b g Topsider (USA)—April Run **Mrs Nerys Dutfield**

MR P. N. DUTFIELD—continued

THREE-YEAR-OLDS

12 **AFTER DAWN (IRE),** b f Brief Truce (USA)—Faakirah **One Over The Eight**
13 **BLISS (IRE),** b f Statoblest—Moira My Girl **Mr W. A. Harrison-Allan**
14 **FLEET LADY (IRE),** b f Don't Forget Me—Yavarro **Mr Harry Dutfield**
15 **KATE LANE (IRE),** b f Petardia—Splendid Yankee **Mrs Nerys Dutfield**
16 **MAGICAL DANCER (IRE),** b f Magical Wonder (USA)—Diva Encore **The Piccolo Boys**
17 **ROYAL AXMINSTER,** b g Alzao (USA)—Number One Spot **Axminster Carpets Limited**
18 **SUN LION (IRE),** b g Shalford (IRE)—Susie Sunshine (IRE) **Mrs Nerys Dutfield**

TWO-YEAR-OLDS

19 B f 25/3 Contract Law (USA)—Curie Express (IRE) (Fayruz) **Mrs Nerys Dutfield**
20 Ch c 13/5 Elmaamul (USA)—Hollow Heart (Wolver Hollow) **Mrs Nerys Dutfield**
21 B f 11/3 Petorius—Make Hay (Nomination) **Mrs Nerys Dutfield**
22 B f 19/5 Tenby—Moira My Girl (Henbit (USA)) **Mrs Nerys Dutfield**
23 B c 19/4 Emarati (USA)—Navarino Bay (Averof) **Mrs Nerys Dutfield**
24 B f 17/3 Petorius—Top Nurse (High Top) **Mrs Nerys Dutfield**

Other Owners: Mr Mike Balcomb, Mr John Boswell, Mr Adrian Coombes, Mr Simon Dutfield, Mr John Frampton, Mr T. J. Keeping, Mr T. Leigh, Mr Peter Meaden, Mr John W. Mitchell, Mr Chris Scott, Mr Matt Tompkins, Mr R. J. Tory, Mr John M. Tutton, Mr J. C. White.

Apprentice: Lisa Somers (7-13).

187 MR C. A. DWYER, Newmarket

Postal: **Cedar Lodge Racing Stables, Hamilton Road, Newmarket, Suffolk, CB8 0NQ.**
Phone: **OFFICE & FAX (01638) 667857 MOBILE (0831) 579844 HOME (01638) 668869**

1 **ALFAHAAL (IRE),** 5, b h Green Desert (USA)—Fair of The Furze **Mr M. M. Foulger**
2 **AQUATIC QUEEN,** 4, b f Rudimentary (USA)—Aquarula **Mr J. Johnston**
3 **BARTHOLOMEW FAIR,** 7, b g Sadler's Wells (USA)—Barada (USA) **Mr David L. Bowkett**
4 **CYRANO'S LAD (IRE),** 9, b g Cyrano de Bergerac—Patiala **Mr M. M. Foulger**
5 **ENGLISH INVADER,** 7, b h Rainbow Quest (USA)—Modica **Mrs Shelley Dwyer**
6 **FINAL STAB (IRE),** 5, b g Kris—Premier Rose **Mrs Shelley Dwyer**
7 **JENNELLE,** 4, b f Nomination—Its A Romp **Mrs J. A. Cornwell**
8 **OXBANE,** 4, b f Soviet Star (USA)—Oxslip **Mr John Purcell**
9 **RON'S ROUND,** 4, ch c Ron's Victory (USA)—Magical Spirit **Formfix**
10 **SEA-DEER,** 9, ch g Hadeer—Hi-Tech Girl **Mr M. M. Foulger**
11 **SWEET SUPPOSIN (IRE),** 7, b h Posen (USA)—Go Honey Go **Mr G. Middlemiss**
12 **URGENT REPLY (USA),** 5, b g Green Dancer (USA)—Bowl of Honey (USA) **The Select Newmarket Partnership**
13 **WARRIOR KING (IRE),** 4, b g Fairy King (USA)—It's All Academic (IRE) **North End Partnership**

THREE-YEAR-OLDS

14 **ARDLEIGH CHARMER,** ch c Theatrical Charmer—Miss Adventure **Roalco Limited**
15 **ARM AND A LEG (IRE),** ch c Petardia—Ikala **Mrs R. P. Aggio**
16 **AVIVA LADY (IRE),** ch f Mac's Imp (USA)—Flying Beauty **Mr R. S. G. Jones**
17 **BLARNEY PARK,** b f Never So Bold—Walking Saint **Blarney Park Racing Club**
18 **BLAZING BILLY,** ch c Anshan—Worthy Venture **Mr R. West**
19 **CATHERINES SONG,** b f Aragon—Songstead **The Select Newmarket Partnership**
20 **DUBLIVIA,** b f Midyan (USA)—Port Isaac (USA) **Mrs Suzanne Costello-Haloute**
21 **ELBA MAGIC (IRE),** b f Faustus (USA)—Dependable **Mr G. Mitchell**
22 **GLAMORGAN (IRE),** b c Petardia—Presentable **Elite Racing Club**
23 **LIVINGSTONE,** b g Dilum (USA)—Batra (USA) **The Select Newmarket Partnership**
24 **PINUP,** gr f Risk Me (FR)—Princess Tara **Mr Mark Barrett**
25 **SADA,** b br f Mujtahid (USA)—Peace Girl **Times of Wigan**
26 **SASSY LADY (IRE),** b f Brief Truce (USA)—Taken By Force **The Select Newmarket Partnership**
27 **SHINDIUM,** b f Presidium—Shining Wood **Mrs Shelley Dwyer**

MR C. A. DWYER—continued

28 SICK AS A PARROT, ch c Casteddu—Sianiski **Mrs Shelley Dwyer**
29 SUPER GEIL, b f Superlative—Mild Deception (IRE) **Mr E. R. Kettenacker**
30 TENDER DOLL (IRE), b f Don't Forget Me—Mistress Vyne **The Select Newmarket Partnership**

TWO-YEAR-OLDS

31 AMISTAD, ch c 22/4 Mystiko (USA)—Ackcontent (USA) (Key To Content (USA)) **Mr E. Haloute**
32 CYQUINTA, b f 25/4 Cyrano de Bergerac—Lady Quinta (IRE) (Gallic League) **Cedar Lodge Racing Club**
33 Ch f 4/4 Second Set (IRE)—Eastern Aura (IRE) (Ahonoora) **Mr B. Hathaway**
34 B f 6/4 Midhish—Eimkar (Junius (USA))
35 ENTHAISINGH, gr f 16/3 Petong—Proper Madam (Mummy's Pet) **Cedar Lodge Racing Club**
36 B f 8/4 Common Grounds—Moon Watch (Night Shift (USA)) **Rous Racing Ltd**
37 Ch f 20/3 Mujtahid (USA)—Simply Marilyn (IRE) (Simply Great (FR)) **Bow Group Ltd**
38 B c 24/4 Cyrano de Bergerac—Woodleys (Tyrnavos) **Mr B. Hathaway**

Other Owners: Mr J. A. Fogarty, Mr D. Foley, Mr I. J. Fowler, Dr A. Haloute, Mr B. Kennedy, Mr Luther G. Miller Iii, Mr T. H. Morris, Mrs Jill Moss, Miss M. Noden, Mrs Christine Rawson.

Jockeys (Flat): L Dettori (8-5, w.a.), S Drowne (8-1, w.a.), K Fallon (8-7, w.a.), F Lunch (8-4, w.a.).

Apprentice: J Gotobed (8-4).

Conditional: K O'Ryan (10-0).

Amateur: Mr K O'Ryan (10-0).

188 MR S. A. EARLE, Marlborough

Postal: **Fox Twitchen, East Kennett, Marlborough, Wiltshire, SN8 4EY.**
Phone: **(01672) 861157 FAX (01672) 861157 MOBILE (0850) 350116**

1 BET YOUR BOOTS, 5, gr g Pragmatic—Hi Boots
2 CHRISTCHURCH (FR), 8, b g Highlanders (FR)—Olchany (FR) **Mr Dennis Breen**
3 CRANE HILL, 8, b g Dancing Brave (USA)—Consolation **Mr Rod Hamilton**
4 CYRILL HENRY (IRE), 9, b g Mister Majestic—Stamina **Champagne and Dreams Partnership**
5 INSPIRE FOUNDATION, 5, ch g Then Again—Flora May **The Inspire Foundation Syndicate**
6 MR SNAGGLE (IRE), 9, ch g Pollerton—Truly Deep **The Plumb Merchants**
7 MY BROTHER, 4, b g Lugana Beach—Lucky Love **Bob & Cora Till**
8 QU'APPELLE, 5, ch g Teamster—Gay Rhythm **Bob & Cora Till**
9 RAKAZONA BEAU, 8, b g Rakaposhi King—Arizona Belle **The Late David Kellow Partnership**
10 SPRING SAINT, 9, ch g Midyan (USA)—Lady of Chalon (USA) **Richard & Carol Stainer**

Other Owners: Mrs Janet Benney, Mr A Bond, Mr A. C. Clift, Mrs R. Earle, Mr R. M. Howard, Exors Of The Late Mr David Kellow, Mrs G. Kellow, Mrs Stanley Perry, Mr C. J. Pye.

Jockeys (NH): C Maude (10-0), B Powell (10-7).

Apprentice: Sara Hartley (8-0).

189 MR M. W. EASTERBY, Sheriff Hutton

Postal: **New House Farm, Sheriff Hutton, York, YO6 7TN.**
Phone: **(01347) 878368 FAX (01347) 878204**

1 **ALMUHIMM (USA),** 6, ch g Diesis—Abbesh (USA) **MP Burke's 5th Family Settlement**
2 **ALPINE HIDEAWAY (IRE),** 5, b g Tirol—Arbour (USA) **Easterby Trailers**
3 **ALU-LADY,** 4, gr f Kalaglow—Mrs Mills **Mr T. Beston**
4 **BANKER COUNT,** 6, b g Lord Bud—Gilzie Bank **Mrs H. Brown**
5 **BEAU BO'S RETURN,** 7, b m Jupiter Island—Formidable Lady **Mr H. Winton**
6 **BEE HEALTH BOY,** 5, b g Superpower—Rekindle **Bee Health Ltd**
7 **BLESSINGINDISGUISE,** 5, b g Kala Shikari—Blowing Bubbles **Mr A. G. Black**
8 **BODFARI NORTH (IRE),** 5, b g Distinctly North (USA)—Dowdstown Miss **Bodfari Stud Ltd**
9 **CAVIAR ROYALE (IRE),** 4, ch c Royal Academy (USA)—
Petite Liqueurelle (IRE) **MP Burke's 5th Family Settlement**
10 **DEE PEE TEE CEE (IRE),** 4, b g Tidaro (USA)—Silver Glimpse **Early Morning Breakfast Syndicate**
11 **DULAS BAY,** 4, b g Selkirk (USA)—Ivory Gull (USA) **Early Morning Breakfast Syndicate**
12 **FLAT TOP,** 7, b g Blakeney—New Edition **Major M. Watson**
13 **FOIST,** 6, b g Efisio—When The Saints **Mr D. F. Spence**
14 **GIPSY PRINCESS,** 4, b f Prince Daniel (USA)—Gypsy's Barn Rat **Mr T. A. Hughes**
15 **HASTA LA VISTA,** 8, b g Superlative—Falcon Berry (FR) **Mr K. Hodgson**
16 4, B g Arzanni—High Affair **Mr S. J. Curtis**
17 **ISSYIN,** 11, ch g Oats—Spiders Web **Mrs H. Brown**
18 **JEDI KNIGHT,** 4, b g Emarati (USA)—Hannie Caulder **Mr K. Hodgson**
19 **LADY SHERIFF,** 7, b m Taufan (USA)—Midaan **Mr E. Mangan**
20 4, B g Millfontaine—Lake Road **Mr H. Winton**
21 **LUCKY BEA,** 5, b g Lochnager—Knocksharry **Bee Health Ltd**
22 **MINSTER GLORY,** 7, b g Minster Son—Rapid Glory **Mrs P. A. H. Hartley**
23 **NORTHERN FALCON,** 5, gr m Polar Falcon (USA)—Bishah (USA) **Mrs P. A. H. Hartley**
24 **NOSHINANNIKIN,** 4, ch g Anshan—Preziosa **Mr S. J. Curtis**
25 **PENSION FUND,** 4, b g Emperor Fountain—Navarino Bay **Mr S. J. Curtis**
26 **PUREVALUE (IRE),** 7, b br g Kefaah (USA)—Blaze of Light **Mrs Jean Turpin**
27 **RIVER DON,** 6, ch g Over The River (FR)—Jane's Daughter **Mrs H. Brown**
28 **ROYAL RESULT (USA),** 5, b br g Gone West (USA)—Norette **M. P. Burke's 5th Family Settlement**
29 **RUSSIAN ASPECT,** 4, br g Al Nasr (FR)—Bourbon Topsy **Mr A. G. Black**
30 **SANDBAGGEDAGAIN,** 4, b g Prince Daniel (USA)—Paircullis **Mrs Christopher Hanbury**
31 4, B g Gildoran—Shalta (FR) **Mr H. Winton**
32 **SILVER STICK,** 11, gr g Absalom—Queen's Parade **Lord Manton**
33 **SOUTHERN CROSS,** 6, ch g Buckley—Muznah **Mr J. H. Holt**
34 **SPARKY,** 4, b g Warrshan (USA)—Pebble Creek (IRE) **Abbots Salford Caravan Park**
35 **STUFFED,** 6, ch g Clantime—Puff Pastry **Early Morning Breakfast Syndicate**
36 **TAPATCH (IRE),** 10, b g Thatching—Knees Up (USA) **Miss V. Foster**
37 **TEDDY'S BOW (IRE),** 4, b br f Archway (IRE)—Gale Force Seven **Mrs Anne Jarvis**
38 **WESTCOURT MAGIC,** 5, b g Emarati (USA)—Magic Milly **Mr K. Hodgson**
39 **WILLIAM'S WELL,** 4, ch g Superpower—Catherines Well **Mr K. Hodgson**

THREE-YEAR-OLDS

40 **ARE YER THERE,** gr g Terimon—Indian Swallow (FR) **Mr D. F. Spence**
41 **BOLERO KID,** b g Rambo Dancer (CAN)—Barrie Baby **Mybank Racing**
42 **BOW PEEP (IRE),** b br f Shalford (IRE)—Gale Force Seven **Mrs Anne Jarvis**
43 **BUZZ THE AGENT,** b g Prince Sabo—Chess Mistress (USA) **Alan Black & Co**
44 **CINDER HILLS,** ch f Deploy—Dame du Moulin **Mr I. Bray**
45 **DANGERMAN (IRE),** ch g Pips Pride—Two Magpies **Mr S. J. Curtis**
46 **DISCO TEX,** b g Rambo Dancer (CAN)—Andbracket **Mybank Racing**
47 **FLOWER O' CANNIE (IRE),** b f Mujadil (USA)—Baby's Smile **Mrs E. Rhind**
48 **KATIE'S KITTY,** b f Noble Patriarch—Catherines Well **Mr K. Hodgson**
49 **MILL END QUEST,** b f King's Signet (USA)—Milva **Mr W. T. Allgood**
50 **MINSTER MOORGATE,** ch f Minster Son—Find The Sun **Mr C. N. Wilmot-Smith**
51 **MY BET,** b f Noble Patriarch—Estefan **Mr W. T. Allgood**
52 **PRINCESS NATALIE,** b f Rudimentary (USA)—X-Data **M. P. Burke's 5th Family Settlement**
53 **RUSSIAN PRINCE (IRE),** b c Soviet Lad (USA)—Sweet Goodbye **Mr S. J. Curtis**

MR M. W. EASTERBY—continued

54 **THE CANNIE ROVER**, ch g Beveled (USA)—Sister Rosarii (USA) **Mrs E. Rhind**
55 **THWING**, b f Presidium—Swinging Baby **Mr R. Mason**
56 **TWO WILLIAMS**, b g Polar Falcon (USA)—Long View **Mr W. L. Caley**
57 **WAIT'N'SEE**, b g Komaite (USA)—Kakisa **Mr M. W. Easterby**
58 **WESTCOURT RUBY**, b f Petong—Red Rosein **Mr K. Hodgson**

TWO-YEAR-OLDS

59 **ABBIE BLUEYES**, b f 9/2 Petong—Abalone **Mr M. W. Easterby**
60 **BODFARI ANNA**, br f 28/4 Casteddu—Lowrianna **Bodfari Stud Ltd**
61 **BODFARI KOMAITE**, b c 26/3 Komaite (USA)—Gypsy's Barn Rat **Bodfari Stud Ltd**
62 **BODFARI SIGNET**, ch c 11/4 King's Signet (USA)—Darakah **Bodfari Stud Ltd**
63 **CUT THE DECK**, b c 6/2 First Trump—Kantikoy **Mr I. Gray**
64 **DOONAREE (IRE)**, b c 12/1 Sadler's Wells (USA)—Rosananti **MP Burke's 5th Family Settlement**
65 **EL JAYTEE**, b c 5/4 Anshan—Better Still (IRE) **Mrs Jean Turpin**
66 **GENTLE JOHNNY (USA)**, b c 2/4 Housebuster (USA)—Latest Scandal (USA) **MP Burke's 5th Family Settlement**
67 B f 15/3 Primo Dominie—Golden Cay **Mr S. J. Curtis**
68 **GRANNY HELEN**, br f 5/2 Reprimand—Peak Squaw **MP Burke Developments Ltd**
69 **HIT THE BEACH**, b c 15/1 Turtle Island (IRE)—Malacca (USA) **Mr I. Bray**
70 **KRISHAN FROLIC**, b f 7/4 Tragic Role (USA)—Kiveton Komet **Mr Lloyd**
71 **LOUGHANLEA (USA)**, b c 5/2 Salt Lake (USA)—Moment of Flight (USA) **MP Burke's 5th Family Settlement**
72 **MARNOR (USA)**, b c 3/3 Diesis—Love's Reward **MP Burke's 5th Family Settlement**
73 **MAYO**, b c 11/3 Nashwan (USA)—Nuryana **MP Burke's 5th Family Settlement**
74 **MILKMAN PAT**, b c 1/2 Polar Falcon (USA)—Langtry Lady **MP Burke's 5th Family Settlement**
75 **MILL END VENTURE (IRE)**, b c 10/3 Namaqualand (USA)—Risk All **Mr W. T. Allgood**
76 **MISS CAMPANULA**, b f 6/4 Rudimentary (USA)—Miss Primula **Mr Jean Torpin**
77 **MUJAGEM**, b f 10/5 Mujadil (USA)—Lili Bengam **Mrs E. Rhind**
78 Ch c 19/1 Whittingham (IRE)—Nellie O'Dowd (USA) **Mr P. Savill**
79 **OREGON DREAM (IRE)**, b f 18/2 Seattle Dancer (USA)—Ibda **Mr I. Bray**
80 **PAT THE FIDDLER (IRE)**, b c 30/3 Night Shift (USA)—Lucky Song (USA) **MP Burke's 5th Family Settlement**
81 **PEAJAY (USA)**, b c 1/5 Dehere (USA)—Petroleuse **MP Burke's 5th Family Settlement**
82 **PIGGY BANK**, b f 13/5 Emarati (USA)—Granny's Bank **Mr S. J. Curtis**
83 **SILVANO'S EXPRESS**, b c 11/4 Sizzling Melody—Penny Hasset **Mr Silvano Scanu**
84 Gr f 8/5 Petong—Spun Gold **Mr K. Hodgson**
85 **STANLEY WIGFIELD (USA)**, b c 16/4 Woodman (USA)—Las Meninas (IRE) **MP Burke's 5th Family Settlement**
86 B f 19/3 Reprimand—Tasmim **Miss V. Foster**
87 **TISSIFER**, b c 26/3 Polish Precedent—Ingozi **MP Burke's 5th Family Settlement**
88 **TULLYNESSLE**, ch f 11/4 King's Signet (USA)—Miss Klew **Brig Racing**

Other Owners: Mrs S. A. Bramall, Mr C. F. Buckton, Mr J. W. P. Curtis, Mrs A. M. Easterby, Mr Peter Easterby, Mr C. Gardiner, Mr J. Hanson, Mr P. A. H. Hartley, Mr Andrew M. Hedley, Mr W. H. Jackson, Mr Philip A. Jarvis, Lady Manton, Mrs Susan E. Mason, Mr K. Mercer, Mr K. E. Rayner, Mr K. J. Simpson, Mr C. F. Spence, Mr D. P. Travers-Clark.

Jockey (Flat): T Lucas (8-5).

Apprentice: S Finnamore (7-12).

Conditional: P Midgley (10-4).

190 MR T. D. EASTERBY, Malton

Postal: **Habton Grange, Great Habton, Malton, North Yorkshire, YO17 0TY.**
Phone: **(01653) 668566 FAX (01653) 668621**

1 **BARNBURGH BOY**, 4, ch g Shalford (IRE)—Tuxford Hideaway **MP Burke Developments Ltd**
2 **BOLLIN FRANK**, 6, b g Rambo Dancer (CAN)—Bollin Emily **Sir Neil Westbrook**
3 **BOLLIN JOANNE**, 5, b m Damister (USA)—Bollin Zola **Lady Westbrook**

MR T. D. EASTERBY—continued

4 **BOLLIN TERRY,** 4, b c Terimon—Bollin Zola **Sir Neil Westbrook**
5 **BRIDLE PATH (IRE),** 7, b g Teenoso (USA)—Hilly Path **Mr Fred Wilson**
6 **CAMIONNEUR (IRE),** 5, b g Cyrano de Bergerac—Fact of Time **Top Freight Ltd**
7 **CASUAL CALL (IRE),** 6, b g Brush Aside (USA)—Nelly Gleason **Mr J. W. Blundell**
8 **CHOPWELL CURTAINS,** 8, ch g Town And Country—Liquer Candy **Durham Drapes Ltd**
9 **CRYSTAL FALLS (IRE),** 5, b g Alzao (USA)—Honourable Sheba (USA) **Mr C. H. Stevens**
10 **CUMBRIAN CHALLENGE (IRE),** 9, ch g Be My Native (USA)—Sixpenny **Cumbrian Industrials Ltd**
11 **CUMBRIAN MAESTRO,** 5, b g Puissance—Flicker Toa Flame (USA) **Cumbrian Industrials Ltd**
12 **DALLY BOY,** 6, b g Efisio—Gay Hostess (FR) **Mr T. H. Bennett**
13 **DAWN MISSION,** 6, b g Dunbeath (USA)—Bustellina **Mrs Jennifer E. Pallister**
14 **DOMINELLE,** 6, b m Domynsky—Gymcrack Lovebird **Sandmoor Textiles Co Ltd**
15 **DOUBLE ACTION,** 4, b g Reprimand—Final Shot **Mr C. H. Stevens**
16 **DURANO,** 7, b g Dunbeath (USA)—Norapa **Mr C. H. Stevens**
17 **EURO SCEPTIC (IRE),** 6, ch g Classic Secret (USA)—Very Seldom **Mr C. H. Stevens**
18 **FOR YOUR EYES ONLY,** 4, b g Pursuit of Love—Rivers Rhapsody **R. Griffin & J. McGrath**
19 **GALLANT MAJOR,** 6, ch g Infantry—Miss Gallant **Mrs C. Johnston**
20 **GALLANTS DELIGHT,** 8, b m Idiot's Delight—Miss Gallant **Mrs C. Johnson**
21 **GOLDEN HELLO,** 7, b g Glint of Gold—Waltz **Mr G. E. Shouler**
22 **GOOD VIBES,** 6, b g Ardross—Harmoney Jane **Mr G. E. Shouler**
23 **HELMSLEY FLIER,** 4, ch g Sula Bula—Penair **Dr J. Hollowood**
24 **HIGH SPIRITS (IRE),** 4, b g Great Commotion (USA)—Spoilt Again **Mrs J. B. Mountifield**
25 **JACK'S JOKER,** 4, b f Gildoran—Fit For A King **Mrs L. Tinnion**
26 **JACKSON PARK,** 5, gr g Domynsky—Hysteria **Mr C. H. Stevens**
27 **JO MELL,** 5, b g Efisio—Militia Girl **C. H. Newton Ltd**
28 **KAITAK (IRE),** 7, ch g Broken Hearted—Klairelle **Mr C. Murphy**
29 **LORD DISCORD,** 4, b g Primo Dominie—Busted Harmony **Mr I. Bray**
30 **MAJOR WEST,** 5, ch g Gunner B—Little Ginger **Mr P. Baillie**
31 **MARTHA'S MOONSTONE,** 4, b f Gildoran—Coral Delight **Mrs L. Tinnion**
32 **MONARCH'S PURSUIT,** 4, b g Pursuit of Love—Last Detail **Mrs Jean P. Connew**
33 **PARTING THE WAVES (IRE),** 5, b g Brush Aside (USA)—Serene River **Mr Jim McGrath**
34 **REVOLT,** 6, b g Primitive Rising (USA)—Fit For A King **Mr C. H. Stevens**
35 **ROYAL MARK (IRE),** 5, b g Fairy King (USA)—Take Your Mark (USA) **Martin Burkes 5th Family Settlement**
36 **RUSK,** 5, b g Pharly (FR)—Springwell **Mrs Jean P. Connew**
37 **RYE CROSSING (IRE),** 8, b g Over The River (FR)—Aran Tour **Mr C. H. Stevens**
38 **SAM CHAMPAGNE (IRE),** 6, b g Lafontaine (USA)—Bumps A Daisy **Mr I. Bray**
39 **SANDMOOR CHAMBRAY,** 7, ch g Most Welcome—Valadon **Sandmoor Textiles Co Ltd**
40 **SCOTTON BANKS (IRE),** 9, b g Le Moss—Boherdeel **Mr I. Bray**
41 **SCOTTON GREEN,** 7, ch g Ardross—Grange Hill Girl **Scotton Developments Ltd**
42 **SHARE OPTIONS (IRE),** 7, b br g Executive Perk—Shannon Belle **Mr Steve Hammond**
43 **SHINING EDGE,** 6, ch g Beveled (USA)—Lustrous **Mr G. Graham**
44 **SILLY MONEY,** 7, b g Silly Prices—Playagain **Mrs Jean P. Connew**
45 **SIMPLY DASHING (IRE),** 7, br g Simply Great (FR)—Qurrat Al Ain **Mr Steve Hammond**
46 **SKILLWISE,** 6, b g Buckley—Calametta **Mr Chris D. Calvert**
47 **SPOOF'S MY GAME,** 5, b g Indian Ridge—Valadon **Mr P. G. Gorvin**
48 **TALE BRIDGE (IRE),** 5, b g Tale Quale—Loobagh Bridge **Mr M. H. Easterby**
49 **THUNDERPOINT (IRE),** 6, b g Glacial Storm (USA)—Urdite (FR) **Kinahan-Puplett-Brown**
50 **WELLINGTON STREET,** 5, b g Roscoe Blake—Catherine Tudor **Mr P. England**
51 **ZAGROS (IRE),** 4, b g Persian Heights—Hana Marie **Caerleon Estates Ltd**

THREE-YEAR-OLDS

52 **BOLLIN ANN,** b f Anshan—Bollin Zola **Lady Westbrook**
53 **BOLLIN ETHOS,** b c Precocious—Bollin Harriet **Sir Neil Westbrook**
54 **BOLLIN PRECIOUS,** b f Precocious—Bollin Emily **Lady Westbrook**
55 **CUMBRIAN CADET,** b g Handsome Sailor—City Sound **Cunbrian Industrials**
56 **CUMBRIAN CARUSO,** b g Primo Dominie—Conquista **Cumbrian Industrials**
57 **DANCING EM,** b f Rambo Dancer (CAN)—Militia Girl **Mr D. Lamplough**
58 **DAWN GAIT,** ch f Fearless Action (USA)—Miller's Gait **Mrs E. Wills**
59 **DILIP SINGH (IRE),** b g Shalford (IRE)—Another Deb **Mr V. S. Bhullar**
60 **DOUBTFUL STEP,** ch f Fearless Action (USA)—Tread Carefully **Mrs E. Wills**

MR T. D. EASTERBY—continued

61 **DURHAM FLYER,** b g Deploy—Hyde Princess **Mr C. H. Stevens**
62 **FRISKY LADY,** b f Magic Ring (IRE)—Epithet **Mr C. H. Stevens**
63 **HOPE VALUE,** b g Rock City—Dee (USA) **Mr M. H. Easterby**
64 **I'M TEF,** b g Noble Patriarch—Who's That Lady **T. E. F. Freight (Scarborough) Ltd**
65 **LADY ROCHELLE,** b f Noble Patriarch—Panic Button **Mr J. J. Lawson**
66 **LAST LAP,** b f Noble Patriarch—Warning Bell **Mrs P. Needham**
67 **LORD OF LOVE,** b g Noble Patriarch—Gymcrak Lovebird **Cumbrian Industrials**
68 **MARTON MOSS (SWE),** b g Polish Patriot (USA)—Arrastra **Mr T. H. Bennett**
69 **NOBLE SAJA,** b g Noble Patriarch—Saja **Ryedale Associates**
70 **OPOPMIL (IRE),** b f Pips Pride—Limpopo **Mr T. H. Bennett**
71 **PANAMA HOUSE,** b c Rudimentary (USA)—Lustrous **Mr P. England**
72 **PENNY WHISTLE,** b f Clantime—Penny Hasset **Mr V. S. Bhullar**
73 **SANDMOOR TARTAN,** b c Komaite (USA)—Sky Fighter **Sandmoor Textiles Co Ltd**
74 **SEMI CIRCLE,** b f Noble Patriarch—True Ring **Mr C. H. Stevens**
75 **SIMPLY GIFTED,** b g Simply Great (FR)—Souveniers **Mr Steve Hammond**

TWO-YEAR-OLDS

76 **AGAINST THE BILL,** b c Petorius—Galka (Deep Diver) **Mr I. Bray**
77 **ASILANA,** b c College Chapel—Uninvited Guest (Be My Guest (USA)) **Mr C. H. Newton**
78 **BELLA EQUULA,** gr f Puissance—Strawberry Pink (Absalom) **Mr P. C. Bourke**
79 **BOLLIN RITA,** b f Rambo Dancer (CAN)—Bollin Harriet (Lochnager) **The Hon Lady Westbrook Syndicate**
80 **BOLLIN ROBERTA,** b f Bob's Return—Bollin Emily (Lochnager) **The Hon Lady Westbrook Syndicate**
81 **BOLLIN ROGER,** b c Rock Hopper—Magdalene (Teenoso (USA)) **Sir Neil Westbrook Syndicate**
82 **BOLLIN ROLAND,** b c Reprimand—Bollin Zola (Alzao (USA)) **The Hon Lady Westbrook Syndicate**
83 **CUMBRIAN BLUE,** b c Weldnaas (USA)—Baroness Gymcrak (Pharly (FR)) **Cumbrian Industrials**
84 **DRAM TIME,** b c Clantime—Chablisse (Radetzky) **Mrs Jennifer E. Pallister**
85 **DURHAM DANCER,** b f Magic Ring (IRE)—Final Shot (Dalsaan) **Mr C. H. Stevens**
86 **ELLIS ISLAND,** ch c Most Welcome—Dry Land (Nonoalco) **Mr R. Tindall**
87 **FLANDERS,** b f Common Grounds—Family At War (USA) (Explodent (USA)) **Mrs Jean P. Connew**
88 **FORGIVEN,** b c Noble Patriarch—Sinners Reprieve (Reprimand) **Habton Farms**
89 **FROSTY,** ch c Lahib (USA)—Chilblains (Hotfoot) **Habton Farms**
90 **GUINEA HUNTER,** b c Pips Pride—Preponderance (Cyrano de Bergerac) **MP Burke Developments Ltd**
91 **MARTON MERE,** ch c Cadeaux Genereux—Hyatti (Habitat) **Mr T. H. Bennett**
92 **MELANJO,** b c River Falls—Chiltern Show (Rambo Dancer (CAN)) **Mr C. H. Newton**
93 **MIXSTERTHETRIXSTER (USA),** b c Alleged (USA)—
Parliament House (USA) (General Assembley (USA)) **Martin Burkes 5th Family Settlement**
94 **PROSPERITY,** b c Catrail (USA)—Bequeath (USA) (Lyphard (USA)) **R. Griffin Syndicate**
95 **RUM POINTER,** b c Turtle Island (IRE)—Osmunda (Mill Reef (USA)) **Martin Burkes 5th Family Settlement**
96 **SPRINGS NOBLEQUEST,** b f Noble Patriarch—Primum Tempus (Primo Dominie) **Springs Equestrian Limited**
97 **SUSAN'S DOWRY,** b f Efisio—Adjusting (Busted) **Habton Farms**
98 **THE HAULIER,** ch c Ardkinglass—Ask Away (Midyan (USA)) **T. E. F. Freight (Scarborough) Ltd**
99 **TIERWORKER,** b c Tenby—On The Tide (Slip Anchor) **Martin Burkes 5th Family Settlement**
100 Ch f In The Wings—Valiant Cry (Town Crier) **Aston House Stud Partnership**
101 B c Noble Patriarch—Who's That Lady (Nordance (USA)) **Habton Farms**

Other Owners: Mr Ian Armitage, Mrs M. E. Armitage, Mr I. Bell, Mr A. D. Bottomley, Mr K. A. Carey, Mrs S. E. M. Cavenagh, Mrs M. H. Easterby, Mrs Sarah Easterby, Mr R. T. Gardner-Brown, Mr Jonathan Gill, Mr James Glass, Mrs Kate Hall, Mrs Anne Henson, Mr H. Key, Mr Declan Kinahan, Mr G. B. Maher, Mr Andy Puplett, Mr A. H. Raby, Mr D. Sherwin, Mr Peter Teasdale, Times Of Wigan.

Jockeys (NH): R Garrity, L Wyer.

Conditional: S Ryan.

Amateur: Alison Deniel.

191 MR P. ECCLES, Lambourn

Postal: **Upshire Farm Racing Stables, Hungerford Hill, Lambourn, Berkshire, RG16 7ZX.**
Phone: **(01488) 73483**

1 **FREDDEN (IRE)**, 5, gr g Castle Keep—Gin An Tonic **Mr Dennis Taylor**
2 **ITS UNBELIEVABLE**, 8, ch g Kalaglow—Avon Royale **Mr Gerald Hopkins**
3 **JOHN BUSH (IRE)**, 4, b g Asir—Philosophical **Mr F. J. Bush**
4 **NOBLE TOM (IRE)**, 6, b g The Noble Player (USA)—Hospitality **Mr Noel Glynn**
5 **PALAMON (USA)**, 5, ch h Sanglamore (USA)—Gantlette **Orchard Press**
6 **SHARP COMMAND**, 5, ch g Sharpo—Bluish (USA) **Mr A. P. Holland**
7 **SPARKLIN'CHAMPAGNE**, 8, b g Pollerton—My Always **Tidmarsh Racing Club**
8 **SPARTS FAULT (IRE)**, 8, ch g King Persian—Clonross Lady **Brian A. Lewendon & Mrs Carol Lewendon**
9 **STATE APPROVAL**, 5, b g Pharly (FR)—Tabeeba **The Claddagh Ring Partnership**
10 **SWING WEST (USA)**, 4, b c Gone West (USA)—Danlu (USA) **Mr Noel Glynn**
11 **WEAVER SQUARE (IRE)**, 9, b g Torus—Canute Villa **Mr Eric Baker**
12 **WESTFIELD MIST**, 6, gr m Scallywag—Melfio Miss **Mrs B. J. Harkins**

THREE-YEAR-OLDS

13 **BRIAN'S BLUE (IRE)**, ch c Statoblest—Lamya **Brian A. Lewendon and Mrs Carol Lewendon**
14 **DIFFICULT JOHN**, b g Reprimand—Kaleidophone **Mr J. P. J. Coles**

Other Owners: Mr G. W. Briscoe, Mrs Pauline Jones, Mr John Minogue, Mr Paul Rowley, Mr B. Thorne, Valley Paddocks Racing Limited.

192 MR B. J. ECKLEY, Brecon

Postal: **Closcedi Farm, Llanspyddid, Brecon, Powys, LD3 8NS.**
Phone: **(01874) 622422**

1 **FLUTTERBUD**, 6, b m Lord Bud—Spartan Flutter **Mr Brian Eckley**
2 **JAUNTY JUNE**, 7, b m Primitive Rising (USA)—Jaunty Jane **Mr Brian Eckley**
3 **NICOLYNN**, 6, ch m Primitive Rising (USA)—Nicolini **Mr Brian Eckley**
4 **SAINT CECILIA**, 5, ch m Orchestra—Among The Gold **Mr Brian Eckley**
5 5, Ch m Glacial Storm (USA)—Trident Missile **Mr Brian Eckley**

193 MR MALCOLM W. ECKLEY, Ludlow

Postal: **Alma House, Brimfield, Ludlow, Shropshire, SY8 4NG.**
Phone: **BRIMFIELD (01584) 711372**

1 **OUT OF THE BLUE**, 6, b m Lochnager—Expletive **Mr Malcolm W. Eckley**

Jockey (Flat): J Williams (8-4, w.a.).

Jockeys (NH): R Dunwoody (10-1, w.a.), M Fitzgerald (10-0, w.a.), A Maguire (10-0, w.a.).

194 MR G. F. EDWARDS, Minehead

Postal: **Summering, Wheddon Cross, Minehead, Somerset, TA24 7AT.**
Phone: **(01643) 831549 MOBILE: (0378) 417660**

1 **CHICKABIDDY**, 10, b m Henbit (USA)—Shoshoni **Mr G. F. Edwards**
2 **CRUISIN ON CREDIT (IRE)**, 7, b g Don't Forget Me—Justine's Way (USA) **Mr G. F. Edwards**
3 **LONGSTONE LAD**, 6, b g Pittacus (USA)—Fatu Hiva (GER) **Mr G. F. Edwards**

MR G. F. EDWARDS—continued

4 **SILENT GUNS (NZ),** 9, b g Guns of Navarone—Acol (NZ) **Mr G. F. Edwards**
5 **THE MINDER (FR),** 11, b br g Miller's Mate—Clarandal **Mr G. F. Edwards**

Jockey (NH): M A Fitzgerald (10-2).

Conditional: D Salter (9-9).

195 MISS S. EDWARDS, Pulborough

Postal: **Coldharbour Farm, Sutton, Pulborough, West Sussex, RH20 1PR.**
Phone: **Tel: (01798) 869219**

1 **BRIGHT FLAME (IRE),** 6, b g Over The River (FR)—Shreelane **Mr Maurice E. Pinto**
2 **CALL HOME (IRE),** 10, b g Callernish—Easter Beauty **Mr Maurice E. Pinto**
3 **CAMDEN ROAD (IRE),** 5, b g Camden Town—Kinnagh Pet **Mr Maurice E. Pinto**
4 **CHRISTY'S PRIDE (IRE),** 6, ch m Kambalda—Caddy Shack **Mr Maurice E. Pinto**
5 **JUST 'N ACE (IRE),** 7, b br g Bustomi—Belace **Mr Maurice E. Pinto**
6 **MINER'S DOUBLE (IRE),** 5, br m Miner's Lamp—Double Bar **Mr Maurice E. Pinto**
7 **NORMANIA (NZ),** 6, b g First Norman (USA)—Brigania (NZ) **Mr Maurice E. Pinto**
8 **SMOKEY ROBOT (IRE),** 5, b g Riberetto—Smokey Queen **Mr Maurice E. Pinto**
9 **THE DANCING SCOT,** 6, ch g Scottish Reel—Lyaaric **Mr Maurice E. Pinto**
10 **THE NEWSMAN (IRE),** 6, b g Homo Sapien—Miller Fall's **Mr Maurice E. Pinto**

Other Owners: Mrs Joseph Abensur.

196 MR C. R. EGERTON, Chaddleworth

Postal: **Heads Farm Stables, Chaddleworth, Newbury, Berkshire, RG20 7EE.**
Phone: **OFFICE (01488) 638771 HOME 638454 FAX 638832 MOBILE (0385) 508058**
email: c.egerton@charles egerton.co.uk **web address:** www.c.egerton.co.uk.

1 **AVANTI EXPRESS (IRE),** 8, b g Supreme Leader—Muckride Lady **Mrs Sarah Stevens**
2 **AZIZZI,** 6, ch g Indian Ridge—Princess Silca Key **Mr Chris Brasher**
3 **BAY CASTER,** 5, b g Gunner B—Marina Bird **Mr D. P. Barrie**
4 **BLACK SECRET,** 5, br m Gildoran—Polypodium **Mr Terry Hubbard & Mr Alan Heard**
5 **BUSHWHACKER,** 4, b g Green Desert (USA)—Missed Again **Mr A. Hayes**
6 **BUSTOPHER JONES,** 4, b g Robellino (USA)—Catkin (USA) **Mr Chris Brasher**
7 **DANTE'S GOLD (IRE),** 7, ch g Phardante (FR)—Gold Bank **Axom**
8 **DECOUPAGE,** 6, b g Bustino—Collage **Mr J. F. Dean**
9 **DIGUP ST EDMUNDS,** 5, b g Bustino—Sharp Glance (IRE) **Sir Clement Freud**
10 **DOUBLE TEMPO (IRE),** 7, b g Orchestra—Break Fast **Bat On Partnership**
11 **FANFARON (FR),** 5, b g Sarpedon (FR)—Ocana IV (FR) **Elite Racing Club**
12 **FRONTAGER (USA),** 8, ch g Irish River (FR)—Arriya **Chaddleworth Partnership**
13 **I'M IMRAN (NZ),** 7, b g Kirmann—True Pleasure (NZ) **The Sita Partnership**
14 **NIKNAKS NEPHEW,** 6, b g Tragic Role (USA)—Bubulina **Mr James Blackshaw**
15 **ONEFORTHEFROG (IRE),** 5, ch g Good Thyne (USA)—Deep Black **The Pink Panther Partnership**
16 **PARADISE NAVY,** 9, b g Slip Anchor—Ivory Waltz (USA) **Elite Racing Club**
17 **PERSIAN ELITE (IRE),** 7, ch g Persian Heights—Late Sally **Elite Racing Club**
19 **RIVER LOSSIE,** 9, b g Bustino—Forres **Mr Chris Brasher**
20 **SHADOW LEADER,** 7, br g Tragic Role (USA)—Hush It Up **Mr James Blackshaw**
21 **STAY WITH ME (FR),** 8, b g Nikos—Live With Me **Mrs Sandra A. Roe**
22 **STRENGTH OF VISION,** 4, b g Unfuwain (USA)—Tootsie Pop (USA) **Mr Austin Allison**
23 **TEAATRAL,** 4, b c Saddlers' Hall (IRE)—La Cabrilla **Bernard Gover Bloodstock Trading Ltd**
24 **UNCLE TERRY,** 5, ch g Phardante (FR)—Music Interpreter **Mr Terry Hubbard & Mr Alan Heard**
25 **WIN THE TOSS,** 6, b g Idiot's Delight—Mayfield (USA) **Miss K. A. Astaire**

MR C. R. EGERTON—continued

THREE-YEAR-OLDS

27 COBRA LADY (IRE), ch f Indian Ridge—Rum Cay (USA) **Mr A. Hayes**
28 DANGERUS PRECEDENT (IRE), ch g Polish Precedent (USA)—Circus Feathers **Mr Chris Brasher**
29 GALLANT FELLOW (FR), ch c Cadeaux Genereux—Hiwaayati **Mr Peter Cook**
30 HAVE A BREAK, b g Most Welcome—Miss Tealeaf (USA) **Direct Salt Supplies Ltd**
31 TAKE TO THE HILLS, b f Danehill (USA)—Akamantis **Mr Chris Brasher**

Other Owners: Mr Mohammed Abouzar, Mrs S. A. Allen, Mr Steven Ashley, Astaire & Partners (Holdings) Ltd, Mr P. F. Banks, Mr J. Barroll-Brown, Mr Graham Bell, Miss June Boden, Mr S. G. Bowkett, Mr D. L. Brooks, Capt. T. Bulwer-Long, Mr G. I. Clay, Mr Barry Cooper, Mr T. Coyle, Mr Nigel Dempster, Mr John W. Egan, Mr T. E. S. Egerton, Mr A. Figg, Mr J. Hall, Mr P. Hammond, Mrs M. Hill, Mr Stewart Holmes, Lord Howland, Mr I. Jacombs, Mr Andy Johnson, Mr Fred Kaufman, Mr Harry Lebowitz, Mrs G. Lord, Mr J. Lorimer, Mr D. A. Lucie-Smith, Mrs Victoria Mitchell, Mr P. B. Mitford-Slade, Mr Barry Nichols, Mr James Osborne, Mr Michael O'Sullivan, Mr Michael Price, Mr M. J. Rees, Mr Andrew Ross, Mrs Alexander Scott, Mr F. Sharman, Mrs M. J. Sharman, Mr Matthew Sharman, Mr Steve Shepperd, Mr Andy J. Smith, Mr Jim W. Smith, Mr Mike Smith, Mr Nigel Smith, Mr P. Stevenson, Mr G. P. Triefus, Mr Tony Trinder, Mr Martin Turnbull, Mr G. Verhoff, Mr N. Viney, Mrs Carolyne Waters, Mr David J. C. Wood.

Jockeys (NH): J A McCarthy (10-0, w.a.), J Osborne (10-0, w.a.), N Williamson (10-0, w.a.).

Amateur: Mr P Phillips (10-5).

197 MR E. A. ELLIOTT, Rushyford

Postal: **Planting House, Windlestone Park, Rushyford, Ferryhill, Co. Durham, DL17 0LZ.**
Phone: **(01388) 720383**

1 BALLYVAUGHAN (IRE), 8, ch g Carlingford Castle—Fahy Quay **Mrs Anne E. Elliott**
2 BARNSTORMER, 12, ch g Carlingford Castle—Sue Bell **Mr Eric A. Elliott**
3 EPONINE, 4, ch f Sharpo—Norska **Mr Eric A. Elliott**
4 MR MCDUCK (IRE), 6, ch g Denel (FR)—Coldwater Morning **Mrs Anne E. Elliott**
5 SELDOM BUT SEVERE (IRE), 8, br g Hawaiian Return (USA)—Goldfoot **Mr Eric A. Elliott**

198 MR BRIAN ELLISON, Lanchester

Postal: **Low Meadows Farm, Lanchester, Co. Durham, DH7 0RE.**
Phone: **HOME 01913 873655 OFFICE 01207 529991 MOBILE 0802 852150 0385 747426**

1 BEACON HILL LADY, 5, b m Golden Lahab (USA)—Homing Hill **Mr Philip Serbert**
2 BHAVNAGAR (IRE), 7, gr g Darshaan—Banana Peel **Mr E. J. Berry**
3 BUYERS DREAM (IRE), 8, b g Adonijah—Twist And Shout **Mr R. Wagner**
4 CHAPARRO AMARGOSO (IRE), 5, b g Ela-Mana-Mou—Champanera **Mr E. J. Berry**
5 CLOVER GIRL, 7, bl m Spin of A Coin—Byerley Rose **Mrs Susan J. Ellison**
6 CROWDED HOUSE (IRE), 10, b br g Mazaad—Standing Ovation **Mrs I. Battla, Mrs Susan J. Ellison**
7 DAIRA, 5, br m Daring March—Ile de Reine **Mrs Susan J. Ellison**
8 DANTES SUN (IRE), 9, b g Phardante (FR)—Shine Your Light **Mrs O. L. Bell, Mrs Susan J. Ellison**
9 DOCTOR BRAVIOUS (IRE), 5, b g Priolo (USA)—Sharp Slipper **Ms Glynis Purcell-Brydon**
10 FATEHALKHAIR (IRE), 6, ch g Kris—Midway Lady (USA) **Mrs Gwen Smith**
11 GO-GO-POWER-RANGER, 5, ch g Golden Lahab (USA)—Nibelunga **Mrs Susan J. Ellison**
12 IN THE FUTURE (IRE), 7, b m Phardante (FR)—Chief Dilke **Bookies Runner**
13 JENDEE (IRE), 10, b g Dara Monarch—Bunch of Blue **Ferrograph Limited**
14 JILLY BEVELED, 6, b m Beveled (USA)—Karens Valentine **Mr C. E. Sherry**
15 JO LIGHTNING (IRE), 5, b g Electric—Santa Jo **Ferrograph Limited**

MR BRIAN ELLISON—continued

16 **JUICE PLUS**, 7, ch g Kris—Highland Light **Mrs Susan J. Ellison**
17 **MAJIC RAIN**, 13, bl g Northern Value—Dinsdale **Mr D. V. Tate**
18 **MAPLE BAY (IRE)**, 9, b g Bold Arrangement—Cannon Boy (USA) **Ferrograph Limited**
19 **MEESONETTE**, 6, ch m Hubbly Bubbly (USA)—Iron Lass **Mrs Susan J. Ellison**
20 **MONIS (IRE)**, 7, ch g Waajib—Gratify **Mr C. E. Sherry**
21 **MOST RICH (IRE)**, 10, b g Dalsaan—Boule de Soie **Mr C. E. Sherry**
22 **PETITE BUSH**, 5, b m Respect—Le Bush **Mr J. G. Robson**
23 **POTATO MAN**, 12, gr g Zambrano—Kit's Future **Mr Chris Foster**
24 **RONNIE THE BUTCHER (IRE)**, 7, b g Northiam (USA)—Goirtin **Mr Ronald McCulloch**
25 **SCRAPMAN**, 5, ch g Backchat (USA)—Saila Thims **Mrs C. L. Bell**
26 **STAKIS CASINOS BOY (IRE)**, 4, ch g Magical Wonder (USA)—Hardiona (FR) **Ashley Carr Racing**
27 **TOSHIBA HOUSE (IRE)**, 7, ch m Le Moss—Santa Jo **Toshiba (UK) Ltd**
28 **TOSHIBA TALK (IRE)**, 6, ch g Horage—Court Ballet **Toshiba (UK) Ltd**
29 **URBAN DANCING (USA)**, 9, ch g Nureyev (USA)—Afifa (USA) **Mr Ronald McCulloch**
30 **WHITEGATESPRINCESS (IRE)**, 7, b m Valiyar—Whitegates Lady **Red Onion**
31 **WHITEGATE'S SON**, 4, ch g Minster Son—Whitegates Lady **Mrs Susan J. Ellison**
32 **WILD BROOK (IRE)**, 8, b g Mandalus—My Lily **Mr Brian Chicken**

THREE-YEAR-OLDS

33 **ASPRILLA (IRE)**, b g Sharp Victor (USA)—Aspire **Mrs C. L. Bell**

Other Owners: Mr S. Bell, Mrs N. B. Bowden, Mr R. W. L. Bowden, Mr Kevin M. L. Brown, Mr Paul Campbell, Mr Kwok Cheng, Mrs L. J. Ellis, Mr L. Ellwood, Mr A. Farrell, Mr I. Fox, Mr J. Hall, Mr Fred Hayne, Mr J. Henderson (Co Durham), Mrs Abigail High, Mrs Adrienne Jackson, Mr K. Morton, Mr T. W. Newton, Mrs Margaret Robertson, Mr J. J. Scanlon, Mrs D. J. Scott, Mr Leslie R. Smith, Mrs Jean Stapleton, Mr C. S. Starbuck, Mr J. Toner.

Jockey (Flat): N Kennedy.

Jockeys (NH): E Callaghan, A Dobbin, D Parker.

Conditional: C McCormack.

199 MR D. R. C. ELSWORTH, Whitsbury

Postal: **Whitsbury Manor Racing Stables, Whitsbury, Fordingbridge, Hants, SP6 3QQ.**
Phone: **OFFICE (01725) 518889 HOME (01725) 518247 FAX (01725) 518747**

1 **AMBER FORT**, 5, gr g Indian Ridge—Lammastide **The Caledonian Racing Society**
2 **ARCO COLORA**, 4, b f Rainbow Quest (USA)—Bella Colora **Helena Springfield Ltd**
3 **BENATOM (USA)**, 5, gr g Hawkster (USA)—Dance Til Two (USA) **Mr T. Harris**
4 **BOOKCASE**, 11, b g Siberian Express (USA)—Colourful (FR) **Adept (80) Ltd**
5 **CURZON STREET**, 4, b f Night Shift (USA)—Pine Ridge **Mr J. McGarry**
6 **GRIEF (IRE)**, 5, ch g Broken Hearted—Crecora **Mr Mike Balcomb**
7 **IVOR'S FLUTTER**, 9, b g Beldale Flutter (USA)—Rich Line **Mr W. I. M. Perry**
8 **LAW COMMISSION**, 8, ch g Ela-Mana-Mou—Adjala **Mr Raymond Tooth**
9 **LONELY HEART**, 4, b f Midyan (USA)—Take Heart **Mr C. J. Harper**
10 **MALE-ANA-MOU (IRE)**, 5, ch g Ela-Mana-Mou—Glasson Lady (GER) **The Oh So Bright Partnership**
11 **MISTER RIVER (IRE)**, 7, ch g Over The River (FR)—Miss Redmarshall **Mrs Ann Shaw**
12 **MOONRAKER'S MIRAGE**, 7, b g Idiot's Delight—Save It Lass **White Horse Racing Ltd**
13 **NEAT FEAT (IRE)**, 7, b g Rising—Imperial Spur **Food Brokers Ltd**
14 **OH SO RISKY**, 11, b g Kris—Expediency (USA) **Mr M. Tabor**
15 **PERSIAN PUNCH (IRE)**, 5, ch g Persian Heights—Rum Cay (USA) **Mr J. C. Smith**
16 **RARE UNITY (IRE)**, 4, ch g Generous (IRE)—Sizes Vary **Lady Dundas, Mrs M. Meredith & A. Wilson**
17 **STATAJACK (IRE)**, 10, b g King of Clubs—Statira **Mr D. R. C. Elsworth**
18 **SUPERCAL**, 4, gr f Environment Friend—Sorayah **The Caledonian Racing Society**

MR D. R. C. ELSWORTH—continued

19 TOM TAILOR (GER), 4, b g Beldale Flutter (USA)—Thoughtful **The A. A. Partnership**
20 WILLOW DALE (IRE), 5, b m Danehill (USA)—Miss Willow Bend (USA) **Michael Jackson Bloodstock Ltd**

THREE-YEAR-OLDS

21 BELCADE, b g Belmez (USA)—Blue Brocade **Mr G. Steinberg**
22 BRIMSTONE (IRE), ch c Ballad Rock—Blazing Glory (IRE) **Seymour Bloodstock (UK) Ltd**
23 CHIPS (IRE), ch c Common Grounds—Inonder **Lucayan Stud**
24 DODO (IRE), b f Alzao (USA)—Dead Certain **Exors of the late Commander G. G. Martin**
25 HILL MAGIC, br c Magic Ring (IRE)—Stock Hill Lass **Michael Jackson Bloodstock Ltd**
26 LADY CHARLOTTE, b f Night Shift (USA)—Circulate **Mr D. R. C. Elsworth**
27 LEAR SPEAR (USA), b c Lear Fan (USA)—Golden Gorse (USA) **Mr Raymond Tooth**
28 MY BOLD BOYO, b c Never So Bold—My Rosie **Mrs W. Protheroe-Beynon**
29 NAPOLEON'S SISTER (IRE), b f Alzao (USA)—Sheer Audacity **Mrs Anne Coughlan**
30 PADDY MCGOON (USA), ch g Irish River (FR)—Flame McGoon (USA) **Mr J. C. Smith**
31 PENDOGGETT (USA), b c Alleged (USA)—Waaria **Mrs M. E. Slade**
32 PUSSY GALORE, b f Pursuit of Love—Zinzi **Mr Raymond Tooth**
33 SEATTLE RIBBON (USA), ch f Seattle Dancer (USA)—Golden Rhyme **Mr J. C. Smith**
34 SILVER SUN, gr f Green Desert (USA)—Catch The Sun **Mr C. J. Harper**
35 TALES OF BOUNTY (IRE), b g Ela-Mana-Mou—Tales of Wisdom **Mrs Michael Meredith**

TWO-YEAR-OLDS

36 Ch f 3/4 Forzando—Abbotswood (Ahonoora)
37 Ch f 13/3 Pips Pride—Algonquin Park (High Line) **Michael Jackson Bloodstock Ltd**
38 B f 14/4 Magic Ring (IRE)—Bay Runner (Bay Express) **Mr R. Frost**
39 CALIWAG (IRE), b c 18/4 Lahib (USA)—Mitsubishi Style (Try My Best (USA)) **The Caledonian Racing Society**
40 Ch f 15/3 Bigstone (IRE)—Dancing Line (High Line)
41 DASHIBA, ch f 22/3 Dashing Blade—Alsiba (Northfields (USA)) **Mr J. C. Smith**
42 DEADLY NIGHTSHADE (IRE), b f 13/3 Night Shift (USA)—
Dead Certain (Absalom) **Exors of the late Commander G. G. Marten**
43 FIRST BALLOT (IRE), b c 27/2 Perugino (USA)—Election Special (Chief Singer) **Mr J. C. Smith**
44 HEAD HONCHO, b c 2/2 Primo Dominie—Ahonita (Ahonoora) **Mr J. C. Smith**
45 Gr f 26/4 Deploy—Julia Flyte (Drone)
46 B c 29/2 Second Set (IRE)—Mali (USA) (Storm Bird (CAN)) **Michael Jackson Bloodstock Ltd**
47 MAPLE (IRE), ch c 17/3 Soviet Lad (USA)—Little Red Rose (Precocious) **Mr G. Steinberg**
48 MISS RIMEX (IRE), b f 13/2 Ezzoud (IRE)—Blue Guitar (Cure The Blues (USA)) **The E. V. Partnership**
49 OTELLO, b c 10/1 Tragic Role (USA)—Yankee Special (Bold Lad (IRE)) **Mrs M. E. Slade**
50 PARADISE COUNTY, b f 17/2 Prince Sabo—Bold County (Never So Bold) **Mrs Penny Sheen**
51 PENMAYNE, ch f 12/1 Inchinor—Salanka (IRE) (Persian Heights) **Mrs M. E. Slade**
52 Ch f 29/3 Magic Ring (IRE)—Pushkar (Northfields (USA)) **Mr C. J. Harper**
53 SANDPOINT, b f 20/5 Lugana Beach—Instinction (Never So Bold) **Mr R. Richards**
54 B f 8/2 Forzando—Sea Clover (IRE) (Ela-Mana-Mou)
55 Ch c 18/2 Seattle Dancer (USA)—Shilka (Soviet Star (USA)) **Michael Jackson Bloodstock Ltd**
56 STRIDHANA, ch c 20/1 Indian Ridge—French Gift (Cadeaux Genereux) **Mr Raymond Tooth**
57 Ch c 14/4 Be My Guest (USA)—Summer Fashion (Moorestyle) **Mr A. J. Thompson**
58 Br c 27/1 Turtle Island (IRE)—Tiavanita (USA) (J O Tobin (USA))
59 B f 2/5 Relief Pitcher—Valls d'Andorra (Free State) **Mr J. Carrington**
60 WOLF TOOTH, ch c 28/3 Wolfhound (USA)—Collide (High Line) **Mr Raymond Tooth**

Other Owners: Mr A. J. Allright, Mrs C. Argeband, Mrs Rosemary Balcomb, Mr Roger Black, Mr Keith Childs, Mr Peter Coe, Mr K. Costello, Mr J. P. Duffy, Mr M. J. Duffy, Mr E. Gadsden, Dr K. M. Henderson, Mr Alistair Hodge, Mr Napier Marten, Mr M. J. Mulgrew, Regal (Witney) Ltd, Mr Ian F. Sandell, Mr J. R. Stott, Mr R. J. Tory, Mrs V. A. Tory, Mrs Rose Vivian, Miss R. Wakeford, Mrs J. Wotherspoon, Mr J. Wotherspoon, Mr R. V. Wright.

Jockeys (Flat): S Drowne, T Quinn.

Jockeys (NH): G Bradley, P Holley (9-7).

200 MISS E. M. V. ENGLAND, Rugby

Postal: **Grove Cottage, Priors Hardwick, Rugby, Warwickshire, CV23 8SN.**
Phone: **(01327) 260437**

1 **COULIN LOCH (IRE)**, 9, b g Long Pond—Flashy Gold **Miss E. M. V. England**
2 **FAIRIES FAREWELL**, 8, ch m Broadsword (USA)—Fairies First **Miss E. M. V. England**

Jockey (NH): Robbie Supple.

201 MR G. P. ENRIGHT, Lewes

Postal: **The Oaks, Old Lewes Racecourse, Lewes, East Sussex, BN7 1UR.**
Phone: **LEWES (01273) 479183 FAX (01273) 479183**

1 **AEDEAN**, 9, ch g Risk Me (FR)—Finlandaise (FR) **Mr M. B. Orpen-Palmer**
2 **COOL SPOT (IRE)**, 10, ch g Boyne Valley—Beagle Bay **Mr Dave Howe**
3 4, B f Warrshan (USA)—Double Dutch **Mr Leonard Fuller**
4 **DUTCH**, 6, ch g Nicholas Bill—Dutch Princess **The Mayfair Partnership**
5 **DUTCH DYANE**, 5, b m Midyan (USA)—Double Dutch **Mr Leonard Fuller**
6 **EL PRESIDENTE**, 5, b g Presidium—Spanish Princess **Mr Chris Wall**
7 **FLOW BACK**, 6, gr g Royal Academy (USA)—Flo Russell (USA) **Mr D. Leon**
8 **FROZEN SEA (USA)**, 7, ch h Diesis—Ocean Ballad **The Oaks Partners**
9 **HAPPY MEDIUM (IRE)**, 5, b g Fairy King (USA)—Belle Origine (USA) **Mrs Anne Devine**
10 **LER CRU (IRE)**, 9, b g Lafontaine (USA)—Kirsova **Mr Stephen Findlay**
11 **NIDOMI**, 11, ch g Dominion—Nicholas Grey **Mr John M. Pegler**
12 **PALACE GUARD**, 6, br g Daring March—Royal Brush **Mr Chris Wall**
13 **PROFESSION**, 7, b g Shareef Dancer (USA)—Mrs Warren (USA) **Mr Frederick Gray**
14 **REAL MADRID**, 7, b g Dreams To Reality (USA)—Spanish Princess **Mr Chris Wall**

TWO-YEAR-OLDS

15 Ch c 25/4 Presidium—Celtic Chimes **Mr Chris Wall**

Other Owners: Mrs E. A. Adair, Mr A. O. Ashford, Mr B. Beagley, Mr E. Benfield, Miss S. L. G. Brown, Mr John Denver, Mr Hugh Doubtfire, Mrs Medeana Findlay, Mrs Jeanne Gray, Miss P. A. Ross.

Jockey (Flat): N Adams (7-10).

Jockey (NH): A McGuire (10-0).

Amateur: Mr S Findlay (9-7).

Lady Rider: Mrs M Enright (8-7).

202 MR T. J. ETHERINGTON, Malton

Postal: **Wold House, Langton Road, Norton, Malton, North Yorkshire, YO17 9QG.**
Phone: **MALTON (01653) 693049 (HOME) 692842 (OFFICE)**

1 **BE BRAVE**, 8, b g Never So Bold—Boo **Mrs Stephanie Parsons**
2 **COURT EXPRESS**, 4, b g Then Again—Moon Risk **Mr J. Pain**
3 **FAMILIE FOOTSTEPS**, 4, br g Primitive Rising (USA)—Ramilie **Miss A. H. Sykes**
4 **IMPISH (IRE)**, 4, ch g Imp Society (USA)—Halimah **Mr Tim Etherington**
5 **MILWAUKEE (IRE)**, 9, ch m Over The River (FR)—Loch Gorman **Mrs J. E. Todd**

MR T. J. ETHERINGTON—continued

6 **MOONRAKING,** 5, gr g Rusticaro (FR)—Lunaire **Mr Ian Bartlett**
7 **OWENS QUEST (IRE),** 8, b m Black Minstrel—Our Quest **London Racing Club Owners Group**
8 **PHALAROPE (IRE),** 10, b g Petorius—Magee **Foreneish Racing**
9 **RHEINBOLD,** 4, br g Never So Bold—Rheinbloom **Mr E. Oliver**
10 **ROCHARISARE,** 9, br g Mummy's Game—Sharseal **H. S. S.**
11 **SIGMA WIRELESS (IRE),** 9, b g Henbit (USA)—Canelle **Mrs J. E. Todd**
12 **VAGABOND CHANTEUSE,** 4, ch f Sanglamore—Eclipsing (IRE) **Mr W. R. Green**
13 **VIOLETTE SABO,** 4, b f Prince Sabo—Kajetana (FR) **R. V. Hughes and Partners**
14 **ZALOTTO (IRE),** 4, b g Polish Patriot (USA)—Honest Penny (USA) **Mr P. D. Savill**

THREE-YEAR-OLDS

15 **AGENT LE BLANC (IRE),** b f Kahyasi—White Witch (USA) **Mr G. E. Oliver**
16 **BALLYKEEFE,** ch g Elmaamul (USA)—Caviar Blini **G. K. Barry**
17 **KAYO,** b c Superpower—Shiny Kay **Mr J. David Abell**
18 **PICCADILLY,** ch f Belmez (USA)—Polly's Pear (USA) **Mr W. R. Green**
19 **SWALLOW WARRIOR (IRE),** b c Warrshan (USA)—Pica **Foreneish Racing**
20 **VICE PRESIDENTIAL,** ch g Presidium—Steelstock **Mr P. D. Savill**
21 B g Past Glories—Zibonny (FR) **Mrs M. C. Butler**

TWO-YEAR-OLDS

22 **KESTRAL,** ch c 6/5 Ardkinglass—Shiny Kay (Star Appeal) **Mr Russell Bradley & Partners**
23 **LEICESTER TIGER,** b c 12/4 Presidium—Glenfield Greta (Gabitat) **Mr J. David & Mrs Julianna Abell**
24 B c 27/2 Anita's Prince—Song Beam (Song) **J. C. Smith**
25 **TRIMILKI (IRE),** b f 5/5 Lahib (USA)—Timmisarra (USA) **Callers and Clerks**
26 B c 11/4 Keen—True Queen (USA) (Silver Hawk (USA)) **Mr J. David & Mrs Julianna Abell**

Other Owners: Mrs M. C. Butler, Mr J. Etherington, Dr D. J. Forecast, Mr Richard Hoiles, Mr R. H. Hudson, Mr K. G. Hunt, Mr W. McNeish, Mr J. Pain, Miss A. H. Sykes, Mr Colin Wilby, Miss Z. C. Willis.

Jockey (Flat): K Darley (w.a.).

Jockeys (NH): R Supple, A Thornton, L Wyer.

203 MR J. M. P. EUSTACE, Newmarket

Postal: **Park Lodge Stables, Park Lane, Newmarket, Suffolk, CB8 8AX.**
Phone: **TEL (01638) 664277 FAX (01638) 664156 MOBILE (0802) 243764**

1 **COMPASS POINTER,** 5, gr g Mazilier (USA)—Woodleys **Mr R. Carstairs**
2 **LAMARITA,** 4, b f Emarati (USA)—Bentinck Hotel **Park Lane Racing & Mrs D. A. La Trobe**
3 **MADAME CHINNERY,** 4, b f Weldnaas (USA)—Bel Esprit **The Chinnery Partnership**
4 **REFUSE TO LOSE,** 4, ch c Emarati (USA)—Petrol **Mr J. C. Smith**
5 **THE WILD WIDOW,** 4, gr f Saddlers' Hall (IRE)—No Cards **Mrs A. Johnstone**
6 **WATERHALL,** 5, b g River God (USA)—Tuneful Queen **Mrs T. S. Matthews**

THREE-YEAR-OLDS

7 **BLACK ARMY,** b c Aragon—Morgannwg (IRE) **Mr K. J. Mercer**
8 **COCKSURE (IRE),** b c Nomination—Hens Grove **Mr J. C. Smith**
9 **DENTARDIA (IRE),** br c Petardia—Modena **Brave Maple Partnership**
10 **INVERGORDON,** ch g Efisio—Kintail **Kissing Tree Partnership**
11 **LITTLE BRAVE,** b c Kahyasi—Littlemisstrouble (USA) **Brave Maple Partnership**

TWO-YEAR-OLDS

12 **ALEGRIA,** b f 10/5 Night Shift (USA)—High Habit (Slip Anchor) **Mr J. C. Smith**
13 **BLUEWATER BAY,** b f 17/2 Lugana Beach—Dominion Blue (Dominion) **Kai Tak racing**
14 **CENTRAL COAST (IRE),** b c 10/3 Hamas (IRE)—Clairification (IRE) (Shernazar) **Mr R. Carstairs**

MR J. M. P. EUSTACE—continued

15 B f 1/4 Puissance—Daymer Bay (Lomond (USA)) **Mr T. Oakley**
16 **ELMS SCHOOLGIRL,** ch f 3/3 Emarati (USA)—Ascend (IRE) (Glint of Gold) **Park Lodge Racing**
17 **EMPYREAN,** b c 5/4 Emarati (USA)—Winter Lightning (Dominion) **Park Lane Racing**
18 **EWENNY,** b f 24/2 Warrshan (USA)—Laleston (Junius (USA)) **Mr & Mrs K. J. Mercer**
19 **PANSY,** br f 28/2 Lugana Beach—Smah (Mtoto) **Racing Post Syndicate**
20 B c 16/4 Scenic—Resiusa (ITY) (Niniski (USA)) **The MacDougall Partnership**
21 **WATER MUSIC,** gr c 2/5 Saddlers' Hall (IRE)—Gleaming Water (Kalaglow) **Mr Raymond Wu**

Other Owners: Mr Gary Coull, Mr Charles Curtis, Mrs James Eustace, Mr A. Frost, Mr A. M. Mitchell.

204 MR J. T. EVANS, Bromyard

Postal: **Yew Tree Cottage, Red Hill Farm, Bredenbury, Bromyard, Herefordshire, HR7 4SY.**
Phone: **(01885) 483535**

1 **BALLYHAMAGE (IRE),** 10, br g Mandalus—Deep Slaney **Mr J. T. Evans**
2 6, B g Lighter—Castleiney **Mr J. T. Evans**
3 **CASTLE OF LIGHT,** 7, b g Lighter—Castleiney **Mr J. T. Evans**
4 6, B g Sexton Blake—Key of The Bar **Mr J. T. Evans**
5 **STAR ADVENTURE,** 6, b g Green Adventure (USA)—Lady Martha **Mr J. T. Evans**

Jockey (NH): R Johnson (10-0).

Amateur: Miss Emma James (10-0).

205 MRS M. EVANS, Haverfordwest

Postal: **Hengoed, Clarbeston Road, Pembrokeshire, SA63 4QL.**
Phone: **(01437) 731336**

1 **KINLOGH GALE (IRE),** 10, b g Strong Gale—Kinlogh Maid **Mr W. J. Evans**
2 **LANDSKER MISSILE,** 9, b m Cruise Missile—Gemmerly Jane **Mr W. J. Evans**

206 MR P. D. EVANS, Welshpool

Postal: **Long Mountain Farm, Leighton, Welshpool, Powys, SY21 8JB.**
Phone: **(01938) 570288 (0860) 668499 (0860) 599101**

1 **ABSTONE QUEEN,** 4, b f Presidium—Heavenly Queen **Mr J. E. Abbey**
2 **CLUED UP,** 5, b m Beveled (USA)—Scharade **Mrs E. J. Williams**
3 **GUTTERIDGE (IRE),** 8, b g Roselier (FR)—Buck's Fairy **BCD Steels Ltd**
4 **ITALIAN SYMPHONY (IRE),** 4, b g Royal Academy (USA)—Terracotta Hut **Mr J. E. Abbey**
5 **LEONATO (FR),** 6, b g Law Society (USA)—Gala Parade **Mr Colin G. R. Booth**
6 **MARINO STREET,** 5, b m Totem (USA)—Demerger **Mr Roy Penton**
7 **MASTER BEVELED,** 8, b g Beveled (USA)—Miss Anniversary **Mrs E. J. Williams**
8 **MAZEED (IRE),** 5, ch g Lycius (USA)—Maraatib (IRE) **Mrs L. A. Windsor**
9 **NAUGHTY PISTOL (USA),** 6, ch m Big Pistol (USA)—Naughty Nile (USA) **Mr Colin G. R. Booth**
10 **PANTHER (IRE),** 8, ch g Primo Dominie—High Profile **Treble Chance Partnership**
11 **RASAYEL (USA),** 8, b m Bering—Reham **Pentons Haulage and Cold Storage Ltd**
12 **REX MUNDI,** 6, b g Gunner B—Rose Standish **Mr J. W. Littler**
13 **SWINO,** 4, b g Forzando—St Helena **Swinnerton Transport Ltd**

MR P. D. EVANS—continued

THREE-YEAR-OLDS

14 **CLASSY CLEO (IRE),** b f Mujadil (USA)—Sybaris **Mr J. E. Abbey**
15 **DEMOLITION JO,** gr f Petong—Fire Sprite **Mr John Pugh**
16 **FULL MOON,** b g Almoojid—High Time (FR) **Mrs E. A. Dawson**
17 **GLASS RIVER,** b c Ardkinglass—Rion River (IRE) **Mr R. F. F. Mason**
18 **INNER KEY,** b g Interrex (CAN)—Key To Enchantment **Mr P. D. Evans**
19 **LARAMANIA,** ch g Safawan—Lara's Baby (IRE) **Lawrence & Vaughan**
20 **MALOZZA,** b f Michelozzo (USA)—Lis Na Mon **Mr D. Maloney**
21 **MICHELEE,** b f Merdon Melody—Hsian **Mr John Pugh**
22 **OPERATIC,** b f Goofalik (USA)—Choir Mistress **Mrs Stephen Allen**
23 **OUT LIKE MAGIC,** ch f Magic Ring (IRE)—Thevetia **Mrs E. A. Dawson**
24 **PINK TICKET,** b f Emarati (USA)—Foreign Mistress **Mr John Pugh**
25 **VELVET STORY,** ch g Aragon—Lucy Manette **Diamond Racing Ltd**

TWO-YEAR-OLDS

26 B f 30/4 River Falls—Bluethroat (Ballymore) **Clayton Bigley Partnership**
27 B g 3/3 Forest Wind (USA)—Celestial Plain (IRE) (Thatching) **Mr P. D. Evans**
28 **CLASSY ABSTONE,** br f 7/3 Tragic Role (USA)—Grey Twig (Godswalk (USA)) **Men Behaving Badly**
29 **FIVE WAYS FLYER,** br f 23/2 Perugino (USA)—Flutinoa (African Song) **Men Behaving Badly**
30 B f 6/5 Beveled (USA)—Foreign Mistress (Darshaan) **Mr J. E. Abbey**
31 Ch f 9/4 Red Sunset—Grave Error (Northern Treat (USA)) **Mr P. D. Evans**
32 **HADEQA,** ch g 17/2 Hadeer—Heavenly Queen (Scottish Reel) **Men Behaving Badly**
33 **HANIBEL DANCER (IRE),** b f 12/5 Elbio—Mistress Muni (IRE) (King of Clubs) **Hanibel Racing**
34 **HANIBEL LADY (IRE),** br f 24/4 Mac's Imp (USA)—Fast Bay (Bay Express) **Hanibel Racing**
35 B f 22/4 Mujadil (USA)—Independent Woman (IRE) (Carmelite House (USA)) **Men Behaving Badly**
36 **JAYCEE SUPERSTAR,** b f 30/3 Cyrano de Bergerac—Sunley Stars (Sallust) **Mr J. Campbell**
37 **JUST ORANGE,** gr g 29/3 Never So Bold—Just Greenwich (Chilibang) **Mrs E. A. Dawson**
38 **LITTLE HENRY,** ch c 4/4 My Generation—White African (Carwhite) **Mr J. G. White**
39 **ORIEL STAR,** b f 10/3 Safawan—Silvers Era (Balidar) **Kendall White**
40 **PAPER FLIGHT,** gr f 21/2 Petong—Tissue Paper (Touch Paper) **Mrs E. A. Dawson**
41 Ch f 3/4 Safawan—Purple Fan (Dalsaan) **Mr J. E. Abbey**
42 **RED CAFE,** ch f 16/3 Perugino (USA)—Test Case (Busted) **Men Behaving Badly**
43 B f 4/3 Tragic Role (USA)—Simmie's Special (Precocious) **Mr J. E. Abbey**
44 **SLIGHTLY DUSTY,** b f 10/2 Depploy—Dusty's Darling (Doyoun) **Mr D. Maloney**
45 **SOMEBODY LOVES ME,** b f 6/3 Distant Relative—Sunita (Owen Dudley) **Men Behaving Badly**
46 **TRYARDIA-ON-AGAIN,** ch f 14/3 Petardia—Trysinger (Try My Best (USA)) **Men Behaving Badly**

Other Owners: Academy Leasing Ltd, Mrs S. Barber, Mr J. R. Bostock, Mr P. Brazier, Mr D. B. Brocklesby, Mr P. G. Evans, Mr John Fowden, Mr Trevor Gallienne, Mr James Glass, Mr Paul Green (Huyton), Mr W. J. Hamilton, Mr M. J. Higgins, Mr M. W. Lawrence, Mr Gordon Mytton, Mr Peter J. Nichol, Mr Mike Nolan, Mr Ralph P. Peters, Mr D. E. Simpson, Mr P. B. Swinnerton, Ms Paula Sylvester, Tern Hill Communications, Mr J. F. Thomas, Mrs C. A. Torkington, Mr M. Vaughan, Mr G. Weaver, Mr J. B. Wilcox, Mr G. E. Wood, Mr M. Woodall.

Jockey (Flat): J F Egan (8-0).

Apprentice: A McCarthy (7-3).

Amateur: Mr A Evans (10-0).

207 MR J. L. EYRE, Hambleton

Postal: **Hambleton House, Sutton Bank, Thirsk, North Yorkshire, YO7 2HA.**
Phone: **(01845) 597481**

1 **ANONYM (IRE),** 6, b g Nashamaa—Bonny Bertha **Wetherby Racing Bureau 28**
2 **ARIAN SPIRIT (IRE),** 7, b m High Estate—Astral Way **Mr Martin West**
3 **BARREL OF HOPE,** 6, b g Distant Relative—Musianica **Mr Peter J. Watson**
4 **BELBAY STAR,** 5, b m Belfort (FR)—Gavea **Miss Anne Simpson & Mr Trevor Welbourn**
5 **BLOOMING AMAZING,** 4, b g Mazilier (USA)—Cornflower Blue **C. H. & D. W. Stephenson Ltd**
6 **BRUTAL FANTASY (IRE),** 4, b g Distinctly North (USA)—Flash Donna (USA) **Diamond Racing Ltd**
7 **CASHMERE LADY,** 6, b m Hubbly Bubbly (USA)—Choir **Mrs Sybil Howe**
8 **CELESTIAL CHOIR,** 8, b m Celestial Storm (USA)—Choir **Mrs Carole Sykes**
9 **CHANCANCOOK,** 5, ch m Hubbly Bubbly (USA)—Majuba Road **Mr J. Chan**
10 **CHEMCAST,** 5, ch g Chilibang—Golden October **Clayton Bigley Partnership Ltd**
11 **COUNT BASIE,** 5, b g Batshoof—Quiet Harbour **Sunpak Potatoes**
12 **DR EDGAR,** 6, b g Most Welcome—African Dancer **Mr A. G. Watson**
13 **FAIRY FINGERS,** 4, b f Treasure Kay—Nellie Moss **Mr W. A. A. Farrell**
14 **FAR AHEAD,** 6, b g Soviet Star (USA)—Cut Ahead **Sunpak Potatoes**
15 **GLADYS ALTHORPE (IRE),** 5, b m Posen (USA)—Gortadoo (USA) **Mr T. S. Ely**
16 **KIRA,** 8, b m Starry Night (USA)—Irish Limerick **Mr J. E. Wilson**
17 **MAGIC MILL (IRE),** 5, b h Simply Great (FR)—Rosy O'Leary **Mr A. S. Scott**
18 **MELS BABY (IRE),** 5, br g Contract Law (USA)—Launch The Raft **Mr John Roberts (Wakefield)**
19 **MR FORTYWINKS (IRE),** 4, ch g Fools Holme (USA)—Dream On **Miss Nuala Cassidy**
20 **MUSIC EXPRESS (IRE),** 4, b f Classic Music (USA)—Hetty Green **Mrs Kate Watson**
21 **NAPOLEON'S RETURN,** 5, gr g Daring March—Miss Colenca **Mr J. E. Wilson**
22 **NIGHT OF GLASS,** 5, b g Mazilier (USA)—Donna Elvira **Mr K. Silvester and Mr B. Silvester**
23 **NIGRASINE,** 4, b c Mon Tresor—Early Gales **Sunpak Potatoes**
24 **OLD HABITS (IRE),** 9, b g Nordance (USA)—Layer Cake **Mr R. W. Thomson**
25 **ONEFOURSEVEN,** 5, b g Jumbo Hirt (USA)—Dominance **Mr J. Roundtree**
26 **ORTOLAN,** 5, gr h Prince Sabo—Kala Rosa **Diamond Racing Ltd**
27 **PINE RIDGE LAD (IRE),** 8, gr g Taufan (USA)—Rosserk **Whitestonecliffe Racing Partnership**
28 **RAINDEER QUEST,** 6, ch m Hadeer—Rainbow Ring **Whitestonecliffe Racing Partnership**
29 **SERIOUS ACCOUNT (USA),** 5, b h Danzig (USA)—Topicount (USA) **Ms Heidi McKenna**
30 **THE BARNSLEY BELLE (IRE),** 5, b m Distinctly North (USA)—La Tanque (USA) **Mr K. Meynell**
31 **THE FED,** 8, ch g Clantime—Hyde Princess **Mr Nicholas Wright**
32 **THE ROAD WEST (IRE),** 9, b g Where To Dance (USA)—Cameo Dancer **Mr Val Kelly**
33 **TIME OF NIGHT (USA),** 5, ro m Night Shift (USA)—Tihama (USA) **Mr J. L. Eyre**
34 **TOTEM DANCER,** 5, b m Mtoto—Ballad Opera **Diamond Racing Ltd**
35 **VALIANT TOSKI,** 7, b h Petoski—Corvelle **Mr Frank Thornton**
36 **WHITLEY GRANGE BOY,** 5, b g Hubbly Bubbly (USA)—Choir **Mrs Carole Sykes**

THREE-YEAR-OLDS

37 **ANDITZ (IRE),** b f Soviet Lad (USA)—Miss Fortunate (IRE) **Mr Peter J. Watson**
38 **AURAMINE (IRE),** ch c Rainbows For Life (CAN)—Les Saintes **Mr M. Gleason**
39 **BAHIA BLANCA SUN (IRE),** b g Tirol—Wild Applause (IRE) **Mr Tony Yates**
40 **BAWSIAN,** b c Persian Bold—Bawaeth (USA) **Mr David Scott**
41 **BRANSTON BERRY (IRE),** ch f Mukaddamah (USA)—Food of Love **Diamond Racing Ltd**
42 **BREAKIN EVEN,** ch g Chilibang—Bee Dee Dancer **Mrs Frank Campbell**
43 **CAPLAW SKEEN,** b g Sure Blade (USA)—Mary From Dunlow **Mr G. P. Bernacchi**
44 **CARAMBO,** b f Rambo Dancer (CAN)—Light The Way **C. H. & D. W. Stephenson Ltd**
45 **CHIMES OF PEACE,** b f Magic Ring (IRE)—Leprechaun Lady **The Secret Seven Partnership**
46 **CUE MAN (IRE),** b c Dancing Dissident (USA)—Albona **Mr J. Roundtree**
47 **CULCRAGGIE,** b c Weldnaas (USA)—Strathrusdale **Mr Guthrie Robertson**
48 **ESSANDESS (IRE),** b f Casteddu—Ra Ra **Mrs Sybil Howe**
49 **FIRST FRAME,** b c Mukaddamah (USA)—Point of Law **Mr J. Roundtree**
50 **HOLY SMOKE,** b f Statoblest—Native Flair **Lady Green**
51 **INTUITIVE,** b f Teenoso (USA)—Hasland
52 **JUST TESTING,** br f Sharpo—Antoinette Jane **Clayton Bigley Partnership Ltd**
53 **LADY RACHEL (IRE),** b f Priolo (USA)—Alpine Spring **Mr Steve Macdonald**

MR J. L. EYRE—continued

54 **MOET (IRE),** b f Mac's Imp (USA)—Comfrey Glen **Mrs Kate Watson**
55 **MUSICAL PET (IRE),** ch f Petardia—Musical Gem (USA) **The Flowerpot Men**
56 **PASS THE REST (IRE),** b c Shalford (IRE)—Brown Foam **Mr J. Roundtree**
57 **SANS RIVALE,** ch f Elmaamul (USA)—Strawberry Song **Dab Hand Racing**
58 **SORRIDAR,** b f Puissance—Sorrowful **Mr K. Birkinshaw**
59 **THE PRESIDENT,** b c Yaheeb (USA)—When The Saints **North Racing Partnership**

TWO-YEAR-OLDS

60 Ch c 13/3 Alhijaz—Bridge Player (The Noble Player (USA)) **Miss Marjorie Thompson**
61 B c 23/4 Jumbo Hirt (USA)—Dominance (Dominion) **Mr J. Roundtree**
62 **DROWNED IN BUBBLY,** b c 29/2 Tragic Role (USA)—Champenoise (Forzando) **Lovely Bubbly Racing**
63 Ch c 18/3 Deploy—Golden Panda (Music Boy) **Mr A. G. Watson**
64 B c 9/4 Aragon—Gwiffina (Welsh Saint) **Sunpak Potatoes**
65 B f 30/1 Shalford (IRE)—Hinari Disk Deck (Indian King (USA)) **Wetherby Racing Bureau**
66 B f 11/2 Soviet Lad (USA)—Piney Lake (Sassafras (FR)) **Mr J. L. Eyre**
67 B c 7/5 Tragic Role (USA)—Princess Yasmin (USA) (Le Fabuleux) **Mr D. Clarkson**

Other Owners: Mr John R. Ashcroft, Mr E. J. Ashton, Mr Harvey Ashworth, Mr Andrew Bates, Mr R. P. Berrow, Mr J. R. Bostock, Mr W. Calder, Mr David Campbell, Mr J. G. Campbell, Mr C. Clark, Mr Anthony Cross, Mr Martin Cruddace, Mr J. Ellis, Mr G. Griffin, Mr Murray Grubb, Mr P. Hampshire, Mr Paul Hemingway, Highgrove Developments Limited, Mr Rowland Hill, Mr John L. Holdroyd, Mr B. Hooper, Mr A. H. Jackson, Miss Donna-Marie Lappin, Mr R. T. Ling, Linkchallenge Limited, Mr J. McCormack, Mr Brian McSweeney, Mr John Morley, Mr George Murray, Mrs Cheryl L. Owen, Mrs Caroline Page, Mr D. Pearson, Mrs Norma Peebles, Mr Roy Peebles, Mrs Maureen Pickering, Mr Alan Pirie, Mr Richard Pitman, Mr Geoff Rawson, Mr E. Richmond, Mrs Elke Scullion, Mr S. P. Sheldon, Mr A. Skelton, Mr J. B. Slatcher, Mrs Pam Slawson, Mr D. A. Smeaton, Mrs Gwen Smith, Mrs Diane Soar, Mr Ernest Spencer, Mr Harry Steckles, Mrs Paula Stringer, Mr D. M. Sutherland, Mrs Eve Sweetman, Mrs Joanne Taylor, The Mirror Punters Club, Ms Melanie Jayne Tyrrell, Mrs Patricia Waldron, Mrs C. A. Ward, Mr N. C. White, Mr M. Willoughby, Mrs Fernanda Windle, Mr Graham Wood, Mr J. J. Wright, Mrs S. J. Yates.

Jockeys (Flat): K Fallon (8-3), R Lappin (8-1), T Williams (7-12).

Jockey (NH): B Storey.

Apprentices: S Buckley (7-12), R Winks (7-12).

Conditional: C Elliot (10-0).

Amateurs: Diana Jones (9-7),

208 MR A. FABRE, Chantilly

Postal: **14 Avenue de Bourbon, 60500 Chantilly, France.**
Phone: **03 44 57 04 98 FAX 03 44 58 14 15**

1 **ALAMO BAY (USA),** 5, b h Nureyev—Albertine
2 **BALLARAT (IRE),** 4, b c Sadler's Wells—Bex
3 **BLUE SKY (IRE),** 4, b c Marignan—Belle Bleue
4 **FLEETING GLIMPSE,** 4, b f Rainbow Quest—Flit
5 **FOR VALOUR (USA),** 5, b h Trempolino—Glitter
6 **FRAGRANT MIX (FR),** 4, b c Linamix—Fragrant Hill
7 **GO BOLDLY (IRE),** 4, b c Sadler's Wells—Diavolina
8 **GRACIE LADY (IRE),** 4, b f Generous—No Distance

MR A. FABRE—continued

9 **LOUP SAUVAGE (USA)**, 4, b c Riverman—Louveterie
10 **NAPOLI EXPRESS (FR)**, 4, b c Persian Bold—Spectatrice
11 **PEINTRE CELEBRE (USA)**, 4, b c Nureyev—Peinture Bleue
12 **PUBLIC PURSE (USA)**, 4, b c Private Account—Prodigious
13 **QUORUM**, 5, b h Sadler's Wells—Green Rock
14 **SIBLING RIVAL (USA)**, 4, b c Quest For Fame—Perfect Sister
15 **VISIONARY (FR)**, 4, b c Linamix—Visor

THREE-YEAR-OLDS

16 **AIGLE NOIR (USA)**, b c Manila—Albertine
17 **ALL HEIGH (FR)**, b c Shirley Heights—Alhawrah
18 **ALLITERATION**, b c Polish Precedent—African Peace
19 **AMBITION**, b c Rainbow Quest—I Want To Be
20 **ANNA PALARIVA (IRE)**, b f Caerleon—Anna of Saxony
21 **ARNAQUEUR (USA)**, b c Miswaki—All Along
22 **ASTORG (USA)**, b f Lear Fan—Action Francaise
23 **BALIZAC (IRE)**, b c Arazi—Lypharita
24 **BANDIT D'HONNEUR (FR)**, b c Pistolet Bleu—Bohemienne
25 **BEAT THE WHEEL (USA)**, b c Time For A Change—Blue Tip
26 **BEQUIA**, b c Shirley Heights—Balabina
27 **BRANCHE D'OR(IRE)**, b f Last Tycoon—Belle Bleue
28 **BRIDELINA (FR)**, b f Linamix—Society Bride
29 **BRILLIANCY (USA)**, b c Alleged—Crystal Gazing
30 **CAMIRING (FR)**, b f Bering—Camikala
31 **CENTRAL LOBBY (IRE)**, b c Kenmare—Style of Life
32 **CHAMBON (IRE)**, b c Epervier Bleu—Charme Discret
33 **CHURCH MIXA (FR)**, b f Linamix—Church Missionary
34 **CIRCE'S SYMBOL**, b c Soviet Star—Circe's Isle
35 **COLOUR DANCE**, b f Rainbow Quest—Balleta
36 **COMPERE**, b c Unfuwain—Comhail
37 **CORUNNA (USA)**, b c Gone West—Kiruna
38 **DANAKIL**, b c Warning—Danilova
39 **DESERT BLOOM (FR)**, b f Last Tycoon—Desert Dawn
40 **DESERT LAND**, b f Green Desert—Bloudan
41 **DIAMONIXA (FR)**, b f Linamix—Diamonaka
42 **DIAMOONA (FR)**, b f Last Tycoon—Diamond Seal
43 **DINKA RAJA (USA)**, b f Woodman—Miss Profile
44 **DISCRET AMOUR (USA)**, b c Riverman—Danseuse de Soir
45 **DIVISION BELL**, b f Warning—Ala Mahlik
46 **DRUM MELODY (USA)**, b f Seeking The Gold—Dolsk
47 **ELANCOURT (FR)**, b c Trempolino—Good To Dance
48 **EPISTOLAIRE (IRE)**, b c Alzao—Epistolienne
49 **ESTUARY (USA)**, b c Riverman—Ocean Ballad
50 **EXTREME ORIENT (FR)**, b c Warning—Repercutionist
51 **FAIRLY GREY (FR)**, b f Linamix—Fairlee Wild
52 **FIRE THUNDER (USA)**, b c Dayjur—Blush With Pride
53 **FLAXEN WELLS (IRE)**, b f Sadler's Wells—Flaxen Hair
54 **FONTEVRAULT (FR)**, b c Subotica—Touville
55 **GARONNE**, b c Zafonic—Nashmeel
56 **GHOST OF YOU**, b f Arazi—Ruffle
57 **GILGAMESH (USA)**, b c Mr Prospector—Danzante
58 **GIVERNEY (IRE)**, b c Fairy King—Golden Bloom
59 **GLISSANDO (IRE)**, b c In The Wings—Across The Ice
60 **GONTCHAROVA (IRE)**, b f Zafonic—Luth de Saron
61 **GUERIDIA (IRE)**, b f Night Shift—Galla Placidia
62 **GUERRE ET PAIX (USA)**, b f Soviet Star—Fire And Shade
63 **HEART HAS WINGS (IRE)**, b c Arazi—J'Ai Deux Amours
64 **HIGHLANDS (FR)**, b c Shirley Heights—Riosamba
65 **HOMME DE LUMIERE (FR)**, b c Arazi—Lumen Dei

MR A. FABRE—continued

66 IN ARCADIA, b c Slip Anchor—Pastorale
67 IRISH SANGUE (USA), b c Irish River—Sangue
68 ISLE DE FRANCE (USA), b f Nureyev—Stella Madrid
69 KARMIBOLA (FR), b f Persian Bold—Karmisha
70 LAURENTIA (USA), b f St Jovite—Lollipop Lies
71 LIMOGES (USA), b f Forty Niner—Louve Bleue
72 LIMPID, b c Soviet Star—Isle of Glass
73 LOUDEAC (USA), b c Riverman—Louveterie
74 LUNE DE MAI, b f Kenmare—Louve Romaine
75 MAGIC ISLE, b f Zafonic—Bermuda Classic
76 MARIA MAGGIORE (GER), b f Mtoto—Mimbet
77 MILK WOOD, b c Zafonic—Welsh Daylight
78 MRS FAIR (FR), b f Always Fair—Mrs Annie
79 MYSTERIOUS MYTH (USA), b f Alleged—Stella Mystika
80 MYSTERY NIGHT (FR), b f Fairy King—Mini Luthe
81 NATIVE JUSTICE (USA), b f Alleged—Fabulous Native
82 NOBELIST, b c Bering—Noble Peregrine
83 NOBLE AIR (IRE), b f Lycius—Beaconaire
84 NORTHERN QUEST (FR), b c Rainbow Quest—Northern Goddess
85 NOVELETTE, b f Darshaan—Nordica
86 NUMA POMPILIUS (FR), b c Sanglamore—Trephine
87 OCEAN OF STORMS (IRE), b c Arazi—Moon Cactus
88 OCTAVE, b f Rainbow Quest—Melodist
89 ODALISQUE (IRE), b f Machiavellian—Ode
90 OSKARBERG, b f Warning—Oscura
91 OURASI (IRE), b c Last Tycoon—Onde Bleu Marine
92 PALATIAL (USA), b f Irish River—Diamond City
93 PALDOUNA (IRE), b f Kaldoun—Palavera
94 PELFRE, b c Suave Dancer—Pelf
95 PENGELLY (USA), b c Woodman—Spur Wing
96 PINE CHIP (USA), b f Nureyev—Peinture Bleue
97 PINK SOVIETSTAIA (FR), b f Soviet Star—Pink Satin
98 PINMIX (FR), b c Linamix—Pinaflore
99 PLEINE LUNE (IRE), b f Alzao—Pampa Bella
100 PRINTANIERE (IRE), b f Thatching—Plume Bleu Pale
101 QUEEN CATHERINE, b f Machiavellian—Russian Royal
102 RUBIS ROYAL (IRE), b c Bluebird—Robertet
103 SAGAMIX (FR), b c Linamix—Saganeca
104 SALINOVA (FR), b f Linamix—Six Love
105 SAMOTHRACE (IRE), b f Arazi—Shani
106 SEA COVE (USA), b f Nureyev—Special Happening
107 SEDDOUK, b c Last Tycoon—Seconde Bleue
108 SEDUCTRICE (USA), b f Kingmambo—Southern Seas
109 SI NOBLE, b c Affirmed—Miss Evans
110 SOLVALLA (USA), b f Nureyev—Shadolawn
111 SPEEDY CROWN (IRE), b c Bering—Symphorine
112 SPIRITUAL, b c Zafonic—Wakria
113 SWADENE (USA), b c Lear Fan—Mount Helena
114 TAMARINO (IRE), b f Caerleon—Fruition
115 TASSLE (IRE), b c Suave Dancer—Satin Pointe
116 THE CARD KING (IRE), b c Sadler's Wells (USA)—Brilleaux
117 THIEF OF HEARTS (IRE), b c In The Wings—Love Smitten
118 TIME CHANGES (USA), b f Danzig—Make Change
119 ULTIMATELY LUCKY (IRE), b c Kris—Oczy Czarnie
120 UNINHIBITED (IRE), b f Lahib—Etiquette
121 VADIMIX (FR), b c Linamix—Vadsa
122 VADLAWYSA (IRE), b f Always Fair—Vadlava
123 VAGABOND (IRE), b c Alzao—Verveine
124 VAINCRE OU MOURIR (FR), b c Groom Dancer—Victoire Bleue
125 VIKING'S COVE (USA), b f Miswaki—Venise

MR A. FABRE—continued

126 VOLONTAIRE (IRE), b c Danehill—Vanille
127 WALTZER, b f Arazi—First Waltz
128 WATERBERG, b c Sadler's Wells (USA)—Pretoria
129 XAAR, b c Zafonic—Monroe
130 YAM (USA), b f Nureyev—Super Staff
131 ZAGHRUTA (USA), b f Gone West—Zaizafon

TWO-YEAR-OLDS

132 ALABAMA (IRE), b f Bluebird—Allons Enfants
133 B c Diesis—Alvernia
134 AMILYNX (FR), b c Linamix—Amen
135 APACHE SONG (USA), b f Dynaformer—Action Francaise
136 ARABIAN SEA (FR), b c Bering—Arabian Dance
137 ARES VALLIS (IRE), b f Caerleon—Hoedown Honey
138 ARIUS, b c Royal Academy—Ville Eternelle
139 BATTAL (USA), b c Persian Bold—Luth de Crystal
140 B f Sadler's Wells—Bex
141 BLUE CLOUD (IRE), b f Nashwan—Batave
142 BLUE SPIRIT (USA), b c Mining—Blue Tip
143 BOUGAINVILLEA (GER), b f Acatenango—Brittania
144 BRIGHT BLUE (FR), b f Linamix—Bohemienne
145 BRIGHT STONE (IRE), b c Bigstone—Bright Moon
146 BROKEN ARROW (FR), b c Bigstone—Belle Bleue
147 CAMIKARIL (FR), b c Akarad—Camikala
148 CARNAC (FR), b c Royal Academy—La Consaca
149 B f Gulch—Chateaubaby
150 CRYSTAL QUEST (IRE), b c Rainbow Quest—Caladesi
151 DALI'S GREY, b f Linamix—Diamonaka
152 DANCING FIRE (USA), b f Dayjur—Danseuse du Soir
153 B c Storm Bird—Dellagrazia
154 B c Deputy Minister—Devon Diva
155 DHARMA (USA), b f Zilzal—Encorelle
156 B c Nureyev—Don't Sulk
157 B c Saint Estephe—Double Line
158 B f Fairy King—Eclat Nocturne
159 FELLOW ROVER, b c Machiavellian—Youm Jadeed
160 FIRST MAGNITUDE (IRE), b c Arazi—Crystal Cup
161 GREAT SPIRIT (USA), b c Irish River—Gold Bird
162 HEALING HANDS, b f Zafonic—One Life
163 HUDSON BAY (FR), b c Ganges—Her Highness
164 INDIAN DANEHILL (IRE), b c Danehill—Danse Indienne
165 IN THE TRIM (IRE), b f Tirol—Pizzazz
166 B c Sadler's Wells—Ispahan
167 B f Machiavellian—Ivrea
168 JET AGE, b c Danehill—Fawaayid
169 KOOTENAI (FR), b f Pistolet Bleu—Keniant
170 KURDISTAN (FR), b c Linamix—Kardanskaia
171 L'OLYMPIQUE (IRE), b c Machiavellian—Lille Hammer
172 B c Kingmambo—Lotka
173 LOUP DES NEIGES (IRE), b c Rainbow Quest—Louve Romaine
174 LOUVE MYSTERIEUSE (USA), b f Seeking The Gold—Louve Bleue
175 LOUVE (USA), b f Irish River—Louveterie
176 B c Be My Guest—Marseillaise
177 MISSISSIPPI (USA), b c Carson City—Mersey
178 B f Sadler's Wells—Modiyna
179 MOUNTAIN SPIRIT (IRE), b f Royal Academy—Martingale
180 MR ACADEMY (IRE), b c Royal Academy—Miss d'Ouilly
181 N'AVOUE JAMAIS (FR), b f Marignan—Newness
182 NOCTUA (GER), b f Hondo Mondo—Nigrita

MR A. FABRE—continued

183 **NORDICAN INCH,** b f Inchinor—Fee des Mers
184 B c Barathea—Overcall
185 **OXALO (GER),** b c Acatenango—Orania
186 **PACE STALKER (USA),** b c Lear Fan—In The Habit
187 **PEACE DRUM,** b c Grand Lodge—Plume Bleu Pale
188 **PEACE SIGNAL (USA),** b f Time For A Change—Peinture Bleue
189 **PEACE TALK (FR),** b f Sadler's Wells—Pampa Bella
190 B c Sadler's Wells—Penza
191 **PERSIANLUX,** b c Persian Bold—Luxurious
192 B c Gone West—Personal Glory
193 **PINAKARAL,** b c Akarad—Pinaflore
194 **PRAIRIE RUNNER (IRE),** b f Arazi—Paix Blanche
195 B c Alydeed—Radiation Delight
196 **RAUCOUS LAD,** b c Warning—Someone Special
197 **RESTLESS WAR (FR),** b c Akarad—Restless Girl
198 **ROYAL ARROW (USA),** b c Dayjur—Buy The Firm
199 **RUSSIAN SHIFT (IRE),** b c Night Shift—Dievotchka
200 B f Gulch—Sabin
201 B f Be My Guest—Secretary Bird
202 **SELLAGINELLA,** b f Konigsstuhl—Sunya
203 B c Sadler's Wells—Sequel
204 B c Exit To Nowhere—Serenad Dancer
205 **SHADOWHUNTER (USA),** b c Riverman—Special Happening
206 B c Lion Cavern—Sharka
207 B c Pleasant Colony—Sha Tha
208 B c Nureyev—Skimble
209 **SLICKLY (FR),** b c Linamix—Slipstream Queen
210 **SOCIAL DUTY (FR),** b c Always Fair—Society Bride
211 **SOLEIL INDIEN (USA),** b c Woodman—Saison
212 **SPIRIT LEADER (USA),** b c Dayjur—Southern Seas
213 B f Irish River—Spit Curl
214 **STANDING ROCK (IRE),** b c Sadler's Wells—Symphorine
215 B c Alleged—Sunny Bay
216 B c Theatrical—Sylph
217 **TELLER OF TALES,** b c Arazi—Water Splash
218 **THE MASK (FR),** b c Saint Estephe—Mare Aux Fees
219 **TOBYWAN,** b c Zafonic—Varsavia
220 B f Rainbow Quest—Trefoil
221 **TRIOMPHANT,** b c Linamix—Te Kani
222 **VALLEE DES REVES (USA),** b f Kingmambo—Venise
223 **VAL ROYAL (FR),** b c Royal Academy—Vadlava
224 **VANISHING WORLD (FR),** b c Bering—Victoire Bleue
225 **VICTORY CRY (IRE),** b f Caerleon—Verveine
226 **VICTORY STAR (FR),** b f Alzao—Vanille
227 B f Rainbow Quest—Wajd
228 **WAR GAME (FR),** b f Caerleon—Walensee
229 **WESTWOOD HO (USA),** b c Gone West—Zaradi Sidi Anna
230 B f Warning—Whitehaven
231 B f Darshaan—White Star Line
232 B f Danzig—Zaizafon

209 MR R. A. FAHEY, Malton

Postal: **Manor House Farm, Butterwick, Brawby, Malton, North Yorkshire, YO17 OPS.**
Phone: **(01653) 628001 FAX (01653) 628001 MOBILE (0411) 210046**

1 **ALSALOPA,** 4, ch g Symbolic—Oxalis **Mrs M. W. Kenyon**
2 **ANTARCTIC STORM,** 5, b g Emarati (USA)—Katie Scarlett **Northumbria Leisure Ltd**
3 **BALA PYJAMA,** 5, b g Henbit (USA)—Rodney's Sister **Aykroyd and Sons Ltd**

MR R. A. FAHEY—continued

4 BALLESWHIDDEN, 6, b g Robellino (USA)—Dame Scarlet **Mr Tommy Staunton**
5 BRIEF SUSPENCE (IRE), 5, b g Distinctly North (USA)—Edwinarowe **A. & K. Lingerie**
6 CASH FOR QUESTIONS (IRE), 6, b g Supreme Leader—Deep Dollar **Mrs P. A. Morrison & Mr P. S. Cresswell**
7 HIGH PREMIUM, 10, b g Forzando—High Halo **Mr J. C. Parsons**
8 HONG KONG CLASSIC, 5, ch m Anshan—Fall About **Mr T. C. Chiang**
9 KALININI (USA), 4, ch g Seattle Dancer (USA)—Kaiserfahrt (GER) **Mr C. H. McGhie**
10 KICKONSUN (IRE), 4, b g High Estate—Damezao **Mr R. A. Fahey**
11 MARATHON MAID, 4, gr f Kalaglow—El Rabab (USA) **John Stephenson & Sons (Nelson) Ltd**
12 MBULWA, 12, ch g Be My Guest (USA)—Bundu (FR) **Northumbria Leisure Ltd**
13 MISS KATIE MAE (IRE), 4, b f Distinctly North (USA)—Cape of Storms **Mr C. Maesepp**
14 MURPHY'S GOLD (IRE), 7, ch g Salt Dome (USA)—Winter Harvest **Mr D. A. Read**
15 NIGHT FLIGHT, 4, gr g Night Shift (USA)—Ancestry **Mr C. H. Stevens**
16 NOYAN, 8, ch g Northern Baby (CAN)—Istiska (FR) **Mr C. H. McGhie**
17 SAM PEEB, 4, b g Keen—Lutine Royal **Mrs M. A. Brown**
18 SAMSPET, 4, ch g Pharly (FR)—Almond Blossom **Mr Peter Tingey**
19 SLASHER JACK (IRE), 7, b g Alzao (USA)—Sherkraine **Mr T. C. Chiang**
20 STEPHENSONS ROCKET, 7, ch g Music Boy—Martian Princess **John Stephenson & Sons (Nelson) Ltd**
21 SUPERIOR PREMIUM, 4, br c Forzando—Devils Dirge **Mr J. C. Parsons**
22 SWAN AT WHALLEY, 6, b g Statoblest—My Precious Daisy **Mrs C. M. Barlow**
23 THE BUTTERWICK KID, 5, ch g Interrex (CAN)—Ville Air **Mr Robert Chambers & Mrs M. W. Kenyon**
24 TOP OF THE FORM (IRE), 4, ch f Masterclass (USA)—Haraabah (USA) **Swan at Whalley Premier Partnership**
25 WINTER SCOUT (USA), 10, ch g It's Freezing (USA)—His Squaw (USA) **Mrs S. M. Russell**

THREE-YEAR-OLDS

26 AMEENA (USA), b f Irish River (FR)—London Pride (USA) **Mr R. Meredith**
27 COLOURS TO GOLD (IRE), ch f Rainbows For Life (CAN)—Brave Ivy **Mr I. Bray**
28 EASTERN PURPLE (IRE), b c Petorius—Broadway Rosie **Mr T. C. Chiang**
29 FIVE OF SPADES (IRE), b g Roi Danzig (USA)—Hellicroft **Mr B. L. Cassidy**
30 HALF A KNICKER, b g Weldnaas (USA)—Queen of The Quorn **Mr J. A. Campbell**
31 B c Ardkinglass—Melaura Belle **Mrs J. Hazell**
32 PIERPOINT (IRE), ch g Archway (IRE)—Lavinia **Mr R. A. Fahey**
33 PREMIUM PURSUIT, b g Pursuit of Love—Music In My Life (IRE) **Mr J. C. Parsons**
34 PREMIUM QUEST, b g Forzando—Sabonis (USA) **Mr J. C. Parsons**
35 RIBBLE ASSEMBLY, ch g Presidium—Spring Sparkle **Swan At Whalley Partnership**
36 RIBBLE PRINCESS, b f Selkirk (USA)—Ricochet Romance (USA) **Swan At Whalley Partnership**
37 ROBERT THE BRUCE, ch g Distinct Native—Kawarau Queen **Mr G. G. Fraser**
38 SCOTCH TIME, ch g Timeless Times (USA)—Scotch Imp **Mr James Ritchie**

TWO-YEAR-OLDS

39 ANNANDALE, ch f 28/2 Balla Cove—Gruinard Bay (Doyoun) **Mr C. H. McGhie**
40 BLUE LINE ANGEL, b g 23/5 Cyrano De Bergerac—Northern Line (Camden Town) **Mr Peter Tingey**
41 FOREIGN EDITOR, ch c 8/3 Magic Ring (IRE)—True Precision (Presidium) **Mr C. Procter**
42 B f 2/4 Sabrehill (USA)—Lambast (Relkino) **Mr R. A. Fahey**
43 MASTER TIROL (IRE), ro c 7/4 Tirol—Inisfail (Persian Bold) **Mr D. A. Read & Mr R. A. Fahey**
44 MORNING GLORY, b f 23/3 Polar Falcon (USA)—Round Midnight (Star Appeal) **Mr A. Brown & Mr R. A. Fahey**
45 Ch f 12/2 Forzando—My Precious Daisy (Sharpo) **Mr R. A. Fahey**
46 Ch c 12/5 Bay Tern (USA)—Naughty Nessie (Celtic Cone) **Mr T. Dyer**
47 PANDJOJOE (IRE), b c 10/4 Archway (IRE)—Vital Princess (Prince Sabo) **Mr J. Dixon**
48 PRINCELY DREAM (IRE), b c 13/4 Night Shift (USA)—Princess of Zurich (IRE) (Law Society (USA)) **Mr I. Bray**
49 B c 4/4 Petorius—Rhinestall (Glenstal (USA))
50 Ch f 13/5 Pursuit of Love—Settlement (USA) (Irish River (FR)) **Mr H. Hurst**
51 Ch c 13/5 Marju (IRE)—Sronica (Midsummer Night II) **Mr J. C. Parsons**
52 TASKONE, ch f 19/5 Be My Chief (USA)—Good As Gold (IRE) (Glint of Gold) **Task Ltd**
53 Br g 8/4 Local Suitor (USA)—Waltz On Air (Doc Marten) **Mr H. Proud & Mr R. A. Fahey**

Other Owners: Miss M. J. Barber, Capt H. H. Barlow, Mrs A. C. Brown, Mrs K. Campbell, Mr T. B. Carr, Mr P. S. Dhariwal, Mrs L. M. Fahey, Mr J. J. Gilmartin, Mrs J. Jackson, Mr K. W. Linfoot, Mr P. Macklam, Mr F. O'Donoghue, Mr H. Proud, Mrs Rosie Richer, Mrs E. Stoker, Mr Peter Teasdale.

Jockey (Flat): A Culhane.

Jockey (NH): L Wyer.

Apprentices: David Egan, R Winston.

Amateur: Mr Lee Russell.

210 MR C. W. FAIRHURST, Middleham

Postal: **Glasgow House, Middleham, Leyburn, North Yorkshire, DL8 4QG.**
Phone: **(01969) 622039 FAX (01969) 622039 MOBILE (0589) 410840**

1 **BARRESBO,** 4, b g Barrys Gamble—Bo' Babbity **North Cheshire Trading & Storage Ltd**
2 **DAMARA,** 4, b f Damister (USA)—Gem-May **Richmond & Paxton**
3 **GILSAN STAR,** 5, b m High Kicker (USA)—Gilsan Grey **Mr G. W. Fenwick**
4 **HIGHFIELD FIZZ,** 6, b m Efisio—Jendor **Mrs P. J. Taylor-Garthwaite**
5 **RAMSEY HOPE,** 5, b h Timeless Times (USA)—Marfen **Mr C. D. Barber-Lomax**
6 **RUDE AWAKENING,** 4, b g Rudimentary (USA)—Final Call **Mr W. Hill**
7 **WARRLIN,** 4, b g Warrshan (USA)—Lahin **Glasgow House Racing Syndicate**

THREE-YEAR-OLDS

8 **PRIX STAR,** ch g Superpower—Celestine **Mr M. J. Grace & Mrs D. Grace**
9 **ROYAL VELVET,** b f Perpendicular—Stellaris **The Brearley & McLain Partnership**
10 **TIMED RIGHT,** ch g Gildoran—Responder **Twinacre Nurseries Ltd**
11 **WINSOME GEORGE,** b g Marju (IRE)—June Moon (IRE) **Mr C. D. Barber-Lomax**

TWO-YEAR-OLDS

12 **ABBAJABBA,** b c 25/3 Barrys Gamble—Bo' Babbity (Strong Gale) **North Cheshire Trading & Storage Ltd**
13 **HAUGHTY LADY,** b f 18/3 Sizzling Melody—
Juris Prudence (IRE) (Law Society (USA)) **Mrs P. J. Dobson & Mr W. J. Dobson**
14 **LADY ANNABEL,** b f 10/2 Alhijaz—Anna Rella (IRE) (Danehill (USA)) **Mr M. Handy**
15 **RINGSIDE JACK,** b c 29/3 Batshoof—Celestine (Skyliner) **M. J. G. Partnership**
16 **SUPER STRIDES,** b f 31/3 Superpower—Go Tally-Ho (Gorytus (USA)) **Mr W. Hill**

Other Owners: Mr J. G. Brearley, Mr D. Bunn, Mr Brian Cann, Daleside Nurseries Ltd, Mr C. W. Fairhurst, Mr D. M. Gardner, Mr David Hawes, Mr George H. Leggott, Mr Iain McLain, Mr Keith Middleton, Mrs V. Paxton, Mrs P. Richmond, Mrs Eve Sweetman.

Jockey (NH): J Callaghan (10-0, w.a.).

Lady Rider: Mrs S Bosley (8-7, w.a.).

211 MR J. R. FANSHAWE, Newmarket

Postal: **Pegasus Stables, Snailwell Road, Newmarket, Suffolk, CB8 7DJ.**
Phone: **(01638) 664525 FAX (01638) 664523**

1 **ALMOND ROCK,** 6, b g Soviet Star (USA)—Banket **C.I.T. Racing Ltd**
2 **ARCTIC OWL,** 4, b g Most Welcome—Short Rations **The Owl Society**
3 **BARFORD SOVEREIGN,** 6, b m Unfuwain (USA)—Barford Lady **Barford Bloodstock**
4 **BE VALIANT,** 4, gr g Petong—Fetlar **Dr Catherine Wills**
5 **BOLD GAIT,** 7, ch g Persian Bold—Miller's Gait **Mrs I. Phillips**
6 **CRAIGIEVAR,** 4, b c Mujadil (USA)—Sweet Home **Mr D. I. Russell**
7 **ETERNITY,** 4, b f Suave Dancer (USA)—Chellita **Dr Catherine Wills**
8 **FAMILY MAN,** 5, ch g Indian Ridge—Auntie Gladys **Family Man Partnership**
9 **FIRED EARTH (IRE),** 10, b g Soughaan (USA)—Terracotta (GER) **Mrs J. Fanshawe**
10 **FLOATING CHARGE,** 4, b g Sharpo—Poyle Fizz **The Leonard Curtis Partnership**
11 **GREEN POWER,** 4, b g Green Desert (USA)—Shaft of Sunlight **Dexa'tex Limited**
12 **HARMONY HALL,** 4, ch g Music Boy—Fleeting Affair **Mr Raymond Tooth**
13 **HEAVENLY RAY (USA),** 4, ch f Rahy (USA)—Highest Truth (USA) **Cheveley Park Stud**

MR J. R. FANSHAWE—continued

14 INVERMARK, 4, b g Machiavellian (USA)—Applecross **Sir David Wills**
15 ONEFORTHEDITCH (USA), 5, gr m With Approval (CAN)—Wee Dram (USA) **Oneforthe ditch Partnership**
16 SMUGGLING, 7, b g Slip Anchor—Strigida **Mr George Taiano**
17 THE TOISEACH (IRE), 7, b g Phardante (FR)—Owens Toi **T. & J. Vestey**
18 TRAVELMATE, 4, b g Persian Bold—Ustka **Barford Bloodstock II**
19 WARNINGFORD, 4, b c Warning—Barford Lady **Barford Bloodstock**

THREE-YEAR-OLDS

20 AMBITIOUS, b f Ardkinglass—Ayodhya (IRE) **Dr Catherine Wills**
21 BEHOLD, ch f Prince Sabo—Be My Lass (IRE) **Cheveley Park Stud**
22 BON SIZZLE, b c Sizzling Melody—Bonne de Berry **Mrs Mary Watt**
23 BRYONY BRIND (IRE), ch f Kris—Bayadere (USA) **Mrs Denis Haynes**
24 EMERALD HEIGHTS, b c Shirley Heights—Lady In Green **Arlington Bloodstock**
25 GATECRASHER, b c Suave Dancer (USA)—Benazir **Mr J. M. Greetham**
26 GLOWING, b f Chilibang—Juliet Bravo **Mrs Jan Hopper**
27 ISLAND RACE, b f Common Grounds—Lake Isle (IRE) **Car Colston Hall Stud**
28 KELD (IRE), b f Lion Cavern (USA)—Society Ball **C.I.T. Racing Ltd**
29 LONACH, gr g Warning—Snowing (USA) **Mrs David Russell**
30 LONDON BE GOOD (USA), ch f Storm Bird (CAN)—Dream Touch (USA) **Mr Joseph Allen**
31 MOLE CREEK, gr f Unfuwain (USA)—Nicholas Grey **Lord Vestey**
32 ONE OF THE FAMILY, b f Alzao (USA)—Someone Special **Helena Springfield Ltd**
33 PERSIANO, ch c Efisio—Persiandale **Miss A. Church**
34 PUBLISHER (USA), b c Kris S (USA)—Andover Way (USA) **Mr Joseph Allen**
35 ROBSART (IRE), b f Robellino (USA)—Sharp Girl (FR) **Lord Vestey**
36 RUBY AFFAIR (IRE), b br f Night Shift (USA)—Tiavanita (USA) **Arlington Bloodstock**
37 SKERRAY, b f Soviet Star (USA)—Reuval **Dr Catherine Wills**
38 TATTINGER, b f Prince Sabo—Tight **Mrs E. Fanshawe**
39 TINA HEIGHTS, b f Shirley Heights—Catina **Mrs James McAllister**
40 B f Soviet Star (USA)—Wantage Park **T. & J. Vestey**

TWO-YEAR-OLDS

41 B f 23/3 Red Ransom (USA)—Andover Way (USA) (His Majesty (USA)) **Mr Joseph Allen**
42 ASTRONOMER, br c 26/4 Ardkinglass—Ayodhya (IRE) (Astronef) **Dr Catherine Wills**
43 BOHEMIA, b f 27/3 Polish Precedent—Horseshoe Reef (Mill Reef (USA)) **Lord Halifax**
44 EILEAN SHONA, b f 17/2 Suave Dancer (USA)—Moidart (Electric) **Dr Catherine Wills**
45 ENLIGHTEN, br c 7/5 Zafonic (USA)—Seek The Pearl **Cheveley Park Stud**
46 ENTWINE, b f Primo Dominie—Splice (Sharpo) **Cheveley Park Stud**
47 EPERNAY, b f 6/3 Lion Cavern (USA)—Decant (Rousillon (USA)) **Cheveley Park Stud**
48 Gr f 25/4 Persian Bold—Faakirah (Dragonara Palace) **Mr W. M. McGregor**
49 FAIR PHOEBE, b f 23/4 Shareef Dancer (USA)—Couleur de Rose (Kalaglow) **Mr J. M. Greetham**
50 Ch f 25/3 Wolfhound (USA)—Fairy Fortune (Rainbow Quest (USA)) **T. & J. Vestey**
51 FIRST FANTASY, b f 4/3 Be My Chief (USA)—Dreams (Rainbow Quest (USA)) **Aylesfield Farms Ltd**
52 Ch c 19/4 Keen—Juliet Bravo (Glow (USA)) **Mrs Jan Hopper**
53 MISTER BLOMBERG (IRE), b c 15/5 Distinctly North—Ruby Realm (Valiyar) **Comet Group PLC**
54 PISTACHIO, gr c 14/2 Unblest—Cashew (Sharrood (USA)) **Lord Vestey**
55 B f 20/4 Shirley Heights—Rose Alto (Adonijah) **T. & J. Vestey**
56 SERPENTINE, ch c 6/3 Grand Lodge (USA)—Lake Pleasant (IRE) (Elegant Air) **Lord Vestey**
57 B c 29/2 Broad Brush (USA)—Sharp Dance (USA) (Dancing Czar (USA)) **Mr Joseph Allen**
58 B f 17/1 Chief's Crown (USA)—Wild Vintage (USA) (Alysheba (USA)) **Car Colston Hall Stud**

Other Owners: Mrs D. Brudenell-Bruce, Miss Bridget Cleverly, Mrs L. Field, Mr R. Field, Mrs J. N. Forman Hardy, Mr N. J. Forman Hardy, Mr K. D. Goodman, Mr J. V. Gredley, Mrs Christine Handscome, Mr T. J. Handscome, Mrs Noreen Hodgson, Mr Peter Hodgson, Dr D. Morgan, Mr Philip Newton, Mr S. D. Swaden, Mr P. Taiano, Miss Helena Weinfeld, Mr Mark Weinfeld.

212 MR P. FARRELL, Taunton

Postal: **Yarde House, Burnworthy Stables, Burnworthy Manor, Churchstanton, Taunton, Somerset, TA3 7DR.**

Phone: **(01823) 601111 MOBILE (0421) 623044 FAX (01823) 601112**

1 6, B g Celio Rufo—Bailieboro **Mr Brian Rowe**
2 **BRAVO STAR (USA),** 13, b g The Minstrel (CAN)—Stellarette (CAN) **Wyvern Racing**
3 **EIRAWE (FR),** 5, b g Lashkari—Ederiya (FR) **Mrs Suzanne Fletcher**
4 **FURRY DAY,** 12, b g Furry Glen—Bright Company **Mr Brian Rowe**
5 **MISTER MAYBE,** 7, b g Damister (USA)—Maybe So **The Mayday Partnership**
6 **MORECEVA (IRE),** 8, ch g Salluceva—Moredee **Mrs Peter Denning**
7 **PABLO'S JET,** 5, b g Pablond—Cilerna Jet **Wyvern Racing**
8 **PRESKIDUL (IRE),** 4, b f Silver Kite (USA)—Dul Dul (USA) **B. R. G. Racers**
9 **SPLASHED,** 4, gr f Absalom—Riverain **Mrs Roz Virasinghe**
10 **UP THE TEMPO (IRE),** 9, ch m Orchestra—Bailieboro **Mr Brian Rowe**
11 8, B m Derring Rose—Wayward Kate **Mrs Suzanne Fletcher**
12 **WINNING TOWN,** 5, ch g Jester—Lurex Girl **B. R. G. Racers**

Other Owners: Mrs L. H. Farrell, Mr Paddy Farrell, Mr David House, Mrs J. House, Ms A. Penn, Mrs J. M. Rees, Mr Matthew Thole, Mrs Jennifer Whitefield.

213 MR P. S. FELGATE, Melton Mowbray

Postal: **Grimston Stud, Grimston, Melton Mowbray, Leicestershire, LE14 3BZ.**

Phone: **(01664) 812019**

1 **BRISTOL GOLD,** 5, b g Golden Heights—The Bristol Flyer **Mr E. Rollinson**
2 **CINNAMON STICK (IRE),** 5, ch g Don't Forget Me—Gothic Lady **Mr P. S. Felgate & Miss K. Scott**
3 **DOUBLE SPLENDOUR (IRE),** 8, b g Double Schwartz—Princess Pamela **Yorkshire Racing Club Owners Group 1990**
4 **GAY BREEZE,** 5, b g Dominion—Judy's Dowry **Mr P. S. Felgate**
5 **GODMERSHAM PARK,** 6, b g Warrshan (USA)—Brown Velvet **Mr H. R. Hornby**
6 **HIGHBORN (IRE),** 9, b br g Double Schwartz—High State **Yorkshire Racing Club Owners Group 1990**
7 **HIGHSPEED (IRE),** 6, ch g Double Schwartz—High State **Mr David R. Wright**
8 **IMP EXPRESS (IRE),** 5, b g Mac's Imp (USA)—Fair Chance **Mr P. S. Felgate**
9 **NO QUARTER GIVEN,** 13, b g Don—Maggie Mine **Mr P. S. Felgate**
10 **ROYAL SOUTH (IRE),** 5, b h Common Grounds—Arkadina's Million **Yorkshire Racing Club Owners Group 1990**
11 **SEANCHAI (IRE),** 5, b g Treasure Kay—Blue Infanta **Mr A. E. Blee**
12 **SOTONIAN (HOL),** 5, br g Statoblest—Visage **Mr Tim Dean**

TWO-YEAR-OLDS

13 **NOW IS THE HOUR,** ch g 26/3 Timeless Times (USA)—Macs Maharanee (Indian King (USA)) **Mr J. Martin**
14 **WOODCUT (IRE),** ch g 21/4 Woods of Windsor (USA—Lady of State (IRE) (Petong) **Yorkshire Racing Club Owners Group 1990**

Other Owners: Mrs N. Gidleywright, Tilstone Lodge Stud, Mrs V. McGeough, Mr Jim Spooner, Mr Dave Walton.

Jockey (Flat): G Hind.

Apprentice: P McCabe.

Lady Riders: Mrs Margaret Crawford, Mrs J Saunders.

214 MR M. J. FETHERSTON-GODLEY, East Ilsley

Postal: **Kennet House Stables, Broad Street, East Ilsley, Newbury, Berkshire, RG20 7LW.**
Phone: **(01635) 281 250 FAX (01635) 281 250 MOBILE (0370) 410983**

1 **BLUSHING GRENADIER (IRE),** 6, ch g Salt Dome (USA)—La Duse **Mr M. J. Fetherston-Godley**
2 **SHANGHAI LIL,** 6, b m Petong—Toccata (USA) **Mr M. J. Fetherston-Godley**
3 **WELCOME HEIGHTS,** 4, b g Most Welcome—Mount Ida (USA) **The Most Welcome Partnership**

THREE-YEAR-OLDS

4 **GUNBOAT DIPLOMACY,** b br c Mtoto—Pepper Star (IRE) **Abigail Limited**
5 **HIGHLAND LORD,** b c Primo Dominie—Tarvie **Mr P. Fetherston-Godley**
6 **PIPPAS PRIDE (IRE),** ch c Pips Pride—Al Shany **Mrs Anthony Vickers**
7 **RUDI KNIGHT,** ch g Rudimentary (USA)—Fleeting Affair **Mr Derek D. Clee**

TWO-YEAR-OLDS

8 Ch f 5/3 Persian Bold—Cindy's Baby (Bairn (USA)) **The Kennet House Partnership**
9 **CORNDAVON (USA),** b f 7/2 Sheikh Albadou—Ferber's Folliers (USA) (Saratoga Six (USA)) **Mrs Julia Scott**
10 B f 17/2 Petardia—Cree's Figurine (Creetown) **Mr Craig Pearman & Partners**
11 B c 26/3 Fayruz—Divine Apsara (Godswalk (USA)) **The Kennet House Partnership**
12 B f 27/3 College Chapel—Meadow Grass (IRE) (Thatching) **The Kennet House Partnership**
13 Gr c 24/2 Petong—Miss Taleca (Pharly (FR)) **The Kennet House Partnership**
14 Ch f 15/5 Forest Wind (USA)—My Destiny (USA) (L'Enjoleur (CAN)) **Mr M. J. Fetherston-Godley**
15 B c 26/3 Second Set (IRE)—Prime Interest (IRE) (Kings Lake (USA)) **The Kennet House Partnership**
16 Ch f 13/3 First Trump—Tarvie (Swing Easy (USA)) **Mr P. Fetherson-Godley**

Other Owners: R. Baly, Mrs R. Buck, Miss N. Carroll, Ms P. J. Carter, Paul Catlin, Mr G. W. Cleaver, Mrs Jean P. Clee, C. Dickens, Mr Andrew Gairdner, M. Kerr-Dineen, P. Phillips, Mr A. Scott, Anne Lady Scott, D. I. Scott, Richard Shepherd, Mr W. L. Smith, Mr David Todd, R. Whitehead.

215 MR D. J. S. FFRENCH DAVIS, Upper Lambourn

Postal: **The Top Yard, Saxon House Stables, Upper Lambourn, Hungerford, Berkshire, RG17 8QH.**
Phone: **OFFICE (01488) 71208 FAX 71214 MOBILE (0831) 118764 HOME (01488) 72342**

1 **AFTER HOURS,** 4, b f Polar Falcon (USA)—Tarasova (USA) **After Hours Partnership**
2 **DANCES WITH HOOVES,** 6, b h Dancing Dissident (USA)—Princesse Legere (USA) **Mr V. Squeglia**
3 **HAWAII STORM (FR),** 10, b g Plugged Nickle (USA)—Slewvindaloo (USA) **Mr C. C. Capel**
4 **IMPULSIF (USA),** 4, ch c Diesis—High Sevens **Mrs Mary Moloney**
5 **MAENAD,** 7, gr m Sharrood (USA)—Now In Session (USA) **Exors of the late Mrs C. A. Robinson**

THREE-YEAR-OLDS

6 **BALLYKISSANN,** ch g Ballacashtal (CAN)—Mybella Ann **Mr Paul De Weck**
7 **COMEOUTOFTHEFOG (IRE),** b g Mujadil (USA)—Local Belle **Mrs Mary Moloney**
8 **MOUNTAIN MAGIC,** b f Magic Ring (IRE)—Nevis **Hargood Limited**

TWO-YEAR-OLDS

9 B c 4/4 Ardkinglass—Hotaria (Sizzling Melody)
10 B f 15/3 Shalford (IRE)—Kept In Style (Castle Keep)
11 **LITTLE CHAPEL,** b f 6/2 College Chapel—Istaraka (IRE) (Darshaan) **North Social Racing Club**
12 **PETAK (IRE),** b f 26/2 Petardia—Wicken Wonder (IRE) (Distant Relative) **Miss H. Senn**
13 B f 3/4 Be My Chief (USA)—Travel Mystery (Godswalk (USA))
14 **WHITS END,** b g 4/5 Whittingham (IRE)—Mybella Ann (Anfield) **Mr Paul De Weck**

Other Owners: Mr Brook Alder, Mrs P. Bedford, Mr A. W. Creighton, Mr D. J. Ffrench Davis, Mrs Susan J. Harraway, Mr G. J. Head, Mr A. W. Jones, Mrs Patrick McCarthy, Mr M. Moloney, Mr P. W. Murphy, Mr S. P. Putnam, Miss M. K. Rossbrook, Ms Renee J. Wheeler.

Jockeys (Flat): T Quinn (w.a.), J Weaver (w.a.).

Jockey (NH): S McNeill.

Conditional: J Magee.

Lady Rider: Miss E Folkes.

216 MR J. G. FITZGERALD, Malton

Postal: **Norton Grange, Norton, Malton, North Yorkshire, YO17 9EA.**
Phone: **MALTON (01653) 692718 FAX MALTON (01653) 600214**

1 **ALZULU (IRE),** 7, b g Alzao (USA)—Congress Lady **Mr D. Buckle**
2 4, Ch g Henbit (USA)—Arachova **Mrs J. G. FitzGerald**
3 **BALLAD MINSTREL (IRE),** 6, gr g Ballad Rock—Sashi Woo **Mr G. E. Shouler**
4 **CAMPASPE,** 6, b m Dominion—Lady River (FR) **Mr J. G. FitzGerald**
5 **CHINA KING (IRE),** 7, b g King's Ride—China Jill **Mr & Mrs Raymond Anderson Green**
6 **CLAVERHOUSE (IRE),** 9, b g Buckskin (FR)—Baby Isle **Mrs Peter Corbett**
7 **CORAL ISLAND,** 4, b g Charmer—Misowni **Mr F. Patten**
8 **DUAL IMAGE,** 11, b g Alzao (USA)—Odette Odile **Datum Building Supplies Limited**
9 **HOUSE CAPTAIN,** 9, br g Oats—Super Princess **Mr & Mrs G. Middlebrook**
10 **JACK ROBBO (IRE),** 6, br g Montelimar (USA)—Derring Lass **H R Atkinson & Co Ltd**
11 **JAVA RED (IRE),** 6, b g Red Sunset—Coffee Bean **Mr Michael Ng**
12 **JUSTIN MAC (IRE),** 7, br g Satco (FR)—Quantas **Mr & Mrs Raymond Anderson Green**
13 4, B g Damister (USA)—Key To The River (USA)
14 4, B g Komaite (USA)—Khadine **Mrs J. G. FitzGerald**
15 **KILDRUMMY CASTLE,** 6, b g Komaite (USA)—Khadine **The Kildrummy Partnership**
16 **LARKSHILL (IRE),** 7, b g Phardante (FR)—Fairy Hollow **Larkshill Engineering Ltd**
17 **MANDICAT (IRE),** 8, b g Mandalus—Apicat **Mrs G. M. Sturges**
18 **MARY FARRELL,** 4, ch f Henbit (USA)—Don't Be Late **Datum Building Supplies Limited**
19 **MEADOW HYMN (IRE),** 7, b g Hymns On High—Nevada Run **Mrs M. Nowell**
20 **NATIVE MISSION,** 11, ch g Be My Native (USA)—Sister Ida **Mr G. E. Shouler**
21 **NIJMEGAN,** 10, b g Niniski (USA)—Petty Purse **Mr W. Hancock**
22 **NO GIMMICKS (IRE),** 6, b g Lord Americo—Catspaw **John Smith's Ltd**
23 **ORANGE IMP,** 5, ch m Kind of Hush—Sip of Orange **Mrs R. A. G. Haggie**
24 **OVERSMAN,** 5, b g Keen—Jamaican Punch (IRE) **Marquesa de Moratalla**
25 **PHAR SMOOTHER (IRE),** 6, br g Phardante (FR)—Loughaderra (IRE) **John Smith's Ltd**
26 **QUANGO,** 6, b g Charmer—Quaranta **Mr L. Milligan**
27 **QUEENSWAY (IRE),** 6, b g Pennine Walk—Polaregina (FR) **Mr G. E. Shouler**
28 5, Ch g Phardante (FR)—Relkal
29 **RUSTIC AIR,** 11, ch g Crash Course—Country Tune **Mrs G. M. Sturges**
30 **SIX CLERKS (IRE),** 5, b g Shadeed (USA)—Skidmore Girl (USA) **Marquesa de Moratalla**
31 **SOUNDS FYNE (IRE),** 9, b g Good Thyne (USA)—Sounds Familiar **Sir Peter O'Sullevan**
32 5, B g Celio Rufo—Star of Monroe
33 **SYMONDS INN,** 4, ch c In The Wings—Shining Eyes (USA) **Marquesa de Moratalla**
34 **WESTERLY (IRE),** 7, b br g Strong Gale—Moonlight Romance **Mrs G. M. Sturges**
35 **WESTERTON (IRE),** 5, b g Glacial Storm (USA)—Killiney Rose **Mr J. S. Murdoch**
36 **WHIP HAND (IRE),** 7, br g Bob Back (USA)—Praise The Lord **Lady Lloyd Webber**
37 **WRANGEL (FR),** 4, ch g Tropular—Swedish Princess **Lady Lloyd Webber**

THREE-YEAR-OLDS

38 **ANOTHER WYN-BANK,** b f Presidium—Wyn-Bank **Mrs Shirley France**
39 B g Rock Hopper—Early Gales
40 B f Caerleon (USA)—Famosa **Mr & Mrs G. Middlebrook**
41 **FINAL CLAIM,** b g Absalom—For Gold **Mr J. G. FitzGerald**
42 **FOX'S LIBEL (IRE),** b c Priolo (USA)—Las Bela **Marquesa de Moratalla**
43 **JAYESS ELLE,** b f Sabrehill (USA)—Sorayah **John Smith's Ltd**
44 **MOONLIGHT FLIT,** b f Presidium—Moonwalker **Mr N. H. T. Wrigley**
45 **MUNDO RARO,** b c Zafonic (USA)—Star Spectacle **Marquesa de Moratalla**
46 **NAJJAR (USA),** gr c El Prado (IRE)—With Strawberries (USA) **John Smith's Ltd**
47 **PRIOLETTE (IRE),** b f Priolo (USA)—Celestial Path **Mr J. Dick**
48 **REAP REWARDS,** gr c Barrys Gamble—Bo' Babbity **Marquesa de Moratalla**
49 **REQUESTOR,** br c Distinctly North (USA)—Bebe Altesse (GER) **Marquesa de Moratalla**
50 **SMOOTH PRINCESS (IRE),** gr f Roi Danzig (USA)—Sashi Woo **Mr J. G. FitzGerald**

TWO-YEAR-OLDS

51 B f 23/3 Local Suitor (USA)—Heart Broken (Bustino)
52 **IRRITANCY,** b c 22/3 Tenby—Anonymous (Night Shift (USA)) **Marquesa de Moratalla**

MR J. G. FITZGERALD—continued

53 B f 3/4 Local Suitor (USA)—La Ciotat (IRE) (Gallic League) **Mr W. Steel**
54 B c 3/3 Slip Anchor—Lady Norcliffe (USA) (Norcliffe (USA)) **Marquesa de Moratalla**
55 MINI LODGE (IRE), ch c 28/1 Grand Lodge (USA)—Mirea (USA) (The Minstrel (CAN)) **Marquesa de Moratalla**
56 MINUIT NOIR (IRE), b c 22/1 Machiavellian (USA)—
Misbegotten (IRE) (Baillamont (USA)) **Marquesa de Moratalla**
57 B c 28/4 Mac's Imp (USA)—Nationalartgallery (IRE) (Tate Gallery (USA))
58 NEVER CAN TELL, ch c 25/1 Emarati (USA)—Farmer's Pet (Sharrood (USA)) **Mr J. Dick**
59 Ch g 29/4 Rainbows For Life—Rasmara (Kalaglow)
60 Ch c 17/2 Primo Dominie—Starr Danias (USA) (Sensitive Prince (USA)) **Marquesa de Moratalla**
61 B c 26/4 Rambo Dancer (CAN)—Steelock (Lochnager)
62 TIME TO WIN, b c 29/4 Timeless Times (USA)—Wyn-Bank (Green God) **Mr Micheal Ng**
63 B c 5/5 Second Set (IRE)—Tradescantia (GER) (Windwurf (GER))
64 B c 10/5 Presidium—Vanishing Trick (Silly Season) **Mr N. H. T. Wrigley**
65 VERACINI, ch f 20/2 Whittingham (IRE)—Zubeyde (IRE) (Bluebird (USA)) **Mr Norman Jackson**
66 B c 3/3 Lugana Beach—White Flash (Sure Blade (USA))

Other Owners: Mrs Anthony Chisenhale-Marsh, Mr Peter Corbett, Mr W. Fenwicke-Clennell, Mrs Santa Fitch-Peyton, Mrs Anita Green, Mrs C. C. Longstaff, Mrs C. L. Parkinson, Major P. H. K. Steveney.

Jockey (Flat): K Fallon (w.a.).

Jockey (NH): P Carberry.

Conditional: F Leahy (9-7).

217 MR F. FLOOD, Grangecon

Postal: **Ballynure, Grangecon, Co. Wicklow, Ireland.**
Phone: **(045) 403136**

1 ANNADOT (IRE), 8, gr m Roselier (FR)—Galliano **Mr R. Kelly**
2 ARBITRAGE MAN (IRE), 6, b g Mandalus—Snow Rose **Mr G. E. Copeland**
3 ASHNIADER (IRE), 4, br f Buckskin (FR)—Galliano **Mr J. Doyle**
4 4, Br g Mandalus—Buck A Tina **Mr M. Walsh**
5 CARRICKDALE BOY (IRE), 7, ch g Buckskin (FR)—Eurolink Sea Baby **Mr P. McParland**
6 CIARA'S PRINCE (IRE), 7, br g Good Thyne (USA)—Sparkling Opera **Mr R. McConn**
7 CNOCAN GLAS (IRE), 6, br g The Bart (USA)—Bunny Brown **Mr W. Cohen**
8 DAMODAR, 9, br g Damister (USA)—Obertura (USA) **Caldbeck Ltd**
9 DRAMATIC DAME (IRE), 5, b m Bukcksin (FR)—Lovely Stranger **Mr R. M. McGearty**
10 EDWARD STREET (IRE), 5, gr m Rhoman Rule (USA)—Sabatta VII **Austin Stacks Syndicate**
11 FINCHPALM (IRE), 8, b g Mandalus—Milan Pride **Mr A. Doyle**
12 HERSILIA (IRE), 7, br m Mandalus—Milan Pride **Mr F. J. O'Reilly**
13 JOES DANTE (IRE), 7, b g Phardante (FR)—Ollatrim Lady **Exors of the late J. Hassett**
14 JOHN JO JOHN (IRE), 6, b g Supreme Leader—Whats The Rush **Mr J. Kearns**
15 KILDARE CHILLER (IRE), 4, ch g Shahrastani (USA)—Ballycuirke **Mrs H. PcParland**
16 KNOCKAULIN, 7, ch g Buckley—Two Shares **Mrs K. L. Urquhart**
17 KNOCKDOO (IRE), 5, ch g Be My Native (USA)—Ashken **Mr H. McParland**
18 LADY OF GRANGE (IRE), 6, b m Phardante—Just Dont Know **Mr R. McConn**
19 LILS LUCK (IRE), 6, ch g Buckskin (FR)—Lils Girl **Mrs D. Reddan**
20 LUCKY CON (IRE), 6, ch m John French—Pearl Reef **Mrs A. Golkel**
21 MOUNTAIN FLIGHT (IRE), 4, b f Prince Rupert (FR)—Mountain Home **Mr P. McNamara**
22 MR MARK (IRE), 6, br g Buckskin (FR)—Lady Karola **Mr R. McConn**
23 NATIVE RUN (IRE), 6, ch g Be My Native (USA)—Sea Guest **Kerry G. A. A.**
24 OUR MEG (IRE), 5, ch m Commanche Run—Guayana (GER) **Mrs D. Reddan**
25 POINT HIRE (IRE), 5, b g Electric—Galliano **Mr L. Kelly**
26 POKONO TRAIL (IRE), 9, ch g Aristocracy—Frank's Choice **Mr R. Murphy**
27 POULGILLIE (IRE), 8, ch g Torus—Carrigart **Mr J. Flood**

MR F. FLOOD—continued

28 **PRE ORDAINED (IRE),** 6, br g Iron Duke (FR)—Miyana (FR) **Dr J. B. O'Connor**
29 **ROSSBEIGH CREEK,** 11, ch g Crash Course—Smile Away **Mr H. Ferguson**
30 **SAINTE JOCELYNE (FR),** 5, br m Roscoe Blake—In Memoriam (IRE) **Mr L. Burke**
31 6, B g Mandalus—Snow Rose **Mr G. E. Copeland**
32 **SPEED BOARD,** 6, b g Waajib—Pitty Pal (USA) **The Web R. C.**
33 **STRONG HICKS (IRE),** 10, ch g Seymour Hicks (FR)—Deep Foliage **Garristown R. C.**
34 5, Ch m The Bart (USA)—Super Sayanarra **Mr J. O'Brien**
35 **THE UILLEANN PIPER (IRE),** 5, br g Lord Americo—Call Me Honey **Mr C. Falls**
36 **TOMMY PAUD (IRE),** 9, br g Asir—Clonroche Floods **Fun Rangers Syndicate**
37 **TOWNLEYHALL (IRE),** 6, ch g Phardante (FR)—Arctic Tartan **Mr G. Kingston**
38 **TO YOUR HONOUR (IRE),** 5, b g Buckskin (FR)—Clasical Influence **Mr H. Dunne**
39 **UNA'S CHOICE (IRE),** 10, ch g Beau Charmeur (FR)—Laurabeg **Mr D. Cahill**
40 **UNFORGOTTEN STAR (IRE),** 5, br g Don't Forget Me—Murroe Star **Mr James Horgan**

Other Owners: Mrs T. Flood, Mr S. Lawlor, Mr D. B. Sanger.

Jockey (NH): F J Flood (9-9).

Apprentice: E Stack (8-0).

Conditional: L Fleming (9-0).

Amateurs: Mr J P Byrne (9-0), Mr B Dolan (9-10).

218 MR R. M. FLOWER, Jevington

Postal: **Devonshire House, Jevington, East Sussex, BN26 5QB.**
Phone: **(01323) 488771 488522 FAX (01323) 488099**

1 **BILLADDIE,** 5, b g Touch of Grey—Young Lady **Mr Richard J. Gurr**
2 **BURNING FLAME,** 5, b m Robellino (USA)—No Islands **Mr Jan Rieck**
3 **COLOUR COUNSELLOR,** 5, gr g Touch of Grey—Bourton Downs **Mrs G. M. Temmerman**
4 **EXECUTIVE OFFICER,** 5, b g Be My Chief (USA)—Caro's Niece (USA) **Mr B. C. Isitt**
5 **FORT KNOX (IRE),** 7, b g Treasure Kay—Single Viking **Mrs D. M. Hickling**
6 **HALF TONE,** 6, gr h Touch of Grey—Demilinga **Mrs G. M. Temmerman**
7 **MASTER BOBBY,** 4, b g Touch of Grey—Young Lady **Mr Richard J. Gurr**
8 **MULTI FRANCHISE,** 5, ch g Gabitat—Gabibti (IRE) **Markirk Racing**
9 **ROYAL LEGEND,** 6, b g Fairy King (USA)—Legend of Arabia **Mr Jan Rieck**
10 **SEJAAL (IRE),** 6, b g Persian Heights—Cremets **Mr Julian P. Snow**
11 **SHARP IMP,** 8, b g Sharpo—Implore **Mrs G. M. Temmerman**
12 **SOOJAMA (IRE),** 8, b g Mansooj—Pyjama Game **Mr M. G. Rogers**
13 **ZAMALEK (USA),** 6, b g Northern Baby (CAN)—Chellingoua (USA) **Miss Victoria Markowiak**
14 **ZORRO,** 4, gr g Touch of Grey—Snow Huntress **Mr G. George**

THREE-YEAR-OLDS

15 **BIT OF A LAD,** gr c Touch of Grey—Lingfield Lass (USA) **Mrs H. Kelleher**
16 Gr f Touch of Grey—Northwold Star (USA) **Mr R. M. Flower**
17 **ROGER ROSS,** b c Touch of Grey—Foggy Dew **Mr H. Lawrence**
18 **SAMMY'S SHUFFLE,** b c Touch of Grey—Cabinet Shuffle **Mrs G. M. Temmerman**
19 Ch g Most Welcome—Silent Loch **Mr R. M. Flower**
20 **SILK PRINCESS,** gr f Touch of Grey—Young Lady **Mr Richard J. Gurr**
21 **ZARIFA,** gr f Touch of Grey—Snow Huntress **Rare Stakes Partnership**

TWO-YEAR-OLDS

22 B c 30/4 Shareef Dancer (USA)—Snow Huntress (Shirley Heights) **Mr R. M. Flower**
23 B c 7/3 Touch Of Grey—Young Lady (Young Generation) **Mr Richard J. Gurr**

Other Owners: Mr K. J. Bowen, Mr Simon Campbell Boreham, Mr Robert N. Dawnbarn, Mr James Evans, Mrs M. V. Hutchinson, Mr P. C. Wager.

219 MR A. L. FORBES, Uttoxeter

Postal: **Hill House Farm, Poppits Lane, Stramshall, Uttoxeter, Staffordshire, ST14 5EX.**
Phone: **(01889) 568145**

1 **BARNABE LAD**, 8, ch g Rabdan—Literary Lady **Mr Tony Forbes**
2 **SALTIS (IRE)**, 6, ch g Salt Dome (USA)—Mrs Tittlemouse **Mr Tony Forbes**

Jockey (NH): Gary Lyons (10-2, w.a.).

220 MR D. M. FORSTER, Darlington

Postal: **Todd Fall Farm, Heighington, Darlington, Co. Durham, DL2 2XG.**
Phone: **(01388) 772441**

1 5, B g Strong Gale—Astral River **Mr D. M. Forster**
2 **CHARMING MOSS (IRE)**, 7, ch g Le Moss—Our Charm **Mr D. M. Forster**
3 4, Gr f Strong Gale—Colleen Glen **Mr D. M. Forster**
4 **GUS BERRY (IRE)**, 5, ch g Montelimar (USA)—Eurolink Sea Baby **Mr D. M. Forster**
5 **KIT SMARTIE (IRE)**, 6, b g Be My Native (USA)—Smart Cookie **Mr D. M. Forster**
6 **SHINING FOUNTAIN (IRE)**, 9, b g Royal Fountain—Ever Shining **Mr D. M. Forster**
7 **THE MIGHTY PARROT (IRE)**, 6, b br g Strong Gale—Nancy's Sister **Mr D. M. Forster**

Jockey (NH): B Storey (10-0).

221 CAPT T. A. FORSTER, Ludlow

Postal: **Downton Hall Stables, Ludlow, Shropshire, SY8 3DX.**
Phone: **(01584) 873688 OFFICE (01584) 874034 HOME (01584) 873525 FAX**

1 **ALBERMARLE (IRE)**, 7, ch g Phardante (FR)—Clarahill **Mr Robert Ogden**
2 **BAGALINO (USA)**, 8, ch g Lyphard (USA)—Bag of Tunes (USA) **Mrs G. J. Phillips**
3 **BLUE WAVE (IRE)**, 6, b g Project Manager—Over The Seas **Anne Duchess of Westminster**
4 **BOLD DOLPHIN**, 8, b g Idiot's Delight—Brave Remark **Mr S. Preston**
5 **BOLD STATEMENT**, 6, ch g Kris—Bold Fantasy **Dowager Lady Cadogan**
6 **BUCK JAKES (USA)**, 10, gr g Turkoman (USA)—Acharmer (USA) **Arcadia Stable**
7 **CHEERFUL ASPECT (IRE)**, 5, b g Cadeaux Genereux—Strike Home **Lady Pilkington**
8 **COOL SPRING (IRE)**, 6, b m Zaffaran (USA)—Daisy Spring **Mr Stephen Lambert**
9 **DOROBO (NZ)**, 10, b g Ivory Hunter (USA)—Mountain Hi (NZ) **Lady Lewinton**
10 **DUBLIN FLYER**, 12, b g Rymer—Dublin Express **Mr J. B. Sumner**
11 **EDMOND (FR)**, 6, b g Video Rock (FR)—Galia III (FR) **Lady Knutsford**
12 **FINAL HAND**, 6, ch g Nearly A Hand—Freuchie **Lord Cadogan**
13 **GALES OF LAUGHTER**, 9, br g Strong Gale—Joca **Lord Leverhulme**
14 **GENERAL WOLFE**, 9, ch g Rolfe (USA)—Pillbox **Winning Line Racing Limited**
15 **GEORGE BULL**, 6, b g Petoski—Firgrove **The Hopeful Partnership**
16 **GIVE ME SPACE**, 5, b m Lochnager—Bit of Space **Mr R. S. Preece & Mr W. C. Davies**
17 **GRAND GOUSIER (FR)**, 4, b g Perrault—Tartifume II (FR) **Mrs G. Leigh**
18 **HAPPY HUSSAR (IRE)**, 5, b g Balinger—Merry Mirth **Mr B. Gibson**
19 **HIGH IN THE CLOUDS (IRE)**, 6, b g Scenic—Miracle Drug (USA) **Mrs Douglas Graham & Mrs John Nesbitt**
20 **HOLLOA AWAY (IRE)**, 6, b g Red Sunset—Lili Bengam **Mr W. F. Reid**
21 **LADY HIGH SHERIFF (IRE)**, 8, b m Lancastrian—Pitalina **Mrs Michael Ward-Thomas**
22 **LANCASTRIAN JET (IRE)**, 7, b g Lancastrian—Kilmurray Jet **Mrs A. E. Heber-Percy**
23 **LANNKARAN (IRE)**, 5, b g Shardari—Lankarana **Mr Simon Sainsbury**
24 **LORD YORK (IRE)**, 6, b br g Strong Gale—Bunkilla **Mr Robert Ogden**
25 **LUCY GLITTERS**, 6, b m Ardross—Henry's True Love **Mr T. F. F. Nixon**
26 **MAJESTIC SOUND (IRE)**, 7, ch g Executive Perk—Little Flame **Lord Leverhulme**
27 **MAJORS LEGACY (IRE)**, 9, b br g Roselier (FR)—Sugarstown **Mrs G. Leigh**

CAPT T. A. FORSTER—continued

28 **MARLBOROUGH (IRE),** 6, br g Strong Gale—Wrekenogan **Mr Robert Ogden**
29 **MARTHA'S SON,** 11, b g Idiot's Delight—Lady Martha **Mr M. Ward-Thomas**
30 **MERLIN'S LAD,** 9, br g Rymer—Seal Marine **Mr H. Messer-Bennetts**
31 **MR MAGNETIC (IRE),** 7, b g Point North—Miss Ironside **Mrs A. L. Wood**
32 **MUSIC THERAPY (IRE),** 8, b g Roselier (FR)—Suny Salome **Mr R. Van Gelder**
33 **POUCHER (IRE),** 8, b g Dock Leaf—Jacqueline Grey **Mrs A. L. Wood**
34 **QUEEN'S RIDE,** 5, gr m King's Ride—Ramelton **Mr M. Ward Thomas**
35 **RECTORY GARDEN (IRE),** 9, b g The Parson—Peace Run **Lord Cadogan**
36 **RING FOR ROSIE,** 7, br m Derrylin—Clear The Course **Mr T. F. F. Nixon**
37 **RIVER MANDATE,** 11, b br g Mandalus—Liffey's Choice **Anne Duchess of Westminster**
38 **RUBY ROSA,** 6, b m Idiot's Delight—Whey **Mr P. J. Hartigan**
39 **SAIL BY THE STARS,** 9, b m Celtic Cone—Henry's True Love **Mr T. F. F. Nixon**
40 **SILVER STANDARD,** 8, b g Jupiter Island—One Half Silver (CAN) **Mr G. W. Lugg**
41 **STAR TRAVELLER,** 7, b g Norwick (USA)—Star of Parnassus **Mrs J.G. Griffith & Mrs Richard Strachan**
42 **STEP ON EYRE (IRE),** 8, b g Step Together (USA)—Jane Eyre **Anne Duchess of Westminster**
43 **SURSUM CORDA,** 7, b g Idiot's Delight—Childhay **Mr M. Ward-Thomas**
44 **TAILORMADE,** 6, ch g Broadsword (USA)—Blades **Mrs A. Reid Scott**
45 **TEINEIN (FR),** 7, b g Dancehall (USA)—Sweet Titania (FR) **Mr Simon Sainsbury**
46 **THE CLARSACH,** 6, ch m Nicholas Bill—Celtic Slave **Mr B. G. Hellyer**
47 **THE PARSONS FOX,** 6, ch g Scallywag—Arctic Mission **Mrs Y. V. Shrubb**
48 **VALIANT (IRE),** 7, b g Salluceva—Torreya **Mrs H. M. Jones**
49 **WANDERING LIGHT (IRE),** 9, b g Royal Fountain—Pleaseme **Anne Duchess of Westminster**
50 **YOUNG SPARTACUS,** 5, b g Teenoso (USA)—Celtic Slave **Mr B. G. Hellyer**

Other Owners: Miss J. I. Abel-Smith, Lady Barlow, Mrs A. Bell-Irving, Mr A. Brewster, Mrs Thomas Buckley, Mrs Ian Cameron, Mrs A. S. Clowes, Mr P. S. Cochran, Mr G. Copley, Mr G. Davison, Mr J. H. Day, Countess Of Eglinton & Winton, Capt. T. A. Forster, Gamston Equine, Mr P. J. Hartigan, Mrs M. D. Hartley, Mrs Diana Hellyer, Mrs W. Hern, Mrs Philip Humphries-Guff, Mr F. N. Iglehart, Mrs David Lewis, Captain T. H. Luckock, Mrs G. W. Lugg, Mrs M. Macaulay, Mrs S. E. Morgan, Mrs I. Norman, Sir Philip Payne-Gallwey B.T., Mrs D. Pridden, Mr Denys Simmons, Major P. G. Verdin, Mrs M. Wiggin.

Jockey (NH): S Wynne (10-0).

Conditional: J Mogford (9-7).

222 MR A. G. FOSTER, Lambourn

Postal: **Bourne House Racing Ltd, Bourne House Stables, Oxford Street, Lambourn, Newbury, RG16 7XS.**
Phone: **TELEPHONE (01488) 73765 MOBILE (0378) 854693 FAX (01635) 253303**

1 **GABLES GIRL,** 7, b m Sousa—Maideed **Mr P. J. Cave**
2 **KEDGE ANCHOR MAN,** 7, b g Bustino—Jenny Mere **Mr Anthony M. Green**
3 **KINGS ANGEL (IRE),** 7, b g King's Ride—Lisbawn Lady **Chance Partnership**
4 **KNOCKBRIT LADY (IRE),** 7, b m Creative Plan (USA)—Rose of Cloneen **Mr D. H. Armitage**
5 **LILLI CLAIRE,** 5, ch m Beveled—Lillicara **Mr Carl Leafe**
6 **MASTER GOODENOUGH (IRE),** 7, ch g Torus—Hilary's Pet **The Moonrakers Partnership**
7 **SALTY GIRL (IRE),** 5, b m Scenic—Sodium's Niece **Miss Juliet E. Reed**
8 **SIMPLE LOGIC,** 4, ch f Aragon—Dancing Chimes **Miss Juliet E. Reed**
9 **SOUND APPEAL,** 4, b f Robellino (USA)—Son Et Lumiere **R. W. and J. R. Fidler**
10 **SWEET BETTSIE,** 4, b f Presidium—Sweet And Sure **Jadecliff Ltd**
11 **TENNESSEE KING (IRE),** 8, gr g Tender King—Monrovia (FR) **Mr D. H. Armitage**
12 **VIBURNUM,** 4, b f Old Vic—Burning Desire

THREE-YEAR-OLDS

13 **BURNING LOVE,** b f Forzando—Latest Flame **Miss Juliet E. Reed**
14 **CHLO-JO,** b f Belmez (USA)—Shaadin (USA) **Mr D. H. Armitage**

MR A. G. FOSTER—continued

15 PRINCESS LONDIS, ch f Interrex (CAN)—Princess Lucianne **Mr C. Richards**
16 REGAL ARROW, br g Superlative—A Little Hot **Regal (Witney) Ltd**
17 SWINGTIME, ch f Beveled (USA)—Superfina (USA) **Mr J. Cook**
18 WEDDING BAND, b f Saddlers' Hall (IRE)—Priceless Bond (USA) **Mr Phil Costello**

TWO-YEAR-OLDS

19 Ch c 25/3 Beveled (USA)—Rekindled Flame (Kings Lake)
20 TSUNAMI, b f 20/4 Beveled (USA)—Alvecote Lady (Touching Wood (USA))

Other Owners: Mr A. Bingley, Mr P. Carter, Mr P. Colley, Mr John Costello, Mr M. C. Cutler, Mrs J. R. Fidler, Mr R. W. Fidler, Mr K. D. Fletcher, Mr D. Goodenough, Mr B. Hiskey, Peter Colley Racing, Mr Andrew Shenston, Skyline Racing Ltd, Mr Colin Smith, Mr George W. Smith, S. W. Transport (Swindon) Ltd, The Woodhaven Stud.

Jockey (Flat): T Sprake (w.a.).

Jockey (NH): B Clifford (10-0).

Conditional: David Creech (10-0).

223 MR J. R. H. FOWLER, Summerhill

Postal: **Rahinston, Summerhill, Co. Meath, Ireland.**
Phone: **(0405) 57014 FAX (0405) 57537**

1 ALMOST REGAL (IRE), 5, b m Jurado (USA)—What A Duchess **Mrs B. J. Fowler**
2 ALTNABROCKY LAD (IRE), 5, b g Be My Native (USA)—Run For Becki **B. D. Smith**
3 BRASS BAND (IRE), 7, br m Orchestra—Credit Card **Mrs B. J. Fowler**
4 COOL IT (IRE), 8, b g Maculata—Cool As Ice **Lady J. Fowler**
5 DEIREFORE (IRE), 8, b m Callernish—Lovely Pine **C. Hanley**
6 FINE DE CLAIRE, 5, b m Teenoso (USA)—Princess Florine (USA) **S. P. Tindall**
7 GRANDA TWO DOGS (IRE), 6, b m Strong Gale—Glory Hunter **C. H. Foley**
8 HAPPY HANGOVER (IRE), 8, ch g Sheer Grit—Rising Dipper **Miss D. Duggan**
9 HI KNIGHT (IRE), 8, b g King's Ride—Le Nuit **M. D. McGrath**
10 5, B g King's Ride—Inagh's Image **S. P. Tindall**
11 JAPAMA (IRE), 7, ch g Nashamaa—Le Nuit **M. D. McGrath**
12 JURESSE (IRE), 5, b m Jurado (USA)—Last Princess **W. Flood**
13 KAMBEAU BAY (IRE), 6, b g Kambalda—Clara Girl **Crosswind Syndicate II**
14 LET US PRAY (IRE), 8, b m The Parson—Loge **B. D. Smith**
15 MAID FOR DANCING (IRE), 9, b m Crash Course—La Flamenca **Mrs B. J. Fowler**
16 5, B m Brush Aside (USA)—Missing Note **J. Liggett**
17 NUISA (IRE), 5, br m Satco (FR)—Le Nuit **M. D. McGrath**
18 OPERA HAT (IRE), 10, br m Strong Gale—Tops O'Crush **Mrs T. K. Cooper**
19 PRIDE OF TIPPERARY (IRE), 7, b m Supreme Leader—Moneyforusall **V. Loughnane**
20 REGAL KNIGHT (IRE), 6, b g King's Ride—Le Nuit **M. D. McGrath**
21 SHINING WILLOW, 8, b m Strong Gale—Lady Buck **S. P. Tindall**
22 STAG PARTY (IRE), 5, b g Buckskin (FR)—Men's Fun **E. Galvin**
23 STRONG RUN (IRE), 5, br g Strong Gale—Arctic Run **M. D. McGrath**
24 UNDER CURRENT (IRE), 5, b g Brush Aside (USA)—Rough Tide **Mrs C. A. Waters**
25 WILD VENTURE (IRE), 10, ch m Le Bavard (FR)—Fast Adventure **Lady J. Fowler**

Jockey (NH): C O'Dwyer (10-0, w.a.),

Conditional: R Burke (9-7).

Amateur: Mr R Geraghty (9-2).

Lady Rider: Miss W Fox (9-7).

224 MR J. C. FOX, Marlborough

Postal: **Highlands Farm Stables, Herridge, Collingbourne Ducis, Marlborough, Wiltshire, SN8 3EG.**
Phone: **(01264) 850218 MOBILE (0402) 880010**

1 **ANNS GIRL,** 5, br m Newski (USA)—Nearly Married **Mrs J. A. Cleary**
2 **CROAGH PATRICK,** 6, b g Faustus (USA)—Pink Pumpkin **Mrs J. A. Cleary**
3 **FALCON RIDGE,** 4, ch g Seven Hearts—Glen Kella Manx **Mrs Anne Coughlan**
4 **HURRICANE HONEY,** 6, ch m Seven Hearts—Movie Market **Miss Sarah-Jane Durman**
5 **INTERMAGIC,** 8, ch g Interrex (CAN)—Tina's Magic **Will To Win Partnership**
6 **KILMEENA LADY,** 4, b f Inca Chief (USA)—Kilmeena Glen **Mrs J. A. Cleary**
7 **LEOPARD PRINCESS,** 5, ch m Seven Hearts—Movie Market **Mr M. Hoaren**
8 **LIZIUM,** 6, b m Ilium—Lizaway **Mr A. W. Weyman**
9 **WENTOBUYABAY,** 5, ch m Henbit (USA)—Deep Ocean **Mrs J. A. Cleary**
10 **WILD NETTLE,** 4, ch f Beveled (USA)—Pink Pumpkin **Mrs J. A. Cleary**

Other Owners: Mr B. D. Alford, Mr A. Gadd, Ms Miriam Mulcahy.

Jockey (NH): S Fox (10-0).

Amateur: Sarah-Jane Durman (8-7).

225 MR R. G. FROST, Buckfastleigh

Postal: **Hawson Stables, Buckfastleigh, Devon, TQ11 0HP.**
Phone: **(01364) 642267 FAX (01364) 643182**

1 **ABAVARD (IRE),** 9, ch g Le Bavard (FR)—Heroanda **Mr D. G. Henderson**
2 **ACCESS ADVENTURER (IRE),** 7, b g Al Hareb (USA)—Olwyn **Miss Elaine D. Williams**
3 **BIDEFORD BAY,** 5, b g Landyap (USA)—Vitapep **Mrs C. Loze**
4 **BISHOPS CASTLE (IRE),** 10, ch g Carlingford Castle—Dancing Princess **Mr Philip Rogers**
5 **BIT OF A TOUCH,** 12, b br g Touching Wood (USA)—Edelliette (FR) **Mr Philip Rogers**
6 **BLUE BLAZER,** 8, b g Bluebird (USA)—View **Mr James Laws**
7 **BRIGHT ECLIPSE (USA),** 5, br g Sunny's Halo (CAN)—Miss Lantana (USA) **Mrs G. Goddard**
8 **CELTIC LAND,** 5, b m Landyap (USA)—Celtic Mist **Mrs J. R. Bastard**
9 **DARK MAURADER,** 5, br g Landyap (USA)—Cawstons Prejudice **Mr J. E. Blake**
10 **DEFENDTHEREALM,** 7, br g Derring Rose—Armagnac Princess **Mr George Standing**
11 **DERBY GILCHREEST (IRE),** 6, b g Strong Gale—Tacova **Mr John Clohisey**
12 **DESERT GREEN (FR),** 9, b g Green Desert (USA)—Green Leaf (USA) **Mr Terry Sanders**
13 **HOLDIMCLOSE,** 8, b g Teamwork—Holdmetight **Mrs C. Loze**
14 **HOLD YOUR RANKS,** 11, b g Ranksborough—Holdmetight **Mrs C. Loze**
15 **IMPETUOUS LADY (USA),** 5, b m Imp Society (USA)—Urakawa (USA) **Mr S. J. Hubbard**
16 **IT'S NOT MY FAULT (IRE),** 10, b g Red Sunset—Glas Y Dorlan **Mr P. D. Jones**
17 **IT'SNOTSIMPLE (IRE),** 6, b m Homo Sapien—Perpetue **Mrs G. A. Robarts**
18 **JONJAS CHUDLEIGH,** 11, ch g Aragon—Lizabeth Chudleigh **Mr R. G. Frost**
19 **KARICLEIGH BOY,** 10, ch g Nearly A Hand—Duvessa **Mr Philip Rogers**
20 **LAND OF MYTH,** 5, b m Landyap (USA)—Travel Myth **Mr P. A. Tylor**
21 **LAYITONTHELINE (IRE),** 9, b g Record Run—Ballyworkan Lass **Mr Philip Rogers**
22 **MISS NIGHT OWL,** 7, ch m Bold Owl—Regal Flame **Mr P. A. Tylor**
23 **MOOR DUTCH,** 7, br g Dutch Treat—Moorland Nell **Mr R. G. Frost**
24 **MR COTTON SOCKS,** 10, ch g Sunyboy—Here We Go **Agriwise**
25 **MR JOLIBEAR,** 6, br g Joligeneration—Moorland Nell **Mr R. G. Frost**
26 **MR PERFECTA,** 5, br g Landyap (USA)—Dona Perfecta **Mr B. P. Burnard**
27 **MR PLAYFULL,** 8, br g Teamwork—Blue Nursery **Mr J. E. Blake**
28 **MYSTIC HILL,** 7, b g Shirley Heights—Nuryana **Mr Jack Joseph**
29 **OBELOS (USA),** 7, ch g Diesis—Fair Sousanne **Mr Terry Sanders**
30 **ON MY TOES,** 7, b m Le Solaret (FR)—On Her Toes **Mr G. Chambers**
31 **PENNYMOOR PRINCE,** 9, b g Pragmatic—Warham Fantasy **Mr N. W. Lake**
32 **POOH STICK,** 8, b g Teamwork—Moorland Nell **Mr R. G. Frost**

MR R. G. FROST—continued

33 **SARASOTA STORM,** 6, b g Petoski—Challanging **Mrs G. A. Robarts**
34 **SOUTHERN RIDGE,** 7, b g Indian Ridge—Southern Sky **Mr N. J. Holdsworth**
35 **SPORTING CHANCE,** 6, ch g Ikdam—Tumbling Ego **Mr H. S. Channon**
36 **STEER POINT,** 7, b g Shaab—Chronicle Lady **Mrs J. R. Bastard**
37 **THE SWAN,** 5, ch m Old Vic—El Vino **Mr Terry Sanders**
38 **VEILED DANCER (IRE),** 5, b m Shareef Dancer (USA)—Fatal Distraction **Mr N. J. Holdsworth**

Other Owners: A.E.C. Electric Fencing Ltd (Hotline), Mrs B. M. Blake, Mrs L. W. Carlson, Mr G. G. A. Gregson, Mrs M. Haimes, Mrs J. Hubbard, Mr A. Loze, Mrs J. McCormack, Mr J. H. Nesbit, Mrs C. Pope, Mr P. D. Rogers, Mr Brian Seaward, Mrs Peggy Smallbone, Mrs Richard Stanley, Mr P. Tosh, Mr M. Venner, Mrs R. Welch, Miss Denise A. Williams.

Jockey (NH): J Frost (10-4).

Conditional: T O'Connor (9-7).

Amateur: Mr A Holdsworth (9-7).

226 MR D. R. GANDOLFO, Wantage

Postal: **Downs Stables, Manor Road, Wantage, Oxfordshire, OX12 8NF.**
Phone: **TEL (01235) 763242 FAX (01235) 764149**

1 **AMBER SPARK (IRE),** 9, ch g The Parson—La Dragoniere **Mr R. E. Brinkworth**
2 **AROUND THE GALE (IRE),** 7, b g Strong Gale—Ring Road **Mr T. J. Whitley**
3 **BALANAK (USA),** 7, b g Shahrastani (USA)—Banque Privee (USA) **Mr W. H. Dore**
4 **BIETSCHHORN BARD,** 8, b g Rymer—Chalet Waldegg **Mr A. W. F. Clapperton**
5 **BLEUSTONE GAMBLER,** 5, ch g Henbit (USA)—H And K Gambler **Mrs C. Skipworth**
6 **BREITHORN PIPER,** 5, b g Scottish Reel—Miss Wrensborough **Mr A. W. F. Clapperton**
7 **BRIGHT NOVEMBER,** 7, b g Niniski (USA)—Brigata **Mr D. R. Gandolfo**
8 **BROGEEN LADY (IRE),** 8, b br m Phardante (FR)—Dewy Clover **Starlight Racing**
9 **CAROLE'S CRUSADER,** 7, ch m Faustus (USA)—Loveville (USA) **Mrs C. Skipworth**
10 **COME ON PENNY,** 7, b m Rakaposhi King—Gokatiego **Mr A. E. Frost**
11 **CRAZY CRUSADER,** 6, gr m Gildoran—Lizzie The Twig **Mr A. E. Frost**
12 **DANTES CAVALIER (IRE),** 8, b g Phardante (FR)—Ring Road **Mr W. H. Dore**
13 **DEYMIAR (IRE),** 6, b g Doyoun—Dedra (FR) **Mr T. J. Whitley**
14 **GALES CAVALIER (IRE),** 10, b g Strong Gale—Ring Road **Starlight Racing**
15 **GARRYLOUGH (IRE),** 9, ch m Monksfield—Clonyn **Mr T. J. Whitley**
16 **GARRYNISK (IRE),** 8, b g Meneval (USA)—Autumn Bounty **Mr T. J. Whitley**
17 **GENERAL TONIC,** 11, ch g Callernish—Jude Lacy **Starlight Racing**
18 **HARDY WEATHER (IRE),** 9, br g Strong Gale—Hardy Colleen **Starlight Racing**
19 **KHALIDI (IRE),** 9, b g Shernazar—Khaiyla **Mr T. J. Whitley**
20 **LADY CASH (IRE),** 5, ch m Sula Bula—Anyone's Fancy **Mr W. H. Dore**
21 **LANDA'S COUNSEL,** 7, b m Pragmatic—Landa's Tipple **Mr James Blackshaw**
22 5, Gr g Scallywag—Le Madame **Mr R. E. Brinkworth**
23 **LOGICAL STEP (IRE),** 8, b g Pragmatic—Stepalong **Mr A. E. Smith**
24 **LOTSCHBERG EXPRESS,** 6, ch m Rymer—Chalet Waldegg **Mr A. W. F. Clapperton**
25 **LUKE WARM,** 8, ch g Nearly A Hand—Hot 'n Scopey **Mr Nigel Stafford**
26 **MOORLANDMERRYMAKER (IRE),** 8, ch m Sheer Grit—Double Cousin **Mrs M. A. Simpson**
27 **MOUSE BIRD (IRE),** 8, b g Glow (USA)—Irish Bird (USA) **Mr Osbert Pierce**
28 **NEW LEAF (IRE),** 6, b g Brush Aside (USA)—Page of Gold **Mrs D. J. Hues**
29 **RIVER LEVEN,** 9, b g Nearly A Hand—Ana Mendoza **Mr D. R. Gandolfo**
30 **ROYAL EVENT,** 7, ch g Rakaposhi King—Upham Reunion **Mr T. J. Whitley**
31 **RYTHM ROCK (IRE),** 9, ch g Swan's Rock—Pryhill **Mr Peter Radcliffe**
32 **SELATAN (IRE),** 6, ch g Shernazar—Seleret (USA) **Starlight Racing**

MR D. R. GANDOLFO—continued

33 **SEYMOURSWIFT**, 8, b m Seymour Hicks (FR)—Swift Sentence **Starlight Racing**
34 **SPRIG MUSLIN**, 6, br m Ra Nova—Wood Heath **Mr D. R. Gandolfo**
35 **TEMPERED STEEL**, 7, ch g Broadsword (USA)—Solatia **Mr G. C. Hartigan**
36 **THE BARGEMAN (NZ)**, 10, b g Lanfranco—Stevadette (NZ) **Mrs Monica Caine**
37 **TIMID JAR (IRE)**, 5, b g Doyoun—Timissara (USA) **Mr T. J. Whitley**
38 **TONKA**, 6, b g Mazilier (USA)—Royal Meeting **Mrs C. A. Webster**
39 **TRYING AGAIN**, 10, b g Northern Game—Wood Heath **Mr W. H. Dore**
40 **WELSH SILK**, 6, b g Weld—Purple Silk **Mrs D. E. Blackshaw**
41 **ZAYNAL (IRE)**, 5, b g Shernazar—Zariya (USA) **Mr T. J. Whitley**

Other Owners: Mr P. F. Boggis, Mr H. Candler, Mr J. P. Carrington, Mr M. F. Cartwright, Mr J. Deeley, Mr S. R. Edwards, Mr George Ennor, Mr Stephen Freud, Miss E. A. Gandolfo, Mrs S. J. Giles, Mrs J. A. Hatcher, Dr G. M. Thelwall Jones, Mrs D. Lousada, Mr G. Macdonald, Mr C. Mackenzie, Mrs David Moon, Mr David O. Moon, Mr G. C. Reilly, Mr Patrick Renahan, Mrs J. M. Snell, Mr K. Styles, Mr Jez Webb.

Jockey (NH): R Dunwoody (w.a.).

Apprentice: Sophie Mitchell (8-5).

Conditional: Sophie Mitchell (9-7).

227 MR N. A. GASELEE, Upper Lambourn

Postal: **Saxon Cottage, Upper Lambourn, Hungerford, Berkshire, RG17 8QN.**

Phone: **LAMBOURN (01488) 71503 FAX (01488) 71585**

1 **ACT OF FAITH**, 8, b g Oats—Ruby's Vision **Mrs R. W. S. Baker**
2 **BAVARD DIEU (IRE)**, 10, ch g Le Bavard (FR)—Graham Dieu **Saguaro Stables**
3 **BERKELEY FRONTIER (IRE)**, 5, ch g Imperial Frontier (USA)—Harristown Rose **Mr R. E. Morris-Adams**
4 **BROOK BEE**, 6, br g Meadowbrook—Brown Bee III **The Saxon Partnership**
5 **BUCKTAIL (NZ)**, 6, b g Conquistarose (USA)—Sans Tache (NZ) **Mr Simon Harrap**
6 **CHRISTMAS GORSE**, 12, b g Celtic Cone—Spin Again **Mr D. R. Stoddart**
7 **CINNAMON CLUB**, 6, b m Derrylin—Cinnamon Run **Club Ten**
8 **CLEAR SKIES (IRE)**, 5, b g Phardante (FR)—Fighting Doleila **Mrs R. W. S. Baker**
9 **DESTINY CALLS**, 8, ch g Lord Avie (USA)—Miss Renege (USA) **Mrs R. W. S. Baker**
10 **FLIPPANCE**, 8, b g Relkino—Stey Brae **Simon Harrap Partnership**
11 **KENTISH BARD (IRE)**, 6, b g Phardante (FR)—Polly Ringling **Miss Caroline Perkins**
12 **LEAP FROG**, 7, ch g Gildoran—Caer-Gai **Mr Robert Cooper**
13 **MAN OF THE MOMENT (IRE)**, 5, b g Mandalus—Approach The Dawn (IRE) **Mr Robert Cooper**
14 **MILLERSFORD**, 7, b g Meadowbrook—My Seer **Mrs Derek Fletcher**
15 **MR CELEBRATION**, 7, br g Hubbly Bubbly (USA)—Westerlands Finis **Mr M. A. Boddington**
16 **MR INVADER**, 11, br g Le Moss—Bruna Magli **Mr M. A. Boddington**
17 **MYSTIC ISLE (IRE)**, 8, b g Callernish—Sleemana **Mrs J. K. Newton**
18 **MY WIZARD**, 11, b g Ile de Bourbon (USA)—Palace Tor **Mrs Angela Brodie**
19 **NO JOKER (IRE)**, 10, b g Jester—Canta Lair **The Jesters**
20 **PURPLE ACE (IRE)**, 6, b g King's Ride—The Best I Can **Sir Christopher Walford**
21 **QUICK SUCCESSION (IRE)**, 5, b g King's Ride—Tony's Lass **Mrs R. W. S. Baker**
22 **SWAZI PRINCESS (IRE)**, 5, b m Brush Aside (USA)—Earn More **Mrs P. T. Orchart**
23 **TOMS LEGACY**, 8, b g Relkino—Talahache Bridge **The Betts Partnership**

Other Owners: Mr Peter Bedford, Mr Keith Benham, Mrs T. C. Betts, Mr A. N. Brooke Rankin, Lieutenant Colonel F. Burnaby Atkins, Mr Tom J. Finley, Miss F. M. Fletcher, Mr G. R. Furse, Exors Of The Late Mrs P. Furse, Mr N. A. Gaselee, Mr John K. Goodman, Major D. Grehan, Mrs B. P. Hall, Brigadier R. W. S. Hall, Don Hookins, Peter Hornby, Mrs J. B. Houlder, Mr Vik Jackson, Mr R. J. Jenks, Mr C. Johns, Mrs Barbara Keene, Mr Robert H. Kieckhefer, Mr Kemper Marley, Mrs Patrick McCarthy, Mrs G. N. Morris-Adams, Mrs Cynthia Mortimer, Mr M. A. F. Newton, Mrs Gordon Pepper, Mrs Tim Perkins, Mr C. H. Petre, Mrs R. Sutcliffe-Smith, Mr Dwight Sutherland, Mr Frank Vessels Iii, Lord Wakeham, Mrs Fulke Walwyn, Mr Peter Walwyn, Brigadier Alan Wheatcroft.

Jockey (NH): C Llewellyn (10-0, w.a.).

228 MR B. GEE, Worksop

Postal: **Highfield Bungalow, Greenway, Carlton-In-Lindrick, Worksop, Nottinghamshire, S81 9EX.**
Phone: **HOME/FAX (01909) 730306 YARD (01909) 731101 OFFICE/FAX (0114) 2483631**

1 **PLATINUM EMPIRE (USA),** 8, b g Nijinsky (CAN)—Kelley's Day (USA) **Mr Brian Gee**

Amateur: Mr Patrick Gee (10-0).

229 MR T. R. GEORGE, Slad

Postal: **Springbank, Slad, Stroud, Gloucestershire, GL6 7QE.**
Phone: **(01452) 814267 FAX (01452) 814246 MOBILE 0860 487426 CAR 0850 793483**

1 **ACT IN TIME (IRE),** 6, b g Actinium (FR)—Anvil Chorus **Mrs G. C. McFerran**
2 **BOB DEVANI,** 12, b g Mandalus—Russell's Touch **Mr Timothy N. Chick**
3 **CARLINGFORD GALE (IRE),** 7, ch m Carlingford Castle—Vul Gale **Mrs Alison Gamble**
4 **COUNTRYMAN (IRE),** 7, ch g Henbit (USA)—Riancoir Alainn **Mr Howard Parker**
5 **CRICKETING,** 6, b g Northern Game—Mandikova **The Wishful Thinkers**
6 **ELBURG (IRE),** 8, b g Ela-Mana-Mou—Iosifa **Mrs Alison Gamble**
7 **FLOOSY,** 7, b m Governor General—Hill Vixen **Mrs J. P. Bissill**
8 **FRANK KNOWS,** 8, ch g Chilibang—Chance Match **Mrs Caroline Peacock**
9 **FRASER CAREY (IRE),** 6, b g Try My Best (USA)—Moortown Lady **Mrs James Burridge**
10 **GENERAL PONGO,** 9, b g Kaytu—Charlotte Mary **Mrs J. K. Powell**
11 **HAVANA RESERVE,** 4, ch g Cigar—Shy Hiker **Mr Giles Gleadell**
12 **HIGH MOOD,** 8, b g Jalmood (USA)—Copt Hall Princess **Mrs E. Farquhar**
13 **HOLY WANDERER (USA),** 9, b g Vaguely Noble—Bronzed Goddess (USA) **Mr Gain Partnership**
14 **HOPPERDANTE (IRE),** 8, ch m Phardante (FR)—Cherry Lodge **Mr M. J. Perkins**
15 **LANLAU (IRE),** 9, b g Lancastrian—Laurenca **Mr T. R. George**
16 **L'IDEFIX (IRE),** 6, ch g Buckskin (FR)—Katty London **Mrs Patrick Stevenson**
17 **LOTTERY TICKET (IRE),** 9, b g The Parson—Beauty Run **Mr Alan Parker**
18 **LYPHARD'S FABLE (USA),** 7, b g Al Nasr (FR)—Affirmative Fable (USA) **Mrs G. C. McFerran**
19 **MACHALINI,** 5, b g Machiavellian (USA)—Trescalini (IRE) **Mrs Alison Gamble**
20 **MASTER LORIEN,** 6, b g Rymer—Lorien Lady **Silkword Racing Partnership**
21 4, Ch g Beveled (USA)—Racemosa **Mr T. R. George**
22 **RIOT LEADER (IRE),** 8, b g Supreme Leader—Calamity Jane **The Riot Partnership**
23 **THE H'PENNY MARVEL (IRE),** 8, b g Sexton Blake—Casacello **Mr T. R. George**
24 **THE PICKLED DUKE (IRE),** 6, gr g Duky—Silk Empress **Mr Timothy N. Chick**

Other Owners: Mr M. G. Corkill, Mr B. Corrigan, Mr M. Davies-Jones, Mrs Wendy Dice, Mr Brian Eacott, Mr John French, Capt. J. A. George, Mrs S. P. George, Miss Margaret Hankin, Mr S. Khalique, Mr Mark Opperman, Mr E. W. Pegna, Mr D. O. Pickering, Mr Tom Regis, Mr Peter Slip, Mr C. N. Walker, Mr Peter Williams, Mr Ken Yeates.

Jockey (NH): R Johnson (10-0, w.a.).

Conditional: D J Kavanagh (9-9).

230 MR RICHARD GIBSON, Chantilly

Postal: **Carrefour De Mont Po, Route Nationale 16, 60260 Lamorlaye, France.**
Phone: **03 44 57 53 00 FAX 03 44 58 15 48**

1 **ARMY OF ONE,** 4, ch c Machiavellian—La Dama Bonita **D. Li**
2 **FIFTY FOUR (USA),** 6, ch h Lyphard—Partygoer **I. Veltman**
3 **LYSANDROS (IRE),** 4, b c Lycius—Trojan Relation **Leprechaun Leisure**
4 **POLAR STAR (FR),** 5, gr g Highest Honor—Arctic River **Alex Lai**
5 **SINECURE (USA),** 4, b c Explodent—Caithness **E. Soderberg**

MR RICHARD GIBSON—continued

THREE-YEAR-OLDS

6 **ALLESSANDRA M (USA),** b f Fortunate Prospect—Italian Beauty **J. de Marcilly**
7 **BELZARINA,** b f Soviet Star—Zabelina **D. Li**
8 **EASTERN LILY (FR),** b f Caerwent—East Riding **D. Li**
9 **GEORDIE (FR),** b c Cardoun—Spinethique **Mme D'Assignies**
10 **KADLASS (FR),** b c Kadounor—Brave Lass **J. D. Martin**
11 **MICHEL DE MOEURS (FR),** b c Northern Fashion—See That Girl **D. Al Johar**
12 **POLARIA (FR),** ch f Hero's Honor—Riviere Polaire **Skymarc Farm**
13 **RED EMPIRE (FR),** b c Subotica—Canesara **O. Lecerf**
14 **ROUDAH (IRE),** b f Suave Dancer—Chicobin **D. Al Johar**
15 **SIR ERIC (FR),** b c Highest Honor—Numidie **E. Sodenberg**
16 **SUAVUS (FR),** b c Suave Dancer—Schezerade **N. Berry**
17 **TERRITORY (IRE),** b c Common Grounds—Chouette **Mme A. Gibson**

TWO-YEAR-OLDS

18 **ARACHNE (FR),** b f 10/4 Shining Steel—Arandora Star (Sagace) **Leprechaun Leisure**
19 Ch f 21/3 Zayyani—Bitter Sweet (Esprit du Nord) **Haras du Logis**
20 **BRAHMANE (FR),** b f 8/3 Diamond Prospect—Babylove Princess (Romildo) **Mme M. A. Bergracht**
21 **EKO NORMANDY (IRE),** ch f 9/2 Midyan—Storm Riding (Storm Bird) **S. Thynell**
22 **ELEUTHERA (FR),** b f 6/4 Mujtahid—Far But Near (Far North) **Horseworld Corporation**
23 Gr f 3/2 Kendor—Helen's Gamble (Spectacular Bid) **S. Thynell**
24 **IVRESSE BERE (FR),** ch f 1/2 Valanjou—Ephelide (Count Pahlen) **Mme M. A. Bergacht**
25 **MOUNTAIN PARK (FR),** b c 4/2 Cricket Ball—Mountain Top (Zino) **M. Hills**
26 **SAINT SERNIN (FR),** b c 11/2 Kendor—Bid Fair (Auction Ring) **E. Sodenberg**
27 B c 4/4 Always Fair—Silent Hill (Temperence Hill) **D. Li**
28 **SLIPPY (FR),** b c 17/2 Sleeping Car—Kiss House (Open House) **Haras du Logis**
29 B f 10/4 Septieme Ciel—Twosome (One For All) **S. Olsson**
30 **ZIBELLO (IRE),** ch c 10/5 Common Grounds—Mariella (Sir Gaylord) **Mme A. Gibson**

Other Owners: K. Eng, T. J. Gibson, B. T. Gibson, M. Lind, M. Opperman, N. Reeves, N. Richards, A. Sorokin, R. Stephenson.

Jockeys (Flat): D Boeuf (8-7, w.a.), S Guillot (8-7, w.a.), S Maillot (7-12).

231 MR J. T. GIFFORD, Findon

Postal: **The Downs, Findon, Worthing, West Sussex, BN14 0RR.**
Phone: **FINDON (01903) 872226 FAX (01903) 877232**

1 **ABSOLUTE LIMIT,** 6, gr g Absalom—Western Line **Mrs J. S. Wootton**
2 **ARDENT BRIDE,** 5, ch m Ardross—Celestial Bride **Mrs S. N. J. Embiricos**
3 **BELVENTO (IRE),** 6, b g Strong Gale—Salufair **Mrs Jean Plackett**
4 **BLACK STATEMENT (IRE),** 8, br g Strong Statement (USA)—Gambell And Dream **Mr Bill Naylor**
5 **BOARDROOM SHUFFLE (IRE),** 7, b g Executive Perk—Eurotin **Mr A. D. Weller**
6 **BRAVE HIGHLANDER (IRE),** 10, b g Sheer Grit—Deerpark Rose **Mr S. N. J. Embiricos**
7 **BURN OUT,** 6, b g Last Tycoon—Obertura (USA) **The Al Yancy Partnership**
8 **CALVARO (IRE),** 7, b g Corvaro (USA)—Jukebox Katie **Mr Bill Naylor**
9 **CARRS ISLAND,** 6, b g Island Set (USA)—Holly Carrs **Mr Bill Naylor**
10 **CHICAGO CITY (IRE),** 5, br g Strong Gale—Orchardstown **Mr S. N. J. Embiricos**
11 **CIPRIANI QUEEN (IRE),** 8, b m Seattle Dancer (USA)—Justsayno (USA) **Tor Royal Racing Club**
12 **CLEAR WATER (IRE),** 6, b g Over The River (FR)—Corvassio **Mr W. E. Gale**
13 **DENVER BAY,** 11, b g Julio Mariner—Night Action **Mr Bill Naylor**
14 **DIVINE RIGHT (IRE),** 5, b g Montelimar (USA)—Scaravie (IRE) **Mr A. D. Weller**
15 **DO ME A FAVOUR (IRE),** 4, b g Classic Memory—Ice Pearl **Mr D. G. Trangmar**
16 **EURO FORUM,** 6, ch g Deploy—Unique Treasure **Mr John Dunsdon**
17 **FLYING ON,** 6, b g Wace (USA)—Quick Exit **Mrs Davina Whiteman**
18 **FOODBROKER STAR (IRE),** 8, gr g Roselier (FR)—Stormy Breeze **Food Brokers Ltd**

MR J. T. GIFFORD—continued

19 FRINGE BENEFIT (IRE), 7, b m Executive Perk—Erins Treasure **Mr R. J. Kershaw**
20 GEORGETOWN, 7, ch g Ballacashtal (CAN)—Wessex Kingdom **Parafix Tapes & Conversions Ltd**
21 GLITTER ISLE (IRE), 8, gr g Roselier (FR)—Decent Dame **Mrs Timothy Pilkington**
22 GROOVING (IRE), 9, b g Callernish—Sams Money **Mrs T. Brown**
23 GUARD OF HONOUR, 6, b g Broadsword (USA)—Celestial Bride **Mr S. N. J. Embiricos**
24 HEADWIND (IRE), 7, b g Strong Gale—Lady In Red **Pell-mell Partners**
25 'IGGINS (IRE), 8, br g Strong Gale—Gale Flash **Pell-mell Partners**
26 IRISH OPTION (IRE), 5, ch g Executive Perk—Erins Treasure **Mrs Jean Plackett**
27 IT'S A GEM, 9, ch g Funny Man—Seed Pearl **Mrs B. M. Biddlecombe**
28 KILLEANEY CARR (IRE), 7, b g Yashgan—Barrack Lady **Miss J. Semple**
29 KILMINGTON (IRE), 9, gr g Roselier (FR)—Hope You're Lucky **Mr H. T. Pelham**
30 KURAKKA (IRE), 5, b g Florida Son—Helens Birthday **Mrs M. C. Sweeney**
31 LIVELY KNIGHT (IRE), 9, b g Remainder Man—Love The Irish **Mr A. D. Weller**
32 LORD ROOBLE (IRE), 7, b g Jolly Jake (NZ)—Missing Note **The Findon Partnership**
33 MANDYS MANTINO, 8, br g Neltino—Mandy's Melody **Mr John Plackett**
34 MARIUS (IRE), 8, b g Cyrano de Bergerac—Nesreen **Miss Jessica Andrews**
35 MERLINS BAY (IRE), 4, b g Nearly A Nose (USA)—Kabarda **Mr John Plackett**
36 MOONSHINE BAY (IRE), 4, b g Executive Perk—Sister of Slane **Mrs Timothy Pilkington**
37 MR CHELSEA (IRE), 5, b g Naheez (USA)—Delay **Felix Rosehstiel's Widow & Son**
38 MR MARKHAM (IRE), 6, b g Naheez (USA)—Brighter Gail **Felix Rosenstiel's Widow & Son**
39 MR PERCY (IRE), 7, ch g John French—Rathvilly Flier **Felix Rosenstiel's Widow & Son**
40 NEW RISING, 6, b g Primitive Rising (USA)—Saucy **Mr Bill Naylor**
41 NONE STIRRED (IRE), 8, b g Supreme Leader—Double Wrapped **Mr Colin Frewin**
42 OFF SHORE (IRE), 5, b g Over The River (FR)—Parson's Princess **Mr A. D. Weller**
43 PROCEED, 6, br g Blakeney—Sayida-Shahira **Mr G. T. Radmore**
44 QUAFF (IRE), 8, b g Buckskin (FR)—Raheen Pearl **Mr A. D. Weller**
45 REDEEMYOURSELF (IRE), 9, b g Royal Fountain—Reve Clair **Mrs T. Brown**
46 RED GUARD, 4, ch g Soviet Star (USA)—Zinzara (USA) **Mr L. A. Hooper**
47 SAN FERNANDO, 12, b g Bulldozer—Burren Orchid **Mrs S. N. J. Embiricos**
48 SKYCAB (IRE), 6, b g Montelimar (USA)—Sams Money **P. H. Betts (Holdings) Ltd**
49 SMINT (IRE), 4, b g Ala Hounak—Fabulous Evening **Food Brokers Ltd**
50 SOLOMAN (IRE), 5, br g Mandalus—Solo Player **Mr R. F. Eliot**
51 STRONG PALADIN (IRE), 7, b g Strong Gale—Kalanshoe **Mrs Angela Brodie**
52 SWEEP CLEAN (IRE), 6, b g Brush Aside (USA)—Quay Blues **Mrs Angela Brodie**
53 TOP NOTE (IRE), 6, ch g Orchestra—Clarrie **Mrs S. N. J. Embiricos**
54 TUDOR ROYAL (IRE), 6, b g Executive Perk—Clashawley **Mrs M. C. Sweeney**
55 VINTAGE CLARET, 9, gr g Funny Man—Vinotino **Mrs J. F. Hall**
56 YORKSHIRE GALE, 12, br g Strong Gale—Mio Slipper **Mr Bill Naylor**
57 ZAISAN (IRE), 5, b br g Executive Perk—Belace **Mrs M. C. Sweeney**

Other Owners: Mr Jon Baldwin, Mr S. P. Barrett, Mr J. Bayer, Mr G. H. L. Bird, Mr Nigel Chamberlain, Mr J. Chromiak, Mr G. K. Duncan, Mr J. Dyer, Ms M. Evans, Mr Richard Gilder, Mr Raymond Anderson Green, Mr R. B. Holt, Mr S. Hurst, Mr D. F. Pengelly, Mrs K. M. Pengelly, Mr P. A. Prince, Mr B. T. Stewart-Brown, Mr T. F. Villiers-Smith, Mr Ian Fenton White, Mr B. M. Wootton.

Jockey (NH): P Hide (10-0).

Conditional: L Aspell (10-0), O Burrows (9-9), W Greatrex (9-7).

Amateur: Mr G Weatherley (10-0).

232 MR PATRICK L. GILLIGAN, Newmarket

Postal: **Sackville House Stables, Sackville Street, Newmarket, Suffolk, CB8 8DX.**
Phone: **(01638) 669151 MOBILE (0802) 679437**

1 **HARVEY'S FUTURE,** 4, b g Never So Bold—Orba Gold **Cavotoro Partnership**
2 **PROTARAS BAY,** 4, b c Superpower—Vivid Impression **Cavotoro Partnership**
3 **RUSHCUTTER BAY,** 5, br g Mon Tresor—Llwy Bren **Treasure Seekers Partnership**

THREE-YEAR-OLDS

4 **JACK RUBY,** b c Risk Me (FR)—Atisayin (USA) **Mr P. R. Dalton**
5 **KALA PATTAR,** b c Thowra (FR)—Manon Lescaut **Dr Susan Barnes**

TWO-YEAR-OLDS

6 **CHIPEWYAS (FR),** b f 18/5 Bering—Litza (FR) (Kenmare (FR)) **Ellis Stud Partnership**
7 B c 10/3 Ezzoud (IRE)—Contraflow (Rainbow Quest (USA)) **Mr P. L. Gilligan**
8 B f 12/5 Mon Tresor—Edith Piaf (Thatch (USA)) **Mr H. Bell**

Other Owners: Mr F. B. Barnes, Mr P. Crowe, Mr M. Flouris, Mr S. Gilligan, Mr S. Searle.

233 MR J. A. GLOVER, Worksop

Postal: **Pinewood Stables, Carburton, Worksop, Nottinghamshire, S80 3BT.**
Phone: **WORKSOP (01909) 475425 (OFFICE) 475962 (HOUSE)**

1 **ALISANDE (IRE),** 6, b m King's Ride—Enchanted Evening **Pell-Mell Partners**
2 **ALZOOMO (IRE),** 6, b g Alzao (USA)—Fandangerina (USA) **Mr L. A. Jackson**
3 **CAPTAIN SCOTT (IRE),** 4, b g Polar Falcon (USA)—Camera Girl **The Write State Partnership**
4 **DAAWE (USA),** 7, b h Danzig (USA)—Capo di Monte **Mrs A. M. Mallinson**
5 **EPWORTH,** 4, b f Unfuwain (USA)—Positive Attitude **Mr B. H. Farr**
6 **KALAMATA,** 6, ch h Kalaglow—Good Try **Mr B. H. Farr**
7 **MISTERTON,** 4, ch g Mystiko (USA)—South Shore **Mr B. H. Farr**
8 **PRINCIPAL BOY (IRE),** 5, br g Cyrano de Bergerac—Shenley Lady **Mr M. O'Horan & Mr C. Moreno**
9 **SHIRAZAN (IRE),** 4, b g Doyoun—Sharaniya (USA) **Mr J. A. Glover**
10 5, B g Seymour Hicks (FR)—Supreme Issue **Mr R. W. Metcalfe**
11 **THREE FOR A POUND,** 4, b g Risk Me (FR)—Lompoa **Hyde Sporting Promotions Limited**
12 **WOODBECK,** 4, b br f Terimon—Arminda **Mr B. H. Farr**

THREE-YEAR-OLDS

13 **BRAZEN HUSSEY,** b f Risk Me (FR)—Rosalka (ITY) **Countrywide Classics Limited**
14 **CLIFTON WOOD (IRE),** b c Paris House—Millie's Lady (IRE) **P. and S. Partnership**
15 **CODED MESSAGE (IRE),** b g Deploy—Princess Carmen (IRE) **Mr P. A. Deal**
16 **LAA JADEED (IRE),** b c Petorius—Sea Mistress **Mr B. Dixon**
17 **LEGEND OF LOVE,** b g Pursuit of Love—Legendary Dancer **Mr S. J. Beard**
18 Br g Full Extent (USA)—Miss Nanna **Mr V. W. Atherton**
19 **NUNTHORPE,** ch f Mystiko (USA)—Enchanting Melody **Mr B. H. Farr**
20 **PIP'S ADDITION (IRE),** ch f Pips Pride—Mint Addition **Miss A. C. Radford**
21 **SANDIA POINT (IRE),** b g Sharpo—Andbell **Mr E. Bennett**
22 **SHAMWARI SONG,** b c Sizzling Melody—Spark Out **Mr V. W. Atherton & Mr J. Lacey**
23 **SWOOSH,** gr g Absalom—Valldemosa **Sports Mania**

TWO-YEAR-OLDS

24 B c 19/5 Scenic—Fashion Parade (Mount Hagen (FR)) **Mr J. A. Glover**
25 B c 14/1 Puissance—Indian Summer (Young Generation) **Mr J. A. Glover**
26 Ch c 5/4 Efisio—Inquirendo (USA) (Roberto (USA)) **Mr B. H. Farr**
27 B c 3/4 Rock City—Latakia (Morston (FR)) **Mr J. A. Glover**
28 B f 7/3 Shareef Dancer (USA)—Little Beaut (Prince Sabo) **Mr M. O'Horan & Mr C. Moreno**
29 B f 9/3 Be My Chief (USA)—Lochbelle (Robellino (USA)) **Mr B. H. Farr**
30 **SAMMAL (IRE),** b g 28/3 Petardia—Prime Site (IRE) (Burslem) **Mrs A. M. Mallinson**
31 B c 12/5 Unblest—Sharp Goodbye (Sharpo) **Countrywide Classics Limited**

MR J. A. GLOVER—continued

32 B c 14/5 Soviet Lad (USA)—Shoubad Melody (Jukebox) **Mr J. A. Glover**
33 Ch f 29/3 Alhijaz—Silver Lodge (Homing) **Mr J. A. Glover**
34 TIKOTINO, ch f 13/4 Mystiko (USA)—Tino-Ella (Bustino) **Mr Ted Revill**
35 WELLOW (IRE), b g 22/5 Unblest—Alpine Sunset (Auction Ring (USA)) **Mr S. B. Whelbourn**

Other Owners: Mrs J. A. Beighton, Mr P. Burdett, Mr J. Chromiak, Mr M. Dews, Mr Brian T. Eastick, Mrs Ann Farrin, Mr T. A. Farrin, Mrs S. Glover, Miss B. Greaves, Mrs S. Jackson, K. P. H. (Equine) Ltd, Mr Christopher Morris, Mr John Pumfrey, Mr Anthony H. Ratcliffe, Mr P. B. Short, Mr Shane Snelling, Mrs C. M. Stevens, Mr W. H. Strawson, Mr James Underwood, Mr Paul Wheeler.

Jockey (Flat): Stephen Williams (8-4).

Jockeys (NH): T Reed, A S Smith.

At the time of going to press, Godolphin had not decided which of their horses would be returning to Europe for the 1998 Flat racing season. An up-to-date list will be published, along with other late teams, in Raceform Update, and copies can also be obtained from the subscription department of Raceform by writing to Raceform Freepost, Compton, Newbury, Berks, RG20 6NL (no stamp required).
1997 International Classification ratings of Godolphin horses appear at the back of the book.

234 COUNTESS GOESS-SAURAU, Marlborough

Postal: **Temple Farm, Rockley, Marlborough, Wiltshire, SN8 1RU.**
Phone: **(01672) 514428 FAX (01672) 514116**

1 DOUBLE OR QUITS, 5, ch m Lord Bud—Highland Waters **Countess Goess-Saurau**
2 PAGE ROYALE (FR), 8, ch m Le Page—Dafka (FR) **Countess Goess-Saurau**

Amateur: Mr A Beedles (10-0).

235 MR J. S. GOLDIE, Glasgow

Postal: **Libo Hill Farm, Uplawmoor, Glasgow, G78 4BS.**
Phone: **(01505) 850212**

1 **FANADIYR (IRE),** 6, b g Kahyasi—Fair Fight **Mr D. Callaghan**
2 **INDIAN SPARK,** 4, ch c Indian Ridge—Annes Gift **Mr Frank Brady**
3 **JOHAYRO,** 5, ch g Clantime—Arroganza **Mr Frank Brady**
4 **KEEP BATTLING,** 8, b g Hard Fought—Keep Mum **Mr J. S. Goldie**
5 **MONTRAVE,** 9, ch g Netherkelly—Streakella **Mr D. St. Clair**
6 **NICHOLAS PLANT,** 9, ch g Nicholas Bill—Bustilly **Mrs M. F. Paterson**
7 **NORTHERN MOTTO,** 5, b g Mtoto—Soulful (FR) **Mr D. Callaghan**
8 **RACHAEL'S OWEN,** 8, ch g Oats—Polly Potter **Die-Hard Racing Club**
9 **RIBBONLETTA,** 4, b f Goldsmiths' Hall—Ribbon Lady **Mrs Ailsa Russell**
10 **SECONDS AWAY,** 7, b g Hard Fought—Keep Mum **Mr J. S. Goldie**
11 **STORMLESS,** 7, b g Silly Prices—Phyl's Pet **Mr D. St. Clair**
12 **TEEJAY'N'AITCH (IRE),** 6, b g Maelstrom Lake—Middle Verde (USA) **Mrs Alice Goldie**
13 **THE MUNRO'S,** 4, b c Safawan—Some Cherry **Aberdeenshire Racing Club**
14 **VINTAGE TAITTINGER (IRE),** 6, b g Nordico (USA)—Kalonji **Die-Hard Racing Club**

THREE-YEAR-OLDS

15 **BAYLHAM,** b g Risk Me (FR)—So Beguiling (USA) **Mr J. S. Goldie**
16 **COSMIC CASE,** b f Casteddu—La Fontainova (IRE) **Mr J. S. Goldie**
17 **RHINEFIELD BEAUTY (IRE),** ch f Shalford (IRE)—Humble Mission **Mr Frank Brady**

Other Owners: Mr J. A. Anderson, Mr J. W. Armstrong, Mrs Kenneth Blair, Mr E. Bruce, Mr Alf Chadwick, Mr Thomas Dyer, Mrs A. Fifer, Mr W. M. Johnstone, Mr Patrick H. Marron, Mr J. C. McGee, Mr Andrew Paterson, Miss Barbara Spittal, Miss Michelle Strawinski, Mr Ronald Wilkie, Mr K. Wilson.

Jockeys (Flat): John Bramhill, Tyrone Williams.

Conditional: Richard McGrath, Scott Taylor.

Amateur: Mr O McPhail.

Lady Rider: Mrs Carol Williams.

236 MR ROBERT H. GOLDIE, Kilmarnock

Postal: **Harpercroft, Old Loans Road, Dundonald, Kilmarnock, Ayrshire, KA2 9DD.**
Phone: **TROON (01292) 317222 FAX (01292) 313585**

1 **AILSA CRAIG,** 6, b g Torus—Mashin Time **Mr Robert H. Goldie**
2 **EASTER OATS,** 11, b m Oats—Ice Lass **Mrs R. H. Goldie**
3 4, B f Le Bavard (FR)—Ice Lass **Mrs R. H. Goldie**
4 **JAVAMAN,** 6, b g Homo Sapien—Brownhill Lass **Mr W. McIntosh**
5 **MISS CAVO,** 7, b m Ovac (ITY)—Ice Lass **Mrs R. H. Goldie**
6 **THE BURGLAR (IRE),** 6, b g Denel (FR)—Night Invader **Mr W. McIntosh**
7 **TIME TO RISE,** 5, b g Primitive Rising (USA)—Mashin Time **Mr Robert H. Goldie**

THREE-YEAR-OLDS

8 B f Denel (FR)—Ice Lass **Mrs R. H. Goldie**

TWO-YEAR-OLDS

9 Br f 29/6 Denel (FR)—Buck To (Buckskin (FR)) **Mrs R. H. Goldie**
10 B f 13/6 Denel (FR)—Ice Lass (Heroic Air) **Mrs R. H. Goldie**

237 MR S. GOLLINGS, Louth

Postal: **Highfield House, Scamblesby, Louth, Lincolnshire, LN11 9XT.**
Phone: **PHONE & FAX (01507) 343204**

1 **AUGUSTAN,** 7, b g Shareef Dancer (USA)—Krishnagar **Mr Robert Jones**
2 **BACKSCRATCHER,** 4, b g Backchat (USA)—Tiernee Quintana **Mrs J. M. Barker**
3 **BLOTOFT,** 6, b g High Kicker (USA)—Foothold **Mr R. N. Forman**
4 **CAUTION,** 4, b f Warning—Fairy Flax (IRE) **Mr Ian & Mrs Irene Thomas**
5 **DR CALIGARI (IRE),** 6, b g My Generation—Mallabee **Mr Dave Mager - Mrs Sue Mager**
6 **EAST BARNS (IRE),** 10, gr g Godswalk (USA)—Rocket Lass **Northern Bloodstock Racing**
7 **ENSHARP (USA),** 12, b g Sharpen Up—Lulworth Cove **Mrs Jayne M. Gollings**
8 **GET THE POINT,** 4, b c Sadler's Wells (USA)—Tolmi **Mr R. L. Houlton**
9 **IN TRUTH,** 10, ch g Dreams To Reality (USA)—Persian Express **Mrs E. Houlton**
10 **MARYS PATH,** 4, b f Rock Hopper—Jasmin Path **Mr R. L. Houlton**
11 **MEMSAHIB OFESTEEM,** 7, gr m Neltino—Occatillo **Tony French & Robert Jones**
12 **NEW INN,** 7, b g Petoski—Pitroyal **Mr Ian K. I. Stewart**
13 **ON MERIT,** 4, b g Terimon—Onika **Northern Bloodstock Racing**
14 **PASSIONATTI,** 4, b f Emarati (USA)—Ration of Passion **Mr A. E. Moss**
15 **PRINCE MOSHAR,** 4, b g Primitive Rising (USA)—Mostimus **Mr A. E. Moss**
16 **RARE TALENT,** 4, b c Mtoto—Bold As Love **John King, Bill Hobson, Graham King**
17 4, Ch f Anshan—Santee Sioux **Mr Ian K. I. Stewart**
18 **SISTER ROSE (IRE),** 7, b m Roselier (FR)—Polarogan
19 **SPRINGFIELD RHYME,** 7, b m Idiot's Delight—Ledee **Mrs M. A. Hall**
20 **TRUTHFULLY,** 5, ch m Weldnaas (USA)—Persian Express **Mrs E. Houlton**
21 **URBAN DANCER (IRE),** 4, ch f Generous (IRE)—Perfect Welcome
22 **VASILIEV,** 10, b g Sadler's Wells (USA)—Poquito Queen (CAN) **Mr R. N. Forman**

THREE-YEAR-OLDS

23 **HARRYS LITTLE GIRL,** gr f Willypous—Slainthe Mhath **Mr Harry Byers**
24 Ch g Carlingford Castle—Hodsock Venture **Mr Keith Brown**
25 B f Nomination—Onika

TWO-YEAR-OLDS

26 B c 4/2 High Estate—Clyde Goddess (IRE) **Mr R. L. Houlton**
27 Ch f 4/4 Rock Hopper—Ikis Girl **Mr Ian K. I. Stewart**
28 B f 12/5 Mystiko (USA)—Maribella **Mr J. Chilton & Mrs V. Chilton**
29 **OMAR SHAREEF,** b c 8/3 Shareef Dancer (USA)—Happy Drome **Mr A. E. Moss**

Other Owners: Mrs A. Allen, Mr P. Allen, Mr A. N. Barrett, Mrs C. Barrett, Mr Gerry Brewer, Mr & Mrs R. H. Coole, Mr Barry Crole, Mr G. D. Dalrymple, Mrs S. E. Forman, Mr S. Gollings, Mr E. Goodhall, Mr John Green, Mr Derek G. M. Holland, Lambert'S Lakes Ltd, Miss P. Phillips, Mr R. A. Redmile, Mr Richard Sanderson, Mr Ralph Taylor.

Jockey (Flat): J Quinn.

Jockeys (NH): R Dunwoody, M A Fitzgerald, K Gaule, A Maguire, A S Smith, Robert Thornton.

Amateur: Mr S Durack.

Lady Rider: Mrs Jayne M Gollings (9-0).

238 MRS A. C. D. GOODFELLOW, Earlston

Postal: **Leadervale House, Earlston, Berwickshire, TD4 6AJ.**
Phone: **EARLSTON (01896) 849541 MOBILE (0831) 133899 FAX (01896) 849567**

1 **CEILIDH BOY,** 12, b g Oats—Charlotte's Festival **Mrs J. D. Goodfellow**
2 **KILCOLGAN,** 11, ch g Le Bavard (FR)—Katula **Mr J. D. Goodfellow**
3 **MISS CHERRY PICKER,** 6, b m Phardante (FR)—Sailing Brig **Major I. C. Straker**
4 **MONKEY WENCH (IRE),** 7, b m Taufan (USA)—Northern Valkyrie **Mrs J. D. Goodfellow**
5 **MORAINE GIRL (IRE),** 5, br m Glacial Storm (USA)—Faha Corner **Mrs J. D. Goodfellow**
6 **PRINCE OF THYNE (IRE),** 9, b br g Good Thyne (USA)—Ryehill Rose **Mr J. D. Goodfellow**
7 **STAN'S YOUR MAN,** 8, b g Young Man (FR)—Charlotte's Festival **Mrs J. D. Goodfellow**
8 **SUNSET FLASH,** 6, b g Good Times (ITY)—Political Prospect **Mr J. D. Goodfellow**
9 **TOUGH TEST (IRE),** 8, ch g Lancastrian—Take Beating **Mr J. D. Goodfellow**

Jockey (NH): B Storey.

239 MR J. H. M. GOSDEN, Newmarket

Postal: **Stanley House Stables, Bury Road, Newmarket, Suffolk, CB8 7DF.**
Phone: **(01638) 669944 FAX (01638) 669922**

1 **ALFANNAN,** 4, b c Lear Fan (USA)—Connecting Link (USA)
2 **DECORATED HERO,** 6, b g Warning—Bequeath (USA)
3 **HANDSOME RIDGE,** 4, ch c Indian Ridge—Red Rose Garden
4 **JASEUR (USA),** 5, b g Lear Fan (USA)—Spur Wing (USA)
5 **LORD OF MEN,** 5, ch h Groom Dancer (USA)—Upper Strata
6 **PERFECT PARADIGM (IRE),** 4, b c Alzao (USA)—Brilleaux
7 **REDBRIDGE (USA),** 4, b c Alleged (USA)—Red Slippers (USA)
8 **RUSSIAN REVIVAL (USA),** 5, ch h Nureyev (USA)—Memories (USA)
9 **SAAFEYA (IRE),** 4, b f Sadler's Wells (USA)—Safa
10 **SABADILLA (USA),** 4, b c Sadler's Wells (USA)—Jasmina (USA)
11 **SAGUARO,** 4, b g Green Desert (USA)—Badawi (USA)
12 **SANTILLANA (USA),** 5, ch h El Gran Senor (USA)—Galway (FR)
13 **SATIN STONE (USA),** 4, b c Mr Prospector (USA)—Satin Flower (USA)
14 **SCATTERGUN,** 4, ch c Rainbow Quest (USA)—Cattermole (USA)
15 **SHANTOU (USA),** 5, b h Alleged (USA)—Shaima (USA)
16 **SHASKA,** 4, ch f Kris—Dance Machine
17 **SONG OF FREEDOM,** 4, ch c Arazi (USA)—Glorious Song (CAN)
18 **SWISS LAW,** 4, b c Machiavellian (USA)—Seductress
19 **THREE CHEERS (IRE),** 4, b br g Slip Anchor—Three Tails
20 **WELLAKI (USA),** 4, ch c Miswaki (USA)—Wellomond (FR)

THREE-YEAR-OLDS

21 **ABYAAN (IRE),** b f Ela-Mana-Mou—Anna Comnena (IRE)
22 **ADOBE,** b c Green Desert (USA)—Shamshir
23 **ALBAADRI,** b c Cadeaux Genereux—Actraphane
24 **ALGUNNAAS,** b c Red Ransom (USA)—Swame (USA)
25 **ALMANDAB (IRE),** b br c Last Tycoon—Fortune Teller
26 **ALRAHAAL (USA),** b br c Diesis—Solar Star (USA)
27 **ARIANT (USA),** ch c Mr Prospector (USA)—Six Months Long (USA)
28 **ASHBILYA (USA),** b f Nureyev (USA)—Storm Fear (USA)
29 **AVELINA,** b f Nashwan (USA)—Balenare
30 **BREVITY,** b c Tenby—Rive (USA)
31 **CADETTE,** ch c Arazi (USA)—Carotene (CAN)
32 **CATAMARAN,** ch c Rainbow Quest (USA)—Cattermole (USA)
33 **COSSACK KING,** b c Soviet Star (USA)—Annie Albright (USA)
34 **DE MILLE (USA),** ch f Nureyev (USA)—Ghaiya (USA)
35 **DENARIUS (USA),** b c Silver Hawk (USA)—Ambrosine (USA)
36 **DESERT TYCOON (IRE),** b c Last Tycoon—Point of Honour

MR J. H. M. GOSDEN—continued

37 **DESIGNER (USA)**, b c Danzig (USA)—Classy Women (USA)
38 **DETERRENT**, b c Warning—Delve (IRE)
39 **DORAID (IRE)**, b c Danehill (USA)—Quiche
40 **EMPIRICAL (USA)**, b f Miswaki (USA)—Louisville (FR)
41 **FETHEROLF (IRE)**, ch c Wolfhound (USA)—Tuxford Hideaway
42 **FINAL TANGO**, b f Danehill (USA)—Sombre Lady
43 **GALLAASH (USA)**, b c Gulch (USA)—In View (USA)
44 **GANDOURA (USA)**, b f Sheikh Albadou—Alqwani (USA)
45 **GATE OF DREAMS**, b c Exit To Nowhere (USA)—Picnicing
46 **GONDOLA (IRE)**, b c Caerleon (USA)—River Memories (USA)
47 **HEBONY**, b f Sabrehill (USA)—Hebba (USA)
48 **HIGH AND MIGHTY**, b c Shirley Heights—Air Distingue (USA)
49 **HIGHEST ACCOLADE**, b f Shirley Heights—Victoress (USA)
50 **ICEBAND (USA)**, ch c Dixieland Band (USA)—Zero Minus (USA)
51 **INCENTIVE**, b c Rainbow Quest (USA)—In The Groove
52 **KILCULLEN (IRE)**, b br g In The Wings—Liffey Lass (USA)
53 **LADY ICARUS**, b f Rainbow Quest (USA)—Sonic Lady (USA)
54 **LAFFAH (USA)**, b c Silver Hawk (USA)—Sakiyah (USA)
55 **LOUIS PHILIPPE (USA)**, b c El Gran Senor (USA)—Naqiyah (USA)
56 **MASHA-IL (IRE)**, b c Danehill (USA)—Valley Lights (IRE)
57 **MASSENET (IRE)**, b c Caerleon (USA)—Massawippi
58 **MIGRATE (USA)**, ch f Storm Bird (CAN)—Home Leave (USA)
59 **MONARCHY (IRE)**, b f Common Grounds—Royal Rumpus
60 **MUBRIK (IRE)**, b c Lahib (USA)—Bequeath (USA)
61 **MUHTATHIR**, ch c Elmaamul (USA)—Majmu (USA)
62 **MYZOMELA (USA)**, b f Kris S (USA)—Myza (USA)
63 **NIKI (IRE)**, b f Fairy King (USA)—Nicola Wynn
64 **OAK VINTAGE (USA)**, b f Seeking The Gold (USA)—Delicate Vine (USA)
65 **OLIVE THE TWIST (USA)**, ch f Theatrical—Lady of The Light (USA)
66 **ORIENTAL**, b c Inchinor—Orient
67 **PERIDOT**, b f Green Desert (USA)—Alinova (USA)
68 **PLAN-B**, b c Polish Precedent (USA)—Draft Board
69 **POLSKA MODELLE (FR)**, ch c Polish Precedent (USA)—Model Village
70 **QUEENS DAGGER (USA)**, b f Rahy (USA)—Katies First (USA)
71 **RAINALD (USA)**, b c Danzig (USA)—Ristna
72 **RAINSTORM**, b c Rainbow Quest (USA)—Katsina (USA)
73 **RIOT**, b c Fairy King (USA)—Lucia Tarditi (FR)
74 **RISING CHORUS (USA)**, b f Gone West (USA)—Devon Diva (USA)
75 **ROMAN KING (IRE)**, b c Sadler's Wells (USA)—Romantic Feeling
76 **SAEEDAH**, ch f Bustino—Galaxie Dust (USA)
77 **SCANDALOUS**, b f Warning—Andaleeb (USA)
78 **SEYAASI (IRE)**, ch c Indian Ridge—Good Policy (IRE)
79 **SHART (IRE)**, b c Last Tycoon—Simaat (USA)
80 **SHOGUN (IRE)**, b c Zafonic (USA)—Sheriyna (FR)
81 **SILVERTOWN**, b c Danehill (USA)—Docklands (USA)
82 **ST BRIDE'S BAY**, b f Caerleon (USA)—La Romance (USA)
83 **TEMPER LAD (USA)**, b c Riverman (USA)—Dokki (USA)
84 **THINK SNOW**, b c Caerleon (USA)—Snow Day (FR)
85 **TITANIC (IRE)**, b c Nashwan (USA)—White Star Line (USA)
86 **TOHUNGA**, b br g Rudimentary (USA)—Refinancing (USA)
87 **TOREERO**, b c Cadeaux Genereux—Free City (USA)
88 **TRENDY INDIAN (IRE)**, ch f Indian Ridge—Moving Trend (IRE)
89 **VIGNETTE (USA)**, b f Diesis—Be Exclusive
90 **WAJORI (USA)**, b c Diesis—Wajna (USA)
91 **WELCOMING**, b c Kris—d'Azy
92 **YAJTAHED (IRE)**, ch c Mujtahid (USA)—Rainstone
93 **YOUNG JOSH**, b c Warning—Title Roll (IRE)
94 **ZELANDA (IRE)**, gr f Night Shift (USA)—Zafadola (IRE)

MR J. H. M. GOSDEN—continued

TWO-YEAR-OLDS

95 Ch c 25/3 Diesis—Affirmative Fable (USA) (Affirmed (USA))
96 B f 9/1 Diesis—Alcando (IRE) (Alzao (USA))
97 **ALSAMEDAH (USA),** b f 21/4 Shadeed (USA)—Alqwani (USA) (Mr Prospector (USA))
98 B br c 9/2 Danzig (USA)—Aquilegia (USA) (Alydar (USA))
99 B br c Dayjur (USA)—Arewehavingfunyet (USA) (Sham (USA))
100 B f 5/1 Red Ransom (USA)—Asdaf (USA) (Forty Niner (USA))
101 Ch f 15/5 Silver Hawk (USA)—Barmistress (USA) (Alydar (USA))
102 Ch c Irish River (FR)—Be Exclusive (Be My Guest (USA))
103 B f 18/3 Fairy King (USA)—Belle Passe (Be My Guest (USA))
104 Ch c 28/4 Elmaamul (USA)—Bizarre Lady (Dalsaan)
105 B c 9/3 Barathea (IRE)—Broadmara (IRE) (Thatching)
106 B br c 16/3 Dayjur (USA)—By Your Leave (USA) (Private Account (USA))
107 Ch c Diesis—Carezza (USA) (Caro)
108 B br f 13/2 Lear Fan (USA)—Carya (USA) (Northern Dancer)
109 **CHOIRGIRL,** b f 2/2 Unfuwain (USA)—Choir Mistress (Chief Singer)
110 **CLANDESTINE,** b f 5/4 Saddlers' Hall (IRE)—Fleeting Affair (Hotfoot)
111 Br f Riverman (USA)—Close Comfort (USA) (Far North (CAN))
112 Ch c 20/2 Woodman (USA)—Crockadore (USA) (Nijinsky (CAN))
113 B f 5/4 Sadler's Wells (USA)—Delage (Bellypha)
114 B br c 9/3 Caerleon (USA)—Depaze (USA) (Deputy Minister (CAN))
115 **DETECTIVE,** ch f 8/2 Wolfhound (USA)—Ivoronica (Targowice (USA))
116 Ch f 24/2 A P Indy (USA)—Dokki (USA) (Northern Dancer)
117 **DONATION,** ch f 16/3 Generous (IRE)—Refinancing (USA) (Forli (ARG))
118 B c 4/4 Personal Hope (USA)—Double The Charm (USA) (Nodouble (USA))
119 Ch f 26/2 Bluebird (USA)—Eastern Shore (Sun Prince)
120 Ch c Woodman (USA)—Eye Drop (USA) (Irish River (FR))
121 B f 26/2 Nashwan (USA)—Fair Rosamunda (Try My Best (USA))
122 B f 31/1 Bigstone (IRE)—Final Decision (Tap On Wood)
123 Br f Lear Fan (USA)—Fitzwilliam Place (Thatching)
124 B c 4/4 Sabrehill (USA)—Flower Arrangement (Lomond (USA))
125 B c 8/5 Silver Hawk (USA)—Glaze (USA) (Mr Prospector (USA))
126 Br c 9/2 Ela-Mana-Mou—Good Enough (IRE) (Simply Great (FR))
127 B f 4/4 Mtoto—Grecian Slipper (Sadler's Wells (USA))
128 Ch c 16/3 Grand Lodge (USA)—Guest Room (IRE) (Be My Guest (USA))
129 Ch f 22/1 Cadeaux Genereux—Gunner's Belle (Gunner B)
130 **HABUB (USA),** b c 2/2 Danzig (USA)—Cheval Volant (USA) (Kris S (USA))
131 B c 25/4 Barathea (IRE)—Hanzala (FR) (Akarad (FR))
132 **HARLEQUIN DANCER,** b c 15/3 Distant Relative—Proudfoot (IRE) (Shareef Dancer (USA))
133 **JADE CHEQUER,** b f 5/4 Green Desert (USA)—Draft Board (Rainbow Quest)
134 **JOIN THE PARADE,** b f 21/2 Elmaamul (USA)—Summer Pageant (Chief's Crown (USA))
135 Br c 18/1 Warning—Jubilee Trail (Shareef Dancer (USA))
136 Ch c 3/4 Common Grounds—Kayu (Tap On Wood)
137 B br c 19/2 Warning—Krill (Kris)
138 **MA-ARIF (IRE),** b br f 25/2 Alzao (USA)—Taqreem (IRE) (Nashwan (USA))
139 **MAMBRINO (USA),** b c 13/3 Kingmambo (USA)—Dream Deal (USA) (Sharpen Up)
140 B c 25/4 Sky Classic (CAN)—Mosella (USA) (Lord At War (ARG))
141 Br bl c 29/1 Silver Hawk (USA)—Mrs West (USA) (Gone West (USA))
142 **MUTAAKID (USA),** b br c 13/4 Dayjur (USA)—Arjuzah (IRE) (Ahonoora)
143 Ch f 9/4 Geiger Counter (USA)—Odori (USA) (The Minstrel (CAN))
144 Ch f 16/3 Trempolino (USA)—Polish Devil (USA) (Devil's Bag (USA))
145 Br f 31/3 Kris S (USA)—Proflare (USA) (Mr Prospector (USA))
146 Ch f 5/2 Selkirk (USA)—Prompting (Primo Dominie)
147 Br c 5/2 Zafonic (USA)—Prophecy (IRE) (Warning)
148 B c 27/2 Catrail (USA)—Quiche (Formidable (USA))
149 Ch c 14/3 Lord At War (ARG)—Right Word (USA) (Verbatim (USA))
150 B f 1/2 Danehill (USA)—Sacristy (Godswalk (USA))
151 **SAMUT (IRE),** b f 6/3 Danehill (USA)—Simaat (USA) (Mr Prospector (USA))
152 Ch f 15/2 Be My Guest (USA)—Scribbling (USA) (Secretariat (USA))

MR J. H. M. GOSDEN—continued

153 **SHANGHAI LADY,** b f 15/3 Sabrehill (USA)—Session (Reform)
154 B c 26/3 Sadler's Wells (USA)—Shannkara (IRE) (Akarad (FR))
155 **SHARP STEPPER,** b f 7/2 Selkirk (USA)—Awtaar (USA) (Lyphard (USA))
156 Ch c 21/2 Indian Ridge—Shih Ching (USA) (Secreto (USA))
157 B c 13/3 Distant Relative—Sinking (Midyan (USA))
158 **SNOOZY,** b f 3/3 Cadeaux Genereux—Quiet Week-End (Town And Country)
159 B c 9/4 Salse (USA)—Stardyn (Star Appeal)
160 Ch c 22/2 Gulch (USA)—Sudden Storm Bird (USA) (Storm Bird (CAN))
161 **TEN KINGDOMS (USA),** b c 19/1 Mr Prospector (USA)—Chinese Empress (USA) (Nijinsky (CAN))
162 B br f 18/4 Doyoun—Vaison La Romaine (Arctic Tern (USA))
163 Ch f 24/1 Selkirk (USA)—Valbra (Dancing Brave (USA))
164 **WAABL (IRE),** b c 27/1 Caerleon (USA)—Amandine (IRE) (Darshaan)
165 **WISHAH (USA),** b f 23/2 Red Ransom (USA)—Ninja Gold (Nijinsky (CAN))

Jockey (Flat): L Dettori (8-4).

Owners: Sheikh Mohammed, Mr K. Abdulla, Exors of the late Mr Herbert Allen Snr, Mr D. Armitage, Cheveley Park Stud, Cotswold Stud, Mr N. Cowan, CTS Racing Partnership, Lady Harrison, Lord Hartington, Hesmonds Stud, Highclere Thoroughbred Racing Ltd, Ms Rachel D. S. Hood, Mr Mark Horton, Mr L. Knight, Mrs M. Jason, Mrs J. Magnier, Sheikh Ahmed al Maktoum, Mr Hamdan al Maktoum, Maktoum al Maktoum, Sheikh Marwan al Maktoum, Mr Nabil Mourad, Pacific Hawk (HK) Ltd, Platt Promotions, Mr C. Ranson, Duke of Roxburghe, Mr Hamad Saeed, Prince Abdul Aziz Bin Saud, Mr P. D. Savill, Mr D. Simpson, Mrs Diane Snowden, Mr Anthony Speelman, Mr George Strawbridge, Mrs Shirley Taylor, The Thoroughbred Corporation, Mrs C. Waters, Mr James Wigan, Mr Ronnie Wood.

240 MRS H. O. GRAHAM, Jedburgh

Postal: **Belses Mill Farm, Ancrim, Jedburgh, Roxburghshire, TD8 6UP.**
Phone: **(01835) 830364**

1 6, B m Primitive Rising (USA)—Celtic Sands **Mrs H. O. Graham**
2 **DEDAY,** 11, gr g Liberated—Pandoras Box **Mrs H. O. Graham**
3 **HOOKY'S TREAT,** 7, b m Dutch Treat—Hookah Girl **Mrs H. O. Graham**
4 **WHISTLE BINKIE,** 12, ch m Slim Jim—Madam Law **Mrs H. O. Graham**

241 MR N. A. GRAHAM, Newmarket

Postal: **Coronation Stables, Newmarket, Suffolk, CB8 9BB.**
Phone: **OFFICE (01638) 665202 FAX (01638) 667849**

1 **BELISARIO (IRE),** 4, b br g Distinctly North (USA)—Bold Kate **Mr Paul G. Jacobs**
2 **BRIGHTER BYFAAH (IRE),** 5, ch g Kefaah (USA)—Bright Landing **Mr Paul G. Jacobs**
3 **CRUMPTON HILL (IRE),** 6, b g Thatching—Senane **Mr T. H. Chadney**
4 **DARK WATERS (IRE),** 5, b g Darshaan—Grecian Sea (FR) **Mr Brian March**
5 **JAZA,** 4, b g Pursuit of Love—Nordica **Mr Paul G. Jacobs**
6 **RUBY ESTATE (IRE),** 7, b m High Estate—Tuesday Morning **Mr C. N. & Mrs J. C. Wright**
7 **SLEEPLESS,** 4, b f Night Shift (USA)—Late Evening (USA) **Mrs Audrey Scotney**

THREE-YEAR-OLDS

8 **LINEAGE,** b f Distant Relative—Hymne d'Amour (USA) **The Earl Cadogan**
9 **MASHAB,** b c Pursuit of Love—Kukri **Mr Hamdan Al Maktoum**
10 **TAUREAN,** b c Dilum (USA)—Herora (IRE) **Mrs Lesley Graham**
11 **THUNDERING PAPOOSE,** b f Be My Chief (USA)—Thunder Bug (USA) **Mr C. N. & Mrs J. C. Wright**
12 **TIDAL WAVE,** b f Distant Relative—Wave Dancer **Mr R. D. Hollingsworth**
13 **TIEBREAKER (IRE),** b g Second Set (IRE)—Millionetta (IRE) **The Tiebreakers**
14 **WIGGING,** b f Warning—Pushy **Bloomsbury Stud**

MR N. A. GRAHAM—continued

TWO-YEAR-OLDS

15 B c 20/2 Lear Fan (USA)—Dixie Duo (USA) **The Thoroughbred Corporation**
16 **GOLD HALO (IRE),** b f 15/2 Strike The Gold (USA)—Halo's Charm (USA) **Mr L. J. Rice**
17 **HINDI,** b c 29/4 Indian Ridge—Tootsiepop (USA) **Mr Hamdan Al maktoum**
18 **MAKARIM (IRE),** ch c 25/2 Generous (IRE)—Emmaline (USA) **Mr Hamdan Al Maktoum**
19 B g 29/4 First Trump—Pepeke **Mr Paul G. Jacobs**
20 **SAMPAN,** b f 30/4 Elmaamul (USA)—Boathouse **Mr R. D. Hollingsworth**
21 **TAWADUD,** ch f 22/3 Arazi (USA)—Cunning **Mr Hamdan Al Maktoum**

Other Owners: Mr P. A. Deal, Mrs Janet Ford, Mr N. A. Graham, Mrs S. Jay, Mr A. Pryor, Mr T. D. Roots, Mr M. J. Silver, Lord Tavistock.

242 MR C. GRANT, Billingham

Postal: **Low Burntoft Farm, Wolviston, Billingham, Cleveland, TS22 5PD.**
Phone: **(01740) 644054**

1 **BIROTEX BOY (IRE),** 5, b g Meneval (USA)—Ballymorris Belle **Birotex**
2 **BOBBY GRANT,** 7, ch g Gunner B—Goldaw **Mr John J. Thompson**
3 **BRAVE EDWIN (IRE),** 8, ch g Le Bavard (FR)—Peace Run **Mrs P. A. Hayes**
4 **CHASING DREAMS,** 7, b g St Columbus—Into Song **Mr D. Eccleston**
5 5, B g Sylvan Express—Dercanny **Mr P. Gibbon**
6 **FERN LEADER (IRE),** 8, b g Supreme Leader—Mossbrook **Mr Robin Ward**
7 **HIGHFIELD PET,** 5, b g Efisio—Jendor **Mrs M. Hunter**
8 **KIERCHEM (IRE),** 7, b g Mazaad—Smashing Gale **Mrs M. Hunter**
9 **MASTER WOOD,** 7, b g Wonderful Surprise—Miss Wood **Mr Roy Robinson**
10 **MONOTONY (IRE),** 5, b g Over The River (FR)—Alamo Bay **Isiris**
11 **MORLEY PRINCE,** 5, b g Daring March—Minature Miss **Mrs H. Scotto**
12 **ROI DE LA CHASSE,** 5, ch g Royal Vulcan—Hunt The Thimble (FR) **The Hon Mrs M. Faulkner**
13 **SANTA BARBARA (IRE),** 7, b m Henbit (USA)—Fiery Rose **Mr B. Hayes**
14 **SHIP THE BUILDER,** 9, ch g Politico (USA)—Early Run **The Shipmates**
15 **SIKANDER A AZAM,** 5, b g Arctic Lord—Shanlaragh **Mr J. E. Greenall**
16 **STILL FRIENDS (IRE),** 5, b g Castle Keep—Majority Straight **Mr Bernard Hathaway**
17 **THE MICKLETONIAN,** 7, ch g K-Battery—Minature Miss **Mrs H. Scotto**
18 **TRIP YOUR TRIGGER (IRE),** 7, ch g Kamehameha (USA)—Half Smashed **Panther Racing**

Other Owners: Mr C. D. Butler, Mrs E. Dresser, Mr Melvyn Johnson, Mr J. H. Richardson, Mr I. Smith.

243 MR L. P. GRASSICK, Cheltenham

Postal: **Postlip Racing Stables, Winchcombe, Cheltenham, Gloucestershire, GL54 5AQ.**
Phone: **HOME (01242) 603124 YARD (01242) 603919**

1 **ALPHA LEATHER,** 7, b g Zambrano—Harvey's Choice **Postlip Racing**
2 **ARTFUL ARTHUR,** 12, b g Rolfe (USA)—Light of Zion **Mrs Pat Beck**
3 4, Ch g Zambrano—Blue Empress **Mr L. H. Ballinger**
4 **FIGHT TO WIN (USA),** 10, b g Fit To Fight (USA)—Spark of Life (USA) **Mr Bernard Partridge**
5 **HIGHTECH TOUCH,** 8, b g Sunley Builds—Caribs Love **Mrs G. Rowan-Hamilton**
6 **HUBERT,** 8, b g Rolfe (USA)—Pilicina **Mr L. H. Ballinger & Mrs P. Whiffen**
7 4, Bl g Zambrano—Lady Crusty **Mr L. P. Grassick**
8 **MARY FRANCIS,** 5, br m Zambrano—Diddy Girl **Mr L. H. Ballinger**
9 **MELVO,** 5, b h Zambrano—Blue Empress **Mr L. H. Ballinger**
10 **POSTLIP ROYALE,** 5, b m Zambrano—Wilhemina Crusty **Mr Alan Waller And Mrs Pat Beck**

THREE-YEAR-OLDS

11 Ch f Derrylin—Goldaw **Mr L. P. Grassick & Mrs S. L. Simmons**
12 **POSTLIP GOLD,** b f Derrylin—Wilhemina Crusty **Mrs Pat Beck & Mr Alan Waller**

MR L. P. GRASSICK—continued

TWO-YEAR-OLDS

13 B g 13/5 Ballacashtal (CAN)—Blue Empress (Blue Cashmere) **Mr L. H. Ballinger**
14 B g 14/5 Ballacashtal (CAN)—Lady Crusty (Golden Dipper) **Mr L. P. Grassick**
15 Gr f 30/4 Whittingham—Miss Crusty (Belfort (FR)) **Mr L. H. Ballinger**
16 B g 9/5 Ballacashtal (CAN)—Wilhemina Crusty (Jester) **Mr L. H. Ballinger**

Other Owners: Mr John Andrews, Mr M. J. Grassick, Mrs T. Grassick, Mr John Harris, Mr R. Mustoe, Mrs D. O'Brien, Mr S. Pope, Mrs S. Pope, Mr Paul Tuck.

Jockey (NH): W Marston (9-10).

Amateur: J R Grassick (9-7).

244 MR M. J. GRASSICK, Curragh

Postal: **Fenpark Stables, Pollardstown, Curragh, Co. Kildare, Ireland.**
Phone: **HOME (045) 436956 YARD (045) 434483 FAX (045) 434483 MOBILE 087 431923**

1 **BELLFAN (IRE)**, 5, b g Taufan (USA)—Fuchsia Belle **Mr Albert Finney**
2 **BLUE JAZZ (IRE)**, 4, b f Bluebird (USA)—Laser Show (IRE) **Mr S. J. Mullin**
3 **BOBBELLA (IRE)**, 4, b f Bob Back (USA)—Fuchsia Belle **Mr Albert Finney**
4 **EXECUTIVE CHOICE (IRE)**, 4, b g Don't Forget Me—Shadia (USA) **Tour Syndicate**
5 **EXECUTIVE DECISION (IRE)**, 4, ch g Classic Music (USA)—Bengala (FR) **Mr Char Kar Sun**
6 **FINAL REMINDER (IRE)**, 7, ch g Don't Forget Me—Pleasant Review (USA) **Mrs S. Grassick**
7 **FLAUNT (IRE)**, 6, b g Persian Bold—Fuchsia Belle **Mrs G. Watt**
8 **GARDD (USA)**, 4, b f Sheikh Albadou—Welsh Garden **Mrs S. Grassick**
9 **GLADIATORIAL (IRE)**, 6, b g Mazaad—Arena **Mrs J. Magnier**
10 **HI-HANDSOME (IRE)**, 7, b g High Estate—Bonnie Bess **Mrs C. Grassick**
11 **JOURNEY**, 5, ch g Tina's Pet—Lady Vynz **Tour Syndicate**
12 4, B f Broken Hearted—Millie's Choice (IRE) **Mr C. O'Loughlin**
13 **MOON ROSE (IRE)**, 4, b f Imperial Frontier—Crown Rose **Mr G. Delaney**
14 **REKONDO (IRE)**, 5, b h Two Timing (USA)—Tuesday Morning **Ricardo Sanz**
15 **RINCE ABHANN (IRE)**, 5, b m Dancing Dissident (USA)—Ballysnip **Mrs M. J. Grassick**
16 **SAN SEBASTIAN**, 4, ch g Niniski (USA)—Top of The League **Ricardo Sanz**
17 **SHALFORD BELLE (IRE)**, 4, ch f Shalford (IRE)—Belle-Cote **Mrs M. J. Grassick**
18 **SIR TRUE BLUE (IRE)**, 6, b g Bluebird (USA)—Very Sophisticated (USA) **Mr J. Crowley**
19 **TERTIA (IRE)**, 4, ch f Polish Patriot (USA)—Traumerei (GER) **Miss S. Von Schilcher**
20 **THE KEEGSTER (IRE)**, 7, ch g Tate Gallery (USA)—Stapara **Mr J. Crowley**
21 **TROPICAL LASS (IRE)**, 4, ch f Ballad Rock—Minnie Tudor **Mr Ken Campbell**
22 **WELSH LION (IRE)**, 4, b c Caerleon (USA)—Welsh Flame **Miss P. F. O'Kelly**

THREE-YEAR-OLDS

23 **ALL HUSH (IRE)**, ch f Highest Honor (FR)—Alamara (IRE) **M. G. Hynes**
24 B f Brief Truce (USA)—Aztec Princess **Mrs S. Grassick**
25 **BRIEF JOURNEY (IRE)**, b f Brief Truce (USA)—Ajona (IRE) **Mrs C. Grassick**
26 **DAWN CHORUS (IRE)**, ch f Mukaddamah (USA)—Singing Millie **Miss S. Von Schilcher**
27 **IMPALDI (IRE)**, b f Imp Society (USA)—Jaldi (IRE) **Mr Albert Finney**
28 **ISHBILIYA (IRE)**, b f Night Shift (USA)—Fantasy Land **Ricardo Sanz**
29 Ch f Be My Native (USA)—Lady Graduate (IRE) **Mrs M. J. Grassick**
30 **LET'S CLIC TOGETHER (IRE)**, b f Don't Forget Me—Mombones
31 **NIGHT PATROL (IRE)**, b f Night Shift (USA)—Naiadoora (IRE) **Mrs C. Grassick**
32 B c Forty Niner (USA)—Palanga (GER) **Miss D. Focke**
33 **RAID**, b c Saddlers' Hall (IRE)—Tabeeba **Mr M. Watt**
34 **SCHUST MADAME (IRE)**, b f Second Set (IRE)—Skisette **Mrs D. Hutch**
35 **SHASTRI (USA)**, b f Alleged (USA)—Sha Tha (USA) **Mrs S. Taylor**
36 **STELLISSIMA (IRE)**, ch f Persian Bold—Ruffling Point **Ricardo Sanz**

MR M. J. GRASSICK—continued

TWO-YEAR-OLDS

37 B f 25/2 Unfuwain (USA)—Alys **Ricardo Sanz**
38 B f 3/3 Up And At 'Em—Badraya (IRE) **Mr Ken Campbell**
39 B f 15/3 St Jovite (USA)—Barelyabride (USA) **Mrs G. Watt**
40 B c 24/4 Acatenango (GER)—Bay Street **Mrs H. Focke**
41 B f 17/4 Marju (IRE)—Braneakins **Mrs B. Brannigan**
42 B f 12/5 Tenby—Finalist **Mr David Clarke**
43 Ch f 8/5 Grand Lodge (USA)—Glendora **Mr B. Cooke**
44 **GROUNDSWELL (IRE)**, b c 7/2 Common Grounds—Fuchsia Belle **Mr Albert Finney**
45 B c 14/5 Caerleon (USA)—Honorine (USA) **Mr G. Canavan**
46 B f 27/4 Selkirk (USA)—Kereolle **Ricardo Sanz**
47 B f 14/3 Mac's Imp (USA)—Kraydel **Mr Jim Moore**
48 B c 7/5 Darshaan—Lisana **Mrs M. Murtagh**
49 B f 2/5 Danzig (USA)—Racing Blue **Mrs H. Focke**
50 **ROSE OF TARA (IRE)**, ch f 25/5 Generous (IRE)—Flame of Tara **Miss P. F. O'Kelly**
51 B c 25/3 Lashkari—She's No Laugh Ben (USA) **Mr R. Weiss**
52 Ch f 4/4 River Falls—Sister Dympna **Mr Sean Corbett**
53 **SPOKANE (IRE)**, ch c 18/6 Indian Ridge—Jaldi (IRE) **Mr Albert Finney**
54 **SUNTRAIL (IRE)**, ch f 8/4 Catrail (USA)—Soleiade **Miss P. F. O'Kelly**
55 Ch f 11/3 Catrail (USA)—Swallowcliffe **Mr M. Duffy**
56 Ch f 17/4 Bluebird (USA)—Tanouma (USA) **Mr F. O'Malley**
57 B f 17/2 Perugino (USA)—Trojan Tale (USA) **Mrs C. Grassick**
58 B f 6/2 Brief Truce (USA)—Viceroy Princess **M. G. Hynes**

Other Owners: H. E. The President Of Ireland, Mrs C. M. Poland.

Jockey (Flat): T J Daly (7-12).

Jockey (NH): P L Malone (9-7).

Apprentices: E Ahern (7-12), D Kinsella (6-7), B M O'Connor (7-12), D Rock (6-10).

245 MR FREDERICK GRAY, Haywards Heath

Postal: **Drewitts, Warninglid, Haywards Heath, West Sussex, RH17 5TB.**
Phone: **(01444) 461235 FAX (01444) 461485**

1 **DAISY RIVER (IRE)**, 6, ch m Over The River (FR)—French Gateaux **Mrs Jeanne Gray**
2 **GOBALINO GIRL (IRE)**, 6, b m Over The River (FR)—Ogan Spa **Mr Frederick Gray**

THREE-YEAR-OLDS

3 **GIGI**, b f Damister (USA)—Carmen Maria **Mrs Jeanne Gray**
4 **GRAN CLICQUOT**, gr f Gran Alba (USA)—Tina's Beauty **Mr Frederick Gray**

Other Owners: Mrs Liz Creber.

Amateur: Mr G Hogan.

246 MR T. R. GREATHEAD, Chipping Norton

Postal: **Chalford Oaks, Oxford Road, Chipping Norton, Oxfordshire, OX7 5QP.**
Phone: **(01608) 642954**

1 **BELLDORAN**, 7, ch g Gildoran—Bellecana **Mrs S. Greathead**
2 **CERIDWEN**, 8, ch m Fearless Action (USA)—Bellecana **Mrs S. Greathead**

MR T. R. GREATHEAD—continued

3 **CHARLAFRIVOLA,** 10, br g Persian Bold—Tattle **Mrs S. Greathead**
4 **CROWN AND CUSHION,** 5, b g High Adventure—Soulieana **Mrs S. Greathead**
5 **CUTTHROAT KID (IRE),** 8, b g Last Tycoon—Get Ahead **Mrs S. Greathead**
6 **WATER MUSIC MELODY,** 5, b m Sizzling Melody—Raintree Venture **Mrs S. Greathead**

Conditional: L Suthern (9-7).

247

THE PROPERTY OF W.J. GREDLEY ESQ

Colours: Yellow, black and yellow striped sleeves, white cap

Trained by **Mr B. W. Hills**, South Bank, Lambourn

1 **INCLUDE ME OUT,** 4, ch g Old Vic—Tafila
2 **JUDICIAL SUPREMACY,** 4, b c Warning—Song Test (USA)
3 **LOGIC,** 4, b f Slip Anchor—Docklands

THREE-YEAR-OLDS

4 **BULLION**, b f Sabrehill (USA)—High And Bright
5 **CHIM CHIMINEY**, b f Sabrehill (USA)—William's Bird (USA)
6 **ECO FRIENDLY**, ch c Sabrehill (USA)—Flower Girl
7 **EI EI**, b c North Briton—Branitska
8 **HIGH DEMAND**, b f Sabrehill (USA)—Tithing (USA)
9 **JANET LINDUP**, b f Sabrehill (USA)—Tartan Pimpernel
10 **MISS BUSSELL**, ch f Sabrehill (USA)—Reel Foyle (USA)
11 **MYSTERIOUS ECOLOGY**, gr f Mystiko (USA)—Ecologically Kind
12 **RELIABLY WON**, b f Sabrehill (USA)—Way To Go
13 **SHARP SARAH**, ch f Sabrehill (USA)—Sarah's Love

TWO-YEAR-OLDS

14 **ALASTAIR SMELLIE**, ch c 24/2 Sabrehill (USA)—Reel Foyle (USA) (Irish River (FR))
15 **BRING SWEETS**, b c 12/2 Sabrehill (USA)—Che Gambe (USA) (Lyphard (USA))
16 **CHIT CHAT (IRE)**, b c 6/5 Mujadil (USA)—Rhoman Ruby (IRE) (Rhoman Rule (USA))
17 **GALLEONS POINT**, b c 1/2 Sabrehill (USA)—Rainbow Ring (Rainbow Quest (USA))
18 **HASTY WORDS (IRE)**, b f 9/2 Polish Patriot (USA)—Park Elect (Ahonoora)
19 **INDUCEMENT**, ch c 10/2 Sabrehill (USA)—Verchinina (Star Appeal)
20 **KING'S CHAMBERS**, ch c 12/3 Sabrehill (USA)—Flower Girl (Pharly (FR))
21 **OCEANS FRIENDLY (USA)**, b f 24/3 Green Dancer (USA)—Sedra (Nebbiolo)
22 **QUIET DIGNITY**, b f 4/5 Unfuwain (USA)—Docklands (On Your Mark)
23 **SO**, b f 14/5 Mystiko (USA)—High And Bright (Shirley Heights)
24 **SPOONFUL OF SUGAR**, b f 21/2 Sabrehill (USA)—Pacific Gull (USA) (Storm Bird (CAN))
25 **THROUGH THE RYE**, ch c 15/3 Sabrehill (USA)—Baharlilys (Green Dancer (USA))
26 **TIGER TALK**, ch c 2/2 Sabrehill (USA)—Tebre (USA) (Sir Ivor)
27 **WILLIAMSHAKESPEARE (IRE)**, b c 9/4 Slip Anchor—Rostova (Blakeney)
28 **ZIPPERGATE**, b c 29/5 Mystiko (USA)—Branitska (Mummy's Pet)
29 **ZMILE**, b c 14/1 Ezzoud (IRE)—Mountain Bluebird (USA) (Clever Trick (USA))

248 MR V. G. GREENWAY, Taunton

Postal: **Higher Vexford Farm, Lydeard St Lawrence, Taunton, Somerset, TA4 3QG.**
Phone: **(01984) 656548**

1 **BLADE OF FORTUNE,** 10, b g Beldale Flutter (USA)—Foil 'em (USA) **Mr V. G. Greenway**
2 **ON ALERT (NZ),** 11, ch g Double Trouble (NZ)—Stand By (NZ) **Mr V. G. Greenway**
3 **TOP SKIPPER (IRE),** 6, b g Nordico (USA)—Scarlet Slipper **Mr V. G. Greenway**
4 **VEXFORD LUCY,** 5, b m Latest Model—Suchong **Mr V. G. Greenway**
5 **VEXFORD MODEL,** 8, b m Latest Model—Suchong **Mr V. G. Greenway**

Other Owners: Mrs M. Greenway, Mr M. G. Greenway.

Amateur: Mr J Tizzard (10-0).

249 MR S. G. GRIFFITHS, Carmarthen

Postal: **Rwyth Farm, Nantgaredig, Carmarthen, Dyfed, SA32 7LG.**
Phone: **(012672) 90321**

1 **NOBLE COLOURS,** 5, b g Distinctly North (USA)—Kentucky Tears (USA) **Mr S. G. Griffiths**
2 **TROJAN LOVE (IRE),** 5, b m Cyrano de Bergerac—Love of Paris **Mr S. G. Griffiths**

250 MR D. M. GRISSELL, Brightling

Postal: **Brightling Park, Robertsbridge, East Sussex, TN32 5HH.**
Phone: **(01424) 838241 FAX (01424) 838378 MOBILE (0378) 498850**

1 **BE MY MOT (IRE),** 6, b m Be My Native (USA)—Madam Butterfly **R. Winchester & Son**
2 **BILLY MOONSHINE,** 6, ch g Nicholas Bill—Indian Moonshine **Mr Graham Haupt**
3 **BRACKENHEATH (IRE),** 7, b g Le Moss—Stable Lass **Mr John Grist**
4 **BUCKLAND LAD (IRE),** 7, ch g Phardante (FR)—Belcraig **Mrs R. M. Hepburn**
5 **EMERALD STATEMENT (IRE),** 8, b g Strong Statement (USA)—Popsi's Darling **The Hon Mrs C. Yeates**
6 **FIRST INSTANCE (IRE),** 8, b g Torus—Red-Leria **Pepin Racing**
7 **JOJO (IRE),** 8, ch g Buckskin (FR)—Autumn Queen **Mr John Grist**
8 **LITTLE CHINK (IRE),** 8, b g Mandalus—Alice Minkthorn **Mrs Eric Boucher**
9 **MAINE MARIE,** 6, b m Northern State (USA)—Marie Galante **Dr Mike Bott**
10 **MIKE'S MUSIC (IRE),** 7, br g Orchestra—Seaville **Mrs Christine Notley**
11 **MR CHATAWAY (IRE),** 7, b g Le Bavard (FR)—Swift Invader **Mrs Eric Boucher**
12 **MULDOVA (IRE),** 5, b g Poet's Dream (IRE)—Marys Choice **Mr D. Curtis & Mr F. J. T. Parsons**
13 **NORMARANGE (IRE),** 8, ch g Lancastrian—Perdeal **Mr D. Curtis**
14 **ROCKHOLM LAD (IRE),** 6, b g Royal Fountain—Rockholm Rosie **Mrs John Grist**
15 **SLEIPNIR,** 5, gr g Executive Perk—Sindur **Mrs John Grist**
16 **SORBIERE,** 11, b g Deep Run—Irish Mint **Mrs R. A. Proctor**
17 **YARSLEY JESTER,** 6, b m Phardante (FR)—Thank Yourself **Mrs Caroline Martin**

Other Owners: Dr J. J. Bourke, Mr J. Draper, Mr T. W. Edmonds, Mrs D. M. Grissell, Mrs Kim Haupt, Mrs R. Howell, Mr D. J. Instance, Mr R. H. Kerr, Mr Christopher Newport, His Honour Judge Peppitt, Mrs Cherry Stupple, Mr M. D. Winchester.

251 MR BRIAN GUBBY, Bagshot

Postal: **Dukes Wood, Bracknell Road, Bagshot, Surrey, GU19 5HX.**
Phone: **DAY 01276 63282 FAX 01276 34445 HOME 01276 471030 MOBILE 0468 867368**

1 **EASY DOLLAR,** 6, ch g Gabitat—Burglars Girl **Brian Gubby Ltd**
2 **LUCAYAN BEACH,** 4, gr g Cyrano de Bergerac—Mrs Gray **Brian Gubby Ltd**

MR BRIAN GUBBY—continued

3 **OMAHA CITY (IRE),** 4, b g Night Shift (USA)—Be Discreet **Brian Gubby Ltd**
4 **SORISKY,** 6, ch g Risk Me (FR)—Minabella **Brian Gubby Ltd**
5 **TRIBAL PEACE (IRE),** 6, ch g Red Sunset—Mirabiliary (USA) **Brian Gubby Ltd**
6 **TULSA (IRE),** 4, b g Priolo (USA)—Lagrion (USA) **Brian Gubby Ltd**

THREE-YEAR-OLDS

7 **IDAHO (IRE),** ch f Common Grounds—Queen's Share **Brian Gubby Ltd**

TWO-YEAR-OLDS

8 **ESTACADO (IRE),** b f 26/3 Dolphin Street (FR)—Raubritter (Levmoss)
9 **POCATELLO,** gr c 4/4 Mystiko (USA)—Ballygriffin Belle (Another Realm)
10 **SPRING AGAIN,** ch f 22/1 Then Again—Spring In Rome (USA) (Forli (ARG))
11 **TIJUANA,** ch f 3/4 Gabitat—Gabibti (IRE) (Dara Monarch)
12 **WINNIPEG (IRE),** ch f 14/4 Mac's Imp (USA)—Cadasi (Persian Bold)

Amateur: Mr James Rees (9-10).

252 MR R. GUEST, Newmarket

Postal: **Chestnut Tree Stables, Exeter Road, Newmarket, Suffolk, CB8 8LR.**
Phone: **(01638) 661508 FAX (01638) 667317 MOBILE (0370) 697976**

1 **DELLUA (IRE),** 4, b f Suave Dancer—Joma Kaanem **Mr Khalid M. Affara**
2 **LYCEUM,** 4, b f Sadler's Wells (USA)—Alysardi (USA) **Matthews Breeding & Racing**
3 **MIDNIGHT SHIFT (IRE),** 4, b f Night Shift (USA)—Old Domesday Book **Mr C. J. Mills**
4 **MONTECRISTO,** 5, br g Warning—Sutosky **Mr Rae Guest**
5 **MOUSEHOLE,** 6, b g Statoblest—Alo Ez **Mrs Janet Linskey**
6 **PRESENT GENERATION,** 5, ch g Cadeaux Genereux—Penny Mint **Mr & Mrs S. Lury**
7 **SLIPSTREAM,** 4, b g Slip Anchor—Butosky **Matthews Breeding & Racing**

THREE-YEAR-OLDS

8 **BARREN LANDS,** b c Green Desert (USA)—Current Raiser **Matthews Breeding and Racing**
9 **BEDTIME STORY,** b f Fairy King (USA)—Prima Domina (FR) **Matthews Breeding and Racing**
10 **INDIAN SPLENDOUR (IRE),** b f Second Set (IRE)—Clover Honey **Mr Vijay Mallya**
11 **JASMINE,** b f Thatching—Jadirah (USA) **Miss K. Rausing**
12 **LITTLE MISS HUFF (IRE),** b f Anita's Prince—Regal Charmer **Mr M. G. Hill**
13 **MAJALIS,** b br f Mujadil (USA)—Rose Barton **Bradmill Ltd**
14 **MILLING (IRE),** b f In The Wings—Princess Pati **Mr C. J. Mills**
15 **MISS DIVOT (IRE),** b f Petardia—Kinosium **Miss Jocelyn M. Booth**
16 **MYSTICAL SONG,** ch f Mystiko (USA)—Jubilee Song **Mr J. Strange**
17 **NATIONALVELVETGIRL,** b f Alhijaz—Bath **Mr A. P. Davies & Partners**
18 **O'KELLY (DEN),** b br f Last Tycoon—Laser Show (IRE) **Mr Nick Elsass**
19 **OUAISNE,** b c Warning—Noirmant **Matthews Breeding & Racing**
20 **PRECIOUS PRINCESS,** br f Precocious—Magyar Princess **Mr J. W. Biswell**
21 **SARAH STOKES (IRE),** b f Brief Truce (USA)—Almaaseh (IRE) **Matthews Breeding and Racing**
22 **TARTAN LASS,** b f Selkirk (USA)—Gwiffina **Matthews Breeding and Racing**
23 **TELEPATHY (IRE),** b f Kahyasi—Timbale d'Argent **Miss K. Rausing**

TWO-YEAR-OLDS

24 **CAPITALIST HERO,** b c 17/2 Barathea (IRE)—Threatening (Warning) **Matthews Breeding & Racing**
25 **EBONY,** b f 23/2 Mujtahid (USA)—Sharia (USA) (Irish River (FR)) **Matthews Beeding & Racing**
26 **INDIAN CITY,** ch f 6/2 Lahib (USA)—Alencon (Northfields (USA)) **Mr Vijay Mallya**
27 B c 19/2 Royal Academy (USA)—Jungle Rose (Shirley Heights) **Mr E. Carter**
28 **JUST DREAMS,** ch f 28/2 Salse (USA)—Pato (High Top) **Matthews Breeding & Racing**
29 **MY FIRST,** b c 30/4 First Trump—Jubilee Song (Song) **Mr C. J. Mills**
30 **RM AGAIN,** b c 8/2 Primo Dominie—La Cabrilla (Carwhite) **RM Design Partmership Ltd**
31 B f 31/3 Lahib (USA)—Rose Barton (Pas de Seul) **Mrs B. Mills & Partners**
32 **TWICKERS,** b f 8/2 Primo Dominie—Songstead (Song) **Mr John Hill**

Other Owners: Mr Peter Hughff, Mr A. D. Linskey, Mrs Lesley Mills, Mr Len Stoten.

Lady Rider: Ms Rachel Flynn.

253 MR W. J. HAGGAS, Newmarket

Postal: **Somerville Lodge, Fordham Road, Newmarket, Suffolk, CB8 7AA.**
Phone: **NEWMARKET (01638) 667013 FAX (01638) 660534**

1 **PEN FRIEND**, 4, b g Robellino (USA)—Nibbs Point (IRE) **Mr B. Haggas**
2 **SEVERITY**, 4, b c Reprimand—Neenah **Girsonfield Ltd.**
3 **YEAST**, 6, b g Salse (USA)—Orient **Mr B. Haggas**

THREE-YEAR-OLDS

4 **ANTHONY MON AMOUR (USA)**, b g Nicholas (USA)—Reine de La Ciel (USA) **Mr Henryk De Kwiatkowski**
5 **BULLET**, b c Alhijaz—Beacon **Mr J. W. Bogie**
6 **CAMOUFLAGE**, b g Salse (USA)—Collage **Mr B. Haggas**
7 **CARNBREA FIRSTLOVE**, b g Pursuit of Love—Carnbrea Snip **Carnbrea Ltd**
8 **CHOCOLATE BOX**, ch f Most Welcome—Short Rations **Mr J. M. Greetham**
9 **DOODLE**, b f Green Desert (USA)—Quillotern (USA) **Mr B. Haggas**
10 **FEN WARRIOR**, b g Pursuit of Love—Kennedys Prima **Jolly Farmers Racing**
11 **HEADHUNTER (IRE)**, b c Last Tycoon—Erzsi **Highclere Thoroughbred Racing Ltd.**
12 **HIT THE SPOT (IRE)**, b f Night Shift (USA)—Winning Feature **Mr M. Tabor & Mrs John Magnier**
13 **INTERNAL AFFAIR (USA)**, b g Nicholas (USA)—Gdynia (USA) **Mr Henryk De Kwiatkowski**
14 **JOLLY HARBOUR**, b f Rudimentary (USA)—Ask Mama **Mrs Henrietta Charlet**
15 **NEWALA**, b f Royal Academy (USA)—African Dance (USA) **Mr J. D. Ashenheim**
16 **PRIME HAND**, ch f Primo Dominie—Rechanit (IRE) **Mrs M. M. Haggas**
17 **RING THE RAFTERS**, b f Batshoof—Soprano **Mr A. Hirschfeld**
18 **SAMATA ONE (IRE)**, b c River Falls—Abadila (IRE) **Mr S. Hassiakos**
19 **SAXON VICTORY (USA)**, b g Nicholas (USA)—Saxon Shore (USA) **Mrs L. A. Wallis**
20 **SENTRY DUTY**, b c Nashwan (USA)—Third Watch **Mr B. Haggas**
21 **SHOCKER (IRE)**, b f Sabrehill (USA)—Fenjaan **Mr Ali K. Al Jafleh**
22 **SHUDDER**, b c Distant Relative—Oublier L'Ennui (FR) **Mr Ali K. Al Jafleh**
23 **TIE BREAK (IRE)**, ch g Second Set (IRE)—Karayasha **Mr M. H. Wilson**

TWO-YEAR-OLDS

24 **ACE OF TRUMPS**, ch c 6/3 First Trump—Elle Reef (Shareef Dancer (USA)) **Fernedge Bloodstock**
25 B c 12/2 Zilzal (USA)—Allegedly (USA) (Sir Ivor) **Dandy Racing Ltd.**
26 B c 10/5 Polar Falcon (USA)—Amina (Brigadier Gerard) **Mr C. Bothway**
27 **ANAIDA (IRE)**, b f 6/4 Perugino (USA)—Wilderness (Martinmas) **Mr Khalifa Dasmal**
28 Ch f 28/4 Polish Patriot (USA)—Blazing Glory (IRE) (Glow (USA))
29 Ch f 6/3 Inchinor—Bonita (Primo Dominie) **Mr A. Hirschfeld**
30 **ESCORT**, b c 31/1 Most Welcome—Benazir (High Top) **Mr J. M. Greetham**
31 **FESTIVE**, b f 1/5 Rudimentary (USA)—Champagne Season (USA) (Vaguely Noble) **Cheveley Park Stud**
32 **FULL EGALITE**, gr c 20/4 Ezzoud (IRE)—Milva (Jellaby) **Mr S. Hassiakos**
33 **FUTURE COUP (USA)**, b c 26/2 Lord at War (ARG)—Holy Moly (USA) (Halo (USA)) **Mr M. Brower**
34 B f 24/4 Rainbows For Life—Gracieuse Amie (FR) (Gay Mecene (USA)) **Mr A. Farook**
35 B c 17/5 Turtle Island (IRE)—Lightino (Bustino) **Dandy Racing Ltd.**
36 **LOCOMOTION (IRE)**, ch c 16/3 Seattle Dancer (USA)—Pipe Opener (Prince Sabo) **Mr W. J. Haggas**
37 B f 23/1 Shirley Heights—Manhattan Sunset (USA) (El Gran Senor (USA)) **Mrs B Bassett**
38 **NUMERATOR**, b f 7/4 Rudimentary—Half A Dozen (Saratoga Six (USA)) **Cheveley Park Stud**
39 **PICTURE PUZZLE**, b f 20/4 Royal Academy (USA)—Cloudslea (USA) (Chief's Crown (USA)) **Mr M. H. Wilson**
40 B c 19/2 Thatching—Pollyfidra (USA) (In Fijar (USA)) **Dandy Racing Ltd**
41 **PREDOMINANT (USA)**, ch c 27/1 Sky Classic—Hard Knocker (USA) (Raja Baba (USA)) **Mr P. Ellick**
42 B c 27/2 Superpower—Syke Lane (Clantime)
43 **TICKLISH**, b f 10/2 Cadeaux Genereux—Exit Laughing (Shaab) **Mr J. Bogie**
44 **TIPSY**, ch f 30/1 Kris—Heady (Rousillon (USA)) **Cheveley Park Stud**
45 **TOP FIT**, b c 21/4 Thatching—Diplomatist (Dominion) **Fung Kwok Hung**
46 Ch c 9/3 Cadeaux Genereux—Tricky Note (Song) **Mr R. Burton**
47 B c 11/3 Sadler's Wells (USA)—Urjwan (USA) (Seattle Slew (USA)) **Highclere Thoroughbred Racing Ltd.**
48 **WELCOME GIFT**, b c 18/4 Prince Sabo—Ausonia (Beldale Flutter (USA)) **Mr M. H. Wilson**
49 **WESTENDER (FR)**, b c 4/4 In The Wings—Trude (GER) (Windwurf (GER)) **Mr Khalifa Dasmal**

Other Owners: Total (Bloodstock) Ltd., Mr Ahmed Al Shafar, Mr E Blitz, Mrs S. M. Crompton, Mr P. A. Deal, Mr S. De Martino, Felix Rosenstiel'S Widow & Son, Mr C. Humphris, Mr S. C. Palmer, Tessona Racing Limited, Mrs P. D. Rossdale.

Apprentice: Jo Hunnam (7-10).

254 MRS D. HAINE, Newmarket

Postal: **C/O June Anne Management, Cardigan Lodge, 3 The Avenue, Newmarket, Suffolk, CB8 9AA.**
Phone: **HOME (01638) 561001 STABLE (01638) 662346**

1 5, Br bl m Executive Perk—Ballyclough Lady **Mrs Diana Haine**
2 **CLASSIC EAGLE,** 5, b g Unfuwain (USA)—La Lutine **Classic Bloodstock PLC**
3 **CRACKLING FROST (IRE),** 10, b br g Green Shoon—Moppet's Last **The Unlucky For Some Partnership**
4 **DIGBY (IRE),** 5, b g Meneval (USA)—Irish Hill Lass **Mrs Diana Haine & Mr E. Fenaroli**
5 **DOYENNE,** 4, gr f Mystiko (USA)—No Chili **Partnership**
6 **FIRE ON ICE (IRE),** 6, b h Sadler's Wells (USA)—Foolish Lady (USA) **Miss M. O'Toole**
7 5, B g Cataldi—Frostbite **Mrs Diana Haine**
8 **IN THE VAN,** 6, b g Bedford (USA)—Sea Countess **Mrs Solna Thomson Jones**
9 **KRASNIK (IRE),** 5, br g Roi Danzig (USA)—Kermesse (IRE) **Mrs Solna Thomson Jones**
10 **LIGHT OF PEACE (IRE),** 5, b h Miner's Lamp—French Academy **Sir Peter & Lady Gibbings**
11 **LUCY WALTERS (IRE),** 6, b m King's Ride—Serpentine Artiste **Miss M. O'Toole**
12 **OCEAN LEADER,** 11, b g Lord Ha Ha—Rough Tide **Gibbings/Mellon Partnership**
13 **PEACE LORD (IRE),** 8, ch g Callernish—French Academy **Sir Peter & Lady Gibbings**
14 **PEACEMAKER (IRE),** 6, br g Strong Gale—Gamonda **Sir Peter & Lady Gibbings**
15 **PRIMITIVE PENNY,** 7, ch m Primitive Rising (USA)—Penny Pink **Mrs Peter Mason**
16 **REGAL RAINBOW (IRE),** 5, br g Royal Fountain—Bow Gello **Gibbings/Mellon Partnership**
17 **SHAKEN UP,** 4, b c Kendor (FR)—Oshawa **Mrs Solna Thomson Jones**
18 **STRAIGHT ON (IRE),** 7, b g Tremblant—Maybird **Mr Gerrard P. Cashin**
19 **SUPREMISM,** 4, b c Be My Chief (USA)—Ever Welcome **Lady Helen Smith & Mr H. Thomson Jones**
20 **SURANOM (IRE),** 6, b h Alzao (USA)—Gracieuse Majeste (FR) **Mrs Ann Leat**
21 **TANGSHAN (CAN),** 4, ch f Zilzal (USA)—Manzanares (USA) **Mrs Solna Thomson Jones**

Other Owners: Mr Jeremy Mason, Mr W. H. Mellen, Mrs E. Mumford, Mr Walter W. Mumford.

Jockey (NH): J F Titley.

Conditional: Martin Mooney (9-7).

255 MR J. S. HALDANE, Mindrum

Postal: **The Yard Cottage, Mindrum, Northumberland, TD12 4QN.**
Phone: **(01890) 850382**

1 **ANTITHESIS (IRE),** 5, b m Fairy King (USA)—Music of The Night (USA) **Mr G. J. Johnston**
2 **FINE TIMES,** 4, br g Timeless Times (USA)—Marfen **Mr J. S. Haldane**
3 **HIGHLANDMAN,** 12, b g Florida Son—Larne **Mrs Hugh Fraser**
4 **NICKYS PERIL,** 6, ch m Nicholas Bill—Priceless Peril **Mr J. S. Haldane**
5 **PARSONS BRIG,** 12, b g The Parson—Tumlin Brig **Mr J. S. Haldane**
6 **RESPECTABLE LAURA,** 7, b m Respect—Laura Lyshill Wood **Mr J. S. Haldane**
7 **SNOOTY ESKIMO (IRE),** 6, ch g Aristocracy—Over The Arctic **The Fraser Racing Partnership**
8 **TIDAL RACE (IRE),** 6, b g Homo Sapien—Flowing Tide **Mrs Hugh Fraser**
9 **TUMLIN OOT (IRE),** 9, b g Amazing Bust—Tumlin Brig **Mrs Hugh Fraser**

Other Owners: Mrs A. J. M. Cockburn, Mr A. M. Crow, Mrs D. Currie, Mr Ernie Fenwick, Mr A. Fraser, Mr Hugh Fraser, Mr Simon Fraser.

256 MR L. MONTAGUE HALL, Tadworth

Postal: **Chartwell Stables, Motts Hill Lane, Tadworth, Surrey, KT20 6BA.**
Phone: **(01737) 814847/370911 FAX (01737) 370911**

1 **AMELIA JANE,** 4, ch f Efisio—Blue Jane **The Racing For Fun Partnership**
2 **BELAMI,** 5, b g Bold Fox—Solbella **Mr Peter Pink**

MR L. MONTAGUE HALL—continued

3 **CRUISING FREE,** 9, b m Cruise Missile—Free Sally **Mr & Mrs Colin Brooks**
4 **FAST FORWARD FRED,** 7, gr g Sharood—Sun Street **The Straight Forward Partnership**
5 **GLOW FORUM,** 7, b m Kalaglow—Beau's Delight (USA) **Miss J. D. Anstee & Partners**
6 **ILLEGALLY YOURS,** 5, br m Be My Chief (USA)—Legal Precedent **Mrs J. Murray**
7 **MIJAS,** 5, ch m Risk Me (FR)—Out of Harmony **The Mijas Partnership**
8 **OOZLEM (IRE),** 9, b g Burslem—Fingers **Brooknight Guarding Ltd**
9 **ROBO MAGIC (USA),** 6, b g Tejano (USA)—Bubble Magic (USA) **Mr A. D. Green and Partners**
10 **THE LAD,** 9, b g Bold Owl—Solbella **Treberth Partnership**
11 **WOTTASHAMBLES,** 7, b br g Arrasas (USA)—Manawa **Dream On Racing Partnership**
12 **ZAFORUM,** 5, b h Deploy—Beau's Delight (USA) **Mr Andy J. Smith**

THREE-YEAR-OLDS

13 **MONOCKY,** b g Mon Tresor—Solbella **Treberth Partnership 2**

Other Owners: Mrs J. L. Agnew, Mr D. J. Campbell, Mr T. Carter, Mr R. Goby, Mrs Jacqueline R. Green, Mr L. Montague Hall, Mr A. P. Johnston, Pinks Gym, Mr G. E. Thompson, Mr Douglas Wooltorton, Mrs Mary B. Wooltorton.

Apprentice: M Harfield (7-13).

257 MISS S. E. HALL, Middleham

Postal: **Brecongill, Coverham, Leyburn, North Yorkshire, DL8 4TJ.**
Phone: **(01969) 640223 FAX (01969) 640223**

1 **FOXES TAIL,** 4, gr g Batshoof—Secret Gill **Mrs Joan Hodgson**
2 **LEIF THE LUCKY (USA),** 9, ch g Lemhi Gold (USA)—Corvine (USA) **Miss Betty Duxbury**
3 **MOVING ARROW,** 7, ch g Indian Ridge—Another Move **Mr G. W. Westgarth**
4 **RUNNING BEAR,** 4, ch g Sylvan Express—Royal Girl **Miss S. E. Hall**
5 **TARA RAMBLER (IRE),** 9, ch g Arapahos (FR)—Tarabelle **Mr J. Hanson**

THREE-YEAR-OLDS

6 **ARAB GOLD,** b g Presidium—Parklands Belle **Mr C. Platts**
7 **DESERT SAND,** b f Tragic Role (USA)—Miss Suntan **Mr J. Hanson**
8 **MOVING PRINCESS,** b f Prince Sabo—Another Move **Mr G. W. Westgarth**
9 **MR LAMB,** gr c Deploy—Caroline Lamb **Mrs T. Hall**
10 **ROOSTER,** b g Roi Danzig (USA)—Jussoli **Mr C. Platts**
11 **TANGO QUEEN,** b f Rambo Dancer (CAN)—Formidable Task **Mr C. Platts**
12 **UNIFORM,** ch f Unfuwain (USA)—Trachelium **Mr C. Platts**

TWO-YEAR-OLDS

13 **DARRAS SKY,** ch c 23/3 Clantime—Sky Music (Absalom) **Skylark Partnership**
14 **GET SET,** ch f 7/2 Keen—Labelon Lady (Touching Wood (USA)) **Mr B. J. McAllister**
15 **GRAVY BOAT (IRE),** b c 6/4 River Falls—Newstreet Princess (Head For Heights) **Miss Betty Duxbury**
16 **INNES,** b f 17/2 Inchinor—Trachelium (Formidable (USA)) **Mr C. Platts**
17 **MISS ELLIE,** b f 20/3 Elmaamul (USA)—Jussoli (Don) **Mr C. Platts**
18 **MOON GLOW (IRE),** b g 8/2 Fayruz—Jarmar Moon (Unfuwain (USA)) **Mr C. Platts**
19 **OTTERINGTON GIRL,** b f 15/2 Noble Patriarch—Bidweaya (USA) (Lear Fan (USA)) **Mrs Joan Hodgson**
20 **ROYAL PRINCESS,** b f 19/2 Rock City—Royal Girl (Kafu) **Miss S. E. Hall**
21 **SIR LAMB,** gr g 15/4 Rambo Dancer (CAN)—Caroline Lamb (Hotfoot) **Mrs T. Hall**
22 **SNOWBERRY,** b f 2/2 Alhijaz—Dear Person (Rainbow Quest (USA)) **Miss Betty Duxbury**
23 **STRIKE IT LUCKY,** ch f 25/1 Deploy—Formidable Task (Formidable (USA)) **Mr C. Platts**

Other Owners: Mrs A. Charlton, Mr William Jarvis, Mr H. Young.

Jockey (Flat): J Weaver (w.a.).

Jockey (NH): N Bentley.

258 MR G. A. HAM, Axbridge

Postal: **Rose Farm, Rooksbridge, Axbridge, Somerset, BS26 2TH.**
Phone: **HOME (01934) 750331 EVENINGS (01934) 733117**

1 **ASTROJOY (IRE)**, 6, ch m Astronef—Pharjoy (FR) **Mrs S. Hutchings**
2 **BRIDIE'S PRIDE**, 7, b g Alleging (USA)—Miss Monte Carlo **Mr K. C. White**
3 **COLETTE'S CHOICE**, 9, b m Alzao (USA)—Le Madrilon (FR) **Mr C. Garland**
4 **FINNIGAN FREE**, 8, ch g Los Cerrillos (ARG)—Philly-Free **Exors of the Late G. E. Rich**
5 **GREEN'S FAIR (IRE)**, 8, b g Carmelite House (USA)—Lockwood Girl **Mr N. G. Ahier**
6 **KIRBY OPPORTUNITY**, 10, ch m Mummy's Game—Empress Catherine **Mr K. C. White**
7 **MINNISAM**, 5, ch g Niniski (USA)—Wise Speculation (USA) **Mr Derek Walker**
8 **NORTHREEL**, 7, ch g Scottish Reel—La Troienne **Mr H. Voitier**
9 **NO SACRIFICE**, 6, b m Revlow—Cool Brae **Mr Mike Cornish**
10 **PRINCE DE BERRY**, 7, ch g Ballacashtal (CAN)—Hoonah (FR) **Mr N. G. Ahier**
11 **RONQUISTA D'OR**, 4, b c Ron's Victory (USA)—Gild The Lily **Mr D. M. Drury**
12 **SAUCY DANCER**, 5, ch m Chilibang—Silent Dancer **Miss S. J. Burgin**
13 **SULA'S DREAM**, 9, b m Sula Bula—Gallic Dream **Miss S. J. Burgin**
14 **TECHNICAL MOVE (IRE)**, 7, br m Move Off—Technical Merit **Mr Mike Cornish**
15 **TWO LORDS**, 6, b g Arctic Lord—Doddycross **Mr W. E. Catstrey**

THREE-YEAR-OLDS

16 B g Arctic Lord—Kellyann **Mr Mike Cornish**

Other Owners: Miss Laura J. Horsey, Mrs M. A. Smith.

Jockey (Flat): S Drowne (w.a.).

Jockey (NH): S Burrough (10-0).

Apprentice: J J Fowle (7-3).

Conditional: R Thornton (w.a.).

Lady Rider: Sophie Mitchell.

259 MR M. D. HAMMOND, Middleham

Postal: **Tupgill Park Stables, Coverham, Leyburn, North Yorkshire, DL8 4TJ.**
Phone: **(01969) 640228 FAX (01969) 640662**

1 **ALCALALI (USA)**, 4, b f Septieme Ciel (USA)—Princess Verna (USA) **Mr Steve Semple**
2 **ALCIAN BLUE**, 7, b g Tina's Pet—Rhiannon **Rykneld Thoroughbred Co**
3 **BROADWATER BOY (IRE)**, 10, b g Miner's Lamp—Down By The River **Mr D. F. Sills**
4 **CAMPAIGN**, 7, b g Sure Blade (USA)—Just Cause **Spectrum**
5 **CATHERINE'S CHOICE**, 5, ch g Primo Dominie—Bambolona **Shore Property Development Ltd**
6 **CELTIC DUKE**, 6, b g Strong Gale—Celtic Cygnet **Mr Trevor Hemmings**
7 **CHARIOT MAN (IRE)**, 6, b br g Mandalus—Mum's Chariot **Mr Trevor Hemmings**
8 **CHIEF MINISTER (IRE)**, 9, br g Rainbow Quest (USA)—Riverlily (FR) **Mr G. Shiel**
9 **COMMANDER GLEN (IRE)**, 6, b g Glenstal (USA)—Une Parisienne (FR) **B. & K. Associates**
10 **COUNT TONY**, 4, ch g Keen—Turtle Dove **Million in Mind Partnership (7)**
11 **CURRENT MONY (IRE)**, 7, ch g Electric—Killiney Rose **Mr S. Monaghan**
12 **DEEP WATER (USA)**, 4, b g Diesis—Water Course (USA) **The County Set**

MR M. D. HAMMOND—continued

13 **EASTERN PROJECT (IRE),** 4, b g Project Manager—Diandra **Mr Steve Semple**
14 **ELPIDOS,** 6, ch g Bold Arrangement—Thalassa (IRE) **Mrs M. Winter**
15 **FASSAN (IRE),** 6, br g Contract Law (USA)—Persian Susan (USA) **M.H.O.G. Racing**
16 **FEEL A LINE,** 4, b g Petong—Cat's Claw (USA) **Punters Haven Racing Club**
17 **FINEWOOD (IRE),** 4, b g Macmillion—Feodora **Finewood Joinery Products Ltd**
18 **FOREVER NOBLE (IRE),** 5, b g Forzando—Pagan Queen **Mrs F. C. Ratter**
19 **FORREST TRIBE (IRE),** 5, b br g Be My Native (USA)—Island Bridge **Mr Trevor Hemmings**
20 **FREEDOM CHANCE (IRE),** 4, ch g Lahib (USA)—Gentle Guest (IRE) **Wetherby Racing Bureau Ltd**
21 **FUTURE'S TRADER,** 5, b g Alzao (USA)—Awatef **Miss Sharon Long**
22 **GEMIKOSIX (FR),** 8, b br g Bikala—Gemia (FR) **Mrs K. Walton**
23 **GLENBOWER,** 6, ch g Primitive Rising (USA)—My Muszka **Mrs S. Watkinson**
24 **GOOD JUDGE (IRE),** 4, b g Law Society (USA)—Cuirie **John Brown & Megan Dennis**
25 **HAM N'EGGS,** 7, b g Robellino (USA)—Rose And The Ring **M.H.O.G. Racing**
26 **HIGH HOPE HENRY (USA),** 5, b g Known Fact (USA)—Parquill (USA) **M.H.O.G. Racing 2**
27 **HONEYSCHOICE (IRE),** 5, b g Distinctly North (USA)—Indian Honey **The Bee Keepers**
28 **HYDRO (IRE),** 7, b g Electric—Loughanmore **Mr Trevor Hemmings**
29 **INVEST WISELY,** 6, ch g Dashing Blade—Saniette **Mr A. G. Chappell**
30 **J J BABOO (IRE),** 5, b g Be My Guest (USA)—Maricica **Mr Roland Roper**
31 **JONA HOLLEY,** 5, b g Sharpo—Spurned (USA) **Mr M. D. Hammond**
32 **KATSAR (IRE),** 6, b g Castle Keep—Welsh Partner **Mr Derek Gennard**
33 **KERNOF (IRE),** 5, b g Rambo Dancer (CAN)—Empress Wu **Mr J. M. Gahan**
34 **KNOW-NO-NO (IRE),** 9, ch g Balboa—Simply Marvellous **Mrs A. Kane**
35 **LAY THE BLAME,** 5, b h Reprimand—Rose And The Ring **J. D. Gordon & E. C. Gordon**
36 **LORD FORTUNE (IRE),** 8, b g Supreme Leader—All Profit **Mr Trevor Hemmings**
37 **LUZCADOU (FR),** 5, b g Cadoudal (FR)—Luzenia (FR) **Mr A. G. Chappell**
38 **MAJOR HARRIS (IRE),** 6, b g Lord Americo—Barntown **Mr H. G. Owen**
39 **MARCHANT MING (IRE),** 6, br g Persian Bold—Hot Curry (USA) **Mr Roland Roper**
40 **MARY'S FEELINGS,** 7, br m Feelings (FR)—Wedderburn **Mr Ian Herd**
41 **MELTEMISON,** 5, b g Charmer—Salchow **Lucky Seven Racing Club**
42 **MISS BARTHOLOMEW,** 8, b m Broadsword (USA)—Aingers Green **Mr D. H. Gibbon**
43 **MONYMAN (IRE),** 8, b g Mandalus—Superdora **Mr Trevor Hemmings**
44 **NORMAN CONQUEST (USA),** 4, ch g Miswaki (USA)—Grand Luxe (CAN) **B. & K. Associates**
45 **OOH AH CANTONA,** 7, b g Crofthall—Chablisse **Mrs Eve Sweetman**
46 **OUTSET (IRE),** 8, ch g Persian Bold—It's Now Or Never **Mr Mark Kilner**
47 **PENNINE PRIDE,** 11, ch g Over The River (FR)—Pats'y Girl **Mrs W. A. Beaumont**
48 **PENNYS FROM HEAVEN,** 4, gr g Generous (IRE)—Heavenly Cause (USA) **S. K. S. C. Racing**
49 **PEPITIST,** 7, b g Bold Owl—Misoptimist **The Gemini Partnership 5**
50 **PIMS GUNNER (IRE),** 10, b g Montelimar (USA)—My Sweetie **Mr A. G. Chappell**
51 **PINK GIN,** 11, ch g Tickled Pink—Carrapateira **Mrs Margaret Francis**
52 **PRINCE OF SAINTS (IRE),** 7, ch g Boyne Valley—Sandy's Daughter **Mr Joe Buzzeo**
53 **PROFLUENT (USA),** 7, ch g Sunshine Forever (USA)—Proflare (USA) **Andy Peake & David Jackson**
54 **RAPIER,** 4, b g Sharpo—Sahara Breeze **Mrs A. Kane**
55 **ROMAN OUTLAW,** 6, gr g Alias Smith (USA)—Roman Moor **Mrs K. Walton**
56 **ROYAL CRIMSON,** 7, b g Danehill (USA)—Fine Honey (USA) **Mrs W. A. Beaumont**
57 **RYALUX (IRE),** 5, b g Riverhead (USA)—Kings de Lema (IRE) **P. Y. D. Ltd**
58 **SIR PETER LELY,** 11, b g Teenoso (USA)—Picture **John Doyle Construction Limited**
59 **STASH THE CASH (IRE),** 7, b g Persian Bold—Noble Girl **Mr G. Shiel**
60 **TARRYTOWN (IRE),** 5, ch g Over The River (FR)—Travel In Style **Mr D. F. Sills**
61 **TAWAFIJ (USA),** 9, ch g Diesis—Dancing Brownie (USA) **Mr S. Laidlaw**
62 **THREE FRANKS (IRE),** 6, b g Step Together (USA)—Reoss **Mr Frank Hanson**
63 **TICKNTIMA,** 4, ch g Precocious—Stolon Time **Mr Andy Peake**
64 **TRACEABILITY,** 5, b g Puissance—Miss Petella **Andy Peake & David Jackson**
65 **TROOPER,** 4, b g Rock Hopper—Silica (USA) **Mr S. T. Brankin**
66 **UK HYGIENE (IRE),** 8, br g Lepanto (GER)—Proceeding **Mr Andy Peake**
67 **VALIANT WARRIOR,** 10, br g Valiyar—Jouvencelle **Mr P. Sellars**
68 **WISE ADVICE (IRE),** 8, b g Duky—Down The Aisle **Mr A. G. Chappell**

MR M. D. HAMMOND—continued

Other Owners: Mr D. E. Allen, Mr Jim Anderson, Mrs R. Auchterlounie, Mr S. Balmer, Mrs L. Barr, Mr A. Bates, Mrs I. Battla, Mr R. Butler, Ms J. Cadman, Mr R. Catterson, Mr M. Chapman, Mrs M. Crane, Mr Philip Curry, Mr D. Gallacher, Mr G. Gobsman, Mr Daniel W. Gray, Mr E. D. Haggart, Mr T. Hanny, Mr D. C. Harrison, Mr W. Haworth, Mr R. Hooper, Mr J. Johnson, Mr Richard Johnson, Mr N. Kelly, Mr S. Kelly, Mr B. Kennedy, Mr J. Kennedy, Mr A. Kettles, Mr R. Lister, Mr Colin J. Long, Mrs M. Lowe, Mr Cornelius Lysaght, Mr M. McCarthy, Mrs C. McGuinness, Mr G. McLaren, Mrs V. Parker, Mrs M. Powney-Jones, Mr D. Ryan, Mr A. Saccomando, Shirebrook Park Management Ltd, Mr A. W. Sinclair, Mr Eddison Skeels, Mr Jimmy Smith, Mr R. J. Stevenson, Mr A. D. Stewart, Mr Tony Sweetman, Miss Ann Venables-Kyrke, Mr A. Walker, Mr S. Waltham, Mr P. Wilkinson, Mrs Patricia M. Wilson, Mrs M. Woolfitt.

Jockeys (NH): D Bentley (10-0), R Garritty (10-3).

Conditional: A Ede, N Horrocks.

Amateur: Mr C Bonner (9-11).

Lady Rider: Mrs A Hammond.

260 MR R. HANNON, Marlborough

Postal: **East Everleigh Stables, Marlborough, Wiltshire, SN8 3EY.**
Phone: **(01264) 850 254 FAX (01264) 850 820**

1 **ANDREYEV (IRE),** 4, ch c Presidium—Missish **Mr J. Palmer-Brown**
2 **BIG BEN,** 4, ch c Timeless Times (USA)—Belltina **Lady Davis**
3 **CALYPSO LADY (IRE),** 4, ch f Priolo (USA)—Taking Steps **Mr I. A. N. Wight & Mrs D. M. Wight**
4 **CAYMAN KAI (IRE),** 5, ch h Imperial Frontier (USA)—Safiya (USA) **Mr I. A. N. Wight & Mrs D. M. Wight**
5 **FAIRY KNIGHT,** 6, b h Fairy King (USA)—Vestal Flame **P. & S. Lever Partners**
6 **HOMESTEAD,** 4, ch g Indian Ridge—Bertrade **Mr Geoffrey C. Greenwood**
7 **INTERDREAM,** 4, b g Interrex (CAN)—Dreamtime Quest **Mr Charles Farr & Mr Mark Heaton**
8 **LOVE HAS NO PRIDE (USA),** 4, gr g El Prado (IRE)—Chili Lee (USA) **Miss L. Regis**
9 **ROFFEY SPINNEY (IRE),** 4, ch c Masterclass (USA)—Crossed Line **Mrs D. F. Cock**
10 **SALTY BEHAVIOUR (IRE),** 4, ch c Salt Dome (USA)—Good Behaviour **Mr J. R. Shannon**
11 **SHARP HAT,** 4, ch c Shavian—Madam Trilby **Mr J. C. Smith**
12 **SHARP SHUFFLE (IRE),** 5, ch g Exactly Sharp (USA)—Style **Mrs H. F. Prendergast**
13 **SHOW FAITH (IRE),** 8, ch g Exhibitioner—Keep The Faith **Mr I. A. N. Wight & Mrs D. M. Wight**
14 **SLIEU WHALLIAN,** 4, b f In The Wings—Ladyfish **Barouche Stud Ltd**
15 **TEST THE WATER (IRE),** 4, ch c Maelstrom Lake—Baliana (CAN) **Mr J. S. Threadwell**
16 **TRIPLE HAY,** 4, ch c Safawan—Davinia **The Broadgate Partnership**

THREE-YEAR-OLDS

17 **ANOTHER FANTASY (IRE),** b f Danehill (USA)—Ariadne **Mrs P. Jubert**
18 **ARPEGGIO,** b c Polar Falcon (USA)—Hilly **Lucayan Stud**
19 **ASPEN (IRE),** br f Scenic—All In White (FR) **Highclere Thoroughbred Racing Ltd**
20 **BEMSHA SWING (IRE),** b br c Night Shift (USA)—Move It Baby (IRE) **Mr Michael Pescod**
21 **BETTRON,** b g Alnasr Alwasheek—Aigua Blava (USA) **Mr R. Gander**
22 **BLAKESET,** ch c Midyan (USA)—Penset **Mrs Caroline Parker**
23 **BLESS 'IM,** b c Presidium—Saint Systems **Mr J. A. Leek**
24 **BLUE SHADOW,** gr c Pips Pride—Lingdale Lass **J. B. R. Leisure Ltd**
25 **BUZZING (IRE),** ch c Ballad Rock—Buzzing Around **Mrs P. Jubert**
26 **CAPTIVATING (IRE),** b f Wolfhound (USA)—Winning Appeal (FR) **M. W. Grant & W. F. Hawkings**
27 **CHURLISH CHARM,** b c Niniski (USA)—Blushing Storm (USA) **Mr Mohamed Suhail**
28 **CLASSIC MANOEUVRE (USA),** ch c Sky Classic (CAN)—Maid of Honor (USA) **Paul & Jenny Green**
29 **CLASSIC MASQUERADE (CAN),** b c Regal Classic (CAN)—Muskoka Command (USA) **Paul & Jenny Green**

MR R. HANNON—continued

30 **CLOAK OF DARKNESS (IRE),** b c Thatching—Madame Nureyev (USA) **Mr Mohamed Suhail**
31 **CORNFLOWER FIELDS,** b f Cadeaux Genereux—Mithl Al Hawa **Mr Mohamed Suhail**
32 **COUNTER STRIKE,** b c Beveled (USA)—Encore L'Amour (USA) **Mr Mahmood Al-Shuaibi**
33 **DAUNTING LADY (IRE),** b f Mujadil (USA)—Dauntess **Mr E. C. Nagell-Erichsen & Partners**
34 **DAWN TREADER (USA),** gr g El Prado (IRE)—Marie de La Ferte **Miss L. Regis**
35 **DISTINCT VINTAGE (IRE),** b c Distinctly North (USA)—Princess Raisa **Mr E. C. Nagell-Erichsen**
36 **ELEGANT HERO (IRE),** b c Common Grounds—Good Relations **Mr Ben Allen**
37 **ELEVENTH DUKE (IRE),** b c Imperial Frontier (USA)—Disregard That (IRE) **Lucayan Stud**
38 **FLAME TOWER (IRE),** ch c Archway (IRE)—Guantanamera (USA) **Mr Mahmood Al-Shuaibi**
39 **GOLDEN REPRIMAND (IRE),** b c Reprimand—Elabella **Mr George E. K. Teo**
40 **GOLDEN STRATEGY (IRE),** b g Statoblest—Lady Taufan (IRE) **Mr George E. K. Teo**
41 **GRAND SLAM (IRE),** b c Second Set (IRE)—Lady In The Park (IRE) **Mr I. A. N. Wight & Mrs D. M. Wight**
42 **GREEBA,** b f Fairy King (USA)—Guanhumara **Barouche Stud Ltd**
43 **GURKHA,** b c Polish Precedent (USA)—Glendera **Gurkha Partnership**
44 **HUNTSWOOD,** b c Warning—Clarista (USA) **Mrs D. F. Cock**
45 **I CRIED FOR YOU (IRE),** b c Statoblest—Fall of The Hammer (IRE) **Mr Bob Lalemant**
46 **I WISH YOU LOVE,** ch c Risk Me (FR)—Sports Delight **Mr Bob Lalemant**
47 **JEWEL (IRE),** b f Cyrano de Bergerac—Renzola **Lady Tennant**
48 **KING DARIUS (IRE),** ch c Persian Bold—Valiant Friend (USA) **Mr E. John Perry**
49 **LIFT THE OFFER (IRE),** ch c Ballad Rock—Timissara (USA) **Broadgate II**
50 **LOBUCHE (IRE),** b c Petardia—Lhotse (IRE) **Mr D. B. Gallop**
51 **LUCKY DOUBLE,** b c Green Desert (USA)—Lady Bentley **Mr Mohamed Suhail**
52 **MAIELLA,** ch f Salse (USA)—Forelino (USA) **Lord Carnarvon**
53 **MIDSUMMER NIGHT (IRE),** b f Fairy King (USA)—Villota **Mr G. Howard-Spink**
54 **MYSTAGOGUE,** ch c Mystiko (USA)—Malibasta **Mr J. S. Threadwell**
55 **NANOUSHKA (IRE),** b f Taufan (USA)—West Chazy (USA) **Thurloe Thoroughbreds II**
56 **NOT ME,** b g Reprimand—Hollow Heart **Mr Paul Jubert**
57 **OVERTURE (IRE),** gr c Fairy King (USA)—Everything Nice **Mr J. A. Lazzari**
58 **PERADVENTURE (IRE),** b c Persian Bold—Missed Opportunity (IRE) **Mr Michael Pescod**
59 **POOL MUSIC,** ch c Forzando—Sunfleet **Mrs Caroline Parker**
60 **PRAETORIAN GOLD,** ch c Presidium—Chinese Princess **The Gold Buster Syndicate (2)**
61 **REJECTED,** b c Puissance—Dalby Dancer **Mr T. G. Holdcroft**
62 **RITUAL RUN,** b c Rudimentary (USA)—Roussalka **Mr Mohamed Suhail**
63 **RON'S PET,** ch g Ron's Victory (USA)—Penny Mint **Mr George E. K. Teo**
64 **SANTONE (IRE),** b c Fairy King (USA)—Olivia Jane (IRE) **Stonethorn Stud Farms Ltd**
65 **SCOTLAND BAY,** b f Then Again—Down The Valley **Mr J. R. Shannon**
66 **SECRET ARCHIVE,** b c Salse (USA)—Lycia (USA) **Mr Mohamed Suhail**
67 **SHAPE SHIFTER (IRE),** ch c Night Shift (USA)—Zabeta **Mr G. Howard-Spink**
68 **SPRITE,** b f Fairy King (USA)—Cubby Hole **Lord Carnarvon**
69 **STORM FROMTHE EAST,** b c Formidable (USA)—Callas Star **Mr N. Hayes**
70 **SURPRISE PRESENT (IRE),** ch c Indian Ridge—Lady Redford **Mr Mohamed Suhail**
71 **TANGO (IRE),** b c Dancing Dissident (USA)—Tunguska **Noodles Racing**
72 **TIYE,** b f Salse (USA)—Kiya (USA) **Lord Carnarvon**
73 **WANDERING WOLF,** ch c Wolfhound (USA)—Circle of Chalk (FR) **Lucayan Stud**
74 **WILD COLONIAL BOY (IRE),** b c Warning—Loch Clair (IRE) **Mr G. Howard-Spink**

TWO-YEAR-OLDS

75 **AL FAHDA,** b f 8/3 Be My Chief (USA)—Fleetwood Fancy (Taufan (USA)) **Brick Kiln Stud**
76 **AMAZING DREAM (IRE),** b f 14/2 Thatching—Aunty Eileen (Ahonoora) **Mrs P. Jubert**
77 **AMY'S GIFT,** b f 11/5 Lahib (USA)—Miss Amy Lou (IRE) (Gallic League) **Mr Ben Allen**
78 **ANNIE APPLE (IRE),** ch f 29/4 Petardia—Art Duo (Artais (USA)) **Mr D. Allen**
79 **BELLA LOUPA,** b f 14/4 Wolfhound (USA)—Quay Line (High Line) **Major A. M. Everett**
80 **BRAVE VALENTINA,** b f 28/3 Cosmonaut—Concorde Lady (Hotfoot) **Lady Davis**
81 **BREW,** b c 24/4 Primo Dominie—Boozy (Absalom) **Mrs R. Heathcote**
82 **BRIMMING OVER,** ch c 3/3 Dashing Blade—Madam Trilby (Grundy) **Mr J. C. Smith**
83 **CABARET QUEST,** ch c 12/4 Pursuit Of Love—
Cabaret Artiste (Shareef Dancer (USA)) **Thurloe Thoroughbreds III**
84 B f 13/2 Distinctly North—Cambridge Lodge (Tower Walk) **The Winning Team (1998)**
85 **CAPPELLA (IRE),** br f 6/4 College Chapel—Mavahra (Mummy's Pet) **Thurloe Thoroughbreds III**
86 **CAPRIOLO (IRE),** ch c 18/4 Priolo (USA)—Carroll's Canyon (IRE) (Hakim (USA)) **Mr John Homer**

MR R. HANNON—continued

87 B f 25/4 Danehill (USA)—Carmelized (CAN) (Key To The Mint (USA)) **T. Ananda Krishnan**
88 CAROUSAL (IRE), b f 25/3 Distinctly North—Mountain Hop (IRE) (Tirol) **Mr T. S. M. Cunningham**
89 CASTILIAN (IRE), b c 28/3 Priolo (USA)—Hertford Castle (Reference Point) **Mr J. C. Smith**
90 CHIEF ABBA, ch c 15/5 Be My Chief (USA)—Themeda (Sure Blade (USA)) **Mr Howard A. Hackett**
91 CLEAR NIGHT, b c 29/5 Night Shift (USA)—Clarista (USA) (Riva Ridge (USA)) **Mr J. A. Lazzari**
92 CREDENZA, ch f 2/2 Superlative—Carousel Music (On Your Mark) **Scott Hardy Partnership**
93 CYBINKA, ch f 24/1 Selkirk (USA)—Sarmatia (USA) (Danzig (USA)) **Lady Howard de Walden**
94 DEMOCRACY (IRE), ch c 31/1 Common Grounds—Inonder (Belfort (FR)) **Highclere Thoroughbred Racing Ltd**
95 DILLIONAIRE, b c 4/4 Dilum (USA)—Running Tycoon (IRE) (Last Tycoon) **Mr J. C. Smith**
96 DOLPHINELLE, b c 22/4 Dolphin Street (FR)—Mamie's Joy (Prince Tenderfoot (USA)) **Mr Tommy Staunton**
97 B f 8/4 Bluebird (USA)—Dubai Lady (Kris) **Royal Ascot Racing Club**
98 END OF STORY (IRE), b c 18/4 Doubletour (USA)—Baliana (CAN) (Riverman (USA)) **High Seas Leisure Limited**
99 ENTROPY, b f 12/3 Brief Truce (USA)—Distant Isle (IRE) (Bluebird (USA)) **Mr T. G. Holdcroft**
100 B c 21/5 Anita's Prince—Gentle Papoose (Commanche Run) **The Gold Buster Syndicate**
101 GOLD ACADEMY (IRE), b c 19/3 Royal Academy (USA)—
Soha (USA) (Dancing Brave (USA)) **Mr George E. K. Teo**
102 GOLDEN FORCE, b c 18/1 Forzando—Silverlocks (Sharrood (USA)) **Mr George E. K. Teo**
103 GOLDEN PRINCE (IRE), gr c 16/4 Polish Patriot—
Cathryn's Song (Prince Tenderfoot (USA)) **Mr George E. K. Teo**
104 GOLDEN SYRUP (IRE), b f 13/3 Dolphin Street (FR)—
Sprint For Gold (USA) (Slew O'Gold (USA)) **Lord Carnarvon**
105 Ch c 24/3 Grand Lodge (USA)—Hemline (Sharpo) **Mr I. A. N. Wight & Mrs D. M. Wight**
106 HONEY BEE, b f 27/3 Alnasr Alwasheek—Mirkan Honey (Ballymore) **Mr P. T. Tellwright**
107 Ch c 26/4 Mujtahid (USA)—Hot Curry (USA) (Sharpen Up) **The Winning Team (1998)**
108 KAIBO, ch c 4/4 Safawan—Jay Gee Ell (Vaigly Great) **Mr I. A. N. Wight & Mrs D. M. Wight**
109 KEY, b f 19/1 Midyan (USA)—Diamond Park (IRE) (Alzao (USA)) **Wyck Hall Stud**
110 B c 28/2 Zieten (USA)—Kiriyaki (USA) (Secretariat (USA)) **Lucayan Stud**
111 LEADING LIGHT (IRE), ch c 6/3 College Chapel—
Valiant Friend (USA) (Shahrastani (USA)) **Mr I. A. N. Wight & Mrs D. M. Wight**
112 LEARNED FRIEND (IRE), ch c 9/2 College Chapel—Caring (Crowned Prince (USA)) **Mr J. C. Smith**
113 LIGHT THE ROCKET (IRE), ch c 23/3 Pips Pride—Coolrain Lady (IRE) (Common Grounds) **Mr Jim Horgan**
114 MAGIC MONDAY (IRE), b f 24/4 Petardia—Ultra (Stanford) **Mr Bill Allan**
115 B c 12/4 Polish Patriot—Marie de Fresnaye (USA) (Dom Racine (FR)) **Absal A. M. Everett**
116 MAYARO BAY, b f 9/4 Robellino (USA)—Down The Valley (Kampala) **Mr J. R. Shannon**
117 METEORITE (IRE), b c 10/5 Bigstone (IRE)—
Winning Appeal (FR) (Law Society (USA)) **M. W. Grant, W. F. Hawkings, T. Bucknall**
118 MY PETAL, gr f 9/3 Petong—Najariya (Northfields (USA)) **Mrs P. R. Jubert**
119 OBAN BALL, ch f 23/3 Pursuit Of Love—Highland Light (Home Guard (USA)) **Lady Howard de Walden**
120 PAL OF MINE, b c 29/2 Zafonic (USA)—Dana Springs (IRE) (Aragon) **Mr G. Howard-Spink**
121 QUEEN OMAH (IRE), b f 14/4 Dolphin Street (FR)—Quilting (Mummy's Pet) **Mr Howard A. Hackett**
122 QUICK SILVER, b f 26/4 Anshan—Tabeeba (Diesis) **Lord Porchester**
123 QUICKSTEP, ch f 19/3 Salse (USA)—Short And Sharp (Sharpen Up) **Lady Tennant**
124 RED DELIRIUM, b c 1/4 Robellino (USA)—Made of Pearl (USA) (Nureyev (USA)) **Mr Terry Neill**
125 RED MAY, br f 23/2 Persian Bold—Stay That Way (Be My Guest (USA)) **Mr Terry Neill**
126 REDOUBLE, b c 28/3 First Trump—Sunflower Seed (Mummy's Pet) **Mr J. P. Kenny**
127 REPUBLIC (IRE), b c 9/3 Anita's Prince—Sweet Finale (Sallust) **Mr Michael Pescod**
128 SAILING SHOES (IRE), b c 19/2 Lahib (USA)—Born To Glamour (Ajdal (USA)) **Mrs Caroline Parker**
129 SARSON, b c 13/3 Efisio—Sarcita (Primo Dominie) **Mr Raymond Tooth**
130 B c 28/4 Alydeed (CAN)—Saucy Action (USA) (Grand Central) **Highclere Thoroughbred Racing Ltd**
131 Ch f 5/4 Bluebird (USA)—Scammony (IRE) (Persian Bold) **T. Ananda Krishnan**
132 SCENIC BEAUTY (IRE), br f 15/2 Scenic—East River (FR) (Arctic Tern (USA)) **Major A. M. Everett**
133 SKY OF HOPE (FR), b c 4/4 Zieten (USA)—Rain Or Shine (FR) (Nonoalco (USA)) **Lucayan Stud**
134 B c 29/2 First Trump—Sound of The Sea (Windjammer (USA)) **Lucayan Stud**
135 SPLIT THE ACES (IRE), gr c 23/4 Balla Cove—Hazy Lady (Habitat) **Mr A. F. Merritt**
136 B c 29/4 Common Grounds—Sports Post Lady (IRE) (M Double M (USA)) **Noodles Racing**
137 SUPER STAR, ch c 23/1 Superlative—International Star (IRE) (Astronef) **Lord Carnarvon**
138 B c 28/2 Never So Bold—Tame Duchess (Saritamer (USA)) **Mr J. Palmer-Brown**
139 B c 20/2 Primo Dominie—Tender Loving Care (Final Straw) **Royal Ascot Racing Club**
140 TIN DRUM (IRE), b c 20/2 Roi Danzig (USA)—Triumphant (Track Spare) **Mr Michael Pescod**

MR R. HANNON—continued

141 TRIPLE RAISE (GER), b f 11/3 Wolfhound (USA)—Timely Raise (USA) (Raise A Man (USA)) **Mr J. C. Smith**
142 Br c 15/4 Tenby—Unaria (Prince Tenderfoot (USA)) **J. B. R. Leisure Ltd**
143 B c 17/3 Mujtahid (USA)—Vian (USA) (Far Out East (USA)) **Mr Saleh Al Homeizi**
144 Ch f 16/2 Pips Pride—Vieux Carre (Pas de Seul) **P. B. Adams, M. W. Grant, W. F. Hawkings**
145 B f 14/4 Doubletour (USA)—Virginia Cottage (Lomond (USA)) **Mr John Homer**
146 WALLACE, ch c 27/4 Royal Academy (USA)—Masskana (IRE) (Darshaan) **Mr J. A. Lazzari**
147 WHY WORRY NOW (IRE), ch f 20/2 College Chapel—Pretext (Polish Precedent (USA)) **Mr N. Hayes**
148 WOODCOTE WARRIOR (IRE), b c 20/3 Barathea (IRE)—Overact (IRE) (Law Society (USA)) **Mrs D. Y. Thomas**
149 ZAHARAM, b g 17/3 Mazaad—Green Pool (Whistlefield) **Mrs J. Reglar**

Other Owners: Aston House Stud, Mr R. A. Bernard, Mrs B. Burchett, Dr A. B. Crowley, Mr T. J. Dale, Mr E. J. Gilbertson, Mr R. D. Green, Mr Peter Hammond, Mr T. Herbert-Jackson, Mr John Hulme, Mr K. S. Jones, Mr Peter Jubert, Mr William J. Kelly, Kennet Valley Thoroughbreds, Mr R. I. Khan, Mr D. A. Lucie-Smith, Mrs John Magnier, Mrs David Nagle, Mr Robert Russell, Mr D. Sieff, Mrs David Sieff, Mr B. T. Stewart-Brown, Lord Tavistock, Mr D. J. Toye, Mr G. P. Triefus, Mr Rupert Wace, Mr N. Warburton, Lady Whent, Mr Jane Withey.

Jockeys (Flat): R Hughes, W J O'Connor, Dane O'Neill (8-0), R Perham (8-4).

Apprentices: P Dobbs (7-12), L Newman (7-3), R Smith (7-12).

261 MRS JESSICA HARRINGTON, Kildare

Postal: **Commonstown Stables, Moone, Co. Kildare.**
Phone: **(0507) 24153 FAX (0507) 24292 CAR (086) 2566129**

1 A LITTLE GRUMPY (IRE), 4, b g Krayyan—Gay Rhapsody **Mrs J. Harrington**
2 BOLTON FOREST (IRE), 5, b g Be My Native (USA)—Tickenor Wood **Mrs J. Harrington**
3 BRUSH WITH TIME (IRE), 6, b m Brush Aside (USA)—Final Filly **Mrs J. Harrington**
4 CAESARS GOLD, 6, ch g Denel (FR)—Lauren's Gem **Caesars Club**
5 CINNIBAR, 5, br m Anshan—Kinkajoo **G. S. Racing Club**
6 CROSSARD (IRE), 6, b g Taufan (USA)—Homosassa **Hugh Curley**
7 DANTE'S BATTLE (IRE), 6, br g Phardante—No Battle **Mrs Margaret Brophy**
8 DRAM HURLER (IRE), 6, ch g Buckskin (FR)—Vintage Harvest **R. Annesley**
9 EDDIE (IRE), 6, b g Orchestra—Bavette **John Peutherer**
10 FERBET JUNIOR (FR), 5, gr g Criminal Law—True Divine **Mr B. Gurney, Mr A. Gurney**
11 4, B f Tirol—Fourp'ny Rock **Mrs J. Harrington**
12 FULL OF VODKA (IRE), 6, b g Moscow Society (USA)—Diathis Coleen **H. N. H. Partnership**
13 GLENPATRICK BLISS (IRE), 5, br m Be My Native (USA)—Our Hollow **Mrs E. Queally & Mrs J. Harrington**
14 GRAPHIC IMAGE (IRE), 8, br g Nearly A Nose (USA)—Just A Bird **Kells Sports & Social Club**
15 KOKO NOR (IRE), 5, b g Royal Academy (USA)—Pu Yi **Mrs J. Costello**
16 LOST ALPHABET (IRE), 5, br g Don't Forget Me—Zenga **James Parkinson**
17 MAKE IT HAPPEN (IRE), 6, br g Supreme Leader—Magic User **H. N. H. Partnership**
18 MARKET LASS (IRE), 6, br m Orchestra—Tor-Na-Grena **Joe Kealing & Partners**
19 MISS ORCHESTRA (IRE), 7, b m Orchestra—Jims Monkey **The BB Horse Racing Club**
20 6, Ch g Electric—Money Incinerator **John Horgan**
21 4, B g Torus—Moppit-Up **Mrs P. Teahon**
22 MULLOVER, 7, ch g Ra Nova—True Divine **Adam Gurney**
23 MUSICAL WHISPER (IRE), 4, ch f Montelimar (USA)—Bella Velutina
24 5, Br m Over The River (FR)—Mwanamio **H.N.H. Syndicate**
25 NATIVE CYNIC (IRE), 5, b g Be My Native (USA)—Ballyline Dancer **Mrs P. Teahon**
26 NUCKLE WOOD (IRE), 6, b m Supreme Leader—Deep Solare **ESB Racing Club**
27 ONMEOWN (IRE), 6, gr m Lafontaine (USA)—Willshego **Kevin Gallagher**
28 PALAMOS (IRE), 6, br g Air Display (USA)—Star Pryse **Mrs J. Harrington & Mr R. Sinclair**
29 PRETTY BEAT UP (IRE), 5, br g Ballad Rock—Alchiea **R. Wood**
30 ROWAN TREE (IRE), 6, b m Castle Keep—Three Friars **George Kent**
31 4, B f Mandalus—Seat of Learning **Mrs E. Queally**

MRS JESSICA HARRINGTON—continued

32 **SHEAN TOWN (IRE),** 5, b g Camden Town—Tops O'Crush **A. Cragie & Brian Smith**
33 **SLANEY NATIVE (IRE),** 5, b g Be My Native—Mean To Me **David Nugent**
34 **SPACE TRUCKER (IRE),** 7, b g Kambalda—Seat of Learning **Mrs E. Queally**
35 4, B f Shernazar—Spin A Coin **Mrs E. Queally**
36 **THATS IT NOW (IRE),** 6, br g King's Ride—Khalice **Tony Farell**
37 **TOM KENNY (IRE),** 8, b g Lhasa—Lady Hapsburg **David Nugent**
38 **TULLABAWN (IRE),** 6, b g Rontino—Reliant Nell **David Reed Scott & Partners**
39 **YONOKA,** 9, ch g Script Ohio (USA)—Sciara **James Parkinson**

THREE-YEAR-OLDS

40 **HAVE MERCI,** b f High Estate—Icecapped **R. Wood**
41 **JOLEAH (IRE),** b f Ela-Mana-Mou—Alchiea **R. Wood**
42 Br g Petorius—Maria Renata **Mrs E. Queally**
43 **TYRONE'S RUNNER (IRE),** b c Lahib—Acara (IRE) **R. Wood**

Jockey (Flat): W Smith (w.a.).

Jockey (NH): John Shortt (w.a.).

Amateur: Mr P Fahey.

262 MR J. L. HARRIS, Melton Mowbray

Postal: **Eastwell Hall Stables, Eastwell, Melton Mowbray, Leicestershire, LE14 4EE.**
Phone: **(01949) 860671 MOBILE (0860) 277138 FAX (01949) 860671**

1 **ARCADY,** 5, b m Slip Anchor—Elysian **Mr J. H. Henderson**
2 **BARWELL BOY,** 4, b g Clantime—Kasu **Cleartherm Ltd**
3 **DOUBLE STAR,** 7, b g Soviet Star (USA)—Startino **Mr A. K. Collins**
4 **GLENRAZIE (IRE),** 5, ch g Kefaah (USA)—Glendera **Mr J. L. Harris**
5 **IMLAK (IRE),** 6, ch g Ela-Mana-Mou—Mashteen (USA) **Mr D. Jackson**
6 **JUSTLIKEJIM,** 7, ch g Say Primula—Trois Filles **Mr Peter Castle**
7 5, Ch m Clantime—Kasu **Mr J. L. Harris**
8 **LORD SABRE,** 5, b g Broadsword (USA)—Lady Hamshire **Mr J. H. Henderson**
9 **MARKET SPRINGER (IRE),** 7, gr g Roselier (FR)—An Carthanach **Mr G. W. Pykett**
10 **PARONOMASIA,** 6, b g Precocious—The Crying Game **Mr Paddy Barrett**
11 **PISUM SATIVUM,** 4, ch f Ron's Victory (USA)—Trojan Desert **Mr Paddy Barrett**
12 **SACHO (IRE),** 5, b h Sadler's Wells (USA)—Oh So Sharp **Mr J. H. Henderson**
13 **SEA VICTOR,** 6, b g Slip Anchor—Victoriana (USA) **Mr J. David Abell**
14 **SIR TASKER,** 10, b h Lidhame—Susie's Baby **Mr J. L. Harris**
15 **SOUTH CHINA SEA,** 4, b f Robellino (USA)—Danzig Harbour (USA) **Mr J. L. Harris**
16 **TEMPTRESS,** 5, br m Kalaglow—Circe **Mr Paddy Barrett**
17 **THAHIB,** 4, b c Polish Precedent (USA)—Hamama (USA) **Dr C. W. Ashpole**

THREE-YEAR-OLDS

18 **BUNNIES OWN,** b f Flockton's Own—Walsham Witch **Mr J. Starbuck**
19 Gr f Neltino—Change of Fortune **Mr R. Fox**
20 **HAUNT THE ZOO,** b f Komaite (USA)—Merryhill Maid (IRE) **Mr H. A. Cushing**
21 **HERNIECE,** b f Weldnaas (USA)—Sizzling Sista **Mrs M. Hills**
22 **SABLE CLOAK,** b f Prince Sabo—Edge of Darkness **Mr J. David Abell**
23 **SHARP LABEL,** ch f Sharpo—Labelon Lady **Mr P. T. Bell**
24 B f Ron's Victory (USA)—Trojan Desert **Mr Paddy Barrett**
25 **VINCENT,** b c Anshan—Top-Anna (IRE) **Mr P. Caplan**

MR J. L. HARRIS—continued

TWO-YEAR-OLDS

26 B f 16/5 Distant Relative—Main Sail (Blakeney) **Mr R. Atkinson**
27 B c 25/2 Bob's Return (IRE)—Saltina (Bustino) **Mr E. Atkinson**

Other Owners: Mrs J. Abell, Mr M. R. Barnes, Mrs M. Bostock, Mr C. Conway, Mr J. F. Coupland, Mrs E. Holmes, Mr M. Holmes, Mr R. W. Huggins, Mr M. F. Hyman, Mr John D. Judge, Mr Roger Langley, Mrs B. Long, Mr David Marston, Mrs Margaret Marston, Mr B. McAllister, Mrs J. D. Sim, Mr W. D. Sim, Mr J. South, Mr D. Wilcox.

Jockey (NH): D Gallagher (w.a.).

Amateur: Mr B Saunders.

263 MR PETER W. HARRIS, Berkhamsted

Postal: **Sallow Copse, Ringshall, Berkhamsted, Hertfordshire, HP4 1LZ.**
Phone: **FAX/OFFICE (01442) 826393/823602 HOUSE/FAX (01442) 842480/842521**

1 AMERICAN WHISPER, 4, b c Dixieland Band (USA)—Only A Rumour **The Confederates**
2 DANIEL DERONDA, 4, b c Danehill (USA)—Kilvarnet **Rainbow Partnership**
3 DIAMOND FLAME, 4, b c Suave Dancer (USA)—Eternal Flame **Dancing Dozen**
4 FLYAWAY HILL (FR), 4, b f Danehill (USA)—Flyaway Bride (USA) **Pendley Fliers**
5 GROOMS GOLD (IRE), 6, ch g Groom Dancer (USA)—Gortynia (FR) **Mrs P. W. Harris**
6 HAYDN JAMES (USA), 4, ch g Danzig Connection (USA)—Royal Fi Fi (USA) **Resplendent Racing Limited**
7 INDIAN BLAZE, 4, ch g Indian Ridge—Odile **Pendley Braves**
8 NORTHERN ANGEL (IRE), 4, b c Waajib—Angel Divine **Mr W. Bruce**
9 NORTHERN BLESSING, 4, b f Waajib—Last Blessing **Twelve Apostles**
10 PREMIER ECLIPSE, 4, b g Primo Dominie—Remany **Twelve Gems**
11 PRIMEVAL, 4, b g Primo Dominie—Class Adorns **Mrs P. W. Harris**
12 PRIMO LARA, 6, ch h Primo Dominie—Clara Barton **Resplendent Racing Limited**
13 SADLER'S BLAZE (IRE), 4, b g Alzao (USA)—Christine Daae **Newly United**
14 SARBARON (IRE), 4, b c Danehill (USA)—Salette **Resplendent Racing Limited**
15 SPENDER, 9, b br g Last Tycoon—Lady Hester **The Entrepreneurs**
16 SUPREME SOUND, 4, b c Superlative—Sing Softly **Mrs P. W. Harris**
17 TO THE ROOF (IRE), 6, b g Thatching—Christine Daae **Mrs P. W. Harris**
18 TWICE AS SHARP, 6, ch h Sharpo—Shadiliya **Formula Twelve**
19 YOUNG PRECEDENT, 4, b br c Polish Precedent (USA)—Guyum **Pendley Knights**

THREE-YEAR-OLDS

20 ABSALOM'S LAD, gr c Absalom—Rose Bouquet **The Absolute Twelve**
21 B g Indian Ridge—Arab Art **Mrs P. W. Harris**
22 BLUEWAIN LADY, b f Unfuwain (USA)—Blue Guitar **The Bluenotes**
23 CANADIAN PUZZLER (USA), gr c With Approval (CAN)—Puzzle Book (USA) **Maple Leafs**
24 DANCING GREY, gr g Petong—Mountain Harvest (FR) **The Mountaineers**
25 DANEHILL FLAME (IRE), b f Danehill (USA)—Hillbrow **The Buckaneers**
26 DANZIG FLYER (IRE), b c Roi Danzig (USA)—Fenland Express (IRE) **Shamrock Four**
27 DAZILYN LADY (USA), ch f Zilzal (USA)—Jetbeeah (IRE) **Knight, Godfrey, Parker**
28 DELCIANA (IRE), b f Danehill (USA)—Delvecchia **Delvecchian Dozen**
29 DESERT SPA (USA), b br c Sheikh Albadou—Healing Waters (USA) **The Chieftains**
30 ELIZA ACTON, b f Shirley Heights—Sing Softly **Mrs P. W. Harris**
31 FORMATION DANCER, ch c Groom Dancer (USA)—Golden Form **Mr M. Winter & Mrs P. W. Harris**
32 GRAND CADEAUX, b c Cadeaux Genereux—Abbey's Gal **Present Company**
33 Ch g Thatching—Happy Smile (IRE) **Mrs P. W. Harris**
34 KOMISTAR, ch c Komaite (USA)—Rosie's Gold **Class Act**
35 LADY OF THE NIGHT (IRE), b f Night Shift (USA)—Joma Kaanem **The Euro Crew**
36 LATIN BAY, b c Superlative—Hugging **Superlative Twelve**

MR PETER W. HARRIS—continued

37 **LEGAL LUNCH (USA),** b c Alleged (USA)—Dinner Surprise (USA) **The Alleged Partnership**
38 **MANTUSIS (IRE),** ch c Pursuit of Love—Mana (GER) **The Romantics**
39 **MISS SYAN,** ch f River Falls—Polaregina (FR) **Syan Ltd**
40 **MUNGO DUFF (IRE),** b c Priolo (USA)—Noble Dust (USA) **J. Jay & Mrs P. W. Harris**
41 **OH HEBE (IRE),** b f Night Shift (USA)—Why So Silent **Mrs P. W. Harris**
42 **RED RISK,** ch g Risk Me (FR)—Red Sails **The Red Connection**
43 **RHEIN HILL (IRE),** b c Danehill (USA)—Rhein Bridge **Danehill Connection**
44 **RISQUE LADY,** ch f Kenmare (FR)—Christine Daae **Godwin Hollis & Lawrence Rice**
45 **RIVER DANCING (IRE),** b c Polish Patriot (USA)—Art Age **The Polishers**
46 **SCOLDED,** b c Reprimand—Lydia Maria **The Bravehearts**
47 **SILVER CASTOR (IRE),** b f Indian Ridge—Bayazida **John Hanshaw**
48 Ch c Indian Ridge—Simply Marilyn (IRE) **Mrs P. W. Harris**
49 **TASTE OF SUCCESS,** b c Thatching—Tastiera (USA) **First Taste**
50 **TOMASZEWSKI (FR),** b c Polish Precedent (USA)—Circus Plume **Mrs P. W. Harris**
51 **VOLONTIERS (FR),** b c Common Grounds—Senlis (USA) **The Commoners**

TWO-YEAR-OLDS

52 B f 30/3 Fly So Free (USA)—Anthem (USA) (Deputy Minister (CAN))
53 Ch f 3/4 With Approval (CAN)—A Taste For Lace (US) (Laomedonte (USA))
54 Ch c 11/4 Beau Genius (CAN)—Aunt Nola (USA) (Olden Times)
55 **BRIGHT HOPE (IRE),** b f 7/2 Danehill (USA)—Crystal Cross (USA) (Roberto (USA)) **Mrs P. W. Harris**
56 **CACHUCHA (USA),** ch f 4/4 Diesis—Baffling Ballerina (USA) (Northern Dancer) **Mrs A Palmer**
57 B c 14/2 Colonial Affair (USA)—Carefree Kate (USA) (Lyphard (USA))
58 Ch f 31/3 Danehill (USA)—Cheviot Amble (IRE) (Pennine Walk)
59 **CHRISMAS CAROL,** b f 14/2 Common Grounds—Stockrose (Horage) **Resplendent Racing Limited**
60 B f 5/4 Primo Dominie—Class Adorns (Sadler's Wells (USA))
61 **FAYBIAN (IRE),** b c 29/3 Fayruz—My Best Susy (IRE) (Try My Best (USA)) **Equine Alliance**
62 B c 11/4 Zafonic (USA)—Free City (USA) (Danzig (USA))
63 B f 24/4 Rudimentary—Guyum (Rousillon (USA))
64 B c 4/5 Royal Academy (USA)—Iswara (USA) (Alleged (USA))

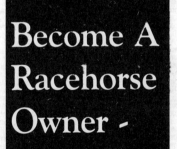

MR PETER W. HARRIS—continued

65 JUNO MARLOWE (IRE), b f 17/3 Danehill (USA)—Why So Silent (Mill Reef (USA)) **Mrs P. W. Harris**
66 KARAMEG (IRE), b f 24/4 Danehill (USA)—House of Queens (IRE) (King of Clubs) **Mr & Mrs G. Knight**
67 KATY NOWAITEE, b f 10/4 Komaite (USA)—Cold Blow (Posse (USA)) **The Stable Maites**
68 B c 16/3 Ela-Mana-Mou—Kilcoy (USA) (Secreto (USA))
69 B c 9/4 Alzao (USA)—Kindjal (Kris)
70 B c 30/3 Kris—Martha Stevens (USA) (Super Concorde (USA))
71 B f 26/4 Common Grounds—Miss Goodbody (Castle Keep)
72 Br f 30/3 Night Shift (USA)—Monoglow (Kalaglow)
73 Ch f 6/4 Thatching—Nora Yo Ya (Ahonoora)
74 B gr c 2/5 Absalom—One Sharper (Dublin Taxi)
75 PALACERA (USA), ch f 19/2 Zilzal (USA)—Placer Queen (Habitat) **Mrs P. W. Harris**
76 B c 21/3 Presidium—Ping Pong (Petong)
77 B c 27/4 Second Set (IRE)—Queen of The Brush (Averof)
78 B c 31/3 Petong—Quick Profit (Formidable (USA))
79 Ch c 12/5 Cadeaux Genereux—Rechanit (IRE) (Local Suitor (USA))
80 Gr f 24/9 Petong—Rose Bouquet (General Assembly (USA))
81 SALESTRIA, b f 16/5 Salse (USA)—Lydia Maria (Dancing Brave (USA)) **Mrs P. W. Harris**
82 B c 12/2 Presidium—Sally Tadpole (Jester)
83 SIR WARNING (USA), b br c 28/2 Warning—Sweet Snow (USA) (Lyphard (USA))
84 B c 25/5 Doyoun—Sovereign Dona (Sovereign Path)
85 B c 13/4 Contract Law (USA)—Sun Gift (Guillaume Tell (USA))
86 Ch c 21/1 Prince Sabo—Tastiera (USA) (Diesis)
87 B c 22/4 Unfuwain (USA)—That'll Be The Day (IRE) (Thatching)
88 B f 14/2 Common Grounds—Windini (Windjammer (USA))

Other Owners: Phillip Abbiss, Amir Abidi, Anita Adams, Diana Adams, Mustafa Ali, Peter Allen, Raymond Amer, Miles Anderton, Stephen Appelbee, Don Archer, Barry Arthurs, Michael Aslett, Derek Auger, Mark Avery, Michael Ayton, Mary Baker, John Ball, Garry Barker, Robert Barnes, Anthony Barry, Jonathan Barthorpe, Melvyn Bass, Andrew Batt, Patrick Beaumont, Mike Beever, Lawrence Benbow, Tony Benford, Derek Bergman, Rosa Bianchi, Gill Biddle, Marjorie Binns, Timothy Blake, John Bliss, Robin Bloomfield, Peter Blower, George Blute, Paul Bolda, Peter Bones, Derek Booth, Gary Bower, John Brady, Gordon Briggs, Beryl Brown, Neville Brown, Raymond Brown, Sharon Brown, Jeff Buckle, Tony Budd, Brenton Burgess, Wayne Burgess, Kenneth Burke, Christine Burt, Chris Bushe, Richard Butler, Lesley Cairns, William Cameron, Colin Campbell, Ian Campbell, Nino Cappuccini, Bernard Cassidy, Frank Cassidy, Richard Chadwick, Jonathan Chilton, Alan Clarke, Jane Clemetson, Rene Clifford, Colin Clilverd, Frank Coen, Colin Cogan, Marjorie & Nigel Cohen, Patrick Coleman, Anthony Collins, John Conroy, Barry Cox, Richard Creese, Emma Crocker, Raymond Crocker, Shirley Culling, John Curtis, Leslie Daffey, Ericka Davis, Gordon Davison, Steve Denham, Tony Depass, John Derry, Dino Dino, Dario Di-Rienzo, John Dixon, Patrick Dolan, Stephen Donnelly, John Donovan, Mary Donovan, Monika Doust, Russell Durnford, David Dutton, Mark East, Varden Ede, Susan Edwards, Judith Eggers, David Eldridge, Linda Ellis, Gary Evans, Neil Evans, Neil Falkner, Clare Farmiloe, Renee Farrington-Kirkham, Brian Findlay, Gerry Fitch, Barry Fitzpatrick, Diane Foster, Howard Foster, Jim Frame, Paul Francis, Bob Franks, Dianne Fraser, Neville Frost, Hugh Gallacher, Gillian Godfrey, Mary Godwin, Bryan Goodman, Clive Goodman, William Gorman, Wendy Goult, Kenneth Graham, Tony Grayston, Walter Griggs, John Grimson, Joseph Groom, Steve Grosvenor, Glenice And Peter Guntrip, Darren Haines, Betty Hale, Alexandra Hall, Kenneth Hall, John Hamshaw, Kazuhito Harada, Scott Harding, Denis Hardy, Terry And Alan Harris, Andrew Harris, Michael Harris, Robert Harris, Roy Harris, Charles Harrison, Cynthia Hart, David Dickson Hastings, David Hayes, John Haygarth, John Hayman, Derek Hemment, Carole Hilton, Michael Hollington, Marlene Hollis, Shani Hollis, Denis Holman, Ron Holmes, Iris Horgan, Richard Horner, Patrick Horsted, Gavin Hough, John Hull, Andy Hyson, Paul Inman, Barry Irons, Sharon Jackson, Jonathan Jay, Rosemarie Jefferson, Hazel Jinks, Wayne John, Peter Johnson, Alan Johnston, Paul Johnston, Joan Jordan, Robert Kaszas, Lenyra Kean, Geoffrey Keane, Ron Keats, Duncan Kelshaw, Alan Kidson, Don Kirby, David Kirk, Angus Kirkland, Christine Knapman, Graham Knight, John Knight, Keith Knight, Lyn Knight, Bernice Lancer, John Landy, Brett Lawrence, Sue Lawry, David Lawson, James Lee, William Lemon, Ethel Lewis, Simon Lewis, Alan Linker, Ian Lobar, David And Elaine Long, Richard Longmuir, Eugene Lowry, Zhu Chang Lu, Steven Lynn, Brenda Macey, Laurence Maguire, Dennis Mahoney, Brian Manfield, Melvyn Manning, Phil Manning, Angelo Mariconda, Barry Martin, Brownlow Martin, Carol Mason, John Mason, Gordon Maver, Barbara May, Eugene McBride, Gerry McCabe, Dennis McCrow, Charles McPhie, Margaret McVey, Stanley Merchack, Richard Miller, Anne And Brian Mitchell, Anne Mitchell, Susan Mitchell, R. Moir, Keith Monk, Pamela Munir, Ron Nappin, Nick Newman, Terry Newsome, Anne Nicholson, Roma Nutt, Anthony Oakes, Patrick O'Boyle, Joseph O'Brien, John O'Gorman, Brendan Olding, Tsuneo Omori, Anita Ooi, Peter Osborne, James Outtridge, Sharon Owen, Chris Page, Maurice Parker, Charles Parris, Graham Parrish, Michael Patrick, Rosemary Peace, Steve Pearson, Steve Perkins, Alwyn Phillips, Robert Phillips, Lesley Pitt, Chris Pittordou,

MR PETER W. HARRIS—continued

Dennis Potter, Gerry Pottinger, Keith Povey, Michael Powell, John Powley, David Pugsley, Lawrence Randall, Justin Readings, Sherridan Rees, Andy Reuthe, David Revell, Bill Rhodes, Eileen Rice, Philip Ring, Allen Rix, Sheila Roberts, Bill And Sylvia Robinson, Lee Robinson, Neil Rodway, Diana And Kevin Rogers, Angela Roper, Meirion Roscoe, David Ross, Paul Rowland, Mel Russell, Ruth Russell, Phil And Mary Rutter, Shoji Sakamoto, Roy Salter, Roger Sanderson, Ian Savage, Malcolm Seagroatt, Sue Seagroatt, Bert Sears, Melvin Seeviour, Martin Shack, Michael Shipperly, Derek Shockledge, Martin Shone, Michael Sibley, Leslie Siffleet, Benita Silverman, Annie Sinclair, Derek Smith, Jim Smith, John Smith, Melvin Smith, Reginald Smith, Stephen Smith, Steve Smith, Terry Smith, Tony Smith, David Snell, Allan And Jan Snow, Ronald Soanes, John Spackman, Andrew Spencer, Roger Spencer, Anthony Standish, Fred Stanford, Karen Stanford, Vince Stanzione, Andrew Suckling, Patrick Sweeney, Harold Sweet, Karen Swinden, Roderick Tankard, Brian Taylor, David Taylor, Frances Taylor, Kenneth Taylor, Jeanne Tebbutt, Geoff Theobald, Peter Thierry, Brian Thorogood, David Tipler, Barbara Tischler, Kevin Toomey, Nigel Toplis, Raymond Torre, Robert Trewhella, Nick Tritton, Peter Truman, Stephanie Tupman, Charles Turner, Robert Turrall-Clarke, Nigel Vaughan, Sue Vine, Gillian Vivian, Michael Wadsworth, Bill Walker, John Walker, Thomas Wallace, Mark Warren, Daniel Watson, Lawrence Watson, Kevin Weaver, Arthur Weller, Martyn Whaley, Patricia Whitmore, Pauline Whitmore, Nigel Whittome, George Willett, Gary Williams, Sally Williams, Allison Willis, Robert Willis, Michael Winter, Roger Wood, Edward Woodford, Anne Wormstone, Gavin Wort, Jonathan Wortley, David Wright, Chris Wyatt, Brian Yeardley, Randolph Yeo.

Lady Rider: Miss Annie Elsey.

264 MR A. H. HARVEY, Bishop's Stortford

Postal: **Wickham Hall, Hadham Road, Bishop's Stortford, Hertfordshire, CM23 1JQ.**
Phone: **OFFICE (01279) 461546 HOME (01279) 654517**

1 **COROMANDEL,** 6, b m Prince Sabo—Jandell (NZ) **Mrs I. A. C. Slade**
2 **DUTY FREE,** 5, b g El Conquistador—Golden Medina **Mrs F. E. Harvey**
3 **EXPANSIVE RUNNER (USA),** 6, b g Explodent (USA)—Scissors (USA) **Mr A. H. Harvey**
4 **HIGH LEARIE,** 8, b g Petoski—Lady Doubloon **Mr Edward Harvey**
5 **KOATHARY (USA),** 7, b g Capote (USA)—Jeffo (USA) **Mr Edward Harvey**
6 4, B g Commanche Run—Manna Rose **Mr Edward Harvey & Mr A. M. Harvey**
7 **OVERRUNNING,** 6, ch m Over The River (FR)—Flo-Jo (DEN) **Mr R. T. S. Matthews**
8 **PAT SAID NO (IRE),** 4, b f Last Tycoon—Fiddle-Faddle **Winning Circle Racing Club Ltd**
9 **PRIME DISPLAY (USA),** 12, ch g Golden Act (USA)—Great Display (FR) **Mrs F. E. Harvey**
10 **SMART CARD,** 5, ch g Nearly A Hand—Moore Stylish **Copenhagen Syndicate**
11 4, B g Nearly A Nose (USA)—Splendidly Gay **Mr Edward Harvey & Mr A. M. Harvey**
12 **THUNDERBIRD,** 6, b m Funny Man—Carlton Valley **The Thunderbird Partnership**
13 **TODD (USA),** 7, b g Theatrical—Boldara (USA) **Mr A. H. Harvey**

Other Owners: Mrs B. B. Carey, Dorspring Limited, Mr David Harvey, Mr N. E. Harvey, Mrs Richard Pilkington.

Jockey (NH): J A McCarthy (10-0).

Amateur: Mr P M McAllister (9-7).

265 MR PATRICK HASLAM, Middleham

Postal: **Castle Stables, Middleham, Leyburn, North Yorkshire, DL8 4QQ.**
Phone: **(01969) 624351 FAX (01969) 624463**

1 **CHINA CASTLE,** 5, b g Sayf El Arab (USA)—Honey Plum **J. M. Davis & T. S. Palin**
2 **GADROON,** 4, ch g Cadeaux Genereux—Greensward Blaze **Dunnington & Smart**
3 **NIGEL'S LAD (IRE),** 6, b g Dominion Royale—Back To Earth (FR) **Mr N. C. Dunnington**
4 **NO GROUSING (IRE),** 4, b g Robellino (USA)—Amenaide **The Glorious Twelfth Syndicate**
5 **OLD HUSH WING (IRE),** 5, b g Tirol—Saneena **Mr John A. Blakey**

MR PATRICK HASLAM—continued

6 **PAGEBOY,** 9, b g Tina's Pet—Edwins' Princess **Lord Scarsdale**
7 **PET EXPRESS,** 4, b g Petoski—Hush It Up **Pet Express (W&R) Ltd**
8 **PIPE MAJOR (IRE),** 6, b g Tirol—Annsfield Lady **Lord Scarsdale**
9 **SELBERRY,** 4, b g Selkirk (USA)—Choke Cherry **Middleham Park Racing VI**
10 **ULTRA BEET,** 6, b g Puissance—Cassiar **Pet Express (W&R) Ltd**

THREE-YEAR-OLDS

11 **ALL OUR BLESSINGS (IRE),** b f Statoblest—Zenga **Middleham Park Racing & Breeding**
12 **AMBER REGENT,** ch g King's Signet (USA)—Silly Sally **Mr S. A. B. Dinsmore**
13 **CELTIC COMFORT,** ch g Executive Man—Annacando **Mr Ray Tutton**
14 **HAPPY WANDERER,** ch g Clantime—Maha **McMurdo/Tutton**
15 **MUSALSE,** b g Salse (USA)—Musical Sally (USA) **Mrs C.Barclay/Middleham Park Racing VIII**
16 **MYSTERY MAN,** gr g Mystiko (USA)—Baileys By Name **Mr N. P. Green**
17 **PIPE MUSIC (IRE),** b g Mujadil (USA)—Sunset Cafe (IRE) **Lord Scarsdale**
18 **PRINCE ASHLEIGH,** b g Anshan—Fen Princess (IRE) **Mr S. A. B. Dinsmore**
19 **ROCKSWAIN (IRE),** ch g Ballad Rock—Uninvited Guest **Mr Martin Wickens**

TWO-YEAR-OLDS

20 **FIORI,** b c 22/4 Anshan—Fen Princess (IRE) (Trojan Fen) **Mr S. A. B. Dinsmore**
21 B f 14/4 Petardia—Hotse (IRE) (Shernazar) **Mr R. A. Popelye**
22 **MAYBE SPECIAL,** b c 17/2 Then Again—With Love (Be My Guest (USA)) **Mr Les Buckley**
23 Ch c 29/2 Executive Man—Recent Events (Stanford) **Mr T. S. Rowley**
24 B c 8/4 Forzando—Shadow Bird (Martinmas) **Middleham Park Racing**
25 **ULTRA CALM (IRE),** ch c 15/2 Doubletour (USA)—Shyonn (IRE) (Shy Groom (USA)) **Pet Express (W & R) Ltd**

Other Owners: Mrs E. Brock, Exors Of The Late Mr J. F. Brock, Mr G. Chapman, Mrs E. Chung, Mr Michael Cook, Mr J. Corbally, Mrs K. F. Corner, Mr John Coyle, Mr M. J. Cunningham, Mr S. P. French, Mr Alan Gleadall, Mr H. Guss, Mr P. F. J. Hamlett, Mrs J. M. Hargreaves, Mr P. C. Haslam, Mr G. Heap, Mr P. Higgins, Mr S. Higgins, Jack Of All Trades Partnership, Mr J. Jarvis, Mrs Peter Lambert, Mr Michael Barrington Moore, Mr David H. Morgan, Viscount Mountgarret, Middleham Park Racing Bureau, Major W. Peyton-Smith, Mr J. A. Preece, Rio Stainless Engineering Limited, Mr J. Soulsby, Mr J. Swinglehurst, Mr G. Wedd, Mr I. Wilson, Mr G. Wood, Col E. C. York.

Jockeys (Flat): L Charnock (7-10), J Weaver (8-4).

Jockey (NH): M Foster (10-0).

Apprentice: P L Goode (7-12).

266 MR N. J. HAWKE, Chard

Postal: **Holemoor House Stables, Coombe St Nicholls, Chard, Somerset, TA20 4AE.**
Phone: **(01460) 66196**

1 **AFTER THE FOX,** 11, b g Athens Treasure—The Deer Hound **Mr A. N. Brooke Rankin**
2 **CHALCUCHIMA,** 5, gr g Reprimand—Ica **The Millenium Group I**
3 **DONNIE BRASCO (IRE),** 5, gr g General Ironside—Royal Liatris **Mr B. Edgely**
4 **EASY LISTENING (USA),** 6, b g Easy Goer (USA)—Queen of Song (USA) **Mr Derek Kacy Flint**
5 **ESSDOUBLEYOU (NZ),** 10, ch g Sambuk—Gardone **S. W. Transport (Swindon) Ltd**
6 **HAPPY HORSE (NZ),** 11, ch g Gaiter (NZ)—Silver Valley (NZ) **Major Ian Manning**
7 **LANHYDROCK GREEN (IRE),** 5, b g Lord Americo—Easter Blade (IRE) **St Mellion Estates Ltd**
8 **MARKSMAN SPARKS,** 8, b g Gunner B—Forty Watts **The Millenium Group I**
9 **MAY SUNSET (IRE),** 8, b g Tremblant—Donegal Queen **The Millenium Group 1**
10 **MUSICAL MONARCH (NZ),** 12, ch g Leader of The Band (USA)—Cheelbrite (NZ) **Mr Sid Williams**
11 **MUTLEY,** 8, b g Rakaposhi King—Ferdee Free **Mr Derek Kacy Flint**
12 **OUR LOTTIE,** 6, ch m Nearly A Hand—Miss Saddler **Mr J. S. Hoare**
13 **PINK SUGAR,** 7, ro m Ayyabaan—Young Sugar Bush **The Millenium Group I**

MR N. J. HAWKE—continued

14 RED PARADE (NZ), 10, b g Church Parade—Infra Ray (NZ) **Mr Russell J. Peake**
15 SANTELLA CAPE, 5, b g Alzao (USA)—Kijafa (USA) **Mrs Ann Hawke**
16 SIERRA NEVADA, 7, ch g Nearly A Hand—Yellow Iris **Mr Pat Bertram**
17 SPARKLING CASCADE (IRE), 6, b m Royal Fountain—Yukon Law **The Seasiders & Partners**
18 ST MELLION LEISURE (IRE), 6, b g Lord Americo—Forthetimebeing **St Mellion Estates Ltd**
19 SWEET SARAH, 4, b f Gold Dust—Tintern Memory **The Millenium Group 1**
20 TOP JAVALIN (NZ), 11, ch g Veloso (NZ)—Buena Vista (AUS) **Mrs Valerie Thum**
21 TREMPLIN (IRE), 7, b m Tremblant—Sweet Slievenamon **Mr Russell J. Peake**
22 TURN UP THE HEAT, 4, ch g Prince of Peace—Trewithien **Mr Russell J. Peake**

Other Owners: Mr H. Bond, Mrs Linda Goddard, Mrs R. Harry, Mrs A. L. Heayns, Mr Trevor Heayns, Mrs J. Hicks, Ms J. A. Hodges, Mr K. Knox, Mr Gary Marquand, Mrs J. A. Peake, Mrs Jackie Reip, Mrs D. R. Whigham.

267 MR JOHN C HAYDEN, Kildare

Postal: **Castlemartin Abbey House Stables, Kilcullen, Co. Kildare, Ireland.**
Phone: **(045) 481598 FAX (045) 481598**

1 5, B g Satco (FR)—Betty's Delight
2 BUTTERFIELD BOY (IRE), 6, b g Mandalus—Disetta
3 EIN TRESOR, 4, b g Mon Tresor—Play The Game
4 FOLLOW THE GUIDE (IRE), 6, b m Strong Gale—Dawn Rising
5 HARBIMONT (IRE), 5, b g Montelimar—Ibrah
6 KING OF THE OCEAN (IRE), 6, b g King's Ride—Jacqueline's Glen
7 4, B g Montelimar (USA)—Mindyourbusiness
8 NURSERY RHYMES (IRE), 4, gr f Common Grounds—Island Goddess
9 ROUNDSTONE DANCER (IRE), 4, b f Dancing Dissident (USA)—Roundstone Lass
10 SHANNON OAK, 6, b g Montelimar (USA)—Mindyourbusiness
11 THE DIRECTOR, 5, b g Prince Rupert (FR)—Caroll's Canyon (IRE)

THREE-YEAR-OLDS

12 MISS CHIQUITA (IRE), b f Waajib—Golden Leap
13 RENAISSANCE DANCER (IRE), b c Petardia—Lute And Lyre (IRE)
14 SHALAZAR (IRE), b g Shernazar—Floren Tink (USA)
15 TIGER WINGS (IRE), b f Thatching—Sialia (IRE)

TWO-YEAR-OLDS

16 B c 17/4 Archway (IRE)—Anoint (Connaught)
17 B c 21/3 Scenic—Fact of Time (Known Fact (USA))
18 B f 2/1 Namaqualand (USA)—Final Contract (IRE) (Shaadi (USA))
19 Ch c 16/3 Pips Pride—Golden Leap (Salmon Leap (USA))
20 B c 18/3 Up And At 'Em—Short Stay (Be My Guest (USA))
21 STRINA (IRE), ch f 4/4 Indian Ridge—Salustrina (Sallust)
22 B f 17/1 Distant Relative—The Bean Sidhe (Corvaro (USA))

Other Owners: Mr Frank Campbell, Castlemartin Racing Club, Mr T. Cox, Mr E. Gilmartin, Mr F. Hannon, J. P. Hardiman, Mrs B. Hayden, Mrs G. Hayden, Mr S. Hayden, Mr Joe Hayes, Mr J. Keeling, Mr S. Kistler, Mrs E. Lalor, Mr E. McAllister, Mr G. McCambridge, Mr P. McCutcheon, M. McGrath, Mr Joe Morgan, Mohammed Al Munro, Dr A. J. O'Reilly, Mrs Chryss O'Reilly, Mr F. O'Toole, Mr S. Ridgeway, Shannon Oak Syndicate, Mrs R. Stewart, Miss M. A. Waters.

Jockeys (Flat): J P Murtagh (w.a.), Willie Supple (w.a.).

Apprentice: Derek Stamp (6-0).

Amateurs: Mr Mark Hayden, Mr P M Kelly.

268 MR D. HAYDN JONES, Pontypridd

Postal: **Garth Paddocks, Efail Isaf, Pontypridd, Mid-Glamorgan, Wales, CF38 1SN.**
Phone: **(01443) 202515 FAX (01443) 201877**

1 **AFRICAN-PARD (IRE),** 6, b g Don't Forget Me—Petite Realm **J. S. Fox and Sons**
2 **ASKERN,** 7, gr g Sharrood (USA)—Silk Stocking **Mr Hugh O'Donnell**
3 **CAPILANO PRINCESS,** 5, b m Tragic Role (USA)—Lady Capilano **Mr H. G. Collis**
4 **ELLAMINE,** 4, b f Warrshan (USA)—Anhaar **Mr G. J. Hicks**
5 **FLEUVE D'OR (IRE),** 4, gr f Last Tycoon—Aldern Stream **Mrs Judy Mihalop**
6 **INTIAASH (IRE),** 6, br m Shaadi (USA)—Funun (USA) **Mr R. Howard Thomas**
7 **MONO LADY (IRE),** 5, b m Polish Patriot (USA)—Phylella **Monolithic Refractories Ltd**
8 **MURRON WALLACE,** 4, gr f Reprimand—Fair Eleanor **Dhes-C Partnership**
9 **NATURAL KEY,** 5, ch m Safawan—No Sharps Or Flats (USA) **Mr Hugh O'Donnell**
10 **PREMIER DANCE,** 11, ch g Bairn (USA)—Gigiolina **J. S. Fox and Sons**
11 **PRINCE OF MY HEART,** 5, ch h Prince Daniel (USA)—Blue Room **Mr G. J. Hicks**
12 **Q FACTOR,** 6, br m Tragic Role (USA)—Dominiana **Mr H. G. Collis**
13 **SELLETTE (IRE),** 4, ch f Selkirk (USA)—Near The End **Mrs Judy Mihalop**
14 **TIMBER BROKER,** 7, ch g Jalmood (USA)—La Petite Noblesse **North Cheshire Trading & Storage Ltd**

THREE-YEAR-OLDS

15 **CRAZEE MENTAL,** b f Magic Ring (IRE)—Corn Futures **Mr Hugh O'Donnell**
16 **GYPSY HILL,** ch f Theatrical Charmer—Mirkan Honey **Mr Kevan R. Kynaston**
17 **KEYSER SOZE,** b g Petong—Lamees (USA) **Mr Hugh O'Donnell**
18 **SUMBAWA (IRE),** ch f Magic Ring (IRE)—Tittlemouse **Mr J. K. Ruggles & Mrs A. R. Ruggles**
19 **TANIMBAR (IRE),** b g Persian Bold—Try My Rosie **Mr J. K. Ruggles & Mrs A. R. Ruggles**

TWO-YEAR-OLDS

20 B f 3/5 Perpendicular—Fool's Errand (Milford) **Mr R. Hacker**
21 Ch c 6/3 Risk Me (FR)—Galejade (Sharrood (USA)) **Mrs Judy Mihalop**
22 B f 1/5 Magic Ring (IRE)—Giblet Pie (Henbit (USA)) **Mrs E. M. Haydn Jones**
23 **HEART SO BLUE,** ch f 6/1 Deploy—Blue Room (Gorytus (USA)) **Mr G. J. Hicks**
24 **INVIRAMENTAL,** b c 29/2 Pursuit Of Love—Corn Futures (Nomination) **Mr Hugh O'Donnell**
25 B f 23/3 Lugana Beach—Mrs Bacon (Balliol) **Mrs S. H. Owen**
26 **PRINCESS FOLEY,** ch f 24/1 Forest Wind (USA)—Taniokey (Grundy) **Foley Steelstock**
27 B f 6/3 Contract Law (USA)—Silent Movie (Shirley Heights) **Monolithic Refractories Ltd**
28 Gr f 2/4 Puissance—Swallow Bay (Penmarric (USA)) **Mrs L. Parry, Mr P. M. Steele-Mortimer**
29 **TEMPRA MENTAL,** ch f 30/1 Midhish—Musical Horn (Music Boy) **Mr Hugh O'Donnell**

Other Owners: Mr D. Brown, Mr R. R. Dunford, Mr R. H. Fox, Mr R. W. Fox, Mr S. Hunter, Jack Brown (Bookmaker) Ltd, Mrs M. O'Donnell, Mrs T. M. Parry, Mr A. Singh, Mr G. Singh, Mr A. Thomson, Mrs Jacqueline Wilkinson.

Jockey (Flat): John Reid (8-4, w.a.).

269 MR H. E. HAYNES, Swindon

Postal: **Red Down Farm, Highworth, Swindon, Wilts, SN6 7SH.**
Phone: **(01793) 762437**

1 **ALHALAL,** 5, ch g Cadeaux Genereux—Vaguely **Mr G. A. Swinbank**
2 **CHANCEY FELLA,** 7, ch g Sylvan Express—Musical Piece **Mrs H. E. Haynes**
3 **CHOISTY (IRE),** 8, ch g Callernish—Rosemount Rose **Mr G. A. Swinbank**
4 **COASTING,** 12, b g Skyliner—Shantung Lassie (FR) **The Reddown High Explosive Partnership**
5 **CONVOY,** 8, gr g Be My Guest (USA)—Be Easy **Mrs H. E. Haynes**
6 **COOL HARRY (USA),** 7, b br g Sir Harry Lewis (USA)—No Chili **Mrs H. E. Haynes**
7 **DAWN CHANCE,** 12, gr g Lighter—Main Chance **Miss Sally R. Haynes**
8 **DON'T TELL TOM (IRE),** 8, b g Strong Statement (USA)—Drop In **Miss Sally R. Haynes**
9 **FIVEALLEYRATH (IRE),** 4, b g Shalford (IRE)—Marazika **Mr G. A. Swinbank**

MR H. E. HAYNES—continued

10 **FREDERICK JAMES,** 4, b c Efisio—Rare Roberta (USA) **Miss Sally R. Haynes**
11 **IHTIMAAM (FR),** 6, b g Polish Precedent (USA)—Haebeh (USA) **Mrs H. E. Haynes**
12 **JOVIAN POND,** 6, b g Jupiter Island—Water Ballet **Miss Sally R. Haynes**
13 **MR JAKE,** 5, b g Safawan—Miss Tealeaf (USA) **Mr G. A. Swinbank**
14 **OBELISK (IRE),** 4, b g Alzao (USA)—Obertura (USA) **Mr G. A. Swinbank**
15 **PANGERAN (USA),** 6, b g Forty Niner (USA)—Smart Heiress **Miss Sally R. Haynes**
16 **PECHE D'OR,** 14, ch g Glint of Gold—Fishermans Bridge **Mrs H. E. Haynes**
17 **RAIN DOCTOR,** 4, b g Lycius (USA)—Rain Date (USA) **Mr G. A. Swinbank**

Jockeys (NH): M Fitzgerald (10-2), A Maguire (10-0), A P McCoy (10-0).

Conditional: R Thornton (9-0).

Amateurs: Mr S Durack (9-7), Mr O McPhail (9-7).

Lady Rider: Miss Fiona Haynes (9-5).

270 MR J. C. HAYNES, Kendal

Postal: **Moss Lea, Levens, Kendal, Cumbria, LA8 8EJ.**
Phone: **(01539) 552280 MOBILE (07771) 511471**

1 **DARIO'S GIRL,** 5, b m Good Times (ITY)—Our Krystle **Mr J. C. Haynes**
2 **GALAXY RAIN,** 7, ch g Smackover—Little Tich **Mr J. C. Haynes**
3 **NORTHERN FLASH,** 4, b g Rambo Dancer (CAN)—Spinster **Mr J. C. Haynes**
4 **TEMPTED (IRE),** 10, ch m Invited (USA)—Fauvette (USA) **Mr J. C. Haynes**

Other Owners: Mr W. E. Moore.

Jockey (NH): D Parker (10-0, w.a.).

Conditional: C McCormack (9-9, w.a.).

271 MR M. J. HAYNES, Epsom

Postal: **21 Chantry Hurst, Epsom, Surrey, KT18 7BW.**
Phone: **HOME EPSOM (013727) 22664 STABLES BURGH HEATH (01737) 351140**

1 **HIGH PRIORITY (IRE),** 5, b h Marju (IRE)—Blinding (IRE) **Mrs Eileen Sheehan**
2 **JOLI FLYERS,** 4, gr c Joli Wasfi (USA)—Hagen's Bargain **Mr Chris J. Buckerfield**
3 **JOLI'S SON,** 4, gr c Joli Wasfi (USA)—Hagen's Bargain **Mr Chris J. Buckerfield**
4 **KING OF TUNES (FR),** 6, b h Chief Singer—Marcotte **Mrs Eileen Sheehan**
5 **KINGSFOLD PET,** 9, b g Tina's Pet—Bella Lisa **George Nye Partnership**
6 **MAD ALEX,** 5, b g Risk Me (FR)—Princess Mona **Mr J. P. Saunders**
7 **OUTSTAYED WELCOME,** 5, b g Be My Guest (USA)—Between Time **Mr M. J. Haynes, Mr Bob Pettis**
8 **PADAUK,** 4, b c Warrshan (USA)—Free On Board **D. Butler, Bob Pettis, M. J. Haynes**

MR M. J. HAYNES—continued

THREE-YEAR-OLDS

9 **ANGELIQUE,** ch f Soviet Star (USA)—Lady Habitat **Mr G. Steinberg**
10 **BERMUDA TRIANGLE (IRE),** b f Conquering Hero (USA)—Bermuda Princess **Mr M. J. Haynes**
11 **ENGLISH LADY (IRE),** b f Fayruz—Paradise Regained **English Lady Classics Ltd**
12 **HELISMAD,** b g Thowra (FR)—Princess Mona **Mr J. P. Saunders**
13 **HICKORY (IRE),** b g Fayruz—La Mortola **Mr G. Steinberg**
14 **KINGSFOLD BLAZE,** b f Mazilier—Kingsfold Flame **Mr Chris J. Buckerfield**
15 **PORTHILLY BUOY,** ch g Keen—Hissma **Porthilly Partners**
16 **PRIMAVERA,** b f Anshan—Fair Maid of Kent (USA) **Mr G Steinberg**

TWO-YEAR-OLDS

17 Ch c 9/4 Lahib (USA)—Anisimova (Kris) **Ansells of Watford**
18 Ch f 6/3 Pip's Pride—Gold Stamp (Golden Act (USA))
19 Ch c 13/4 Safawan—Sister Sal (Bairn (USA))
20 Gr f 23/3 Lugana Beach—Thames Glow (Kalaglow)

Other Owners: Mrs M. L. Ansell, Mr David M. Butler, Mr G. R. Butterfield, Mr W. G. Carpenter, Mr M. A. Evans, Mr D. J. Gander, Mr Eddie Gleeson, Larkrise Ostrich Farm Ltd, Mr W. E. Moore, Exors Of The Late Mr G. E. Nye, Mrs Y. M. Nye, Mrs M. Rauch, Mr Anthony Roche, Mr J. P. Saunders, Mr Alan Walder.

Apprentice: M Cornally (8-0).

Lady Rider: Miss Y Haynes (9-7).

272 MR P. A. HAYWARD, Netheravon

Postal: **Copperfield, Haxton, Netheravon, Wiltshire, SP4 9PY.**
Phone: **(01980) 670585**

1 **BO'JUST,** 6, b m Bold Fort—Just Blair **Mr P. Hayward**
2 **COURAGEOUS KNIGHT,** 9, gr g Midyan (USA)—Little Mercy **Mr L. Kirkwood**
3 **CRYSTAL VALE,** 5, b m Sulaafah (USA)—Swift Turtle **J. H. & M. E. Stranger**
4 **EMBER,** 5, b m Nicholas (USA)—Cinderwench **Mr A. P. King**
5 **GRANBY BELL,** 7, b g Ballacashtal (CAN)—Betbellof **Mr H. A. Watton**
6 **I RECALL (IRE),** 7, b g Don't Forget Me—Sable Lake **Mrs S. A. Coplestone**
7 **ISCA MAIDEN,** 4, b f Full Extent (USA)—Sharp N' Easy **The Welsh Connection**
8 **JILLY WOO,** 4, gr f Environment Friend—William's Bird (USA) **Mrs J. Wotherspoon**
9 **KASHAN (IRE),** 10, b g Darshaan—Kamanika (FR) **Miss E. J. Wright**
10 **SPRING TO GLORY,** 11, b g Teenoso (USA)—English Spring (USA) **Mr A. J. Byrne**

THREE-YEAR-OLDS

11 **NOTTY,** ch f Nicholas Bill—Silver Empress **Mrs S. A. Coplestone**

Other Owners: Mr B. C. Brown, Mrs Marilyn J. Mein, Mr J. Sawyer, Mr J. H. Strange, Mrs M. E. Stranger, Mr P. B. Woodley.

Jockey (NH): B Fenton (10-0).
Apprentice: M Henry.

273 MRS C. HEAD, Chantilly

Postal: **32 Avenue du General Leclerc, 60500 Chantilly, France.**
Phone: **(33) 3 44 57 01 01 FAX (33) 3 44 58 53 33**

1 **BANAFSAJEE,** 4, b f Pleasant Colony—Sous Entendu **Gainsborough Stud**
2 **BRIGHT FINISH,** 4, b f Zilzal—Bialy **Gainsborough Stud**
3 **DANCING KRIS,** 5, b h Kris—Liska's Dance **Wertheimer et Frere**
4 **DAYLIGHT IN DUBAI,** 4, ch c Twilight Agenda—Lady Godolphin **Mr P. Savill**
5 **DELIMARA,** 4, b f In The Wings—Mariella **Mr G. A. Oldham**
6 **FACULTY,** 4, b c Known Fact—Arewehavingfunyet **Prince Khalid Abdulla**
7 **FILM NOIR,** 4, b c Alleged—Black Princess **Wertheimer et Frere**
8 **FUMARELLI,** 4, ch c Trempolino—Bellarida **Wertheimer et Frere**
9 **HANKSLEW,** 4, b c Seattle Slew—Fabulous Hostess **Wertheimer et Frere**
10 **HIGHEST HIGH,** 4, b c Highest Honor—Haute Autorite **Wertheimer et Frere**
11 **MAJORIEN,** 4, b c Machiavellian—Green Rosy **Gainsborough Stud**
12 **NIJINSTIC,** 4, ch c Caerleon—Young Hostess **Wertheimer et Frere**
13 **OCCUPANDISTE,** 5, b m Kaldoun—Only Seule **Wertheimer et Frere**
14 **PALERMO,** 4, b c Green Desert—Caprarola **Mr G. A. Oldham**
15 **PAS DE REPONSE,** 4, b f Danzig—Soundings **Wertheimer et Frere**
16 **PRETENDANT,** 4, b c Seeking The Gold—Pallanza **Wertheimer et Frere**
17 **QUESTNEYEV,** 4, b c Rainbow Quest—Mona Stella **Wertheimer et Frere**
18 **RAINGAY,** 4, b c Saumarez—Solveig **Wertheimer et Frere**
19 **RECONDITE,** 4, b c Polish Patriot—Recherchee **Mr P. Savill**
20 **SICULO,** 4, b c Highest Honor—Vanya **Mr G. A. Oldham**
21 **SILVER FUN,** 4, b f Saumarez—Riviere d'Argent **Wertheimer et Frere**
22 **SPECIAL DISCOUNT,** 4, b c Nureyev—Look Sensational **Wertheimer et Frere**
23 **ZAPATAFAR,** 5, b h Lyphard—Viva Zapata **Wertheimer et Frere**

THREE-YEAR-OLDS

24 **ACCESS TO FAME,** b f Ferdinand—Twin Cities **Mr Mastey**
25 **AIR SUPREMO,** b c Shadeed—Fly To The Moon **Gainsborough Stud**
26 **AL AFREATA,** ch f Bering—La Francesa **Sheikh Mohammed bin Khalifa Al Thani**
27 **AMUSING TIME,** b f Sadler's Wells—Ozone Friendly **Gainsborough Stud**
28 **ANTHELION,** b f Stop The Music—Autumn Glory **Prince Khalid Abdulla**
29 **ANYSHEBA,** b f Alysheba—Animatrice **Wertheimer et Frere**
30 **APALEON,** b c Caerleon—Apachee **Wertheimer et Frere**
31 **ARAZINA,** b f Arazi—Valses Pour Moi **Wertheimer et Frere**
32 **ARGENTINNSKY,** b c Groom Dancer—Riviere d'Argent **Wertheimer et Frere**
33 **ARTHURIAN,** b c Sanglamore—Trampship **Prince Khalid Abdulla**
34 **AUTORITARIAN,** b c Shirley Heights—Haute Autorite **Wertheimer et Frere**
35 **AZOT,** b c Deputy Minister—Angelina Ballerina **Wertheimer et Frere**
36 **BAUBLE,** ch c Sanglamore—Princess Borghese **Prince Khalid Abdulla**
37 **BRIGHT PORSPECT,** b f Miswaki—Lucky State **Wertheimer et Frere**
38 **BROOKLYN'S GOLD,** b c Seeking The Gold—Brooklyn's Dance **Wertheimer et Frere**
39 **CAUSED CONFUSION,** b c Miswaki—Reassert **Gainsborough Stud**
40 **CHATEAU COUNTRY,** b c Lear Fan—Mt Morna **Gainsborough Stud**
41 **CONTEXT,** b f Zafonic—Twixt **Prince Khalid Abdulla**
42 **CORTONA,** b f Caerleon—Olbia **Mr G. A. Oldham**
43 **DANZIGOER,** b c Danzig—Partygoer **Wertheimer et Frere**
44 **DIABLENEYEV,** b c Nureyev—La Pitie **Wertheimer et Frere**
45 **DIVINE APPEAL,** b f El Gran Senor—Maribiya **Wertheimer et Frere**
46 **DIVINEYEVA,** b f Nureyev—Divine Danse **Wertheimer et Frere**
47 **DIXIT,** b c Diesis—Ixtapa **Prince Khalid Abdulla**
48 **DOUBLE ACCOUNT,** b c Sillery—Fabulous Account **Wertheimer et Frere**
49 **FABULOUS,** ch f Seeking The Gold—Gorgeous **Mr R. Clay**
50 **FAIRWAY QUEEN,** b f Theatrical—Fairway Flag **Mr John Moore**
51 **FLAG CONNECTION,** b c Alleged—Lassie Connection **Wertheimer et Frere**
52 **FLAMING SONG,** b f Darshaan—Pale Blue **Wertheimer et Frere**
53 **FRONT BENCH,** b c Arazi—Fetish **Prince Khalid Abdulla**
54 **FROZEN GROOM,** b c Bering—Danagroom **Wertheimer et Frere**

MRS C. HEAD—continued

55 GENOVESE, b c Generous—Superstore **Prince Khalid Abdulla**
56 GOLD AWAY, b c Goldneyev—Blushing Away **Wertheimer et Frere**
57 GREEN RUN, b f Green Dancer—Black Princess **Wertheimer et Frere**
58 HALOMOR, b c Sanglamore—Amene **Wertheimer et Frere**
59 HOSTESSANTE, b f Pleasant Colony—Fabulous Hostess **Wertheimer et Frere**
60 IRISH FASHION, b c Nashwan—L'Irlandaise **Wertheimer et Frere**
61 IRISH FLARE, b f Irish River—Insijaam **Mr Mastey**
62 KARAPUCHA, b f Kaldoun—Soviet Squaw **Wertheimer et Frere**
63 LASTING FRIENDSHIP, b c Diesis—Etoile d'Amore **Gainsborough Stud**
64 LASTMAN, b c Fabulous Dancer—Rivala **Wertheimer et Frere**
65 LOVING CLAIM, b f Hansel—Ville d'Amore **Gainsborough Stud**
66 LUNATA, b f Marju—Rained Off **Mr G. A. Oldham**
67 LUNCHTIME, b f Known Fact—Arewehavingfunyet **Prince Khalid Abdulla**
68 MAGICAL HAWK, b f Silver Hawk—Sum **Mr Edward J. Kelly Jr**
69 MASTER TERN, b c Generous—Young Hostess **Wertheimer et Frere**
70 MEMORIES, b f Darshaan—Saveur **Aylesfield Farm**
71 MUD BAND, b f Dixieland Band—Galitizine **Wertheimer et Frere**
72 NOBLE WANDERER, b c Nashwan—Tajfah **Gainsborough Stud**
73 ONLY QUEST, b c Saumarez—Only Seule **Wertheimer et Frere**
74 OR BLEU, b f Rainbow Quest—Riviere d'Or **Wertheimer et Frere**
75 OTAVALO, b c Diesis—Lacovia **Mr G. A. Oldham**
76 PHOTOGRAPHIE, b f Trempolino—Vintage **Wertheimer et Frere**
77 PIEDS DE PLUME, b f Seattle Slew—Featherhill **Wertheimer et Frere**
78 PRINCE REVIEWER, b c Nureyev—Only Queens **Gainsborough Stud**
79 PROSPECTHEUS, b c Gone West—Valthea **Wertheimer et Frere**
80 PROUD HEART, b f Caerleon—Porphyrine **Gainsborough Stud**
81 QUEENSWAY, b f Zafonic—Shapaara **Mrs Alexandra J. Chandris**
82 RENAZIG, b c Polish Precedent—Renashaan **Wertheimer et Frere**
83 RIVER BRIDGE, b f Sanglamore—Batchelor's Button **Aylesfield Farm**
84 RIVER FLARE, b f Riverman—Proflare **Prince Khalid Abdulla**
85 ROYAL ALLEGIANCE, b c Kris—Wilayif **Gainsborough Stud**
86 RUSSYSKIA, b f Green Dancer—Marie de Russy **Wertheimer et Frere**
87 SADLER'S SECRET, b c Sadler's Wells—Athyka **Wertheimer et Frere**
88 SAND PROSPECTOR, b c Dixieland Band—Soundings **Wertheimer et Frere**
89 SCARLET PIMPERNEL, b c Night Shift—Working Model **Mr James Wigan**
90 SEEKING THE DREAM, b c Seeking The Gold—Chapel of Dreams **Mr Edward J. Kelly Jr**
91 SENSATIONAL DANCER, b c Goldneyev—Polish Looks **Wertheimer et Frere**
92 SESTINO, b c Shirley Heights—Stellina **Mr G. A. Oldham**
93 SHOTWELL, b c Pistolet Bleu—Gerbera **Wertheimer et Frere**
94 SMARTLY TAX, b c Miswaki—Smartly Styled **Wertheimer et Frere**
95 SPECIAL QUEST, b c Rainbow Quest—Mona Stella **Wertheimer et Frere**
96 SUCH IS LIFE, b c Zilzal—Hiaam **Gainsborough Stud**
97 TETRAVELLA, b f Groom Dancer—Vanya **Mr G. A. Oldham**
98 TIYI, b f Fairy King—Reine d'Egypte **Wertheimer et Frere**
99 TRES STRICT, b c Irish River—Strictly Raised **Wertheimer et Frere**
100 TYPONEX, b c Last Tycoon—Polyxena **Wertheimer et Frere**
101 URGENT MOVE, b f Chief's Crown—Lady B Gay **Mr Mastey**
102 VELLANO, b c Lycius—Maresca **Mr G. A. Oldham**
103 WAKI DECREE, b f Miswaki—Papal Decree **Wertheimer et Frere**
104 WITH THE FLOW, b c Irish River—Principale **Mr M. W. Jenney**

TWO-YEAR-OLDS

105 ACCOUNTING, b f Sillery—Fabulous Account **Wertheimer et Frere**
106 ANTIQUE PEARL, b f Darshaan—Touch And Love **Gainsborough Stud**
107 AQUIRE NOT DESIRE, b c Woodman—Forladiesonly **Gainsborough Stud**
108 B f Stop The Music—Autumn Glory **Prince Khalid Abdulla**
109 B c Lear Fan—Averti **Prince Khalid Abdulla**
110 BEAUTIMIX, b f Linamix—Raise A Beauty **Wertheimer et Frere**
111 BICBIC, b c Seattle Slew—Corrazona **Wertheimer et Frere**

MRS C. HEAD—continued

112 **BLUE BOMBER,** b c Darshaan—Pale Blue **Wertheimer et Frere**
113 **BROOKLYN'S STORM,** b f Storm Cat—Brooklyn's Dance **Wertheimer et Frere**
114 **CRYSTAL MAGICIAN,** b c Cadeaux Genereux—Miss Temerity **Gainsborough Stud**
115 **DANANEYEV,** b c Goldneyev—Danagroom **Wertheimer et Frere**
116 **DANCE WITH KELLY,** b c Devil's Bag—Dance With Grace **Wertheimer et Frere**
117 **DANSEUR MONDAIN,** b c Dancing Spree—Polish Looks **Wertheimer et Frere**
118 **DANZIGAWAY,** b f Danehill—Blushing Away **Wertheimer et Frere**
119 **ELEANOR'S PRIDE,** b f Barathea—Escaline **Gainsborough Stud**
120 **EMERALD PARK,** b c Zilzal—Greenland Park **Gainsborough Stud**
121 **EMPIRENEYEV,** b c Nureyev—La Pitie **Wertheimer et Frere**
122 B f Gone West—Euphonic **Prince Khalid Abdulla**
123 **FAST AND FIRE,** b c Gulch—Petit Diable **Wertheimer et Frere**
124 **FRANC,** b c Woodman—Adventurous Di **Mr W. Kelly**
125 **FRANKLY FINE,** b f Fairy King—Melting Gold **Gainsborough Stud**
126 **FREDAINES,** b c Unfuwain—La Francesa **Prince Saud bin Khalifa**
127 **GOLD BUST,** b f Nashwan—Riviere d'Or **Wertheimer et Frere**
128 **GOLDEN MARVEL,** b c Linamix—Horphaly **Wertheimer et Frere**
129 **GREEN INDY,** b f A P Indy—Valthea **Wertheimer et Frere**
130 **GROUPINSKY,** b c Green Dancer—La Groupie **Wertheimer et Frere**
131 **HALF QUEEN,** b f Deputy Minister—At The Half **Wertheimer et Frere**
132 **HALOMIX,** b f Linamix—Amene **Wertheimer et Frere**
133 **HEADWAY,** b c Exit To Nowhere—Shapaara **Mrs Alexandra J. Chandris**
134 **IDEAL LADY,** b f Seattle Slew—Insijaam **Gainsborough Stud**
135 **IRISH PRIZE,** b c Irish River—Cadeaux d'Amie **Gainsborough Stud**
136 B f Generous—Ivorine **Prince Khalid Abdulla**
137 B c Diesis—Ixtapa **Prince Khalid Abdulla**
138 B c Dayjur—Jeano **Mr W. Kelly**
139 **JUVENIA,** b f Trempolino—Vintage **Wertheimer et Frere**
140 B c Affirmed—Kinema **Prince Khalid Abdulla**
141 **KINGSTYLE,** b c Kingmambo—Smartly Styled **Wertheimer et Frere**
142 **LIBERTAIRE,** b f Highest Honor—Liberia **Prince Saud bin Khaled**
143 **LITTLE REDSKIN,** b f Petit Loup—Filigree **Aylesfield Farm**
144 **LYPHARD AGAIN,** b c Lyphard—Blushing Tamara **Mr Mastey**
145 **MIDNIGHT FOXTROT,** b c Kingmambo—Vana Turns **Gainsborough Stud**
146 **MILAZZO,** b c Lycius—Maresca **Mr G. A. Oldham**
147 **MOIAVA,** b f Bering—Mona Stella **Wertheimer et Frere**
148 B c Generous—Moss **Prince Khalid Abdulla**
149 **MUDMAN,** b c Dixieland Band—Galitizine **Wertheimer et Frere**
150 B c Zieten—Muirfield **Mr P. Savill**
151 B f Nashwan—Nawaiet **Gainsborough Stud**
152 **NE COUPEZ PAS,** b c Nureyev—Soundings **Wertheimer et Frere**
153 **NINAKI,** b f Miswaki—Young Hostess **Wertheimer et Frere**
154 **PARTINA,** b f Bluebird—Lambada **Mr G. A. Oldham**
155 **PATRONA BAVARIA,** b f Generous—Silicon Bavaria **Wertheimer et Frere**
156 **PERFECT COPY,** b f Deputy Minister—Seewillo **Wertheimer et Frere**
157 **PESCARA,** b f Common Grounds—Mackla **Mr G. A. Oldham**
158 B c Sillery—Plania **Mr P. Savill**
159 **POLYQUEST,** b c Rainbow Quest—Polyxena **Wertheimer et Frere**
160 B f Sanglamore—Princess Borghese **Prince Khalid Abdulla**
161 **QUIET DREAM,** b f Seattle Slew—Partygoer **Wertheimer et Frere**
162 **RENALEON,** b c Generous—Renashaan **Wertheimer et Frere**
163 **RING QUEEN,** b f Fairy King—Ring Beaune **Wertheimer et Frere**
164 **RIVER MELODY,** b f Riverman—Sophisbe **Mr Mastey**
165 **SABRINSKY,** b c Polish Precedent—Charmante Dame **Wertheimer et Frere**
166 **SAINTE GIG,** b f Saint Cyrien—Vallee des Fleurs **Wertheimer et Frere**
167 **SALLIVERA,** b f Sillery—Mabrova **Wertheimer et Frere**
168 **SANDBAND,** b c Dixieland Band—Minstrel Girl **Wertheimer et Frere**
169 **SECRET WELLS,** b f Sadler's Wells—Athyka **Wertheimer et Frere**
170 **SERENA'S DAY,** b f Sillery—Batchelor's Button **Aylesfield Farm**
171 **SHEBANE,** b f Alysheba—Belle Sultane **Wertheimer et Frere**

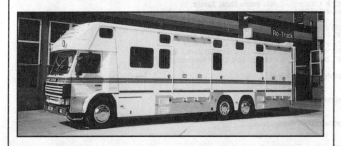

MRS C. HEAD—continued

172 **SILVER UNION,** b f Bering—Light Fresh Air **Gainsborough Stud**
173 **SKY BLEU,** b c Pistolet Bleu—Makarova **Wertheimer et Frere**
174 **SPECIAL LAD,** b c Zilzal—Etoile d'Amore **Gainsborough Stud**
175 **STARLIGHT FESTIVAL,** b c Green Desert—Fasateen **Gainsborough Stud**
176 B f Unfuwain—Superstore **Prince Khalid Abdulla**
177 B f Gone West—Tennis Lady **Mr W. Kelly**
178 **TERMANIA,** b f Shirley Heights—Bubbling Danseuse **Wertheimer et Frere**
179 **TRAPEZINA,** b f Saumarez—Only Seule **Wertheimer et Frere**
180 **TROMBOLI,** b c Kaldoun—Gerbera **Wertheimer et Frere**
181 **TRUMBLEWEED,** b c Gone West—Princesse Kathy **Wertheimer et Frere**
182 B c Warning—Tunaria **Prince Khalid Abdulla**
183 **VALNERINA,** b f Caerleon—Lady Capulet **Mr G. A. Oldham**
184 **VAOUEST,** b c Gone West—Rivala **Wertheimer et Frere**
185 **VERTIMI,** b c Green Dancer—Minimata **Wertheimer et Frere**
186 B f Zafonic—Welsh Daylight **Prince Khalid Abdulla**
187 B f Selkirk—Woodwardia **Prince Khalid Abdulla**
188 **YES I WILL,** b f Danzig—Let's Elope **Mr Dennis Marks**
189 **ZIGGY GOLD,** b c Danzig—Gold Splash **Wertheimer et Frere**

Jockey (Flat): O Doleuze.

Apprentice: N Guesdon.

Amateur: Mr P Hamel.

Lady Rider: Dominique Clerc.

274 MR M. J. B. HEATON-ELLIS, Wroughton

Postal: **Barbary Castle Farm, Wroughton, Swindon, SN4 0QZ.**
Phone: **(01793) 815009 FAX (01793) 845080**

1 **ABSOLUTLY EQUINAME (IRE),** 7, gr g Roselier (FR)—Cotton Gale **Mr F. J. Sainsbury**
2 **ARTERXERXES,** 5, b g Anshan—Hanglands **Mr P. G. Lowe & Partners**
3 **ARTFUL DANE (IRE),** 6, b h Danehill (USA)—Art Age **S. P. Lansdown Racing**
4 **BEAUCATCHER (IRE),** 4, b f Thatching—Gale Warning (IRE) **Mrs R. F. Lowe**
5 **BRAVE ENVOY,** 4, b g High Estate—Restless Anna **Mr Tom Burge**
6 **CHANDLER'S HALL,** 4, b g Saddlers' Hall (IRE)—Queen's Visit **Sir Peter Cazalet**
7 **ETHBAAT (USA),** 7, b br g Chief's Crown (USA)—Alchaasibiyeh (USA) **The Over The Bridge Partnership**
8 **GIRL OF MY DREAMS (IRE),** 5, b m Marju (IRE)—Stylish Girl (USA) **Miss V. H. Owen**
9 **GOLDEN MELODY,** 4, b f Robellino (USA)—Rose Chanelle **Amity Finance Ltd**
10 **HIGH ALLTITUDE (IRE),** 10, b g Coquelin (USA)—Donna Cressida **Mr F. J. Sainsbury**
11 **LITTLE MISS LUCY,** 4, b f Petoski—Puki Puki **Mr Richard Lissack**
12 **LORD HIGH ADMIRAL (CAN),** 10, b g Bering—Baltic Sea (CAN) **Elite Racing Club**
13 **MELLORS (IRE),** 5, b h Common Grounds—Simply Beautiful (IRE) **Mr T. P. Jones**
14 **MULLITOVER,** 8, ch g Interrex (CAN)—Atlantic Air **Mrs D. B. Mulley**
15 **NAME YOUR GAME (CAN),** 4, b g Charlie Barley (USA)—Original Script (CAN) **Mrs June M. Sifton**
16 **RATHKEAL (IRE),** 7, gr g Roselier (FR)—Fandango Lady **S. P. Lansdown Racing**
17 **SILVER SECRET,** 4, ro c Absalom—Secret Dance **Mr F. J. Sainsbury**
18 **SPEEDY CLASSIC (USA),** 9, br g Storm Cat (USA)—
Shadows Lengthen **South Wales Shower Supplies T/A Faucets**
19 **THE NEGOTIATOR,** 4, ch g Nebos (GER)—Baie des Anges **Mr F. J. Sainsbury**
20 **VENDOON (IRE),** 8, b g Sanchi Steeple—Lovely Venture **Mrs Francoise Jansen**
21 **WILD SKY (IRE),** 4, br g Warning—Erwinna (USA) **The Gold Partnership**
22 **WOODY'S BOY (IRE),** 4, gr g Roi Danzig (USA)—Smashing Gale **Mr Vic Woodason**
23 **ZOOM UP (IRE),** 4, ch g Bluebird (USA)—Senane **Mr K. Maeda**

MR M. J. B. HEATON-ELLIS—continued

THREE-YEAR-OLDS

24 **ABU CAMP,** b c Indian Ridge—Artistic Licence **Mr John Manser**
25 **BEDEVILLED,** ch c Beveled (USA)—Putout **Mr David A. Caruth**
26 **RISKY GIRL,** ro f Risk Me (FR)—Jove's Voodoo (USA) **Mr F. J. Sainsbury**
27 **SUGAR DANCE,** b c Salse (USA)—Springtime Sugar (USA) **Mr John Manser**
28 **THE GENE GENIE,** b c Syrtos—Sally Maxwell **R. P. & M. Berrow**
29 **THIRD COUSIN (IRE),** b c Distant Relative—Queen Caroline (USA) **Mr P. G. Lowe**

TWO-YEAR-OLDS

30 B f 2/6 Mukaddamah (USA)—Adocentyn (USA) (Upper Nile (USA)) **Mrs Jane Joynson**
31 **FARFRAE,** ch f 17/2 Emarati (USA)—Hanglands (Bustino) **Mr S. P. Tindall**
32 B f 9/2 Aragon—Gentle Stream (Sandy Creek) **Mr M. Heaton-Ellis**
33 Ch c 31/3 Magical Wonder (USA)—Gleeful (Sayf El Arab (USA)) **Mr M. Heaton-Ellis**
34 B c 11/3 Common Grounds—Inanna (Persian Bold) **Mrs Caroline Parker**
35 Ch c 14/4 Common Grounds—North Telstar (Sallust) **Fieldspring Racing**
36 B f 22/2 Pursuit Of Love—Pillowing (Good Times (ITY)) **Mrs A. N. Campbell-Harris**
37 Ch c 16/4 Thatching—Up To You (Sallust) **Mr M. Heaton-Ellis**

Other Owners: The Hon Adam Barker, The Hon Mrs C. Colman, Mr P. E. Cooper, Lt. Gen. Sir Sam Cowan, Mr J. M. Davidson, Mr Mel Davies, Mr D. Gold, The Hon Jolyon Grey, Mr P. G. Horrocks, Mr S. P. Lansdown, Mr T. H. Luckock, Mr David Mort, Mr John Newsome, Miss M. Noden, Mr N. Parker, Mr R. Pennant Jones, Mr I. Peter Sedgwick, Mr David Shorthouse, Mrs Janet Wain, Mrs D. C. Woodason, Mrs D. Yeats Brown.

Jockeys (Flat): A Clark (w.a.), S Drowne.

Jockeys (NH): D Gallagher (w.a), B Powell (w.a.).

Apprentices: A Daly (7-12), Jonjo Fowle (7-2).

275 MR P. R. HEDGER, Chichester

Postal: **Eastmere Stables, Eastergate Lane, Eastergate, Chichester, West Sussex, PO20 6SJ.**
Phone: **(01243) 543863 FAX 543913**

1 **AUTUMN COVER,** 6, gr g Nomination—Respray **Mr G. A. Alexander**
2 **BRILLIANT RED,** 5, b g Royal Academy (USA)—Red Comes Up (USA) **Mrs M. J. George**
3 **CANDLE SMOKE (USA),** 5, b g Woodman (USA)—Light The Lights (FR) **Mr M. K. George**
4 **DERRY'S GLORY,** 6, ch g Derrylin—Boreen's Glory **Mr P. R. Hedger**
5 **GOLDEN MILE (IRE),** 5, b m King's Ride—Gold Label **Mrs M. N. Tufnell**
6 **HAYLING STAR,** 4, ch f Out of Hand—Lurex Girl **Mr Bill Broomfield**
7 **KEDWICK (IRE),** 9, b g Be My Guest (USA)—Lady Pavlova **Mrs Joyce Griffiths**
8 **MAC OATES,** 5, b g Bairn (USA)—Bit of A Lass **Mr D. N. Larke**
9 **MADAME MAXI,** 4, ch f Ron's Victory (USA)—New Pastures **Mr P. R. Hedger**
10 **RUNNING WATER (IRE),** 5, b g Commanche Run—Paupers Spring **Mr Howard Spooner**
11 **SECRET SPRING (FR),** 6, b g Dowsing (USA)—Nordica **Mr M. K. George**
12 **SMART IN VELVET,** 8, gr m Scorpio (FR)—Cool Down **Mrs Jacqueline Elizabeth Hooker**
13 **SPICK AND SPAN,** 4, b g Anshan—Pretty Thing **Ess and Ess**
14 **SPY KNOLL,** 4, b c Shirley Heights—Garden Pink (FR) **Mr M. K. George**
15 **SUPER MAC (IRE),** 5, b g Milk of The Barley—Super Amber **Mrs A. Trigg**
16 **UMBERSTON (IRE),** 5, b g Nabeel Dancer (USA)—Pivotal Walk (IRE) **Mr Howard Spooner**
17 **UNFORGETABLE,** 6, ch g Scottish Reel—Shercol **Mr D. O'Connor**
18 **VERONICA FRANCO,** 5, b m Darshaan—Maiden Eileen **Mr J. J. Whelan**

MR P. R. HEDGER—continued

TWO-YEAR-OLDS

19 B f 1/5 Chaddleworth (IRE)—Gaynor Goodman (IRE) (Fayruz) **Mr Ian Hutchins**

Other Owners: Mr Norman Briant, Mrs C. Goodsell, Mr Malcolm M. Hooker, Mr K. T. Ivory, Mr A. K. Johnson, Mrs J. E. M. Powell, Mrs H. R. A. Spooner, Mr I. L. Weaver, Mr R. J. Patrick Weaver, Mr Nic Wellington, Mr E. Whelan.

Jockey (NH): M Richards (10-0, w.a.).

276 MR C. J. HEMSLEY, Witney

Postal: **Fairspear Equestrian Centre, Fairspear Road, Leafield, Witney, Oxfordshire, OX8 5NT.**
Phone: **YARD (01993) 878279/878551 HOME/FAX (01993) 844554**

1 6, B m Noalto—Adrian's Girl **A. W. S. Contracts (G.B.)**
2 **FAIRSPEAR LADY (IRE)**, 8, ch m Remainder Man—Lady Eleanor **Mr W. E. Dudley**
3 **FOREST FLIGHT (IRE)**, 6, ch g Standaan (FR)—Camanime **A. W. S. Contracts (G.B.)**
4 **HONEST GEORGE**, 7, b g Cruise Missile—Colourful Girl **Mr Aubrey Ellis**
5 **HOTPOT**, 5, br g Hotfoot—Miss Polly Peck **Mr W. E. Dudley**
6 **HUGE MISTAKE**, 9, b g Valiyar—Nicoletta **Wychwood Racing Partnership**
7 **HUGH DANIELS**, 10, b g Adonijah—Golden Realm **Mr Brett Hemsley**
8 **LADY OF THE DAWN**, 4, b f Tina's Pet—Distant Sound **Mrs D. M. Hickman**
9 **PLUVIUS (IRE)**, 6, ch g Be My Native (USA)—Planet Star **Mr W. E. Dudley**
10 **SUPER NOVA**, 7, b g Ra Nova—Windrush Song **Mr W. E. Dudley**
11 **SWEET EMMALINE**, 4, b f Emarati (USA)—Chapelfell **Mrs Jill Hemsley**
12 4, Gr f Baron Blakeney—Windrush Song **Mr W. E. Dudley**

Other Owners: Mr A. J. Collins, Mr J. C. Hickman, Mr Alan Woodley.

Amateur: Miss Anne Dudley (8-9).

277 MR N. J. HENDERSON, Lambourn

Postal: **Seven Barrows, Lambourn, Hungerford, Berkshire, RG17 8UH.**
Phone: **LAMBOURN (01488) 72259 OR 72300 FAX (01488) 72596**

1 **ALL GONG**, 4, br g Kris—Bonne Ile **Mr Anthony Speelman**
2 **ARDENTINNY**, 5, gr m Ardross—Charlotte Gray **Mr G. P. P. Stewart**
3 **ARTEMIS (IRE)**, 6, b g Strong Gale—Ethel's Daughter **W.V. M.W. & Mrs E.S. Robins**
4 **AUTO PILOT (NZ)**, 10, b g Gay Apollo—Dairne (NZ) **S. W. Transport (Swindon) Ltd**
5 **BALLET HIGH (IRE)**, 5, b g Sadler's Wells (USA)—Marie d'Argonne (FR) **Lady Lloyd Webber**
6 **BARNA BOY (IRE)**, 10, b g Torus—Barna Beauty **Mr Lynn Wilson**
7 **BASSEY (IRE)**, 5, b g Be My Native (USA)—Evergreen Lady **The Barrow Boys**
8 **BAY FUSILIER**, 5, b g Mazilier (USA)—Kingsfold Flash **Mrs P. Sherwood**
9 **BE BRAVE (FR)**, 5, b m Green Forest (USA)—Belle Brava (USA) **Lord MacLaurin**
10 **BIG MATT (IRE)**, 10, b g Furry Glen—Stoirin **Mr T. Benfield and Mr W. Brown**
11 **BLAST FREEZE (IRE)**, 9, b m Lafontaine (USA)—Lady Helga **Pioneer Heat-Treatment**
12 **BORO SOVEREIGN (IRE)**, 5, b g King's Ride—Boro Penny **Mr Lynn Wilson**
13 **CALON LAN (IRE)**, 7, b g Bustineto—Cherish **Mr Howard Brown**
14 **CAMERA MAN**, 8, ch g Scorpio (FR)—Something To Hide **Mrs P. Shaw**
15 **CELIO BRAVO (IRE)**, 6, b g Celio Rufo—Swuzzlebubble **W.V. M.W. & Mrs E.S. Robins**
16 **CLASSY LAD (NZ)**, 8, b br g Golden Elder—Barrel (NZ) **Mr Michael Buckley**
17 **COMMANDANT (IRE)**, 5, b g Good Thyne (USA)—Slave Run **W.V. M.W. & Mrs E.S. Robins**
18 **CONQUERING LEADER (IRE)**, 9, b m Supreme Leader—Fair Invader **Mrs R. A. Proctor**
19 **DEAR DO**, 11, b br g Swinging Rebel—Earlsgift **Mr C. J. Edwards**

MR N. J. HENDERSON—continued

20 **DEPUTY LEADER (IRE)**, 6, b g Florida Son—Larne
21 **EBULLIENT EQUINAME (IRE)**, 7, b g Zaffaran (USA)—Corvina **Mr Lynn Wilson**
22 **EMBANKMENT (IRE)**, 8, b g Tate Gallery (USA)—Great Leighs **Lady Tennant**
23 **FIDDLING THE FACTS (IRE)**, 7, b br m Orchestra—Facts 'n Fancies **Mrs E. Roberts**
24 **FLEETING MANDATE (IRE)**, 6, br g Mandalus—Mistress Sarah **Mrs P. Sherwood**
25 **FREELINE FONTAINE (IRE)**, 6, b br g Lafontaine (USA)—Mandavard (IRE) **Mr Irving Struel**
26 **FRIENDSHIP (IRE)**, 6, b g Strong Gale—Apicat **Mr T. Benfield and Mr W. Brown**
27 **FUJIYAMA CREST (IRE)**, 6, b g Roi Danzig (USA)—Snoozy Time **Mr Roger Baines**
28 **GARNWIN (IRE)**, 8, b g Strong Gale—Lisnamandra **Pioneer Heat-Treatment**
29 **GARRISON FRIENDLY (IRE)**, 5, b g Buckskin (FR)—Ikeathy **Major Christopher Hanbury**
30 **GET REAL (IRE)**, 7, br g Executive Perk—Lisa's Music **Pioneer Heat-Treatment**
31 **GOLDEN EAGLE**, 6, b g Ardross—Leading Line **Mr Peter Oldfield**
32 **GOLDEN SPINNER**, 11, ch g Noalto—Madame Russe **Sir Peter Miller**
33 **HIDEBOUND (IRE)**, 6, b g Buckskin (FR)—Merry Run **W.V. M.W. & Mrs E.S. Robins**
34 **HOODED HAWK (IRE)**, 7, b g Henbit (USA)—Kessella **Mr C. M. Hamer**
35 **KING'S BANKER (IRE)**, 7, b g King's Ride—Wren's Princess **Mr J. E. H. Collins**
36 **KISSAIR (IRE)**, 7, b g Most Welcome—Salonniere (FR) **Mr Terry Benson**
37 **LADY PETA (IRE)**, 8, b g The Parson—Smooth Run **Mr B. M. Collins**
38 **LAKEFIELD LEADER (IRE)**, 7, b g Supreme Leader—Debonair Dolly **Newbury Racehorse Owners Group**
39 **LITENING CONDUCTOR**, 8, b g Strong Gale—Music Interpreter **Count Konrad Goess-Saurau**
40 **MAGIC CIRCLE (FR)**, 6, b g Bering—Lucky Round **Mr T. Benfield and Mr W. Brown**
41 **MAJESTIC AFFAIR (IRE)**, 6, b g Brush Aside (USA)—Hazel Gig **Knights' Racing**
42 **MARAUDER (IRE)**, 5, b g Yashgan—Sweet Slievenamon **W.V. M.W. & Mrs E.S. Robins**
43 **MELODY MAID**, 6, b m Strong Gale—Ribo Melody **Mr R. J. Parish**
44 **MIGHTY MONARCH (IRE)**, 5, b g King's Ride—Foxy Jane **W.V. M.W. & Mrs E.S. Robins**
45 **MOUNTAIN PATH**, 8, b g Rakaposhi King—Donna Farina **Mr Anthony Speelman**
46 **MOUNTAIN STORM (IRE)**, 6, b g Strong Gale—Luminous Run **Mr Anthony Speelman**
47 **OH DONNA (IRE)**, 6, b m Lafontaine (USA)—Red Donna **Mrs Johnny Reed**
48 **OLD DECENCY (IRE)**, 7, b g Aristocracy—Boro Cent **Mr Michael Blackburn**
49 **OVER THE WAY (IRE)**, 8, b br g Over The River (FR)—Biddy The Crow **Mrs Elaine Baines**
50 **PASHTO**, 11, b g Persian Bold—Epure **Mr Raymond Tooth**
51 **PERFECT VENUE (IRE)**, 5, b h Danehill (USA)—Welsh Fantasy **The Martin Partnership**
52 **PHARSTAR (IRE)**, 7, b g Phardante (FR)—Winter Fox **W.V. M.W. & Mrs E.S. Robins**
53 **PHILIP'S WOODY**, 10, b g Sula Bula—Pine Gypsy **Mr K. G. Knox**
54 **PIETRO BEMBO (IRE)**, 4, b g Midyan (USA)—Cut No Ice
55 **POINTED REMARK (IRE)**, 7, ch g Exactly Sharp (USA)—King's Chase **Mr Peter S. Winfield**
56 **POSH SPICE (IRE)**, 7, b m Neshad (USA)—Escalado **Mr Erik Thorbek**
57 **ROARING SPRING (IRE)**, 8, b g Callernish—Sister Cecelia **Lady Lloyd Webber**
58 **ROYAL TOAST (IRE)**, 6, b g Supreme Leader—Hats Off **Mrs Christopher Edwards**
59 **SALMON BREEZE (IRE)**, 7, ch g Kambalda—Channel Breeze **The Salmon Racing Partnership**
60 **SCARROTS**, 4, b c Mazilier (USA)—Bath **Million in Mind Partnership (7)**
61 **SECURON GALE (IRE)**, 6, br g Strong Gale—Thousand Flowers **Mrs R. A. Proctor**
62 **SERENUS (USA)**, 5, b g Sunshine Forever (USA)—Curl And Set (USA) **W.V. M.W. & Mrs E.S. Robins**
63 **SESAME SEED (IRE)**, 10, b g Wassl—Halva **Mr Raymond Tooth**
64 **SHARPICAL**, 6, b g Sharpo—Magical Spirit **Thurloe Thoroughbreds II**
65 **SILVER WIZARD (USA)**, 8, b h Silver Hawk (USA)—Cherie's Hope (USA) **W.V. M.W. & Mrs E.S. Robins**
66 **SILVER WONDER (USA)**, 4, ch g Silver Hawk (USA)—Upper Class Lady (USA) **W.V. M.W. & Mrs E.S. Robins**
67 **SOPHOMORE**, 4, b c Sanglamore (USA)—Livry (USA)
68 **SOVEREIGN BELLE**, 5, b m Ardross—Ribo Melody **Mr Brian J. Griffiths**
69 **SOVEREIGNS PARADE**, 6, ch g Chromite (USA)—Queen's Visit **Mr Raymond Tooth**
70 **STAY LUCKY (NZ)**, 9, b g Sir Sydney (NZ)—Against The Odds (NZ) **Mr Michael Buckley**
71 **STORMYFAIRWEATHER (IRE)**, 6, b g Strong Gale—Game Sunset **Mrs Christopher Hanbury**
72 **SUBLIME FELLOW (IRE)**, 8, b g Phardante (FR)—Whakapohane **Mr Rory McGrath**
73 **SUMMER SPELL (USA)**, 5, b br g Alleged (USA)—Summertime Lady (USA) **W.V. M.W. & Mrs E.S. Robins**
74 **SUNDAY VENTURE (NZ)**, 6, b g Lucky Ring—Guimpe (NZ) **Mr F. J. Sainsbury**
75 **TEMPESTUOUS LADY (IRE)**, 7, b m Sexton Blake—Lady-Easton **Mrs E. Roberts**
76 **TRISTRAM'S IMAGE (NZ)**, 7, b g Tristram's Edition (NZ)—Angel Face (NZ) **Mr S. Keeling**
77 **VERIDIAN**, 5, b g Green Desert (USA)—Alik (FR) **Thurloe Thoroughbreds III**
78 **WALLABY BLOWED**, 6, b m Strong Gale—Rosie Furlong **Mrs Christopher Wells**
79 **WAYFARERS WAY (USA)**, 7, ch g Manastash Ridge (USA)—Miss Daytona (USA) **Lady Tennant**

MR N. J. HENDERSON—continued

80 WAYNFLETE (IRE), 7, b g Strong Gale—Sister Delaney **Lord Arran**
81 WHAT'S THE BUZZ, 7, ch g Ardross—Cherry Opal **Lady Lloyd Webber**
82 WINTER GALE (IRE), 6, b br g Strong Gale—Winter Fox **W.V. M.W. & Mrs E.S. Robins**
83 WOOLOOMOOLOO (IRE), 6, b g Lapierre—Halation's Flair **The Gap Partnership**

Other Owners: Queen Elizabeth, Mr J. Adeane, Amtrak Express Parcels Ltd, Mr P. R. Anders, Mr M. R. Baxter, Dr J. J. Bourke, Mr Ben Brooks, Mr N. C. Clark, Mr Mark Coley, Mrs Brenda Frewin, Lady Annabel Goldsmith, Mrs D. A. Henderson, Mr J. R. Henderson, Mrs John Henderson, H. & T. Walker Ltd, Mr A. C. D. Ingleby-Mackenzie, Mr M. B. J. Kimmins, Mr M. C. Knight, Mrs Hugh Maitland-Jones, Mr C. Marner, Mr G. D. P. Materna, Mr Ed McGrath, Mr D. R. Midwood, Mr D. Minton, Mr G. C. Mordaunt, Mr M. J. Morrison, Mr Martin Myers, Mr R. W. Newman, Major-Gen J. D. G. Pank, Mr Oliver Pawle, Lord Pembroke, Mr G. H. Peter-Hoblyn, Mr J. W. Randall, Mr P. N. Roberts, Mr G. A. Rogers, Mr D. J. W. Ross, Mrs Basil Samuel, Mr J. A. B. Stafford, Lord Swaythling, Mrs Margaret Turner, Mr Michael White, Mr B. R. Wilsdon.

Jockeys (NH): M A Fitzgerald (10-0), J R Kavanagh (10-0).

Conditional: T C Hagger, T C Murphy, L Vickers.

278 MRS R. G. HENDERSON, Okehampton

Postal: **Heath Hills, Folly Gate, Okehampton, Devon, EX20 3AE.**
Phone: **(01837) 52914**

1 BLAZING BATMAN, 5, ch g Shaab—Cottage Blaze **Mr W. J. Henderson**
2 BLAZING MIRACLE, 6, b m Shaab—Cottage Blaze **Mrs R. G. Henderson**
3 FIDDLERS PIKE, 17, b g Turnpike—Fiddlers Bee **Mrs R. G. Henderson**
4 KALOORE, 9, ch g Ore—Cool Straight **Mrs J. Alford**
5 ZAGGY LANE, 6, b g Prince of Peace—Meldon Lady **Mrs E. Rossiter**

Other Owners: Miss A. D. Furniss, Mrs J. D. Harding, Mrs Joan Henderson.

Conditional: D Salter (9-9).

Amateur: Mr W J Henderson (10-0).

Lady Rider: Mrs R G Henderson (10-0).

279 LADY HERRIES, Littlehampton

Postal: **Angmering Park, Littlehampton, West Sussex, BN16 4EX.**
Phone: **HOME (01903) 871421 YARD (01903) 871460 FAX (01903) 871609**

1 ALAMEDA, 4, b g Formidable (USA)—Albiflora (USA) **Lady Herries**
2 AMAZE, 9, b g Natroun (FR)—Entrancing **Lady Katharine Phillips**
3 ANDANITO (IRE), 7, b g Darshaan—Newquay **Bonusprint**
4 BAJAN (IRE), 7, br g Taufan (USA)—Thatcherite **Lady Sarah Clutton**
5 CARDIGAN BAY (IRE), 4, b g Slip Anchor—Welsh Dancer **Mr E. Reitel**
6 CASTLE COURAGEOUS, 11, b g Castle Keep—Peteona **Lady Mary Mumford**
7 DANISH RHAPSODY (IRE), 5, b g Danehill (USA)—Ardmelody **Mr Chris Hardy**
8 DISTINCTIVE DREAM (IRE), 4, b g Distincly North (USA)—Green Side (USA) **Mr R. Bremner**

LADY HERRIES—continued

9 **DRAGON LORD,** 4, b g Warning—Cockatoo Island **Mr P. D. Savill**
10 **EAGLE DANCER,** 6, b g Persian Bold—Stealthy **Mr E. Reitel**
11 **ELFLAND (IRE),** 7, b g Fairy King (USA)—Ridge The Times (USA) **The High Flying Partnership**
12 **FALLAH,** 4, b g Salse (USA)—Alpine Sunset **Mr P. D. Savill**
13 **GRAND SPLENDOUR,** 5, b m Shirley Heights—Mayaasa (FR) **Mr Andy Holder**
14 **GULF HARBOUR (IRE),** 4, b g Caerleon (USA)—Jackie Berry **Mrs M. Cowdrey**
15 **HARBOUR DUES,** 5, b h Slip Anchor—Quillotern (USA) **Hesmonds Stud**
16 **HEIGHT OF HEIGHTS (IRE),** 5, b g Shirley Heights—Azallya (FR) **Mrs Denis Haynes**
17 **INFATUATION,** 5, b g Music Boy—Fleeting Affair **Lady Katharine Phillips**
18 **INSEPARABLE,** 6, ch m Insan (USA)—Lady Gerardina **Mrs B. V. Chennells**
19 **ISLE OF PEARLS (USA),** 8, b g Theatrical—Margaritaville (USA) **Mr L. G. Lazarus**
20 **LIATHACH,** 7, b g Shirley Heights—Reuval **Seymour Bloodstock (UK) Ltd**
21 4, B g Damister (USA)—Lydia Rose **Lady Herries**
22 **MARALINGA (IRE),** 6, ch g Simply Great (FR)—Bellinzona **Mr D. K. R. & Mrs J. B. C. Oliver**
23 **MCKEEVER (IRE),** 6, ch g Wood Chanter—Preside **Mr A. L. Merry**
24 **MEILLEUR (IRE),** 4, b g Nordico (USA)—Lucy Limelight **The Cottage Racing Partnership**
25 **MOON BLAST,** 4, gr g Reprimand—Castle Moon **Angmering Park Stud**
26 **MOON COLONY,** 5, b g Top Ville—Honeymooning (USA) **Mrs Berta Lazarus**
27 **MOWELGA,** 4, ch c Most Welcome—Galactic Miss **Hesmonds Stud**
28 **NANTON POINT (USA),** 6, b g Darshaan—Migiyas **The High Flying Partnership**
29 **RIVER NORTH (IRE),** 8, ch g Lomond (USA)—Petillante (USA) **Lady Herries**
30 **ROCK FALCON (IRE),** 5, ch g Polar Falcon (USA)—Rockfest (USA) **Mr E. Reitel**
31 **ROLLING STONE,** 4, b c Northern Amethyst—First Sapphire **Mr Brian Cooper & Ms Elaine Reffo**
32 **RUSSIAN WRITER,** 5, b g Soviet Star (USA)—Speed Writing (USA) **Mr George Ward**
33 **SAFETY IN NUMBERS,** 8, b g Slip Anchor—Winter Queen **Lady Herries**
34 **SANS EGALE (FR),** 4, ch f Lashkari—Lady Gerardina **Mrs B. V. Chennells**
35 **SILLY MID-ON,** 4, b f Midyan (USA)—Height of Folly **Lady Sarah Clutton**
36 **SOFYAAN (USA),** 5, b g Silver Hawk (USA)—Tanwi **Mr E. Reitel**
37 **STAND TALL,** 6, b g Unfuwain (USA)—Antilla **Mr Chris Hardy**
38 **STRAZO (IRE),** 5, b g Alzao (USA)—Ministra (USA) **Mr E. Reitel**
39 **TAUFAN'S MELODY,** 7, b g Taufan (USA)—Glorious Fate **All At Sea**
40 **TIBETAN,** 6, b g Reference Point—Winter Queen **Mrs Wendy Brown**
41 **TYKEYVOR (IRE),** 8, b g Last Tycoon—Ivoronica **Seymour Bloodstock (UK) Ltd**

THREE-YEAR-OLDS

42 **ACT OF FOLLY,** b f Midyan (USA)—Height of Folly **Lady Herries**
43 **AMAZING FACT (USA),** b g Known Fact (USA)—Itsamazing (USA) **Mr L. G. Lazarus**
44 **CARBON,** b br g Batshoof—Reyah **Mr I. G. Corke**
45 **DAUNTING (IRE),** br f Formidable (USA)—Durun **Hesmonds Stud**
46 **DRAKENSBERG,** b g Bering—Theme (IRE) **Mrs Berta Lazarus**
47 **FIRST IMPRESSION,** b c Saddlers' Hall (IRE)—First Sapphire **Ms Elaine Reffo & Mr Brian Cooper**
48 **FLYING GILDA,** b f Gildoran—Megan's Flight **Lord Cowdrey**
49 **FOREST DREAM,** b f Warrshan (USA)—Sirenivo (USA) **Lord Cowdrey**
50 **IMPERATOR (IRE),** b c Mac's Imp (USA)—Secret Hideaway (USA) **Imperial Arms Partnership**
51 **LAKE BARINGO,** b c Robellino (USA)—Kisumu **Angmering Park Stud**
52 **MALAYAN MOON,** ch g Kris—Moon Carnival **Angmering Park Stud**
53 B g Batshoof—On To Glory **Lady Herries**
54 **PORTENT,** ch f Most Welcome—Foreseen **Hesmonds Stud**
55 **SWIFT ALLIANCE,** b c Belong To Me (USA)—One Quick Bid (USA) **Mrs H. A. Cameron-Rose**
56 **TOM FOOLING,** b g Batshoof—Crosby Triangle **T. F. Jackson & Partner**

TWO-YEAR-OLDS

57 **ALLZI (USA),** ch f 25/2 Zilzal (USA)—All For Hope (USA) **Hesmonds Stud**
58 **ARCTIC LOVE,** ch f 15/2 Polar Falcon (USA)—Lovers Tryst (USA) **Angmering Park Stud**
59 **BALLADONIA,** b f 11/4 Primo Dominie—Susquehanna Days (USA) **Mr D. K. R. Oliver & Mrs J. B. C. Oliver**
60 **BOLD FAIRY (IRE),** b f 21/1 Fairy King (USA)—Copsewood (IRE) **Maj Gen Guy Watkins & Sir William Purves**
61 **CELTIC FLING,** b f 9/4 Lion Cavern (USA)—Celtic Ring **Angmering Park Stud**
62 **DISTANT MOON,** b c 8/2 Distant Relative—Moon Carnival **Mr George Ward**
63 **FARAWAY MOON,** gr f 31/3 Distant Relative—Moon Magic **Angmering Park Stud**
64 **FORSIO,** b c 26/4 Efisio—Foreseen **Hesmonds Stud**

LADY HERRIES—continued

65 B f 4/2 Alhijaz—Frustration **Angmering Park Stud**
66 **MAGIC FLUTE,** ch f 12/4 Magic Ring (IRE)—Megan's Flight **Angmering Park Stud**
67 **ROCKOBIE,** ch c 20/3 Rock City—Bolshoi Belle (USA) **Hesmonds Stud**
68 **SADDLE MOUNTAIN,** b f 5/3 Saddlers' Hall (IRE)—Rainbow Mountain **Hesmonds Stud**
69 **SPEY DANCER,** b c 1/4 Suave Dancer (USA)—River Spey **Hesmonds Stud**
70 **STAND ASIDE,** b c 28/5 In The Wings—Honourable Sheba (USA) **Mr Chris Hardy**
71 **THALGAU (IRE),** br f 25/4 College Chapel—Sally St Clair **Mr Chris Hardy**
72 **TOTAL DELIGHT,** b c Mtoto—Shesadelight **Hesmonds Stud**

Other Owners: Mr Peter Bennett Jones, Mr T. Bond, Mr David Bowerman, Mr Nigel Clutton, Mr Tim Coghlan, Mr Richard J. Cohen, Ms Daisy Collins, Mr John Constable, Mr Richard Cooper, Mr Graham Cowdrey, Mr Mark Davies Jones, Mr C. Donnarumma, Mr S. D. Edmonds, Mr Nicholas Freeman, Mr R. Godson, Mr Charles Green, Mrs Edna Joyce Green, Mr Roy Greenslade, Mr & Mrs David Hardy, Mr & Mrs C Ion'Savage, Mr Alan Keys, Mr John M. D. Knight, Mrs Linda McCalla, Mr Charles McClure, Mr Neil Midgley, Mr Garth Milne, Group Capt A. Mumford, Mr & Mrs C O'Grady, Mr Brian O'Regan, Mr Terry Osborne, Mr H. Owen, Mr Christopher Reeves, Mr Lewis Rudd, Mr Mike Scott, Mr K. B. Symonds, Mr Francis Ward, Mrs George Ward, Mr Michael H. Watt, Mr Peter Willett.

Lady Rider: Mrs M Cowdrey.

280 MR J. HETHERTON, Malton

Postal: **Highfield Stables, Beverley Road, Malton, North Yorkshire, YO17 9PJ.**
Phone: **OFFICE/FAX (01653) 696778 MOBILE (0410) 922396**

1 **ALL ON,** 7, ch m Dunbeath (USA)—Fresh Line **Mr N. Hetherton**
2 **BACK ROW,** 4, b f In The Wings—Temple Row **Mr C. D. Barber-Lomax**
3 **BATOUTOFTHEBLUE,** 5, br g Batshoof—Action Belle **Dr C. I. Emmerson**
4 **EXCLUSION,** 9, ch g Ballad Rock—Great Exception **Mr James Byrne**
5 **GLORIOUS DANCER,** 4, b f Past Glories—Precious Ballerina **Mr M. Williamson**
6 **HEIGHTH OF FAME,** 7, b g Shirley Heights—Land of Ivory (USA) **Dr W. D. Mackenzie And Janet Elvans**
7 **HULLBANK,** 8, b g Uncle Pokey—Dubavarna **Mr V. J. M. Haigh**
8 **IMPETUS,** 4, b g Puissance—Cold Line **Mr N. Hetherton**
9 **JACK THE LAD (IRE),** 4, b g Shalford (IRE)—Indian Honey **Keith West Partnership**
10 **LEGAL ISSUE (IRE),** 6, b h Contract Law (USA)—Natuschka **Mr B. Valentine**
11 **PHARLY DANCER,** 9, b g Pharly (FR)—Martin-Lavell Mail **Mr A. Marucci**
12 **ROYAL CITIZEN (IRE),** 9, b g Caerleon (USA)—Taking Steps **Qualitair Holdings Limited**
13 **SASKIA'S HERO,** 11, ch g Bairn (USA)—Comtec Princess **Qualitair Holdings Limited**
14 **SWYNFORD CHARMER,** 4, ch g Charmer—Qualitairess **Qualitair Holdings Limited**
15 **SWYNFORD DREAM,** 5, b g Statoblest—Qualitair Dream **Qualitair Holdings Limited**
16 **SWYNFORD PRIDE,** 6, ch g Siberian Express (USA)—Qualitair Princess **Qualitair Holdings Limited**
17 **TOSS AND TUMBLE,** 4, b f Syrtos—Breakfast In Bed **Mrs S. Barber**
18 **ZORBA,** 4, b g Shareef Dancer (USA)—Zabelina (USA) **Mr C. D. Barber-Lomax**

THREE-YEAR-OLDS

19 Br gr g Terimon—Comtec Princess **Qualitair Holdings Limited**
20 **GLORY OF LOVE,** b c Belmez (USA)—Princess Lieven **Mr Cliffe Rowlands**
21 **LUDERE (IRE),** ch g Desse Zenny (USA)—White Jasmin **Mr B. Valentine**
22 **MEANS BUSINESS (IRE),** ch g Imp Society (USA)—Fantasise (FR) **Keith West Partnership**
23 **PERCY,** ch g Precocious—Manna Green **Mrs O. K. Steele**
24 **POETTO,** ch g Casteddu—Steamy Windows **Mr H. R. Hewitt**
25 **PRIDDY GREEN,** b f Formidable (USA)—No Can Tell (USA) **Barbara Sadler**
26 **TOM,** gr c Petong—Wanton **Mr C. D. Barber-Lomax**
27 **WILTON,** ch c Sharpo—Poyle Amber **Mr George A. Moore**

MR J. HETHERTON—continued

TWO-YEAR-OLDS

28 **BLUE HAZE,** ch c 25/5 Ardkinglass—Cold Line (Exdirectory) **Mr N. Hetherton**
29 **EVENING SCENT,** b f 19/2 Ardkinglass—Fresh Line (High Line) **Mr N. Hetherton**
30 Br f 9/5 Cyrano de Bergerac—Steppey Lane (Tachypous)

Other Owners: Mr E. Chaney, Mr Paul Dancer, Mrs P. Gibbon, Mrs I. Gibson, Dr W. Donald Mackenzie, Peter Sadler, Mr R. W. Swiers, Mr K. C. West, Miss K. Williamson, Mr W. S. Wright.

Jockey (Flat): Neil Kennedy (7-10).

Apprentice: Tom Siddall (8-3).

Conditional: Tom Siddall (9-7).

Amateur: Mr James Byrne (10-10).

Lady Rider: Miss Annie Elsey (8-12).

281 MR P. W. HIATT, Banbury

Postal: **Six Ash Farm, Hook Norton, Banbury, Oxfordshire, OX15 5DB.**
Phone: **(01608) 737255**

1 **BIG TREAT (IRE),** 6, b g Be My Guest (USA)—Cavurina **Mr P. W. Hiatt**
2 **CANARY BLUE (IRE),** 7, b m Bluebird (USA)—Norfolk Bonnet **Mr P. W. Hiatt**
3 **COCHITI,** 4, b f Kris—Sweet Jaffa **The Equus Club**
4 **MILL DANCER (IRE),** 6, b m Broken Hearted—Theatral **Mr P. W. Hiatt**
5 **MYOSOTIS,** 4, ch g Don't Forget Me—Ella Mon Amour **Red Lion (Chipping Norton) Partnership**
6 **ROYAL CIRCUS,** 9, b g Kris—Circus Ring **Mr P. W. Hiatt**
7 **ROYAL CONCUBINE,** 5, ch m Rich Charlie—Town Flirt **Mr P. W. Hiatt**
8 **SAUCY NUN (IRE),** 6, ch m Orchestra—Port Flyer **Mr P. W. Hiatt**

Other Owners: Mr Hywel Davies, Mr Paul Souch, Mr Paul Viner.

Jockey (NH): D Bridgwater (9-9).

Conditional: E Husband (9-11).

282 MRS C. M. HICKS, Naunton

Postal: **Hill Farm, Aylworth, Naunton, Cheltenham, Gloucestershire, GL54 3AH.**
Phone: **(01451) 850981 OR (01451) 850226**

1 **BRAVE FRIEND (IRE),** 6, b br m Beau Sher—Ashford House **Mr M. G. Green**
2 **CHARLIES DELIGHT (IRE),** 10, b g Welsh Term—Pilgrim Soul **Artisan Partnership**
3 **COMMIN' UP,** 5, b m Primo Dominie—Ridalia **Artisan Partnership**
4 **INTERREGNUM,** 4, ch f Interrex (CAN)—Lillicara (FR) **Mrs J. A. Thomson**
5 **IODER WAN (IRE),** 6, b m Phardante (FR)—Good Credentials **Mr G. M. Thomson**

MRS C. M. HICKS—continued

6 **LOFTY DEED (USA),** 8, b g Shadeed (USA)—Soar Aloft (USA) **Mrs C. Hicks**
7 **MAPENGO,** 7, b g Salse (USA)—Premiere Cuvee **Mrs Vera Williams**
8 **PURE AIR,** 6, b g Derrylin—Pure Poetry **Mrs C. Hicks**
9 **STRONG SPICE (IRE),** 7, b br m Strong Gale—Yukon Law **Mrs C. Hicks**
10 **VITA NUOVA (IRE),** 7, ch m Phardante (FR)—Park Breeze (IRE) **The Stanton Seven**
11 **WELL BANK,** 11, b g Tudor Diver—Technical Merit **Mrs C. Hicks**

Other Owners: Mr G. Bannar, Mr M. Coopey, Mr Howard Dawson, Mr A. G. Dewhurst, Mr John D. Higgs, Mr N. J. Hughes, Mr S. P. Hughes, Mr J. R. P. McNamara, Mr W. Nobes, Mr M. Pearson, Mrs J. Thompstone.

283 MR B. W. HILLS, Lambourn

Postal: **South Bank Stables, Lambourn, Hungerford, Berkshire, RG17 7LL.**
Phone: **OFFICE LAMBOURN (01488) 71548 FAX LAMBOURN (01488) 72823**

1 **BUSY FLIGHT,** 5, br h Pharly (FR)—Bustling Nelly **Mr S. Wingfield Digby**
2 **CADEAUX CHER,** 4, ch g Cadeaux Genereux—Home Truth **Mr N. N. Browne**
3 **FURTHER FLIGHT,** 12, gr g Pharly (FR)—Flying Nelly **Mr S. Wingfield Digby**
4 **IN COMMAND (IRE),** 4, b c Sadler's Wells (USA)—Flying Melody **Maktoum Al Maktoum**
5 **LOOKOUT,** 4, b f Salse (USA)—Sea Pageant **Mr R. D. Hollingsworth**
6 **MITHALI,** 5, b h Unfuwain (USA)—Al Bahathri (USA) **Mr Hamdan Al Maktoum**
7 **MUSALSAL (IRE),** 4, b c Sadler's Wells (USA)—Ozone Friendly (USA) **Maktoum Al Maktoum**
8 **PRAIRIE FALCON (IRE),** 4, b c Alzao (USA)—Sea Harrier **Lady Harrison**
9 **SHOWBOAT,** 4, b c Warning—Boathouse **Mr R. D. Hollingsworth**
10 **STATE FAIR,** 4, b c Shirley Heights—Lobinda **Mr Ray Richards**
11 **THE FLY,** 4, gr c Pharly (FR)—Nelly Do Da **Mrs J. M. Corbett**
12 **THE PUZZLER (IRE),** 7, br g Sharpo—Enigma **Lady Richard Wellesley**

THREE-YEAR-OLDS

13 **ALMUROOJ,** b f Zafonic (USA)—Al Bahathri (USA) **Mr Hamdan Al Maktoum**
14 **ALOHA DANCER (IRE),** b f Danehill (USA)—Spire **Mr J. R. Fleming**
15 **ANDALISH,** b f Polish Precedent (USA)—Risanda **Mr K. Abdulla**
16 **ASCOT CYCLONE (USA),** ch f Rahy (USA)—Dabaweyaa **Mr Salem Bel Obaida**
17 **ASYAAD (USA),** b c Zilzal (USA)—Shihama (USA) **Mr Salem Bel Obaida**
18 **BOMBASTIC,** ch c Polish Precedent (USA)—Fur Hat **H.R.H. Prince Fahd Salman**
19 **BRISTOL CHANNEL,** b f Generous (IRE)—Shining Water **Mr K. Abdulla**
20 **CHATTAN,** b c Lycius (USA)—Chanzi (USA) **Abdullah Saeed Bul Hab**
21 **CHEROKEE BAND (USA),** b br c Dixieland Band (USA)—Cherokee Darling (USA) **Maktoum Al Maktoum**
22 **CHRYSOLITE (IRE),** ch c Kris—Alamiya (IRE) **Mr A. D. Shead**
23 **DEFIANCE,** b c Warning—Princess Athena **Mr Ray Richards**
24 **ELHABUB,** b c Lion Cavern (USA)—Million Heiress **Mr Hamdan Al Maktoum**
25 **EPSOM CYCLONE (USA),** ch c Rahy (USA)—Aneesati **Mr Salem Bel Obaida**
26 **EXPECT TO SHINE,** b f Fairy King (USA)—Anjaab (USA) **Maktoum Al Maktoum**
27 **FAIRY ROCK (IRE),** b f Fairy King (USA)—Safe Home **Mr John C. Grant**
28 **FEMME MECHANTE (USA),** ch f Zilzal (USA)—Cormorant Wood **Maktoum Al Maktoum**
29 **GENOA,** b f Zafonic (USA)—Yawl **Mr R. D. Hollingsworth**
30 **GUARANTEED,** b c Distant Relative—Pay The Bank **Mr Wafic Said**
31 **HIGH AND LOW,** b f Rainbow Quest (USA)—Cruising Height **Mr K. Abdulla**
32 **HIPPOCRACY,** b f Unfuwain (USA)—Marielou (FR) **Hippocracy Partnership**
33 **INCEPTA,** b c Selkirk (USA)—Ringlet (USA) **Mr A. L. R. Morton**
34 **JOINT REGENT (USA),** br c St Jovite (USA)—Ice Fantasy (USA) **Maktoum Al Maktoum**
35 **KANZ PRIDE (USA),** ch f Lion Cavern (USA)—Kanz (USA) **Mr D. J. Deer**
36 **KHALAS,** b c Wolfhound (USA)—Absaar (USA) **Mr Hamdan Al Maktoum**
37 **LA-FAAH (IRE),** ch c Lahib (USA)—Rawaabe (USA) **Mr Hamdan Al Maktoum**
38 **LAST CHRISTMAS,** b c Salse (USA)—State Ball **Mr A. D. Shead**
39 **LAST REPUTATION,** b f Zafonic (USA)—Reputation **Mr R. E. Sangster**
40 **LIDO (IRE),** ch c Waajib—Licimba (GER) **Mr Guy Reed**
41 **MAGIC OF ALOHA (IRE),** ch f Diesis—Satz (USA) **Mr J. R. Fleming**

MR B. W. HILLS—continued

42 MANNEQUIN (IRE), b f In The Wings—Pretty Lady **Mohammed Al Nabouda**
43 MOON TANGO, b f Last Tycoon—Dance It (USA) **K. Al-Said**
44 NIGHT VIGIL (IRE), b c Night Shift (USA)—Game Plan **Mr Saif Ali**
45 PENROSE (IRE), ch f Wolfhound (USA)—Mill Path **Mr Madhad Ali**
46 PLEASE, b f Kris—Tanz (IRE) **Mrs Jane Bailey**
47 PRINCESS SCEPTRE, ch f Cadeaux Genereux—Sans Blague (USA) **Sceptre Racing**
48 PROLIX, ch c Kris—Ajuga (USA) **Mr K. Abdulla**
49 PURE NOBILITY (IRE), br c Darshaan—Ma Pavlova (USA) **Mr Bassam Freiha**
50 RAINBOW HIGH, b c Rainbow Quest (USA)—Imaginary (IRE) **Mr K. Abdulla**
51 RAINBOW WAYS, b c Rainbow Quest (USA)—Siwaayib **Maktoum Al Maktoum**
52 RED BORDEAUX, b c Alzao (USA)—Marie de Flandre (FR) **Mr Wafic Said**
53 RED RABBIT, b f Suave Dancer (USA)—Turban **Mr S. P. Tindall**
54 RICHMOND HILL, b c Sabrehill (USA)—Mrs Warren (USA) **Mr Saif Ali**
55 SADDLERS' ROE (IRE), b g Saddlers' Hall (IRE)—Ladyfish **Ford Farm Racing**
56 SEA MAGIC (IRE), b br f Distinctly North (USA)—Danger Ahead **Mr Ray Richards**
57 SECRET BOURNE (USA), b f Exbourne (USA)—Secret Angel **Mr K. Abdulla**
58 SENSORY, b c Selkirk (USA)—Illusory **Mr K. Abdulla**
59 SHFOUG (USA), b f Sheikh Albadou—Pure Misk **Mr Hilal Salem**
60 SILVER STRAND (IRE), b f Waajib—Jendeal **Miss Susan McIntyre**
61 SINHALA (USA), ch f Affirmed (USA)—Sin Lucha (USA) **Mr K. Abdulla**
62 SPRING FEVER, b c Indian Ridge—Tender Moment (IRE) **Mr Ray Richards**
63 STYLISH STORM (USA), b f Storm Bird (CAN)—Purify (USA) **Newbyth Stud**
64 THE GLOW-WORM (IRE), b c Doyoun—Shakanda (IRE) **Mrs J. M. Corbett**
65 THE SANDFLY (USA), b f Sheikh Albadou—Sweet Simone (FR) **Mrs J. M. Corbett**
66 UP AT THE TOP (IRE), b f Waajib—Down The Line **Mrs E. Roberts**
67 WAY OUT YONDER, b c Shirley Heights—Patsy Western **Maktoum Al Maktoum**

TWO-YEAR-OLDS

68 Ch c 26/4 Sanglamore (USA)—Ajuga (USA) (The Minstrel (CAN)) **Mr K. Abdulla**
69 ANSGATE LADY (IRE), b f 5/5 Polish Patriot (USA)—Tales of Wisdom (Rousillon (USA)) **Mr Gareth J. Thomas**
70 Ch f 3/3 Nashwan (USA)—Balliasta (USA) (Lyphard (USA)) **Mr K. Abdulla**
71 BIG FANDANGO, b f 28/4 Bigstone (IRE)—Dance It (USA) (Believe It (USA)) **K. Al-Said**
72 BODFARI MUKA (IRE), ch c 13/3 Mukaddamah (USA)—Precious Egg (Home Guard (USA)) **Bodfari Stud Ltd**
73 BODFARI VISTA, b f 15/1 Scenic—Tomard (Thatching) **Bodfari Stud Ltd**
74 BURMA BABY (USA), ch c 14/4 Woodman (USA)—Rangoon Ruby (Sallust) **Maktoum Al Maktoum**
75 CALCUTTA, b c 21/2 Indian Ridge—Echoing (Formidable (USA)) **Mrs J. M. Corbett**
76 CHESHIRE CAT (IRE), b f 7/3 Ezzoud (IRE)—Riyda (Be My Guest (USA)) **Mr Christopher Wright**
77 Ch c 1/4 Generous (IRE)—Colza (USA) (Alleged (USA)) **Mr K. Abdulla**
78 Gr f 21/3 Anshan—Crackling (Electric)
79 CRAGGY MOUNTAIN, ch c 12/2 Cadeaux Genereux—Jet Ski Lady (USA) (Vaguely Noble) **Maktoum Al Maktoum**
80 DAHSHAH, ch f 26/4 Mujtahid (USA)—Rawaabe (USA) (Nureyev (USA)) **Mr Hamdan Al Maktoum**
81 DANGEROUS DANCER, b f 12/2 Warning—Silabteni (USA) (Nureyev (USA)) **Mr Stephen Crown**
82 ELMUTABAKI, b c 24/3 Unfuwain (USA)—Bawaeth (USA) (Blushing Groom (FR)) **Mr Hamdan Al Maktoum**
83 EVIE HONE (IRE), ch f 24/3 Royal Academy (USA)—Tochar Ban (USA) (Assert) **Mr Jeremy Gompertz**
84 FAMILY TREE (IRE), ch f 19/3 Soviet Lad (USA)—The Woman In Red (Red Regent) **Mr J. Hanson**
85 FANCY THAT (IRE), b f 23/3 Shalford (IRE)—Clancy's Corner (IRE) (Auction Ring (USA)) **Mr Guy Reed**
86 B c 11/2 Exbourne (USA)—Fast Flow (USA) (Riverman (USA)) **Mr K. Abdulla**
87 GENTLE DAME, ch f 21/2 Kris—Cascassi (USA) (Nijinsky (CAN)) **Maktoum Al Maktoum**
88 GOLDEN SNAKE (USA), b c 18/4 Danzig (USA)—Dubian (High Line) **Mr Mohammed Obaida**
89 GOLD RUSH (IRE), b c 2/3 Namaqualand (USA)—Shillay (Lomond (USA)) **Mr Guy Reed**
90 GRACIOUS PLENTY (IRE), ch f 10/3 Generous (IRE)—Formide (USA) (Trempolino (USA)) **Mr E. D. Kessly**
91 GUEST OF HONOUR, gr f 10/3 Petong—Special Guest (Be My Guest (USA)) **Mr Christopher Hanbury**
92 GUNNER SAM, ch c 26/3 Emarati (USA)—Minne Love (Homeric) **Mr R. W. Miller**
93 HAPPY LADY (FR), b f 7/3 Cadeaux Genereux—Siwaayib (Green Desert (USA)) **Maktoum Al Maktoum**
94 HAWATTEF (IRE), b f 1/3 Mujtahid (USA)—Madary (CAN) (Green Desert (USA)) **Mr Hilal Salem**
95 B c 2/2 Barathea (IRE)—High Hawk (Shirley Heights) **Sheikh Mohammed**
96 HULA ANGEL (USA), b f 19/3 Woodman (USA)—Jode (USA) (Danzig (USA)) **Mr J. R. Fleming**
97 Ch c 18/4 Grand Lodge (USA)—Irish Sea (IRE) (Irish River (FR)) **Sheikh Mohammed**
98 B c 9/3 Sadler's Wells (USA)—Khalafiya (Darshaan) **Sheikh Mohammed**
99 KHUDUD, b f 3/3 Green Desert (USA)—Braari (USA) (Gulch (USA)) **Mr Hamdan Al Maktoum**

MR B. W. HILLS—continued

100 **KIND SIR,** b c 15/2 Generous (IRE)—Noble Conquest (USA) (Vaguely Noble) **Mr A. D. Shead**
101 **KING FOR A DAY,** b c 18/1 Machiavellian (USA)—Dizzy Heights (USA) (Danzig (USA)) **Maktoum Al Maktoum**
102 **LIBERTY LINES (USA),** b c 9/5 Zilzal (USA)—Bold'n Determined (USA) (Bold And Brave (USA)) **Maktoum Al Maktoum**
103 **LITTLE NELL,** b f 29/5 Pharly (FR)—Nelly Do Da (Derring-Do) **Mrs J. M. Corbett**
104 **LOUGH SWILLY (IRE),** b c 16/1 Mukaddamah (USA)—Flooding (USA) (Irish River (FR)) **Mr John C. Grant**
105 **MADAM WAAJIB (IRE),** ch f 23/4 Waajib—Clogher Head (Sandford Lad) **Mrs J. C. Raper**
106 **MAKEBELIEVE ISLAND (IRE),** b c 7/3 Namaqualand (USA)—Zalamera (Rambo Dancer (CAN)) **Mr A. D. Shead**
107 Br c 22/2 Warning—Mettlesome (Lomond (USA)) **Mr K. Abdulla**
108 **MISS UNIVERSE (IRE),** gr f 10/2 Warning—Reine d'Beaute (Caerleon (USA)) **Mrs J. M. Corbett**
109 B c 24/1 Dayjur (USA)—Model Bride (USA) (Blushing Groom (FR)) **Mr K. Abdulla**
110 **MOON RIVER WONDER (IRE),** b c 17/2 Doyoun—Bayazida (Bustino) **Mr A. D. Shead**
111 **MOSS ROSE,** ch f 1/4 Wolfhound (USA)—Champagne 'n Roses (Chief Singer) **Mrs A. D. Bourne**
112 **MUNJIZ (IRE),** b c 8/5 Marju (IRE)—Absaar (USA) (Alleged (USA)) **Mr Hamdan Al Maktoum**
113 **MUSICAL TONES (USA),** b f 24/5 Diesis—Arsaan (USA) (Nureyev (USA)) **Maktoum Al Maktoum**
114 B c 1/5 Irish River (FR)—Never A Care (USA) (Roberto (USA)) **Mr K. Abdulla**
115 **NIGHT VENTURE (USA),** b c 28/3 Dynaformer (USA)—Charming Ballerina (IRE) (Caerleon (USA)) **Maktoum Al Maktoum**
116 **NIMBLE JACK,** b c 6/3 Dilum (USA)—Yah Dancer (Shareef Dancer (USA)) **Mr R. W. Miller**
117 B c 21/3 Mtoto—Octavia Girl (Octavo (USA)) **Mr John Leat**
118 **PESHTIGO (USA),** b c 7/5 Kris S (USA)—Fume (USA) (Secretariat (USA)) **Maktoum Al Maktoum**
119 **PIAF,** b f 28/1 Pursuit Of Love—Pippas Song (Reference Point) **Mr S. P. Tindall**
120 **PROSPEROUS (IRE),** ch f 4/4 Generous (IRE)—Amwag (USA) (El Gran Senor (USA)) **Mr R. A. Scarborough**
121 B f 19/2 Deploy—Questionable (Rainbow Quest (USA)) **Mr K. Abdulla**
122 **QUIGLEYS POINT (IRE),** b c 22/4 Royal Academy (USA)—Remind Me (USA) (Riverman (USA)) **Mr John C. Grant**
123 **RAINBOW STAGE (USA),** b f 6/1 Lear Fan (USA)—Certain Flair (Danehill (USA)) **Mr R. A. N. Bonnycastle**
124 **RAS SHAIKH (USA),** b f 10/2 Sheikh Albadou—Aneesati (Kris) **Mr Salem Bel Obaida**
125 **RELATE BACK (IRE),** ch c 4/4 College Chapel—Kip's Sister (Cawston's Clown) **Mr J. Hanson**
126 **RIGGING,** b f 28/2 Warning—Pilot (Kris) **Mr R. D. Hollingsworth**
127 B c 13/4 Kris—Ringlet (USA) (Secreto (USA))
128 Ch f 24/2 Generous (IRE)—Risanda (Kris) **Mr K. Abdulla**
129 **ROSES FROM RIDEY (IRE),** b f 25/1 Petorius—Minnie Habit (Habitat) **Mr R. A. N. Bonnycastle**
130 **SHEER NATIVE,** b f 19/2 In The Wings—Native Magic (Be My Native (USA)) **Mr R. J. Arculli**
131 **SHEER VIKING (IRE),** b c 26/4 Danehill (USA)—Schlefalora (Mas Media) **Mr R. J. Arculli**
132 B f 12/2 Caerleon (USA)—Shining Water (Kalaglow) **Mr K. Abdulla**
133 Ch f 16/1 Summer Squall (USA)—Sin Lucha (USA) (Northfields (USA)) **Mr K. Abdulla**
134 **SPANKER,** ch f 7/5 Suave Dancer (USA)—Yawl (Rainbow Quest (USA)) **Mr R. D. Hollingsworth**
135 Ch f 15/2 Irish River (FR)—Stellaria (USA) (Roberto (USA)) **Mr K. Abdulla**
136 **ST MAGNUS (IRE),** gr c 19/3 Petorius—More Magnanimous (King Persian) **Mrs J. M. Corbett**
137 **SUMMER BOUNTY,** b c 12/4 Lugana Beach—Tender Moment (IRE) (Caerleon (USA)) **Mr Ray Richards**
138 **TESS,** b f 1/2 Emarati (USA)—Everdene (Bustino) **Mr S. P. Tindall**
139 B f 21/3 Polish Precedent—Trampship (High Line) **Mr K. Abdulla**
140 **TRAWLING,** b f 20/1 Mtoto—Ghost Tree (IRE) (Caerleon (USA)) **Mrs H. Theodorou**
141 **TUDOR HALL (IRE),** ch f 8/2 Thatching—Confidence Boost (USA) (Trempolino (USA)) **Sceptre Racing**
142 **TURAATH (IRE),** b c 7/3 Sadler's Wells (USA)—Diamond Field (USA) (Mr Prospector (USA)) **Mr Hamdan Al Maktoum**
143 **WEAVER OF WORDS,** b f 24/2 Danehill (USA)—Canadian Mill (USA) (Mill Reef (USA)) **Maktoum Al Maktoum**
144 B f 4/3 Brief Truce (USA)—Winged Victory (IRE) (Dancing Brave (USA))
145 **YELLOW RIBBON (IRE),** b f 30/4 Hamas (IRE)—Busker (Bustino) **Mr A. N. Foster**

Horses owned by Mr W. J. Gredley appear under "The Property of W. J. Gredley, Esq."

Other Owners: Mrs J. M. Broscombe, Mr Seymour Cohn, Mr A. K. Collins, Mr Del Francis, Mr W. J. Gredley, Mr C. W. Kennard, Mr Paul H. Locke, Mr Paul McNamara, Sir Eric Parker, Mrs Simon Polito, Mr John Sillett, Mr C. B. Smith, Mr R. J. C. Upton, Mr William Wood, Mrs J. R. Woodhouse.

Apprentices: A Nicholls (7-5), J D Smith (8-2).

Amateur: Mr C B Hills (10-2).

284 MR J. W. HILLS, Lambourn

Postal: **Hill House Stables, Folly Road, Lambourn, Hungerford, Berkshire, RG17 8QE.**
Phone: **(01488) 73144 FAX (01488) 73099**

1 **ARRIVING**, 4, br f Most Welcome—Affirmation **Wyck Hall Stud**
2 **AWESOME POWER**, 12, b g Vision (USA)—Majestic Nurse **Mr Garrett J. Freyne**
3 **CHINA RED (USA)**, 4, br g Red Ransom (USA)—Akamare (FR) **Mr N. N. Browne And Partners**
4 **CRIMSON TIDE (IRE)**, 4, b c Sadler's Wells (USA)—Sharata (IRE) **Mr Christopher Wright**
5 **DIMINUTIVE (USA)**, 5, b g Diesis—Graceful Darby (USA) **Gainsbury Partnership**
6 **DOMINANT DUCHESS**, 4, b f Old Vic—Andy's Find (USA) **Mrs Diana Patterson**
7 **REUNION (IRE)**, 4, br f Be My Guest (USA)—Phylella **Highclere Thoroughbred Racing Ltd**
8 **SHERIFF**, 7, b g Midyan (USA)—Daisy Warwick (USA) **Mr Terry Milson**

THREE-YEAR-OLDS

9 **AZULINO (IRE)**, gr f Bluebird (USA)—Page Blanche (USA) **Mr K. Y. Lim**
10 **BOLD KING**, br c Anshan—Spanish Heart **Avon Industries Ltd**
11 **BROOKSIE**, b g Efisio—Elkie Brooks **Mrs Shirley Trotman**
12 **CADILLAC JUKEBOX (USA)**, b br c Alleged (USA)—Symphonic Music (USA) **Mr Freddy Bienstock**
13 **CAGE AUX FOLLES (IRE)**, b c Kenmare (FR)—Ivory Thread (USA) **Mr Christopher Wright**
14 **CANONIZE (IRE)**, b f Alzao (USA)—Cecina **Mr George Tong**
15 **COALMINERSDAUGHTER (IRE)**, b f Dynaformer (USA)—Sportin' Notion (USA) **Mr Freddy Bienstock**
16 **COLD FRONT**, br c Polar Falcon (USA)—Chandni (IRE) **Mr George Tong**
17 **DOATING (IRE)**, b f Doyoun—Hayat (IRE) **Mr J. W. Robb**
18 **DOCKSIDER (USA)**, ch c Diesis—Pump (USA) **Mr Freddy Bienstock**
19 **ESPRESSO**, br g Faustus (USA)—Shikabell **Espresso Racing**
20 **FAYRANA (IRE)**, b f Fayruz—Paryiana (IRE) **Racegoers Club Owners Group (1997)**
21 **FLUSH (FR)**, b br f Warning—Garden Pink (FR) **Mr G. Lowe; The Losers Owners Group**
22 **FRANCESCA'S FOLLY**, b f Efisio—Nashville Blues (IRE) **Mr Freddy Bienstock**
23 **GENERAL SAM (USA)**, b br g Houston (USA)—Irish Wisdom (USA) **Mr Freddy Bienstock & Gary J. Player**
24 **KRISPY KNIGHT**, ch c Kris—Top Table **Mr Derek D. Clee**
25 **LA ISLA BONITA**, ch f Lion Cavern (USA)—La Dama Bonita (USA) **Mr Christopher Wright**
26 **LA LYONESSE**, b f Lion Cavern (USA)—Princess Sioux **Mr & Mrs P. Homewood**
27 **LEMON BRIDGE (IRE)**, b c Shalford (IRE)—Sharply **Mr Martin Myers**
28 **MEMPHIS DANCER**, b f Shareef Dancer (USA)—Wollow Maid **Mr Martin Boase**
29 **MISS GREEN**, b f Greensmith—Miss Comedy **Miss J. Wilkinson**
30 **NAUTICAL STAR**, b c Slip Anchor—Comic Talent **Mr Michael Wauchope**
31 **NIGHT FLYER**, b c Midyan (USA)—Scandalette **The Jampot Partnership**
32 **NOCTURNE (IRE)**, b f Tenby—Phylella **Highclere Thoroughbred Racing Ltd**
33 **ON THE RIGHT SIDE**, b g Pursuit of Love—La Masse **Mr R. J. McCreery**
34 **POLAR MIRAGE**, br f Polar Falcon (USA)—Miss Oasis **The Jampot Partnership**
35 **RED LEGGINGS**, b f Shareef Dancer (USA)—Anchorage (IRE) **Mrs Claire Smith**
36 **RING OF TRUTH**, b f Magic Ring (IRE)—Great Aim **Mr Michael Wauchope**
37 **ROI DE DANSE**, ch c Komaite (USA)—Princess Lucy **Mr A. N. Miller**
38 **SHORT ROMANCE (IRE)**, b f Brief Truce (USA)—Lady's Turn **Abbott Racing Partners**
39 **STALWART LEGION (IRE)**, b f Distinctly North (USA)—La Posada **Royal British Legion Racing Club**
40 **TOPAZ**, b c Alhijaz—Daisy Topper **The Topaz Partnership**

TWO-YEAR-OLDS

41 **ADORA'S DREAM (IRE)**, b c 21/1 Mujtahid (USA)—Shady Bank (USA) (Alleged (USA)) **Mr George Tong**
42 **ALIGN**, gr f 13/3 Petong—Affirmation (Tina's Pet) **Wyck Hall Stud**
43 **CAERDYDD FACH**, b f 3/2 Bluebird (USA)—Waitingformargaret (Kris) **Derek & Jean Clee**
44 **CASINO ROYALE**, b c 5/4 Royal Academy (USA)—Sharata (IRE) (Darshaan) **Mr Christopher Wright & Partners**
45 B c 12/4 El Gran Senor (USA)—Celtic Loot (USA) (Irish River (FR)) **Mr N. Hubbard & Mrs J. Magnier**
46 **CUBISM (USA)**, b c 4/4 Miswaki (USA)—Seattle Kat (USA) (Seattle Song (USA)) **Mr K. Y. Lim**
47 **DOMINANT DANCER**, ch f 15/2 Primo Dominie—Footlight Fantasy (USA) (Nureyev (USA)) **Mr L. Godfrey & Partners**
48 **FADWA**, b f 12/5 Mizoram (USA)—Mey Madam (Song) **Mr Z. Galadari**
49 B c 9/5 Sadler's Wells (USA)—Fair of The Furze (Ela-Mana-Mou) **Mr Freddy Bienstock & Partners**
50 **FAIR WARNING**, b c 13/3 Warning—Fairy Bluebird (Be My Guest (USA)) **Mr Michael Wauchope & Partners**
51 B c 17/2 Fairy King (USA)—Fashion Front (Habitat)

MR J. W. HILLS—continued

52 **FIRST CUT (USA),** b f 13/5 Diesis—Super Jamie (USA) (Nijinsky (CAN)) **Mr K. Y. Lim**
53 **FOREST KING (IRE),** b c 21/3 Forest Wind (USA)—Paryiana (IRE) (Shernazar) **Mr R. Styles, Mr R. Tarring**
54 B f 6/2 Teenoso (USA)—Formal Affair (Rousillon (USA)) **Mrs Claire Smith**
55 **GARDENIA (IRE),** b f 28/4 Sadler's Wells (USA)—Formulate (Reform) **Abbott Racing Partners**
56 **GLINT IN HER EYE,** b f 9/3 Arazi (USA)—Wind In Her Hair (IRE) (Alzao (USA)) **Abbott Racing Partners**
57 **ICE PACK,** gr f 14/2 Mukaddamah (USA)—Mrs Gray (Red Sunset) **Inpacks**
58 B f 19/4 Aragon—Ingerence (FR) (Akarad (FR)) **Abbott Racing Partners**
59 B f 1/3 Absalom—Just Irene (Sagaro) **Mr G. Noble**
60 **KNIGHTHOOD,** b c 16/2 Highest Honor (FR)—
Picardy (Polish Precedent (USA)) **Highclere Thoroughbred Racing Ltd**
61 **MADAGASCAR,** b f 11/3 Puissance—Tabyan (USA) (Topsider (USA)) **Mr Martin Myers**
62 **MAESTEG,** b f 25/1 Reprimand—Eluned May (Clantime) **Derek & Jean Clee**
63 B f 14/5 Green Desert (USA)—Mahabba (USA) (Elocutionist (USA)) **Mr D. Caruth & Partners**
64 B c 29/3 Barathea (IRE)—Miss Demure (IRE) (Shy Groom (USA)) **Sara Warren & Amanda Hubbard**
65 B c 22/3 Common Grounds—Miss Siddons (Cure The Blues (USA))
66 Gr f 16/3 Bustino—Nichodoula (Doulab (USA)) **Mrs Claire Smith**
67 **NO MERCY,** ch c 4/2 Faustus (USA)—
Nashville Blues (IRE) (Try My Best (USA)) **Mr Freddy Bienstock & Mr J. W. Hills**
68 B f 9/3 Inchinor—Poyle Fizz (Damister (USA)) **The Jampot Partnership**
69 **QUICKSILVER GIRL,** b f 10/4 Danehill (USA)—
Crime of Passion (Dragonara Palace (USA)) **Mr Christopher Wright**
70 **REGAL PHILOSOPHER,** b c 19/2 Faustus (USA)—Princess Lucy (Local Suitor (USA)) **Trajan Partners**
71 **RESTIGNE (FR),** b c 1/4 Polytain (FR)—Dissidence (IRE) (Dancing Dissident (USA))
72 **SAFERJEL,** b f 14/2 Elmaamul (USA)—Band of Fire (USA) (Cheif's Crown (USA)) **Mr Z. Galadari**
73 B f 13/3 Royal Academy (USA)—Samnaun (USA) (Stop The Music (USA)) **Mr W. Coleman & Partners**
74 **TIME MILL,** b c 19/2 Shirley Heights—Not Before Time (IRE) (Polish Precedent (USA)) **Mr George Tong**

Other Owners: Mr Daniel Abbott, Mrs Margaretha Allen, Astaire & Partners (Holdings) Ltd, Mr Derek Auburn, Mr T. W. Bailey, Mr R. J. Bolam, Mrs Joan Buckingham, Mr Keith Buckingham, Mr Richie Burrows, Dr J. A. Chandler, Dr Frank S. B. Chao, Mr D. J. Chapman, Mr Robert Cottam, Exors The Late Lady D'Avigdor-Goldsmid, Mr Christoper Davis, Mr D. J. Deer, Sir Simon Dunning, Mr Kenneth Gervase-Williams, Mr Dale J. Gibson, Miss L. M. Gold, Mr J. Hawkes, Mr M. Hawkes, Mr D. Hopson, Mrs S. Hopson, Mr Stewart R. Hunt, Mr R. Hunter, Mr J. B. Johnstone, Sultan Al Kabeer, Mr Abdulla Al Khalifa, Mrs S. M. Lim, Mr C. Marner, Mr T. V. More, Mr T. Morning, Mr C. R. Nelson, Mr William J. Patterson, Mr J. H. Richmond-Watson, Mrs Sonia Rogers, Mr Anthony Savin, Mr N. P. Savin, Mr I. Peter Sedgwick, Mr P. Sedgwick, Mr Ken Sharp, Mr C. B. Smith, Mrs W. Tulloch, Mr C. R. Utting, Mr Nic Warren, Mr P. F. Warren, Miss Z. Whitmore, Willsford Racing Incorporated.

Jockeys (Flat): M Henry (7-8), M Hills (8-0), R Hills (8-0).

Apprentices: P Clarke (7-10), S Dickerson (7-10).

Lady Rider: Miss Eve Johnson Houghton (9-7).

285 MR R. P. C. HOAD, Lewes

Postal: **Windmill Lodge Stables, Spital Road, Lewes, East Sussex, BN7 1LS.**

1 **CELTIC LILLEY,** 8, ch m Celtic Cone—Pal Alley **Mrs J. E. Taylor**
2 **CODE RED,** 5, b g Warning—For Action (USA) **Mr R. P. C. Hoad**
3 **DESERT PRESIDENT,** 7, ch g Polish Precedent (USA)—Majestic Kahala (USA) **Mrs J. E. Taylor**
4 **HEAD FOR HEAVEN,** 8, b g Persian Heights—Believer **Mrs C. O'Connell/Mr A. Nairn/Mr R. Hoad**
5 **NOT FORGOTTEN (USA),** 4, b g St Jovite (USA)—Past Remembered (USA)

TWO-YEAR-OLDS

6 Ch c 11/4 Mazaad—Donalee (Don) **Mrs Julie Hoad**

286 MR A. G. HOBBS, Kingsbridge

Postal: **Wotton Farm, Woodleigh, Kingsbridge, Devon, TQ7 4DP.**
Phone: **(01548) 550805 FAX (01548) 550805 MOBILE (0378) 153473**

1 **AMOTHEBAMBO (IRE),** 5, b g Martin John—Twilight In Paris **Mrs Maureen Shenkin**
2 **BURLINGTON SAM (NZ),** 10, b g Veloso (NZ)—Bees Knees (NZ) **Mrs Jackie Reip**
3 **DRAMATIC ACT,** 5, gr m Tragic Role (USA)—Curious Feeling **Mrs D. Hollingsworth**
4 **EASTDON GOLD DUST,** 5, b g Gold Dust—Aunt Etty **Mr M. A. Swift**
5 **FOUNTAINS (USA),** 4, b g Danzig (USA)—Coxwold (USA) **Mrs Maureen Shenkin**
6 **HELD TO RANSOM,** 6, ch g Revlow—Chantage **Mr J. J. O'Connor**
7 **JAY EM ESS (NZ),** 9, b g Blue Razor (USA)—Bonafide (FR) **Mr M. D. Anderson**
8 **MARINE SOCIETY,** 10, b g Petoski—Miranda Julia **Bideford Tool Ltd**
9 **MIRAMARE,** 8, br g Sulaafah (USA)—Skilla **Mr M. A. Swift**
10 **MISSED THE BOAT (IRE),** 8, b g Cyrano de Bergerac—Lady Portobello **Bideford Tool Ltd**
11 **MON AMIE,** 8, ch g Right Regent—Woodcourt Gold **Mr John Lister**
12 **NEVER IN DEBT,** 6, ch g Nicholas Bill—Deep In Debt **Mr M. R. Clough**
13 **NIGHT TIME,** 6, b g Night Shift (USA)—Gathering Place (USA) **Mrs Maureen Shenkin**
14 **NINE O THREE (IRE),** 9, b g Supreme Leader—Grenache **Bideford Tool Ltd**
15 **OYSTER,** 5, b g Kris—Made of Pearl (USA) **Mr Edward Retter**
16 **PALACE PARADE (USA),** 8, ch g Cure The Blues (USA)—Parasail (USA) **Bideford Tool Ltd**
17 **SALLY SCALLY,** 6, ch m Scallywag—Petite Cone **Mr Edward Retter**
18 **ST MELLION DRIVE,** 8, b g Gunner B—Safeguard **St Mellion Estates Ltd**
19 **TAKETHETOPOFF (IRE),** 5, br m Accordion—Fandikos (IRE) **Mr Geoffrey Hobbs**
20 4, B g Astronef—War Ballad (FR) **Mrs Maureen Shenkin**
21 **WILLOWS ROULETTE,** 6, b g High Season—Willows Casino **Miss Jayne Brace**

TWO-YEAR-OLDS

22 **MAGIC VALENTINE,** b f 14/2 Magic Ring (IRE)—Oublier L'Ennui (FR) (Bellman (FR)) **Mrs Jackie Reip**

Other Owners: Mr D. H. Barons, Mr A. J. Chapman, Miss R. M. Gardner, Mr R. Harding, Mrs D. N. Harris, Mr A. G. Hobbs, Mr Alan A. Jones, Dr Ian R. Shenkin, Miss Joanne Tremain, Unity Farm Holiday Centre Ltd.

Conditional: G Shenkin (9-10).

Amateur: J Young (10-7).

287 MR P. J. HOBBS, Minehead

Postal: **Sandhill, Bilbrook, Minehead, Somerset, TA24 6HA.**
Phone: **(01984) 640366 CAR (0860) 729795 FAX (01984) 641124**

1 **AAL EL AAL,** 11, br g High Top—Last Card (USA) **Mrs Christine Hake**
2 **ALPINE JOKER,** 5, b g Tirol—Whitstar **The Cobra Partnership**
3 **AMLAH (USA),** 6, gr g Storm Bird (CAN)—Old Mother Hubbard (USA) **Mr Salvo Giannini**
4 **ANOTHER COCKPIT,** 6, b g Petoski—Tommys Dream **The Cockpit Crew**
5 **ASHWELL BOY (IRE),** 7, b g Strong Gale—Billys Pet **A. B. S. Racing**
6 **ASKING FOR KINGS (IRE),** 5, b g Thatching—Lady Donna **Mr Jim Weeden**
7 **ATAVISTIC (IRE),** 6, b g Architect (USA)—Saceili **Mrs Jill Emery, Mr A.Staple, Mr E.Morris**
8 **BABBLING BROOK (IRE),** 6, ch g Meneval (USA)—Sparkling Stream **Mr A. Stennett & Mrs J. M. Stennett**
9 **BARRIE STIR,** 6, b g Law Society (USA)—Avahra **Waterloo**
10 **BEACON SILVER,** 4, b f Belmez (USA)—Nettle **Mr Ron Croft**
11 **BELLS LIFE (IRE),** 9, b g The Parson—Affability **Mr R. Gibbs**
12 **BON VOYAGE (USA),** 6, b g Riverman (USA)—Katsura (USA) **The French Relation Partnership**
13 **BORN TO PLEASE (IRE),** 6, ch g Waajib—Gratify **A. B. S. Racing**
14 **BROWN WREN,** 7, b m Kinglet—Brown Veil **Mrs A. G. Lawe**
15 **BRUSH WITH FAME (IRE),** 6, b g Brush Aside (USA)—Cheeney's Gift **J & B Gibbs & Sons Ltd**

MR P. J. HOBBS—continued

16 **BULKO BOY (NZ)**, 6, br g Pandemonium—Comedy of Errors (NZ) **Nobodys Partnership**
17 **CLIFTON BEAT (USA)**, 7, b h Danzatore (CAN)—Amenity (FR) **Mr D. B. O'Connor**
18 **CLONGOUR (IRE)**, 8, ch g Capricorn Line—Momentary Affair **Mr Liam Mulryan**
19 **CLUB CARIBBEAN**, 6, br m Strong Gale—Murex **Mr S. P. Marsh**
20 **CONNAUGHT CRACKER**, 8, ch g Gunner B—Burlington Belle **Mrs Angela Tincknell**
21 **COUNTRY GOSSIP**, 6, ch m Scorpio (FR)—Royal Chitchat **Mr J. G. Charlton**
22 **CRACK ON**, 8, ch g Gunner B—Wing On **Mr D. R. Peppiatt**
23 **CRYSTAL JEWEL**, 6, b m Lir—Crystal Comet **Mrs Izabel Palmer**
24 **DR LEUNT (IRE)**, 7, ch g Kefaah (USA)—Not Mistaken (USA) **Mr Peter Emery & Mr A. Staple**
25 **EDGEMOOR PRINCE**, 7, b g Broadsword (USA)—Stubbin Moor **The Racing Hares**
26 **EDIMBOURG**, 12, b g Top Ville—Miss Brodie (FR) **Mrs Iva Winton**
27 **EDIPO RE**, 6, b h Slip Anchor—Lady Barrister **Mr Tony Eaves**
28 **FAUSTINO**, 6, gr g Faustus (USA)—Hot Case **The Bilbrook '4'**
29 **FOREST MUSK (IRE)**, 7, b g Strong Gale—Brown Forest **The Brushmakers**
30 **GOOD LORD MURPHY (IRE)**, 6, br g Montelimar (USA)—Semiwild (USA) **The Country Side**
31 **GREENBACK (BEL)**, 7, b g Absalom—Batalya (BEL) **Mr Jack Joseph**
32 **GREENFIELD GEORGE (IRE)**, 7, b g Royal Fountain—Meenia **Mrs Karola Vann**
33 **GREENHIL TARE AWAY**, 10, b g Oats—Burlington Belle **Mrs P. F. Payne**
34 **HACK ON**, 6, b m Good Thyne (USA)—Wing On **Mrs A. E. Goodwin**
35 **HAWKFIELD (IRE)**, 9, b g Persian Bold—Oh Carol **The Hedonists**
36 **HYLTERS CHANCE (IRE)**, 7, ch g Zaffaran (USA)—Stickey Stream **Mrs Karola Vann**
37 **IN THE BLOOD (IRE)**, 7, b g Henbit (USA)—Polly's Slipper **Mr I. L. Shaw**
38 **ISIS DAWN**, 6, b m Rakaposhi King—Dawn Encounter **Major R. Darell**
39 **ISITOFF**, 5, b g Vague Shot—Plum Blossom (USA) **Mr C. J. Butler**
40 **JABIRU (IRE)**, 5, b br g Lafontaine (USA)—Country Glen **Mrs R. J. Skan**
41 **JAQUIES GLEN (IRE)**, 5, b m King's Ride—Jacqueline's Glen **The Yearlings Limited**
42 **KARICLEIGH MAN**, 8, b g El Conquistador—Duvessa **Mr H. R. C. Catherwood**
43 **KAZ KALEM (IRE)**, 6, b g Lancastrian—Kilclare Lass **Mr & Mrs D. Thompson**
44 **KIBREET**, 11, ch g Try My Best (USA)—Princess Pageant **Mrs Jill Emery & Mr Terry Warner**
45 **KNUCKLEBUSTER (IRE)**, 8, b g Bustineto—Diana Harwell **Mrs D. Poore**
46 **LIFE'S WORK**, 6, b g Lyphento (USA)—Travail Girl **The Four Double-U's**
47 **MADISON COUNTY (IRE)**, 8, b g The Parson—Lucie Fort **Mr B. K. Peppiatt**
48 **MAYBRIDGE LADY**, 5, ch m Lighter—Shadow Play **Mrs J. F. Deithrick**
49 **MILFORD SOUND**, 5, b g Batshoof—Nafis (USA) **Mrs Karola Vann**
50 **NAZIR (FR)**, 4, b g Art Francais (USA)—Nabita (FR) **Mr Peter Emery**
51 **NEARLY A DOCTOR**, 5, ch g Nearly A Hand—Gay Ticket **St Bartholomews & The Royal London Turf**
52 **NORLANDIC (NZ)**, 6, ch g First Norman (USA)—April Snow (NZ) **The Till House Partnership**
53 **NOT FOR PARROT (IRE)**, 6, ch g Be My Native (USA)—Sugar Quay **Mr R. Broomhall**
54 **ORSWELL LAD**, 9, b g Pragmatic—Craftsmans Made **Mr R. M. E. Wright**
55 **ORSWELLTHATENSWELL**, 7, b g Ballacashtal (CAN)—A'Dhahirah **Mr R. M. E. Wright**
56 **PAIR OF JACKS (IRE)**, 8, ch g Music Boy—Lobbino **Gordano Buccaneers**
57 **PENNCALER (IRE)**, 8, ch g Callernish—Pennyland **Mrs Anona Taylor**
58 **PLEASURE SHARED (IRE)**, 10, ch g Kemal (FR)—Love-In-A-Mist **Mr Tony Eaves & Mrs J. Grant**
59 **POLAR PROSPECT**, 5, b g Polar Falcon (USA)—Littlemisstrouble (USA) **Mr & Mrs Don Last and Bill Yates**
60 **PREMIER BAY**, 4, b c Primo Dominie—Lydia Maria **Mr E. M. Thornton**
61 **PRIDE OF KASHMIR**, 5, gr g Petong—Proper Madam **Frank & Cicely Berry**
62 **RAGAMUFF**, 7, b g El Conquistador—Ragsi **Mrs P. G. Wilkins**
63 **RICHMOND LADY**, 5, ch m Broadsword (USA)—Wing On **Mr James Burley**
64 **RIVER MULLIGAN (IRE)**, 6, ch g Over The River (FR)—Miss Manhattan **St Mellion Estates Ltd**
65 **ROSCORRIE**, 5, b g Roscoe Blake—Corrie's Girl **Mr & Mrs J. Northover**
66 **ROYAL POT BLACK (IRE)**, 7, b br g Royal Fountain—Polly-Glide **Mr A. Loze**
67 **ROYAL SPARK**, 6, b g Lighter—Royal Rushes **Mr Peter Luff**
68 **SADLER'S REALM**, 5, b g Sadler's Wells (USA)—Rensaler (USA) **B. D. Racing**
69 **SAMLEE (IRE)**, 9, b g Good Thyne (USA)—Annie Buskins **White Lion Partnership**
70 **SAXON DUKE**, 7, b g Saxon Farm—Bucks Princess **Saxon Duke Partnership**
71 **SAXON MEAD**, 8, ch g Saxon Farm—Great Chance **Mr H. R. C. Catherwood**
72 **SHARP THYNE (IRE)**, 8, b g Good Thyne (USA)—Cornamucla **Mrs Christopher Hodgson**
73 **SHROPSHIRE GALE (IRE)**, 7, b g Strong Gale—Willow Fashion **Mr A. Stennett & Mrs J. M. Stennett**
74 **SLIEMA CREEK**, 4, gr g Beveled (USA)—Sea Farer Lake **Mr Jack Joseph**

MR P. J. HOBBS—continued

75 **STORMY PASSAGE (IRE)**, 8, b g Strong Gale—Perusia **Mr Peter Luff**
76 **SULLIVANS LIFE (IRE)**, 5, b g Strong Gale—Affability **Mr R. Gibbs**
77 **TIDAL FORCE (IRE)**, 7, br g Strong Gale—Liffey Travel **Mr Ian S. Steers**
78 **TWIN FALLS (IRE)**, 7, b g Trempolino (USA)—Twice A Fool (USA) **Mr Rod Hamilton**
79 **TYPICAL WOMAN (IRE)**, 7, b br m Executive Perk—Beau Jo **Mr A. H. Bulled**
80 **VILLAGE KING (IRE)**, 5, b g Roi Danzig (USA)—Honorine (USA) **Capt. E. J. Edwards-Heathcote**
81 **WARNER FOR PLAYERS (IRE)**, 7, b g Good Thyne (USA)—Bramble Hatch **Mr Terry Warner**

Other Owners: Mr B. B. Akerman, Allied Manufacturing Company, Mr A. J. Allright, Mr G. J. F. Baer, Mr Q. J. F. Baer, Mr Phil Blair, Mr I. F. Brown, Mrs A. H. Bulled, Mr D. Carey, Mr Seamus Carroll, Mrs S. C. Cockshott, Miss H. L. Cope, Mr J. Cope, Mr Thomas Corbett, Mrs B. Davies, Mr R. W. Devlin, Miss I. D. Du Pre, Mrs J. Edwards-Heathcote, Mr A. G. Fear, Mrs A. Frank, Mrs J. Gibbs, Mr Bill Gibson, Mr I. Gould, Mr Neil Graham, Mr J. R. Hall, Mrs M. E. Heappey, Mrs S. L. Hobbs, Mrs B. J. House, Mr Gordon E. Innes, In Touch Racing Club, Mr R. Joyce, Mr B. Knight, Knightsbridge Bc, Mr I. A. Laming, Mr S. C. Lee, Mrs S. P. Marsh, Col R. J. Martin, Mr S. Martin, Maybridge Chemical Company Limited, Sir Harry Moore, Mr Michael Neville, Mr M. J. Ogborne, Mr Frank Palk, Mr A. Palmer, Mr Victor G. Palmer, Mr V. J. Pennington, Mr L. Perring, Mr J. A. Pickford, Mr B. S. Port, Mr D. A. Rees, Mr S. D. Reeve, Mr C. H. Saunders, Mr N. C. Savery, Mr D. Sheldon, Mr R. K. Simmons, Mr A. Stevens, Mr G. W. Stevenson, Terry Warner Sports, Mr W. Tincknell, Mr J. Tudor, Unity Farm Holiday Centre Ltd, Mr C. J. M. Walker, Mr Michael Warner, Mr C. K. Watkins, Mr A. M. Watts, Mr David J. Wood, Mr Jeffrey H. Wright, Mr Andrew P. Wyer.

Jockeys (NH): R Dunwoody (10-0), G Tormey (10-0).

Amateurs: Mr P Flynn (9-7), Mr R Widger (10-7).

288 MR R. J. HODGES, Somerton

Postal: **Footstep, Cedar Lodge, Charlton Adam, Somerton, Somerset TA11 7AR.**
Phone: **CHARLTON MACKRELL (01458) 223922 FAX (01458) 223969**

1 **ABTAAL**, 8, b g Green Desert (USA)—Stufida **Mr P. Slade**
2 **AFICIONADO (IRE)**, 4, b g Marju (IRE)—Haneena **Mrs C. J. Cole**
3 **ALMAPA**, 6, ch g Absalom—More Fun **Mr P. Slade**
4 **COUNTRY TARQUIN**, 6, b h Town And Country—High Finesse **Miss C. A. James**
5 **FENWICK**, 11, b g Magnolia Lad—Isobel's Choice **Major A. W. C. Pearn**
6 **FIVE BOYS (IRE)**, 6, b g King Luthier—Riverside Willow **Mrs S. J. Maltby**
7 **FULL OF BOUNCE (IRE)**, 7, b g Corvaro (USA)—Keep The Link **Fieldspring Racing**
8 **GLOWING PATH**, 8, b g Kalaglow—Top Tina **Mr P. Slade**
9 **HIGHTOWN CAVALIER**, 7, b g Thowra (FR)—Hightown Fontana **Miss R. Dobson**
10 **INDIAN RUN (IRE)**, 9, b g Commanche Run—Excitingly (USA) **Mr P. Slade**
11 **JAYANMAY**, 4, gr g Arzanni—Princess Story **Mr S. J. Norman**
12 **LINE OF CONQUEST**, 8, b g El Conquistador—High Finesse **Miss C. A. James**
13 **MASTER MILLFIELD (IRE)**, 6, b g Prince Rupert (FR)—Calash **Mr P. Slade**
14 **MISTER JOLSON**, 9, br g Latest Model—Impromptu **Mr Bob Froome**
15 **MOONLIGHT ESCAPADE (IRE)**, 7, b g Executive Perk—Baybush **Mr P. Slade**
16 **MORSTOCK**, 8, gr g Beveled (USA)—Miss Melmore **Mrs M. Fairbairn**
17 **MYTTONS MISTAKE**, 5, b g Rambo Dancer (CAN)—Hi-Hunsley **Mr P. Slade**
18 **NORTHERN SADDLER**, 11, ch g Norwick (USA)—Miss Saddler **Mr Richard J. Evans**
19 **NORTHERN SINGER**, 8, ch g Norwick (USA)—Be Lyrical **Mr Joe Panes**
20 **PRIMITIVE STREAK**, 7, b g Primitive Rising (USA)—Purple Streak **Mrs Jonathan Bennett**
21 **SAILEP (FR)**, 6, ch g Holst (USA)—Sweet Cashmere (FR) **Mr P. Slade**
22 **TAKE A FLYER (IRE)**, 8, b g Air Display (USA)—Venus of Stretham **Mr Ron Osborne**
23 **TINKER OSMASTON**, 7, br m Dunbeath (USA)—Miss Primula **Mr John Luff**
24 **URBAN LILY**, 8, ch m Town And Country—Laval **Mrs C. J. Cole**
25 **WAYWARD KING**, 6, b g Rakaposhi King—Wayward Pam **Fieldspring Racing**

MR R. J. HODGES—continued

THREE-YEAR-OLDS

26 KATHIES PET, b f Tina's Pet—Unveiled **Mrs E. A. Tucker**

Other Owners: Mr P. E. Axon, Mr George W. Baker, Mrs S. Barraclough, Mr T. Bartlett, Mr David B. Beal, Mrs P. A. Bradshaw, Mr Malcolm A. Brereton, Mr Robert Bridgman, Mrs K. N. Burge, Mr G. Carey, Mr A. J. Coleman, Mr J. N. Coventry, Mr Frank E. Crumpler, Mr Jock Cullen, Mr B. Dennett, Mr J. W. Dufosee, Mrs E. A. Eagles, Mrs E. J. Edwards, Mrs A. M. Evans, Fayers Brown Racing Ltd, Mr A. G. Fear, Mr V. S. Fox, Mrs Liz Froome, Gardens Entertainments Ltd, Mr Andrew Gifford, Mr L. W. Goult, Mr Percy J. Harris, Mr R. J. Hodges, Mr J. N. Hutchinson, Mrs A. L. J. Inshaw, Mr A. C. James, Mrs E. M. J. James, Mr R. E. James, Mr S. E. James, Mr G. Keirle, Mrs Barbara Lock, Mr P. Maltby, Mr David Mort, Mr J. W. Mursell, Mr J. Newsome, Mr Terry Pasquale, Mr D. J. F. Phillips, Pineapple Clothing Co Ltd, Mr P. F. Popham, Mr S. Poree, Mrs Anna L. Sanders, Mrs D. D. Scott, Mrs K. Sellers, Mr R. T. Sercombe, Mr G. Small, Mr K. Small, Mr D. H. Smith, Mrs C. Snart, Lt. Col. E. L. Stocker, Mrs P. R. Stocker, Unity Farm Holiday Centre Ltd, Mr Terry Warner, Mr Paul Wheeler, Mrs B. Whettam, Mr M. White, Mr C. M. Wilson.

289 MR T. HOGAN, Nenagh

Postal: **Fattheen House, Nenagh, Co. Tipperary, Ireland.**
Phone: **HOUSE (067) 33924 YARD 32846 MOBILE (087) 2332111**

1 **AGENT SCULLY (IRE),** 4, b f Simply Great (FR)—Crecora **P. McLoughney & J. Hogan**
2 5, B g Farhaan—Ballywhackeen **T. Hogan**
3 **GLEN GIRL (IRE),** 8, ch m Mister Lord (USA)—Noddy **Mrs G. Hogan**
4 **LIOS NA MAOL (IRE),** 7, b m Jeu de Paille (FR)—Pollyville **Mrs G. Hogan**
5 5, Ch m Rising—My Baloo **Kenyon Syndicate**
6 **MYSTERY BUCK (IRE),** 9, b g Buckskin (FR)—Nualas Choice **Mrs J. Hogan**
7 **ROSES NIECE (IRE),** 5, br m Jeu de Paille (FR)—Pollyville **Landesborough Syndicate**
8 **WHERES THE GOOSE (IRE),** 5, b m Jeu de Paille (FR)—Catchthegoose **D. F. J. Kelly**

Other Owners: R. Elliot, K. L. T. Syndicate, G. M. Lee, G. Maloney, J. Murray.

Jockey (NH): K F O'Brien.

Conditional: M D Murphy.

Amateurs: Mr P Fenton (w.a.), Miss K Rudd.

290 MR A. F. HOLLINGSWORTH, Feckenham

Postal: **Lanket House, Crofts Lane, Feckenham, Redditch, Worcestershire, B96 6PU.**

1 **HIJACKED,** 4, b g True Song—Scamper **Mr A. Hollingsworth**
2 **JIMMY MORREL,** 7, br g Baron Blakeney—Tower Bay **Mr A. Hollingsworth**
3 **MITCHELLS BEST,** 12, br g True Song—Emmalina **Mr A. Hollingsworth**
4 **MR HATCHET (IRE),** 7, ch g Executive Perk—Aubretia (USA) **Mr A. Hollingsworth**
5 **SHADOWGRAFF,** 8, b m Scorpio (FR)—Panatate **Mr A. Hollingsworth**
6 **SHADOW WALKER,** 14, b g Bigivor—Panatate **Mr A. Hollingsworth**
7 **SHARP ALICE,** 7, b m Lighter—Scamper **Mr A. Hollingsworth**
8 **SIDELINER,** 10, ch g Green Shoon—Emmalina **Mr A. Hollingsworth**
9 **STAR CHANGES,** 5, b g Derrylin—Sweet Linda **Mr A. Hollingsworth**

291 MR R. HOLLINSHEAD, Upper Longdon

Postal: **Lodge Farm, Upper Longdon, Rugeley, Staffordshire, WS15 1QF.**
Phone: **ARMITAGE (01543) 490298 FAX (01543) 490490**

1 **BOLD ARISTOCRAT (IRE),** 7, b g Bold Arrangement—Wyn Mipet **Mrs J. Hughes**
2 **BOLD SARAH,** 4, ch f Bold Arrangement—Miss Sarajane **Mr J. Smyth**
3 **C-HARRY (IRE),** 4, ch c Imperial Frontier (USA)—Desert Gale **Mr D. Coppenhall**
4 **CRISSEM (IRE),** 5, b m Thatching—Deer Emily **Mrs Christine Johnson**
5 **DARU (USA),** 9, gr g Caro—Frau Daruma (ARG) **Mrs J. Hughes**
6 **DIVIDE AND RULE,** 4, b c Puissance—Indivisible **Mr M. Johnson**
7 **EASTLEIGH,** 9, b g Efisio—Blue Jane **Mr R. Hollinshead**
8 **HEATHYARDS LADY (USA),** 7, b m Mining (USA)—Dubiously (USA) **Mr L. A. Morgan**
9 **KARADENI (IRE),** 4, gr g Linamix (FR)—Kareferya (USA) **Mrs E. J. Galpin**
10 **LOCH STYLE,** 5, b g Lochnager—Simply Style **Mrs B. Ramsden**
11 **MALIHABAD (IRE),** 9, ch g Shahrastani (USA)—Mill River (FR) **Miss Sarah Hollinshead**
12 **MUJOVA (IRE),** 4, b c Mujadil (USA)—Kirsova **Mr J. D. Graham**
13 **NOUFARI (FR),** 7, b g Kahyasi—Noufiyla **Mr Ed Weetman**
14 **PATINA,** 4, ch f Rudimentary (USA)—Appledorn **Barouche Stud Ltd**
15 **RATHLEA,** 4, b c Risk Me (FR)—Star of Jupiter **Mrs Robert Heathcote**
16 **RESPECTABLE JONES,** 12, ch g Tina's Pet—Jonesee **Miss Sarah Hollinshead**
17 **SCENICRIS (IRE),** 5, b m Scenic—Princesse Smile **Mrs Christine Johnson**
18 **SHAKIYR (FR),** 7, gr g Lashkari—Shakamiyn **L & R Roadlines**
19 **SING WITH THE BAND,** 7, b m Chief Singer—Ra Ra Girl **The Tree R's**
20 **SKELTON COUNTESS (IRE),** 5, ch m Imperial Frontier (USA)—Running Brook **Mr G. Bailey**
21 **SKELTON SOVEREIGN (IRE),** 4, b c Contract Law (USA)—Mrs Lucky **Mr G. Bailey**
22 **SOSTENUTO,** 5, b m Northern State (USA)—Pride of Ayr **Mrs B. E. Woodward**
23 **SUALTACH (IRE),** 5, b h Marju (IRE)—Astra Adastra **Mr Noel Sweeney**
24 **TANIYAR (FR),** 6, b g Glenstal (USA)—Taeesha **Mrs J. Hughes**
25 **UNDERSTUDY,** 4, b f In The Wings—Pipina (USA) **Mr R. Hollinshead**
26 **U-NO-HARRY (IRE),** 5, b h Mansooj—Lady Roberta (USA) **Mr D. Coppenhall**
27 **WEET-A-MINUTE (IRE),** 5, ro h Nabeel Dancer (USA)—Ludovica **Ed Weetman (Haulage & Storage) Ltd**
28 **WEETMAN'S WEIGH (IRE),** 5, b h Archway (IRE)—Indian Sand **Ed Weetman (Haulage & Storage) Ltd**
29 **WHISPER LOW (IRE),** 4, ch f Shalford (IRE)—Idle Gossip **Mr D. Lowe**
30 **WHO DEALT,** 4, ch f Nalchik (USA)—Lana's Secret **Mr Brian J. Rogerson**
31 **WINN'S PRIDE (IRE),** 7, b g Indian Ridge—Blue Bell Girl **Mrs W. L. Bailey**

THREE-YEAR-OLDS

32 **CHASETOWN CAILIN,** b f Suave Dancer (USA)—Kilvarnet **Chasetown Civil Engineering Ltd**
33 **FARNDON PRINCESS,** b f Nomination—Ankara's Princess (USA) **Mr J. D. Graham**
34 **FIELDGATE FLYER (IRE),** b f Sabrehill (USA)—Orba Gold (USA) **Mr G. A. Farndon**
35 **GLENSTAL LAD,** b c Nomination—Glenstal Princess **Mr J. D. Graham**
36 **HEATHYARDS SHEIK,** b c Alnasr Alwasheek—Wilsonic **Mr L. A. Morgan**
37 **LAWFUL CONTRACT (IRE),** br g Contract Law (USA)—Lucciola (FR) **Mr J. Doxey**
38 **MAGGICE,** b f Magic Ring (IRE)—Ice Chocolate (USA) **Mr J. A. Forsyth**
39 **MISS LACROIX,** b f Picea—Smartie Lee **Miss Norma Harris**
40 **NOBLE PATRIOT,** b c Polish Patriot (USA)—Noble Form **Mr P. D. Savill**
41 **SILVER HOPE (IRE),** ch c Silver Kite (USA)—Cloven Dancer (USA) **Mr John Smallman**
42 **SING FOR ME (IRE),** b br f Songlines (FR)—Running For You (FR) **Miss Sarah Hollinshead**
43 **TRAKELOR,** b f Most Welcome—French Cooking **Mr L. A. Morgan**
44 **WHACKER-DO (IRE),** ch c Archway (IRE)—Denowski **Clayton Bigley Partnership Ltd**

TWO-YEAR-OLDS

45 **ALANA'S CAVALIER (IRE),** b c 6/3 Forest Wind (USA)—Annais Win **The Tree R's**
46 **AVONDALE GIRL (IRE),** ch f 15/2 Case Law—Battle Queen **Mr C. Lynch**
47 Ch c 12/4 Political Merger—Bridewell Belle **Mrs S. Edwards**
48 **GILLY WEET,** b f 25/2 Almoojid—Sindos **Mrs G. Weetman**
49 Gr c 22/4 Tragic Role (USA)—Gold Belt (USA)
50 **GOLDEN REEF,** b c 14/4 Puissance—Cloudy Reef **Mr M. Johnson**
51 **HEATHYARDS JAKE,** b c 29/3 Nomination—Safe Bid **Mr L. A. Morgan**

MR R. HOLLINSHEAD—continued

52 **OTAHUNA,** b c 19/3 Selkirk (USA)—Stara **Mr J. D. Graham**
53 **SANTANDRE,** ch c 22/3 Democratic (USA)—Smartie Lee **Mr G. Lloyd**
54 **TENBY HEIGHTS (IRE),** b c 5/4 Tenby—Alpine Spring **Mr J. D. Graham**
55 **THE LAST WORD,** b c 14/2 Cosmonaut—Jolizal **Mr & Mrs N. Lunn**
56 **THE RAIN LADY,** b f 31/1 Lugana Beach—Rain Splash **Mr John Smallman**
57 **WEET U THERE (IRE),** b c 29/4 Forest Wind (USA)—Lady Aladdin **Ed Weetman (Haulage & Storage) Ltd**
58 B c 15/5 Unblest—Zaydeen

Other Owners: Dr M. A. Clarke, Miss B. Connop, Mrs B. Facchino, Mrs D. A. Hodson, Mr D. R. Horne, Mr John M. Jackson, Mrs S. Meredith-Bennett, Mr Ray Robinson, D. J. Smart, Mrs K. D. Smart.

Jockey (NH): G Lyons (10-2).

Apprentices: S Clarke (7-7), D Hayden (7-12), P Quinn (7-0).

Amateur: Mr M Rimell (10-0).

Lady Rider: Mrs Jane Galpin (8-7).

292 MR CON HORGAN, Pulborough

Postal: **Recitation House 3, Coombelands Stables, Pulborough, West Sussex, RH20 1BP.**
Phone: **OFFICE (01798) 874511 FAX (01798) 874511 MOBILE (0850) 365459**

1 **COUNTRY THATCH,** 5, b g Thatching—Alencon **Mrs B. Sumner**
2 **DESERT TIME,** 8, b br g Green Desert (USA)—Supper Time **Spoof Racing**
3 **GOLD MILLENIUM (IRE),** 4, gr g Kenmare (FR)—Gold Necklace **Mrs L. M. Horgan**
4 **OLIVO (IRE),** 4, ch g Priolo (USA)—Honourable Sheba (USA) **Mr J. L. Harrison**
5 **PISTOL (IRE),** 8, ch g Glenstal (USA)—First Wind **Mrs B. Sumner**
6 **PRINCE ZANDO,** 4, b g Forzando—Paradise Forum **Mrs B. Sumner**
7 **REGAL ACADEMY (IRE),** 4, b f Royal Academy (USA)—Polistatic **Mrs B. Sumner**
8 **RISING SPRAY,** 7, ch g Waajib—Rose Bouquet **Mr J. T. Heritage**
9 **ROY BOY,** 6, b g Emarati (USA)—Starky's Pet **Mr Bill Brown**
10 **SOVEREIGN CREST (IRE),** 5, gr g Priolo (USA)—Abergwrle **Mrs B. Sumner**
11 **THATCHMASTER (IRE),** 7, b g Thatching—Key Maneuver (USA) **Mrs B. Sumner**
12 **VICTOR BLUM (USA),** 5, b g Dr Blum (USA)—Victoria Elena (USA) **Mr R. Del Rosario**
13 **WARREN KNIGHT,** 5, b g Weldnaas (USA)—Trigamy **Mrs B. Sumner**

THREE-YEAR-OLDS

14 **FORBES PARK,** b c Alzao (USA)—Rose Alto **Mr B. R. Tantoco**
15 **FRANKLIN LAKES,** ch c Sanglamore (USA)—Eclipsing (IRE) **Mr B. R. Tantoco**
16 **KEY ACADEMY,** b f Royal Academy (USA)—Santa Linda (USA) **Mrs B. Sumner**
17 **MY PLEDGE (IRE),** b c Waajib—Pollys Glow (IRE) **Mrs B. Sumner**

TWO-YEAR-OLDS

18 **CHERE ELISE,** b f 28/3 Be My Chief (USA)—William's Bird (USA) (Master Willie) **Mr M. J. Simmonds**
19 **PURPLE FLAME (IRE),** b f 10/1 Thatching—Poustatic (Free State) **Mrs B. Sumner**
20 B c 17/4 Imp Society (USA)—Straw Boater (Thatch (USA)) **Mr G. Steinberg**
21 B br c 26/2 Second Set (IRE)—Tiffany's Case (IRE) (Thatching) **Mr John Kelsey-Fry**
22 **TYROLEAN LOVE (IRE),** b f 19/1 Tirol—Paradise Forum (Prince Sabo) **Mrs B. Sumner**
23 Gr c 22/2 Petong—Wasimah (Caerleon (USA)) **Mr B. R. Tantoco**

Other Owners: Mr Royston Brown, Mrs Mette Campbell, Mr K. A. Dack, Friary Bloodstock Company Ltd, Mrs S. Greenaway, Mr A. Hudson.

293 MRS S. L. HORNER-HARKER, Yarm

Postal: **Saltergill Park, Low Worsall, Yarm, North Yorkshire, TS15 9PG.**
Phone: **TEL & FAX (01642) 788825 MOBILE (0467) 368706**

1 **ADMISSION (IRE),** 8, br g Glow (USA)—Admit **Miss L. Horner**
2 **ENIGMA BELL,** 5, b g Rambo Dancer (CAN)—Skelton **Mr P. A. Horner-Harker**
3 **FORTY WINKS,** 7, gr g Zambrano—Miss Levantine **Mrs Sarah Horner-Harker**
4 **KING FLY,** 8, ch g Saxon Farm—Deep Goddess **Mr P. A. Horner-Harker**
5 **NINTH SYMPHONY,** 4, ch g Midyan (USA)—Good As Gold (IRE) **Mrs Sarah Horner-Harker**
6 **RULE OUT THE REST,** 7, ch g Scallywag—Saucy Eater **Mrs Sarah Horner-Harker**
7 **STELLAR FORCE (IRE),** 7, br g Strong Gale—Glenroe Star **Mrs J. Horner**

294 MR H. S. HOWE, Tiverton

Postal: **The Old Smithy, Oakfordbridge, Tiverton, Devon, EX16 9JA.**
Phone: **(01398) 351224 (0802) 506344 MOBILE**

1 **ANOTHER BULA (IRE),** 7, b g Cardinal Flower—Celtic Lace **Mr Stuart Howe**
2 **APACHEE FLOWER,** 8, ch m Formidable (USA)—Molucella **Mr John Tackley**
3 **DUNKERY BEACON,** 12, b g Casino Boy—Crown Member VII **Mr Stuart Howe**
4 **MISS SOUTER,** 9, b m Sulaafah (USA)—Glenn's Slipper **Mr John Bull**
5 **MOORLOUGH BAY (IRE),** 8, ch g Abednego—Monica's Pet **The Trojan Partnership**
6 **PURPLE LACE,** 6, b m Salse (USA)—Purple Prose **Mr Kevin Daniel Crabb**
7 **RUMPELSTILTSKIN,** 6, ch g Sharpo—Ouija **Mr Kevin Daniel Crabb**
8 **SHEILAS DREAM,** 5, b m Inca Chief (USA)—Windlass **Mr George Searle**
9 **SILVER GULL (IRE),** 7, gr g Step Together (USA)—Popsi's Darling **J. Bull, A. Cleave & T. Hamlin**
10 **STORM POINT (IRE),** 10, ch g Kambalda—Glenbrien Dusky **Mr R. J. Parish**
11 **STRATTON FLYER,** 8, b m Mas Media—Empress Valley **Mr Stuart Howe**

THREE-YEAR-OLDS

12 **JAYBEE SILVER,** gr f Mystiko (USA)—Pipistrelle **Mr John Bull**

Other Owners: Mr C. J. Harris, Mr C. R. Hollands, Mr Graham Kinson, Mr K. P. Neil, Mr M. J. Peachey, Miss Kate Spurway, Mr H. Veysey, Mr R. F. Walker.

Jockeys (Flat): F Lynch, S Whitworth.

Jockeys (NH): D Bridgwater, A P McCoy, B Powell.

Lady Rider: Miss E J Jones.

295 MR P. HOWLING, Newmarket

Postal: **Wellbottom Lodge, Moulton Paddocks, Bury Road, Newmarket, Suffolk, CB8 7BU.**
Phone: **MOBILE (0836) 721029 (01638) 668503**

1 **BOBBY SWIFT,** 4, ch g Wing Park—Satin Box **Wing Park Progeny Syndicate**
2 **CASTLE ASHBY JACK,** 4, gr g Chilibang—Carly-B (IRE) **Mr Richard Berenson**
3 **HOPEFUL BID (IRE),** 9, b g Auction Ring (USA)—Irish Kick **Mr D. C. Patrick**
4 **JIBEREEN,** 6, b g Lugana Beach—Fashion Lover **Mr Liam Sheridan**
5 **MOON STRIKE (FR),** 8, b br g Strike Gold (USA)—Lady Lamia (USA) **Mr A. Foustok**
6 **SASEEDO (USA),** 8, ch g Afleet (CAN)—Barbara's Moment (USA) **Mr M. Fustok & Mr R. Fustok**
7 **SWEET MAGIC,** 7, ch g Sweet Monday—Charm Bird **Mr C. Hammond**
8 **TOPTON (IRE),** 4, b g Royal Academy (USA)—Circo **Mr Liam Sheridan**

MR P. HOWLING—continued

9 **WILD PALM,** 6, b g Darshaan—Tarasova (USA) **Mr S. Fustok**
10 **ZESTI,** 6, br g Charmer—Lutine Royal **Mrs J. Lewis**

THREE-YEAR-OLDS

11 **ANGELINA,** b f Most Welcome—Mystic Crystal (IRE) **Mr A. Foustok**
12 **HIGH GAIN,** b f Puissance—Femme Formidable **Red Kite Racing**
13 **HOPPIT,** b f Rock Hopper—Pellinora (USA) **Manor Farm Packers**
14 **LAVACA RIVER,** b c Primo Dominie—Rose Music **King Size Racing**
15 **LEGAL LARK (IRE),** ro g Case Law—Park Silver **Mr C. Hammond**
16 **MARAHILL LAD,** b c Mazilier (USA)—Harmonious Sound **Mr Liam Sheridan**
17 **PINSHARP (IRE),** b c Sharp Victor (USA)—Binnissima (USA) **Mr K. Weston**
18 **RED PEPPER (IRE),** br g Chilibang—Magic Flame **Rosefield UK Ltd**
19 **SANTARENE (IRE),** b f Scenic—Rising Spirits **Mr R. N. Khan**
20 **TOP GEAR (IRE),** ch c Case Law—Fleur-de-Luce **Mr Liam Sheridan**

TWO-YEAR-OLDS

21 B f 10/5 Batshoof—Dara Dee (Dara Monarch) **Mrs J. M. Khan**
22 **FIRST HUSSAR,** b c 15/4 Primo Dominie—Third Movement (Music Boy) **Mr P. Gwilliam**
23 **PIETRA,** b f 16/4 Puissance—Femme Formidable (Formidable (USA)) **Mr P. Gwilliam**
24 **SAMIYAH (IRE),** b f 30/4 Anshan—Fujaiyrah (In Fijar (USA))
25 B c 3/3 Chilibang—Swing O'The Kilt (Hotfoot) **Mr A. Foustok**
26 Ch c 8/5 Absalom—Very Good (Noalto) **Chart Enterprises Ltd**
27 Ch f 28/3 Sabrehill (USA)—Ymirkhan (FR) (Kashmir II) **Mr M. Fustok & Mr R. Fustok**

Other Owners: Mr R. W. Bainbridge, Mr Robert Baker, Mr Mike Fochtmann, Mr J. Hammond, Mr B. C. Marshall, Mrs S. Patrick, Mr Max Pocock, Mr I. D. Purkiss, Mr P. Rawson, Mr Roger Cole Shilton, Six Furlongs Racing, Mr Bobby Swift, Mr P. D. Woodward, Mr C. N. Wright.

Jockeys (Flat): Paul Eddery (8-2), J Quinn (7-7).

Lady Rider: Miss I Foustok.

296 MR G. A. HUBBARD, Woodbridge

Postal: **Worlingworth Hall Stud, Worlingworth, Woodbridge, Suffolk, IP13 7NS.**
Phone: **(01728) 628243 (01728) 628554 ASST TRAINER (01473) 230168 (ADMIN)**

1 **AMBROSIA (IRE),** 5, b m Strong Gale—Scotsman Ice **Mr G. A. Hubbard**
2 **BALI STRONG (IRE),** 4, b g Strong Gale—Greavesfind **Mr G. A. Hubbard**
3 **BELMARITA (IRE),** 5, ch m Belmez (USA)—Congress Lady **Mr G. A. Hubbard**
4 **BESSIE BROWNE (IRE),** 6, b m Strong Gale—Shuil Ub **Mr G. A. Hubbard**
5 **CAPSOFF (IRE),** 5, b m Mazaad—Minerstown (IRE) **Mr G. A. Hubbard**
6 **ERNEST WILLIAM (IRE),** 6, b br g Phardante (FR)—Minerstown (IRE) **Mr G. A. Hubbard**
7 **EXECUTIVE KING (IRE),** 7, br g Executive Perk—Leith Hill **Mr G. A. Hubbard**
8 **GIPSY GEOF (IRE),** 7, b g Miner's Lamp—Princess Menelek **Mr G. A. Hubbard**
9 **GOLD SCHEME (IRE),** 5, b g Creative Plan (USA)—Miss Rex **Mr G. A. Hubbard**
10 **HI HEDLEY (IRE),** 8, b g Henbit (USA)—Verbana **Mr G. A. Hubbard**
11 **JAVELIN COOL (IRE),** 7, gr g Roselier (FR)—Wonderful Lilly **Mr G. A. Hubbard**
12 **LORD KHALICE (IRE),** 7, b g King's Ride—Khalice **Mr G. A. Hubbard**
13 **MELTON MADE (IRE),** 5, br g Strong Gale—Pamela's Princess **Mr G. A. Hubbard**
14 **MERILENA (IRE),** 8, b m Roselier (FR)—Scotsman Ice **Mr G. A. Hubbard**
15 **MONKS SOHAM (IRE),** 10, b g The Parson—Kadaga **Mr G. A. Hubbard**
16 **OCCOLD (IRE),** 7, b g Over The River (FR)—My Puttens **Mr G. A. Hubbard**
17 **PEALINGS (IRE),** 6, gr g Wood Chanter—Ten-Cents **Mr G. A. Hubbard**
18 **PETTAUGH (IRE),** 10, b g The Parson—Bright Record **Mr G. A. Hubbard**
19 **POLISH RHYTHM (IRE),** 5, b m Polish Patriot (USA)—Clanjingle **Mr G. A. Hubbard**
20 **RUN FOR DANTE (IRE),** 8, b g Phardante (FR)—Shallow Run **Mr G. A. Hubbard**

MR G. A. HUBBARD—continued

21 **SAXTEAD MILL (IRE)**, 5, b g King's Ride—Toi Figures **Mr G. A. Hubbard**
22 **SILLE ME (IRE)**, 6, ch g Over The River (FR)—Alamo Bay **Mr G. A. Hubbard**
23 **SOUTHOLT (IRE)**, 10, b g Deep Run—Girseach **Mr G. A. Hubbard**
24 **STRONG ARROW (IRE)**, 5, b g Strong Gale—Caesonia **Mr G. A. Hubbard**
25 **STRONG PROMISE (IRE)**, 7, b br g Strong Gale—Let's Compromise **Mr G. A. Hubbard**
26 **SUPER RAPIER (IRE)**, 6, b g Strong Gale—Misty Venture **Mr G. A. Hubbard**
27 **THERMECON (IRE)**, 7, ch g Phardante (FR)—Brosna Girl **Mr G. A. Hubbard**

Jockey (NH): Pat Verling (9-7).

Conditional: Grant Bazin (10-2), Nathan Rossiter.

297 MR J. S. HUBBUCK, Hexham

Postal: **High House Farm, Highford Lane, Hexham, Northd, NE46 2LZ.**

1 **BLAZING DAWN**, 11, b g Deep Run—Men's Fun **Mr J. S. Hubbuck**
2 **SHAHGRAM (IRE)**, 10, gr g Top Ville—Sharmada (FR) **Mr J. S. Hubbuck**

298 MR D. T. HUGHES, Kildare

Postal: **Osborne Lodge, Kildare, Co. Kildare, Ireland.**
Phone: **(045) 521490 FAX (045) 521643 MOBILE (0862) 534098**

1 5, B g Royal Fountain—Aelia Paetina **Frank Prendergast**
2 **AMAKANE LADY (IRE)**, 9, b m King Persian—Kitty Ellis **Thierry Delcros**
3 **ATLANTIC RUN (IRE)**, 5, b g Commanche Run—Lancastrian Height (IRE) **Martin Howley**
4 **AUNTY DAISY (IRE)**, 6, b m Satco (FR)—Maun **J. Stafford**
5 **BATTERSTOWN BOY (IRE)**, 6, b g Satco (FR)—Doon Royal **Desmond O'Sullivan**
6 **BEAKERS BUDDY (IRE)**, 5, b g Cardinal Flower—Better Opportunity **M. P. Whelan**
7 **BLUE WAVE (IRE)**, 6, b g Project Manager—Over The Seas **Mrs Pauline Donnelly**
8 **CATCHABLE**, 4, b g Pursuit of Love—Catawba **Sean Mulryan**
9 **CONNIES BUCK (IRE)**, 6, ch g Buckskin (FR)—Con Lady **T. J. Culhane**
10 5, Ch g Torus—Deep Pine **D. T. Hughes**
11 **DUST GALE (IRE)**, 9, b m Strong Gale—Dusty Hall **Jed Pierse**
12 **EVELYN ANTHONY (IRE)**, 7, b m Phardante (FR)—Last Sprite **Michael Ward Thomas**
13 **EVENKEEL (USA)**, 6, b g Horage—Corozal **Francis G. Kenny**
14 **EXECUTIVE LAWYER (IRE)**, 7, b g Executive Perk—Aluda Queen **Mary Farrell Ward**
15 **FORTYNINEPLUS (IRE)**, 7, b g Torus—Gipsey Jo **Cloverway Racing Club**
16 **GUEST PERFORMANCE (IRE)**, 6, b g Be My Guest (USA)—Bold And Bright (FR) **Sean Mulryan**
17 **HEMISPHERE (IRE)**, 9, b g Dominion—Welsh Fantasy **Kevin McNulty**
18 4, B g Montelimar (USA)—Herbal Lady **D. T. Hughes**
19 **INDIAN MAGIC (IRE)**, 9, b m Montelimar (USA)—Indian Beauty **Mrs D. T. Hughes**
20 **JOHNNY'S DREAM (IRE)**, 8, b g Trimmingham—Maypole Hie **Mrs T. M. Moriarty**
21 **KAMACTAY (IRE)**, 6, b g Kambalda—Miss Agloso **H. A. Campbell**
22 **KEAL RYAN (IRE)**, 5, b g Petorius—Paddy's Joy **Cloverway Racing Club**
23 **MACON EXPRESS (IRE)**, 5, ch g Rhoman Rule (USA)—Dolmen Ballad **G. McConnell**
24 **MARGIN CALL (IRE)**, 4, b f Tirol—Chive **Glen Martin**
25 **MERCHANTS QUAY (IRE)**, 7, ch g Executive Perk—Foolish Lady **Andrew Redmond**
26 **MISS DALE (IRE)**, 5, b m Lord Americo—Jackson Miss **Mrs Nancy Doyle**
27 **MISTY MOMENTS (IRE)**, 7, b g Supreme Leader—Con Lady **Mrs T. M. Moriarty**
28 **PHARAOH (IRE)**, 5, b g Phardante (FR)—Daffydown Lady **James Kelly**
29 **PRINCE DE LOIR**, 4, b c Be My Chief (USA)—Princesse Vali (FR) **Mrs T. M. Moriarty**
30 **RATHBAWN PRINCE (IRE)**, 6, ch g All Haste (USA)—Ellis Town **Brian Macmahon**
31 **RED EBREL (IRE)**, 6, b m Red Sunset—Park Silver **Emerald Racing Syndicate**

MR D. T. HUGHES—continued

32 ROUNDWOOD (IRE), 9, b g Orchestra—Another Bless **M. P. Whelan**
33 SPIONAN (USA), 5, ch h Gold Seam (USA)—More Berries (FR) **Mrs D. T. Hughes**
34 SUPER DEALER (IRE), 6, b g Supreme Leader—Death Or Glory **Sean Muiryan**
35 SYCAMORE BOY (USA), 4, b g Woodman (USA)—Kafiyah (USA) **P. Joseph Kelly**
36 THINKERS CORNER (IRE), 6, b g Executive Perk—Aluda Queen **Brian MacMahon**
37 TONITA'S CHOICE (IRE), 4, b f Silver Kite (USA)—Carriglegan Girl **Mrs Francis Ryan**
38 TOO MANY CHIEFS (IRE), 9, b g Treasure Hunter—Young Express **Mrs James Nicholson**
39 WET PATCH (IRE), 6, b g Common Grounds—Disco Girl (FR) **Seven To Eleven Syndicate**
40 WOLSELEY LORD (IRE), 6, br g Lord Americo—Ballygoman Maid **Laurence Byrne**
41 5, B g Brush Aside (USA)—Zitas Toi **Mrs Kay Owens**

Jockey (NH): Garrett Cotter (9-0).

Apprentice: Paul Wade (8-0).

Conditional: Kieran Kelly (9-0).

Amateur: Mr A Dempsey (10-0).

Lady Rider: Breeda Wall (8-0).

299 MR JOHN R. HUGHES, Ludlow

Postal: **Gorsty Farm, Maryknoll, Ludlow, Shropshire, SY8 2HD.**
Phone: **(01584) 874064 FAX (01584) 873256**

1 6, B m Executive Perk—Amy Fairy **J. L. Needham**
2 ARIOSO, 10, b m True Song—Most **J. L. Needham**
3 BE MY ROMANY (IRE), 6, ch m Be My Native (USA)—Romany Fortune **Miss J. Needham**
4 CALLINDOE (IRE), 8, b br m Callernish—Winsome Doe **J. L. Needham**
5 CHERRY ORCHID, 11, b br g Callernish—Cherry Token **J. L. Needham**
6 LASTOFTHEVIKINGS, 13, ch g Cisto (FR)—Vivyiki **J. L. Needham**
7 LEINTHALL PRINCESS, 12, b m Prince Regent (FR)—Due Consideration **J. L. Needham**
8 LEINTHALL THISTLE (IRE), 9, b br m Mandalus—Phantom Thistle **J. L. Needham**
9 ONE MORE DIME (IRE), 8, b m Mandalus—Deep Dollar **J. L. Needham**
10 OVER THE WREKIN, 11, ch g Over The River (FR)—Wrekin Rose **J. L. Needham**
11 6, B m Lafontaine (USA)—Rathmill Syke **J. L. Needham**
12 WESTERN SUN, 8, b g Suny Boy—Running Valley **J. L. Needham**

Other Owners: Miss C. Nicholas, Mrs D. Smith.

Jockey (NH): B Fenton.

Conditional: G Hogan.

300 LORD HUNTINGDON, West Ilsley

Postal: **Hodcott House, West Ilsley Stables, West Ilsley, Newbury, Berkshire, RG20 7AE.**
Phone: **OFFICE (01635) 281747 HOME (01635) 281725 FAX (01635) 281720**

1 **BATHE IN LIGHT (USA),** 4, ch f Sunshine Forever (USA)—Ice House **Coriolan Partnership**
2 **BYZANTIUM,** 4, b c Shirley Heights—Dulceata (IRE) **Mr R. Van Gelder**
3 **DARING FLIGHT (USA),** 4, b c Danzig (USA)—Life At The Top **Mr Henryk De Kwiatkowski**
4 **DURST,** 4, ch f Risk Me (FR)—Farras **Lord Huntingdon**
5 **FARAWAY LASS,** 5, b m Distant Relative—Vague Lass **Mr J. Rose**
6 **FINAL GLORY,** 4, ch f Midyan (USA)—Lady Habitat **Sir Gordon Brunton**
7 **HURTLEBERRY (IRE),** 5, b m Tirol—Allberry **Mrs Ian Pilkington**
8 **KING PARROT (IRE),** 10, br g King of Spain—Red Lory **Lord Huntingdon**
9 **LA PERRUCHE (IRE),** 5, b m Cyrano de Bergerac—Red Lory **Mr S. Hastings-Bass**
10 **MATCHLESS,** 5, b g Efisio—Mandrian **Mr J. Rose**
11 **MONGOL WARRIOR (USA),** 5, b h Deputy Minister (CAN)—Surely Georgie's (USA) **Mr Henryk De Kwiatkowski**
12 **PERSEVERE,** 4, b f Pursuit of Love—Seastream (USA) **Mrs A. Rothschild**
13 **PIQUANT,** 11, b br g Sharpo—Asnoura (MOR) **Lord Huntingdon**
14 **PRESENT SITUATION,** 7, ch g Cadeaux Genereux—Storm Warning **Mr Chris van Hoorn**
15 **PRINCE OF INDIA,** 6, b g Night Shift (USA)—Indian Queen **Sir Gordon Brunton**
16 **RENOWN,** 6, b g Soviet Star (USA)—Starlet **D. H. Caslon Partners**
17 **SHIFTING TIME,** 4, b f Night Shift (USA)—Timely Raise (USA) **Mr Tim Corby**
18 **SMART DOMINION,** 4, b c Sharpo—Anodyne **Mr George Ward**
19 **SWEET WILHELMINA,** 5, b m Indian Ridge—Henpot (IRE) **Mr Chris van Hoorn**
20 **VISCOUMTESS BRAVE (IRE),** 4, b br f Law Society (USA)—Vadrouille (USA) **Mr Pietro Somaini**
21 **WESTERN SONATA (IRE),** 5, b m Alzao (USA)—Musique Classique (USA) **Mr Ken Nishikawa**

THREE-YEAR-OLDS

22 **BROWNING,** b g Warrshan (USA)—Mossy Rose **Mr Stanley J. Sharp**
23 **CADW (IRE),** b c Cadeaux Genereux—Night Jar **Mr J. T. Thomas**
24 **DISTINCTIVE DANCE (USA),** b c Distinctive Pro (USA)—Allison's Dance (USA) **Mr George Ward**
25 **DOM SHADEED,** b g Shadeed (USA)—Fair Dominion **Mr David Shirley**
26 **EMINENT,** ch c Alnasr Alwasheek—Vague Lass **Mr J. Rose**
27 **EMPHATIC (IRE),** ch c Ela-Mana-Mou—Sally Rose **Lord Weinstock**
28 **FLICKER,** b f Unfuwain (USA)—Lovers Light **The Hodcott Syndicate**
29 **IONIAN SPRING (IRE),** b c Ela-Mana-Mou—Well Head (IRE) **Lord Weinstock**
30 **PROSPECTRESS (USA),** ch f Mining (USA)—Seductive Smile (USA) **Mrs S. Y. Thomas**
31 **SILKEN DALLIANCE,** b f Rambo Dancer (CAN)—A Sharp **Lord Crawshaw**
32 **SMART SQUALL (USA),** b c Summer Squall (USA)—Greek Wedding (USA) **Mr George Ward**
33 **SPIRITO,** b c Mystiko (USA)—Classic Beam **The W. I. Syndicate**
34 **TOTOM,** b f Mtoto—A Lyph (USA) **Mr Chris van Hoorn**
35 **WILD CANARY,** ch f Groom Dancer (USA)—Nest **Lord Carnarvon**
36 **WREN (IRE),** ch f Bob Back (USA)—In The Rigging (USA) **Anglia Bloodstock Syndicate**

TWO-YEAR-OLDS

37 **ARAGANT (FR),** b br c 1/3 Aragon—Soolaimon (IRE) (Shareef Dancer (USA)) **Mrs S. U. Thomas**
38 Ch f 22/2 College Chapel—Be Nimble (Wattlefield) **Lord Huntingdon**
39 **DRESSING GOWN,** b f 2/4 Night Shift (USA)—Kiya (USA) (Dominion) **Lord Carnarvon**
40 **FIRST FAMILY (IRE),** b c 27/3 Polish Precedent—Happy Kin (USA) (Bold Hitter (USA)) **Lord Weinstock**
41 **JUST WHIZZ,** b c 28/4 Efisio—Jade Pet (Petong) **Mr P. Crane**
42 B f 12/3 High Estate—Paul's Lass (IRE) (Al Hareb (USA)) **Coriolan Partnership**
43 **RELATIVE SHADE,** b f 7/2 Distant Relative—In The Shade (Bustino) **Mr George Ward**
44 B f 24/2 Mukaddamah (USA)—Scanno's Choice (IRE) (Pennine Walk) **Anglia Bloodstock Syndicate**
45 **SUSANNE,** b f 29/4 Batshoof—Clarandal (Young Generation) **Mr S. Hastings-Bass**
46 **TIGER HUNT (IRE),** b c 26/5 Rainbow Quest (USA)—Gay Hellene (Ela-Mana-Mou) **Lord Weinstock**
47 **TRICKS (IRE),** b f 10/2 First Trump—Party Line (Never So Bold) **Miss C. Holmes a Court**

Other Owners: The Queen, Mr D. Carleton Paget, Mrs A. F. B. Crawshaw, Mr R. S. Dawes, Capt. E. Edmonstone, Mr Richard J. Evans, Mr K. H. Fischer, Mr Geoffrey C. Greenwood, Lady Halifax, Lord Halifax, Mrs Peter Hastings, Mr M. H. Leapman, Countess Of Lonsdale, Maverick Productions Ltd, Mr George A. Moore, Mr G. C. Mordaunt, Mr M. L. Oberstein, Mr John E. Rose, Mrs Amanda Simmons, Mr R. A. Simmons, Mrs K. M. Thomas.

Apprentices: Christopher Cogan (7-0), Aimee Cook (7-13), Steven Harrison (7-0).

301 DON E. INCISA, Middleham

Postal: **Thorngill, Coverham, Middleham, Leyburn, North Yorkshire, DL8 4TJ.**
Phone: **WENSLEYDALE (01969) 640653 FAX (01969) 640694**

1 **FRENCH GINGER,** 7, ch m Most Welcome—French Plait **Don Enrico Incisa**
2 **GOLD EDGE,** 4, ch f Beveled (USA)—Golden October **Don Enrico Incisa**
3 **GWESPYR,** 5, ch g Sharpo—Boozy **Don Enrico Incisa**
4 **MAREMMA,** 4, b f Robellino (USA)—Maiden Way **Don Enrico Incisa**
5 **MCGILLYCUDDY REEKS (IRE),** 7, b m Kefaah (USA)—Kilvarnet **Don Enrico Incisa**
6 **MINT CONDITION,** 4, ch g Superlative—Penny Mint **Don Enrico Incisa**
7 **NOBBY BARNES,** 9, b g Nordance (USA)—Loving Doll **Don Enrico Incisa**
8 **ORIOLE,** 5, b g Mazilier (USA)—Odilese **Don Enrico Incisa**
9 **PICKENS (USA),** 6, b g Theatrical—Alchi (USA) **Don Enrico Incisa**
10 **PLEASURE TRICK (USA),** 7, br g Clever Trick (USA)—Pleasure Garden (USA) **Don Enrico Incisa**
11 **SOUPERFICIAL,** 7, gr g Petong—Duck Soup **Mrs Christine Cawley**

THREE-YEAR-OLDS

12 **DONNA'S DOUBLE,** ch c Weldnaas (USA)—Shadha **Don Enrico Incisa**
13 **FLORENCE ASHER,** b f Shardari—Filicaia **Razza Dormello Olgiata**
14 **JUST NOBBY,** b g Totem (USA)—Loving Doll **Don Enrico Incisa**

TWO-YEAR-OLDS

15 **FRANCE LAMBERT,** gr f Tirol—Filicaia (Sallust) **Razza Dormello Olgiata**

Jockey (Flat): Kim Tinkler (7-10).

302 MR R. INGRAM, Epsom

Postal: **Wendover Stables, Burgh Heath Road, Epsom, Surrey, KT17 4LX.**
Phone: **STABLES (01372) 748505 HOME (01372) 749157 MOBILE (0374) 239372**

1 **ANOTHER MONK (IRE),** 7, b g Supreme Leader—Royal Demon **Mr Paul Naughton**
2 **BLUE FLYER (IRE),** 5, b g Bluebird (USA)—Born To Fly (IRE) **Mr B. Scott**
3 **CLONOE,** 4, b g Syrtos—Anytime Anywhere **McKernan - O'Neill**
4 **DESERT WAR (IRE),** 7, ch m Military Attache (USA)—War Demon **Mr Paul Naughton**
5 **GENERAL GLEESON (IRE),** 6, ch g Jackson's Drift (USA)—Lady General **The Emerald Gang**
6 **JAMIES FIRST (IRE),** 5, ch g Commanche Run—Avionne **Mr Roger Ingram**
7 **JUNIKAY (IRE),** 4, b g Treasure Kay—Junijo **Ellangowan Racing Partners**
8 **PERSIAN CONQUEST (IRE),** 6, b g Don't Forget Me—Alaroos (IRE) **Mr B. Scott**
9 **RANDOM KINDNESS,** 5, b g Alzao (USA)—Lady Tippins (USA) **949 Racing**
10 **RIFIFI,** 5, ch g Aragon—Bundled Up (USA) **Brooknight Guarding Ltd**
11 **RUN OF BUST (IRE),** 5, b m Commanche Run—Busteds Fancy **Four Bars Racing**
12 **SAN GLAMORE MELODY (FR),** 4, b g Sanglamore (USA)—Lypharitissima (FR) **949 Racing**
13 **TOMAL,** 5, b g King Amongst Kings—Jacinda **Mr Roger Ingram**
14 **TUIGAMALA,** 7, b g Welsh Captain—Nelliellamay **Mrs Sharon Ingram**

THREE-YEAR-OLDS

15 Ch c Most Welcome—Avionne **Four Bars Racing**
16 **BLUE LAMP (USA),** ch f Shadeed (USA)—Matter of Time **Mr B. Scott**
17 **KANTONE (IRE),** ch g Petardia—Green Life **Mr B. Scott**
18 **RAPID RELIANCE,** b f Emarati (USA)—Chiquitita **Brooknight Guarding Ltd**

TWO-YEAR-OLDS

19 B c 12/5 Castaddu—Nelliellamay (Super Splash (USA)) **Sharon Ingram**

Other Owners: Mr C. G. Adams, Mr Gerry Boyer, Mr Peter J. Burton, Mr S. R. Cloutte, Mr P. J. Donnison, Mr G. D. Everett, Mr H. Everett, Mr Eddie Gleeson, Mr G. L. Mills, Mr H. G. Norman, Ms Linda Pearce, Mr Andrew Ross.
Jockey (Flat): A McGlone (8-2, w.a.).

Jockey (NH): A Maguire (10-0).

Lady Rider: Mrs Sharon Ingram (9-7).

303 MR C. F. C. JACKSON, Malvern

Postal: **Whitehouse Farm, Tanhouse Lane, Cradley, Malvern, Worcestershire, WR13 5JX.**
Phone: **(01886) 880463**

1 **FONTAINEROUGE (IRE),** 8, gr g Millfontaine—How Are You **Mr C. F. C. Jackson**
2 **FRED FUGGLES,** 6, ch g Green Adventure (USA)—Wald Konigin **B. H. R. W. Racing Partnership**
3 5, B m Teenoso (USA)—Miss Nero **Mr C. F. C. Jackson**
4 **MIXED OPINION (IRE),** 5, b g Be My Guest (USA)—Outside Pressure **Mr C. F. C. Jackson**
5 **MOONLIGHTER,** 8, b m Lighter—Skidmore **Gold Top Racing**
6 **NERO'S GEM,** 7, b m Little Wolf—Miss Nero **Mr R. Yates**
7 4, B g Derrylin—Scally Dancer **Mr T. Lowe**
8 **VISCOUNT TULLY,** 13, b g Blakeney—Cymbal **Mr C. F. C. Jackson**
9 **WHITEBONNET (IRE),** 8, b g Rainbow Quest (USA)—Dawn Is Breaking **Mr C. F. C. Jackson**

THREE-YEAR-OLDS

10 B g North Col—Thetford Chase **Mrs A. Jackson**

TWO-YEAR-OLDS

11 Ch g North Col—Thetford Chase **Mrs A. Jackson**

Other Owners: Mr Sean Bryan, Mr D. Craddock, Mr David M. Foster, Mr P. Holland, Mr D. J. Pardy, Mr J. Ranford, Mrs Jackie S. Wassall.

Lady Rider: Miss S Jackson.

304 MR F. S. JACKSON, Lowdham

Postal: **Hill View, Old Epperstone Road, Lowdham, Nottinghamshire, NG14 7JA.**
Phone: **(0115) 9663970/(0115) 9663832**

1 **CAPTAIN SAM,** 5, b g Jendali (USA)—Scotgavotte (FR) **Mr F. S. Jackson**
2 **CARLY-J,** 7, b m Cruise Missile—Porto Louise **Mr F. S. Jackson**
3 **LITERARY SPARK,** 10, ch g Kalaglow—My Lady Muriel (USA) **Mr F. S. Jackson**
4 **TOM'S SURPRISE,** 5, ch g Jendali (USA)—Porto Louise **Mr F. S. Jackson**

Amateur: Mr Nick Kent (10-0).

305 MR E. L. J. D JAMES, Hungerford

Postal: **Mask Cottage, Front Street, East Garston, Hungerford, Berkshire, RG17 7EU.**
Phone: **HOME (01488) 648280/(01488) 648077 MOBILE (0802) 886307**

1 **ABOVE SUSPICION (IRE),** 6, b g Henbit (USA)—Cash Discount **Mrs J. N. Humphreys**
2 **ALBERTINA,** 6, b m Phardante (FR)—Rambly Gold **The East Garston Partnership**
3 **BEVELED CRYSTAL,** 4, ro f Beveled (USA)—Countess Mariga **Mrs J. E. M. Powell**
4 **BIG BEN DUN,** 12, b g The Parson—Shanban **Miss N. Carroll**
5 **CAWARRA BOY,** 10, b g Martinmas—Cawarra Belle **Mrs Margaret Kenyon Holden**
6 **CRADLERS,** 10, ch g Sunley Builds—Countess Mariga **The Cradlers Partnership**
7 **DESIGNER LINES,** 5, ch g Beveled (USA)—Parrot Fashion **Mr R. A. Shaw**
8 6, B g Roselier (FR)—Dusky's Lady **Mrs D. Davidson & Mrs P. James**
9 **ESPY,** 15, b g Pitpan—Minorette **Mr E. James**
10 **FINNIGAN'S LOT (IRE),** 4, b g Lancastrian—Light Bidder **Mr P. A. Brazier**
11 **HOTSPUR STREET,** 6, b g Cadeaux Genereux—Excellent Alibi (USA) **Mrs D. C. Samworth**
12 **SWAN STREET (NZ),** 7, b g Veloso (NZ)—Azatla (NZ) **The Swan Street Partnership**
13 **TOLA COLA,** 6, b g Rakaposhi King—Cooks Lawn **Lady Cobham**

MR E. L. J. D JAMES—continued

THREE-YEAR-OLDS

14 **DARE,** b g Beveled (USA)—Run Amber Run **Mr Nicholas Cowan**
15 **SHECANDO (IRE),** ch f Second Set (IRE)—Carado **Mr Nicholas Cowan**
16 **UNIVERSAL LADY,** b f Beveled (USA)—Lady of Itatiba (BEL) **Universal Conference & Incentive Trv Ltd**

TWO-YEAR-OLDS

17 B c 22/4 Deploy—Alwal
18 B f 21/4 Robellino (USA)—Fair Minded
19 B f 10/5 Petong—Mo's Star

Other Owners: Mrs S. Allen, Mrs C. Barrows, Mr V. R. Bedley, The Earl Of Burlington, Lady Burnham, Mr F. Bury, Mr A. Capping, Mr Aldo Corradi, Mrs S. Crofton, Mrs S. Crofton-Atkins, Miss E. J. Denton, Mr R. C. Denton, Mr P. Deweck, Lady Eyre, Mr R. M. Fleming, Mrs S. Gilmour, Mr R. Hestor, Mrs J. Heywood Lonsdale, Mr G. Hulse, Mr C. James, Mrs C. J. James, Mr D. Keswick, Mr T. Keswick, Mr Jake Leslie-Melville, Mrs Hugh Lewin, Mrs J. Macdonald, Mrs J. Martin, Mr G. Mather, Mrs A. McAlpine, Mr G. Patterson, Mr Daniel Richards, Mr S. S. H. Shirazi, Mrs A. Steele, Mr C. Tonge, Mrs D. Tonge, Mr Freddie Tulloch, Mrs Carol J. Welch.

Lady Rider: Miss S Samworth.

306 MR A. P. JARVIS, Aston Upthorpe

Postal: **Frimley Stables, Aston Upthorpe, Didcot, Oxfordshire, OX11 9EE.**
Phone: **(01235) 851341 FAX (01235) 851361 MOBILE (0370) 785551**

1 **BROADWAY MELODY,** 4, b f Beveled (USA)—Broadway Stomp (USA) **Mrs Ann Jarvis**
2 **CHAIRMANS CHOICE,** 8, ch g Executive Man—Revida Girl **Mrs D. B. Brazier**
3 **DIVINE MISS-P,** 5, ch m Safawan—Faw **Town and Country Tyre Services Limited**
4 **EUROBOX BOY,** 5, ch g Savahra Sound—Princess Poquito **Mr N. Coverdale**
5 **GEE BEE BOY,** 4, ch c Beveled (USA)—Blue And White **Grant & Bowman Limited**
6 **GEE BEE DREAM,** 4, ch f Beveled (USA)—Return To Tara **Grant & Bowman Limited**
7 **JAZZMAN (IRE),** 6, b g Black Minstrel—Carbery Star **Mrs Ann Jarvis**
8 **JELLABY ASKHIR,** 6, b h Salse (USA)—Circus Act **Essa Bin Mubarak Al-Khalifa**
9 **MATTIMEO (IRE),** 5, b g Prince Rupert (FR)—Herila (FR) **Mrs Monica Keogh**
10 **MONICASMAN (IRE),** 8, br g Callernish—Sengirrefcha **Mr N. Coverdale**
11 **MOON SONG,** 4, b f Presidium—Martian Melody **Mrs D. B. Brazier**
12 **RUSSIAN RULER (IRE),** 4, b g Bering—Whitecairn **Mr A. L. R. Morton**
13 **THE BAT,** 5, b h Chauve Souris—Jamra **Mrs P. Stroud**

THREE-YEAR-OLDS

14 **ACEBO LYONS (IRE),** b f Waajib—Etage **Mr Terence P. Lyons II**
15 **ALLEGIANCE,** b g Rock Hopper—So Precise (FR) **Mrs Ann Jarvis**
16 **ARCANE STAR (IRE),** b c Arcane (USA)—Chatsworth Bay (IRE) **B. T. G. Partnership**
17 **BLUNDELL LANE (IRE),** ch c Shalford (IRE)—Rathbawn Realm **Mr N. Coverdale**
18 **CLARITY (IRE),** b f Scenic—Cristalga **Mr A. L. R. Morton**
19 **COUNT DE MONEY (IRE),** b g Last Tycoon—Menominee **Mr L. Fust**
20 **CROFTERS EDGE,** ch c Beveled (USA)—Zamindara **Crofter's Edge**
21 **EMMA'S SECRET (IRE),** ch f Arcane (USA)—Moodybint **Mrs Ann Jarvis**
22 **KAYOKO (IRE),** b f Shalford (IRE)—Karamana **Mrs Ann Jarvis**
23 **KIERANS BRIDGE (IRE),** ch f Arcane (USA)—Rhein Valley (IRE) **Mr G. S. Bray**
24 **MOONSTONE (IRE),** b f Statoblest—Opening Day **Mrs D. B. Brazier**
25 **MUGELLO,** b f Emarati (USA)—Fleur de Foret (USA) **Mrs Ann Jarvis**
26 **MUJI,** b f Safawan—Tame Duchess **Town and Country Tyre Services Limited**
27 **OCEAN LINE (IRE),** b c Kefaah (USA)—Tropic Sea (IRE) **Mr Michael Everett**
28 **SASSY (IRE),** b f Imp Society (USA)—Merrie Moment (IRE) **Mr A. L. R. Morton**

MR A. P. JARVIS—continued

TWO-YEAR-OLDS

29 B c 24/2 Mac's Imp (USA)—Almasa (Faustus (USA)) **Mrs Ann Jarvis**
30 B c 16/1 Catrail (USA)—Athens Belle (IRE) (Groom Dancer (USA)) **Mr Ambrose Turnbull**
31 B c 15/3 Forest Wind (USA)—Ballinlee (IRE) (Sky Liner) **Mrs Ann Jarvis**
32 B c 17/4 Lion Cavern (USA)—Bellagio (Busted) **Mrs Ann Jarvis**
33 B f 15/5 Mukaddamah (USA)—Blue Bell Lady (Dunphy) **Mrs Ann Jarvis**
34 B f 30/4 Perugino (USA)—Children's Hour (Mummy's Pet) **Mrs Ann Jarvis**
35 B f 27/4 Beveled (USA)—Cranfield Charger (Northern State (USA)) **Anne Wren**
36 B c 27/4 High Estate—Fairy Magic (IRE) (Fairy King (USA)) **Mrs Ann Jarvis**
37 B f 26/2 Pips Pride—Friendly Song (Song) **Mrs Ann Jarvis**
38 B c 22/3 Shalford (IRE)—Glendale Joy (IRE) (Glenstal (USA)) **Mrs Ann Jarvis**
39 B f 10/4 Perugino (USA)—Height of Elegance (Shirley Heights) **Mrs Ann Jarvis**
40 B f 5/3 Anshan—Jade Mistress (Damister (USA))
41 B f 31/3 Prince Sabo—Lady St Lawrence (USA) (Bering) **Mrs Ann Jarvis**
42 B c 5/4 Keen—Last Finale (USA) (Stop The Music (USA)) **Mr Ambrose Turnbull**
43 B c 11/2 Soviet Lad (USA)—Late Date (Goldhill) **Mr Ambrose Turnbull**
44 B f 10/3 Tenby—Lavezzola (IRE) (Salmon Leap (USA)) **Mr Ambrose Turnbull**
45 B c 9/4 Roi Danzig (USA)—Merrie Moment (IRE) (Taufan (USA)) **Mrs Ann Jarvis**
46 B f 3/4 Emarati (USA)—Moreton's Martha (Derrylin) **Mrs D B Brazier**
47 B c 7/3 Timeless Times (USA)—Parijoun (Manado) **Mrs Ann Jarvis**
48 B f 30/4 Reprimand—Poyle Amber (Sharrood (USA)) **Mrs Ann Jarvis**
49 B c 22/4 Safawan—Sky Fighter (Hard Fought) **Mrs Ann Jarvis**

Other Owners: Axo Sport Uk Limited, Miss S. A. Bloxam, Mr M. I. Glass, Mr Brian T. Griffiths, Mr N. J. Mitchell, Mr D. W. W. Norris, Mr Dennis O'Gara, Mr I. B. O'Rorke, Mr S. A. Sprenger.

Apprentice: C Carver (7-10).

307 MR M. A. JARVIS, Newmarket

Postal: **Kremlin House Stables, Fordham Road, Newmarket, Suffolk, CB8 7AQ.**
Phone: **(01638) OFFICE 661702 HOME 662519 FAX 667018**

1 POLAR PRINCE (IRE), 5, b h Distinctly North (USA)—Staff Approved **Mrs Christine Stevenson**

THREE-YEAR-OLDS

2 ANEMOS (IRE), ch c Be My Guest (USA)—Frendly Persuasion **Mr Andreas Michael**
3 BARRETTSTOWN, ch g Cadeaux Genereux—Sagar **Midcourts Limited**
4 BERAYSIM, b f Lion Cavern (USA)—Silk Braid (USA) **Sheikh Ahmed Al Maktoum**
5 CAMPARI (IRE), ch f Distinctly North (USA)—Foolish Flight (IRE) **Mr Jack Fisher**
6 COLLEVILLE, gr f Pharly (FR)—Kibitka (FR) **Mr K. G. Powter**
7 COMPOSITION, ch f Wolfhound (USA)—Tricky Note **Mr Saeed Manana**
8 COSMIC COUNTESS (IRE), b f Lahib (USA)—Windmill Princess **The Cosmic Greyhound Racing P'nship 11**
9 DASHING CHIEF (IRE), b c Darshaan—Calaloo Sioux (USA) **Lord Harrington**
10 DREAM POWER (IRE), ch c In The Wings—Gelder Shiel **Sheikh Ahmed Al Maktoum**
11 ELBARREE (IRE), b g Green Desert (USA)—Walimu (IRE) **Sheikh Ahmed Al Maktoum**
12 FAIRY THREE, b f Vague Shot—Fairy Free **Mrs Celia Miller**
13 FRANKIE FAIR (IRE), b f Red Sunset—Animate (IRE) **Mr Michael Hill**
14 Ch c Arazi (USA)—Gesedeh **Sheikh Ahmed Al Maktoum**
15 GOLDTUNE, b f Damister (USA)—Tantalizing Song (CAN) **Mr N. S. Yong**
16 HAAJRA (IRE), b f Polish Precedent (USA)—Hejraan (USA) **Sheikh Ahmed Al Maktoum**
17 ITSONLYGILLY, b f Terimon—Letterewe **Mr Joss Collins**
18 JABAL HADEED (IRE), b c Caerleon (USA)—Emilia Romagna (USA) **Sheikh Ahmed Al Maktoum**
19 JAMORIN DANCER, b c Charmer—Geryea (USA) **Mrs L. D. McLardy Smith**
20 LADY OF THE DANCE, b f Tragic Role (USA)—Waltz **Mr T. G. & Mrs M. E. Holdcroft**
21 MERRY PRINCE (IRE), b g Roi Danzig (USA)—Queen of The Brush **Mr D. Fisher**

MR M. A. JARVIS—continued

22 **MIDNIGHT STING,** gr f Inchinor—Halvoya **The West's Awake Racing Partnership**
23 **RADAR (IRE),** b c Petardia—Soignee **Mr John E. Sims**
24 **RAINMAKER,** b c Last Tycoon—Starr Danias (USA) **Thurloe Thoroughbreds II**
25 **SAFE SHARP JO (IRE),** ch g Case Law—Kentucky Wildcat **Mrs Greta Sarfaty Marchant**
26 **SHOHRA WA JAAH,** b g Mtoto—Pipina (USA) **Sheikh Ahmed Al Maktoum**
27 **STAR,** b f Most Welcome—Marista **Mr T. G. Warner**
28 **TECHNICIAN (IRE),** ch g Archway (IRE)—How It Works **Mr M. Sinclair**
29 **TOWAAHI (IRE),** ch f Caerleon (USA)—Untold **Sheikh Ahmed Al Maktoum**
30 **ZEENEH,** b f Machiavellian (USA)—Possessive Dancer **Sheikh Ahmed Al Maktoum**
31 **ZOBAIDA (IRE),** b f Green Desert (USA)—Charmante (USA) **Sheikh Ahmed Al Maktoum**

TWO-YEAR-OLDS

32 Ch c 25/2 Diesis—Afaff (Nijinsky (CAN)) **Mr & Mrs Raymond Anderson Green**
33 B c 12/2 Shirley Heights—Albertville (USA) (Polish Precedent (USA)) **Sheikh Ahmed Al Maktoum**
34 Ch c 26/2 Be My Guest (USA)—Almost A Lady (IRE) (Entitled) **Ms Beata Sadowska**
35 **BEST PORT (IRE),** b c 6/2 Be My Guest (USA)—Portree (Slip Anchor) **Lord Harrington**
36 B br f 6/5 Binalong (USA)—Blue Grass Field (Top Ville) **Mr Jose Quiros**
37 **CHI CHI'S PRIDE (IRE),** b c 30/4 Pips Pride—Kew Gift (Faraway Son (USA)) **Mr Yusof Sepiuddin**
38 **COMPENSATION (IRE),** gr c 2/2 Turtle Island (IRE)—Fontenoy (Lyphard's Wish (FR)) **Mr D. Fisher**
39 **CYRO,** b g 3/2 Cyrano De Bergerac—Odile (Green Dancer (USA)) **Mr T. G. Warner**
40 **EL MOBASHERR (USA),** b c 7/3 Machiavellian (USA)—Sheroog (USA) (Shareef Dancer (USA)) **Sheikh Ahmed Al Maktoum**
41 **ESTIME (FR),** b f 14/3 Caerleon (USA)—Almuhtarama (IRE) (Rainbow Quest (USA)) **Sheikh Ahmed Al Maktoum**
42 B c 18/4 Barathea (IRE)—Fair Shirley (IRE) (Shirley Heights) **Sheikh Ahmed Al Maktoum**
43 Gr c 27/3 Terimon—Flammable (IRE) (Prince Rupert (FR)) **Ms Beata Sadowska**
44 B c 4/3 Saddlers' Hall (IRE)—Full Orchestra (Shirley Heights) **Mr Mohammed Bin Hendi**
45 B br c 15/4 Dayjur (USA)—Gesedeh (Ela-Mana-Mou) **Sheikh Ahmed Al Maktoum**
46 **GOLD CRAFT,** b c 7/3 Be My Chief (USA)—Kukri (Kris) **Mr M. Milan**
47 B c 7/2 Shirley Heights—Historiette (Chief's Crown (USA)) **Sheikh Ahmed Al Maktoum**
48 B f 13/2 Mtoto—Jasoorah (IRE) (Sadler's Wells (USA)) **Sheikh Ahmed Al Maktoum**
49 Gr c 2/2 Elmaamul (USA)—Kibitka (FR) (Baby Turk) **Mr K. G. Powter**
50 B c 8/2 Zafonic (USA)—Lady Blackfoot (Prince Tenderfoot (USA)) **Sheikh Ahmed Al Maktoum**
51 **LONDON ROSE (USA),** b f 6/2 Machiavellian (USA)—United Kingdom (USA) (Danzig (USA)) **Sheikh Ahmed Al Maktoum**
52 B c 29/2 Cadeaux Genereux—Marienbad (FR) (Darshaan) **Mr Saif Ali**
53 **MINLAND (IRE),** b c 19/3 Namaqualand (USA)—Arfjah (Taufan (USA)) **Mr Yusof Sepiuddin**
54 **MORVINO,** b c 21/4 Night Shift (USA)—Hard Task (Formidable (USA)) **Thurloe Thoroughbreds III**
55 **PEBBLE MOON,** gr c 29/1 Efisio—Jazz (Sharrood (USA)) **Mr John E. Sims**
56 B f 10/4 Lion Cavern (USA)—Possessive Dancer (Shareef Dancer (USA)) **Sheikh Ahmed Al Maktoum**
57 B c 21/3 Be My Chief (USA)—Prudence (Grundy) **Mr & Mrs Raymond Anderson Green**
58 **RAAHAT ALGHARB (USA),** b f 5/2 Gone West (USA)—Mount Helena (Danzig (USA)) **Sheikh Ahmed Al Maktoum**
59 Ch f 22/2 Gone West (USA)—Sans Escale (USA) (Diesis) **Mr Mohammed Bin Hendi**
60 Br f 29/1 Mtoto—Slow Jazz (USA) (Chief's Crown (USA)) **Mr Saeed Abdullah Humaid**
61 B c 16/4 In The Wings—So Romantic (IRE) (Teenoso (USA)) **Mr Saif Ali**
62 **SWEET CHARITY (IRE),** ch f 14/4 Bigstone (IRE)—Tolstoya (Northfields (USA)) **Mrs Christine Stevenson**
63 Ch f 10/4 Superlative—Tantalizing Song (CAN) (The Minstrel (CAN)) **Mr N. S. Yong**
64 Ch f 13/2 Trempolino (USA)—Tegwen (USA) (Nijinsky (CAN)) **Abdullah Saeed Bul Hab**
65 B f 18/4 Polish Precedent—Top of The League (High Top) **Sheikh Ahmed Al Maktoum**
66 **TOUGH GUY (IRE),** b c 11/1 Namaqualand (USA)—Supreme Crown (USA) (Chief's Crown (USA)) **Sqdn-Ldr R. A. Milsom**

Other Owners: Miss V. C. Arnold, Mr R. L. Capon, Mr P. G. Carty, Mrs Charlotte Collins, Danehill Homes Limited, Mr Bob Davis, Mr T. P. Gaughan, Mrs Gay Jarvis, Mr M. A. Jarvis, Mr A. D. Latter, Mr J. V. Layton, Mr R. P. Marchant, Mrs H. Michael, Mr Oliver Pawle, Mr J. M. Poland, Mr B. Schmidt-Bodner, Mrs Beryl Sims, Mrs Dorothy M. Solomon, Mr Peter J. Stevenson, Mr T. H. S. Trotter, Mr M. H. Yong, Mr Bob Young.

308 MR W. JARVIS, Newmarket

Postal: **Phantom House Stables, Fordham Road, Newmarket, Suffolk, CB8 7AA.**
Phone: **HOME (01638) 662677 OFFICE (01638) 669873 FAX (01638) 667328**

1 **ALEZAL,** 4, b c Anshan—Dance On The Stage **Mr Howard Spooner**
2 **BACHELORS PAD,** 4, b g Pursuit of Love—Note Book **Mrs Doris N. Allen**
3 **COLD STEEL,** 4, b g Warrshan (USA)—Rengaine (FR) **Mr A. A. Penney & Partners**
4 **DOUBLE-O,** 4, b g Sharpo—Ktolo **R. K. Bids Ltd**
5 **FARHANA,** 5, b m Fayruz—Fahrenheit **Mr A. Foustok**
6 **GANGA (IRE),** 4, ch f Generous (IRE)—Congress Lady **Cuadra Africa**
8 **LORD OLIVIER (IRE),** 8, b g The Noble Player (USA)—Burkina **Miss V. R. Jarvis**
9 **MR FROSTY,** 6, b g Absalom—Chadenshe **Mr D. G. Wright & Partners**
10 **PASSION FOR LIFE,** 5, b g Charmer—Party Game **Canisbay Bloodstock Ltd**
11 **VRENNAN,** 4, ch f Suave Dancer (USA)—Advie Bridge **Canisbay Bloodstock Ltd**

THREE-YEAR-OLDS

12 **ABSENTEE,** br f Slip Anchor—Meliora **Lord Howard de Walden**
13 **BERSAGLIO,** ch c Rainbow Quest (USA)—Escrime (USA) **Lord Howard de Walden**
14 **CLEF OF SILVER,** b c Indian Ridge—Susquehanna Days (USA) **Silver Clef Racing Venture**
15 **DHIRINA (FR),** ch f Bering—Dixiella (FR) **Mr A. Foster**
16 **DOWER HOUSE,** ch c Groom Dancer (USA)—Rose Noble (USA) **Lord Howard de Walden**
17 **HASTATE,** b g Persian Bold—Gisarne (USA) **Lord Howard de Walden**
18 **IVY BIRD (IRE),** b f Contract Law (USA)—Hollyberry (IRE) **Mr William Jarvis & Mr W. McIlveen**
19 **KING PRIAM (IRE),** b g Priolo (USA)—Barinia **Miss V. R. Jarvis**
20 B g Polish Precedent (USA)—Ktolo **R. K. Bids Ltd**
21 **LATE NIGHT OUT,** b c Lahib (USA)—Chain Dance **Mr J. M. Greetham**
22 **LA TIZIANA,** b f Rudimentary (USA)—Tizona **The Phantom House Partnership**
23 **MISS HILLSIDE,** b f Reprimand—Miss Butterfield **Miss V. R. Jarvis**
24 **MOON GORGE,** b f Pursuit of Love—Highland Light **Lady Howard de Walden**
25 **SIMLET,** b g Forzando—Besito **Mrs Doris N. Allen**
26 **SOUTH BEACH,** b f Magical Wonder (USA)—Puget Dancer (USA) **Buckram Oak Holdings**

TWO-YEAR-OLDS

27 **ASTRAKAN (IRE),** ch c 6/5 Lycius (USA)—Star Ridge (USA) (Storm Bird (CAN)) **Buckram Oak Holdings**
28 **BELLECOUR,** ch c 13/3 Royal Academy (USA)—Escrime (USA) (Sharpen Up) **Lord Howard de Walden**
29 **BUCKLE (IRE),** b f 15/2 Common Grounds—Maratona (Be My Guest (USA)) **Mr A. Foster**
30 **CRESSET,** ch c 19/4 Arazi (USA)—Mixed Applause (USA) (Nijinsky (CAN)) **Lord Howard de Walden**
31 **CYRAN PARK,** b c 30/4 Cyrano de Bergerac—Kimberley Park (Try My Best (USA)) **J K Racing**
32 **FINAL LAP,** b c 29/5 Batshoof—Lap of Honour (Final Straw) **Mr T. C. Blackwell & Partners**
33 Ch f 31/1 Barathea (IRE)—Fly Dont Run (USA) (Lear Fan (USA)) **Mr K. P. Seow**
34 **HIGHLAND WELCOME,** b g 25/2 Most Welcome—Highland Hannah (IRE) (Persian Heights) **Mr J. M. Ratcliffe**
35 **INDUNA,** ch f 4/4 Grand Lodge (USA)—Kerkura (USA) (Riverman (USA)) **Lord Howard de Walden**
36 **KATTEGAT,** b c 13/3 Slip Anchor—Kirsten (Kris) **Lord Howard de Walden**
37 **KING TUT,** ch c 6/5 Anshan—Fahrenheit (Mount Hagen (FR)) **Mr A. Fustok**
38 B c 17/3 Fayruz—Lightning Laser (Monseigneur (USA))
39 **MISS PUISSANCE,** b f 27/2 Puissance—Romantic Saga (Prince Tenderfoot (USA)) **The Shed Full Partnership**
40 B f 22/4 Slip Anchor—Miss Up N Go (Gorytus (USA)) **Judith Prescott**
41 **PLURALIST,** b c 27/2 Mujadil (USA)—Encore Une Fois (IRE) (Shirley Heights) **The Pluralist Partnership**
42 **ROSE CROIX (USA),** b f 4/2 Chief's Crown (USA)—La Papagena (Habitat) **Lord Howard de Walden**
43 **SEVENTY ONE,** b c 1/4 Indian Ridge—Rahwah (Northern Baby (CAN)) **Mr Louis Lo**
44 B c 26/1 Zieten (USA)—Siddon Pretty (IRE) (Darshaan) **Noodles Racing**
45 **SUPER ZOE,** b f 11/5 Bustino—Chain Dance (Shareef Dancer (USA)) **Mr J. M. Greetham**
46 b c 9/1 Glitterman (USA)— Speckofsun (USA) (Sunny North (USA)) **Mr H. J. W. Steckmest & Partners**
47 Ch f 1/3 Grand Lodge (USA)—Swordlestown Miss (USA) (Apalachee (USA)) **Mrs W. B. Dearman & Mrs Bell**
48 **THUNDER BAY (IRE),** b c 22/4 Grand Lodge (USA)—
Velinowksi (Malinowski (USA)) **Mrs John Magnier & Mr Michael Tabor**
49 **TRUANT (USA),** b c 4/2 Alleged (USA)—
Top Roberto (USA) (Topsider (USA)) **Highclere Thoroughbred Racing Ltd**

MR W. JARVIS—continued

50 TYLER'S TOAST, ch c 3/2 Grand Lodge (USA)—Catawba (Mill Reef (USA)) **Lady Howard de Walden**
51 VILLA WANDA, ch f 1/3 Grand Lodge (USA)—Gisarne (USA) (Diesis) **Lord Howard de Walden**

Other Owners: Mr James Aiken, Mr Sam Alder, Mr Thomas R. Capehart, Mr David Carr, Mr A. K. Collins, Mr Charles Curtis, Mr W. B. Dearman, Mr John Dewan, Mrs A. Finn, Mrs Ray Fowler, Mr & Mrs Jimmy George, Mr Peter D. Gram, Mr Hugh Gregory, Mrs A. Grimm, Mr Kit Guavardhana, Mr Richard Hannon, Mr A. L. Harrison, Mr Tim Hedin, Mr I. C. Hill Wood, Mr Adam Hollywood, Mr D. Lonergan, Mr N. McCrea, Mr P. McKenna, Mr Andrew Miller, Mr Martin Mitchell, Mr D. Murrell, Mr Olsen, Miss Victoria Owen, Mr N. Phillips, Mr Nigel Rich, Mr W. Robertson, Mr Patrick Savage, David Sheffield, Mr Ian Southerden, Mrs Joanna Stockbridge, Neil Warnock, Mr N. S. Yong.

309 MR J. M. JEFFERSON, Malton

Postal: **Newstead Cottage Stables, Norton, Malton, North Yorkshire, YO17 9PJ.**
Phone: **(01653) 697225 MOBILE (0410) 502044**

1 **ANABRANCH,** 7, br m Kind of Hush—An-Go-Look **Mrs M. Barker**
2 **BEN CRUACHAN (IRE),** 8, b g King's Ride—Vale of Peace **The Caldeonian Racing Club**
3 **CAIUS (IRE),** 5, ch g Eurobus—Market Romance **Mr & Mrs J. H. Riley**
4 **CORPORATION POP (IRE),** 4, b g King's Ride—My Sunny South **Mr & Mrs J. M. Davenport**
5 **COUNT JOE (IRE),** 5, b g Persian Mews—Bold Kim **Mrs Christine Sharratt**
6 **DANBYS GORSE,** 6, ch g Presidium—Dohty Baby **Mr D. T. Todd**
7 **DANYERMAN,** 5, ch g Sylvan Express—Janie-O **Mr Peter Nelson**
8 **DATO STAR (IRE),** 7, br g Accordion—Newgate Fairy **Mrs K. Riley/Mrs M. Guthrie/Mr J. Donald**
9 **FAIR FARM LAD,** 6, b g Derring Rose—Miss Orby **Mr & Mrs H. Copley**
10 **FALCON'S IMAGE (USA),** 7, b g Silver Hawk (USA)—Will of Victory **Mr T. Pryke & Partners**
11 **FORCAROL,** 4, ch f Primitive Rising (USA)—Sable Hill **Yorkshire Racing Club Owners Group**
12 **GO-INFORMAL,** 7, ch g Primitive Rising (USA)—Sable Hill **Mr R. G. Marshall & Partners**
13 **JUST JAKE,** 5, b g Jendali (USA)—Dohty Baby **Mrs M. Barker**
14 **KINGS MEASURE (IRE),** 5, b g King's Ride—Snoqualmie **Mr John H. Wilson & Partners**
15 **KNAYTON KNIGHT (IRE),** 5, gr g Satco (FR)—No Slow **Mr & Mrs J. M. Davenport**
16 **LITTLE WASTER (IRE),** 6, b g Lord Americo—Lilac Queen **Mr J. Hellens**
17 **LORD TORRIDON (IRE),** 5, b g Torus—Minizen Lass **The Caledonian Racing Club**
18 **MADGE MCSPLASH,** 6, ch m Insan (USA)—Highland Waters **Mr & Mrs J. M. Davenport**
19 **MAGIC BLOOM,** 12, br m Full of Hope—Mantavella **Mr Peter Nelson**
20 **MR KELBURNE (IRE),** 6, b g Le Bavard (FR)—Torus Light **Kelburne Construction Ltd**
21 **MR WALT,** 5, ch g Bedford (USA)—Springhill Song **Mr & Mrs Caffney**
22 **NORTHERN GENERAL,** 5, b g Gunner B—Garvenish **Messrs Donald, Dixon, Marshall, Brough**
23 **NORTHERN SQUIRE,** 10, b g Uncle Pokey—Kit's Future **Mrs M. E. Dixon, Mr & Mrs J. Davenport**
24 **OVER THE BECK (IRE),** 5, b g Over The River (FR)—Echo Creek (IRE) **Mr Richard Collins**
25 **PENTLAND SQUIRE,** 7, b g Belfort (FR)—Sparkler Superb **Mrs M. E. Dixon & Partners**
26 4, B f Gunner B—Pugilistic **Partnership**
27 **RED BROOK,** 6, ch g Weld—Scrambird **Dr B. H. Seal**
28 **RUN FOR THE MILL,** 6, b g Primitive Rising (USA)—Brydonna **Mrs M. A. Roper**
29 **SCARBA,** 10, b g Skyliner—Looking For Gold **Yorkshire Racing Club Owners Group**
30 **SUAS LEAT (IRE),** 8, b br g Clearly Bust—Paico Lane **Mr & Mrs J. M. Davenport**
31 **THE CHASE,** 7, gr g Komaite (USA)—Torrington's Hope **Mr D. T. Todd**
32 **THE TIGER HUNTER,** 7, b g Primitive Rising (USA)—Highland Waters **Mr & Mrs J. M. Davenport**
33 **TULLYMURRY TOFF (IRE),** 7, b g King's Ride—Cooleogan **Mr John H. Wilson and Mr J. H. Riley**
34 **WELLSWOOD (IRE),** 5, ch g Montelimar (USA)—Many Views **Mr R. G. Marshall & Mr D. G. Savala**

THREE-YEAR-OLDS

35 **COUNT KENI,** ch g Formidable (USA)—Flying Amy **Mrs Christine Sharratt**
36 **ELLERBECK,** b f Priolo (USA)—Cadisa **Mr & Mrs J. M. Davenport**
37 **STONE BECK,** b f Lapierre—Dovey **Mr & Mrs J. M. Davenport**

Other Owners: Mr David Blackett, Mr S. R. Caley, Mr A. R. Dixon, Mr John Donald, Mr Morton Elliott, Mr W. A. Fouracres, Mr Bryan Gordon, Mr G. Griffin, Mr J. B. Harrison, Mr B. C. S. Kemp, Mr A. Lomas, Mr G. D. Stephenson, Mr D. Willis.

Jockey (Flat): K Fallon.

Jockey (NH): M Dwyer.

Conditional: E Callaghan (10-0), M Newton (9-7).

310 MR J. R. W. JENKINS, Royston

Postal: **Kings Ride, Baldock Road, Royston, Hertfordshire, SG8 9NN.**
Phone: **(01763) 241141 FAX (01763) 248223 HOME (01763) 246611**

1 **AIRBORNE BLUE,** 7, gr g Kuwait Beach (USA)—Sobralia **Mrs Celia Whicher**
2 **BLUE CHEESE,** 4, gr f Mystiko (USA)—Legal Sound **The Cheese Gang**
3 **CHRIS'S LAD,** 7, b g Thowra (FR)—Stockline **Mrs Susan McCarthy**
4 **DESERT CHALLENGER (IRE),** 8, b g Sadler's Wells (USA)—Verily **Andrews Freight Services Ltd**
5 **DIESEL DAN (IRE),** 5, b g Mac's Imp (USA)—Elite Exhibition **Mr M. A. Ward**
6 **DJAIS (FR),** 9, ch g Vacarme (USA)—Dame de Carreau (FR)
7 4, B f Teenoso (USA)—Dutch Princess **Mr P. W. Piper**
8 **FOREIGN RULE (IRE),** 4, b g Danehill (USA)—Guida Centrale **Mrs Susan McCarthy**
9 **FRENCH COUNTY (IRE),** 6, b g Executive Perk—Donegal Moss **County Constructions Ltd**
10 **GLIDE PATH (USA),** 9, ch g Stalwart (USA)—Jolly Polka (USA) **Mr B. Shirazi**
11 **HAL HOO YAROOM,** 5, b h Belmez (USA)—Princess Nawaal (USA) **Ellis & Partners (Stockbrokers) Ltd**
12 **HIGH IN THE SKY,** 5, b g Ilium—Sweet Canyon (NZ) **Mr S. Powell**
13 **HORNBEAM,** 4, b c Rich Charlie—Thinkluckybelucky **Mr K. C. Payne**
14 **LEGENDARY LOVER (IRE),** 4, b c Fairy King (USA)—Broken Romance (IRE) **Come Racing Ltd**
15 **LINDEN'S LAD (IRE),** 4, b c Distinctly North (USA)—Make Or Mar **Electronic & Software Publications Ltd**
16 **MINOR KEY (IRE),** 8, b g Orchestra—Maid of Moyode **The Royston Racers**
17 **MONTONE (IRE),** 8, b g Pennine Walk—Aztec Princess **Mr B. Shirazi**
18 **NAWAR (FR),** 8, b g Kahyasi—Nabita (FR) **Mr T. H. Ounsley**
19 **SHEATH KEFAAH,** 5, ch h Kefaah (USA)—Wasslaweyeh (USA) **Mr K. C. Payne**
20 **TELLION,** 4, b g Mystiko (USA)—Salchow **Come Racing Ltd**
21 **THE STAGER (IRE),** 6, b g Danehill (USA)—Wedgewood Blue (USA) **Mr Julian Duncan**
22 **TIM (IRE),** 8, b g Sexton Blake—Wingau (FR) **Mr P. W. Piper**
23 **TOP SPIN,** 9, b g Niniski (USA)—Spin
24 **TUKANO (CAN),** 7, ch g Halo (USA)—Northern Prancer (USA) **Mrs T. McCoubrey**
25 **ZAFARELLI,** 4, gr g Nishapour (FR)—Voltigeuse (USA) **Mr R. M. Ellis**

THREE-YEAR-OLDS

26 B f Merdon Melody—Dubitable
27 B f Warrshan (USA)—Dutch Princess **Mr P. W. Piper**
28 **FINAL SETTLEMENT (IRE),** b g Soviet Lad (USA)—Tender Time **The Meek Partnership**
29 **SOLO SPIRIT,** b f Northern Park (USA)—Brown Taw **Mrs I. Hampson**
30 **THE SILK THIEF,** b c Thowra (FR)—Fine N Fancy **Mrs M. A. Bateley**

TWO-YEAR-OLDS

31 B f Mizoram (USA)—Brown Taw (Whistlefield) **Mrs Carol Davis**
32 B f Merdon Melody—Cymbal (Ribero) **Norman Hill Plant Hire Ltd**
33 Ch c Democratic (USA)—English Mint (Jalmood (USA)) **Mrs S. Peirce**
34 B f Beveled (USA)—In The Papers (Aragon) **Mr S. Powell**
35 Br g Distinctly North (USA)—Make Or Mar (Daring March)
36 B g Anshan—Minteen (Teenoso (USA)) **Mrs S. Peirce**
37 B f Shadeed (USA)—Trattoria (USA) (Alphabatim (USA)) **Mr K. Dasmal**

Other Owners: Mr P. B. Allingham, Andutra Limited, Mr S. A. Barningham, Mr Peter Bond, Mr S. Curran, Mrs Ann Denny, Mrs D. G. Dobson, Mr D. H. W. Dobson, Mr M. Desmond Fitzgerald, Mr B. Fitzpatrick, Mrs Gina Fitzpatrick, Mr R. Fox, Mr D. B. Francis, Mr R. Gajadhar, Mr M. J. Gingell, Ms H. Gordon, Exors Of The Late Mr Doug Hagger, Mr R. A. Hazelby, Mr Harry Hobson, Miss L. E. Horsham, Mrs Wendy Jenkins, Mr J. Kenny, Mr T. Long, Mr J. McBarron, Mr A. H. McDonald, Mrs J. E. Meek, Mr James Midgley, Mr Gregory Molen, Mr David Morris, Mrs Jennefer M. Morris, Morton Thornton & Company, Mr F. G. Newberry, Mr Mike Newell, Mr R. Noy, Miss J. Robson, Mr E. Rossbacher, Mrs P. A. Rossbacher, Mr Roger Seymour, Mr H. B. Shouler, Mrs Madeline Skinner, Mr Tony Skinner, Mr R. F. Smith, Mrs D. Stedman, Mr Charles Stewart, Mr Andy Taylor, Mr J. M. Taylor, Technical Standards Services Ltd, Miss J. L. Watson, Mr Basil White, Mrs Nigel Wrighton, M. Young.

311 MR W. P. JENKS, Bridgnorth

Postal: **Wadeley Farm, Glazeley, Bridgnorth, Shropshire, WV16 6AD.**
Phone: **OFFICE (01746) 789288 FAX (01746) 789535**

1 **BARNAGEERA BOY (IRE),** 9, b g Indian King (USA)—Saint Simbir **Mrs C. S. Wilson**
2 **DANZIG ISLAND (IRE),** 7, b g Roi Danzig (USA)—Island Morn (USA) **The Glazeley Partnership**
3 **EDWARD SEYMOUR (USA),** 11, b g Northern Baby (CAN)—Regal Leader (USA) **Mr W. Jenks**
4 **EXALTED (IRE),** 5, b g High Estate—Heavenward (USA) **Mrs Bryan Jenks**
5 **HOODWINKER (IRE),** 9, b g Supreme Leader—Merrybash **Mr P. A. Howell**
6 **JEMARO (IRE),** 7, b g Tidaro (USA)—Jeremique **Mr Jeremy Beasley**
7 **JOLTO,** 9, b g Noalto—Joytime **Mr Peter Barclay**
8 **KALADROSS,** 7, ch g Ardross—Calametta **Mr Roy Howell**
9 **KARZHANG,** 6, b g Rakaposhi King—Smokey Baby **Mr Jeremy Beasley**
10 **MICHIGAN BLUE,** 6, b g Rakaposhi King—Starquin (IRE) **Mr P. A. Howell**
11 **POLITICAL POWER,** 7, b g Politico (USA)—Pauper Moon **Mr W. J. Sinker**
12 5, B g Rakaposhi King—Raise The Dawn **Mr W. Jenks**
13 **ROSMARINO,** 8, br g Persian Bold—No More Rosies **Mr Roy Howell**
14 **SANCHOLLING,** 6, ch g Executive Perk—In My View **Mr W. Jenks**
15 **SMOKING GUN,** 5, b g Gunner B—Smokey Baby **Mrs Diane Snowden**
16 **THE POLECAT (IRE),** 6, b m Supreme Leader—Protrial **Mrs Douglas Graham**
17 5, B m Good Thyne (USA)—Victorious Belle (IRE) **Mr W. Jenks**

Other Owners: Dr B. Alexander, Mrs D. E. Bromley, Mr R. L. Burton, Mrs M. A. Hickman, Mr W. R. Milner, Mr Michael Stoddart, Mr D. J. Ward.

Jockey (NH): Tom Jenks (10-0).

Amateur: Mr R Burton (10-4).

Lady Rider: Miss A Sykes (9-7).

312 MR A. E. M. JESSOP, Chelmsford

Postal: **Flemings Farm, Warren Road, South Hanningfield, Chelmsford, Essex, CM3 8HU.**
Phone: **(01268) 710210**

1 **ARTIC MEADOW,** 7, ch m Little Wolf—Meadow Maid **Mr A. Jessop**
2 **GOVERNORS BLUE,** 7, b m Governor General—How Blue **Mrs Gloria Jessop**
3 **THE WEATHERMAN,** 10, b g Official—Deep Depression **Mrs Gloria Jessop**

313 MR F. JESTIN, Wigton

Postal: **Hilltop, Brocklebank, Wigton, Cumbria, CA7 8DL.**

1 **BOLD IRENE (IRE),** 7, gr m Peacock (FR)—Bold And True **Mr F. Jestin**
2 **DONNA'S DANCER (IRE),** 4, ch g Magical Wonder (USA)—Ice On Fire **Mr F. Jestin**
3 **SPECTRE BROWN,** 8, b g Respect—My Goddess **Mr F. Jestin**
4 **SPRING LOADED,** 7, b g Last Tycoon—Time For Romance **Mr F. Jestin**
5 **WINTER RAMBLE,** 12, ch g Avocat—Little Anthea **Mr F. Jestin**

Amateur: Mr H Finegan (10-7).

314 MRS L. C. JEWELL, Sutton Valence

Postal: **Southfield Stables, South Lane, Sutton Valence, Maidstone, Kent, ME17 3AZ.**
Phone: **(01622) 842788 MOBILE (0585) 379773**

1 **ARMS BAN (IRE),** 5, b g Executive Perk—Safety Feature **Gallagher Equine Ltd**
2 5, B g Gildoran—Artalinda **Mrs S. Haedon**
3 **BARBRALLEN,** 6, b m Rambo Dancer (CAN)—Barrie Baby **Mr Peter J. Allen**
4 **CHALLENGER ROW (IRE),** 8, b g Colmore Row—Tunguska **No Need To Argue Partnership**
5 **CHARTER LANE (IRE),** 8, b g Toravich (USA)—Ulster Belle **Mrs A. Emanuel**
6 **CLEVER DICK,** 13, b g Cosmo—Princess Albertina (FR) **Mrs P. S. Donkin**
7 **COTTAGE COUNSEL (IRE),** 6, b g Kambalda—Lady McQuaid **Gallagher Equine Ltd**
8 **EMALLEN (IRE),** 10, b g Prince Regent (FR)—Peperonia **Mr Peter J. Allen**
9 **FORWARD MISS,** 4, br f Bold Arrangement—Maiden Bidder **Mr J. S. S. Hollins**
10 **GALLANT LORD (IRE),** 9, ch g Mister Lord (USA)—Knockantota Star **Mr Peter J. Allen**
11 **JUST A BEAU,** 7, b g Just A Monarch—Piphue Rosie **Mrs P. S. Donkin**
12 **KATATONIC (IRE),** 5, b g Waajib—Miss Kate (FR) **Sadlers Estate Agents**
13 **NORTH END LADY,** 7, b m Faustus (USA)—Truth Will Out **Mr Eamonn J. Sullivan**
14 **PHILOSOPHIC,** 4, b g Be My Chief (USA)—Metaphysique (FR) **Gallagher Equine Ltd**
15 **PRINCESS ROSHEEN,** 6, ch m Kinglet—Dark Rosheen **Mrs T. C. Betts**
16 **RUTH'S GAMBLE,** 10, b g Kabour—Hilly's Daughter **Mrs A. Emanuel**
17 **SERIOUS TRUST,** 5, b h Alzao (USA)—Mill Line **Mr Peter J. Allen**
18 **SMART GUY,** 6, ch g Gildoran—Talahache Bridge **Mrs P. S. Donkin**
19 **STEAM ON,** 7, ch g Common Grounds—Oh My Joy **Gallagher Equine Ltd**
20 **SUPREME THOUGHT,** 6, b m Emarati (USA)—Who's That Girl **Mr Barry Morton**

THREE-YEAR-OLDS

21 **GOTTABECRAKCERS,** b g General Wade—Park Vista **No Need to Argue Partnership**

Other Owners: Mrs S. M. Gee, Mr Brian Matthews, Mrs Linda Matthews, Mr A. Mitford-Slade, Mr Victor Semple, Mrs C. F. Willis, Mr D. N. Yeadon.

Jockeys (NH): J Kavanagh, D Leahy (10-0).

Conditional: Sophie Mitchell (9-7).

315 MISS C. JOHNSEY, Chepstow

Postal: **Devauden Court, Devauden, Chepstow, Gwent, NP6 6PL.**
Phone: **(01291) 650248/(01291) 650695 MOBILE (0468) 012666 FAX (01291) 650637**

1 **BROWN MELODY (IRE),** 5, b g Little Bighorn—Zozimus **Mr T. A. Johnsey**
2 **CLAUDIA ELECTRIC (IRE),** 6, ch m Electric—Lepida **Mrs Margaret Johnsey**
3 **FANCY NANCY (IRE),** 7, b m Buckskin (FR)—Lils Melody **Mr T. A. Johnsey**
4 **FLUSHING SPIRIT (IRE),** 6, ch m Henbit (USA)—Formia Spirit **Mr T. A. Johnsey**
5 **LEGAL ARTIST (IRE),** 8, b g Tate Gallery (USA)—Dowdstown Miss **Mr T. A. Johnsey**
6 **LOUGH LEIN SPIRIT (IRE),** 7, b g Henbit (USA)—Formia Spirit **Mrs Margaret Johnsey**
7 **MR CUDDLE,** 6, gr g Roselier (FR)—Quarry Machine **Mr T. A. Johnsey**
8 **RED HOT ROBBIE,** 5, ch g Gildoran—Quarry Machine **Mr T. A. Johnsey**
9 **RUSHAWAY,** 7, b g Robellino (USA)—Brush Away **Wheeler Dealers**
10 **SPRIGHTLEY PIP (IRE),** 7, gr g Roselier (FR)—Owen's Rose **Beacon Estates Ltd**
11 **STRONG MAGIC (IRE),** 6, br g Strong Gale—Baybush **Mr T. A. Johnsey**
12 **SUMMIT,** 7, b g Salse (USA)—Reltop **Mr T. A. Johnsey**
13 **TRAVELLING MAN (IRE),** 6, b g Le Bavard (FR)—Monks Rambler **Mr T. A. Johnsey**

Other Owners: Chepstow Plant Hire Ltd, Mr P. F. Hicks, Miss Clair Johnsey, Mr Kevin Johnsey, Mr Gary Plumley.

Jockey (NH): Dean Gallagher.

316 MRS A. E. JOHNSON, Newmarket

Postal: **The Old Twelve Stables, Moulton Paddocks, Newmarket, Suffolk, CB8 8QJ.**
Phone: **(01638) 660048 MOBILE (0411) 108612**

1 **CAERFILLY DANCER,** 4, ch f Caerleon (USA)—Darnelle
2 **CHANGE THE REIGN,** 11, b g King's Ride—Reformed Rule **Mr E. D. Nicolson**
3 **COTTESMORE,** 7, b g Broadsword (USA)—Celestial Bride **Mr S. N. J. Embiricos**
4 **DRIFT,** 4, b g Slip Anchor—Norgabie **Mr G. W. Byrne**
5 **FABULOUS FRANCY (IRE),** 10, ch g Remainder Man—Francie's Treble **Mr E. D. Nicolson**
6 **FRIENDLY KNIGHT,** 8, b g Horage—Be A Dancer **Mr Mark Johnson**
7 **GANDOUGE GLEN,** 11, b g Furry Glen—Gandouge Lady **Mr S. N. J. Embiricos**
8 **GENERAL MONTY,** 6, b g Vague Shot—State Free **Mrs Pat Appleby**
9 **KING HIGH,** 11, b g Shirley Heights—Regal Twin (USA) **Mr Tim Bryce**
10 **KINGS ATHLETE (IRE),** 5, b m King's Ride—Super Athlete **Mr C. W. Cooper**
11 **MAGICAL BLUES (IRE),** 6, b g Magical Strike (USA)—Blue Bell Girl **Mrs A. E. Johnson**
12 **NEVER THINK TWICE,** 5, b g Never So Bold—Hope And Glory (USA) **Mr Danny Baker**
13 **NEWTOWN ROSIE (IRE),** 9, gr m Roselier (FR)—Sicilian Princess **Mr A. Zafiropulo**
14 **PEGASUS BAY,** 7, b g Tina's Pet—Mossberry Fair **Mr Don Cantillon**
15 **RAGLAN ROAD,** 14, b g Furry Glen—Princess Concorde **Mr Mark Johnson**
16 **RUTH'S BOY (IRE),** 9, br g Lord Ha Ha—Club Belle **Chasers II**
17 **STANBROOK LASS,** 5, ch m Broadsword (USA)—Dontella's Girl **Mr D. R. Barnard**
18 **STAR OF DAVID (IRE),** 10, b g Mister Lord (USA)—Knockantota Star **Mrs S. N. J. Embiricos**
19 **SWEET SEVENTEEN,** 5, gr m Touch of Grey—Westminster Waltz **Mr Derek Weeden**
20 **WIND RIVER (IRE),** 6, b g Strong Gale—River of Wine **Mrs S. N. J. Embiricos**

Other Owners: Mrs E. D. Nicolson, Mr F. Prescott.

Jockey (Flat): J Quinn (7-10).

Jockey (NH): R Johnson.

Amateur: Mr A Jacobs (9-7).

Lady Rider: Miss A E Embiricos (10-2).

317 MR J. H. JOHNSON, Crook

Postal: **White Lea Farm, Crook, Co. Durham, DL15 9QN.**
Phone: **01388 762113 CAR PHONE 0860 31964 FAX 01388 768278 MOBILE 0589 280887**

1 **ABERCROMBY CHIEF,** 13, br g Buckskin (FR)—Free For Ever **Mr Ian Davidson**
2 6, Ch g Over The River (FR)—Augustaeliza (IRE) **Mr J. Howard Johnson**
3 **BABY JAKE (IRE),** 8, ch g Over The River (FR)—Our June **Mr George Tobitt**
4 5, B g Salluceva—Bold And True **Mr J. Howard Johnson**
5 **BOUNDTOHONOUR (IRE),** 6, b g Rashar (USA)—Densidal **Mr Peter Gormley**
6 **BRANDY CROSS (IRE),** 9, br g Strong Statement (USA)—Rescued **Mr Michael Thompson**
7 4, Ch g Abednego—Clairellen **Mr J. Howard Johnson**
8 **CLAVERING (IRE),** 8, br g Good Thyne (USA)—Caffra Mills **Mr Chris Heron**
9 **DIRECT ROUTE (IRE),** 7, b g Executive Perk—Mursuma **Mr Michael Thompson**
10 **DOUBLE AGENT,** 5, ch g Niniski (USA)—Rexana **Hertford Offset Limited**
11 **DOWN THE FELL,** 9, b g Say Primula—Sweet Dough **Mrs S. Johnson**
12 **DUKE OF PERTH,** 7, ch g Scottish Reel—Own Free Will **Mr W. M. G. Black**
13 **EDEN DANCER,** 6, b g Shareef Dancer (USA)—Dash **Mr Geoffrey Hamilton**
14 4, B g Rakaposhi King—Edwina's Dawn **Mr Peter Gormley**

MR J. H. JOHNSON—continued

15 **FORBES (IRE)**, 7, b g Strong Gale—Gold Label **Mrs M. W. Bird**
16 **FORESTAL**, 6, b g Glenstal (USA)—Foreno **Mr Billy Maguire**
17 **FOREVER GREY (IRE)**, 6, gr m Celio Rufo—Princess Moy **The Scottish Steeplechasing Partnership**
18 **GLOBAL LEGEND**, 8, b g Oats—Mirthful **Gordon Brown/Bert Watson**
19 **HIBERNATE (IRE)**, 4, ch g Lahib (USA)—Ministra (USA) **Cragside Contractors II**
20 **HIGHLAND VIEW (IRE)**, 8, b g Phardante (FR)—Chatty Di **Mr R. W. L. Bowden**
21 **IRISH WILDCARD (NZ)**, 10, b g Lyphard's Trick (USA)—Courageous Mahoney (NZ) **Mr Peter Gormley**
22 **JOE WHITE**, 12, ch g Tampero (FR)—Fiery Rose **Mr J. Howard Johnson**
23 **KIBBY BANK**, 9, gr g Pragmatic—Alcide Inn **Mr J. Henderson (Co Durham)**
24 **LETHAL COCKTAIL (IRE)**, 9, ch g Bob Back (USA)—Naughty Lass **Mrs J. M. Corbett**
25 **LYMAX**, 4, ch g Lycius (USA)—Most Amusing **Mr W. M. G. Black**
26 **MAJOR HAGE (IRE)**, 7, gr g Over The River (FR)—Kilross **Mr J. Henderson (Co Durham)**
27 **MINELLA EXPRESS (IRE)**, 9, b g The Parson—Dream Toi **The Braw Partnership**
28 **MISTER MUDDYPAWS**, 8, b g Celtic Cone—Jane's Daughter **Mr J. Howard Johnson**
29 **MISTER ROSS (IRE)**, 8, b g Mister Lord (USA)—Ross Rag **Gordon Brown/Bert Watson**
30 **MORCELI (IRE)**, 10, gr g Mouktar—Safiah (FR) **Mrs J. M. Corbett**
31 **MY SHENANDOAH (IRE)**, 7, br g Derrylin—Edwina's Dawn **Mr Peter Gormley**
32 **NERONIAN (IRE)**, 4, ch g Mujtahid (USA)—Nimieza (USA) **J. R. Featherstone, D. R. Bird**
33 **NOT GUILTY (IRE)**, 6, b g Electric—Just Darina **Mr Peter Gormley**
34 **NOUKARI (IRE)**, 5, b g Darshaan—Noufiyla **Carna Transport (Ireland) Ltd**
35 **ONYOUROWN (IRE)**, 5, b g Treasure Kay—Mursuma **Mr Thomas Harty**
36 **OVER THE MASTER (IRE)**, 6, ch g Over The River (FR)—Covette **Mr D. M. Fulton**
37 **PENTLANDS FLYER (IRE)**, 7, b g Phardante (FR)—Bunkilla **Mrs M. W. Bird**
38 **PILKINGTON (IRE)**, 8, b g Roselier (FR)—Little Bloom **Mrs Alurie O'Sullivan**
39 **RADANPOUR (IRE)**, 6, b g Kahyasi—Rajpoura **Mr Terry Pollock**
40 **RAG DOLL**, 6, b m Buckskin (FR)—Nightlinger **The Sun Punters Club**
41 **RIVER UNSHION (IRE)**, 8, ch g Aristocracy—Smurfette **Mr R. J. Crake**
42 **SANDABAR**, 5, b g Green Desert (USA)—Children's Corner (FR) **Mr W. Williams**
43 **SCOTMAIL BOY (IRE)**, 5, b g Over The River (FR)—Princess Paula **Gordon Brown & Bert Watson**
44 **SEATTLE ART (USA)**, 4, b g Seattle Slew (USA)—Artiste **B. & W. Partnership**
45 **SKY HIGH**, 4, b g Shirley Heights—Sky Love (USA) **Mr J. Howard Johnson**
46 **SLAVE'S CHOICE**, 5, b g Arctic Lord—Panning **Mr T. W. Ellwood**
47 5, B g Arctic Lord—Soraway **Mr J. Howard Johnson**
48 **THEGIFT**, 5, b g Say Primula—Fair Echo **Mr Gordon Bear**
49 **THE KEEK (IRE)**, 6, b m Brush Aside (USA)—Fairgoi **Mr J. Howard Johnson**
50 **THE WASP (IRE)**, 6, gr g Lancastrian—Moll of Kintire **Mrs J. M. Corbett**
51 **TOM BRODIE**, 8, b g Ardross—Deep Line **Mrs M. W. Bird**
52 4, Gr g Grey Desire—Warchant **Mr J. Howard Johnson**
53 **WHITEGATES WILLIE**, 6, b g Buckskin (FR)—Whitegates Lady **Mr R. W. L. Bowden**
54 **WINTER BELLE (USA)**, 10, b g Sportin' Life (USA)—Belle O'Reason (USA) **Mrs M. W. Bird**
55 **YOUNG TOMO (IRE)**, 6, b g Lafontaine (USA)—Siege Queen **Mr Michael Thompson**

TWO-YEAR-OLDS

56 B g Arctic Lord—Soraway **Mr J. Howard Johnson**

Other Owners: Mr T. Alderson, Mr J. G. Askew, Mr P. A. Brannan, Mr John Crayston, Durham Drapes Ltd, Mr D. W. Ellwood, Mr D. Gardiner, Mr J. Garratt, Mr D. Gill, Mr Christopher Hewitt, Mr Barry Hughes, Mr Maurice Hutchinson, Miss Lucy S. Johnson, Mr R. M. Kirkland, Mr Ken Knox, Mr K. L. Larnach, Mr M. E. L. Maydon, Mr Kevin McCormick, Mr Brian McNichol, Mr D. Phelan, Group Captain J. A. Prideaux, Mr R. G. Ross, Mrs Annette Stenner, Mr Ron Wilde.

Jockeys (NH): P Carberry (w.a.), A Dobbin, A Smith.

Conditional: E G Callaghan.

318 MR P. R. JOHNSON, Cannock

Postal: **Pinetrees Farm, Stafford Road, Huntington, Cannock, Staffordshire, WS12 4PX.**
Phone: **(01543) 502962**

1 **GEORGE ASHFORD (IRE),** 8, b g Ashford (USA)—Running Feud **Mr P. Johnson**
2 **RITA'S CHOICE,** 5, gr m Scallywag—Headbee **Mrs L. V. Durnall**
3 5, Ch g Denel (FR)—Tactique (FR) **Mr P. Johnson**

319 MR ROBERT W. JOHNSON, Newcastle Upon Tyne

Postal: **Grange Farm, Newburn, Newcastle Upon Tyne, NE15 8QA.**
Phone: **(01912) 674464**

1 **AIDE MEMOIRE (IRE),** 9, b m Don't Forget Me—Pharjoy (FR) **Mr P. Kelly & Mr J. Thornton**
2 **FENLOE RAMBLER (IRE),** 7, b g Wylfa—Monks Rambler **Mr Robert Johnson**
3 **GILDORAN SOUND,** 5, b m Gildoran—Sound of Laughter **Mr Robert Johnson**
4 **I'M TYSON (NZ),** 10, b g Tights (USA)—Rose of Hawa (AUS) **Mr Robert Johnson**
5 **LADYHAUGH,** 5, b m Respect—Larriston Lady VII **Mr Robert Johnson**
6 **REVE DE VALSE (USA),** 11, ch g Conquistador Cielo (USA)—Dancing Vaguely (USA) **Mr Robert Johnson**
7 **RYSANSHYN,** 6, b m Primitive Rising (USA)—Shining Bann **Mr Robert Johnson**
8 **SHINING TYNE,** 4, b g Primitive Rising (USA)—Shining Bann **Mr Robert Johnson**

Jockey (NH): K Johnson (10-0).

Amateur: Mr P Johnson (10-9).

320 MRS S. M. JOHNSON, Madley

Postal: **Carwardine Farm, Madley, Hereford, HR2 9JQ.**
Phone: **(01981) 250214**

1 **DERRING BRIDGE,** 8, b g Derring Rose—Bridge Ash **Mr I. K. Johnson**
2 **KING PADDY (IRE),** 6, b g King's Ride—Nebechal **Mrs S. A. Evans**
3 **RUSTY BRIDGE,** 11, b g Rustingo—Bridge Ash **Mr I. K. Johnson**

Jockey (NH): Richard Johnson (9-7).

321 MR G. F. JOHNSON HOUGHTON, Newmarket

Postal: **19 Lisburn Road, Newmarket, Suffolk, CB8 8HS.**
Phone: **(01638) 602467 MOBILE (0585) 753154**

1 **ALCOVE,** 7, ch g Faustus (USA)—Cubby Hole **Mrs S. Collins**
2 **BERTIE BAVARD,** 6, ch g Le Bavard (FR)—Acushla Macree **Mrs R. F. Johnson Houghton**
3 **MIAMI MOON,** 4, ch f Keen—Two Moons **Mr M. B. Clemence**
4 **PROTOTYPE,** 7, b g Governor General—Sweet Enough **Mr R. B. Holt**
5 **TOO CLEVER BY HALF,** 10, b g Pragmatic—Acushla Macree **Mrs R. F. Johnson Houghton**
6 **TUWUN,** 6, gr m Neltino—Fanta's Girl **The Easy Racing Partnership**

Other Owners: Mr T. E. Boylan, Mr C. Deadman, Mr A. Goodsir, Mr Gordon Johnson Houghton, Mrs H. Johnson Houghton, Mr K. Santana, Santos Racing.

Jockey (NH): A Thornton (10-0).

Lady Rider: Eve Johnson Houghton (9-0).

322 MR R. F. JOHNSON HOUGHTON, Didcot

Postal: **Woodway, Blewbury, Didcot, Oxfordshire, OX11 9EZ.**
Phone: **(01235) 850480 FAX (01235) 851045 MOBILE (0836) 599232**

1 **CENTRE STALLS (IRE),** 5, b h In The Wings—Lora's Guest **Mr Anthony Pye-Jeary**
2 **EXPRESS AGAIN,** 6, b g Then Again—Before Long **Mr R. F. Johnson Houghton**
3 **SASSY STREET (IRE),** 5, b g Danehill (USA)—Sassy Lane **Mr R. F. Johnson Houghton**
4 **SHAARID (USA),** 10, b g El Gran Senor (USA)—Summer Silence (USA) **Mr Peter Oldfield**
5 **SPUNKIE,** 5, ch g Jupiter Island—Super Sol **Mr Jim Short**

THREE-YEAR-OLDS

6 **BAYLEAF,** ch f Efisio—Bayonne **Lady Rothschild**
7 **FORGOTTEN STAR (IRE),** b br f Don't Forget Me—Sterna Star **Mr R. F. Johnson Houghton**
8 **KING'S HUSSAR,** b g Be My Chief (USA)—Croire (IRE) **Mr W. H. Ponsonby**
9 **MANUFAN,** b c Sabrehill (USA)—The Last Empress (IRE) **Mr Anthony Pye-Jeary**
10 **PHANTOM WATERS,** b f Pharly (FR)—Idle Waters **Mr R. E. Crutchley**
11 **SQUABBLE,** b f Reprimand—Hability **Mr T. D. Holland-Martin**
12 **TEREYNA,** gr f Terimon—Lareyna **Mrs P. Robeson**

TWO-YEAR-OLDS

13 **BAYONET,** b f 19/4 Then Again—Lambay (Lorenzaccio) **Lady Rothschild**
14 Ch c 16/4 Bigstone (IRE)—Classic Opera (Lomond (USA)) **Mr C. W. Sumner**
15 B c 28/3 Handsome Sailor—Eye Sight (Roscoe Blake) **Lord Leverhulme**
16 B c 2/4 Handsome Sailor—Harifa (Local Suitor (USA)) **Lord Leverhulme**
17 B c 23/3 In The Wings—Icy Tundra (Shaadi (USA)) **Mr Anthony Pye-Jeary**
18 Ch f 6/5 Thatching—Keepers Lock (USA) (Sunny's Halo (CAN))
19 B c 12/4 Namaqualand (USA)—Madam Loving (Vaigly Great) **Mr Anthony Pye-Jeary**
20 **PETUCHINO (IRE),** b f 8/3 Petardia—Cappuchino (IRE) (Roi Danzig (USA)) **Woodway Racing**
21 Ch f 14/4 King's Signet (USA)—Shall We Run (Hotfoot) **Mrs R. F. Johnson Houghton**
22 **ST CLAIR,** b c 29/3 Distant Relative—Bayonne (Bay Express) **Lady Rothschild**
23 B g 10/2 Grand Lodge (USA)—Wild Abandon (USA) (Graustark)

Other Owners: Mrs Bruce Bossom, Mr Bob Crocker, Mrs R. E. Crutchley, Mr Anthony Harrison, Dr J. A. E. Hobby, Mr D. T. Horn, Mr Bob Lanigan, Mr R. C. Naylor, Mr S. J. D. Posford, Mrs Wendy J. Price, Mr J. W. Rowles, Mr Keith Wills.

Jockey (Flat): J Reid (w.a.).

Lady Rider: Miss E A Johnson Houghton (9-7).

323 MR M. S. JOHNSTON, Middleham

Postal: **Kingsley House Racing Stables, Middleham, Leyburn, North Yorkshire,DL8 4PH.**
Phone: **(01969) 622237 FAX (01969) 622484**

1 **AS-IS,** 4, b g Lomond (USA)—Capriati (USA) **Mr R. Robinson (Wigan)**
2 **ATLANTIC DESIRE (IRE),** 4, b f Ela-Mana-Mou—Bold Miss **Atlantic Racing Limited**
3 **CELESTIAL KEY (USA),** 8, br g Star de Naskra (USA)—Casa Key (USA) **Mr Markus Graff**
4 **CLOUD INSPECTOR (IRE),** 7, b g Persian Bold—Timbale d'Argent **Mr Markus Graff**
5 **DOUBLE TRIGGER (IRE),** 7, ch h Ela-Mana-Mou—Solac (FR) **R. W. Huggins, R. C. Moules, J. Clopet**
6 **ETTERBY PARK (USA),** 5, b g Silver Hawk (USA)—Bonita Francita (CAN) **Mr & Mrs G. Middlebrook**
7 **GAELIC STORM,** 4, b c Shavian—Shannon Princess **H. C. Racing Club**
8 **GOTHENBERG (IRE),** 5, b h Polish Patriot (USA)—Be Discreet **Brian Yeardley Continental Ltd**
9 **INDIGO DAWN,** 4, b f Rainbow Quest (USA)—Dame Ashfield **Greenland Park Ltd**
10 **MISTER ASPECTO (IRE),** 5, b g Caerleon (USA)—Gironde (USA) **Aspecto Clothing Co Ltd**
11 **MUNAAJI (USA),** 7, b g Storm Cat (USA)—Growth Rate (USA) **Mr J. Mercer & Mr M. H. Goodbody**

MR M. S. JOHNSTON—continued

12 **ONE FOR BAILEYS,** 4, b g Unfuwain (USA)—Three Stars **G. R. Bailey Ltd (Baileys Horse Feeds)**
13 **PLAN FOR PROFIT (IRE),** 4, b g Polish Patriot (USA)—Wild Sable (IRE) **Professional Racing Partnership**
14 **SHONTAINE,** 5, b g Pharly (FR)—Hinari Televideo **Mr Paul Dean**
15 **SORBIE TOWER (IRE),** 5, b h Soviet Lad (USA)—Nozet **P. D. Q.**
16 **STAR RAGE (IRE),** 8, b g Horage—Star Bound **Mr J. David Abell**
17 **TILER (IRE),** 6, br g Ballad Rock—Fair Siobahn **Mrs C. Robinson**
18 **TOUCH'N'GO,** 4, b g Rainbow Quest (USA)—Mary Martin **Greenland Park Ltd**

THREE-YEAR-OLDS

19 **ADULTRESS (IRE),** ch f Ela-Mana-Mou—Adarika **Mrs Sonia Rogers**
20 **AIX EN PROVENCE (USA),** b c Geiger Counter (USA)—Low Hill **J. R. Featherstone, D. R. Bird**
21 **ALBERICH (IRE),** b c Night Shift (USA)—Tetradonna (IRE) **Mr J. David Abell**
22 **ALCONLEIGH,** ch c Pursuit of Love—Serotina (IRE) **Mr J. David Abell**
23 **AMSICORA,** b f Cadeaux Genereux—Santi Sana **Mr Ettore Landi**
24 **ANITA MARIE (IRE),** b f Anita's Prince—Fandangerina (USA) **Greenland Park Ltd**
25 **ASSET MANAGER,** b c Night Shift (USA)—Hud Hud (USA) **Maktoum Al Maktoum**
26 **ATLANTIC VIKING (IRE),** b c Danehill (USA)—Hi Bettina **Atlantic Racing Limited**
27 **BOULEVARD ROUGE (USA),** b f Red Ransom (USA)—Beetwentysix (USA) **Mr K. Hodgson**
28 **CAROL SINGER (USA),** b f Geiger Counter (USA)—Wake Up Noel (USA) **Mr & Mrs G. Middlebrook**
29 **CORPUS CHRISTI (IRE),** b g Royal Academy (USA)—Christi Dawn (USA) **Mr J. Godfrey**
30 **DARWELL'S FOLLY (USA),** ch c Blushing John (USA)—Hispanolia (FR) **S & P Darwell Ltd**
31 **DOUBLE BLADE,** b c Kris—Sesame **The 2nd Middleham Partnership**
32 **DOUBLE EDGED,** ch c Sabrehill (USA)—Island Lake **The 2nd Middleham Partnership**
33 **ELABELLOU (IRE),** b f Ela-Mana-Mou—Salabella **Montagu Bloodstock Ltd**
34 **EQUITY PRINCESS,** b f Warning—Hawait Al Barr **Maktoum Al Maktoum**
35 **FAIRY TREE (USA),** b f Rahy (USA)—Magic Gleam (USA) **Maktoum Al Maktoum**
36 **FIZZED,** ch f Efisio—Clicquot **Duke of Roxburghe, Marquis of Hartington**
37 **FREE SPIRIT (IRE),** b f Caerleon (USA)—Soha (USA) **Mr & Mrs G Middlebrook**
38 **FRUITS OF LOVE (USA),** b c Hansel (USA)—Vallee Secrete (USA) **Mr M Doyle**
39 **GYPSY PASSION (IRE),** ch c Woodman (USA)—Rua d'Oro (USA) **Mr P. D. Savill**
40 **HIGHLAND FLING (IRE),** b f Mtoto—Highland Ball **The Celtic Connection**
41 **IRELAND'S EYE (IRE),** b c Shareef Dancer (USA)—So Romantic (IRE) **Sheikh Mohammed**
42 **JOHN BOWDLER MUSIC,** b c Soviet Star (USA)—Arianna Aldini **Mr Paul Dean**
43 **KAMEEZ (IRE),** ch f Arazi (USA)—Kalikala **Mr Ali Saeed**
44 **KOKANEE (USA),** b c Nureyev (USA)—River Mystery (USA) **Sheikh Mohammed**
45 **LAND OF DREAMS,** b f Cadeaux Genereux—Sahara Star **Maktoum Al Maktoum**
46 **LEND A HAND,** b c Great Commotion (USA)—Janaat **Maktoum Al Maktoum**
47 **LINDESBERG,** b f Doyoun—Be Discreet **Brian Yeardley Continental Ltd**
48 **LOCHDENE (IRE),** b c Robellino (USA)—Cat's Claw (USA) **Mr J. S. Morrison & Mr M. D. Shrigley**
49 **LONG BOND (IRE),** ch c Kris—Compton Lady (USA) **Mr Markus Graff**
50 **LOVE ACADEMY,** b c Royal Academy (USA)—Quiet Week-End **Mr M. Doyle**
51 **LOVE KISS (IRE),** b c Brief Truce (USA)—Pendulina **Mr M. Doyle**
52 **MADMAN'S MIRAGE (FR),** b g Green Desert (USA)—Layaali (USA) **J. S. Morrison & R. A. Dalglish**
53 **MISTY MOOR,** b f Wolfhound (USA)—Corley Moor **Greenland Park Ltd**
54 **MUFEED,** b c Shirley Heights—English Spring (USA) **Sheikh Mohammed**
55 **MY LOST LOVE,** b g Green Desert (USA)—Love of Silver (USA) **Mr Ali Saeed**
56 **NASKHI,** b f Nashwan (USA)—Calpella **Mr Saeed Manana**
57 **NETTA RUFINA (IRE),** ch c Night Shift (USA)—Age of Elegance **Miss Belinda E. Lee**
58 **NORTH OFTHE BORDER,** b c Primo Dominie—Valika **Mr Robert Aird**
59 **NUIT D'OR (IRE),** ch g Night Shift (USA)—Sister Golden Hair (IRE) **J. R. Featherstone, D. R. Bird**
60 **PRINCELY HEIR (IRE),** b c Fairy King (USA)—Meis El-Reem **Maktoum Al Maktoum**
61 **PROFIT MAKER (USA),** b g Hansel (USA)—Bineyah (IRE) **Maktoum Al Maktoum**
62 **RAFTING (IRE),** b f Darshaan—White Water (FR) **Mr Alan Lillingston**
63 **RANGATIRA (IRE),** ch c Royal Academy (USA)—Chief's Quest (USA) **Mr J. W. Robb**
64 **ROI BRISBANE,** b c Roi Danzig (USA)—Crystal Cup (USA) **Mr John Hodge**
65 **SADEEBAH,** b g Prince Sabo—Adeebah (USA) **Mr J. David Abell & Mrs J Abell**
66 **SAINT ANN (USA),** b f Geiger Counter (USA)—Swan Princess **Mr & Mrs G Middlebrook**
67 **SHARP CRACKER (IRE),** b f Hamas (IRE)—Ascensiontide **Mrs I. Bird**
68 **SHARP PLAY,** b c Robellino (USA)—Child's Play (USA) **Mrs I. Bird**
69 **SINON (IRE),** ch c Ela-Mana-Mou—Come In **Ridings Racing**

MR M. S. JOHNSTON—continued

70 **SOME MIGHT SAY,** b c Be My Chief (USA)—Willowbed **Stable Investments**
71 **SPIRIT OF LOVE (USA),** ch c Trempolino (USA)—Dream Mary (USA) **Mr A. W. Robinson**
72 **ST HELENSFIELD,** ch c Kris—On Credit (FR) **Mr Paul Dean**
73 **STINGRAY (IRE),** b c Darshaan—Sovereign Dona **Mr M. J. Pilkington**
74 **SWAYBUS,** ch f Pursuit of Love—Gong **Mrs Jacqueline Conroy**
75 **TOUCHEZ DU BOIS (IRE),** ch c Cadeaux Genereux—Fire Flash **Mr R. W. Huggins**
76 **TRIGGER HAPPY (IRE),** ch f Ela-Mana-Mou—Happy Tidings **Mr R. W. Huggins**
77 **URCHIN (IRE),** b f Fairy King (USA)—Safe Haven **Mr M. J. Pilkington**
78 **WHITE HEART,** b g Green Desert (USA)—Barari (USA) **Maktoum Al Maktoum**
79 **YOUNICO,** b c Nordico (USA)—Young Wilkie **Mr C. H. Greensit**

TWO-YEAR-OLDS

80 **AMARICE,** b f 13/5 Suave Dancer (USA)—Almitra (Targowice (USA)) **Mrs S. O'Brien**
81 B br f 5/2 Hansel (USA)—Aquakiss (FR) (Kings Lake (USA)) **Mr & Mrs G. Middlebrook**
82 **ARABIAN DESERT,** b c 27/1 Tragic Role (USA)—Arabian Nymph (Sayf El Arab (USA)) **Mr Ziad A. Galadari**
83 **BEDOUIN SONG (USA),** ch c 29/1 Sheikh Albadou—Philharmonia (Caerleon (USA)) **Mr M. Broke & Mr J. Lazzari**
84 **BID ME WELCOME,** b c 3/5 Alzao (USA)—Blushing Barada (USA) (Blushing Groom (FR)) **Maktoum Al Maktoum**
85 **BRANSTON MAX,** b c 5/4 Turtle Island (IRE)—Tuxford Hideaway (Cawston's Clown) **Mr J. David Abell**
86 B f 23/1 Sheikh Albadou—Brava (GER) (Arratos (FR)) **Mr J Conroy**
87 **COMPLIMENTARY PASS,** b f 12/5 Danehill (USA)—Capo di Monte (Final Straw) **Maktoum Al Maktoum**
88 B f 2/2 Night Shift (USA)—Crystal City (Kris) **Mr P D Savill**
89 Ch f 23/3 Polish Patriot (USA)—Curie Abu (Crofter (USA)) **Mr J. Henderson**
90 B c 19/5 Saddlers' Hall (IRE)—Dame Ashfield (Grundy) **Greenland Park Ltd.**
91 B c 19/4 Housebuster (USA)—Exactly So (Caro) **Mr J. A. Farmer**
92 B f 13/5 Indian Ridge—Gayshuka (Lord Gayle (USA)) **Hertford Offset Ltd**
93 Ch f 14/3 Lycius (USA)—Gold Braisim (IRE) (Jareer (USA)) **Mr W. Johnstone**
94 B c 29/3 Robellino (USA)—Greenvera (USA) (Riverman (USA)) **Mr P. D. Savill**
95 **HORMUZ (IRE),** b c 18/2 Hamas (IRE)—Balqis (USA) (Advocator) **Brian Yeardley Continental Ltd.**
96 B f 6/4 Dayjur (USA)—Humility (USA) (Cox's Ridge (USA)) **Mr J. S. Morrison**
97 B c 01/5 Fairy King (USA)—Idle Chat (USA) (Assert) **Atlantic Racing Limited**
98 **IMPLIED (USA),** b c 4/2 Alleged (USA)—Watercolourtwo (USA) (Secreto (USA)) **Brian Yeardley Continental Ltd**
99 B c 22/5 Hansel (USA)—Jolie Bold (USA) (Bold Forbes (USA)) **Mr M. Doyle**
100 **LAABED,** b c 1/3 Mizoram (USA)—Petite Butterfly (Absalom) **Mr Ziad A. Galadari**
101 Ch f 13/2 Polish Patriot (USA)—Lady Coombe (Brigadier Gerard) **Mr I. Harland**
102 **LOVE DIAMONDS (IRE),** b c 22/2 Royal Academy (USA)—Baby Diamonds (Habitat) **Mr M. Doyle**
103 **LUMIERE DE MA VIE (USA),** b c 2/3 Ghazi (USA)—Ma Biche (USA) (Key To The Kingdom (USA)) **Mrs S. Yeardley**
104 **MAYBEE,** b f 5/5 Then Again—Miss Ritz (Robellino (USA)) **Mrs D. Schreiber**
105 **OPULENCE,** ch f 18/5 Arazi (USA)—Janaat (Kris) **Maktoum Al Maktoum**
106 **PENNY MOOR,** b f 29/3 Polish Precedent—Corley Moor (Habitat) **Greenland Park Ltd**
107 Br f 11/3 Hamas (IRE)—Pericolo (IRE) (Kris) **Hereford Offset Ltd**
108 Br c 06/5 Mujtahid (USA)—Pursue (Auction Ring (USA)) **Mr F. McNamee**
109 Ch f 27/4 Polish Patriot (USA)—Recherchee (Rainbow Quest (USA)) **Mr P. D. Savill**
110 B c 17/2 Batshoof—Rectitude (Runnymede) **Mr R Smith**
111 B f 23/4 Royal Academy (USA)—Respectfully (USA) (The Minstrel (CAN)) **Atlantic Racing Limited**
112 **ROYAL MOUNT,** ch c 14/5 Cadeaux Genereux—Hawait Al Barr (Green Desert (USA)) **Maktoum Al Maktoum**
113 B c 20/2 Polar Falcon (USA)—Sarabah (IRE) (Ela-Mana-Mou) **Mr J. David Abell**
114 **SEVERENCE FEE (IRE),** ch c 27/2 Polish Precedent—Funoon (IRE) (Kris) **Maktoum Al Maktoum**
115 B f 25/4 Turtle Island (IRE)—Shamiyda (USA) (Sir Ivor) **Sheikh Mohammed**
116 **SOCIETY SNOOP (IRE),** b c 29/1 Warning—Aljood (Kris) **Maktoum Al Maktoum**
117 **SPITZBERGEN,** ch c 20/4 Polar Falcon (USA)—Soba (Most Secret) **Brian Yeardley Continental Ltd**
118 **STOLEN TEAR (FR),** ch c 6/3 Cadeaux Genereux—Durrah (USA) (Nijinsky (CAN)) **Maktoum Al Maktoum**
119 B c 21/5 Imperial Frontier—Superb Investment (IRE) (Hatim (USA)) **Mr Markus Graff**
120 **TELL THEM ALL,** ch c 26/3 Kris—Just Cause (Law Society (USA)) **Maktoum Al Maktoum**
121 B c 27/4 Robellino (USA)—Thimblerigger (Sharpen Up) **The Double Baileys Partnership**
122 B f 8/5 Zafonic (USA)—Trescalini (IRE) (Sadler's Wells (USA)) **Maktoum Al Maktoum**
123 **TURTLE,** b c 02/4 Turtle Island (IRE)—Kate Marie (USA) (Bering) **Mr M. J. Pilkington**
124 B c 23/3 Clantime—Tyrian Belle (Enchantment) **Mr A. Mathieson**

MR M. S. JOHNSTON—continued

125 B f 28/1 Sheikh Albadou—Urbacity (USA) (Fappiano (USA)) **Mr & Mrs G. Middlebrook**
126 B f 30/1 Bering—Walliser (Niniski (USA)) **Mr A Miller**
127 B f 4/4 Mujadil (USA)—Welsh Note (USA) (Sharpen Up) **Mrs I. Bird**
128 B f 18/4 Thatching—Wild Applause (IRE) (Sadler's Wells (USA)) **Walter S. Partnership**
129 B c 25/2 Chief's Crown (USA)—With Style (CAN) (Smarten (USA)) **Mr M. Doyle**
130 ZEITZ (FR), b c 10/5 Zieten (USA)—Zarzaya (USA) (Caro) **Brian Yeardley Continental Ltd.**

Other Owners: Mr J. W. Armstrong, Mr R. J. Barbiaux, Mr P. J. Biggins, Lady Bolton, Mr P. Bolton, Mr C. C. Buckley, Mrs D. J. Buckley, Miss K. M. Butters, Mrs H. Conroy, Mr William Cook, Mr J. D. Cotterill, Mr W. Cully, Mr & Mrs J. Digby, Mrs Julian Dixon, Mr Christopher Donald, Mr Jim Ennis, Mrs J. Farmer, Mr J. A. Forsyth, Miss Jane Gilbert, Mr Charles Gillis, Mr J. R. Good, Mrs P. Good, Mr W. A. Greensit, Mr H. J. Hambley, Mr J. F. Hanna, Mr Simon Hodges, Mrs M. E. Holdcroft, Mr T. G. Holdcroft, Mr Richard B. Huckerby, Mrs N. J. Huggins, Mr John Hulme, Mr I. M. Jones. Mr S. Kimberley, Mrs Andrea King, Mr A. D. Latter, Mark Johnston Racing Ltd., Mr P. McMahon, Mr B. G. A. Mills, Mrs V. A. Mills, Mr Grant C. Mitchell, Mrs Liz Nelson, Mrs J. Pennell, Mr R. N. Pennell, Mrs Gillian Quinn, Mr Ian Robinson, Roldvale Limited, Dr Fuk To Chang, Mrs J. D. Trotter, Mr P. Venner, Mr D. Wadham, Mr A. Watson, Mr James Wigan, Mr W. J. P. Yellop.

Apprentices: Ian Grantham (7-7), Keith Sked (7-7).

Lady Rider: Mrs C Williams (9-0).

324 MR A. P. JONES, Eastbury

Postal: **Eastbury Cottage Stables, Eastbury, Lambourn, Newbury, Berkshire, RG16 7JJ.**
Phone: **PHONE & FAX (01488) 72637 MOBILE (0831) 167346 HOME (01488) 71729**

1 CAPITAIN, 9, b g Idiot's Delight—Crosa **Mr S. C. Jones**
2 COLWAY PRINCE (IRE), 10, b g Prince Tenderfoot (USA)—El Cerrito **Mr A. A. King**
3 COPPER SHELL, 4, ch g Beveled (USA)—Luly My Love **Mr A. A. King**
4 COUNTRY STORE, 9, ch m Sunyboy—Pollys Owen **Westfield Racing**
5 COUNTRY TOWN, 8, b m Town And Country—Little Member **Mr R. Barton**
6 FESTIVAL (FR), 5, gr g Mourtazam—Oseille IV **Mr A. A. King**
7 FIN BEC (FR), 5, b g Tip Moss (FR)—Tourbrune (FR) **Mr A. A. King**
8 GREEN KING, 6, b g Green Adventure (USA)—Devine Lady **Mr A. P. Jones**
9 INCANDESCENT, 4, b f Inca Chief (USA)—Heavenly State **Mrs Gail Gaisford**
10 SHARP PROGRESS, 5, b g Inca Chief (USA)—Sharp Venita **Mr A. P. Jones**
11 SILVER LINING, 4, b g Beveled (USA)—Seymour Ann **The Lambourn Racing Club**
12 SOLO GENT, 9, br g Le Bavard (FR)—Go-It-Alone **The Eastbury Racing Club**
13 TINKER'S CUSS, 7, ch m Nearly A Hand—Little Member **Mr A. Briars**

THREE-YEAR-OLDS

14 Ch g Beveled (USA)—Cotehele **Mr A. A. King**
15 B f Miner's Lamp—Crosa **Mr A. P. Jones**
16 FAUTE DE MIEUX, ch c Beveled (USA)—Supreme Rose **Mrs V. Youell**
17 MINJARA, b c Beveled (USA)—Honey Mill **Mrs V. Youell**
18 MISS SCOOTER, ch f Beveled (USA)—Donosa **Mr A. P. Jones**
19 SECRET TANGO, ch f Interrex (CAN)—Seymour Ann **Mr D. White**

TWO-YEAR-OLDS

20 Ch f 27/4 Interrex (CAN)—Albion Polka (Dance In Time (CAN)) **Mr F. A. Ezen**
21 B f Minshaanshu Amad—Noble Soul (Sayf El Arab (USA)) **Mr F. A. Ezen**
22 B c 26/1 Minshaanshu Amad—To The Point (Sharpen Up) **Mr J. F. O'Donovan**

Other Owners: 14th Field Regiment Royal Artillery, Mr P. Armour, Mr G. Ball, Mrs M. I. Barton, Mr R. Bourne, Mr W. Bush, Mr A. Drake, Mr R. Eagles, Mr Larry Loake, Mr P. Newell, Mr M. R. Parkins, Mr T. R. Parkins, Mr G. E. R. Paulin, Mr J. C. P. G. Scutt, Mrs A. G. L. Walker, Major R. G. Wilson.

Jockeys (Flat): R Cochrane, T Sprake.

Jockeys (NH): S McNeill, G Upton.

Conditional: G Hogan.

Amateur: Mr E James.

325 MR BOB JONES, Newmarket

Postal: **Boyden End House, Wickhambrook, Newmarket, Suffolk, CB8 8XX.**
Phone: **(01440) 820342/820664 OR (0831) 822129 FAX (01440) 820958**

1 **CANOVAS HEART,** 9, b g Balidar—Worthy Venture **Mr M. J. Osborne and Mrs J. Woods**
2 **GAIN LINE (USA),** 5, b g Dayjur (USA)—Safe Play (USA) **Legend Racing Club**
3 5, Ch g Phardante (FR)—Glen Laura **Mr & Mrs P. Marioni**
4 **GREAT CHIEF,** 5, ch g Be My Chief (USA)—Padelia **Mrs S. Buckland**
5 **JACK BUTTON (IRE),** 9, b g Kings Lake (USA)—Tallantire (USA) **Mrs S. A. Jones**
6 **LE TETEU (FR),** 5, b h Saint Andrews (FR)—Nouvelle Star (USA) **Mrs J. Woods And Mrs Sally Jones**
7 **MOUNT GENIUS (USA),** 5, b br g Beau Genius (CAN)—Mount Jackie (USA) **Mrs S. Buckland And Mrs J. Woods**
8 **MUKHLLES (USA),** 5, b h Diesis—Serenely (USA) **Mr Bob Jones**
9 **WATCH ME GO (IRE),** 9, b g On Your Mark—Nighty Night **Mr Bob Jones**

THREE-YEAR-OLDS

10 **ASHANGEM,** ch g Risk Me (FR)—Dancing Belle **Hobbs Racing Partnership**
11 **CHALIAPIN,** b g Tragic Role (USA)—Last Note **B. O. W. Partnership**
12 **EIFFEL TIGER (IRE),** b br g Paris House—Rosa Bengala **Mrs Joan Marioni**
13 **HIGHBURY LEGEND,** ch g Mazilier (USA)—Jans Contessa **Sandbaggers Club**
14 **YANSHAN,** b g Anshan—Joy of Freedom **Mrs S. Osborne**

TWO-YEAR-OLDS

15 B f 21/4 Northern Park (USA)—Lovely Lagoon (Mill Reef (USA)) **Crafton Stud**

Other Owners: Armorex Limited, Mr B. Benson, Mr David S. Blake, Mr Frederick Clarke, Mr D. A. Eagles, Mr Robert H. Eagles, Mr K. Chan Wan Fong, Mr D. C. Hobbs, Mr M. G. Mackenzie, Mr E. McCay, Mr C. F. Monticolombi, Mrs V. Paxton, Mrs P. Richmond, Mr B. M Saumtally, Mr A. Ward, Mrs M. Warwick, Mrs Judit Woods.

Jockeys (Flat): N Day (8-6), M Wigham (8-6).

Jockey (NH): R Dunwoody (w.a.).

Apprentice: Gemma Jones (7-10).

Lady Rider: Miss Diana Jane Jones (9-7).

326 MR C. H. JONES, Cheltenham

Postal: **The Flat, Grove Farm House, Cold Aston, Cheltenham, Gloucestershire, GL54 3BN.**
Phone: **(01451) 821277 MOBILE (0973) 404770**

1 **COUNTRY CONCORDE,** 8, b g Ilium—Countrypop **Mr Bob Coles**
2 **PHROSE,** 8, b g Pharly (FR)—Rose Chanelle **Miss B. Small**
3 **POCONO KNIGHT,** 8, gr g Petong—Avahra **Mrs R. C. Jones**
4 **RAKAPOSHI IMP,** 8, ch m Rakaposhi King—Spartan Imp **Mr T. W. H. Dancer**
5 4, B f Welsh Captain—Rymer's Fancy **Mr T. W. H. Dancer**
6 **SWEETLY DISPOSED (IRE),** 10, b g Celio Rufo—Castle Creeper **Mr Timothy Eager**
7 **THE GADFLY,** 6, br g Welsh Captain—Spartan Imp **Mr T. W. H. Dancer**
8 **THE MILLSTONE,** 7, b g Welsh Captain—Blue Mint **Mr T. W. H. Dancer**

Jockey (NH): G Upton (10-1).

Conditional: L Suthern (9-7, w.a.).

Amateur: Miss B Small (8-9).

327 MR G. ELWYN JONES, Lampeter

Postal: **Lluestnewydd, Bettws, Lampeter, Dyfed, SA48 8PB.**
Phone: **(01570) 493261**

1 **JUST BECAUSE (IRE),** 6, ch g Sharp Charter—Lakefield Lady **Mr G. Elwyn Jones**
2 **PRIME MINISTER,** 4, ch c Be My Chief (USA)—Classic Design **Mr G. Elwyn Jones**
3 **RAVEN'S ROOST (IRE),** 7, b g Taufan (USA)—Al Zumurrud **Mr G. Elwyn Jones**

Jockey (NH): P McLoughlin (9-7).

Lady Rider: Miss P Jones (9-7).

328 MRS M. A. JONES, Lambourn

Postal: **Stork House, Baydon Road, Lambourn, Hungerford, Berkshire, RG17 8NU.**
Phone: **LAMBOURN (01488) 72409 MOBILE (0374) 492069 FAX (01488) 72409**

1 **BE LUCKY COLIN (IRE),** 7, ch g Buckley—Maladiction **Mr C. Flear**
2 **BROWN SEAL,** 6, b m Arctic Lord—Brown Veil **Mrs P. Corbett**
3 **BURFIELD BOY (IRE),** 7, b g Eve's Error—Lady Wolver **Mrs Barbara Sharpe**
4 **CALDAMUS,** 6, gr g Scallywag—Portodamus **Mr P. R. Warwick**
5 **CALLING TIME,** 5, ch g Rakaposhi King—Kentucky Calling **Mr F. J. Sainsbury**
6 **CAMDEN FELLOW (IRE),** 5, b g Camden Town—Decent Brandy **Mr M. Sawers**
7 **COLORFUL AMBITION,** 8, b g Slip Anchor—Reprocolor **Mr F. J. Sainsbury**
8 **DAMIEN'S CHOICE (IRE),** 6, b g Erin's Hope—Reenoga **Mr M. Sawers**
9 **DIFFICULT DECISION (IRE),** 7, ch g John French—Lady Mala **Mr F. J. Sainsbury**
10 **ELA MATA,** 6, br g Dancing Brave (USA)—Princess Genista **Mr F. J. Sainsbury**
11 **GOLDWYN (USA),** 6, b g Rainbow Quest (USA)—Golden Treasury (USA) **Crown Pkg & Mailing Svs Ltd**
12 **HI MARBLE (IRE),** 7, ch m Wylfa—Red Marble **Risk Takers**
13 **INTO THE SWING,** 9, b g Neltino—Audela **Mr F. J. Sainsbury**
14 **INTO THE WEB (IRE),** 7, br g Noalto—Elenas Beauty **Mr F. J. Sainsbury**
15 **JANGLYNYVE,** 4, ch f Sharpo—Wollow Maid **Mr F. J. Sainsbury**
16 **JATHIB (CAN),** 7, ch g Trempolino (USA)—Noble Gaze (USA) **Crown Pkg & Mailing Svs Ltd**
17 **JOLLY JAMES (IRE),** 7, b g Jolly Jake (NZ)—Taca (USA) **Brigadier Racing**
18 **JUST GRAND (IRE),** 4, b g Green Desert (USA)—Aljood **Mr F. J. Sainsbury**
19 **LIGHT VENEER,** 13, ch g Touching Wood (USA)—Oscilight **Mr Louis Jones**
20 **LIVELY ENCOUNTER (IRE),** 7, b g Jeu de Paille (FR)—A Bit of Honey **Mr F. J. Sainsbury**
21 **LORD EDGAR (IRE),** 6, br g Lord Americo—Coolreagh Princess **Mr F. J. Sainsbury**
22 **LOVE ME DO (USA),** 4, b g Minshaanshu Amad (USA)—I Assume (USA)
23 5, Ch g Heavenly Manna—Mad Rodger
24 **MALLAM MIST (IRE),** 6, gr g Roselier (FR)—Rocks Rose **Mr F. J. Sainsbury**
25 **MANOLETE,** 7, b g Hard Fought—Andalucia **Mr C. Flear**
26 **MELROY (IRE),** 7, b g Le Bavard (FR)—Blackrath Beauty **Mr F. J. Sainsbury**
27 **MERCILESS COP,** 4, ch g Efisio—Naturally Bold **The Par Four**
28 **MOCK TRIAL (IRE),** 5, b g Old Vic—Test Case **Mr F. J. Sainsbury**
29 **MORE DASH THANCASH (IRE),** 8, ch g Stalker—Gobolino **Mr F. J. Sainsbury**
30 **MUTI (USA),** 4, b g El Gran Senor (USA)—Marie de Chantilly (USA)
31 **PACIFIC RIDGE (IRE),** 7, gr g Roselier (FR)—Pacific Ocean **Mr F. J. Sainsbury**
32 4, Ch c Un Desperado (FR)—Red Marble
33 **ROYAL SHREWSBURY,** 8, ch g Cruise Missile—Hay-Hay
34 6, B g Satco (FR)—Safe And Happy
35 **SHERMAN POTTER,** 7, b g Celestial Storm (USA)—Corinthia (USA) **The Blaze Partnership**
36 **SICARIAN,** 6, b g Kris—Sharka **Mr F. J. Sainsbury**
37 **SILVER SIROCCO (IRE),** 6, gr g Razzo Forte—Oronocco Gift **Mr F. J. Sainsbury**

MRS M. A. JONES—continued

38 SILVER TREASURE (IRE), 7, gr g Cataldi—Languid **Mr N. P. Vigart**
39 SNOW BOARD, 9, gr g Niniski (USA)—Troja **Mr F. J. Sainsbury**
40 SON OF ANSHAN, 5, b g Anshan—Anhaar **Mr F. J. Sainsbury**
41 SURPRISE GUNNER, 8, b g Gunner B—Heckley Loch **Unregistered Partnership**
42 THE DEEJAY (IRE), 4, ch g Desse Zenny (USA)—White Jasmin **Mr F. J. Sainsbury**
43 TREASURE AGAIN (IRE), 9, b g Treasure Hunter—Ten Again **Mr John Hugo Gwynne**
44 URON V (FR), 12, b g Cap Martin (FR)—Jolivette (FR) **Mrs E. M. Bousquet-Payne**
45 WHATEVER NEXT (IRE), 5, ch g Phardante (FR)—Carney's Hill **Mr F. J. Sainsbury**
46 WORTHY MEMORIES, 9, b m Don't Forget Me—Intrinsic **Mrs E. M. Bousquet-Payne**

THREE-YEAR-OLDS

47 B g Discover (USA)—Stark Home (USA)

TWO-YEAR-OLDS

48 B g 3/3 Unblest—Santa Patricia (IRE)

Other Owners: Mr & Mrs T. Ballantyne, Mr D. J. Bussell, Mr Julien Bussell, Miss L. G. Chapman, Mr Brian Davies, Mr L. M. Dodds, Mrs W. J. George, Mr Lou Giaracuni, Mr L. J. Gwynne, Mr M. Hornby, Mr G. Irlam, Mr David F. Lacey, Mrs M. Lacey, Mr C. M. De B. Lipscomb, Mr M. Maloney, Mrs M. Martin, Mr & Mrs J. McClurg, Mr M. Morris, Mr A. O'Brien, Mr J. O'Brien, Mr C. Palmer, Mr M. Pugh, Mr Jim Sly, Mrs Sue Smith, Theresa Smith, Mr D. Stopps, Mr D. J. Thomas.

Jockeys (NH): Derek Byrne (10-0), R Dunwoody (10-0, w.a.), M A Fitzgerald (10-0, w.a.), A P McCoy (9-10).

Conditional: M Dunne (9-7), S Hearn (9-7).

Amateur: Mr B Kendellen (9-7).

329 MR P. J. JONES, Marlborough

Postal: **Fox Twitchen, East Kennett, Marlborough, Wiltshire, SN8 4EY.**
Phone: **(06782861) 427**

1 BARBARY FALCON, 8, b g El Conquistador—Dusty Run **Mr P. J. Jones**
2 LUCYS RED SLIPPER, 6, ch m Newski (USA)—Slipalong **Mr P. J. Jones**
3 LUSCOMBE, 5, b g Tirol—Slipalong **Mr P. J. Jones**

330 MR T. M. JONES, Guildford

Postal: **Brook Farm, Albury, Guildford, Surrey, GU5 9DJ.**
Phone: **SHERE (01483) 202604 (01483) 203749**

1 DIGWANA (IRE), 5, b g Digamist (USA)—Siwana (IRE) **Mr T. M. Jones**
2 LITTLE PILGRIM, 5, b g Precocious—Bonny Bright Eyes **Mr Richard L. Page**
3 LITTLE PROGRESS, 4, b g Rock City—Petite Hester **Mr T. M. Jones**
4 SEXTON'S MIRROR (IRE), 6, ch g Sexton Blake—Aries Star **Mervyn J. Evans**
5 WARNING BOARD, 7, b g Bairn (USA)—Candle In The Wind **Mr T. M. Jones**

THREE-YEAR-OLDS

6 COMMANDER CONN, b c Perpendicular—Bonny Bright Eyes **Mr Richard L. Page**

TWO-YEAR-OLDS

7 WHO GOES THERE, ch f 2/5 Wolfhound (USA)—Challanging (Mill Reef (USA)) **Resthill Partnership**

Other Owners: Mr John Brookes, Mrs John Brookes, Mr Barrie Catchpole, Mr R. Le Blanc.

Jockey (Flat): R Perham.

331 MR F. T. J. JORDAN, Leominster

Postal: **Butt Oak Farm, Risbury, Leominster, Herefordshire, HR6 0NQ.**
Phone: **PHONE AND FAX (01568) 760281**

1 **ARC (IRE)**, 4, b c Archway (IRE)—Columbian Sand (IRE) **Mrs A. Roddis**
2 **CARLINGFORD LASS (IRE)**, 8, ch m Carlingford Castle—Clanwilla **Mr F. Jordan**
3 **CHEQUERS BOY**, 7, b g Sweet Monday—Some Kathy **Mr A. Corfield**
4 **CHIEF MOUSE**, 5, b g Be My Chief (USA)—Top Mouse **Mr Bill Gavan**
5 **CRACKSMAN**, 5, b g Scallywag—Furstin **Mr D. Pugh**
6 **CRAZY HORSE DANCER (USA)**, 10, b g Barachois (CAN)—Why Pass (USA) **Mrs A. Roddis**
7 **DAUNT**, 6, b g Darshaan—Minute Waltz **Supercraft Ind & Farm Buildings Ltd**
8 **DONNRUA (IRE)**, 7, ch m Denel (FR)—Lough Hill Lady **Mr Bill Woodward**
9 **EAGLE CANYON (IRE)**, 5, b br g Persian Bold—Chrism **Mr T. R. Sanders**
10 **FINNURE (IRE)**, 6, ch g Lancastrian—Wayward Express **Mr M. K. Roddis**
11 **FIRST BEE**, 7, b m Gunner B—Furstin **Mr D. Pugh**
12 **FIRST CRACK**, 13, b m Scallywag—Furstin **Mr D. Pugh**
13 **FUNKY**, 5, ch m Classic Music (USA)—Foreno **Mr K. Hind**
14 4, B f Rakaposhi King—Furstin
15 **GO BRITANNIA**, 5, b g Machiavellian (USA)—Chief Celebrity (USA) **Fenside Waste Ltd**
16 **GO KATIE**, 6, ch m Gunner B—Gokatiego **Mr F. Jordan**
17 **GOLD'N SHROUD (IRE)**, 7, b g Shy Groom (USA)—Launch The Raft **Mr J. W. Delahay**
18 **GUNNY'S GIRL**, 7, ch m Scallywag—Girl In Green **War Rick Gun Vic Partnership**
19 **JOLLY BOAT**, 11, br g Lord Ha Ha—Mariner's Dash **Mr M. J. Bevan**
20 **KING OF BABYLON (IRE)**, 6, b g Persian Heights—My My Marie **Miss L. M. Rochford**
21 **KYLE DAVID (IRE)**, 6, gr g Peacock (FR)—Aunty Babs **Supercraft Ind & Farm Buildings Ltd**
22 **LOCH NA GLEANN (IRE)**, 6, b m Homo Sapien—Lough Hill Lady **Mr M. Robinson**
23 4, Ch f Denel (FR)—Lough Hill Lady **Mr John Hanner**
24 **LOUGH TULLY (IRE)**, 8, ch g Denel (FR)—Lough Hill Lady **Mr R. A. Hancocks**
25 **MARSAYAS (IRE)**, 5, ch g Classic Music (USA)—Babiana (CAN) **G. Pickering & J. P. Hames**
26 **MR GOON HILLY**, 8, b g Idiot's Delight—Queen of The Nile **Mr R. A. Hughes**
27 **MY BILLY BOY**, 9, b g Puget (USA)—Dragon Fire **Mr R. A. Hughes**
28 **NUNS LUCY**, 7, ch m Toirdealbhach—Nuns Royal **G. Pickering & J. P. Hames**
29 **ROCKET MAN (IRE)**, 5, b g Denel (FR)—Sofa River (FR) **Mr P. Wise**
30 **ROSS SPORTING**, 6, b g Derring Rose—Cheetah's Spirit **Mr Alan Price**
31 **ROYAL EXPRESSION**, 6, b g Sylvan Express—Edwins' Princess **Mrs A. Roddis**
32 **ROYAL SALUTE**, 6, ch g Royal Vulcan—Nuns Royal
33 **SAINT CIEL (USA)**, 10, b h Skywalker (USA)—Holy Tobin (USA) **Tam Racing**
34 **SHADY EMMA**, 6, ch m Gunner B—Shady Legacy **Mr D. Pugh**
35 **SHAMATEUR (IRE)**, 4, b g Ela-Mana-Mou—Sharp Slipper **Mr R. O'Ryan**
36 **SHIFTING MOON**, 6, b g Night Shift (USA)—Moonscape **Mrs K. Roberts-Hindle**
37 **SONG FOR JESS (IRE)**, 5, b m Accordion—Ritual Girl **Mr F. Jordan**
38 **STAR PERFORMER (IRE)**, 7, b g Petorius—Whitstar **Crafty Cockneys**

Other Owners: Mr P. J. A. Bomford, Mr R. Bourton, Mr Ricky Dolphin, Mr C. F. Gummow, Mr Robert Gunthorpe, Mr M. Kear, Mr David Martin, Mr John McPhee, Mr Mike Mifflin, Mrs E. J. Norton, Mr R. H. Preece, Mr David Pugh, Mr Paul Robson.

Jockeys (NH): D Byrne, A P McCoy (w.a.).

Conditional: B J Clarke (9-7), R J Hodges (9-11).

332 MRS J. JORDAN, Yarm

Postal: **Staindale Lodge, Picton, Yarm, Cleveland, TS15 0AE.**
Phone: **(01642) 701061**

1 **ALYPORTENT**, 4, b g Warning—Alilisa (USA) **Mr J. E. Hulme**
2 **AMBUSCADE (USA)**, 12, ch g Roberto (USA)—Gurkhas Band (USA) **Mrs J. Jordan**

MRS J. JORDAN—continued

3 **BLAZING IMP (USA),** 5, ch g Imp Society (USA)—Marital (USA)
4 **DARING LAD,** 5, b g Daring March—Kept Waiting **Mr J. O. Addison**
5 **DOCTOR'S REMEDY,** 12, br g Doc Marten—Champagne Party **Mr J. O. Addison**
6 **GORODENKA BOY,** 8, ch g Then Again—Simply Jane **Mrs J. Jordan**
7 **MARLINGFORD,** 11, ch g Be My Guest (USA)—Inchmarlo (USA) **Mrs J. Brennan**
8 **PERFECT GRACE,** 4, b f Lord David S (USA)—Luce Bay **Mrs M. Mathews**
9 **THISONESFORMAGGIE,** 5, ch m Scottish Reel—Touch My Heart **Mr M. W. Mitchell**

Other Owners: Mr N. Fletcher, Mr B. Phizacklea, Mr P. Szuszkewicz.

Apprentice: Jenny Murphy (7-10).

333 MR J. JOSEPH, Amersham

Postal: **Cherry Tree Farm, Coleshill, Amersham, Buckinghamshire, HP7 0LE.**
Phone: **(01494) 722239 (01494) 432992 FAX**

1 **ANIF (USA),** 7, b g Riverman (USA)—Marnie's Majik (USA) **Mr Jack Joseph**
2 **BUNDERBURG (USA),** 8, b br g Nureyev (USA)—Hortensia (FR) **Mr Jack Joseph**
3 **CABOCHON,** 11, b g Jalmood (USA)—Lightning Legacy (USA) **Mr Jack Joseph**
4 **CAVO GRECO (USA),** 9, b g Riverman (USA)—Cypria Sacra (USA) **Mr Jack Joseph**
5 **GREEN LANE (USA),** 10, ch g Greinton—Memory Lane (USA) **Mr Jack Joseph**
6 **KARACHI,** 8, b g Nishapour (FR)—Lady Dacre **Mr Jack Joseph**
7 **MILZIG (USA),** 9, b g Ziggy's Boy (USA)—Legume (USA) **Mr Jack Joseph**
8 **PINKERTON'S PAL,** 7, ch g Dominion—White Domino **Mr Jack Joseph**

Other Owners: Allied Manafacturing Company, Sarena Plastics.

334 MR R. T. JUCKES, Abberley

Postal: **Worsley Racing Stables, Abberley, Worcester, Worcestershire, WR6 6BQ.**
Phone: **GREAT WITLEY (01299) 896471 OR (01299) 896522**

1 **ABDUCTION,** 5, ch g Risk Me (FR)—Spirit Away **Mr R. T. Juckes**
2 **ALBEMINE (USA),** 9, b g Al Nasr (FR)—Lady Be Mine (USA) **Mr A. C. W. Price**
3 **ARABIAN BOLD (IRE),** 10, br g Persian Bold—Bodham **Mr A. C. W. Price**
4 **BOBBY VIOLET,** 6, b g Starch Reduced—Otterden **Mr P. Sandy**
5 **CHANGED TO BAILEYS (IRE),** 4, b g Distinctly North (USA)—Blue Czarina **Mr R. T. Juckes**
6 **HOH DOWN (IRE),** 4, b f Fairy King (USA)—Tintomara (IRE) **Mr A. C. W. Price**
7 **JALCANTO,** 8, ch g Jalmood (USA)—Bella Canto **Mr A. C. W. Price**
8 **JUST FOR A REASON,** 6, b g Siberian Express (USA)—Artaius Rose (FR) **Mr A. C. W. Price**
9 **LANCER (USA),** 6, ch g Diesis—Last Bird (USA) **Mr A. C. W. Price**
10 **PEDALTOTHEMETAL (IRE),** 6, b m Nordico (USA)—Full Choke **Mr A. C. W. Price**
11 **PRECIOUS ISLAND,** 5, b m Jupiter Island—Burmese Ruby **Mr J. W. Ellis**
12 **SUPERCHARMER,** 4, ch g Charmer—Surpassing **Mr A. C. W. Price**
13 **SWEET AMORET,** 5, b m Forzando—Primrose Way **Mr Stuart Hibbert**
14 **SWISS COAST (IRE),** 4, b g Mujadil (USA)—Rose A Village **The Good Fun Racing Club**

THREE-YEAR-OLDS

15 **ROMANTIC SECRET,** ch f Executive Man—Tria Romantica **Mrs K. C. Price**

Other Owners: Mr P. M. Clarke, Mr Tom Hayes, Mr Barry Hine, Mrs M. Minett, Mr P. R. Peplow, Mr J. Wilson Walker.

Jockey (NH): G Lyons.

Lady Rider: Miss E M Jones (8-7).

335 MR H. M. KAVANAGH, Bodenham

Postal: **Mereside, Church Road, Bodenham, Hereford, HR1 3JU.**
Phone: **(01568) 797048**

1 **SARA BELLA,** 5, br m Rolfe (USA)—Sandra Bella **Mrs S. Kavanagh**

THREE-YEAR-OLDS

2 Br f Teenoso (USA)—Raise The Dawn

336 MR T. KEDDY, Alfrick

Postal: **The Last Empire Stables, Crews Hill, Alfrick, Worcester, Worcestershire, WR6 5HF.**
Phone: **(01886) 884144**

1 **CONNEL'S CROFT,** 6, ch g Rich Charlie—Technology (FR) **BCD Steels Ltd**
2 **ESKLEYBROOK,** 5, b g Arzanni—Crystal Run VII **Mr V. Y. Gethin**
3 **JIMMY THE GILLIE,** 12, b br g Sunley Builds—Lac Royale **Mr Jim Lewis**
4 **JUSTJIM,** 6, b g Derring Rose—Crystal Run VII **Mr V. Y. Gethin**
5 **KAYTU'S CAROUSEL,** 9, ch m Kaytu—Touching Clouds **Miss Anita Gibbons**
6 **LIME STREET BLUES (IRE),** 7, b g Digamist (USA)—Royal Daughter **The Blues Partnership**
7 **MR MOTIVATOR,** 8, b g Rolfe (USA)—National Clover **Mr V. Y. Gethin**
8 5, B m Little Wolf—Orange Spice **Rebecca Whitcombe**
9 **TAJAR (USA),** 6, b g Slew O' Gold (USA)—Mashaarif (USA) **The Veg Chef Partnership**
10 **WEEKEND WORKER,** 7, b g Rustingo—Crystal Run VII **Mr V. Y. Gethin**

THREE-YEAR-OLDS

11 **ISABELLA,** ch f Primo Dominie—Scossa (USA) **Mr M. Olden**

Other Owners: Mrs J. Chidley-Brown, Mr Simon Gegg, Mr D. I. Harding, Mr C. J. Hitchings, Mr Ray Jones, Mr David Milburn.

337 MR A. KELLEWAY, Newmarket

Postal: **Charnwood Stables, Hamilton Road, Newmarket, Suffolk.**
Phone: **(01638) 661461 FAX (01638) 666238**

1 **DOVEDON STAR,** 4, b f Unfuwain (USA)—Whitstar **Mr Michael C. Whatley**
2 **FRESH FRUIT DAILY,** 6, b m Reprimand—Dalmally **Mr Kevin Hudson**
3 **URSA MAJOR,** 4, b c Warning—Double Entendre **Mr Michael C. Whatley**

THREE-YEAR-OLDS

4 **HOT TOPIC (IRE),** ch f Desse Zenny (USA)—Sajanjal **Mr Osvaldo Pedroni**

TWO-YEAR-OLDS

5 Ch f 19/3 Risk Me (FR)—Celtic River (Caerleon (USA)) **Mr P. A. Kelleway**
6 Ch f 7/1 Caerleon (USA)—Darayna (IRE) (Shernazar) **Scuderia Golden Horse SRL**
7 Gr c 19/1 Environment Friend—Emeraude (Kris) **Scuderia Golden Horse SRL**
8 Ch c 26/2 Be My Chief (USA)—Hence (USA) (Mr Prospector (USA)) **Mr P. A. Kelleway**
9 **ORO STREET (IRE),** b c 7/3 Dolphin Street (FR)—Love Unlimited (Dominion) **Mr Osvaldo Pedroni**

Other Owners: Mrs Sandra Woodley.

338 MISS G. M. KELLEWAY, Whitcombe

Postal: **Racing Stables, Whitcombe Manor, Whitcombe, Dorchester, Dorset, DT2 8NY.**
Phone: **OFFICE (01305) 257353 FAX (01305) 257354 MOBILE (0802) 855484**

1 **ALJAZ,** 8, b g Al Nasr (FR)—Santa Linda (USA) **The Guernsey Racing Partnership**
2 **ANAK-KU,** 5, ch g Efisio—City Link Lass **H.R.H. Sultan Ahmad Shah**
3 **FATHER DAN (IRE),** 9, ch g Martin John—Sonia John **Mr Howard Rowland**
4 **FRIENDLY BRAVE (USA),** 8, b g Well Decorated (USA)—Companionship (USA) **Tempus Fugit Partnership**
5 **GALAPINO,** 5, b g Charmer—Carousella **Glendale Partnership Ltd**
6 **GOLDEN LILY,** 5, ch m Interrex (CAN)—Gold Risk **Mrs M. Fairbairn**
7 **GOLDEN POUND (USA),** 6, b g Seeking The Gold (USA)—Coesse Express (USA) **Mr A. P. Griffin**
8 **IVOR'S DEED,** 5, b g Shadeed (USA)—Gena Ivor (USA) **Mr A. P. Griffin**
9 **LA MODISTE,** 5, b m Most Welcome—Dismiss **Mr John Purcell**
10 **MAJOR CHANGE,** 6, gr g Sharrood (USA)—May The Fourteenth **The Two In One Partnership**
11 **MIKE'S DOUBLE (IRE),** 4, br g Cyrano de Bergerac—Glass Minnow (IRE) **The Money Men**
12 **OPERA BUFF (IRE),** 7, br g Rousillon (USA)—Obertura (USA) **Mr D. W. Watson**
13 **OVER KEEN,** 4, b f Keen—Shift Over (USA) **Miss J. A. Challen**
14 **PERICLES,** 4, b g Primo Dominie—Egalite (FR) **Miss Gay Kelleway**
15 **PUTERI WENTWORTH,** 4, b f Sadler's Wells (USA)—Sweeping **H.R.H. Sultan Ahmad Shah**
16 **RUSSIAN MUSIC,** 5, b g Forzando—Sunfleet **The Seventh Heaven Partnership**
17 **TARRY,** 5, b m Salse (USA)—Waitingformargaret **The Pieces Of Eight Partnership**
18 **TOMMY TORTOISE,** 4, b c Rock Hopper—Wish You Well **Mr Tommy Staunton**
19 **WAASEF,** 5, b g Warning—Thubut (USA) **Another Seventh Heaven Partnership**
20 **YET AGAIN,** 6, ch g Weldnaas (USA)—Brightelmstone **Mr A. P. Griffin**

THREE-YEAR-OLDS

21 **ADMIRE,** b f Last Tycoon—Belle Isis (USA) **Miss Gay Kelleway**
22 **ALEANBH (IRE),** ch c Classic Secret (USA)—Highdrive **Mr Tommy Staunton**
23 **BE MY WISH,** b f Be My Chief (USA)—Spinner **Mr T. Tran**
24 **DANCING WOLF (IRE),** b f Wolfhound (USA)—Aigue **Mrs I. C. C. Hayes**
25 **DAPHNE'S DOLL (IRE),** b f Polish Patriot (USA)—Helietta **Mrs Alan Gordon**
26 **FIRST MASTER,** ch c Primo Dominie—Bodham **Three's Lucky Partnership**
27 **GLENDALE RIDGE (IRE),** b g Indian Ridge—English Lily **Glendale Partnership Ltd**
28 **HONEY SUCKLE,** br f Petong—May The Fourteenth **Mrs C. J. Powell**
29 **HOPEFUL STAR (IRE),** ch c Pips Pride—Mijouter (IRE) **The Hopeful Millionaires**
30 **LISA'S PRIDE (IRE),** ch f Pips Pride—Brazilian Princess **Mr A. P. Griffin**
31 **NANCY MALONEY (IRE),** b f Persian Bold—Snoozy Time **Miss Jo Crowley**
32 **POLY BLUE (IRE),** ch f Thatching—Mazarine Blue (USA) **Sheet & Roll Convertors Ltd**
33 **SOFT TOUCH (IRE),** b f Petorius—Fingers **Mind The Gap Partnership**
34 **SOVIET BUREAU (IRE),** ch c Soviet Lad (USA)—Redwood Hut **Mr A. P. Griffin**

TWO-YEAR-OLDS

35 **ANOTHER RAINBOW (IRE),** b f 15/3 Rainbows For Life—Phylella (Persain Bold) **Pot Of Gold**
36 B f 24/4 Soviet Lad (USA)—Ballylesson Girl (IRE) (Nashamaa) **Glendale Partnership Ltd**
37 **BARON DE PICHON (IRE),** b c 29/3 Perugino (USA)—Ariadne (Bustino) **The Money Men**
38 Ch g 16/3 Risk Me (FR)—Capriati (USA) (Diesis) **Roldvale Ltd**
39 **DUSTY DANCER,** ch c 8/3 Risk Me (FR)—Eternal Triangle (USA) (Barachois (CAN)) **Mr Belcher**
40 B c 22/4 Shareef Dancer (USA)—Inderaputeri (Bold Fort) **H. R. H. Sultan Ahmad Shah**
41 **JELLYBEEN (IRE),** ch f 28/4 Petardia—Lux Aeterna (Sandhurst Prince) **Mr N. Parker**
42 **KEEN ABLAZE,** b c 5/5 Keen—Miss Coco (Swing Easy (USA)) **Mr A. P. Griffin**
43 B f 24/4 Fairy King (USA)—More Fizz (Morston (FR)) **The Money Men**
44 B c 4/2 Pursuit Of Love—Nsx (Roi Danzig (USA)) **H. R. H. Sultan Ahmad Shah**
45 Ch c 7/3 Cosmonaut—Paircullis (Tower Walk) **Rainbow Racing (UK) Ltd**
46 **PULAU PINANG (IRE),** ch f 30/4 Dolphin Street (FR)—Inner Pearl (Gulf Pearl) **Mrs A. Ooi**
47 B f 5/3 Risk Me (FR)—Sunday Sport's Pet (Mummy's Pet) **Mr F. O'Rourke**
48 B c 24/3 Soviet Lad (USA)—Symphonic Poem (USA) (Arts And Letters (USA)) **Mr A. P. Griffin**
49 **TOUCH UP (IRE),** ch c 21/4 Up And At 'Em—Fingers (Lord Gayle (USA)) **Sheet & Roll Convertors Ltd**
50 B c 7/2 Whittingham (IRE)—Uae Flame (IRE) (Polish Precedent (USA)) **Mr Massa**
51 B f 27/1 Soviet Lad (USA)—Woody's Colours (USA) (Caro) **Mr A. P. Griffin**
52 Ch c 12/4 Lion Cavern (USA)—Zealous Kitten (USA) (The Minstrel (CAN)) **Miss Gay Kelleway**

MISS G. M. KELLEWAY—continued

Other Owners: Mr John Davey Beverton, Mr Peter R. Bolton, Mrs C. Bracher, Mr R. S. Briggs, Mr Nigel Davies, Mr Nigel Dearman, Mr Brian T. Eastick, Mr T. A. Edwards, Mr B. T. Ferguson, Mr C. R. Fleet, Mr Andrew Goodall, Mr D. G. Hardisty, Invoshire Ltd, Mr B. W. J. Irons, Mr M. S. Kariolis, Mr S. R. Leoni, Mr R. F. Merrett, Mrs Christine Mills, Mrs Liz Nelson, Mrs M. E. O'Shea, Mr K. Panos, Mr A. Pao, Mrs Gilly Pembroke, Mr A. E. Salvage, Mr M. G. Sly, Mrs Lynne Smith, Mr C. F. Sparrowhawk, Mr Mike F. Sullivan, Mr Raymond Tooth, Mr Rex Towers, Mr B. Tregurtha, Whitcombe Manor Racing Stables Limited, Mr David Whitefield, Mr I. Wicks, Mr Chris Wilkinson, Mrs L. M. Wundke.

Jockey (Flat): K Fallon (w.a.).

Jockey (NH): D Bridgwater (w.a.).

Apprentice: A P Whelan (8-3).

Amateurs: Mr Marcus Armytage, Mr S Durack.

Lady Riders: Miss Sarah Kelleway (8-0), Miss Lucy Vollaro (8-7).

339 MR G. P. KELLY, Sheriff Hutton

Postal: **3 Church End Cottages, Sheriff Hutton, Yorkshire, YO6 1PY.**
Phone: **STABLES (01347) 878518 HOME (01347) 878770**

1 **CHILLED WINE,** 4, gr f Chilibang—Persian Joy **Mr R. Midgley**
2 **DALLAI (IRE),** 7, b g Dance of Life (USA)—Wavetree **Mr G. P. Kelly**
3 **DISTANT KING,** 5, b g Distant Relative—Lindfield Belle (IRE) **Mr A. Barrett**
4 **ELISSA,** 12, ch m Tap On Wood—Blakewood **Mr G. P. Kelly**
5 **GINGER FLOWER,** 9, ch m Niniski (USA)—Monterana **Miss Jayne Sunley**
6 **LAUDIBLE,** 13, ch g Formidable (USA)—Clouds **Mr G. P. Kelly**
7 **MARSH'S LAW,** 11, br g Kala Shikari—My Music **Mr Cooper Wilson**

Other Owners: Mr M. W. Easterby, Mr R. Naylor.

Jockeys (Flat): Alex Greaves (8-3), G Parkin (8-3).

Jockey (NH): P Midgley (10-0).

Apprentice: S Finnamore (7-12).

Amateurs: Mr M Keswick (9-7), Mr C Mulhall (10-9).

Lady Rider: Miss Sarah Brotherton (9-7).

340 MR W. T. KEMP, Duns

Postal: **Drake Myre, Grants House, Duns, Berwickshire, TD11 3RL.**
Phone: **(01361) 850242**

1 **BALLYLINE (IRE),** 7, b g Electric—Miss Dikler **The 49 Partnership**
2 **CHIEF CHIPPIE,** 5, b g Mandalus—Little Katrina **The 49 Partnership**
3 **COPPERHURST (IRE),** 7, ch m Royal Vulcan—Little Katrina **Mr W. T. Kemp**
4 **D'ARBLAY STREET (IRE),** 9, b g Pauper—Lady Abednego VII **Green For Luck**
5 **DENTON LAD,** 4, b g Prince Sabo—Dahlawise (IRE) **Mrs M. Irwin**
6 **FARNDALE,** 11, gr g Vaigly Great—Beloved Mistress **Mr A. J. Thurgood**

THREE-YEAR-OLDS

7 **FILEY BRIGG,** b f Weldnaas (USA)—Dusty's Darling **Drakemyre Racing**
8 B g Terimon—Forever Together **Mr W. T. Kemp**
9 **NGAERE PRINCESS,** br f Terimon—Zippy Zoe **Drakemyre Racing**

TWO-YEAR-OLDS

10 Ch f 7/5 Hatim (USA)—Glenrock Dancer (IRE) (Glenstal (USA)) **Mr W. T. Kemp**

Other Owners: Miss D. M. M. Calder, Mrs A. Ellis, Mr G. McGuiness, Mr J. B. Mitchell, Mr Tommy Naughton, Mrs Sue Waite, Mrs S. J. Wood.

Jockey (Flat): K Fallon (w.a.).

Conditional: C McCormack, R McGrath.

Amateur: Mr S Durack.

341 MR S. E. KETTLEWELL, Middleham

Postal: **Tupgill Park Stables, Middleham, Leyburn, N. Yorkshire, DL8 4TJ.**
Phone: **OFFICE (01969) 640411 FAX 640494 HOSTEL 640295 MOBILE (0421) 614983**

1 **AEOLINA (FR),** 4, b br f Kaldoun (FR)—Folia **Mr J. Tennant**
2 **BARITONE,** 4, b g Midyan (USA)—Zinzi **Mr S. E. Kettlewell**
3 **CHIEF OF KHORASSAN (FR),** 6, br g Nishapour (FR)—Amber's Image **Middleham Park Racing II**
4 **EASBY BLUE,** 6, b g Teenoso (USA)—Mellie **Mr G. R. Orchard**
5 **EASBY JOKER,** 10, b g Idiot's Delight—Be Spartan **Mr G. R. Orchard**
6 4, B g Arctic Lord—Gilzie Bank **Mr S. E. Kettlewell**
7 **GOOD HAND (USA),** 12, ch g Northjet—Ribonette (USA) **Uncle Jacks Pub**
8 **HI MUJTAHID (IRE),** 4, ch g Mujtahid (USA)—High Tern **Mr W. B. Imison**
9 **HOWYOUDOING,** 8, ch g Meadowbrook—Reigate Head **Mrs G. Handley**
10 **JACK FLASH,** 4, ch g Primitive Rising (USA)—Moss Pink (USA) **Miss L. Wilson**
11 **JUST BOB,** 9, b g Alleging (USA)—Diami **Mr J. Fotherby**
12 **LUCKY MOVE,** 5, b g Move Off—Mandrake Princess **Mr J. R. Wilson**
13 **MEMPHIS BLUES (IRE),** 6, b m Buckskin (FR)—Orinda Way **Mr J. E. Titley**
14 **ROSEATE LODGE,** 12, b g Habitat—Elegant Tern (USA) **Mr Jon Firth**
15 **SUNSET HARBOUR (IRE),** 5, br m Prince Sabo—City Link Pet **Mr J. Tennant**

THREE-YEAR-OLDS

16 B g Aragon—Almadaniyah **Mr S. E. Kettlewell**
17 **DISPOL EMERALD,** b f Emarati (USA)—Double Touch (FR) **Mr S. E. Kettlewell**
18 **DRAIN DOCTOR,** b g State Diplomacy—Stilvella **Drain Doctor Plumbing Ltd**
19 **ERRO CODIGO,** b g Formidable (USA)—Home Wrecker (DEN) **Mr D. Neale**
20 **GOOD ON YER,** b f Reprimand—Princess Eurolink **Hollinbridge Racing**
21 **STRINGERS (IRE),** ch c Shalford (IRE)—Rebecca's Girl (IRE) **Mr J. S. Calvert**

MR S. E. KETTLEWELL—continued

TWO-YEAR-OLDS

22 B g 30/4 Perpendicular—Pendle's Secret (Le Johnstan) **Mrs P. Simpson**

Other Owners: Mr D. Barker, Mrs C. M. Beresford, Mr Roy Chadwick, Mr Don Chapman, Mr A. Craven, Mr Graham De Caux, Mr Franco Fantoni, Mr R. Fenwick-Gibson, Mr S. P. French, Mr James Hughes, Mr J. R. Kettlewell, Mr P. G. Leadley, Mrs B. A. Meechan, Northumbria Leisure Ltd, Mr T. S. Palin, Mr J. P. Severn, Mrs E. Stoker, Mr Trevor Ward, Mr T. Whalley, Mr R. Wood, Mr David R. Wright.

Jockey (Flat): J Fortune.

Jockeys (NH): R Johnson (w.a.), P Niven (w.a.).

Apprentice: Paul Fredericks (8-0).

Conditional: G Lee (w.a.).

342 MR J. S. KING, Swindon

Postal: **Elmcross House, Broad Hinton, Swindon, Wiltshire, SN4 9PF.**
Phone: **(01793) 731481 MOBILE (0836) 245393 & (0378) 976114**

1 **A N C EXPRESS,** 10, gr g Pragmatic—Lost In Silence **Mr H. K. Porter**
2 **AVONCLIFF,** 5, ch m Sharp Deal—Dusty Run **Dajam Ltd**
3 **CAPENWRAY (IRE),** 9, br g Supreme Leader—Godetia **Mr B. K. Peppiatt**
4 **CLAYMORE LAD,** 8, b g Broadsword (USA)—Cannes Beach **Marlborough Racing Partnership**
5 **COOL GUNNER,** 8, b g Gunner B—Coolek **Mr Richard Peterson**
6 **COOLREE (IRE),** 10, b g Gianchi—Positron **Mr B. T. R. Weston**
7 **COUNTRY BEAU,** 6, b g Town And Country—Chanelle **Mrs J. J. Peppiatt**
8 **DORANS GROVE,** 4, b f Gildoran—Binny Grove **Miss J. Cunningham**
9 **DUBELLE,** 8, b m Dubassoff (USA)—Flopsy Mopsy **Mr W. J. Lee**
10 **EHTEFAAL (USA),** 7, b g Alysheba (USA)—Bolt From The Blue (USA) **Mrs Marygold O'Kelly**
11 **EKEUS (IRE),** 8, ch g Henbit (USA)—Flying Early **Miss S. Douglas-Pennant**
12 5, B m Broadsword (USA)—Flopsy Mopsy **Mrs P. M. King**
13 **FOLESCLAVE (IRE),** 6, b m Brush Aside (USA)—Strong Slave (IRE) **The Marlborough Racing/Askew Partnership**
14 **FORTUNES COURSE (IRE),** 9, b m Crash Course—Night Rose **Mrs A. J. Garrett**
15 **FORTUNES FLIGHT (IRE),** 5, b g Tremblant—Night Rose **Mrs A. J. Garrett**
16 **FORTUNES ROSE (IRE),** 6, b m Tremblant—Night Rose **Mrs A. J. Garrett**
17 **GAZUMPER (NZ),** 5, b g Veloso (NZ)—Gardone **Mr R. B. Denny**
18 **HIGHLY PRIZED,** 4, b g Shirley Heights—On The Tiles **Mrs Marygold O'Kelly**
19 **HILLSWICK,** 7, ch g Norwick (USA)—Quite Lucky **Mr M. G. A. Court**
20 **INCHCAILLOCH (IRE),** 9, b g Lomond (USA)—Glowing With Pride **Mr F. J. Carter**
21 4, Br g Orchestra—Jane Bond **Mr Jim Kinloch**
22 **KING OF THE BLUES,** 6, b g Rakaposhi King—Colonial Princess **Mr Ian Watkins**
23 **LIGHTENING LAD,** 10, b g Pragmatic—Miss Lightening **Mr Richard Peterson**
24 5, B g Hollow Hand—Marand
25 **MARCHMAN,** 13, b g Daring March—Saltation **Mrs P. M. King**
26 **MEASURED STEP (IRE),** 7, b g Nearly A Hand—Silent Twirl **Mr Matt McBride**
27 **MINER'S BILL (IRE),** 7, br g Miner's Lamp—Lady Tarsel **Wish Racing**
28 **MISTER CHIPS,** 7, b g Macmillion—Nikali **Mr D. R. Peppiatt**
29 **MISTER ODDY,** 12, b g Dubassoff (USA)—Somerford Glory **Mrs R. M. Hill**
30 **MONUMENT,** 6, ch g Cadeaux Genereux—In Perpetuity **Mr V. Askew**
31 **MR MUSIC MAN (IRE),** 5, b g Accordion—A New Rose (IRE) **Mr N. A. Gill**
32 **POLKERRIS,** 7, b g Malaspina—Pearl Stud **Mr T. L. Morshead**

MR J. S. KING—continued

33 **RELATIVE CHANCE,** 9, b g Relkino—Chance A Look **Miss S. Douglas-Pennant**
34 **RUPERT BLUES,** 6, b g Thowra (FR)—Atlantic Line **Mr Robert Skillen**
35 **SEEF,** 4, b g Slip Anchor—Compton Lady (USA) **Mr Richard Peterson**
36 **SHARIAKANNDI (FR),** 6, b g Lashkari—Shapaara **Mr S. Clough**
37 5, B g Cruise Missile—Shoa
38 **SILENTLY,** 6, b g Slip Anchor—Land of Ivory (USA) **Mr G. G. Grayson**
39 **SOL MUSIC,** 6, ch g Southern Music—Tyqueen **The G. & P. Partnership**
40 **SPRUCE LODGE,** 5, b g Full Extent (USA)—Miss Ticklemouse **Mrs W. Jarrett**
41 **TIFFANY,** 5, b m Nader—Pharoah's Pet **Mr N. M. Giddings**
42 **TWIN TIME,** 4, b f Syrtos—Carramba (CZE) **Dajam Ltd**
43 **TWO SOCKS,** 5, ch g Phountzi (USA)—Mrs Feathers **Mrs Satu Marks**
44 **VALLIS VALE,** 8, ch m St Colombus—Barge Mistress **Mr Stephen Andrews**
45 **WALK ON BY,** 4, gr g Terimon—Try G's **Mrs R. M. Hill**
46 **WISHFUL VENTURE,** 6, b g Lyphento (USA)—Corniche Rose **Wish Racing**

Other Owners: Mr G. Birt, Mrs B. C. Dice, Mr F. P. Forbes, Mr John D. Hatherley, Mr Michael P. Hill, Mrs Carrie Janaway, Mr J. S. King, Mr Alan Lee, Mr E. J. Mangan, Mr Mark O'Connor, Mr Eric Penny, Mr Nigel Rich, Mr K. D. Shepherd, Miss G. Sowerby, Mr Peter Thomas.

343 MR T. R. KINSEY, Ashton

Postal: **Peel Hall, Ashton, Chester, CH3 8AY.**
Phone: **(01829) 751230**

1 **ALBERT BLAKE,** 11, b g Roscoe Blake—Ablula **Mrs T. R. Kinsey**
2 **FIBREGUIDE TECH,** 15, b g Uncle Pokey—Starcat **Mrs T. R. Kinsey**
3 **HORTON-CUM-PEEL (IRE),** 7, b g Swan's Rock—Lady Beecham **Mrs T. R. Kinsey**
4 **PO CAP EEL,** 8, b m Uncle Pokey—Hejera **Mrs T. R. Kinsey**
5 **SCORPOTINA,** 9, b m Scorpio (FR)—Ablula **Mrs T. R. Kinsey**
6 **STEEL GOLD,** 8, gr g Sonnen Gold—Ablula **Mrs T. R. Kinsey**

344 MR F. KIRBY, Northallerton

Postal: **High Whinholme Farm, Danby Wiske, Northallerton, North Yorkshire, DL7 0AS.**
Phone: **(01325) 378213 FAX (01325) 378213**

1 **DESPERATE DAYS (IRE),** 9, b g Meneval (USA)—Grageelagh Lady **Mr Fred Kirby**
2 **MCLOUGHLIN (IRE),** 9, ch g Orchestra—Boyne Bridge **Mr Fred Kirby**
3 **MENOO WHO (IRE),** 6, ch g Keen—Flying Anna **Mr Fred Kirby**
4 **SUPERGOLD (IRE),** 5, ch g Keen—Superflash **Mr Fred Kirby**
5 **WHINHOLME LASS (IRE),** 6, b m Mister Lord (USA)—Deep Down **Mr Fred Kirby**

Jockey (NH): W Dwan (10-0).

345 MR J. KIRBY, Wantage

Postal: **Pewit Farm, The Ridgeway, Manor Road, Wantage, Oxfordshire, OX12 8LY.**
Phone: **PHONE/FAX (01235) 767987**

1 **TISSISAT (USA),** 9, ch g Green Forest (USA)—Expansive **Mr John Kirby**

346 MISS H. C. KNIGHT, Wantage

Postal: **West Lockinge Farm, Wantage, Oxfordshire, OX12 8QF.**
Phone: **(01235) 833535 FAX 820110 MOBILE (0860) 110153 CAR (0589) 805597**

1 **ASK IN TIME (IRE),** 6, br g Jeu de Paille (FR)—C B M Girl **Mr Darren C. Mercer**
2 **BAYLINE STAR (IRE),** 8, b g Callernish—Blooming Rose **Mr Jim McCarthy**
3 **BENEFIT-IN-KIND (IRE),** 6, br g Executive Perk—Tanarpa **The Earl Cadogan**
4 **BLOWING ROCK (IRE),** 6, b g Strong Gale—Poor Elsie **Mrs Peter Andrews**
5 **BRAMBLEHILL CHIEF (IRE),** 7, b g Satco (FR)—Duchess **Mr Michael H. Watt**
6 **BRUSH OFF (IRE),** 5, b g Brush Aside (USA)—Bavello **Mr M. E. R. Allsopp**
7 **CELTIC SEASON,** 6, b g Vital Season—Welsh Flower **Four No Trumps Partnership**
8 **CLOUDY BILL,** 6, ch g Nicholas Bill—Welsh Cloud **Mr M. J. Howard**
9 **COLONEL BLAZER,** 6, b g Jupiter Island—Glen Dancer **Mr T. W. Biddlecombe**
10 **COXWELL COSSACK,** 5, ch g Gildoran—Stepout **Mrs P. A. Allsopp**
11 **DARAKSHAN (IRE),** 6, b g Akarad (FR)—Dafayna **Mr Michael H. Watt**
12 **DEBUTANTE DAYS,** 6, ch m Dominion—Doogali **Mrs Shirley Bradher**
13 **DICTUM (IRE),** 7, ch g Phardante (FR)—Secret Top **Mrs R. A. Humphries**
14 **DIE FLEDERMAUS (IRE),** 4, b g Batshoof—Top Mouse **Lady Vestey**
15 **DURNFORD BAY (IRE),** 5, b g Denel (FR)—Chamowen **R. W. Giles**
16 **EASTHORPE,** 10, b g Sweet Monday—Crammond Brig **Mr Martin Broughton**
17 **EDREDON BLEU (FR),** 6, b g Grand Tresor (FR)—Nuit Bleue III (FR) **Mr Jim Lewis**
18 **EZANAK (IRE),** 5, b g Darshaan—Ezana **The West Lockinge Partnership**
19 **FERRYHILL (IRE),** 5, b g Over The River (FR)—Eden Valley **Mrs R. A. Humphries**
20 **FULL OF OATS,** 12, b g Oats—Miss Melita **Mr Martin Bradford**
21 **GARETHSON (IRE),** 7, b g Cataldi—Tartan Sash **Mr & Mrs Derek Anderson**
22 **GORMAN (IRE),** 6, br g Lord Americo—Alcmena's Last **Miss H. Knight**
23 **GREY SMOKE,** 8, gr g Alias Smith (USA)—Salira **The Earl Cadogan**
24 **HARDLY (IRE),** 5, ch g Good Thyne (USA)—Monks Lass (IRE) **The Earl Cadogan**
25 **HEART,** 5, ch m Cadeaux Genereux—Recipe **Mr Chris & Mrs Shirley Brasher**
26 **HE FLIES BY NIGHT,** 9, b g Bold Owl—Premier Susan **Mrs Z. S. Clark**
27 **INTO THE CLAN (IRE),** 6, b g Be My Native (USA)—Polls Joy **Mr Ken Liscombe**
28 **KARSHI,** 8, b g Persian Bold—Kashmiri Snow **Lord Vestey**
29 **LEADING NOTE (USA),** 4, ch f Blushing John (USA)—Beat (USA) **The Leaders**
30 **LITTLE HULTON,** 5, b m Teenoso (USA)—Deep Line **Patrick Burling Developments Ltd**
31 **LORD OF THE FLIES (IRE),** 5, b br g Lord Americo—Beau's Trout **Winter Madness**
32 **MAID FOR ADVENTURE (IRE),** 7, br m Strong Gale—Fast Adventure **Mr Chris Brasher**
33 **MIM-LOU-AND,** 6, b g Glacial Storm (USA)—Tina's Melody **J. D. Martin**
34 **MUHTADI (IRE),** 5, br g Marju (IRE)—Moon Parade **The C. I. G. S. Partnership**
35 **NEMISTO,** 4, gr g Mystiko (USA)—Nemesia **The Nemisto Partnership**
36 **OATIS REGRETS,** 10, b g Oats—Joscilla **Mr D. C. G. Gyle-Thompson**
37 **OBAN,** 8, ch g Scottish Reel—Sun Goddess (FR) **Lord Hartington**
38 **OLD FASHIONED WAY (IRE),** 4, ch g Cardinal Flower—Anniversary Waltz **Mrs Guy Knight**
39 **ORCHID HOUSE,** 6, b m Town And Country—Tudor Orchid **Simon Bullimore**
40 **PARTY LEADER (IRE),** 5, b g Supreme Leader—Sally Dale **The SPS Group Ltd**
41 **PERSROLLA,** 4, br f Persian Bold—Primrolla **Lord Vestey**
42 **PONGO WARING (IRE),** 9, b g Strong Gale—Super Cailin **Mrs J. K. Peutherer**
43 **QUIBBLING,** 4, b f Salse (USA)—Great Exception **T. A. F. Frost**
44 **RAMALLAH,** 9, b g Ra Nova—Anglophil **The Maidens Green Partnership**
45 **RED BLAZER,** 7, ch g Bustino—Klewraye **Miss H. Knight**
46 **RHOSNEIGR BAY (IRE),** 5, b g Brush Aside (USA)—Necochea **Patrick Burling Developments Ltd**
47 **RIVER BAY (IRE),** 7, b m Over The River (FR)—Derrynaflan **Riverwood Racing**
48 **ROYAL BLAZER,** 4, br g Bustino—Explosiva (USA) **Miss H. Knight**
49 **SHILLING (IRE),** 4, b f Bob Back (USA)—Quiche **Million in Mind Partnership (7)**
50 **SINGLE SOURCING (IRE),** 7, b g Good Thyne (USA)—Lady Albron **Mr V. J. Adams**
51 **SLEEPTITE (FR),** 8, gr g Double Bed (FR)—Rajan Grey **Mr Chris & Mrs Shirley Brasher**
52 **SOUNDS LIKE FUN,** 7, b g Neltino—Blakeney Sound **Mrs H. Brown**
53 **STOMPIN,** 7, b g Alzao (USA)—Celebrity **Mr Martin Broughton**
54 **STORM DUST,** 9, b g Celestial Storm (USA)—Mary Sunley **Mr R. J. Sunley Tice**
55 **STORM FORECAST (IRE),** 6, b g Strong Gale—Cooleogan **Lord Vestey**
56 **STRIKE A LIGHT (IRE),** 6, b g Miner's Lamp—Rescued **Graham Kendrick & Partners**

MISS H. C. KNIGHT—continued

57 **SUPREME LADY (IRE),** 7, b m Supreme Leader—Tudor Lady **The Supreme Lady Partnership**
58 **SYDNEY TWOTHOUSAND (NZ),** 8, b g Sir Sydney (NZ)—Quite A Surprise (NZ) **Mr Michael H. Watt**
59 **TANGO KING,** 4, b c Suave Dancer (USA)—Be My Queen **Lord Swaythling**
60 **TELLICHERRY,** 9, br m Strong Gale—Quadro **Mr R. J. Jenks**
61 **THYNE'S VENTURE (IRE),** 6, ch g Good Thyne (USA)—Kath's Venture **Mrs Z. S. Clark**
62 **TIED FOR TIME (IRE),** 6, b g Montelimar (USA)—Cornamucla **Miss L. Robertson**
63 **TIGHT FIST (IRE),** 8, b g Doulab (USA)—Fussy Budget **Mrs A. M. Davis**
64 **TRAIL BOSS (IRE),** 7, b g The Noble Player (USA)—Jackson Miss **Mr Martin Broughton**
65 **WADE ROAD (IRE),** 7, b g King's Ride—Branstown Lady **The Earl Cadogan**
66 **WHAT A FUSS,** 5, b g Great Commotion (USA)—Hafwah **Mrs Denise Shefras**
67 **WINNOW,** 8, ch m Oats—Anglophil **Enigma Racing**
68 **WISHING WILLIAM (IRE),** 6, b g Riot Helmet—Forest Gale **Executive Racing**

Other Owners: Mr Ben Allen, Mr N. B. Attenborough, Mr B. M. Barrett, Mr S. G. Boyle, Mr Ben Brooks, Mr S. W. Broughton, Mr Hector H. Brown, Mr N. C. Clark, Mrs C. Clatworthy, Mrs D. Clatworthy, Mr Tom Cutts, Dr B. J. Eppel, Mr T. G. Fox, Roger Giles, Mr Graham Goode, Mr G. C. Green, Mrs Helen Greenshields, Mr H. Harrison, Mr Brian M. Hartigan, Mr Allan Hepworth, Mr John Holmes, Mr John Hornsey, Independent Twine Manufacturing Co Ltd, Mrs Nicholas Jones, Mrs M. Kelsey Fry, Mr M. B. J. Kimmins, Mr Richard Last, Mr J. R. Lavelle, Mr R. J. Lavelle, Mrs R. J. Lavelle, Mr John Loader, Mr Jim McGrath, Mr D. Minton, Mr H. O'Neill, Mr R. J. Parish, Mr Ian Rees, Mr G. A. Rogers, Mr W. S. Rogers, Mr Roger Sayer, Sir Anthony Scott, Dr George Scott, Mr H. R. Siegle, Ms Marie Steele, Mr H. Stephen Smith, Mr D. F. Sumpter, Mr John B. Sunley, Mr Harold Winton, Winton Bloodstock Ltd.

Jockeys (NH): J Culloty (9-7), J F Titley (10-0).

347 MR S. G. KNIGHT, Taunton

Postal: **Vincents Farm, Lower West Hatch, Taunton, Somerset, TA3 5RJ.**
Phone: **(01823) 480320 MOBILE (0378) 549452**

1 **CASPIAN BELUGA,** 10, b br g Persian Bold—Miss Thames **L. J. H. Partnership**
2 **KETCHICAN,** 6, b g Joligeneration—Fair Melys (FR) **Mr Terry Keiler**
3 **KIMBER HILL LAD,** 5, ch g Jester—Good Appeal **Mrs Wendy Murphy**
4 **LITTLE HOOLIGAN,** 7, b br g Rabdan—Nutwood Emma **Mr G. W. Hackling**
5 **NORMAN'S CONVINCED (IRE),** 8, b g Convinced—A Nice Alert **Somerset White Lining Ltd**
6 **SPLASH OF BLAKENEY,** 7, b m Blakeney Point—Upper Persuasion **Mr Gordon C. Fox**
7 **TRUST DEED (USA),** 10, ch g Shadeed (USA)—Karelia (USA) **Mr Malcolm Enticott**

THREE-YEAR-OLDS

8 **AUDEEN,** ch f Keen—Aude La Belle (FR) **Mrs Val Rapkins**
9 **GINNIESHOPE,** ch f Never So Bold—Sweet Home **Mrs Ginny Withers**

TWO-YEAR-OLDS

10 **ANOTHER LOVER,** ch f 23/2 Then Again—Love Street (Mummy's Pet) **Mrs Ginny Withers**
11 **KINGFISHERS BONNET,** b f 18/4 Hamas (IRE)—Mainmast (Bustino) **Mr P. J. Wightman**
12 **MASTER OF FASHION,** ch g 19/4 Triune—Fashion Princess (Van Der Linden (FR)) **Mr J. A. F. Cairns**
13 **NOTAGAINTHEN,** b f 3/2 Then Again—Fairy Ballerina (Fairy King (USA)) **Mrs Ginny Withers**

Other Owners: Mr Mike Boon, Mrs J. M. Greed, Mr A. L. Hawkings, Mrs P. M. Underhill, Mr Raymond Wright.

Jockey (NH): G Upton.

Conditional: D Salter.

348 MR C. LAFFON-PARIAS, Chantilly

Postal: **38, Avenue du General Leclerc, 60500 Chantilly, France.**
Phone: **(333) 44 57 53 75 FAX (333) 44 57 52 43**

1 **CARAMBA KELLY,** 4, b f Mtoto—Harefoot **Dartap**
2 **COTTON KISSER,** 4, b c Suave Dancer—Glim **E. Hinojosa**
3 **DYHIM DIAMOND,** 4, ch c Night Shift—Happy Landing **Gainsborough Stud**
4 **PSICOSSIS,** 5, b h Slip Anchor—Precious Jade **E. Hinojosa**
5 **RIPOSTO,** 4, ch c Night Shift—Kahara **J. Gispert**

THREE-YEAR-OLDS

6 **ACQUIRENDA,** ch f Arazi—Rimsh **C. Cealy**
7 **BAYOURIDA,** b f Slew O' Gold—Bellarida **Wertheimer et Frere**
8 **BETICO,** b g Fabulous Dancer—Ternia **Lomba**
9 **BRAVE CHARGER,** b c Nureyev—Sunset Rose **Gainsborough Stud**
10 **BUSY SIGNAL,** b c Bering—Liska's Dance **Wertheimer et Frere**
11 **ENJOLEUR,** b c Exit To Nowhere—En Avant **Mr Blair Down**
12 **EVENING CHARM,** b f Bering—Miss Fyor **Gainsborough Stud**
13 **FLAG CONNECTION,** b c Alleged—Lassie Connection **Wertheimer et Frere**
14 **FRAME OF MIND,** b c Unfuwain—Namatanga **J. Gonzalez**
15 **GREEN DELIGHT,** b f Green Desert—Capo di Monte **Gainsborough Stud**
16 **HERMITE,** b f St Jovite—Heaven Knows **Mr Alfred S. Y. Hui**
17 **HIDDEN COSTS,** b c Zafonic—Overcast **Gainsborough Stud**
18 **LEGGS,** ch c Be My Chief—Song Test **E, Hinojosa**
19 **LONE BID,** b c Priolo—Lobmille **Mr Jose Gonzales**
20 **MALAGA,** ch f Lion Cavern—Lady Liska **Dartap**
21 **MIRAMAR,** b c Bering—Mariana **A. Head**
22 **MUMTAAZ,** b c Warning—Jameelaty **Gainsborough Stud**
23 **MY LIFE,** b f Common Grounds—Key of Life **Gainsborough Stud**
24 **PASSING BEAUTY,** b f Green Desert—Pumpona **Gainsborough Stud**
25 **PHARATTA,** b f Fairy King—Sharata **Dartap**
26 **QUALITY GIFT,** gr br f Last Tycoon—Manntika **Gainsborough Stud**
27 **SPAGO,** b c Seeking The Gold—Spaulding **Mme C. Morange**
28 **STIFELIO,** b c Last Tycoon—Blue River **J. Gispert**
29 **TINGED WITH GOLD,** ch c Kris—Touch And Love **Gainsborough Stud**
30 **TOOFMAN,** b c Lahib—Pennsylvania **F. Sanz Blanco**
31 **TRES STRICT,** b c Irish River—Strictly Raised **Wertheimer et Frere**
32 **WHICH HAND,** ch c Indian Ridge—Madame Crecy **Gainsborough Stud**
33 **ZAKOUSKY,** b f Arazi—Zartota **Mr Alfred S. Y. Hui**

TWO-YEAR-OLDS

34 **AMERICAN QUEEN,** b f Fairy King—Apachee **Wertheimer et Frere**
35 Ch f Catrail—Arctic Winter **J. Hormaeche**
36 B c Arazi—Beloved Visitor **Gainsborough Stud**
37 **BLUE BOMBER,** b c Darshaan—Pale Blue **Wertheimer et Frere**
38 **CELINDA,** b f Bering—Consolation **J. Gonzales**
39 **DANANEYEV,** b c Goldneyev—Danagroom **Wertheimer et Frere**
40 B f Sillery—Free Hair **R. Santulli**
41 **FUSHAN,** b f Petit Loup—Fujitiva **E. Hinojosa**
42 B c Saddlers' Hall—Gift of Glory **E. Hinojosa**
43 Ch f Grand Lodge—Gracious Line **F. Hinojosa**
44 **HAZIDA,** b f Exit To Nowhere—Minaudeuse **Dartap**
45 **HEXAGON,** ch c Kris—Hint of Silver **C. Gispert**
46 B c Petit Loup—Lailati **Gainsborough Stud**
47 B c Sabrehill—Loxandra **Stilvi Compagnia**
48 B c Lycius—Miss Fyor **Gainsborough Stud**
49 **MYSTERIOUS LAND,** gr f Kaldoun—Mysterious Move **Dr W. K. Baumann**
50 B c Bering—North Haneena **F. Sanz Blanco**
51 **PALLADO,** b c Bigstone—Perle d'Irlande **F. Hinojosa**
52 **PAOLA,** b f Fabulous Dancer—Pride of Baino **Mme de Chambure**

MR C. LAFFON-PARIAS—continued

53 **PLISSETSKAIA,** b f Caerleon—Soviet Squaw **Wertheimer et Frere**
54 **SATEN,** b f Zieten—Safriya **J. Gonzalez**
55 **SPADOUN,** b c Kaldoun—Tolga **J. Gonzalez**
56 Ch f Persian Bold—Very Charming **Gainsborough Stud**
57 **VIL DESTIN,** b c Exit To Nowhere—Nativelee **Stilvi Compagnia**

349 MR D. A. LAMB, Seahouses

Postal: **East Fleetham, Seahouses, Northumberland, NE68 7UX.**
Phone: **(01665) 720260 OR (01665) 720837**

1 **BLAKENEY BOY,** 8, b g Blakeney—Leylandia **Mr D. A. Lamb**
2 **BROADGATE FLYER (IRE),** 4, b g Silver Kite (USA)—Fabulous Pet **Mr D. A. Lamb**
3 **BUCKS GALA (IRE),** 6, b g Buckskin (FR)—Queen's Gala **Mr D. A. Lamb**
4 **CALLERNOY (IRE),** 8, b g Callernish—Pats'y Girl **Exors of the late Mr R. R. Lamb**
5 **DARK MIDNIGHT (IRE),** 9, br g Petorius—Gaelic Jewel **Mr D. A. Lamb**
6 **GAME POINT,** 9, b m Broadsword (USA)—Running Game **Exors of the late Mr R. R. Lamb**
7 **GERMAN LEGEND,** 8, br g Faustus (USA)—Fairfields **Mr D. G. Pryde**
8 **GUILE POINT,** 7, b m Bybicello—Abergeen **Mr I. D. Jordon**
9 **KING PIP (IRE),** 6, ch g Phardante (FR)—Caesonia **Mr D. A. Lamb**
10 **KINGS MINSTRAL (IRE),** 8, ch g Andretti—Tara Minstral VII **Exors of the late Mr R. R. Lamb**
11 **MARCUS ROYALE,** 11, b g Royal Fountain—Marcus Lady **Mr D. A. Lamb**
12 **OUR FRANKIE,** 6, b g Respect—Brig House **Mr D. A. Lamb**
13 **PERSIAN GRANGE (IRE),** 8, ch g King Persian—Little Grange **Mr D. G. Pryde**
14 **PERSUASIVE TALENT (IRE),** 7, ch g Exhibitioner—Giorradana **Exors of the late Mr R. R. Lamb**
15 **SIGNAL POINT,** 7, b g Bybicello—Flying Tee **Mr I. D. Jordon**
16 **SNOOK POINT,** 11, b g Bybicello—Tarisma **Mr I. D. Jordon**
17 **THE ENERGISER,** 12, ch g Energist—Be An Angel **Exors of the late Mr R. R. Lamb**
18 **TO BE THE BEST,** 8, ch g Superlative—Early Call **Exors of the late Mr R. R. Lamb**
19 **ZAMBUSTER,** 10, b g Zambrano—Marcus Lady **Mr D. A. Lamb**

Other Owners: Mr K. L. Larnach.

Jockey (NH): J Burke (10-0).

350 MRS K. M. LAMB, Seahouses

Postal: **Burnhouse Farm, Seahouses, Northumberland, NE68 7UZ.**
Phone: **(01665) 720251 FAX (01665) 720251**

1 **DONT FORGET CURTIS (IRE),** 6, b g Don't Forget Me—Norse Lady **Mrs K. M. Lamb**
2 **FISH QUAY,** 15, ch g Quayside—Winkle **Mrs K. M. Lamb**
3 **FOREVER SHY (IRE),** 10, b g Sandalay—Cill Damhnait **Mrs K. M. Lamb**
4 **QUEENSBORO LAD (IRE),** 10, b g Euphemism—Yukon Lil **Mrs K. M. Lamb**
5 **RUBISLAW,** 6, ch g Dunbeath (USA)—Larnem **Mrs K. M. Lamb**
6 **SON OF TEMPO (IRE),** 9, b g Sandhurst Prince—Top Love (USA) **Mrs K. M. Lamb**

Lady Rider: Miss S Lamb (9-7).

351 MRS S. LAMYMAN, Lincoln

Postal: **Ruckland Manor, Louth, Lincolnshire, LN11 8RQ.**
Phone: **(01507) 533260**

1 **AJDAR,** 7, b g Slip Anchor—Loucoum (FR) **Mr P. Lamyman**
2 **BOMBADIL,** 6, b g Gunner B—Sugar Token **Mr P. Lamyman**
3 **JAMAICAN FLIGHT (USA),** 5, b h Sunshine Forever (USA)—Kalamona (USA) **Mr P. Lamyman**
4 **LACHESIS,** 5, ch m Lycius (USA)—Chance All (FR) **Mr J. McManamon**
5 **LYSANDER,** 6, ch g Takachiho—Apple At Night **Mr P. Lamyman**
6 **MAGNUS MAXIMUS,** 6, b g Takachiho—L'Oraz **Mr P. Lamyman**
7 **MODEST HOPE,** 11, b g Blushing Groom (FR)—Key Dancer (USA) **Mr J. McManamon**
8 **PROTOCOL (IRE),** 4, b c Taufan (USA)—Ukraine's Affair (USA) **Mr P. Lamyman**
9 **SCORCHED AIR,** 8, b m Elegant Air—Misfire **Mr P. Lamyman**
10 **SISTER ROSZA (IRE),** 10, b m Roselier (FR)—Glentoran Valley **Mr P. Lamyman**
11 **SUMO,** 5, ch g Superlative—Model Lady **Mrs Jennifer Woodward**

Other Owners: Mr Lewis Parker.

352 MRS J. L. LE BROCQ, Jersey

Postal: **St Etienne, Rue D'Elysee, St Peters, Jersey.**
Phone: **(01534) 481461**

1 **DUTOSKY,** 8, b m Doulab (USA)—Butosky **Miss J. V. May**
2 **FORCING BID,** 4, b g Forzando—Cox's Pippin (USA) **Mr & Mrs H. R. Moszkowicz**
3 **GLORY BEE,** 14, ch g Bold Owl—Sweet Minuet **Miss J. V. May, Mrs J. Le Brocq**
4 **GREEN'S FAIR (IRE),** 8, b g Carmelite House (USA)—Lockwood Girl **Mr N. G. Ahier**
5 **SWEEPING STATEMENT,** 4, b f Statoblest—Sweep Along (IRE) **Miss J. V. May, Mrs J. Le Brocq**
6 **THE WAD,** 5, br g Emarati (USA)—Fair Melys (FR) **Miss J. V. May**
7 **TRUE KNOT,** 9, b m True Song—Ganglion **Mrs J. Le Brocq**
8 **WHOTHEHELLISHARRY,** 5, ch g Rich Charlie—Ballagarrow Girl **Miss J. V. May**
9 **WILDMOOR,** 4, ch g Common Grounds—Impropriety **Miss J. V. May**

Other Owners: Mr Godfrey Amy, Mr Chris Benest, Mr John Berry, Mr Nick Blake, Mrs Gaye Martin, Mr Francis Pembrook.

Jockeys (Flat): P Bloomfield, G Duffield (8-1, w.a.), M Fenton (8-1), R McGhin (8-3).

Jockeys (NH): P Holley (10-0), A Maguire (10-0, w.a.), B Powell (w.a.).

Amateurs: Mr C De P Berry (10-10), Mr J C De P Berry (10-7), Mr T Verdon (10-0).

Lady Riders: Mrs P Drew (9-0), Mrs J Le Brocq (8-4).

353 MR ROBIN LE PENNEC, Jersey

Postal: **Green Bank Racing Stables, St Peters, Jersey, JE3 7AH.**
Phone: **HOME (01534) 483296 YARD (01534) 483800**

1 4, B g Prince of Cill Dara—Come On Doll **All Bright Cleaning Services**
2 **NEWBURY COAT,** 8, b g Chilibang—Deanta In Eirinn **Mrs E. E. Le Pennec**
3 **RIGHTACRES LAD,** 7, ch g Librate—Sue Clare **Mr A. J. Le Pennec**
4 4, Br g Prince of Cill Dara—Sacred River **Mrs E. E. Le Pennec**

Other Owners: Mr P. H. A. Court, Miss P. Philo.

Jockey (NH): P Holley (10-0, w.a.).

Amateur: Mr T Verdon (9-10).

354 MR S. J. LEADBETTER, Berwick-upon-Tweed

Postal: **Ladykirk Stables, Berwick-upon-Tweed, TD15 1SU.**
Phone: **(01289) 382519**

1 **BAGOTS PARK,** 9, ro g Alias Smith (USA)—Newfield Green **Mr S. J. Leadbetter**
2 **BLUE COLLAR,** 7, b g Bybicello—Over Dinsdale **Mr S. J. Leadbetter**
3 **DAVARA,** 12, gr g Dawn Johnny (USA)—News Belle **Mr D. W. Nicholson**
4 **DUNDYVAN,** 16, ch g Crimson Beau—Flora Day **Mr S. J. Leadbetter**
5 **JUPITER LORD,** 7, b g Jupiter Island—Angelic Appeal **Mr S. J. Leadbetter**
6 **PADDY HAYTON,** 17, br g St Paddy—Natenka **Mr S. J. Leadbetter**
7 **ROBARA,** 8, b br g Another Realm—Kate Kimberley **Mr D. W. Nicholson**

Amateur: Mr R Shiels (10-10).

355 MR AUGUSTINE LEAHY, Kilmallock

Postal: **"Lorien" Clogher, Kilmallock, Co. Limerick, Ireland.**
Phone: **(063) 90676 (087) 580296 FAX (063) 90676**

1 **BEAU CYRANO (IRE),** 6, b g Cyrano de Bergerac—Only Great **White Star Holdings**
2 **BE MY FOLLY (IRE),** 6, ch m Astronef—Folly Gale **Miss M. McGrath**
3 **COULTHARD (IRE),** 5, ch h Glenstal (USA)—Royal Aunt **Mrs E. Leahy**
4 **HAKKINEN (IRE),** 7, ch g Rising—Shenley Annabella **Winners Circle Racing Club**
5 4, B c Fools Holme (USA)—Hotel du Lac
6 **INDESTRUCTIBLE (IRE),** 10, ch g Duky—Chatty Actress **J. P. McManus**
7 **IRVINE (IRE),** 6, b g Rising—Garryfine Cross **Mrs E. Leahy**
8 4, Ch g Moscow Society (USA)—Lyphards Anemone **M. Wilmott**
9 **MOSTA (IRE),** 5, b m Moscow Society (USA)—Shenley Annabella **M. M. Power**
10 **MUSCOVITE MARBLE (IRE),** 5, b m Moscow Society (USA)—Mrs Foley **C. Creed**
11 **PAS POSSIBLE (IRE),** 6, b g The Bart (USA)—Pollette **T. G. Curtin**
12 **PHARDY (IRE),** 7, b g Phardante (FR)—Enchanted Lady **Gan Ceann Syndicate**
13 **REGIT (IRE),** 8, b g Duky—Shenley Annabella **Mrs E. Leahy**
14 **SEA FISHER (IRE),** 7, b g Mulhollande (USA)—Escape Path **J. P. McManus**
15 4, B f Soviet Lad (USA)—She Is The Boss
16 4, B f Topanoora—Tender Always **Miss S. J. Leahy**
17 4, Gr f Batshoof—To Oneiro
18 **TRICKERY (IRE),** 4, b f Cyrano de Bergerac—Beguiled (IRE) **Capt. E. Williams**
19 **VISCOUNT (IRE),** 5, b g Jolly Jake (NZ)—Chelsea Charmer **Mrs G. E. Jones**

THREE-YEAR-OLDS

20 **BLACKWATER STAR (IRE),** ch f Island Reef—Sadowa **Lisselan Farms**
21 B g Archway (IRE)—Dora Gayle
22 **MYSTERIOUS MISS (IRE),** b f Imp Society (USA)—Hotel du Lac
23 **RUBINHO (IRE),** ch c Shalford (IRE)—Perle's Fashion **Miss M. McGrath**

TWO-YEAR-OLDS

24 B f 29/3 Polish Patriot (USA)—Beguiled (IRE) (Be My Guest (USA)) **Capt. E. Williams**
25 B f 29/1 Archway (IRE)—Hench Woman (Henbit (USA))
26 B f 29/3 Namaqualand (USA)—Irish Affaire (IRE) (Fairy King (USA))
27 B c 22/4 Contract Law (USA)—Kilboy Concorde (African Sky)
28 B f 24/5 Balla Cove—Manela Lady (Ela-Mana-Mou)
29 B f 30/4 Tirol—Scottish Gaelic (USA) (Highland Park (USA))
30 B f 15/3 Lucky Guest—Tender Always (Tender King)

Other Owners: T. Begley, Blackwater Motors, Lady Melissa Brooke, D. Cotter, J. F. Dorrian, Ford Homestead Horse Centre, R. Goodwin, Patsy Byrnes Synd, J. Quane, T. F. Sheehan, Ian Williams.

Conditional: M J Collins (9-7).

Lady Rider: S J Leahy (8-10).

356 MR R. R. LEDGER, Sittingbourne

Postal: **Sorrento, School Lane, Borden, Sittingbourne, Kent, ME9 8JS.**
Phone: **(01795) 423360**

1 **TARTAN GLORY,** 8, b m Roman Glory—Spartan Flame **Mr R. R. Ledger**
2 **UPWARD SURGE (IRE),** 8, ch g Kris—Sizes Vary **Mr R. R. Ledger**
3 **WILTOSKI,** 10, b g Petoski—Cojean (USA) **Mr R. R. Ledger**

Jockey (NH): A Thornton.

Lady Rider: Mrs Nicky Ledger (9-0).

357 MR RICHARD LEE, Presteigne

Postal: **The Bell House, Byton, Presteigne, Powys, LD8 2HS.**
Phone: **(01544) 267672 FAX 260247 CAR (0831) 846550 MOBILE(0836) 537145**

1 **AMONG ISLANDS,** 7, b m Jupiter Island—Queen of The Nile **Mr R. A. Hughes**
2 **ANOTHER COMEDY,** 8, b g El Conquistador—Miss Comedy **The Another Comedy Partnership**
3 **CATWALKER (IRE),** 7, b g Reasonable (FR)—Norse Lady **Mr Richard Lee**
4 5, B g Contract Law (USA)—Celeritas
5 **COLD COMFORT,** 6, b g Arctic Lord—Main Brand **Mr G. Snell**
6 **DEBT OF HONOR,** 10, ch g Deep River—Vulgan's Honor **Mrs Bill Neale**
7 **GOLDEN MILLENIUM,** 6, ch m Radical—Belmont Lady **Gigmill Racing Club**
8 **GOOD FOR A LOAN,** 11, b g Daring March—Game For A Laugh **Mr T. M. J. Curry**
9 **JOSHUA'S VISION (IRE),** 7, b g Vision (USA)—Perle's Fashion **J & D Racing**
10 **LILILO (IRE),** 6, b g Vision (USA)—Persian Royale **Mr Richard Lee**
11 **LITTLE GAINS,** 9, b g Nearly A Hand—Flavias Cottage **Mr Bob Brazier**
12 **MACGEORGE (IRE),** 8, b g Mandalus—Colleen Donn **Mr J. H. Watson**
13 **MANAMOUR,** 11, br g Mandalus—Fifi L'Amour **Mr R. L. C. Hartley**
14 **MISTER BLAKE,** 8, b g Damister (USA)—Larive **Mr W. D. Edwards**
15 **ORIENTAL BOY (IRE),** 6, b g Boreen (FR)—Arctic Sue **Oriental Boy Partnership**
16 **PLAY GAMES (USA),** 10, ch g Nijinsky (CAN)—Playful Queen (USA) **Mr J. O. Beavan**
17 **SHOPLATCH,** 5, ch g Phardante (FR)—Ethels Course **Mr Gareth Samuel**
18 **SNOWBOY (IRE),** 6, br g Celio Rufo—Laurestown Rose **Mr George Brookes**
19 **STARDANTE (IRE),** 6, b g Phardante (FR)—Borecca **Risk Factor Partnership**
20 **SUPER COIN,** 10, b g Scorpio (FR)—Penny Princess **Mr George Brookes**
21 5, B m Kala Shikari—Turn Up The Wick **Mr W. Arblaster**

Other Owners: Mr N. Abbott, Mr G. H. S. Bailey, N. J. Barrowclough, Mrs J. A. Beavan, Mr R. A. Beavan, Mr J. C. Coales, Mr B. Connolly, Dudley Coombes, Mr P. A. Dickinson, Mr D. E. Edwards, Mr Richard Edwards, Mr J. A. Evans, R. Geffen, Mr P. Gowman, David Harris, Mr B. Hinchcliff, Mr John M. Jackson, J & J Slitting Services, Mrs C. Lee, Mr D. R. Lee, Mr Patrick H. Lee O.B.E., T. Loftus, Mr B. Lynn, K. McCormac, Mr Richard Money, Mr Jim Mottram, Mr Des Murray, Mr W. J. Perchard, Mr P. T. G. Phillips, Miss Tracey Quinn, Mr W. Quinn, Mr Will Roseff, Mr R. Samuel, Mr Raymond Smith, Mr J. Stewart, Mr Martin Stillwell, Walgrove International Ltd.

Jockeys (NH): R Johnson, A Maguire (10-0).

Conditional: Ian Pike (9-7).

Amateur: Mr S Durack (9-7).

358 MR J. P. LEIGH, Gainsborough

Postal: **Mount House Stables, 12 Long Lane, Willoughton, Gainsborough, Lincolnshire.**
Phone: **(01427) 668210**

1 **CATTLY HANG (IRE)**, 8, b g King's Ride—Lawless Secret **Mr W. G. N. Morgan**
2 **INFLATION**, 4, b f Primo Dominie—Fluctuate **Mr J. W. Rowles**
3 **JOHNNIE THE JOKER**, 7, gr g Absalom—Magic Tower **Miss M. Carrington Smith**
4 **ROCKIE THE JESTER**, 4, b g Rock Hopper—Magic Steps **Mr J. P. Leigh**

THREE-YEAR-OLDS

5 **LADY OF SPAIN**, ch f Aragon—Myth **Mr J. W. Rowles**
6 **ROUGE**, gr f Rudimentary (USA)—Couleur de Rose **Mr J. M. Greetham**

Other Owners: Mr John L. Evans, Mrs E. A. Quayle, Mr C. G. Rowles Nicholson.

359 MR G. LEWIS, Epsom

Postal: **Thirty Acre Barn, Shephard Walk, Headley, Epsom, Surrey, KT18 6BX.**
Phone: **ASHTEAD (01372) 277662 OR 277366 FAX (01372) 277366**

1 **CARLTON (IRE)**, 4, ch g Thatching—Hooray Lady **City Slickers**
2 **EASTERN PROPHETS**, 5, b g Emarati (USA)—Four Love **Mrs J. M. Purches**
3 **MUARA BAY**, 4, gr c Absalom—Inca Girl **Mr P. A. Idris**
4 **PRIX DE CLERMONT (IRE)**, 4, b g Petorius—Sandra's Choice **The Jet Stream Partnership**
5 **REFERENDUM (IRE)**, 4, b c Common Grounds—Final Decision **Highclere Thoroughbred Racing**
6 **RIGHT MAN**, 4, gr c Robellino (USA)—High Matinee **Mr G. V. Wright**
7 **TIGRELLO**, 4, ch c Efisio—Prejudice **Mr A. M. Al-Midani**

THREE-YEAR-OLDS

8 **AIR ATTACHE (USA)**, b c Sky Classic (CAN)—Diplomatic Cover (USA) **Mr Khalifa Dasmal**
9 **ELA-ANDRULLA (IRE)**, b f Rainbows For Life (CAN)—Rep's Retton (USA) **Mrs Andry Muinos**
10 **IMANI**, b f Danehill (USA)—Santarem (USA) **Mr R. N. Khan**
11 **IVORY LEAGUE**, b f Last Tycoon—Ivory Lane **Mr R. D. Hubbard**
12 **LAUREN'S LAD**, ch c Tachyon Park—Glory Isle **Mrs Linda McCalla**
13 **MANDHAR (IRE)**, b c Scenic—Clonross Lady **Mr Abdulla Al Khalifa**
14 **MANTLES PRINCESS**, b f Rock City—Teslemi (USA) **Mr David Barker**
15 **MISS GILLY**, b f Thowra (FR)—Mey Madam **The Smine Partnership**
16 **NATALIE'S PET**, b f Merdon Melody—Tripolitaine (FR) **Mrs Linda McCalla**
17 **PURE COINCIDENCE**, b c Lugana Beach—Esilam **Mrs Andry Muinos**
18 **PURE MAGIC**, b c Magic Ring (IRE)—Confection **Mr G. Lewis**
19 **ROYAL SHYNESS**, b f Royal Academy (USA)—Miss Demure **Mr R. D. Hubbard**
20 **SAINTLY THOUGHTS (USA)**, b br c St Jovite (USA)—Free Thinker (USA) **Mr Khalifa Dasmal**
21 **SURPRESA CARA**, ch f Risk Me (FR)—Yukosan **Ms E. A. Whelton**

TWO-YEAR-OLDS

22 Ch c 28/2 Paris House—Auction Maid (IRE)
23 Ch c 23/3 Emarati (USA)—Bentinck Hotel
24 **CEDAR WELLS (USA)**, b c 8/5 Desert Secret (IRE)—Sans Sorrow (USA) **Mr & Mrs Z. Kantis**
25 **COMMONWEALTH (IRE)**, b c 4/4 Common Grounds—Silver Slipper **Highclere Thoroughbred Racing Ltd**
26 **DIVING FOR PEARLS**, ch c 3/4 Petardia—Island Heather (IRE) **Mr David Waters**
27 Ch c 20/3 Pips Pride—Dorado Llave (USA) **Noodles Racing**
28 B f 16/3 Lugana Beach—Esilam **Mr Max Muinos**
29 Ch c 26/1 Clantime—First Play **Lucayan Stud**
30 B c 16/5 Minshaanshu Amad—Glory Isle
31 **LATCH LIFTER**, b c 26/4 Prince Sabo—Thevetia **Mr David Barker**
32 Ch c 20/4 Archway (IRE)—Lauretta Blue (IRE)
33 **MANZONI**, b c 5/1 Warrshan (USA)—Arc Empress Jane (IRE) **Mr David Barker**
34 B c 1/2 Cyrano de Bergerac—May Light

MR G. LEWIS—continued

35 **NEPTUNE,** b c 16/4 Dolphin Street (FR)—Seal Indigo (IRE) **Highclere Thoroughbred Racing Ltd**
36 B br c 18/2 First Trump—Oriental Air (IRE) **Mr G. H. P. Pritchard**
37 B f 15/1 Ardkinglass—Petrina Bay
38 **SHABAASH,** b c 27/2 Mujadil (USA)—Folly Vision (IRE) **Mr S. Chatwal**
39 Ch c 14/3 Soviet Lad (USA)—Stop The Cavalry
40 **SYRAH,** br f 24/3 Minshaanshu Amad—La Domaine **White Bear Ltd**
41 **TAYAR,** ch c 8/4 Mystiko (USA)—Tahnee **Mr & Mrs Z. Kantis**
42 **WHYDAH,** br f 17/5 Suave Dancer (USA)—Calandra (USA) **White Bear Ltd**

Other Owners: Ms M. L. Bartoli, Mr R. Bell, Mr Manolo Castilla, Mr R. Hannon, Mr Roger Harding, Mr A. A. Hussain, Mr W. J. P. Jackson, Mrs J. M. Khan, Mr R. N. Khan, Mrs G. Lamprell, Mr S. Lamprell, Mr Geoff Lewis, Mr V. McCalla, Mr Jim McCarthy, Mr J. N. G. Moreton, Mr D. Purches, Mr A. Schipper, Mr Michael H. Watt, Mr John Wetherell.

Jockeys (Flat): Pat Eddery (8-4, w.a.), Paul Eddery (8-0).

Apprentice: D Denby (8-0).

360 MR N. P. LITTMODEN, Wolverhampton

Postal: **Phoenix Stables, Wolverhampton Racecourse, Gorsebrook Road, Wolverhampton, WV6 0PE.**
Phone: **(01902) 688558 (0370) 964865 MOBILE (01902) 688558 FAX**

1 **ANNIE,** 4, gr f Thethingaboutitis (USA)—Rue de Remarque **Mrs D. Burton**
2 **AXEMAN (IRE),** 6, b g Reprimand—Minnie Tudor **Mr J. Barton**
3 **BURNING (USA),** 6, b g Bering—Larnica (USA) **Mr T. Peters**
4 **CASHAPLENTY,** 5, ch g Ballacashtal (CAN)—Storm of Plenty **Mr J. R. Salter**
5 **CRETAN GIFT,** 7, ch g Cadeaux Genereux—Caro's Niece (USA) **Mr T. Clarke**
6 **DENNIS WISE,** 5, ch g High Kicker (USA)—Poppin Gill **Mr N. P. Littmoden**
7 **DUNSTON DURGAM (IRE),** 4, b c Durgam (USA)—Blazing Sunset **Mr T. Walker**
8 **EVEZIO RUFO,** 6, b g Blakeney—Empress Corina **Mr T. Clarke**
9 **FAILED TO HIT,** 5, b g Warrshan (USA)—Missed Again **M. C. S. D. Racing**
10 **FLOOD'S HOT STUFF,** 4, gr f Chilibang—Tiszta Sharok **Mr Philip Kirby**
11 **HEAD GARDENER (IRE),** 4, b g Be My Chief (USA)—Silk Petal **The Gardening Partnership**
12 **HELLO MISTER,** 7, b h Efisio—Ginnies Petong **M. C. S. D. Racing**
13 **KING OF PERU,** 5, b h Inca Chief (USA)—Julie's Star (IRE) **M. C. S. D. Racing**
14 **MOOR DANCE MAN,** 8, b g Seymour Hicks (FR)—Cute Dancer **Mr N. P. Littmoden**
15 **MULLAGH HILL LAD (IRE),** 5, b g Cyrano de Bergerac—Fantasise (FR) **The Bramble Partnership**
16 **MYSTERIUM,** 4, gr g Mystiko (USA)—Way To Go **Mrs G. L. Taylor**
17 **NORTH ARDAR,** 8, b g Ardar—Langwaite **Mr P. Stringer**
18 **OVER THE MOON,** 4, ch f Beveled (USA)—Beyond The Moon (IRE) **Trojan Racing**
19 **POSIE CHAIN,** 5, b m Rakaposhi King—Call Me Daisy **Mrs P. M. Daniel**
20 **SHERATON GIRL,** 4, b f Mon Tresor—Sara Sprint **The Happy Partnership**
21 **TALLULAH BELLE,** 5, b m Crowning Honors (CAN)—Fine A Leau (USA) **Trojan Racing**

THREE-YEAR-OLDS

22 **ACHILLES,** ch c Deploy—Vatersay (USA) **Achilles International Ltd**
23 **BLACK JET,** b g Durgam (USA)—Blazing Sunset **Mr T. Clarke**
24 **BLUE KITE,** ch c Silver Kite (USA)—Gold And Blue (IRE) **Mr T. Clarke**
25 **DRYAD,** ch c Risk Me (FR)—Lizzy Cantle **Mr Brian D. Cantle**
26 **FROLICKING,** b f Mujtahid (USA)—Perfect Desire (USA) **Foley Steelstock**
27 **GRALMANO (IRE),** b c Scenic—Llangollen (IRE) **Coleorton Moor Racing**
28 **IMBACKAGAIN (IRE),** b g Mujadil (USA)—Ballinclogher (IRE) **M. C. S. D. Racing**
29 **MOONLIGHTANDROSES,** b f Aragon—Lively (IRE) **Mrs G. Jennings**
30 **ONE SINGER,** ch c Anshan—Moushka **Clayton Bigley Partnership**
31 **POLLYDUU,** ch f Casteddu—Polly Packer **Mr David Hall**

MR N. P. LITTMODEN—continued

32 ROSIE JAQUES, b f Doyoun—Premier Princess **La Piette Partnership**
33 SUPER RASCAL, b g Superpower—Gild The Lily **Guy, Hart & Plyvine**
34 TEEPLOY GIRL, b f Deploy—Intoxication **Evergreen Partnership**
35 B f Timeless Times (USA)—Woodbegood **R.A.M. Racecourses Ltd**

TWO-YEAR-OLDS

36 ACHILLES STAR, ch c 9/4 Deploy—Norbella (Nordico (USA)) **Achilles International Ltd**
37 BLUE STAR, b c 5/4 Whittingham (IRE)—Gold And Blue (IRE) (Bluebird (USA)) **Mr T. Clarke**
38 JOEY THE JOLLY, b c 16/3 Belfort (FR)—Divine Penny (Divine Gift) **Mr & Mrs N. Wolstencroft**
39 B f 27/3 Ardkinglass—Kajetana (FR) (Caro) **Mr T. Clarke**
40 B f 3/3 Up And At 'Em—Lady-Mumtaz (Martin John) **Trojan Racing**
41 B f 7/2 Distant Relative—Moments Joy (Adonijah) **Trojan Racing**
42 NATIVE QUEST, b c 14/4 Alhijaz—Adana (FR) (Green Dancer (USA)) **Mr Nilesh Unadkat**
43 PC'S EUROCRUISER (IRE), b c 29/3 Fayruz—Kuwait Night (Morston (FR)) **P. C.'s Racing Partners**
44 PERUVIAN STAR, b c 9/3 Emarati (USA)—Julie's Star (IRE) (Thatching) **M.C.S.D. Racing**
45 B c 27/3 Case Law—Shahrazad (Young Emperor) **Mr N. P. Littmoden**
46 Gr c 31/3 Paris House—Thatched Roof (IRE) (Thatching) **Mr T. Clarke**

Other Owners: Mr M. Bishop, Mr Chris Bradbury, Mr P. C. Burgess, Exors Of The Late Mr M. J. Burton, Miss Stephanie Clark, Mr J. W. C. Coxon, Mr A. Ewen, Mrs P. A. Farr, Mr O. A. Gunter, Mr G. S. Hartshorn, Mr A. Holmes, Mrs J. E. Lloyd, Mr S. C. Matthews, Mr P. McCauley, Mr Barry J. McClean, Mrs Maggie McClean, Mr S. Myatt, Brigadier A. H. Parker Bowles, Mr Terry Pritchard, Mr John Pugh, Mr G. H. Senior, Mr P. C. Smith, Ms Patricia Watson, Mr P. A. Whiteman.

Jockeys (Flat): J Weaver (8-4), S Whitworth (8-4).

Apprentice: K Pierrepont (8-2).

Amateur: Mr J Tyler-Morris (8-12).

361 MR R. E. A. LIVERMORE, Usk

Postal: **Red House Farm, Pen-Y-Cae Mawr, Usk, Monmouthshire, Wales, NP5 1LX.**
Phone: **(01291) 650774**

1 BARON'S HEIR, 11, b g Town And Country—Lady London **Mrs J. L. Livermore**
2 CO-TACK, 13, ch g Connaught—Dulcidene **Mrs J. L. Livermore**
3 FONSMILE, 9, b m Cruise Missile—Fonmon **Mrs J. L. Livermore**
4 NOTANOTHERONE (IRE), 10, b g Mazaad—Maltese Pet **Mrs J. L. Livermore**
5 4, Gr g Fools Holme (USA)—Phar Lapa **Mrs J. L. Livermore**

362 MR B. J. LLEWELLYN, Bargoed

Postal: **Ffynonau - Duon Farm, Pentwyn, Fochriw, Bargoed, Mid-Glamorgan, CF8 9NR.**
Phone: **(01685) 841259 FAX (01685) 841259**

1 CAPABILITY BROWN, 11, b g Dominion—Tomfoolery **Mr David S. Lewis**
2 CHARLIE CHANG (IRE), 5, b g Don't Forget Me—East River (FR) **Mr A. P. Gent**
3 DISTANT STORM, 5, ch g Pharly (FR)—Candle In The Wind **Mr D. H. Driscoll**
4 DRAMA KING, 6, b g Tragic Role (USA)—Consistent Queen **Mrs Vicki Guy**
5 FLASHMAN, 8, b g Flash of Steel—Proper Madam **Mr B. J. Llewellyn**
6 GAJAN (IRE), 4, b g Ela-Mana-Mou—Delightful Time **John Williams Transport (Newport) Ltd**
7 GALLOPING GUNS (IRE), 6, ch g Conquering Hero (USA)—Jillette **Mr Patrick Harrington**
8 GUNMAKER, 9, ch g Gunner B—Lucky Starkist **Mr B. J. Llewellyn**
9 IRISH SEA (USA), 5, b g Zilzal (USA)—Dunkellin (USA) **Mr Salvo Giannini**

MR B. J. LLEWELLYN—continued

10 LORD NITROGEN (USA), 8, b br g Greinton—Jibber Jabber (USA) **Mr B. J. Llewellyn**
11 NORD LYS (IRE), 7, b g Nordico (USA)—Beach Light **Mr B. J. Llewellyn**
12 NORTHERN OPTIMIST, 10, b m Northern Tempest (USA)—On A Bit **Mackworth Snooker Club PT**
13 ORANGE PLACE (IRE), 7, ch g Nordance (USA)—Little Red Hut **Lodge Cross Partnership**
14 PRIZEFIGHTER, 7, b g Rambo Dancer (CAN)—Jaisalmer **Mr J. Milton**
15 STRIKE-A-POSE, 8, ch m Blushing Scribe (USA)—My Bushbaby **Mr B. J. Llewellyn**
16 XENOPHON OF CUNAXA (IRE), 5, b g Cyrano de Bergerac—Annais Nin **Mr Alan J. Williams**

Other Owners: Mr K. Butt, Mrs T. P. Davichand, Mr Dilwyn Davies, Mr Des Edwards, Mr S. Harrison, Mr N. Heath, Mr I. Jones, Mr Gary Mills, Mr Eamonn O'Malley, Mr G. E. Parr, Mr J. V. Rawlings.

Jockey (Flat): Tyrone Williams.

Amateur: Mr John Lewis Llewellyn (10-5).

363 MR F. LLOYD, Bangor-on-Dee

Postal: **Althrey Woodhouse, Bangor-on-Dee, Wrexham, Clwyd, LL13 0DA.**
Phone: **(01978) 780356 FAX (01978) 780427**

1 ALTHREY ARISTOCRAT (IRE), 8, ch g Aristocracy—Fairy Island **Mr F. Lloyd**
2 ALTHREY CAPTAIN (IRE), 8, ch g Hardboy—Shimering Star **Mr F. Lloyd**
3 ALTHREY FLAME (IRE), 5, b m Torus—Keep The Cut **Mr F. Lloyd**
4 ALTHREY GALE (IRE), 7, b g Supreme Leader—Greek Gale **Mr F. Lloyd**
5 ALTHREY LEADER (IRE), 8, b g Supreme Leader—Shannon Belle **Mr F. Lloyd**
6 ALTHREY PRINCESS (IRE), 5, b m Brush Aside (USA)—Torus Court **Mr F. Lloyd**
7 ALTHREY RULER (IRE), 5, b g Phardante (FR)—Keego's Aunt **Mr F. Lloyd**
8 ALTHREY SAINT (IRE), 5, b g Orchestra—Butty Miss **Mr F. Lloyd**
9 ALTHREY TORCH (IRE), 6, b g Torus—Keep The Cut **Mr F. Lloyd**

364 MR L. R. LLOYD-JAMES, Malton

Postal: **4 Wayfaring Close, Malton, North Yorkshire, YO17 9DW.**
Phone: **(01653) 696872 OFFICE 690200 MOBILE (0802) 872900 OR (0410) 162024**

1 AVANT HUIT, 6, ch m Clantime—Apres Huit
2 FRENCH GINGER, 7, ch m Most Welcome—French Plait
3 MARAUD, 4, ch g Midyan (USA)—Peak Squaw (USA)
4 MARY HAYNE, 5, ch m Handsome Sailor—The Huyton Girls
5 OHNONOTAGAIN, 6, b m Kind of Hush—Dear Glenda
6 STAR OF THE ROAD, 4, b c Risk Me (FR)—Astrid Gilberto

THREE-YEAR-OLDS

7 Gr f Barrys Gamble—Balgownie
8 DOUBLE POWER, ch f Superpower—Double Decree
9 B g Puissance—Fontaine Lady
10 B f Barrys Gamble—Keep Mum

Other Owners: Mr David Dyer, Miss L. M. Helliwell, Mrs C. Lloyd-James, Mrs Cheryl L. Owen, Mr J. C. Owen, Mr S. F. Stubbings, R. Vardy.

Jockey (Flat): R Cochrane (w.a.).

Jockey (NH): L Wyer (w.a.).

Apprentice: C Lowther (w.a.).

Conditional: M Newton (9-7).

Amateur: Mr J Tizzard (w.a.).

365 MR ALAN LOCKWOOD, Malton

Postal: **Fleet Cross Farm, Brawby, Malton, North Yorkshire,YO17 0QA.**
Phone: **(01751) 431796**

1 **ANOTHER PICEA,** 5, b g Picea—Atoka **Mr Chester Bosomworth**
2 **CUMBERLAND BLUES (IRE),** 9, b g Lancastrian—Tengello **Mr John L. Holdroyd**
3 **GLAD SHE'S GONE,** 7, gr g Move Off—Absent Lady **Mrs A. Lockwood**
4 **GOODHEAVENS MRTONY,** 11, b g Carwhite—Golden October **Mrs Carole Sykes**
5 **PEEP O DAY,** 7, b m Domynsky—Betrothed **Mr John L. Holdroyd**
6 **TYNDRUM GOLD,** 8, br g Sonnen Gold—Firwood **Mr John L. Holdroyd**

Lady Rider: Miss Alyson J Deniel (9-7).

366 MR D. R. LODER, Newmarket

Postal: **Graham Lodge, Birdcage Walk, Newmarket, Suffolk, CB8 0NE.**
Phone: **(01638) 662233 FAX (01638) 665596**

1 **APPREHENSION,** 4, b c In The Wings—First Kiss
2 **DREAM OF NURMI,** 4, ch g Pursuit of Love—Finlandaise (FR)
3 **GENEROUS LIBRA,** 4, b g Generous (IRE)—Come On Rosi
4 **GRACEFUL LASS,** 4, b f Sadler's Wells (USA)—Hi Lass
5 **MANOLO (FR),** 5, b g Cricket Ball (USA)—Malouna (FR)
6 **PRIENA (IRE),** 4, ch f Priolo (USA)—Isabena
7 **YAROB (IRE),** 5, ch h Unfuwain (USA)—Azyaa

THREE-YEAR-OLDS

8 **ALYRIVA (USA),** b c Alydeed (CAN)—Portio (USA)
9 **AMBIGUOUS,** ch c Arazi (USA)—Vaguely
10 **BEACON BLAZE,** ch f Rudimentary (USA)—Beacon Hill
11 **BILLIONAIRE,** b c Distant Relative—Miss Plum
12 **BINT KALDOUN (IRE),** b f Kaldoun (FR)—Shy Danceuse (FR)
13 **BLUEBELLE,** b f Generous (IRE)—Hi Lass
14 **CAPTAIN LOGAN (IRE),** b c Fairy King (USA)—Heaven High
15 **COURT LANE (USA),** b f Machiavellian (USA)—Chicarica (USA)
16 **DARING DEREK (USA),** ch c Naevus (USA)—Gatap (USA)
17 **DESERT PRINCE (IRE),** b c Green Desert (USA)—Flying Fairy
18 **DIKTAT,** br c Warning—Arvola
19 **ETHEREAL,** b c Fairy King (USA)—Secret Seeker (USA)
20 **FRANKIE FERRARI (IRE),** b c Common Grounds—Miss Kelly
21 **GENEROUS ROSI,** b c Generous (IRE)—Come On Rosi
22 **GOLDEN FORTUNE,** ch f Forzando—Short And Sharp
23 **HALF-HITCH (USA),** b f Diesis—Marling (IRE)
24 **IDENTICAL (IRE),** b f Machiavellian (USA)—Flawless Image (USA)
25 **KAREFREE KATIE (USA),** b f Lac Ouimet (USA)—Dame Cecilia (USA)
26 **LIBRA STAR (USA),** b c Hermitage (USA)—Aromalibra (USA)
27 **LONG SIEGE (IRE),** ch c Brief Truce (USA)—Sugarbird
28 **LOVERS KNOT,** b f Groom Dancer (USA)—Nemea (USA)
29 **LUCAYAN INDIAN (IRE),** ch c Indian Ridge—Eleanor Antoinette (IRE)
30 **MASTER CASTER (IRE),** b g Night Shift (USA)—Honourable Sheba (USA)
31 **MIRACLE ISLAND,** b c Jupiter Island—Running Game
32 **NAME OF LOVE (IRE),** b f Petardia—National Ballet
33 **OPENING MEET,** ch f Wolfhound (USA)—Carnival Spirit
34 **PAARL ROCK,** ch c Common Grounds—Markievicz (IRE)
35 **PARADISE SOUL (USA),** b f Dynaformer (USA)—River Valley (FR)
36 **PIXIELATED (IRE),** b f Fairy King (USA)—Last Embrace (IRE)
37 **PRIMA FACIE,** b f Primo Dominie—Soluce
38 **QUEEN SALOTE,** b f Mujtahid (USA)—Island Ruler
39 **SPECIAL TREAT,** b f Wolfhound (USA)—Just A Treat (IRE)

MR D. R. LODER—continued

TWO-YEAR-OLDS

40 Ch c 23/4 College Chapel—Alpine Symphony (Northern Dancer)
41 ARABIAN MOON (IRE), ch c 16/5 Barathea (IRE)—Excellent Alibi (USA) (Exceller (USA))
42 B c 16/3 Rainbow Quest (USA)—Awaasif (CAN) (Snow Knight)
43 BEMUSE, b f 7/2 Forzando—Barsham (Be My Guest (USA))
44 B f 3/4 Indian Ridge—Benedicite (Lomond (USA))
45 BERGAMO, b c 3/3 Robellino (USA)—Pretty Thing (Star Appeal)
46 B c 11/5 Dolphin Street (FR)—Biraya (Valiyar)
47 B f 13/4 Dayjur (USA)—Blue Note (FR) (Habitat)
48 B c 26/3 In The Wings—Bogus John (CAN) (Blushing John (USA))
49 B f 3/2 Polish Precedent—Braiswick (King of Spain)
50 BRAZILIAN MOOD (IRE), b c 12/4 Doyoun—Sea Mistress (Habitat)
51 CAERAU, ch f 2/2 Nashwan (USA)—Charming Life (Habitat)
52 B c 2/5 Polar Falcon (USA)—Choire Mhor (Dominion)
53 B c 3/4 Storm Bird (CAN)—Croquetallie (USA) (Alydar (USA))
54 B f 9/4 Storm Cat (USA)—Diminuendo (USA) (Diesis)
55 ELBAZ (USA), ch c 6/4 Thorn Dance (USA)—Stuttering (USA) (Ack Ack (USA))
56 FAIRY QUEEN (IRE), b f 28/1 Fairy King (USA)—Dedicated Lady (IRE) (Pennine Walk)
57 Ch c 12/3 Cadeaux Genereux—Fernlea (USA) (Sir Ivor)
58 FIUMINCINO (IRE), b c 28/2 Barathea (IRE)—Lacovia (USA) (Majestic Light (USA))
59 B f 23/4 Darshaan—Flawless Image (USA) (The Minstrel (CAN))
60 B c 18/3 Distant Relative—Frasquita (Song)
61 B c 1/4 Nashwan (USA)—Hebba (USA) (Nureyev (USA))
62 Ch c 5/3 Common Grounds—House of Fame (USA) (Trempolino (USA))
63 HOUSTON TIME (USA), ch c 18/1 Rahy (USA)—Band (USA) (Northern Dancer)
64 Gr c 2/2 Machiavellian (USA)—Indian Skimmer (USA) (Storm Bird (CAN))
65 JUNE GRACE, b f 11/2 Efisio—Reyah (Young Generation)
66 KING MIDAS, b c 21/3 Bluebird (USA)—Ellebanna (Tina's Pet)
67 KING OBERON (IRE), b c 17/2 Fairy King (USA)—Annenberg (Slip Anchor)
68 LAST WARNING, b c 22/3 Warning—Dancing Crystal (Kris)
69 LOVE STORY (IRE), b c 9/2 Green Desert (USA)—Takwim (Taufan (USA))
70 B f 27/1 Dixieland Band (USA)—Marillette (USA) (Diesis)
71 B f 16/4 Woodman (USA)—Memories of Pam (USA) (Graustark)
72 NEWSCASTER, b c 3/5 Bluebird (USA)—Sharp Girl (FR) (Sharpman)
73 Ch f 14/1 Cadeaux Genereux—Norpella (Northfields (USA))
74 PILGRIM'S WAY (USA), b f 10/5 Gone West (USA)—Marling (IRE) (Lomond (USA))
75 B c 7/3 Gone West (USA)—Polish Style (USA) (Danzig (USA))
76 PRETTY WOMAN (IRE), b f 22/2 Alzao (USA)—Simply Gorgeous (Hello Gorgeous (USA))
77 B c 23/3 Danzig (USA)—Priceless Pearl (USA) (Alydar (USA))
78 RAJWHAN (USA), br c 3/4 Lear Fan (USA)—Samra (USA) (Solford (USA))
79 RESERVATION, ch f 30/3 Common Grounds—Chief's Quest (USA) (Chief's Crown (USA))
80 ROSIE DREAM (IRE), ch f 23/4 Cadeaux Genereux—Impudent Miss (Persian Bold)
81 SPIRIT WILLING (IRE), b f 3/4 Fairy King (USA)—Pro Patria (Petingo)
82 B c 9/3 Silver Hawk (USA)—Strait Lane (USA) (Chieftain II)
83 Ch f 13/2 Zafonic (USA)—Sweet Mover (USA) (Nijinsky (CAN))
84 B f 21/2 Cadeaux Genereux—Tansy (Shareef Dancer (USA))
85 B c 27/4 Efisio—Thakhayr (Sadler's Wells (USA))
86 B f 15/2 Barathea (IRE)—Tribal Rite (Be My Native (USA))
87 Ch c 20/4 Woodman (USA)—Triple Tiara (USA) (Majestic Light (USA))
88 TRUE LOVE, gr f 26/3 Robellino (USA)—Cumbrian Melody (Petong)
89 UNICAMP, ch f 18/2 Royal Academy (USA)—Honeyspike (IRE) (Chief's Crown (USA))
90 B f 19/3 Barathea (IRE)—Upend (Main Reef)

Owners: Jaber Abdullah, Cuadra Africa, Chris Brasher, Earl Of Burlington, Casting Partners, Cheveley Park, Derek Clee, M. Conti, Mrs P. T. Fenwick, W. E. A. Fox, S. Frisby, Abdullah Saeed Bul Hab, Trevor Harris, Lady Harrison, Highclere Thoroughbred Racing, Mohammed Jaber, Lord Lloyd Webber, E. J. Loder, Lucayan Stud, Hadi Mashood, Sheikh Mohammed, Mohammed Al Nabouda, J. Bonifacio C. Nogueira, P. D. Player, Duchess Of Roxburghe, Ali Saeed, Wafic Said, Faisal Salman, Mrs D. Snowden, Salem Suhail, M. Watt.

Apprentice: Gavin Faulkner (8-1).

367 MR J. E. LONG, Woldingham

Postal: **Main Yard, Tillingdowns, Woldingham, Caterham, Surrey, CR3 7JA.**
Phone: **CATERHAM (01883) 348250**

1 **ANOTHER FIDDLE (IRE)**, 8, b g Waajib—Elmar **Mrs D. Crick**
2 **HAWTHORNE GLEN**, 11, b g Furry Glen—Black Gnat **Mrs O. C. Foster**
3 **KOMODO (USA)**, 6, ch g Ferdinand (USA)—Platonic Interest (USA) **Mrs A. Warren**
4 **MOYLOUGH REBEL**, 5, ch g Hotfoot—Stellajoe **Mrs A. Warren**
5 **MY SON TOM**, 9, b g My Dad Tom (USA)—Narinne **Mrs O. C. Foster**
6 **PREMIER LEAGUE (IRE)**, 8, gr g Don't Forget Me—Kilmara (USA) **The Harkander Partnership**
7 **SARUM**, 12, b g Tina's Pet—Contessa (HUN) **Mr Terry Waters**
8 **SPRINTFAYRE**, 10, b g Magnolia Lad—Headliner **Mrs O. C. Foster**
9 **WILL I FLY**, 12, b g What A Guest—Monalda (FR) **Mrs O. C. Foster**

TWO-YEAR-OLDS

10 **ISLE OF THORNS**, b f 26/3 Infantry—Dumerica (Yukon Eric (CAN)) **Mr Tim Kenward**

Other Owners: Mr Ken Argent, Mr Adrian Boylan, Mr J. King, Mr John Nicholson, Mr J. J. Ryan.

Jockey (Flat): Leesa Long (8-3).

Jockey (NH): Leesa Long (10-0).

Conditional: G Gallagher.

Amateurs: Mr R Blyth (10-0), Mr T Waters (10-0).

Lady Rider: Miss S Colville.

368 MR L. LUNGO, Carrutherstown

Postal: **Hetland Hill Farm, Carrutherstown, Dumfriesshire, DG1 4JX.**
Phone: **(01387) 840691 FAX (01387) 840323**

1 **ASHGROVE DANCER (IRE)**, 8, ch g Roselier (FR)—Leith Hill **Mrs Barbara Lungo**
2 **BAWARA (IRE)**, 4, b g Slip Anchor—Alwatar (USA) **Mrs Barbara Lungo**
3 **BIRKDALE (IRE)**, 7, gr g Roselier (FR)—Clonroche Lady **Mr Edward Birkbeck**
4 **BONNY RIGG (IRE)**, 6, b m Phardante (FR)—Open Your Eyes **Roman Wall Racing**
5 **CADS DELIGHT (IRE)**, 7, b g Fine Blade (USA)—Fanlight Fanny **Mrs Barbara Lungo**
6 **CASTLE BAY (IRE)**, 7, ch g Castle Keep—Castle Pearl **Mr G. A. Arthur**
7 **CELTIC GIANT**, 8, ch g Celtic Cone—Hester Ann **Mr R. J. Gilbert**
8 **CHUMMY'S SAGA**, 8, ch g Caerleon (USA)—Sagar **Mrs I. Curran**
9 **CLERICAL COUSIN (IRE)**, 9, b g The Parson—Copp On **Mrs Barbara Lungo**
10 **CORSTON JOKER**, 8, b g Idiot's Delight—Corston Lass **Mr A. S. Lyburn**
11 **DORLIN CASTLE**, 10, b g Scorpio (FR)—Gorgeous Gertie **Mrs D. C. Greig**
12 **DOWSHI**, 7, b m Baron Blakeney—Molinello **Mr Guy Willoughby**
13 **FLUTTERBY LADY**, 5, b m Bedford (USA)—Aserbaidschan (GER) **Brundeanlaws Racing Club**
14 **HOLLOW PALM (IRE)**, 7, b g Hollow Hand—Meneroyal **Mr A. S. Lyburn**
15 **IFALLELSEFAILS**, 10, b g Pollerton—Laurello **Mrs Barbara Lungo**
16 **ISLAND PATH (IRE)**, 5, b m Jupiter Island—Lifestyle **Mr J. Nelson**
17 **JOHNNY JOE (IRE)**, 5, ch g Camden Town—Lissanuhig **Currie Group**
18 **KALAJO**, 8, b g Kala Shikari—Greenacres Joy **Mr M. J. McGovern**

MR L. LUNGO—continued

19 **KIRSTENBOSCH,** 11, b g Caerleon (USA)—Flower Petals **Mrs Barbara Lungo**
20 **KRIS GREEN (IRE),** 4, ch c Kris—Green Lucia **Mrs Barbara Lungo**
21 **LINROYALE KING,** 7, b g Sulaafah (USA)—Nearly A Lady **Mrs Barbara Lungo**
22 **LORD OF THE LOCH (IRE),** 7, b br g Lord Americo—Loughamaire **Mr Ken Batey**
23 **MENSHAAR (USA),** 6, b g Hawkster (USA)—Klassy Imp (USA) **Miss S. Blumberg**
24 **MIKE STAN (IRE),** 7, b g Rontino—Fair Pirouette **Mr J. M. Crichton**
25 **MISTER TRICK (IRE),** 8, br g Roselier (FR)—Fly Fuss **Mr Edward Birkbeck**
26 **NODDLE (USA),** 10, ch g Sagace (FR)—Formartin (USA) **Mr J. C. Galbraith**
27 **NOOSA SOUND (IRE),** 8, br g Orchestra—Borecca **Mr Andrew W. B. Duncan**
28 **NOW YOUNG MAN (IRE),** 9, br g Callernish—Claddagh Pride **Mrs Barbara Lungo**
29 **OAT COUTURE,** 10, b g Oats—Marjoemin **Ashleybank Investments Limited**
30 **OUT ON A PROMISE (IRE),** 6, b g Night Shift (USA)—Lovers' Parlour **London & Clydeside Properties Ltd**
31 **PALACE OF GOLD,** 8, b g Slip Anchor—Salacious **Mr Andrew W. B. Duncan**
32 **PARSON'S LODGE (IRE),** 10, ch m The Parson—Loge **Mrs S. J. Matthews**
33 **PHAR ECHO (IRE),** 7, b g Phardante (FR)—Borecca **S. H. C. Racing**
34 **PLUMBOB (IRE),** 9, br g Bob Back (USA)—Naujella **Mr Andrew W. B. Duncan**
35 **PORTER PADDY (IRE),** 6, b g Nashamaa—Princess Rapunzel **Mrs Barbara Lungo**
36 **SHOW YOUR HAND (IRE),** 10, ch g Aristocracy—Sister's Prize **Strathayr Publishing Ltd**
37 **SUMTHYNE SPECIAL (IRE),** 6, b g Good Thyne (USA)—Condonstown Rose **Mr J. M. Crichton**
38 **SUPERTOP,** 10, b br g High Top—Myth **Mrs Barbara Lungo**
39 **SWANBISTER (IRE),** 8, b g Roselier (FR)—Coolentallagh **Colonel D. C. Greig**
40 **THE NEXT WALTZ (IRE),** 7, b g Buckskin (FR)—Loge **Mrs Michael Royds**
41 **TO-DAY TO-DAY (IRE),** 5, b g Waajib—Balela **Colonel D. C. Greig**
42 **VALIGAN (IRE),** 5, gr g Roselier (FR)—Wonderful Lilly **Mr Ronald Thorburn**
43 **WEE TAM,** 9, b g Silver Season—Bishop's Song **Miss Amanda Creedon**

Other Owners: Mrs G. A. Arthur, Miss E. Birkbeck, Mr A. N. Brooke Rankin, Mrs F. A. B. Burn, Mr John Corr, Mr James Craig, Mrs P. R. Crawford, Miss Hazel Crichton, Mr C. J. Ewart, Mrs T. Fogarty, Mr G. G. Fraser, Mr Arthur Gillespie, Mr James Glass, Mrs S. D. Gourlay, Mr Paul Green, Mrs E. P. Henry, Mr J. G. Hickie, Mr Malcolm Hind, Mr William Jardine, Mrs A. S. J. Johnston, Sir D. Landale, Mr David S. Leggate, Mrs Nicola Leggate, Mackinnon Mills, Mrs A. G. Martin, Mr A. S. McGimpsey, Mr J. A. Ogle, Mrs J. K. Peutherer, Mrs A. E. Robertson, Rycon Limited, Mr J. R. Simpson, Miss Jennifer Taylor, Miss Emma Tazey, Mr Fred Wilson.

Conditional: W Dowling.

Amateur: Mr B Gibson.

369 MR GER LYONS, Dunsany

Postal: **Glenburnie Stables, Dunsany, Co. Meath, Ireland.**
Phone: **(046) 25666 FAX (046) 26166 E-mail: gerlyons@IOL.IE**

1 **BOBSANNA (IRE),** 6, b m Bob Back—Kirei **Alitobahn Syndicate**
2 **CAREFREE LEGEND (IRE),** 5, ch g Carefree Dancer—Mainham **Medusa Syndicate**
3 **COUNTY CAPTAIN (IRE),** 5, b g Electric—Miss Daraheen **Hanlon's Four Syndicate**
4 **DIFFICULT TIMES (IRE),** 6, ch g Ela-Mana-Mou—Loveshine **Mr P. M. Dowling**
5 **DIVINE DANCER (IRE),** 5, ch m Carmelite House—Aljasur **Mr Eddie Campbell**
6 **EN-JAY-BEE (IRE),** 4, b g Classic Music—Simply Inch **Just One More Syndicate**
7 **GRANNY CLARK (IRE),** 5, b m Welsh Term—Black-Crash **Mrs Alix Stevenson**
8 4, B g Salt Dome—Irena
9 **MONTELACITY (IRE),** 6, b m Montelimar—Bahamas Bank **Beechfield Syndicate**
10 **MULKEY PRINCE (IRE),** 7, b g Lancastrian—Waltzing Shoon **Mrs Mary Keville**
11 **MYSTERY LADY (IRE),** 5, b m Distinctly North—Aunt Eileen **Mysterious Men Syndicate**
12 **NATIVE RHYTHM (IRE),** 4, ch f Lycius—Perfect Time **Mr F. A. McNulty**
13 **SPIRIT DANCER (IRE),** 5, ch g Carmelite House—Theatral **Mrs Alix Stevenson**
14 **SUPER SHRONE (IRE),** 4, b g Imp Society—Bonny's Niece **Serious Session Syndicate**
15 **YES VOTE (IRE),** 4, b f Taufan—Arab Scimetar **Kitchen Syndicate**

MR GER LYONS—continued

THREE-YEAR-OLDS

16 BLACK ROCK CITY, br g Rock City—Jomel Amou **Hard Hat Syndicate**
17 CANARD VALU (IRE), b g Lahib—Athassel Rose **Mrs Alix Stevenson**
18 DELIRIOUS TANTRUM (IRE), b f Taufan—Shrewd Girl **Serious Session Syndicate**
19 FIDDLER'S ROCK (IRE), b g Ballad Rock—Rockbourne **Christina Gilsennan**
20 LADY FOR LIFE (IRE), b f Rainbows For Life—Tartan Lady **Mr Eddie Campbell**
21 SHAMBODIA (IRE), b f Petardia—Lucky Fountain **Lynne Lyons**
22 Ch f Ela-Mana-Mou—Silk Blend **Mr P. M. Dowling**
23 B g Marju—Summer Palace
24 TERRAHAWK (IRE), b g Imp Society—Ludovica **Mrs Alix Stevenson**
25 TIFOSI (IRE), b f Mujadil—That's Easy **Lynne Lyons**
26 TITTLE TATTLE (IRE), b f Soviet Lad—Saint Cynthia **Mr P. M. Dowling**
27 WHIZAWAY (IRE), ch f Archway—Plunket's Choice **Mr P. M. Dowling**
28 B f Insan—Yukon Lil **Medusa Syndicate**

TWO-YEAR-OLDS

29 B c 12/3 Prince Sabo—Ashdown (Pharly) **Glenburnie Racing Club**
30 B c 31/1 Alnasr Alwasheek—Classical Vintage (Stradavinsky) **Glenburnie Racing Club**
31 FIELDHOUSE ROSE (IRE), b f 12/3 Woods of Windsor—Smart Pet (Petong) **Mr C. Marks**
32 B c 21/4 Pips Pride—Hard To Stop (Hard Fought) **Glenburnie Racing Club**
33 B f 21/5 Imperial Frontier—Hay Knot (Main Reef) **Glenburnie Racing Club**
34 B f 8/2 Prince Sabo—Henpot (Alzao) **Ms Mel Reddy**
35 LUCKY PLAYER (IRE), ch c 17/4 Lucky Guest—Miss Player (The Noble Player) **Anomoine Ltd**
36 Gr c 18/4 Forest Wind—Mia Georgina (Never So Bold) **Ms Mel Reddy**
37 Ch f 4/3 Forest Wind—Morgiana (Godswalk) **Glenburnie Racing Club**
38 PILGRIM STAR (IRE), b f 27/3 Marju—Fireheba (Fire of Life) **Mr F. A. McNulty**
39 B c 7/4 Petardia—Rainbow Vision (Prince Tenderfoot) **Lynne Lyons**
40 B f 1/4 Great Commotion—Rockbourne (Midyan) **Glenburnie Racing Club**
41 B f 13/4 Mukadammah—Rousalong (Rousillon) **Ms Mel Reddy**
42 B c 7/4 Petardia—Steel Duchess (Yashgan) **Glenburnie Racing Club**
43 Ch c 18/3 Formidable—Thimbalina (Salmon Leap) **Glenburnie Racing Club**
44 B c 26/3 Soviet Lad—Vital Spirit (Tachypous) **Mr P. M. Dowling**
45 B c 23/3 Petong—Waveguide (Double Form) **Glenburnie Racing Club**

370 MRS N. J. MACAULEY, Melton Mowbray

Postal: **The Sidings, Saltby Road, Sproxton, Melton Mowbray, Leicestershire, LE14 4RA.**
Phone: **(01476) HOME 860578 OFFICE 860090 FAX 860611 MOBILE (0441) 004444**

1 BENTICO, 9, b g Nordico (USA)—Bentinck Hotel **Twenty Twenty Racing**
2 BLAZER'S BABY, 4, ch f Norton Challenger—Qualitair Blazer **Miss S. Rudge**
3 ELTON LEDGER (IRE), 9, b g Cyrano de Bergerac—Princess of Nashua **The Posse**
4 KIPPANOUR (USA), 6, b g Alleged (USA)—Innsbruck **Mr G. Wiltshire**
5 NAPIER STAR, 5, b m Inca Chief (USA)—America Star **Mr P. M. Heaton**
6 NOBALINO, 4, ch c Sharpo—Zipperti Do **Mr Maurice Kirby**
7 RIVAL BID (USA), 10, b g Cannonade (USA)—Love Triangle (USA) **Twenty Twenty Racing**
8 ROCHEA, 4, br f Rock City—Pervenche **Mr J. Teasdale**
9 SHE'S A CRACKER, 4, b f Deploy—Red Secret (IRE) **Mr Maurice Kirby**
10 SOMMERSBY (IRE), 7, b g Vision (USA)—Echoing **Mr Andy Peake**
11 SUPERMODEL, 6, gr m Unfuwain (USA)—Well Off **Miss S. Rudge**
12 VADO VIA, 10, b m Ardross—Brigado **Miss S. Rudge**

THREE-YEAR-OLDS

13 DANZINO (IRE), b g Roi Danzig (USA)—Luvi Ullmann **Mr G. Horsford**
14 LAPIMI, b f Lapierre—Miami Pride **Mr J. Teasdale**
15 SHARP MONKEY, b c Man Among Men (IRE)—Sharp Thistle **Mr J. Teasdale**
16 SHE'S A GEM, b f Robellino (USA)—Rose Gem (IRE) **Mr Maurice Kirby**
17 TILBURG, b f High Kicker (USA)—Touch My Heart **Mr J. Teasdale**

MRS N. J. MACAULEY—continued

TWO-YEAR-OLDS

18 **GIFTO WE'RE GONZO,** b c 7/2 Minshaanshu Amad (USA—Princess Lucianne (Stanford) **Mr Frank McEntee**
19 B f 18/3 Clantime—Lightning Belle (Belfort (FR)) **Mr J. Teasdale**

Other Owners: Mr John Hine, Mrs N. Macauley, Mr Jeffrey Ross.

Jockeys (Flat): D Biggs, S Drowne, S Webster.

Apprentice: P McCabe.

Lady Riders: Miss J Harrison (9-0), Miss K Moore (8-7).

371 MR W. J. W. MACKIE, Church Broughton

Postal: **The Bungalow, Barton Blount, Church Broughton, Derby, DE65 5AN.**
Phone: **BURTON-ON-TRENT (01283) 585604 MOBILE (0421) 938070**

1 **ARABIAN HEIGHTS,** 5, ch g Persian Heights—Arabian Rose (USA) **Mr J. H. Dickinson**
2 **BARKINGATTHEMOON,** 4, b g Seymour Hicks (FR)—China's Way (USA) **Mr F. A. Dickinson**
3 **BARTY BOY (IRE),** 6, b g Buckskin (FR)—Black Tulip **The Bartlett Family**
4 **BERNERA,** 6, br g Rakaposhi King—Isle Maree **Mr N. J. Sessions**
5 **CAHERLOW (IRE),** 7, ch g Kambalda—Wrens Lass **Harlow Bros Ltd**
6 **CHARLEY LAMBERT (IRE),** 7, b g Strong Gale—Frankford Run **Mr R. M. Mitchell and Mr D. G. Savala**
7 **DIVERTIMIENTO,** 7, b g Night Shift (USA)—Aunt Jemima **Mr B. J. Wood**
8 **ESKIMO KISS (IRE),** 5, b m Distinctly North (USA)—Felicitas **Mrs Sue Adams**
9 **FAIRLY SHARP (IRE),** 5, b m Glenstal (USA)—Bengala (FR) **Ms Caroline F. Breay**
10 **JIMMY O'DEA,** 11, br g Funny Man—Premier Nell **Mr J. S. Harlow**
11 **LAUNCHSELECT,** 7, b g Alleging (USA)—Polished Queen **Mr J. S. Harlow**
12 **LISLAUGHTIN ABBEY,** 6, ch g Nicholas Bill—Kates Fling (USA) **Mr P. M. Bradley**
13 **MRS ROBINSON (IRE),** 7, b m The Parson—Celtic Connection **Mr V. Wilson**
14 **MUSTANG SCALLY,** 4, b f Makbul—Another Scally **Mr F. A. Dickinson**
15 **NAHRI (USA),** 7, ch g Riverman (USA)—Welden (USA) **Mrs Sue Adams**
16 **PINGO HILL (IRE),** 6, ch g Salt Dome (USA)—Andarta **Mr R. J. Wright**
17 **SHU GAA (IRE),** 5, ch g Salse (USA)—River Reem (USA) **Mr R. M. Kirkland**
18 **SLEETING,** 5, ch g Lycius (USA)—Pluvial **Mr Colin Moore**
19 **SOLDIER MAK,** 5, ch g Infantry—Truly Blest **Rose And Crown, Boylestone**
20 **STAR SELECTION,** 7, b g Rainbow Quest (USA)—Selection Board **Mr R. M. Mitchell**
21 **TRUVARO (IRE),** 7, b g Corvaro (USA)—Trudy Belle **Mrs Sue Adams**
22 **WILLOW MILL,** 6, ch m Nicholas Bill—Sound of Laughter **Mrs B. A. Burgass**

Other Owners: Mr S. P. Adams, Mr J. C. Archer, Mr A. H. Bartlett, Mr P. A. Bartlett, Mr N. Brown, Mr S. R. Francis, Mr Tim Kelly, Mrs J. Mackie, Mr P. Nugent, Mr J. A. Provan, Mrs J. E. Small, Mr A. J. Wall, Mr V. Wilson, Mr A. J. Winterton.

372 MR A. B. MACTAGGART, Hawick

Postal: **Greendale, Hawick, Roxburghshire, TD9 7LH.**
Phone: **(01450) 372086 FAX (01450) 372086 MOBILE (0860) 139698**

1 **BABY JANE,** 4, b f Old Vic—Sutosky **Mrs Ann E. M. Wright**
2 **BERRYMOSS (IRE),** 6, b g Le Moss—Velindre **Kelso Lowflyers**
3 **CHEENY'S D'OR,** 4, b f Le Coq d'Or—Cheeny's Brig **Mr B. Mactaggart**
4 **CONTRAVENE (IRE),** 4, b f Contract Law (USA)—Vieux Carre **Mr T. K. Easdon**
5 **DALTON LADY,** 4, b f Roscoe Blake—Drom Lady **Mr R. W. Armstrong & Mr B. Mactaggart**

MR A. B. MACTAGGART—continued

6 **FOX SPARROW,** 8, b g Sharpo—Wryneck **Mr B. Todd**
7 **INGLE DENE,** 5, b g Skyliner—Dreamy Desire **Souter Racing**
8 **INGLETONIAN,** 9, b g Doc Marten—Dreamy Desire **Mrs Hilary Mactaggart**
9 **LEET BRIG,** 7, b g Pitpan—Gilzie Bank **Mr H. Brydon**
10 **LOST IN THE POST (IRE),** 5, ch g Don't Forget Me—Postie **Mr J. M. Rudkin**
11 **LUMBACK LADY,** 8, b m State Diplomacy (USA)—Jalome **Mr J. McKinnon**
12 **OVER THE BURN,** 6, b g Over The River (FR)—Sharp Vixen **Mrs P. McNeill**
13 **PHARTOOMANNY (IRE),** 8, b m Phardante (FR)—Deep Whistle **Mr F. D. A. Snowden**
14 **PUPIL MASTER (IRE),** 4, b g Masterclass (USA)—Lamya **Radio Borders Racing**
15 **SNUFF BOX (IRE),** 5, b g Brush Aside (USA)—Nickel Run **Mr C. J. Cookson**
16 **TIRINITY,** 6, b m Respect—Miss Appleyard **Mrs I. A. Forrest**
17 **TREASURE HILL (IRE),** 4, ch g Roi Danzig (USA)—Grass Court **Mr J. Stephenson**
18 **WELL APPOINTED (IRE),** 9, b g Petorius—So Stylish **Drumlanrig Racing**

THREE-YEAR-OLDS

19 **JOOGLIE BRIG (IRE),** b f Le Coq d'Or—Cheeny's Brig **Mr B. Mactaggart**
20 **LADY OF THE LUNE,** b f Skyliner—Hot Feet **Mrs K. Howells**
21 **SI SENORITA,** b f Young Senor (USA)—Raunchy Rita **Mrs Ann E. M. Wright**

TWO-YEAR-OLDS

22 B g Glacial Storm (USA)—Cheeny's Brig **Mr B. Mactaggart & Mr R. J. Cowper**
23 **STORMY BEECH,** b g 1/6 Glacial Storm (USA)—Cheeny's Brig (New Brig) **Mr B. Mactaggart & Mr R. J. Cowper**

Other Owners: Mr Colin Barnfather, Mrs Frances Godson, Mr M. W. Graham, Mr J. B. Jeffrey, R. M. Landale, Mr Andrew Minto, Mr David Morrison, Mr Des Redhead, Mr J. Ross, Mr Frank Steele, Mr D. Sundin, Mr Tommy Todd.

Jockey (NH): B Storey (10-0, w.a.).

Conditional: G Lee (9-7, w.a.).

373 MR M. J. MADGWICK, Denmead

Postal: **Forest Farm, Forest Road, Denmead, Hampshire, PO7 6UA.**
Phone: **(01705) 258313**

1 **CERTAIN SURPRISE,** 4, b f Grey Desire—Richesse (FR) **Mrs H. Veal**
2 **FOUNTAIN VILLE (IRE),** 5, b g Supreme Leader—Bonne Royale **Mr J. D. Brownrigg**
3 **LOCH PATRICK,** 8, b g Beveled (USA)—Daisy Loch **Miss E. M. L. Coller**
4 **MANDALADY (IRE),** 5, br m Mandalus—Coppenagh Girl **Mr J. D. Brownrigg**
5 **MEMORY'S MUSIC,** 6, b g Dance of Life (USA)—Sheer Luck **Mr W. V. Roker**
6 **NEWBY END (IRE),** 4, br g Over The River (FR)—Comeallye **Mr J. D. Brownrigg**
7 **NORDANSK,** 9, ch g Nordance (USA)—Free On Board **Mr T. Smith**
8 **OUT LINE,** 6, gr m Beveled (USA)—Free Range **Miss D. M. Green**
9 **SHARP DEED (IRE),** 4, ch g Sharp Victor (USA)—Fabulous Deep (USA) **Mr W. V. Roker**
10 **SIMPLY (IRE),** 9, b g Simply Great (FR)—Be A Dancer **Mr Paul Gibbons**

THREE-YEAR-OLDS

11 **LOCH LAIRD,** b g Beveled (USA)—Daisy Loch **Miss E. M. L. Coller**
12 **PREMIER JET,** br f Dilum (USA)—Lady Shikari **Mr T. G. N. Burrage**
13 **SWEET SENORITA,** b f Young Senor (USA)—Sweet N' Twenty **Mr W. E. Baird**
14 **TWOFORTEN,** b c Robellino (USA)—Grown At Rowan **Mr T. G. N. Burrage**

Other Owners: Mr A. R. Aylett, Mr C. P. Fulford, Mr H. F. George, Mrs C. Knight, Mr D. Knight, Miss J. Smith.

Jockeys (Flat): M Fenton (8-0), T Quinn (8-0), J Reid (8-6).

Jockeys (NH): R Dunwoody, B Fenton.

374 MR K. MAHDI, Newmarket

Postal: **Green Ridge Stables, Hamilton Road, Newmarket, CB8 7JQ.**
Phone: **(01638) 666185 FAX (01638 666184**

1 **ALFAHAD,** 5, b h Doyoun—Moogie **Mr A. Al-Radi**
2 **ALMUSHTARAK (IRE),** 5, b h Fairy King (USA)—Exciting **Mr H. Al-Mutawa**
3 **AWASSI (IRE),** 5, b h Fairy King (USA)—Phantom Row **Mr H. Al-Mutawa**
4 **DESERT WARRIOR (IRE),** 4, b c Fairy King (USA)—Highland Girl (USA) **Mr H. Al-Mutawa**
5 **JAWAH (IRE),** 4, br g In The Wings—Saving Mercy **Mr H. Al-Mutawa**
6 **MOUNT HOLLY (USA),** 4, b c Woodman (USA)—Mount Helena **Mr H. Al-Mutawa**
7 **MUTABARI (USA),** 4, ch c Seeking The Gold (USA)—Cagey Exuberance (USA) **Mr H. Al-Mutawa**
8 **PERSICA,** 5, b m Persian Bold—Nadina **Mr H. Al-Mutawa**
9 **SECRET BALLOT (IRE),** 4, b c Taufan (USA)—Ballet Society (FR) **Mr Waleed Al-Mutawa**
10 **TRAIKEY (IRE),** 6, b h Scenic—Swordlestown Miss (USA) **Sheik Ahmad Yousuf Al Sabah**
11 **TREATY (USA),** 4, b c Trempolino (USA)—Zonda **Mr H. Al-Mutawa**
12 **ZAALEFF (USA),** 6, ch h Zilzal (USA)—Continual (USA) **Mr H. Al-Mutawa**
13 **ZUGUDI,** 4, b c Night Shift (USA)—Overdrive **Sheik Ahmad Yousuf Al Sabah**

THREE-YEAR-OLDS

14 **AL MABROOK (IRE),** b c Rainbows For Life (CAN)—Sky Lover **Mr H. Al-Mutawa**
15 **BE MY CHANCE,** ch c Be My Chief (USA)—Appleton Heights **Mr H. Al-Mutawa**
16 **CHILLISIMA,** ch f Alnasr Alwasheek—Eccolina **Miss Debbie Mountain**
17 **ENJOY ME,** b c Puissance—Glint of Victory **Mr H. Al-Mutawa**
18 **KHALED (IRE),** b c Petorius—Felin Special **Mr H. Al-Mutawa**
19 **LORENZO (IRE),** b br c Distinctly North (USA)—Stephens Guest (IRE) **Mr H. Al-Mutawa**
20 **MY TYSON (IRE),** b c Don't Forget Me—Shuckran Habibi **Mr H. Al-Mutawa**
21 **TATTOO,** b f Casteddu—Ebony Park **Mr H. Al-Mutawa**

TWO-YEAR-OLDS

22 B f 11/5 Deploy—Adorable Cherub (USA) (Halo (USA)) **Mr H. Al-Mutawa**
23 Ch f 15/4 Be My Chief (USA)—Appleton Heights (Shirley Heights) **Sheikh Ahmad Yousuf Al Sabah**
24 B f 28/4 Merdon Melody—Balidilemma (Balidar) **Mr H. Al-Mutawa**
25 Br f 2/4 Perugino (USA)—Betelgeuse (Kalaglow) **Mr H. Al-Mutawa**
26 B c 7/5 Fairy King (USA)—Decadence (Vaigly Star) **Mr H. Al Mutawa**
27 Ch f 19/2 Inchinor—Kinkajoo (Precocious) **Mr H. Al-Mutawa**
28 B c 23/3 Warning—Lomond Blossom (Lomond (USA)) **Sheikh Ahmad Yousuf Al Sabah**
29 B c 18/3 Hamas (IRE)—Millie's Lady (IRE) (Common Grounds) **Mr H. Al-Mutawa**
30 B f 5/5 Efisio—Miss Witch (Highline) **Mr H. Al-Mutawa**
31 B f 7/5 Skyliner—Phantom Singer (Relkino) **Mr H. Al Mutawa**
32 Gr c 21/2 Petong—Princess Eurolink (Be My Guest (USA)) **Mr H. Al-Mutawa**
33 B c 17/4 Nashwan (USA)—Select Sale (Auction Ring (USA)) **Mr H. Al-Mutawa**
34 Gr f 6/3 Chilibang—Sizzling Sista (Sizzling Melody) **Mr H. Al-Mutawa**
35 Ch c 5/4 Weldnaas (USA)—The Boozy News (USA) (L'Emigrant (USA)) **Mr H. Al-Mutawa**

Apprentice: Mark Baird (7-7).

375 MR P. J. MAKIN, Marlborough

Postal: **Bonita Racing Stables, Ogbourne Maisey, Marlborough, Wilts, SN8 1RY.**
Phone: **MARLBOROUGH (01672) 512973 FAX (01672) 514166**

1 **ALWAYS ON MY MIND,** 4, b f Distant Relative—Fleur Rouge **Mascalls Stud**
2 **BABA SADHU,** 4, b g Mazilier (USA)—La Jambalaya **Mrs P. J. Makin**
3 **CROWDED AVENUE,** 6, b g Sizzling Melody—Lady Bequick **Mr T. W. Wellard**
4 **DOUBLE BOUNCE,** 8, b g Interrex (CAN)—Double Gift **Mrs P. Scott-Dunn**
5 **GONE FOR A BURTON (IRE),** 8, ch g Bustino—Crimbourne **Mr H. P. Carrington**
6 **KINGS HARMONY (IRE),** 5, b g Nordico (USA)—Kingston Rose **Ten of Hearts**
7 **OGGI,** 7, gr g Efisio—Dolly Bevan **Skyline Racing Ltd**

MR P. J. MAKIN—continued

8 **PALATIAL STYLE,** 11, b g Kampala—Stylish Princess **Skyline Racing Ltd**
9 **SHARP REBUFF,** 7, b h Reprimand—Kukri **Mr D. M. Ahier**
10 **TOP OF THE GREEN (IRE),** 4, b g Common Grounds—Grayfoot **Mr Terence Molossi**
11 **WELVILLE,** 5, b g Most Welcome—Miss Top Ville (FR) **Mr T. G. Warner**
12 **WILCUMA,** 7, b g Most Welcome—Miss Top Ville (FR) **Mr T. G. Warner**
13 **ZIDAC,** 6, b br g Statoblest—Sule Skerry **Mr Brian Brackpool**

THREE-YEAR-OLDS

14 **BOUND TO PLEASE,** b c Warrshan (USA)—Hong Kong Girl **D. A. Poole**
15 **CITY DANCE,** b br f Rock City—Fen Dance (IRE) **Mr D. M. Ahier**
16 **DE-WOLF,** gr f Petong—Doppio **Mr Barrie C. Whitehouse**
17 **DIAMOND DRILL (USA),** b c Geiger Counter (USA)—Decollete (USA) **Exors of the Late S. Mitchell**
18 **DOVER SOUL,** ch f Absalom—Whirling Words **Mr R. P. Marchant**
19 **EL FUERTE,** b g Perpendicular—Sleekit **E. J. R. Roberts & Mrs Stanley Cayzer**
20 **FAIRY LIGHTS (IRE),** b f Fairy King (USA)—Gay Fantastic **Dr Carlos E. Stelling**
21 **GEM,** b f Most Welcome—Miss Top Ville (FR) **Mr T. G. Warner**
22 **HENRY HEALD,** br g Anshan—Zalfa **Miss H. Joly**
23 **IL DESTINO,** b c Casteddu—At First Sight **Skyline Racing Ltd**
24 **JUST DESERTS,** b f Alhijaz—What A Pet **Mr David Gibson**
25 **L'ESTABLE FLEURIE (IRE),** b f Common Grounds—Dorado Llave (USA) **Mr Liam Queally**
26 **MAAS (IRE),** br c Elbio—Payne's Grey **Mr Brian Brackpool**
27 **MUYASSIR (IRE),** b c Brief Truce (USA)—Twine **Mr William Otley**
28 **POINT OF DISPUTE,** b g Cyrano de Bergerac—Opuntia **Mrs B. J. Carrington**
29 **RING DANCER,** b c Polar Falcon (USA)—Ring Cycle **Mrs Tricia Mitchell**
30 **SHEILA-B,** ch f Formidable (USA)—Good Woman **Mr D. L. C. Hodges**
31 **STARTRECK,** b f Night Shift (USA)—Shirley Superstar **Helena Springfield Ltd**
32 **STATUA (IRE),** b f Statoblest—Amata (USA) **Skyline Racing Ltd**
33 **TREBLE TERM,** ch f Lion Cavern (USA)—Treble Hook (IRE) **Mrs P. J. Makin**
34 **VISTA ALEGRE,** b g Petong—Duxyana (IRE) **Mrs A. E. Dennis**
35 **VITTORIA,** b f Rudimentary (USA)—Carlton Glory **Skyline Racing Ltd**
36 **WOLFHUNT,** b c Wolfhound (USA)—Vayavaig **Mrs Eileen Queally**

TWO-YEAR-OLDS

37 Br c 23/2 Petong—Azola (IRE) (Alzao (USA)) **T. W. Wellard Partnership**
38 **CREME DE CASSIS,** ch f 27/1 Alhijaz—Lucky Flinders (Free State) **Mrs B. Thorne**
39 Gr c 15/3 Reprimand—Dolly Bevan (Another Realm) **Skyline Racing Ltd**
40 **FANTASTIC BELLE (IRE),** b f 22/4 Night Shift (USA)—Gay Fantastic (Ela-Mana-Mou) **Dr Carlos E. Stelling**
41 **FANTASTIC DANCE (USA),** br f 20/2 Imperial Ballet (IRE)—
Fantastic Bid (USA) (Auction Ring (USA)) **Dr Carlos E. Stelling**
42 Br f 10/4 Alhijaz—Hong Kong Girl (Petong) **Mrs B. Shelton**
43 **IMPERIAL BEAUTY (USA),** b f 25/2 Imperial Ballet (IRE)—
Multimara (USA) (Arctic Tern (USA)) **Dr Carlos E. Stelling**
44 B f 2/3 Alhijaz—Irenic (Mummy's Pet) **Ten Of Hearts**
45 B f 17/4 Warning—Kindergarten (Trempolino (USA)) **Bakewell Bloodstock Ltd**
46 B g 29/4 Elbio—Madam Slaney (Prince Tenderfoot (USA)) **Mr R. P. Marchant**
47 **NOZOMI,** br f 20/3 Mujadil (USA)—Crimbourne (Mummy's Pet) **Mr R. P. Marchant**
48 Ch f 28/3 Wolfhound (USA)—Peperonata (IRE) (Cyrano de Bergerac) **Skyline Racing Ltd**
49 **PRESUMED (USA),** b f 12/3 Dynaformer (USA)—Prebend (USA) (L'Emigrant (USA)) **Dr Carlos E. Stelling**
50 Br f 5/3 Pips Pride—Royal Wolff (Prince Tenderfoot (USA))
51 **SALSA DANCER (IRE),** b f 8/4 Seattle Dancer (USA)—Rince Deas (IRE) (Alzao (USA)) **Dr John P. Ryan**
52 B f 30/4 Grand Lodge (USA)—Salvezza (IRE) (Superpower) **Skyline Racing Ltd**
53 **SING FOR ROSIE,** br f 25/4 Petong—Turbo Rose (Taufan (USA)) **Mrs B. Thorne**
54 B c 18/4 Wolfhound (USA)—Swame (USA) (Jade Hunter (USA)) **Mr P. Wragg**
55 Ch f 1/4 Lion Cavern (USA)—Tenderetta (Tender King) **Skyling Racing Ltd**
56 **TURNOFACARD,** ch f 9/4 First Trump—Barbary Court (Grundy) **Mr A. W. Schiff**

Other Owners: Mr K. Brackpool, Mr J. P. Carrington, Mr Joseph Chan, Mrs Frank Clothier, Mr H. R. Dobinson, Mrs L. Donald, Mr D. R. J. Foster, Mr K. E. Gregory, Mr Peter Harriman, Mr Barry Hearn, Mrs Susan Hearn, Mrs Greta Sarfaty Marchant, Mrs Lucille Melotti, Mr Gerry Moss, Mr R. G. Percival, Mr John Rathmell, Mr Geoff Roberts, Mr J. R. Roberts, Mr Derek Sadler, Mr Nicholas Schofield, Mr B. Shelton, Mr N. Taylor, Mrs J. Veitch, Sir Christopher Walford, Mrs Sarah Walker, Mrs L. Whitehouse.

Apprentice: David Griffiths (8-4).

376 MR JAMES J. MANGAN, Mallow

Postal: **Curraheen, Conna, Mallow, Co. Cork, Ireland.**
Phone: **(058) 59116**

1 **CHOICE OF KINGS (IRE),** 6, b m King's Ride—Ursula's Choice **Mrs M. C. O'Connor**
2 **DIAMOND MELODY (IRE),** 7, b g Torus—Sylvan Storm **Brogue Syndicate**
3 **HARBOUR LEADER (IRE),** 6, b g Supreme Leader—Buckskins Chat **Mr Michael Healy**
4 **JIMMY DAN (IRE),** 6, b g Lord Americo—French Academy **Directors Decision Syndicate**
5 **MIRACLE ME (IRE),** 6, b g Supreme Leader—Castleblagh **Mrs G. Magnier**
6 **MR K'S WINTERBLUES (IRE),** 8, br m Strong Gale—Speedy Lady **Mrs T. Kouwenberg**
7 **STROLL HOME (IRE),** 8, ch g Tale Quale—Sales Centre **Mrs M. Mangan**

Other Owners: Miss E. Harris, D. A. Lucey, Mrs P. J. Magnier, Miss Ann McCarthy, Mrs M. Mulcahy, John T. Raole, Yawl Bay Seafood Ltd.

Amateur: Mr J G Sheehan (10-2).

377 MR C. J. MANN, Upper Lambourn

Postal: **Whitcoombe Park Stables, Upper Lambourn, Hungerford, Berkshire, RG17 8RA.**
Phone: **(01488) 71717/73118 FAX (01488) 73223 MOBILE (0421) 888333**

1 **ALQAIRAWAAN,** 9, b g Ajdal (USA)—Clare Island **Mr Jack Joseph**
2 **ANOTHER COURSE (IRE),** 10, b g Crash Course—Regal Guard **Miss S. Barraclough**
3 **BIMSEY (IRE),** 8, b h Horage—Cut It Out **Mr Aidan J. Ryan**
4 **BLUESHAAN (IRE),** 5, b g Darshaan—Pale Blue **The Lavender Cottage Partnership**
5 **CARROLLS ROCK (IRE),** 7, b g Delamain (USA)—Hello Del **C'est La Vie Racing Partnership**
6 **CASTLE ARROW (IRE),** 5, b g Mansooj—Soulful **The Tramp Partnership**
7 **CELIBATE (IRE),** 7, ch g Shy Groom (USA)—Dance Alone (USA) **Stamford Bridge Partnership**
8 **CHECK THE DECK (IRE),** 7, b g Hollow Hand—Anaglog Dream **Mrs L. G. Turner**
9 **CLIFTON SET,** 7, b g Northern State (USA)—Brave Maiden **Mrs Christine Fennell**
10 **COLOSSUS OF ROADS,** 9, b g Rymer—Dear Jem **Mr David F. Wilson**
11 **DECIDE YOURSELF (IRE),** 8, b g Tumble Gold—Wrong Decision **Mr David F. Wilson**
12 **DENHAM HILL (IRE),** 7, ch g Electric—Barrow Breeze **Mr J. E. Brown**
13 5, Ch g Watchman (NZ)—Dewi (NZ) **Mr Charlie Mann**
14 **DRUMMOND WARRIOR (IRE),** 9, b g Rontino—Speckled Leinster **Mr David F. Wilson**
15 **EASY BREEZY,** 8, b g Strong Gale—Mill Shine **Granville J. Harper & Partners**
16 **EDGE AHEAD (IRE),** 8, b g Le Bavard (FR)—Blackrath Beauty **Mr T. Thomson Jones**
17 **ERUDIT II (FR),** 6, b g Missolonghi (USA)—Quelle Etoile V (FR) **Mr J. E. Funnell**
18 **FAKIR D'AVRILLY (FR),** 5, b g Bakilani (FR)—Jouvence (FR) **Mrs P. Dodd**
19 **FARNESE (FR),** 5, b br m Roi de Rome (USA)—Royaute (FR) **The British Volunteer Partnership**
20 **GLORIOUS ENCOUNTER,** 4, b g Pursuit of Love—Swellegant
21 **GOING FOR BROKE,** 4, b g Simply Great (FR)—Empty Purse **Watubust Racing**
22 **GOOD JOB,** 6, b m King's Ride—Oh So Ripe **Pertemps Ltd**
23 **HADIDI,** 4, b g Alzao (USA)—Sesame **Stamford Bridge Partnership**
24 **HIGH SUMMER,** 8, b g Green Desert (USA)—Beacon Hill **Mr David F. Wilson**
25 **HOLBORN HILL (IRE),** 6, gr g Riberetto—Grey Tor **Mr J. E. Brown**
26 **IADES BOY (NZ),** 7, b g Iades (FR)—Phero's Bay (NZ) **Mr J. D. I. Bell**
27 **IVY BOY (IRE),** 8, ch g Riot Helmet—Ivy Run **The Gianluca Partnership**
28 **JACKSON FLINT,** 10, b g Nishapour (FR)—Scamperdale **Mrs L. G. Turner**
29 **KING OF THIEVES (IRE),** 6, b g Executive Perk—Tom's Crofter **Mr J. D. I. Bell**
30 **LISTE ROUGE (USA),** 5, b g Red Ransom (USA)—Bestseller's List (USA) **Charlton Bloodstock**
31 **LORD TOMANICO (FR),** 6, b g Tirol—Lady Beauvallon **Mr Charlie Mann**
32 **MONTE'S MAGIC (NZ),** 5, ch g Omnicorp (NZ)—Miss Beaufort (NZ) **Monte's Racing Partnership**
33 **MULTY (IRE),** 6, b br g Posen (USA)—Geraldville **The Izz That Right Partnership**
34 **NATIVE SHORE (IRE),** 6, b m Be My Native (USA)—Castle Stream **Charles Andrew Robin Angus Partnership**
35 **NORMANDY DUKE (NZ),** 6, ch g First Norman (USA)—Royal Step (NZ) **Mrs I. Coles**

MR C. J. MANN—continued

36 **PROFESSOR PAGE (IRE),** 8, b g Spanish Place (USA)—Knight's Princess **Bryan & Ann Beacham**
37 **PROVINCE,** 5, b g Dominion—Shih Ching (USA) **Mr J. E. Brown**
38 **RANGITIKEI (NZ),** 7, b g Alleged Dash (USA)—Suelga (NZ) **Mrs J. M. Mayo**
39 **REWARD,** 4, gr ro g Highest Honor (FR)—Intimate Guest **Mr Athole Still**
40 **SANTELLA BOY (USA),** 6, b g Turkoman (USA)—Dream Creek (USA) **The Link Leasing Partnership**
41 **SNOWY PETREL (IRE),** 6, b g Petorius—Bronzewing **The Icy Fire Partnership**
42 **SOCIETY MAGIC (USA),** 5, b g Imp Society (USA)—Lady Kirtling (USA) **Monte's Racing Partnership**
43 **TAKE THE BUCKSKIN,** 11, b g Buckskin (FR)—Honeyburn **Mr David F. Wilson**
44 **TIME FOR ACTION (IRE),** 6, b g Alzao (USA)—Beyond Words **Mr Martin Myers**
45 **TOTAL JOY (IRE),** 7, gr g Persian Bold—Caranina (USA) **Mr P. M. Warren**
46 **TRUANCY,** 5, b g Polar Falcon (USA)—Zalfa **Mr J. E. Funnell**
47 **VIRTUOSO,** 4, ch g Suave Dancer (USA)—Creake **Mrs M. Devine**
48 **WASP RANGER (USA),** 4, b g Red Ransom (USA)—Lady Climber (USA) **Charlton Bloodstock**

Other Owners: Mr D. P. Barrie, Mr A. Bavin, Mr B. R. H. Burrough, Mr M. Charlton, Mr C. D. Cunningham, Mr C. J. Dartmouth, Mr John Davies (Stonehill), Mr R. E. Good, Mrs A. E. Goodwin, Mr A. Granados, Mr J. F. Hansberry, Mr J. A. Kendall, Mr Ian Kirkham, Mrs Viviann Linden, Mr R. P. B. Michaelson, Mr A. Mitchell, Mr M. J. Morrison, Mr Larry Murphy, Mr C. R. Nugent, Mr G. Osztreicher, Mrs Jean Peacock, Mr J. M. Quinn, Miss A. Roberts, Mrs C. Tate, Mr A. M. Tolhurst, Mr A. W. Turczyniak, Mr G. Willey, Mr Michael J. Williams, Mr Noel Wilson, Mr R. P. Woolford, Mr P. H. Young.

Jockey (NH): R Dunwoody (w.a.).

Conditional: Jamie Magee (9-11).

Amateur: Mr K R O'Ryan (10-0).

378 MR G. G. MARGARSON, Newmarket

Postal: **Machell Place, Old Station Road, Newmarket, Suffolk, CB8 0DW.**
Phone: **(01638) 602070 FAX (01638) 668043 MOBILE (0860) 19830**

1 **BLOOD ORANGE,** 4, ch c Ron's Victory (USA)—Little Bittern (USA)
2 **CABCHARGE GEMINI,** 4, b g High Kicker (USA)—Miss Noname
3 **DIESAN (USA),** 7, b g Diesis—Bold Courtesan (USA)
4 **EILEEN'S LADY,** 4, b f Mtoto—Laughsome
5 **GENERAL ASSEMBLY (IRE),** 6, b g Pharly (FR)—Hastening
6 **KOSEVO (IRE),** 4, b g Shareef Dancer (USA)—Kallista
7 **MARCASSIN,** 4, b g Unfuwain (USA)—Coir 'a' Ghaill
8 **MOLLY MUSIC,** 4, b f Music Boy—Carlton Glory
9 **ROCKCRACKER (IRE),** 6, ch g Ballad Rock—Forest Blaze (USA)
10 **SINGFORYOURSUPPER,** 4, ch f Superlative—Suzannah's Song
11 **TINKLERS FOLLY,** 6, ch g Bairn (USA)—Lucky Straw

THREE-YEAR-OLDS

12 **ASTRAL RHYTHM,** b c Scorpio (FR)—Suzannah's Song
13 **A TOUCH OF FROST,** gr f Distant Relative—Pharland (FR)
14 **JAY GEE (IRE),** b f Second Set (IRE)—Polynesian Goddess (IRE)
15 **SHAMBLES,** ch f Elmaamul (USA)—Rambadale
16 **SPEEDFIT TOO (IRE),** b c Scenic—Safka (USA)
17 **TOUCHANOVA,** gr f Touch of Grey—Mazurkanova

TWO-YEAR-OLDS

18 **FROSTED AIRE,** ch c 7/3 Chilibang—Suzannah's Song (Song)
19 **GEMINI GUEST (IRE),** ch c 14/2 Waajib—Aldhabyih (General Assembly (USA))

MR G. G. MARGARSON—continued

20 HONEY GUEST (IRE), ch f 16/3 Roi Danzig (USA)—Kuwah (IRE) (Be My Guest (USA))
21 POLAR PEAK, ch f 24/2 Polar Falcon (USA)—Hilly (Town Crier)

Other Owners: Mr P. E. Axon, Mr T. S. Child, Computer Cab (Racing Club) Ltd, The Craftsmen, Mr J. Gilman, Mr J. D. Guest, Mr William Hattersley, Mr D. Martin, Mr S. M. Martin, Mrs Jean Mitchell, Shambles Partnership, Mrs Jill Sinclair, Mr M. Sinclair, Mr Mark Sommers, The Four Jays Partnership, Mr J. Whiting, Mrs Patricia Williams.

379 MR D. MARKS, Upper Lambourn

Postal: **Lethornes, Lambourn, Hungerford, Berks, RG17 8QS.**
Phone: **(01488) 71767 FAX (01488) 73783**

1 **CHILI BOUCHIER (USA),** 4, br f Stop The Music (USA)—Low Approach **Mr Peter J. Pearson**
2 **DARIUS THE GREAT (IRE),** 6, ch g Persian Heights—Derring Dee **Mr C. R. Buttery**
3 **LA MENORQUINA (USA),** 8, b m Woodman (USA)—Hail The Lady (USA) **Mr Joe Arden**
4 **PARAMOUNT LEADER,** 6, b g Presidium—Dragusa **Joe And Pat Arden**
5 **PRIVATE FIXTURE (IRE),** 7, ch g The Noble Player (USA)—Pennyala **Mr John M. Jackson**

TWO-YEAR-OLDS

6 **HATHNI KHOWND,** b f 10/3 Reprimand—Rattle Along (Tap On Wood) **Mr G. J. King**
7 **KEYHOLE KATE,** b f Nomination—Nikitria (Robellino (USA)) **Mr P. Oppenheimer**
8 **MUDDY WATERS,** ch f 3/5 Salse (USA)—Rainbow Fleet (Nomination) **Mr R. J. F. Brothers**

Other Owners: Mrs E. A. Chevis, Mr D. J. Crenin, C. H. Davies, Mr P. A. Heath, Mr Denis Marchant, Mr D. Marks, M. O'Halloran, Mr John N. Simpson.

Jockey (Flat): P Eddery (w.a.).

Jockey (NH): J McCarthy (10-0, w.a.).

Lady Rider: Miss Kelly Marks (9-7).

380 MRS L. A. MARSHALL, Morpeth

Postal: **Togston Hall Farmhouse, North Togston, Amble, Morpeth, Northd, NE65 0HR.**
Phone: **(01665) 712699**

1 **ARISTODEMUS,** 9, b g Politico (USA)—Easter Jane **Mrs L. Marshall**
2 **DONOVANS REEF,** 12, b g Cool Guy (USA)—Mother Machree **Mrs L. Marshall**
3 **REGAL DOMAIN (IRE),** 7, gr g Dominion Royale—Adaraya (FR) **Mrs L. Marshall**

THREE-YEAR-OLDS

4 B f Silver Season—By The Bye **Mr S. Marshall**

TWO-YEAR-OLDS

5 **MISS MATTIE ROSS,** b f 28/7 Milieu—Mother Machree (Bing II) **Mr S. Marshall**

381 MR R. F. MARVIN, Southwell

Postal: **The Hunter Yard, Southwell Racecourse, Southwell, Nottinghamshire, NG25 OTS**
Phone: **(01636) 814481 EX 41 (01636) 814943 (0441) 198718**

1 **AFAAN (IRE)**, 5, ch h Cadeaux Genereux—Rawaabe (USA) **Mr E. Gray**
2 **AJNAD (IRE)**, 4, b g Efisio—Lotte Lenta **Mr E. Gray**
3 **BLACK BOY (IRE)**, 9, br g Auction Ring (USA)—Relic Spirit **Mr David G. Woods**
4 **BOBALUNA**, 5, b h Inca Chief (USA)—Davemma **Mr E. Gray**
5 **KOMASEPH**, 6, b g Komaite (USA)—Starkist **Mr R. W. Jaines**
6 **NO PRETENCE**, 4, b c Forzando—Minne Love **Miss Megan Phipps**
7 **ROYALE FINALE (IRE)**, 4, ch g Royal Academy (USA)—Final Farewell (USA) **Mr A. Radford**
8 **WILD CITY (USA)**, 4, b g Wild Again (USA)—Garvin's Gal (USA) **Mr P. J. Cronin**

THREE-YEAR-OLDS

9 **PORT OF CALL (IRE)**, ch g Arazi (USA)—Port Helene **Mr R. F. Marvin**

Jockey (Flat): T G McLaughlin (8-4).

Jockey (NH): W Worthington (10-0).

Lady Rider: Mrs M Morris (9-0).

382 MR N. B. MASON, Brancepeth

Postal: **Brancepeth Manor Farm, Crook, Co. Durham, DL15 9AS.**
Phone: **OFFICE (0191) 5673767 FARM (0191) 3736277/3736803 FAX (0191) 5642089**

1 **AFTER GRACE**, 8, ch m Gunner B—Take My Hand **Mr N. B. Mason**
2 **ARIZONA BOLD**, 5, b g Skyliner—Bold Event **Mr N. B. Mason**
3 **BATTERY FIRED**, 9, ch g K-Battery—Party Cloak **Mr N. B. Mason**
4 **BLAZING COUNTY (IRE)**, 7, b g Mandalus—Johns County **Mr N. B. Mason**
5 **BRANCEPETH BELLE (IRE)**, 8, b m Supreme Leader—Head of The Gang **Mr N. B. Mason**
6 **CARLEY LAD (IRE)**, 10, br g Crash Course—Leveret **Mr N. B. Mason**
7 **CLASSIC CONTACT**, 12, b g Whistling Top—Fosseway Folly **Mr N. B. Mason**
8 **DAMZA**, 6, b g Damister (USA)—So Precise (FR) **Mr N. B. Mason**
9 **EMPEROR'S MAGIC (IRE)**, 7, ch g Over The River (FR)—Sengirrefcha **Mr N. B. Mason**
10 **FIRST IN THE FIELD**, 7, ch m King of Clubs—Mighty Fly **Mr N. B. Mason**
11 **HAPPY GALE (IRE)**, 5, b m Strong Gale—Mighty Fly **Mr N. B. Mason**
12 **ICEFIRE DANCER**, 5, b m Arctic Lord—Super Gambler **Mr N. B. Mason**
13 **JOHNS THE BOY**, 12, b g Kambalda—Liskennett Girl **Mr N. B. Mason**
14 **JOKERS CHARM**, 7, b g Idiot's Delight—By The Lake **Mr N. B. Mason**
15 **KING'S COUNTRY (IRE)**, 6, b g King's Ride—Tatlock **Mr N. B. Mason**
16 **LITTLE TUSKA (IRE)**, 8, gr g Step Together (USA)—Peek-A-Boo **Mr N. B. Mason**
17 **MAJOR TROOP**, 9, br g State Trooper—Highflyer Park **Mr N. B. Mason**
18 **NASAYER (IRE)**, 8, b g Asir—Tourney's Girl **Mr N. B. Mason**
19 **NOSAM**, 8, b g Idiot's Delight—Socher **Mr N. B. Mason**
20 **RADICAL REFORM (IRE)**, 9, ch g Radical—Fountain Blue **Mr N. B. Mason**
21 **RED MARAUDER**, 8, ch g Gunner B—Cover Your Money **Mr N. B. Mason**
22 **RED STRIKER**, 4, ch g Gunner B—Cover Your Money **Mr N. B. Mason**
23 **REDSWAY (IRE)**, 7, ch g Tremblant—Clerihan Miss **Mr N. B. Mason**
24 **RUBON PRINCE (IRE)**, 7, ch g Kambalda—Oh Clare **Mr N. B. Mason**
25 **SEABURN**, 8, b g State Trooper—Star Display **Mr N. B. Mason**
26 **TITAN THAI (IRE)**, 9, b g Supreme Leader—Thai Nang **Mr N. B. Mason**
27 **TOTAL TRUANT**, 6, ro m Scallywag—Southend Scallywag **Mr N. B. Mason**
28 **WONDER GIRL**, 6, b m Bedford (USA)—Super Gambler **Mr N. B. Mason**
29 **XAIPETE (IRE)**, 6, b g Jolly Jake (NZ)—Rolfete (USA) **Mr N. B. Mason**

Jockeys (NH): D Gallagher, R Guest, R Thornton.

Conditional: C McCormack.

Amateurs: Mr M Carrol, Mr S Durack.

Lady Rider: Miss M O'Sullivan.

383 MR K. MCAULIFFE, Lambourn

Postal: **Delamere Cottage Stables, Folly Road, Lambourn, Berkshire, RG17 8QE.**
Phone: **(01488) 73999 FAX (01488) 73888 MOBILE (0802) 368846**

1 **AVANTI BLUE,** 4, b g Emarati (USA)—Dominion Blue **Folly Road Racing Partners (1996)**
2 **DRIMARD (IRE),** 7, ch g Ela-Mana-Mou—Babilla (USA) **Mr K. McAuliffe**
3 **FOLLY ROAD (IRE),** 8, b g Mister Lord (USA)—Lady Can **Mr K. McAuliffe**
4 **GENERAL SONG (IRE),** 4, b c Fayruz—Daybreaker **General Horse Advertising SRL**
5 **MYSTIC QUEST (IRE),** 4, b g Arcane (USA)—Tales of Wisdom **Delamere Cottage Racing Partners (1996)**

THREE-YEAR-OLDS

6 **FAYEZ,** ch c Interrex (CAN)—Forest Nymph **Mr A. Ezen**
7 **LEGS BE FRENDLY (IRE),** b c Fayruz—Thalssa **BABK Racing**
8 **MAGIC SPRING (IRE),** ch f Persian Bold—Oasis **Fieldspring Racing**
9 **PRINCE OF SALSA,** b g Emarati (USA)—Salinas **The PBT Group**
10 **SARA MOON CLASSIC (IRE),** b c Fayruz—Irish Affaire (IRE) **Highgrove Developments Limited**
11 **SHANTUNG (IRE),** ch f Anshan—Bamian (USA) **K & B Wetherell, Mrs Burke, C. Krosinsky**
12 **SILVER JOY,** b f Silver Kite (USA)—Oh My Joy **Gallagher Equine Ltd**
13 **SMOOTH SAILING,** gr g Beveled (USA)—Sea Farer Lake **Mr A. R. Parrish**
14 **STORM CAT,** ch c Interrex (CAN)—Albion Polka **Mr A. Ezen**
15 **TIPPITT BOY,** b c Prince Sabo—Space Travel **Highgrove Developments Limited**

TWO-YEAR-OLDS

16 B c Mukaddamah (USA)—Brockley Hill Lass (IRE) **Mr E. D. Kessly**
17 B f Persian Bold—Cliveden Gail (IRE) **Mr G. Tong**
18 Ch c River Falls—Heart To Heart (IRE) **The PBT Group & C. Krosinsky**
19 Gr c Petong—Holyrood Park **Mr E. Jameson**
20 B c Presidium—Judys Girl (IRE)
21 B c Presidium—Petitesse **Highgrove Developments Limited**
22 B c Casteddu—Rosie Dickins **Delamere Cottage Racing (1998)**
23 Gr f Beveled (USA)—Sea Farer Lake
24 B c Noble Patriarch—Simply Candy (IRE) **Miami Bloodstock**
25 B c Distant Relative—Singing Nelly
26 **SWAMPY,** b c Second Set (IRE)—Mystery Lady (USA) **Gallagher Equine Ltd**
27 Gr f Up And At 'em—Thalssa
28 **THAMES DANCER (USA),** ch c Green Dancer (USA)—Hata (FR) **Mr J. S. Dunningham**
29 **TRAGIC DANCER,** b c Tragic Role (USA)—Chantallee's Pride **Mr E. Treadwell & Mr P. Chung**
30 Ch c College Chapel—Valmarana (USA) **Gallagher Equine Ltd**

Other Owners: Mr N. Abbott, Mr T. L. Adams, Mr D. F. Allport, Mr D. H. Armitage, Mrs Dorothy Barclay, Mr Peter Barclay, Mrs Brenda Burke, Mr G. Carey, Mr R. J. Cummings, Mr D. D. Davies, Dragon Industrial Services, D. J. Evans, Mr Keith A. France, Mr Pat Hennerty, Hoh Supply Limited, Mr Ronald Howe, Mount Juliet, Mr N. C. Kersey, Mrs J. M. Langmead, Mr T. Mohan, Mr P. Petrovic, Mrs H. Raw, Mr Paul A. Rhodes, Mrs J. M. Ryan, Mrs C. Snart, Mr Jorg Vasicek, Mr John Wicks.

384 MR D. MCCAIN, Cholmondeley

Postal: **Bankhouse, Cholmondeley, Malpas, Cheshire, SY14 8AL.**
Phone: **(01829) 720352 FAX (01829) 720475 MOBILE (0836) 780879**

1 **ANALOGICAL,** 5, br m Teenoso (USA)—The Howlet
2 **BIYA (IRE),** 6, ch g Shadeed (USA)—Rosie Potts **Champ Chicken Co**
3 **BRAVE AIR (FR),** 4, b f Nashwan (USA)—Decided Air (IRE) **Mr M. Pollitt**
4 **CIRCULATION,** 12, b g Town And Country—Veinarde **Clayton Bigley Partnership Ltd**
5 **COBLE,** 4, b g Slip Anchor—Main Sail **Clayton Bigley Partnership Ltd**
6 **COME ON RISK ME,** 7, ch g Risk Me (FR)—Star Rose (FR) **Harry Ormesher**
7 **COMMERCIAL ARTIST,** 12, b g Furry Glen—Blue Suede Shoes **Mr L. A. Morgan**
8 **COOLINNY (IRE),** 9, b g Torus—Lady Driver **Champ Chicken Co**

MR D. MCCAIN—continued

9 CRAFTY CHAPLAIN, 12, ch g The Parson—She's Clever **Champ Chicken Co**
10 DESERT CALM (IRE), 9, br g Glow (USA)—Lancette **Mr R. N. Fuller**
11 4, B g Mandalus—Disetta
12 EBEN AL HABEEB (IRE), 7, ch g Nashwan (USA)—Family Style (USA) **The Bankhouse Confederacy**
13 EUROLINK SHADOW, 6, b g Be My Chief (USA)—Miss Top Ville (FR) **Champ Chicken Co**
14 4, B g Gildoran—Fille de Soleil
15 FOLLOW DE CALL, 8, b g Callernish—Designer **Champ Chicken Co**
16 GENTRY, 7, b g Aristocracy—Remember Don
17 GUNNARISKIT, 6, ch g Gunner B—Kirsheda
18 HEATHYARDS PEARL (USA), 4, gr f Mining (USA)—Dance Dance Dance (IRE) **Mr L. A. Morgan**
19 4, Br g Fools Holme (USA)—Injection **Mr R. Bellamy**
20 6, B m Derrylin—Little Oats
21 LOTHIAN COMMANDER, 6, ch g Alias Smith (USA)—Lothian Lightning **Mr Roger Bellamy**
22 8, B g Executive Man—Mickley Vulstar
23 MISS LAMBRINI, 5, ch m Henbit (USA)—Miss Club Royal **Halewood International Ltd**
24 5, B g Gunner B—My Aisling
25 4, B g Precious Metal—My Solitaire
26 NADIAD, 12, b g Darshaan—Naveen
27 NEVERMIND HEY, 4, b f Teenoso (USA)—The Howlet **Clayton Bigley Partnership Ltd**
28 PACKITIN PARKY, 5, b g Rakaposhi King—Divine Affair (IRE) **A. A. Packaging Ltd**
29 PADDINGTON JONES (IRE), 5, b g Camden Town—Bann River **Mr John Singleton**
30 RAINHAM, 11, b g Sadler's Wells (USA)—Edge of Town **Shaw Hill Golf Club**
31 SHAWKEY (IRE), 5, ch g Nashwan (USA)—Rosia Bay **Clayton Bigley Partnership Ltd**
32 SMUGURS (IRE), 4, ch f Masterclass (USA)—Blue Vista (IRE) **Harry Ormesher**
33 6, B g Pablond—Sovereign's Oak
34 THE EENS, 6, b g Rakaposhi King—Snippet **Shaw Hill Golf Club (Sage Cott Props Ltd**
35 THE FENCE SHRINKER, 7, b g Ballacashtal (CAN)—Whose Lady (USA) **Champ Chicken Co.**
36 THE SECRET GREY, 7, gr g Rakaposhi King—Locketts Lane **Clayton Bigley Partnership Ltd**
37 TILL TOMORROW, 7, ch m Executive Man—Saheej (USA) **Champ Chicken Co**
38 TREMENDISTO, 8, b g Petoski—Misty Halo **Mr L. A. Morgan**
39 4, B g Gildoran—Valiant Vision **Mr J. Singleton**
40 VERTICAL AIR, 5, b g Pablond—Joyful's Girl **Champ Chicken Co**
41 ZUHAIR, 5, ch g Mujtahid (USA)—Ghzaalh (USA) **Clayton Bigley Partnership Ltd**

THREE-YEAR-OLDS

42 HEATHYARDS HERO, b g Puissance—Heathyards Gem **Mr L. A. Morgan**
43 B g Teenoso (USA)—Let Me Finish
44 B f Dilum (USA)—Lucky Song **Harry Ormesher**
45 MICKLEOVER, ch g Mazaad—Overdraft
46 B g Teenoso (USA)—Miss Club Royal **Halewood International Ltd**
47 PERFECT LADY, gr f Petong—Petit Peu (IRE) **Harry Ormesher**
48 SAFI, b c Generous (IRE)—Jasarah (IRE)
49 SHARP PET, b f Petong—Harmony Park **Harry Ormesher**
50 B g Henbit (USA)—Snippet

TWO-YEAR-OLDS

51 B c 4/2 Puissance—Kentucky Tears (USA) (Cougar (CHI)) **Mr M. Pollitt**
52 B c 15/5 Alflora (IRE)—Miss Club Royal (Avocat) **Halewood International Ltd**
53 TIHEROS GLENN, ch c 21/4 Toxotis—Warthill Girl (Anfield) **Mrs H. F. Mahr**
54 B g 26/5 Terimon—Wave Dancer (Dance In Time (CAN))

Other Owners: Mr Richard Abbott, Mr C. Barker, Mrs S. K. Maan, Mrs D. McCain, Mr I. N. Meadows, Mr R. J. Rossiter, Mr G. Gary Salters.

Jockey (NH): T Jenks.

Amateur: Mr G Lake (9-0).

385 MR J. C. MCCONNOCHIE, Stratford-on-Avon

Postal: **Bankfield Racing Stables, Billesley Road, Wilmcote, Stratford-on-Avon, Warwickshire, CV37 9XG.**
Phone: **(01789) 415607 MOBILE (0831) 788565**

1 **ARMATEUR (FR)**, 10, b g Miller's Mate—Artistically (USA) **Major H. R. M. Porter**
2 **BELLE BARONESS**, 8, gr m Baron Blakeney—Ribobelle **Mr J. C. McConnochie**
3 **CAPTAIN ROSE**, 6, b g Soldier Rose—Miss Oxstall's **Mrs Richard Evans**
4 **CHAMPAGNE GOLD**, 11, ch g Bairn (USA)—Halkissimo **Mr J. C. McConnochie**
5 **COUNTERBALANCE**, 11, b m Orchestra—Lysanders Lady **Derwent Dene Farm**
6 **IVY BREEZE (IRE)**, 7, br m Phardante (FR)—Ivy Run **Mr S. E. Constable**
7 **PEARL'S CHOICE (IRE)**, 10, b br m Deep Run—Vendevar **The Choice Set Partnership**
8 **PHARDANTE'S WAY (IRE)**, 7, b g Phardante (FR)—Zitas Toi **Mr S. E. Constable**
9 **REGAL BLUFF**, 6, ch g Regal Steel—Bangkok Boss **Miss M. T. Sheridan**
10 **SIDNEY**, 9, b g Chabrias (FR)—Staboe Lady **Miss E. M. V. England**
11 **THE PEELER (IRE)**, 5, b g Orchestra—Miss Nancy **Mr S. E. Constable**
12 **TOPPERILLO**, 9, b g El-Birillo—Kramenna **Mrs R. E. Stocks**
13 **VAGUE HOPE (IRE)**, 6, b g Strong Gale—Misty's Wish **Mr Aiden Murphy**

Other Owners: Ms Barbara Ashby-Jones, Mr J. A. Bianchi, Mr S. Forster, Miss P. Elizabeth Porter, Mr D. J. Renney, Mr A. J. Stocks, Miss Judith Wilkinson.

Jockeys (NH): R Bellamy, S McNeill, A Thornton, S Wynne.

Amateur: Mr Matthew Mancini (10-0).

386 MR G. M. MCCOURT, Wantage

Postal: **Antwick Stud, Letcombe Regis, Wantage, Oxfordshire, OX12 9LH.**
Phone: **OFFICE (01235) 764456 HOUSE (01235) 763137 FAX (01235) 764456/763137**

1 **AINSI SOIT IL (FR)**, 7, b br g Amen (FR)—Crinolene (FR) **A-Men Partnership**
2 5, B g King's Ride—Arumah **Mr & Mrs Malcolm Batchelor**
3 **BARRANAK (IRE)**, 6, b g Cyrano de Bergerac—Saulonika **Mr M. MacCarthy**
4 4, Br g Actinium (FR)—Beautiful Glen **Mr Stanley Nixon**
5 **BILLY BOX**, 6, gr g Lord Bud—Counter Coup **Mr Alec Tuckerman**
6 **CAPTAIN KHEDIVE**, 10, ch g Deep Run—Wing On **Khedive Partnership**
7 **CASSIO'S BOY**, 7, b g Presidium—Cassio Lil **Lyonshall Racing**
8 **CATEMPO (IRE)**, 8, b g Cataldi—Raise The Tempo **Mr E. Sanjack**
9 **C D BOY (IRE)**, 5, b g Lord Americo—October Lady **C. D. Northern Ltd**
10 **CERTAIN SHOT**, 7, b g Little Wolf—Duckdown **McCourt Fine Meats Ltd & D. J. Rushen**
11 **HALMANERROR**, 8, gr g Lochnager—Counter Coup **Caulkheads Racing**
12 **HAWAIIAN YOUTH (IRE)**, 10, ch g Hawaiian Return (USA)—Eternal Youth **Mr David Czarnetzki**
13 **JUMP JET (IRE)**, 5, b g Lord Americo—Polly Ringling **Mr R. Cohen & Mr J. Constable**
14 5, Ch g Rakaposhi King—Just Pam **Mr J. Duggan**
15 **KEY TO**, 4, b f Interrex (CAN)—Key To Enchantment **Mr Christopher Shankland**
16 **LAGUNA BAY (IRE)**, 4, b f Arcane (USA)—Meg Daughter (IRE) **Town And Country Services Limited**
17 **LANCE ARMSTRONG (IRE)**, 8, b g Lancastrian—Wolver Rose **Mr G. L. Porter**
18 **NATURAL PARK (IRE)**, 5, gr g Roselier (FR)—Minstrel Park **Mr R. Cohen & Mrs B. Gerber**
19 **ORPHAN SPA (IRE)**, 7, ch g Phardante (FR)—Knockdrumagh **Mrs B. Taylor**
20 **PEDLAR'S CROSS (IRE)**, 6, b g Lancastrian—Fine Debut **Mr A. F. Merritt**
21 **PLAYLORD**, 5, b g Arctic Lord—Show Rose **Mr John Mandeville**
22 **PUNKAH (USA)**, 5, b g Lear Fan (USA)—Gentle Persuasion **McCourt Fine Meats Ltd & D. J. Rushen**
23 **RANAHINCH (IRE)**, 5, b m Persian Mews—Parsfield **The Futurist Partnership**
24 **REAR WINDOW**, 4, b g Night Shift (USA)—Last Clear Chance (USA) **Dawn Build Ltd**
25 **RED CURATE (IRE)**, 7, b g Radical—Parsfield **Mrs M. Turner & Mr C. White**
26 **RUNS IN THE FAMILY**, 6, b m Distant Relative—Stoney Dale **Mr Geoffrey C. Wood**

MR G. M. MCCOURT—continued

27 **SELECT STAR (IRE)**, 4, b g Arcane (USA)—Chevrefeuille **Mr G. McCourt**
28 **SHIMBA HILLS**, 10, b g Scorpio (FR)—Leading Line **Mrs K. A. Stuart**
29 4, Gr g Thethingaboutitis (USA)—Shrood Biddy **Mr S. D. Gray**
30 **SISTER STEPHANIE (IRE)**, 9, b br m Phardante (FR)—Soul Lucy **The Antwick Partnership**
31 **THUMBS UP**, 12, b g Fidel—Misclaire **Mrs B. Taylor**
32 **WHERE'S MIRANDA**, 6, ch m Carlingford Castle—Cindie Girl **Mrs B. Taylor**
33 **WHISPERING PINES (NZ)**, 5, b g Cache of Gold (USA)—Woodhill (NZ) **Mr J. J. Boulter**

TWO-YEAR-OLDS

34 B f 25/4 Runnett—Romantic Melody (Battle Hymn) **Mercaston Consultants Ltd**

Other Owners: Mr R. O. Addis, Mr J. Ayres, Mr T. R. Bull, Mr P. Cassidy, Mr Robert Cox, Mr M. A. Dore, Mr D. G. Ellis, Mr M. C. Englert, Mr P. G. Fry, Mr A. J. Graham, Mr A. P. Hartley, Mr D. M. Huglin, Mr W. D. Jamieson, Mr Robin Jones, Mr Edward Matthews, Middx Packaging Ltd, Mr A. K. Nash, Mr Wayne Neville, Mr Steven Pattinson, Mr Mike Perkins, Mr Andy Piggott, Mr G. Rouse, Mr Andy Turner, Mrs Margaret Turner, Mr B. T. Weisberg, Mr Christopher White.

Jockeys (NH): David Bridgwater (9-10), D J Moffatt (10-0).

Apprentice: Ross Studholme (8-12).

Conditional: Richard Hobon (9-7).

Amateur: Mr David Harney (10-7).

387 MR RAY MCGHIN, Exning

Postal: **Harraton Stables, Chapel Street, Exning, Suffolk, CB8 7HA.**
Phone: **(01638) 552009 FAX (01638) 750203**

1 **BILL MOON**, 12, ch g Nicholas Bill—Lunar Queen **Miss J. Feilden**
2 **DARYABAD (IRE)**, 6, b g Thatching—Dayanata **The C & M Racing Partnership**
3 **DON'T DROP BOMBS (USA)**, 9, ch g Fighting Fit (USA)—Promised Star (USA) **Miss J. Feilden**
4 **MELLERIO**, 8, ch g Jalmood (USA)—Arrangement **Mr K. Santana**
5 **MISS PIN UP**, 9, gr m Kalaglow—Allander Girl **Mr R. McGhin**

THREE-YEAR-OLDS

6 **PREMIER BARON**, b c Primo Dominie—Anna Karietta **M. Squance**

Other Owners: Mrs J. L. Beschizza, Mr P. J. Feilden, Mr M. Morris, Mr C. Paskin, Mr S. Paskin.

Amateur: Mr Ken Santana (9-7).

Lady Rider: Miss J Feilden (9-0).

388 MR T. P. MCGOVERN, Lewes

Postal: **Grandstand Stables, Old Lewes Racecourse, Lewes, East Sussex, BN7 1UR.**
Phone: **(01273) 487813**

1 **ANIMATO (IRE)**, 4, b g Eurobus—Audata (FR) **Mr Mark Holman**
2 **BALLYGRIFFIN LAD (IRE)**, 9, ch g Carlingford Castle—Calfstown Night **Mr Tommy Breen**

MR T. P. MCGOVERN—continued

3 CREST WING (USA), 5, b g Storm Bird (CAN)—Purify (USA) **Mr Tommy Breen**
4 FISIO SANDS, 9, b m Efisio—Sayida-Shahira **The Best Of Luck Partnership**
5 KAREN'S TYPHOON (IRE), 7, b g Strong Gale—Pops Girl **Mr Mark Holman**
6 LASTOFTHEBLAKENEYS, 5, b m Blakeney—Sayida-Shahira **Miss V. I. Willis**
7 MILLMOUNT (IRE), 8, ch m Be My Guest (USA)—Cooliney Princess **Mr Tommy Breen**
8 SILVER SANDS, 4, gr f Chilibang—Sayida-Shahira **The Best Of Luck Partnership**
9 SLEETMORE GALE (IRE), 8, b m Strong Gale—Lena's Reign **Mr D. O. Walsh**
10 WALKING TALL (IRE), 7, ch g Hatim (USA)—Futility **The Walking Tall Partnership**

Other Owners: Mr N. Abbott, Mr A. C. Baker, Mr C. Blanchard, Mr B. T. Buckley, Mr T. Clarke, Mr Paul Gibbons, Mr J. Holman, T. P. McGovern, Mr J. E. Mills, Mr K. Powell, Mr J. Washington, Mrs S. A. Willis.

389 MRS C. MCINNES SKINNER, Melton Mowbray

Postal: **John O'Gaunt House, Melton Mowbray, Leicestershire, LE14 2RE.**
Phone: **(01664) 454327**

1 LITTLE TINCTURE (IRE), 8, ch g Meneval (USA)—Lakefield Lady **Mrs T. J. McInnes Skinner**
2 SHEELIN LAD (IRE), 10, ch g Orchestra—Aryumad **Mrs T. J. McInnes Skinner**
3 YOUNG MINER, 12, ch g Monksfield—Tassel Tip **Mrs T. J. McInnes Skinner**

Jockey (NH): G Upton (10-2, w.a.).

Conditional: Sophie Mitchell (w.a.).

390 MR R. MCKELLAR, Carluke

Postal: **The Lodge, Waygateshaw House, Nr. Braidwood, Carluke, Lanarkshire, Scotland.**
Phone: **(01555) 750910**

1 ANOTHER NIGHTMARE (IRE), 6, b m Treasure Kay—Carange **GM Engineering**
2 4, Ch c French Gondolier (USA)—Doulally **Mr J. G. Hickie**
3 GRAND HOTEL (IRE), 4, ch c Be My Guest (USA)—State Treasure (USA) **Mr Gordon B. Cunningham**
4 HUTCHIES LADY, 6, b m Efisio—Keep Mum **Mrs Linda McKellar**
5 ON THE OFF CHANCE, 6, ch g French Gondolier (USA)—Off And On **Mr J. G. Hickie**
6 OPERATIC DANCER, 7, b g Germont—Indian Dancer **Mr Peter Howell**
7 SERIOUS HURRY, 10, ch g Forzando—Lady Bequick **Mrs Linda McKellar**
8 THE VALE (IRE), 6, b g Satco (FR)—Lady Kasbah **Mr Willie Smith**
9 VALES ALES, 5, b g Dominion Royale—Keep Mum **Mrs Linda McKellar**

THREE-YEAR-OLDS

10 B f Lashkari—Inneen Alainn **Mrs S. Nichol**

Other Owners: Mr C. P. Bone, Mr G. A. Martin, Mr J. C. McGee, Mr C. M. McKenna, Mr George Murray, Mrs Kathleen Murray, Mr Ray Vardy.

Jockeys (Flat): J K Fanning, T Williams.

Conditional: D Parker (w.a.).

Amateurs: Mr C Dunbar (10-7), Mr R Hale (9-7, w.a.).

Lady Rider: Mrs C Williams (9-0).

391 MR W. G. MCKENZIE-COLES, Taunton

Postal: **Bells Cottage, Lydeard St Lawrence, Taunton, Somerset, TA4 3RN.**
Phone: **LYDEARD ST LAWRENCE (01984) 667334**

1 **AT IT AGAIN (IRE)**, 9, ch g Regular Guy—Pollys Grind **Mr W. G. McKenzie-Coles**
2 **LOUIS RENEE (IRE)**, 7, ch g Cardinal Flower—Moon Lock **Mr W. G. McKenzie-Coles**
3 **SUPREME CRUSADER (IRE)**, 7, br g Supreme Leader—Seanaphobal Lady **Mr W. G. McKenzie-Coles**
4 **TOM TUGG (IRE)**, 8, b g Supreme Leader—Healys Pass **Mrs R. McKenzie-Coles**

Jockeys (NH): C Maude, W J McFarland.

Conditional: Sophie Mitchell (9-7).

392 MR W. J. MCKEOWN, Newcastle

Postal: **East Wideopen Farm, Wideopen, Newcastle-upon-Tyne, NE13 6DW.**
Phone: **TEL (0191) 236 7545 FAX (0191) 236 2959**

1 **DISSINGTON TIMES**, 4, ch g Timeless Times (USA)—Zam's Slave **DA & W Wyllie**
2 **EASTCLIFFE (IRE)**, 6, ch g Zaffaran (USA)—Missing Note **Mrs L. E. McKeown**
3 **HECKLEY DANCER**, 6, b g Dancing High—Heckley Surprise **Mr J. L. Gledson**
4 4, B g Over The River (FR)—Moppet's Last **Mrs J. Joyce**
5 **MORNING STAR**, 4, b f Statoblest—Moushka **Mrs L. E. McKeown**
6 **MOST WANTED (IRE)**, 5, ch m Priolo (USA)—Dewan's Niece (USA) **Mr G. Allan**
7 **MR OSCAR**, 6, b g Belfort (FR)—Moushka **Mr W. McKeown**
8 **NAUGHTY FEELINGS**, 4, b g Feelings (FR)—Pohet **Mr W. J. Laws**
9 4, B g King's Ride—Nebechal **Mr W. McKeown**
10 **PORTMAN**, 6, b g Sulaafah (USA)—Bride **Mrs L. E. McKeown**
11 **SIR BOB (IRE)**, 6, br g Aristocracy—Wilden **Mrs L. E. McKeown**
12 **VANADIUM ORE**, 5, b g Precious Metal—Rockefillee **Mr E. H. E. Garth Ormond**

THREE-YEAR-OLDS

13 **DISSINGTON ME**, b f Presidium—Zam's Slave **DA & W Wyllie**
14 **ELLENBER**, ch g Risk Me (FR)—Brig of Ayr **Mrs L. E. McKeown**
15 **SAINTES**, b g Be My Chief (USA)—Latakia **Mr W. McKeown**
16 **WEE CHRISTY (IRE)**, gr c Contract Law (USA)—Eternal Optimist **Christy Golfing Society**

Other Owners: Miss Gwen Gibson, Mr A Hynd, Mr John Smart, Mr I. A. Smith, Mr J. Taylor, Mrs L. A. Tinnion.

393 MRS V. MCKIE, Twyford

Postal: **'Twyford Mill', Twyford, Buckingham, MK18 4HA.**
Phone: **STEEPLE CLAYDON (01296) 730707 FAX: (01296) 730806**

1 **AMERICAN STYLE (IRE)**, 6, b g Lord Americo—Spindle Tree **Twyford Bloodstock**
2 **ARMALA**, 13, ch g Deep Run—Bardicate **Mrs C. Houston**
3 6, B g Brush Aside (USA)—Baranee **Twyford Bloodstock**
4 **BELARUS (IRE)**, 6, b g Waajib—Kavali **Mr M. H. D. Barlow**
5 **BLACK STAG (IRE)**, 9, b br g Phardante (FR)—Light Whisper **Mr T. J. Ovens**
6 **FASHION MAKER (IRE)**, 8, b g Creative Plan (USA)—Cailin Alainn **Mr J. B. Sumner**
7 **GROGARRY LODGE**, 6, ch g Gildoran—Misty Fort **Mrs V. McKie**
8 **HIGH INTAKE**, 6, b g Primitive Rising (USA)—Cornetta **Twyford Bloodstock**
9 5, Ch g Phardante (FR)—Lena's Reign **Twyford Bloodstock**
10 4, B g Infantry—Littledrunkgirl **Twyford Bloodstock**
11 4, B f Crested Lark—Mrs Pepperpot **Twyford Bloodstock**

MRS V. MCKIE—continued

12 **MY BETSY,** 4, gr f Absalom—Formidable Task **Twyford Bloodstock**
13 **MY SECRET (IRE),** 6, b g Montelimar (USA)—Ballinoe Lass **Mr M. H. D. Barlow**
14 **OVER AND UNDER (IRE),** 5, ch g Over The River (FR)—Silver Gala **Twyford Bloodstock**
15 **PERFECT MINSTREL (IRE),** 7, b g Black Minstrel—Ashford Doll **Twyford Bloodstock**
16 **ROUGH TIGER (IRE),** 5, ch g Glacial Storm (USA)—Mourne Trix **Mr M. H. D. Barlow**
17 **TORIAN (IRE),** 7, b g Torus—Brave Intention **Twyford Bloodstock**
18 **WELSH SPINNER (IRE),** 7, b g Corvaro (USA)—Welsh Tan **Twyford Bloodstock**

Other Owners: Lady Richard Wellesley.

Jockey (NH): W Marston (10-0).

394 MR B. A. MCMAHON, Tamworth

Postal: **Woodside Farm, Hopwas Hill, Tamworth, Staffordshire, B78 3EB,**
Phone: **(01827) 62901 FAX (01827) 68361**

1 **COURSE FISHING,** 7, ch g Squill (USA)—Migoletty **Mr G. D. Bull**
2 **CREES SQAW,** 6, b m Cree Song—Elsocko **Mr J. C. Fretwell**
3 **GO FOR THE DOCTOR,** 8, b g Doctor Wall—Mary Mile **Mr S. Edwards**
4 **HOLLOWAY MELODY,** 5, ch m Cree Song—Holloway Wonder **Mrs Rita Gibson**
5 **ISIT IZZY,** 6, b m Crofthall—Angie's Girl **Mrs Angela Beard**
6 **JACK JENNINGS,** 5, ch h Deploy—Lareyna **Mr G. Whitaker**
7 **LOOK WHO'S CALLING (IRE),** 5, b g Al Hareb (USA)—House Call **Mr S. Edwards**
8 **NOMINATOR LAD,** 4, b c Nomination—Ankara's Princess (USA) **Mr J. D. Graham**
9 **OUT OF SIGHT (IRE),** 4, ch c Salse (USA)—Starr Danias (USA) **Mr D. J. Allen**
10 **PRESENT CHANCE,** 4, ch c Cadeaux Genereux—Chance All (FR) **Mr Ian Guise**
11 **ROVING MINSTREL,** 7, ch h Cree Song—Klairove **Mrs J. McMahon & Mr Tommy Staunton**
12 **ROYAL CASCADE (IRE),** 4, b g River Falls—Relative Stranger **Mrs J. McMahon**
13 **SILVER MOON,** 4, gr f Environment Friend—High And Bright **Mr M. Sturgess & Mrs J. McMahon**
14 **SUPERBIT,** 6, b g Superpower—On A Bit **Mr Neville H. Smith**
15 **THE GAY FOX,** 4, gr c Never So Bold—School Concert **Mr G. Whitaker**
16 **TONNERRE,** 6, b g Unfuwain (USA)—Supper Time **Mr Ian Guise**
17 **YABINT EL SULTAN,** 4, ch f Safawan—Dalby Dancer **G. S. D. Ltd & Mrs J. McMahon**
18 **YEOMAN OLIVER,** 5, b h Precocious—Impala Lass **Mr Michael G. T. Stokes**

THREE-YEAR-OLDS

19 **AKARITA (IRE),** b f Akarad (FR)—Safita **Barouche Stud Ltd**
20 **GENERAL KLAIRE,** b br f Presidium—Klairover **Mr Tommy Staunton**
21 **JIMMY TOO,** b c Nomination—Cutlass Princess (USA) **Mr J. D. Graham**
22 **POSITIVE AIR,** b f Puissance—Breezy Day **Mr R. Thornhill**
23 **PRESS AHEAD,** br c Precocious—By Line **Mr R. L. Bedding & Mr Tommy Staunton**
24 **RA RA RASPUTIN,** b c Petong—Ra Ra Girl **Mr D. J. Allen**
25 **REVENGE IS SWEET,** b c Absalom—Welsh Secret **Mr Ian Guise & Mr J. R. Smith**
26 **RUSSIAN ROMEO (IRE),** b c Soviet Lad (USA)—Aotearoa (IRE) **Mr R. L. Bedding**
27 **SALLY'S DANCER,** b f Shareef Dancer (USA)—Spica (USA) **Mrs Sally Fields**
28 **SHARWAY LADY,** b f Shareef Dancer (USA)—Eladale (IRE) **Sharway Contracts**
29 **THE DOWNTOWN FOX,** b c Primo Dominie—Sara Sprint **Mr G. Whitaker**
30 **TRAVELLING CLOCK,** ch c Deploy—Travel Mystery **Mr R. L. Bedding & Mr G. Whitaker**
31 **YORKIES BOY,** gr c Clantime—Slipperose **Mrs H. Beddis**

TWO-YEAR-OLDS

32 Ch c 22/3 Formidable (USA)—Careful Dancer
33 B c 14/3 Sizzling Melody—Elsocko **Mrs J. McMahon**
34 B f 27/3 Never So Bold—Highland Rowena **Mrs J. McMahon**
35 B c 27/2 Sizzling Melody—Little Tich **Mrs J. McMahon**
36 **LUCKY COVE,** gr c 26/4 Lugana Beach—Port-Na-Blath **Mr J. R. Smith**

MR B. A. MCMAHON—continued

37 MISS PIPPIN, ch f 1/6 Rudimentary (USA)—Appledorn **Mr M. Sturgess**
38 MY TESS, b f 6/4 Lugana Beach—Barachois Princess (USA) **Mr J. D. Graham**
39 B c 3/3 Sizzling Melody—Nilu (IRE) **Zm Hussein**
40 NOW LOOK HERE, b c 30/4 Reprimand—Where's Carol **Mr S. Edwards**
41 PERUGINO BAY (IRE), b c 14/2 Perugino (USA)—Dublah (USA) **Mr J. C. Fretwell**
42 B f 16/3 Sizzling Melody—Ra Ra Girl **Mr D. J. Allen**
43 ROYAL DOLPHIN, b c 2/2 Dolphin Street (FR)—Diamond Lake **Mr R. L. Beddis**
44 B c 27/4 Be My Chief (USA)—Swift Return
45 TESS TOO, b f 23/3 Lugana Beach—Ankara's Princess (USA) **Mr J. D. Graham**
46 WEE JIMMY, b c 3/3 Lugana Beach—Cutlass Princess (USA) **Mr J. D. Graham**
47 YABINT EL SHAM, b f 13/4 Sizzling Melody—Dalby Dancer **G. S. D. Ltd & Mrs J. McMahon**

Other Owners: Mrs S. E. Allen, Mr J. W. Butler, Mr C. G. Conway, Mrs B. Facchino, Mr K. P. Holland, Mrs Christopher Lee-Jones, Mrs L. Mathew, Mrs Mary Meddings, Mr Stefan Uppstrom, Mr P. F. Youd.

Jockeys (Flat): J Fortune, L Newton (8-0).

Apprentices: F Boyle (7-2), D Kilcourse (6-0), S Righton (7-7).

395 MR B. J. MCMATH, Newmarket

Postal: **Wolver Hollow Cottage, Marriott Stables, Hamilton Road, Newmarket, Suffolk, CB8 0NY.**
Phone: **NEWMARKET (01638) 665868 MOBILE (0411) 129575 FAX (01638) 665868**

1 ACTION JACKSON, 6, b g Hadeer—Water Woo (USA) **Mr R. G. Levin**
2 BOB'S SAINTLY AIM, 4, b f Mazilier (USA)—Great Aim **Mr Robert Clark**
3 CHIMBORAZO, 7, ch g Salse (USA)—Pale Gold (FR) **Mrs Lisa Olley**
4 DOCKLANDS LIMO, 5, b h Most Welcome—Bugle Sound **Mrs Lisa Olley**
5 MEDLAND (IRE), 8, ch g Imperial Frontier (USA)—Miami Dancer **The Happy Go Lucky Partnership**
6 MILNGAVIE, 8, ch g Pharly (FR)—Wig And Gown **Mrs Lisa Olley**
7 NARBONNE, 7, b m Rousillon (USA)—Historical Fact **Saracen Racing**
8 OH NO ROSIE, 7, ch m Vital Season—Rosie Oh **Mr P. Venner**
9 RETOTO, 4, ch f Totem (USA)—Responder **The Likely Bunch**
10 ZIBAK (USA), 4, br g Capote (USA)—Minifah (USA) **Mrs Lisa Olley**

THREE-YEAR-OLDS

11 DAN HOI (IRE), ch c Roi Danzig (USA)—Honorine (USA) **Mrs Lisa Olley**
12 DOCKLANDS EXECUTIVE, b g Nomination—Khadino **Mrs Lisa Olley**
13 B f Lahib (USA)—Gentle Guest (IRE) **Mr M. Armitt**
14 JOCK'S DREAM, b f Noble Patriarch—Bold Sophie **The Happy Go Lucky Partnership**
15 RED HEAD AND DOTTY, ch f Risk Me (FR)—Sharper Still **Mr Martin Clark**

TWO-YEAR-OLDS

16 MEZZA LUNA, b f 6/2 Distant Relative—Cox's Pippin (USA) (Cox's Ridge (USA)) **Mr R. G. Levin**

Other Owners: Mr C. Cowlard, Miss M. Dawson, Mr C. Glassett, Mr M. Glassett, Mr B. Harris, Mr C. Hitchcock, Mr G. W. Holland, Mr H. Hughes, Mr David W. Jones, Mr Len Terrell.

Jockeys (Flat): R Cochrane (w.a.), E Johnson (7-7).

Jockey (NH): C Llewellyn (10-0, w.a.).

396 MR M. D. MCMILLAN, Bibury

Postal: **The Glebe House, Bibury, Cirencester, Gloucestershire, GL7 5NS.**
Phone: **(01285) 740341 FAX (01285) 740592**

1 5, Ch m Le Moss—La Verite **Mr M. D. McMillan**
2 **REAL LUCILLE,** 6, b m Idiot's Delight—La Verite **Mr M. D. McMillan**
3 **TACO'S REVENGE,** 5, b g Henbit (USA)—Taco **Mr M. D. McMillan**

Other Owners: Mrs A. T. McMillan.

397 MR MARTYN MEADE, Malmesbury

Postal: **Ladyswood, Sherston, Malmesbury, Wilts, SN16 0JL.**
Phone: **OFFICE (01666) 840880 HOME (01666) 840465 FAX (01666) 840073**

1 **GI LA HIGH,** 5, gr m Rich Charlie—Gem of Gold **Ladyswood Racing Club**
2 **LUNAR MIST,** 5, b m Komaite (USA)—Sugar Token **Mrs P. A. Barratt**
3 **LUNAR MUSIC,** 4, b f Komaite (USA)—Lucky Candy **Mr Paul J. Dixon**
4 **NIGHTINGALE SONG,** 4, b f Tina's Pet—Songlines **Mr Stephen Bayless**
5 **NORNAX LAD (USA),** 10, b g Northern Baby (CAN)—Naxos (USA) **Ladyswood Racing Club**
6 **WALK THE BEAT,** 8, b g Interrex (CAN)—Plaits **Ladyswood Racing Club**
7 **WHAT HAPPENED WAS,** 4, b f Deploy—Berberana **Mr Paul J. Dixon**

THREE-YEAR-OLDS

8 **ANNIE HALL,** b f Saddlers' Hall (IRE)—Rainbow Fleet **Mr Stephen Bayless**
9 **BLUSHING VICTORIA,** b f Weldnaas (USA)—Bollin Victoria **Mr Paul J. Dixon**
10 B f Alhijaz—Captivate **Mr Martyn Meade**
11 **COOL WATERS,** b f Puissance—Keep Cool (FR) **Mrs Susan Keable**
12 **DANCE TO THE BEAT,** b f Batshoof—Woodleys **The Country Life Partnership**
13 **DAYS OF GRACE,** gr f Wolfhound (USA)—Inshirah (USA) **Mr Stephen Bayless**
14 **IMPULSIVE DECISION (IRE),** gr f Nomination—Siva (FR) **Ladyswood Racing Club**
15 **INDY KNIGHT (IRE),** ch f Indian Ridge—Bag Lady **Mr & Mrs D. Clee**
16 **JASMINE TEA,** ch f Alhijaz—Come To Tea (IRE) **Mr Stephen Bayless**
17 **LAWLESS BRIDGET,** b f Alnasr Alwasheek—Geoffrey's Sister **Mr R. M. West**
18 **SCENE (IRE),** b f Scenic—Avebury Ring **Mr Paul J. Dixon**
19 **SEA IMP (IRE),** b f Mac's Imp (USA)—Sea Glen (IRE) **Mr Paul J. Dixon**
20 **SHANNON SQUAW,** b f Be My Chief (USA)—Shannon Princess **Mr B. P. Ryan**
21 **TRACKER,** b f Bustino—Make A Signal **Mr P. A. Deal**

TWO-YEAR-OLDS

22 B f Petong—Bellyphax **C. I. T. Racing**
23 B c Savahra Sound—Lucky Sarah **Mrs P. A. Barratt**
24 B c Savahra Sound—Sugar Token **Mrs P. A. Barratt**
25 B c Savahra Sound—Sweet And Lucky **Mr Paul J. Dixon**

Other Owners: Mrs M. Bayless, Mr David Caddy, Mr A. Crute, Mr Howard Groves, Mr John W. Lawson.

398 MR N. MEADE, Navan

Postal: **Tu Va Stables, Castletown, Navan, Co. Meath, Ireland.**
Phone: **(046) 54197 or 54278 FAX (046) 54459**

1 **ADVOCAT (GER),** 8, br g Dancing Brave (USA)—Amethysia (GER)
2 **ALMIRA (IRE),** 5, b m King's Ride—Higher Again (IRE)
3 **ALWAYS A PAUPER (IRE),** 9, b g Pauper—Pickled Girl
4 **BAILENAGUN (IRE),** 5, b g Castle Keep—Miss Teto

MR N. MEADE—continued

5 **BOB THE BROKER (IRE),** 4, b g Bob Back (USA)—Java Jive
6 5, B g Torus—Bonne Bouche
7 5, B g Glacial Storm (USA)—Candora
8 **CARDINAL HILL,** 4, b g Thowra (FR)—Phyl
9 **CHURCH PLACE (IRE),** 5, b g Persian Mews—Hurry Miss
10 **CLIFFS OF DOONEEN (IRE),** 5, b g Be My Native (USA)—Zalazula
11 5, Gr m Roselier (FR)—Clonarctic Slave
12 **COCKNEY LAD (IRE),** 9, ch g Camden Town—Big Bugs Bomb
13 **COMMANCHE NATIVE (IRE),** 4, b g Commanche Run—Native High Line
14 **CONFIDENTIALITY (IRE),** 6, b g Le Bavard (FR)—Allured
15 **COQ HARDI VENTURE (IRE),** 7, b g Roselier (FR)—Big Polly
16 **DARDJINI (USA),** 8, b g Nijinsky (CAN)—Darara
17 **DISTANT STAR (IRE),** 8, ch g Buckskin (FR)—Tipperary Star
18 **EARP,** 6, b g Anita's Prince—Ottavia Abu
19 **EMBELLISHED (IRE),** 6, b h Scenic—Embroidery
20 **ETON GALE (IRE),** 9, b g Strong Gale—Lough Street
21 **FANE LASSY (IRE),** 5, b m Homo Sapien—Rowlandstown Lass
22 **FIDDLERS BOW VI,** 10, b g Said To Be Fidel—Dam Unknown
23 **FINOEL (IRE),** 6, b g Phardante (FR)—Mary May
24 **FISHIN JOELLA (IRE),** 6, ch m Gone Fishin—Flying Jennie
25 4, Br g Phardante (FR)—Flash Parade
26 4, Ch g Phardante (FR)—Gaelic Sport
27 **GLOBAL DIAMOND (IRE),** 4, b f Classic Music (USA)—Herila (FR)
28 5, B g Strong Gale—Grabel
29 **GREENSTEAD (USA),** 5, b h Green Dancer (USA)—Evening Air (USA)
30 **HEATHER VILLE (IRE),** 6, b m Yashgan—Terracotta (GER)
31 **HEIST,** 9, ch g Homeboy—Pilfer
32 **HILL SOCIETY (IRE),** 6, b g Law Society (USA)—Sun Screen
33 **JOHNNY BRUSHASIDE (IRE),** 5, b g Brush Aside (USA)—Flash Parade
34 **JUGGERNAUT (IRE),** 4, b c Fools Holme (USA)—Shining Jug
35 **KILCALM KING (IRE),** 6, b g King's Ride—Arctic Run
36 **KINGS BANQUET,** 5, b g Supreme Leader—Culinary
37 **KIRIBATI (IRE),** 5, b g Digamist (USA)—Brolga
38 **LUNA FLEUR (IRE),** 5, b m Shardari—Medicosma (USA)
39 **MARSUL (USA),** 4, b br g Cozzene (USA)—Beside (USA)
40 5, Gr g Camden Town—Martins Times (IRE)
41 **MEGALIER (IRE),** 5, gr g Roselier (FR)—Bavardmore
42 **MICK MAN (IRE),** 7, b g Electric—Belle Chanel
43 **MIDNIGHT LOVER,** 4, ch f Beveled (USA)—Hens Grove
44 **MONAVALE (IRE),** 6, b m Strong Gale—Running Board (IRE)
45 **MUTHEER,** 4, b c Rainbow Quest (USA)—Awaasif (CAN)
46 **NATIVE DARA (IRE),** 5, b g Be My Native (USA)—Birchwood
47 **NATIVE ESTATES (IRE),** 6, b g Be My Native (USA)—Sesetta
48 **NOMADIC,** 4, gr c Kenmare (FR)—Legend of Arabia
49 4, Ch g Be My Native (USA)—Nordic Fling
50 5, B g Altountash—Not At All
51 **OHIO (IRE),** 5, b g Marju (IRE)—Royaleffort
52 **OLIVER'S ISLAND,** 4, b g Teenoso (USA)—Sea Island
53 **OMRACH OIGHEAR (IRE),** 5, b m Glacial Storm (USA)—Amber Ballad
54 **ONLY THE BEST (IRE),** 5, ch g Phardante (FR)—Rather Grand
55 **PERFECT (IRE),** 6, br g Castle Keep—Peaceful Rose
56 **PHARLUCY (IRE),** 7, b br m Phardante (FR)—Soul Lucy
57 **RIVER PILOT,** 4, b g Unfuwain (USA)—Cut Ahead
58 **RIVER RHYME (IRE),** 5, b m Riverhead (USA)—Kept In The Dark
59 **RODRIGO (IRE),** 5, b g Good Thyne (USA)—Magic Minstrel
60 **ROSES OF PICARDY (IRE),** 5, br m Roselier (FR)—Super Leg
61 **SALLIE'S GIRL (IRE),** 5, b m Un Desperado (FR)—Katerina
62 **SAVING BOND,** 6, ch g Digamist (USA)—Marine Life
63 **SHAWAHIN,** 6, b g Nashwan (USA)—Bempton
64 **SIGMA COMMS (IRE),** 5, b g Don't Forget Me—River Serenade (USA)

MR N. MEADE—continued

65 STAGALIER (IRE), 6, gr m Roselier (FR)—Big Polly
66 4, B g Be My Native (USA)—Sugar Quay
67 THE BRIEF (IRE), 6, b g Mandalus—Another Space
68 THREE KINGS, 5, gr g Arzanni—Chancebeg
69 TOSCANINI (IRE), 5, b g Homo Sapien—Maria Tudor
70 TREASURE DOME (IRE), 4, b g Treasure Kay—Royal Saint (USA)
71 TRUE ROCK, 4, b g Rock City—Prydwen
72 WALK ON MIX (FR), 6, gr g Linamix (FR)—Walk On Air
73 WALT (IRE), 8, b g King's Ride—Random What
74 WYATT (IRE), 8, br g Roselier (FR)—Big Polly
75 YOUNG BUCK (IRE), 4, ch g Glacial Storm (USA)—Lady Buck

THREE-YEAR-OLDS

76 DEILGINIS, b c Ardkinglass—Greenhill Lass
77 ROCK ICE, b g Rock Hopper—Strike Home
78 SUNSHINE STREET (USA), b c Sunshine Forever—Meadow Spirit (USA)
79 WINNING RONNIE (IRE), b c Royal Academy (USA)—Miss Sandman

TWO-YEAR-OLDS

80 B c 22/1 Night Shift (USA)—Echoes of Eternity (USA) (Cougar (CHI))
81 B c 3/4 Mtoto—Miquette (FR) (Fabulous Dancer (USA))
82 Ch g 29/2 Sunshine Forever—Romarctic (USA) (Arctic Tern (USA))

Apprentice: Patrick Stringer.

Conditional: Barry Geraghty.

Amateurs: Mr T Gibney, Mr G Harford.

399 MR M. G. MEAGHER, Ormskirk

Postal: **'Brookfields', Charity Lane, Westhead, Ormskirk, Lancashire, L40 6LG.**
Phone: **(01695) 579334**

1 CRABBIE'S PRIDE, 5, ch g Red Sunset—Free Rein **Turks Head Racing Club**
2 GAD YAKOUN, 5, ch g Cadeaux Genereux—Summer Impressions (USA) **Mr M. R. Johnson**
3 HOLDERS HILL (IRE), 6, b g Tirol—Delightful Time **Mr C. E. Whiteley**
4 5, B m Montelimar (USA)—Lilac Lass **Mr Dennis Patrick Flynn**
5 NEWBRIDGE BOY, 5, b g Bustino—Martyrdom (USA) **Mr Alan Draper**
6 ORDOG MOR (IRE), 9, ch g Boreen (FR)—Minorette **Mr M. R. Johnson**
7 4, Br g Lear Fan (USA)—Rain Wind (USA) **Mrs K. Meagher**
8 REAL FIRE (IRE), 4, b g Astronef—Golden Arum **Mr Mike Saunders**
9 SEFTON BLAKE, 4, b g Roscoe Blake—Rainbow Lady **Sefton Surfacing Co. Ltd**
10 SILVER PRIDE, 8, b g Silver Season—La Furze **Mr A. Bayman**
11 TANSEEQ, 7, b g Green Desert (USA)—Kawkeb (USA) **Miss N. C. Taylor**
12 5, B br g Montelimar (USA)—Tender Tan **Mr S. McManaman**

TWO-YEAR-OLDS

13 B c 15/2 Theatrical Charmer—Excavator Lady (Most Secret) **Aim High Partnership**
14 B f 22/4 Rambo Dancer (CAN)—Having Fun (Hard Fought) **Mr M. R. Johnson**
15 B c 20/1 Rudimentary (USA)—Legal Precedent (Star Appeal) **Mr Peter Deecon**
16 Ch c 12/3 Forest Wind (USA)—Pam Story (Sallust) **Mr M. R. Johnson**
17 B f 23/4 Tragic Role (USA)—Rainbow Lady (Jaazeiro (USA)) **Mr J. Pickavance**

Other Owners: Mr J. E. Ball, Mr K. Carbery, Mr Allan Collier, Mr B. Collier, Mr G. Ferrigno, Mr E. Marsh, Mr W. B. Marshall, Mrs P. Saunders, Mr M. Somers.

Jockey (Flat): J Fortune (8-3, w.a.).

Jockeys (NH): D Byrne (10-0, w.a.), L Wyer (10-0, w.a.).

Apprentice: Paul Fessey (7-7, w.a.).

Conditional: F Leahy (9-11, w.a.).

400 MR B. J. MEEHAN, Upper Lambourn

Postal: **Tumbleweed Cottage, Upper Lambourn, Hungerford, Berkshire, RG17 8QT.**
Phone: **OFFICE (01488) 73656/73636 HOME 73125 FAX 73633 MOBILE (0836) 754254**

1 **CATHEDRAL (IRE),** 4, b g Prince Sabo—Choire Mhor **Kennet Valley Thoroughbreds**
2 **DANCETHENIGHTAWAY,** 4, gr f Efisio—Dancing Diana **Mr G. A. Bosley**
3 **EASYCALL,** 4, b c Forzando—Up And Going (FR) **Easycall Partnership**
4 **LIFE OF RILEY,** 4, ch c Caerleon (USA)—Catina **Mr John Manley**
5 **MR MAJICA,** 4, b c Rudimentary (USA)—Pellinora (USA) **Mr C. J. Metcalfe**
6 **POLAR ECLIPSE,** 5, ch g Polar Falcon (USA)—Princess Zepoli **Mr J. R. Good**
7 **ROYAL AMARETTO (IRE),** 4, b c Fairy King (USA)—Melbourne Miss **The Harlequin Partnership**
8 **ROYALE (IRE),** 4, b f Royal Academy (USA)—Societe Royale
9 **TOMBA,** 4, ch c Efisio—Indian Love Song **Mr J. R. Good**
10 **TUMBLEWEED RIDGE,** 5, ch h Indian Ridge—Billie Blue **The Tumbleweed Partnership**
11 **WHITE EMIR,** 5, b g Emarati (USA)—White African **The Three Bears Racing**
12 **ZELDA ZONK,** 6, b m Law Society (USA)—Massive Powder **Mrs Christine Painting**

THREE-YEAR-OLDS

13 **ADJUTANT,** b c Batshoof—Indian Love Song **Mr J. R. Good**
14 **AMERICAN COUSIN,** b g Distant Relative—Zelda (USA) **Middleham Park Racing XIV**
15 **ASINBOX (IRE),** ch g Persian Bold—Traveling Dancer (FR) **Miss J. Semple**
16 **BELLE DE NUIT (IRE),** b f Statoblest—Elminya (IRE) **Mr Richard Withers**
17 **CAPTAIN JONES (IRE),** ch c Imp Society (USA)—Thatcherite **E. H. Jones (Paints) Ltd**
18 **CORTACHY CASTLE (IRE),** ch c Pips Pride—Maricica **Mrs E. A. Lerpiniere**
19 **DALI,** b g Rock City—Supreme Kingdom **Mr J. R. Good**
20 **DILKUSHA (IRE),** b g Indian Ridge—Crimson Glen **Mr Trevor Painting**
21 **DOBERMAN (IRE),** br g Dilum (USA)—Switch Blade (IRE) **Mr John Manley**
22 **FLAK JACKET,** b g Magic Ring (IRE)—Vaula **Kennet Valley Thoroughbred II**
23 **GIPSY MOTH,** b f Efisio—Rock The Boat **Mrs K. J. Crangle**
24 **GUILDHALL,** b c Saddlers' Hall (IRE)—Queen's Visit **Merlyn Racing**
25 **IMSHISHWAY (IRE),** b c Royal Academy (USA)—Mama Lucia **Mr A. S. Helaissi**
26 **KIM'S BRAVE,** b g Deploy—Princess Dina **Mr J. K. Sim**
27 **KING OF MOMMUR (IRE),** b c Fairy King (USA)—Monoglow **The Three Bears Racing**
28 **KRISAMBA,** ch c Kris—Lia's Dance **Mr B. Schmidt-Bodner**
29 **MADAME JONES (IRE),** ch f Lycius (USA)—Gold Braisim (IRE) **E. H. Jones (Paints) Ltd**
30 **MIDSUMMER ROMANCE (IRE),** b f Fairy King (USA)—Jealous One (USA) **Mr Theo Waddington**
31 **MISTER RAMBO,** b g Rambo Dancer (CAN)—Ozra **Abbott Racing Limited**
32 **MORGAN LE FAY,** b f Magic Ring (IRE)—Melody Park **Lord Portman**
33 **ONLY IN DREAMS,** b f Polar Falcon (USA)—Dream Baby **Mascalls Stud**
34 **SOVIET GIRL (IRE),** b f Soviet Star (USA)—Crystal City **Mr F. C. T. Wilson**
35 **STONE OF DESTINY,** ch c Ballad Rock—Shamasiya (FR) **Mr P. Heath**
36 **TITANIUM DANCER (IRE),** ch g Common Grounds—Grayfoot **Ms A. M. Cone-Farran**
37 **TUMBLEWEED HERO,** b c Alzao (USA)—Julip **The Third Tumbleweed Partnership**
38 **TUMBLWEED PROSPECT,** ch g Lion Cavern (USA)—Ring of Pearl **The Second Tumbleweed Partnership**
39 **YULARA (IRE),** b f Night Shift (USA)—Fifth Quarter
40 **ZURYAF (IRE),** b c Fayruz—The Way She Moves **Abbott Racing Limited**

TWO-YEAR-OLDS

41 B f 26/2 Pursuit Of Love—Addicted To Love (Touching Wood (USA)) **Mascalls Stud**
42 **ANNAPURNA,** b f 10/3 Brief Truce (USA)—National Ballet (Shareef Dancer (USA)) **Thurloe Thoroughbreds**
43 **ARCTIC CHAR,** br f 20/2 Polar Falcon (USA)—Breadcrumb (Final Straw) **Miss G. Abbey**
44 B c 23/4 Puissance—Aryaf (CAN) (Vice Regent (CAN)) **Mr T. Hyde**
45 Ch c 16/3 Pips Pride—Aubretia (USA) (Hatchet Man (USA)) **Mr J. McCarthy**
46 B c 18/2 Thatching—Bedspread (USA) (Seattle Dancer (USA)) **Mr Trevor Painting**
47 **BLUE LASER (IRE),** b g 1/2 Mujtahid (USA)—Dazzling Fire (IRE) (Bluebird (USA)) **Miss J. Semple**
48 **BRIEF ENCOUNTA (FR),** b c 27/2 Brief Truce (USA)—
Villa Blanca (SPA) (Rheffisimo (FR)) **Abbott Racing Limited**
49 Ch g 17/3 College Chapel—Cathy Garcia (IRE) (Be My Guest (USA)) **Mr P. Burdett**
50 **CHALLENGES (FR),** b c 21/3 Zieten (USA)—La Toscanella (FR) (Riverton (FR)) **Mr J. Gutkin**
51 **COOLING CASTLE (FR),** b g 21/4 Sanglamore (USA)—Syphaly (USA) (Lyphard (USA)) **Mrs E. A. Lerpiniere**

MR B. J. MEEHAN—continued

52 COSMO JACK (IRE), b g 31/3 Balla Cove—Foolish Law (IRE) (Law Society (USA)) **Mr M. Peart**
53 CRICKET'S SONG (IRE), b f 9/2 College Chapel—
The Multiyorker (IRE) (Digamist (USA)) **Kennett Valley Thoroughbreds III**
54 CRITO, ch g 18/5 Efisio—Furry Dance (USA) (Nureyev (USA)) **Mr R. Bernard**
55 B f 8/4 Perugino—Danger Ahead (Mill Reef (USA)) **Mrs D. A. La Trobe**
56 Ch c 4/4 Thatching—Daphne Indica (IRE) (Ballad Rock) **The Fourth Tumbleweed Partnership**
57 DRAMATIZE (IRE), ch g 6/3 Great Commotion (USA)—Silk Cord (Sallust) **Mr N. Attenborough**
58 EL PICADOR, b c 14/3 Aragon—Hawaiian Bloom (USA) (Hawaii) **Mr M. Lanfranchi**
59 EL TANGO, ch g 20/2 Risk Me (FR)—Princess Tara (Prince Sabo) **Mr M. Lanfranchi**
60 FRANTIC, b f 17/1 Be My Chief (USA)—Nazmiah (Free State) **Mr Al-Helaissi**
61 B f 8/4 Dolphin Street (FR)—Galapagos (Pitskelly) **Mr J. Blackshaw**
62 GIPSY ROSE LEE (IRE), b f 17/2 Marju (IRE)—Rainstone (Rainbow Quest (USA)) **Mrs K. J. Crangle**
63 INDIANA DANCER (IRE), ch c 16/4 Indian Ridge—
Mardi Gras Belle (USA) (Masked Dancer (USA)) **The Two's Company Partnership**
64 Br f 4/2 Rock City—Indian Love Song (Be My Guest (USA)) **Mr J. R. Good**
65 IRISH MELODY (IRE), ch f 28/3 Mac's Imp (USA)—Musical Gem (USA) (The Minstrel (CAN)) **Mrs R. Egan**
66 LA PAOLA, ch f 26/4 Common Grounds—Lotte Lenta (Gorytus (USA)) **Mr G. Battocchi**
67 Ch g 12/3 Forest Wind—Larentia (Salse (USA)) **Mr J. Blackshaw**
68 LA TAVERNETTA, ch f 17/3 Magical Wonder (USA)—
Carolina Rua (USA) (L'Emigrant (USA)) **Mrs A. Forde & Partners**
69 LEGAL VENTURE (IRE), ch g 12/3 Case Law—We Two (Glenstal (USA)) **Mrs B. Bell**
70 Gr f 4/3 Efisio—Lindy Belle (Alleging (USA)) **Mr P. Christey**
71 MOST-SAUCY, br f 31/1 Most Welcome—So Saucy (Teenoso (USA)) **Wyck Hall Stud**
72 B c 13/4 Namaqualand—Now Then (Sandford Lad) **Mr B. Schmidt-Bodner**
73 OPTIONAL, ch f 10/3 Prince Sabo—My Polished Corner (Tate Gallery (USA)) **Wyck Hall Stud**
74 Ch c 5/4 Lion Cavern (USA)—Precious Jade (Northfields (USA)) **Mr F. C. T. Wilson**
75 PRINCESS LATIFA, b f 8/3 Wolfhound (USA)—Moorish Idol (Aragon) **Mr J. Lazzari**
76 RIMMAS (IRE), b c 29/4 River Falls—Abbessingh (Mansingh (USA)) **The Chantilly Partnership**
77 SARAH'S SONG (IRE), b f 16/1 Warning—Two And Sixpence (Chief's Crown (USA)) **Mrs Susan Roy**
78 SECRET HAVEN, br f 16/3 Lugana Beach—Embroglio (USA) (Empery (USA)) **Mr David Powell**
79 SEPTEMBER HARVEST (USA), ch c 18/3 Mujtahid (USA)—
Shawgatny (USA) (Danzig Connection (USA)) **Mr J. Dunningham**
80 SKY STORM, ch c 20/4 Lycius (USA)—Beijing (USA) (Northjet) **Mrs A. Forde**
81 B f 19/3 Polish Precedent—Stack Rock (Ballad Rock) **Mr F. C. T. Wilson**
82 B c 29/2 Mon Tresor—Starisk (Risk Me (FR)) **High Seas Leisure**
83 SUSAN'S PRIDE (IRE), b c 10/4 Pips Pride—Piney Pass (Persian Bold) **Mrs Susan Roy**
84 TASSO DANCER, gr f 29/4 Dilum (USA)—Dancing Diana (Raga Navarro (ITY)) **Mrs J. Tredwell**
85 TUMBLEWEED GLEN (IRE), ch c 20/2 Mukaddamah (USA)—
Mistic Glen (IRE) (Mister Majestic) **The Fifth Tumbleweed Partnership**
86 TUMBLEWEED QUARTET, b c 25/2 Manila (USA)—
Peggy's String (USA) (Highland Park (USA)) **The Tumbleweed Partnership**
87 TWI DANCER (IRE), b f 7/4 Thatching—Houwara (IRE) (Darshaan) **Mrs B. Bell**
88 WHITEWATER BOY, b g 16/5 Emarati (USA)—Chacewater (Electric) **Lime Street Racing**
89 Ch f 19/1 Risk Me (FR)—Yukosan (Absalom) **Roldvale Ltd**

Other Owners: Mr Stanley Adams, D. Allen, Mr F. D. Allison, Amity Finance Ltd, Mr G. D. Anderson, Mr N. Andrew, Mr P. Anthony, Mrs D. E. Blackshaw, Lady Bolton, Mr C. Bosley, Mr Michael Broke, Mr Geoff Buck, Mrs A. Clarkin, Mr Alan Cunliffe, Mrs Ruth Egan, Mr Luigi Ferraris, Mrs V. Ford, Mrs P. Good, Mr R. Harding, Mr Barry Hearn, Mrs Susan Hearn, Mr A. S. Hill, Mr K. Hill, Mr K. N. T. Holland, Mr J. Johnston, Mr D. Johnstone, Mrs C. Laskin, Mrs L. Lerpiniere, Mr G. P. Lewis, Mrs N. L. Lewis, Mr J. Mangiacapra, Mr A. Mason, Mrs Susan McCarthy, Mr C. J. McGale, Mrs S. Mead, Mr B. J. Meehan, Mr C. J. Meehan, Mrs Eithne Meehan, Mr H. Meredith, Mr Stephen W. Molloy, Mr R. P. North, Mr T. S. Palin, Mr John W. Parker, Mr Oliver Pawle, Mr D. Purches, Mr N. W. Rimington, Mr N. J. F. Robinson, Mr Barry Root, Mr L. D. Rowley, Mr G. Scott, Mr D. M. Simpson, Mr John Smith (Roehampton), Miss D. M. Stafford, Mr Nigel Stafford, Mr I. H. Stephenson, Mr Athole Still, Mr C. J. Surr, Mr Wayne B. Sweeting, Mr C. Taylor, Mr B. L. P. Tebbutt, Mr D. H. L. Thompson, Mr J. S. Threadwell, Mr T. S. Treacy, Mrs Sheila Tucker, Mr Stephen Tucker, Mr G. Vialli, Vintage Services Limited, Mr K. Wetherell, Ms A. M. Whaley, Mr Keith Wills.

Jockeys (Flat): B Doyle, M Tebbutt (8-6).

Jockeys (NH): B Powell, G Upton.

Apprentice: G Hannon (8-0).

Lady Rider: Miss Jane Allison.

401 MR S. MELLOR, Swindon

Postal: **Pollardstown Racing Stables, Foxhill, Wanborough, Swindon, Wilts, SN4 0DR.**
Phone: **(01793) 790230 FAX (01793) 790871**

1 **AMERICANVAL (FR),** 10, b g Kashneb (FR)—Ravenna III (FR) **Mr Stan Mellor**
2 **ANLACE,** 9, b m Sure Blade (USA)—Ascot Strike (USA) **The Felix Bowness Partnership**
3 **AWAFEH,** 5, b g Green Desert (USA)—Three Piece **Mrs S. C. Haine**
4 **BONE SETTER (IRE),** 8, b g Strong Gale—Princess Wager **Lord Leverhulme**
5 **CHARLIE HAWES (IRE),** 9, b g Euphemism—Eyecap **Silver Knight Exhibitions Ltd**
6 **CHEROKEE FLIGHT,** 4, b g Green Desert (USA)—Totham **Silver Knight Exhibitions Ltd**
7 **ERLKING (IRE),** 8, b g Fairy King (USA)—Cape of Storms **The Ridgeway Ramblers**
8 **EZZY'S BOY,** 10, b g Welsh Captain—Pearl Bound **Mr Stewart Wilson**
9 **FLIC ROYAL (FR),** 5, gr g Royal Charter (FR)—Flika d'Or (FR) **Ken Jaffa, John Lewis & David Shalson**
10 **FLOTILLA,** 4, b g Saddlers' Hall (IRE)—Aim For The Top (USA) **Silver Knight Exhibitions Ltd**
11 **FOREVER DREAMING (IRE),** 7, b g Le Moss—On A Dream **Mr Stan Mellor**
12 **HARDING,** 7, b g Dowsing (USA)—Orange Hill **Mr S. P. Tindall**
13 **MASON (IRE),** 6, ch g Simply Great (FR)—Viva Ronda **Mr S. P. Tindall**
14 **MONTECOT (FR),** 9, b g Le Riverain (FR)—Pour Ta Pomme (FR) **Sir Michael Connell**
15 **MORNING SUIT,** 4, b g Reprimand—Morica **Mr Stan Mellor**
16 **NESSUN DORO,** 6, b g Hallgate—Bamdoro **Paul Porter & Partners**
17 **RED PHANTOM (IRE),** 6, ch g Kefaah (USA)—Highland Culture **Silver Knight Exhibitions Ltd**
18 **ROYAL ARCTIC (IRE),** 8, ch g Sandalay—Remindful **Mr T. D. J. Syder**
19 **SEOD RIOGA (IRE),** 9, br g Down The Hatch—Jackie's Pet **Mr S. P. Tindall**
20 **SHANAGORE WARRIOR (IRE),** 6, b g Arapahos (FR)—Our Linda **Mr S. P. Tindall**
21 **SHEPHERDS REST (IRE),** 6, b g Accordion—Mandy's Last **The Odd Dozen**
22 **STAR OF DUNGANNON,** 5, b g Forzando—Key To The River (USA) **Mr Stan Mellor**
23 **STORM TIGER (IRE),** 7, b g Strong Gale—Happy Party **W. R. Partnership**
24 **TAARISH (IRE),** 5, b g Priolo (USA)—Strike It Rich (FR) **Studer & Partners**
25 **THE CHEESE BARON,** 7, b g Idiot's Delight—Stella Roma **T. D. J. Syder & S. M. D. Oliver**

THREE-YEAR-OLDS

26 **CHIKA SHAN (IRE),** b c Archway (IRE)—Judy's Pinch **Jafeica Partnership**
27 **LADY FELIX,** br f Batshoof—Volcalmeh **The Felix Bowness Partnership**

TWO-YEAR-OLDS

28 **ALMAYMONA (IRE),** ch f 19/2 Pips Pride—Suppression **Sheikh Salim Al-Fairuz**
29 **ALMAZIONA,** ch f 14/3 Formidable (USA)—Flying Amy **Sheikh Salim Al-Fairuz**
30 Ch g 13/3 Fayruz—Tender Encounter **Silver Knight Exhibitions Ltd**
31 Ch g 25/4 Risk Me (FR)—Treble Top (USA) **The Bandbox Brigage**

Other Owners: Mr L. J. Boswell, Mr Felix Bowness, Mr R. H. Brookes, Mr Laurence B. Butters, Mr Terry Hardy, Mr Michael Harrold, Mr D. J. Horne, Mr H. Kayne, Mr T. Liggins, Mr F. E. Maslin, Mr P. A. Porter, Dr S. M. Readings, Mr Stuart J. Smith, Amale Studer, Mr A. D. Tomkinson, Mrs S. Warren.

Jockey (Flat): M Wigham (8-7, w.a.).

Conditional: C Webb (9-7).

402 MISS M. K. MILLIGAN, Middleham

Postal: **Fell View Stables, East Witton, Middleham, Leyburn, North Yorkshire, DL8 4SG.**
Phone: **(01969) 23221 OFFICE (01969) 24105 HOME (01969) 23541 FAX**

1 **AMAZING SAIL (IRE),** 5, b g Alzao (USA)—Amazer (USA) **Maritime**
2 **BEAU MATELOT,** 6, b g Handsome Sailor—Bellanoora **Mr Adrian Buckley**
3 **DOCKMASTER,** 7, b g Dominion—Surf Bird **Mr J. D. Gordon**
4 **FAIR AND FANCY (FR),** 7, b g Always Fair (USA)—Fancy Star (FR) **The F. And F. Partnership**

MISS M. K. MILLIGAN—continued

5 **JACK YEATS (IRE),** 6, b g Don't Forget Me—Petty Session **Mr J. D. Gordon**
6 **JEEPERS (IRE),** 7, gr g Nearly A Nose (USA)—Broker Aems **Mr A. Mordain**
7 **LA PERDOMA,** 4, b f Sylvan Express—Oratava Valley **Jumbo Racing Club**
8 **LORD PAT (IRE),** 7, ch g Mister Lord (USA)—Arianrhod **Dr B. I. McLain**
9 **MY BUSTER,** 6, ch g Move Off—Young Lamb **Mrs J. M. L. Milligan**
10 **ORIEL LAD,** 5, b g Colmore Row—Consistent Queen **Mr Dave Teasdale**
11 **PRELUDE TO FAME (USA),** 5, b g Affirmed (USA)—Dance Call (USA) **Jumbo Racing Club**
12 **THE TOASTER,** 11, b g Furry Glen—Foolish Lady **The Aunts**
13 **THIS IS MY LIFE (IRE),** 9, b g General View—Bluemore **Panther Racing Ltd**

Other Owners: Mr Graham Angell, Mrs D. L. Barrett, Mr Geoff Bridges, Mrs J. B. Buckley, Mrs A. J. M. Cockburn, Mr Philip Curry, Mr G. Duckett, Mr E. C. Gordon, Mr F. D. Jackson, Dr D. J. Layfield, Miss Kate Milligan, Mrs S. Murray-Usher, Dr Roy Palmer, Mr B. J. Rae, Mrs Judith Robson, Mr Eddison Skeels, Miss A. M. Smith, Mr J. J. H. Walker, Mr S. Ward, Mr M. J. Willan.

Lady Rider: Pauline Robson.

403 MR B. R. MILLMAN, Cullompton

Postal: **The Paddocks, Kentisbeare, Cullompton, Devon, EX15 2DX.**
Phone: **(01884) 266620 FAX (01884) 266620 MOBILE (0585) 168447**

1 **ARCTIC CHANTER,** 6, b g Arctic Lord—Callope (USA) **Exe Valley Racing**
2 **ATLANTIC MIST,** 5, ch g Elmaamul (USA)—Overdue Reaction **The Wardour Partnership**
3 **BOATER,** 4, b g Batshoof—Velvet Beret (IRE) **Mr A. Loze**
4 **BROUGHTONS TURMOIL,** 9, b g Petorius—Rustic Stile **Mr R. Marlow**
5 **CLIFTON GAME,** 8, b g Mummy's Game—Brave Maiden **Oping Enterprises**
6 **CLIFTON MATCH,** 6, gr m Nicholas Bill—Brave Maiden **Oping Enterprises**
7 **FLYING ARTIST,** 6, b m Naskracker (USA)—Rising Artist **Mr J. F. Jones**
8 **HERBSHAN DANCER,** 4, b g Warrshan (USA)—Herbary (USA) **The Kingtroll Racing Partnership**
9 **JAILBREAKER,** 11, ch g Prince of Peace—Last Farewell **The Jay Partnership**
10 **KENDAL CAVALIER,** 8, gr g Roselier (FR)—Kenda **Mr Michael Wingfield Digby**
11 **KEWARRA,** 4, b g Distant Relative—Shalati (FR) **Mr G. Palmer**
12 **MAGIC BREEZE,** 5, ch m Jester—Stormbound **Mr B. Hammond**
13 **POLLY LEACH,** 8, b m Pollerton—Come On Gracie **Mr M. G. Willey**
14 **RUBY TWO SHOES,** 5, b m Revlow—Miss Burgundy **Tarka Racing**
15 **SHALATEENO,** 5, b m Teenoso (USA)—Shalati (FR) **Mr G. Palmer**
16 **SONG OF KENDA,** 6, b m Rolfe (USA)—Kenda **J. Logan/M. Sechiari/M. Wingfield Digby**
17 **THERHEA (IRE),** 5, b g Pennine Walk—Arab Art **Ray Gudge, Colin Lewis, Malcolm Calvert**
18 **WORLD EXPRESS (IRE),** 8, b g Jareer (USA)—Eight Mile Rock **The Dragisic Partnership**

THREE-YEAR-OLDS

19 **LORD KINTYRE,** b c Makbul—Highland Rowena **Mr M. Calvert**
20 **POLISH SPIRIT,** b c Emarati (USA)—Gentle Star **Mr & Mrs V. G. Palmer**
21 **SEE MORE FLOWERS,** b f Seymour Hicks (FR)—Flower of Tintern **Mr S. R. Bowley**
22 **SHALAD'OR,** b f Golden Heights—Shalati (FR) **Mr G. Palmer**
23 **SHEILA-B,** b f Formidable (USA)—Good Woman **Mr D. L. C. Hodges**
24 **SILVER SYMPHONY,** gr f Kylian (USA)—Brave Maiden **Mr G. Palmer**
25 **TEMPUS FUGIT,** ch f Timeless Times (USA)—Kabella **The Keepers**
26 **ZEPPO (IRE),** ch c Fayruz—Chase Paperchase **The Plyform Syndicate**

TWO-YEAR-OLDS

27 **DIABLO DANCER (IRE),** b c 12/5 Deploy—Scharade **Kentisbeare Quartet**
28 Ch c 27/3 Alnasr Alwasheek—La Belle Vie **Mr R. Lawson**
29 **LORD ROCHESTER,** b c 23/1 Distant Relative—Kentfield **Mr Ray Gudge**

MR B. R. MILLMAN—continued

30 LORD STROLLER, b c 26/3 Petong—Breakfast Boogie **Mr Mike Geering**
31 B c 18/1 Rainbows For Life—Nawadder
32 NICK'S CHOICE, b c 1/3 Sula Bula—Clare's Choice **Mr John Brookman**
33 POLRUAN, ch c 13/2 Elmaamul (USA)—Trelissick **Messrs Wingfield Digby, Sechiari, Hunter**
34 REDEPLOY, b c 10/2 Deploy—Baino Clinic (USA) **Take Six Partnership**
35 B c 23/4 Inchinor—Sveltissima **D Fisher, M Nicholls, D Clark, R Martin**

Other Owners: Mr M. Bevan, Mr W. J. Butt, Prof H. Coakham, Mr D. Coles, Mr A. J. Conway, Mrs J. D. Coombes, Mr M. Dragisic, Mr Derek Dymond, Mrs John C. Edwards, Mrs J. Gliddon, Mr H. Gooding, Mr E. J. Grigg, Mr Dave Harris, Mr J. W. Haydon, Mr M. J Iles, Mr A. J. King, Mr D. J. Longhurst, Mr Jamie McPhee, Mr B. R. Millman, Dr John Newman, Mr T. D O'Sullivan, Mrs M. Palmer, Mr G. R. Poole, Mr Henry Rix, Mr M. R. Terry, Mr M. J. Trollope, Mr J. R. Upton, Mr S. E. White, Mr Robert Wright.

Jockeys (Flat): Brett Doyle (w.a.), Tim Sprake.

Apprentice: Cheryl Noseworthy (7-10).

Conditional: Darren Salter.

Amateur: Mr Matthew Frith (9-10).

404 MR T. G. MILLS, Epsom

Postal: **Loretta Lodge, Tilley Lane, Headley, Epsom, Surrey, KT18 6EP.**
Phone: **(01372) 377209 (01372) 386578**

1 BLUE RIVER (IRE), 4, ch c River Falls—Royal Resident **Mr M. J. Legg**
2 BROTHER ROY, 5, b g Prince Sabo—Classic Heights **Mr T. G. Mills**
3 DOUBLE RUSH (IRE), 6, b g Doulab (USA)—Stanza Dancer **Mr Tony Murray**
4 GREENWICH FORE, 4, b g Formidable (USA)—What A Challenge **Mr T. G. Mills**
5 HAYES WAY (IRE), 4, b c Lahib (USA)—Edgeaway **Mr T. G. Mills**
6 JUNIE (IRE), 4, ch f Astronef—Numidia **Mr T. G. Mills**
7 JUST ALEX (IRE), 4, b g River Falls—Picnic Basket **Mr Tony Murray**
8 LAW DANCER (IRE), 5, b g Alzao (USA)—Judicial (USA) **Mr T. J. Oswin**
9 MY HERO (IRE), 4, b f Bluebird (USA)—Risacca (ITY) **Bill Brown and Peter Pepper Partnership**
10 NORTHERN SUN, 4, b g Charmer—Princess Dancer **John Humphreys (Turf Accountants) Ltd**
11 PHAL, 4, b g Derrylin—Royal Birthday **Mr Glen Antill**
12 PROPER BLUE (USA), 5, b h Proper Reality (USA)—Blinking (USA) **Mr M. J. Legg**
13 SODEN (IRE), 4, b f Mujadil (USA)—Elminya (IRE) **Albert Soden Ltd**
14 TEAR WHITE (IRE), 4, b g Mac's Imp (USA)—Exemplary **A. W. Lawson & Co Ltd**

THREE-YEAR-OLDS

15 ETOILE DANCER, ch g Suave Dancer (USA)—Padelia **Mrs Stephanie Merrydew**
16 JUST IN TIME, b c Night Shift (USA)—Future Past (USA) **Mrs Pauline Merrick**
17 TELALANJON, b c Tirol—Akkazao (IRE) **John Humphreys (Turf Accountants) Ltd**
18 THATS LIFE, b c Mukaddamah (USA)—Run Faster (IRE) **Mr T. G. Mills**

TWO-YEAR-OLDS

19 ALL THE WAY (IRE), b c 7/6 Shirley Heights—Future Past (USA) (Super Concorde (USA)) **John Humphreys (Turf Accountants) Ltd**
20 Ch c 30/3 Be My Chief (USA)—Blink Naskra (USA) (Naskra (USA)) **Mrs Stephanie Merrydew**
21 COLLELE BLUE (IRE), b f 4/3 College Chapel—Mitsubishi Centre (IRE) (Thatching) **Mr M. J. Legg**
22 Br c 4/2 Puissance—Lominda (IRE) (Lomond (USA)) **Mr T. G. Mills**
23 B c 2/3 Sabrehill (USA)—Petite Rosanna (Ile de Bourbon (USA)) **Chancery Bourse Investments Ltd**

MR T. G. MILLS—continued

24 Gr f 29/2 Perugino (USA)—Soubrette (Habat) **Mr G. J. King**
25 SWING JOB, b f 12/1 Ezzoud (IRE)—Leave Her Be (USA) (Known Fact (USA)) **Shipman Racing**

Other Owners: Mr V. A. D'Haens, Mr Peter Hannon, Sherwoods Transport Ltd, Mr F. G. Shipman.

Jockeys (Flat): T Quinn (8-2, w.a.), J Reid (8-6, w.a.).

Apprentice: Lisa Hackett (7-7).

Amateur: Mr J Darby (10-2).

405 MR C. W. MITCHELL, Dorchester

Postal: **White House, Buckland Newton, Dorchester, Dorset, DT2 7DE.**
Phone: **(01300) 345276**

1 COLD FEET, 7, b m Arctic Lord—Hammerhill **Mr C. W. Mitchell**
2 DUCKLING, 8, b m White Prince (USA)—Romful Donna **Mr C. W. Mitchell**
3 MISS SECRET, 8, b m El Conquistador—Harts Lane **Mr C. W. Mitchell**
4 WALTER'S DESTINY, 6, ch g White Prince (USA)—Tearful Sarah **Mr C. W. Mitchell**

406 MR N. R. MITCHELL, Dorchester

Postal: **East Hill Stables, Piddletrenthide, Dorchester, Dorset, DT2 7QY.**
Phone: **PIDDLETRENTHIDE (01300) 348739 & FAX**

1 CLASSIC PAL (USA), 7, b g Danzatore (CAN)—Welsh Garden **Mr P. C. Tory**
2 DRESS DANCE (IRE), 8, b g Nordance (USA)—Pitaya **Mrs J. R. Powell**
3 GAMAY, 8, b g Rymer—Darling Rose **Mr J. J. Boulter**
4 KEEP ME IN MIND (IRE), 9, b g Don't Forget Me—Gold Trinket **Mr P. C. Tory**
5 KING OF THE DAWN, 7, b br g Rakaposhi King—Dawn Encounter **Mr J. J. Boulter**
6 MAREMMA GALE (IRE), 10, b g Strong Gale—My Halo **Mr R. L. Scorgie**
7 NODDADANTE (IRE), 8, b g Phardante (FR)—Loughcopple **Mr N. R. Mitchell**
8 ORCHARD LADY, 8, ch m Rich Charlie—Ballagarrow Girl **Mrs A. E. Davis**
9 QUEEN OF THE SUIR (IRE), 9, ch m Carlingford Castle—Miss Daraheen **Mr R. L. Scorgie**
10 TURN OF THE TIDE, 5, ch g Riverwise (USA)—Cut Above The Rest **Mr Piers Butler**

Other Owners: Mr Terry Cooper, Mr G. Goode, Exors Of The Late Mr J. Goode, Mrs E. Mitchell, Mr S. L. Mitchell, Mrs R. L. Scorgie, Mr R. C. Whitaker.

Conditional: S Mitchell (8-0).

Amateur: Mr N R Mitchell (11-3).

407 MR PAT MITCHELL, Newmarket

Postal: **Hamilton Stables, Hamilton Road, Newmarket, Suffolk, CB8 7JQ.**
Phone: **NEWMARKET (01638) 660013 FAX (01638) 660013 E-mail: gbg61@dial.pipe.com**

1 CARROLLS MARC (IRE), 10, b g Horage—Rare Find **Mrs Gail Dunlop**
2 CLASSIC FIND (USA), 5, b br g Lear Fan (USA)—Reve de Reine (USA) **Classic Bloodstock Plc**
3 4, B g Conquering Hero (USA)—Erck

MR PAT MITCHELL—continued

4 MOI CANARD, 5, ch h Bold Owl—Royal Scots Greys **Mrs Anna L. Sanders**
5 WADERS DREAM (IRE), 9, b g Doulab (USA)—Sea Mistress **Mrs Anna L. Sanders**

THREE-YEAR-OLDS

6 B g Almoojid—Misty Arch

TWO-YEAR-OLDS

7 B f 27/5 Anshan—Operelle **Mr Sam McBride**
8 PRINCESS MO, b f 27/4 Prince Sabo—Morica **Miss J. Bunting & Partners**

Other Owners: Mr D. Cruikshank, Mrs Sandy Herridge, Mrs R. S. Johnston, Mrs Catherine Reed, Mr Paul Reed, Mr G. Tweed, Mr D. Waldock.

408 MR PHILIP MITCHELL, Epsom

Postal: **Downs House, Epsom Downs, Surrey, KT18 5ND.**
Phone: **(01372) 273729 FAX (01372) 278701 MOBILE (0836) 231462**

1 AMADOUR (IRE), 5, b g Contract Law (USA)—Truly Flattering **Lovine Partnership**
2 CEDRIC TUDOR, 5, b g Picea—English Mint **Mrs S. Peirce**
3 CULTURAL ICON (USA), 6, br g Kris S (USA)—Sea Prospector (USA) **Mrs Patricia Mitchell**
4 FANCY DESIGN (IRE), 5, b m Cyrano de Bergerac—Crimson Robes **Mrs V. M. Harris**
5 MISS IMP (IRE), 4, b f Mac's Imp (USA)—Be Nimble **Mrs Carol Williamson**
6 RED RAJA, 5,b br g Persian Heights—Jenny Splendid **Mr J. R. Ali**
7 RUNNING STAG (USA), 4, b c Cozzene (USA)—Fruhlingstag (FR) **Mr Richard J. Cohen**
8 SOVIET KING (IRE), 5, b g Soviet Lad (USA)—Finessing **Mrs Patricia Mitchell**
9 THE FUGATIVE, 5, b m Nicholas (USA)—Miss Runaway **Mr J. A. Redmond**
10 WARRIO, 8, b g Battle Hymn—River Damsel **Mr R. Cheetham**
11 WING OF A PRAYER, 4, b g Statoblest—Queen Angel **Thurloe Thoroughbreds**

THREE-YEAR-OLDS

12 MISTER TRICKY, ch c Magic Ring (IRE)—Splintering **Mr G. P. Triefus**
13 OMAR'S ODYSSEY (IRE), ch c Sharifabad (IRE)—Tales of Homer **Mr Richard J. Cohen**
14 SERGEANT IMP (IRE), b g Mac's Imp (USA)—Genzyme Gene **Mr W. R. Mann**
15 SPECIAL PERSON (IRE), ch f Ballad Rock—Hada Rani **Matthews Breeding and Racing**

TWO-YEAR-OLDS

16 DUTY SQUADRON (IRE), b c 6/1 Mac's Imp (USA)—Guess Who **Mr W. R. Mann**
17 B f 12/1 Magic Ring (IRE)—Naulakha **Chint Racing Club**
18 Ch c 20/2 Aragon—Salinas **Mr P. Mitchell**

Other Owners: Mr H. Al-Mandeel, Mrr Derek Crowson, Mr G. V. Eliades, Mr Greg Gregory, Mr G. R. Harris, Mr D. W. Johnson, Mrs R. A. Johnson, Mr J. Lamote, Mr Michael Stewart, Mr John Ullman.

Jockey (Flat): A Clark.

Jockey (NH): J Osborne (w.a.).

Amateur: Mr C Bickley (10-0).

Lady Rider: Miss H Mitchell (9-0).

409 MRS HELEN MOBLEY, Brackley

Postal: **Homelands Farm, Farthinghoe, Brackley, Northants, NN13 5NU.**
Phone: **(01295) 710297 FAX (01295) 712066**

1 **BUTLERS MATCH (IRE),** 8, ch g Matching Pair—Millys Last **Mrs Helen Mobley**
2 **CHILLY LAD,** 7, b g High Kicker (USA)—Miss Poll Flinders **Mr Alan Mobley**
3 **DOEVILLE,** 5, ch m Crested Lark—Shotsville **Mrs Helen Mobley**
4 **MADAM MATCH (IRE),** 7, b m Matching Pair—Millys Last **Mrs Helen Mobley**
5 **SHADRACH,** 7, b g Neltino—Fay Valantine **Mrs Katie Sunderland**
6 **SPERRIN VIEW,** 12, ch m Fidel—Baroness Vimy **Mrs Katie Sunderland**
7 **TELL THE BOYS (IRE),** 10, b g Montelimar (USA)—Disco Beat **Mr John Nicholls**
8 **WHAT CHANCE (IRE),** 10, ch m Buckskin (FR)—Grainne Geal **Mrs Helen Mobley**

THREE-YEAR-OLDS

9 **VILLIAN,** b f Kylian (USA)—Shotsville **Mrs Helen Mobley**

Other Owners: Mr C. W. Booth.

Jockey (NH): Carl Llewellyn (10-0).

Lady Rider: Mrs Katie Sunderland (8-7).

410 MR D. MOFFATT, Cartmel

Postal: **Pit Farm Racing Stables, Cartmel, Grange-Over-Sands, Cumbria, LA11 6PJ.**
Phone: **CARTMEL (015395) 36689 FAX (015395) 36236 YARD (015395) 36713**

1 **BEGORRAT (IRE),** 4, ch g Ballad Rock—Hada Rani **Mr Mike Flynn**
2 **DOUBLE DASH (IRE),** 5, gr g Darshaan—Safka (USA) **The Sheroot Partnership**
3 **GRANDMAN (IRE),** 7, b g Executive Perk—Gerise **Mr F. Hewer**
4 **HOME COUNTIES (IRE),** 9, ch g Ela-Mana-Mou—Safe Home **Ms A. Hartley**
5 **INGLEBOROUGH,** 4, b g Barrys Gamble—Dreamy Desire **The Vilprano Partnership**
6 **LAGEN BRIDGE (IRE),** 9, gr g Decent Fellow—Suir **Mrs Eileen M. Milligan**
7 **MIDDLE BAY (IRE),** 7, ch g Le Bavard (FR)—Patricia's Joy **Bruce Partnership**
8 **MULLINS (IRE),** 7, b g Mandalus—Nire's Pride **Mr A. G. Milligan**
9 **RUNNING GREEN,** 7, b g Green Desert (USA)—Smeralda (GER) **Die-Hard Racing Club**
10 **SILVER HOWE,** 5, gr g Move Off—Vinovia **Cartmel Racing**
11 **TRIBAL MISCHIEF,** 4, br f Be My Chief (USA)—Lammastide **Mr G. R. Parrington**
12 **VILPRANO,** 7, b g Ra Nova—Village Princess **The Vilprano Partnership**

THREE-YEAR-OLDS

13 **ANKA LADY,** b f Precocious—Hicklam Millie **Mr Fred Coulson**
14 **ANNIEMITCHELLSLASS,** b f Noble Patriarch—Fair Janet **Die-Hard Racing Club**
15 **HAPPY DAYS,** b g Primitive Rising (USA)—Miami Dolphin **Mr J. W. Barrett**

TWO-YEAR-OLDS

16 **BAYARD LADY,** b f 1/4 Robellino (USA)—Lurking (Formidable (USA)) **Bay Horse Racing Syndicate**
17 **HAYSTACKS (IRE),** b c 13/3 Contract Law (USA)—Florissa (FR) (Persepolis (FR)) **Mr A. G. Milligan**
18 Ch f 9/2 Bold Arrangement—Jersey Maid (On Your Mark) **Mr P. G. Airey**

Other Owners: Mrs Gloria Bath, Mr K. Bowron, Mr E. Bruce, Mrs Lynn Campion, Mr J. H. Collins, Mrs S. S. Coulson, Mr A. Douglas, Mr Thomas Dyer, Mr John D. Ferguson, Mr Edward Graham, Mr W. Graham, Mr Mike Keating, Metropolitan Properties Ltd, Mr A. R. Mills, Mrs Jennie Moffatt, Roxy Cinemas (Dalton) Ltd, Sir Sanderson Temple, Mrs G. A. Turnbull, Mr R. R. Whitton, Mr J. D. Wilson.

Apprentice: Darren Moffatt (7-4. w.a.).

Conditional: D J Moffatt (10-4, w.a.).

411 MR PETER MONTEITH, Rosewell

Postal: **Whitebog Farm, Rosewell, Midlothian, EH24 9AY.**
Phone: **(0131 440) 2309 MOBILE (0585) 060296 FAX (0131 440) 2226**

1 4, B g Lugana Beach—Annie Ra **Mr P. Monteith**
2 **ARRADALE,** 10, b g Ardross—Mary Park **The Low Flyers (Thoroughbreds) Ltd.**
3 **BREYDON,** 5, ch g Be My Guest (USA)—Palmella (USA) **The Dregs Of Humanity**
4 **BROADCAST,** 5, b m Broadsword (USA)—Olympian Princess **Mrs J. Wood**
5 **ISLE OF RHUM,** 6, b g Jupiter Island—Carribean Sound **Hamilson House Limited**
6 **LORD PODGSKI (IRE),** 7, b g Lord Americo—Linoski **Mrs G. Smyth**
7 **MARISOL (IRE),** 5, b m Mujtahid (USA)—Stanerra's Star **Mr Allan W. Melville**
8 **MASTER BAVARD (IRE),** 10, ch g Le Bavard (FR)—Honey Come Back **Mr Allan W. Melville**
9 **MOMONTAI,** 4, ch g Tina's Pet—Don't Loiter **Mr Alan Guthrie**
10 **MR KNITWIT,** 11, ch g Kambalda—Clonaghadoo **Coupar Capital Racing**
11 5, Ch m Feelings (FR)—Pinkie Hill **Mr P. Monteith**
12 **PROPHITS PRIDE (IRE),** 6, ch g Carmelite House (USA)—Asinara **Mrs Maud Monteith**
13 **RALLEGIO,** 9, b g Alleging (USA)—Radigo **Mr A. R. M. Galbraith**
14 **ROSSEL (USA),** 5, b g Blushing John (USA)—Northern Aspen (USA) **Mr Allen W. Melville**
15 **RUSTY BLADE,** 9, b g Broadsword (USA)—Sea Sand **Mrs M. I. Nisbet**
16 **SHE'S A WINNER (IRE),** 5, ch m Classic Music (USA)—Eyre Square (IRE) **Mr P. Monteith**
17 **SHONARA'S WAY,** 7, b m Slip Anchor—Favorable Exchange (USA) **Mr Alan Guthrie**
18 **SILLYMORE,** 5, b m Silly Prices—Admire-A-More **Mrs M. I. Nisbet**
19 **SUNNY LEITH,** 7, b g Feelings (FR)—Pinkie Hill **Mr G. M. Cowan**
20 **TRIENNIUM (USA),** 9, ch g Vaguely Noble—Triple Tipple (USA) **Mr M. C. Boyd**
21 **TRIGGERFISH,** 6, b g Broadsword (USA)—Sea Sand **Mrs M. I. Nisbet**
22 **VALEDICTORY,** 5, b g Slip Anchor—Khandjar **Mr I. Bell**
23 4, B g Jendali (USA)—Young Mary **Mr Alan Guthrie**

THREE-YEAR-OLDS

24 Ch g Feelings (FR)—Pinkie Hill **Mr P. Monteith**
25 **SUN DANCING (IRE),** ch f Magical Wonder (USA)—Lockwood Girl **Mr P. Monteith**

Other Owners: Mr R. M. S. Allison, Mr W. M. G. Black, Miss J. Campbell, Mr Tony Caplan, Mr A. Dawson, Miss C. E. J. Dawson, Mr D. J. Fairbairn, Mr J. A. G. Fiddes, Mr T. P. Finch, Mr A. D. T. Fletcher, Mr L. Grant, Miss H. B. Hamilton, Mr G. W. Laing, Mr J. E Langley, Mr T. H. Littleton, Exors Of The Late Mr William McKinlay, Kelso Members Lowflyers Club, Mrs V. Nyberg, Mr John Pirie, Mr R. L. Ritchie, Mr Guthrie Robertson, Mr W. A. Robertson, Dr J. Simpson, Mrs A. F. Tullie, Mr John Wilson, Mrs R. M. Wood.

Jockey (NH): A Dobbin (10-0).

Conditional: I Jardine (9-7).

412 MR A. L. MOORE, Naas

Postal: **Dereens, Naas, Co. Kildare, Ireland.**
Phone: **(045) 876292 FAX (045) 876292**

1 **ARDSHUIL,** 9, b g Pennine Walk—Ordina (FR) **N. McCarthy**
2 **ARE YOU SAILING (IRE),** 6, ch g Maelstrom Lake—Nielsine **Mrs A. L. T. Moore**
3 **BACK BAR (IRE),** 10, b g Strong Gale—Ballingee Marge **P. J. McCarthy**
4 **CAVALIER D'OR (USA),** 7, b g Diesis—Luth d'Or (FR) **J. P. McManus**
5 **CHATEAU MARTIN (IRE),** 6, b g Castle Keep—Bonny Joe **A. J. O'Reilly**
6 **DEE ELL,** 12, ch g Little Wolf—Sagora **Mrs A. L. T. Moore**
7 **DIGIN FOR GOLD (IRE),** 7, b g Miner's Lamp—Supreme Slave **D. McCarthy**
8 **EMERALD GALE (IRE),** 8, b g Strong Gale—Kilbrogan **D. Tierney**
9 **FADOUDAL DU COCHET (FR),** 5, b g Cadoudal (FR)—Eau de Vie (FR) **Mrs A. L. T. Moore**

MR A. L. MOORE—continued

10 **FISCAL GALE (IRE)**, 6, b g Strong Gale—Dunleer Duchess **R. Ryan**
11 **FOLLIDAY (FR)**, 5, b g Sharken (FR)—Oliday (FR) **F. Cruess-Callaghan**
12 **GOOD GLOW**, 8, b g Jalmood (USA)—Dame Scarlet **Miss E. Lawlor**
13 **GRAPHIC EQUALISER (IRE)**, 6, b g Accordian—Top Girl (IRE) **B. R. A. S. K. Syndicate**
14 **GREY GUY (IRE)**, 6, gr g Shernazar—Rasmara **F. Conroy**
15 **HEAVY HUSTLER (IRE)**, 7, b g Strong Gale—Balingale **Mrs R. Hale**
16 **HIGH GALE (IRE)**, 6, b g Strong Gale—High Board **R. Auld**
17 **HORS BORD (FR)**, 6, b g Esprit du Nord (USA)—Honey Hill (FR) **Long Neck Syndicate**
18 **JEFFELL**, 8, gr g Alias Smith (USA)—Saleander **T. Bailey**
19 **KADOUKO (FR)**, 5, b g Cadoudal (FR)—Perle Bleue (FR) **George Ward**
20 **KILSPINDIE**, 7, b g Niniski (USA)—Kilavea (USA) **Lyreen Syndicate**
21 **KLAIRON DAVIS (FR)**, 9, b g Rose Laurel—Styrene (FR) **C. Jones**
22 **LORD DAL (FR)**, 5, b g Cadoudal (FR)—Lady Corteira (FR) **Mrs T. Hyde**
23 **LORD EDENBURY (IRE)**, 7, b g Lord Americo—Supposeyouare **Edenbury Syndicate**
24 **LORD OF THE DANCE (IRE)**, 6, b g Mister Lord (USA)—Pachamama **D. J. Lenihan**
25 **MAJOR JAMIE (IRE)**, 7, b g Welsh Term—Jamie's Lady **C. Nolan**
26 **MANHATTAN CASTLE (IRE)**, 9, b g Strong Gale—Allamanda (FR) **P. Fitzpatrick**
27 **MILLER KING (IRE)**, 9, gr g Aristocracy—Bramble Mill **Mrs D. Guinness**
28 **MOORE'S MELODIES (IRE)**, 7, b g Orchestra—Markree Castle **F. Clarke**
29 **MORE THAN A STROLL (IRE)**, 6, ch g Pennine Walk—Jenny's Child **Mrs A. L. T. Moore**
30 **MULDALUS (IRE)**, 6, b g Mandalus—Some Gossip **S. Mulryan**
31 **NORTHERN GALAXY (IRE)**, 6, b g Pennine Walk—Etoile Grise **Mrs S. M. Collins**
32 **OVER EAGER (IRE)**, 6, b g Over The River (FR)—Kincsem **J. P. McManus**
33 **OWENDUFF (USA)**, 8, ch g Irish River (FR)—Principle (USA) **F. Cruess-Callaghan**
34 **PAT HARTIGAN (IRE)**, 8, ch g Orchestra—Oriental Star **J. P. McManus**
35 **PENNY NATIVE (IRE)**, 6, ch g Be My Native (USA)—Penny Maes **F. Conroy**
36 **REGENCY RAKE**, 6, b g Ti King (FR)—Midnight Owl (FR) **Mrs J. J. McGettigan**
37 **ROYAL MARINE (IRE)**, 6, b g King's Ride—Eurolink Sea Baby **J. P. McManus**
38 **RYHANE (IRE)**, 9, b g Erin's Hope—Ballrue Lady **Mrs B. M. McKinney**
39 **SCENT ON (IRE)**, 6, b g Roselier (FR)—Sweet Run **Skybar Syndicate**
40 **TARTHOOTH (IRE)**, 7, ch g Bob Back (USA)—Zoly (USA) **Mrs H. De Burgh**
41 **TENDER SITUATION**, 7, b g Gildoran—Balancing Act **T. Ryan**
42 **THE QUADS**, 6, b g Tinoco—Queen's Royale **Told You So Syndicate**
43 **TYNDARIUS (IRE)**, 7, b g Mandalus—Lady Rerico **J. M. Walker**
44 **VEREDARIUS (FR)**, 7, b g Le Nain Jaune (FR)—Villa Verde (FR) **Mrs A. L. T. Moore**
45 **WHALE OF A KNIGHT (IRE)**, 9, b g Buckskin (FR)—Three Ladies **S. Galvin**
46 **WINDGAP HILL (IRE)**, 7, b g Supreme Leader—Deep Adventure **Sunny South Syndicate**
47 **WOODLAND KING (IRE)**, 6, b g King's Ride—Bilma (IRE) **C. Hanbury**
48 **WYLDE HIDE**, 11, b g Strong Gale—Joint Master **J. P. McManus**

Jockeys (NH): B Cash (10-0), C O'Dwyer (10-0).

Conditional: D O'Sullivan (9-7).

Amateur: Mr G Donnelly (10-4).

Lady Rider: Miss A Moore (10-0).

413 MR G. L. MOORE, Brighton

Postal: **4 Downland Close, Woodingdean, Brighton, Sussex, BN2 6DN.**
Phone: **(0802) 580993 MOBILE (01273) 620106 HOME (01273) 620405 YARD & FAX**

1 **ALHOSAAM**, 4, b c Belmez (USA)—Leipzig **Speedline Telecom**
2 **ANNOUNCING**, 4, b g Old Vic—d'Azy **Miss K. Shine**
3 **APOLLO RED**, 9, ch g Dominion—Woolpack **Mr A. Moore**

MR G. L. MOORE—continued

4 **BANZHAF (USA),** 5, ch g Rare Performer (USA)—Hang On For Effer (USA) **Mr Bryan Pennick**
5 **BARBASON,** 6, ch g Polish Precedent (USA)—Barada (USA) **Mr F. L. Hill**
6 **BARRIER RIDGE,** 4, ch g Lycius (USA)—Star Ridge (USA) **Mrs C. Hockeridge**
7 **BE TRUE,** 4, b g Robellino (USA)—Natchez Trace **Mr F. L. Hill**
8 **BIGWIG (IRE),** 5, ch h Thatching—Sabaah (USA) **Mrs Elizabeth Kiernan**
9 **CHEEKY CHARLIE,** 6, b g Jupiter Island—Double Shuffle **Mr Phil Collins**
10 **CHEWIT,** 6, gr g Beveled (USA)—Sylvan Song **Ballard (1834) Limited**
11 **DAYDREAMER (USA),** 5, b g Alleged (USA)—Stardusk (USA) **Mrs Rita Bates**
12 **DEEPLY VALE (IRE),** 7, b g Pennine Walk—Late Evening (USA) **Speedline Telecom**
13 **DURHAM,** 7, ch g Caerleon (USA)—Sanctuary **Mr Matthew Thole**
14 **ELA AGAPI MOU (USA),** 5, b g Storm Bird (CAN)—Vaguar (USA) **Action II**
15 **GUEST ALLIANCE (IRE),** 6, ch g Zaffaran (USA)—Alhargah **Ballard (1834) Limited**
16 **HARDY DANCER,** 6, ch g Pharly (FR)—Handy Dancer **Mr Peter L. Higson**
17 **HATTA SUNSHINE (USA),** 8, b g Dixieland Band (USA)—Mountain Sunshine (USA) **Mr R. Kiernan**
18 **HEAVENLY HAND,** 4, ch f Out of Hand—My Home **Mr A. Moore**
19 **INKWELL,** 4, b g Relief Pitcher—Fragrant Hackette **Joe Bates (Bloodstock) Ltd**
20 **INVOCATION,** 11, ch g Kris—Royal Saint (USA) **Mr R. Kiernan**
21 **JUBILEE SCHOLAR (IRE),** 5, b g Royal Academy (USA)—Jaljuli **Mr M. V. Johnston**
22 **KAFIL (USA),** 4, b br c Housebuster (USA)—Alchaasibiyeh (USA) **Mr C. F. Sparrowhawk**
23 **KI CHI SAGA (USA),** 6, ch g Miswaki (USA)—Cedilla (USA) **Mr Danny Bloor**
24 **KINNINO,** 4, b g Polish Precedent (USA)—On Tiptoes **Mr F. L. Hill**
25 **LIFT BOY (USA),** 9, b g Fighting Fit (USA)—Pressure Seat (USA) **Mr A. Moore**
26 **MARYJO (IRE),** 9, b m Tale Quale—Down The Aisle **Mr R. Kiernan**
27 **MERSEY BEAT,** 4, ch c Rock Hopper—Handy Dancer
28 **MISCONDUCT,** 4, gr f Risk Me (FR)—Grey Cree **Mrs Sheila White**
29 **MOST WELCOME NEWS,** 6, b g Most Welcome—In The Papers **Mr A. S. Reid**
30 **MR NEVERMIND,** 8, b g The Noble Player (USA)—Salacia **Mr K. Higson**
31 **MUHANDIS,** 5, b h Persian Bold—Night At Sea **Mr F. L. Hill**
32 **NAHRAWALI (IRE),** 7, b g Kahyasi—Nashkara **Mr C. F. Sparrowhawk**
33 **NO EXTRAS (IRE),** 8, b g Efisio—Parkland Rose **Mr K. Higson**
34 **NO PATTERN,** 6, ch g Rock City—Sunfleet **Mr K. Higson**
35 **NORDIC SPREE (IRE),** 6, b g Nordico (USA)—Moonsilk **Mr Roger John Jones**
36 **PALO BLANCO,** 7, b m Precocious—Linpac Mapleleaf **Mr A. S. Reid**
37 **QUAKERS FIELD,** 5, b h Anshan—Nosey **Mr B. V. Pennick**
38 **ROMAN REEL (USA),** 7, ch g Sword Dance—Our Mimi (USA) **Mrs J. Moore**
39 **ROYAL CARLTON (IRE),** 6, b g Mulhollande (USA)—Saintly Angel **Mrs Mary Doyle**
40 **SHAHRUR (USA),** 5, b br g Riverman (USA)—Give Thanks **Mrs Elizabeth Kiernan**
41 **SHALSTAYHOLY (IRE),** 4, ch f Shalford (IRE)—Saintly Guest **J. B. R. Leisure Ltd**
42 **SODA POP (IRE),** 4, b c River Falls—Riviere Salee (FR) **Mr C. F. Sparrowhawk**
43 **STOPPES BROW,** 6, b g Primo Dominie—So Bold **Mr C. J. Pennick**
44 **SUPPLY AND DEMAND,** 4, b g Belmez (USA)—Sipsi Fach **Action**
45 **WAIKIKI BEACH (USA),** 7, ch g Fighting Fit (USA)—Running Melody **Mrs J. Moore**
46 **WARM SPELL,** 8, b g Northern State (USA)—Warm Wind **Mr K. Higson**
47 **WHISKY WILMA,** 6, b m Gildoran—Danny d'Albi **Heart of the South Racing (2)**
48 **WOT NO FAX,** 5, ch g Sharrood (USA)—Priors Dean **Kerniquip's Racing Partnership**
49 **ZABRISKIE,** 4, b c Polish Precedent (USA)—Somfas (USA) **Mr R. Kiernan**

THREE-YEAR-OLDS

50 **BANK ON HIM,** b g Elmaamul (USA)—Feather Flower **Mr T. W. Leung**
51 **PRINCE OXLEY,** ch c King's Signet (USA)—Precious Air (IRE) **Mr Bryan Pennick**
52 **PRIVATE SEAL,** b g King's Signet (USA)—Slender **Mr Bryan Pennick**
53 **RESPOND,** b f Reprimand—Kina (USA) **Mr C. J. Pennick**
54 **ZADA,** b c Distant Relative—Handy Dancer **Mr Bryan Pennick**

TWO-YEAR-OLDS

55 B c 30/3 Priolo (USA)—Dauntess (Formidable (USA)) **Allen Associates**
56 Gr c 8/3 Barathea (IRE)—Dazzlingly Radiant (Try My Best (USA)) **Action II**
57 **KARINGA PRINCE,** gr c 31/1 Karinga Bay—Silent Sister (Kind of Hush) **Mr C. F. Sparrowhawk**
58 **MY EMILY,** b f 13/3 King's Signet (USA)—Flying Wind (Forzando) **B. V. Pennick**

MR G. L. MOORE—continued

59 ROUTE SIXTY SIX, gr f 14/3 Brief Truce (USA)—Lyphards Goddess (IRE) (Lyphard's Special (USA)) **J. B. R. Leisure Ltd**
60 ZOLA POWER, ch f 1/3 Efisio—Caroline Connors (Fairy King (USA)) **Miss Nadia Benjamin**

Other Owners: Mr David Allen, Mrs Dyanne Benjamin, Mr A. J. Doyle, Mrs Mary Doyle, Mr A. L. Green, Mr Duncan Heath, Mr Jim Horgan, Mr D. R. W. Jones, Mrs L. B. Jones, Mrs E. Keep, Mr P. Kernahan, Mr M. Morris, Mr C. J. Pennick, Miss S. Pennick, Mrs Caroline Penny, Mr John Penny, Miss Julie Reeves, Mr Stephen L. Ross, Miss Karen Shine, Mr B. Smith, Mrs Linda Stone, Mr Simon M. T. Tse.

Jockey (Flat): C Morris (8-2).

Apprentices: Cheryl Bone (8-4), R Brisland (7-3).

Conditional: M Batchelor (8-7).

Amateur: Mr I Mongon (8-4).

Lady Rider: Mrs J Moore.

414 MR G. M. MOORE, Middleham

Postal: **Warwick Lodge Stables, Middleham, Leyburn, North Yorkshire, DL8 4PB.**
Phone: **WENSLEYDALE (01969) 623823**

1 **BOLD ACCOUNT (IRE),** 8, b g Strong Statement (USA)—Ogan Spa **Mr John Robson**
2 **BOLD BOSS,** 9, b g Nomination—Mai Pussy **Mr John Robson**
3 **BOLD FOUNTAIN (IRE),** 7, b g Royal Fountain—Glitter On **Mr John Robson**
4 **BROMFORD HOUSE (IRE),** 5, b g Brush Aside (USA)—Shuilernish **Mr A. W. Sergeant**
5 **BURNT IMP (USA),** 8, ch g Imp Society (USA)—Flaming Reason (USA) **N. B. Mason (Farms) Ltd**
6 **COURSE DOCTOR (IRE),** 6, ch g Roselier (FR)—Faultless Girl **Mr Richard Johnson**
7 **DIAMOND BEACH,** 5, b g Lugana Beach—Cannon Boy (USA) **Valueplace Ltd**
8 **FARMERS SUBSIDY,** 6, ch g Primitive Rising (USA)—Em-Kay-Em **White Hart In Hawes Partnership**
9 **GALE AHEAD (IRE),** 8, br g Strong Gale—Caddy Girl **Mr John Robson**
10 **GAUTBY HENPECKED,** 5, ch m Henbit (USA)—Mervins **L N P Racing**
11 **GLENUGIE,** 7, b g Insan (USA)—Excavator Lady **Mr Frazer Hines**
12 **GOLLACCIA,** 4, gr f Mystiko (USA)—Millie Grey **Mrs H. I. S. Caizini**
13 **HANDSOME ANTHONY (IRE),** 7, b g Lancastrian—Gilded Empress **Mr Sean Graham**
14 **HOBBS CHOICE,** 5, b m Superpower—Excavator Lady **Miss Liz Hobbs**
15 **HOUSE OF DREAMS,** 6, b g Darshaan—Helens Dreamgirl **J. & M. Leisure Ltd**
16 **JOE LUKE (IRE),** 6, b g Satco (FR)—Garden County **Mrs Margi Winter**
17 **MAFTUN (USA),** 6, ch g Elmaamul (USA)—Allesheny **Anmaf Partnership**
18 **NONIOS (IRE),** 7, b g Nashamaa—Bosquet **Mrs Susan Moore**
19 **OUT BY NIGHT (IRE),** 7, b g Phardante (FR)—Love And Idleness **Mr A. J. Coupland**
20 **PALADUS (IRE),** 6, b g Mandalus—Lucy's Pal **Mr M. Gleason**
21 **PAPARAZZO,** 7, b g Posen (USA)—Royale Warning (USA) **Mrs R. D. Peacock**
22 **PEBBLE BEACH (IRE),** 8, gr g Roselier (FR)—Indian Idol **The Pebble Beach Partnership**
23 **PETERSEN HOUSE (IRE),** 4, b g Ikdam—Corrib Gipsy **Mr R. I. Graham**
24 **REEDS,** 4, b g Thatching—Bayadere (USA) **North Briton Racing**
25 **ROYAL SPRUCE (IRE),** 7, b g Step Together (USA)—Lacken Lady **Mrs Susan Moore**
26 **ROYAL VACATION,** 9, b g King of Spain—Crane Beach **Mr G. P. Edwards**
27 **SANTA JET (IRE),** 7, b g Henbit (USA)—Santa Anita Jet **Mr G. P. Edwards**
28 **SCOTMAIL LAD (IRE),** 4, b g Ilium—Nicholas Ferry **Gordon Crown/Bert Watson**
29 **SHANAVOGH,** 7, b g Idiot's Delight—Honeybuzzard (FR) **Mr Sean Graham**

MR G. M. MOORE—continued

30 **STONESBY (IRE),** 6, b g The Bart (USA)—Maid In The Mist **Mr Eric Atkinson**
31 **TIME WARRIOR (IRE),** 7, ch g Decent Fellow—Oonagh's Teddy **Mrs Susan Moore**
32 **WEE RIVER (IRE),** 9, b g Over The River (FR)—Mahe Reef **Mr Sean Graham**
33 **WELSH MARCH (IRE),** 6, b g Over The River (FR)—Welsh Tan **Mr John Robson**

TWO-YEAR-OLDS

34 B f 22/4 Timeless Times (USA)—Tangalooma (Hotfoot) **A. S. & J. A. Whitwham**

Other Owners: Mr D. J. Bushell, Mr J. S. Calvert, Mr K. D. Goodman, Mrs J. M. Gray, Mr Geoffrey Hamilton, Mr J. Hamilton, Mr M. W. Harrison, Mr G. Hayton, Mr N. Honeyman, Mr M. G. R. Hoskins, Mrs Bet Jones, Mrs Linda Leckie, Mr John Lishman, Mr N. B. Mason, Mrs Margaret McSweeney, Mr Andy Middleton, Mr A. F. Monk, Mr Chris Moreno, Mrs G. Newborough, Mr J. P. Paternoster, Mrs D. N. B. Pearson, Mr J. A. Poirrette, Mrs K. A. Sowerby, Mr P. E. Sowerby, Mr G. E. Stevenson, Mr J. Tennant, Thornfield Developments Ltd, Mr R. W. Tunstall, Ms Sigrid Walter.

Jockeys (NH): N Bentley (10-0), J Callaghan (10-0).

Conditional: N Hannity (10-0), T Hogg (10-0).

Amateur: Mr Gordon Markham (10-0).

415 MR J. S. MOORE, Hungerford

Postal: **Parsonage Farm Racing Stables, Newbury Road, East Garston, Hungerford, Berkshire, RG17 7ER.**
Phone: **HOME/YARD (01488) 648822 MOBILE (0860) 811127 FAX (01488) 648185**

1 **AQUAVITA,** 4, b f Kalaglow—Aigua Blava (USA) **Mr Ernie Houghton**
2 **CHIEF'S LADY,** 6, b m Reprimand—Pussy Foot **Mr D. J. White**
3 **EXPRESS CRUSADER (IRE),** 5, b g New Express—Ribot Ann **Mr S. M. Boddy**
4 **FOLEYS QUEST (IRE),** 4, b f River Falls—Katie's Delight **Mr Ernie Houghton**
5 **FRESH ROSE MARY (IRE),** 6, b m Welsh Term—Clare's Sheen **Mr J. S. Moore**
6 **JOCTOR DON (IRE),** 6, b br g Pitpan—Thats Irish **Mrs Derek Strauss**
7 **NA HUIBHEACHU (IRE),** 7, ch g Nostrum (USA)—Royal Slip **Mr P. Kelly**
8 **ORONTES (USA),** 4, b g Lomond (USA)—Chateau Princess (USA) **The Once Bitten Partnership**
9 **PATSY GRIMES,** 8, b m Beveled (USA)—Blue Angel **Mr J. K. Grimes**
10 **RIVERSIDE GIRL (IRE),** 4, b f River Falls—Ballywhat (IRE) **Mr J. R. Franklin**
11 **ROSS DANCER (IRE),** 6, b g Ajraas (USA)—Crimson Crown **Mr Gerard P. O'Loughlin**
12 **RUMBUSTIOUS,** 4, b f Rambo Dancer (CAN)—Persian Alexander **Mr Christopher Curtis**
13 **SHARPEST,** 4, ch g Sharpo—Anna Karietta **Mr Terry Pasquale**
14 **STAPLEFORD LADY,** 10, ch m Bairn (USA)—Marie Galante (FR) **P. C. and Mrs S. I. Fry**
15 **WITNEY-DE-BERGERAC (IRE),** 6, b g Cyrano de Bergerac—Spy Gin **Mr Ernie Houghton**
16 **WITNEY O'GRADY (IRE),** 5, ch g Ring of Ford—Cbm Girl **Mr Ernie Houghton**

THREE-YEAR-OLDS

17 **ASTROLFELL (IRE),** ch f River Falls—Indian Starlight **Mrs P. Ratcliff**
18 **BLUE MONK (IRE),** ch c Bluebird (USA)—High Habit **Mr Alex Gorrie**
19 **CAROL GRIMES,** b f Beveled (USA)—Come To Good **Mr J. K. Grimes**
20 **DANCING AL,** br g Alnasr Alwasheek—Lyne Dancer **Miss L. D. Martin**
21 **FIRE GODDESS,** ch f Magic Ring (IRE)—Into The Fire **Mrs Victoria Goodman**
22 **LADY LEW (IRE),** ch f River Falls—Tropical Desert (IRE) **Mr Lewendon**
23 **LA GALLERIA,** ch f Royal Academy (USA)—Two And Sixpence (USA) **Mr D. J. Walker**
24 **MAGNI MOMENTI,** b f King's Signet (USA)—Halka **Miss S. Clarke**
25 **MAKE IT SO,** ch f Henbit (USA)—H And K Gambler **The Pratt Partnership**
26 **MISLEAD (IRE),** b f Distinctly North (USA)—Chez Nous (IRE) **Mr P. Henley**

MR J. S. MOORE—continued

27 NISABA (IRE), b f Belmez (USA)—Nibabu (FR) **Mr Ernest H. Moore**
28 B f Rock City—Sayida-Shahira **Mrs S. A. Willis**
29 VICKY JAZZ, ch f Alhijaz—Kinkajoo **Mr J. S. Moore**

TWO-YEAR-OLDS

30 Ch c 22/3 Ardkinglass—Angel's Sing (Mansingh (USA))
31 B c 12/3 Elmaamul (USA)—Cache (Bustino) **Mr Alex Gorrie**
32 B f 25/3 Unblest—Collected (IRE) (Taufan (USA))
33 Ch c 19/3 Simply Great (FR)—Donna Katrina (Kings Lake (USA)) **Mrs Victoria Goodman**
34 B f 26/3 Deploy—Dramatic Mood (Jalmood (USA)) **Mr P. Henley**
35 B f 28/1 Tirol—Kirsova (Absalom) **Mr Kevin Reddington**
36 B f 22/4 Balla Cove—Penultimate Cress (IRE) (My Generation) **Mrs Victoria Goodman**
37 Ch f 23/2 Forest Wind (USA)—Popcorn (Pharly (FR))
38 Ch g 20/4 Imp Society (USA)—Rose 'n Reason (IRE) (Reassonable (FR)) **Mr Ernie Houghton**
39 B c 9/6 First Trump—Sayida-Shahira (Record Run) **Mrs S. A. Willis**
40 B c 27/4 Risk Me (FR)—Sporting Lass (Blakeney)
41 B g 30/3 Balla Cove—Spy Girl (Tanfirion) **Mr Ernie Houghton**
42 Ch f 7/5 Forest Wind (USA)—Tropical Desert (IRE) (King Persian)
43 B f 27/2 Tirol—Tuesday Morning (Sadler's Wells (USA)) **Mrs A. Speyer**

Other Owners: B & E Bloodstock Limited, Mr Chris Bradbury, Mr P. M. Breakspear, Mrs A. Burton, Mr P. Colley, Mr L. F. Doherty, Mr Liam Doherty, Mr R. Hannon, Mr Ian Hutchins, Mr C. Kyriakou, Mr M. Moore, Mr J. Newsome, Mrs M. A. O'Neill, Mrs P. M. Ratcliffe, Miss Juliet E. Reed, Exors Of The Late Mr D. G. Sprackland, Mrs A. M. Upsdell, Mr David Wildash, Mrs C. M. Williams.

Jockey (NH): W McFarland (10-0).

Apprentice: P P Murphy (7-10).

Conditional: P Henley, J Keehan (9-7).

Amateur: Mr S Durack.

Lady Rider: Mrs S J Moore (8-0).

416 MR B. C. MORGAN, Burton-on-Trent

Postal: **Stoneyford Farm, Barton-Under-Needwood, Burton-on-Trent, Staffordshire, DE13 8BW.**
Phone: **TEL/FAX (01283) 575304 MOBILE (0831) 171531**

1 5, B g Rolfe (USA)—Arctic Lion **Needwood Racing Ltd**
2 FLYING FLIP, 4, b f Rolfe (USA)—Needwood Sprite **Mr Tim Leadbeater**
3 MR KERMIT, 7, b g Rolfe (USA)—Sea Dart **Mr D. G. Blagden**
4 NEEDWOOD EPIC, 5, b m Midyan (USA)—Epure **Needwood Racing Ltd**
5 NEEDWOOD LEGEND, 5, b br h Rolfe (USA)—Enchanting Kate **Needwood Racing Ltd**
6 NEEDWOOD MUPPET, 11, b g Rolfe (USA)—Sea Dart **Mr D. G. Blagden**
7 NEEDWOOD NUTKIN, 5, b m Rolfe (USA)—Needwood Nut **Gromit Racing**
8 NEEDWOOD POPPY, 10, b m Rolfe (USA)—Needwood Nap **Mr Tim Leadbeater**
9 6, B g Rolfe (USA)—Sea Dart **Needwood Racing Ltd**

THREE-YEAR-OLDS

10 B f Rolfe (USA)—Enchanting Kate **Needwood Racing Ltd**
11 NEEDWOOD SPIRIT, b c Rolfe (USA)—Needwood Nymph **Needwood Racing Ltd**

MR B. C. MORGAN—continued

12 **NEEDWOOD SPITFIRE,** b f Rolfe (USA)—Lime Brook **Needwood Racing Ltd**
13 Ch f Gunner B—Needwood Sprite **Mr Tim Leadbeater**
14 Ch g Gunner B—Sea Dart **Needwood Racing Ltd.**
15 **THE LIMPING CAT (IRE),** b c Emarati (USA)—Little Madam **Mr G. Whitaker**

TWO-YEAR-OLDS

16 B c 31/1 Sizzling Melody—Enchanting Kate (Enchantment) **Needwood Racing Ltd**
17 B c 30/4 Magic Ring (IRE)—Hithermoor Lass (Red Alert) **Mr G. Whitaker**
18 B c 4/4 Sizzling Melody—Lime Brook (Rapid River) **Needwood Racing Ltd.**
19 B f 24/5 Sizzling Melody—Needwood Nut (Royben) **Needwood Racing Ltd**
20 B c 7/3 Sizzling Melody—Needwood Poppy (Rolfe (USA)) **Needwood Racing Ltd**
21 B c 20/5 Sizzling Melody—Needwood Sprite (Joshua) **Mr Tim Leadbeater**
22 B c 12/7 Sizzling Melody—Sea Dart (Air Trooper) **Needwood Racing Ltd.**

Other Owners: Mr Tim Hampton, Mr B. C. Morgan, Mr Robin Salmon.

Jockey (NH): Luke Harvey (10-0).

Lady Rider: Miss Sarah Phizacklea (8-7).

417 MR K. A. MORGAN, Melton Mowbray

Postal: **Hall Farm Stables, Waltham On The Wolds, Melton Mowbray, Leicestershire, LE14 4AJ.**
Phone: **(01664) 464711 OR 464488 FAX (01664) 464492 MOBILE(0468) 996103**

1 **ARCTIC AFFAIR (IRE),** 5, b m Glacial Storm (USA)—Moonlight Romance **Mr Rex Norton**
2 **COINTOSSER (IRE),** 5, b m Nordico (USA)—Sure Flyer (IRE) **Mr T. R. Pryke**
3 **CORRIMULZIE (IRE),** 7, ch g Phardante (FR)—Scott's Hill **Roemex Ltd**
4 **COUNT OF FLANDERS (IRE),** 8, b g Green Desert (USA)—Marie de Flandre (FR) **Mr K. A. Morgan**
5 **DINO'S MISTRAL,** 5, b g Petong—Marquessa d'Howfen **Mr R. G. Marriott**
6 **FARHAN (USA),** 4, b g Lear Fan (USA)—Mafatin (IRE) **Mrs R. M. Burgess**
7 **GLANMERIN (IRE),** 7, b g Lomond (USA)—Abalvina (FR) **Mr Rex Norton**
8 **GOLD OF ARABIA (USA),** 5, b g Seeking The Gold (USA)—Twitchet (USA) **Mr W. Tyler**
9 **HURRICANE HARRY,** 6, br g Strong Gale—Chancer's Last **Mrs M. Bisjill**
10 **JEANANN,** 5, b m Primitive Rising (USA)—Jean Jeanie **Mr Tony Evans**
11 **JUNIPER HILL,** 6, b g Dragonara (FR)—Sombreuil **Mrs P. A. L. Butler**
12 **LAGAN,** 5, b g Shareef Dancer (USA)—Lagta **Wild Racing**
13 **MARIGLIANO (USA),** 5, b g Riverman (USA)—Mount Holyoke **Mr T. R. Pryke**
14 **MEZZORAMIO,** 6, ch g Cadeaux Genereux—Hopeful Search (USA) **Mr T. R. Pryke**
15 **MOOBAKKR (USA),** 7, b br g Mr Prospector (USA)—Without Feathers (USA) **Mr Peter N. Davis**
16 **MUHASSIL (IRE),** 5, ch g Persian Bold—Nouvelle Star (AUS) **Mr R. W. Walpole**
17 **MUSAFI (USA),** 4, b g Dayjur (USA)—Ra'a (USA) **D & M Cased Hole**
18 **NIFAAF (USA),** 6, b m Silver Hawk (USA)—Betty Money (USA) **Mr A. A. Penney**
19 **NIGHT DANCE,** 6, ch h Weldnaas (USA)—Shift Over (USA) **Racecourse Medical Officers Association**
20 **NOBLE HERO,** 4, b g Houston (USA)—Noble Devorcee (USA) **D & M Cased Hole**
21 **NOCATCHIM,** 9, b g Shardari—Solar **Mr Richard Chandler**
22 **OPERA FAN (IRE),** 6, b g Taufan (USA)—Shannon Lady **Mr J. A. Outwin**
23 **PONTEVEDRA (IRE),** 5, b m Belmez (USA)—Pretoria **Mrs P. A. L. Butler**
24 **RUSSIAN BEAR,** 7, ch g Celestial Storm (USA)—Alma Ata **Bear Necessities**
25 **SECRET SOURCE,** 4, b c Alleged (USA)—Lake Dianchi (USA) **Mr K. A. Morgan**
26 **SHAMILLE DANCER,** 4, b f Show-A-Leg—Grand Teton **Seabourne Partnership**
27 **SHARK (IRE),** 5, b g Tirol—Gay Appeal **Mr M. J. Harmer**
28 **STURGEON (IRE),** 4, ch c Caerleon (USA)—Ridge The Times (USA) **Mr J. Cleeve**
29 **TO BE HONEST LIKE,** 5, b m Totem (USA)—Alma Ata **Mr K. A. Morgan**
30 **WAMDHA (IRE),** 8, b m Thatching—Donya **Mr T. R. Pryke**
31 **WASSL STREET (IRE),** 6, b g Dancing Brave (USA)—One Way Street **Mr Rex Norton**

MR K. A. MORGAN—continued

32 **WEATHER ALERT (IRE),** 7, b g Dance of Life (USA)—Ask The Wind **Mr K. A. Morgan**
33 **WELSH MOUNTAIN,** 5, b g Welsh Captain—Miss Nelski **Mrs P. A. L. Butler**
34 **YOUNG MARCIUS (USA),** 4, ch g Green Dancer (USA)—Manhatten Miss **Miss Alison Silkman**

THREE-YEAR-OLDS

35 **SAFFLEUR,** b f Safawan—Hinari Hi Fi **D. & M. Caseohole**
36 **SCOLDING,** b f Reprimand—Tinkerbird **Mr Michael Worth**
37 **WALTHAM BLACKBIRD,** b f Tigani—Heemee **Hall Farm Syndicate**
38 **WALTHAM DOVE,** br g Gypsy Castle—Dovetail **Hall Farm Syndicate**
39 **WALTHAM KINGFISHER,** b f Presidium—Lindrake's Pride **Hall Farm Syndicate**
40 **WALTHAM SKYLARK,** b f Puissance—Pear Drop **Hall Farm Syndicate**

TWO-YEAR-OLDS

41 **ROBELLA,** ch f 26/4 Keen—Afrabela (African Sky) **Mrs A. Balderstone**

Other Owners: Mr M. H. Beesley, Mr Gordon Boreland, Mr S. Cavender, Mr G. Davis, R. Dingley, Mr Roger England, Mr P. T. Facer, Mr D. J. Jarvis, Mr Philip Kenley, Mr Alan Kerr, Mr P. G. Kerr, Dr D. J. Layfield, Mr B. Leatherday, Miss T. C. Mahdjate, Mr W. B. Mawson, Mr Bill Nuttell, Mr G. W. O'Keefe, Mr John H. Price, Mr Harry Redknapp, Mr A. P. Roche, Mr D. H. Seidel, Mrs Alison Silkman, Mr R. A. Simcox, Mr Richard Simpson, Mr Paul Stock, Mr K. W. Weale, Mr J. Wild, Mr J. N. Wild, Mr N. R. Wild, Mr Keith Wills.

Jockey (NH): Aidie Smith (9-12, w.a.).

Conditional: R Massey (9-7), P Morris (9-9).

Amateur: B Foster (10-2).

418 MR C. P. H. MORLOCK, Wantage

Postal: **Raceyard Cottage Stables, Kingston Lisle, Wantage, Oxfordshire, OX12 9QH.**
Phone: **HOME/FAX (01367) 820510 MOBILE (0468) 923444**

1 **ABOVE THE CUT (USA),** 6, ch g Topsider (USA)—Placer Queen **J. P. M. & J. W. Cook**
2 **ABSOLUTELY HOPEFUL,** 5, ch g Nearly A Hand—Owena Deep **Mr Michael Padfield**
3 **ANOTHER RUMPUS,** 6, b g Mr Fluorocarbon—Premier Susan **The Trogs**
4 **BANNY HILL LAD,** 8, gr g Pragmatic—Four M's **Mr Andrew F. Sawyer**
5 **CACHALOT,** 6, b g Buzzards Bay—Deep Ocean **Mr Dwight Makins**
6 **CORDIAL KNIGHT (USA),** 5, b g Night Shift (USA)—Temperence Cordial (USA) **J. P. M. & J. W. Cook**
7 **CURRACLOE ROSE,** 5, gr m Roselier (FR)—Cotton Gale **Not Over Big Partnership**
8 **EASY BUCK,** 11, b g Swing Easy (USA)—Northern Empress **J. P. M. & J. W. Cook**
9 **FILSCOT,** 6, b g Scottish Reel—Fililode **Mr J. Wild & Partners**
10 6, B g Strong Gale—Flash 'n' Run **Mr C. P. H. Morlock**
11 **GOD SPEED YOU (IRE),** 9, gr g Roselier (FR)—Pitmark **Wallop**
12 **HALONA,** 8, b m Pollerton—Premier Susan **Mrs Z. S. Clark**
13 5, B m Supreme Leader—Henry Woman (IRE) **Mr C. P. H. Morlock**
14 **ICKFORD OKEY,** 6, b g Broadsword (USA)—Running Kiss **Mr P. J. Morgan**
15 **LOCH NA KEAL,** 6, b m Weldnaas (USA)—Keyanloch **Mr S. Kimber**
16 **MY DAWN,** 5, b m River God (USA)—Sea Rambler **Mr A. Figg, Mr D. Redvers**
17 **NATIVE CHARM (IRE),** 6, b m Be My Native (USA)—Tumvella **Pell-mell Partners**
18 **NOTHING TO IT,** 7, b g Lyphento (USA)—Corniche Rose **Pell-mell Partners**
19 **NUTFIELD DOWN,** 7, b g Gildoran—Loch Rose **Mr Andrew Wilson**
20 **ROBELLITA,** 4, b g Robellino (USA)—Miellita **Angels Racing Syndicate**
21 **STEVE FORD,** 9, gr g Another Realm—Sky Miss **Mr P. J. Morgan**
22 **SUPREME TROGLODYTE (IRE),** 6, b m Supreme Leader—Clontinity Queen **The Trogs**
23 **THREADS,** 5, b m Bedford (USA)—Relkusa **Mr C. P. H. Morlock & Partners**

MR C. P. H. MORLOCK—continued

24 ULURU (IRE), 10, b g Kris—Mountain Lodge **Mr P. J. Morgan**
25 WOODHOUSE BAY (IRE), 5, b m Zaffaran (USA)—Mixed Blends **Mrs J. Maitland-Jones**

Other Owners: Mr W. P. Baines, Mrs Maurice Bosley, Mr A. N. Brooke Rankin, Mr N. Cassidy, Mr J. Chromiak, Mr Bernard Fox, Mr Richard Gilder, Mr R. J. Graham, Mr W. B. Griffiths, Miss E. Gwynne, Mr R. A. Instone, Mr P. M. Joslin, Mrs Penelope Makins, Mr J. J. T. Miller, Mr M. Miller, Sir Peter Miller, Mrs K. Morgan, Mr W. R. Morlock, Mr C. T. Nash, Mrs Tessa Padfield, Mr Richard Venn, Mr R. A. Winstanley.

Jockey (NH): J R Kavanagh (10-0).

Conditional: M Handley (9-7).

Amateur: Mr M Armytage (10-7).

419 MR DAVID MORRIS, Newmarket

Postal: **Hackness Villa, Exeter Road, Newmarket, Suffolk, CB8 8LP.**
Phone: **(01638) 667959 FAX (01638) 667959**

1 **A BREEZE,** 4, br g Precocious—Wasimah **Mr D. Morris**
2 **BAY OF ISLANDS,** 6, b g Jupiter Island—Lawyer's Wave (USA) **Bloomsbury Stud**
3 **EIDER HILL,** 4, b f Alawir (FR)—Matrah **Mr B. Cornish**
4 **MISSILE TOE (IRE),** 5, b g Exactly Sharp (USA)—Debach Dust **Stag and Huntsman**
5 **MR ROUGH,** 7, b g Fayruz—Rheinbloom **Mr D. Morris/Mr T. Clifford/Mr P. Hayes**
6 **PINCHINCHA (FR),** 4, b g Priolo (USA)—Western Heights **Mr T. J. Wells**
7 **SAIFAN,** 9, ch g Beveled (USA)—Superfrost **Mr D. Morris**
8 **YOUNG ANNABEL (USA),** 5, ch m Cahill Road (USA)—Only For Eve (USA) **Baker Street Six**

THREE-YEAR-OLDS

9 **AIRS IMAGE,** ch f Bustino—Western Star **Chippenham Lodge Stud**
10 **BULLISH,** gr g Terimon—Kovalevskia **Bloomsbury Stud**
11 **CAPERCAILLIE,** ch g Deploy—Tee Gee Jay **Future Electrical Services Ltd**
12 **GUILSBOROUGH,** br c Northern Score (USA)—Super Sisters (AUS) **Mason Racing Limited**
13 **TAJMIL (IRE),** ch f Wolfhound (USA)—Nouvelle Star (AUS) **Bloomsbury Stud**

TWO-YEAR-OLDS

14 **COCKATRICE,** b f 18/2 Petong—Noble Peregrine (Lomond (USA)) **The Hon D. Sieff, Mr R. Holmes**
15 B f 11/5 Feelings (FR)—Kala's Image (Kala Shikari) **Mrs S. I. Parry**
16 Ch f 20/3 Emarati (USA)—Nice Lady (Connaught) **Mr David Barrie, Mr P. Mason**
17 Ch c 17/4 Balla Cove—Royal Golden (IRE) (Digamist (USA)) **Mr Jim Brown**
18 Br f 17/4 Komaite (USA)—Super Sisters (AUS) (Call Report (USA)) **Mr P. Mason**

Other Owners: Mr Robin Akehurst, Mrs L. Brook, Mr J. Burns, Mr E. J. Cantillon, Mr D. Cobb, Mr J. S. Dunlop, Mr J. R. Dutton, Miss C. Fagerstrom, Mr J. J. Higgins, J. B. R. Leisure Ltd, Mr Ronald Johnson, Mr B. McAllister, Mrs Linda Morris, Mr A. J. Phillips, Mr G. Read, Mr Roger Cole Shilton, Hon W. H. Smith, Ms Wendy Smith, Mr Roy Taiano, Lord Tavistock, The Mirror Punters Club.

Jockey (Flat): Nigel Day.

Lady Rider: Zoe Burkett.

420 MR DERRICK MORRIS, Epsom

Postal: **Ermyn Lodge Stables 'A', Shepherds Walk, Epsom, Surrey, KT18 6DF.**
Phone: **(01372) 279308/725592 FAX (01372) 279308 MOBILE (0421) 988439**

1 **DUCHESS OF ERMYN,** 5, gr m Unfuwain (USA)—Trois Vallees **J. Daniels**
2 **ERMYNS PET,** 7, gr g Petoski—Trois Vallees **J. Daniels**
3 **MISTER ERMYN,** 5, ch g Minster Son—Rosana Park **J. Daniels**
4 **SOPHIE MAY,** 7, b m Glint of Gold—Rosana Park **J. Daniels**
5 **WONDERBOY (IRE),** 4, ch g Arazi (USA)—Alsaaybah (USA) **J. Daniels**

THREE-YEAR-OLDS

6 Ch g Out of Hand—Stellajoe **J. Daniels**

Jockey (NH): D Morris (10-0).

421 MR M. MORRIS, Fethard

Postal: **Everardsgrange, Fethard, Co. Tipperary, Ireland.**
Phone: **(052) 31474 FAX (052) 31654**

1 **ALEXANDRA KING (IRE),** 4, ch g Classic Secret (USA)—Castlemagner (IRE) **A. J. O'Reilly, Mr N. O'Callaghan**
2 **BOSS DOYLE (IRE),** 6, b g Lapierre—Prolific Scot **Mrs Ann Daly**
3 **BROWNIE RETURNS (IRE),** 5, b g Dry Dock—What A Brownie **Mrs Ann Daly**
4 5, B g Lafontaine (USA)—Buck A Tina **Mr M. Peters**
5 **CAPTAIN WALLACE (IRE),** 6, b g Supreme Leader—The Priory **Mrs P. F. N. Fanning**
6 **CRISTYS PICNIC (IRE),** 8, b g Tremblant—My Maizey **Ramojo Syndicate**
7 **CROI,** 8, b g Lancastrian—Our Chrisy **Mr G. Fitzmaurice**
8 **EMPOWERMENT (IRE),** 8, ch g Be My Native (USA)—Fun
9 5, Ch g Naheez (USA)—Flowering Moss (IRE) **Mr M. Peters**
10 **FOXCHAPEL KING (IRE),** 5, b g Jolly Jake (NZ)—Monatrim **A. J. O'Reilly**
11 **HARDYCOMESTOHARDY (IRE),** 5, b g Be My Native (USA)—Bid For Fun (IRE) **Mrs Miles Valentine**
12 **HIS SONG (IRE),** 5, ch g Accordion—Pampered Finch VII **Mr David Lloyd**
13 **ILLEGAL ALIEN (IRE),** 8, b g Duky—Dontellvi **Mr M. F. Morris**
14 **JOLLY JOHN (IRE),** 7, b h Jolly Jake (NZ)—Golden Seekers **Mrs P. F. N. Fanning**
15 5, B g Brush Aside (USA)—Kilbrack **Mrs J. Fanning**
16 **LA GAZELLE (IRE),** 6, b m Executive Perk—Our Quest **A. J. O'Reilly**
17 **LYRE HILL (IRE),** 4, b f Strong Gale—Baby Clair **Mrs J. Fanning**
18 **MASTER OF ILLUSION (IRE),** 5, ch g Castle Keep—Galloping Gold VII **Mrs M. Jordan**
19 **MILLA'S DELIGHT (IRE),** 7, br g Boreen (FR)—Brook Lady **Mr David Lloyd**
20 **MILLA'S MAN (IRE),** 6, b g Satco (FR)—Rullahola **Mr David Lloyd**
21 **MORAL SUPPORT (IRE),** 6, ch g Zaffaran (USA)—Marians Pride **Mrs K. Ronan**
22 **MYFAVOURITEMARTIAN (IRE),** 8, b g Strong Gale—Le Idol **Mrs Sharon Nelson**
23 **NEW CO,** 10, ch g Deep Run—True Minstrel **Exors of the late Mrs L. C. Ronan**
24 **PHARADISO (IRE),** 7, ch g Phardante (FR)—Sugar Shaker **A. J. O'Reilly**
25 **PHILL THE WALTZ (IRE),** 6, b g Supreme Leader—Queen's Run (IRE) **Dundrum Hotel & Golf Syndicate**
26 5, B g Buckskin (FR)—Polarville **Mr M. Peters**
27 5, B g Royal Fountain—Portane Miss **Mr M. Peters**
28 **PUGET BLUE (IRE),** 5, b g Lord Americo—Kyle Cailin **Mrs Ann Daly**
29 4, B g Glacial Storm (USA)—Shuil Ub **Mrs Ann Daly**
30 **SOMEMANFORONEMAN (IRE),** 4, b g Asir—Wintry Shower **The Birdie RC**
31 **SUIR FIND (IRE),** 6, b g Executive Perk—Mantle Hill **Mrs P. F. N. Fanning**
32 **THATSWHATITHOUGHT (IRE),** 6, b g Boreen (FR)—Denali **Mrs Miles Valentine**
33 **THE BUTCHER BOY,** 5, ch g Broadsword (USA)—Annie'll Do **Ramojo Syndicate**
34 **THE CAVIAR MAN (IRE),** 6, br g Homo Sapien—Scots Maid **Mrs Sharon Nelson**
35 **THE OOZLER (IRE),** 5, b g Montelimar (USA)—Tikrara (USA) **The Birdie RC**
36 **WEE ICEMAN (IRE),** 6, b g Buckskin (FR)—Island Walk **The Birdie RC**

Jockeys (NH): D Casey, C O'Dwyer (w.a.).

422 MR H. MORRISON, East Ilsey

Postal: **Summerdown, East Ilsley, Newbury, Berkshire, RG20 7LB.**
Phone: **(01635) 281678 (01635) 281746 FAX (0836) 687799 MOBILE**

1 **FLETCHER,** 4, b g Salse (USA)—Ballet Classique (USA) **Lady Margadale**
2 **FRENCHMAN'S CREEK,** 4, b g Emperor Fountain—Hollow Creek **Mr H. Morrison**
3 **TAYOVULLIN (IRE),** 4, ch f Shalford (IRE)—Fifth Quarter **Mr H. Morrison**

THREE-YEAR-OLDS

4 **BALA,** ch f Casteddu—Baladee **Lord Margadale**
5 Ch f Imp Society (USA)—Cool Dancer
6 **GRINKOV (IRE),** b br g Soviet Lad (USA)—Tallow Hill **Rosanne Dobson & Partners**
7 **MANE FRAME,** b c Unfuwain (USA)—Moviegoer **A, J & M. Arbib**
8 **ROY,** ch g Keen—Billante (USA) **The D. T. M. Partnership**
9 **SALIGO (IRE),** b f Elbio—Doppio Filo **The Beach Club**
10 **STOP OUT,** b f Rudimentary (USA)—Breakaway **Sheran Macdonald-Buchanan & Partners**

TWO-YEAR-OLDS

11 B c 30/3 Alhijaz—Doppio (Dublin Taxi)
12 **FUDGE,** b f 28/5 Polar Falcon (USA)—My Candy (Lorenzaccio)
13 Ch f 16/5 Pips Pride—Hazar (IRE) (Thatching)
14 B f 16/3 Forest Wind (USA)—Kaya (GER) (Young Generation)
15 **RAINDROP,** b f 11/3 Primo Dominie—Thundercloud (Electric)
16 **SALALAH,** gr f 13/3 Lion Cavern (USA)—Sea Fret (Habat)
17 B c 18/4 Highest Honor (FR)—Villella (Sadler's Wells (USA))
18 B f 28/5 Rudimentary (USA)—Zepha (Great Nephew)

Late Namings

WINDSTORM (IRE), b f Forest Wind (USA) — Kaya (GER) (Young Generation)
ENNOBLE, b c Highest Honor (FR) — Villella (Sadler's Wells (USA))

Other Owners: Miss C. Allsopp, Mr J. A. Arbib, Mr A. L. Brockbank, Mr D. Brooke, Mrs Ann Cooley, Mr Peter Deal, Fonthill Stud, The Hon. J. Greenall, Mr Rupert Hambro, Mr R. Jenks, Mr Nicholas Kaye, Capt J. Macdonald-Buchanan, Mr A. J. Morrison, Hon. Miss Mary Morrison, Mrs P. Nicoll, Hon. W. H. Smith, Alison Stanley, Mr H. A. B. Stroud, Mr Tim Sutton, Viscount Trenchard, Viscountess Trenchard, Mr J. R. Weatherby, Mrs A. White, Mr James Williams, Mr Richard Williams.

Jockey (Flat): C Rutter (w.a.).

Jockey (NH): T Jenks (w.a.).

Amateur: Mr Robert Latham (10-0).

423 MRS E. MOSCROP, Seaton Burn

Postal: **East Brenkley Stables, Brenkley, Seaton Burn, Newcastle Upon Tyne, NE13 6BT.**
Phone: **(0191) 2362145**

1 **OLE OLE,** 12, br g Boreen (FR)—Night Caller **Mrs E. Moscrop**
2 **PLATINI (IRE),** 7, b g Gallic League—Tardy (USA) **Mr George R. Moscrop**
3 **TANGO IN PARIS (ARG),** 8, ch g Bates Motel (USA)—What A Bang (USA) **Mrs E. Moscrop**

Amateur: Mr G R Moscrop (10-7).

424 MR M. P. MUGGERIDGE, Newbury

Postal: **5 Cherry Orchard, Great Shefford, Newbury, Berkshire, RG17 7BU.**
Phone: **HOME (01488) 648715 YARD 73532 FAX (01488) 72909 MOBILE (0973) 661226**

1 **BOLSHOI (POL),** 4, b g All Hands On Deck (USA)—Becky Sharp
2 **BRIDEPARK ROSE (IRE),** 10, b m Kemal (FR)—Elite Lady **Mr Tom Segrue**
3 **FIELDRIDGE,** 9, ch g Rousillon (USA)—Final Thought **The Charleston Partnership**
4 **ILEWIN,** 11, br g Ile de Bourbon (USA)—City Swinger **Middx Packaging Ltd**
5 **LITTLE SAHEFFORD,** 6, ch g Ballacashtal (CAN)—Wolstenbury **Mr John Liddiard**
6 **MISTRAL LORD (IRE),** 4, br g Fairy King (USA)—Walkyria **Zephyr Racing**
7 4, Br g Accordion—Ritual Girl **Mr Andrew Rybak**
8 **SOVEREIGN,** 4, b f Interrex (CAN)—Shiny Penny **The Charleston Partnership**
9 **SPUMANTE,** 6, ch g Executive Man—Midler **The Charleston Partnership**

THREE-YEAR-OLDS

10 **MOON ANGEL,** ch f Beveled (USA)—Beyond The Moon (IRE) **The Gaelic Five**
11 **SUPREME ANGEL,** br f Beveled (USA)—Blue Angel **The Least Moved Partnership**
12 **SYLPHIDE,** b f Balley Royal (USA)—Shafayif **Zephyr Racing**

TWO-YEAR-OLDS

13 B f Magical Wonder (USA)—Shes A Dancer (IRE)

Other Owners: Ms P. Angus, Mrs M. Bennett, Mr L. F. Chamberlain, Mr K. H. Eng, Mr A. A. King, Mr A. F. Leighton, Mr G. Robinson, Mr D. J. Ryan, Mr Ian Seville, Ms A. J. B. Smalldon, Mr G. White.

Jockeys (NH): Sean Curran (10-0), Brendan Powell.

425 MR WILLIAM R. MUIR, Lambourn

Postal: **Linkslade, Wantage Road, Lambourn, Hungerford, Berkshire, RG17 8UG.**
Phone: **OFFICE (01488) 73098 HOME 73748 FAX 73490 MOBILE (0831) 457074**

1 **ALMATY (IRE),** 5, b h Dancing Dissident (USA)—Almaaseh (IRE) **Mrs H. Levy**
2 **ALSAHIB (USA),** 5, b g Slew O' Gold (USA)—Khwlah (USA) **Mr S. Channing-Williams**
3 **AL'S ALIBI,** 5, b h Alzao (USA)—Lady Kris (IRE) **Mr R. Haim**
4 **AVERTI (IRE),** 7, b h Warning—Imperial Jade **Mr D. J. Deer**
5 **BRECON,** 5, b br h High Estate—No Can Tell (USA) **The Four Willies Partnership**
6 **CALAMANDER (IRE),** 4, b f Alzao (USA)—Local Custom (IRE) **Philip Blacker Studio Partnership**
7 **DANESMAN (IRE),** 5, b g Danehill (USA)—Vernonhills **The Four Willies Partnership**
8 **DARBY FLYER,** 5, b g Dominion Royale—Shining Wood **Jacklin Ltd**
9 **DAVIS ROCK,** 4, ch f Rock City—Sunny Davis (USA) **Mrs H. Levy**
10 **DAYRELLA,** 4, ch f Beveled (USA)—Divissima **Dulverton Equine**
11 **FERNY HILL (IRE),** 4, b c Danehill (USA)—Miss Allowed (USA) **Ms Monique Van Bakel**
12 **GREENSPAN (IRE),** 6, b g Be My Guest (USA)—Prima Ballerina (FR) **Camelot Racing**
13 **JUST NICK,** 4, b g Nicholas (USA)—Just Never Know (USA) **Mr D. G. Clarke**
14 **LONGWICK LAD,** 5, ro h Chilibang—Bells of St Martin **Mrs Marion Wickham**
15 **LUCKY TOUCH,** 5, ch g Broadsword (USA)—Solatia **Ridgebarn Farm Stud**
16 **ONE SHOT (IRE),** 5, b g Fayruz—La Gravotte (FR) **Mr R. Haim**
17 **ORSAY,** 6, gr g Royal Academy (USA)—Bellifontaine (FR) **Mr D. J. Deer**
18 **PEARTREE HOUSE (IRE),** 4, b c Simply Majestic (USA)—Fashion Front **Fayzad Thoroughbred Ltd**
19 **PRINCESS DANIELLE,** 6, b m Prince Daniel (USA)—Bells of St Martin **Mrs Marion Wickham**
20 **PRIVATE AUDIENCE (USA),** 5, b h Private Account (USA)—Monroe (USA) **Mr J. Davies**
21 **QUIET ARCH (IRE),** 5, b g Archway (IRE)—My Natalie **Mr J. Davies**
22 **RISCATTO (USA),** 4, b g Red Ransom (USA)—Ultima Cena (USA) **Mr F. Hope**
23 **ROUFONTAINE,** 7, gr m Rousillon (USA)—Bellifontaine (FR) **Piercefield Stables**
24 **SHADOOF,** 4, b c Green Desert (USA)—Bermuda Classic **Mrs H. Levy**
25 **SHARAF (IRE),** 5, b g Sadler's Wells (USA)—Marie de Flandre (FR) **Mrs H. Levy**
26 **SHEER FACE,** 4, b c Midyan (USA)—Rock Face **Mr A. J. de V. Patrick**

MR WILLIAM R. MUIR—continued

27 **TAILWIND,** 4, ch g Clantime—Casbar Lady **Mr R. Haim**
28 **TAYSEER (USA),** 4, ch g Sheikh Albadou—Millfit (USA) **Mrs H. Levy**
29 **THE GREEN GREY,** 4, gr g Environment Friend—Pea Green **Mrs Barbara Jean Martin**
30 **WARP DRIVE (IRE),** 4, ch g Bluebird (USA)—Red Roman **Mrs Danita Winstanly**
31 **WILD RITA,** 6, ch m Risk Me (FR)—Ma Pierrette **Perspicacious Punters Racing Club**

THREE-YEAR-OLDS

32 **ACID TEST,** ch c Sharpo—Clunk Click **Mr A. J. de V. Patrick**
33 **ALPEN WOLF (IRE),** ch g Wolfhound (USA)—Oatfield **Mr R. Haim**
34 **ALTISHAAN,** b f Darshaan—Altiyna **Mr D. J. Deer**
35 **ANGEL EYES,** b f Batshoof—Fair And Wise **Mr A. J. de V. Patrick**
36 **ARRY MARTIN,** b c Aragon—Bells of St Martin **Mrs Marion Wickham**
37 **ASTROLOGER,** b c Soviet Star (USA)—Taalif **Mr D. Edginton**
38 **BOLD LEGACY (IRE),** ch c Mujtahid (USA)—Lagrion (USA) **Mr C. L. A. Edginton**
39 **DA BOSS,** b c Be My Chief (USA)—Lady Kris (IRE) **Mr R. Haim**
40 B f Risk Me (FR)—Dark Kristal (IRE)
41 **FLYING BOLD (IRE),** ch c Persian Bold—Princess Reema (USA) **Mrs H. Levy**
42 **LADY LAPHROAIG (FR),** ch f Elmaamul (USA)—Venerate (IRE) **Friends of Laphroaig**
43 B f Chilibang—My Diamond Ring **Mrs Marion Wickham**
44 **PAPILLON SAUVAGE,** b f Theatrical Charmer—Gotcher **Mr P. A. Bourdon**
45 **PERCY-P,** ch c Superpower—Song's Best **Perspicacious Punters Racing Club**
46 **POLISH PILOT (IRE),** b c Polish Patriot (USA)—Va Toujours **Mrs Barbara Jean Martin**
47 B c Almoojid—Quite A Lark **Mrs A. McMillan**
48 **ROXY,** b f Rock City—Hyatti **Mrs J. M. Muir**
49 **TULLICH REFRAIN,** b f Petardia—Norfolk Serenade **Mr M. P. Payton**

TWO-YEAR-OLDS

50 B c 14/3 Marju (IRE)—Blueberry Walk (Green Desert (USA)) **Fayzad Thoroughbred Limited**
51 B f 10/3 Rudimentary (USA)—Charlton Athletic (Bustino) **Mr B. Adams & Mr T. Gleeson**
52 Gr c 8/2 Forznado—Frighten The Life (Kings Lake (USA))
53 **HUG ME ROB,** b f 10/3 Robellino (USA)—Hug Me (Shareef Dancer (USA)) **Mr C. L. A. Edginton**
54 B c 15/4 Wolfhound (USA)—Imperial Jade (Lochnager) **Mr D. J. Deer**
55 Ch c 16/2 Woodman (USA)—Kanz (USA) (The Minstrel (CAN)) **Mr D. J. Deer**
56 Br f 15/2 Ballacashtal (CAN)—Legendary Lady (Reprimand) **Mrs H. Mills**
57 B f 8/5 Petardia—Lune de Miel (Kalamoun) **Camelot Racing**
58 Br c 1/3 Polar Falcon (USA)—Maestrale (Top Ville) **Mrs D. Edginton & Mrs E. Clowes**
59 **MY MAN FRIDAY,** b c 5/4 Lugana Beach—My Ruby Ring (Blushing Scribe (USA)) **Mrs Marion Wickham**
60 B c 7/2 Indian Ridge—Nightitude (Night Shift (USA)) **V. S. Fleet**
61 **PASSIONS PLAYTHING,** ch c 12/4 Pursuit Of Love—Maiyaasah (Kris) **Miss J. Halford**
62 B c 16/3 Midyan (USA)—Polly Worth (Wolver Hollow) **Mr A. J. de V. Patrick**
63 B f 16/4 Rock City—Shernborne (Kalaglow) **Mr S. Lamb**
64 B c 10/3 Dolphin Street (FR)—Solas Abu (IRE) (Red Sunset)
65 B f 8/3 Ardkinglass—Song's Best (Never So Bold) **Mr D. J. Deer**
66 **SOUHAITE (FR),** b c 29/3 Salse (USA)—Parannda (Bold Lad (IRE)) **Mrs Danita Winstanly**
67 **THRUST,** b c 26/4 Prince Sabo—La Piaf (FR) (Fabulous Dancer (USA)) **Mrs H. Levy**
68 **TIGER GRASS (IRE),** gr c 23/2 Ezzoud (IRE)—Rustic Lawn (Rusticaro (FR)) **Mr M. Caddy**
69 B c 28/2 College Chapel—Trull (Lomond (USA))
70 B c 3/2 Common Grounds—Warg (Dancing Brave (USA)) **Parkside Partnership**
71 **WATER LOUP,** b f 14/2 Wolfhound (USA)—Heavenly Waters (Celestial Storm (USA)) **Mr J. Haim**

Other Owners: Mr A. T. Beverley-Jones, Mr P. A. Brannan, Mr B. Bull, Mrs A. E. Chapman, Mr Timothy N. Chick, Mr P. Clarke, Mr R. P. Clarke, Mr Glynne Clay, Miss Lynda Cox, Mrs D. Cunningham-Reid, Mr Stephen L. Darby, Mr J. Garratt, Mr Martin P. Graham, Miss C. A. Green, Mr Christopher Harris, Mr R. Harrison, Mr J. Jannaway, Mr K. Jeffery, J. P. Group Limited, Mr L. Kadzidlo, Mrs Lorna Keat, Dr Don S. McIntosh, Mrs M. McMillan, Mr George Merodoulakis, Mr John O'Mulloy, Mrs Jacqueline Peirce, Mr Richard Peirce, Mr L. A. Pickett, Mr S. C. Scowen, Mrs J. Seaden, Mr R. Shaw, Mr D. J. Sheppard, Mr Peter Sheppard, The Sussex Stud Limited, Mr Robert L. Thompson, Mr D. G. Wheatley, Mr P. J. Wheatley, Mrs Irene White, Mr Duncan J. Wiltshire.

Jockeys (Flat): Martin Dwyer (7-10), John Reid (8-6, w.a.).

Jockey (NH): Mark Richards (10-0).

Apprentice: Jason Wilkinson (8-5).

Conditional: Aaron Bates (9-10).

426 MR A. B. MULHOLLAND, Hambleton

Postal: **Hambleton Lodge, Hambleton, Sutton Bank, Thirsk, North Yorkshire, YO7 2HA.**
Phone: **(01845) 597288 FAX (01845) 597288 MOBILE (0410) 466314**

1 **CHADLEIGH LANE (USA),** 6, ch g Imp Society (USA)—Beauty Hour (USA) **The Gloria Darley Racing Partnership**
2 **IMPERIAL LINE (IRE),** 4, ch g Mac's Imp (USA)—Ellaline **Hambleton Racing Partnership**
3 **KOMLUCKY,** 6, b m Komaite (USA)—Sweet And Lucky **Hambleton Lodge Equine Premix Ltd**
4 **MA BULSIE,** 5, b m Beveled (USA)—Cool Run **The Gloria Darley Racing Partnership**
5 **MUSTARD,** 5, ch m Keen—Tommys Dream **Exors of the late G. Turner**
6 **MY SALTARELLO (IRE),** 4, b g Salt Dome (USA)—Daidis **Mr R. Wylie**
7 **RENNYHOLME,** 7, ch g Rich Charlie—Jacqui Joy **The Gloria Darley Racing Partnership**

THREE-YEAR-OLDS

8 **COOL AFFAIR (IRE),** ch g Statoblest—Ukraine's Affair (USA) **The Gloria Darley Racing Partnership**
9 **COOL MYSTERY,** ro c Mystiko (USA)—Romantic Saga **The Gloria Darley Racing Partnership**
10 **COOL PROSPECT,** b c Mon Tresor—I Ran Lovely **The Gloria Darley Racing Partnership**
11 **COOL SECRET,** gr c Petong—Cool Run **The Gloria Darley Racing Partnership**
12 B f Teenoso (USA)—Lindisfarne Rose **Mr P. Jackson**
13 **SPECIALIST DANCER,** ch c Krisinsky (USA)—China Crisis **Partnership**
14 B f Youn Senor (USA)—Tommys Dream **Mr A. Mulholland**

TWO-YEAR-OLDS

15 **BELLE OF HEARTS,** gr f 30/3 Belfort (FR)—Three of Hearts **Mrs V. Dixon**
16 **POETS PRIDE,** br f 24/4 Cyrano de Bergerac—Pattis Pet **The 2 Jays Partnership**

Other Owners: Mr D. Benyon, Mr W. A. Bleasdale, Mr R. N. Bracher, Mr Hugh Cholmley, Mr R. C. Crawford, Mr Ron Davison, Mr J. E. Gray, Mr Les Hartridge, Mr J. H. Henmy, Mr William Humes, Mrs H. Kavanagh, Mrs E. B. Lewis, Ms C. Robinson, W. N. Smith, Mr B. Tudor, Mr Jack Whittingham.

Jockeys (Flat): T Lucas (8-3), D Wright (7-10).

Jockey (NH): L Wyer (10-0).

Apprentice: R Winston (7-7).

Amateur: Mr R Wylie (10-0).

427 MR M. MULLINEAUX, Tarporley

Postal: **Southley Farm, Alpraham, Tarporley, Cheshire, CW6 9JD.**
Phone: **(01829) 261440**

1 **BRUMON (IRE),** 7, b g Sadler's Wells (USA)—Loveliest (USA) **Mr P. T. Hollins**
2 **CHESTER WREN,** 4, b f Handsome Sailor—Chester Belle **Mr C. W. Jenkins**
3 **DAWN'S DELLA,** 5, gr m Scottish Reel—Easter Swallow **Mr R. Kinsey & Mr K. Benson**
4 **MY ABBEY,** 9, b m Hadeer—Rose Barton **Mr P. Lawton & Abbey Racing**
5 7, B g Seymour Hicks (FR)—Princess Bella **Mr R. A. Royle**
6 **SKY RUNNER,** 7, ch g Scallywag—Space Drama **Mr R. G. E. Owen**
7 **SOME DEW,** 5, ch g Handsome Sailor—Dew **Mr M. Humphreys**
8 **THE ROUNDSILLS,** 4, ch g Handsome Sailor—Eye Sight **Lord Leverhulme**
9 **TRAVEL BOUND,** 13, b g Belfalas—Sugar Shaker **Mr M. Mullineaux**

THREE-YEAR-OLDS

10 B f Derrylin—Misty Sky **Mr M. Mullineaux**

MR M. MULLINEAUX—continued

TWO-YEAR-OLDS

11 **SUGAR CUBE TREAT,** b f 7/2 Lugana Beach—Fair Eleanor **Mr P. Lawton & Abbey Racing**

Other Owners: Mr T. S. Wallace.

Amateurs: Mr T. D. B. Barlow (11-0), Mr S Prior (10-7).

428 MR J. W. MULLINS, Amesbury

Postal: **Wilsford Stables, Wilsford-Cum-Lake, Amesbury, Salisbury, Wiltshire, SP4 7BL.**
Phone: **(01980) 626344 FAX (01980) 626344 MOBILE (0402) 559634**

1 **ALPINE MUSIC (IRE),** 4, b g Tirol—Holy Devotion **Mrs Sally Mullins**
2 **ALWAYS GREENER (IRE),** 7, gr m Vision (USA)—Great Meadow **Mr Peter Houghton**
3 **BENBULBIN (IRE),** 8, b g Supreme Leader—Loose Key **Mr C. D. Tilly**
4 **CONQUER THE KILT,** 7, b g El Conquistador—Kilton Joy **Mr F. G. Matthews**
5 **GAME DILEMMA,** 7, b m Sulaafah (USA)—Stagbury **Mr Ian M. McGready**
6 **GERRY'S PRIDE (IRE),** 7, b g Corvaro (USA)—Doll Acre **Mr G. E. Heard**
7 **GINKA,** 7, b m Petoski—Pine **Mrs M. L. Bruce**
8 **HOLLY HATCH,** 6, b m Sulaafah (USA)—Stagbury **Mrs U. Wainwright**
9 **KENTFORD TINA,** 7, b m Nearly A Hand—Notina **Mr D. I. Bare**
10 **MAKHPIYA PATAHN (IRE),** 6, br g Nestor—Our Mare Mick **Mr Geoff Skillen**
11 **PARAHANDY (IRE),** 8, b g Lancastrian—Dishcloth **Mr G. E. Heard**
12 **PENNY APPEAL,** 4, ch f Clantime—Petroc Concert **Mr T. K. Pearce**
13 4, Ch f Clantime—Petroc Concert **Mr T. K. Pearce**
14 **PUP'S PET,** 4, b f Petoski—Saucey Pup **Mr F. G. Matthews**
15 4, B g Camden Town—Quick Romance **Mr Seamus Mullins**
16 **QUISTAQUAY,** 6, b m El Conquistador—Busy Quay **Mr D. I. Bare**
17 **SCORING PEDIGREE (IRE),** 6, b g King Luthier—Quick Romance **Wilsford Racing Partnership**
18 **STEAMBURD,** 8, b m Dowsing (USA)—No Control **Mr Patrick Everard**
19 **STONEHENGE SAM (IRE),** 6, b g Asir—Astrina's Daughter **The Stonehenge Racing Partnership**
20 **STRONG CHOICE (IRE),** 6, b m Strong Gale—Innocent Choice **Mrs Sandra McCarthy**
21 4, B f Phardante (FR)—Swift Melody **Mr Gerard Mullins**
22 **THE LAND AGENT,** 7, b g Town And Country—Notinhand **Mr D. I. Bare**
23 **VIA DEL QUATRO (IRE),** 6, b m Posen (USA)—Gulistan **Ian McGready, Rob McGready, Adam Day**

THREE-YEAR-OLDS

24 **SHALABELLA (IRE),** br f Shalford (IRE)—Perfect Swinger **Mrs Jeni Fisher**

Other Owners: 14th Field Regiment Royal Artillery, Mrs J. M. Bailey, Exors Of The Late Mrs Heather Bare, Mr Denis Barry, Miss Suzannah Cotterill, Mr P. J. Donnelly, Mrs Jeni Fisher, Mr Brian S. Heath, Mr D. J. Line, Mr Rob McCready, Mr J. H. Mead, Mr Jim Milward, Mr Ralph P. Peters, The Army Air Corps Racing Club, Mrs C. A. Weatherley, Mr R. D. Weatherley, Col R. I. Webb-Bowen, Mr G. Wiltshire.

Conditional: D Turner.

Amateur: Major S Robinson.

429 MR F. MURPHY, Leyburn

Postal: **Wynbury Stables, West Witton, Leyburn, North Yorkshire, DL8 4LR.**
Phone: **TELEPHONE & FAX (01969) 622289 MOBILE (0421) 398034**

1 **ANOTHER VENTURE (IRE)**, 8, br g Tanfirion—Fitz's Buck **The Northern Boys**
2 **APACHE RAIDER**, 6, b g Dancing Brave (USA)—Calandra (USA) **Mrs E. A. Kettlewell**
3 **APPEARANCE MONEY (IRE)**, 7, b m Dancing Dissident (USA)—Fussy Budget **Irish Festival Racing Club**
4 **ARDRINA**, 7, b m Ardross—Ina's Farewell **L. G. M. Racing**
5 **ASTRO LINES (IRE)**, 4, b g Classic Secret (USA)—Fado's Delight
6 **BALLYMANA BOY (IRE)**, 5, b g Commanche Run—Spring Chimes **Mr K. Flood**
7 **BOOKING NOTE (IRE)**, 5, b m Brush Aside (USA)—Our Gale **Mr K. Perry**
8 **COOLAW (IRE)**, 5, b g Miner's Lamp—Mijette **Mrs R. D. Cairns & Mr F. Murphy**
9 **COUNT KARMUSKI**, 6, b g Ardross—Trimar Gold **Mr P. E. Atkinson**
10 **DR BONES (IRE)**, 5, b br g Durgam (USA)—Rose Deer **Mrs Ann Fortune**
11 **EPICA**, 7, b g Picea—Aladyat **The Desperate Men**
12 **FRENCH HOLLY (USA)**, 7, b g Sir Ivor—Sans Dot **Mr K. Flood**
13 **GRACELAND**, 6, ch m Buckley—Ina's Farewell **Mr Kevin Boddy**
14 **HEAVENS ABOVE**, 6, br g Celestial Storm (USA)—Regal Wonder **R. & G. Leonard**
15 **HIGH PYRENEES**, 6, b g Shirley Heights—Twyla **Mr John Stephenson**
16 **IRISH STAMP (IRE)**, 9, b g Niniski (USA)—Bayazida **Mr P. O'Donnell**
17 **JOE BUZZ (IRE)**, 6, b g Phardante (FR)—Dosie Deegan **Mr Joe Buzzeo**
18 **JORIDI LE FORIGE (IRE)**, 7, b g Seclude (USA)—Rose Deer **Mrs Ann Fortune**
19 **LAND OF CHIEFS (IRE)**, 5, b g Little Bighorn—Monmore **Mr K. Lee**
20 **LORD OF THE RINGS**, 6, b g Arctic Lord—Sister of Gold **Oak Wood Racing**
21 **MAC'S SUPREME (IRE)**, 6, b g Supreme Leader—Merry Breeze **Mr B. McEntaggart**
22 **OFF PISTE SALLY**, 6, b m Newski (USA)—Sols Joker **Commander Peter Longhurst**
23 **OSCAIL AN DORAS (IRE)**, 9, b g Avocat—Candora **Mrs Rhys Thomas Williams**
24 **PADDY'S RETURN (IRE)**, 6, b g Kahyasi—Bayazida **Mr P. O'Donnell**
25 **POSTAGE STAMP**, 11, b g The Noble Player (USA)—Takealetter **Mr P. O'Donnell**
26 **PROFIT AND LOSS**, 7, b m Ardross—Clear As Crystal **Mrs A. Walter**
27 **PROLIFIC AGENCY (IRE)**, 5, b g Lancastrian—Superlee (IRE) **The Diamond Ad. Partnership**
28 **STAGE FRIGHT**, 7, b g Sure Blade (USA)—First Act **Mrs J. Dyde & Mr J. Gordon**
29 **STONED IMACULATE (IRE)**, 4, ch f Durgam (USA)—Rose Deer **Mr M. Rowsell**
30 **SUPREME SPICE (IRE)**, 5, b m Supreme Leader—Deep Serenade **Dream Racing Club**
31 **TORUS SPA (IRE)**, 7, ch g Torus—Deep Spa **Mr P. O'Donnell**
32 **WOODBRIDGE (IRE)**, 9, b g Royal Fountain—Monday's Pet **Mr K. Lee & Mr I. Davis**

THREE-YEAR-OLDS

33 **FLIGHT FOR FREEDOM**, b f Saddlers' Hall (IRE)—Ana Troccolo **Mrs Samantha Dare**
34 **FLYING HIGH (IRE)**, b c Fayruz—Shayista **Mr B. Batey**
35 **WYNBURY FLYER**, ch g Risk Me (FR)—Woolcana **Wynbury Racing**

TWO-YEAR-OLDS

36 B c 3/4 Saddlers' Hall (IRE)—Anatroccolo **Mr K. Lee & Mrs Samantha Dare**
37 B c 8/2 Lashkari—Dushenka **Mr K. Lee**
38 B c 1/5 Then Again—Fair Attempt **Mrs Samantha Dare**

Other Owners: Mr John Byrne, Mr Thomas Corbett, Mr Thomas Elves, Mr J. Fleming, Dr N. J. Gavin, Mr George Graham, Mr A. Hunter, Mr Brian Hunter, Mr R. Joseph, Miss Marie Kearns, Mr P. J. O'Donnell, Mr C. C. Pounder, Mr G. A. Ray-Hills, Mr David Scott, Ms G. Scott, Mr L. Seaton, Mrs G. P. Seymour, Mr Martin Smith (Sunderland), Mrs S. J. Sugden, Mr B. D. Tipler, Mr Richard Wheeler.

Jockeys (Flat): R Cochrane (8-3, w.a.), K Fallon (w.a.).

Jockeys (NH): Paul Carberry (10-0), M Foster (w.a.), A Maguire (w.a.).

Amateur: Mr Paul Murphy (10-0).

Lady Rider: Miss Elizabeth Doyle (9-4).

430 MR P. G. MURPHY, Bristol

Postal: **Racecourse Farm, Portbury, Bristol, Avon, BS20 9SM.**
Phone: **OFFICE (01275) 373581 FAX (01275) 375053 MOBILE (0831) 410409**

1 **ANOTHER NIGHT (IRE),** 4, ch g Waajib—Little Me **Megan Dennis & Craig Shields**
2 **HOCANTELL,** 7, b m Primitive Rising (USA)—Princess Nora **Mrs K. B. Elliott**
3 **JALB (IRE),** 4, b g Robellino (USA)—Adjacent (IRE) **Family And Friends**
4 **JIGSAW BOY,** 9, ch g Homeboy—Chiparia **Mrs Louise Murphy**
5 **KHAYAL (USA),** 4, b g Green Dancer (USA)—Look Who's Dancing (USA) **Mr Gordon James Cossey**
6 **LIMELIGHT,** 4, b f Old Vic—Nellie Dean **S. B. Partners**
7 4, B g Henbit (USA)—Moheli **Bram Davis**
8 **PARADE RACER,** 7, b g Derring Rose—Dusky Damsel **Mr Andrew G. Chapman**
9 **QUIET MOMENTS (IRE),** 5, b g Ron's Victory (USA)—Saint Cynthia **Mrs Louise Murphy**
10 **REAGANESQUE (USA),** 6, b g Nijinsky (CAN)—Basoof (USA) **Mrs John Spielman**
11 **SEBASTOPOL,** 9, b g Royal Match—Saucy Sprite **Mr Derrick Page**
12 **SHADIAAN (IRE),** 4, b g Darshaan—Shakanda (IRE) **Michael Blackburn & John Brown**
13 **SHOOTING LIGHT (IRE),** 5, b g Shernazar—Church Light **Mr J. M. Brown**
14 **SIBERIAN MYSTIC,** 5, gr m Siberian Express (USA)—Mystic Crystal (IRE) **Glenferry And Partners**
15 **SIR JOEY (USA),** 9, ch g Honest Pleasure (USA)—Sougoli **Mrs A. G. Sims**
16 **VOILA PREMIERE (IRE),** 6, b g Roi Danzig (USA)—Salustrina **Mr B. W. Gaule**
17 **WILL TO WIN,** 4, b f Mazilier (USA)—Adana (FR) **Mrs Pat Wyatt**
18 **YAK ALFARAJ,** 4, b c Sadler's Wells (USA)—Clara Bow (USA) **Miss J. Collison**
19 4, B g Bedford (USA)—Young Mistress **Mrs Louise Murphy**

THREE-YEAR-OLDS

20 **WILLA WOOSTER,** b f Sure Blade (USA)—Bertrade **Miss Amanda J. Rawding**

TWO-YEAR-OLDS

21 **DICK'S AT HOME,** b g Whittingham (IRE)—Homemaker (Homeboy) **Racecourse Farm Racing**

Other Owners: Mr Kerry Barker, Mr T. F. Dundon, Mr W. E. Dundon, Mr D. J. Dunne, Mr A. R. G. Else, Mr J. H. Forbes, Mr John W. Ford, Mr C. Garland, Glenferry Building & Maintenance Ltd, Mr W. L. Gorman, Mr P. J. Green, Mr Geoffrey C. Greenwood, Mr S. Hadley, Mrs C. Halliday, Mrs Sandy Herridge, Mrs S. Hutchings, Mr J. McGlinchey, Mr Raymond Miquel, Mr D. C. Roberts, Mr N. C. Rolfe, Mr D. Tylden-Wright, Mr R. D. Willis.

Jockey (Flat): S Drowne.

Jockey (NH): R Farrant.

431 MR D. J. G. MURRAY SMITH, Market Harborough

Postal: **The Old Rectory, Gumley, Market Harborough, Leicestershire, LE16 7RX.**
Phone: **(01162) 792201 MOBILE (0385) 920352**

1 **ANDAMAN,** 4, b c Riverman (USA)—Balleta (USA) **Mrs Susan Nash**
2 **BRYNKIR,** 4, b g Batshoof—Felinwen **The 96 Partnership**
3 **DENBRAE (IRE),** 6, b g Sure Blade (USA)—Fencing **Mr Michael Mellersh**
4 **GRUNGE (IRE),** 10, b br g Crash Course—Hills of Fashion **Mrs Susan Nash**
5 **HELIOS,** 10, br g Blazing Saddles (AUS)—Mary Sunley **Box 40 Racing**
6 **JELALI (IRE),** 5, b g Last Tycoon—Lautreamont **The Fort Partnership**
7 **KANCELSKIS (IRE),** 9, ch g Buckskin (FR)—Left Hand Woman **The Joiners Arms Racing Club Quarndon**
8 **MENDOZA,** 4, b g Rambo Dancer (CAN)—Red Poppy (IRE) **Bid Defence Partnership**
9 **NAKHAL,** 5, b g Puissance—Rambadale **Ms Diana Wilder**
10 **NIKITA'S STAR (IRE),** 5, ch g Soviet Lad (USA)—Sally Chase **Nikita's Partners**
11 **OLD ROUVEL (USA),** 7, b g Riverman (USA)—Marie de Russy (FR) **Mrs R. D. Cowell**
12 **PAVANA (IRE),** 4, b g Groom Dancer (USA)—Ma Pavlova (USA) **Ms Diana Wilder**
13 **PRINCE DANZIG (IRE),** 7, ch g Roi Danzig (USA)—Veldt **Mr A. H. Ulrick**

MR D. J. G. MURRAY SMITH—continued

14 **PRINCESS ZELDA (FR)**, 4, b f Defensive Play (USA)—Brisk Waters (USA) **Mr D. Murray Smith**
15 **RIVER CAPTAIN (USA)**, 5, ch g Riverman (USA)—Katsura (USA) **Ms Diana Wilder**
16 **WOODLAND NYMPH**, 4, gr f Norton Challenger—Royal Meeting **The Woodland Partners**

THREE-YEAR-OLDS

17 **APPIAN DAME (IRE)**, b f Mukaddamah (USA)—Apapa Port **Mr D. Twomey**
18 **FELONY (IRE)**, ch c Pharly (FR)—Scales of Justice **Ms Diana Wilder**
19 **ROLLING HIGH (IRE)**, ch c Roi Danzig (USA)—Sally Chase **Mr D. Twomey**
20 **THE IMPOSTER (IRE)**, ch c Imp Society (USA)—Phoenix Dancer (IRE) **Mr D. Murray Smith**

TWO-YEAR-OLDS

21 B c 11/4 Paris House—Glenfield Portion (Mummy's Pet) **Manny Bernstein**

Other Owners: Mr M Brittain, Mrs S. Ashcroft, Mr D. G. Barnes, Mr C. Carter, Mr R. D. Cowell, Mr D. H. Cowgill, Mr A Farmer, Mr M Farmer, Mrs B Hale, Mr K. Hamill, Mr G. W. Hughes, Mr N Jackson, Miss D. Lancia, Mr T Martin, Mrs R. Philp, Mr K. Poynter, Miss S. Price, Mr Christopher P. Riley, Lady D. M. Watts.

Jockey (NH): Dean Gallagher (w.a).

Amateurs: Miss Susan Brown, Miss Alex Wells.

432 MR F. P. MURTAGH, Carlisle

Postal: **Hurst Farm, Ivegill, Carlisle, Cumbria, CA4 ONL.**
Phone: **(017684) 84649 MOBILE (0421) 720250**

1 **AULBY (IRE)**, 4, b f Mandalus—Miss Ranova **Mr R. Hall**
2 **BUSHMILLS**, 5, ch m Genuine Gift (CAN)—Princess Zenobia **Mr R. R. Bainbridge**
3 **CRIFFEL STAR**, 6, b m Leading Star—Criffel Mist **Mrs K. Q. Holliday**
4 **FEN TERRIER**, 6, b m Emarati (USA)—Kinz **Mr K. G. Fairbairn**
5 **FUNNY YE KNOW (IRE)**, 9, ch g Fidel—Culkeern **Mr Denis Tumelty**
6 **HANSEL'S STREAK**, 6, br g Majestic Streak—Hansel's Meadow VII **Mrs A. J. McMath**
7 **HURST FLYER**, 6, gr m Neltino—True Missile **Mr J. Proudfoot**
8 **MILL-DOT**, 6, b g Petoski—Bright-One **Mr Steven Roper**
9 **MOVIE MAKER (IRE)**, 10, b g Remainder Man—Night Moves **Mr J. Proudfoot**
10 **PERKS OF THE JOB (IRE)**, 6, br g Executive Perk—Siba Vione **Mrs A. J. McMath**
11 **POINT DUTY**, 8, b g Reference Point—Vilikaia (USA) **Mr J. J. Henderson**
12 **ROCHEBURG (IRE)**, 5, b g Be My Native (USA)—Greek Gale **Mr K. G. Fairbairn**
13 **SARMATIAN (USA)**, 7, br g Northern Flagship (USA)—Tracy L (USA) **Mr Steven Roper**
14 **SNIPER**, 6, ch g Gunner B—Highfrith **Clayton Bigley Partnership Ltd**
15 **TENERIFE GIRL**, 5, b m Risk Me (FR)—Sir Tangs Gift **Mr J. Proudfoot**

Other Owners: Mr W. J. Eland, Mr L. Irving, Mr F. P. Murtagh, Mr Norman Park, Mr Ken Roper.

Jockeys (NH): A Dobbin, R J Supple.

433 MR W. J. MUSSON, Newmarket

Postal: **Saville House, St Mary's Square, Newmarket, Suffolk, CB8 0HZ.**
Phone: **(01638) 663371 FAX (01638) 667979**

1 **ALWAYS A PLEASURE**, 7, b m Chauve Souris—Pleasure Bid **Mr R. D. Musson**
2 **BATSMAN**, 4, b g Batshoof—Lady Bequick **Ex-Recession Partnership**
3 **BINTANG TIMOR (USA)**, 4, ch g Mt Livermore (USA)—Frisky Kitten (USA) **Broughton Thermal Insulation**

MR W. J. MUSSON—continued

4 **BOLD FAITH,** 5, b m Warning—Bold And Beautiful **Jumbo Limited**
5 **BROUGHTON BLAZE,** 7, b g Faustus (USA)—Summer Posy **Broughton Thermal Insulation**
6 **BROUGHTONS CHAMP,** 6, b g Dowsing (USA)—Knees Up (USA) **Broughton Bloodstock**
7 **BROUGHTONS ERROR,** 4, ch g Most Welcome—Eloquent Charm (USA) **Broughton Thermal Insulation**
8 **BROUGHTONS FORMULA,** 8, b g Night Shift (USA)—Forward Rally **Crawford Gray & Aylett**
9 **BROUGHTONS LURE (IRE),** 4, ch f Archway (IRE)—Vaal Salmon (IRE) **Broughton Bloodstock**
10 **CHILDREN'S CHOICE (IRE),** 7, b m Taufan (USA)—Alice Brackloon (USA) **Mrs A. V. Totman**
11 **DAUPHIN (IRE),** 5, b br g Astronef—Va Toujours **Mrs Rita Brown**
12 **ELLA LAMEES,** 4, b f Statoblest—Lamees (USA) **Billings & Broughton**
13 **GONE SAVAGE,** 10, b g Nomination—Trwyn Cilan **Broughton Thermal Insulation**
14 **GREENAWAY BAY (USA),** 4, ch g Green Dancer (USA)—Raise N' Dance (USA) **Asterlane Ltd**
15 **INDIUM,** 4, b g Groom Dancer (USA)—Gold Bracelet
16 **LOGANLEA (IRE),** 4, br f Petong—White's Pet **Mrs P. A. Linton**
17 **MUTADARRA (IRE),** 5, ch g Mujtahid (USA)—Silver Echo **Mrs Rita Brown**
18 **NOTHING DOING (IRE),** 9, b g Sarab—Spoons **Broughton Bloodstock**
19 **NUBILE,** 4, b f Pursuit of Love—Trojan Lady (USA) **Mr Lloyd Bennett**
20 **PLEADING,** 5, b g Never So Bold—Ask Mama **Mr Lloyd Bennett**
21 **SOUTHERN MEMORIES (IRE),** 8, b g Don't Forget Me—Our Pet **Broughton Thermal Insulation**
22 **TURRILL HOUSE,** 6, b m Charmer—Megabucks **J. R. Hawksley & C. H. Pettigrew**

THREE-YEAR-OLDS

23 **BROUGHTONS MILL,** gr g Ron's Victory (USA)—Sandra's Desire **Windmill Racing**
24 **FERNS MEMORY,** ch f Beveled (USA)—Sharp Venita **Fern Components Ltd**
25 **FLEUR-DE-LYS,** ch f King's Signet (USA)—Kind of Cute **Mr W. J. Musson**
26 **HETRA HEIGHTS (USA),** b f Cox's Ridge (USA)—Top Hope **Mr K. L. West**
27 **MAGIC MORNING,** ch g Magic Ring (IRE)—Incarnadine **Mrs Rita Brown**
28 **MICKS DOUBLE,** ch g Ron's Victory—Princess Dancer **Mr M. W. Goodey**
29 **SAMPOWER LADY,** ch f Rock City—Travel On **Sampower Racing Club**

TWO-YEAR-OLDS

30 B c 18/3 Risk Me (FR)—Bernstein Bette (Petong) **Asterlane Ltd**
31 B f 22/3 Chaddleworth (IRE)—Broughtons Pet (IRE) (Cyrano de Bergerac) **Broughton Bloodstock**
32 Br f 17/3 Petardia—Island Adventure (Touching Wood (USA)) **The Square Table**
33 B f 2/5 Chaddleworth (IRE)—Princess Dancer (Alzao (USA)) **Broughton Bloodstock**
34 B g 19/3 Rock Hopper—Sweet Quest (Rainbow Quest (USA)) **Mr Mike Hawkett**
35 Br g 10/3 Deploy—Unique Treasure (Young Generation) **Mr Mike Hawkett**
36 B f 21/2 Forest Wind (USA)—Volkova (Green Desert (USA)) **Mrs Rita Brown**

Other Owners: Mrs V. Albert, Mr S. Antram, Mr Roger Aylett, Mr K. G. Balfour, Mr M. Barby, Mr Michael Billings, Mr J. L. Brian, Mrs C. J. Broughton, Mr M. E. Broughton, Mr Con Dower, Mr A. Fletcher, Mr B. N. Fulton, Mr T. Crawford Gray, Mr R. Harsher, Mr D. Hawkridge, Mr J. Huckett, Mr R. Huke, Mr J. M. Husband, Mr R. Liddiard, Mr A. Lyons, Mr P. J. McBride, Mr A. McMillan, Mr J. Mellows, Mr J. T. D. Musson, Mr T. O'Dell, Mr Mike Perkins, Mr H. Shipstone, Mr P. Tacon, Mr A. T. Thompkins, Mr S. Tkaczynski, Mrs A. N. Ward, Mr G. Wiltshire.

Jockey (Flat): Declan O'Shea (7-10).

Apprentice: Philip Shea (8-2).

434 MRS A. M. NAUGHTON, Richmond

Postal: **High Gingerfield, Hurgill Road, Richmond, North Yorkshire, DL10 4TD.**
Phone: **(01748) 822803**

1 **ALL THE GAS (IRE),** 7, b g Convinced—Moredee **Lady Sarah Barry**
2 **CASEY CASEY (IRE),** 9, b g Bishop of Orange—Dara's Last **Lady Sarah Barry**
3 **CHASE THE ACE (IRE),** 5, b g Un Desperado (FR)—Forty Kisses **Lady Sarah Barry**
4 7, B g Good Thyne (USA)—Churchlands Madam **Miss J. M. Thompson**

MRS A. M. NAUGHTON—continued

5 **JAMAICA BRIDGE,** 8, b g Doulab (USA)—Mill Hill (USA) **Mr B. Hough**
6 **KENTUCKY DREAMS,** 8, b g Dreams To Reality (USA)—Kentucky Tears (USA) **Mrs A. M. Naughton**
7 **MADE OF STEEL (IRE),** 9, b g Flash of Steel—Kew Gift **Lady Sarah Barry**
8 **SHANNON SHOON (IRE),** 6, b g Zaffaran (USA)—Carrick Shannon **Mrs A. M. Naughton**
9 **SWEET MEADOW,** 4, b g Sylvan Express—River Bark **Mr D. H. Montgomerie**
10 **THE BIRD O'DONNELL,** 12, b g Monksfield—Sheila's Flame **Lady Sarah Barry**
11 **UP FOR RANSOME (IRE),** 9, b g Boyne Valley—Fauvette (USA) **Mrs C. T. Woodley**
12 **WINDYEDGE (USA),** 5, ch g Woodman (USA)—Abeesh (USA) **Mrs A. M. Naughton**

Other Owners: Mrs A. J. Calvert, Mr Ian P. Davies, Mr Hugh Gething, Mr B. M. Johnson, Davies Philip, Mrs M. P. Neatby, Mr Michael O'Grady, Mr B. T. Price, Exors Of The Late Mr Eric Scarth, Mr Dave Tuckwell, Ms Diane Tunstall.

Jockeys (NH): Martin Foster (10-0), John Supple (10-0).

Amateur: Mr T J Barry (10-7).

435 MR T. J. NAUGHTON, Epsom

Postal: **The Durdans, Chalk Lane, Epsom, Surrey, KT18 7AX.**
Phone: **(01372) 745112 FAX (01372) 741944**

1 **ALLSTARS DANCER,** 5, b m Primo Dominie—Danzig Harbour (USA) **Mr T. J. Naughton**
2 **CABCHARGE BLUE,** 6, b m Midyan (USA)—Mashobra **Mr J. J. Wise**
3 **CHERRY GARDEN (IRE),** 5, b g Treasure Kay—Door To Door (USA) **Mr T. J. Naughton**
4 **COMANCHE COMPANION,** 8, b m Commanche Run—Constant Companion **Hever Racing Club**
5 **DIZZY TILLY,** 4, b f Anshan—Nadema **Mrs S. Leech**
6 **HEVER GOLF GLORY,** 4, b c Efisio—Zaius **Hever Racing Club**
7 **HEVER GOLF HERO,** 5, b g Robellino (USA)—Sweet Rosina **Hever Racing Club**
8 **HEVER GOLF MAGIC (IRE),** 4, ch f Ballad Rock—Track Twenty Nine (IRE) **Hever Racing Club**
9 **HEVER GOLF MOVER,** 4, ch f Efisio—Joyce's Best **Hever Racing Club**
10 **HEVER GOLF ROCKET,** 4, b g Efisio—Truly Bold **Hever Racing Club**
11 **HEVER GOLF ROSE,** 7, b m Efisio—Sweet Rosina **Hever Racing Club**
12 **KEEN COMPANION,** 5, b m Keen—Constant Companion **Mr S. J. Simmons**
13 **MOGIN,** 5, b m Komaite (USA)—Misdevious (USA) **The Dream Partnership**
14 **NOPALEA,** 4, b f Warrshan (USA)—Nophe (USA) **Mr T. J. Naughton**
15 **OLD SCHOOL HOUSE,** 5, ch h Polar Falcon (USA)—Farewell Letter (USA) **Mr T. J. Naughton**
16 **SONG OF SKYE,** 4, b f Warning—Song of Hope **Mr E. J. Fenaroli**
17 **YOUDONTSAY,** 6, ch m Most Welcome—Fabulous Luba **Mr Tom Nicholls**

THREE-YEAR-OLDS

18 **HEVER GOLF MACHINE,** ch c Rudimentary (USA)—Stop Press (USA) **Hever Racing Club**
19 **HEVER GOLF PASSION (IRE),** b f Pips Pride—Base Camp **Hever Racing Club**
20 **HEVERGOLF PRINCESS (IRE),** ch f Petardia—High Profile **Hever Racing Club**
21 **HEVER GOLF RANGER,** b c Efisio—Bold Green (FR) **Hever Racing Club**
22 **LADY JAZZ,** b f Night Shift (USA)—Penamint **Miss L. A. Elliott**
23 **MISS SKYE (IRE),** b f Common Grounds—Swift Chorus **Mr E. J. Fenaroli**
24 **NIHAL,** br f Machiavellian (USA)—Wanisa (USA) **Hever Racing Club**

TWO-YEAR-OLDS

25 B c 2/5 Polish Patriot (USA)—Ever So Artful (Never So Bold)
26 Br f 19/4 Tirol—Felsen (IRE) (Ballad Rock) **Mr G. Archer**
27 B f 29/2 Midyan (USA)—Lady Anfield (Anfield) **Mr T. J. Naughton**
28 B f 14/4 Petardia—Lhotse (IRE) (Shernazar)
29 Ch c 15/2 Mujtahid (USA)—Next Episode (USA) (Nijinsky (CAN))
30 Br f 16/3 Second Set (IRE)—Primo Stampari (Primo Dominie)

MR T. J. NAUGHTON—continued

31 SECOND REMINDER (IRE), b f 16/4 Risk Me (FR)—Where's The Money (Lochnager) **Mr A. Callard**
32 B f 19/2 Puissance—Sojourn (Be My Guest (USA)) **Mr J. J. Wise**
33 B f 7/3 Petardia—Steffi (Precocious)
34 B c 10/3 Second Set (IRE)—Why Not Glow (IRE) (Glow (USA)) **Mr E. J. Fenaroli**

Other Owners: Mr D. Borrows, Mr L. Dutton, Mr A. A. Evenden, Mrs E. Jackman, Mr T. O'Flaherty, Mrs P. Payne, Mr R. A. Popely, Mrs A. Wise.

Jockeys (Flat): Pat Eddery (w.a.), J Weaver (w.a.).

436 MR JAMES NEVILLE, Newport, Gwent

Postal: **Cefn Llogell Racing Stables, Coed Kernew, Newport, Gwent, NP1 9UD.**
Phone: **(01633) 680978 FAX (01633) 680926**

1 ALBERT THE LION (IRE), 6, gr g Celio Rufo—Esker Lady **Mr J. Neville**
2 APRIL SEVENTH (IRE), 7, br g Stalker—Ring-Em-All **Park Industrial Supplies (Wales) Ltd**
3 CARACOL, 9, b g Ore—Fit For A King **Mr C. G. Bolton**
4 CARLYS QUEST, 4, ch g Primo Dominie—Tuppy (USA) **John Williams Transport (Newport) Ltd**
5 COTTEIR CHIEF (IRE), 7, b g Chief Singer—Hasty Key (USA) **Mr J. Neville**
6 DANGEROUS WATERS, 5, b m Risk Me (FR)—Queen's Lake **Mr J. Neville**
7 DUBLIN TREASURE (IRE), 6, b g Treasure Kay—Dublin Millennium **Mr George Moore**
8 GIBBON BOY, 5, ch g Clantime—Touch O' Spirit **Mr J. Neville**
9 GUNNER B SPECIAL, 5, ch g Gunner B—Sola Mia **The Eagle Racing Partnership**
10 ILLINEYLAD, 4, b g Whitehall Bridge—Illiney Girl **Mrs T. O'Toole**
11 KOMPLETELY, 4, b f Komaite (USA)—Lucky Councillor **Mrs P. A. Barratt**
12 LE KHOUMF (FR), 7, ch g Son of Silver—Bentry (FR) **Mr David S. Lewis**
13 LORD MCMURROUGH (IRE), 8, b g Mister Lord (USA)—Penny Buskins **Mr J. Neville**
14 MAKE READY, 4, b f Beveled (USA)—Prepare (IRE) **Mr J. Neville**
15 MINSTER'S MADAM, 7, ch m Minster Son—Figrant (USA) **Mr J. Neville**
16 MOBAYE (FR), 4, ch g Le Nain Jaune (FR)—Sainte Etoile (FR) **Mr J. Neville**
17 OLYMPIAN, 11, ch g High Line—Elysian **Mr J. Neville**
18 OUT RANKING (FR), 6, b m Le Glorieux—Restless Nell **Mr David S. Lewis**
19 PICEA'S PAST, 4, b g Picea—Atoka **Mr J. Neville**
20 RITTO, 8, b g Arctic Tern (USA)—Melodrama **Park Industrial Supplies (Wales) Ltd**
21 ROBINGO (IRE), 9, b g Bob Back (USA)—Mill's Girl **Mr J. Neville**
22 ROBORETTE (FR), 5, b m Robore (FR)—Bentry (FR) **Mr T. A. Wadsworth**
23 ROYALE ANGELA (FR), 6, ch g Garde Royale—Santa Angela (FR) **Mr J. Neville**
24 ROYAL THEN (FR), 5, ch g Garde Royale—Miss Then (FR) **Mr T. A. Wadsworth**
25 SQUIRE YORK, 8, b g Bairn (USA)—Alice Parry **Mr J. Powell-Tuck**
26 SWIFT MAIDEN, 5, gr m Sharrood (USA)—Gunner Girl **Mr J. Neville**
27 TARA GALE (IRE), 6, b m Phardante (FR)—Smashing Gale **Mr A. J. Williams**
28 THE CROPPY BOY, 6, b g Arctic Lord—Deep Cut **Winterbourne Plant Ltd**
29 TIMELY MAGIC (IRE), 6, b g Good Thyne (USA)—Magic Quiz **Mr J. Neville**
30 TRIPLE TRIUMPH (IRE), 5, b m Welsh Term—Sno-Sleigh **Mr George Moore**
31 UNITED FRONT, 6, br g Be My Chief (USA)—Julia Flyte **Mr T. Beresford**
32 VERYVEL (CZE), 7, b g Paico—Vernea (CZE) **Mr David S. Lewis**

Other Owners: Mr F. J. Ayres, Mr Bernard G. Barry, Beacon Estates Ltd, Mrs K. M. Berry, Mr James Bradley, Mr Peter Corrigan, Mr James Creemer, Mr Nigel Gay, Mr B. J. G. Haines, Mr S. Harrison, Mr A. R. Jackson, Mr Michael R. Jaye, Mr D. A. Johnson, Mr John Jones, Mrs P. J. Lee, Magnum Construction Ltd, Mr Stephen Norman, Mr D. Spencer, Mr B. E. V. Thomas, Mr M. R. Thompson, Mrs S. A. Turner.

Conditional: Tom Dascombe, Lee Pitcher (9-7).

Amateur: Miss Nadine Richards (8-7).

437 MR D. NICHOLLS, Thirsk

Postal: **Tall Trees, Sessay, Thirsk, North Yorkshire, YO7 3ND.**
Phone: **(01845) 501470 FAX (01845) 501666 MOBILE (0498) 575747**

1 **ALAMEIN (USA),** 5, ch g Roi Danzig (USA)—Pollination **R. J. W. Limited**
2 **BILKO,** 4, gr g Risk Me (FR)—Princess Tara **Contrac Promotions Ltd**
3 **BREAK THE RULES,** 6, b g Dominion—Surf Bird **Mr John Wilman**
4 **CENSOR,** 5, b g Kris—Mixed Applause (USA) **Mr G. H. Leatham**
5 **DON PEPE,** 7, b g Dowsing (USA)—Unique Treasure **Mrs E. Aird**
6 **DOUBLE OSCAR (IRE),** 5, ch g Royal Academy (USA)—Broadway Rosie **Trilby Racing**
7 **EUROQUEST,** 4, b g Ron's Victory (USA)—Raaya **Mr W. G. Swiers**
8 **FANCY A FORTUNE (IRE),** 4, b g Fools Holme (USA)—Fancy's Girl (FR) **E. W. & M. Tuer**
9 **FIRE DOME (IRE),** 6, ch g Salt Dome (USA)—Penny Habit **Mr J. Ranson**
10 **GRAND CHAPEAU (IRE),** 6, b g Ballad Rock—All Hat **Mr David Faulkner**
11 **HURGILL LADY,** 4, ch f Emarati (USA)—Gitee (FR) **Mrs C. Blakebrough**
12 **JAWHARI,** 4, b c Lahib (USA)—Lady of The Land **Mr B. Franks**
13 **KNAVE'S ASH (USA),** 7, ch g Miswaki (USA)—Quiet Rendezvous (USA) **R J H Limited**
14 **LENNOX LEWIS,** 6, b g Superpower—Song's Best **Mr P. S. Platt**
15 **LUNCH PARTY,** 6, b g Beveled (USA)—Crystal Sprite **Mr S. Aitken**
16 **NERVOUS REX,** 4, b g Reprimand—Spinner **Mr B. Franks**
17 **NEWTONS CORNER (IRE),** 4, ch g Masterclass (USA)—Princess Galicia **Girls On Top**
18 **NIZAAL (USA),** 7, ch g Diesis—Shicklah (USA) **Mr S. Aitken**
19 **NO CLICHES,** 5, ch g Risk Me (FR)—Always On A Sunday **Mr Mark A. Leatham**
20 **PAINT IT BLACK,** 5, ch g Double Schwartz—Tableaux (FR) **Mr M. A. Scaife**
21 **PROUD NATIVE (IRE),** 4, b g Imp Society (USA)—Karamana **Mr P. Savill**
22 **RAMBO WALTZER,** 6, b g Rambo Dancer (CAN)—Vindictive Lady (USA) **Mr W. G. Swiers**
23 **SENSE OF PRIORITY,** 9, ch g Primo Dominie—Sense of Pride **Mr M. A. Scaife**
24 **SHARE DELIGHT (IRE),** 4, b c Common Grounds—Dorado Llave (USA) **Mr V. Greaves**
25 **SIHAFI (USA),** 5, ch g Elmaamul (USA)—Kit's Double (USA) **Mr John Gilbertson**
26 **SPOTTED EAGLE,** 5, ch g Risk Me (FR)—Egnoussa **Mr W. G. Swiers**
27 **SUE ME (IRE),** 6, b br g Contract Law (USA)—Pink Fondant **Mr T. G. Meynell**
28 **TART (FR),** 5, br m Warning—Sharp Girl (FR) **Mr M. A. Scaife**
29 **TREASURE TOUCH (IRE),** 4, b g Treasure Kay—Bally Pourri (IRE) **Mr N. Honeyman**
30 **TYPHOON EIGHT (IRE),** 6, b h High Estate—Dance Date (IRE) **Mr D. Lambie**
31 **VENTURE CAPITALIST,** 9, ch g Never So Bold—Brave Advance (USA) **Mr W. G. Swiers**
32 **YA MALAK,** 7, b g Fairy King (USA)—La Tuerta
33 **YOURS IN SPORT,** 4, b g Slip Anchor—Birthdays' Child **Mrs D. M. Swinburn**
34 **ZAIN DANCER,** 6, ch g Nabeel Dancer (USA)—Trojan Lady (USA) **Mr S. Aitken**

THREE-YEAR-OLDS

35 **ALLMAITES,** b c Komaite (USA)—Darling Miss Daisy **R J H Limited**
36 **ANOTHER CENTURY,** gr g Belfort (FR)—Miss Cuddles **Mr B. Franks**
37 **CHINAIDER (IRE),** b f Mujadil (USA)—We Two **Mr Mark A. Leatham**
38 **ELLA FALLS (IRE),** ch f Dancing Dissident (USA)—Over Swing (FR) **Mr J. Ranson**
39 **EURO VENTURE,** b g Prince Sabo—Brave Advance (USA) **Mr W. G. Swiers**
40 **GIFTED BAIRN (IRE),** b f Casteddu—Latin Mass **Mr J. P. Hames**
41 **JAYIR (IRE),** b g Mujtahid (USA)—Arylh (USA) **A. A. Bloodstock Ltd**
42 **LEATHER AND SCRIM (IRE),** b f Imperial Frontier (USA)—Yola (IRE) **First Past The Post**
43 **MR FUND SWITCH,** ch g Chilibang—Purple Fan **Mr Justin R. Aaron**

TWO-YEAR-OLDS

44 **COEUR DU LION,** b f 28/2 Whittingham (IRE)—The Fernhill Flyer (IRE) (Red Sunset) **Contrac Promotions Ltd**
45 **LITTLE CINNAMON,** ch c 22/1 Timeless Times (USA)—Belltina (Belfort (FR)) **Miss K. Jansen**
46 **SWEET SHE AINT,** b f 29/3 King's Signet (USA)—Just Run (IRE) (Runnett) **R. J. H. Limited**

Other Owners: Mr E. C. Alton, Mrs D. Bainbridge, Mr A. Barker, Mrs Monica Caine, Mr Ian W. Glenton, Mr D. Hale, Mr G. A. Harker, Mr P. I. Harker, Mr K. Hind, Mr B. Hooper, Mr Robin Johnson, Mr A. Langley, Mr Douglas Leach, Mr Keith Middleton, Mr Jeff Mortonson, Mr R. Naylor, Mr W. Palfreeman, Mr Lewis Parker, Mr G. Pickering, Mr M. A. Proudfoot, Mr Reg Richardson, Mrs M. Sharland, Mr S. A. Short, Mr Dave Teasdale, Mr Geoffrey Thompson, Mr H. J. Walker, Mr T. Welsh.

Jockey (Flat): Alex Greaves (8-4).

438 MR P. F. NICHOLLS, Shepton Mallet

Postal: **Heighes House, Manor Farm Stables, Ditcheat, Shepton Mallet, Somerset, BA4 6RD.**
Phone: **(01749) 860656 FAX (01749) 860523 MOBILE (0468) 612213**

1 **ASK ANTONY (IRE)**, 8, gr g Roselier (FR)—Lady Casita **Mr Geoff Bond**
2 **BELMONT KING (IRE)**, 10, b g Kemal (FR)—The Potwalluper **Mrs Billie Bond**
3 **BENGERS MOOR**, 7, b g Town And Country—Quilpee Mai **Mr J. R. Townshend**
4 **BLUE LAWS (IRE)**, 8, b g Bluebird (USA)—Claretta (USA) **Mr Jeffrey Hordle**
5 **BORO VACATION (IRE)**, 9, b g Ovac (ITY)—Boro Quarter **Mrs C. I. A. Paterson**
6 **BRAMBLEHILL BUCK (IRE)**, 9, gr g Roselier (FR)—Buckybrill **T. and J. A. Curry**
7 **BUCK'S PALACE**, 5, ch g Buckley—Lady Geneva **Mr Paul K. Barber and Mr J. A. Keighley**
8 **CALL EQUINAME**, 8, gr g Belfort (FR)—Cherry Season **Mick Coburn, P. K. Barber, C. Lewis**
9 **CALLING WILD (IRE)**, 8, b g Callernish—Chestnut Vale **Hunt & Co (Bournemouth) Ltd**
10 **CHERRY GLEN (IRE)**, 7, ch m Executive Perk—Cherry Run **Mr K. J. Mitchell**
11 **CHERRYNUT**, 9, b g Idiot's Delight—Merry Cherry **Hunt & Co (Bournemouth) Ltd**
12 **COURT MELODY (IRE)**, 10, b g Whistling Deer—Overwood Grove **Mr Mick Coburn**
13 **CROWN EQUERRY (IRE)**, 8, b br g Strong Gale—Ballybrowney Gold **Mr Robert Ogden**
14 **DANCETILLYOUDROP (IRE)**, 7, b g Clearly Bust—Keep Dancing **Mr Derek Millard**
15 **DINES (IRE)**, 6, b g Phardante (FR)—Dippers Daughter **T.Chappell,T.Curry,D.Nichols&J.Blackwell**
16 **DROMHANA (IRE)**, 8, ch g Le Bavard (FR)—Honey Come Back **J.Blackwell,T.Chappell,T.Curry&D.Nichols**
17 **FLAKED OATS**, 9, b g Oats—Polly Toodle **Mr E. B. Swaffield**
18 **GALATASORI JANE (IRE)**, 8, b m Mister Lord (USA)—Ardsallagh **Mr B. L. Blinman**
19 **GENERAL CRACK (IRE)**, 9, ch g Lancastrian—Barna Havna **Mr Paul K. Barber and Mr J. A. Keighley**
20 **GIGI BEACH (IRE)**, 7, ch g Roselier (FR)—Cranagh Lady **Mrs Susan Humphreys**
21 **GORRAN**, 4, br g Belfort (FR)—Con Carni **Mr M. Monsley**
22 **HAVE TO THINK**, 10, b g Impecunious—Dusty Run **John Blackwell, Terry Curry, Des Nichols**
23 **HERBERT BUCHANAN (IRE)**, 8, ch g Henbit (USA)—Our Siveen **Five For Fun**
24 **IDEAL PARTNER (IRE)**, 9, ch g Ovac (ITY)—Castle Demon **T. and J. A. Curry**
25 **JAC DEL PRINCE**, 8, b g Teofane—Star Shell **Mr D. P. Millward**
26 **KINGS WITNESS (USA)**, 5, b g Lear Fan (USA)—Allison's Deeds **Mr Jeffrey Hordle**
27 **KNIGHT TEMPLAR (IRE)**, 5, b g Roselier (FR)—Rathsallagh Tartan **Mr Robert Ogden**
28 **LAKE KARIBA**, 7, b g Persian Bold—Gold Bracelet **The Lake Kariba Partnership**
29 **LANSDOWNE**, 10, b g High Top—Fettle **Mr R. F. Denmead**
30 **LARRY'S LORD (IRE)**, 9, ch g Lord Chancellor (USA)—
Archers Dream **John Blackwell, Terry Curry, Des Nichols**
31 **LATIN MISTRESS**, 6, b m Scallywag—Miss Nero **Mr R. H. Dunn**
32 **LINTON ROCKS**, 9, b g Town And Country—Top Soprano **The Hon Mrs Townshend**
33 **MANDALAY MAN (IRE)**, 5, br g Mandalus—Nice Little Earner **Mr Derek Millard**
34 **MERAWANG (IRE)**, 5, b g Shahrastani (USA)—Modiyna **Forever Hopefuls**
35 **MINELLA DERBY (IRE)**, 8, br g Sexton Blake—Black-Crash **Mr B. C. Kilby**
36 **MISCHIEF STAR**, 5, b m Be My Chief (USA)—Star Face **Mr Mick Coburn**
37 **MISTER ONE**, 7, b br g Buckley—Miss Redlands **Mr J. A. Keighley and Mr Paul K. Barber**
38 **MRS EM**, 6, b m Nicholas Bill—Sleepline Comfort **Mr G. Z. Mizel**
39 **MR STRONG GALE (IRE)**, 7, br g Strong Gale—Fleeting Sunshine **Mr T. G. A. Chappell**
40 **MUTUAL AGREEMENT**, 11, ch m Quayside—Giolla's Bone **Mr Edward Darke**
41 **NEARLY AN EYE**, 7, ch g Nearly A Hand—Kitty Come Home **Mr Paul K. Barber and Mr J. A. Keighley**
42 **NEWLANDS-GENERAL**, 12, ch g Oats—Spartiquick **Mr C. Murphy**
43 **OTTOWA (IRE)**, 8, b g Roselier (FR)—Queenie Kelly **Mr Paul K. Barber**
44 **PROFESSOR STRONG (IRE)**, 10, b br g Strong Gale—Chapter Four **B. C. Kilby, J. C. Blackwell & T. Curry**
45 **RURAL RUN (IRE)**, 7, b m Commanche Run—Country Character **Trading Thoroughbreds Ltd**
46 **SEAHAWK RETRIEVER**, 9, ch g Treasure Hunter—Sister Claire **Mrs Robert Blackburn**
47 **SEE MORE BUSINESS (IRE)**, 8, b g Seymour Hicks (FR)—
Miss Redlands **Mr J. A. Keighley and Mr Paul K. Barber**
48 **STORM DAMAGE (IRE)**, 6, b g Waajib—Connaught Lace **Storm Damage Partnership**
49 **STORM RUN (IRE)**, 8, b g Strong Gale—Summerville Lass **Mrs Penny Mitchell**
50 **STRONG CHAIRMAN (IRE)**, 7, br g Strong Gale—The Furnituremaker **Hunt & Co (Bournemouth) Ltd**
51 **STRONG TARQUIN (IRE)**, 8, br g Strong Gale—Trumpster **Mr C. I. A. Paterson**
52 **SUNLEY BAY**, 12, gr g Sunley Builds—Menrise Bay **Mrs Marianne G. Barber**
53 **THE LORD ROBERTS (IRE)**, 5, b g Strong Gale—Thousand Flowers **Mr Derek Millard**
54 **THURSDAY NIGHT (IRE)**, 7, ch g Montelimar (USA)—Alsazia (FR) **Mr B. L. Blinman**

MR P. F. NICHOLLS—continued

55 TORDUFF EXPRESS (IRE), 7, b g Kambalda—Marhabtain **Two Plus Two**
56 UNION STATION (IRE), 6, b g Homo Sapien—Way Ahead **Fieldspring Racing**
57 WHAT A HAND, 10, ch g Nearly A Hand—Kiki Star **Mr F. A. Bonsal**
58 WILLIAM O'DEE (NZ), 9, b g Exceptionnel—Fiducia O'Dee (NZ) **Mr B. C. Kilby**
59 WITH IMPUNITY, 9, br g Sula Bula—Sleepline Comfort **Mr G. Z. Mizel**
60 WONDERFULL POLLY (IRE), 10, ch m Pollerton—Wonderful Lilly **Mr J. G. Olds**

Other Owners: Exors Of The Late Mr J. W. Aplin, Mr G. Carey, Mrs Mary Coburn, Mr R. G. Eddy, Mr T. C. Frost, Mr C. Garland, Mr K. Harris, Mr R. Holbrook, Mr T. Hubbard, Mrs John Jackson, Mr E. N. Liddiard, Mr R. J. Metherell, Mrs Bridget Nicholls, Mr R. M. Phillips, Seaborough Manor Limited, Mr J. V. Sinnott, Mrs C. Snart, Mrs Carole Solman, Mrs D. Viney, Mr R. T. Wilkins.

Jockey (NH): T J Murphy.

Conditional: L Cummins (9-7).

Amateur: Mr Joe Tizzard (9-12).

439 MR DAVID NICHOLSON, Temple Guiting

Postal: **Ford Farm Racing, Jackdaws Castle, Temple Guiting, Cheltenham, Gloucestershire, GL54 5XU.**
Phone: **(01386) 584209 (01386) 584219 FAX (01386) 584218**

1 ACHILL RAMBLER, 5, b m Rakaposhi King—One More Try **Getjar Limited**
2 AIR SHOT, 8, b g Gunner B—Dans Le Vent **Mrs Peter Prowting**
3 ANZUM, 7, b g Ardross—Muznah **The Old Foresters Partnership**
4 ARCTIC CAMPER, 6, b g Arctic Lord—Mayotte **Lady Harris**
5 BAKKAR (IRE), 4, b c Darshaan—Bayyasa (IRE) **M. P. Burke's 5th Family Settlement**
6 BANJO (FR), 8, b g Beyssac (FR)—Fabinou (FR) **Mr Darren C. Mercer**
7 BARONET (IRE), 8, gr g Roselier (FR)—Shuil Agragh **Mrs David Thompson**
8 BAROSE, 5, ro g Baron Blakeney—Rose of Texas **Mrs A. A. Shutes**
9 BARTON BANK, 12, br g Kambalda—Lucifer's Daughter **Mrs J. Mould**
10 BILLYGOAT GRUFF, 9, b g Afzal—Autumn Ballet **Mr Peter D. Cooper**
11 BRAMBLEHILL DUKE (IRE), 6, b g Kambalda—Scat-Cat **South Wales Shower Supplies T/A Faucets**
12 BUCKHOUSE BOY, 8, b g Relkino—Teapot Hall **The Bawtry Boys**
13 CALL IT A DAY (IRE), 8, b g Callernish—Arctic Bavard **Mrs Jane Lane**
14 CAMITROV (FR), 8, b g Sharken (FR)—Emitrovna (FR) **Mr Jim Lewis**
15 CASTLE OWEN (IRE), 6, b g Castle Keep—Lady Owenette (IRE) **Lord Vestey**
16 CASTLE SWEEP (IRE), 7, b g Castle Keep—Fairy Shot **Lord Vestey**
17 CERTAINLY STRONG (IRE), 8, b m Strong Gale—Arctic Verb **Mr Nick Skelton**
18 CHERRY PIE, 6, b m Rakaposhi King—Merry Cherry **Mr Denis Barry**
19 CHERYL'S LAD (IRE), 8, b g Mister Majestic—Two's Company **Mrs Elaine Baines**
20 CHICODARI, 6, b g Shardari—Chicobin (USA) **Mr J. F. Horn**
21 CIRCUS STAR, 5, b g Soviet Star (USA)—Circus Act **The Ringmasters**
22 COOLE HILL (IRE), 7, b br m Strong Gale—Cool Girl **Messrs B. Winfield and J. Potter**
23 CRABAPPLE HILL (IRE), 6, gr g Duca di Busted—Tender Galatea **Mrs Elaine Baines**
24 DARKWOOD BAY (USA), 7, b br h Green Dancer (USA)—Unyielding (USA) **Mr Raymond Tooth**
25 DESTIN D'ESTRUVAL (FR), 7, b g Port Etienne (FR)—Vocation (FR) **Mr Darren C. Mercer**
26 DIRTY DOZEN (IRE), 6, b g Brush Aside (USA)—Blooming Rose **Mrs Claire Smith**
27 DISALLOWED (IRE), 5, b m Distinctly North (USA)—Miss Allowed (USA) **M. P. Burke's 5th Family Settlement**
28 DREAM RIDE (IRE), 8, b g King's Ride—Night Dreamer **Gerry Mordaunt & Christopher Clarke**
29 DUKE'S MOUNT (IRE), 8, b g King's Ride—Georgiana **Mrs Claire Smith**
30 EASY FEELIN (IRE), 6, b br g Lord Americo—Quick Frozen **M. P. Burke's 5th Family Settlement**
31 EDDY'S SON (IRE), 6, b g Brush Aside (USA)—Light The Lamp **Mrs J. Mould**

MR DAVID NICHOLSON—continued

32 **ELFLAA (IRE)**, 7, b br g Sure Blade (USA)—Miss Gris (USA) **Mr Raymond Tooth**
33 **EMPEROR BUCK (IRE)**, 10, b g Buckskin (FR)—Gilded Empress **Mrs Claire Smith**
34 **ESCARTEFIGUE (FR)**, 6, b g Start Fast (FR)—Dona Clara **Mr Darren C. Mercer**
35 **FESTIVE TEAK (IRE)**, 6, b br g King's Ride—Take Me Home **Mr Darren C. Mercer**
36 **FLYING GUNNER**, 7, ch g Gunner B—Dans Le Vent **Mrs R. J. Skan**
37 **FOREST IVORY (NZ)**, 7, ch g Ivory Hunter (USA)—Fair And Square (NZ) **The Old Foresters Partnership**
38 **GENERAL CLAREMONT (IRE)**, 5, gr g Strong Gale—Kasam **Mr K. G. Manley**
39 **GOOD VIEW (IRE)**, 6, ch g Good Thyne (USA)—Whosview **In The Frame**
40 **GREVILLE AGAIN (IRE)**, 9, ch g Phardante (FR)—Maravo **Mrs H. J. Clarke**
41 **HAILSTORM (IRE)**, 5, ch g Glacial Storm (IRE)—Sindys Gale **Mr Peter Clinton**
42 **HATCHAM BOY (IRE)**, 8, br g Roselier (FR)—Auling **Mr R. Maryan Green**
43 **HILLESDEN (IRE)**, 5, ch g Executive Perk—She's Clever **Mr M. R. Deeley**
44 **HURRICANE LAMP**, 7, b g Derrylin—Lampstone **Mr & Mrs F. C. Welch**
45 **IAMUS**, 5, ch g Most Welcome—Icefern **M. P. Burke's 5th Family Settlement**
46 **IN THE ROUGH (IRE)**, 7, b g Strong Gale—Cherrydawn **Mrs L. R. Lovell**
47 **ISLAND SANCTUARY (IRE)**, 4, ch c Fools Holme (USA)—Church Light **Million in Mind Partnership (7)**
48 **JACK TANNER (IRE)**, 9, b br g Roselier (FR)—Felicity Lot **Lady Harris**
49 **JUSTUCE ALONE (IRE)**, 5, ch g Over The River (FR)—Another Dutchess **The Poppet Partnership**
50 **KADI (GER)**, 9, b g Shareef Dancer (USA)—Kaisertreue (GER) **Mr J. E. Brown**
51 **KEANO (IRE)**, 9, ch g Phardante (FR)—Nickel Run **Midavon Partnership**
52 **KILBRIDE LAD (IRE)**, 4, b g Mac's Imp (USA)—Cordon **Mr Peter Wetzel**
53 **KING LUCIFER (IRE)**, 9, b g King's Ride—Cahore **Mr A. J. Davies**
54 **KING ON THE RUN (IRE)**, 5, b g King's Ride—Fly Run **Lady Harris**
55 **L'OPERA (FR)**, 5, ch g Old Vic—Ma Pavlova (USA) **Sheikh Ahmed Al Maktoum**
56 **MACMORRIS (USA)**, 5, b g Silver Hawk (USA)—Andover Cottage (USA) **Mr Raymond Tooth**
57 5, Ch m Ardross—Madam-M **Mrs J. Mould**
58 **MIGHTY MOSS (IRE)**, 7, b g Moscow Society (USA)—Derry Girl **Mr K. Hutsby**
59 **MOTOQUA**, 6, b m Mtoto—Neeran **Mrs E. W. Pegna & Mrs Ian Smith**
60 **MULLIGAN (IRE)**, 8, ch g Callernish—Anaglogs Pet **Lady Harris**
61 **MUSKHILL**, 7, b g Law Society (USA)—Greencastle Hill **Midcourts**
62 **NAKIR (FR)**, 10, b g Nikos—Nabita (FR) **Mr Jim Lewis**
63 **NAMOODAJ**, 5, b g Polish Precedent (USA)—Leipzig **All The King's Men**
64 **NATIVE RECRUIT (IRE)**, 5, ch g Be My Native (USA)—Castle Stream **Mr Jerry Wright**
65 **NISHAMIRA (IRE)**, 6, gr m Lashkari—Nishila (USA) **M. P. Burke Developments Limited**
66 **NOISY MINER (IRE)**, 6, b g Kambalda—Furry Lady **Mrs R. J. Skan**
67 **OI MOTHER (IRE)**, 6, b m Strong Gale—Pops Girl **Aiden Murphy And Nick Skelton**
68 **OVER THE COUNTRY**, 6, b g Over The River (FR)—Country Seat **M. P. Burke's 5th Family Settlement**
69 **PEARL EPEE**, 9, b m Broadsword (USA)—Pearly's Orphan **Mrs A. A. Shutes**
70 **PENNYBRIDGE (IRE)**, 9, ch g Orchestra—Little Snob **Mr Joel McCleary**
71 **PERSIAN SWORD**, 12, b g Broadsword (USA)—Sorraia **Ford Farm Racing**
72 **PHARANEAR (IRE)**, 8, b g Camden Town—Monas River **Stainless Threaded Fasteners Ltd**
73 **POTTER AGAIN (IRE)**, 6, b m Brush Aside (USA)—Polly Puttens **Mr J. E. Potter**
74 **POTTER'S BAY (IRE)**, 9, br g Strong Gale—Polly Puttens **Mrs J. E. Potter**
75 **POTTER'S GALE (IRE)**, 7, br m Strong Gale—Polly Puttens **Mr J. E. Potter**
76 **RANDOM ASSAULT (NZ)**, 9, b g Random Chance (NZ)—Lady Frisco (NZ) **The Random Lot**
77 **REAL ESTATE**, 4, b c High Estate—Haitienne (FR) **Mrs J. Mould**
78 **REGAL ABSENCE (IRE)**, 6, br g King's Ride—Aw Gone **P. R. D. Fasteners Ltd**
79 **REGAL CHANCE**, 5, b g Cisto (FR)—Regal Flutter **Mrs A. A. Shutes**
80 **RELKEEL**, 9, b g Relkino—Secret Keel **Trustees of the late Brig C. B. Harvey**
81 **RICHES TO RAGS (IRE)**, 8, ch g Castle Keep—Merry Buskins **The Riches To Rags Partnership**
82 **ROWINGTON**, 7, b g Ardross—Cherry Crest **Mrs Jane Lane**
83 **RUSSELL ROAD (IRE)**, 6, br g Phardante (FR)—Burren Gale (IRE) **Mrs L. Field**
84 **SAMAKAAN (IRE)**, 5, b g Darshaan—Samarzana (USA) **Lady Harris**
85 **SAMUEL WILDERSPIN**, 6, b g Henbit (USA)—Littoral **County Graphix Colour Limited**
86 **SANMARTINO (IRE)**, 6, b h Salse (USA)—Oscura (USA) **Mr K. Abdulla**
87 **SARAS DELIGHT**, 6, b g Idiot's Delight—Lady Bess **Mrs D. Jackson**
88 **SHANKAR (IRE)**, 7, gr g Shareef Dancer (USA)—Sibelle d'Oa (FR) **International Plywood Plc**
89 **SHEEPCOTE HILL (IRE)**, 7, b g Corvaro (USA)—Misty Boosh **Mr J. E. Brown & Mrs Sue Faccenda**
90 **SHINING LIGHT (IRE)**, 9, b g Crash Course—Arumah **The Deeley Partnership**
91 **SMOKEY JOE (IRE)**, 6, br g Lord Americo—Badsworth Madam **Roach Foods Limited**

MR DAVID NICHOLSON—continued

92 **SOLDAT (USA)**, 5, b g Bering—Sans Prix (USA) **Mr Darren C. Mercer**
93 **SOUNDS STRONG (IRE)**, 9, br g Strong Gale—Jazz Bavard **Mrs David Thompson**
94 **SPENDID (IRE)**, 6, b g Tidaro (USA)—Spendapromise **Mrs Stewart Catherwood**
95 **STONE'S THROW**, 5, b g Roscoe Blake—Lampstone **Mr & Mrs F. C. Welch**
96 **STORM ALERT**, 12, b g Strong Gale—Jet Travel **Mrs Dawn Perrett**
97 **SYMPHONY'S SON (IRE)**, 7, b g Orchestra—Garden of Roses **Mrs J. Mould**
98 **THE CAPTAIN'S LADY**, 6, ch m Infantry—The Lady's Wish **Miss A. J. Murray**
99 **THE CAPTAIN'S WISH**, 7, ch g Infantry—The Lady's Wish **Miss A. J. Murray**
100 **TIUTCHEV**, 5, b g Soviet Star (USA)—Cut Ahead **The Liars Poker Partnership**
101 **TOBY BROWN**, 5, b g Arzanni—Forest Nymph (NZ) **Mr A. Stennett & Mrs J. M. Stennett**
102 **TURNING TRIX**, 11, b g Buckskin (FR)—Merry Run **Mr Mel Davies**
103 **VIKING FLAGSHIP**, 11, b g Viking (USA)—Fourth Degree **Roach Foods Limited**
104 **WINDROSS**, 6, b g Ardross—Dans Le Vent **Mrs Peter Prowting**
105 **ZABADI (IRE)**, 6, b g Shahrastani (USA)—Zerzaya **Lady Harris**
106 **ZAFARABAD (IRE)**, 4, gr g Shernazar—Zarafa **Mrs Elaine Baines**
107 **ZAITOON (IRE)**, 7, b g Waajib—Sawlah **Cheltenham Racing Ltd**
108 **ZARALASKA**, 7, ch g Shernazar—Eskimo Spring (USA) **Lady Harris**

Other Owners: Mr Hugh Arthur, Mrs Diana Attwood, Mr Roger Baines, Mrs Pam Bates, Mr Terry Benson, Mr Robert Benton, Mr Ben Brooks, Cheveley Park Stud, Mr Stanley W. Clarke, Mrs C. A. Coombs, Mr T. W. Coombs, Mr J. R. A. Crabtree, Mrs A. J. Davies, Mr P. A. Deal, Mrs Audrey Deeley, Mr D. I. B. Dick, Mr S. B. Duncombe, Mr R. S. Field, Mrs Anne Fisher, Mr Graham Goode, Mr A. J. Heappey, Mr H. Hutsby, Mr D. J. Jackson, Mr Joseph E. Keeling, Knightsbridge Bc, Mr Frank P. Krasovec, Mr David M. Mason, Miss V. Medwell, Mr I. R. Metcalfe, Mr D. Minton, Mr J. B. R. Morris, Mr R. G. Murray, Mr Gordon Mytton, Mr Charles F. Newman, Mr C. G. Nicholl, Mr M. R. Oliver, Mrs M. A. Powis, Mr P. G. Rattenberry, Mr K. E. Rayner, Mr L. M. Rutherford, Mr R. Sheehan, Mr K. J. Simpson, Mr C. B. Smith, Mr M. R. Smith, Miss F. M. Stone, Mr J. A. H. West, Mr Andrew P. Wyer.

Jockeys (NH): Richard Johnson (10-0), Adrian Maguire (10-0).

Conditional: Gerry Hogan (9-12), Robert Massey (9-9), Robert Thornton.

Amateurs: Mr Richard Burton (10-0), Mr Fred Hutsby (10-0), Mr Oliver McPhail (9-7).

440 MR G. R. S. NIXON, Selkirk

Postal: **Oakwood Farm, Ettrickbridge, Selkirk, Selkirkshire, Scotland, TD7 5HJ.**
Phone: **(01750) 52245**

1 **DELIGHTFOOL**, 7, gr m Idiot's Delight—Parselle **Mr & Mrs G. R. S. Nixon**
2 **JUST HUSH**, 5, b m Kind of Hush—Royal Huntress **Mr & Mrs G. R. S. Nixon**
3 5, B m Rakaposhi King—Kilglass **Mr & Mrs G. R. S. Nixon**
4 4, Ch g Ardar—Kincherinchee **Mr & Mrs G. R. S. Nixon**
5 **POLITICAL MANDATE**, 5, br m Respect—Political Mill **Mr & Mrs G. R. S. Nixon**
6 4, Ch g Mirror Boy—Political Mill **Mr & Mrs G. R. S. Nixon**
7 **POLITICAL TOWER**, 11, b g Politico (USA)—Crosby Waves **Mr Mrs G. R. S. Nixon**
8 **SPRINGLEA TOWER**, 5, b g Meadowbrook—Tringa (GER) **Mr & Mrs G. R. S. Nixon**

Jockey (NH): A Dobbin.

441 MRS S. NOCK, Stow-on-the-Wold

Postal: **Smenham Farm, Icomb, Stow-on-the Wold, Cheltenham, Gloucestershire, GL54 1JQ.**
Phone: **(01451) 831688 (01451) 831404 FAX**

1 **COOL RUNNER**, 8, b g Sunyboy—Nosey's Daughter **Mr Gerard Nock**
2 **OPERETTO (IRE)**, 8, b g Orchestra—Love From Judy **Mr Gerard Nock**
3 **SENOR EL BETRUTTI (IRE)**, 9, gr g Roselier (FR)—Rambling Gold **Mr Gerard Nock**

442 MR D. A. NOLAN, Wishaw

Postal: **Riverside Racing Stables, 227a Bonkle Road, Newmains, Wishaw, Lanarkshire, ML2 9QQ.**
Phone: **(01698) 381829 FAX (01698) 381829**

1 **AYE READY**, 5, ch g Music Boy—Cindy's Princess
2 **BEST KEPT SECRET**, 7, b g Petong—Glenfield Portion **Mrs J. McFadyen-Murray**
3 **DESERT LORE**, 7, b g Green Desert (USA)—Chinese Justice (USA) **Mrs J. McFadyen-Murray**
4 **DONNA'S DANCER (IRE)**, 4, ch g Magical Wonder (USA)—Ice On Fire **Mr F. Jestin**
5 **LORD ADVOCATE**, 10, br g Law Society (USA)—Kereolle **Mrs J. McFadyen-Murray**
6 **LORD CORNELIOUS**, 5, b h Lochnager—Title **Mrs J. McFadyen-Murray**
7 **PALLIUM (IRE)**, 10, b g Try My Best (USA)—Jungle Gardenia **Mrs J. McFadyen-Murray**
8 **POWER GAME**, 5, b g Puissance—Play The Game **Mrs J. McFadyen-Murray**
9 **RAGTIME COWGIRL**, 5, ch m Aragon—Echo Chamber **Mrs J. McFadyen-Murray**
10 **RAPID MOVER**, 11, ch g Final Straw—Larive **Mrs J. McFadyen-Murray**
11 **RATTLE**, 5, b g Mazilier (USA)—Snake Song **Mr J. Kelly**
12 **SCHOOL OF SCIENCE**, 8, b g Then Again—Girl's Brigade **Mrs J. McFadyen-Murray**
13 **SIX FOR LUCK**, 6, b g Handsome Sailor—Fire Sprite **Mrs J. McFadyen-Murray**
14 **SOCIETY TIMES (USA)**, 5, b g Imp Society (USA)—Mauna Loa (USA) **Mrs J. McFadyen-Murray**
15 **SPEKTRA**, 6, br m Respect—My Goddess **County Car Parks**

THREE-YEAR-OLDS

16 **SOLO SONG**, ch f Executive Man—Aosta **The Low Flyers (Thoroughbreds) Ltd**
17 **THE ANGEL GABRIEL**, ch c My Generation—Minsk **Mrs J. McFadyen-Murray**
18 **THE OTHER RISK**, b g Risk Me (FR)—First Fastnet **The Low Flyers (Thoroughbreds) Ltd**

Other Owners: Mr G. Coburn, Mr Grant Dalgetty, Mr J. C. Furlong, Mr J. Macintyre, Mr A. S. McPherson, Mrs K. Russell.

Jockey (Flat): Tim Sprake.

Jockeys (NH): Mike Maloney, Brian Storey.

Apprentices: Keith Sked, Neil Varley (7-7).

Amateur: Mr Richard Hale.

Lady Rider: Ms Diana Carter.

443 MR JOHN NORTON, Barnsley

Postal: **Globe Farm, High Hoyland, Barnsley, South Yorkshire, S75 4BE.**
Phone: **(01226) 387633 FAX (01226) 387633**

1 **ALZOTIC (IRE),** 5, b g Alzao (USA)—Exotic Bride (USA) **Mr Billy Parker**
2 **BAASM,** 5, b g Polar Falcon (USA)—Sariah **Bradlor Developments Limited**
3 **CANDY'S DELIGHT,** 5, b m Dunbeath (USA)—Simply Candy (IRE) **Mr Jeff Slaney**
4 **COMMUNITY SERVICE (IRE),** 7, b m Homo Sapien—Perpetue **Ecosse Racing**
5 **EFAAD (IRE),** 7, b g Shaadi (USA)—Krismas River **Mr J. Norton**
6 **FORTUNE HUNTER (IRE),** 4, ch g Lycius (USA)—Cardomine **Mr Antony Waters**
7 **LANDLER,** 5, b g Shareef Dancer (USA)—Les Dancelles **Bradlor Developments Limited**
8 **LAST ACTION,** 5, gr m Lyphento (USA)—Sunlit **Mr J. Norton**
9 **MISHRAF (USA),** 4, b g Sheikh Albadou—My Shafy **Mr J. Norton**
10 **MUDLARK,** 6, b g Salse (USA)—Mortal Sin (USA) **Mr J. Norton**
11 5, Gr g Supreme Leader—Nanny Kehoe **Mr John Richard Norton**
12 **NORTH MOSS,** 5, b g Scorpio (FR)—Bint Al Arab **Mr David McDuffie**
13 **POLAR REFRAIN,** 5, ch m Polar Falcon (USA)—Cut No Ice **Mr Graham Brooksbank**
14 5, B m Infantry—Princess Constanza **Mr J. Norton**
15 **SAHARA REEM (IRE),** 4, b f Don't Forget Me—River Reem (USA) **Mr J. Norton**
16 **SCOBI,** 4, ch g Scottish Reel—Bint Al Arab **Mr David McDuffie**
17 **SHARED RISK,** 6, ch g Risk Me (FR)—Late Idea **Mr Graham Brooksbank**
18 **SQUANDAMANIA,** 5, b g Ela-Mana-Mou—Garden Pink (FR) **Mr J. Norton**
19 **SUDDEN SPIN,** 8, b g Doulab (USA)—Lightning Legacy (USA) **Mr Billy Parker**
20 **TAZIBARI,** 4, b f Barry's Gamble—Jersey Maid **Cowga Partners**
21 4, B g Henbit (USA)—Touch of Luck (FR) **Mr J. Norton**

THREE-YEAR-OLDS

22 B g Seymour Hicks (FR)—Joyfulness (FR) **Mr John Richard Norton**

TWO-YEAR-OLDS

23 B f 29/3 Presidium—Joie de Patina (Forzando) **Mr John Richard Norton**

Other Owners: Bradlor Developments Limited, Mr P. J. Burns, Mr John D. Ferguson, Mr Edward Graham, Mr Mattie O'Toole.

444 MR J. J. NOSEDA, Newmarket

Postal: **Shalfleet, Bury Road, Newmarket, Suffolk, CB8 7BX.**
Phone: **(01638) 664010 FAX (01638) 664100**

1 **MUSICAL PURSUIT,** 4, b c Pursuit of Love—Gay Music (FR)
2 **TEOFILIO (IRE),** 4, ch c Night Shift (USA)—Rivoltade (USA)

THREE-YEAR-OLDS

3 **CALL THE BOSS (USA),** b c Chief's Crown (USA)—Laz's Joy (USA)
4 **EMERALD HUNTER (USA),** b c Quest For Fame—In Jubilation (USA)
5 **ISABELLA,** ch f Primo Dominie—Scossa (USA)
6 **KING'S COLOURS (USA),** b c Gold Legend (USA)—Aly's Delight (USA)
7 **MORNINGTON,** b c Shirley Heights—Habibay
8 **NAUTICAL WARNING,** b c Warning—Night At Sea
9 **WILD EAGLE,** ch c Lion Cavern (USA)—Krameria

TWO-YEAR-OLDS

10 Br f 17/2 Twilight Agenda (USA)—Alpha Rascal (USA) (Alphabatim (USA))
11 B f 12/3 Reprimand—Babycham Sparkle (So Blessed)
12 **CALYPSO (IRE),** b c 10/5 Turtle Island (IRE)—Music of The Night (USA) (Blushing Groom (FR))
13 **CATAPULT (IRE),** b c 14/3 Catrail (USA)—Flimmering (Dancing Brave (USA))

MR J. J. NOSEDA—continued

14 B c 13/4 Salse (USA)—Celebrity (Troy)
15 Ch f 26/1 Cadeaux Genereux—Chatterberry (Aragon)
16 **DESARU (USA),** br c 22/1 Chief's Crown (USA)—Team Colors (USA) (Mr Prospector (USA))
17 **DIAMOND DECORUM (IRE),** ch c 27/4 Fayruz—Astra Adastra (Mount Hagen (FR))
18 B f 15/3 Deposit Ticket (USA)—Dogwood Lane (USA) (Alydar (USA))
19 B c 7/4 Bluebird (USA)—Evangola (Persian Bold)
20 B c 1/4 Sadler's Wells (USA)—Guess Again (GER) (Stradavinsky)
21 Ch f 25/4 Kris—Habibay (Habitat)
22 **INDIAN WARRIOR,** b c 24/3 Be My Chief (USA)—Wanton (Kris)
23 **KINGRHUMBA (USA),** b c 4/6 Kingmambo (USA)—Lady Ice (CAN) (Vice Regent (CAN))
24 **MELBEN,** b c 19/3 Dolphin Street (FR)—Shapely Test (USA) (Elocutionist (USA))
25 **MISTER POPPINS (IRE),** ch c 27/3 Lahib (USA)—From The Rooftops (IRE) (Thatching)
26 **MY OWN LOVELY LEE (IRE),** b f 31/3 College Chapel—Pairc-Na-Lee (IRE) (Fairy King (USA))
27 B f 27/3 Bustino—Nadia Nerina (CAN) (Northern Dancer)
28 Br f 16/5 Sea Hero (USA)—Northern Valley (USA) (Northern Dancer)
29 B f 5/5 Cadeaux Genereux—Piffle (Shirley Heights)
30 B c 2/4 Cyrano de Bergerac—Plie (Superlative)
31 **POLAR FAIR,** ch f 5/2 Polar Falcon (USA)—Fair Country (Town And Country)
32 B c 3/3 Then Again—Primitive Gift (Primitive Rising (USA))
33 **PRINCE PROSPECT,** b c 8/4 Lycius (USA)—Princess Dechtra (IRE) (Bellypha)
34 **RAIN IN SPAIN,** b c 21/3 Unfuwain (USA)—Maria Isabella (FR) (Young Generation)
35 **RANELLE (USA),** ch f 10/2 Rahy (USA)—Aspenelle (CAN) (Vice Regent (CAN))
36 **RANSOM CALL (USA),** b c 31/3 Red Ransom (USA)—Playcaller (USA) (Saratoga Six (USA))
37 B f 21/3 Nureyev (USA)—Saratoga Sea (USA) (Saratoga Six (USA))
38 Gr f 12/5 Royal Academy (USA)—Secret Sunday (USA) (Secreto (USA))
39 **SNOWY RANGE (USA),** br f 31/1 Seattle Slew (USA)—November Snow (USA) (Storm Cat (USA))
40 **SONG 'N DANCE MAN,** b c 19/2 Prince Sabo—Born To Dance (Dancing Brave (USA))
41 **TOKOLOSHE KING (IRE),** b c 28/4 Fairy King (USA)—Belize Tropical (USA) (Baillamont (USA))
42 **TOMASEAN,** b c 27/2 Forzando—Bunny Gee (Last Tycoon)
43 **TOUCH OF LOVE,** b c 20/1 Pursuit of Love—Nitouche (Scottish Reel)
44 **VIBRANCE (IRE),** b c 22/3 College Chapel—Shalara (Dancer's Image (USA))
45 **VICTORY ROLL,** b c 4/4 In The Wings—Persian Victory (IRE) (Persian Bold)
46 B f 18/1 Danehill (USA)—Wannabe (Shirley Heights)
47 Br c 3/4 Alydeed (CAN)—Years (USA) (Secretariat (USA))
48 **YOU RANG HERE (USA),** ch f 12/3 Dehere (USA)—Phone Booth (USA) (Phone Trick (USA))

Owners: Asian Racing & Breeding Ltd, Lady Sarah Berry, Mr J. Breslin, Sir Gordon Brunton, Mrs P. Chambers, Mr S. Crown, Cypress Farms, Mr T. Dalton, Diamond Racing, Ecurie Pharos, Fieldspring Racing, Mr J. Fitzgerald, Hesmonds Stud, Mr & Mrs D. Hicks, Mr K. Y. Lim, Mrs J. Magnier, Mr N. Mandell, Mr B. McAllister, Mr B. Nielsen, Mr M. Olden, Mrs C. Parker, Mr H. Rosenblatt, Mrs J. M. Ryan, Mr P. D. Savill, Mr B. Schmidt-Bodner, Mr J. K. Sim, Mr W. R. Swinburn Snr, Mr M. Tabor, Mrs M. Tillman, Mr Goncalo Borges Torrealba, Mr Peter S. Winfield.

445 MR CHARLES O'BRIEN, Kildare

Postal: **Ridge Manor Stables, Rathbride, Kildare, Ireland.**
Phone: **(045) 522607 FAX (045) 522609**

1 **ASHLEY PARK (IRE),** 4, b c Sadler's Wells (USA)—Maiden Concert
2 **BURDEN OF PROOF (IRE),** 6, b h Fairy King (USA)—Belle Passe
3 **DR JOHNSON (USA),** 4, ch c Woodman (USA)—Russian Ballet (USA)
4 **QUEST OF PASSION (USA),** 4, b f Saumarez—Autocratic

THREE-YEAR-OLDS

5 **ACADEMIC WORLD (IRE),** b c Royal Academy (USA)—Lisadell (USA)
6 **AD INFINITUM (IRE),** b c Rainbows For Life—Scapa (USA)
7 **ALCADIA (IRE),** ch f Thatching—Soltura (IRE)
8 **ALONZO (IRE),** b c Alzao (USA)—Rosa Mundi (USA)
9 **CAMPO CATINO (IRE),** br c Woodman (USA)—Karri Valley (USA)

MR CHARLES O'BRIEN—continued

10 **DANCING HOPE (IRE),** b f Mujtahid (USA)—Dancing Home
11 **GEISHA GIRL,** b f Nashwan (USA)—Miznah (IRE)
12 **GENUINE (FR),** b f Generous (IRE)—Rive de Sud (USA)
13 **GOLDEN CHIMES (USA),** ch c Woodman (USA)—Russian Ballet (USA)
14 **HIGH SEAS (IRE),** b g Pips Pride—Summit Talk
15 **HILLSIDE ROSE (IRE),** b f Danehill (USA)—Miss Belgravia (USA)
16 **JARNAC (FR),** b c Saumarez—Green Moon (FR)
17 **LIEGE (IRE),** b f Night Shift (USA)—Wedding Bouquet
18 **LOWER CHAPEL,** ch f Sharpo—Humble Pie
19 **NIGHT IN TOWN (IRE),** b g Night Shift (USA)—Samite (FR)
20 **PRECIOUS CHOICE (USA),** ch f Jade Hunter (USA)—Brorita (USA)
21 **RAINSWEPT,** ch g Selkirk (USA)—Pluvial

TWO-YEAR-OLDS

22 B c 13/3 Bluebird (USA)—Abet (USA) (Alleged (USA))
23 Br c 12/2 Lion Cavern (USA)—Allegra (Niniski (USA))
24 B c 18/5 College Chapel—Arcade (Rousillon (USA))
25 Br c 10/3 Hamas (IRE)—Banana Peel (Green Dancer (USA))
26 **CANALETTO,** b c 4/2 Royal Academy (USA)—Diavolina (USA) (Lear Fan (USA))
27 **DONATUS (IRE),** b c 28/4 Royal Academy (USA)—La Dame du Lac (USA) (Round Table)
28 **FRANCHETTI,** b c 11/2 Unfuwain (USA)—Lady Shipley (Shirley Heights)
29 **HIGHWAY ONE ELEVEN (IRE),** b c 22/4 Polar Falcon (USA)—Finger of Light (Green Desert (USA))
30 **JEWEL IN THE CROWN (USA),** b f 7/3 Seeking The Gold—Christabelle (USA) (Northern Dancer)
31 **KILKENNY CASTLE (IRE),** b c 13/3 Grand Lodge (USA)—Shahaamh (IRE) (Reference Point)
32 B f 27/4 Danehill (USA)—Maiden Concert (Condorcet (FR))
33 B br f 4/3 Darshaan—Mild Intrigue (USA) (Sir Ivor)
34 B f 11/3 Machiavellian (USA)—Misallah (IRE) (Shirley Heights)
35 Ch c 27/4 College Chapel—Red Roman (Solinus)
36 **ROMANCIA (USA),** ch f 17/4 Woodman (USA)—Russian Ballet (USA) (Nijinsky (CAN))
37 **SAN ROCCO,** ch c 20/3 Thatching—Oatfield (Great Nephew)
38 Ch c 2/5 College Chapel—Soltura (IRE) (Sadler's Wells (USA))
39 **TREBIZOND (IRE),** b c 4/4 Sadler's Wells (USA)—Karri Valley (USA) (Storm Bird (CAN))

Owners: Dr C. Bascape, Mrs J. Brosnan, P. A. Byrne, Dr Anne Heffernan, Mrs John Magnier, J. P. McManus, Mrs P. Myerscough, Dr M. V. O'Brien, M. E. Parrish, Ms M. M. Ridgway, P. D. Savill, Mr M. Tabor.

446 MR D. C. O'BRIEN, Tonbridge

Postal: **Knowles Bank, Capel, Tonbridge, Kent, TN11 0PU.**
Phone: **(01892) 824072**

1 **AUGUST TWELFTH,** 10, b g Full of Hope—Espanita
2 **BECKENHAM INSIGHT,** 4, b f Efisio—Capel Lass **Mrs S. Harris**
3 **CAMP FOLLOWER,** 5, b g Warrshan (USA)—House Maid **Mrs J. Scudder**
4 **CLEMENS,** 6, b m Full of Hope—Mossaka (FR)
5 **DAZZLING,** 5, b m Rambo Dancer (CAN)—Azaiyma **Mr Graham Pasquill**
6 **DRAGON'S BACK (IRE),** 5, ch g Digamist (USA)—Classic Choice **Mrs J. Scudder**
7 **EQUITY'S DARLING (IRE),** 6, b m Law Society (USA)—Curie Abu
8 **ILLUMINATE,** 5, b g Marju (IRE)—Light Bee (USA) **Mr J. S. Court**
9 **JEWELLER'S WELLS (USA),** 6, ch g Alleged (USA)—Artic Eclipse (USA)
10 **KELLY MAC,** 8, b g Precocious—Ridalia
11 **LANCE'S PET,** 4, b f Warning—Snub **Mr Lance Lodge**
12 **MIDNIGHT TIMES,** 4, b f Timeless Times (USA)—Midnight Lass **Mrs V. O'Brien**
13 **NANCYS GEM,** 4, b f Most Welcome—Nancy Chere (USA) **Mr Lance Lodge**
14 **REGAL AURA (IRE),** 8, ch g Glow (USA)—Dignified Air (FR)
15 **SALAMAN (FR),** 6, b g Saumarez—Merry Sharp **Mrs V. O'Brien**
16 **SIFWA,** 4, ch f Safawan—Wigeon **Mr A. Runacre**

MR D. C. O'BRIEN—continued

17 SNOW CLOUD, 4, b f Today And Tomorrow—Fancy Pages **Mrs V. O'Brien**
18 4, B f Ardross—Targon Girl
19 YOUNG MAZAAD (IRE), 5, b g Mazaad—Lucky Charm (IRE)

THREE-YEAR-OLDS

20 ARIES BOY, ch c Risk Me (FR)—Fancy Pages **Mrs V. O'Brien**
21 KAGSI, br f King's Signet (USA)—Azaiyma **Mr Graham Pasquill**
22 KING'S MISTRESS, ch f King's Signet (USA)—Rectory Maid **Mrs V. O'Brien**

TWO-YEAR-OLDS

23 Ch f 16/4 Dilum (USA)—Emmer Green (Music Boy)
24 B c 18/2 Presidium—Espanita (Riboboy (USA))
25 Br f 23/4 Today And Tomorrow—Vital Witness (Garda's Revenge (USA))

Other Owners: Mr G. Battocchi, Mrs R. M. Blake, Mrs V. Costello, Mr Bernard O'Brien, Mr D. C. O'Brien, Ms G. J. Walker, Mrs Helen Yeadon.

Jockey (Flat): G Bardwell.

Apprentice: D Burchell (7-3).

447 MR E. J. O'GRADY, Thurles

Postal: **Killeens, Ballynonty, Thurles, Co. Tipperary, Ireland.**
Phone: **(052) 56156 FAX (052) 56466**

1 ALLATRIM (IRE), 8, b m Montelimar (USA)—Robertina (USA) **E. R. Madden**
2 BALAWHAR (IRE), 8, b g Doyoun—Bayazida **Michael Tabor**
3 BALLINCARA (IRE), 5, b g Broadsword (USA)—Four Sport **P. McLoughney**
4 BALLYDONNELLY (IRE), 6, br g Be My Native (USA)—Madam Milan **S. P. Tao**
5 BIGHEARTED ARTHUR (IRE), 6, b g Strong Gale—Orlinda **M. Toritt**
6 BLOWN AWAY (IRE), 7, b g Strong Gale—Buck Away **B. Duffy**
7 BRUSH THE FLAG (IRE), 6, b g Brush Aside (USA)—Shanaway **A. P. Wyse**
8 CARMEN FAIR (IRE), 6, br m Strong Gale—Let's Compromise **Mrs L. McCallan**
9 CLAYHITHE (IRE), 5, b g Un Desperado (FR)—Sandbank (IRE) **S. P. Tao**
10 CLEMENTE, 5, b m Robellino (USA)—Gravad Lax **F. A. McNulty**
11 COILLTE AN CEOIL (IRE), 5, gr g Wood Chanter—Miss Fanackapan **Mrs N. P. Conneely**
12 COUNTRY FLAVOUR (IRE), 5, b g Un Desperado (FR)—Candy Princess **Country Club Syndicate**
13 GIMME FIVE, 11, b g Deep Run—Cill Dara **John P. McManus**
14 GO ROGER GO (IRE), 6, b g Phardante (FR)—Tonto's Girl **John P. McManus**
15 IMPOSSIBLE QUICK (IRE), 5, b g Brush Aside (USA)—Pampered Run **R. MacSharry**
16 IMPULSIVE DREAM (IRE), 7, b g Miner's Lamp—Nellie's Dream **Scott Lloyd**
17 KERANI (USA), 6, b g Arctic Tern (USA)—Kerita **Michael Watt**
18 KERRY ORCHID, 10, gr g Absalom—Matinata **P. Curling**
19 LAURA LUGS (IRE), 6, b g Strong Gale—Geeaway **David A. Lloyd**
20 LEAPING LORD (IRE), 5, b g Mister Lord (USA)—Sauce Serene **Simon Tindall**
21 MALABAR, 5, b g Be My Native (USA)—Quadro **R. Jenks**
22 MEET AND GREET (IRE), 4, b g Bob Back (USA)—Hostess **J. S. Gutkin**
23 NICHOLLS CROSS (IRE), 6, b g Mandalus—Milan Pride **David A. Lloyd**
24 NICK DUNDEE (IRE), 6, b g Supreme Leader—Silent Run **Mrs John Magnier**
25 OAKLAND HILLS (IRE), 5, b g Mandalus—Meanwood **P. Myerscough**
26 OFF THE COAST, 4, b g Slip Anchor—Mulvilla **J. S. Gutkin**
27 OKAY OCEE (IRE), 6, ch g Executive Perk—Susan McCann **James O'Connor**
28 ONE MORE SPIN (IRE), 5, b br h Tirol—Manela Lady **J. S. Gutkin**
29 ORMOND STYLE (IRE), 4, b g Commanche Run—For Love Nor Money **P. McLoughney**
30 PAY THE MAN (IRE), 6, ch g Remainder Man—Bail Out **John P. McManus**
31 SARCASTIC (IRE), 5, b m Lafontaine (USA)—Cutty Sark **C. Hansard**

MR E. J. O'GRADY—continued

32 **SHRUG (IRE),** 5, b g Brush Aside (USA)—Diane's Glen **Michael Watt**
33 **SMILING AWAY (IRE),** 5, b m Phardante (FR)—Judysway **The Bridge Syndicate**
34 **STORMING AHEAD (IRE),** 6, b g Strong Gale—Distant Castle **Mrs A. Catherwood**
35 **STORMON (IRE),** 5, b g Glacial Storm (USA)—Jodi's Money **The Cards Syndicate**
36 **STRONG FOCUS (IRE),** 6, b g Strong Gale—Scotch News **David A. Lloyd**
37 **THE BARGE (IRE),** 5, b g Un Desperado (FR)—Marble Owen **K. Murphy**
38 **THELADYSNECKLACE,** 4, b f Anshan—Kinkajoo **W. A. Barrett**
39 **TIME FOR A RUN,** 11, b g Deep Run—Hourly Rate **John P. McManus**
40 **TIME TO LEAD (IRE),** 8, b g Supreme Leader—Hourly Rate **John P. McManus**
41 **WILLOWMOUNT (IRE),** 5, br g Niels—The Hofsa **M. McGread**

THREE-YEAR-OLDS

42 **BLACK ORPHEUS (IRE),** b g Astronef—Cri Basque **Dr J. Torsney**

Other Owners: M. Goodbody, Mr D. McKey, Mrs Myerscough.

Amateur: Mr P Fenton (10-0).

448 MR J. J. O'NEILL, Penrith

Postal: **Ivy House, Skelton Wood End, Penrith, Cumbria, CA11 9UB.**
Phone: **(017684) 84555 FAX (017684) 84559 MOBILE (0831) 399500**

1 **ALL THE ACES,** 11, gr g Roselier (FR)—Alice Starr **Mr J. P. McManus**
2 **ARDRONAN (IRE),** 8, b g Roselier (FR)—Molly Coddle **Mrs L. R. Joughin**
3 **AREN'T WE LUCKY (IRE),** 5, b h Project Manager—Keshia **Maj. Straker, M. O'Connor, P.S. Thompson**
4 **BEACHY HEAD,** 10, gr g Damister (USA)—No More Rosies **Mr M. Tabor**
5 **CAMBRIAN DAWN,** 4, b c Danehill (USA)—Welsh Daylight **Mr A. K. Collins**
6 **CASH FLOW (IRE),** 7, b g Mister Lord (USA)—Turn A Coin **Mrs L. R. Joughin**
7 **CLIFTON FOX,** 6, b g Deploy—Loveskate (USA) **Mr J. P. McManus**
8 **COMMANCHE TRIX (IRE),** 5, ch m Commanche Run—Funtrix **Mrs A. R. Thompson**
9 **COPPEEN JEWEL (IRE),** 5, br g Arapahos (FR)—Castleview Rose **Mr Fred Coulson**
10 **ESCALATE,** 4, ch c Groom Dancer (USA)—Brosna (USA) **Mr A. K. Collins**
11 **FARNEY GLEN,** 11, b g Furry Glen—Windara **Mrs A. I. Meller**
12 **FINISTERRE (IRE),** 5, b g Salt Dome (USA)—Inisfail **Les Femmes Fatales**
13 **FORZAIR,** 6, b g Forzando—Persian Air **Clayton Bigley Partnership Ltd**
14 **FOUR FROM HOME (IRE),** 6, ch g Carlingford Castle—Loving Way **G. & P. Barker Ltd/Globe Engineering**
15 **FRONT LINE,** 11, ch g High Line—Caroles Delight **Mr J. P. McManus**
16 **GIVE BEST,** 7, ch g Dunbeath (USA)—Cold Line **Mr J. P. McManus**
17 **GLOBE RUNNER,** 5, b h Adbass (USA)—Scenic Villa **G. & P. Barker Ltd/Globe Engineering**
18 **INCH WAY (IRE),** 6, b br g Kambalda—Glenaveel **High Green Partnership**
19 **IVY HOUSE (IRE),** 10, b g Orchestra—Gracious View **Mrs L. R. Joughin**
20 **JENNIE'S PROSPECT,** 7, b g Rakaposhi King—Jennie Pat **Mrs R. H. Thompson**
21 **JUST AN EXCUSE (IRE),** 5, b g Project Manager—Over The Seas **Peter Thompson Mark Derry Mark O'Connor**
22 **JUST ONE QUESTION (IRE),** 8, b g Torus—Stormy Night **Anne Duchess of Westminster**
23 **JYMJAM JOHNNY (IRE),** 9, b g Torus—Inventus **Pallet Recycling Services**
24 **LEGAL RIGHT (USA),** 5, b g Alleged (USA)—Rose Red (USA) **Mrs John Magnier**
25 **LORD OF THE WEST (IRE),** 9, b g Mister Lord (USA)—Caroline's Girl **Anne Duchess of Westminster**
26 **MAGSLAD,** 8, ch g Jumbo Hirt (USA)—Welsh Diamond **Mr David Alan Harrison**
27 **MARYCEE (IRE),** 4, b f King's Ride—Miss Lamb **Mr D. O'Connor**
28 **MR RESTRICTOR (IRE),** 5, b g Un Desperado (FR)—Tasmania Star **Mr P. Byrne**
29 **NAUGHTY FUTURE,** 9, ch g Scallywag—Sea Rambler **Mr A. K. Collins**
30 **NEEDLE MATCH,** 5, ch h Royal Academy (USA)—Miss Tatting (USA) **Clayton Bigley Partnership Ltd**
31 **SAGEBRUSH ROLLER,** 10, br g Sharpo—Sunita **Mr A. K. Collins**
32 **SEGALA (IRE),** 7, b g Petorius—Cerosia **Mr F. S. Williams**
33 **SHINING EXAMPLE,** 6, ch g Hadeer—Kick The Habit **Mrs L. R. Joughin**
34 **SLEEPY RIVER (IRE),** 7, ch g Over The River (FR)—Shreelane **Mrs Jonjo O'Neill**

MR J. J. O'NEILL—continued

35 **SLIDEOFHILL (IRE),** 9, ch g Le Bavard (FR)—Queen Weasel **Mr J. P. McManus**
36 **SMOKEY FROM CAPLAW,** 4, b g Sizzling Melody—Mary From Dunlow **Mr G. P. Bernacchi**
37 **SOLWAY BREEZE (IRE),** 5, b m King's Ride—Spicey Cut **Mr David Alan Harrison**
38 **SUBMARINE,** 4, b g Slip Anchor—Meliora **Mr A. K. Collins**
39 **VITAL ISSUE (IRE),** 6, b br g Electric—Dreamello **Anne Duchess of Westminster**
40 **WATER FONT (IRE),** 6, b g Lafontaine (USA)—Belle Savenay **G. & P. Barker Ltd/Globe Engineering**
41 **WHAT JIM WANTS (IRE),** 5, b g Magical Strike (USA)—Sally Gone (IRE) **Clayton Bigley Partnership Ltd**

THREE-YEAR-OLDS

42 **ANKA LADY,** b f Precocious—Hicklam Millie **Mr Fred Coulson**
43 **BARRELBIO (IRE),** b g Elbio—Esther **Mr A. Sweeney and Mr I. Cross**
44 **EARLY PURPLE,** b f Keen—Beautiful Orchid **Mr E. A. Brook**
45 **GLOBE RAIDER,** b g Safawan—Polola **G. & P. Barker Ltd/Globe Engineering**
46 **HAY DANZIG (IRE),** ch f Roi Danzig (USA)—Hay Knot **Pointerfarm Racing Partnership**
47 **MANILA MOON (USA),** b c Manila (USA)—Sign Language (USA) **Clayton Bigley Partnership Ltd**
48 **NEBUCHADNEZZAR,** gr g Absalom—Golden Decoy **Miss G. Joughin**
49 **NORTHUMBRIAN BELLE (IRE),** b f Distinctly North (USA)—La Bella Fontana **Mrs I. C. C. Hayes**
50 **ON THE MAT,** b g Reprimand—Secret Freedom (USA) **Clayton Bigley Partnership Ltd**
51 **TEARAWAY,** gr c Efisio—Hoosie **Mr A. K. Collins**
52 **THANKS KEITH,** ch g Risk Me (FR)—Nannie Annie **Clayton Bigley Partnership Ltd**
53 **TURF MOOR (IRE),** b f Mac's Imp (USA)—Tuft Hill **Valley Paddocks Racing Limited**
54 **UP THE CLARETS (IRE),** b g Petardia—Madeira Lady **Valley Paddocks Racing Limited**

TWO-YEAR-OLDS

55 Ch f 25/3 Savahra Sound—Be My Sweet (Galivanter) **Mr P. Dixon**
56 **DYNAMIC DANCER,** ch c 12/2 King's Signet (USA)—Eleckydo (Electric) **Clayton Bigley Partnership Ltd**
57 **MUCKLE MAVIS,** b f 18/3 Nomadic Way—The Muckle Quine (Hubbly Bubbly (USA)) **Miss G. Joughin**
58 Br f 13/3 Terimon—Singing Forever (Chief Singer) **Mrs L. R. Joughin**
59 B f 3/3 Rock Hopper—Super Sally (Superlative) **Miss G. Joughin**

Other Owners: Dr Linda Barber, Mr A. Barry, Miss Carol A. Blott, Mr R. A. N. Bonnycastle, Mrs B. J. Carrington, Mr J. P. Carrington, Mr N. Cawood, Mrs D. Chacewicz, Mrs A. Chapman, Mrs S. S. Coulson, Miss Yvonne Edwards, Mr John J. Elliot, Mrs Caroline Fallows, Mr L. H. Gilmurray, Mr Paul Green (Huyton), Mr S. S. G. Hayes, Mrs Judy Hunt, Mr P. G. Johnston, Miss Sandra E. Johnston, Mrs Hilary Kerr, Mr John Leat, Mr Geoff Mason, Mr T. Mattinson, Mr Russell McAllister, Mr R. P. McNaught, Mr C. J. Murphy, Mrs Mavis Murphy, Mr L. E. Newey, Mrs Agnes Parkinson, Mr Mark Physick, Mr Warren Lee Primhak, Red Nab Racing Ltd, Mr Brian Robb, Mr Geoff Salters, Mr R. E. Sangster, Mr Allan J. Schaverien, Mrs Maralyn Seed, Mr Richard Seed, Mrs D. Singleton, Mr S. Stirling, Mrs Carmel Sweeney, Mr Jeremy J. Thompson, Mr R. J. C. Upton, Mr Derek Wilson, Mr J. J. Wright.

Jockey (NH): A Roche (10-0).

Apprentice: S Olley (8-11).

Conditional: L Cooper (9-7), D Jewett, R McGrath.

Lady Rider: Miss Sarah Kerswell (9-9).

449 MR O. O'NEILL, Cheltenham

Postal: **Cleeve Lodge, Cleeve Hill, Cheltenham, Gloucestershire, GL52 3PW.**
Phone: **(01242) 673275**

1 **ALLEZ CYRANO (IRE),** 7, b g Alzao (USA)—Miss Bergerac **Mr J. A. Danahar**
2 **A S JIM,** 7, b g Welsh Captain—Cawston's Arms **Mrs H. Jones**
3 **BEACON LANE (IRE),** 5, br g Strong Gale—Sharpaway **Mr Frank Clarke**

MR O. O'NEILL—continued

4 **B MY LOVELY,** 8, ch m Gunner B—Poets Day **Mr Michael J. Brown**
5 **CLEEVE CASTLE,** 6, ch g Carlingford Castle—Hilly Path **Mrs M. Allen & Partners**
6 **DEE DEE,** 6, b m Buckskin (FR)—Special Venture **Mr V. Hever**
7 **EMERALD LAMP (IRE),** 7, b g Miner's Lamp—Mary Kate **Mr Frank Clarke**
8 **KATIE'S JOKER,** 12, b g Idiot's Delight—Roller Skate **Mr J. Russell**
9 **LEGUARD EXPRESS (IRE),** 10, b g Double Schwartz—All Moss **Mr John C. Gilbert**
10 **MAZAMET (USA),** 5, b g Elmaamul (USA)—Miss Mazepah (USA) **Mr Frank Clarke**
11 **MELODY PRINCESS,** 5, b m Ardross—Letteressie **Mr Frank Clarke**
12 **METRO FASHION (IRE),** 7, ch g Carlingford Castle—Good Resemblance **Mr Frank Clarke**
13 **NEW ROSS (IRE),** 6, gr g Roselier (FR)—Miss Lucille **Mr Frank Clarke**
14 **OLD IRISH,** 5, gr g Old Vic—Dunoof **Mr Frank Clarke**
15 **SHARAZAN (IRE),** 5, b g Akarad (FR)—Sharaniya (USA) **Mr Frank Clarke**
16 **SIR ALIDAF,** 4, b g Broadsword (USA)—Bolton Flyer **Mr K. G. Boulton**
17 **TOP DOLLAR (IRE),** 5, b g Brush Aside (USA)—Deep Dollar **Mr Frank Clarke**

THREE-YEAR-OLDS

18 **DARING NEWS,** b g Risk Me (FR)—Hot Sunday Sport **Mr Frank Clarke**

Other Owners: Mr R. Allen, Mr S. Bowett, Mr W. Edwyn-Jones, Mrs L. J. O'Neill, Mr W. T. Robinson, Miss H. Smith.

Jockey (Flat): J V Slattery (8-6).

Jockey (NH): J V Slattery (10-0).

Conditional: H J Oliver (9-7).

450 MR J. F. P. O'REILLY, Barnsley

Postal: **Burntwood Racing, Brierley Common, Brierley, Nr Barnsley, S72 9ET.**
Phone: **(01226) 711123 (0379) 895265 MOBILE**

1 **BANNERET (USA),** 5, b g Imperial Falcon (CAN)—Dashing Partner **Burntwood Sports Ltd**
2 **BELMONT BUCCANEER,** 6, ch g Forzando—Sharp Celine **Bod Racing Partnership**
3 **FLO'S CHOICE (IRE),** 4, b f Dancing Dissident (USA)—Miss Siddons **Burntwood Sports Ltd**
4 **JUDDY,** 4, ch g Clantime—Two's Up **Burntwood Sports Ltd**
5 **LAKE ARIA,** 5, b m Rambo Dancer (CAN)—Hinge **Mrs M. P. Neatby**
6 **NITE OWLER,** 4, b g Saddlers' Hall (IRE)—Lorne Lady **Burntwood Sports Ltd**
7 **WELLCOME INN,** 4, ch g Most Welcome—Mimining **Burntwood Sports Ltd**

THREE-YEAR-OLDS

8 **BILLY OWL (IRE),** ch c Shalford (IRE)—Ounavarra **Burntwood Sports Ltd**

TWO-YEAR-OLDS

9 **CRYSTAL LASS,** b f 19/4 Ardkinglass—That's Rich (Hot Spark) **White House Racing Club, Mr J. Edwards**

Other Owners: Mrs M. Ford, Mr R. K. Ford, Mr Tony Gore, Mr John Hays, Mr M. Rowley, Mr J. T. Wilkinson.

451 MR J. G. M. O'SHEA, Westbury-on-Severn

Postal: **Tudor Racing Stables, Elton, Westbury-on-Severn, Gloucestershire, GL14 1JN.**
Phone: **OFFICE/FAX (01452) 760835 HOME (01594) 516201 MOBILE (0411) 146688**

1 **ALPINE MIST (IRE),** 6, gr g Nishapour (FR)—Afeefa **Catch-42**
2 **BARLEY MEADOW (IRE),** 6, ch g Phardante (FR)—Foredefine **Mr Gary Roberts**
3 **BAYERD (IRE),** 7, b g Strong Gale—Bracka Pigeon **T. G. K. Construction Ltd**

MR J. G. M. O'SHEA—continued

4 **BELL STAFFBOY (IRE)**, 9, b g Phardante (FR)—Trumpster **K. W. Bell & Son Ltd**
5 **BEVELED MILL**, 4, b f Beveled (USA)—Lonely Shore **Mr Tom Jones**
6 **CHIEF GALE (IRE)**, 6, b g Strong Gale—Distant Lady **T. G. K. Construction Ltd**
7 **COLONEL HOOK**, 6, b g Almutanabbi—Come On Clover **Mrs B. J. Lockhart**
8 **DANNY BELL (IRE)**, 5, b g Be My Native (USA)—Rhein Valley (IRE) **Mr K. W. Bell**
9 **DUBLIN RIVER (USA)**, 5, b g Irish River (FR)—Vivre Libre (USA) **Mr K. W. Bell**
10 **FASIL (IRE)**, 5, ch g Polish Patriot (USA)—Apple Peel **Mr Tony Usher**
11 **GIMME (IRE)**, 8, b g Sheer Grit—Barrow Breeze **Mr Brian O'Kane**
12 **GO BALLISTIC**, 9, br g Celtic Cone—National Clover **Mrs B. J. Lockhart**
13 **GOLDEN DRUM (IRE)**, 8, ch g Black Minstrel—Four In A Row **McMahon (Contractors Services) Ltd**
14 **GRANNY NIX**, 8, gr m Zambrano—Ginara **Mr & Mrs J. C. Donnelly**
15 **ISLAND VISION (IRE)**, 8, b g Vision (USA)—Verandah **Mr Gary Roberts**
16 **KERIALI (USA)**, 5, b g Irish River (FR)—Kerita **Mr Tony Usher**
17 **LANDED GENTRY (USA)**, 9, b g Vaguely Noble—Phydilla (FR) **K. W. Bell & Son Ltd**
18 **LORD FOLEY (NZ)**, 6, b g Cache of Gold (USA)—Gay Beat (NZ) **Foley Steelstock**
19 **MAJOR BILL (IRE)**, 7, ch g Cheval—Pineway VII **Mr John Pugh**
20 **MENDELUCI (IRE)**, 6, b g Nordico (USA)—Favourite Niece **Mr Robert Mullett**
21 **MISS ROBERTO (IRE)**, 5, ch m Don Roberto (USA)—Frau Ahuyentante (ARG) **M. G. Lilwall and Partners (2)**
22 **NORDIC PRINCE (IRE)**, 7, b g Nordance (USA)—Royal Desire **Mr Brian O'Kane**
23 **OH DEARIE ME**, 6, b m Puissance—Tyrian Princess **The Cross Racing Club**
24 5, Br m Strong Gale—Orra Beg **Mr Graham Brown**
25 **ROYAL RAPPORT**, 5, ch g Rich Charlie—Miss Camellia **Mr Gary Roberts**
26 **SEPTEMBER BREEZE (IRE)**, 7, ch m Henbit (USA)—Deepwater Woman **Best Racing**
27 **SHILLELAGH OAK**, 8, ch g Nishapour (FR)—Sweet Ecstasy **Mr C. E. Moir**
28 **SIGMA RUN (IRE)**, 9, b g The Parson—Splendid Run **K. W. Bell & Son Ltd**
29 **SPARTAN HEARTBEAT**, 5, b g Shareef Dancer (USA)—Helen's Dream **Mr K. W. Bell**
30 **TANGO MAN (IRE)**, 6, ch g King Luthier—Amour Libre **T. G. K. Construction Ltd**
31 **TOM-MOSS**, 6, b g Le Moss—Val's Jem **Mr Ray Salter**
32 **WALTER'S DREAM (IRE)**, 8, b br g Strong Gale—Wonder Alice **Pentons (Haulage & Storage)**

THREE-YEAR-OLDS

33 **GARAJ**, ch c Alhijaz—Sunley Stars **Mr Gary Roberts**
34 **IMPERIAL COURT (IRE)**, b c Imperial Frontier (USA)—Fandikos (IRE) **M. G. Lilwall & Partners**
35 **JOLLYHACK**, b c Mon Tresor—Spiritofaffection **T. Bell, P. McDonald, J. McGowan**

Other Owners: Allfor, Mr M. D. Anderson, N. G. H. Ayliffe, Mr K. W. Bell, Mrs Teresa Bell, Mr R. P. Berrow, Mr Martin Bradley, Mr Sean Bryan, Mr T. Connop, Mr R. J. Cummings, Mr J. C. Donnelly, Mrs S. P. Donnelly, Mr Tony Fletcher, Foley Steelstock, Mr S. Gallagher, Mr R. H. Harris, Mr Anthony C. Hughes, Mr M. G. Lilwall, Mr H. G. Llewellyn, Mr T. P. Macdonald, Mr C. R. McDonagh, Mr J. P. McGowan, Mr Peter Munro, Mr Ian D. Newman, Mrs Alurie O'Sullivan, Mr S. Pack, Ms Jill Palmer, Mr M. R. Parkes, Mr Barry Sale, Mr W. Sanderson, Mr Anthony W. Smith, Mr D. Thode, Mr Barry Veasey, Mr A. J. Yeates.

Jockeys (NH): M A Fitzgerald (10-0), A P McCoy (10-0).

Conditional: Michael Brennan, Adrian Scholes, Martin Smith.

Amateur: Mr Martin Fitzgerald.

452 MR EUGENE M. O'SULLIVAN, Mallow

Postal: **Brittas, Lombardstown, Mallow, Co. Cork.**
Phone: **(022) 47116/47304 FAX (022) 47588 MOBILE (086) 541398**

1 **ABSENT CITIZEN (IRE)**, 5, b m Supreme Leader—Boreen Citizen **E. J. O'Sullivan**
2 4, Br g Man Among Men (IRE)—Against You **E. M. O'Sullivan**
3 **ANOTHER EXCUSE (IRE)**, 10, br g Mandalus—Alan's Rosalinda **Kilshannig R. S.**

MR EUGENE M. O'SULLIVAN—continued

4 **AUGUSTA BROOK (IRE)**, 5, br m Over The River (FR)—Augusta Victoria **Terence O'Donnell**
5 **BALLYHEST FOUNTAIN (IRE)**, 7, b m Royal Fountain—Ride The Waves **D. O'Reilly**
6 **BLAZE O'BOY (IRE)**, 5, b g Blaze O' Gold (USA)—Fernshaw **Miss E. Sykes**
7 **BOSS MORTON (IRE)**, 7, b g Tremblant—Sandy Kelly **M. C. O'Sullivan**
8 5, Ch g Ballacashtal (CAN)—Carolynchristensen **N. W. Rimmington**
9 **CITIZEN BILL (IRE)**, 4, ch g Alphabatim (USA)—Elgran Citizen **E. J. O'Sullivan**
10 **COPE WITH REALITY (IRE)**, 5, b g Danehill (USA)—Reality **Fiona O'Sullivan**
11 **DHA FOCALEILE (IRE)**, 5, br g Be My Native (USA)—Stamp of Glory **Denis Fehan**
12 **EXCUSE ME SIR (IRE)**, 5, br g Glacial Storm (USA)—Knockarctic **Kilshannig R. S.**
13 **FINNOW THYNE (IRE)**, 8, br g Good Thyne (USA)—Mother Cluck **Ivor Dulohery**
14 **GLACIAL VIEW (IRE)**, 5, ch g Glacial Storm (USA)—Ara View **J. White & D. Grumley**
15 4, Ch f Project Manager—Gorm **Terence O'Donnell**
16 **GORTBOFINA LADY (IRE)**, 5, ch m Phardante (FR)—Welsh Thorn **Fiona O'Sullivan**
17 **GORTROE GUY (IRE)**, 6, b g Carlingford Castle—Calfstown Night **Anne O'Sullivan**
18 **HICKEY'S TAVERN (IRE)**, 5, ch g Black Minstrel—Wait For Gillian **Sean Hickey**
19 **JACK FLA (IRE)**, 6, ch g Electric—Run Artiste **Churchtown R. S.**
20 **LITTLE ROO (IRE)**, 6, b m King's Ride—Quetta's Dual **E. Murray**
21 **LOCKBEG LASS (IRE)**, 6, b m Supreme Leader—Super Sayanarra **Ringaskiddy R. C.**
22 **LOFTUS LAD (IRE)**, 10, b g Le Bavard (FR)—Maeves Invader **Ringaskiddy R. C.**
23 **MEEANDTWO (IRE)**, 5, b g Torus—Marble Miller (IRE) **C. Meehan & Patrick Twomey**
24 **MURIEL'S PRIDE (IRE)**, 7, br m Mister Lord (USA)—Toombeola **D. Sharp Bolster**
25 **NEWBERRY ROSE (IRE)**, 6, br m Black Minstrel—Bellusis **E. J. O'Sullivan**
26 **ROCK ON LORD (IRE)**, 6, b m Mister Lord (USA)—Run In Time **Patrick Mulcahy**
27 **SAM VAUGHAN (IRE)**, 9, ch g Milk of The Barley—Kentstown Girl **Maura Moylan**
28 **SHIRODKAR (IRE)**, 6, b g Supreme Leader—Progello **Grand Crew R. S.**
29 **SUPREME CITIZEN (IRE)**, 6, b g Supreme Leader—Kelenem **E. J. O'Sullivan**

THREE-YEAR-OLDS

30 Ch g Phardante (FR)—Boreen Citizen **E. J. O'Sullivan**
31 B g Alphabatim (USA)—John's Rose **Fiona O'Sullivan**
32 Br f Be My Native (USA)—Kelenem **E. J. O'Sullivan**
33 B f Alphabatim (USA)—Lyndon Rose **Fiona O'Sullivan**

Other Owners: Mr Denis A. Linehan, John G. Linehan, C. Meehan, Miss E. Murphy.

Jockeys (NH): Garrett Cotter (9-4), Michael Murphy (9-7).

Amateurs: Mr Brendan O'Sullivan (10-7), Mr William O'Sullivan (10-7), Mr John A Sheehan (9-7).

Lady Rider: Fiona O'Sullivan (9-7).

453 MRS S. M. ODELL, Chipping Norton

Postal: **Little Brook House, Little Tew, Chipping Norton, Oxfordshire, OX7 4JJ.**
Phone: **(01608) 683249**

1 **DAYS OF LIGHTNING**, 5, b m Lightning Dealer—Orleans Spring **Mr W. J. Odell**
2 **DAYS OF THUNDER**, 10, ch g Vaigly Great—Silent Prayer **Mr W. J. Odell**
3 **RYTON RUN**, 13, b g Deep Run—Money Spinner **Mr W. J. Odell**

454 MR J. A. B. OLD, Wroughton

Postal: **Upper Herdswick Farm, Hackpen, Burderop, Wroughton, Wiltshire, SN1 0RH.**
Phone: **(01793) 845200 (OFFICE) CAR (0836) 721459 FAX (01793) 845201**

1 **ARFER MOLE (IRE),** 10, b g Carlingford Castle—Sharpaway **Mr W. E. Sturt**
2 **ARKLEY ROYAL,** 7, b g Ardross—Lady Geneva **Mr John Bickel**
3 **BARRISTERS BOY,** 8, b g Rakaposhi King—Thevicarsdaughter **The Rumpole Partnership**
4 **BOXGROVE MAN (IRE),** 8, br g Mandalus—Kittykelvin **Lord Lloyd-Webber**
5 **BRACEY RUN (IRE),** 8, b g The Parson—Outdoor Ivy **Doubleprint**
6 **CAPTAIN WALTER (IRE),** 8, b h Supreme Leader—Deep Captain **Mr W. E. Sturt**
7 **CHAI-YO,** 8, b g Rakaposhi King—Ballysax Lass **Mr Nick Viney**
8 **CLEVER REMARK,** 9, b g Idiot's Delight—Brave Remark **Mrs Jan Smith**
9 **COLLIER BAY,** 8, b g Green Desert (USA)—Cockatoo Island **Mr W. E. Sturt**
10 **COUNTRY HOUSE,** 7, b m Town And Country—Mearlin **The Country House Syndicate**
11 **DANGEROUS GUEST (IRE),** 6, b g Deploy—Guest List
12 **DAWN LEADER (IRE),** 7, b g Supreme Leader—Tudor Dawn **Bonusprint**
13 **DEEP C DIVA (IRE),** 6, b m Supreme Leader—Deep Adventure **Lady Lloyd Webber**
14 **DUNBURY FLYER (IRE),** 6, ch g Be My Native (USA)—Miss Umm (IRE) **Mr Graham Dalziel**
15 **EL FREDDIE,** 8, b g El Conquistador—Unto Rose **Mr J. A. B. Old & Partners**
16 **FRANK BYRNE,** 6, b g Rakaposhi King—Polarita **Mr W. E. Sturt**
17 **FRYS NO FOOL,** 8, b g Idiot's Delight—Scotch And Ice **Frys No Fool Partnership**
18 **GARY DUKE (FR),** 4, b g Iron Duke (FR)—Mary Long Grass (FR) **Mr W. E. Sturt**
19 **JEFFERIES,** 9, br g Sunyboy—Scotch Princess **Miss S. Blumberg, Mr J. M. Sage**
20 **JUYUSH (USA),** 6, b h Silver Hawk (USA)—Silken Doll (USA) **Mr W. E. Sturt**
21 **KING MOLE,** 7, b g Rakaposhi King—Sayshar **Mr Denis Milne, Mrs J. Fowler**
22 **KINGS CHERRY (IRE),** 10, b g King's Ride—Another Cherry **Mr T. J. Swaffield**
23 **KLONDIKE CHARGER (USA),** 4, b g Crafty Prospector (USA)—Forever Waving (USA) **Mrs Jan Smith**
24 **LOMBARDIC (USA),** 7, b h Private Account (USA)—If Winter Comes (USA) **Bonusprint**
25 **LORD JIM (IRE),** 6, b g Kahyasi—Sarah Georgina **Mrs S. Y. Thomas**
26 **MANDALAY,** 9, b g Mandalus—Hurricane Hattie **Auld Alliance**
27 7, Ch g Gildoran—Milltown Lady **Mr J. A. B. Old**
28 **NATIVE KING (IRE),** 6, b h Be My Native (USA)—Outdoor Ivy **Mr George Ward**
29 **PETE THE PARSON (IRE),** 9, b g The Parson—Gemelek **Mr W. E. Sturt**
30 **POLAR RAMBLER (IRE),** 7, br g Strong Gale—The Wren's Nest **Tripleprint**
31 **PRINCE KINSKY,** 5, ch h Master Willie—Princess Lieven **Mrs Anne Bickel**
32 **RED LIGHTER,** 9, ch g Lighter—Miss Redlands **Mrs C. H. Antrobus**
33 **SIMPSON,** 13, ch g Royal Match—Black Penny **Mr John Bickel**
34 **SIR TALBOT,** 4, b g Ardross—Bermuda Lily **Mr W. E. Sturt**
35 **SONG OF THE SWORD,** 5, b g Kris—Melodist (USA) **Lady Lloyd Webber**
36 **SPACEAGE GOLD,** 9, b g Sunyboy—Chancer's Last **Mr Graham Dalziel**
37 **SUPREME GENOTIN (IRE),** 9, b g Supreme Leader—Inagh's Image **Mr W. E. Sturt**
38 **THREE FARTHINGS,** 8, b g Derring Rose—Black Penny **Mr K. R. Britten**
39 **TRAPPER CREEK (IRE),** 6, ch h Henbit (USA)—Trapper Jean **Tripleprint**
40 **UPHAM SURPRISE,** 10, b g Sula Bula—Upham Lady **Mr J. A. B. Old**
41 **WISE KING,** 8, b g Rakaposhi King—Sunwise **Mr Denis Milne**
42 **WRECKLESS MAN,** 11, br g Mandalus—Wreck-Em-All **Mr J. A. B. Old**
43 **YAHMI (IRE),** 8, b g Law Society (USA)—Hogan's Sister (USA) **Mr W. E. Sturt**

Other Owners: Mr Charles Arkwright, Mr D. W. Blomeley, Mr J. Chromiak, Mr M. G. A. Court, Mrs Anne-Marie Dartnall, Mrs C. R. Davison, Lady Camilla Dempster, Mr Nigel Dempster, Mr J. L. Eddis, Mr S. Emmet, Miss C. Foster, Mr R. P. Fry, Mrs S. Gill, Harlequin Software Consultants Ltd, Mr Chris Jenkins, Mr M. W. Lampkin, Mr Martin Lovatt, Mr H. B. Lowe, Mr D. Martin-Betts, Mr W. Osborne-Young, Mrs Alison Smith, Mr Adrian Spooner, Mr D. F. Turner.

Jockey (NH): C Llewellyn (10-0, w.a.).

455 MR G. R. OLDROYD, York

Postal: **The Stables, Common Farm, Upper Hemsley, York, YO4 1JX.**
Phone: **(01759) 373007**

1 **ARCHELLO (IRE)**, 4, b f Archway (IRE)—Golden Room **Mr E. Gale**
2 **DANCE MELODY**, 4, b f Rambo Dancer (CAN)—Cateryne **Mr D. W. B. Meldrum**
3 **DISPOL DIAMOND**, 5, b m Sharpo—Fabulous Rina (FR) **Mrs D. Drewery**
4 **DISPOL PRINCE**, 5, b g Risk Me (FR)—Gemma Kaye **Mr Robert E. Cook**
5 **GRAMPSAWINNA**, 10, b m Peter Wrekin—Seabright Smile **Miss Angela Bennett**
6 **GREENACRES LADY**, 8, b m Seymour Hicks (FR)—Moon Lady **Miss Angela Bennett**
7 **MU-ARRIK**, 10, b br h Aragon—Maravilla **Mr Robert E. Cook**
8 **NUKUD (USA)**, 6, b g Topsider (USA)—Summer Silence (USA) **Mr Robert E. Cook**

THREE-YEAR-OLDS

9 **CRYSTAL LOUGH (IRE)**, b f Maelstrom Lake—Holy Water **Mr W. F. Burton**
10 **CRYSTAL WATERS (IRE)**, b f River Falls—Annie's Glen (IRE)
11 **GAELIC QUINIE (IRE)**, b f River Falls—Eliza Wooding **Mr William Riddell**
12 **PABELLA BLUEBIRD (IRE)**, b f Mac's Imp (USA)—Blue Diana (IRE) **Mr C. Raine**
13 **REPOSE (IRE)**, gr f Posen (USA)—Dream Trader **Ms Janet McLeod**

TWO-YEAR-OLDS

14 B c 17/3 Inchinor—Actress (Known Fact (USA))
15 **CORBYPARK (IRE)**, ch f 17/4 College Chapel—Karoi (IRE) (Kafu) **Mrs D. Drowesy**
16 Ch f 26/4 Soviet Lad—Great Pleasure (GER) (Star Appeal)
17 B f 15/4 Treasure Kay—Mighty Special (IRE) (Head For Heights)
18 Gr f 8/5 Archway (IRE)—Zanskar (Godswalk (USA))

Other Owners: Mr Mick Burrows, Mrs G. M. Cook, Mr P. Drewery, Mr Adrian Goodings, Mr W. B. Imison, Mr G. R. Oldroyd, Mr C. Wright, Mr J. F. Wright.

Jockey (Flat): K Hodgson (8-5).

Amateur: Mr William Wenyon (9-12).

456 MR J. K. M. OLIVER, Hawick

Postal: **Hassendean Bank, Hawick, Roxburghshire, TD9 8RX.**
Phone: **(01450) 870216 MOBILE (0374) 426017 FAX (01450) 870357**

1 **ARCTIC SANDY (IRE)**, 8, ch g Sandalay—Reach Here **Mr & Mrs Raymond Anderson Green**
2 **DUSKY DANTE (IRE)**, 4, b f Phardante (FR)—Red Dusk **Dusky Dante Partnership**
3 **EVENING DUSK (IRE)**, 6, b m Phardante (FR)—Red Dusk **Mrs Fiona Rintoul**
4 **GOLDEN FIDDLE (IRE)**, 10, b g Strong Gale—Belle Mackay **Mr W. Stuart Wilson**
5 **HALLRULE (IRE)**, 4, ch g Be My Native (USA)—Phantom Thistle **Mr J. K. M. Oliver, Mrs F. Percy-Davis**
6 **HONEY SPICE**, 6, b m Henbit (USA)—Honeyburn **Mr J. K. M. Oliver**
7 **I'M STILL HERE**, 4, gr g Skyliner—Miss Colenca **Mrs J. M. Berry**
8 **STORMY FABLE (IRE)**, 5, b g Lafontaine (USA)—Galeshula **Mr T. J. Summerfield**
9 **THORNWOOD (IRE)**, 6, ch g Phardante (FR)—Arctic Mistress **The British Beef Partnership**
10 **TIMBUCKTOO**, 11, b g Buckskin (FR)—Rugged Glen **Mrs P. M. Guild**

THREE-YEAR-OLDS

11 Ch g Phardante (FR)—Red Dusk **Mr J. K. M. Oliver**

TWO-YEAR-OLDS

12 B f 10/5 Minster Son—Gilmanscleuch (IRE) (Mandalus) **Mr J. K. M. Oliver**
13 B f 18/6 Royal Fountain—Red Dusk (Deep Run) **Mr J. K. M. Oliver**

MR J. K. M. OLIVER—continued

Other Owners: Mr Philip Allison, Mr J. Berry, Mrs Peta Culham, Mr Ian Davidson, Mr J. G. Dudgeon, Mr Eric Gillie, Mrs Anita Green, Mr Philip O'Brien, Mrs J. K. M. Oliver, Mr Joe Richardson, Mr Ted Rodgers, Pat Shaw, Mr John A. Sleigh, T D Stowe, Mr R. P. Walker.

Jockey (NH): B Storey (w.a.).

Conditional: S Melrose.

Lady Rider: Miss Sandra Forster (10-0).

457 MR H. ORDE-POWLETT, Leyburn

Postal: **Wensley Hall, Wensley, Leyburn, North Yorkshire, DL8 4HN.**
Phone: **(01969) 623674 OR 623981**

1 **ANTRIM COUNTY,** 13, ch g Deep Run—Gothic Arch **Mr H. A. N. Orde-Powlett**
2 **GIKONGORO,** 5, ch g Dominion—Sea Charm **Mr H. A. N. Orde-Powlett**
3 **HUSO,** 10, ch g Sharpo—Husnah **Mr H. A. N. Orde-Powlett**

Amateurs: Mr Harry Orde-Powlett (10-10), Mr W. Ben Orde-Powlett (10-0).

458 MR E. H. OWEN, Denbigh

Postal: **Y Wern, Llandyrnog, Denbigh, Clwyd, Wales, LL16 4HW.**
Phone: **LLANDYRNOG (01824) 790264**

1 **INCEY WINCEY,** 6, b m Idiot's Delight—Muffet's Spider **Mrs Julia Owen**
2 **MUIZENBERG,** 11, b g Mashhor Dancer (USA)—Allotria **Mrs Julia Owen**

459 MR JOHN M. OXX, Kildare

Postal: **Creeve, Currabeg, Kildare, Ireland.**
Phone: **0455 21310 FAX 0455 22236**

1 **ADMIRAL WINGS (IRE),** 4, b g In The Wings—Folkboat **A. Gannon**
2 **COLOMBIAN GREEN (IRE),** 4, b c Sadler's Wells (USA)—Sharaya (USA) **Mr Benny Kwong**
3 **DABALI (IRE),** 4, b c Doyoun—Dabiliya **H. H. Aga Khan**
4 **DARROUZETT (IRE),** 4, b f Darshaan—Hebba (USA) **Sheikh Mohammed**
5 **DONA ROYALE (IRE),** 4, b f Darshaan—Sovereign Dona **Mr R. Griffin**
6 **EBADIYLA (IRE),** 4, b f Sadler's Wells (USA)—Ebaziya (IRE) **H. H. Aga Khan**
7 **FORT MORGAN (USA),** 4, b c Pleasant Colony—Colorado Dancer **Sheikh Mohammed**
8 **RAIYOUN (IRE),** 5, b h Doyoun—Raymouna (IRE) **H. H. Aga Khan**
9 **RAYOUNI (IRE),** 4, b c Zayyani—Raymouna (GER) **H. H. Aga Khan**
10 **RENGE,** 4, ch f Generous—Lyphard's Lady **Mr T. Wada**
11 **SOMERTON REEF,** 4, gr c Mystiko (USA)—Lady Reef **Mr P. J. Austin**
12 **SYMBOLI KILDARE (IRE),** 5, b h Kaldoun (FR)—Quiche **Mr T. Wada**
13 **VIA SALERIA,** 4, b f Arazi—Alexandrie **S. Hanson**
14 **WINGED HUSSAR,** 5, b g In The Wings—Akila **Dundalk Racing Club**
15 **WOODSIA,** 4, b f Woodman—Aquaba **Sheikh Mohammed**

EQUINE NUTRITIONAL CONSULTANCY

Helping Clients to Stay Lengths Ahead

Advisors to English and Irish Champion Trainers and Leading Producers of Thoroughbred Bloodstock

While many companies are just trying to sell you products – come to us for completely independent advice on how to effectively maximise the benefits of your feeding and supplemental programmes

OUR REFERENCES AND THE CONSISTENT RESULTS OF OUR CLIENTS SPEAK FOR THEMSELVES

For more Information on how to join this elite group contact:
Pamela Kinslow BA MSc – ENC Limited – Jasmine Cottage,
East Garston, Berkshire UK RG17 7EX – Tel/Fax: 01488-648683

MR JOHN M. OXX—continued

THREE-YEAR-OLDS

16 **ABANDONMENT,** b f Caerleon—Fermoy **Sheikh Mohammed**
17 **ABSOLUTA,** b f Royal Academy—Leyete Gulf **Mrs F. G. Wilson**
18 **AFARAD,** b c Slip Anchor—Afasara **H. H. Aga Khan**
19 **ALLOTROPE,** b c Nashwan—Graphite (USA) **Sheikh Mohammed**
20 **ANAZEEM,** b f Irish River—Anaza **H. H. Aga Khan**
21 **BADILA,** b f Doyoun—Badaraya **H. H. Aga Khan**
22 **BANIYKKA,** b f Doyoun—Banaja **H. H. Aga Khan**
23 **BAYYADI,** b c Doyoun—Bayyasa **H. H. Aga Khan**
24 **BELDARIAN,** b f Last Tycoon—Sorbus **G. W. Jennings**
25 **BIG TIPPER (USA),** b c El Gran Senor—It Will Be Forever **L. Neil Jones**
26 **BOSANQUET (USA),** b f Pleasant Colony—Beat (USA) **Sheikh Mohammed**
27 **BUDDY AND SODA,** ch f Imperial Frontier—Tikarna **B. Brindley**
28 **CANZONA,** gr c Kenmare—Gay Nocturne **Lady Clague**
29 **CHALNA,** b f Darshaan—Chalon **Sheikh Mohammed**
30 **CROMWELL,** b g Last Tycoon—Catherine Parr **Sheikh Mohammed**
31 **CYDONIE,** b f Hansel—Cydalia **Mrs A. J. F. O'Reilly**
32 **DABAYA,** br f In The Wings—Dabiliya **H. H. Aga Khan**
33 **DEYSANIYA,** ch f Lycius—Denizliya **H. H. Aga Khan**
34 **ELECTORATE,** b f Caerleon—Elect **Sheikh Mohammed**
35 **ENZELI,** b c Kahyasi—Ebaziya **H. H. Aga Khan**
36 **EYMIR,** ch c Polish Patriot—Eviyrna **H. H. Aga Khan**
37 **GOLDEN CAT,** b f Storm Cat—Eurobird **G. W. Jennings**
38 **HANZANAR,** b c Alzao—Hanzala **H. H. Aga Khan**
39 **HARIYMI,** gr c Woodman—Harouniya **H. H. Aga Khan**
40 **HAZARAMA,** b f Kahyasi—Hazaradjat **H. H. Aga Khan**
41 **HIMRANI,** b c Shernazar—Himaya **H. H. Aga Khan**
42 **ILLYRIA,** ch f Nashwan—Idraak **Sheikh Mohammed**
43 **IMPUDENT REBECCA,** gr f Linamix—Touraya **Mrs A. Coughlan**
44 **KATIYAR,** gr c Kenmare—Katiyfa **H. H. Aga Khan**
45 **KERIYOUN,** b c Storm Bird—Kerita **H. H. Aga Khan**
46 **KHAIRKA,** gr f Tirol—Khairkana **H. H. Aga Khan**
47 **KHALIANDAK,** gr c Doyoun—Khalisiyn **H. H. Aga Khan**
48 **KHATANI,** b c Kahyasi—Khanata **H. H. Aga Khan**
49 **KHATELA,** b f Shernazar—Khatima **H. H. Aga Khan**
50 **LOYAL DEED,** b c Alleged (USA)—Reloy (USA) **Sheikh Mohammed**
51 **MADAME CURIE,** b f Polish Precedent—Last Exit **Mrs A. Gurney**
52 **MARDANI,** b c Fairy King—Marmana **H. H. Aga Khan**
53 **MARITANA,** b f Rahy—Mariella (USA) **Sheikh Mohammed**
54 **MASARKAL,** b c Kahyasi—Masarika **H. H. Aga Khan**
55 **MAZURKA,** b f Polish Precedent—Kashtala **Sheikh Mohammed**
56 **MESSILA ROSE,** b f Darshaan—Golden Cay **Khaled D. S. Al-Sabah**
57 **MILLE MIGLIA,** b f Caerleon—Madame du Barry **D. Hoefemeier**
58 **MISTER BOLD,** ch c Persian Bold—Madiya **Mrs D. Reddan**
59 **MORA,** ch f Second Set—Broadway Royal **Mrs F. G. Wilson**
60 **NICOLA BELLA,** b f Sadler's Wells—Valley of Hope **L. Neil Jones**
61 **NOVIAN,** br f Doyoun—Naevog **Mrs J. J. Byrne**
62 **OUTSPOKEN,** ch c Arazi (USA)—Oh So Sharp **Sheikh Mohammed**
63 **PIRRO,** ch c Persian Bold—Kindness Itself **Lady Clague**
64 **PLAYACTING,** b c Forty Niner—Mystery Play **Sheikh Mohammed**
65 **QUEVILLY,** b c Rainbow Quest—Nadma (USA) **Sheikh Mohammed**
66 **RHINE VALLEY,** b f Danzig—Lake Valley **Sheikh Mohammed**
67 **RIDGEWOOD RUBY,** b f Indian Ridge—Glen Kella Manx **Mrs A. Coughlan**
68 **RITE OF SPRING,** ch f Niniksi—Riverstreak **Dundalk Racing Club**
69 **ROYAL HOUSE (FR),** b f Royal Academy—Reine Caroline **Mrs A. O'Neill**
70 **SANAKA,** b f Kahyasi—Sanamia **H. H. Aga Khan**
71 **SANCHEZ,** ch f Wolfhound (USA)—Flamenco Wave **Sheikh Mohammed**
72 **SARWANI,** gr g Fayruz—Sarafia **H. H. Aga Khan**

MR JOHN M. OXX—continued

73 **SCANDISK,** b f Kenmare—Yankee Lady **Parco SRL**
74 **SHAFOAN,** ch c Sharpo—Rani **Sheikh Mohammed**
75 **SHAH OF PERSIA,** b c Darshaan—Equal Eloquence **J. D. Clague**
76 **SHAIYMARA,** b f Darshaan—Shaiyra **H. H. Aga Khan**
77 **SHAQUILLE,** br c Thatching—Louzitania **Parco SRL**
78 **SPECIALIST (USA),** b c Caerleon—Self Assured **Sheikh Mohammed**
79 **STRIKE HARD,** b f Green Desert (USA)—Chinese Justice **Sheikh Mohammed**
80 **SUMMER STYLE,** ch f Indian Ridge—Summer Fashion **D. B. Davis**
81 **TAKARIAN,** b c Doyoun—Takarouna **H. H. Aga Khan**
82 **TARASI,** b c Green Dancer—Tarafa **H. H. Aga Khan**
83 **WHITE FANG,** b f Wolfhound (USA)—Ivory Dawn **Sheikh Mohammed**
84 **WINONA,** b f Alzao—My Potters **Lady Clague**
85 **WOODWIN,** ch f Woodman—Klarifi **G. W. Jennings**

TWO-YEAR-OLDS

86 **ANSAR,** b c 2/2 Kahyasi—Anaza (Darshaan) **H. H. Aga Khan**
87 B f 28/3 In The Wings—Arctic Appeal (Ahonoora) **Sheikh Mohammed**
88 B c 5/2 Catrail—Atsuko (Mtoto) **Mrs A. J. F. O'Reilly**
89 Ch f 27/3 Night Shift—Ballet Shoes (Ela-Mana-Mou) **Mrs A. J. F. O'Reilly**
90 Br c 8/3 Catrail—Ballykett Lady (Sir Ivor) **Exors of the late N. Keating**
91 Ch c 17/2 Polish Precedent—Calounia (Pharly) **H. H. Aga Khan**
92 B f 5/3 Warning—Chanzi (El Gran Senor) **Sheikh Mohammed**
93 B c 1/5 Nureyev—Colour Chart (Mr Prospector) **Sheikh Mohammed**
94 B c 4/5 Persian Bold—Dabtiya (Shirley Heights) **H. H. Aga Khan**
95 Ch f 29/3 Lycius—Dance Festival (Nureyev) **Sheikh Mohammed**
96 B c 29/3 Indian Ridge—Dawnsio (Tate Gallery) **Lady Clague**
97 **EVIYRN,** b c 18/4 In The Wings—Evrana (Nureyev) **H. H. Aga Khan**
98 B f 29/3 Hamas—Folkboat (Kalaglow) **A. Gannon**
99 B c 6/4 Caerleon—Game Plan (Darshaan) **Sheikh Mohammed**
100 B c 8/5 Royal Academy—Go Honey Go (General Assembly) **Mr & Mrs R. Shroff**
101 Ch f 19/2 Zafonic—Gothic Dream (Nashwan) **Lady Clague**
102 B f 6/3 Caerleon—Graphite (Mr Prospector) **Sheikh Mohammed**
103 **HAMMERING,** b c 13/2 Hamas—Cachet (Warning) **Mrs C. Burns**
104 **HIRAPOUR,** b c 28/4 Kahyasi—Himaya (Mouktar) **H. H. Aga Khan**
105 Ch f 3/3 Wolfhound—Ice Pool (Diesis) **Sheikh Mohammed**
106 B f 16/4 Kris—Idle Gossip (Lyphard) **Killeen Castle Stud**
107 B f 24/1 El Gran Senor—Image of Truth (In Reality) **Mrs A. J. F. O'Reilly**
108 B f 10/4 Alzao—Kashka (The Minstrel) **Lady Clague**
109 B f 17/5 Common Grounds—Klarifi (Habitat) **G. W. Jennings**
110 B f 6/5 Selkirk—Last Exit (Dominion) **Mrs A. Gurney**
111 B f 26/4 Lycius—La Vue (Reviewer) **Sheikh Mohammed**
112 **LIGHT RIVER,** ch f 14/3 Irish River—Lirica (Blushing Groom) **Mrs A. J. F. O'Reilly**
113 **LITTLE GIANT,** b c 2/4 Caerleon—Ballerina (Dancing Brave) **L. Neil Jones**
114 B c 25/1 Darshaan—Lypharita (Lightning) **Sheikh Mohammed**
115 **MANGWANA (USA),** b f 16/3 Dehere—Yanuka (Pitcairn) **Mrs F. G. Wilson**
116 B br c 14/3 Machiavellian—Massaraat (Nureyev) **Sheikh Mohammed**
117 B f 7/3 Green Desert—My Potters (Irish River) **Lady Clague**
118 B f 1/3 Silver Hawk—Mystery Play (Sadler's Wells) **Sheikh Mohammed**
119 B c 30/5 Pleasant Colony—Night Secret (Nijinsky) **Sheikh Mohammed**
120 B f 29/2 Sabrehill—Nobly Born (The Minstrel) **Sheikh Mohammed**
121 Ch c 22/2 Arazi—Outstandingly (Exclusive Native) **Sheikh Mohammed**
122 **PAMPITA (USA),** ch f 29/1 Affirmed—Style N' Elegance (Alysheba) **Mrs F. G. Wilson**
123 B f 29/4 Arazi—Park Appeal (Ahonoora) **Sheikh Mohammed**
124 B f 22/5 Theatrical—Reloy (Liloy) **Sheikh Mohammed**
125 B c 15/5 Woodman—Sahara Sun (Alysheba) **Mrs A. J. F. O'Reilly**
126 B f 6/5 Nashwan—Samsova (Shareef Dancer) **Sheikh Mohammed**
127 **SISTER BELLA,** b f 9/1 Sadler's Wells—Valley of Hope (Riverman) **L. Neil Jones**
128 B f 16/2 Sadler's Wells—Skating (Mill Reef) **Sheikh Mohammed**
129 B c 19/4 Darshaan—Sorbus (Busted) **Sheikh Mohammed**
130 B f 25/1 Darshaan—Sovereign Touch (Pennine Walk) **Killeen Castle Stud**

MR JOHN M. OXX—continued

131 B f 26/5 Fairy King—Tap On Air (Caerleon) **Sheikh Mohammed**
132 B c 26/2 Sadler's Wells—Tarsila (High Top) **Sheikh Mohammed**
133 Ch f 23/3 Arazi—Twyla (Habitat) **Sheikh Mohammed**
134 B f 23/2 Sadler's Wells—Valdara (Darshaan) **Sheikh Mohammed**
135 B c 7/5 Seattle Dancer—What A Candy (Key To The Mint) **J. F. Malle**
136 Ch c 3/4 Woodman—Windmill Point (Storm Bird) **Sheikh Mohammed**

Jockeys (Flat): D Hogan (8-8), J P Murtagh (8-10), P J Smullen (8-4).

Apprentices: C Gannon (7-2), K Lavelle (7-2), S O'Keeffe (8-3), L O'Neill (8-0), I Power (7-0).

460 MR BRYN PALLING, Cowbridge

Postal: **Ty-Wyth-Newydd, Tredodridge, Cowbridge, South Glam, CF71 7UL.**
Phone: **COWBRIDGE (01446) 760122 FAX (01446) 760067**

1 ARCTIC THUNDER (USA), 7, b g Far North (CAN)—Flying Cloud (USA) **Merthyr Motor Auctions**
2 BEAU VENTURE (USA), 10, ch h Explodent (USA)—Old Westbury (USA) **Mrs A. L. Stacey**
3 BELLE'S BOY, 5, b g Nalchik (USA)—Ty-With-Belle **Mrs M. M. Palling**
4 BONNE VILLE, 4, gr f Good Times (ITY)—Ville Air **Millbrook Associates**
5 BROOKSEES DREAM, 4, ch f Glacial Storm (USA)—Good Holidays **Mr Caleb Davies**
6 CARRANITA (IRE), 8, b m Anita's Prince—Take More (GER) **Mr Humphrey Okeke & Mrs Rena Davies**
7 CHICKAWICKA (IRE), 7, b h Dance of Life (USA)—Shabby Doll **Merthyr Motor Auctions**
8 HAROLDON (IRE), 9, ch g Heraldiste (USA)—Cordon **Lamb Brook Associates**
9 HIL RHAPSODY, 4, ch f Anshan—Heavenly Note **Mrs M. M. Palling**
10 HOPPERETTA, 4, b f Rock Hopper—Can Can Girl **Rhiwbina Racing**
11 I'LL SOON KNOW, 11, ch m Known Fact (USA)—Soolyn
12 MEADOWS BOY, 6, b g Derrylin—What A Coup **Mr Richard Edwards**
13 MOSCOW MIST (IRE), 7, b g Soviet Star (USA)—Ivory Dawn (USA) **Merthyr Motor Auctions**
14 MR BERGERAC (IRE), 7, b g Cyrano de Bergerac—Makalu **Mr P. R. John**
15 PARDAN, 4, b g Pharly (FR)—Silent Pool **Mrs M. M. Palling**
16 ROSE OF GLENN, 7, b m Crofthall—May Kells **Mr S. Sullivan**
17 SUPER RITCHART, 10, b g Starch Reduced—Karousa Girl **The Gradon Associates**
18 THOUGHTFUL KATE, 4, b f Rock Hopper—Beloved Visitor (USA) **Mr D. F. L'Estrange**

THREE-YEAR-OLDS

19 ANITA AT DAWN (IRE), br f Anita's Prince—Dawn Is Breaking **Merthyr Motor Auctions**
20 ARBENIG (IRE), b f Anita's Prince—Out On Her Own **Mr A. Smallwood & Mr Alan Evans**
21 ARIAN DA, ch f Superlative—Nell of The North (USA) **Mr J. Hamilton-Jones**
22 BALANITA (IRE), b g Anita's Prince—Ballybannon **Merthyr Motor Auctions**
23 BALLASILLA, b f Puissance—Darussalam **Merthyr Motor Auctions**
24 BOYOBOY (IRE), b c Paris House—Webbiana **Merthyr Motor Auctions**
25 CHIKAL, b g Nalchik (USA)—Ty-With-Belle **Mrs M. M. Palling**
26 DIM OTS, b f Alhijaz—Placid Pet **Mrs D. J. Hughes**
27 FAST TEMPO (IRE), b f Statoblest—Bellinzona **Mr W. H. Elliott**
28 LILANITA, b f Anita's Prince—Jimlil **Mrs M. M. Palling**
29 MEADGATE'S DREAMER (IRE), br f Petardia—Avidal Park **Meadgate Homes Limited**
30 MISS PARADISO (IRE), b f Anita's Prince—Heavenly Blessed **Rhiwbina Racing**
31 NIGHT AUCTION (IRE), b f Night Shift (USA)—Maria Stuarda **Merthyr Motor Auctions**
32 PERECAPA (IRE), b f Archway (IRE)—Cupid Miss **Davies And Williams Partnership**
33 RUZEN (IRE), b c Fayruz—Stifen **Five To Follow**
34 SANTA FAYE (IRE), b f Fayruz—Florissa (FR) **Mrs R. M. Williams**

TWO-YEAR-OLDS

35 DIM OFAN, b f Petong—Wilsonic **Mrs D. J. Hughes**
36 Ch f Timeless Times (USA)—Hill of Fare **Mrs J. Phillips**
37 Ch f Case Law—Nishiki (USA)

MR BRYN PALLING—continued

Other Owners: Mr D. Baker, Mr D. Brennan, Mr M. G. Bridgeman, Mr J. L. Brown, Mr G. Button, Mr D. E. Crompton, Mrs F. C. Crompton, Mr J. R. Davies, Mr John H. Davies, Mr T. P. Davies, Mr W. G. Davies, Mr Nigel B. Davis, Mr R. N. Edwards, Mr D. Egan, Mrs B. J. Harkins, Mrs L. Hedlund, Mr D. H. Hudd, Mr P. Hudd, Mr S. D. Hudd, Mr K. J. Mercer, Mrs S. Mercer, Mr M. L. Merriman, Mr N. Phillips, Mrs Anita Quinn, Mr K. N. Rideout, Mr A. L. Roberts, Mr S. E. Salineni, Mr T. H. Stuart, Mr P. A. Sutton, Mrs A. Taylor, Mr D. R. Thomas, Mr G. J. Thomas, Mr M. A. Tilke, Mr E. B. Turner, Mr M. Unsworth, Mr M. Williams, Mr Paul A. Young.

Jockey (Flat): T J Sprake (7-11).

Jockey (NH): R Farrant (10-0).

461 MR I. PARK, Stockton-on-Tees

Postal: **2 Willow Bank, Durham Lane, Eaglescliffe, Stockton, Cleveland, TS16 0PY.**
Phone: **(01642) 580263**

1 **ALLMERE (IRE)**, 7, b m Electric—Beswick Paper Lady **Mrs C. Park**
2 **KINDA GROOVY**, 9, b g Beveled (USA)—Tory Blues **Mr Ian Park**

Jockey (NH): Nick Smith (10-0).

Lady Rider: Miss Fiona Wilson (9-0).

462 MR C. PARKER, Lockerbie

Postal: **Douglas Hall Farm, Lockerbie, Dumfriesshire, DG11 1AD.**
Phone: **(01576) 510232 FAX (01576) 510232**

1 **ACKZO**, 5, b g Ardross—Trimar Gold **Mr & Mrs Raymond Anderson Green**
2 **BOARDING SCHOOL**, 11, b g Glenstal (USA)—Amenity (FR) **Mr & Mrs Raymond Anderson Green**
3 **BUNNYMAN (IRE)**, 4, gr g Henbit (USA)—Viking Rocket **Mr & Mrs Raymond Anderson Green**
4 **DELICEO (IRE)**, 5, b g Roselier (FR)—Grey's Delight **Mr & Mrs Raymond Anderson Green**
5 **JAUNTY GENERAL**, 7, b g Governor General—Ash Gayle **Mr E. Waugh**
6 **KIMDALOO (IRE)**, 6, b g Mandalus—Kimin **Mr & Mrs Raymond Anderson Green**
7 **LATIN LEADER**, 8, b g Primo Dominie—Ravaro **Mr & Mrs Raymond Anderson Green**
8 **MAYDOO (IRE)**, 5, br m Mandalus—Fayafi **Mr & Mrs Raymond Anderson Green**
9 **MISTER WOODSTICK (IRE)**, 5, b g Distinctly North (USA)—Crannog **Mr & Mrs Raymond Anderson Green**
10 **NATURAL TALENT**, 6, ch g Kris—Tropicaro (FR) **Mr & Mrs Raymond Anderson Green**
11 **N'INSISTEZ PAS (FR)**, 4, b g Le Nain Jaune (FR)—Rusa Fee (FR) **Mr & Mrs Raymond Anderson Green**
12 **NUTTY SOLERA**, 8, ch g Henbit (USA)—Friendly Cherry **Mr & Mrs Raymond Anderson Green**
13 **OH SO COSY (IRE)**, 5, br g Mandalus—Milan Pride **Mr & Mrs Raymond Anderson Green**
14 **PACIFIC WAR (IRE)**, 9, b g Bluebird (USA)—Exgravity (USA) **Mr H. R. Grant**
15 **PAPPA CHARLIE (USA)**, 7, b g Manila (USA)—Lassie's Lady (USA) **Mr Raymond Anderson Green**
16 **PHANTOM HAZE**, 5, gr g Absalom—Caroline Lamb **Jacksons Timber**
17 **RET FREM (IRE)**, 5, b g Posen (USA)—New Light **Mr & Mrs Raymond Anderson Green**
18 **SETATRAP**, 5, b g Lord Bud—Royal Scarlet **Mr A. Wight**
19 **SHE'S ALL HEART**, 5, b m Broken Hearted—Tina's Brig **Mr K. Milligan, Mr D. Griffiths**
20 **SHINEROLLA**, 6, b g Thatching—Primrolla **Mr & Mrs Raymond Anderson Green**
21 **SPARKY GAYLE (IRE)**, 8, b g Strong Gale—Baybush **Mr & Mrs Raymond Anderson Green**
22 **TEELIN BAY (IRE)**, 6, b g Be My Native (USA)—Fahy Quay **Mr & Mrs Raymond Anderson Green**
23 **THE BOOZING BRIEF (USA)**, 5, b g Turkoman (USA)—Evening Silk (USA) **Mr & Mrs Raymond Anderson Green**
24 **TRUMP**, 9, b g Last Tycoon—Fleeting Affair **Mr & Mrs Raymond Anderson Green**
25 **WAYUPHILL**, 11, b m Furry Glen—Queen Weasel **Mr & Mrs Raymond Anderson Green**

Other Owners: Mr E. A. Brook, Mr G. G. Fraser, Mr M. C. Mackenzie, Mr Derrick Mossop, Mrs L. Mossop, Mr R. Nichol, Mr R. F. Stewart, Mr David A. Taglight, Mr J. Waugh.

Jockeys (NH): David Parker, Brian Storey.

Amateurs: Mr Tristan Davidson, Mr Andrew Parker (10-0).

Lady Rider: Miss Pauline Robson.

463 MR J. E. PARKES, Malton

Postal: **12 Whitewall Cottages, Norton, Malton, North Yorkshire, YO17 9EH.**
Phone: **(01653) 697570**

1 **ARCTIC FLORA,** 6, b m Arctic Lord—School Run **Mr W. A. Sellers**
2 **BALI-PET,** 4, b g Tina's Pet—Baligay **Mr R. Flegg**
3 **BLUCANOO,** 8, ch m Lighter—Lunar Monarch **Mr D. Furman**
4 **FLAG FEN (USA),** 7, br g Riverman (USA)—Damascus Flag (USA) **Mr Vince Dolan**
5 **GENUINE JOHN (IRE),** 5, b g High Estate—Fiscal Folly (USA) **Mrs G. M. Z. Spink**
6 **IJAB (CAN),** 8, b g Ascot Knight (CAN)—Renounce (USA) **Mrs Lynn Parkes**
7 **KAILAN SCAMP,** 5, gr m Palm Track—Noble Scamp **Mrs G. M. Z. Spink**
8 **KEEN TO PLEASE,** 4, ch f Keen—Tasseled (USA) **Mrs B. Cooney**
9 **KILNAMARTYRA GIRL,** 8, b m Arkan—Star Cove **Mr P. J. Cronin**
10 **OUR CAROL (IRE),** 6, br m Buckskin (FR)—Hampton Grange **Mr Vince Dolan**
11 **SALINGER,** 10, b g Rousillon (USA)—Scholastika (GER) **Mr Vince Dolan**
12 **SHEEFIN (IRE),** 4, b f Danehill (USA)—Starlust **Academy Partnership**
13 **YOUR THE LIMIT (IRE),** 5, b g Don't Forget Me—Excruciating (CAN) **Mrs B. Cooney**

THREE-YEAR-OLDS

14 **ALMOST GOT IT,** ch f St Ninian—Star Leader **Mr C. W. Moore**
15 **BALANCE THE BOOKS,** b f Elmaamul (USA)—Psylla **Mrs G. Comer**

Other Owners: Mr J. E. P. Childs, Mr Niall Enright, Mr P. Fiske, Mr J. Parkes, H. H. Prince Yazid Saud, Mr J. Shine.

464 MR J. R. PAYNE, Dulverton

Postal: **Lower Holworthy Farm, Brompton Regis, Dulverton, Somerset, TA22 9NY.**

1 **SPIRIT LEVEL,** 10, ch m Sunley Builds—Tuneful Flutter **Mr J. R. Payne**

Amateur: Mr R J Payne (10-7).

465 MR J. W. PAYNE, Newmarket

Postal: **Frankland Lodge, Hamilton Road, Newmarket, Suffolk, CB8 7JQ.**
Phone: **NEWMARKET (01638) 668675 FAX (01638) 668675 MOBILE (0850) 133116**

1 **AL MUALLIM (USA),** 4, b c Theatrical—Gerri N Jo Go (USA) **Al Muallim Partnership**
2 **ARDENBAR,** 6, b m Ardross—Barwell **Mr T. J. Wyatt**
3 **DANCER'S CHIEF,** 4, ch g Suave Dancer (USA)—Kijafa (USA) **Mrs J. W. Payne**
4 **GENEROUS PRESENT,** 5, ch g Cadeaux Genereux—Dance Move **Mrs J. W. Payne**
5 **KWEILO,** 4, b g Mtoto—Hug Me **Mr Marwan Tabsh**
6 **MECHILIE,** 4, b f Belmez (USA)—Tundra Goose **Sir Simon Lycett Green**
7 **SCUD MISSILE (IRE),** 7, b g Persian Heights—Desert Bluebell **Mr J. P. Power**
8 **SQUADDIE,** 6, ch g Infantry—Mendelita **Mr J. P. Power**
9 **TRUCULENT,** 5, b g Jupiter Island—Maureen Mhor **Mrs E. Lake**

THREE-YEAR-OLDS

10 **DRAGONHEART,** b g Prince Sabo—Nazakat **Mr T. H. Barma**
11 **RAISE A KING,** b g Ardkinglass—Bias **Mr Marwan Tabsh**
12 **ZILLION (IRE),** b g Priolo (USA)—Arab Scimetar (IRE) **Mr Marwan Tabsh**

TWO-YEAR-OLDS

13 **DOLPHIN FRIENDLY,** b f 26/4 Dolphin Street (FR)—Sound Performance (IRE) (Ahonoora) **The Frankland Lodgers**
14 B g 1/3 Northern Park (USA)—Kotsina (Top Ville) **Mr Alex Penman**

MR J. W. PAYNE—continued

15 **RAISE A GRAND (IRE),** ch c 13/3 Grand Lodge (USA)—Atyaaf (USA) (Irish River (FR)) **Nagy El Azar**
16 **RED LION,** ch c 1/5 Lion Cavern (USA)—Fleur Rouge (Pharly (FR)) **Nagy El Azar**
17 **TAYIF,** gr c 26/3 Taufan (USA)—Rich Lass (Broxted) **Nagy El Azar**
18 **YA BALESH,** b c 19/3 Priolo (USA)—Ichnusa (Bay Express) **Nagy El Azar**

Other Owners: Mr & Mrs J. Bowyer, Mr Gerald Cooper, Mr M. Djojomartono, M. Gallo, Mr Sean C. Gollogly, A. Hillman, Mrs V. Hillyard, Mr G. Jabre, Lucayan Stud, Mr E. Melville, Thomas Morley, Roy Murphy, Mr & Mrs D. Rees, Mr A. E. Sexton.

Lady Rider: Mrs Sally Cahill (7-12).

466 MR R. E. PEACOCK, Malmesbury

Postal: **Oliver House Stud, Chedglow, Malmesbury, Wiltshire, SN16 9EZ.**
Phone: **(01666) 577238**

1 **ALTHREY BLUE (IRE),** 9, b g Milk of The Barley—Hua Hin **Mr F. Lloyd**
2 **ALTHREY PILOT (IRE),** 7, br g Torus—Black Pilot **Mr F. Lloyd**
3 **BURNING COST,** 8, br m Lochnager—Sophie Avenue **Mr R. E. Peacock**
4 **CALL MY GUEST (IRE),** 8, b g Be My Guest (USA)—Overcall **Mr Derek D. Clee**
5 **DREAM CARRIER (IRE),** 10, b g Doulab (USA)—Dream Trader **Mr R. E. Peacock**
6 **FIGHTER SQUADRON,** 9, ch g Primo Dominie—Formidable Dancer **Mr R. E. Peacock**
7 4, Gr g Absalom—Girl's Brigade **Mr Derek D. Clee**
8 6, Ch g Gunner B—Morstons Maid **Mrs P. Hutchinson**
9 **NUNS CONE,** 10, ch g Celtic Cone—Nunswalk **Mrs Alurie O'Sullivan**
10 **QUEENS STROLLER (IRE),** 7, b m Pennine Walk—Mount Isa **Mr R. E. Peacock**
11 **ROKER JOKER,** 7, b g Jupiter Island—Trikkala Star **Mrs P. Hutchinson**
12 **SHEEP STEALER,** 10, gr g Absalom—Kilroe's Calin **Mr R. E. Peacock**
13 **TA-RA-ABIT (IRE),** 5, br m Tornabuoni—Frigid Lady **Mr Paul Stringer**
14 **TOMMY TEMPEST,** 9, ch g Northern Tempest (USA)—Silently Yours (USA) **Mr R. E. Peacock**
15 **WRITTEN AGREEMENT,** 10, ch g Stanford—Covenant **Mr R. E. Peacock**

THREE-YEAR-OLDS

16 **KNIGHTCRACKER,** b f Cadeaux Genereux—Top Treat (USA) **Mr Derek D. Clee**

Other Owners: Mrs Jean P. Clee, Miss P. Kissock-Smith.

Jockeys (Flat): J Bramhill (7-5), Seb Sanders (8-0, w.a.).

Jockeys (NH): A P McCoy (10-0, w.a.), S McNeill (10-0, w.a.).

Apprentice: Ian Hudson (8-8).

Conditional: Christopher Webb (9-9).

Lady Rider: Mrs Carmen Peacock (9-4).

467 MR B. A. PEARCE, Lingfield

Postal: **Churchill Stud, West Park Road, Newchapel, Lingfield, RH7 6HT.**
Phone: **(01342) 833989**

1 **CHEMIN-DE-FER,** 6, b g Darshaan—Whitehaven **Mr Richard J. Gray**
2 **CHURCHILL'S SHADOW (IRE),** 4, b c Polish Precedent (USA)—Shy Princess (USA) **Mr Richard J. Gray**
3 **DISTANT DYNASTY,** 8, br g Another Realm—Jianna **Mr Martin J. Gibbs**
4 **ELA-MENT (IRE),** 6, b g Ela-Mana-Mou—Dorado Llave (USA) **Mr C. M. Kwai**
5 **GOODBYE GATEMEN (IRE),** 4, gr g Soviet Lad (USA)—Simple Love **Mrs E. N. Nield**
6 **JESTER MINUTE,** 4, gr g Jester—Jealous Lover **S B Components**
7 **SHARP MOVE,** 6, ch m Night Shift (USA)—Judeah **S B Components**
8 **SURGICAL SPIRIT,** 8, b m Lighter—Sheba Queen **Mr B. Lee**
9 **VICTORIA HOUSE (IRE),** 4, b f River Falls—Double Grange (IRE) **Mr G. Boyer**
10 **WHAT IS THE PLAN (IRE),** 9, b g Mandalus—Hills Approach **Mr D. Newman**
11 **YELLOW DRAGON (IRE),** 5, b g Kefaah (USA)—Veldt **Mr C. M. Kwai**
12 **YOUNG BUTT,** 5, ch g Bold Owl—Cymbal **Mr D. Newman**

THREE-YEAR-OLDS

13 **ERIKA'S YOUNG MAN,** b c Unfuwain (USA)—Tearful Reunion **Mr Richard J. Gray & Partners**
14 **FALKENBERG (FR),** ch g Polish Precedent (USA)—Mithi Al Gamar (USA) **Mr J. Salter**

Other Owners: Mr R. Acland, Mr N. A. Bedward, Mrs Maureen Bell, Mr P. Iacovou, Mrs R. Nash, Mr Brian Arthur Pearce, Mr J. S. Scott, Mr A. H. Weller.

Jockey (Flat): D McCabe.

Apprentices: M Dwyer, C Lowther.

Amateur: Mr S Durack.

Lady Rider: Miss Leesa Long.

468 MR J. PEARCE, Newmarket

Postal: **Wroughton House, 37 Old Station Road, Newmarket, Suffolk, CB8 8DT.**
Phone: **NEWMARKET (01638) 664669 OFFICE (01638) 669891 FAX (01638) 669891**

1 **ANJOU,** 6, b g Saumarez—Bourbon Topsy **Mr G. H. Tufts**
2 **ATHENRY,** 5, b h Siberian Express (USA)—Heresheis **Mr A. J. Thompson**
3 **BELLAS GATE BOY,** 6, b g Doulab (USA)—Celestial Air **Mr Jeff Pearce**
4 **BE WARNED,** 7, b g Warning—Sagar **Mr A. J. Thompson**
5 **BUTRINTO,** 4, ch g Anshan—Bay Bay
6 **CAN CAN CHARLIE,** 8, gr g Vaigly Great—Norton Princess **Mr G. H. Tufts**
7 **CONIC HILL (IRE),** 7, ch g Lomond (USA)—Krisalya **Mr Jeff Pearce**
8 **ESPERTO,** 5, b g Risk Me (FR)—Astrid Gilberto **Mrs Anne V. Holman-Chappell**
9 **FILIAL (IRE),** 5, b g Danehill (USA)—Sephira **Mr D. Leech**
10 **GOLD BLADE,** 9, ch g Rousillon (USA)—Sharp Girl (FR) **Mr Arthur Old**
11 **GUESSTIMATION (USA),** 9, b g Known Fact (USA)—Best Guess (USA) **The Exclusive Two Partnership**
12 **HARVEY WHITE (IRE),** 6, b br g Petorius—Walkyria **The Harvey White Partnership**
13 **HEUBACH BOY,** 4, b g Belmez (USA)—North Pacific (USA) **Mr K. B. Philbin**
14 **JEAN PIERRE,** 5, b g Anshan—Astolat **Mr P. D. Burnett**
15 **JOHN TUFTY,** 7, ch g Vin St Benet—Raffles Virginia **Mr G. H. Tufts**
16 **JUCINDA,** 4, gr f Midyan (USA)—Catch The Sun **Mrs Samantha Whitson**
17 **LAMBSON,** 11, b g Petorius—Julie Be Quick (USA) **Mr & Mrs Ian Hall**

MR J. PEARCE—continued

18 **LUCY TUFTY,** 7, b m Vin St Benet—Manor Farm Toots **Mr G. H. Tufts**
19 **NAGOBELIA,** 10, b g Enchantment—Lost Valley **Mr Jeff Pearce**
20 **NORTH REEF (IRE),** 7, b h Danehill (USA)—Loreef **Storeforce Limited**
21 **NOSEY NATIVE,** 5, b g Cyrano de Bergerac—Native Flair **Mr Jeff Pearce**
22 **PERTEMPS MISSION,** 4, b g Safawan—Heresheis
23 **PETOSKIN,** 6, b g Petoski—Farcical **Mrs Jean Routledge**
24 **PILIB (IRE),** 7, b g Salt Dome (USA)—Princess Elinor **Fijon Partnership**
25 **PROSPECTOR'S COVE,** 5, b g Dowsing (USA)—Pearl Cove **Saracen Racing**
26 **PURE SWING,** 5, b g Shareef Dancer (USA)—Mrs Warren (USA) **U.K. Letterbox Marketing Ltd**
27 **RETENDER (USA),** 9, br g Storm Bird (CAN)—Dandy Bury (FR) **Mr Jeff Pearce**
28 **ROMANY CREEK (IRE),** 9, b g Trimmingham—Rare Picture **Mr A. J. Thompson**
29 **SOUND OF THUNDER,** 7, gr g Risk Me (FR)—Astral Suite **Mrs Lucy Gibbons**
30 **STYLISH WAYS (IRE),** 6, b g Thatching—Style of Life (USA) **Mr Ian Hall**
31 **SUPERLEAGUE SAINTS,** 5, b m Teenoso (USA)—Ruth's River **The Saints Partnership**
32 **SUPER PARK,** 6, b g Superpower—Everingham Park **Mr Jeff Pearce**
33 **SWYNFORD KING,** 6, b g Jalmood (USA)—Maputo Princess **Qualitair Holdings Limited**
34 **TOUJOURS RIVIERA,** 8, ch g Rainbow Quest (USA)—Miss Beaulieu **Exdreco**
35 **TROPICAL BEACH,** 5, b g Lugana Beach—Hitravelscene **Mr A. J. Thompson**

THREE-YEAR-OLDS

36 **ALWAYS LUCKY,** gr f Absalom—Petitesse **G. Byrne**
37 **COOL VIBES,** b c Rock City—Meet Again **Jim Furlong**
38 **CRY FOR FREEDOM,** b f Komaite (USA)—Heresheis
39 **ELLEGANT GENT,** b c Pharly (FR)—Ellegant Model **Hazaar Partnership**
40 **EXCLUSIVELY,** gr f Absalom—Peters Pleasure **Exclusive 2 Partnership**
41 **PRIMARY COLOURS,** b f Saddlers' Hall (IRE)—Go For Red (IRE) **Saracen Racing**
42 **WAVE OF OPTIMISM,** ch g Elmaamul (USA)—Ballerina Bay

TWO-YEAR-OLDS

43 **TIME TO TELL,** b f 5/3 Keen—Meet Again **Jim Furlong**
44 **TOP OF THE MORNING,** b f 29/2 Keen—Kelimutu **Jennie Furlong**

Other Owners: Hon. Robert P. Acton, Mr M. J. Baxter, Mr C. C. Brown, Mrs K. J. Crangle, Mr J. L. Davison, Mr I. Fuhrmann, Mr W. J. Goddard, Mrs Kate Hall, Mr N. M. Hanger, Mr G. T. Harvey, Mr Terry Harvey, Mr Tom Hayes, Mr G. W. Holland, Mr D. J. Maden, Miss Ann Pauline Meadows, Mr J. G. Nunn, Miss Islee S. Oliva, Mrs P. O'Shea, Mrs Lydia Pearce, Mrs Diane Christine Roche, Captain J. L. Round-Turner, Mr Peter Routledge, Storeforce Limited, Mr Ryszard W. Varasella, Mr David White, Mr Peter Wymann.

Jockeys (Flat): Gary Bardwell (7-7, w.a.), M Wigham.

Lady Rider: Mrs Lydia Pearce (8-7).

469 MR J. E. PEASE, Chantilly

Postal: **Villa Primerose, Chemin des Aigles, 60500 Chantilly, France.**
Phone: **03 44 58 19 96/03 44 57 23 09 FAX 03 44 57 59 90**

1 **BLUEBELL DANCER (USA),** 4, ch f Sovereign Dancer (USA)—O My Darling (USA) **Peter Pritchard**
2 **EKATERINA (USA),** 4, b f Danzig (USA)—Relko (FR) **George Strawbridge**
3 **HELEN SPRINGS (USA),** 4, ch f Silver Hawk (USA)—First Approach (USA) **George Strawbridge**
4 **HOMING INSTINCT,** 4, b f Arctic Tern (USA)—Singapore Girl (FR) **George Strawbridge**
5 **HUDO (USA),** 8, b h Hero's Honor (USA)—Jardin de Nuit (USA) **The Niarchos Family**
6 **KAIZEN (FR),** 4, b c Saumarez—Karannja (USA) **J. D. Champalbert**
7 **LA BIJOU (FR),** 4, b f Caerwent—La Magnifique (FR) **W. Wolf**
8 **LABYRINTH (FR),** 4, b f Exit To Nowhere (USA)—Olvarria (FR) **L. Roy**
9 **PAXOS (USA),** 4, b c Slew O' Gold (USA)—Puppet Dance (USA) **The Niarchos Family**

MR J. E. PEASE—continued

10 **PERSONAL BEST (IRE)**, 4, ch f Kris—Penultimate (USA) **G. W. Leigh**
11 **PIPERI (IRE)**, 4, b c Machiavellian (USA)—Gwydion (USA) **The Niarchos Family**
12 **SMART ALEC**, 6, b g Diesis—Ahead **G. W. Leigh**
13 **WITH FIRE (USA)**, 4, b c Gulch (USA)—Fran's Valentine (USA) **George Strawbridge**

THREE-YEAR-OLDS

14 **ALIOTH (FR)**, b f Turgeon (USA)—Silicon Lady (FR) **John Goelet**
15 **ANNORA SPRINGS (USA)**, b f Kris S (USA)—First Approach (USA) **George Strawbridge**
16 **ASHKIRK**, b f Selkirk (USA)—Land of Ivory (USA) **George Strawbridge**
17 **BALSAMITA (FR)**, b f Midyan (USA)—Balsamine **J. E. Pease**
18 **BLUE ROCK**, ch c Selkirk (USA)—Bague Bleue (IRE) **George Strawbridge**
19 **CLAYBROOK (FR)**, br c Sillery (USA)—Cubique (USA) **George Strawbridge**
20 **CREESE (USA)**, ch f Diesis—Name And Fame (USA) **The Niarchos Family**
21 **ELAANDO**, b c Darshaan—Evocatrice **F. Van Oppenheim**
22 **ENCENS**, b f Common Grounds—Idyllic (USA) **The Niarchos Family**
23 **HAPPY HEART (FR)**, b f Exit To Nowhere (USA)—Light of Hope (USA) **The Niarchos Family**
24 **HONEYTRAP (FR)**, b f Primo Dominie—Singapore Girl (FR) **George Strawbridge & J. Wiga**
25 **IONOSPERE**, b c Green Desert (USA)—Ionian Sea **George Strawbridge**
26 **KALISTINA (FR)**, b f Sillery (USA)—Key Role **A. R. Baechler**
27 **MEDIEVAL (IRE)**, b c Bluebird (USA)—Maid of Erin (USA) **The Niarchos Family**
28 **MEDUSA (FR)**, b f Machiavellian (USA)—Beaute Dangereuse (USA) **The Niarchos Family**
29 **MILLIGAN (FR)**, b c Exit To Nowhere (USA)—Madigan Mill **H. Seymour & A. R. Chalk**
30 **MONARC (FR)**, b c Arctic Tern (USA)—Mysouko (FR) **George Strawbridge**
31 **NATIONAL PORTRAIT (IRE)**, b f Royal Academy (USA)—Proskona (USA) **G. W. Leigh**
32 **PERFIDIA (USA)**, b f Danzig (USA)—Madam North (CAN) **G. W. Leigh**
33 **PETRONILLA (USA)**, b f Lyphard (USA)—Central City **George Strawbridge**
34 **RES JUDICATA**, b c Rainbow Quest (USA)—Whakilyric (USA) **The Niarchos Family**
35 **RING OF FIRE (USA)**, b f Nureyev (USA)—Imperfect Circle (USA) **The Niarchos Family**
36 **ROYAL DOUNE (FR)**, gr f Kaldoun (FR)—Princesse Bee (FR) **L. Roy**
37 **TOURNESOL (FR)**, gr f Turgeon (USA)—Olvarria (FR) **J. E. Pease**
38 **WHISTLE STOP (USA)**, b c Shadeed (USA)—Glitter (FR) **Mrs A. J. Richards**
39 **WINSOME**, b f Kris—Ahead **G. W. Leigh**

TWO-YEAR-OLDS

40 B c 20/5 Selkirk (USA)—Bague Bleue (IRE) **George Strawbridge**
41 **BLANCHE DUBOIS (FR)**, ch f 24/1 Suave Dancer (USA)—Nouvelle Lune (FR) **J. D. Dewaurin**
42 B c 3/6 Green Dancer (USA)—Central City **George Strawbridge**
43 Ch c 27/4 Nureyev (USA)—Chimes of Freedom (USA) **The Niarchos Family**
44 B f 18/2 Alzao (USA)—Dazzling Heights **Peter Pritchard**
45 Ch c 25/4 Mr Prospector (USA)—East of The Moon (USA) **The Niarchos Family**
46 B f 28/1 Nashwan (USA)—Glowing Ardour **George Strawbridge**
47 **HAMPTON MAZE**, b c 6/3 Exit To Nowhere (USA)—Passerella (FR) **L. G. Albertini**
48 B f 26/5 Dayjur (USA)—Heartbreak (USA) **George Strawbridge**
49 B f 28/4 Kingmambo (USA)—Imperfect Circle (USA) **The Niarchos Family**
50 B c 13/4 Selkirk (USA)—Ionian Sea **George Strawbridge**
51 B f 19/5 Red Ransom (USA)—Kazadancoa (FR) **George Strawbridge**
52 **KIANELL (FR)**, b c 16/3 Fairy King (USA)—Belle Cordia (USA) **L. Roy**
53 B c 14/3 Kris—Land of Ivory (USA) **George Strawbridge**
54 Ch c 9/2 Storm Cat (USA)—Lightning Fire **The Niarchos Family**
55 **MOONLIGHT'S BOX (USA)**, b f 2/2 Nureyev (USA)—Coup de Genie (USA) **The Niarchos Family**
56 **RAMBLING FEVER**, b f 28/1 Be My Chief (USA)—Thalestria (FR) **Mrs A. J. Richards**
57 **SLEIPNEIR (FR)**, b c 15/3 Akarad (FR)—Silicon Lady (FR) **John Goelet**
58 B c 4/4 Green Desert (USA)—Snow Bank (IRE) **George Strawbridge**
59 B f 10/5 Private Terms (USA)—Snowbowl (USA) **George Strawbridge**
60 B f 27/3 Polish Precedent—Snowtop **George Strawbridge**
61 **SWEET ADENINE (IRE)**, b f 3/4 Fairy King (USA)—Exgravity (USA) **John Goelet**
62 **TARIKA (USA)**, ro f 16/4 Cozzene (USA)—Reiko (FR) **George Strawbridge**
63 **TURMERIC (FR)**, b c 20/5 Turgeon (USA)—Balsamine **J. E. Pease**

MR J. E. PEASE—continued

64 B c 13/4 Caerleon (USA)—Urmia **George Strawbridge**
65 B f 15/1 Red Ransom (USA)—White Corners (USA) **George Strawbridge**
66 B f 22/3 Silver Hawk (USA)—Wiener Wald (USA) **N. J. Forman Hardy/Car Colston Hall Stud**

Jockey (Flat): C Asmussen.

Apprentice: F Champagne.

470 MR M. A. PEILL, Thirsk

Postal: **Burtree House Racing Stables, Hutton Sessay, Thirsk, North Yorkshire, YO6 3AY.**
Phone: **(01845) 501333 OR 501104 FAX (01845) 501333**

1 **BRACKENTHWAITE,** 8, ch g Faustus (USA)—Cosset **Mr J. B. Slatcher**
2 **CANONBIEBOTHERED,** 7, ch m Liberated—Play Mount **Mr A. S. McGimpsey**
3 **DAVID'S WAY (IRE),** 9, b g Fresh Breeze (USA)—Croziers Glimmer **Mr D. J. Lever**
4 **FANTASY FLIGHT,** 4, b f Forzando—Ryewater Dream **Mr Michael Ng**
5 **HE'S GOT WINGS (IRE),** 5, b g In The Wings—Mariella **Mr D. J. Lever**
6 **HIP HOP (IRE),** 9, gr g Phardante (FR)—Iron Mermaid **Mr D. J. Lever**
7 **MARBLE MAN (IRE),** 8, ch g Henbit (USA)—Flameing Run **Mr D. J. Lever**
8 **PLUM FIRST,** 8, b g Nomination—Plum Bold **Mr J. B. Slatcher**
9 **SERAPE,** 5, b m Primo Dominie—Absaloute Service **Ms V. B. Foster**
10 **SUJUD (IRE),** 6, b m Shaadi (USA)—Sit Elnaas (USA) **Mr D. J. Lever**
11 **SYCAMORE LODGE (IRE),** 7, ch g Thatching—Bell Tower **Mr D. J. Lever**

Other Owners: Mr Malcom Emmerson, Mrs J. R. Ramsden, Mr K. Smith.

Jockey (Flat): J Carroll (w.a.).

Jockey (NH): D Bentley.

471 MISS L. A. PERRATT, Ayr

Postal: **Cree Lodge, 47 Craigie Road, Ayr, KA8 0HD.**
Phone: **PHONE/FAX (01292) 266232 MOBILE (0468) 176768**

1 **ANOTHER EPISODE (IRE),** 9, b g Drumalis—Pasadena Lady **Hay-Sutherland**
2 **BIFF-EM (IRE),** 4, ch g Durgam (USA)—Flash The Gold **Cree Lodge Racing Club**
3 **BRAVE MONTGOMERIE,** 4, ch g Most Welcome—Just Precious **Mr C. J. C. McLaren**
4 **DIET,** 12, b g Starch Reduced—Highland Rossie **Miss L. A. Perratt**
5 **DON'T CARE (IRE),** 7, b m Nordico (USA)—Eyeliner (USA) **Mr C. J. C. McLaren**
6 **GOLDEN SADDLE (IRE),** 4, b f Waajib—Flying Beckee (IRE) **Mr F. Johnson**
7 **LEADING PRINCESS (IRE),** 7, gr m Double Schwartz—Jenny Diver (USA) **Mrs Ruth S. S. Wyllie**
8 **MANFUL,** 6, b g Efisio—Mandrian **Mr C. D. Barber-Lomax**
9 **MILETRIAN CITY,** 5, gr g Petong—Blueit (FR) **Mr Andy Dickie**
10 **MISTER WESTSOUND,** 6, b g Cyrano de Bergerac—Captivate **David Sutherland-Ian Hay**
11 **PHILMIST,** 6, b m Hard Fought—Andalucia **Mr C. D. Barber-Lomax**
12 **SHORTSTAFF (IRE),** 9, b g Strong Gale—Earn More **Mr T. P. Finch**
13 **SUNDAY MAIL TOO (IRE),** 6, b m Fayruz—Slick Chick **Mr T. P. Finch**

THREE-YEAR-OLDS

14 **FRIAR TUCK,** ch c Inchinor—Jay Gee Ell **Cree Lodge Racing Club**
15 **HO LENG (IRE),** ch g Statoblest—Indigo Blues (IRE) **Mr Alan Guthrie**
16 **JACMAR (IRE),** br c High Estate—Inseyab **Mr John G. Marett**

MISS L. A. PERRATT—continued

17 MISS VIVIEN, b f Puissance—Madam Bold **Lostford Manor Stud**
18 RYEFIELD, b c Petong—Octavia **Mrs Elaine Aird**
19 SELKIRK ROSE (IRE), b f Pips Pride—Red Note **Mr Jim McLaren**
20 SNOWBALLS, gr c Chilibang—Golden Panda **Cree Lodge Racing Club**
21 TROPHY CENTRE, b f Paris House—Kentucky Tears (USA) **Cree Lodge Racing Club**

TWO-YEAR-OLDS

22 AJJAE (IRE), b c 9/3 High Estate—Lake Ormond (Kings Lake (USA)) **Mr Andy Dickie**
23 B f 28/2 Tirol—All In White (FR) (Carwhite)
24 Ch c 9/4 Casteddu—Bellatrix (Persian Bold) **Scottish Bloodstock Agency**
25 EFFANDEMM (IRE), ch c 16/4 Up And At 'Em—Bermuda Princess (Lord Gayle (USA)) **Mr F. Johnstone**
26 B f 11/4 Mujadil (USA)—Fleur de Luce (Tumble Wind (USA))
27 B f 23/1 Fayruz—Gaelic Song (Mansingh (USA))
28 B f 9/3 Minshaanshu Amad—Me Spede (Valiyar)
29 B f 6/2 Be My Chief (USA)—One Half Silver (CAN) (Plugged Nickle (USA)) **Lostford Manor Stud**
30 Ch c 14/3 Forest Wind (USA)—Ravensdale Rose (IRE) (Henbit (USA)) **Scottish Bloodstock Agency**
31 Gr f 22/2 Petong—Russell Creek (Sandy Creek) **Clayton Bigley Partnership Ltd**
32 B c 7/4 Up And At 'Em—Shoka (FR) (Kaldoun (FR)) **Clayton Bigley Partnership Ltd**
33 B c 8/2 Warrshan (USA)—Silver Venture (USA) (Silver Hawk (USA)) **Scottish Bloodstock Agency**
34 B c 9/4 River Falls—Tribal Rhythm (IRE) (Double Schwartz)

Other Owners: Mrs Caroline Ashworth, Mr J. Berry, Mr A. R. Breeze, Mr J. M. Craig, Miss Heather Galbraith, Mr L. Hamilton, Mr T. Hughes, Mrs V. E. Hughes, Mr Paul G. Jacobs, Mrs M. M. Johnson, Mrs S. Kennedy, Lightbody Of Hamilton Ltd, Mrs Geraldine Marett, Mr Jim McLaren, Mr R. McLean, Mr J. W. M. M. Richard, Mrs A. E. Robertson, Mrs Every Roosmoalecocq, Mrs Ailsa Russell, Mr John Scanlon, Mr R. F. Stewart, Mr David White (Bothwell), Mr Ronald Wyllie.

Jockeys (Flat): G Duffield (w.a.), J K Fanning (w.a.), Neil Kennedy, J Weaver (w.a.).

Jockeys (NH): A Maguire (w.a.), P Niven (w.a.), L O'Hara.

Apprentice: John McAuley (7-3).

Amateurs: Mr James Dellahunt (10-10), Mr M Lightbody, Mr J J McLaren.

Lady Rider: Miss Linda A Perratt (9-0).

472 MRS A. J. PERRETT, Pulborough

Postal: **Coombelands Racing Stables, Pulborough, West Sussex, RH20 1BP.**
Phone: **OFFICE (01798) 873011 HOME 874894 FAX 875163 MOBILE (0410) 075970**

1 AMANCIO (USA), 7, b g Manila (USA)—Kerry Ring (USA) **Mr Paul H. Locke**
2 BETTER OFFER (IRE), 6, b g Waajib—Camden's Gift **Lady Harrison**
3 CATCHMENT, 4, ch g Persian Bold—Cachou (USA) **Mr G. Harwood**
4 CLINKING, 7, b g Glint of Gold—Kai **Mr G. Harwood**
5 CONSORT, 5, b h Groom Dancer (USA)—Darnelle **Mrs S. L. Whitehead**
6 DEVILISH CHARM (USA), 4, ch g Devil's Bag (USA)—Popularity (USA) **Mr Peter Wiegand**
7 FAR DAWN (USA), 5, b h Sunshine Forever (USA)—Dawn's Reality (USA) **Mr Peter Wiegand**
8 FINE THYNE (IRE), 9, ch g Good Thyne (USA)—Bring Me Sunshine **Mr Peter Wiegand**
9 FURTHER OUTLOOK (USA), 4, gr g Zilzal (USA)—Future Bright (USA) **Lady Harrison**
10 HANBITOOH (USA), 5, b g Hansel (USA)—Bitooh **Mr Fred Cotton**
11 HAWKSBILL HENRY (USA), 4, ch g Known Fact (USA)—Novel Approach (USA) **Mr G. Harwood**

MRS A. J. PERRETT—continued

12 **KAYVEE,** 9, gr g Kaldoun (FR)—Secret Life (USA) **Mr J. H. Richmond-Watson**
13 **KING KATO,** 5, b g Unfuwain (USA)—Sharmood (USA) **Mrs Jenny Ells**
14 **LAUREL SEEKER (USA),** 4, b g Mining (USA)—L'On Vite (USA) **Mr G. Harwood**
15 **METEOR STRIKE (USA),** 4, ch g Lomond (USA)—Meteoric **Mr S. P. Tindall**
16 **NORTHERN FLEET,** 5, b h Slip Anchor—Kamkova (USA) **Racing For Pleasure**
17 **PROSPERO,** 5, b g Petong—Pennies To Pounds **Mrs Gaynor Scruton**
18 **RENZO (IRE),** 5, b g Alzao (USA)—Watership (USA) **Mr K. J. Buchanan**
19 **TOUGH ACT,** 4, b g Be My Chief (USA)—Forelino (USA) **Mrs R. Doel**
20 **TRANSOM (USA),** 7, b br g Private Account (USA)—Trestle (USA) **Mr Seymour Cohn**
21 **TU DEAR,** 7, b m Lighter—Nelodor **Mrs S. L. Whitehead**

THREE-YEAR-OLDS

22 **EDWARDIAN,** ch c Sanglamore (USA)—Woodwardia (USA) **Mr K. Abdulla**
23 **FLAMBOYANT BELLE,** b f Lahib (USA)—Mainmast **The PBT Group**
24 **JANE LECHAT,** b f Teenoso (USA)—Richards Kate **Mr S. P. Tindall**
25 **LEAR'S CROWN (USA),** b f Lear Fan (USA)—Crowning Ambition (USA) **Mr K. Abdulla**
26 **RAFTERS MUSIC (IRE),** b c Thatching—Princess Dixieland (USA) **Mr C. Duncan**
27 **TEMERAIRE (USA),** b c Dayjur (USA)—Key Dancer (USA) **Mr K. Abdulla**
28 **THE GAMBOLLER (USA),** b c Irish Tower (USA)—Lady Limbo (USA) **Mr Simon Karmel**

TWO-YEAR-OLDS

29 B c 3/3 In The Wings—Autumn Tint (USA) (Roberto (USA)) **Mr K. Abdulla**
30 **BLUE (IRE),** b c 12/3 Bluebird (USA)—Watership (USA) (Foolish Pleasure (USA)) **Mr & Mrs K. J. Buchanan**
31 **CRYSTAL CREEK (IRE),** b c 28/2 River Falls—Dazzling Maid (IRE) (Tate Gallery (USA)) **Mr Fred Cotton**
32 B f 20/4 Polar Falcon (USA)—Doubles (Damister (USA)) **Mr K. Abdulla**
33 B c 7/4 Danehill (USA)—Liaison (USA) (Blushing Groom (FR)) **Mr K. Abdulla**
34 B f 12/5 Danehill (USA)—Our Reverie (USA) (J O Tobin (USA)) **Mr & Mrs K. J. Buchanan**
35 Ch f 25/4 Generous (IRE)—Phaleria (USA) (Lyphard (USA)) **Mr K. Abdulla**
36 B c 4/2 Stop The Music (USA)—Ranales (USA) (Majestic Light (USA)) **Mr K. Abdulla**
37 B c 20/4 Grand Lodge (USA)—Repetitious (Northfields (USA)) **Mr Seymour Cohn & Sir Eric Parker**
38 B f 9/5 Sanglamore (USA)—Sand Grouse (USA) (Arctic Tern (USA)) **Mr K. Abdulla**
39 Gr c 28/1 Northern Park (USA)—Yamamah (Siberian Express (USA)) **Mr B. Keay**

Other Owners: Mr T. L. Adams, Mr Alan Archer, Atlantic Foods Ltd, Mrs Lola Black, Mr B. S. Creber, Mr J. B. Dale, Mr C. J. Eagle, Mr C. J. Ells, Mr T. G. Fox, Mr G. C. Green, Mrs G. Harwood, Major Charles Hennings, Mrs M. R. Landau, Mr Selwyn Lewis, Mr P. J. Mellon, Mr Ron Miller, Miss E. A. Nagle, Major R. E. Norris, Mr Timothy J. Pope, Mr Paul A. Rhodes, Mrs C. Silvester, Mr Peter Silvester, Tessona Racing Limited, Mr David Todd, Mr Mark Tracey, Mrs A. E. V. Wadman.

Amateur: Mrs Amanda Perrett (9-3).

473 MR R. T. PHILLIPS, Lambourn

Postal: **Beechdown Farm, Sheepdrove, Lambourn, Newbury, Berkshire, RG17 7UN.**
Phone: **OFFICE (01488) 73072 HOME 73378 FAX (01488) 73500 MOBILE (0374) 832715**

1 **BEECHDOWN,** 6, b g Arctic Lord—Save It Lass **Reading Evening Post**
2 **BULLFINCH,** 5, ch g Anshan—Lambay **Lady Lewinton**
3 **COLD LAZARUS,** 4, br g Warning—Indian Pink (USA) **Mr John Mills**
4 **DEEP REFRAIN (IRE),** 8, b g Mandalus—Deep Serenade **The 10th of July Partnership**
5 **DELIGHT (FR),** 7, b g Vorias (USA)—Etoile du Berger III (FR) **Pride Of Africa Partnership**
6 **DISTANT ECHO (IRE),** 8, b g Seamanship—Ripperidge **Mr Mel Fordham**
7 **DOCKLANDS COURIER,** 6, b g Dominion—High Quail (USA) **Mrs Lisa Olley**
8 **FROGMARCH (USA),** 8, ch g Diesis—La Francaise (USA) **Mr John Mills**
9 **FURSAN (USA),** 5, b g Fred Astaire (USA)—Ancient Art (USA) **Mr Richard Phillips**
10 **JOBINGO,** 10, b br g Rustingo—Ruths Image **Mrs Jenny Trier**
11 **KARABURAN,** 4, b g Shareef Dancer (USA)—Kalmia **Mr John Mills**

MR R. T. PHILLIPS—continued

12 **LAAZIM AFOOZ,** 5, b g Mtoto—Balwa (USA) **Nut Club Partnership**
13 **MIGHTY PHANTOM (USA),** 5, b m Lear Fan (USA)—Migiyas **Torrance Racing**
14 **MONEYPOINT SAM (IRE),** 6, ch g Moscow Society (USA)—Ripperidge **Mr Mel Fordham**
15 **NOBLE LORD,** 5, ch g Lord Bud—Chasers' Bar **Mr G. Lansbury**
16 **SURE TO DREAM (IRE),** 5, b m Common Grounds—Hard To Stop **Dozen Dreamers Partnership**
17 **TIME WON'T WAIT (IRE),** 9, b g Bulldozer—Time Will Wait **Old Berks Partnership**
18 **T J GOODTYME (IRE),** 6, ch g Riberetto—Daily Rate **Mr B. Gorman**
19 5, B g Old Vic—Valiant Cry **The Mug Club**
20 **WILLIE B BRAVE (IRE),** 7, b g Buckskin (FR)—Ranamacken **Mr Richard Phillips**
21 **ZYGO (USA),** 6, b g Diesis—La Papagena **The Beechdowners**

Other Owners: S. A. Aldridge, R. Bailey, Mr N. Barham, Miss D. Barnett, Mrs R. Baxter, Mrs E. Beckett, Mr A. Blackman, Mr D. Bladon, Mr P. Bowden, Mr J. Bratley, Mr G. Brega, Mr I. Brown, Mr B. J. Caulfield, Mr A. Chalk, Mrs Jean Chalk, Mrs Mary Chalk, Mrs S. Collins, Mr J. Cover, Mr S. Day, Mr P. A. Deal, Mr B. Fulton, Count K. Goess-Saurau, Mrs Sallie Good, R. W. Green, Mr A. Groves, Mr R. Holt, Mr Jeremy Hulme, Mr J. Inverdale, Mr P. Johnsen, Angela Kaye, Mrs T Ruck Keene, W. Laule, Mrs F. Leach, The Hon C. Leigh, Sir Christopher Lewinton, Mrs T. Loyd, Mr J. E. Marchbanks, Mr Jeff McCarthy, Mr Terry Milson, Mr F. A. Mirando, P. M. Murphy, Mr J Nelson, Mr M Nichols, Mrs S Nicholson, O. O'Herlihy, Mr B. O'Keefe, Miss Angela Paulley, Mr J. S. Phillips, Mr T. Phillips, Mr A. Rackham, Mr R. Richards, Mrs M. Richardson, Mrs A. L. Rook, Sybil Ruscoe, Mr R. Salmon, Mr F. Shekleton, Mr M. Sissons, Mr S. M. Smith, Mrs B. Sumner, Mr T. Voorspuy, Mr P. Wallner, Mr R. Whitehead, Mrs P. D. Wild, Mr A. Wright, Mrs J Youdan, Lt. Col A. Young.

474 MRS T. D. PILKINGTON, Stow-on-the-Wold

Postal: **Hyde Mill, Stow-on-the-Wold, Cheltenham, Gloucestershire, GL54 1LA.**
Phone: **(01451) 830641**

1 **FUTONA,** 6, ch m Fearless Action (USA)—Chaise Longue **Mrs T. D. Pilkington**
2 **HYDEMILLA,** 8, b m Idiot's Delight—Bellaloo **Mrs T. D. Pilkington**
3 **ROSEHALL,** 7, b br m Ardross—Coral Delight **Mrs T. D. Pilkington**

475 MR MARTIN PIPE, Wellington

Postal: **Pond House, Nicholashayne, Wellington, Somerset, TA21 9QY.**
Phone: **OFFICE (01884) 840715 FAX (01884) 841343**

1 **ABOO HOM,** 4, b c Sadler's Wells (USA)—Maria Waleska **Kammac Plc**
2 **ALLEGATION,** 8, b g Dominion—Pageantry **Martin Pipe Racing Club**
3 **AMITGE (FR),** 4, ch f Vaguely Pleasant (FR)—Ribbon In Her Hair (USA) **Phil Lake, Huw Lake**
4 **BELMOREBRUNO,** 8, b g Pitpan—Direct Call **Mrs Audrey J. Hartnett**
5 **BERYLLIUM,** 4, b g Tragic Role (USA)—Flower Princess **Mr Malcolm B. Jones**
6 **BLOWING WIND (FR),** 5, b br g Fabulous Dancer (USA)—Bassita **Mr P. A. Deal**
7 **BOLD STREET (IRE),** 8, ch g Shy Groom (USA)—Ferry Lane **Codan Trust Company Limited**
8 **BRIGHSTONE,** 5, ch h Cadeaux Genereux—High Fountain **Richard Green (Fine Paintings)**
9 **CADOUGOLD (FR),** 7, b g Cadoudal (FR)—Fontaine Aux Faons (FR) **Mr D. A. Johnson**
10 **CHALLENGER DU LUC (FR),** 8, b g Chamberlin (FR)—Islande II (FR) **Mr D. A. Johnson**
11 **CHAMPLEVE (FR),** 5, gr g Kendor (FR)—Nilmeen (FR) **Mr D. A. Johnson**
12 **CIRCLE OF MAGIC,** 4, gr f Midyan (USA)—Miss Witch **Mr Jim Weeden**
13 **COUCHANT (IRE),** 7, b g Petoski—Be Easy **Teltone Racing**
14 **COURBARIL,** 6, b g Warrshan (USA)—Free On Board **Richard Green (Fine Paintings)**
15 **CYBORGO (FR),** 8, b g Cyborg (FR)—Quintessence III (FR) **County Stores (Somerset) Holdings Ltd**
16 **CYFOR MALTA (FR),** 5, b br g Cyborg (FR)—Force Nine (FR) **Mr D. A. Johnson**
17 **DAMAS (FR),** 7, b br g Video Rock (FR)—Queue de Pie (FR) **Knight Hawks Partnership**
18 **DAMIER BLANC (FR),** 9, b g Damister (USA)—Roche Blanche (FR) **Mr T. Painting & Mrs C. Painting**
19 **DANJING (IRE),** 6, b g Danehill (USA)—Beijing (USA) **Knight Hawks Partnership**
20 **DARAYDAN (IRE),** 6, b g Kahyasi—Delsy (FR) **Mr D. A. Johnson**

MR MARTIN PIPE—continued

21 **DEANO'S BEENO,** 6, b g Far North (CAN)—Sans Dot **Axom**
22 **DECYBORG (FR),** 7, ch g Cyborg (FR)—Kelinda (FR) **Mr Terry Neill**
23 **DIWALI DANCER,** 8, gr g Petong—Dawn Dance (USA) **Mr B. E. Case**
24 **D'NAAN (IRE),** 5, b g Royal Academy (USA)—Festive Season (USA) **Mrs P. B. Browne**
25 **DOCTOOR (USA),** 8, ch g Cozzene (USA)—To The Top (USA) **Mr A. F. Walls & Karen Whitehead**
26 **DOLCE NOTTE (IRE),** 8, b m Strong Gale—Caratasca (FR) **County Stores (Somerset) Holdings Ltd**
27 **DOM SAMOURAI (FR),** 7, gr g Dom Pasquini (FR)—Miss Dianon (FR) **Mr B. A. Kilpatrick**
28 **EUDIPE (FR),** 6, b g Useful (FR)—Toskaninie (FR) **Mr D. A. Johnson**
29 **EVANGELICA (USA),** 8, b m Dahar (USA)—Rebut (USA) **Martin Pipe Racing Club**
30 **EVER SMILE (FR),** 11, ch g Be My Guest (USA)—Smiling (FR) **Mr David L'Estrange**
31 **FABULON (FR),** 5, gr g Kadrou (FR)—Thais Kervernet (FR) **Mr D. A. Johnson**
32 **FARFADET V (FR),** 5, b g Quart de Vin (FR)—Jolivette (FR) **C. M., B. J. & R. F. Batterham II**
33 **FATALISTE (FR),** 4, b c Nikos—Faracha (FR) **Mr Trevor Painting**
34 **FILL THE BILL (IRE),** 6, b h Bob Back (USA)—Neat Dish (CAN) **Mrs P. B. Browne**
35 **FLEET CADET,** 7, ch h Bairn (USA)—Pirogue **Sir John Swaine**
36 **FORCE DIVINE (FR),** 4, b f L'Emigrant (USA)—Force d'Attaque (FR) **Mr T. M. Hely-Hutchinson**
37 **FRIENDLY HOUSE (IRE),** 9, b g Fools Holme (USA)—Perle's Fashion **Mrs Sarah Buckley**
38 **GABOVA (FR),** 4, ch f Galetto (FR)—Borisova (FR) **Martin Pipe Racing Club**
39 **GAMBLING GUNNER,** 6, ch g Gunner B—Walnut Way **Mrs J. Robshaw**
40 **GENERAL MOUKTAR,** 8, ch g Hadeer—Fly The Coop **Mr A. S. Helaissi**
41 **GRAY PASTEL (IRE),** 4, gr g Al Nasr (FR)—Gay Pastel (FR) **Lord Donoughmore**
42 **GYSART (IRE),** 9, br g Good Thyne (USA)—Cute Play **Mrs R. Cobbold**
43 **HARBOUR ISLAND,** 6, b g Rainbow Quest (USA)—Quay Line **Mr Malcolm B. Jones**
44 **INDIAN ARROW (NZ),** 10, b g Show King (AUS)—Beatitude (NZ) **Joe & Joanne Richards**
45 **INDIAN DELIGHT,** 8, b g Uncle Pokey—Drinkers Delight **Joe & Joanne Richards**
46 **INDIAN JOCKEY,** 6, b g Indian Ridge—Number Eleven **Mr Stuart M. Mercer**
47 **INDIAN TRACKER,** 8, b g Oats—Sovereign Castle **Joe & Joanne Richards**

MR MARTIN PIPE—continued

48 **IRANOS (FR),** 6, b g Labus (FR)—Misvaria (FR) **Mr B. A. Kilpatrick**
49 **IRISH BANKER,** 7, ch g Derrylin—Cover Your Money **Mr David Jenks**
50 **IRKUTSK (USA),** 7, b g Nureyev (USA)—Herb Wine (USA) **Martin Pipe Racing Club**
51 **IRSAL,** 4, ch c Nashwan (USA)—Amwag (USA) **Richard Green (Fine Paintings)**
52 **JAZZ TRACK (IRE),** 4, b c Sadler's Wells (USA)—Minnie Hauk (USA) **Mr Malcolm B. Jones**
53 **JOLIVER (IRE),** 10, b g Strong Gale—Preacher's Gem **Mr C. R. Fleet**
54 **KASTERLEE (FR),** 4, ch f Stay For Lunch (USA)—Flowerdale (FR) **St Mellion Estates Ltd**
55 **KEEN DANCER,** 4, ch g Keen—Royal Shoe **Mrs Alison Farrant & Mr Frank Farrant**
56 **KEN RISK (FR),** 6, gr g Kendor (FR)—Swiss Risk (FR) **Mr Jim Weeden**
57 **KNOCK LEADER (IRE),** 6, b g Supreme Leader—Julie Mack **Mr Antony Sofroniou**
58 **LOLITA (FR),** 4, b f Hellios (USA)—Silver Dime (FR) **Southern Counties Finance & Leasing**
59 **LUV-U-FRANK (IRE),** 9, b g Good Thyne (USA)—Callula **Mr Frank Farrant & Mrs Alison Farrant**
60 **MAKE A STAND,** 7, ch g Master Willie—Make A Signal **Mr P. A. Deal & Mr M. C. Pipe**
61 **MANILENO,** 4, ch g K-Battery—Andalucia **Mr Stuart M. Mercer**
62 **MEDAILLE MILITAIRE,** 6, gr h Highest Honor (FR)—Lovely Noor (USA) **Mr James Hartnett**
63 **MELT THE CLOUDS (CAN),** 5, ch g Diesis—Population **Promo-Sherring Ltd**
64 **MIDAS,** 7, b g Rambo Dancer (CAN)—Curzon House **D. G. & D. J. Robinson**
65 **MISS ONDEE (FR),** 4, b f Dress Parade—Lady Caroline (FR) **C. M., B. J. & R. F. Batterham**
66 **MITE EQUAL,** 5, b g Presidium—Dissolution **Mr Heeru Kirpalani**
67 **MOZEMO,** 11, ch g Remezzo—Mo Storeen **Codan Trust Company Limited**
68 **MR DARCY,** 6, b g Dominion—Rose Chanelle **Mr Roger Nicholls**
69 **MYSTIK DAY,** 4, b g Mystiko (USA)—Swell Time (IRE) **Mr R. Stanley**
70 **NOBEL LAD,** 4, b c Highest Honor (FR)—Aldbourne **Mr James Hartnett**
71 **NORDIC BREEZE (IRE),** 6, b br g Nordico (USA)—Baby Clair **Mr Malcolm B. Jones**
72 **NORDIC VALLEY (IRE),** 7, b g Nordico (USA)—Malia **Pond House Racing**
73 **NORTHERN STARLIGHT,** 7, b g Northern State (USA)—Ganadora **Mr Arthur Souch**
74 **OLIVER'S SECRET (IRE),** 8, b g Sandalay—Cold Arctic **Mr C. R. Fleet**
75 **ORMANIA (FR),** 5, b m Synefos (USA)—Normania Hall (FR) **Mr Terry Neill**
76 **OR ROYAL (FR),** 7, gr g Kendor (FR)—Pomme Royale (FR) **Mr D. A. Johnson**
77 **PEKAY,** 5, b g Puissance—K-Sera **Moran, Nelson & Newman**
78 **PETITE RISK,** 4, ch f Risk Me (FR)—Technology (FR) **Mr A. J. Lomas**
79 **POMME SECRET (FR),** 5, b g Assert—Thalestria **Elite Racing Club**
80 **POTENTATE (USA),** 7, b br g Capote (USA)—Gay Fantastic **Mr Jim Weeden**
81 **PRIDWELL,** 8, b g Sadler's Wells (USA)—Glowing With Pride **Jones, Berstock and Fleet Partnership**
82 **RAINBOW STAR (FR),** 4, b br g Saumarez—In The Star (FR) **Mr Arthur White**
83 **ROBERT'S TOY (IRE),** 7, b g Salt Dome (USA)—Zazu **Mr Clive D. Smith**
84 **ROSEVALLEY (IRE),** 8, b g Boyne Valley—Rosebrook **A.J. & Mrs J.I. Whiting**
85 **ROYAL DIVERSION (IRE),** 5, b m Marju (IRE)—Royal Recreation (USA) **Richard Green (Fine Paintings)**
86 **RUNAWAY PETE (USA),** 8, b g Runaway Groom (CAN)—
Pete's Damas (USA) **Mr J. Smeaden & Mrs J. Smeaden**
87 **RUNNING DE CERISY (FR),** 4, ch g Lightning (FR)—Niloq (FR) **Mr P. A. Deal**
88 **SERENDIPITY (FR0,** 5, b g Mtoto—Bint Damascus (USA) **Mr M. Horton**
89 **SHAHRANI,** 6, b g Lear Fan (USA)—Windmill Princess **Mr A. S. Helaissi and Mr S. Helaissi**
90 **SHIKAREE (IRE),** 7, b g Salt Dome (USA)—Piculet **Martin Pipe Racing Club**
91 **ST MELLION STREAM (IRE),** 6, b g Heavenly Manna—Prime Preacher **St Mellion Estates Ltd**
92 **STRONG TEL (IRE),** 8, b g Strong Gale—Arctic Snow Cat **Mr Terry Neill**
93 **SUPERMICK,** 7, ch g Faustus (USA)—Lardana **Mr P. Clarke**
94 **TAMARINDO (FR),** 5, b g Galetto (FR)—Rainbow Rainbow **Mr D. A. Johnson**
95 **TERAO,** 12, b g Furry Glen—Bodyline **Mr B. A. Kilpatrick**
96 **THE FRENCH FURZE (IRE),** 4, ch g Be My Guest (USA)—Exciting **Mr Jim Ennis**
97 **THEME ARENA,** 5, b m Tragic Role (USA)—Sea Siesta **Mr Antony Sofroniou**
98 **TORBOY (IRE),** 8, b g Torus—Song of Love **Mr Paul Green**
99 **TORCH VERT (IRE),** 6, b g Law Society (USA)—Arctic Winter (CAN) **Mr Paul Green**
100 **TOTALLY YOURS (IRE),** 5, b m Classic Music (USA)—Dominia **Knight Hawks Partnership**
101 **ULTIMATE SMOOTHIE,** 6, b g Highest Honor (FR)—Baino Charm (USA) **Isca Bloodstock**
102 **UNSINKABLE BOXER (IRE),** 9, b g Sheer Grit—Softly Sarah **Mr Paul Green**
103 **VA UTU,** 10, b g Balliol—Flame **Mr Arthur Souch**
104 **VENT D'AOUT (IRE),** 4, ch f Imp Society (USA)—Barncogue **Elite Racing Club**
105 **WATER FLOWER,** 4, b f Environment Friend—Flower Girl **Avalon Surfacing Ltd**
106 **YUBRALEE (USA),** 6, ch g Zilzal (USA)—Kentucky Lill (USA) **Mr D. A. Johnson**

MR MARTIN PIPE—continued

Other Owners: Mr A. J. Allright, Alpenford Ltd, Mr D. M. Beresford, Mr T. Beresford, Mr D. A. Berstock, Mr Roger Bibby, Mr G. C. Bisgrove, Miss H. A. Bisgrove, Nrs M. A. Bisgrove, Miss S. Blumberg, Mr David Broadway, Mrs Mary Burke, Mr P. G. Bush, Mr G. Cherel, Mrs H. J. Clarke, Mr Stanley W. Clarke, Mr B. J. Craig, Datum Building Supplies Limited, Mr Les Draper, Miss J. Du Plessis, Mr R. E. Evans, Mr John Fasey, Mr Mick Fletcher, Mr Tony Fletcher, Mrs H. Forde, Mr Peter Fyvie, Mr W. J. Gredley, Mr Tony Hill, Mr A. Holdham, Mr M. Holmes, Mr J. N. Hutchinson, Mr Michael R. Jaye, Mrs D. Jenks, Mr G. B. Jennings, John Doyle Construction Limited, Mr E. C. Jones, Mr P. J. Keary, Mr L. G. Kennard, Mr Andrew Killean, Mr Kevin A. C. Kinch, Mrs Sarah Ling, Mr A. Long, Mrs Angie Malde, Mr I. D. McEwen, Mr P. McMahon, Mr N. G. Mills, Mr Joe Moran, Mr N. Morgan, Mr Liam Mulryan, Mr Gerald Myers, Mr Vincent Nally, Mr Noel Nation, Mr Steve Nelson, Mr Nick Newman, Miss M. Noden, Mr W. A O'Gorman, Mr William O'Leary, Mr Eugene O'Neill, Palladium Ltd, Mr Graham Parker, Mr Ron Peake, Mr David Pengelly, Mrs Pam Pengelly, Mr T. Perkins, Mr Graham Phippen, Mrs M. C. Pipe, Mrs Y. J. Reynolds, Mrs Jean Robinson, Mr S. J. Robshaw, Miss F. C. Russell, Mr T. J. R. Sanders, Exors Of The Late Mr Eric Scarth, Mrs L. M. Sewell, Mr Brian Simpkins, Mr John H. Smith, Somerset White Lining Ltd, Mr Stef Stefanou, Mrs I. M. Steinman, Mr J. D. Steinman, Mr C. J. Underwood, Mr Roger Warren, Mr A. M. Wellstead, Mr Bob Wheatley, Mrs L. M. Wundke.

Jockeys (NH): J Lower (10-4), A P McCoy.

Conditional: C Durham (9-10), J Hulet (9-7), G Supple (9-9).

Amateurs: Mr G Elliott (9-9), Mr Ashley Farrant (10-12).

476 MRS J. PITMAN, Upper Lambourn

Postal: **Weathercock House, Upper Lambourn, Hungerford, Berkshire, RG17 8QT.**
Phone: **LAMBOURN (01488) 71714 FAX (01488) 72196**

1 **AMTRAK EXPRESS,** 11, ch g Black Minstrel—Four In A Row **Amtrak Express Parcels Ltd**
2 **ARDFINNAN (IRE),** 5, b g Torus—O Tuk Deep **Willsford Racing Incorporated**
3 **ARITHMETIC,** 8, ch g Torus—Graphics Eska **Robert & Exors Late Elizabeth Hitchins**
4 **ARTADOIN LAD (IRE),** 5, b g King's Ride—Nun Merrier **Mr J. Shaw**
5 **AUDLEY LASS (IRE),** 5, b m Strong Gale—Audley Lady **Robert & Exors Late Elizabeth Hitchins**
6 **BALLADUR (USA),** 5, b g Nureyev (USA)—Ballinderry **Peters and Lee**
7 **BENJAMIN JONES,** 6, b g Teenoso (USA)—Mizzie Lizzie **Mr M. K. Florey**
8 **BROGANIER (IRE),** 6, b g Royal Fountain—Sleemana **Robert & Exors Late Elizabeth Hitchins**
9 **BROWJOSHY (IRE),** 5, b g Zaffaran (USA)—Keeping Company **B. D. L. Racing**
10 **BUSTER BOB (IRE),** 8, b br g Clearly Bust—Possible **Robert & Exors Late Elizabeth Hitchins**
11 **CABALLUS (USA),** 5, b g Danzig Connection (USA)—Rutledge Place (USA) **Salammi Racing**
12 **CARAS ROSE (IRE),** 6, gr g Roselier (FR)—Glencara **Robert & Exors Late Elizabeth Hitchins**
13 **CATHAY (IRE),** 6, gr g Roselier (FR)—Coolentallagh **Robert & Exors Late Elizabeth Hitchins**
14 **CHERRYMORE (IRE),** 7, br g Cataldi—Cherry Bow **Robert & Exors Late Elizabeth Hitchins**
15 **CHILLED (IRE),** 6, b g Mandalus—Phantom Thistle **Mrs T. Brown**
16 **CONNOR MACLEOD (IRE),** 5, ch g Torus—Blackrath Gem **Autofour Engineering**
17 **CONSPIRITO (IRE),** 5, b g Orchestra—Fly Fuss **Robert & Exors Late Elizabeth Hitchins**
18 4, Ch g Tale Quale—Corrielek **Mrs Evelyn Hankinson**
19 **COUNT CAMPIONI (IRE),** 4, b g Brush Aside (USA)—Emerald Flair **Garrett Gibbon Racing**
20 **CRANDON BOULEVARD,** 5, b g Niniski (USA)—Last Clear Chance (USA) **Ms S. Morris**
21 **DAISY (IRE),** 5, br m Yashgan—Water Sprite **Robert & Exors Late Elizabeth Hitchins**
22 **DARK CHALLENGER (IRE),** 6, b br g Brush Aside (USA)—Great Aunt Emily **Legs Only Partnership**
23 **DEMI CENTURY (IRE),** 6, b g Mandalus—Cloonaheen Girl **Mr Stewart Andrew**
24 **EGYPT MILL PRINCE,** 12, b g Deep Run—Just Darina **Mr S. R. Webb**
25 **ELYSIAN HAWK,** 5, ch g Heavenly Manna—Honeybuzzard (FR) **Robert & Exors Late Elizabeth Hitchins**
26 **EVER BLESSED (IRE),** 6, b g Lafontaine (USA)—Sanctify **The Ever Blessed Partnership**
27 **FLORES (IRE),** 6, b br g Air Display (USA)—Shining Green **Robert & Exors Late Elizabeth Hitchins**
28 **GINGER FOX (USA),** 5, ch g Diesis—Over Your Shoulder (USA) **Mr Martin Van Doorne**
29 **GOODTHYNE LADY (IRE),** 4, br f Good Thyne (USA)—Audley Lady **Robert & Exors Late Elizabeth Hitchins**

MRS J. PITMAN—continued

30 **GOODTIME GEORGE (IRE),** 5, b g Strong Gale—Game Sunset **Mrs M. J. Bone**
31 **HARLEQUIN CHORUS,** 8, ch g Jester—Raise The Dawn **Harlequin Software Consultants Ltd**
32 **HINEMOA (IRE),** 5, gr m Mandalus—Misty Joy **Mrs H. R. Cross**
33 **HIPPARQUE (FR),** 4, gr g Highest Honor (FR)—Hylandra (USA) **Mr W. Saunders**
34 **IDIOT'S LADY,** 9, b m Idiot's Delight—Lady Ling **Mrs J. Ollivant**
35 **INDEFENCE (IRE),** 7, b g Conquering Hero (USA)—Cathryn's Song **Indef Limited**
36 **INFERNO (IRE),** 5, ch g Zaffaran (USA)—Marians Pride **Mr B. R. H. Burrough**
37 4, B g Henbit (USA)—Irish Mint **Willsford Racing Incorporated**
38 **JET BOYS (IRE),** 8, b g Le Bavard (FR)—Fast Adventure **The Jet Stationery Company Limited**
39 **JET FILES (IRE),** 7, ro g Roselier (FR)—Deepdecending **The Jet Stationery Company Limited**
40 **JET RULES (IRE),** 8, b g Roselier (FR)—Bell Walks Fancy **The Jet Stationery Company Limited**
41 **JET SPECIALS (IRE),** 5, b g Be My Native (USA)—Glencuragh **The Jet Stationery Company Limited**
42 **JET TABS (IRE),** 6, b g Roselier (FR)—Bell Walks Fancy **The Jet Stationery Company Limited**
43 **JIBBER THE KIBBER (IRE),** 9, br g Good Thyne (USA)—Mia's Girl **Mr J. Hitchins**
44 **JUST ALBERT (IRE),** 8, b g Roselier (FR)—Carrigaun Lass **The Jet Stationery Company Limited**
45 **LORD REGAL (IRE),** 7, br g Aristocracy—Regular Maid **Crombie Club Racing**
46 **MAN OF THE MATCH,** 8, b g Vital Season—Kate The Shrew **Mrs Elizabeth Pearce**
47 **MASTER HARRY (IRE),** 6, b g Strong Gale—Another Miller **Robert & Exors Late Elizabeth Hitchins**
48 **MAURACHAS (IRE),** 8, ch g Good Thyne (USA)—Fodder Beet VII **Mr R. W. Guilding**
49 **MERRY SHOT (IRE),** 6, b g Cataldi—Borgina **Robert & Exors Late Elizabeth Hitchins**
50 **MISS BRECKNELL (IRE),** 9, b m Supreme Leader—Just Darina **Willsford Racing Incorporated**
51 **MUDAHIM,** 12, b g Shareef Dancer (USA)—Mariska (FR) **In Touch Racing Club**
52 **NAHTHEN LAD (IRE),** 9, b g Good Thyne (USA)—Current Call **Mr J. Shaw**
53 **NOBLE ATHLETE (IRE),** 6, br g King's Ride—Bowerina **Mr G. & L. Johnson**
54 **OTAGO HEIGHTS (NZ),** 6, b g Gold And Ivory (USA)—Mountain Heights (NZ) **Hunt Allen Cross Partnership**
55 5, B g Mandalus—Phantom Thistle **Mrs T. Brown**
56 **POT BLACK UK,** 7, b g Joligeneration—Golden Home **Pot Black (UK) Ltd**
57 **PRINCEFUL (IRE),** 7, b g Electric—Iram **Robert & Exors Late Elizabeth Hitchins**
58 **QUEENS HARBOUR (IRE),** 4, b g Brush Aside (USA)—Queenie Kelly **Mr Philip Matton**
59 **RADOMSKO,** 6, b g Polish Precedent (USA)—Mahabba (USA) **Jebel Ali Racing Stables**
60 **RELKANDER,** 8, b g Relkino—Arctic Ander **Mrs Maureen Buckley**
61 **RENARDINE BOY (IRE),** 5, ch g Carlingford Castle—Lady Hiltop **Miss N. F. Thesiger**
62 **RICARDO,** 4, b g Sanglamore (USA)—Nurica (USA) **Mailcom Plc & Mr Pat Whelan**
63 **ROSSELL ISLAND (IRE),** 7, br g Strong Gale—Fraoch Ban **Robert & Exors Late Elizabeth Hitchins**
64 **ROUYAN,** 12, b g Akarad (FR)—Rosy Moon (FR) **Mr Peter Mines**
65 **SALEEL (IRE),** 6, b g Salse (USA)—Kentfield **Jebel Ali Racing Stables**
66 **SALFORD QUAY (IRE),** 5, b g King's Ride—Super Lane **Mr A. J. Thompson**
67 **SCARLET EMPEROR (IRE),** 4, b g Supreme Leader—Red Donna **Mr Robert Hitchins**
68 **SECRET GIFT,** 5, ch m Cadeaux Genereux—Triste Oeil (USA) **Regal Racing**
69 **SILVER THYNE (IRE),** 6, br g Good Thyne (USA)—Fitz's Buck **Robert & Exors Late Elizabeth Hitchins**
70 **SMARTY (IRE),** 5, b br g Royal Fountain—Cahernane Girl **Mrs T. Brown**
71 **SMITH'S PERK (IRE),** 5, b g Executive Perk—Sister of Slane **Mr Arthur Smith**
72 **SMITH TOO (IRE),** 10, br g Roselier (FR)—Beau St **Smith Mansfield Meat Co Ltd**
73 **TELUK (IRE),** 7, ch g Sula Bula—Little Union **Robert & Exors Late Elizabeth Hitchins**
74 **TENNESSEE TWIST (IRE),** 8, b g Buckskin (FR)—Darjoy **Halewood International Ltd**
75 **THE HAPPY MONARCH (IRE),** 6, gr g Roselier (FR)—Larrys Glen **Mrs J. Ollivant**
76 **TUSCANY HIGHWAY (IRE),** 9, ch g Aristocracy—Johnnie's Lass **Mr A. Loze**
77 6, B g Sharrood (USA)—Valiyen **J. & A. Young (Leicester) Ltd**
78 **VITAMAN (IRE),** 9, b g King's Ride—Sea Cygnet **Larkhall Nat Hlth/Cantassium Vitamins**
79 **WAR PAINT (IRE),** 6, gr g Zaffaran (USA)—Rosy Posy (IRE) **Autofour Engineering**
80 **WREKENGALE (IRE),** 8, br g Strong Gale—Wrekenogan **Robert & Exors Late Elizabeth Hitchins**
81 **YEOMAN SAILOR (IRE),** 4, b g Roselier (FR)—Liffey Lady **Mrs Jill Eynon & Mr Robin Eynon**
82 **YOUNG BALDRIC,** 11, gr g Politico (USA)—No Don't **Mr B. R. H. Burrough**

Other Owners: Mr R. S. Allen, Mrs Richard Allen, Mr Roger Baines, Mr Mike Bateman, Mr D. A. Brown, Mr Brian Buckley, Mr Roger Davies, Mr M. J. Farrell, Mr J. A. Gent, Mr P. Harvey, Mr J. S. G. Haslem, Mr J. C. Hitchins, Mr Stewart R. Hunt, Mr G. I. Isaac, Jenny Pitman Racing Ltd, Mrs Kathy Kaplan, Mrs J. M. Kennedy, Mr Michael Kershaw, Mrs David Laing, Mr C. J. R. Lee, Mr N. J. Lipczynski, Sheikh Ahmed Al Maktoum, Mr A. E. T. Mines, Sheikh Mohammed, Mr M. Oberstein, Mr Eddie Shotton, Mr John Skull, Mr D. W. Stait, Mr M. A. Strong, Mr P. M. Tilley, Dr Robert Woodward.

Jockey (NH): R Farrant (10-0).

477 MR M. A. PITMAN, Upper Lambourn

Postal: **Saxon House Stables, Upper Lambourn, Hungerford, Berkshire, RG17 8QH.**
Phone: **YARD (01488) 73311 HOME (01488) 648006 FAX (01488) 71065**

1 **BANK AVENUE,** 7, b g Buckley—Woodram Delight **Mr S. D. Hemstock**
2 **CAROL'S DREAM (USA),** 6, ch h Risen Star (USA)—Merle Halton (USA) **Mr M. Pitman**
3 **COKENNY BOY,** 13, b g Abednego—Northern Push **Mr S. D. Hemstock**
4 **DIEGO,** 5, b g Belmez (USA)—True Queen (USA) **Peter J. Douglas Engineering**
5 **EXPRESS GIFT,** 9, br g Bay Express—Annes Gift **M. W. Horner, H. Young, and D. S. Arnold**
6 **FATHER MCCARTEN (IRE),** 5, ch g Be My Native (USA)—Mossiness **Mr Malcolm C. Denmark**
7 **JOLI GOOD FUN,** 7, gr g Joli Wasfi (USA)—Millend Twiggy VII **Mrs Marion Bowden**
8 **KEEP ME STRAIGHT (IRE),** 4, b g Castle Keep—Majority Straight **Mr D. Goodman & Mr D. S. Arnold**
9 **MARBLE CITY (IRE),** 5, br g Young Man (FR)—Marble Bash (IRE) **Mr Malcolm C. Denmark**
10 **MIMOSA,** 5, ch m Midyan (USA)—Figini **In The Frame**
11 **SAILIN MINSTREL (IRE),** 7, ch g Arapahos (FR)—Amoristic Love (IRE) **Mr R. Robinson**
12 **SANTABLESS (IRE),** 5, b g Zaffaran (USA)—Nimbi **Mr D. Goodman & Mr D. S. Arnold**
13 **SILENT CRACKER,** 6, br g Teenoso (USA)—Silent Surrender **Silent Partners**
14 **SILENT ROSE,** 5, b br m Petoski—Silent Surrender **Silent Partners**
15 **STRONG STUFF (IRE),** 8, b g Strong Gale—Must Rain **Mr M. Chavoush**
16 **SUPERIOR FINISH,** 12, br g Oats—Emancipated **Mr R. Robinson**
17 **TORSONS COMET (IRE),** 10, ch g Torus—Miss Fidget **Mrs S. Watts**
18 **URGENT SWIFT,** 5, ch g Beveled (USA)—Good Natured **Mr A. L. R. Morton**
19 **VENETIAN STORM,** 4, b f Glacial Storm (USA)—Milworth **Mr R. Bull**
20 **WAKEEL (USA),** 6, b g Gulch (USA)—Raahia (CAN) **Mr M. Chavoush**

Other Owners: Axo Sport Uk Limited, Mr E. G. M. Beard, Mrs C. A. Coombs, Mr T. W. Coombs, Mrs L. Douglas, Mr Peter J. Douglas, Mr N. C. Padden, Mr Richard Pitman, Mrs Richard Pitman, Mr D. W. Potter, Mrs E. A. Robinson, Mrs E. R. Smith, Mr M. R. Thompson.

478 MR S. I. PITTENDRIGH, South Wylam

Postal: **Bradley Hall Farm, South Wylam, Northd, NE41 8JP.**
Phone: **(01661) 852676**

1 **FLY EXECUTIVE,** 7, b g Executive Perk—March Fly **Mr S. I. Pittendrigh**
2 **HIGHLAND MISS,** 8, gr m Highlands—Umtali **Mr S. I. Pittendrigh**
3 **MANDIKA,** 10, b g Flash of Steel—Bushti Music **Mr S. I. Pittendrigh**
4 **MERCS AND PERKS (IRE),** 7, b g Executive Perk—Merseyside **Mr S. I. Pittendrigh**
5 **NOBODYS FLAME (IRE),** 10, b g Dalsaan—Hamers Flame **Mr S. I. Pittendrigh**
6 7, Gr g Le Bavard (FR)—Perato **Mr S. I. Pittendrigh**
7 **PERSIAN SYMPHONY (IRE),** 7, ch m Persian Heights—River Serenade (USA) **Mr S. I. Pittendrigh**

Amateurs: Mr S I Pittendrigh (10-7), Mr C Wilson.

479 MS L. C. PLATER, Newcastle-upon-Tyne

Postal: **The Stables, Little Harle, Kirkwhelpington, Newcastle-upon-Tyne, NE19 2PD.**
Phone: **(01830) 540424**

1 **BOLD ECHO,** 6, b m Silly Prices—Fair Echo **Mr D. Sundin**
2 **DASHMAR,** 11, b g Rare One—Ballinattin Girl **Mr D. Sundin**
3 **MR MCQUAKER,** 5, b g Past Glories—Mary McQuaker **Mr D. Sundin**
4 **STRATHMORE LODGE,** 9, b m Skyliner—Coliemore **Mr D. Sundin**
5 **ZOOT MONEY,** 6, gr m Scallywag—Moonduster **Mr D. Sundin**

Jockey (NH): D Bentley.

Lady Rider: Ms P Robson (9-0).

480 MR ROBERT E. POCOCK, Bridgwater

Postal: **Stringston Farm, Holford, Bridgwater, Somerset, TA5 1SX.**
Phone: **(01278) 741236 FAX (01278) 741240**

1 **DUST OF LIFE,** 8, b m War Hero—Yellow Wagtail **Mr T. E. Pocock**
2 5, B g Zambrano—Indian Election **Mr T. E. Pocock**
3 **MISSED THE MATCH,** 8, ch g Royal Match—Miss Levantine **Mr T. E. Pocock**
4 **ROSE GARDEN,** 9, b m Pragmatic—Indian Rose **Mr T. E. Pocock**

481 MR M. J. POLGLASE, Newmarket

Postal: **Heyward Place, Hamilton Road, Newmarket, Suffolk, CB8 7JQ.**
Phone: **(01638) 560125 FAX (01638) 560859 EVENINGS (01638) 664459**

1 **I SEE YOU SYDNEY (AUS),** 4, ch g Al Hareb (USA)—Sorrento (AUS) **Mr K. S. Lee**
2 **LADY GODIVA,** 4, b f Keen—Festival Fanfare **Keen Racing**
3 **MISS BARCELONA (IRE),** 4, b f Mac's Imp (USA)—National Ballet **Mr M. J. Polglase**
4 **OTTO E MEZZO,** 6, b g Persian Bold—Carolside **J. P. M. & J. W. Cook**
5 **STELLAR LINE (USA),** 5, ch g Zilzal (USA)—Stellaria (USA) **Odyssey Racing**
6 **SUN ALERT (USA),** 4, b f Alysheba (USA)—Sunerta (USA) **Mr K. S. Lee**
7 **SUPREME MAIMOON,** 4, b c Jareer (USA)—Princess Zena **Mr R. Newton**
8 **SWIFT,** 4, ch g Sharpo—Three Terns (USA) **General Sir Geoffrey Howlett**

THREE-YEAR-OLDS

9 **DAHLIDYA,** b f Midyan (USA)—Dahlawise (IRE) **General Sir Geoffrey Howlett**
10 **LEOFRIC,** b c Alhijaz—Wandering Stranger **Keen Racing**
11 **MAGIC FALLS (IRE),** b c River Falls—Simply Inch **Mr K. S. Lee**
12 **MAKE BELIEVE,** ch f Caerleon (USA)—Sleeping Beauty **Mr K. S. Lee**
13 **RECOGNITION,** b c Rock City—Star Face **Mr K. S. Lee**
14 **SHIRA-A,** b c Soviet Star (USA)—Hamama (USA) **Mr K. S. Lee**

TWO-YEAR-OLDS

15 **PIP'S BRAVE,** b c 21/5 Be My Chief (USA)—Pipistrelle **Mr M. J. Polglase**

Other Owners: Mr Mark Bury, Mr Tim Dean, Mr F. M. McClymont, Mr Nilesh Unadkat, Mrs Liz Wilkinson.

482 MR C. L. POPHAM, Taunton

Postal: **Bashford Racing Stables, West Bagborough, Taunton, Somerset, TA4 3EF.**
Phone: **(01823) 432769 (0831) 209875**

1 **BUDDY DIVER,** 5, b g Revlow—Rely-On-Pearl **Ms Sian Gale**
2 **CHURCHTOWN CHANCE (IRE),** 8, b m Fine Blade (USA)—Churchtown Breeze **Avalon Racing**
3 **COOL WEATHER (IRE),** 10, b g Kemal (FR)—Arctic Tack **Mr R. J. Hart**
4 **GENTLEMAN JIM,** 8, b g Nearly A Hand—Jenpoint Jessy **Roy Hart Motors Partnership**
5 **ILANDRA (IRE),** 6, b m Roi Danzig (USA)—Island Goddess **Brewers Arms Racing Club**
6 **KONGIES MELODY,** 7, b m Sousa—Pullandese **Mr K. L. Dare**
7 **KOO'S PROMISE,** 7, bl m Lepanto (GER)—Koo-Ming **G. A. Warren Limited**
8 **NATIONAL FIASCO,** 5, b g Pragmatic—Lady Barunbe **Mr B. R. Bartlett**
9 **ROBINS PRIDE (IRE),** 8, b g Treasure Hunter—Barney's Sister **Weeks, Staple, Littlejohns & Dascombe**
10 **ROVESTAR,** 7, b g Le Solaret (FR)—Gilberts Choice **Mr G. Burr**
11 **SANDS POINT,** 8, b g Rakaposhi King—Jacqueline Jane **Mrs C. R. Hayton**

Other Owners: Mrs A. E. Baker, Mr G. J. Dascombe, Mr A. J. Hutchings, Mr Paul B. Jordain, Mr P. Littlejohns, Mr T. Needham, Mr D. J. Newton, Mr C. L. Popham, Mrs Sue Popham, R. J. Heathman (County Contractors) Ltd, Mr A. Skidmore, Mr A. Staple, Mr G. Waterman, Mr Richard Weeks, Mr C. D. J. West.

483 MR J. C. POULTON, Lewes

Postal: **Balmer Farm, Brighton Road, Lewes, East Sussex, BN7 3JN.**
Phone: **(01273) 603824/621303 FAX (01273) 603824**

1 **BLURRED IMAGE (IRE),** 7, ch g Exactly Sharp (USA)—Bear's Affair **Mr Gerald West**
2 **BUILT IN HEAVEN,** 6, ch m Sunley Builds—Saintly Chorus **Mr Gerald West**
3 **CHERRY LEE,** 6, b m Buckley—Cherry Opal **Mr Gerald West**
4 **DUKE OF LEE,** 8, b g Buckley—La Margarite **Mr Gerald West**
5 **IT'S WALLACE,** 5, b g Bedford (USA)—Rua Batric **Gerald West William Charlton Juliet Touw**
6 4, B f Bedford—Lac Royale **Mr Gerald West**
7 **MY NAD KNOWS,** 5, b g Derrylin—Early Run **Mr Julian Poulton**
8 **PROPERO,** 13, b g Electric—Nadwa **Mr Gerald West**
9 4, B f Headin' Up—Spartan Native **Mr Gerald West**
10 **SPEEDY SNAPS PRIDE,** 6, gr g Hallgate—Pineapple's Pride **Mr Gerald West**
11 **SPRINGFIELD DANCER,** 7, b m Rambo Dancer (CAN)—Nebiha **Mr & Mrs M. Jones**
12 **STAR ISLAND,** 5, b g Jupiter Island—Gippeswyck Lady **Mr Gerald West**
13 **WHITE IN FRONT,** 7, ch g Tina's Pet—Lyaaric **Mr Gerald West**

TWO-YEAR-OLDS

14 B f 23/3 Toulon—Aryumad (Goldhill) **Mr Gerald West**
15 Ch f 25/4 Gran Alba (USA)—Harristown Rose (Miami Springs) **Mr Gerald West**
16 B c 10/5 Sir Harry Lewis (USA)—Letterewe (Alias Smith (USA)) **Mr Gerald West**

Other Owners: Mr J. McSpirit, Mr M. C. Wells, Mr J. West, Mrs N. West.

Jockeys (NH): J Culloty, T J Murphy (10-0), Andrew Thornton (w.a.).

Conditional: L P Aspell (10-0, w.a.), G Gallagher (10-0).

Lady Rider: Miss Leesa Long (10-0).

484 MR J. R. POULTON, Lewes

Postal: **White Cottage, Stud Farm, Telscombe, Lewes, East Sussex, BN7 3HZ.**
Phone: **(01273) 300127 HOME (01273) 302486 YARD (01273) 302486 YARD**

1 **ARNIE (IRE),** 6, b g Double Schwartz—The Moneys Gone **Mr Mike Culling**
2 **ARRASAS LADY,** 8, ch m Arrasas (USA)—Sharelle **Mr T. Armour**
3 **EAU SO SLOE,** 7, b g Baron Blakeney—Final Attraction **Mrs J. Druce**
4 **GIKO,** 4, b g Arazi (USA)—Gayane **V. R. V. Partnership**
5 **INTO DEBT,** 5, b m Cigar—Serious Affair **Mrs J. Druce**
6 **LADYBOWER (IRE),** 6, b m Pennine Walk—Eimkar **Mr F. Willson**
7 **MEGA TID,** 6, b g Old Vic—Dunoof **Come Racing Ltd**
8 **OLD GOLD N TAN,** 5, b g Ballacashtal (CAN)—Raleigh Gazelle **Mr T. Armour**
9 **ONE IN THE EYE,** 5, br h Arrasas (USA)—Mingalles **Mr T. Armour**
10 **PRIVATE PERCIVAL,** 5, b g Arrasas (USA)—Romacina **Mrs C. D. Poulton**
11 **STEADY READY GO (IRE),** 6, b g Night Shift (USA)—Smeralda (GER) **V. R. V. Partnership**
12 **WRN PRINCESS,** 4, ch f Handsome Sailor—Sovereign Rose **Come Racing Ltd**
13 **ZURS (IRE),** 5, b g Tirol—Needy **Glendale Partnership Ltd**

THREE-YEAR-OLDS

14 Ch c Henbit (USA)—Romacina **Miss Victoria Markowiak**

Other Owners: Mr J. L. C. O'Brien, Mrs David Page, Mrs Rose Vivian, Miss Vanda Vivian.

Jockeys (Flat): S Drowne (8-1, w.a.), A Morris (8-2).

Apprentice: R Mullen (7-3, w.a.).

Conditional: J Magee (9-11).

Lady Rider: Mrs C Poulton (9-7).

485 MR W. G. PREECE, Telford

Postal: **Uppington Smithy, Uppington, Telford, Shropshire, TF6 5HN.**
Phone: **(01952) 740249 FAX (01952) 740434 MOBILE (0802) 676040**

1 **BATTY'S ISLAND,** 9, b g Town And Country—Just Something **Mrs Mary Price**
2 **CAIUS CALIGULA (USA),** 7, b g Risen Star (USA)—L'Incestueuse (USA) **Mr M. Ephgrave**
3 **DOSSES DAN (IRE),** 6, b h Danehill (USA)—Flyaway Bride (USA) **Mr M. Ephgrave**
4 **GOATSFUT (IRE),** 8, ch g Le Bavard (FR)—Kilbricken Glen **Mr D. Jones**
5 **GUNNER SID,** 7, ch g Gunner B—At Long Last **Mrs Mary Price**
6 **NAGARA SOUND,** 7, b g Lochnager—Safe 'n' Sound **The Wroxeter Race Club**
7 **NIRVANA PRINCE,** 9, ch g Celestial Storm (USA)—Princess Sunshine **Mr D. Portman**
8 **NIRVANA PRINCESS,** 6, ch m Glacial Storm (USA)—Princess Sunshine **Mr D. Portman**
9 **ON THE GREEN,** 5, br m Pharly (FR)—Regal Wonder **H. S. & E. M. Yates**

Other Owners: Mr G. L. Edwards, Mr R. A. Jones, Mr Andy Li, Miss J. L. Portman, Mr D. Pugh, Mr P. Russell, Mr Cecil W. Wardle, Mr Eddie Wicks.

Amateur: Mr H Ephgrave.

486 MR P. PRENDERGAST, Kildare

Postal: **Melitta Lodge, Kildare, Co. Kildare, Ireland.**
Phone: **(045) 521288 FAX (045) 521875**

1 **ANITA'S LAD (IRE),** 5, ch g John French—Hidden Hand (USA) **Mr Terence Coleman**
2 **BARKERSFORD (IRE),** 4, ch g Shalford (IRE)—Grand Morning **Mrs R. Castle**
3 5, Ch g Un Desperado (FR)—Conductress **Ms M. Horan**
4 **EASTENDER (IRE),** 5, b g Camden Town—Latoya **Mrs Heather Whiteside**
5 **FIRMOUNT CROSS (IRE),** 6, b g Be My Native (USA)—Latoya **Mr Aidan Walsh**
6 **HOH INVADER (IRE),** 6, b g Accordion—Newgate Fairy **Mr D. Allport**
7 4, B g Executive Perk—Latoya
8 **MR MONGOOSE (IRE),** 6, b g Accordion—Temarie (FR) **Mrs Whitehead**
9 **PIXIE DANCER,** 4, b c Rambo Dancer (CAN)—Nicholess **Ms M. Horan**
10 **PRINCE ALEX (IRE),** 4, b g Night Shift (USA)—Finalist (USA)
11 **TARAJAN (USA),** 6, ch g Shahrastani (USA)—Tarafa **Ms M. Horan**
12 **UNCLE WAT,** 6, b g Ardross—First Things First **Ms M. Horan**
13 **UNION TOWN (IRE),** 4, b g Generous (IRE)—Exclusive Life (USA) **Ms M. Horan**

THREE-YEAR-OLDS

14 **ARANTXA SANCHEZ (IRE),** ch f Indian Ridge—Grand Morning (IRE)
15 **AUNTY CATHERINE (IRE),** b f Mujadil (USA)—Nation's Game **Mr M. Horan**
16 **EN RETARD (IRE),** b br f Petardia—Regal Society (IRE) **Mr Aidan Walsh**
17 **JIMMY THE GREEK (IRE),** b g Tenby—Some Fun **Ms M. Horan**
18 B f Phardante (FR)—Latoya

TWO-YEAR-OLDS

19 B c Housebuster (USA)—Crimson Contender (USA) (Monsieur Chaplain) **Ms M. Horan**
20 B c 10/4 Case Law—Miss Quotation (Sexton Blake) **Ms M. Horan**
21 B c 21/2 Brief Truce (USA)—Ukud (USA) (Woodman (USA)) **Ms M. Horan**

487 SIR MARK PRESCOTT BT, Newmarket

Postal: **Heath House, Newmarket, Suffolk, CB8 8DU.**
Phone: **(01638) 662117 FAX (01638) 666572**

1 **FARMOST,** 5, ch g Pharly (FR)—Dancing Meg (USA) **Mr W. E. Sturt**
2 **HYDE PARK (IRE),** 4, b c Alzao (USA)—Park Elect **Mr Neil Greig**
3 **PASTERNAK,** 5, b h Soviet Star (USA)—Princess Pati **Mr Graham Rock**
4 **RUDIMENTAL,** 4, b g Rudimentary (USA)—Full Orchestra **Cheveley Park Stud**
5 **WIZARD KING,** 7, b h Shaadi (USA)—Broomstick Cottage **Sheikh Ahmed bin Saeed Al Maktoum**

THREE-YEAR-OLDS

6 **ALBORADA,** gr f Alzao (USA)—Alouette **Miss K. Rausing**
7 **ALTITUDE (IRE),** b c Alzao (USA)—Elevate **Mrs F. R. Watts**
8 **BREAK FOR PEACE (IRE),** b f Brief Truce (USA)—Run Bonnie **Sharp But Fair Partnership**
9 **CALCHAS (IRE),** b g Warning—Nassma (IRE) **Sheikh Ahmed bin Saeed Al Maktoum**
10 **CHASING RAINBOWS,** b f Rainbow Quest (USA)—Height of Passion **Cheveley Park Stud**
11 **CRITICAL AIR,** b g Reprimand—Area Girl **Mr Neil Greig**
12 **FAR CRY (IRE),** b g Pharly (FR)—Darabaka (IRE) **Mr W. E. Sturt**
13 **FEARLESS,** b f Groom Dancer (USA)—Fearless Revival **Cheveley Park Stud**
14 **FLAWLESS,** b f Warning—Made of Pearl (USA) **Cheveley Park Stud**
15 **FREEDOM QUEST (IRE),** b c Polish Patriot (USA)—Recherchee **Mr W. E. Sturt**
16 **GIRLIE SET (IRE),** b f Second Set (IRE)—Heavenward (USA) **Mr G. S. Shropshire**
17 **GRAZIA,** b f Sharpo—Dance Machine **Mr Cyril Humphris**
18 **HUNT HILL (IRE),** b c High Estate—Royaltess **Lord Swaythling**
19 **MACH ONE (FR),** b g Sanglamore (USA)—Douceur (USA) **Mr Roger Barby**
20 **MITCH PASSI (IRE),** ch g Exit To Nowhere (USA)—Stormed (USA) **Mr B. Haggas**
21 **MOUNTAIN SONG,** b c Tirol—Persian Song **Eclipse Thoroughbreds**

SIR MARK PRESCOTT BT—continued

22 **MYSTERY GUEST (IRE),** b g Alzao (USA)—Lora's Guest **Mr G. Moore**
23 **NORSKI LAD,** b c Niniski (USA)—Lady Norcliffe (USA) **Hesmonds Stud**
24 **ODETTE,** b f Pursuit of Love—On Tiptoes **Mr J. W. Rowles**
25 **ON CALL,** gr f Alleged (USA)—Doctor Bid (USA) **Cheveley Park Stud**
26 **PEDRO (IRE),** b c Brief Truce (USA)—Mrs Fisher (IRE) **Mr G. D. Waters**
27 **POLAR MIST,** b g Polar Falcon (USA)—Post Mistress (IRE) **Mr Neil Greig**
28 **PRESSURISE,** ch g Sanglamore (USA)—Employ Force (USA) **Mr Charles Walker & Mr Jonathon Carroll**
29 **PRIMATICCIO (IRE),** b g Priolo (USA)—Martinova **Mr Cyril Humphris**
30 **REGENT,** ch c Zafonic (USA)—Queen Midas **H.R.H. Prince Fahd Salman**
31 **SHIPLEY GLEN,** b c Green Desert (USA)—Lady Shipley **Mrs L. Burnet**
32 **SILENT WARNING,** b c Ela-Mana-Mou—Buzzbomb **Eclipse Thoroughbreds**
33 **SMART (IRE),** b f Last Tycoon—Belle Origine (USA) **Mr A. S. Reid**
34 **TARASHAAN,** b g Darshaan—Tarasova (USA) **Mr E. B. Rimmer**
35 **TIGHTROPE,** b c Alzao (USA)—Circus Act **Mr W. E. Sturt**
36 **TREASURE ISLAND,** b f Rainbow Quest (USA)—Cockatoo Island **Lord Derby**

TWO-YEAR-OLDS

37 **BAHRAIN (IRE),** ch c 17/3 Lahib (USA)—Twin Island (IRE) (Standaan (FR)) **H.R.H Prince Fahd Salman**
38 **BORDER GLEN,** b c 25/2 Selkirk (USA)—Sulitelma (USA) (The Minstrel (CAN)) **Mr L. A. Larratt**
39 **CARABINE (USA),** gr f 19/3 Dehere (USA)—Caracciola (FR) (Zeddaan) **Miss K. Rausing**
40 **CHICODOVE,** b f 6/3 In the Wings—Chicobin (USA) (J O Tobin (USA)) **Hesmonds Stud**
41 **COVER GIRL (IRE),** ch f 14/4 Common Grounds—Peace Carrier (IRE) (Doulab (USA)) **The Speculators**
42 **DANSKER (IRE),** b c 24/3 Darshaan—Nassma (IRE) (Sadler's Wells (USA)) **Sheikh Ahmed bin Saeed Al Maktoum**
43 **DREAMING,** b f 26/1 Polar Falcon (USA)—Dream Baby (Master Willie) **Cheveley Park Stud**
44 **EN GRISAILLE,** gr f 8/4 Mystiko (USA)—Hickleton Lady (IRE) (Kala Shikari) **Mr H. R. Moszkowicz**
45 **EYEBALLS OUT,** b c 3/2 Polar Falcon (USA)—Jacquelina (USA) (Private Account (USA)) **John Brown & Megan Dennis**
46 **FLYING OFFICER,** ch c 15/5 Efisio—Area Girl (Jareer (USA)) **Mr Neil Greig**
47 **GIGETTA (IRE),** ch f 31/3 Brief Truce (USA)—Mrs Fisher (IRE) (Salmon Leap (USA)) **Mr Alvaro Maccioni**
48 **HIDDEN MAGIC,** b c 12/3 Magic Ring (IRE)—Magic Milly (Simply Great (FR)) **Platinum Syndicate Limited**
49 **HYPHEN,** ch c 6/4 Most Welcome—Finlandaise (FR) (Artic Tern (USA)) **Mr B. Haggas**
50 **INDIAN BAZAAR (IRE),** ch c 26/2 Indian Ridge—Bazaar Promise (Native Bazaar) **Eclipse Thoroughbreds**
51 **LINCOLN DEAN,** b c 27/1 Mtoto—Play With Me (IRE) (Alzao (USA)) **Mr Cyril Humphris**
52 **LOVE AFFAIR,** b f 1/3 Be My Chief (USA)—Post Mistress (IRE) (Cyrano de Bergerac) **Mr Neil Greig**
53 **MAGIC LIGHT (IRE),** b c 23/3 Dilum (USA)—Wynona (IRE) (Cyrano de Bergerac) **Mr H. D. Kelly**
54 **MOLYNEUX,** b c 12/2 Marju (IRE)—Mahasin (USA) (Danzig (USA)) **Mr A. Speelman**
55 **MOON SHOT,** gr c 11/3 Pistolet Bleu (IRE)—La Luna (USA) (Lyphard (USA)) **Eclipse Thoroughbreds**
56 **MY LASS,** b f 22/1 Elmaamul (USA)—Be My Lass (IRE) (Be My Guest (USA)) **Cheveley Park Stud**
57 **NOBLE ONE,** ch f 9/3 Primo Dominie—Noble Destiny (Dancing Brave (USA)) **Cheveley Park Stud**
58 **NO WARNING,** b c 4/6 Warning—Norgabie (Northfields (USA)) **Hesmonds Stud**
59 **PHUKET PARK,** gr f 13/5 Petong—Peace In The Park (IRE) (Ahonoora) **Mr J. R. Newton**
60 **POLAR ICE,** b c 30/3 Polar Falcon (USA)—Sweet Slew (USA) (Seattle Slew (USA)) **Cheveley Park Stud**
61 **QUILT,** b f 25/4 Terimon—Quaranta (Hotfoot) **Lord Fairhaven**
62 **RAJMATA (IRE),** br f 27/2 Prince Sabo—Heart of India (IRE) (Try My Best (USA)) **Mrs C. R. Philipson**
63 B g 18/2 Rainbows For Life—Sandy Maid (Sandy Creek) **Thurcoe Partnership**
64 **SOVEREIGN ABBEY (IRE),** b f 16/3 Royal Academy (USA)—Elabella (Ela-Mana-Mou) **Mr G. S. Shropshire**
65 **SUMMER NIGHT,** b f 7/4 Nashwan (USA)—Shimmering Sea (Slip Anchor) **Miss K. Rausing**
66 **SUNNY CHIEF,** ch c 17/4 Be My Chief (USA)—Sunny Davis (USA) (Alydar (USA)) **Hesmonds Stud**
67 **SWAGGER,** ch c 28/1 Generous (IRE)—Widows Walk (Habitat) **Mr G. Moore**
68 **THE BALTIC,** ch c 8/5 Emarati (USA)—Harold's Girl (FR) (Northfields (USA)) **Lord Swaythling**
69 **TREASURY,** ch f 27/3 Generous (IRE)—Atlantic Flyer (USA) (Storm Bird (CAN)) **Cheveley Park stud**
70 **TRIPLE DASH,** ch c 10/4 Nashwan (USA)—Triple Joy (Most Welcome) **Hesmonds Stud**
71 **UNERRING,** b f 12/1 Unfuwain (USA)—Serotina (IRE) (Mtoto) **Lord Roborough**
72 **WAIN MOUNTAIN,** b c 20/3 Unfuwain (USA)—Mountain Memory (High Top) **Hesmonds Stud**
73 **WHITE TRUFFLE (USA),** ch f 24/2 Dehere (USA)—Familiar (USA) (Diesis) **Mr Faisal Salman**

SIR MARK PRESCOTT BT—continued

Other Owners: Mr Bruce Cairnduff, Mr J. P. Carroll, Mr Charles J. Catt, Mr David Coe, Mr Stephen Crawley, Mr R. S. Dawes, Mrs Megan Dennis, The Hon Miss Gillian Douglas-Pennant, Mr Roger T. Ferris, Lady Margaret Fortescue, Mr Chris Jenkins, Mr J. Johnston, Miss Lawson Johnston, Mrs Rosemary Moszkowicz, Major C. R. Philipson, Tessona Racing Limited, Mrs Ann Thurlow, Mr Charles C. Walker.

Jockeys (Flat): G Duffield (8-2), C Nutter (8-4), S. Sanders (8-3).

Apprentice: C Luno (7-10).

Amateur: Mr C Vigors (10-10).

488 MR C. J. PRICE, Leominster

Postal: **Brockmanton Hall, Brockmanton, Leominster, Herefordshire, HR6 0QU.**
Phone: **(01568) 760695**

1 **SPARKLING DOVE,** 5, ch m Lighter—Nimble Dove **Mr Cecil J. Price**

489 MR RICHARD J. PRICE, Hereford

Postal: **Criftage Farm, Ullingswick, Hereford, Herefordshire, HR1 1JG.**
Phone: **HEREFORD (01432) 820263**

1 **DOUBLY SHARP (USA),** 4, ch g Diesis—Nijana (USA) **Mr Don Gould**
2 **DOVE FROM ABOVE,** 5, b g Henbit (USA)—Sally's Dove **Mr R. J. Price**
3 **FASTINI GOLD,** 6, b g Weldnaas (USA)—La Carlotta **Mr A. E. Price**
4 **GINGER WATT (IRE),** 6, ch g Electric—Deirdre Oge **Mr Hugh B. McGahon**
5 **LADY ROSEBURY,** 8, b m Derring Rose—Foxbury **Mrs C. W. Middleton**
6 **LE GRAND GOUSIER (USA),** 4, ch c Strawberry Road (AUS)—Sandy Baby (USA) **Mrs S. G. Davies**
7 **LOCHLASS (IRE),** 4, b f Distinctly North (USA)—Littleton Song **My Left Foot Racing Syndicate**
8 **MR BUDDY BLUE (IRE),** 5, gr g Carmelite House (USA)—Haut Lafite **Mrs J. M. Kitson**
9 **PICK-N-CRUISE,** 6, b m Cruise Missile—Pickled Tink **Mrs C. W. Middleton**
10 **PRIDEWOOD FUGGLE,** 8, b g Little Wolf—Quick Reply **Mrs B. Morris**
11 **PRIDEWOOD PICKER,** 11, b g Joshua—Guinea Feather **Mrs B. Morris**
12 **RISKING,** 5, b m Risk Me (FR)—Dark Kristal (IRE) **Mr Bill Davies**
13 **WOLFBURY,** 10, ch m Little Wolf—Foxbury **Mrs C. W. Middleton**

Other Owners: Mr M. J. Barnell, Mrs I. D. Broadbent, Mrs Chris Davies, Mr P. J. Hoare, Mr J. P. Price, Mr P. E. Price, Mr R. T. Price, Mr A. Shields.

490 MR P. A. PRITCHARD, Shipston-on-Stour

Postal: **The Gate House, Whatcote, Shipston-on-Stour, Warwickshire, CV36 5EF.**
Phone: **TYSOE (01295) 680689**

1 **DEEP SONG,** 8, ch g True Song—Rapagain **Mr P. A. Pritchard**
2 4, Ch g Risk Me (FR)—Hallowed **Woodlands (Worcestershire) Ltd**
3 5, Br g Rich Charlie—Hallowed **Woodlands (Worcestershire) Ltd**
4 **MISS FORTINA,** 6, b m Belfort (FR)—Lady Martina **Mr P. A. Pritchard**
5 **WOODLANDS ENERGY,** 7, b m Risk Me (FR)—Hallowed **Woodlands (Worcestershire) Ltd**
6 **WOODLANDS GENHIRE,** 13, ch g Celtic Cone—Spartella **Woodlands (Worcestershire) Ltd**
7 **WOODLANDS LAD TOO,** 6, b g Risk Me (FR)—Hallowed **Woodlands (Worcestershire) Ltd**

THREE-YEAR-OLDS

8 B f Risk Me (FR)—Hallowed **Woodlands (Worcestershire) Ltd**

Other Owners: Mr J. Digweed, Mr R. W. Stowe.

Jockey (NH): R Bellamy (10-0).

Amateurs: Mr F Hutsby (10-0), Mr J Pritchard (10-7).

491 DR P. L. J. PRITCHARD, Purton

Postal: **Pond House, Purton, Berkeley, Gloucestershire, GL13 9HY.**
Phone: **(01453) 811989 E-Mail: 101655.157@compuserve.com**

1 **JIM VALENTINE,** 12, br g Furry Glen—Duessa **Mrs T. Pritchard**
2 4, B f North Col—Midnight Mystic
3 **SALCOMBE HARBOUR (NZ),** 14, ch g English Harbour—Faux Leigh (NZ) **Mrs T. Pritchard**
4 **WHO'S TO SAY,** 12, b g Saher—Whisht **Mrs T. Pritchard**

Other Owners: Dr P. Pritchard.

Amateur: Dr P L J Pritchard (9-11).

492 MR P. D. PURDY, Bridgwater

Postal: **Fyne Court Farm, Broomfield, Bridgwater, Somerset, TA5 2EQ.**
Phone: **(01823) 451632 (0860) 392786 CAR PHONE**

1 **COURT NANNY,** 4, ch f Nicholas Bill—Tudor Sunset **Mr P. D. Purdy**
2 **FLASHFEET,** 8, b g Rousillon (USA)—Miellita **Mr P. D. Purdy**
3 **LAJADHAL (FR),** 9, gr g Bellypha—Rose d'Amour **Mr P. D. Purdy**
4 **RIPSNORTER (IRE),** 9, ch h Rousillon (USA)—Formulate **Mr P. D. Purdy**
5 **SUTTON BALLAD,** 4, b f Emperor Fountain—Crescent Cottage **Mr P. D. Purdy**
6 **SUTTON LION,** 6, b g Lyphento (USA)—Crescent Cottage **Mr P. D. Purdy**
7 **TUDOR BLONDE,** 7, ch m Pablond—Cottage Melody **Mr P. D. Purdy**
8 **TUDOR COTTAGE,** 8, ch g Town And Country—Cottage Melody **Mr P. D. Purdy**
9 **TUDOR NICKOLA,** 6, ch m Nicholas Bill—Cottage Melody **Mr P. D. Purdy**
10 **TUDOR TOWN,** 10, b g Town And Country—Cottage Melody **Mr P. D. Purdy**
11 **VERRO (USA),** 11, ch g Irish River (FR)—Royal Rafale (USA) **Mr P. D. Purdy**

THREE-YEAR-OLDS

12 **GREY COURT,** ro g Gran Alba (USA)—Tudor Sunset **Mr P. D. Purdy**

TWO-YEAR-OLDS

13 **COURT SENOR,** gr g 28/5 Gran Alba (USA)—Tudor Sunset **Mr P. D. Purdy**
14 **EMPEROR SUTTON,** ch g 17/5 Emperor Fountain—Crescent Cottage **Mr P. D. Purdy**

Lady Rider: Miss Alison Jane Purdy (9-2).

493 MR J. J. QUINN, Malton

Postal: **Bellwood Cottage Stables, Settrington, Malton, North Yorkshire, YO17 8NP.**
Phone: **(01944) 768370 MOBILE (0370) 500028 FAX (01944) 768370**

1 **BOWLERS BOY,** 5, ch g Risk Me (FR)—Snow Wonder **Bowlers Racing**
2 **B THE ONE,** 7, b g Gunner B—Half Asleep **Andrew Page & John Pollard**
3 **COTTAGE PRINCE (IRE),** 5, b g Classic Secret (USA)—Susan's Blues **Mrs Kay Thomas**
4 **ERINY (USA),** 9, br g Erins Isle—Memorable Girl (USA) **Lady Anne Bentinck**
5 **EYE OF THE STORM (IRE),** 7, b g Strong Gale—Belon Brig **Mr John Stone**
6 **FIRST LIGHT,** 6, b g Lord Bud—New Dawning **Four Wise Men**
7 **INDICATOR,** 6, b g Reference Point—Comic Talent **Lady Anne Bentinck**
8 **IN GOOD FAITH,** 6, b g Beveled (USA)—Dulcidene **Mrs S. Quinn**
9 **L A TOUCH,** 5, b m Tina's Pet—Silvers Era **New Perceptions**
10 **MURRAY'S MAZDA (IRE),** 9, ch g M Double M (USA)—Lamya **Mr Murray Grubb**
11 **NEVER SAD NEWSBOY,** 5, b g Gildoran—Lawnswood Miss **Anne Penney & Carol Bloom**

MR J. J. QUINN—continued

12 **PERPETUAL LIGHT,** 5, b m Petoski—Butosky **The Four Point Partnership**
13 **RING OF VISION (IRE),** 6, br g Scenic—Circus Lady **Mr Harold Bray**
14 **RUM LAD,** 4, gr g Efisio—She's Smart **Mr B. Shaw**
15 **SIMON SAYS,** 8, b g Giacometti—Mrs Scattercash **Mr D. Simpson**
16 **TIPPERARY SUNSET (IRE),** 4, gr g Red Sunset—Chapter And Verse **Mr Harold Bray**
17 **TWENTY WINKS,** 5, b m Gunner B—Half Asleep **Mrs P. Nicholson**

THREE-YEAR-OLDS

18 **LAVERNOCK LADY,** b f Don't Forget Me—Danissa **Home Countries**
19 **MISS MAIN STREET (IRE),** b f Shalford (IRE)—Bonvin **Mr T. S. Robinson**
20 **OLLIE'S CHUCKLE (IRE),** b g Mac's Imp (USA)—Chenya **Mrs Maggie Pearson**
21 **PREMIUM PRINCESS,** b f Distant Relative—Solemn Occasion (USA) **Premium Bloodstock Plc**
22 **SMART PRINCE,** gr g Prince Sabo—She's Smart **Mr B. Shaw**

TWO-YEAR-OLDS

23 **ARCHIE BABE (IRE),** ch g Archway (Ire)—Frensham Manor **Carol Bloom & Karen Mapp**
24 B f Robellino (USA)—By Candlelight (IRE) **Mr Derrick Bloy**
25 Gr f Petardia—Chapter And Verse **Manx Mirrors Ltd**
26 B g Cosmonaut—Could Have Been **Mrs S. Quinn**
27 B f Weldnaas (USA)—Heemee **Mr B. Adamson**
28 B c Ardkinglass—Infra Blue (IRE) **Mrs S. Quinn**
29 **LADY NAIRN,** b f Mujadil (USA)—Animate (IRE) **Mr Murray Grubb**
30 B g Mac's Imp (USA)—Miss Ming **Bowlers Racing**
31 **SMART PREDATOR,** gr c Polar Falcon (USA)—She's Smart **Mr B Shaw**
32 **WESTWOOD VIEW,** b f Puissance—Long View **The Westwood Partnership**

Other Owners: Mrs G. Barnes, Mr S. Bowett, Mr Richard Dawson, Mr C. J. Eagle, Mr C. R. Galloway, Mr P. R. Gooder, Mr Paul Hogan, Mr P. F. Hope, Mr H. B. Hughes, Mr Ian Muir, Mr S. Robinson, Mr C. A. Rosen, Mr Jack Simmons, Mrs Marie Taylor, Mr P. M. Taylor.

Jockey (Flat): J Fortune (w.a).

Jockey (NH): L Wyer (10-0, w.a.).

494 MR MICK QUINN, Wantage

Postal: **East Manton Stables, Sparsholt, Wantage, Oxon, OX12 9PJ.**
Phone: **(01235) 751433 FAX (01235) 751433**

1 **BLUE NOPPER,** 4, b f Rock Hopper—Kimble Blue **M Q Racing**
2 **INVIGILATE,** 9, ch g Viking (USA)—Maria da Gloria **M. Quinn**
3 **MUHTAFEL,** 4, b c Nashwan (USA)—The Perfect Life (IRE) **Frank Adams Partnership**
4 **PRINCE OF SPADES,** 6, ch g Shavian—Diamond Princess **M & K Sports Promotions**

THREE-YEAR-OLDS

5 **APPYABO,** ch g Never So Bold—Cardinal Palace **M. Quinn**
6 **ESTOPPED (IRE),** b g Case Law—Action Belle **Mrs S. G. Davies**
7 **FAIRY DOMINO,** ch f Primo Dominie—Fairy Fortune **R. G. Sturmey & M. Quinn**
8 **KATIE'S CRACKER,** b f Rambo Dancer (CAN)—Tea-Pot **J. Miller**
9 **MISS DANGEROUS,** b f Komaite (USA)—Khadine **M. Quinn**
10 **TIGGY SILVANO,** b f Tigani—Infanta Maria **M. Quinn**

TWO-YEAR-OLDS

11 B f 10/5 Pips Pride—Londubh (Efisio) **M. Quinn**
12 B g 19/3 Komaite (USA)—Malcesine (IRE) (Nureyev (USA)) **Maygain Ltd**
13 **SUMO AGAIN,** ch c 3/4 Then Again—Foresta Verde (USA) (Jaazeiro (USA)) **Sumo Quinn Partnership**
14 B f 16/2 Inchinor—Valkyrie (Ahonoora) **Peter Wood**

Other Owners: Frank Adams, Paul Cook, Nigel Dearman, Barry Edwards.

Jockey (Flat): A Whelan (8-0).

Apprentices: E Joyce (7-10), P P Murphy (8-2).

Lady Rider: Miss K Davies.

495 MRS J. R. RAMSDEN, Thirsk

Postal: **Breckenbrough Ltd, Breckenbrough House Farm, Breckenbrough, Thirsk, North Yorkshire, YO7 4EL.**

Phone: **(01845) 587226 FAX (01845) 587443**

1 **BENZOE (IRE),** 8, b g Taufan (USA)—Saintly Guest **Mr Tony Fawcett**
2 **BISHOPS COURT,** 4, ch g Clantime—Indigo **Mr D. R. Brotherton**
3 **FAMOUS DEAL (IRE),** 5, b g Brush Aside (USA)—Dambydale **Mr Paul Green**
4 **FOREST ROBIN,** 5, ch g Formidable (USA)—Blush Rambler (IRE) **Mrs J. R. Ramsden**
5 **HOH EXPRESS,** 6, b g Waajib—Tissue Paper **Platinum Syndicate Ltd**
6 **KING UNO,** 4, b g Be My Chief (USA)—The Kings Daughter **J. & M. Leisure Ltd**
7 **MADISON MIST,** 4, gr f Mystiko (USA)—Hi-Li **Mrs Alison Iles**
8 **MITHAK (USA),** 4, b g Silver Hawk (USA)—Kapalua Butterfly (USA) **Platinum Syndicate Ltd**
9 **MOUCHE,** 4, b br f Warning—Case For The Crown (USA) **Mr M. J. Simmonds**
10 **MUNGO PARK,** 4, b g Selkirk (USA)—River Dove (USA) **Mrs H. M. Carr**
11 **NORTHERN ACCORD,** 4, b g Akarad (FR)—Sioux City **Mrs J. R. Ramsden**
12 **RUDI'S PET (IRE),** 4, ch c Don't Forget Me—Pink Fondant **Mr Jonathan Ramsden**
13 **TAFFS WELL,** 5, br g Dowsing (USA)—Zahiah **Mr Jonathan Ramsden**
14 **THE REAL MCCOY,** 4, b g Deploy—Mukhayyalah **Mrs J. R. Ramsden**
15 **TOP CEES,** 8, b g Shirley Heights—Sing Softly **Mr R. E. Sangster**

THREE-YEAR-OLDS

16 **ANSTAND,** b c Anshan—Pussy Foot **Mr Bernard Hathaway**
17 **CONVENER,** ch g Be My Chief (USA)—Bold County **Mrs J. R. Ramsden**
18 **DISCRIMINATION,** b f Efisio—Prejudice **L. C. and A. E. Sigsworth**
19 **DROIT DE SEIGNEUR (USA),** b g Chief's Crown (USA)—Sly Damsel (USA) **Charlton Bloodstock Ltd**
20 **ELEANOR'S BISCUIT,** b f Silly Prices—Jenifer Browning **Mr J. E. Swiers**
21 **FAR REMOVED (IRE),** b c Distant Relative—Cormorant Creek **Lord Swaythling**
22 **NAVIASKY (IRE),** b br g Scenic—Black Molly (IRE) **Mr Nigel Munton**
23 **NOBLE DEMAND (USA),** b g Red Ransom (USA)—Noble Nordic (USA) **Mrs Alison Iles**
24 **NORDIC PIRJO,** b f Nordico (USA)—Victoria Mill **Mr P. J. Carr**
25 **NUCLEAR DEBATE (USA),** b g Geiger Counter (USA)—I'm An Issue (USA) **Mr J. R. Chester**
26 **ONE NIGHT STAND,** ch g Pursuit of Love—Relatively Easy **Mrs D. Ridley**
27 **RAY OF SUNSHINE (IRE),** ch g Rainbows For Life (CAN)—Maura's Guest (IRE) **Charlton Bloodstock Ltd**
28 **SHALYAH (IRE),** ch f Shalford (IRE)—Baheejah **Mr J. David Abell**
29 **SHARP SHOOTER (IRE),** b g Sabrehill (USA)—Kermesse (IRE) **Mrs D. Ridley**
30 **SURPRISED,** b g Superpower—Indigo **Mr D. R. Brotherton**
31 **TORSO,** b g Rudimentary (USA)—Tosara **Lord Swaythling**

TWO-YEAR-OLDS

32 **ASTONISHED,** ch c 12/3 Weldnaas (USA)—Indigo **Mr D. R. Brotherton**
33 **BODFARI QUARRY,** b f 14/4 Efisio—Last Quarry **Bodfari Stud Ltd**
34 **BODFARI STREET,** ch c 7/4 Dolphin Street (FR)—As Sharp As **Bodfari Stud Ltd**
35 **CAPITALIST,** br c 12/3 Bigstone (IRE)—Pinkie Rose (FR) **Platinum Syndicate Ltd**
36 **CODICIL,** ch f 14/3 Then Again—Own Free Will **Mr M. Houlston**
37 **COURTESAN,** b f 9/2 Pursuit of Love—Case For The Crown (USA) **Mr M. J. Simmonds**
38 **ELVIS REIGNS,** b c 10/2 Rock City—Free Rein **Mr Bernard Hathaway**
39 B c 24/3 Persian Bold—Emerald Waters **Mr Paul Green**
40 **FAIRTOTO,** b c 9/4 Mtoto—Fairy Feet **Mrs Joan L. Egan**
41 **KINLANO,** b c 1/4 Cyrano De Bergerac—Kinlacey **Mr Bernard Hathaway**
42 B f 24/4 Bluebird (USA)—Maribiya (FR) **Mr J. M. & Mrs E. E. Ranson**
43 **PINMOOR HILL (IRE),** b c 22/3 Saddlers' Hall (IRE)—Pennine Pink (IRE) **Mr P. Morrison**
44 **PREPOSITION,** b c 15/4 Then Again—Little Emmeline **Mr Bernard Hathaway**
45 **PRINCE CONSORT,** b c 17/5 Clantime—Miss Petella **Mr P. Savill**
46 **RIVERBLUE,** b c 18/3 Bluebird (USA)—La Riveraine (USA) **Mrs Joan L. Egan**
47 **SABRILA,** ch f 22/5 Sabrehill (USA)—Tafila **Mrs J. R. Ramsden**
48 **SCOOP (IRE),** b f 30/3 Scenic—Big Stores **Mr Nigel Munton**
49 **SHOT SILK,** ch f 1/5 Kris—Flaming Rose (USA) **Mrs J. Trotter**
50 B c 26/4 Mtoto—Sibley **Mr M. J. Simmonds**

MRS J. R. RAMSDEN—continued

51 SILVER GYRE (IRE), b f 7/4 Silver Hawk (USA)—Kraemer (USA) **Mrs Joan L. Egan**
52 SQUARE DANCER, b c 31/3 Then Again—Cubist (IRE) **Mr Bernard Hathaway**
53 STORMIN (IRE), b c 12/1 Perugino (USA)—Unalaska (IRE) **Mrs Joan L. Egan**
54 TARASCO (FR), b f 19/4 Deploy—Moucha (FR) **Mrs D. Ridley**
55 TIBBIE SHIELS, b f 6/2 Deploy—Bajina
56 B c 19/2 Night Shift (USA)—Top Knot **Mr Paul Green**

Other Owners: Mr Michael Payton, Lord Petersham, Swiss Partners, Mr Colin Webster.

Jockey (Flat): J Fortune (8-6).

Jockey (NH): R Garritty (10-4).

Apprentice: C West (8-0).

Conditional: D Thomas (10-0).

Amateurs: Mr A Balding (11-0), Mr S Swiers (10-7).

Lady Rider: Miss E Ramsden (8-7).

496 MR C. I. RATCLIFFE, Welburn

Postal: **Teal Cottage Stud, Teal House, Welburn, North Yorkshire, YO6 7EJ.**

1 6, B g Satco (FR)—Maureens Dote **Mr C. I. Ratcliffe**
2 MORCAT, 9, ch m Morston (FR)—Ancat Girl **Mr C. I. Ratcliffe**

Amateur: Mr C I Ratcliffe (10-7).

497 MR W. RAW, Richmond

Postal: **Uckerby Mill, Scorton, Richmond, North Yorkshire, DL10 6DA.**

1 ANOTHER RED, 10, ch g Move Off—Daleena **Mr W. Raw**
2 OH BROTHER, 5, br g Move Off—Scally's Girl **Mr W. Raw**

498 MR W. G. REED, Hexham

Postal: **Moss Kennels, Haydon Bridge, Hexham, Northd, NE47 6NL.**
Phone: **HALTWHISTLE (01434) 344201 MOBILE (0585) 934343**

1 CELTIC COMMA, 7, b m Celtic Cone—Lor Darnie **Miss Rosemary Jeffreys**
2 MEADOW BEE, 6, b g Meadowbrook—Regal Bee **Mr W. G. Reed**
3 MEADOWBURN, 8, b m Meadowbrook—Miss Hubbard **Mrs G. Reed**
4 MILL BEE, 5, b m Meadowbrook—Brown Bee III **Mr W. G. Reed**
5 OTTADINI (IRE), 6, br m Cardinal Flower—Anniversary Waltz **Mr R. G. Fairs**
6 STINGING BEE, 7, b g Respect—Regal Bee **Mr W. G. Reed**

Other Owners: Mrs D. F. Culham, Mr Geoffrey D. Dance, Mrs G. Reed, Mr J. Walby.

Jockey (NH): W T Reed (10-6).

499 MRS G. R. REVELEY, Saltburn

Postal: **Groundhill Farm, Lingdale, Saltburn, Cleveland, TS12 3HD.**
Phone: **(01287) 650456 FAX (01287) 653095 MOBILE (0802) 449085**

1 **ALI'S ALIBI,** 11, br g Lucifer (USA)—Moppit-Up **Mrs B. Kearney**
2 **ALPINE PANTHER (IRE),** 5, b g Tirol—Kentucky Wildcat **Mr P. D. Savill**
3 **ANGUS-G,** 6, br g Chief Singer—Horton Line **Mrs J. V. Kehoe & Partners**
4 **ARCTIC FOX (IRE),** 6, b g Glacial Storm (USA)—Fleeting Vixen **Mr Jeremy Mitchell**
5 **ARDARROCH PRINCE,** 7, b g Chief Singer—Queen's Eyot **Mr W. G. McHarg**
6 **AUDREY'S PEARL (IRE),** 4, b f Waajib—Inner Pearl **Mr R. McArdle**
7 **BERKELEY BOUNDER (USA),** 6, b g Diesis—Top Socialite (USA) **Mr R. Hilley**
8 **BILLY BUSHWACKER,** 7, b g Most Welcome—Secret Valentine **Mr T. S. Child**
9 **BODEGA BAY,** 6, b g Primitive Rising (USA)—Keldholme **Mr H. Young**
10 5, Gr g Roselier (FR)—Boreen Bro **Lightbody of Hamilton Ltd**
11 **BRAMBLES WAY,** 9, ch g Clantime—Streets Ahead **Mr Nigel E. M. Jones**
12 **BRIGHTER SHADE (IRE),** 8, b g Sheer Grit—Shady Doorknocker **Mr D. S. Hall**
13 **BROCTUNE BAY,** 9, b g Midyan (USA)—Sweet Colleen **C. C. Buckley and Partners**
14 **BROCTUNE GOLD,** 7, b g Superpower—Golden Sunlight
15 **BROCTUNE LINE,** 4, ch g Safawan—Ra Ra **Mr D. Playforth**
16 **BRODESSA,** 12, gr g Scallywag—Jeanne du Barry **The Mary Reveley Racing Club**
17 **BROTHER OF IRIS (IRE),** 5, b g Decent Fellow—Granita Cafe (FR) **M.H.G. Systems Ltd**
18 **CAB ON TARGET,** 12, br g Strong Gale—Smart Fashion **Mr N. Hurst & Partners**
19 **CALDER KING,** 7, ch g Rakaposhi King—Name The Game **Laurel (Leisure) Ltd**
20 **CARRICK TROOP (IRE),** 5, gr g Roselier (FR)—Over The Pond (IRE) **Major J. C. K. Young**
21 **CASTLE CLEAR (IRE),** 5, b g Castle Keep—Rose of Allendale **Mr R. Hilley**
22 **CATHEDRAL BELLE,** 4, ch f Minster Son—Corn Lily **Mrs Susan McDonald**
23 **CHARITY CRUSADER,** 7, b g Rousillon (USA)—Height of Folly **The Mary Reveley Racing Club**
24 **CLASSICAL DANCE (IRE),** 4, b g Classic Music (USA)—Eyre Square (IRE) **Mrs M. I. Jackson & Partners**
25 **COPPER ISLAND,** 5, br g Durgam (USA)—Queen's Eyot **Mr W. G. McHarg**
26 **COUNTRY ORCHID,** 7, b m Town And Country—Star Flower **Mrs J. V. Kehoe**
27 **DESERT FIGHTER,** 7, b g Green Desert (USA)—Jungle Rose **Mr A. Frame**
28 **DRAGONS BAY (IRE),** 9, b g Radical—Logical View **Mr P. C. W. Owen**
29 **DURGAMS FIRST (IRE),** 6, ch g Durgam (USA)—Miromaid **The Mary Reveley Racing Club**
30 4, B g Insan (USA)—Elteetee **Mr H. Robinson & Partners**
31 **ELUSIVE STAR,** 8, b m Ardross—Star Flower **Mr W. Ginzel**
32 **ENDOWMENT,** 6, ch g Cadeaux Genereux—Palm Springs **Mr R. Hilley**
33 **EXECUTIVE DESIGN,** 6, b g Unfuwain (USA)—Seven Seas (FR) **Mr L. T. Foster**
34 **FLYING NORTH (IRE),** 5, b g Distinctly North (USA)—North Kildare (USA) **Dr Glyn Meredith**
35 **FOR CATHAL (IRE),** 7, b g Legal Circles (USA)—Noble For Stamps **Mr D. S. Hall**
36 **FOUNDRY LANE,** 7, b g Mtoto—Eider **Mr A. Sharratt**
37 **FULLOPEP,** 4, b g Dunbeath (USA)—Suggia **Mr & Mrs W. J. Williams**
38 **GALEN (IRE),** 7, br g Roselier (FR)—Gaye Le Moss **Mrs T. E. Sharratt**
39 **GIOLLA VALLEY (IRE),** 4, b g Boyne Valley—Bean Giolla **The Mary Reveley Racing Club**
40 **GLACIAL PRINCESS (IRE),** 5, b m Glacial Storm (USA)—Just Darina **Mr and Mrs S. Cadzow**
41 **GUS CUNNINGHAM,** 6, br g Bustomi—Crazie Annie **Mr J. Goddard**
42 **HARFDECENT,** 7, b g Primitive Rising (USA)—Grand Queen **Mr A. G. Knowles**
43 **HIGHBANK,** 6, b g Puissance—Highland Daisy **Mr Peter M. Dodd**
44 **HIGHBEATH,** 7, b g Dunbeath (USA)—Singing High **Mr A. Sharratt**
45 **HIT THE CANVAS (USA),** 7, ch g At The Threshold (USA)—Also Royal (USA) **Mr Jeremy Mitchell**
46 **IBN MASIRAH,** 4, b g Crowning Honors (CAN)—Masirah **Mr G. Thomson**
47 **IMUSTAMIT,** 8, b g Sula Bula—You Can Be Sure **Kehoe Partnership**
48 **INDIANA PRINCESS,** 5, b m Warrshan (USA)—Lovely Greek Lady **Wentdale Racing Partnership**
49 **INTO THE BLACK (IRE),** 7, ch g Over The River (FR)—Legal Fortune **Mr J. Huckle**
50 **JESSICA ONE (IRE),** 7, b m Supreme Leader—Lochadoo **Mr W. H. Strawson**
51 **JOE SHAW,** 5, ch g Interrex (CAN)—Super Lady **Mr F. Gillespie**
52 **JUNE'S RIVER (IRE),** 5, ch g Over The River (FR)—June Bug
53 **KATHRYN'S PET,** 5, b m Blakeney—Starky's Pet **Mr Bill Brown**
54 **KIDLAW,** 10, b g Good Times (ITY)—Bedfellow **Mr J. Walby**
55 **KILCREGGAN,** 4, b g Landyap (USA)—Lehmans Lot **Mr C. Anderson**
56 **KIMBERLEY BOY,** 8, b g Mtoto—Diamond House **Mrs Susan McDonald**

MRS G. R. REVELEY—continued

57 **LEDGENDRY LINE,** 5, b g Mtoto—Eider **The Home & Away Partnership**
58 **LINEA-G,** 4, ch f Keen—Horton Line **Mr W. Ginzel**
59 **LINGDALE LAD (IRE),** 4, b g Remainder Man—Pampered Sally **The Lingdale Optimists**
60 **LINLATHEN,** 8, ch g Move Off—Loch Brandy **Mrs J. A. Niven**
61 **LIPPY LOUISE,** 6, b m Buckley—Kersti Dunn **Mr D. G. Williamson**
62 **LORD LAMB,** 6, gr g Dunbeath (USA)—Caroline Lamb **Mr A. Sharratt & Mr J. E. Renton**
63 **LURPAK LEGEND (IRE),** 4, br g Castle Keep—Welsh Tan **MD Foods Plc**
64 **MARELLO,** 7, br m Supreme Leader—Clonmello **Mr & Mrs W. J. Williams**
65 **MENTAL PRESSURE,** 5, ch g Polar Falcon (USA)—Hysterical **Mr P. D. Savill**
66 **MERRY MASQUERADE (IRE),** 7, b g King's Ride—Merry Madness **Mr G. S. Brown & Lady Legard**
67 **MONACO GOLD (IRE),** 6, b g Durgam (USA)—Monaco Ville **Mr D. McGonagle**
68 **MONDRAGON,** 8, b g Niniski (USA)—Le Lutine **Mr D. Young & Mrs G. R. Reveley**
69 **MONICA'S CHOICE (IRE),** 7, b g Shaadi (USA)—Tendermark **Mrs E. A. Murray**
70 **MR BOSTON,** 13, b g Halyudh (USA)—Edith Rose **Mr M. K. Oldham**
71 **MR BUSBY,** 5, b g La Grange Music—Top-Anna (IRE) **Mr P. Caplan**
72 **MR LIU,** 4, ch g Nomadic Way (USA)—Kersti Dunn
73 **MR LURPAK,** 6, b g Minster Son—Ixia
74 **MR TEES COMPONENTS,** 6, br g Strong Gale—Culinary **Tees Components Ltd**
75 **NOBLE NORMAN,** 7, b g Grey Desire—Pokey's Pet **Mr M. S. Vernon**
76 **NO MORE HASSLE (IRE),** 5, ch g Magical Wonder (USA)—Friendly Ann **The No Hassle Partnership**
77 **NORTHERN MAESTRO,** 4, ch g Rock Hopper—Thimbalina **Mr A. Sharratt**
78 **OCTOBER MIST (IRE),** 4, gr g Roselier (FR)—Bonny Joe **Mrs M. B. Scholey**
79 **OLD RED (IRE),** 8, ch g Ela-Mana-Mou—Sea Port **Mr A. Flannigan & Mrs G. R. Reveley**
80 **ONCE MORE FOR LUCK (IRE),** 7, b g Petorius—Mrs Lucky **The Mary Reveley Racing Club**
81 **OPULENT,** 7, b g Robellino (USA)—One Half Silver (CAN) **Mrs E. Hawkey**
82 **PAUSE FOR THOUGHT,** 5, b g Bairn (USA)—Mill d'Art **The Thoughtful Partnership**
83 **PEPPER POT BOY (IRE),** 6, b g Lapierre—That's It **Mr A. J. MacDonald**
84 **PHEASANTS DELIGHT,** 8, ch m K-Battery—Johanna Keys **Mr Geoff Pickering**
85 **RANDOM HARVEST (IRE),** 9, br g Strong Gale—Bavello **Mr C. C. Buckley**
86 **RHOSSILI BAY,** 10, b g Idiot's Delight—Hitting Supreme **Mr & Mrs W. J. Williams**
87 **ROBBO,** 4, b g Robellino (USA)—Basha (USA) **Mrs D. Scarth**
88 **SAD MAD BAD (USA),** 4, b g Sunny's Halo (CAN)—Quite Attractive (USA) **Mr P. D. Savill**
89 **SAINT EXPRESS,** 8, ch g Clantime—Redgrave Design **Mr D. S. Hall**
90 **SEDVICTA,** 6, b g Primitive Rising (USA)—Annes Gift **The Mary Reveley Racing Club**
91 **SEVEN TOWERS (IRE),** 9, b g Roselier (FR)—Ramble Bramble **Mrs E. A. Murray**
92 **SHAFFISHAYES,** 6, ch g Clantime—Mischievous Miss **Mr P. Davidson-Brown**
93 **SILVER MINX,** 6, gr g Bold Fox—Annie Bee **Mrs E. A. Kettlewell**
94 **SMART SPIRIT (IRE),** 4, b f Persian Bold—Sharp Ego (USA) **Mrs Stephanie Smith**
95 **SON OF IRIS,** 10, br g Strong Gale—Sprats Hill **M.H.G. Systems Ltd**
96 **SOUSSE,** 5, b m Warrshan (USA)—Mona **Wentdale Racing Partnership**
97 **STRAFFAN GOLD (USA),** 4, b c Lear Fan (USA)—Oro Bianco (USA) **Mr P. D. Savill**
98 **STRONG MINT (IRE),** 7, br g Strong Gale—Derrygold **Mr J. Good**
99 **SUGAR MILL,** 8, b g Slip Anchor—Great Tom **Mr C. C. Buckley**
100 **SUPERPRIDE,** 6, b g Superpower—Lindrake's Pride **Mrs Muriel Ward**
101 **SUSHI BAR (IRE),** 7, gr g Petorius—Sashi Woo **Tremousser Partnership**
102 **TERDAD (USA),** 5, ch g Lomond (USA)—Istiska (FR) **Mr Les De La Haye**
103 **TILLYBOY,** 8, b g Little Wolf—Redgrave Creative **The Mary Reveley Racing Club**
104 **TOM'S RIVER (IRE),** 6, ch g Over The River (FR)—Nesford **Jemm Partnership**
105 **TOTEM FOLE,** 5, gr g Totem (USA)—Tenez La Corde **Mrs Susan McDonald**
106 **TROJAN HERO (SAF),** 7, ch g Raise A Man (USA)—Helleness (SAF) **Mr C. C. Buckley**
107 **TROJAN RISK,** 5, ch g Risk Me (FR)—Troyes **Andy Peake & David Jackson**
108 **TURNPOLE (IRE),** 7, br g Satco (FR)—Mountain Chase **Mr & Mrs W. J. Williams**
109 **UNCLE DOUG,** 7, b g Common Grounds—Taqa **Mr D. D. Saul**
110 **VALLEY OF HOPE,** 5, b m Meadowbrook—Farm Consultation **Mr J. Walby**
111 **WHAT A TALE (IRE),** 6, b g Tale Quale—Cherish **Jemm Partnership**
112 **WOODFIELD GALE (IRE),** 5, b g Strong Gale—Excitable Lady **Mrs M. B. Scholey**
113 **WOODFIELD RIDE (IRE),** 5, b g King's Ride—Kim's Choice **Mrs M. B. Scholey**
114 **WOODFIELD VISION (IRE),** 7, ch g Castle Keep—Comeragh Vision **Frickley Holdings Ltd**
115 **WOTSTHEPROBLEM,** 6, b g Rymer—Alfie's Own **Mr A. Flannigan**
116 **WYNYARD DAMSEL,** 5, b m Silly Prices—The White Lion **Mr D. S. Hall**

MRS G. R. REVELEY—continued

117 WYNYARD KNIGHT, 6, b g Silly Prices—The White Lion **Sir John Hall**
118 WYNYARD LADY, 7, ch m Say Primula—The White Lion **Lady Mae Hall**

THREE-YEAR-OLDS

119 BLUE ANCHOR, b c Robellino (USA)—Fair Seas **Mr D. R. Wellicome**
120 BORDER STARLETTE (IRE), b f Ela-Mana-Mou—Fillette Lalo (FR) **Mr D. Young**
121 Gr g Roselier (FR)—Bright Boreen
122 CELESTIAL WELCOME, b f Most Welcome—Choral Sundown **The Welcome Alliance**
123 FLAXEN PRIDE (IRE), ch f Pips Pride—Fair Chance **G. Fawcett And Partners**
124 FREE, ch c Gone West (USA)—Bemissed (USA) **Mr P. D. Savill**
125 B g Risk Me (FR)—Lady Warninglid
126 PENNYS PRIDE (IRE), b f Pips Pride—Mursuma **Partnership**
127 Br f Roi Danzig (USA)—Suggia **Mr A. Sharratt**
128 B g Commanche Run—Swift Tide **Mrs E. A. Murray**
129 TIGI, ch f Tigani—Molly Brazen **Mr Geoff Pickering**
130 WATCHING BRIEF (IRE), b f Brief Truce (USA)—Lady's Bridge (USA) **Mr J. Shack & Mr G. M. Barnard**

TWO-YEAR-OLDS

131 CHOK-DI, b c Beveled (USA)—Pendona (Blue Cashmere) **Desert Rats Racing Club**
132 B c Mtoto—Glenfinlass (Lonond (USA)) **Mr P. D. Savill**
133 ON ICE (IRE), ch c Pursuit of Love—Ice Chocolate (USA) (Icecapade (USA)) **Mr J. Shack**
134 PENGUIN BAY, b c Rock Hopper—Corn Lily (Aragon) **Mrs Susan McDonald**

Other Owners: Mrs D. Addison, Mr Malcolm Bailey, Mr Mike J. Beadle, Mr G. Black, Mr K. E. Bodenham, Mrs S. F. Bodenham, Mr H. Bowman, Mr M. Bradley, Mr B. Callaghan, Carnoustie Racing Club Ltd, Mr M. Chandler, Mrs Angela Chatterton, Mr Hugh Chatterton, Mrs Linda Corbett, Mr W. Crawford, Mr A. D. Crombie, Mr Dan Daly, Mr I. L. Davies, Mr A. L. Deal, Mr Michael Dunbar, Mrs Gillian Dunmore, Mr J. A. Evans, Mr P. A. Evans, Mr Guy Faber, Mr Ernie Fenwick, Mrs Marie Foster, Mr R. Foster, Mr Robert Fraser, Mr Brian W. Goodall, Mr David Grant, Mr David A. Green, Mrs O. Harrison, Mr Keith Hogg, Mrs Marie C. Hooton, Mr John Jackson, Mrs G. Jenyns, Mr R. W. S. Jevon, Mrs E. Jordan, Mr Drew Kerr, Mr E. W. Kettlewell, Mr J. Laird, Mr K. Lee, Mr P. Longstaff, Mr Robert Macgregor, Mr C. Maesepp, Mr R. Manners, Mr W. Manners, Mr J. F. Mernagh, Mr G. P. D. Milne, Mrs S. D. Murray, Mr R. J. Nash, Mr Ian Nicol, Mr Alexander Paterson, Mr M. J. Paver, Mr D. Pearson, Mr Alan Pirie, Miss C. J. Raines, Mr John Reveley, Mr K. G. Reveley, Mr G. A. Robinson, Mr James T. Robinson, Mr R. G. Russ, Mrs M. Saul, Miss E. Saunders, Mr R. R. J. Scott, Miss E. Shepherd, Mr R. H. Shepherd, Mrs J. Simmonds, Mr Gerry Slater, Mr Norman Smith, Mr John Snaith, Mrs C. Steel, Mrs Margaret Stewart, Mr Jim Struth, Mrs Mary Thompson, Mrs M. B. Thwaites, Mr J. A. Torn, Mr P. A. Tylor, Waldridge Developments Ltd, Mr D. B. Ward, Lady Susan Watson, Wentdale Const Ltd, Mr Ron Whitehead, Mr Harry Whitton, Mr David Wild, Mr Ronald Wilkie, Mr John Wills, Mr John S. Wilson, Mr Owen Watson Wilson.

Jockeys (Flat): A Culhane, K Darley (8-1).

Jockeys (NH): P Niven (10-4), N Smith (10-0).

Apprentice: S Copp (8-5).

Conditional: M Herrington (9-7), G Lee (9-7), M H Naughton (9-9).

Amateur: Mr T J Comerford (9-7).

500 MR P. M. RICH, Llangovan

Postal: **Llangwendr Farm, Llangovan, Nr Monmouth, NP5 4BT.**
Phone: **(01291) 690864 (01633) 262791 FAX (01633) 262791**

1 **ARDRICH,** 4, b g Ardross—Randama **Mr P. M. Rich**
2 **BUS WAY GIRL,** 5, b m Itsu (USA)—Ridgeway Girl **Mr J. Parfitt**
3 **CLUBS ARE TRUMPS (IRE),** 7, b g King of Clubs—Aberklair **Mr J. Parfitt**
4 **DEEDEEJAY,** 5, b m Cigar—Miss Patdonna **Ms H. Lewis**
5 **FERRUFINO (IRE),** 10, b g Montekin—Fauchee **Mr P. M. Rich**
6 **GRANNY RICH,** 4, b f Ardross—Weareagrandmother **Mr P. M. Rich**
7 **NAIYSARI (IRE),** 10, gr g Mouktar—Naiymat **Mr P. M. Rich**
8 **PLAS-HENDY,** 12, ch g Celtic Cone—Little Cindy II **Mr P. M. Rich**
9 **RICH TYCOON (IRE),** 9, b g Buckskin (FR)—Stolen Gold **Mr P. M. Rich**

THREE-YEAR-OLDS

10 **OSO RICH,** b g Teenoso (USA)—Weareagrandmother **Mr P. M. Rich**

501 MR G. W. RICHARDS, Greystoke

Postal: **The Stables, Greystoke, Penrith, Cumbria, CA11 0TG.**
Phone: **(017684) 83392 FAX (017684) 83933**

1 **ACAJOU III (FR),** 10, b g Cap Martin (FR)—Roxane II (FR) **Mr Robert Ogden**
2 **ADDINGTON BOY (IRE),** 10, br g Callernish—Ballaroe Bar **Gott Foods Limited**
3 **ALARMIST,** 4, b g Warning—Wryneck **Dr Kenneth S. Fraser**
4 **BALLON,** 8, b m Persian Bold—La Vosgienne **Whitworth Racing**
5 **BETTER TIMES AHEAD,** 12, ro g Scallywag—City's Sister **Mr E. Briggs**
6 **BOURBON DYNASTY (FR),** 5, b g Rainbow Quest (USA)—Bourbon Girl **Independent Twine Manufacturing Co Ltd**
7 **CINEMA PARADISO,** 4, b g Polar Falcon (USA)—Epure **Mr Edward Melville**
8 **COLONEL IN CHIEF (IRE),** 8, br g Strong Gale—Sirrahdis **Mr Robert Ogden**
9 **COMMITTED SCHEDULE (IRE),** 7, b g Saxon Farm—Padykin **The Schedule Partnership**
10 **DEFENCE COUNSEL (IRE),** 6, b g Darshaan—Maryinsky (USA) **Mr A. Snipe**
11 **DERANNIE (IRE),** 6, b br g Phardante (FR)—Dasa Girl **Mrs Stewart Catherwood**
12 **EARLY MORNING LIGHT (IRE),** 9, gr g Idiot's Delight—Primrose Wood **Mrs Ann Starkie**
13 **EDELWEIS DU MOULIN (FR),** 6, b g Lute Antique (FR)—Tulipe du Moulin (FR) **Mr Robert Ogden**
14 **ESQUIMAU (IRE),** 7, gr g Roselier (FR)—Shallow Run **Mr A. D. Stewart**
15 **ETERNAL CITY,** 7, b g Kind of Hush—Dark City **Mr R. Tyrer**
16 **FEELS LIKE GOLD (IRE),** 10, b g Oats—Drom Lady **Independent Twine Manufacturing Co Ltd**
17 **GALE BLAZER,** 5, br m Strong Gale—Royal Blaze **Mr Antony Wakeham**
18 **GALESHAN (IRE),** 6, b g Strong Gale—Shan's Pal **Mr J. Hales**
19 **GLINGER (IRE),** 5, b g Remainder Man—Harilla **Mr James Westoll Jnr**
20 **GUILT OF A SINNER (IRE),** 5, b g Spanish Place (USA)—Riseaway **Mr P. R. Harrison**
21 **JAMBO BWANA,** 5, ch g Henbit (USA)—Four Friends **Mr D. E. Harrison**
22 **JAY JAY BEE (IRE),** 5, b g Montelimar (USA)—Sanctify **Mr D. Whelan**
23 **JESSOLLE,** 6, gr m Scallywag—Dark City **Mr C. R. Fleet**
24 **JOCKS CROSS (IRE),** 7, ch g Riberetto—Shuil Le Dia **Mrs Gill Harrison**
25 **KERIO RIVER (IRE),** 5, ch m Over The River (FR)—Lulu's Daughter **Lord Cavendish**
26 **KILLBALLY BOY (IRE),** 8, b g Strong Gale—Rare Dream **Everaldo Partnership**
27 **LINDEN'S LOTTO (IRE),** 9, b g Kambalda—Linden **Crocketts Racing Club**
28 **LINWOOD,** 7, gr m Ardross—Silva Linda **Emral Lakes Partnership**
29 **LOSTRIS (IRE),** 7, b m Pennine Walk—Herila (FR) **Mr K. Knox**
30 **LOTHIAN COMMODORE,** 8, gr g Alias Smith (USA)—Lothian Lightning **Mr D. A. Whitaker**
31 **MCGREGOR THE THIRD,** 12, ch g Nearly A Hand—Arctic Dawn **Mrs D. A. Whitaker**
32 **MISTER GORDON (IRE),** 6, b g Strong Gale—Woodford Princess **Mrs Stewart Catherwood**
33 **MONK CASTLE (IRE),** 5, b g Supreme Leader—Ballyheda's Love **Mr Alistair Duff**
34 **MR FRANGIPANI (IRE),** 7, ch g Phardante (FR)—Croom Cross **Ashleybank Investments Limited**
35 **NEEDLE THREAD,** 6, gr m Henbit (USA)—Linen Thread **Gott Foods Limited**

MR G. W. RICHARDS—continued

36 **NO FINER MAN (IRE)**, 7, b g Lord Americo—Ballaroe Bar **Gott Foods Limited**
37 **ONE MAN (IRE)**, 10, gr g Remainder Man—Steal On **Mr J. Hales**
38 **PAPERISING**, 6, b g Primitive Rising (USA)—Eye Bee Aitch **The Jockeys Whips**
39 **PARSONS BOY**, 9, ch g The Parson—Kylogue Daisy **Mr B. Ridge & Mr D. Hewitt**
40 **PILE DRIVER (IRE)**, 5, b g Brush Aside (USA)—Master Nidee **Taranto De Pol**
41 **RAINING STAIRS (IRE)**, 7, b g Orchestra—Strong Gale Lass **Dr Kenneth S. Fraser**
42 **REAL TONIC**, 8, bl g Strong Gale—Primrose Wood **Mr Robert Ogden**
43 **SALMON CELLAR (IRE)**, 5, ch g Roselier (FR)—Perfect Excuse **Mr George Graham (Cumbria)**
44 **SEVEN MILE GALE (IRE)**, 6, b g Strong Gale—Moonlight Romance **Mr M. Binnington**
45 **SKANE RIVER (IRE)**, 7, ch g Over The River (FR)—Miami High **Mr W. J. Peacock**
46 **SOLOMON'S DANCER (USA)**, 8, b br g Al Nasr (FR)—Infinite Wisdom (USA) **Mr J. Hales**
47 **STEPHEN'S BRAE**, 6, b g Scorpio (FR)—Pendella **Dr Kenneth S. Fraser**
48 **SULAAMAN**, 7, b g Sulaafah (USA)—Kiki Star **Mrs A. Robertson**
49 **TARTAN TRADEWINDS**, 11, b g Strong Gale—Tipperary Special **Ashleybank Investments Limited**
50 **THE GREY MONK (IRE)**, 10, gr g Roselier (FR)—Ballybeg Maid **Mr Alistair Duff**
51 **THE OPERATOR (IRE)**, 7, b g Kefaah (USA)—Come In **Greystoke Stables Ltd**
52 **TOBY**, 5, b g Jendali (USA)—Au Revoir Sailor **Mr R. Tyrer**
53 **TOGGI DANCER (NZ)**, 5, b g Victory Dance—Solfatara (NZ) **Ashleybank Investments Ltd**
54 **TOP ACE**, 6, b g Statoblest—Innes House **Jumping Prospects Racing**
55 **TRIX OF THE TRADE (IRE)**, 5, ch g Air Display (USA)—Game Trix **Mrs Stewart Catherwood**
56 **TROUBLED MAN (IRE)**, 7, b g Mandalus—Small Trouble **Mrs Gill Harrison**
57 **UNGUIDED MISSILE (IRE)**, 10, br g Deep Run—Legaun **Mr D. E. Harrison**
58 **WHISPERING STEEL**, 12, b g Furry Glen—Shady Grove **Mr J. Michael Gillow**
59 **WILLIAM OF ORANGE**, 6, ch g Nicholas Bill—Armonit **Special Reserve Racing**
60 **WISE GUNNER**, 5, ch m Gunner B—Edelweiss **Mr Jim Ennis**

THREE-YEAR-OLDS

61 **REGAL ISLAND**, b g Pharly (FR)—Regal Wonder **Mrs Linda Bott**

Other Owners: Mr T. Alderson, Mr R. G. Bartholomew, Mr P. W. Boylett, Mrs J. A. Broad, Mrr I. T. Buchanan, Mrs A. Cross, Mr Jimmy Dudgeon, Mr Roddy Duff, Mr J. Dungan, Mr J. M. Elliott, Mr Robert J. Elliott, Mr K. M. Everitt, Miss L. Hales, Mr T. Hebdon, Mrs V. D. Hodgkiss, Mrs J. W. Hutchinson, Mr K. S. Jones, Mr W. K. Jones, Mrs P. A. Knox, Mr S. Leece, Mr J. M. Newbould, Mr J. Noone, Mr J. A. Pratt, Mrs T. R. Riley, Mr Malcolm Wassall, Mrs C. Welwood.

Jockeys (NH): A Dobbin (10-0), B Harding (10-0).

Conditional: R Burns (10-0).

502 MR GRAHAM RICHARDS, Pontypridd

Postal: **1 Tynewydd Cottage, Llanfabon, Cilfynydd, Pontypridd, Mid Glam, CF37 4HP.**
Phone: **(01443) 453189 FAX (01443) 453189**

1 **COLONIAL OFFICE (USA)**, 12, ch g Assert—Belles Oreilles (CAN) **Mr Graham Richards**
2 **POLO KIT (IRE)**, 7, b g Trempolino (USA)—Nikitina **Mr Graham Richards**
3 **REACH FOR GLORY**, 9, b g Reach—Carlton Glory **Mr Graham Richards**

Jockeys (NH): C Llewellyn, A Thornton.

Conditional: Mark Griffiths (9-7), John Power.

Amateur: Mr Steven Blackwell (10-0).

Lady Rider: Miss S Bosley.

503 MRS LYDIA RICHARDS, Chichester

Postal: **Lynch Farm, Hares Lane, Funtington, Chichester, West Sussex, PO18 9LG.**
Phone: **HOME (01243) 574882 YARD (01243) 574379 MOBILE (0374) 120935**

1 **AUNT DAPHNE,** 4, b f Damister (USA)—Forbearance **Mr R. D. Letby**
2 **EAU DE COLOGNE,** 6, b g Persian Bold—No More Rosies **D. and M. Evans**
3 **FICHU (USA),** 10, b g Sharpen Up—Mousseline de Soie (FR) **Mr B. Seal**
4 **JURASSIC CLASSIC,** 11, gr g Leading Man—Statfold Pride **Brian Seal & Roger Rees**
5 **JUST NIP,** 5, b g Lord Bud—Popping On **B. Seal, D & M Evans**
6 **KEEN BID (IRE),** 7, b g Alzao (USA)—Gaychimes **Mr B. Seal**
7 **LIMOSA,** 7, b m Jalmood (USA)—Larive **Mrs Lydia Richards**
8 **ONEOFUS,** 9, b g Lochnager—Mountain Child **Mr R. D. Letby**
9 **SIOUX TO SPEAK,** 6, b g Mandrake Major—Sioux Be It **The Sioux Partnership**
10 **WEAPONS FREE,** 7, b g Idiot's Delight—Sea Kestrel **The Sioux Partnership**

Other Owners: Mr Alan Bailey, Mr I. Bell, Mr K. L. Dalwood, Four Seasons Racing Ltd, Mr J. S. Gowling, Mr P. D. Luckin, Mr G. C. Reilly, Mr Tony Rooth, Mr Ron Stone, Mr David M. White, Mr W. G. R. Wightman.

Jockey (NH): M Richards (10-0).

504 MRS S. L. RICHARDSON, Cheltenham

Postal: **Owdeswell Manor, Andoversford, Cheltenham, Gloucestershire, GL54 4LD.**
Phone: **(01242) 820297 (01242) 820505**

1 **LORD MAX,** 6, br g Arctic Lord—Thames Air **Mrs S. L. Richardson**
2 **PHOEBE THE FREEBEE (IRE),** 7, ch m Phardante (FR)—Stormy Night **Mrs S. L. Richardson**
3 **SHUIL POIPIN (IRE),** 9, b br m Buckskin (FR)—Shuil Comeragh **Wickfield Farm Partnership**

Other Owners: Mrs P. J. Fairbarns, Mr R. G. Fairbarns.

505 MR P. C. RITCHENS, Tidworth

Postal: **'Hillview', 91 Parkhouse Road, Shipton Bellinger, Tidworth, Hampshire, SP9 7YE.**
Phone: **HOME (01980) 843088 YARD (01264) 781140**

1 **BARGIN BOY,** 9, ch g Undulate (USA)—Chaddy **Mr R. Catton**
2 **BLANCHLAND,** 9, gr g Bellypha—Premier Rose **Mr Jock Cullen**
3 **BLAZER MORINIERE (FR),** 9, b g Montevideo II—Kimberlite (FR) **Mr John Pearl**
4 **BROAD LADY,** 4, b f Broadsword (USA)—Lady Solstice **Mr R. Catton**
5 **EL CID (IRE),** 8, b g Presidium—Sheer Nectar **Mr P. Ritchens**
6 **FROZEN DROP,** 11, b g Le Bavard (FR)—Frozen Ground **Mr Jock Cullen**
7 **GRATOMI (IRE),** 8, b g Bustomi—Granny Grumble **Mr John Pearl**
8 **JADIDH,** 10, b m Touching Wood (USA)—Petrol **Mr Don Hazzard**
9 **KAIFOON (USA),** 9, b g Woodman (USA)—Kitchen (USA) **Mr John Pearl**
10 **MONKSANDER,** 12, b g Monksfield—Maudie's Choice **Mr John Pearl**
11 **NEW STATESMAN,** 10, br g Politico (USA)—Nova Ray **Mr L. J. Garrett**
12 **PORLOCK CASTLE,** 5, b g Thowra (FR)—Miss Melmore **Mrs B. D. Adams**
13 **RAQIB,** 7, b g Slip Anchor—Reine Maid (USA) **Mr A. Kidd, Mr A. Johnson**

Other Owners: Mrs B. Bishop, Mr D. Tye, Mr S. W. Ullyott.

Jockey (NH): S Fox (10-0).

506 MRS P. ROBESON, Newport Pagnell

Postal: **Fences Farm, Tyringham, Newport Pagnell, Buckinghamshire, MK16 9EN.**
Phone: **(01908) 611255 FAX (01908) 611255**

1 **BROADBILL,** 5, gr g Broadsword (USA)—Tangara **Mrs P. Robeson**
2 **MOUNTAIN LORY,** 4, ch f Ardross—Lady Stock **Mrs P. Robeson**
3 **SHAHBOOR (USA),** 4, b g Zilzal (USA)—Iva Reputation (USA) **Sir Evelyn De Rothschild**
4 **TAWNY WARBLER,** 6, b m Teenoso (USA)—Arctic Warbler **Mrs P. Robeson**
5 **TEETON NISHABALL,** 8, gr m Nishapour (FR)—Charlton Athletic **Mrs Joan Tice**
6 **TEETON THOMAS,** 9, b g Sunley Builds—Royal Darwin **Mrs Joan Tice**
7 **WREN WARBLER,** 8, ch m Relkino—Arctic Warbler **Mrs P. Robeson**

THREE-YEAR-OLDS

8 **AUK,** ch g Absalom—Lady Stock **Mr P. Robeson**

507 MR C. G. ROE, Chalford

Postal: **Hyde Park Farm, Lower Hyde, Chalford, Gloucestershire, GL6 8NZ.**
Phone: **(01453) 885487 FAX (01453) 88 5204**

1 **BAD BERTRICH (IRE),** 7, b g Waajib—Sweet Unison (USA) **Peter Mikhail**
2 **BLUE HAVANA,** 6, br m Cigar—Welsh Bluebell **Mr Harold Berlinski**
3 **MUMMY'S MOLE,** 7, gr g Le Solaret (FR)—Tups
4 **RISKY ROSE,** 6, b m Risk Me (FR)—Moharabuige **Mike Perry**
5 **SAMAKA HARA (IRE),** 6, b g Taufan (USA)—Aunt Hester (IRE)
6 **SPARKS R FLYING,** 5, gr g Le Solaret (FR)—Almelikeh **Mrs Margaret Blake**
7 **SPENCER STALLONE,** 5, b g Rambo Dancer (CAN)—Armour of Light **Mr Harold Berlinski**
8 **SUNGIA (IRE),** 9, b g Orchestra—Lysanders Lady **Mr Graeme Roe**
9 **TEAM PROJECT (IRE),** 4, gr g Project Manager—Ashco (IRE) **Michael Kier, Mike Perry, Ralph Snedden**
10 **TUPENNY SMOKE,** 6, b m Cigar—Tups **Paul Davis**

THREE-YEAR-OLDS

11 B g Puissance—Our Aisling **Roe Racing Ltd**

Other Owners: Ms Caroline F. Breay, Martin And Mandy Evans, Mr I. Fox, Mr G. B. Perry, Roe Byfield Advertising.

Jockey (Flat): M Fenton (8-1, w.a.).

Jockeys (NH): Richard Dunwoody (10-2, w.a.), J M Moffat (10-4).

Conditional: S Graham (10-0).

508 MR W. M. ROPER, Curragh

Postal: **Maddenstown Lodge, The Curragh, Co. Kildare, Ireland.**
Phone: **(045) 441798 MOBILE (086) 8234279**

1 **BROKEN RITES (IRE),** 5, b g Broken Hearted—Lady Wise **N. B. Wachman**
2 **CLEAR BLUE WATER (IRE),** 5, b h Dancing Dissident—Fair Song **Mr W. P. Roper**
3 **FIRE IN HER EYES (IRE),** 4, ch f Montelimar (USA)—Glowing Embers
4 **HONOR'S STAG (USA),** 4, ch c Blushing John (USA)—Bobbinette (USA) **Mr W. P. Roper**
5 6, B g Montelimar (USA)—Hurricane Dandy **Mr W. P. Roper**
6 **ISLE OF IONA (IRE),** 7, b g St Columbus—Slave's Bangle **Ms Winifred O'Malley**

MR W. M. ROPER—continued

7 **JIMMY O'GOBLIN,** 11, ch g Deep Run—Natural Shine **Mr F. Clarke**
8 **LEESHA (IRE),** 4, b f Ela-Mana-Mou—Esh Sham (USA) **Mrs H. McGalmont**
9 **LITTLE LEFT GIRL (IRE),** 5, b m Salluceva—Little Rich Girl **Mr E. Newell**
10 **LORGLANE LADY (IRE),** 7, ch m Lancastrian—City Dame **Mr D. Murphy**
11 4, B f Saddlers' Hall (IRE)—Nordic Beauty (USA) **Mr P. N. Reynolds**
12 **QUOTE UNQUOTE,** 5, b g Fayruz—Miss Quotation **Mr W. M. Roper**
13 **SOMERSET PRIDE (IRE),** 8, br m Supreme Leader—Susie Wuzie **Ms Winifred Smalley**
14 **SWEET DESPERADO (IRE),** 4, br f Un Desperado (FR)—Sucre Fan (IRE) **Mrs R. Snow**
15 **TALYGARN,** 7, gr g Faustus (USA)—Lucky Song **Mr Alan Cook**
16 **TIDAL PRINCESS (IRE),** 6, b m Good Thyne (USA)—Gemini Gale **Mr W. M. Roper**
17 **UP IN THE AIR (IRE),** 8, br g Tremblant—Burton Brown **Mr B. Burke**

THREE-YEAR-OLDS

18 B g Lashkari—Buzz Along **Mr D. Cornwall**

TWO-YEAR-OLDS

19 **LAKE HOUSE (IRE),** ch f 19/3 Be My Guest (USA)—
Lake Poopo (IRE) (Persian Heights) **Mrs C. S. Gaisford St Lawrence**
20 **LEAGHILLAUN (IRE),** b f 23/4 Turtle Island (IRE)—
Heads We Called (IRE) (Bluebird (USA)) **Mr C. S. Gaisford St Lawrence**
21 B f 2/4 Namaqualand (USA)—Merrie Laughter (Morston (FR)) **Mr R. T. Macauley**
22 Gr c 9/5 Dolphin Street (FR)—Miss Mitchell (Sexton Blake) **Mr W. M. Roper**

Other Owners: Mr Ken Crow, Mr A. Hamilton, M. Killilea, John Lynch, P. Quigley, Mr K. Sinanan.

Apprentice: Angela Matthews (7-7).

509 MR B. S. ROTHWELL, Malton

Postal: **2 Honeysuckle Cottage, Musley Bank, Malton, North Yorkshire, YO17 0TD.**
Phone: **HOME (01653) 696384 MOBILE (0411) 474904**

1 **ASK FOR BARNEY (IRE),** 9, ch g Phardante (FR)—Coolbawn Lady **JMG Promotions Ltd**
2 **BILLY BRIGHTON,** 8, br g Nomination—Bright-One **Mr Peter Rawson**
3 **BITRAN,** 8, gr g Midyan (USA)—Bishah (USA) **Miss A. L. Wright**
4 **BOLD TOP,** 6, ch g Bold Owl—Whirlygigger **Mrs G. M. Z. Spink**
5 **FORESHORE MAN,** 7, b g Derrylin—Royal Birthday **JMG Promotions Ltd**
6 **FORGET PARIS (IRE),** 5, gr m Broken Hearted—Miss Deauville **Mr Brian Rothwell**
7 **GOLD PIGEON (IRE),** 9, b m Goldhill—Bracka Pigeon **JMG Promotions Ltd**
8 **HAZARD A GUESS (IRE),** 8, ch g Digamist (USA)—Guess Who **JMG Promotions Ltd**
9 **HEVER GOLF CHARMER,** 4, b g Precocious—Callas Star **The Action Racing Club Ltd**
10 **INSIDER TRADER,** 7, b g Dowsing (USA)—Careless Whisper **Mrs H. M. Carr**
11 **JACK FLUSH (IRE),** 4, b g Broken Hearted—Clubhouse Turn (IRE) **Mr D. Smith**
12 **LAST TRY (IRE),** 7, ch g Try My Best (USA)—Alpenwind **Mr H. J. Harenberg**
13 **LINDRICK LADY (IRE),** 4, b f Broken Hearted—Fiodoir **Mr S. P. Hudson**
14 **NIGHT CHORUS,** 4, b g Most Welcome—Choral Sundown **Mr R. M. J. Macnair**
15 **QUEENS CONSUL (IRE),** 8, gr m Kalaglow—Queens Connection **Miss Heather L. Davison**
16 **SUNDAY'S MAN (IRE),** 8, br g Tanfirion—Call-Me-Tara **Mr Brian Rothwell**
17 **WILLERFOSS (IRE),** 8, b g Roselier (FR)—Some Gossip **Mr Michael Saunders**

THREE-YEAR-OLDS

18 **ALBRIGHTON,** b g Terimon—Bright-One **Mr Peter Rawson**
19 **BEECHWOOD QUEST (IRE),** b f River Falls—Egalite (IRE) **Mr Brian Valentine**
20 **JACKERIN (IRE),** b g Don't Forget Me—Meanz Beanz **The BDT Partnership**
21 **JACOBINA,** b f Magic Ring (IRE)—Mistitled (USA) **Mr J. M. Ranson & Mrs E. E. Ranson**
22 **KING OF DANCE,** ch g King's Signet (USA)—Times **Mrs S. St Quinton**

MR B. S. ROTHWELL—continued

TWO-YEAR-OLDS

23 B f 9/4 Teenoso (USA)—Bright-One **Mr Peter Rawson**
24 **COUNTY TIMES,** br g 18/5 Timeless Times (USA)—Misty Rocket **The Three County Partnership**
25 **GOWITHTHEFLOW (IRE),** b c 27/1 River Falls—Astral Way **Mrs H. M. Carr**
26 Br g 9/4 Risk Me (FR)—Hot Sunday Sport **JMG Promotions Ltd**
27 B f 22/4 Reprimand—Lady Leman
28 B f 20/5 Dilum (USA)—Lismore
29 B g 11/5 Case Law—Peep of Day (USA)
30 **ROSE'S TREASURE (IRE),** b f 1/3 Treasure Kay—Euro Miss (IRE) **Mr J. Kee**
31 Ch f 27/2 Forest Wind (USA)—Siofra Beag
32 Ch g 24/3 Forest Wind (USA)—Tinnycross
33 **TUULI (IRE),** b c 7/3 Forest Wind (USA)—Rifaya (IRE) **Mrs H. M. Carr**

Other Owners: Mr G. Aldus, Mr F. Arnott, Mrs L. Beharrell, Mrs H. A. Burn, Mr P. J. Carr, Mr J. K. Carson, Mr David Hewson, Mrs Liz Hunt, Mr D. H. A. Macnair, Mr Jeffrey Newton, Mrs B. Oughtred, Mr John H. Price, Mr J. Senior, Mr A. Spence, Mr E. St Quinton, Mr M. Tucker, Victor Chandler (Equus) Ltd, Mr B. Walker (Hull), Mr Richard Wastling, Mr K. Wills, Mr J. B. Young.

510 MR J. DE ROUALLE, Lamorlaye

Postal: **17 Rue Charles Pratt, 60260 Lamorlaye, France.**
Phone: **44 21 37 37 FAX: 44 21 37 28**

1 **DESIDERIO (FR),** 4, b g Pistolet Bleu—Rose River **Michael Watt**
2 **FARASAN (IRE),** 5, b h Fairy King—Gracieuse Majeste **Prince A. A. Faisal**
3 **FIFTY FOUR (USA),** 6, ch h Lyphard—Partygoer **K-H Eng**
4 **FRANCE ORCHESTRA,** 4, gr f Linamix—Canesara **Yves Lamarche**
5 **MICHAELANGELO (FR),** 5, b h Lear Fan—Illusive Icicle **NP Bloodstock Ltd**
6 **MONT D'ARNAUD,** 4, b c Double Bed—Mill Lady **Sir J. Goldsmith**
7 **ORYX,** 4, ch c Polish Precedent—Rafha **Prince A. A. Faisal**
8 **PIN PINICAILLE,** 4, b c Lead On Time—Coincidence **J. Baguenault de Puchesse**
9 **SUNDAY HORSE,** 6, b h Caerwent—Coincidence **J. Veil-Picard**
10 **TIRANIA,** 4, gr f Highest Honor—Tirana **Alan F. S. Li**

THREE-YEAR-OLDS

11 **AZUENA (IRE),** b f Night Shift—Pearl Marine **Comtesse J. de Roualle**
12 **BARBOLA (USA),** ch c Diesis—Barboukh **Bob McCreery**
13 **BINT ZACK (FR),** b f Fabulous Dancer—Scimitarlia **Hakam Zakaria**
14 **BRAVE BLEU (FR),** b c Agent Bleu—Belle Fabi **Comtesse J. de Roualle**
15 **BUCKWOOD,** b f Saumarez—Badiane **K-H Eng**
16 **GALUPPI (FR),** ro c Tel Quel—Grisellina **Jean-Pierre Zaouch**
17 **HABANA (FR),** ch c Bering—Avricourt **Alan F. S. Li**
18 **IJA NAJD,** b c Slip Anchor—Docklands **Diab Al Johar**
19 **JARNAIL (FR),** br c General Holme—Va Et Vient **S.N.C. de la Tete de Bray**
20 **KSAR BLEU (FR),** b c Pistolet Bleu—Lady Prima **Joseph Kaida**
21 **L'AMI DE TOUJOURS (FR),** b c Bakharoff—Parannda **Max Boukobza**
22 **LAST MANGO (IRE),** b c Caerleon—Last Flair **Antoinette Tamagni**
23 **MARY THE SECOND (IRE),** b f Marju—Marienthal **K-H Eng**
24 **ONE WAY (FR),** b f Exit To Nowhere—April Shower **Mabel de Forest**
25 **PASSE DU DIABLE (FR),** gr f Kaldoun—Coincidence **Sir J. Goldsmith**
26 **SCOTTISH HONOR (FR),** br c Highest Honor—Scottish Bride **Mabel de Forest**
27 **TAX EVASION,** ch c Kendor—Allegory **Hakam Zakaria**
28 **WILLTORUN (FR),** b c Highest Honor—Cat Storm **Alan F. S. Li**
29 **ZACK LUTE (FR),** b c Panoramic—Lute String **Hakam Zakaria**

TWO-YEAR-OLDS

30 **ABOU SAFIAN (IRE),** ch c Bluebird—Kind of Cute **Diab Al Johar**
31 **ANGELINA CAROLINA (IRE),** ch f Kris—Angelina Ballerina **Haras de la Perelle**

MR J. DE ROUALLE—continued

32 **APRIL ALLEGRO (FR),** br c Doyoun—April Lee **Rigby Bloodstock Ltd**
33 **APRILIA (FR),** ch f Bakharoff—Angel Victory **Alain Brandebourger**
34 **BARAWIN (FR),** b f Fijar Tango—Baratoga **Rigby Bloodstock Ltd**
35 **BEAUTE (FR),** br f Highest Honor—Gold Pebble **Jean de Souza Lage**
36 **BELLE CARDOUNE (FR),** b f Cardoun—Belle de Namur **Joseph Kaida**
37 **COMILLAS (FR),** gr f Kaldoun—Rive du Sud **Bering S. A.**
38 **DOUCHA (FR),** ch f Shining Steel—Windelia **Jean-Pierre Zaouch**
39 **EDEN ROCK (FR),** b f Exit To Nowhere—Go The Music **Gerard Ben Lassin**
40 **EL MILAGRO (FR),** gr c Exit To Nowhere—Coincidence **J-M Peycelon**
41 **FIRST CHOICE (FR),** b f Exit To Nowhere—Allwaki **Michael Watt**
42 **FOX STORY (IRE),** ch f Petit Loup—Notre Histoire **Alan F. S. Li**
43 **GIRARE (IRE),** b c Arctic Tern—Kirova **Michael Watt**
44 **GUADANINO (FR),** b c Akarad—Eau de Nuit **Joseph Kaida**
45 **HONORABLE LADY (FR),** ch f Highest Honor—Baddi Bird **Terry A. Straeter**
46 **KING OLAV (USA),** ch c Chief's Crown—Bilakna **K-H Eng**
47 **KNIGHT OF HONOUR (FR),** ch c Highest Honor—Joie de Nuit **Alan F. S. Li**
48 **LADY ELIANE (FR),** b f Tenby—Pearl Marine **Comtesse J. de Roualle**
49 **LADY RAGNHILD,** b f Selkirk—Madame Crecy **K-H Eng**
50 **LESOTEK (FR),** b f Lesotho—Tekinia **S.N.C. de la Tete de Bray**
51 **LITTLE ANCHOR (FR),** gr f Kendor—Petite Ancre **Alan F. S. Li**
52 **MARIE D'ISLAND (FR),** b f Turtle Island—Pick Marie **K-H Eng**
53 **MIKHAEL,** b c Fijar Tango—Scimitarlia **Hakam Zakaria**
54 **MISS JAMS (FR),** b f Showbrook—La Roseliere **Joseph Kaida**
55 **MYSTERIOUS SOUND (USA),** b f Danzig—Iva Reputation **K-H Eng**
56 **NAJLA (IRE),** b f Catrail—Las Bela **Diab Al Johar**
57 **OLINKA (USA),** b f Wolfhound—Optimistic Lass **Haras de la Perelle**
58 **PUNTAL (FR),** b c Bering—Saveur **Bering S. A.**
59 **QUEEN OF NORWAY (USA),** ch f Woodman—Qena **K-H Eng**
60 **SCOTTISH GLEN (FR),** ro c Kendor—Scottish Bride **Mabel de Forest**
61 **SHIMMERING GAZE,** b f Green Desert—Shining Eyes **Rigby Bloodstock Ltd**
62 **SKI RACER (FR),** b f Ski Chief—Shahoune **K-H Eng**
63 **SPRING FLAKE (FR),** b c Zieten—April Shower **Mabel de Forest**
64 **VALDAIA,** b f Sadler's Wells—Vale of Truth **Haras de la Perelle**
65 B f Lahib—Valley Lights **Andreas Putsch**
66 **ZACK EXIT (FR),** b c Exit To Nowhere—Lute String **Hakam Zakaria**

511 MR J. C. ROUGET, Pau

Postal: **Chemin De La Foret, Bastard, 64000 Pau, France.**
Phone: **59 33 27 90 FAX 59 33 29 30**

1 **AMITIE FATALE,** 4, ch f Night Shift—Adjarida **Ecurie M3 Elevage**
2 **ASTRONOMY,** 4, b f Cricket Ball—Arcidia **Mrs J. F. Dupont**
3 **AUDIGNON,** 5, br h Highest Honor—Juvenka **B. Ducasse**
4 **BALLE DE GOLF,** 4, b f Homme de Loi—Baloa **Mrs J. F. Dupont**
5 **BARAGUEY,** 4, ch g Marignan—Liberty Nell **R. Bousquet**
6 **BONUS EVENTUS,** 4, ch c Alwuhush—Femme de Fer **J. M. Soriano**
7 **CHLEPNYR,** 4, b g Last Tycoon—Zircon Lady **A. Bidart**
8 **CONSTANCE DO,** 5, ch m Risk Me—The Boozy News **Mrs A. Corcoral**
9 **DIAMANT DU ROI,** 7, br g Top Ville—Wish For Diamonds **Mrs R. Chandioux**
10 **DORSODURO,** 5, gr g Highest Honor—Sioux City **J. P. Rios**
11 **FOLMANIE,** 5, ch m Blushing John—Philarmonia **Mrs M. de Chambure**
12 **FUN HARBOUR,** 5, ch g Funambule—Clef des Ondes **A. Lapoterie**
13 **GARITZ,** 4, b c Alzao—Lobbino **A. Bidart**
14 **GUEST OF ANCHOR,** 5, b m Slip Anchor—Intimite Guest **Ecurie I. M. Fares**
15 **HIGH NORMANDY,** 4, b g Highest Honor—Numidie **Ecurie I. M. Fares**
16 **HIGH TIARA,** 4, b f Highest Honor—Noble Tiara **Ecurie I. M. Fares**
17 **HONOR OF BAINO,** 5, b g Highest Honor—Baino Bluff **Ecurie I. M. Fares**

MR J. C. ROUGET—continued

18 **IOANNINA,** 4, b f Lesotho—Miss Banjer **Mrs J. F. Dupont**
19 **JE REVE,** 5, ch g Risk Me—First Fastnet **C. Gour**
20 **JOUMART,** 4, b c Kendor—Dinner Out **Ecurie des Mousquetaires**
21 **JUSTFUL,** 4, gr c Highest Honor—Just Class **Ecurie I. M. Fares**
22 **KALDOUNSKA,** 4, b f Kaldoun—Prologue **Mrs G. Forien**
23 **KANJI,** 5, ch m Polish Patriot—Kamada **Ph. Martin**
24 **KEEP PLAYING,** 4, ch c Highest Honor—Playing For Keeps **Ecurie I. M. Fares**
25 **LUROY,** 5, br g Esprit du Nord—Lumiere du Feu **A. Caro**
26 **MA CHERIE DANCER,** 4, b f Shareef Dancer—Sword Lily **N. Mourad**
27 **MALOUET,** 5, gr g Kendor—Mi Longa **J. F. Gribomont**
28 **MASSIMO,** 4, gr c Lead On Time—Mi Longa **J. F. Gribomont**
29 **MUDEJAR,** 4, ch c Bering—Vaguely Money **A. Bidart**
30 **MY PRICKLY,** 4, ch g Be My Guest—Prickle **Mrs J. F. Dupont**
31 **NEBLI,** 4, ch g Blushing John—No One Bundles **A. Caro**
32 **PRO SILBER,** 4, b c Sanglamore—Pro Sugar **Ecurie La Clauzade**
33 **RAINCLOUD,** 4, b f Rainbow Quest—Discomatic **Mrs A. Rothschild**
34 **RUNNING MAN,** 4, ch g General Holme—Rudolfina **R. Bousquet**
35 **SHAHRAZAD,** 4, b f Bering—Shardazar **Ecurie I. M. Fares**
36 **SHAKA,** 4, b c Exit To Nowhere—Serafica **R. Bousquet**
37 **SLEW BAY,** 4, b f Beaudelaire—Slew of Fortune **J. Biraben**
38 **SUN KICKS,** 4, b g Saumarez—For Kicks **Ecurie La Clauzade**
39 **SYMBOLETHO,** 4, b g Lesotho—Symbolique **H. Chamarty**
40 **TOUR DE TABLE,** 8, ch g Fast Topaze—Dame des Roches **A. Caro**

THREE-YEAR-OLDS

41 **AKAR BABY,** b f Akarad—Lypheor Baby **Ecurie I. M. Fares**
42 **BADDI HEIGHTS,** b f Shirley Heights—Baddi Baddi **Ecurie I. M. Fares**
43 **BAIKONOUR,** b f Kadounor—Boydara **R. Labeyrie**
44 **BARANGAY,** b c Manila—Femme de Fer **J. M. Soriano**
45 **BOUCCANEER,** b c Hero's Honor—Shahoune **R. Bousquet**
46 **BRILLIANT,** b f Bering—Eliante **Ecurie I. M. Fares**
47 **CHARMING LILI,** b f Sharpo—Lili Cup **Ecurie I. M. Fares**
48 **DAME FOLY,** b f Exit To Nowhere—River Sharp **B. Ducasse**
49 **DOIGTS D'OR,** b g Sanglamore—Doigts de Fee **C. Gour**
50 **DONNYBROOK,** b c Tel Quel—Fragrant Baby **C. Gour**
51 **ESTHONIAN,** b c Bering—Chester County **R. Bousquet**
52 **FARABUTTO,** b c Fabulous Dancer—Ourla **L. Cattan**
53 **FIFTH HIGH,** b f Quiet American—Hill Pleasure **J. M. Soriano**
54 **FOR FUN,** b f Exit To Nowhere—Faintly **J. C. Gour**
55 **FORMIDABLE NOOR,** b f Efisio—Lovely Noor **Ecurie I. M. Fares**
56 **FOR MORE,** b f Sanglamore—For Kicks **Ecurie La Clauzade**
57 **FORTUNA,** b f Kaldoun—For Lasha **Ecurie La Clauzade**
58 **FRUIT CUP,** b c Strawberry Road—Host of Angels **J. C. Gour**
59 **HIGHEST NOBLES,** b f Highest Honor—Noble Tiara **Ecurie I. M. Fares**
60 **HONORABLE MONEY,** b c Highest Honor—Vaguely Money **Ecurie I. M. Fares**
61 **HONORABLE WEDGE,** b c Highest Honor—Wedge Cut **Ecurie I. M. Fares**
62 **IDAZKARI,** b f Shadeed—Secrets Told **Ecurie des Mousquetaires**
63 **IPPON,** b c Pursuit of Love—Lady Reem **R. Bousquet**
64 **IVORY MOUNTAIN,** b c Salse—Ivory Moment **Ecurie I. M. Fares**
65 **JUST AN OASIS,** b c Green Desert—Just Class **Ecurie I. M. Fares**
66 **KADANCE VILLE,** b f Fabulous Dancer—Kadouville **S. Boucheron**
67 **KLIFFDHEN,** b c Exit To Nowhere—Touraille **R. Bousquet**
68 **KNIGHT OF HONOR,** b f Highest Honor—Sir Hollow **Ecurie I. M. Fares**
69 **KOOKABARRA,** b c Kendor—Comete de Halley **R. Bousquet**
70 **L'AGENAISE,** ch f Epervier Bleu—Orangerie **Mrs B. Clin**
71 **L'ARROSEE,** b f Woodman—Air de Noblesse **Ecurie des Mousquetaires**
72 **LEGITIME DEFENSE,** b f Highest Honor—Clear Hero **L. Cattan**
73 **LEOVILLE,** b f Zilzal—Femme Trompeuse **A. Holmes**
74 **MAFETENG,** b g Lesotho—Kenalya **K. Benfell**

MR J. C. ROUGET—continued

75 **MASTER NIKO**, b c Nikos—Mi Longa **J. F. Gribomont**
76 **MAZEL TRICK**, b c Phone Trick—Mazatleca **C. Gour**
77 **METISSE**, b f Kingmambo—Maximova **J. T. L. Jones**
78 **MIASMATIC**, b f Warning—Tiger Flower **Sheikh Mohammed**
79 **MIOURA**, b f Saumarez—Quality And Style **R. Bousquet**
80 **PALATIAL AFFAIRE**, b f Kingmambo—Party Cited **G. Tanaka**
81 **PAYS TO WIN**, b g Septieme Ciel—Aglasini **Mrs B. Clin**
82 **PEARL RARE**, b g Kadrou—Lady Pearl **H. Chamarty**
83 **PHIDIAS**, b c Pharly—Juvenka **Ecurie I. M. Fares**
84 **PLASTIQUEUSE**, b f Quest For Fame—Platinum Chain **A. S. Y. Hui**
85 **PRINCESSE DE VIANE**, b f Kaldoun—Life On The Road **A. Toulet**
86 **PRIVATE PARTY**, b f Fabulous Dancer—Numero Privee **Ecurie I. M. Fares**
87 **PRO GOLD**, b f Saumarez—Pro Sugar **Ecurie La Clauzade**
88 **QUEEN'S ELECT**, b f Sabrehill—Nobly Born **Sheikh Mohammed**
89 **REINE DE CHINE**, b f Shining Steel—Reine de Grace **A. Lapoterie**
90 **REINE DE PALMYRE**, ch f General Assembly—Wish For Diamonds **Mrs R. Chandioux**
91 **REPRIMAND THE LADY**, b f Reprimand—Lady Dowery **Ecurie I. M. Fares**
92 **RISKY BET**, b g Risk Me—Star Rose **J. C. Gour**
93 **RISKY MOONLIGHT**, b f Risk Me—Moonlight Princess **C. Gour**
94 **ROCKET MAN**, b c Take Risks—Rebellita **Mrs M. de Chambure**
95 **RYTHME ENDIABLE**, b c Lear Fan—Rosyphard **J. T. L. Jones**
96 **SECRETS AND LIES**, b f Polish Patriot—Fanfan **Mrs J. F. Dupont**
97 **SETHOS**, b c Exit To Nowhere—Silent Circle **R. Bousquet**
98 **SNOWFLAKES**, b g Always Fair—Snowy **J. C. Gour**
99 **SNOW POLINA**, b f Trempolino—Snow House **Ecurie La Clauzade**
100 **SO FREE**, b c Fly So Free—Munchkin Michele **J. C. Gour**
101 **SORTIE DE BAL**, b f Hero's Honor—Sharp Sunrise **A. Caro**
102 **STAGE EXIT**, ch f In The Wings—Approche **J. Wigan**
103 **STARGARD**, b f Polish Precedent—Princess Genista **Sheikh Mohammed**
104 **STEEPLE**, ch f Selkirk—Contralto **J. Wigan**
105 **SUAVE MARIE**, b f Suave Dancer—Mary's Dance **R. Bousquet**
106 **SWEET VICTORY**, b g Polish Precedent—Optimistic Lass **Sheikh Mohammed**
107 **TEXAS TORNADO**, b c Last Tycoon—No Sugar Baby **A. Bidart**
108 **TRENCAVEL**, b g Kendor—Heartfelt **A. Caro**
109 **TULIPE NOIRE**, b f Alleged—Black Tulip **Faisal Salman**
110 **TXOTXONGILO**, b g Mountain Cat—Assuita **A. Lapoterie**
111 **USHIMATA**, b c Weldnaas—The Boozy News **R. Bousquet**
112 **VIBRANT**, b f Machiavellian—Vilikaia **Sheikh Mohammed**
113 **VILLAFRANCA**, b f In The Wings—Ville Eternelle **Ecurie La Clauzade**
114 **WAZA ARI**, b g Petong—Reem El Fala **R. Bousquet**
115 **WIND DRAFT**, b f Lear Fan—Arctic Lead **C. Gour**
116 **YVABEN**, b c Noblequest—Lady Hawke **P. Nogues**
117 **ZAMBEZI**, b f Rahy—Zonda **Sheikh Mohammed**

TWO-YEAR-OLDS

118 **AGRAVAIN**, b c Turtle Island—Benevole **R. Bousquet**
119 **AIDAMON**, b c Affirmed—Black Tulip **Ecurie I. M. Fares**
120 **AIGLIN**, br c Unfuwain—Frosting **R. Bousquet**
121 **AKKAR HERO**, b c Pharly—Miss Ivory Coast **Ecurie I. M. Fares**
122 **ANDKIT**, b f Alleged—Chimes Bird **Ecurie I. M. Fares**
123 **BAMBOLINA**, b f Great Palm—Alhucema **L. de Quintanilla**
124 **BAZBINA**, b f Highest Honor—Elite Guest **Ecurie I. M. Fares**
125 **BEIT MILLAT**, b f Alleged—Powder Storm **Ecurie I. M. Fares**
126 **CABARDES**, ch c Shining Steel—Heartfelt **A. Caro**
127 **CHER DOCTEUR**, b c Dear Doctor—Callia **H. Chamarty**
128 **CRUELLE**, ch f Irish River—Company **N. Radwan**
129 Ch f Sanglamore—Divine Valse **Mrs A. Forien**
130 **EAU DE RIZ**, br f Al Nasr—Akline **A. Caro**
131 **ESCANDALOSO**, b c Reprimand—Forest of Arden **Mrs A. Corcoral**

MR J. C. ROUGET—continued

132 **EXIT TO VILLE,** b f Exit To Nowhere—Kadouville **S. Boucheron**
133 **FILS DE VIANE,** b c Kadounor—Life On The Road **A. Toulet**
134 **FNEIDIK,** ch c Highest Honor—Shaquick **Ecurie I. M. Fares**
135 **HERMINE,** b f Kaldoun—Habigael **Haras d'Etreham**
136 **INAVOUABLE,** b f Septieme Ciel—Jeany's Halo **Ecurie des Mousquetaires**
137 **JAPAN EXILE,** b f Arazi—Terre de Feu **J. F. Gribomont**
138 **JET STEEL,** b c Shining Steel—Jetty **Mrs J. Vaslin**
139 B f Dixieland Band—Jon's Singer **Ecurie I. M. Fares**
140 **KEN PIPER,** gr f Kendor—Queen's Piper **R. Labeyrie**
141 **KIWAHU,** ch f Galetto—Fabuleuse Cherie **L. Cattan**
142 **KOBEIAT,** gr c St Jovite—La Carene **Ecurie I. M. Fares**
143 B f Shirley Heights—Lady Dowery **Ecurie I. M. Fares**
144 **LOCKERGREEN,** b c Sillery—Pommes Sautees **R. Bousquet**
145 **LUSSINO,** b c Esprit du Nord—Lumiere de Feu **A. Caro**
146 **MORDIOU,** br c Cyrano de Bergerac—Play The Game **R. Bousquet**
147 **MYTH AND REALITY,** gr f Linamix—Melite **J. F. Gribomont**
148 B f Grand Lodge—Nabila **J. Wigan**
149 **NO NIGHT,** br c Night Shift—No Sugar Baby **A. Bidart**
150 **OKABANGO,** b c Unfuwain—Riveryev **L. de Quintanilla**
151 **OLD BEINO,** gr f Highest Honor—Aldbourne **Ecurie I. M. Fares**
152 **PATHETIC,** ch c Mountain Cat—Arctic Interlude **Mrs A. Corcoral**
153 **PIBALE,** b f Mutjahid—Bint Albadou **M. Daguzan-Garros**
154 **POUDRIERE,** b f Trempolino—Miracles Happen **Ecurie des Mousquetaires**
155 **PRETTY MOON,** gr f Linamix—Mondsee **Mrs R. Ades**
156 **PRINCE DOM,** b c Homme de Loi—Princesse Mimi **R. Bousquet**
157 **RAFTERY,** b c Nashamaa—Go On Fiddling **Mrs A. Corcoral**
158 **RISKY BUSINESS,** b f Ski Chief—La Chiava **H. Chamarty**
159 **RIVER ABOUALI,** ch f Bluebird—Litani River **Ecurie I. M. Fares**
160 **ROSEANBO,** b c Nashamaa—Fragrant Baby **A. Bidart**
161 **SEPTIEME NEIGE,** b c Septieme Ciel—Snow House **Ecurie La Clauzade**
162 B f Bering—Shardazar **Ecurie I. M. Fares**
163 **SHINING CARA,** gr c Shining Steel—Frances Cara **L. de Quintanilla**
164 **SHY NIGHT,** b f Barathea—Shy Danseuse **Mrs R. Ades**
165 **STAR OF AKKAR,** b f Distant Relative—Donna Star **Ecurie I. M. Fares**
166 **SUAVE BABY,** ch c Suave Dancer—La Grande Cascade **R. Bousquet**
167 **SUPER QUERCUS,** ch c Hero's Honor—Ginger Candy **J. P. Rios**
168 **SUPREME ALLIANCE,** gr f Kendor—Painted Flower **R. Bousquet**
169 **TALIBORE,** ch c Highest Honor—Zapata Beauty **R. Bousquet**
170 **TIKREET,** ch f Dixieland Band—Hawk Beauty **Ecurie I. M. Fares**
171 **TOP QUERCUS,** b c Diamond Prospect—Money Can't Buy **J. Meuche**
172 **TOP SEED,** gr f Cardoun—Theatrical Victory **Baron G. de Rothschild**
173 **TRIPOLI,** b c Always Fair—Highest Pleasure **Ecurie I. M. Fares**

Jockeys (Flat): J R Dubosc, P H Dumortier, J B Eyquem.

512 MR R. ROWE, Pulborough

Postal: **Ashleigh House Stables, Sullington Lane, Storrington, Pulborough, West Sussex, RH20 4AE.**
Phone: **(01903) 742871 MOBILE (0831) 345636**

1 **A CHEF TOO FAR,** 5, b g Be My Chief (USA)—Epithet **The Hove Racing Club**
2 **BAY LOUGH (IRE),** 7, b m Lancastrian—Cauriedator **Mr Guy Luck**
3 **BLACK CHURCH,** 12, ch g Torus—Chantry Blue **Dr B. Alexander**
4 **BLESS ME SISTER (IRE),** 9, b m Lafontaine (USA)—Ilawn
5 **BRASSIS HILL (IRE),** 7, b g Marktingo—Mystery Woman **The Sleeping Partnership**
6 **BULA VOGUE (IRE),** 8, b m Phardante (FR)—Bulabos **The In Vogue Partnership**
7 **CASH FOR BASH (IRE),** 8, b g Mandalus—Money For Honey **Capt A. Pratt**

MR R. ROWE—continued

8 **CELTIC FIREFLY,** 6, ch m Cruise Missile—Celtic Art **J. W. P. Sulllivan & G. W. Elphick**
9 **CLAREGARY (IRE),** 5, b m Brush Aside (USA)—Adare Lady **Mr C. Cornwell**
10 **DESERT MELODY (IRE),** 6, b g Carlingford Castle—Jasmine Melody **Mrs P. V. Crocker**
11 **EULOGY (IRE),** 8, ch g Paean—Daly Preacher **Mr Nicholas Cooper**
12 **FEAR CLISTE (IRE),** 7, b g Homo Sapien—Glenravel **Mr Frank Arthur**
13 **FLORLESS GUY (IRE),** 10, b g Floriferous—Wine List **Mr M. P. Sampson**
14 **FRAZER ISLAND (IRE),** 9, br g Phardante (FR)—Avransha **Dr B. Alexander**
15 **I'M SUPPOSIN (IRE),** 6, b h Posen (USA)—Robinia (USA) **Mr Nicholas Cooper**
16 **IRISH FROLIC (IRE),** 6, b g Jareer (USA)—Grey Marble **The Nicky Watts Partnership**
17 **KARAR (IRE),** 8, b g Shardari—Karaferya (USA) **Mrs Margaret Sampson**
18 **KILORAN BAY,** 7, b m Lyphento (USA)—Love You Rosy **Mr N. Blair**
19 **KYBO'S REVENGE (IRE),** 7, ch g Carlingford Castle—Mettle Kettle **The Hon Mervyn Greenway**
20 **LEAD VOCALIST (IRE),** 9, ch m Orchestra—Eternal Youth **Capt A. Pratt**
21 **MATAMOROS,** 6, gr g Kalaglow—Palama (USA) **Mrs P. V. Crocker**
22 **MAZZINI (IRE),** 7, b g Celio Rufo—Dontellvi **Mr Nicholas Cooper**
23 **MILLFRONE (IRE),** 8, ch g Millfontaine—Frone **Winterfields Farm Ltd**
24 **MONTROE (IRE),** 6, gr g Roselier (FR)—Cathedral Street **Miss Meriel Tufnell**
25 **MULLINTOR (IRE),** 7, b g King Luthier—Latin Verses **Mr T. Thompson**
26 **NATIVE PLAYER (IRE),** 6, b g Be My Native (USA)—Kilbricken Bay **Mr Nicholas Cooper**
27 **NESCAF (NZ),** 8, b g Gold Blend (USA)—Urania (NZ) **Mr Tim Clowes**
28 **NO MATTER (IRE),** 7, br g Roselier (FR)—Nataf **Mr Nicholas Cooper**
29 **PADDY'S WOLF,** 7, b g Little Wolf—Paddy's Delight **Mr Grahame A. Dedman**
30 **PAVLOVA (IRE),** 8, ch m Montelimar (USA)—Light Foot **Mrs Margaret McGlone**
31 **RHEIN LADY,** 4, b f Gildoran—Houston Belle **The Cinder Syndicate**
32 **RIVER MONARCH,** 7, b h Just A Monarch—Costa Beck **Mr B. J. White**
33 **ROISIN CLOVER,** 7, ch m Faustus (USA)—Valiyen **The Clockhouse Press Ltd**
34 **SEVENTH WAVE,** 6, b m Gildoran—Ribobelle **Mr David Hill & Mr Tim Chandler**
35 **SIR DANTE (IRE),** 7, ch g Phardante (FR)—Tumvella **Mr Peter R. Wilby**
36 **SIR TOBY (IRE),** 5, bl g Strong Gale—Petite Deb **Miss Meriel Tufnell**
37 **SIR VALENTINE (IRE),** 4, b g Be My Native (USA)—Tumvella **Capt A. Pratt**
38 **SOUTHDOWN LAD,** 4, b g Henbit (USA)—Stupid Cupid **The Exclusive Partnership**
39 **SUFFOLK ROAD,** 11, br g Yashgan—Maybird **Mr Leon Best**
40 **THE TEN AMIGOS (IRE),** 7, b g Tremblant—Light Foot
41 **THUHOOL,** 10, b g Formidable (USA)—Wurud (USA) **Mr C. Cornwell**
42 **YEOMAN WARRIOR,** 11, b g Tug of War—Annies Pet **Mrs Heather Alwen**

THREE-YEAR-OLDS

43 **FLINDERS,** b f Henbit (USA)—Stupid Cupid **The Exclusive Partnership**

Other Owners: Mr A. L. Abrahams, Mr J. C. H. Berry, Mr Alistair Blades, Dr W. Bogie, Mr David Coe, Mr S. P. Cooper, Mrs A. E. Dawes, Miss Genevieve Donovan, Mr D. T. Ellingham, Faulkner West & Co Ltd, Mr J. Ferguson, Mrs C. Gregory, Mr K. E. Gregory, Mr M. G. Hardy, Mr T. Hunter Blair, Mr I. Kerman, Mr Robin A. Lamb, Mr M. I. Lewis, Mr Quin Lovis, Mr N. J. McKibbin, Mr C. J. Messer, Mr R. C. Murdoch, Miss Henrietta Neville, Lady Neville, Mr W. Packham, Mr J. A. Porteous, Mr B. J. Reid, Mr Richard Rowe, Mr M. P. Sadler, Mrs L. Sanders, Mr R. J. Sharp, Mrs B. Sopp, Mr A. Taylor, Mr George Tobitt, Mr Clive Turner, Mrs F. A. Veasey, Mrs G. Watts.

Jockey (NH): D O'Sullivan (10-2).

Conditional: Andrew Garrity (9-7).

513 MISS M. E. ROWLAND, Lower Blidworth

Postal: **Kirkfields, Calverton Road, Lower Blidworth, Nottingham, NG21 0NW.**
Phone: **(01623) 794831**

1 **ABINGER,** 6, ch g Absalom—Western Singer **Mr T. W. J. Edmonds**
2 **BOHOLA PETE (IRE),** 7, ch g Orchestra—Deep Link **Mr Tim Brown**

MISS M. E. ROWLAND—continued

3 **DACHA (IRE)**, 6, b g Soviet Star (USA)—Shadywood **Mrs Nicky Chambers**
4 **DRAMATIST (IRE)**, 7, b g Homo Sapien—Frostbite **Miss M. E. Rowland**
5 **FALCARRAGH (IRE)**, 8, b g Common Grounds—Tatra **Miss M. E. Rowland**
6 **GOLDLINER BAILEY**, 6, ch g Royal Vulcan—Semi-Colon **Miss M. E. Rowland**
7 **I'M A DREAMER (IRE)**, 8, b g Mister Majestic—Lady Wise **Miss M. E. Rowland**
8 **INSPIRATIONAL (IRE)**, 4, ch f Lahib (USA)—Sun Breiz (FR)
9 **LEAR DANCER (USA)**, 7, b br g Lear Fan (USA)—Green Gown **Miss M. E. Rowland**
10 **LOVABLE OUTLAW (IRE)**, 7, br g Henbit (USA)—Sweet Tulip **Mr T. W. J. Edmonds**
11 **LOVE VENTURE**, 4, b f Pursuit of Love—Our Shirley **Miss M. E. Rowland & Mr Bob Tanner**
12 **MINNESOTA FATS (IRE)**, 6, b br g Little Bighorn—Pepper Cannister **Mr T. W. J. Edmonds**
13 5, B m Strong Gale—Rednael **Miss M. E. Rowland**
14 **ROYAL MOUNTBROWNE**, 10, b g Royal Vulcan—Star Shell **Mrs J. E. O'Kane**
15 **TEEJAY'S FUTURE (IRE)**, 7, b m Buckskin (FR)—Lolos Run VII **Mr J. C. Hind**
16 **THE BOULD VIC (IRE)**, 6, b g Bold Arrangement—Silojoka **The Leicestershire Connection**
17 **UP THE CREEK (IRE)**, 6, br m Supreme Leader—Jacob's Creek (IRE) **Miss M. E. Rowland**

THREE-YEAR-OLDS

18 B f Pips Pride—Swift And Early (IRE) **Mr Tim Brown**

Other Owners: Mr R. A. Aston, Mrs Lesley Beauchamp, Mr Rick Beauchamp, Mrs Susan Foster, Mrs Bambi Hornbuckle, Mr Alan Moulton, Mr J. Revell, Mrs J. J. Spence.

Jockey (NH): Gary Lyons (10-2).

Conditional: G Hogan, P Midgley (10-4).

Lady Rider: Miss S Wright (9-0).

514 MR A. DE ROYER-DUPRE, Chantilly

Postal: **3 Chemin des Aigles, 60500 Chantilly, France.**
Phone: **(4) 4580303 FAX (4) 4573938**

1 **ADJILANI (IRE)**, 5, b h Lashkari—Adjriyna **H. H. Aga Khan**
2 **AERDEE (FR)**, 4, gr f Highest Honor—Valse Hesitation **Mlle M. Bliard**
3 **ALIPS (FR)**, 4, ch f Beaudelaire—New Miss **Marquise de Moratalla**
4 **ALIWAIYN (IRE)**, 4, b c Shernazar—Aleema **H. H. Aga Khan**
5 **ASTARABAD (USA)**, 4, b c Alleged—Anaza **H. H. Aga Khan**
6 **DIYAWARA (IRE)**, 4, b f Doyoun—Diya **H. H. Aga Khan**
7 **DONKEY ENGINE**, 4, b c Fairy King—City Ex **Marquise de Moratalla**
8 **FADO (FR)**, 5, b h Unfuwain—Lusitana **Mr E. Fierro**
9 **HAMIRPOUR (IRE)**, 5, b h Shahrastani—Hamaliya **H. H. Aga Khan**
10 **MARIN MARIE (FR)**, 6, b h Fabulous Dancer—Marie de Fontenoy **Marquise de Moratalla**
11 **NOMBRE PREMIER**, 4, gr c Kendor—Sabiola **Marquise de Moratalla**
12 **NOUSAIYRA (IRE)**, 4, b f Be My Guest—Noufiyla **H. H. Aga Khan**
13 **PORBANDAR (IRE)**, 4, b c Shahrastani—Parapa **Mr Beniamino Arbib**
14 **QUENDU**, 4, gr c Kendor—Quintefolle **Marquise de Moratalla**
15 **RED GUEST (IRE)**, 4, ch c Be My Guest—Mika Red **Mr Bob Lalemant**
16 **SAFARID (FR)**, 4, b g Al Nasr—Safariyna **H. H. Aga Khan**
17 **SAMAPOUR (IRE)**, 4, b c Kahyasi—Samneeza **H. H. Aga Khan**
18 **SAZAIYMAR (FR)**, 6, b g Doyoun—Samirza **H. H. Aga Khan**
19 **SHENABI (IRE)**, 4, b c Kenmare—Shashna **H. H. Aga Khan**
20 **TAJOUN (FR)**, 4, b g General Holme—Taeesha **H. H. Aga Khan**
21 **TIRAAZ (USA)**, 4, b c Lear Fan—Tarikhana **H. H. Aga Khan**
22 **ZAYANA (IRE)**, 5, b m Darshaan—Zaydiya **H. H. Aga Khan**

MR A. DE ROYER-DUPRE—continued

THREE-YEAR-OLDS

23 **ABIYAN (IRE)**, b c Doyoun—Abasiya **H. H. Aga Khan**
24 **ADJISA (IRE)**, b f Doyoun—Adjiriyna **H. H. Aga Khan**
25 **ALIMADJID (IRE)**, b c Last Tycoon—Aleema **H. H. Aga Khan**
26 **ALWIYDA (USA)**, b f Trempolino—Alimana **H. H. Aga Khan**
27 **ANEYDIA (IRE)**, b f Kenmare—Aneyza **H. H. Aga Khan**
28 **ARRET DE PRINCE**, ch c Arazi—La Tirana **Marquise de Moratalla**
29 **ASHGARI (IRE)**, b c Selkirk—Ashtarka **H. H. Aga Khan**
30 **BASIE BLUES**, b f Alzao—Boat Race **Mr Bob Lalemant**
31 **CHARGE D'AFFAIRES**, b c Kendor—Lettre de Cachet **Marquise de Moratalla**
32 **DABIYAL (IRE)**, b c High Estate—Dabara **H. H. Aga Khan**
33 **DARALIYA (IRE)**, b f Kahyasi—Daralinsha **H. H. Aga Khan**
34 **DARGHAR (IRE)**, b c Kahyasi—Daralaka **H. H. Aga Khan**
35 **DARIALANN (IRE)**, b c Kahyasi—Delsy **H. H. Aga Khan**
36 **DARYAPOUR (IRE)**, b c Kahyasi—Daroura **H. H. Aga Khan**
37 **DAYMARTI (IRE)**, b c Caerleon—Daltawa **H. H. Aga Khan**
38 **DAYMOON (USA)**, b f Dayjur—Moonlight Serenade **Mme Marlene Brody**
39 **DOLFIKAR (IRE)**, b c Darshaan—Dounya **H. H. Aga Khan**
40 **EDELORA (IRE)**, b f Doyoun—Ederiya **H. H. Aga Khan**
41 **ERDIJIYA (IRE)**, b f Kahyasi—Erdiya **H. H. Aga Khan**
42 **GRILLON (FR)**, gr c Exit To Nowhere—Un Peu Grise **Baron Guy de Rothschild**
43 **HARITHABAD (FR)**, b c Ela-Mana-Mou—Haratiyna **H. H. Aga Khan**
44 **ILAHABAD (IRE)**, b c Kahyasi—Ilmiyya **H. H. Aga Khan**
45 **IN A MELLOW TONE**, b f Exit To Nowhere—Elka **Mr Bob Lalemant**
46 **KARSIYAKA (IRE)**, b f Kahyasi—Karlafsha **H. H. Aga Khan**
47 **KASSIYAN**, b c Niniski—Kassiyda **H. H. Aga Khan**
48 **KHAZIM (FR)**, b c Akarad—Khariyda **H. H. Aga Khan**
49 **KONIYA (IRE)**, b f Doyoun—Kozana **H. H. Aga Khan**
50 **LA JOLLA SLEW (USA)**, b c Seattle Slew—C Sharp **Mr Hubert Guy**
51 **LIYANA (IRE)**, b f Shardari—Lisana **H. H. Aga Khan**
52 **LORDMARE (FR)**, gr c Kenmare—Continuite **Baron Guy de Rothschild**
53 **MANNSARA (IRE)**, b f Royal Academy—Masslama **H. H. Aga Khan**
54 **MASALARIAN (IRE)**, b c Doyoun—Masamiyda **H. H. Aga Khan**
55 **MASALI (IRE)**, b c Darshaan—Masmouda **H. H. Aga Khan**
56 **MEDASAN (FR)**, b c Darshaam—Meadow Green Lady **H. H. Aga Khan**
57 **MON PREFERE (FR)**, ch c Pistolet Bleu—Salve **Mr Bob Lalemant**
58 **NAFASAPOUR (IRE)**, b c Subotica—Nafzawa **H. H. Aga Khan**
59 **NAKIYA (FR)**, b f Kendor—Nabagha **H. H. Aga Khan**
60 **OBJECT OF VERTU (FR)**, b f Kendor—Quintefolle **Marquise de Moratalla**
61 **ON A CLEAR DAY**, b c Exit To Nowhere—Marcotte **Mr Bob Lalemant**
62 **PALASARI (IRE)**, b c Doyoun—Parapa **H. H. Aga Khan**
63 **PANTOUFLARD**, gr c Kendor—Belle Doche **Marquise de Moratalla**
64 **PARAJA (IRE)**, b f Doyoun—Parnala **H. H. Aga Khan**
65 **PASHMIYNA (FR)**, b f Highest Honor—Valse Hesitation **Mlle M. Bliard**
66 **PENSE BETE (FR)**, b c Always Fair—Une Pensee **Baron Guy de Rothschild**
67 **POLLY'S FLEET (USA)**, ch f Afleet—Polly's Harde **Mr Henri Mastey**
68 **PRINCE NOCTURNE (IRE)**, b c Night Shift—Reine du Ciel **Baron Guy de Rothschild**
69 **QUEEN MAMBO (USA)**, b f Kingmambo—Margot **Mme Marlene Brody**
70 **REDCLIFF (FR)**, ch c General Holme—Rudolfina **Mr Bob Lalemant**
71 **RIVER BRAVE (USA)**, b c Riverman—Brave Hearted **Mme Marlene Brody**
72 **SARAGANN (IRE)**, b c Danehill—Sarliya **H. H. Aga Khan**
73 **SEARCH FOR LOVE (FR)**, b f Groom Dancer—Merry Quest **Mme O. Bryant**
74 **SENANJAR (IRE)**, b c Kahyasi—Sendana **H. H. Aga Khan**
75 **SHAMARZIAN (IRE)**, b c Thatching—Shamarzana **H. H. Aga Khan**
76 **SHAMSIYANI (IRE)**, b c Shernazar—Shamsiya **H. H. Aga Khan**
77 **SHERANA (IRE)**, b f Alleged—Sherarda **H. H. Aga Khan**
78 **SUBSIDY**, ch c Midyan—Sabiola **Marquise de Moratalla**
79 **TALKASHA (IRE)**, b f Doyoun—Talwara **H. H. Aga Khan**
80 **TARBAZAN (IRE)**, b c Don't Forget Me—Tazmeen **H. H. Aga Khan**

MR A. DE ROYER-DUPRE—continued

81 TIRIYMA (IRE), b f Thatching—Tijara **H. H. Aga Khan**
82 VARAPOUR (IRE), b c Kenmare—Vearia **H. H. Aga Khan**
83 ZAINTA (IRE), b f Kahyasi—Zaila **H. H. Aga Khan**
84 ZALAIYKA (FR), b f Royal Academy—Zanadiyka **H. H. Aga Khan**
85 ZANAKANN (FR), b c Last Tycoon—Zanata **H. H. Aga Khan**
86 ZARAWA (IRE), b f Kahyasi—Zarna **H. H. Aga Khan**

TWO-YEAR-OLDS

87 ALBANY SOUND (IRE), b f Superlative—Salt Peanuts **Mr Bob Lalemant**
88 B c 29/1 Zayyani—Balance **H. H. Aga Khan**
89 BEHRANI (IRE), b c 10/4 Linamix—Behera **H. H. Aga Khan**
90 CHEVRE FOLLE (IRE), b f Warning—Fermiere **Baron Guy de Rothschild**
91 CHICAGO PEACE (IRE), b f Saint Cyrien—Petchili **J. H. Metzger**
92 COZY MORN (USA), b c Cozzene—Morning Games **Mme Marlene Brody**
93 DABARPOUR (IRE), b c 23/3 Alzao—Dabara **H. H. Aga Khan**
94 DAJAZAR (IRE), b c 1/4 Seattle Dancer—Dajarra **H. H. Aga Khan**
95 DONA BEIJA (FR), b f Caerleon—Didjala **Marquise de Moratalla**
96 DOUNINE, b f Kaldoun—Flabbergasted **Mme Marlene Brody**
97 EUPHRATES (USA), b f Cox's Ridge—Syria **Mme Marlene Brody**
98 B c Zinaad—Fadaki Hawaki **Marquise de Moratalla**
99 FIVE THORNS (IRE), b c Danehill—Sabiola **Marquise de Moratalla**
100 B c Royal Academy—Girouette **Marquise de Moratalla**
101 B c Night Shift—Gold Flair **Mr Bob Lalemant**
102 HAPPY ROSE (IRE), b f Linamix—Indian Rose **Baron Guy de Rothschild**
103 HARLEM NOCTURNE (IRE), b c Be My Guest—Chalarone **Mr Bob Lalemant**
104 B f Barathea—Howlin' **Marquise de Moratalla**
105 IMAGINAIRE (USA), b c Quest For Fame—Hail The Dancer **Mr J. R. de Arago Bozano**
106 JUSTICIAR, b c Kendor—Gerante **Marquise de Moratalla**
107 B f 24/2 Linamix—Kalajana **H. H. Aga Khan**
108 KANONETTE (FR), b f Kaldoun—Neomeris **Mr Dwight Kendall**
109 B f 3/2 Subotica—Karikata **H. H. Aga Khan**
110 KHARIYALI (FR), b c 29/2 Lycius—Khariyda **H. H. Aga Khan**
111 MACHICABULA (IRE), b c Vert Amande—Lusitana **Mr E. Fierro**
112 B f Superlative—Marcotte **N.V. B.S.I.**
113 B c 11/5 Darshaan—Meadow Glen Lady **H. H. Aga Khan**
114 MERIDIANA (FR), b f Kaldoun—Incroyable **Baron Guy de Rothschild**
115 B f 7/4 Green Desert—Nabagha **H. H. Aga Khan**
116 B c 18/3 Catrail—Naziriya **H. H. Aga Khan**
117 NIGHT WALKER, b c Kendor—Svetlana **Marquise de Moratalla**
118 NUIT D'OPALE (IRE), b f Hero's Honor—Fleur du Ciel **Baron Guy de Rothschild**
119 OU BIEN OU BIEN (USA), b c Roanoke—Nangela Dear **J. H. Metzger**
120 PAS D'HEURE (IRE), b f Arazi—La Tirana **Marquise de Moratalla**
121 RED EAGLE (FR), b f Epervier Bleu—Red Silk **J. H. Metzger**
122 ROSE DES ANDES (IRE), b f Royal Academy—Rose Paille **Baron Guy de Rothschild**
123 B c 20/4 Zayyani—Sharmada **H. H. Aga Khan**
124 SHARP SHIFT (FR), b c Night Shift—Sharp Change **Marquise de Moratalla**
125 SOUS VAILLANT (IRE), b c Kendor—Soloi **Marquise de Moratalla**
126 STUFF GOWN, b c Reprimand—Subaru **Marquise de Moratalla**
127 B c 27/3 Night Shift—Tashtiyana **H. H. Aga Khan**
128 THATCHAYA (FR), b f Thatching—Sharbaya **Mr Dwight Kendall**
129 THEORY OF LAW, b f Generous—Lettre de Cachet **Marquise de Moratalla**
130 WHENLIGHTSARELOW (IRE), b f Brief Truce—Tender Baby **Mr Bob Lalemant**
131 WILD APPEAL (USA), b c Wild Again—Appealing Missy **Mme Marlene Brody**
132 B f 8/5 Linamix—Zanadiyka **H. H. Aga Khan**

Jockey (Flat): Gerald Mosse.

Apprentice: Jimmy Simon.

515 MISS L. V. RUSSELL, Kinross

Postal: **Arlary House, Milnathort, Kinross, Tayside, Scotland, KY13 7SJ.**
Phone: **OFFICE (01577) 862482 YARD 865512 FAX 861171 MOBILE (07970) 645261**

1 **ABBEY LAMP (IRE)**, 9, b g Miner's Lamp—Abbey Lodge **Panther Racing Ltd**
2 **BARDAROS**, 9, b g Lighter—Suttons Hill **Mr Peter J. S. Russell**
3 **BLAZING TRAIL (IRE)**, 10, gr g Celio Rufo—Bally Sovereign **Mr S. Bruce**
4 **CHARLIE FOXTROT (IRE)**, 6, b g Be My Native (USA)—Zalazula **Mr Peter J. S. Russell**
5 **CICERONE**, 8, br g Tina's Pet—Emma Royale **The Drumpellier Partnership**
6 **CLASSIC CREST (IRE)**, 7, ch g Persian Heights—Blunted **Miss Lucinda V. Russell**
7 **FIVELEIGH BUILDS**, 11, b g Deep Run—Giolla Donn **Miss Lucinda V. Russell**
8 **GREENHILL RAFFLES**, 12, ch g Scallywag—Burlington Belle **Mr Peter J. S. Russell**
9 **GYPSY KING (IRE)**, 10, b g Deep Run—Express Film **Mr M. F. B. Nicholson**
10 **HEE'S A DANCER**, 6, b g Rambo Dancer (CAN)—Heemee **Mr M. F. B. Nicholson**
11 **INNOVATE (IRE)**, 6, b m Posen (USA)—Innate **Mr Peter K. Dale**
12 **INVER RED (IRE)**, 10, ch g Roselier (FR)—Churchtown Girl **The Gypsy King Partnership**
13 **MOVAC (IRE)**, 9, br g Ovac (ITY)—Mountain Glee **Mr Tommy Naughton**
14 **MR MATCHIT (IRE)**, 6, b g Mandalus—Twitchit **Mr Peter J. S. Russell**
15 **PATTER MERCHANT**, 9, ch g Import—El Chaperall **Mr P. B. Hall**
16 **PHARKULA (IRE)**, 5, b m Phardante (FR)—Sikulu (IRE) **The Pharkula Partnership**
17 **ROCKET RUN (IRE)**, 10, b g Orchestra—Roselita **Mr Peter J. S. Russell**
18 **SPEAKER'S HOUSE (USA)**, 9, b g Lear Fan (USA)—Bring Me Flowers (FR) **Mrs C. G. Greig**
19 **STONEY BURKE (IRE)**, 9, b g Niels—Stoney Broke **Miss E. C. A. Noble**
20 **TWO FOR ONE (IRE)**, 9, b br g Strong Gale—Shatana **Mrs C. G. Greig**
21 **UNCLE BERT (IRE)**, 8, b g Ovac (ITY)—Sweet Gum (USA) **Mrs C. C. Greig**
22 **WAR WHOOP**, 6, ch g Mandrake Major—Mohican **Leading Star Racing**
23 **WHITE DIAMOND**, 10, b g Touching Wood (USA)—Dimant Blanche (USA) **Mr Peter J. S. Russell**
24 **WINDTHROP**, 5, ch g Dancing High—Malandot **Mrs J. Grieve**
25 **WOODFORD GALE (IRE)**, 8, b g Strong Gale—Woodford Princess **Kelso Members Lowflyers Club**

Other Owners: Mr W. Agnew, Diana Blythe, Mr P. Brierley, Mr Alan Cairns, Dr Anne Gillespie, Mrs J. M. Grimston, R. M. Landale, Mr J. Rodger, Mr R. Wardlaw.

Jockeys (NH): M R Foster (10-0), A R Thornton (10-0).

Conditional: D Reid (9-7).

Amateur: Mr M S G Bradburne (10-0).

516 MR B. J. M. RYALL, Yeovil

Postal: **Higher Farm, Rimpton, Yeovil, Somerset, BA22 8AD.**
Phone: **MARSTON MAGNA (01935) 850222**

1 **BOZO (IRE)**, 7, b g Kefaah (USA)—Hossvend **Mr B. J. M. Ryall**
2 **COUNTRY KRIS**, 6, b g Town And Country—Mariban **Mr B. J. M. Ryall**
3 4, B g Then Again—Mariban **Mr. B. J. M. Ryall**
4 **SPRING GRASS**, 10, br m Pardigras—Spring River **Mr B. J. M. Ryall**
5 **SPRING HEBE**, 8, b m Pragmatic—Spring River **Mr B. J. M. Ryall**
6 **SUKAAB**, 13, gr g Nishapour (FR)—Nye (FR) **Mr B. J. M. Ryall**
7 **WIN A HAND**, 8, b m Nearly A Hand—Mariban **Mr B. J. M. Ryall**

517 MR M. J. RYAN, Newmarket

Postal: **Cadland, 35 Old Station Road, Newmarket, Suffolk, CB8 8DT.**
Phone: **(01638) 664172 FAX 560248**

1 **CAPE SIREN,** 4, b f Warning—Cape Race (USA)
2 **CONTRARIE,** 5, b m Floose—Chanita
3 **DAFFODIL EXPRESS (IRE),** 5, b m Skyliner—Miss Henry
4 **DOC RYAN'S,** 4, b c Damister (USA)—Jolimo
5 **EL DON,** 6, b g High Kicker (USA)—Madam Gerard
6 **GOLD CLIPPER,** 4, b c High Kicker (USA)—Ship of Gold
7 **GOLDEN HADEER,** 7, ch h Hadeer—Verchinina
8 **KINGCHIP BOY,** 9, b g Petong—Silk St James
9 **SIDNEY THE KIDNEY,** 4, b f Mystiko (USA)—Martin-Lavell Mail
10 **SILK ST JOHN,** 4, b g Damister (USA)—Silk St James
11 **SUGAR REEF,** 4, br g High Kicker (USA)—Miss Poll Flinders
12 **SWEETNESS HERSELF,** 5, ch m Unfuwain (USA)—No Sugar Baby (FR)
13 **TOCCO JEWEL,** 8, br m Reesh—Blackpool Belle
14 **TOP JEM,** 4, b f Damister (USA)—Sharp Top

THREE-YEAR-OLDS

15 **FRECKLES,** b f High Kicker (USA)—Ship of Gold
16 **LADY ROCKSTAR,** b f Rock Hopper—Silk St James
17 **NORCROFT JOY,** b f Rock Hopper—Greenhills Joy
18 **PRINCESS OLIVIA,** b f Prince Sabo—Les Amis
19 **WILD LILLY,** b f Elmaamul (USA)—Chrisanthy

TWO-YEAR-OLDS

20 **AN SMEADUBH (IRE),** b f Dolphin Street (FR)—Forest Berries (IRE)
21 **AN SUILIN,** b f Magic Ring (IRE)—Toulal
22 Ch f Superlative—Dame du Moulin
23 B f Night Shift (USA)—Gena Ivor (USA)
24 Ch f Grand Lodge (USA)—Mrs Musgrove
25 **MURPHY'S LAW,** b g High Kicker (USA)—Mio Mementa
26 Ch f High Kicker (USA)—Sharp Top

Owners: Mr L. Audus, Mr P. E. Axon, Mr M. J. Baxter, Mr M. A. Beaven, Mr D. Bell, Mr M. Byron, Collectors Investments Ltd, Mr M. R. Currell, Mr William Dixon, Mr P. J. Donnison, Mr Keith Dunn, Extraman Ltd, Mr P. J. Flavin, Mrs P. Foley, Mr W. Foley, Mr A. Gorrie, Mr Alex Gorrie, Mr Jeffrey Green, Mrs Jean Hodge, Mr A. J. Hollis, Mr B. Holmes, Mr S. J. Lavallin, Mrs M. J. Lavell, Mr Michael Maloney, Mr John Malpass, Mr P. Marron, Mr G. Morphy, Mr Don Morris, Miss J. Nicholls, Norcroft Park Stud, Mrs M. J. Ryan, Mr M. J. Ryan, Mr David Sheen, Mrs W. L. Sole, Mrs Patricia J. Williams.

518 MISS B. SANDERS, Epsom

Postal: **Chalk Pit Stables, Headley Road, Epsom, Surrey, KT18 6BW.**
Phone: **ASHTEAD (01372) 278453 FAX (01372) 276137**

1 **BON GUEST (IRE),** 4, ch c Kefaah (USA)—Uninvited Guest **Mrs P. J. Sheen**
2 4, Br g Arctic Lord—Charossa **Mrs J. M. Laycock**
3 **DIAMOND LADY,** 6, ch m Nicholas Bill—Charossa **Mrs J. M. Laycock**
4 **DOUBLE FLIGHT,** 4, b f Mtoto—Sariah **The Middleweek-Leon Partnership**
5 **LA CHATELAINE,** 4, b f Then Again—La Domaine **Mr T. J. Blake**
6 **REHAAB,** 5, b m Mtoto—Top Treat (USA) **Mrs J. M. Laycock**
7 **ROWLANDSONS CHARM (IRE),** 5, b m Fayruz—Magic Gold **Mr J. M. Quinn**
8 **ROYAL ROULETTE,** 4, ch f Risk Me (FR)—Princess Lily **Mrs P. J. Sheen**
9 **SUPERIOR FORCE,** 5, ch g Superlative—Gleeful **Copyforce Ltd**

THREE-YEAR-OLDS

10 **COSMIC GIRL,** gr f Wolfhound (USA)—Remany **Mrs P. J. Sheen**

MISS B. SANDERS—continued

TWO-YEAR-OLDS

11 B f 11/2 Elmaamul (USA)—Sabaya (USA) (Seattle Dancer (USA)) **Copyforce Ltd**
12 Ch c 25/4 Mystiko (USA)—Surpassing (Superlative) **Copyforce Ltd**

Other Owners: Mr Leonard Fuller, Gallagher Materials Ltd, Sir Freddie Laker, Miss Helen Laycock, Miss Sarah Laycock, Mr M. E. Leon, Mr J. Middleweek, Mr M. D. Middleweek, Mr Giles W. Pritchard-Gordon, Mrs Anita Reid, Miss Brooke Sanders, Exors Of The Late Mr R. V. Smyth, Victor Chandler (Equus) Ltd, Mr T. M. Wales.

Jockey (Flat): S Sanders (w.a.).

Jockey (NH): M Richards (w.a.).

Lady Rider: Miss Holly Mitchell (8-12).

519 MR M. S. SAUNDERS, Wells

Postal: **Blue Mountain Farm, Wells Hill Bottom, Haydon, Wells, Somerset, BA5 3EZ.**
Phone: **(01749) 841011**

1 ASTRAL INVADER (IRE), 6, ch g Astronef—Numidia **Mr M. S. Saunders**
2 CONDITION RED, 5, b m Sayf El Arab (USA)—Forever Mary **Mr M. S. Saunders**
3 FABULOUS MTOTO, 8, b h Mtoto—El Fabulous (FR) **Mr N. R. Pike**
4 MILTON ABBOT, 5, b g Full Extent (USA)—Auto Connection **Mr Peter A. Brazier**
5 MUTASAWWAR, 4, ch g Clantime—Keen Melody (USA) **Mr M. S. Saunders**
6 RED TIME, 5, br g Timeless Times (USA)—Crimson Dawn **Mr M. S. Saunders**
7 REPERTORY, 5, b g Anshan—Susie's Baby **Mr M. S. Saunders**
8 SONGSHEET, 5, b m Dominion—Songstead **Mrs J. Turner**
9 WARRING, 4, b g Warrshan (USA)—Emerald Ring **Mr Chris Scott**

Other Owners: Mr E. W. Jones, Mr F. E. Jones, Mrs Denise Saunders, Mr A. R. Thirkill.

Jockey (Flat): S Drowne.

Apprentice: P P Murphy.

Lady Rider: Miss K Jones.

520 DR J. D. SCARGILL, Newmarket

Postal: **Red House Stables, Hamilton Road, Newmarket, Suffolk, CB8 OTE.**
Phone: **(01638) 663254 FAX (01638) 667767**

1 DEFINED FEATURE (IRE), 5, ch m Nabeel Dancer (USA)—Meissarah (USA) **Mr Derek W. Johnson**
2 GO FOR GREEN, 4, br f Petong—Guest List **Manor Farm Packers Ltd**
3 HERR TRIGGER, 7, gr g Sharrood (USA)—Four-Legged Friend **The Inn Crowd**
4 JAWANI (IRE), 10, b g Last Tycoon—Fabled Lady **Mrs Susan Scargill**

THREE-YEAR-OLDS

5 BIN FAA, b g Superlative—A Nymph Too Far (IRE) **The Vibrations**
6 BOBBYDAZZLE, ch f Rock Hopper—Billie Blue **Mrs Bobby Cohen**

DR J. D. SCARGILL—continued

7 **DOUBLIN' BAY (IRE)**, b f Roi Danzig (USA)—Nizamiya **The S P Partnership**
8 **DOWNSIZING (IRE)**, b f Tirol—In For More **Mrs Susan Scargill**
9 **FIRST DANCE**, b f Primo Dominie—Soviet Swan (USA) **Mr A. C. Edwards**
10 **PIPS SONG (IRE)**, ch g Pips Pride—Friendly Song **Mr Phillip Edwards**
11 B f Petoski—Price of Sentiment (IRE) **Mr Basil White**
12 **QUITE HAPPY (IRE)**, b f Statoblest—Four-Legged Friend **Mr Jonathan Crisp**
13 **THEME TUNE**, b f Dilum (USA)—Souadah (USA) **Mr G. W. Cossey**

TWO-YEAR-OLDS

14 B f 20/3 Komaite (USA)—A Nymph Too Far (IRE) (Precocious) **Mrs M. Coppitters**
15 Ch c 17/3 Mukaddamah (USA)—Cookawara (IRE) (Fairy King (USA)) **Premier Bloodstock Partners**
16 B c 31/3 Wolfhound (USA)—Desert Girl (Green Desert (USA)) **Premier Bloodstock Partners**
17 **JAYESAY (IRE)**, gr c 9/5 Mystiko (USA)—Scravels Saran (IRE) (Indian King (USA)) **Mr Derek W. Johnson**
18 Ch f 25/4 Dolphin Street (FR)—Karamana (Habitat) **P. A. & D. G. Sakal**
19 **NOM FRANCAIS**, b f 20/1 First Trump—Eastern Ember (Indian King (USA)) **Mr Maurice Sakal**
20 B f 26/2 Solo Native (USA)—Pal's Girl (IRE) (Cyrano de Bergerac) **W. J. de Ruiter**

Other Owners: Mr C. Ambler, P. Blythe, Mrs V. Boyley, J. W. Boyley, G. Bridgford, J. Custerson, Mr R. A. Dalton, C. J. Dont, D. Farey, I. Farnsworth, A. Fleming, Mr Robert A. Gladdis, C. Gould, M. Jakes, M. Leeson, J. Nicholls, Mr M. Reditt, Mrs P. Reditt, Mr M. Sakal, F. Spring, A. Taylor, W. Taylor, P. Treacy, M. Underwood, Mrs R. Watson, J. Wetherall, Mr C. A. Wotton.

Jockeys (Flat): R Cochrane (w.a.), J Quinn (w.a.).

521 MR B. SCRIVEN, Taunton

Postal: **Cogload Farm, Durston, Taunton, Somerset, TA3 5AW.**
Phone: **NORTH CURRY (01823) 490208**

1 **GABISH**, 13, b g Try My Best (USA)—Crannog **Mr B. Scriven**
2 **PLATO'S REPUBLIC (USA)**, 7, b br g Woodman (USA)—Jura Mist (USA) **Mr B. Scriven**
3 **ROCQUAINE**, 12, ch g Ballad Rock—Lola Sharp **Mr B. Scriven**

Conditional: G Supple (w.a.).

522 MRS J. SCRIVENS, Tiverton

Postal: **Barricane Stables, Bowdens Lane, Shillingford, Tiverton, Devon, EX16 9BU.**
Phone: **(01398) 331232 (0850) 733683 MOBILE**

1 **FOREMAN**, 5, b g Timeless Times (USA)—Skiddaw Bird **Mrs J. Scrivens**
2 4, B g Silver Owl—Holnicote **Mrs J. Scrivens**
3 5, B g Newski (USA)—Holnicote **Mrs J. Scrivens**
4 **JAY JAYS DREAM**, 12, b m Shaab—Traverser **Mrs J. Scrivens**
5 **JAY JAY'S VOYAGE**, 15, b g Saunter—Traverser **Mrs J. Scrivens**
6 **MORDROS**, 8, b g Interrex (CAN)—Jay Jays Dream **Mrs J. Scrivens**
7 **TAILSPIN**, 13, b g Young Generation—Mumtaz Flyer (USA) **Mrs J. Scrivens**

Jockey (NH): T G Dascombe (10-0).

523 MR D. SHAW, Newark

Postal: **Averham Park Farm, Averham, Newark, Nottinghamshire, NG23 5RU.**

1 **BARKSTON WARRIOR,** 4, b g Totem (USA)—Bold Difference **Mr T. H. Morris**
2 **BROADSTAIRS BEAUTY (IRE),** 8, ch g Dominion Royale—Holy Water **Mrs Judy Hunt**
3 **CHEERFUL GROOM (IRE),** 7, ch g Shy Groom (USA)—Carange **Mr Bill Cahill & Mr D. Mulvihill**
4 **DOCS DILEMMA (IRE),** 9, br g Decent Fellow—Talkative Princess **Mr Paul Murphy**
5 **GLIMMERING HOPE (IRE),** 4, b g Petorius—Angevin **Mr J. S. Lammiman**
6 **JACK SAYS,** 4, b g Rambo Dancer (CAN)—Madam Cody **Mr K. Nicholls**
7 **MUTAHADETH,** 4, ch g Rudimentary (USA)—Music In My Life (IRE) **G. S. D. Imports Ltd**
8 **ORNATE (IRE),** 4, b g Arazi (USA)—Pretty Lady **Mr J. C. Fretwell**
9 **STATE OF CAUTION,** 5, b g Reprimand—Hithermoor Lass **Mr J. C. Fretwell**
10 **STATOYORK,** 5, b g Statoblest—Ultimate Dream **Mr J. C. Fretwell**
11 **SYLVAN SABRE (IRE),** 9, b g Flash of Steel—Flute (FR) **Mr J. C. Fretwell**
12 **THEATRE MAGIC,** 5, b g Sayf El Arab (USA)—Miss Orient **Green Diamond Racing**
13 **VICTORIA DAY,** 6, b m Reference Point—Victoress (USA) **Mr Paul Murphy**
14 **YOU'RE AGOODUN,** 6, ch g Derrylin—Jennie Pat **Mr J. S. Lammiman**

THREE-YEAR-OLDS

15 **AVERHAM STAR,** ch g Absalom—Upper Sister **Mr G. E. Griffiths**
16 **HOGAIF (IRE),** ch g Persian Bold—Camarat **Mr J. C. Fretwell**
17 **SAND HAWK,** ch g Polar Falcon (USA)—Ghassanah **Mr J. C. Fretwell**

TWO-YEAR-OLDS

18 Ch f 2/4 Savahra Sound—Ace Girl **P. Dixon**
19 B c 11/5 Scenic—Amata (USA) **Rayton Racing**
20 B f 1/3 Batshoof—Attila The Honey **Mr Paul Murphy**
21 B c 18/2 Forest Wind (USA)—Beautyofthepeace (IRE) **Mr G. E. Griffiths**
22 Gr c 26/3 Paris House—Track Twenty Nine (IRE) **Rayton Racing**

Other Owners: Mr K. Bainbridge, Mr P. J. Burke, Mr Ray Enfield, Mr Tony Enfield, Mr B. G. Peacock, Mr K. G. Radford, Mr K. Sherman, Mr G. L. Tanner, Mr A. M. Wragg.

Jockey (Flat): J.K Fanning (8-2, wa).

Jockey (NH): A Smith (10-0, w.a).

524 MR J. J. SHEEHAN, Findon

Postal: **Woodmans Stables, London Road, Ashington, West Sussex, RH20 3AU.**
Phone: **YARD (01903) 893031 MOBILE (0410) 495951**

1 **COLERIDGE,** 10, gr g Bellypha—Quay Line **Mr P. J. Sheehan**
2 **ELEGANT DANCE,** 4, ch f Statoblest—Furry Dance (USA) **Mrs Christina Dowling**
3 **HIGH PRIORITY (IRE),** 5, b h Marju (IRE)—Blinding (IRE) **Mrs Eileen Sheehan**
4 4, Gr f Shavian—Innerglow **Mrs Christina Dowling**
5 **KING OF TUNES (FR),** 6, b h Chief Singer—Marcotte (FR) **Mrs Eileen Sheehan**
6 **ROCK TO THE TOP (IRE),** 4, b c Rudimentary (USA)—Well Bought (IRE) **Mrs Christina Dowling**
7 **ROMAN ACTOR,** 6, b g Tragic Role (USA)—Christines Lady **Mrs Eileen Sheehan**
8 **ROMAN ACTRESS,** 5, b m Tragic Role (USA)—Christines Lady **Mrs Eileen Sheehan**

TWO-YEAR-OLDS

9 Ch c 17/4 Up And At 'Em—Classic Choice (Patch) **Mr P. J. Sheehan**
10 B f 18/3 Mukaddamah (USA)—Shenley Lass (Prince Tenderfoot (USA)) **Mrs T. L. Harman**

Jockey (Flat): R Cochrane.

Jockey (NH): J Culloty.

525 MR FINBARR SHEEHY, Cork

Postal: **Shanagore, Innishannon, Co. Cork, Ireland.**
Phone: **(021) 775840 MOBILE (087) 2308266**

1 **ANOTHER LAFONTAINE (IRE),** 7, b g Lafontaine (USA)—Marfisa **D. F. Sheehy**
2 **CALMOS,** 11, ch g Callernish—Mossy's Niece **G. A. Murphy**
3 **DESERTMORE (IRE),** 8, b g King's Ride—Pillow Chat **B. O'Brien**
4 **FESTIVAL TRIUMPH (IRE),** 5, ch g The Bart (USA)—Bridgetown Girl **F. Sheehy**
5 **FOUNTAIN BID (IRE),** 6, b g Royal Fountain—Lilford Castle **F. Sheehy**
6 **GOOD TIME MELODY (IRE),** 5, b g Good Thyne (USA)—Raashideah **D. F. Sheehy**
7 **INHERIT THE SUN (IRE),** 5, b g Lahiq (USA)—Eden Dale **F. Sheehy**
8 **MCKENNAS MAGIC (IRE),** 4, b g Magical Wonder (USA)—Tumble Dale **D. F. Sheehy**
9 **MENELEK LORD (IRE),** 4, b g Yashgan—Higcham **D. F. Sheehy**
10 **RIVERSIDE RUN (IRE),** 5, b g Commanche Run—Annamoss **D. F. Sheehy**
11 **STRONG RED PINE (IRE),** 6, b g Electric—Red Pine **F. Sheehy**
12 **SWAN'S WISH (IRE),** 9, ch g Swan's Rock—Wish Again **M. O'Driscoll**
13 **THE HILL HAS MOVED (IRE),** 5, ch g Ore—Quotation **D. F. Sheehy**
14 **THE SEVENTH SCROLL (IRE),** 5, b g Brush Aside (USA)—Garryduff Lass **D. F. Sheehy**

THREE-YEAR-OLDS

15 **BLUE MUSIC (IRE),** ch g Keen—Coast Wind (USA) **F. Sheehy**
16 **LYPHARD BELLE,** b f Noble Patriarch—Skiddaw Bird **D. F. Sheehy**
17 **PRINCELY SPARK (IRE),** ch c Balla Cove—Tigeen **D. F. Sheehy**

TWO-YEAR-OLDS

18 B c 12/3 College Chapel—Idle Gossip (Runnett) **D. F. Sheehy**

Other Owners: John Cuffe, Richard Egan, Michael O'Connell, Barry O'Driscoll, Edward O'Driscoll.

Jockeys (Flat): D P McDonogh (w.a.), J Spencer.

Jockeys (NH): E Ahern (w.a.), Eamon Fehily, N D Fehily, J Shortt (w.a.), N Williamson (w.a.).

Lady Rider: Ms Susan Leahy (w.a.).

526 MR M. I. SHEPPARD, Ledbury

Postal: **Home Farm Cottage, Eastnor, Ledbury, Herefordshire, HR8 1RD.**
Phone: **FAX (01531) 634846 MOBILE (0370) 625061**

1 **BEAR HUG,** 5, b g Polar Falcon (USA)—Tender Loving Care **Mr K. Jones**
2 5, B g Almutanabbi—Call-Me-Sally **Mr C. A. Fuller**
3 **CLOBEEVER BOY,** 8, b g Shaab—Clover Bee **Mrs J. K. Spear**
4 **HONEYBED WOOD,** 10, ch m Town And Country—Bremhill Rosie **R. Herbert, T. Doxsey and M. Drake**
5 **LITTLE GUNNER,** 8, ch g Gunner B—Love of Kings **Mr A. W. Bailey**
6 **MARGI BOO,** 5, ch m Risk Me (FR)—Louisianalightning **S. B. I. Racing**
7 **NOW WE KNOW (IRE),** 10, ch g Denel (FR)—Struell Course **R. Herbert, T. Doxsey and M. Drake**
8 **OAKMONT (IRE),** 5, b g Pennine Walk—Heartland **Mr Simon Gegg**
9 **ODDA'S CHAPEL,** 5, b g Little Wolf—Pity's Pet **Mr David A. Hunt**
10 **RUSH OF BLOOD (IRE),** 4, b f Nordico (USA)—Crimson Robes **Rush Of Blood Racing**
11 **SEEK THE FAITH (USA),** 9, ch g Pilgrim (USA)—Bundler (USA) **Mr R. H. F. Matthews & Mrs K. H. Bullock**
12 **SOUTHWICK PARK,** 6, ch m Little Wolf—Carry On Fighting **Mr David A. Hunt**

Other Owners: Mr G. W. Caines, Mr T. A. Couchman, Mrs C. L. Goodinson, Mr M. G. Hynes, Mr G. M. Spencer, Mr John D. Thomas, Mr E. Wharton-Smith.

Amateur: Mr J M Pritchard (11-0).

527 MR O. M. C. SHERWOOD, Upper Lambourn

Postal: **Rhonehurst House, Upper Lambourn, Hungerford, Berkshire, RG17 8RG.**
Phone: **(01488) 71411 HOSTEL 72263 FAX 72786 MOBILES 0860 361142 0836 215639**

1 **ABBEY STREET (IRE),** 6, b g Old Vic—Racquette **Mr B. T. Stewart-Brown**
2 **AERION,** 7, b g Ardross—Swallowfield **The Chamberlain Addiscott Partnership**
3 **ALLTIME DANCER (IRE),** 6, b g Waajib—Dance On Lady **Mr H. M. Heyman**
4 **ANNA SOLEIL (IRE),** 5, b g Red Sunset—Flying Anna **Mr M. G. St Quinton**
5 **BARTON HOLT,** 6, b g Nicholas Bill—Arctic Advert **Mr J. Palmer-Brown**
6 **BEAR CLAW,** 9, b g Rymer—Carmarthen Honey **Roach Foods Limited**
7 **BERUDE NOT TO (IRE),** 9, b g Roselier (FR)—Decent Debbie **Mr G. Addiscott**
8 **BLOWN WIND (IRE),** 7, b g Strong Gale—Raise A Queen **Mr B. T. Stewart-Brown**
9 **BOULEVARD BAY (IRE),** 7, b g Royal Fountain—Cairita **Lady Helen Smith**
10 **BREATH OF SCANDAL (IRE),** 7, br g Strong Gale—Her Name Was Lola **Lady Lloyd Webber**
11 **CALLISOE BAY (IRE),** 9, b br g Callernish—Granagh Bay **Mr R. Waters**
12 **CHARMING GIRL (USA),** 7, b m L'Emigrant (USA)—Charming Pan (FR) **Mr C. Coxen**
13 **CHEROKEE CHIEF,** 7, ch g Rakaposhi King—Coole Pilate **Mr A. Boyd-Rochfort**
14 **CITIZEN KANE (IRE),** 4, b g Sadler's Wells (USA)—Princess Tiara **Mr B. T. Stewart-Brown**
15 **COOL AS A CUCUMBER (IRE),** 7, ch g Ballad Rock—Siberian Princess **Rashleigh Arms Charlestown St Austell**
16 **COULTON,** 11, ch g Final Straw—Pontevecchio Due **Mr M. G. St Quinton**
17 5, B g Roselier (FR)—Decent Debbie **Mr B. T. Stewart-Brown**
18 **DOCS BOY,** 8, b g Rakaposhi King—Jennie Pat **Mr D. J. W. Ross**
19 **DONNINGTON (IRE),** 8, b g Good Thyne (USA)—Eljay **Mr B. T. Stewart-Brown**
20 **EARLY DRINKER,** 10, gr g Gabitat—Blow My Top **Mr S. Channing-Williams**
21 **ELY'S HARBOUR (IRE),** 7, gr g Roselier (FR)—Sweet Run **Mrs Jean R. Bishop**
22 **EMINENCE JAUNE (FR),** 6, b g Le Nain Jaune (FR)—Samara IV (FR) **D. & G. Mercer**
23 **FALMOUTH BAY (IRE),** 9, b g Miner's Lamp—Vita Veritas **Mr James Morton**
24 **FATHER SKY,** 7, b g Dancing Brave (USA)—Flamenco Wave (USA) **Mr Kenneth Kornfeld**
25 **FLAMENGO (FR),** 5, b g Bayolidaan (FR)—Raiatea (FR) **Mrs M. A. Bull**
26 **GREEN GREEN DESERT (FR),** 7, b g Green Desert (USA)—Green Leaf (USA) **Mr Darren C. Mercer**
27 **HIM OF PRAISE (IRE),** 8, b g Paean—Tamed **Mr M. G. St Quinton**
28 **ITS WORTH A BOB,** 6, b g Gildoran—Rolling Dice **Mrs A. M. Murray**
29 **KADOU NONANTAIS (FR),** 5, b g Cadoudal (FR)—Belle Nonantaise (FR) **Mr Darren C. Mercer**
30 **KEEP IT ZIPPED (IRE),** 8, gr g Roselier (FR)—Bodalmore Kit **Mrs Luisa Stewart-Brown**
31 **KING OF SPARTA,** 5, b g Kefaah (USA)—Khaizaraan (CAN) **Mr Darren C. Mercer**
32 **KINGSLAND TAVERNER,** 7, ch g True Song—Princess Hecate **Mr R. Northall**
33 **KINGSMARK (IRE),** 5, gr g Roselier (FR)—Gaye Le Moss **Mr Robert Ogden**
34 **KONVEKTA KING (IRE),** 10, br g Mandalus—Realma **Konvekta Ltd**
35 **KRISCLIFFE,** 5, ch h Kris—Lady Norcliffe (USA) **Mr P. A. Idris**
36 **LARGE ACTION (IRE),** 10, b g The Parson—Ballyadam Lass **Mr B. T. Stewart-Brown**
37 **LARKUS AURELIUS (IRE),** 5, br g Ardross—First Things First **The Chamberlain Addiscott Partnership**
38 **LITTLE CRUMPLIN,** 6, b g Pablond—Speckyfoureyes **Mr M. G. St Quinton**
39 **LORD OF THE RIVER (IRE),** 6, br g Lord Americo—Well Over **Mr B. T. Stewart-Brown**
40 **MERLINS DREAM (IRE),** 9, ch g Callernish—Mystical Moonshine **Mr W. S. Watt**
41 **MORGANS HILL (IRE),** 6, b g Strong Gale—Tengello **Mrs Jean R. Bishop**
42 **NOT FOR TURNING (IRE),** 7, b g Roselier (FR)—Coolcanute **Mr Charles F. Engel**
43 **OLD BRIDGE (IRE),** 10, ch g Crash Course—What A Duchess **Mr K. C. B. Mackenzie**
44 **PERSIAN BOY (IRE),** 6, b g Brush Aside (USA)—Bargara **Mr K. G. Manley**
45 **POLO RIDGE (IRE),** 6, gr g Phardante (FR)—Fane Bridge **Mr James Morton**
46 **READY MONEY CREEK (IRE),** 7, ch g Phardante (FR)—Chestnut Vale **Roach Foods Limited**
47 **ROBERTO RIVA,** 5, b g Shirley Heights—Rustle of Silk **Mr Robert Ogden**
48 **ROYAL ACTION,** 5, b g Royal Academy (USA)—Ivor's Honey **Mr B. Harris**
49 **ROYAL TOMMY (IRE),** 6, b g Royal Fountain—Cherry Token **Mr L. G. Kimber**
50 **SAINT JOE (IRE),** 5, b g Roselier (FR)—Dusky's Lady **St Josephs Partnership**
51 **SERGEYEV (IRE),** 6, ch h Mulhollande (USA)—Escape Path **Mr B. T. Stewart-Brown**
52 **SHIFT AGAIN (IRE),** 6, b m Siberian Express (USA)—Pushkinia (FR) **Mr R. J. Bassett**
53 **SIERRA BAY (IRE),** 8, b g Castle Keep—Beau's Trout **Mr R. Waters**
54 **SIOUX FALLS (IRE),** 5, b g Mandalus—Dandy Poll **Roach Foods Limited**
55 **SIR LEONARD (IRE),** 8, b g Strong Gale—Boro Penny **Mrs Jean R. Bishop**

MR O. M. C. SHERWOOD—continued

56 **SOUTHERLY WIND,** 4, b g Slip Anchor—Karavina **Lady Lloyd Webber**
57 **SPRING GALE (IRE),** 7, b g Strong Gale—Orospring **M. Crabb, B. Ead, P. May, M. Moore**
58 **STEFPHONIC (IRE),** 5, b m Orchestra—Markree Castle **Mr B. T. E. Shrubsall**
59 **STONE RIDGE (IRE),** 6, b g Indian Ridge—Cut In Stone (USA) **Mrs Chris Harrington**
60 **SUNUVUGUN,** 6, b g Gunner B—Final Melody **Roach Foods Limited**
61 **TAKEAMEMO (IRE),** 5, ch m Don't Forget Me—Persian Myth **Sherwood Partnership Owners Club**
62 **TAKE IT EASY (IRE),** 6, ch g Orchestra—Permanent Lady **Mr B. T. Stewart-Brown**
63 **TAPPERS KNAPP (IRE),** 6, b g Brush Aside (USA)—Gales Money **Mr Nigel Chamberlain**
64 **THE IN-LAWS (IRE),** 4, ch f Be My Guest (USA)—Amboselli **Mr C. Coxen**
65 **THE MINE CAPTAIN,** 11, b g Shaab—Bal Casek **Mr Gerald W. Evans**
66 **TUCKERS TOWN (IRE),** 6, br g Strong Gale—Moate Gypsy **Mrs Jean R. Bishop**
67 **WELCOME CALL (IRE),** 8, ch g Callernish—Well Over **Mr B. T. Stewart-Brown**

THREE-YEAR-OLDS

68 Br g Strong Gale—Just Dont Know **Mr D. M. C. Sherwood**

Other Owners: Mrs D. L. Addiscott, Miss Mary W. Arkle, Mr W. J. Bridge, Mr J. K. Carson, Mrs P. C. Chamberlain, Miss Liz Clark, Mr Peter Davis, Mr J. Dougall, Mr R. F. Eliot, Mr R. B. Holt, Mr I. A. Low, Mr John McMullen, Mrs C. J. Morcom, Mr R. G. Morcom, Mr Rodney Morcom, Mr Julian Palfreyman, Mr R. B. Pearson, Countess C. H. Plymouth, Mr M. J. Rivett-Carnac, The Hon Mrs S. Sherwood, Mr S. Sherwood, Mr V. J. Walsh.

Jockeys (NH): J McCarthy (10-0), J Osborne (10-0), M Richards (10-0).

Conditional: C Honour.

528 MISS L. C. SIDDALL, Tadcaster

Postal: **Stonebridge Farm, Colton, Tadcaster, North Yorkshire, LS24 8EP.**
Phone: **(01904) 744291 FAX (01904) 744291 MOBILE (0378) 216694/92**

1 **AHBEJAYBUS (IRE),** 9, b g Muscatite—Miami Dancer **Mrs S. E. Cooper**
2 **DAN DE MAN (IRE),** 7, br g Phardante (FR)—Slave De **David J. Poulter Partnership**
3 **DONA FILIPA,** 5, ch m Precocious—Quisissanno **Mr A. Emmerson**
4 **FEATHERSTONE LANE,** 7, b g Siberian Express (USA)—Try Gloria **Mr D. Parker**
5 **FRONTIER FLIGHT (USA),** 8, b g Flying Paster (USA)—Sly Charmer (USA) **Miss L. C. Siddall**
6 **INNOCENT GEORGE,** 9, b g Hallgate—Are You Guilty **Mr Edward C. Wilkin**
7 **LEAP IN THE DARK (IRE),** 9, br h Shadeed (USA)—Star Guide (FR) **Mrs D. J. Morris**
8 6, B g Buckskin (FR)—Left Hand Woman **Mr D. Wyatt**
9 **MEADOW BLUE,** 5, b m Northern State (USA)—Cornflower (USA) **Mr M. R. Marklow**
10 **MR CHRISTIE,** 6, b g Doulab (USA)—Hi There **David Mann Partnership**
11 **OAKBURY (IRE),** 6, ch g Common Grounds—Doon Belle **Miss L. C. Siddall**
12 **SAMANID (IRE),** 6, b g Shardari—Samarzana (USA) **Magnum Construction Ltd**
13 **SILENT VALLEY,** 4, b f Forzando—Tremmin **Mrs S. E. Cooper**
14 **SPARKLING HARRY,** 4, ch g Tina's Pet—Sparkling Hock **Lynn Siddall Racing**
15 **SUPERFRILLS,** 5, b m Superpower—Pod's Daughter (IRE) **Podso Racing**
16 **THE OTHER MAN (IRE),** 8, b g Remainder Man—Amelioras Gran **Stonebridge Racing**

TWO-YEAR-OLDS

17 Ch c 11/5 Formidable (USA)—Irish Limerick **Mrs S. E. Cooper**
18 Gr c Mtoto—Pepper Star (IRE) **David Mann Partnership**

Other Owners: Mr H. Banks, Mrs P. J. Clark, Mrs K. Dyer, Mrs Valerie Emmerson, Miss J. Goodyear, Mrs P. M. Hornby, Miss L. Ibbotson, Mrs Theresa O'Toole, Mr Arthur Pooley, Mr Anthony Sugare, Mr R. J. Wilkinson, Mrs A. Wyatt.

Jockey (NH): A Thornton (10-0, w.a.).

Apprentice: T Siddall (8-3).

Conditional: T Siddall (9-7).

529 MR RODNEY SIMPSON, Wendover

Postal: **Russell Farm, Cobblers Hill, Wendover, Buckinghamshire, HP22 6QD.**
Phone: **(01296) 696980 FAX (01296) 696978**

1 **BELZAO,** 5, b g Alzao (USA)—Belle Enfant **Mr G. Piper**
2 **CHAHAYA TIMOR (IRE),** 6, b g Slip Anchor—Roxy Hart **Mr Philip Haslam**
3 **CHARLIE SIDDLE,** 4, b g Thowra (FR)—Figrant (USA) **Mr C. B. Siddle**
4 **CHARLOTTE'S BOY,** 5, ch g Sunley Builds—Rush Lady **Major B. Gatensbury**
5 **CHIEFTAIN'S CROWN (USA),** 7, ch g Chief's Crown (USA)—Simple Taste (USA) **Miss J. Rumford**
6 **CHILLI BOOM,** 4, gr f Chilibang—Silent Sun **Wendover Dean Racing Club**
7 **DELAMAINS GOLD (IRE),** 7, b g Delamain (USA)—Some Fortune **Mr G. Piper**
8 **DRUNA (FR),** 4, ch f Garde Royale—Bentry (FR) **Mrs C. F. O'Hara**
9 **FLIRTING AROUND (USA),** 4, b c Silver Hawk (USA)—Dancing Grass (USA)
10 **FLYING EAGLE,** 7, b g Shaadi (USA)—Fly Me (FR) **Mr T. F. Maycock**
11 **KRYSTALLOS,** 6, b g Polish Precedent (USA)—Dancing Crystal **Mr G. Piper**
12 **LADY MARGARETTA,** 7, b m Rolfe (USA)—Needwood Fortune **Miss J. Rumford**
13 **MAJOR'S LAW (IRE),** 9, b g Law Society (USA)—Maryinsky (USA) **Miss J. Rumford**
14 **NIPPER REED,** 8, b g Celestial Storm (USA)—Figrant (USA) **Mr G. Piper**
15 **PHARSILK (IRE),** 9, ch g Phardante (FR)—Boule de Soie **Miss J. Rumford**
16 **RESERVATION ROCK (IRE),** 7, ch g Ballad Rock—Crazyfoot **Mr G. Piper**
17 **RISE ABOVE (IRE),** 4, b f Simply Great (FR)—La Tanque (USA) **Mr G. Piper**
18 **SILESIA (IRE),** 4, b c Sadler's Wells (USA)—Ghariba
19 **TASHKENT,** 6, b g Thowra (FR)—Royal Bat **Miss J. Rumford**
20 **TELLAPORKY,** 9, b g Bold Fort—Ab Dabh **Mr Rod Simpson**
21 **VENICE BEACH,** 6, b g Shirley Heights—Bold And Beautiful **Ms K. Churchill**
22 **YO-MATE,** 7, b g Komaite (USA)—Silent Sun **Miss L. A. Elliott**

THREE-YEAR-OLDS

23 **BOLLAN,** b g Democratic (USA)—Faustelerie **Mr G. Piper**
24 **DE LA HAYE,** b f Puissance—Hibiscus Ivy (AUS) **Wendover Dean Racing Club**
25 **EVENING CHORUS (USA),** b c Shadeed (USA)—Evening Air (USA) **Mr G. Piper**
26 **OPENING NIGHT,** b g Theatrical Charmer—First Time Over **Miss J. Rumford**
27 **ZEPTEPI (IRE),** b f Astronef—Tangle Thorn **Kings Cross Racing**

Other Owners: Mr Antony Charles Brown, Mr Nigel Guy, Mrs Wendy Hasilam, Mrs I. Y. Taylor.

530 MRS D. E. SLACK, Appleby

Postal: **Stoneriggs, Hilton, Appleby, Cumbria, CA16 6LS.**
Phone: **(017683) 51354**

1 **FORTUNE HOPPER,** 4, gr g Rock Hopper—Lots of Luck **Mr A. Slack**
2 **I'M THE MAN,** 7, ro g Say Primula—Vinovia **Mr A. Slack**
3 **JONAEM (IRE),** 8, b g Mazaad—Priors Mistress **Mrs Evelyn Slack**

531 MRS P. M. SLY, Peterborough

Postal: **Singlecote, Thorney, Peterborough, PE6 0PB.**
Phone: **(01733) 270212**

1 **BASSENHALLY,** 8, ch g Celtic Cone—Milly Kelly **Thorney Racing Club**
2 **BUKEHORN,** 7, b g Bold Owl—Milly Kelly **Mrs P. M. Sly**
3 **DANGER FLYNN (IRE),** 8, b g Boreen (FR)—Stramillian **Mr R. Brazier**
4 **DOUBLE MATT,** 6, b g Double Schwartz—Kasarose **Mrs P. M. Sly**
5 **ECHENTONE,** 7, gr g Aydimour—Miss Pilgrim **Mr J. R. Bainbridge**
6 **GRIFFINS BAR,** 10, b g Idiot's Delight—Milly Kelly **Mr M. S. Smith**

MRS P. M. SLY—continued

7 **HOT DOGGING,** 5, b m Petoski—Mehtab **Thorney Racing Club**
8 **LADY-H,** 5, ch m Never So Bold—Courtesy Call **Mrs P. M. Sly**
9 **LONGSHORE,** 5, ch g Lord Bud—Milly Kelly **Mr M. S. Smith**
10 **MISS PINK,** 4, gr f Arzanni—Ewe Lamb **Mr M. H. S. Sly**
11 **MOLSUM,** 5, ch g Lord Bud—Rosie Cone **Mrs P. M. Sly**
12 **NELTEGRITY,** 9, b g Neltino—Integrity **Mrs Irene Dobney**
13 **NORMANTON,** 4, gr g Petong—Mehtab **Mrs P. M. Sly**
14 **POU NOU (IRE),** 5, gr g Roselier (FR)—Flashy Treasure **Mr Robin Sturgess**
15 **SINGLESOLE,** 13, ch g Celtic Cone—Milly Kelly **Mrs P. M. Sly**

THREE-YEAR-OLDS

16 **ALLATON (IRE),** ch g Shalford (IRE)—Confirmed Friend **Mr T. Crowson, Mr A. J. Speechley**
17 **SENOR HURST,** b g Young Senor (USA)—Broadhurst **Mrs P. M. Sly**

TWO-YEAR-OLDS

18 B f 17/4 Presidium—Ewe Lamb **Mrs P. M. Sly**

Other Owners: Mr F. Allan, Mr J. L. Burt.

Jockey (Flat): A Culhane (w.a.).

Jockey (NH): W Marston (w.a.).

Lady Rider: Miss Louise Allen (9-7).

532 MR D. SMAGA, Lamorlaye

Postal: **17 Voie de la Grange des Pres, 60260 Lamorlaye, France.**
Phone: **03 44 21 50 05 FAX 03 44 21 53 56**

1 **ABU'L FAZL (FR),** 5, b h Legend of France (USA)—Mevlana (IRE) **Alain Maubert**
2 **BOB DEL MARE (FR),** 4, b c Sanglamore (USA)—Femme Femme (USA) **Ecurie Leader**
3 **DART BOARD (IRE),** 4, b f Darshaan—Trojan Miss **Lord A. Weinstock**
4 **GLIVANA (FR),** 4, b f Highest Honor (FR)—Glifahda (FR) **Baron T. Van Zuylen**
5 **LEGAT DE FRANCE (FR),** 4, b g Always Fair (USA)—Luna Maya (FR) **Ecurie du Club Galop**
6 **MAMI WATTA (USA),** 4, b f Mining (USA)—Ten Downing Street (USA) **M. Lagasse**
7 **MARILDO,** 11, b h Romildo—Marike **David Smaga**
8 **MARRAST (FR),** 5, b h Groom Dancer (USA)—Mary Linoa (USA) **Christian Serre**
9 **MODERN TIMES (FR),** 5, b h Lead On Time (USA)—Glifahda (FR) **Baron T. Van Zuylen**
10 **NEXT WINNER (FR),** 8, b h Irish River (FR)—Pleasant Way (USA) **David Smaga**
11 **PRESBOURG (FR),** 4, b c Sanglamore (USA)—Plytroca (USA) **Alain Lequeux**
12 **ROYAL CASTLE (IRE),** 4, b c Caerleon (USA)—Sun Princess **Lord A. Weinstock**
13 **STAR OF FEMME (FR),** 6, b h Saint Cyrien—Femme Femme **David Smaga**
14 **STRAWBERRY FIELDS (FR),** 4, b c Saint Cyrien (FR)—Willchris (USA) **Mme O. A. Scemama**
15 **TROJAN SEA (USA),** 7, b h Bering—Trojan Miss **Lord A. Weinstock**
16 **VARXI (FR),** 4, b c Kaldoun (FR)—Girl of France **Baron T. Van Zuylen**

THREE-YEAR-OLDS

17 **ACTION MAN (FR),** b c Perrault—Estada (FR) **Baron T. Van Zuylen**
18 **COLOR SCHEME (FR),** b f Antheus (USA)—Perfect Rainbow **Baron T. van Zuylen**
19 **COOLRAOUL (FR),** b f Suave Dancer (USA)—Canaletto (FR) **Ecurie M3 Elevage**
20 **DAME EDITH (FR),** b f Top Ville—Girl of France **Baron T. Van Zuylen**
21 **FAIRDANE (FR),** b f Always Fair (USA)—Avellaneda (FR) **Ecurie Seutet**
22 **FIBONACCI (IRE),** b c Alzao (USA)—Kate Marie (USA) **Anthony Holmes**
23 **FREDERICTION (USA),** b c Red Ransom (USA)—Laughing Empress (USA) **Ecurie Chalhoub**

MR D. SMAGA—continued

24 **HAMMERKLAVIER (IRE)**, b c Soviet Star (USA)—Victory Chorus **Lord A. Weinstock**
25 **LANDING LIGHT (IRE)**, b c In The Wings—Gay Hellene **Lord A. Weinstock**
26 **LIBRIO**, b c Priolo (USA)—Light The Sky (FR) **Mme O. A. Scemama**
27 **MAGIC SILLERY (FR)**, b f Sillery (USA)—Willchris (USA) **David Smaga**
28 **MAINMISE (USA)**, b f Septieme Ciel (USA)—Maxencia (FR) **Anthony Holmes**
29 **MARIE AU NIEL'S (USA)**, b f Housebuster (USA)—Calltheminstrel (CAN) **M. Lagasse**
30 **MISS BERBERE (FR)**, b f Bering—Miss Afrique (FR) **Ecurie Seutet**
31 **MISTER MAGIC (FR)**, b c Saumarez—Glifahda (FR) **Baron T. Van Zuylen**
32 **NAMIX (FR)**, gr c Linamix (FR)—Nashra (FR) **Alain Lequeux**
33 **REINE AMANDINE (FR)**, ch f Marignan (USA)—Azyadee (FR) **Alain Maubert**
34 **RUDBECKIA (FR)**, b f High Estate—Painted Flower (IRE) **Jacques Liscia**
35 **SARALEA (FR)**, b f Sillery (USA)—Solidarite (USA) **Mme de Chambure**
36 **SEA QUEST (IRE)**, b f Rainbow Quest (USA)—Grecian Sea (FR) **Lord A. Weinstock**
37 **SQUAW (IRE)**, b f Commanche Run—Karelia (USA) **Lord A. Weinstock**
38 **TIGER LAND (USA)**, b f Machiavellian (USA)—Rainbow Wood **Alaina Lequeux**
39 **TRAIN BLEU (FR)**, b c Pistolet Bleu (IRE)—Kenaria (FR) **Baron T. Van Zuylen**
40 **ZSOFIA (FR)**, ch f Tropular—New Saya (FR) **Alain Lequeux**

TWO-YEAR-OLDS

41 **COLOUR SCHEME (FR)**, b f Perrault—Perfect Rainbow **Baron T. Van Zuylen**
42 **DANGER MONEY (IRE)**, b c Danehill (USA)—Troyanna **Lord A. Weinstock**
43 **DINNER TIME (FR)**, ch f Bering—Dinner Out (USA) **Mme El Sharif**
44 **FAIRY STAR (FR)**, b f Fairy King (USA)—Energie Solaire (USA) **Madame Ades-Hazan**
45 **FRANCE'S HONOR (FR)**, gr c Highest Honor (FR)—Girl of France **Baron T. Van Zuylen**
46 **KANSA (FR)**, gr f Linamix (FR)—Kartabula (FR) **Haras d'Etreham**
47 Gr c Kaldoun (FR)—Manureva (USA) **Mme de Chambure**
48 **MARY LINDA**, b f Grand Lodge (USA)—Mary's Dance (IRE) **David Smaga**
49 **MISS BEDOUINE (FR)**, b f Bering—Miss Afrique (FR) **Ecurie Seutet**
50 **OLD MARSH (IRE)**, b c Grand Lodge (USA)—Lolly Dolly **Mme F. Darty**
51 **PERIANDRE (FR)**, b c Perrault—Emerald City **Baron T. Van Zuylen**
52 **RAIN DROP (FR)**, b f Pistolet Bleu (IRE)—Titian Queen **Baron T. Van Zuylen**
53 **RED ALERT (IRE)**, b c Warning—Well Head (IRE) **Lord A. Weinstock**
54 **SAO (IRE)**, b f Dolphin Street (FR)—Scarlet Slipper **Mme de Chambure**
55 **SIDE SADDLE (IRE)**, b f Saddlers' Hall (IRE)—Athene (IRE) **Lord A. Weinstock**
56 **STARKEN (FR)**, gr c Kendor (FR)—Sparkling Plenty (FR) **Mme O. A. Scemama**

Jockey (Flat): D Boeuf.

Apprentice: R Thomas.

533 MR B. SMART, Lambourn

Postal: **Sherwood Stables, Folly Road, Hungerford, Berkshire, RG17 8QE.**
Phone: **LAMBOURN (01488) 71632 FAX (01488) 73859 MOBILE (0374) 946070**

1 **BASMAN (IRE)**, 4, b c Persian Heights—Gepares (IRE) **Mr L. Alvarez Cervera**
2 **DAHIYAH (USA)**, 7, b g Ogygian (USA)—Sticky Prospect (USA) **Mr W. Clifford**
3 **DICK TURPIN (USA)**, 4, br g Red Ransom (USA)—Turn To Money (USA) **The Dyball Partnership**
4 **MASTER MULLIGAN**, 5, b g Then Again—Sagora **Mrs L. M. Dresher**
5 **POLGWYNNE**, 4, ch f Forzando—Trelissick **Mr W. Clifford**
6 **QUESTAN**, 6, b g Rainbow Quest (USA)—Vallee Dansante (USA) **Mr B. Smart**
7 **RESEMBLANCE**, 4, b f State Diplomacy (USA)—Pretty Pollyanna **Mrs V. R. Smart**
8 **RIVER JUNCTION (IRE)**, 7, b g Cyrano de Bergerac—Lovestream **The Dyball Partnership**
9 **SIBERIAN HENRY**, 5, b g Siberian Express (USA)—Semperflorens **Mr C. S. Tateson**
10 **SUPER SAFFRON**, 8, b m Pollerton—Sagora **Mr R. B. Warren**
11 **THALJANAH (IRE)**, 6, ch g In The Wings—Dawn Is Breaking **Mr W. Clifford**
12 **THE NED**, 7, b g Kinglet—Galetzky **Mr Mike Perkins**

MR B. SMART—continued

THREE-YEAR-OLDS

13 **BASENJI,** b g Wolfhound (USA)—Guyum **Fleet Of Foot Partnership**
14 **BRYAN'S JOY,** b f Saddlers' Hall (IRE)—Artist's Glory **Mr R. B. Warren**
15 **GOLD HAWK,** ch c Weldnaas (USA)—Bel Esprit **Mrs C. A. Dickson**
16 **HIGH JINKS,** b c High Estate—Waffling **Sharp Racing**
17 **JACKIES WEBB,** b f Selkirk (USA)—Hawayah (IRE) **Mr Norman E. Webb**
18 **KING SLAYER,** b c Batshoof—Top Sovereign **Mr A. Khaleq**
19 **LADY EIL,** ch f Elmaamul (USA)—Oakbrook Tern (USA) **Mr J. A. Griffin**
20 **NAKED OAT,** b g Imp Society (USA)—Bajina **The Superioat Partnership**
21 **SEVEN,** ch g Weldnaas (USA)—Polly's Teahouse **The Smart Set**
22 **SUELLAJOY,** ch f Weldnaas (USA)—Jeethgaya (USA) **Mr K. H. Burks**
23 **ZELAH (IRE),** b f Alzao (USA)—Marie Noelle (FR) **Mr John M. Hawker**

TWO-YEAR-OLDS

24 **BLIZZARD,** gr f 7/2 Petong—Tempesta Rossa (IRE) (Persian Heights) **The Dyball Partnership**
25 **BLUE PERU (IRE),** b f 8/3 Perugino (USA)—Blue Czarina (Sandhurst Prince) **The Dyball Partnership**
26 B c 8/3 Lugana Beach—Gay Ming (Gay Meadow) **Mr W. Clifford**
27 **PATRIOT,** b c 17/1 Whittingham (IRE)—Gibaltarik (IRE) (Jareer (USA)) **Mr W. Clifford**
28 **PECULIARITY,** b c 17/3 Perpendicular—Pretty Pollyanna (General Assembly) **The Family Partnership**
29 Ch f 18/2 Weldnaas (USA)—Scottish Lady (Dunbeath (USA)) **Partnership**
30 B c 15/4 Batshoof—Top Sovereign (High Top) **Mr A. Khaleq**

Other Owners: Mrs P. A. Clark, Mr E. Crisp, Mr Paul Curtis, Mrs Bernice M. Cuthbert, Mr D. J. S. Dyball, Mrs G. S. Forbes, Mr Michael Jeffery, Miss N. Jefford, Mr D. Jones, Mr J. Nelson, Mr Steve Nelson, Mr N. Newman, Mrs E. Sharp, Mr I. G. Sharp, Mr A. Tuohey.

Jockey (Flat): J Stack.

Jockey (NH): C Llewellyn (w.a.).

Lady Rider: Miss V Marshall (8-5).

534 MR A. D. SMITH, Westward Ho

Postal: **Duckhaven Stud, Cornborough Road, Westward Ho, Bideford, Devon, EX39 1AA.**
Phone: **(01237) 478648 FAX (01237) 476239**

1 **FLYING ANGEL,** 4, b f Almoojid—Silvie **Duckhaven Stud**
2 **IN CAHOOTS,** 5, gr g Kalaglow—Royal Celebrity (USA) **Duckhaven Stud**
3 **NIGEL'S CHOICE,** 6, gr g Teenoso (USA)—Warm Winter **Duckhaven Stud**
4 **PEYTON JONES,** 5, b g Presidium—York Street (USA) **Duckhaven Stud**
5 **REMEMBER STAR,** 5, ch m Don't Forget Me—Star Girl Gay **Duckhaven Stud**
6 **SEAMUS,** 4, ch g Almoojid—Royal Celebrity (USA) **Duckhaven Stud**
7 **SURCOAT,** 11, b g Bustino—Mullet **Duckhaven Stud**

Other Owners: Mr A. D. Smith, Mrs J. M. Smith.

535 MR ALFRED SMITH, Beverley

Postal: **Heath Racing Stables, Newbald Road, Beverley, North Humberside, HU17 8EF.**
Phone: **(01482) 882520**

1 **BRIGHT GOLD,** 4, ch g Clantime—Miss Brightside **Mr A. H. Grant**
2 **CAPTAIN FLINT,** 4, b br g Bedford (USA)—Sun Yat Chen **Mrs G. Wood**
3 **LITTLE CONKER,** 10, ch g All Systems Go—L'Irondelle **Mr Alfred Smith**
4 **MR EGLANTINE,** 6, ch g Mr Fluorocarbon—Sweet Rosa **Westwood Racing**
5 **PRIMITIVE LIGHT,** 8, ch m Primitive Rising (USA)—Ring of Flowers **Mr Alfred Smith**
6 **RISKY FLIGHT,** 4, ch g Risk Me (FR)—Stairway To Heaven (IRE) **Mrs Sheila Oakes**
7 **TIP IT IN,** 9, gr g Le Solaret (FR)—Alidante **Mrs M. Dunning**

THREE-YEAR-OLDS

8 **ITSNOTYETNAMED,** b c Kasakov—Wych Willow **Just For Fun Partnership**

Other Owners: Mr James Bowden, Mr P. Dixon, Mr Malcom Douglas, Mr K. A. Johnson, Mr Paul Laverack, Mr John Allan Milburn, Mr R. A. Nicklin, Mr P. W. Punter, Mr J. Strudwick, Mr David Tate.

536 MR C. SMITH, Wellingore

Postal: **Thompsons Bottom Farm, Temple Bruer, Wellingore, Lincoln, LN5 0DE.**
Phone: **(01526) 833245 TELEPHONE AND FAX (0378) 149188 MOBILE**

1 **BLASTER WATSON,** 7, ch g Kind of Hush—Economy Pep **Mr M. W. Flint**
2 **CAN SHE CAN CAN,** 6, b m Sulaafah (USA)—Dominance **The Hunting Ten Partnership**
3 **CAPTAIN TANDY (IRE),** 9, ch g Boyne Valley—Its All A Dream **Mr D. E. Sims**
4 **CHEEKA,** 9, ch g Dawn Johnny (USA)—Lallax **Mr David J. Thompson**
5 **COPPER CABLE,** 11, ch g True Song—Princess Mey **Mr T. I. Gourley**
6 **KALA SUNRISE,** 5, ch h Kalaglow—Belle of The Dawn **Mr A. E. Needham**
7 **MACS HERO,** 8, b g Scallywag—Celtickerry
8 **PLEASURE TIME,** 5, ch g Clantime—First Experience **Mr A. E. Needham**
9 **ROTHERFIELD PARK (IRE),** 6, b m High Estate—Alriyaah **Mr David J. Thompson**
10 **ROYAL RIGGER,** 5, gr m Reprimand—Overdraft
11 4, B f Teenoso—Sayshar (USA)
12 4, B f Flockton's Own—Trent Lane **Mr J. Payne**

THREE-YEAR-OLDS

13 **MARGARET'S DANCER,** b g Rambo Dancer (CAN)—Cateryne **Mr Gordon Batty**
14 **TOM DOUGAL,** b c Ron's Victory (USA)—Fabulous Rina (FR) **Mrs N. Stewart**

TWO-YEAR-OLDS

15 B f 4/3 Distinctly North—Dear Heart (Blakeney)
16 B c 16/4 Rock City—Free Skip (Free State)
17 Ch c 2/3 Clantime—Lady Pennington (Blue Cashmere)
18 Ch f 30/3 Superlative—Miss Display (Touch Paper)
19 **PALVIC LADY,** b f 3/3 Cotation—Palvic Grey (Kampala)
20 **RAINBOW RAVER (IRE),** ch f 13/4 Rainbows for Life—Foolish Passion (USA) (Secretariat (USA))
21 **SERGEANT YORK,** b c 7/4 Be My Chief (USA)—Metaphysique (FR) (Law Society (USA))

Other Owners: Mrs Christina M. Griffin, Mr P. Lamyman, Mr H. G. Norman, Mrs Alexander Scott, Dowager Lady Scott, Miss S. A. Sempers, Mr B. Sharpe, Mr P. J. Sharpe, Mrs Rita Smith, Mr Terry Thorp, Mr C. Tompkins.

Jockey (NH): M Ranger (10-0).

537 MR DENYS SMITH, Bishop Auckland

Postal: **Holdsforth Farm, South Church Road, Bishop Auckland, Co. Durham, DL14 6DJ.**
Phone: **(01388) 603317 OR 606180 FAX**

1 **BOLD BRIEF,** 4, b g Tina's Pet—Immodest Miss **P. & I. Darling**
2 **CADEAUX PREMIERE,** 7, b g Cadeaux Genereux—Clare Island **Lumsden & Carroll Construction Ltd**
3 **DENSBEN,** 14, b g Silly Prices—Eliza de Rich **Mrs Janet M. Pike**
4 **DOMINDROSS,** 6, ch g Ardross—Plum Tree **Mr Denys Smith**
5 **DURAID (IRE),** 6, ch g Irish River (FR)—Fateful Princess (USA) **Mr A. Suddes**
6 **GEORGE DILLINGHAM,** 8, b g Top Ville—Premier Rose **Mr Jim Blair**
7 **KARISMA (IRE),** 5, b g Tirol—Avra (FR) **Mr D. Vic Roper**
8 **OAKLEY,** 9, ch g Nicholas Bill—Scrub Oak **Duke of Sutherland**
9 **RECCA (IRE),** 6, b g Detroit Sam (FR)—French Note **Mr Denys Smith**
10 **SPANISH VERDICT,** 11, b g King of Spain—Counsel's Verdict **Cox & Allen (Kendal) Ltd**
11 **STYLISH INTERVAL,** 6, ch g Interrex (CAN)—Super Style **Mr Ian Darling**
12 **THE LAMBTON WORM,** 4, b g Superpower—Springwell **Lord Durham**
13 **TWO ON THE BRIDGE,** 4, b g Chilibang—Constant Companion **Mr Denys Smith**
14 **VAL DE RAMA (IRE),** 9, b g Lafontaine (USA)—Port Magee **Mr D. Morland**

THREE-YEAR-OLDS

15 Ch g Most Welcome—Hawaiian Bloom (USA) **Mr Denys Smith**
16 **MISS SALSA DANCER,** ch f Salse (USA)—Thakhayr **Mr Jim Blair**
17 **PLEASANT DREAMS,** ch f Sabrehill (USA)—Tafila **Mr Jim Blair**
18 **PRIDE OF BRYN,** br f Efisio—Alpine Sunset **Mr Jim Blair**

TWO-YEAR-OLDS

19 **DAY-BOY,** b g 21/2 Prince Sabo—Lady Day (FR) (Lightning (FR)) **Duke Of Sutherland**
20 **DIPPLE,** b f 31/3 Komaite (USA)—Rynavey (Rousillon (USA)) **Duke Of Sutherland**

Other Owners: Mr J. A. Bianchi, Carlton Appointments (Aberdeen) Ltd, Lord Lambton, Mr R. O. Manners, Mr J. R. Wharton.

Jockey (Flat): K Fallon (w.a.).

Jockey (NH): P Niven (w.a.).

Lady Rider: Miss Melanie Carson (8-5).

538 MR J. P. SMITH, Rugeley

Postal: **Coldwell Cottage, Coldwell, Gentleshaw, Rugeley, Staffordshire, WS15 4NJ.**
Phone: **(01543) 686587 MOBILE: (0802) 758977**

1 **ARR EFF BEE,** 11, b g Crooner—Miss Desla **Mr P. R. Wheeler**
2 **BEE DEE BEST (IRE),** 7, b g Try My Best (USA)—Eloquent Charm (USA) **Mr J. P. Smith**
3 **CERBERA,** 9, b g Caruso—Sealed Contract **Mr P. R. Wheeler**
4 **DARING RYDE,** 7, b g Daring March—Mini Myra **Mrs H. J. Bannister**
5 **DESLA'S DEVIL,** 6, b g Devil To Play—Miss Desla **Mr Brian Marsh**
6 **MY SWAN SONG,** 13, b g Soul Singer—Palmaria **Mr Brian McGowan**
7 **WHAT THE DEVIL,** 5, ch m Devil To Play—Whats Yours Called **Mrs Frances Draper**

Other Owners: Mr M. A. Beckett, Mr Dennis Newton.

539 MR JULIAN S. SMITH, Tirley

Postal: **Tirley Court, Tirley, Gloucester, GL19 4HA.**
Phone: **(01452) 780208 FAX (01452) 780 461**

1 **GRAND APPLAUSE (IRE)**, 8, gr g Mazaad—Standing Ovation **Mr Geo Taylor**
2 **HANDY LASS**, 9, b m Nicholas Bill—Mandrian **Mr G. W. Hackling**
3 **LITTLE JOE (IRE)**, 9, br g Cataldi—Linanbless **Mr F. G. Smith**
4 **MURRAY'S MILLION**, 6, b g Macmillion—Random Select **Cotswold Connection**
5 **SENSE OF VALUE**, 9, br m Trojan Fen—War Ballad (FR) **Mr Donald Smith**
6 **TIRLEY GALE**, 6, b g Strong Gale—Mascara VII **Mr Donald Smith**
7 **TIRLEY MISSILE**, 12, ch g Cruise Missile—Tic-On-Rose **Mr J. D. Hankinson**

Other Owners: Mr John Eaton, Mr D. J. Eckley, Mr Alec Wynes.

Amateur: Mr O McPhail.

540 MR N. A. SMITH, Upton Snodsbury

Postal: **Court Farm Stables, Court Farm, Upton Snodsbury, Worcester, WR7 4NN.**
Phone: **OFFICE (01905) 381077 FAX (01905) 381077 MOBILE (0589) 808202**

1 4, B f Ron's Victory (USA)—Camp Chair **Mr Edwin Smith**
2 **FORTYTWO DEE (IRE),** 8, b m Amazing Bust—Maggie's Way **Triumph International Limited**
3 **LADY PENDRAGON,** 9, b m Oats—Impressive Reward (USA) **Mr J. I. D. Paine**
4 **NOVA SCOTIA,** 7, b m Ra Nova—Arctic Gipsy **Mr D. Newberry**
5 **PETRACO (IRE),** 10, b g Petorius—Merrie Moira **Mrs Penny Day**
6 **SILENT ACTION (USA),** 6, b br g Greinton—Heather Bee (USA) **Mrs G. C. List**
7 **TARAKHEL (USA),** 5, ch g Seattle Dancer (USA)—Tarafa **Mr N. A. Smith**
8 4, B f Roi Danzig (USA)—Viceroy Express **Mr N. A. Smith**

THREE-YEAR-OLDS

9 **SUN DANCER,** b g Sizzling Melody—Petite Melusine (IRE) **High Wood Racing**

Other Owners: Mrs S. Snelling, Mr Shane Snelling.

Jockey (Flat): S D Williams.

Jockey (NH): M Sharratt (10-0).

541 MR RALPH JOHN SMITH, Northleach

Postal: **Penhill Farm, Salperton, Northleach, Gloucestershire, GL54 4ED.**
Phone: **(01242) 820869**

1 **BUZZARDS BELLBUOY,** 9, b g Buzzards Bay—Bella Travaille **Mr N. H. Gardner**
2 **CASUAL COTTAGE (IRE),** 4, b f Thatching—Non Casual **Mr A. A. Wright**
3 **KINGSDOWN TRIX (IRE),** 4, b g Contract Law (USA)—Three of Trumps **The Penhill Partnership**
4 5, B m Then Again—Massawa (FR) **Mr R. J. Smith**
5 **STRAY HARMONY,** 8, ch m Noalto—Kitty Come Home **Winwood Connell Partnership**
6 **TALENT SPOTTER,** 11, b g Strong Gale—Twelve Steps **Mrs L. J. Griffiths**
7 **THE BARRINGTON FOX,** 5, b g Arctic Lord—Brown Coast **The Fox Inn Partnership**
8 **VERDE LUNA,** 6, b g Green Desert (USA)—Mamaluna (USA) **Ms Isabella Ziemba**

Other Owners: Mr J. L. Aizpuru, Mrs M. J. Arnold, Mrs S. Connell, Mrs J. Mould, Mr Paul Porter, Mr M. P. Wareing, Mrs S. L. Winwood.

Jockey (NH): C Maude.

Conditional: X Aizpuru, G Hogan.

Amateur: Mr S Joynes.

542 MRS S. J. SMITH, Bingley

Postal: **Craiglands Farm, High Eldwick, Bingley, West Yorkshire, BD16 3BE.**
Phone: **BRADFORD (01274) 564930**

1 **ABSOLUTE FOLLY,** 6, gr g Absalom—Agreloui **Mrs S. Smith**
2 **AHRAYDOUBLEYOU,** 5, b br g Teenoso (USA)—Minigale **R. Mellish, Mrs A. Skene & W. S. Skene**

MRS S. J. SMITH—continued

3 **ALIAS CHUBB,** 7, gr g Alias Smith (USA)—Chubby Ears **Mrs S. Smith**
4 **ARDENT SCOUT,** 6, b g Ardross—Vidette **R. Mellish, Mrs A. Skene & W. S. Skene**
5 **AUSSIE BOB,** 6, b g Nearly A Hand—No Politics **Mrs S. Smith**
6 **BASILICUS (FR),** 9, b g Pamponi (FR)—Katy Collonge (FR) **Mrs S. Smith**
7 **BIT OF A DREAM (IRE),** 8, b g Henbit (USA)—Time And Patience **Mrs S. Smith**
8 **BRAMBLEBERRY,** 9, gr g Sharrood (USA)—Labista **Hampers Racing**
9 **CAP IN HAND,** 6, ch g Nearly A Hand—Beringa Bee **The Cartmel Syndicate**
10 **COLMARANN,** 6, ch m Good Thyne (USA)—Brandy Run **Mr K. Fisher**
11 **COVERDALE LANE,** 11, ch m Boreen (FR)—Princess Concorde **Mr Jim Pilkington**
12 **CURRENT SPEECH (IRE),** 7, b g Thatching—Lady Aladdin **Mrs S. Smith**
13 **CUTHILL HOPE (IRE),** 7, gr g Peacock (FR)—Sicilian Princess **Mrs Emma Gilchrist**
14 **DANA POINT (IRE),** 6, br g Phardante (FR)—Wallpark Princess **Mrs S. Smith**
15 **DANDY DES PLAUTS (FR),** 7, b g Cap Martin (FR)—Pagode (FR) **Mr J. L. Walbank**
16 **DESERT BRAVE (IRE),** 8, b g Commanche Run—Desert Pet **T and B Benson**
17 **DIDDY RYMER,** 8, b m Rymer—Doddycross **Brampton Royal Oak**
18 **EIRESPRAY (IRE),** 7, ch g Executive Perk—Shannon Spray **Mr Trevor Hemmings**
19 **FENWICK'S BROTHER,** 8, ch g Domitor (USA)—Topsey Lorac **Mr David Campbell**
20 **FIVE FLAGS (IRE),** 10, ch g Le Moss—Lovenos **Mr Keith Middleton**
21 **FORT ZEDDAAN (IRE),** 8, b g Trojan Fort—Jasminia **Mrs S. Smith**
22 **GAELIC BLUE,** 8, ch g Celtic Cone—Giollaretta **Mr Trevor Hemmings**
23 **GEMS LAD,** 11, ch g Broadsword—Dolben Gem **Miss J. Wood**
24 **GO NATIVE (IRE),** 6, br g Be My Native (USA)—Terrama Sioux **Mr Trevor Hemmings**
25 **HARD TRY,** 6, gr g Sharrood (USA)—Trynova **Mrs S. Smith**
26 **KARENASTINO,** 7, b g Neltino—Karena Park **Miss J. Wood**
27 **KENMORE-SPEED,** 11, gr g Scallywag—Quick Exit **Mr K. M. Dacker**
28 **KEY GRIP (IRE),** 7, br g Black Minstrel—Estrella **Hyndburn Bridge Racing**
29 **KING OF THE BURREN (IRE),** 8, b g King's Ride—Strandhill **Mrs S. Smith**
30 **LUCKY GANESHA,** 5, b m Komaite (USA)—Lucky Monashka **Mrs S. Smith**
31 **MOONSHINE DANCER,** 8, b g Northern State (USA)—Double Birthday **Aarons Archer Partnership**
32 **MO'S BOY,** 7, b g Sulaafah (USA)—Ridans Girl **Mr D. Clayton**
33 **MY BOY JOSH,** 6, ch g Risk Me (FR)—Merry Kate **Mrs S. Smith**
34 **NEWTON MIST,** 7, ch g Scorpio (FR)—Westamist **Mrs S. Smith**
35 **ONE MORE FLING (IRE),** 5, b g Satco (FR)—Highway's Last **Michael Jackson Bloodstock Ltd**
36 **PERUVIAN GALE,** 9, b g Strong Gale—Peruvian Lady **Mr J. L. Walbank**
37 **PIN MONY,** 6, b g Henbit (USA)—Shuil Run **Mr Trevor Hemmings**
38 **POWDER PRIM,** 7, b m Primitive Rising (USA)—Powder Horn **Mrs Enid Brindle**
39 **REGAL ROMPER (IRE),** 10, b g Tender King—Fruit of Passion **Mrs S. Smith**
40 **ROCKY MY BOY,** 4, ch g Rock City—Flying Flynn **Mr J. Henderson**
41 **SOTATTIE,** 5, b m Teenoso (USA)—Celtic Cygnet **Mr Trevor Hemmings**
42 **SUL FOSSO,** 6, b g Skyliner—Sveltissima **Mrs S. Smith**
43 **SWEEP GENTLY,** 6, b g Brush Aside (USA)—Gentle Madam **Mr Trevor Hemmings**
44 **THE LAST FLING (IRE),** 8, ch g Avocat—Highway's Last **Michael Jackson Bloodstock Ltd**

Other Owners: Mr David Aarons, Miss Angela Brindle, Mr Keith Hammill, Mr M. F. Jackson, Mr J. Kemp, Mr Brian McNichol, Mrs B. Perrin, Mr S. Powell, Mr R. Preston, Mrs J. B. Pye, Mr D. A. Stephenson, Mr J. Townson, Mrs C. E. Van Praagh, Mr N. Wilby, Mr Richard Younger.

Jockey (NH): Richard Guest (10-0).

Conditional: D Elsworth, G F Ryan, R Wilkinson (9-7).

Amateur: Mr Jos Saville.

543 MR J. G. SMYTH-OSBOURNE, Towcester

Postal: **Highfields Stables, Adstone, Towcester, Northamptonshire, NN12 8DS.**
Phone: **(01327) 860840 FAX (01327) 860810 MOBILE (0410) 946701**

1 **ALAMODE,** 4, b f Statoblest—Alo Ez **Mrs V. Dawes & Partners**
2 **ARCTIC FANCY (USA),** 5, ch g Arctic Tern (USA)—Fit And Fancy (USA) **The Cool Customers**
3 **JO MAXIMUS,** 6, b g Prince Sabo—Final Call **Mr J. G. Smyth-Osbourne**
4 **KINGS ASSEMBLY,** 6, b h Presidium—To The Point **The Ever Hopefuls**
5 **MOON FAIRY,** 4, ch f Interrex (CAN)—Zamoon **Firm Of M. D. G. Black**
6 **TRIPLE TERM,** 4, b g Terimon—Triple Reef **Sir Michael Connell**

THREE-YEAR-OLDS

7 **ABUNDANCE,** b f Cadeaux Genereux—Flourishing (IRE) **Mr P. Player**
8 **ALZAHRA,** ch f Interrex (CAN)—Flirty Lady **Mrs J. Harmsworth & Mrs A. Dorler**
9 **CITADEL,** b f Emarati (USA)—Round Tower **Lady Rothschild**
10 **CULTURED KING (IRE),** b g Imp Society (USA)—Regina St Cyr (IRE) **The Highfields Partnership**
11 **ELLA PEE-ELLE,** b f Elmaamul (USA)—Alipampa (IRE) **Mr T. Rossiter**
12 **FOUND AT SEA,** ch f Handsome Sailor—Close Call **Mrs K. Campbell Fraser**
13 **GRECIAN PRINCE,** ch c Risk Me (FR)—Troyes **Spice Partnership**
14 **HALSE COPSE,** b f Robellino (USA)—Rengaine (FR) **Grafton Farmers**
15 **INCHAHOY,** ch f Inchinor—Ackcontent (USA) **Mr A. Doran**
16 **MOON MISSION,** b f Interrex (CAN)—Zamoon **Firm of M. D. G. Black**
17 **SULTANA,** b f Unfuwain (USA)—Lambay **Lady Rothschild**
18 **SWEET REWARD,** ch c Beveled (USA)—Sweet Revival **Mr C. Tateson**
19 **THELONIUS (IRE),** ch c Statoblest—Little Sega (FR) **Mrs E. T. Smyth-Osbourne & Partners**

TWO-YEAR-OLDS

20 B f 25/4 Pips Pride—Mint Addition (Tate Gallery (USA)) **GNI Partnership**
21 B f 9/3 Safawan—Stoneydale (Tickled Pink)
22 B f 15/2 Bluebird (USA)—Swift Pursuit (Posse (USA))

Other Owners: Mr B. A. Bell, Mr M. D. G. Black, Mr M. J. G. Black, Mrs S. L. Carne, Mr J. H. S. Denham, Mrs S. A. Dore, Mrs L. Ekon, Mr Charles Farr, Mrs G. Imerman, Mr W. R. Johnson, Brig M. R. Koe, Mrs A. Lawrence-Dorler, Mr A. H. McDonald, Mr T. J. Ovens, Mr Tony Skinner, Mr P. J. Softley, Mr P. A. Upperton, Mr J. A. Whiting.

544 MR L. A. SNOOK, Sturminster Newton

Postal: **Lower Ridge Farm, Kings Stag, Sturminster Newton, Dorset, DT10 2AU.**
Phone: **TEL: (01258) 817364 FAX (01258) 817771**

1 **COLONEL PETER,** 5, b g Right Regent—Raja Moulana **Mr Laurie Snook**
2 **MIGAVON,** 8, b m Sharrood (USA)—Migoletty **Mr Laurie Snook**
3 **QUINTA ROYALE,** 11, b g Sayyaf—Royal Holly **Mr Laurie Snook**
4 **RAJADORA,** 6, b m Golden Heights—Raja Moulana **Mr Laurie Snook**
5 **RAMSBURY RIDGE,** 6, br m Golden Heights—Idyllic Glen **Mr Laurie Snook**
6 **TOM DIAMOND,** 6, ch g Right Regent—Shavegreen Holly VII **Mr Laurie Snook**

545 MR V. ST JOHN SOANE, Hungerford

Postal: **Mabberlys, Front Street, East Garston, Hungerford, Berkshire, RG17 7EU.**
Phone: **(01488) 648180 FAX (01488) 648181**

1 **BARANOV (IRE),** 5, b g Mulhollande (USA)—Silojoka **Mrs T. Cross**
2 **DELTA SOLEIL (USA),** 6, br h Riverman (USA)—Sunny Roberta (USA) **American Connection**
3 **ITSINTHEPOST,** 5, b m Risk Me (FR)—Where's The Money **First Class**
4 **KALASADI (USA),** 7, b g Shahrastani (USA)—Kassiyda **Mr G. A. Libson**
5 **KING OF SWING (IRE),** 6, b g Lancastrian—Romantic Rhapsody **The Troubadours-Four Seasons Racing**

MR V. ST JOHN SOANE—continued

6 **MATOAKA,** 4, b f Be My Chief (USA)—Echoing **The Stargazers**
7 **MY BEST VALENTINE,** 8, b h Try My Best (USA)—Pas de Calais **The Valentines**
8 **SALTY JACK (IRE),** 4, b c Salt Dome (USA)—Play The Queen (IRE) **Salts Of The Earth**
9 **SHADES OF LOVE,** 4, b c Pursuit of Love—Shadiliya **The Pursuers**
10 **THE BOOLEY HOUSE (IRE),** 8, b g Sheer Grit—Chalk It Down **The Booley Bunch**
11 **TWIN CREEKS,** 7, b g Alzao (USA)—Double River (USA) **The Armchair Jockeys**

THREE-YEAR-OLDS

12 **HOT SUNSHINE,** b c Sharpo—Sunflower Seed **Mr Saleh Al Homeizi**
13 **KALA,** b f Alhijaz—Flushing Meadow (USA) **Mr David L. Bayliss**
14 **NORMAN ARCHER (IRE),** b c Archway (IRE)—Foxy Fairy (IRE) **Mrs M. Watts & Miss R. Hatley**
15 **PADDY DEUX,** b c Perpendicular—Plie **Mrs T. Cross**
16 **PERSIAN SABRE,** b f Sabrehill (USA)—Wassl's Sister **Persian War Racing**
17 **RISKY MONEY,** b c Risk Me (FR)—Where's The Money **The Risky Investors-Four Seasons Racing**
18 **SECRET HARMONY,** gr f Mystiko (USA)—Mimram Melody **The Mystics-Four Seasons Racing**

TWO-YEAR-OLDS

19 **CREME DE CASSIS,** ch f 27/1 Alhijaz—Lucky Flinders (Free State) **Mrs P. Smith & Partners**
20 B f 1/5 Fairy King (USA)—Hana Marie (Formidable (USA)) **Mr S. Al-Homaizi**
21 B f 17/4 Cyrano de Bergerac—I Fear Nothing (Kalaglow)
22 B f 2/4 Petong—Miss Clarinet (Pharly (FR))
23 **MUMMY NOSE BEST,** b f 10/4 Cyrano de Bergerac—Wendy's Way (Merdon Melody) **The Fillies Fanciers**
24 **PENNY BLACK,** br f 25/1 Cyrano de Bergerac—Cow Pastures (Homing) **Mrs J. Stepper & Partners**
25 **PRIESTESS (IRE),** b f 9/4 Magical Wonder—Forest Treasure (USA) (Green Forest (USA)) **Forest Five**
26 **SING FOR ROSIE,** br f 25/4 Petong—Turbo Rose (Taufan (USA)) **Mrs B. Thorne - Four Seasons Racing**
27 B f 24/4 Soviet Lad (USA)—Tallow Hill (Dunphy) **The Red Brigade**

Other Owners: Mr D. Adams, Mr A. L. Alper, Mr R. Barrs, Mr M. Bayley, Mr J. M. Beever, Mr D. Bevan, Mr P. Bignell, Mr D. J. Billinghurst, Mr R. Brant, Mr G. Bridgford, Mr C. Brown, Mr A. Budd, Mr Kenneth D. Bull, Mr K. Chittock, Mrs Irene Clifford, Mr N. Cohen, Mr M. Corcoran, Mr E. Cottam, Mr N. K. Croft, Mr J. Curtis, Mr L. Daffey, Mr A. Derrett, Mrs S. Dixon, Mr R. Eagle, Mr R. Fulford-Smith, Mrs R. J. Gillett, Mr M. W. Goodall, Miss C. Gray, Mr B. W. Greaves, Mrs Jean Greaves, Mr J. Green, Mr A. Greenhalch, Mr S. Grosvenor, Mr R. Haigh, Mr D. Hale, Mr David Harris, Mr S. Harris, Mr G. Harrison, Mr S. Herbert, Mrs C. Hutchings, Mr R. Hutchings, Miss C. Jones, Mr M. Kavanagh, Mr S. Laughton, Mr Marco Lehmann, Mr K. Love, Mrs J. Margetts, Mrs B. May, Mr J. McDougall, Mr W. McGaffin, Mr M. Merron, Mr B. Mitchell, Mr J. Mitchell, Mr K. Mockler, Mr R. Murray, Mr P. Myers, Mr D. F. Norton, Mr B. Parker, Mr R. J. Pedder, Mr A. R. Perry, Exors Of The Late Mr D. E. Popham, Miss C. Rice, Mr A. Rix, Mr Neil Rodway, Miss J. Roisson, Mr M. Ronald, Mr E. Rossbacher, Mr P. Rowland, Mrs E. Rowley-Williams, Mr C. Savage, Mr D. Savage, Mr S. Shaw, Mr S. Shepherd, Mr S. Slack, Mr Stephen G. Smith, Mr E. Sparkes, Mr M. Springett, Mr K. R. Steeper, Mr D. Sutherland, Mr G. Taylor, Mr J. Taylor, Mrs B. Thorne, Mr L. Tsokallis, Miss S. Wale, Mr B. Ward, Whitelight Engineering Ltd, Mr C. Yoe.

Jockeys (Flat): R Cochrane (w.a.), R Perham, C Rutter.

546 MR M. E. SOWERSBY, York

Postal: **Southwold Farm, Goodmanham Wold, Market Weighton, York, East Yorkshire, YO4 3LZ.**
Phone: **(01430) 810534 MOBILE (0402) 557335**

1 **CIMMERIAN,** 4, ch f Aragon—Relatively Easy **Mr Michael Ralph**
2 **COIS NA FARRAIGE (IRE),** 5, b g Nashamaa—Persian Sparkler **Mr M. E. Sowersby**
3 **GENERAL HAVEN,** 5, ch g Hadeer—Verchinina **Mr T. W. Heseltine**
4 **GIVUS A CALL (IRE),** 8, ch g Callernish—Theinthing **Mr A. Milner**
5 **JUNIOR BEN (IRE),** 6, b g Tirol—Piney Pass **Racing Ladies**
6 6, B g Good Times (ITY)—Mountain Child **Mr S. F. Stubbings**
7 **MR FUDGE,** 11, gr g Broadsword (USA)—Blades **Mrs Jean W. Robinson**
8 **NODDY'S BUCK,** 5, b br m Rakaposhi King—Miss Buckstar **Mr Michael Robson**

MR M. E. SOWERSBY—continued

9 **OUR KRIS,** 6, b g Kris—Our Reverie (USA) **Mrs Ruth Sellers**
10 **SAXON FAIR,** 9, ch g Saxon Farm—Fair Kitty **Mr A. Milner**
11 **STRONG JOHN (IRE),** 10, b g Strong Gale—Deep Khaletta **Mr S. Birkinshaw**

Other Owners: Mrs C. A. Birkinshaw, Mr Paul Clifton, Mrs S. E. Hight, Mr A. Reynard.

Conditional: M H Naughton.

547 MR J. L. SPEARING, Severn Stoke

Postal: **Kinnersley Racing Stables, Kinnersley, Severn Stoke, Worcestershire, WR8 9JR.**
Phone: **(01905) 371054 FAX (01905) 371054**

1 **BANKHEAD (IRE),** 9, gr g Roselier (FR)—Coolcanute **Mrs Liz Brazier**
2 **BRIDGES ROLLER (IRE),** 6, b g Dry Dock—Popular View **Midland Wheel Club**
3 **COLINS CHOICE,** 4, ch f Risk Me (FR)—Give Me A Day **Mr Colin Ross**
4 **DIGITAL OPTION (IRE),** 4, b g Alzao (USA)—Elevated **Inthebing Ltd**
5 **DON'T WORRY MIKE,** 4, ch g Forzando—Hat Hill **Inthebing Ltd**
6 **FINE HARVEST,** 12, b g Oats—Kayella **Miss A. Shirley-Priest**
7 **GRATE TIMES,** 4, b g Timeless Times (USA)—Judys Girl (IRE) **Mr J. Spearing**
8 **HIGH DOMAIN (IRE),** 7, b g Dominion Royale—Recline **Mr Stephen Borsberry**
9 **JUCEA,** 9, b m Bluebird (USA)—Appleby Park **Mr A. A. Campbell**
10 **LORD JUSTICE (IRE),** 6, ch g Mister Lord (USA)—Natural Majority **The Lord Justice Partnership**
11 **MADAM LUCY,** 4, ch f Efisio—Our Aisling **Inthebing Ltd**
12 **MARKET MAYHEM,** 8, b g Revlow—Miss Burgundy **Mr Alan C. Cadoret**
13 **MISTY RAIN,** 4, br f Polar Falcon (USA)—Ballerine (USA) **Last Chance Racing**
14 **MOONLIGHT AIR,** 7, br m Bold Owl—Havon Air **Mrs P. Badger**
15 **MR SPECULATOR,** 5, ch g Kefaah (USA)—Humanity **Mr E. E. Bowers & Mrs B. J. Speller**
16 **QUEEN'S PAGEANT,** 4, ch f Risk Me (FR)—Mistral's Dancer **Mrs Robert Heathcote**

THREE-YEAR-OLDS

17 **BELLE DE MONTFORT,** b f Presidium—Judys Girl (IRE) **Junior Nel Partnership**
18 **GAME BIRD,** b f Absalom—Mistral's Dancer **Mrs Robert Heathcote**
19 **MONCHANIA,** ch f Mon Tresor—Sugar Owl **Mrs B. J. Speller**
20 **VAX RAPIDE,** ch f Sharpo—Vax Lady **Vax Limited**

TWO-YEAR-OLDS

21 B f Anshan—College Supreme
22 **EMARINA,** b f 4/3 Emarati (USA)—Cushina **Mr D. Dobson & Mr J. Nichols**
23 **LORD BERGERAC,** b c 15/3 Cyrano de Bergerac—Vax Lady **Mr A. J. Brazier & Mrs L. Brazier**
24 Ch f Risk Me (FR)—Mandrake Madam

Other Owners: Abbots Salford Caravan Park, Mr Alan Bosley, Mr G. M. Eales, Mr R. A. Giles, Mr J. D. Groves, Mr Robert Ham, Mr Barrie James, Mrs P. Joynes, Mrs A. Kemp, Mrs P. Lipscomb, M. F. C. A. Ltd, Non-Stop Promotions & Marketing Ltd, Mr R. Rainbow, Mr Michael Tennet, Mr Graham Treglown, Mr N. F. Williams.

Jockey (NH): D Bridgwater (w.a.).

Lady Riders: Miss Caroline Spearing (9-0), Miss Teresa Spearing (9-0).

548 MR R. C. SPICER, Spalding

Postal: **The Gallops, Dozens Bank, West Pinchbeck, Spalding, Lincolnshire, PE11 3ND.**
Phone: **(01775) 640068**

1 **GOLDEN ACE (IRE),** 5, ch g Archway (IRE)—Gobolino **Mr G. D. J. Linder**
2 **LEITRIM COTTAGE (IRE),** 7, b g Yashgan—New Talent **B & M McHugh Civil Engineering**
3 **SEVEN CROWNS (USA),** 5, b g Chief's Crown (USA)—Ivory Dance (USA) **Mrs N. J. Nichols**
4 **SOUND THE TRUMPET (IRE),** 6, b g Fayruz—Red Note **Mrs N. J. Nichols**
5 **VICTOR ROMEO,** 9, b g Nomination—Be My Sweet **Mrs P. M. Spicer**
6 **WE'RE IN THE MONEY,** 14, ch m Billion (USA)—Fandance **Mrs A. Chinn**

THREE-YEAR-OLDS

7 **DEVON REEF,** ch f Bandmaster (USA)—Reef Bay (IRE) **L. Kasparian**
8 B c Mazaad—Venetian Joy **L. Kasparian**

TWO-YEAR-OLDS

9 B f Superlative—Girl Next Door **M. G. & J. Vines**

Other Owners: K. Appleby, D. Wall.

549 MR T. STACK, Golden

Postal: **Thomastown Castle, Golden, Co. Tipperary, Ireland.**
Phone: **(062) 54129 FAX (062) 54399**

1 **AMERICAN RENAISANS (IRE),** 5, b h Sadler's Wells—Tough Lady
2 5, B h Phardante—Bubbling
3 **BURNT TOAST (IRE),** 4, b f Night Shift—House of Queens
4 **GALE AGAIN,** 11, br g Strong Gale—Going Again
5 **HELSINGOR (IRE),** 5, b h Danehill—Assya
6 5, B h King's Ride—Lantern Lass
7 **LAST EDITION (IRE),** 7, ch g Executive Perk—Miss Furlong
8 **RECORD ENTRY,** 4, b c Emarati—Thorner Lane
9 **ROSETA (IRE),** 6, ch g Roselier—Urrin Valley VII
10 **SCOTTISH SONG,** 5, b g Niniski—Miss Saint-Cloud
11 **SHORT SHIFT (IRE),** 5, ch m Mac's Imp—Clipper Queen
12 **TOP SAINT (IRE),** 4, gr g Topanoora—God's Kiss

THREE-YEAR-OLDS

13 **ANNUAL VISIT (IRE),** b f Alzao—Melinte
14 **BAND OF ANGELS (IRE),** b f Alzao—Rose of Jericho
15 **BIRD OF PREY (IRE),** b f Last Tycoon—Red Partridge
16 **BYLINY (IRE),** ch f Archway—Minami
17 **CAUSEWAY BAY (IRE),** gr c Kenmare—Starring Role
18 **DOCTOR GODDARD,** b g Niniski—Kamada
19 **HALLUCINATION (IRE),** b f Last Tycoon—Welsh Berry
20 **JUINEVERA (IRE),** b f Tenby—Atlantic Dream
21 **KINNEAR (IRE),** b c Last Tycoon—Tough Lady
22 B f Be My Native—Line of Reason
23 **SCAPULA,** b f Elmaamul—Benedicite
24 **SIR CADOR (IRE),** b c Waajib—Seaworthy
25 **STOPWATCH (IRE),** b c Lead On Time—Rose Bonbon
26 **TARASCON (IRE),** b f Tirol—Breyani
27 **TIME LIMIT (IRE),** b f Alzao—Assya
28 **TODOS SANTOS (IRE),** b c Caerleon—Stellar Empress
29 **WEDLOCK (IRE),** b f Last Tycoon—Squire's Daughter

MR T. STACK—continued

TWO-YEAR-OLDS

30 **BETWEEN THE ACTS (IRE)**, ch f 27/1 El Gran Senor—Tendermark
31 **CHALLENGER DEEP (IRE)**, b c 13/4 Tirol—Assya
32 **CYMBELINE (IRE)**, b f 7/3 Tenby—Festive Season
33 **FEDERAL HALL (IRE)**, b c 12/4 Perugino—Unyielding
34 **FEMININE MYSTIQUE (IRE)**, b f 13/4 Dolphin Steet—Squire's Daughter
35 **GLOBE THEATRE (IRE)**, b c 15/3 Tirol—Starring Role
36 **MOUNT VERNON (IRE)**, b c 27/5 Darshaan—Chellita
37 **NASHOBA (IRE)**, gr f 17/3 Caerleon—Grise Mine
38 **PASSIONATE PILGRIM (IRE)**, b c 25/2 Pursuit of Love—Troyanos
39 **PROVINCIAL LADY (IRE)**, b f 15/5 Caerleon—Porphyrine
40 **SOCIAL CONTRACT (IRE)**, ch c 3/4 Seattle Dancer—Paparazzi
41 **STAR LIGHT**, ch f 13/3 Thatching—Tootling
42 **TUSCALOOSA**, b f 10/2 Robellino—Title Role
43 B f 27/3 Brief Truce—Zing Ping

Owners: Mr M. A. Begley, Mr Peter Brennan, Mr P. A. Byrne, Mr T. Corden, Ms W. Cousins, Mr K. Doyle, Mr D. B. Gallop, Mr Hosokawa, Miss Y. Hosokawa, Miss C. Lynch, Mrs John Magnier, Mr John Magnier, Mr J. P. McManus, Mr J. F. O'Malley, Mr Peter Piller, Mrs J. Rowlinson, Mr R. E. Sangster, Mrs T. Stack.

Jockey (Flat): P J Smullen (8-3).

Apprentice: Michael Black (8-2).

Amateurs: S P Hennessy (10-0), Mr B Kinnane (10-0), Mr J A Stack (9-10).

550 MISS V. A. STEPHENS, Taunton

Postal: **Rock Farm, Tolland, Lydeard St Lawrence, Taunton, Somerset, TA4 3PP.**
Phone: **(01984) 667427**

1 4, Ch f Jester—Rose Red City **Mr D. G. Stephens**
2 **SEACHEST**, 9, ch m Stanford—Seajan **Mr D. G. Stephens**
3 **SPACE CAPPA**, 10, br g Capitano—Space Speaker **Mr D. G. Stephens**
4 **WILLET TOWER**, 6, b g Joligeneration—Rose Red City **Mr D. G. Stephens**
5 **WILLET WIZARD**, 5, ch g Jester—Rose Red City **Mr D. G. Stephens**

Lady Rider: Miss V A Stephens (9-7).

551 MR A. C. STEWART, Newmarket

Postal: **Clarehaven, Bury Road, Newmarket, Suffolk, CB8 7BY.**
Phone: **(01638) 667323 FAX (01638) 666389**

1 **MO-ADDAB (IRE)**, 8, b g Waajib—Tissue Paper **Mr S. J. Hammond**

THREE-YEAR-OLDS

2 **A DESERT TOO FAR**, b c Green Desert (USA)—Always Far (USA) **Sheikh Ahmed Al Maktoum**
3 **AGWAAS (IRE)**, ch f Rainbow Quest (USA)—El Fabulous (FR) **Sheikh Ahmed Al Maktoum**
4 **CORONET**, b f Be My Chief (USA)—Thorner Lane **Mrs K. L. Stewart**
5 **CRUINN A BHORD**, b f Inchinor—Selection Board **Lord Derby**
6 **DMOWSKI**, b c Polish Precedent (USA)—Pfalz **P. Saunders And R. George**
7 **DUSHAAN**, ch c Anshan—Soon To Be **Sheikh Ahmed Al Maktoum**

MR A. C. STEWART—continued

8 **ELSHAMMS,** ch f Zafonic (USA)—Gharam (USA) **Mr Hamdan Al Maktoum**
9 **GLENMEAD,** ch c Polish Precedent (USA)—Fair Country **Mr Robin Paterson**
10 **KHAFAYA,** b f Unfuwain (USA)—Mahrah (USA) **Mr Hamdan Al Maktoum**
11 **MARWEH,** b c Prince Sabo—Born To Dance **Mr Hamdan Al Maktoum**
12 **MESHTY (IRE),** b g Lahib (USA)—Merry Devil (IRE) **Sheikh Ahmed Al Maktoum**
13 **MUTAMAM,** b c Darshaan—Petal Girl **Mr Hamdan Al Maktoum**
14 **OUDALMUTEENA (IRE),** b c Lahib (USA)—Roxy Music (IRE) **Mr Hamdan Al Maktoum**
15 **RAKEEB (USA),** ch c Irish River (FR)—Ice House **Mr Hamdan Al Maktoum**
16 **RANNA,** b f Warning—Jasoorah (IRE) **Sheikh Ahmed Al Maktoum**
17 **RUSSIAN PARTY (IRE),** ch c Lycius (USA)—Sherkova (USA) **Sheikh Ahmed Al Maktoum**
18 **SAFE YAMAANI,** ch c Efisio—Lucca **Sheikh Ahmed Al Maktoum**
19 **SERDAAL,** b c Warning—Negeen (USA) **Sheikh Ahmed Al Maktoum**
20 **TANSHAN,** ch c Anshan—Nafla (FR) **Mr M. Hawkes**
21 **TEROOM,** br c Mtoto—Ballad Opera **Sheikh Ahmed Al Maktoum**
22 **THE DARK FLYER,** b g Batshoof—Sveltissima **Mr Chris Brasher**
23 **YAJREE (IRE),** b c Selkirk (USA)—Ustka **Sheikh Ahmed Al Maktoum**

TWO-YEAR-OLDS

24 **ALFATH (USA),** ch c 13/1 Diesis—Lady Express (IRE) (Soviet Star (USA)) **Mr Hamdan Al Maktoum**
25 **ALHASAD (USA),** b c 23/1 Sheikh Albadou—
Valley Prospector (USA) (Northern Prospect (USA)) **Mr Hamdan Al Maktoum**
26 B f 21/1 Wolfhound (USA)—Ameerat Jumaira (USA) (Alydar (USA)) **Sheikh Ahmed Al Maktoum**
27 **AZIMAH,** b f 16/1 Unfuwain (USA)—Rafif (USA) (Riverman (USA)) **Mr Hamdan Al Maktoum**
28 B f 14/4 Marju (IRE)—Azm (Unfuwain (USA)) **Sheikh Ahmed Al Maktoum**
29 Ch f 24/4 Lycius (USA)—Balwa (USA) (Danzig (USA)) **Sheikh Ahmed Al Maktoum**
30 Ch c 17/4 Kris—Cambara (Dancing Brave (USA)) **Sheikh Ahmed Al Maktoum**
31 **CASIMIR,** b c 24/2 Roi Danzig (USA)—Have A Cut (IRE) (Al Hareb (USA)) **Mr P. T. McGuinness**
32 Ch c 15/2 Diesis—Dream Play (USA) (Blushing Groom (FR)) **Sheikh Ahmed Al Maktoum**
33 Br c 12/2 Sadler's Wells (USA)—Dwell (USA) (Habitat) **Sheikh Ahmed Al Maktoum**
34 **EL SARAJ,** ch c 18/3 Night Shift (USA)—Mareha (IRE) (Cadeaux Genereux) **Mr Hamdan Al Maktoum**
35 **FREYA (IRE),** b f 29/4 Fayruz—My Croft (Crofter) **Mr R. Axworthy & Mr N. J. Fish**
36 **HYPERACTIVE (IRE),** b c 30/1 Perugino (USA)—Hyannis (FR) (Esprit du Nord (USA)) **Racing For Gold**
37 **INDIGO BAY (IRE),** b c 26/3 Royal Academy (USA)—Cape Heights (Shirley Heights) **Clare Hall Racing Ltd**
38 B f 8/2 Doyoun—Iviza (IRE) (Sadler's Wells (USA)) **Sheikh Ahmed Al Maktoum**
39 **JENNY SPINNER (IRE),** b f 24/4 Bluebird (USA)—Run To Jenny (Runnett) **Major J. H. de Burgh**
40 **LEARNED FELLOW (IRE),** ch c 21/4 College Chapel—Shanamara (IRE) (Shernazar) **Racing For Gold**
41 **OPEN SECRET (IRE),** b br f 19/3 Mac's Imp (USA)—Lady Montekin (Montekin) **Racing For Gold**
42 Ch c 20/3 Irish River (FR)—Patricia (USA) (Assert) **Sheikh Ahmed Al Maktoum**
43 **PITTODRIE (IRE),** b br c 23/3 Petardia—Evictress (IRE) (Sharp Victor (USA)) **Racing For Gold**
44 **RAJI,** b c 9/5 Green Desert (USA)—Cancan Madame (USA) (Mr Prospector (USA)) **Mr Hamdan Al Maktoum**
45 **RHAPSODY,** b f 23/1 Rudimentary (USA)—Kennedy's Prima (Primo Dominie) **Milton Park Stud & Lady Southey**
46 Gr c 29/4 Petong—Scarlet Veil (Tyrnavos) **S. J. Hammond/I. Chamberlain/N. J. Fish**
47 Ch f 5/2 Rainbow Quest (USA)—Selection Board (Welsh Pageant) **Lord Derby**
48 B c 24/4 Green Desert (USA)—Shadha (USA) (Devil's Bag (USA)) **Sheikh Ahmed Al Maktoum**
49 Ch c 2/4 Rahy (USA)—So Romantic (USA) (El Gran Senor (USA)) **Racing For Gold**
50 **SURE FUTURE,** b c 27/3 Kylian (USA)—Lady Ever-So-Sure (Malicious) **R. George, P. Saunders, A. K. Collins**
51 **TIERGARTEN (IRE),** b f 23/4 Brief Truce (USA)—Lady In The Park (Last Tycoon) **Mrs D. Domvile**

Other Owners: Mr A. J. Arkwright, Mr D. P. Barrie, Mr D. Boden, Mrs Shirley Brasher, Mrs J. Chamberlain, Mr R. Clemons, Lord Dalment, Mr A. C. Dolbey, Mr H. Fraser, Mr D. Guyer, Sir Stephen Hastings, Mr R. W. Hill-Smith, Mr R. Lambert, Mr C. Lane, Mr A. D. Martens, Mr C McMillan, Mrs D. Nastasi, Mr A. Ovett, Mr A. Pickering, Mr M. J. Rees, Mrs A. Savage, Mr D. C. Stewart, Mr D. Theobald, Mr A. C. Yolland.

Jockey (Flat): M Roberts (w.a.).

Amateur: Mr V Lukaniuk (9-0).

552 MISS ANN STOKELL, Claverdon

Postal: **Arden Park Stables, Manor Lane, Claverdon, Warwickshire, CV35 8NH.**
Phone: **(01926) 842464 MOBILE (0468) 436678**

1 **BARQAISH,** 11, br g Jalmood (USA)—Adeebah (USA) **Arden Racing Club**
2 **CLASSIC DAME (FR),** 5, gr m Highest Honor (FR)—Reem El Fala (FR) **Ms Caron Stokell**
3 **ERICOLIN (IRE),** 8, ch g Ahonoora—Pixie Erin **Ms Caron Stokell**
4 **FLOWER FAYRE,** 5, b m North Col—Reef Native **Mr Ken Dale**
5 **HIGHLY CHARMING (IRE),** 6, b g Shirley Heights—Charmante Dame (FR) **Mr N. Jinks**
6 **SANDRIFT,** 9, ch m Glint of Gold—Olivian **Mr M. F. Barraclough**
7 4, B f Syrtos—Sussex Queen **Mr M. F. Barraclough**
8 **TIM SOLDIER (FR),** 11, ch g Tip Moss (FR)—Pali Dancer (FR) **Mr M. F. Barraclough**
9 **WEEHEBY (USA),** 9, ch g Woodman (USA)—Fearless Dame (USA) **The DANA Partnership**

THREE-YEAR-OLDS

10 **ROCKLINE EXPRESS,** b g Welsh Captain—Velvet Asity **Rockline Industries Ltd**

Other Owners: Mr D. J. Griffin, Mr A. Lucas, Mr A. Peters, Mr J. Savage, Mr Raymond Tooth, Mr Nigel Wall.

Jockeys (NH): R Supple, G E Tormey.

Apprentice: P P Murphy.

Conditional: X Aizpuru, R Thornton.

Lady Rider: Miss Ann Stokell (9-7).

553 MR F. S. STOREY, Carlisle

Postal: **Low Dubwath, Kirklinton, Carlisle, Cumbria, CA6 6EF.**
Phone: **KIRKLINTON (0122 875) 331**

1 **NOIR ESPRIT,** 5, br g Prince Daniel (USA)—Danse d'Esprit **Mr F. S. Storey**
2 **SHATRAVIV,** 10, b m Meadowbrook—M-N-Ms Lass **Mr F. S. Storey**

Jockey (NH): B Storey (9-10).

554 MRS J. M. STOREY, Kelso

Postal: **Halterburnhead Farm, Kelso, Roxburghshire, TD5 8PP.**

1 **ALLERBANK,** 7, b g Meadowbrook—Allerdale **Mr C. Storey**
2 **BLYTH BROOK,** 6, b g Meadowbrook—The Bean-Goose **Mrs S. A. Sutton**
3 **ENSIGN EWART (IRE),** 7, ch g Buckskin (FR)—Clonea Fog **Major M. W. Sample**
4 **HAPPY BLAKE,** 7, b g Blakelight—Happy To Play **Mrs C. J. Todd**
5 **JACQUES THE LAD (IRE),** 6, bl g Strong Gale—Rent A Card **Mr James R. Adam**
6 **JUDICIOUS CAPTAIN,** 11, b g New Member—Injudicious **Mr James R. Adam**
7 **PLEASEDASPUNCH (IRE),** 6, br g Convinced—Ferdee Free **Chartres, Bramley, Scott & Storey**
8 **ROYAL PASS,** 5, ch g Royal Vulcan—Final Joy **Mr C. Storey**
9 **SHAY GAP (IRE),** 5, br g Yashgan—Anavore **Mr M. H. Walton**
10 **STOCK OPTION (IRE),** 5, b g Executive Perk—Clondo Blue (IRE) **Mr J. R. Anthony**

MRS J. M. STOREY—continued

11 **TELLHERPATIT (IRE)**, 5, ch m Torus—Lady Sese **Mrs Jane M. Storey**
12 **WEEJUMPAWUD**, 8, b m Jumbo Hirt (USA)—Weewumpawud **Mr C. Storey**
13 **WUDIMP**, 9, b g Import—Weewumpawud **Mr C. Storey**

Other Owners: Mrs E. Bramley, Mrs R. M. Chartres, Mrs Murray Scott.

555 MR W. STOREY, Consett

Postal: **Grange Farm & Stud, Muggleswick, Consett, Co. Durham, DH8 9DW.**
Phone: **(01207) 55259 OR (0860) 510441 FAX (01207) 55607**

1 **BOYZONTOOWA (IRE)**, 6, b g Beau Sher—Lindabell **Mr John J. Maguire**
2 **CHARTER**, 7, b g Reference Point—Winter Queen **Victor Chandler (Equus) Ltd**
3 **COLWAY RITZ**, 4, b g Rudimentary (USA)—Million Heiress **Mr Ray Coleman**
4 **DR WOODSTOCK**, 4, br g Rock City—Go Tally-Ho **Mr D. O. Cremin**
5 **GENTLE ANGEL (IRE)**, 7, br m Roselier (FR)—Autumn Saphire **Mr Neil D. McDiarmid**
6 **GREAT EASEBY (IRE)**, 8, ch g Caerleon (USA)—Kasala (USA) **Mr D. C. Batey**
7 **HERE COMES HERBIE**, 6, ch g Golden Lahab (USA)—Megan's Move **Mr H. S. Hutchinson**
8 **NATIVE SONG**, 5, b m Hatim (USA)—Ivors Melody **Invicta Bloodstock**
9 **OPAQUE**, 6, b g Shirley Heights—Opale **Mr G. J. Keary**
10 **SPECULATIVE**, 4, b c Suave Dancer (USA)—Gull Nook **Mr Tony Stafford**
11 **TIPPING TINA**, 5, b m King's Ride—Jeanarie **Mr D. C. Batey**
12 **WEAVER GEORGE (IRE)**, 8, b g Flash of Steel—Nephrite **Regent Decorators Ltd**
13 **ZAAHIR (IRE)**, 4, b g Marju (IRE)—Abhaaj **Mr D. C. Batey**
14 **ZAMHAREER (USA)**, 7, b g Lear Fan (USA)—Awenita **Mr D. C. Batey**

THREE-YEAR-OLDS

15 **CHETANI'S MOVE**, ch f Golden Lahab (USA)—Megan's Move **Mr H. S. Hutchinson**
16 **DEECEEBEE**, b g Rudimentary (USA)—Do Run Run **Mr D. C. Batey**
17 **HIDING PLACE**, b f Saddlers' Hall (IRE)—Sanctuary Cove **Mr Tony Stafford**
18 **SUGGEST**, b g Midyan (USA)—Awham (USA) **Mrs M. Tindale**

Other Owners: Bellcoil Ltd, Mr D. Callaghan, Mr Victor Chandler, Mr C. A. Clark, Mr B. Crunden, Mr Elliott Dickman, Mr J. M. Elliott, Mr John Herring, Mr H. Hurst, Mr Peter Mines, Mr Alan Osborne, Mr Norman Park, Mr C. Paskin, Mr C. B. Rennison, Mr Anthony Roche, Mr W. Storey, Mr Richard Thompson, Mr Foster Watson, Mr A. Whiting, Mr J. A. Wilkinson.

Lady Rider: Miss S Storey (8-7).

556 MR M. STOUTE, Newmarket

Postal: **Freemason Lodge, Bury Road, Newmarket, Suffolk, CB8 7BT.**
Phone: **NEWMARKET (01638) 663801 FAX (01638) 667276**

1 **AMONG MEN (USA)**, 4, b c Zilzal (USA)—Questionablevirtue (USA)
2 **CLERKENWELL (USA)**, 5, b h Sadler's Wells (USA)—Forlene
3 **DELILAH (IRE)**, 4, b f Bluebird (USA)—Courtesane (USA)
4 **GREEK PALACE (IRE)**, 4, b c Royal Academy (USA)—Grecian Sea (FR)
5 **ILLUSION**, 4, b c Green Desert (USA)—Time Charter
6 **INSATIABLE (IRE)**, 5, b h Don't Forget Me—Petit Eclair
7 **MULTICOLOURED (IRE)**, 5, b h Rainbow Quest (USA)—Greektown
8 **NICOLE PHARLY**, 4, b f Pharly (FR)—Debbie Harry (USA)
9 **SILENCE REIGNS**, 4, b g Saddlers' Hall (IRE)—Rensaler (USA)
10 **STAR INVADER**, 4, b c Nashwan (USA)—Sahara Star

MR M. STOUTE—continued

11 TANAASA (IRE), 4, b c Sadler's Wells (USA)—Mesmerize
12 WHITEWATER AFFAIR, 5, ch m Machiavellian (USA)—Much Too Risky
13 WIND CHEETAH (USA), 4, b br c Storm Cat (USA)—Won't She Tell (USA)

THREE-YEAR-OLDS

14 AIM HIGH, b c Sadler's Wells (USA)—Aim For The Top (USA)
15 ALIABAD (IRE), b br c Doyoun—Alannya (FR)
16 ALIGNMENT (IRE), b f Alzao (USA)—Scots Lass
17 ALLY (FR), b g Zilzal (USA)—Holy Tobin (USA)
18 ANGSTROM (IRE), b g Alzao (USA)—Anna Petrovna (FR)
19 ASTRAPI, b f Last Tycoon—Graecia Magna (USA)
20 BESHARA (IRE), b gr f Doyoun—Shakamiyn
21 BRAVE REWARD (USA), b c Lear Fan (USA)—A Tad Better (USA)
22 CANDESCENT, b f Machiavellian (USA)—Nearctic Flame
23 CAREFUL TIMING, b f Caerleon (USA)—By Charter
24 CARIBBEAN MONARCH (IRE), b c Fairy King (USA)—Whos The Blonde
25 CHARMED EXISTENCE (IRE), b f Sadler's Wells (USA)—Broadway Joan (USA)
26 CLOSE SHAVE, b c Warning—La Barberina (USA)
27 CONFIDANTE (USA), b f Dayjur (USA)—Won't She Tell (USA)
28 CORELLI, b c Machiavellian (USA)—Musical Bliss (USA)
29 DANCING PHANTOM, b c Darshaan—Dancing Prize (IRE)
30 DARK SHELL (IRE), b c Darshaan—Grecian Urn
31 DESERT ACADEMY (IRE), b c Green Desert (USA)—Sit Alkul (USA)
32 DOUBLE CLASSIC (USA), br c Riverman (USA)—Adam's Angel (USA)
33 ENCHANT, ch f Lion Cavern (USA)—Belle Et Deluree (USA)
34 EXCLUSIVE, ch f Polar Falcon (USA)—Exclusive Order (USA)
35 FIRST CLASS TICKET (USA), b f Northern Flagship (USA)—White Feather (USA)
36 FIRST CONSUL (USA), ch c Rubiano (USA)—Sunflower Fields (USA)
37 GLEAMING HILL (USA), b c Marquetry (USA)—Mountain Sunshine (USA)
38 GREEK DANCE (IRE), b c Sadler's Wells (USA)—Hellenic
39 HIGHWAYMAN (IRE), b c Danehill (USA)—Millerette
40 INDIAN IMP, b f Indian Ridge—Morina (USA)
41 JAAZIM (USA), b c Silver Hawk (USA)—Alvear (USA)
42 KARASI (IRE), b c Kahyasi—Karamita
43 KILIMANJARO, b c Shirley Heights—Darara
44 KIMONO (IRE), b f Machiavellian (USA)—Kiliniski
45 KNIFE EDGE (USA), b br c Kris S (USA)—My Turbulent Miss (USA)
46 LONESOME DUDE (CAN), b c With Approval (CAN)—Local Lass
47 LUCREZIA (IRE), b f Machiavellian (USA)—Troyanna
48 MARIDPOUR (IRE), b c Shernazar—Maridana (USA)
49 MAWSOOF, b c Alzao (USA)—Guilty Secret (IRE)
50 MILLITRIX, br f Doyoun—Galatrix
51 MINSTREL'S DANCE (CAN), b f Pleasant Colony (USA)—Minstrelsy (USA)
52 MISLEADING LADY, b f Warning—Much Too Risky
53 MOON MASQUERADE (IRE), b br f Darshaan—Moon Parade
54 MR CAHILL (USA), b c Cahill Road (USA)—Sympathetic Miss (USA)
55 MUHIB (USA), b c Red Ransom (USA)—Sensorious (CAN)
56 NORTHERN MAJOR (USA), b c Northern Flagship (USA)—Majeboo (USA)
57 PALAIS (IRE), b c Darshaan—Dance Festival
58 PEAK PATH (IRE), b c Polish Precedent (USA)—Road To The Top
59 RAMBLING ROSE, ch f Cadeaux Genereux—Blush Rambler (IRE)
60 RED TULLE (USA), b f A P Indy (USA)—Namaqua (USA)
61 RUSHED (IRE), b g Fairy King (USA)—Exotic Bride (USA)
62 SCENT OF SUCCESS (USA), b f Quiet American (USA)—Mousquet (USA)
63 SECRET SAVER (USA), ch c Green Dancer (USA)—Vachti (FR)
64 SHALAMA (IRE), b f Kahyasi—Shademah
65 SHANA, b f Darshaan—Vivre En Paix
66 SINGER SARGENT (USA), ch c Kingmambo (USA)—Puppet Dance (USA)
67 SKY ROCKET, ch c Storm Cat (USA)—Oriental Mystique

MR M. STOUTE—continued

68 TRIDENT (USA), b c Red Ransom (USA)—Lady di Pomadora (USA)
69 VIRTUOUS, b f Exit To Nowhere (USA)—Exclusive Virtue (USA)
70 WAHJ (IRE), ch c Indian Ridge—Sabaah (USA)

TWO-YEAR-OLDS

71 B c 7/2 Indian Ridge—Above Water (IRE) (Reference Point)
72 B f 19/4 Green Desert (USA)—Alinova (USA) (Alleged (USA))
73 ALL OUR HOPE (USA), b f 19/4 Gulch (USA)—Knoosh (USA) (Storm Bird (CAN))
74 B c 4/3 Polish Precedent (USA—Anna Matrushka (Mill Reef (USA))
75 ARIEL (IRE), b f 24/4 Caerleon (USA)—Arousal (Rousillon (USA))
76 ATYAB (USA), b f 27/4 Mr Prospector (USA)—Muhbubh (USA) (Blushing Groom (FR))
77 AUDITION, b f 3/2 Machiavellian (USA)—Dance To The Top (Sadler's Wells (USA))
78 AUGURY, b f 26/3 Warning—Phyliel (USA) (Lyphard (USA))
79 AUSPICIOUS, b f 26/1 Shirley Heights—Blessed Event (Kings Lake (USA))
80 Br c 5/3 Nureyev (USA)—Aviara (USA) (Cox's Ridge (USA))
81 B f 1/4 Rahy (USA)—Blue Daisy (USA) (Shahrastani (USA))
82 BLUE RIBBON (IRE), b c 31/3 Bluebird (USA)—Sweet Justice (Law Society (USA))
83 Ch f 7/3 Irish River (FR)—Bounding Away (CAN) (Vice Regent (CAN))
84 B f 24/4 Kris—By Charter (Shirley Heights)
85 CHICKIE'S DISCO, b f 3/2 Shirley Heights—African Dance (USA) (El Gran Senor (USA))
86 CITY STANDARD (IRE), b c 19/5 Rainbow Quest (USA)—City Fortress (Troy)
87 CLOUDY SKY (IRE), b c 18/2 Sadler's Wells (USA)—Dancing Shadow (Dancer's Image (USA))
88 B f 6/6 Alzao (USA)—Dafinah (USA) (Graustark)
89 DARAWAD (IRE), b c 21/4 Bluebird (USA)—Dawala (USA) (Lashkari (IRE))
90 DARK TROJAN (IRE), b c 4/4 Darshaan—Trojan Miss (Troy)
91 DOUNYAPOUR (IRE), b c 23/3 Lahib (USA)—Dounya (USA) (Caro)
92 DUELLING GIRL (USA), b f 21/2 Dayjur (USA)—Carduel (USA) (Buckpasser)
93 EMILY'S LUCKY CHARM (USA), br c 12/2 Lear fan (USA)—Emily's Charm (CAN) (Dom Alaric (FR))
94 ENTIKAA (IRE), b c 2/5 Sadler's Wells (USA)—Miranisa (Habitat)
95 FABULOUS, b f 13/4 Fabulous Dancer (USA)—Loon (FR) (Kaldoun (FR))
96 Ch c 27/1 Machiavellian (USA)—Fair Maid of Kent (USA) (Diesis)
97 FANTASTIC LIGHT (USA), b c 13/2 Rahy (USA)—Jood (USA) (Nijinsky (CAN))
98 B f 4/2 Fairy King (USA)—Favoridge (USA) (Riva Ridge (USA))
99 Ch c 27/4 Diesis—First Tracks (USA) (Alleged (USA))
100 FLAMING QUEST, b c 9/3 Rainbow Quest (USA)—Nearctic Flame (Sadler's Wells (USA))
101 FORTIFY, b f 11/3 Machiavellian (USA)—Talon d'Aiguille (USA) (Big Spruce (USA))
102 Ch f 30/1 Woodman (USA)—Good Example (FR) (Crystal Glitters (USA))
103 B c 10/4 Danehill (USA)—Graecia Magna (USA) (Private Account (USA))
104 HALAKANN (IRE), b c 15/2 Doyoun—Halaka (IRE) (Shernazar)
105 HAND OVER THE CASH (USA), b c 7/2 Red Ransom (USA)—Ambigua (IRE) (Alydar (USA))
106 Br f 12/3 Mr Prospector (USA)—Heart of Joy (USA) (Lypheor)
107 HIGHEST PEAK (USA), ch c 4/3 Mt Livermore (USA)—Disconiz (USA) (Northern Dancer)
108 HIGH POLICY (IRE), ch c 25/4 Machiavellian (USA)—Road To The Top (Shirley Heights)
109 HOPES ARE HIGH (IRE), b c 18/2 Ezzoud (IRE)—Ma Petite Cherie (USA) (Caro)
110 B c 14/5 Green Desert (USA)—Hyabella (Shirley Heights)
111 B c 12/2 Caerleon (USA)—Idraak (Kris)
112 Ch f 15/4 Irish River (FR)—Imagining (USA) (Northfields (USA))
113 IMPRESARIO, b c 16/4 Sadler's Wells (USA)—Exclusive Order (USA) (Exclusive Native (USA))
114 Ch f 24/1 Woodman (USA)—Informatrice (USA) (Trempolino (USA))
115 Ch c 17/4 Caerleon (USA)—Jaljuli (Jalmood (USA))
116 JAMEELA (IRE), b f 15/4 Danehill (USA)—Legend of Arabia (Great Nephew)
117 Gr c 9/4 Silver Hawk (USA)—Kazoo (Shareef Dancer (USA))
118 KING ADAM (IRE), b c 6/2 Fairy King (USA)—Sailor's Mate (Shirley Heights)
119 B f 22/2 Rainbow Quest (USA)—Kissing Cousin (IRE) (Danehill (USA))
120 LIONESS, b f 4/3 Lion Cavern (USA)—Pidona (Baillamont (USA))
121 LITTLE ROCK, b c 5/2 Warning—Much Too Risky (Bustino)
122 LONESOME, b f 12/2 Night Shift (USA)—Pine Ridge (High Top)
123 B c 5/5 Ezzoud (IRE)—Lovely Noor (USA) (Fappiano (USA))
124 B c 6/3 Caerleon (USA)—Malvern Beauty (Shirley Heights)
125 MARY STUART (IRE), b f 16/6 Nashwan (USA)—Scots Lass (Shirley Heights)

MR M. STOUTE—continued

126 B c 1/3 Polish Precedent—Mashmoon (USA) (Habitat (USA))
127 **MESSENGER MISS (USA),** b f 21/3 Danehill (USA)—Foreign Courier (USA) (Sir Ivor)
128 **MUKHTAAL,** b c 16/4 Machiavellian (USA)—On The House (FR) (Be My Guest (USA))
129 **NATIONAL ANTHEM,** b c 17/1 Royal Academy (USA)—Heart's Harmony (Blushing Groom (FR))
130 Ch c 30/4 Lion Cavern (USA)—Negligent (Ahonoora)
131 **NUFUTH (USA),** ch f 3/3 Nureyev (USA)—On Your Guard (USA) (Alydar (USA))
132 B c 19/3 Grand Lodge (USA)—Olean (Sadler's Wells (USA))
133 B c 6/3 Indian Ridge—One Wild Oat (Shareef Dancer (USA))
134 B c 16/5 Caerleon (USA)—Petticoat Lane (Ela-Mana-Mou (USA))
135 **POP QUEEN,** ch f 6/4 Nashwan (USA)—Pick of The Pops (High Top)
136 **PRECOCIOUS MISS (USA),** b f 14/3 Diesis—Kissogram Girl (USA) (Danzig (USA))
137 B c 29/3 Danzig (USA)—Queena (USA) (Mr Prospector (USA))
138 B c 1/3 Gulch (USA)—Queen's View (FR) (Lomond (USA))
139 **RAIN GOD,** b c 20/2 Rainbow Quest (USA)—Mystic Goddess (USA) (Storm Bird (CAN))
140 **RELENTLESS REVENGE (USA),** b c 20/2 Strolling Along (USA)—Bold Courtesan (USA) (Bold Bidder)
141 Gr f 3/4 Machiavellian (USA)—Rusian Royal (USA) (Nureyev (USA))
142 **SEABOUND,** b f 14/2 Prince Sabo—Shore Line (High Line)
143 **SEA PICTURE (IRE),** b f 14/4 Royal Academy (USA)—Grecian Sea (FR) (Homeric)
144 B c 4/3 Polish Precedent (USA—Secret Obsession (USA) (Secretariat (USA))
145 **SERDAL (USA),** b c 26/1 Gulch (USA)—Ginny Dare (USA) (Pilgrim (USA))
146 Br c 7/1 Silver Hawk (USA)—Silken Doll (USA) (Chieftain II)
147 B f 8/2 Machiavellian (USA)—Sonic Lady (USA) (Nureyev (USA))
148 **SPARKLING,** ch f 21/2 Kris—Sister Sophie (Effervescing (USA))
149 Br c 29/2 Dynaformer (USA)—Spirited Missus (USA) (Distinctive (USA))
150 Ch c 27/3 Indian Ridge—Spring Daffodil (Pharly (FR))
151 **SUMOOD,** b f 4/2 Rainbow Quest (USA)—Bella Ballerina (Sadler's Wells (USA))
152 B c 18/5 Sadler's Wells (USA)—Surmise (USA) (Alleged (USA))
153 B f 21/2 Alzao (USA)—Swan Heights (Shirley Heights)
154 **TELECASTER (IRE),** ch c 5/5 Indian Ridge—Monashee (USA) (Sovereign Dancer (USA))
155 **THE NOBLEMAN (USA),** b c 9/3 Quiet American (USA)—Furajet (USA) (The Minstrel (CAN))
156 B f 6/6 Green Desert (USA)—Time Charter (Saritamer (USA))
157 **TITANIA,** b f 16/4 Fairy King (USA)—Warning Light (High Top)
158 B c 10/5 Bluebird (USA)—Triode (USA) (Sharpen Up)
159 B c 9/2 Midhish—Tudor Loom (Sallust)
160 Ch c 11/4 Indian Ridge—Upward Trend (Salmon Leap (USA))
161 **WOOD POUND (USA),** b c 9/3 Woodman (USA)—Poundzig (USA) (Danzig (USA))
162 B c 14/4 Caerleon (USA)—Zafadola (IRE) (Darshaan)

Owners: Mr Mitaab Abdullah, Mrs M. Arbib, Mr J. D. Ashenheim, Mr R. Barnett, Mr David Barrie, Cheveley Park Stud, Mr Athos Christodoulou, Mr Luciano Gaucci, Mr & Mrs Paul Green, Mr J. M. Greetham, Mr S. Hanson, Lady Harris, Mrs Denis Haynes, Helena Springfield Ltd, Highclere Thoroughbred Racing Ltd, Mr Abdulla Al Khalifa, H. H. Aga Khan, Lord Lloyd-Webber, Capt J. Macdonald Buchanan, Mrs John Magnier, Maktoum Al Maktoum, Mr Hamdan Al Maktoum, Sheikh Mohammed, Mr M. Nagashima, Niarchos Family, Mr J. H. Richmond-Watson, Sir Evelyn De Rothschild, H. R. H. Prince Fahd Salman, Mr P. D. Savill, Mr Pierpont Scott, Mr W. H. Scott, Mrs G. A. E. Smith, Mr George Strawbridge, Mr Saeed Suhail, Mrs Doreen M. Swinburn, Mr M. Tabor, The Royal Ascot Racing Club, Lord Weinstock, Mr Peter Wetzel, Mr James Wigan, Mr Ralph C. Wilson Jr.

557 MR A. P. STREETER, Uttoxeter

Postal: **Anfield House Racing Stables, New Road, Uttoxeter, Staffordshire, ST14 5DT.**
Phone: **HOME/FAX (01889 568919 MOBILE (0976) 386227**

1 **ALASKAN HEIR,** 7, b g Northern State (USA)—Royal Meeting **Mr J. Burton**
2 **APACHE PARK (USA),** 5, b g Alleged (USA)—Fairly Magic (USA) **Mr M. Eley**
3 **BONYALUA MILL,** 4, gr f Chilibang—Candesco **Mrs Brenda Jeffery**
4 **BOSSYMOSS (IRE),** 9, b g Le Moss—Annes Wedding **Mrs Margaret James**
5 **CENTAUR EXPRESS,** 6, b g Siberian Express (USA)—Gay Twenties **Centaur Racing Ltd**

MR A. P. STREETER—continued

6 **CLASSIC EXHIBIT**, 9, b g Tate Gallery (USA)—See The Tops **Principal Racing**
7 **GAVASKAR (IRE)**, 9, b g Indian King (USA)—Sovereign Bloom **Mr D. W. Stevens**
8 **GRACEFUL DOLLY**, 5, b m Tina's Pet—Sea Crossing (FR) **Hydro-Brake**
9 **JILLS JOY (IRE)**, 7, b g Law Society (USA)—Cooliney Princess **Mr R. Baker**
10 **LEGATEE**, 7, ch m Risk Me (FR)—Legal Sound **South Normanton Racing**
11 **MAD MILITANT (IRE)**, 9, b g Vision (USA)—Ullapool **Mr K. Nicholls**
12 **MEG'S MEMORY (IRE)**, 5, b m Superlative—Meanz Beanz **Centaur Racing Ltd**
13 **MY WEE MAN (IRE)**, 7, b g Carlingford Castle—Pollerun Slave **Peter J. Douglas Engineering**
14 **NEWHALL PRINCE**, 10, b g Prince Ragusa—Doyles Folly **Mr B. W. Trubshaw**
15 **ONEOFTHEOLDONES**, 6, b g Deploy—Waveguide **Mr R. Baker**
16 **ROCK SCENE (IRE)**, 6, b g Scenic—Rockeater **Mrs J. Hughes**
17 **SALSKA**, 7, b m Salse (USA)—Anzeige (GER) **Mr P. L. Clinton**
18 **STICKY MOMENTS**, 6, b g Grey Desire—Richesse (FR) **Best Racing**
19 **TILTY (USA)**, 8, b g Linkage (USA)—En Tiempo (USA) **Cheadle Racing**
20 **YOUNG DALESMAN**, 5, br g Teenoso (USA)—Fabulous Molly **Mr B. J. Garrett**

THREE-YEAR-OLDS

21 **OPTIMISTIC CHRIS**, b g Pharly (FR)—Gay Twenties **Optimistic Racing**

TWO-YEAR-OLDS

22 Ch c 25/3 Ardkinglass—Bella Maggio (Rakaposhi King) **Mr B. J. Garrett**

Other Owners: Mr Chris Adams, Mrs L. Allen, Mr Brian Bailey, Mr Alan Baxter, Mr T. Beck, Mr Joe Bland, Mr Derek Boulton, Mr Peter J. Douglas, Mr Frank Dronzek, Mr R. Foster, Mr Paul Hollinshead, Mr David Kastelan, Mr J. E. Lea, Miss C. A. Mather, Mr A. T. McAllister, Mr Marek Pawlitta, Mr M. Rhodes, Mrs J. Salt, Mr C. Shaw, Mr Clive Staddon, Mr J. T. S. Stimpson, Mrs M. Stimpson, Mr Barry Thacker, Mrs Marcia Titterton, Mr N. Titterton, Mr Timothy Watts, Mr Brian Wells, Mr W. Wibberley, Mr B. Wilne, Mr S. Wilson.

Jockey (NH): T Eley (10-0).

Apprentice: R Havlin (8-4, w.a.).

558 MRS L. STUBBS, Marlborough

Postal: **Highland Farm Racing Stables, Collingbourne Ducis, Marlborough, Wiltshire, SN8 3EG.**
Phone: **(01264) 850094 MOBILE (0802) 453666**

1 **GUNNERS GLORY**, 4, b g Aragon—Massive Powder **Mr Ian Blakey**
2 **KHALIK (IRE)**, 4, br g Lear Fan (USA)—Silver Dollar **Mr A. P. Griffin**
3 **MUMKIN**, 4, b c Reprimand—Soon To Be **Mr R. P. Johns**
4 **MYRMIDON**, 4, b g Midyan (USA)—Moorish Idol **Mr Michael Worth**
5 **MYSTICAL**, 4, gr f Mystiko (USA)—Midnight Imperial **Mrs Zelda R. Farr**
6 **RAKIS (IRE)**, 8, b br g Alzao (USA)—Bristle **Mr P. G. Shorrock**
7 **SMARTER CHARTER**, 5, br h Master Willie—Irene's Charter **Mr A. P. Griffin**
8 **WITCHFINDER (USA)**, 6, b g Diesis—Colonial Witch (USA) **Mr Maurice Parker**

THREE-YEAR-OLDS

9 **CELTIC VENTURE**, ch c Risk Me (FR)—Celtic River (IRE) **Mr R. P. Johns**
10 **CHAMELI**, b f Nordico (USA)—Try Vickers (USA) **Mrs Christine Griffiths**
11 **CHIKAPENNY**, b f Mon Tresor—Arabian Nymph **Mr Maurice Parker**
12 **DESERT NATIVE**, b f Formidable (USA)—Desert Nomad **Mrs L. Stubbs**
13 **LADY SO BOLD**, ch f Bold Arrangement—Lady Blues Singer **Mr A. P. Griffin**
14 **LONGBOWMAN**, ch g Prince Sabo—Nuit de Lune (FR) **Mr Doug Kirk**

MRS L. STUBBS—continued

TWO-YEAR-OLDS

15 Ch f 19/3 Dilum (USA)—Ansellady **Mr Joseph C. Smith**
16 Ch f 6/2 Kasakov—Kabella
17 **RUNAWAY BAY,** gr c 28/4 Lugana Beach—Absaloui
18 Gr c 30/5 Mizoram (USA)—Ziggi's Girl (IRE)

Other Owners: Mr M. S. Griffiths, Mr Darren Kirk, Mr D. M. Smith, Mr J. P. Spencer, Mr O. J. Williams.

Jockeys (Flat): J F Egan, D Harrison, S Whitworth.

559 MR K. R. SUPPLE, Wrotham

Postal: **1 Park Farm Cottage, Park Farm, Wrotham, Kent, TN15 7RE.**
Phone: **(01732) 885237 YARD (01634) 253350**

1 **SEYMOUR WHO,** 5, b g Seymour Hicks (FR)—Normazoo **Mrs S. M. Supple**

Jockey (NH): R J Supple (10-0, w.a.)..

Conditional: G Supple (9-7).

560 CAPT. D. SWAN, Cloughjordon

Postal: **Modreeny, Cloughjordon, Co. Tipperary, Ireland.**
Phone: **(0505) 42221 FAX (0505) 42128**

1 **AN MAINEACH (IRE),** 9, br g Lafontaine (USA)—Swanny Jane **C. Pettigrew**
2 **ARCHELEC (IRE),** 6, b g Farhaan—Truly Deep **Mrs Orla Finulane**
3 **BALLYRIHY (IRE),** 7, br g Farhaan—Ceoil Eireann **Miss B. Collison**
4 **BALOO'S PERK (IRE),** 6, b m Executive Perk—Lucky Baloo **Kevin Clarke**
5 **BARNA BREEZE (IRE),** 6, br g Farhaan—Barna Beauty **Miss B. Collison**
6 **BARNA LAD (IRE),** 8, ch g Torus—Barna Beauty **Miss B. Collison**
7 **BARNA LASS,** 7, b m Lafontaine (USA)—Barna Beauty **Miss B. Collison**
8 **COMMANCHE RETREAT (IRE),** 5, ch g Commanche Run—Fillo **Mr D. O'Meara**
9 **DONADINO (IRE),** 5, br g Be My Native—Atteses **Mr J. P. McManus**
10 **ELECTRIC PRINCESS (IRE),** 6, b m Electric—Santa Anita Jet **Racing Exiles Syndicate**
11 **GO GO HENRY (IRE),** 6, br g Roselier (FR)—Glencairn Lass **Capt D. G. Swan**
12 **KING OF THE GREEKS (IRE),** 5, b g Mandalus—Greek Tan **Capt D. G. Swan**
13 **LIKE A LION (IRE),** 7, b g Farhaan—Marble Miller (IRE) **Mrs Orla Finulane**
14 **LORD OF THE CHASE (IRE),** 5, ch g Le Bavard (FR)—Katy Quick **Mr Thomas Keane**
15 **MARCUSMYMAN (IRE),** 6, b g Lafontaine (USA)—Goose Loose **Mrs R. Orr**
16 **MIGHTY MARBLE (IRE),** 6, br m Satco (FR)—Marble Owen **Mr Robert Hodgins**
17 **MILEY SWEENEY,** 11, ch g Le Moss—Abbeyside **Stephen O'Connor Miley**
18 **OONAGH'S STAR (IRE),** 6, b g Brush Aside (USA)—Kimstar **Mr J. P. McManus**
19 **PERSIAN DREAM (IRE),** 5, b m Mazaad—Irish Dream **C. Pettigrew**
20 **SAVANAGH (IRE),** 4, b f Brush Aside (USA)—Sesetta **Capt D. G. Swan**
21 **SCAR (IRE),** 7, ch g Orchestra—Linda Dudley **Francis G. Kenny**
22 **ST BARTS (IRE),** 6, ch g Eve's Error—Eileen Fancy **J. Connolly**
23 **TREASURE CHANT (IRE),** 8, b g Treasure Hunter—Ring Twice **Michael V. Hough**

Jockey (NH): C F Swan (9-7, w.a.).

Conditional: Joseph Donnelly (10-0).

Amateur: Mr John O'Meara (9-0).

Lady Riders: Miss M L Olivefalk (9-7), Miss N Swan (9-7).

561 MRS A. SWINBANK, Richmond

Postal: **Hurgill Lodge, Richmond, North Yorkshire, DL10 4TA.**
Phone: **(01748) 850444 FAX (01748) 850819 MOBILE (0802) 496332**

1 6, B g Le Moss—Bullawn Lady **Mrs Ann Swinbank**
2 **BURNING TRUTH (USA),** 4, ch g Known Fact (USA)—Galega **Middleham Park Racing**
3 **CHARMING ADMIRAL (IRE),** 5, b g Shareef Dancer (USA)—Lilac Charm **Mrs Linda Corbett**
4 **COLOUR CODE,** 6, ch g Polish Precedent (USA)—Reprocolor **Mr Bill Walker**
5 **CRAIGARY,** 7, b g Dunbeath (USA)—Velvet Pearl **Mr James A. Cringan**
6 **DAWN LAD (IRE),** 9, b g Lancastrian—Lek Dawn **Mr Arnie Flower**
7 6, Gr g Roselier (FR)—Derrymore's Mossy **G. B. Tulnbull Ltd**
8 **DOMINO FLYER,** 5, b g Warrshan (USA)—Great Dilemma **Mr S. Smith**
9 **FIELD OF VISION (IRE),** 8, b g Vision (USA)—Bold Meadows **Mr David C. Young**
10 5, B h Belfort (FR)—Fishpond **Mrs Ann Swinbank**
11 **ILE DISTINCT (IRE),** 4, b g Dancing Dissident (USA)—Golden Sunlight **Windsor Room Syndicate**
12 **IRISH BUZZ (IRE),** 6, b g Satco (FR)—Brisbee **Mr Jim McCarthy**
13 **KITTOCHSIDE LAD,** 8, br g Destroyer—Chalkies Pet **Scotnorth Racing Ltd**
14 **LANACAR LANE,** 6, b g Northern State (USA)—My Polyanna **Scotnorth Racing Ltd**
15 **MILTON,** 5, ch g Groom Dancer (USA)—Gold Flair **Mrs Julie Martin**
16 **OHIO ROYALE,** 4, ch g Shalford (IRE)—Jupiter's Message **Mr William Riddell**
17 **PARLANCA BAY (IRE),** 6, b g Lancastrian—Parsons Law **Mrs L. J. Tounsend**
18 **PHARMISTICE (IRE),** 7, b g Phardante (FR)—Lucylet **Mr John Halliday**
19 **QUARTERSTAFF,** 4, b g Charmer—Quaranta **Mr S. Smith**
20 **RAED,** 5, b h Nashwan (USA)—Awayed (USA) **Mr David C. Young**
21 **RISING DAWN (IRE),** 6, ch g Rising—Bawnard Lady **Mr Eddie Shotton**
22 **SAM'S MAN (IRE),** 8, b g Lancastrian—Boston Rose **Townstock Partnership**
23 **SILLARS STALKER (IRE),** 10, b g Stalker—Mittens **Sillars Civil Engineering Ltd**
24 **SILVER PENNY,** 8, gr m Silly Prices—Vinovia **Mrs H. M. Woods**
25 **SNOW KINGDOM (IRE),** 4, b g Akarad (FR)—Whitesville (IRE) **Leicestershire Thoroughbred Racing Club**
26 **SOUTHERN BELLE,** 4, b f Dixi (BEL)—Run Milady **Scotnorth Racing Ltd**
27 **SURTSEY,** 4, ch g Nashwan (USA)—Fire And Shade (USA) **G. B. Tulnball Ltd**
28 **TEME VALLEY,** 4, b g Polish Precedent (USA)—Sudeley **Mr Eddie Shotton**
29 **THE KHOINOA (IRE),** 8, b g Supreme Leader—Fine Drapes **The Jolly Boys Partnership**
30 **TIRMIZI (USA),** 7, b g Shahrastani (USA)—Tikarna (FR) **Mr S. Smith**
31 **TROODOS,** 12, b g Worlingworth—My Polyanna **Scotnorth Racing Ltd**
32 **VENI VIDI VICI (IRE),** 5, b h Fayruz—Divine Apsara **Mrs Ann Swinbank**

THREE-YEAR-OLDS

33 **ANGELIC ASSEMBLY,** b f Presidium—Angels Answer (IRE) **Mrs Ellie Holder**
34 **DOUGS DREAM (IRE),** ch f Mac's Imp (USA)—Lomond Heights (IRE) **Mr Doug Marshall**
35 B f Last Tycoon—Habichess **Mrs Ann Swinbank**
36 **IMPERIAL HONEY (IRE),** b f Imperial Frontier (USA)—Indian Honey **Mr Eddie Shotton**
37 **MISSED DOMINO,** ch f Ron's Victory (USA)—Far Claim (USA) **Mr S. Smith**
38 **REPTON,** ch g Rock City—Hasty Key (USA) **Mrs Julie Martin**
39 Gr f Absalom—Saltina **Mrs Ann Swinbank**

TWO-YEAR-OLDS

40 **ALI YA YA,** b f 22/1 Puissance—Manor Adventure (Smackover) **Mrs Julie Martin**
41 **CRYSTAL ROSIE,** gr f 7/4 Ardkinglass—Indian Crystal (Petong) **Mr J. Carter**
42 B f 13/4 Fayruz—Depaypur (Touch Paper) **Mr Nigel Fisher**
43 Ch f 7/4 Polar Falcon (USA)—Kaliala (FR) (Pharly (FR)) **Mr Eddie Shotton**
44 **LEAPING CHARLIE,** b c 14/4 Puissance—Impala Lass (Kampala) **Mr J. Carter**

Other Owners: Ms J. A. Bostock, Mr C. Bradwell, Mr F. P. Byrne, Mr A. Campbell, Mr J. Carter, Mr I. Fox, Mrs D. L. Holder, Mr A. E. Lea, Mr David R. Martin, Mr Adam Menzies, Panther Racing Ltd, Mr N. R. Pullan, Mr Tim Townsend, Upex Electrical Distributors Ltd.

Jockey (Flat): George Duffield (w.a.).

Jockey (NH): John Supple (10-0).

Amateur: Mr Chris Wilson (10-6).

Lady Rider: Miss Lorna Preston.

562 MR D. G. SWINDLEHURST, Carlisle

Postal: **Lynefoot, Westlinton, Carlisle, Cumbria, CA6 6AJ.**
Phone: **(01228) 74289**

1 **ALAN'S PRIDE (IRE),** 7, b m Supreme Leader—Mantilla Run **Mr D. J. Swindlehurst**
2 **DIPADOR (IRE),** 6, b m Satco (FR)—Joy's Toy **Mr D. J. Swindlehurst**
3 **GRANDERISE (IRE),** 8, b g Digamist (USA)—Miss Morgan **Mr D. J. Swindlehurst**
4 **TALL MEASURE,** 12, b g High Top—Millimeter (USA) **Mr D. J. Swindlehurst**

Jockey (NH): B Storey (10-0, w.a.).

Amateur: Mr D J Swindlehurst (10-7).

563 MR T. P. TATE, Tadcaster

Postal: **Castle Farm, Hazlewood, Tadcaster, North Yorkshire, LS24 9NJ.**
Phone: **(01937) 836036 FAX (01937) 530011 Mobile: (0802) 197494**

1 **A DAY ON THE DUB,** 5, b g Presidium—Border Mouse **The Ivy Syndicate**
2 **AGHAWADDA GOLD (IRE),** 6, b g Peacock (FR)—Portane Miss **The Ivy Syndicate**
3 **ASK TOM (IRE),** 9, b g Strong Gale—On The Scratch **Mr B. T. Stewart-Brown**
4 **BLACK ICE (IRE),** 7, b g Cataldi—Turbulent Lass **Sir Simon Lycett Green**
5 **HARDACRE,** 4, b g Phardante (FR)—Dublin Ferry **Sir Simon Lycett Green**
6 **JOSS BAY,** 6, ch g Nearly A Hand—Maranzi **Mrs J. Young**
7 **KATIE BAGGAGE (IRE),** 6, b m Brush Aside (USA)—Red Celtic **Mr Michael G. H. Adcock**
8 **LEVITICUS (IRE),** 4, b g Law Society (USA)—Rubbiera (IRE) **Mrs S. L. Worthington**
9 **LITTLE TWIG (IRE),** 5, b m Good Thyne (USA)—Red Celtic **Mr Michael G. H. Adcock**
10 **LO STREGONE,** 12, b g The Parson—Somers Castle **Mrs Sylvia Clegg & Mrs S. L. Worthington**
11 **MAJOR TOM (IRE),** 4, ch g Mister Lord (USA)—Crash Street **Mr T. P. Tate**
12 **SPIRIT OF STEEL,** 5, gr g Arzanni—Miss Redlands **Mr B. T. Stewart-Brown**
13 **THE SNOW BURN,** 5, ch g River God (USA)—Rose Rambler **The Ivy Syndicate**
14 **WHAT A FIDDLER (IRE),** 5, ch g Orchestra—Crowenstown Miss **Mr C. E. Whiteley**

THREE-YEAR-OLDS

15 **ORLEANS (IRE),** b g Scenic—Guest House **Mr C. E. Whiteley**
16 **RIOJA,** ch g Anshan—Executive Flare **Mrs Sylvia Clegg**

TWO-YEAR-OLDS

17 **FERRET EDDIE (IRE),** ch c Be My Guest (USA)—Musical Essence **The Ivy Syndicate**
18 **KINGFISHER GOLD (IRE),** b c Perugino (USA)—Cerosia **Mr C. E. Whiteley**

Other Owners: Mr D. M. W. Hodgkiss, Mrs S. Hodgkiss, Mrs T. P. Tate.

Jockey (NH): R Garrity (10-0).

Amateur: Mr W Burnell (10-0).

564 MRS L. C. TAYLOR, Chipping Warden

Postal: **Blackgrounds Farm, Chipping Warden, Banbury, Oxfordshire, OX17 1LZ.**
Phone: **(01295) 660267 FAX (01295) 660267**

1 **ALPA'S HONOR (FR)**, 6, b m Hero's Honor (USA)—Quiet Thoughts **Mrs L. C. Taylor**
2 **CABILLE (FR)**, 6, ch g Lesotho (USA)—Ironique (FR) **Mrs L. C. Taylor**
3 **CHURCH LAW**, 11, gr g Sexton Blake—Legal Argument **Mrs L. C. Taylor**
4 **DOMAINE DE PRON (FR)**, 7, ch g Brezzo (FR)—Pasiphae (FR) **Mrs L. C. Taylor**
5 **FUNNY GENIE (FR)**, 5, b g Genereux Genie—Sauteuse de Retz (FR) **Mrs L. C. Taylor**
6 **GRUNDON (IRE)**, 9, br g Mandalus—Buckskin Lady **Mrs L. C. Taylor**
7 **KNOCKANARD (IRE)**, 6, br g Executive Perk—Trianqo **Mrs W. Morrell**

565 MR D. T. THOM, Newmarket

Postal: **Exeter Stables, Church Street, Exning, Newmarket, Suffolk, CB8 7EH.**
Phone: **HOME (01638) 577675 FAX (01638) 577675**

1 **BEAU BRUNO**, 5, b g Thatching—Lady Lorelei **Mr D. E. Jenkins**
2 **CAPTAIN MARMALADE**, 9, ch g Myjinski (USA)—Lady Seville **Mrs Alison Thom**
3 **CLARENCE COURT**, 9, gr g Old Lucky—Lady Melynda VII **Mr J. P. Lee-Woolf**
4 **DUNABRATTIN**, 5, b h Blakeney—Relatively Smart **Harraton Racing Partnership**
5 **LIATHACH**, 7, b g Shirley Heights—Reuval **Mr M. Melluish**
6 **SLIGHTLY SPECIAL (IRE)**, 6, ch g Digamist (USA)—Tunguska **Mrs R. Nash**
7 **THE LADY CAPTAIN**, 6, b m Neltino—Lady Seville **Mr Jack Ashurst**
8 **VISTEC EXPRESS (IRE)**, 8, b g Salse (USA)—Kriswick **Shamrock Horseboxes Ltd**

THREE-YEAR-OLDS

9 **BIZZIE LIZZIE**, gr f Touch of Grey—Lovely Lizzie **Mr R. Foulds**
10 **KATIES TREAT (IRE)**, ch f Superpower—Fancied **Mrs R. Nash**
11 **RUTHS GEM (IRE)**, ch f Imperial Frontier (USA)—Hossvend **Mrs R. Nash**
12 **TACT**, b f Deploy—Yes **Mr W. F. Coleman**

TWO-YEAR-OLDS

13 **DANNY DEEVER**, b c 29/4 Deploy—Yes **Mr W. F. Coleman**

Other Owners: Mr J. M. Dyson, Miss S. Graham, Mr M. W. Littlewort, Mrs J. A. Purdy.

Lady Riders: Miss Julia Feilden, Miss Diana Jones (9-0).

566 MRS D. THOMAS, Bridgend

Postal: **Pen-Y-Lan Farm, Aberkenfig, Bridgend, Mid Glam, CF32 9AN.**
Phone: **(01656) 720254**

1 **EASY OVER (USA)**, 12, ch g Transworld (USA)—Love Bunny (USA) **Mrs D. Thomas**
2 **SANDVILLE LAD**, 6, gr g Librate—Inglifield **Mrs D. Thomas**
3 **SHREWD JOHN**, 12, b g John French—Seal Shrew **Mrs D. Thomas**

567 MR RONALD THOMPSON, Doncaster

Postal: **No 2 Bungalow, Haggswood Racing Stable, Stainforth, Doncaster, South Yorkshire, DN7 5PS.**
Phone: **(01302) 845904 FAX (01302) 845904**

1 **ALLEMANDE (IRE)**, 6, b h Nashwan (USA)—Dance Festival **Mr Stephen Jones**
2 **BROUGHTON'S PRIDE (IRE)**, 7, b m Superpower—French Quarter **Mrs J. Morris**
3 **CAPTAIN CARAT**, 7, gr g Handsome Sailor—Gem of Gold **P. D. Q. Express Security Services**

MR RONALD THOMPSON—continued

4 **HEVER GOLF ANGEL (IRE),** 4, b f Mujadil (USA)—Doon Belle **Haggswood Partnerships**
5 **HOH MAJESTIC (IRE),** 5, b g Soviet Lad (USA)—Sevens Are Wild **Mr Ronald Thompson**
6 **KALICK,** 5, b g Komaite (USA)—Lucky Relikon **P. D. Q. Express Security Services**
7 **M-I-FIVE (IRE),** 7, ch g Classic Secret (USA)—B J Moon **Haggswood Partnerships**
8 **MIRUS,** 5, ch g Tina's Pet—Water Stock **Mr J. Bradwell**
9 6, B m Ra Nova—Moon Game **Mrs J. Carney**
10 **SKYERS TRYER,** 4, b f Lugana Beach—Saltina **Mrs J. Carney**
11 **STORM DANCE,** 7, b g Celestial Storm (USA)—Moonlight Fling **Haggswood Partnerships**

THREE-YEAR-OLDS

12 Ch g Dancing Monarch—Arcadian Princess
13 **CANDY TWIST,** b f Deploy—Simply Candy (IRE) **Mr J. Bradwell**
14 B f King's Signet (USA)—Debsy Do (USA)
15 B g Mazaad—Glazepta Final
16 **KARENARAGON,** b f Aragon—Rosy Sunset (IRE) **Mr Allan Howling**
17 **MAEDALEY,** b f Charmer—Carousella **Haggswood Partnerships**
18 **NEW DESIRE,** b g Then Again—Unjha
19 **SKYERS A KITE,** b f Deploy—Milady Jade (IRE) **Mrs J. Carney**
20 **VET'S DECEIT (IRE),** ch g Statoblest—Maniusha **Mr Ronald Thompson**

TWO-YEAR-OLDS

21 Ch f 10/5 Anshan—Baby Flo (Porto Bello) **Mrs J. Carney**
22 B f 1/4 Alhijaz—Kalvee Dancer (Kalaglow) **Mrs J. Carney**
23 Ch c 23/3 King Among Kings—Market Blues (Porto Bello)
24 B g 9/2 Noble Patriarch—Naufrage (Main Reef)
25 B f 6/5 Merdon Melody—Thabeh (Shareef Dancer (USA))

Other Owners: Mrs M. E. Boggon, Mr R. Holford, Mr D. G. Poole, Mrs M. Thompson.

Jockey (Flat): V Halliday (8-4).

Conditional: A Todd (9-0).

568 MR A. M. THOMSON, Greenlaw

Postal: **Lambden Burns, Greenlaw, Duns, Berwickshire, TD10 6UN.**

1 **BENGHAZI,** 14, b br g Politico (USA)—Numerous **Mr A. M. Thomson**
2 **CORNKITTY,** 11, b m Oats—Kitty Castle **Mr D. M. Thomson**

Other Owners: Mrs B. K. Thomson, Mrs M. C. Thomson.

569 MRS DOROTHY THOMSON, Milnathort

Postal: **Tillyrie Farm, Milnathort, Kinross, KY13 7SW.**
Phone: **(01577) 863418 FAX (01577) 863418**

1 **ALLFORUS (IRE),** 6, gr m Sula Bula—Kissing Gate **The Kelso Connection**
2 5, B m Teeenoso (USA)—Anita's Choice **Scottish Racing Club**
3 **BLOOMING SPRING (IRE),** 9, b m Strong Gale—Ask The Boss **The Coutts McGregor Clan**
4 5, B g Respect—Cool Date **Mrs V. Gilmour**
5 **FINER FEELINGS,** 6, b m Feelings (FR)—High Caraval **Mrs Dorothy Thomson**
6 **FLOWER OF DUNBLANE,** 7, ch m Ardross—Anita's Choice **Mrs Dorothy Thomson**
7 **HEAVENLY THOUGHT,** 7, ch m Alias Smith (USA)—Moonbreaker **Mrs Jean McGregor**

MRS DOROTHY THOMSON—continued

8 **JOWOODY,** 5, ch m Gunner B—Maskwood **Tagwood Syndicate**
9 **MISS COLETTE,** 10, b m Meadowbrook—Miss Colonnette **Mr Robert Drysdale**
10 5, B g Lighter—Moonbreaker **Mrs Dorothy Thomson**
11 **MORE CHAMPAGNE,** 8, ch m Little Wolf—Anita's Choice **The Border Hotel**
12 **MUSIC BLITZ,** 7, b g Sizzling Melody—Sunny Waters **The Coutts McGregor Clan**
13 **NORDIC GIFT (DEN),** 5, ch g Bold Arrangement—Nordic Rose (DEN) **Mrs E. G. Jorgensen**
14 **NORDISK LEGEND,** 6, b g Colmore Row—Nordic Rose (DEN) **Punters Haven Racing Club**
15 **PEGGY GORDON,** 7, b m Feelings (FR)—Megan's Way **Frank Flynn and Richard Madden**
16 **PESSIMISTIC DICK,** 5, b g Derrylin—Tycoon Moon **The Tam Pepper Partnership**
17 **TONY'S FEELINGS,** 10, b g Feelings (FR)—Meg's Mantle **Die-Hard Racing Club**
18 4, B g Feelings (FR)—Wedderburn **Mrs Dorothy Thomson**

Other Owners: Mr Jim Anderson, Mrs C. G. Braithwaite, Mr E. Bruce, Capt Ben Coutts, Mr & Mrs Day, Mr Thomas Dyer, Mr Frank Flynn, Mr M. Griese, Mr J. W. Hazeldean, Mr R. Madden, Mrs Daphne Pease, Mr J. Thomson, Mr L. Wright.

Jockeys (NH): Liam O'Hara, David Parker.

Lady Rider: Miss P Robson.

570 MR N. B. THOMSON, Shaftesbury

Postal: **Duncliffe Home Farm, Stour Row, Shaftesbury, Dorset, SP7 0QW.**
Phone: **EAST STOUR (01747) 838262**

1 **BOOZYS DREAM,** 7, b g All Fair—Miss Moth **Mr Gordon Legg**
2 **FOUROFUS,** 9, b g Wassl—Que Sera **Mr N. B. Thomson**
3 **INDIAN CROWN,** 8, b m Welsh Captain—Indian Cash **Mr Philip Buckley**
4 **MASCALLS LADY,** 13, b m Nicholas Bill—Whisper Gently **Mrs Madge Cox**
5 **MISS NORWAIT,** 8, b m Norwick (USA)—Miss Kuwait **Mr R. N. Short**
6 **TAXBUSTER,** 6, b g Welsh Captain—Indian Cash **Taxbusters**
7 6, Ch m Sharp Deal—Toddy Noddy **Mrs L. K. Jeans**
8 **WEST LODGE LADY,** 13, ch m Crooner—Rose of France **Mrs Madge Cox**

Other Owners: Mrs J. Wills, Mr M. J. Witt.

571 MR R. W. THOMSON, Hawick

Postal: **Millcourt, Cavers, Hawick, Roxburghshire, TD9 8LN.**
Phone: **(01450) 372668**

1 5, Ch m Henbit (USA)—Queen's Darling **Mr R. W. Thomson**
2 **RUBER,** 11, b g Mljet—Chip of Gold **Mr R. W. Thomson**

Jockeys (NH): D Parker, B Storey (10-0).

Lady Rider: Miss P Robson.

572 MR G. E. THORNER, Wantage

Postal: **Upper Manor Farm, Letcombe Regis, Wantage, Oxfordshire, OX12 9LD.**
Phone: **WANTAGE (01235) 763003**

1 **ARCTIC LODGE (IRE)**, 6, b g Arctic Lord—Mogen **Mr Graham Thorner**
2 **HUNTING MONARCH (IRE)**, 6, b g King's Ride—Kylogue's Delight **Mr P. A. Deal**
3 **JUST A ROADIE (IRE)**, 5, b g Good Thyne (USA)—Lochda **Miss A. Jones**
4 **LASTO ADREE (IRE)**, 7, b g Shernazar—Summer Palace **Miss J. Newell**
5 **MAETERLINCK (IRE)**, 6, b g Bluebird (USA)—Entracte **Mr Graham Thorner**
6 **MONKS JAY (IRE)**, 9, b g Monksfield—Boro Penny **Mr J. A. Cover**
7 **ROYAL ANNABELLA**, 7, b m Rambo Dancer (CAN)—Malise **Miss A. Jones**
8 **STAUNCH RIVAL (USA)**, 11, b g Sir Ivor—Crystal Bright **Mrs Penny Mitchell**
9 **SUNDAY MARKET (USA)**, 4, b g Lear Fan (USA)—Sunday Bazaar (USA) **Mr Graham Thorner**
10 **WENTWORTH (USA)**, 6, b g Diesis—Line Call (USA) **Miss J. Newell**
11 **ZABARI (IRE)**, 5, b g Soviet Star (USA)—Zafadola (IRE) **Mr P. J. Orme**

Other Owners: Mr N. Boyd, Mr Alan W. Clarke, Mr R. K. Curtis, Mr I. R. Disney, Mr Jeremy Edwards, Miss D. M. Harris, Mr J. D. Hussey, Mr Bill Ivens, Mr Russell James, Mr Frank R. Jarvey, Mr Keith Ogden, Mr Crispin Wall, Mr J. D. T. Wall, Mr J. P. C. Wall.

Jockeys (NH): D Bridgwater, B Powell.

Conditional: Clare Thorner (10-0).

Lady Rider: Clare Thorner.

573 MR C. W. THORNTON, Middleham

Postal: **Spigot Lodge, Coverham, Leyburn, North Yorkshire, DL8 4TL.**
Phone: **(01969) 623350 LADS HOSTEL (01969) 622252 FAX (01969) 624374**

1 **BONGO**, 4, b g Efisio—Boo Hoo **Mr Guy Reed**
2 **BONNIE LASSIE**, 4, gr f Efisio—Normanby Lass **Mr Guy Reed**
3 **CITTADINO**, 8, b g Good Thyne (USA)—Slave's Bangle **Mr D. B. Dennison**
4 **GOOD DAY**, 4, gr g Petong—Courtesy Call **Mr Guy Reed**
5 **HANAJIR (IRE)**, 4, b f Cadeaux Genereux—Muhit (USA) **Mr Guy Reed**
6 **MUSTANG**, 5, ch g Thatching—Lassoo **Mr Guy Reed**
7 **NEW DAWN**, 4, ch f Rakaposhi King—Raise The Dawn **Mr Trevor Grice**
8 **POLAR KING (IRE)**, 5, b g Glacial Storm (USA)—Our Little Lamb **Mr I. Bray**
9 **PRIDE OF BRIXTON**, 5, b g Dominion—Caviar Blini **Mr Guy Reed**
10 **PRIORESS (IRE)**, 4, b f Supreme Leader—Lohunda Lady **Mr Simon Brown**
11 **QUEEN'S SPEECH (IRE)**, 5, b m Supreme Leader—Announcement **Mr I. Bray**
12 **RAJAH**, 5, b br g Be My Chief (USA)—Pretty Thing **Mr Guy Reed**
13 **RANCHEROS**, 4, b g Mandrake Major—Sioux Be It **Mr Guy Reed**
14 **ROUND ROBIN (IRE)**, 4, ch g Royal Academy (USA)—Flying Fantasy **Mr Guy Reed**
15 **SIDE BY SIDE (IRE)**, 5, b m Brush Aside (USA)—Jupiter Miss (USA) **Mr Simon Brown**
16 **SIOUX**, 4, ch f Kris—Lassoo **Mr Guy Reed**
17 **SON OF ARAGON**, 4, b g Aragon—Golden Swallow (NZ) **Mr W. G. Thornton**
18 **TAM O'SHANTER**, 4, gr g Persian Bold—No More Rosies **Mr Guy Reed**
19 **TRIBUNE**, 7, ch g Kefaah (USA)—Quick J **Hexagon Racing**

THREE-YEAR-OLDS

20 **AMAZONIAN**, b c Formidable (USA)—Red Rose Garden **Mr Guy Reed**
21 **BEST OF OUR DAYS**, b c Clantime—Uptown Girl **Mr Guy Reed**

MR C. W. THORNTON—continued

22 **BLOW ME A KISS,** ch f Kris—Lassoo **Mr Guy Reed**
23 **BLUE MOON (IRE),** b c Scenic—Debach Delight **Mr Guy Reed**
24 **BUZZ,** b c Anshan—Ryewater Dream **Mr Guy Reed**
25 **DEB'S DELIGHT,** ch f Most Welcome—Adana (FR) **Mr Guy Reed**
26 **ENVOY,** b c Presidium—Chief Dancer **Mr Guy Reed**
27 **FEARLESS BRAVE,** b c Aragon—Siouan **Mr Guy Reed**
28 **GLIDER (IRE),** b f Silver Kite (USA)—Song of The Glens **Mr Guy Reed**
29 **HUSSAR (IRE),** ch c Shalford (IRE)—How Gorgeous **Mr Guy Reed**
30 **RIGOLETTO,** ch c Machiavellian (USA)—Sally Brown **Mr Guy Reed**
31 **ROMA,** b f Second Set (IRE)—Villasanta **Mr Guy Reed**
32 **SHIFTING,** ch f Night Shift (USA)—Preening **Mr Guy Reed and Mrs Ailsa Daniels**
33 **STACCATO,** b c Forzando—Fast Car (FR) **Mr Guy Reed**
34 **TAJ MAHAL (IRE),** b c High Estate—Verthumna **Mr Guy Reed**
35 **WHIRLWIND,** b c Puissance—Yours Or Mine (IRE) **Mr Guy Reed**

TWO-YEAR-OLDS

36 **ALEXANDER,** b c 19/2 Be My Chief (USA)—Arminda (Blakeney) **Mr Guy Reed**
37 **INDIAN PLUME,** b c 23/2 Efisio—Boo Hoo (Mummy's Pet) **Mr Guy Reed**
38 **MISS DOODY BUSINESS,** br f 4/3 Formidable (USA)—Miss Doody (Gorytus (USA)) **Racegoers Club Owners Group**
39 **SCARLET,** ch f 5/3 Bluebird (USA)—Taza (Persian Bold) **Mr Guy Reed**
40 **SHALL WE DANCE,** b f 7/2 Rambo Dancer (CAN)—Anger Fire (Nashwan (USA)) **Mr Guy Reed**
41 **SPY (IRE),** br c 15/2 Mac's Imp (USA)—Mystery Bid (Auction Ring (USA)) **Mr Guy Reed**

Other Owners: Mr P. W. Bayston, Mrs Joy Bendall, Mr Geoff Bonson, Mr G. H. Brittain, Mr J. R. Churchill, Miss L. M. Gold, Mr J. Hanson, Racegoers Club Spigot Lodge Owners Group, Mr R. W. Rose, Mr I. Townsend, Mr M. E. Twibell, Mrs S. Waddup.

Jockey (Flat): Dean McKeown (8-4, w.a.).

Jockey (NH): M Foster (10-0).

574 MR W. H. TINNING, York

Postal: **High Street Farm, Thornton-Le-Clay, York, Yorkshire, YO6 7TE.**
Phone: **MALTON (01653) 618996**

1 **CHADWICK'S GINGER,** 10, ch m Crofthall—Knight Hunter **Mr W. H. Tinning**
2 **MEMBERS WELCOME (IRE),** 5, b g Eve's Error—Manuale Delutente **Mr W. H. Tinning**
3 **RIGHTY HO,** 4, b g Reprimand—Challanging **Mr W. H. Tinning**

575 MR D. M. TODHUNTER, Ulverston

Postal: **The North Lodge, Priory Road, Ulverston, Cumbria, LA12 9RX.**
Phone: **(01229) 580529 MOBILE (0976) 440082**

1 **AMOEBIC (IRE),** 5, b g Prince Rupert (FR)—Redington Belle **Mrs Rita Butler**
2 **BUABHALL MOR,** 5, ch g Nishapour (FR)—Share A Friend **Mr Paul Fitzpatrick**
3 4, B g Glacial Storm (USA)—Castleblagh **J. L. Racing**
4 **CHIPPED OUT,** 8, gr g Scallywag—City's Sister **Domino Racing**
5 **DIVVLING,** 4, br g Golden Heights—Fast Dancer **Mrs J. Rowlinson**
6 **EMBRYONIC (IRE),** 6, b g Prince Rupert (FR)—Belle Viking (FR) **Mrs D. Miller**
7 **FAN D'ESTRUVAL (FR),** 5, ch g Quart de Vin (FR)—Pommette III **Mr Robert Ogden**
8 **HAG'S WAY (IRE),** 8, ch g Roselier (FR)—Lucifer's Way **Mrs Alurie O'Sullivan**

MR D. M. TODHUNTER—continued

9 **HIGHLAND WAY (IRE),** 10, b g Kemal (FR)—Peace Run **Mr J. D. Gordon**
10 **ICONIC,** 4, b g Reprimand—Miami Melody **Great Head House Estates Limited**
11 **KWIKPOINT,** 4, ch g Never So Bold—Try The Duchess **Great Head House Estates Limited**
12 **LACONIC (IRE),** 4, b g Fools Holme (USA)—Advantageous **Great Head House Estates Limited**
13 **MAITRE DE MUSIQUE (FR),** 7, ch g Quai Voltaire (USA)—Mativa (FR) **Mr Robert Ogden**
14 5, Ch m Gunner B—March At Dawn **Mr J. Lomax**
15 **MOONLIGHT VENTURE,** 6, b g Jupiter Island—Moonlight Bay **Mr Smalley**
16 **NAWTINOOKEY,** 8, gr m Uncle Pokey—Abrasive **G. C. G. Racing Partnership**
17 **NIGHT EXPRESS,** 4, ch g Night Shift (USA)—New Edition **Barley Lion Racing**
18 **PARIAH (IRE),** 9, b g Derring Rose—Proverb Lady **Mrs D. Miller**
19 **PREMIER CRU (IRE),** 6, b g Strong Gale—Diana's Mile **Mr Robert Ogden**
20 **PRIME EXAMPLE (IRE),** 7, ch g Orchestra—Vanessa's Princess **Mr Robert Ogden**
21 **REALLY USEFUL (IRE),** 6, b g Strong Gale—Arctic Match **Mr Robert Ogden**
22 **SALEM BEACH,** 6, b m Strong Gale—Ellen Greaves **Mrs David Marshall**
23 **SLAUGHT SON (IRE),** 10, br g Roselier (FR)—Stream Flyer **Mrs D. Miller**
24 **STRONG BRAVE (IRE),** 4, b g Strong Gale—Kemaldor **Mr J. D. Gordon**
25 **SWING BAR,** 5, b m Sadeem (USA)—Murex **Mr S. P. Marsh**
26 **TINDLES BIBLE,** 6, b g Le Coq d'Or—Wedderburn **Mr Keith Jackson**
27 **VALHALLA (IRE),** 5, b g Brush Aside (USA)—Eimers Pet **Mrs D. Miller**
28 **WILLIE HORNE,** 5, b g Batshoof—Folle Idee (USA) **Great Head House Estates Limited**

THREE-YEAR-OLDS

29 **CURRICULUS (IRE),** ch g Sharp Victor (USA)—Felsen (IRE) **Mrs D. Miller**

TWO-YEAR-OLDS

30 Ch f Pips Pride—Grayfoot **Great Head House Estates Limited**

Other Owners: Mr A. M. Davidson, Mr P. Dawson, Leeds Plywood And Doors Ltd, Mr W. A. McCoubrey, Mr George Watson.

Jockey (Flat): J Carroll (w.a.).

Jockeys (NH): P Carberry, P Niven.

Conditional: C McCormack.

Amateur: Mr R Hale.

576 MR J. A. R. TOLLER, Whitsbury

Postal: **Majors Farm, Whitsbury, Fordingbridge, Hampshire, SP6 3QG.**
Phone: **(01725) 518220 FAX (01725) 518520 MOBILE (0467) 848077**

1 **AT LARGE (IRE),** 4, b g Night Shift (USA)—Lady Donna **Duke of Devonshire**
2 **COMPTON PLACE,** 4, ch c Indian Ridge—Nosey **Duke of Devonshire**
3 **HURGILL DANCER,** 4, b g Rambo Dancer (CAN)—Try Vickers (USA) **Mr G. Cooper & Partners**
4 **LITERARY SOCIETY (USA),** 5, ch h Runaway Groom (CAN)—Dancing Gull (USA) **Lady Celina Carter**
5 **MARCH STAR (IRE),** 4, b f Mac's Imp (USA)—Grade A Star (IRE) **Mr N. O'Callaghan**
6 **OTHER CLUB,** 4, ch g Kris—Tura **Duke of Devonshire**
7 **RODERICK HUDSON,** 6, b g Elmaamul (USA)—Moviegoer **Duke of Devonshire**
8 **RUSSIAN ROSE (IRE),** 5, b m Soviet Lad (USA)—Thornbeam **Ash Partnership**
9 **SANDICLIFFE (USA),** 5, b m Imp Society (USA)—Sad Song (USA) **Ash Partnership**

MR J. A. R. TOLLER—continued

10 **THE DILETTANTI (USA),** 5, br g Red Ransom (USA)—Rich Thought (USA) **Duke of Devonshire**
11 **VIRTUAL REALITY,** 7, b g Diamond Shoal—Warning Bell **Ash Partnership**
12 **ZIMIRI,** 4, ch c Keen—Annabrianna **Rannerdale, D. G. & N. A. Fraser**

THREE-YEAR-OLDS

13 **BESEECHING (IRE),** b br f Hamas (IRE)—Na-Ammah (IRE) **Mr P. C. J. Dalby**
14 **DUCK ROW (USA),** ch c Diesis—Sunny Moment (USA) **Duke of Devonshire**
15 **KRISTA,** ch f Kris—Tura **Mr C. N. Hart**
16 **LYCIAN (IRE),** b g Lycius (USA)—Perfect Time (IRE) **Mr A. Ilsley**
17 **MADAME CLAUDE (IRE),** b f Paris House—Six Penny Express **Mr P. C. J. Dalby**
18 **PARTING ECHO,** ch g Aragon—Annabrianna **Forum Trustees Limited A/C Rannerdale**
19 **PETARGA,** b f Petong—One Half Silver (CAN) **Mrs R. W. Gore-Andrews**
20 **PURNADAS ROAD (IRE),** ch f Petardia—Choral Park **Mr R. A. C. Toller**
21 **SPANISH EYES,** b f Belmez (USA)—Night Transaction **Mr Alan Gibson**
22 **TEAPOT ROW (IRE),** b c Generous (IRE)—Secrage (USA) **Duke of Devonshire**

TWO-YEAR-OLDS

23 **BLACKHEATH (IRE),** ch c 21/5 Common Grounds—Queen Caroline (USA) (Chief's Crown (USA)) **Mr G. H. Toller**
24 **BUN ALLEY,** b c 7/2 Be My Guest (USA)—Neptunalla (Slip Anchor) **Duke of Devonshire**
25 B f 16/3 Petardia—Business Centre (USA) (Digamist (USA)) **Partnership**
26 **FRANKINCENSE (IRE),** gr c 1/3 Paris House—Mistral Wood (USA) (Far North (CAN)) **Duke of Devonshire**
27 B f 20/3 Sir Harry Lewis (USA)—Lady Minstrel (Tudor Music) **Mr M. E. Wates**
28 **NULLI SECUNDUS,** b c 10/4 Polar Falcon (USA)—Exclusive Virtue (USA) (Shaeed (USA)) **Duke Of Devonshire**
29 **SEWARDS FOLLY,** b f 6/2 Rudimentary (USA)—Anchorage (IRE) (Slip Anchor) **Mr G. M. Cobey**
30 B c 19/3 Unblest—Starinka (Risen Star (USA)) **The Gap Partnership**
31 **UMBRIAN GOLD (IRE),** b f 20/2 Perugino (USA)—Golden Sunlight (Ile de Bourbon (USA)) **Mrs R. W. Gore-Andrews**

Other Owners: Mr J. Austin, Mrs M. E. Austin, Mr J. Findlay, Mrs C. N. Hart, Mr M. G. H. Heald, Mr A. J. Morrison, Lady Sophie Morrison, Mr Andrew Singleton, Mr Simon Smith, Mr L. Straszewski, Mrs Charles Toller, Mrs J. Toller, Mrs J. B. Williams, Mr Philip Wroughton.

Jockey (Flat): S Sanders.

577 MR M. H. TOMPKINS, Newmarket

Postal: **Flint Cottage Stables, Rayes Lane, Newmarket, Suffolk, CB8 7AB.**
Phone: **NEWMARKET (01638) 661434 FAX (01638) 668107**

1 **BLOWING AWAY (IRE),** 4, b br f Last Tycoon—Taken By Force **Mark Tompkins Racing**
2 **BLURRED (IRE),** 5, ch g Al Hareb (USA)—I'll Take Paris (USA) **Trafalgar Racing Club and Partners**
3 **BOBBY'S DREAM,** 6, b m Reference Point—Kiralyi (FR) **Mrs Patricia M. Kalman**
4 **CIRO'S PEARL (IRE),** 4, b f Petorius—Cut It Fine (USA) **Mr J. H. Shannon**
5 **CLAIRESWAN (IRE),** 6, ch g Rhoman Rule (USA)—Choclate Baby **Mrs Beryl Lockey**
6 **COOL EDGE (IRE),** 7, ch g Nashamaa—Mochara **Mr Henry B. H. Chan**
7 **FANTAIL,** 4, b c Taufan (USA)—Eleganza (IRE) **Pamela, Lady Nelson of Stafford**
8 **MISSED CALL (IRE),** 6, b g Phardante (FR)—Una's Run **Mr M. H. Tompkins**
9 **NICHOL FIFTY,** 4, b g Old Vic—Jawaher (IRE) **Mr Lloyd Bedack**
10 **OCKER (IRE),** 4, br g Astronef—Violet Somers **Mr T. N. Claydon**
11 **PARROT'S HILL (IRE),** 5, b g Nashamaa—Cryptic Gold **Mark Tompkins Elite**
12 **ROYAL SCIMITAR (USA),** 6, ch g Diesis—Princess of Man **P. J. M. Racing**
13 **SATCOTINO (IRE),** 7, b m Satco (FR)—Autumn Bounty **Grangewood (Sales & Marketing) Ltd**
14 **SKY DOME (IRE),** 5, ch g Bluebird (USA)—God Speed Her **Miss D. J. Merson**
15 **STAUNCH FRIEND (USA),** 10, b g Secreto (USA)—Staunch Lady (USA) **Mrs M. H. Tompkins**
16 **TAKE COVER (IRE),** 7, b g Meneval (USA)—Bad Weather **Adrienne and Michael Barnett**
17 **THE MOOR (IRE),** 7, br g Strong Gale—Maid of Moyode **Miss D. J. Merson**

MR M. H. TOMPKINS—continued

18 TOPATORI (IRE), 4, ch f Topanoora—Partygoer **Mr M. P. Bowring**
19 TYROLEAN DREAM (IRE), 4, b g Tirol—Heavenly Hope **Mr P. Heath**
20 WESTMINSTER (IRE), 6, ch g Nashamaa—Our Galadrial **Mr Michael C. Jenkins**

THREE-YEAR-OLDS

21 CAMPIONE (IRE), b c Common Grounds—Kyrenia **Mrs Patricia M. Kalman**
22 CHIST (USA), b br c Lear Fan (USA)—Morna **Mrs Jane Bailey**
23 CROMER PIER, b g Reprimand—Fleur du Val **Mrs P. D. Sealey**
24 DUTCH LAD, b c Alnasr Alwasheek—Double Dutch **Mr S. Dean**
25 EMPIRE STATE (IRE), b g High Estate—Palm Dove (USA) **Miss D. J. Merson**
26 FRITTON (IRE), br g Petardia—Calash **Mr P. F. Riseborough**
27 B g Be My Native (USA)—Gales Chariot
28 HANUMAN HIGHWAY (IRE), b g Alzao (USA)—Cherry Ridge **P. J. M. Racing**
29 LUCKY ME (IRE), gr c Maledetto (IRE)—Silver Heart **Mr Michael H. Keogh**
30 MACCA LUNA (IRE), b f Kahyasi—Medicosma (USA) **Mr B. McAllister**
31 MARK TIME, b c Pursuit of Love—Quiet Harbour **Mr J. A. Fuller**
32 NORTHERN LASS (IRE), br f Rainbows For Life (CAN)—Intrepid **Mrs Brian Grice**
33 OPTIMISTIC, b f Reprimand—Arminda **Mystic Meg Limited**
34 PAS DE MEMOIRES (IRE), b c Don't Forget Me—Bally Pourri (IRE) **Mr P. D. Savill**
35 QILIN (IRE), b f Second Set (IRE)—Usance (GER) **Mr Ian Lochhead**
36 RIVER BEAT (IRE), b g River Falls—Aughamore Beauty (IRE) **Grangewood (Sales & Marketing) Ltd**
37 RUDE SHOCK, gr g Rudimentary (USA)—Frighten The Life **Mr J. H. Ellis**
38 SAFARI SAM (IRE), b g Cyrano de Bergerac—Light Hand **Mr Robert Levitt**
39 TEN BOB (IRE), br c Bob Back (USA)—Tiempo **Mrs M. H. Tompkins**
40 THREE ANGELS (IRE), b g Houmayoun (FR)—Mullaghroe **Mr Bernard Bloom**
41 TROJAN WOLF, ch c Wolfhound (USA)—Trojan Lady (USA) **Mr Kenneth MacPherson**
42 WINNING SAINT (IRE), ch c St Jovite (USA)—Winning Heart **Mr Michael H. Keogh**
43 WORTH THE EFFORT, b f Beveled (USA)—Haiti Mill **Adrienne & Michael Barnett**

TWO-YEAR-OLDS

44 APPLES AND PEARS (IRE), b f 25/4 High Estate—Tiempo (King of Spain) **Mrs M. H. Tompkins**
45 BATANTA, br f 24/4 Bob's Return (IRE)—Atlantic Air (Air Trooper) **Mrs Alison Ruggles**
46 BIG CHIEF, ch c 31/3 Be My Chief (USA)—Grove Daffodil (Salt Fome (USA)) **P. H. Betts (Holdings) Ltd**
47 B c 19/5 Aragon—Double Dutch (Nicholas Bill) **Mr L. Fuller**
48 EBLANA (IRE), b f 30/4 Maledetto (IRE)—Dublin Millennium (Dalsaan) **Mr Michael H. Keogh**
49 FANETTA (IRE), b f 14/4 Taufan (USA)—Bold Fille (IRE) (Bold Arrangement) **Pamela, Lady Nelson of Stafford**
50 FIFTH AVENUE, b f 2/2 Unfuwain (USA)—Pencil Sharpener (USA) (Sharpen Up) **Miss D. J. Merson**
51 GABRIEL (IRE), b f 6/3 River Falls—Los Angeles (IRE) (Double Schwartz) **Mr Michael H. Keogh**
52 GAPTON BOB (IRE), b c 30/3 Bob's Return (IRE)—Bradwell (IRE) (Taufan) **Mr P. F. Riseborough**
53 B c 11/4 Tirol—Gay Appeal (Star Appeal) **Mr Richard R. Flatt**
54 Ch f 31/3 Bob's Return (IRE)—Gazettalong (Taufan) **Mark Tompkins Racing**
55 Ch c 13/2 Mujtahid (USA)—Gingerly (USA) (Ferdinand (USA))
56 INTENSITY, b c 10/4 Bigstone (IRE)—Brillante (FR) (Green Dancer (USA)) **Mr J. Lovat**
57 IT'S OUR SECRET (IRE), ch c 17/4 Be My Guest (USA)—Lady Dulcinea (ARG) (General (FR)) **Mrs M. Barwell**
58 LIGHT FINGERED (IRE), ch c 14/2 Soviet Lad (USA)—Light Hand (Star Appeal) **Mr Robert Levitt**
59 MASONIC (IRE), ch c 22/4 Grand Lodge (USA)—Winning Heart (Horage) **Mrs Beryl Lockey**
60 MEGA (IRE), b f 14/5 Petardia—Gobolino (Don) **Mystic Meg Limited**
61 MENSA, ch c 28/4 Rudimentary (USA)—Musianica (Music Boy) **Mrs Beryl Lockey**
62 SEVEN STARS, b c 27/2 Rudimentary (USA)—Carlton Glory (Blakeney) **Magnificent Seven**
63 B c 18/5 Distinctly North—Slightly Latin (Ahonoora) **Flint-Fairyhouse Partnership**
64 B c 26/4 Superlative—Westering (Auction Ring (USA))
65 B c 3/3 Distinctly North—Winscarlet North (Garland Knight) **Mr Richard R. Flatt**

Other Owners: Mrs Sara J. Alldread, Mr D. J. Anderson, Mr N. Bedack, Mr J. Bowers, Mrs P. R. Bowring, Mr B. G. Chan, Mr George H. Gibson, Mr P. S. Green, Mrs Nicola Guest, Mr R. V. Lewis, Mrs V. A. Lewis, Mr Conrad Lockey, Mr Chris Machin, Mr S. M. McAnulty, Mr Colin Russell, Mr David J. Winter.

Jockey (Flat): D Biggs (8-0).

578 MRS P. LAXTON TOWNSLEY, Godalming

Postal: **Mendips, The Common, Dunsfold, Godalming, Surrey, GU8 4LA.**
Phone: **(01483) 200849 MOBILE (0836) 205579**

1 **ALKA INTERNATIONAL,** 6, b g Northern State (USA)—Cachucha **Mr Paul Townsley**
2 **DONT GAMBLE,** 12, gr g Spin of A Coin—Dontlike **Mrs J. H. M. Mackenzie**
3 **FATHER FORTUNE,** 10, b g The Parson—Irish Mint **Mr Paul Townsley**
4 **FOR JOSH (IRE),** 9, ch g Hard Fought—Twice Regal **Mr Paul Townsley**
5 **JELLYBAND,** 10, ro g Baron Blakeney—General's Daughter **Mr Paul Townsley**
6 **MAYGAIN (IRE),** 5, b g Kefaah (USA)—Sistina **Mr M. Logah**
7 **MULTI LINE,** 8, ch m High Line—Waterford Cream **Mrs Pru Townsley**
8 **RUN BAVARD (IRE),** 10, ch g Le Bavard (FR)—Serenade Run **Mr Paul Townsley**
9 **ZIPALONG,** 7, b g Idiot's Delight—Evening Song **Mrs Pru Townsley**
10 **ZIPALONGKATIE,** 6, b m Lightning Dealer—Second Swallow **Mr Nick Garrick**
11 **ZIP YOUR LIP,** 8, b g Ra Nova—Centaur Star **Mr Paul Townsley**

Other Owners: Mr Paul McQueenie, Mr & Mrs J. Thompson.

Amateur: Mr Paul Townsley (11-0).

Lady Riders: Miss C Townsley (9-0), Miss L Townsley (10-0).

579 MR M. P. TREGONING, Lambourn

Postal: **Kingwood House Stables, Lambourn, Berkshire, RG17 7RS.**
Phone: **(01488) 73300 FAX (01488) 71728**

1 **GHALIB (IRE),** 4, ch c Soviet Star (USA)—Nafhaat (USA) **Mr Hamdan Al Maktoum**
2 **MADMUN (IRE),** 4, ch g Cadeaux Genereux—Kates Cabin **Mr Hamdan Al Maktoum**
3 **MUTAZZ (USA),** 6, b g Woodman (USA)—Ghashtah (USA) **Mr M. P. N. Tregoning**
4 **RASHIK,** 4, ch c Cadeaux Genereux—Ghzaalh (USA) **Mr Hamdan Al Maktoum**
5 **SHAYA,** 4, ch c Nashwan (USA)—Gharam (USA) **Mr Hamdan Al Maktoum**

THREE-YEAR-OLDS

6 **ASHIRAH (USA),** b f Housebuster (USA)—Manwah (USA) **Mr Hamdan Al Maktoum**
7 **HAWADETH,** ch c Machiavellian (USA)—Ghzaalh (USA) **Mr Hamdan Al Maktoum**
8 **KADIR,** b br c Unfuwain (USA)—Rafif (USA) **Mr Hamdan Al Maktoum**
9 **LIGHT SHIP,** b f Warning—Bireme **Mr R. D. Hollingsworth**
10 **MUNEERA (USA),** ch f Green Dancer (USA)—Hard Knocker (USA) **Mr Hamdan Al Maktoum**
11 **NEBL,** ch f Persian Bold—Maraatib (IRE) **Mr Hamdan Al Maktoum**
12 **ROYAL BOUNTY (IRE),** b f Generous (IRE)—Queen Helen **Lord Weinstock**
13 **SABHAAN,** b c Green Desert (USA)—Al Theraab (USA) **Mr Hamdan Al Maktoum**
14 **SIFAT,** b f Marju (IRE)—Reine Maid (USA) **Mr Hamdan Al Maktoum**
15 **TAALLUF (USA),** b f Hansel (USA)—Tatwij (USA) **Mr Hamdan Al Maktoum**
16 **THAAYER,** b c Wolfhound (USA)—Hamaya (USA) **Mr Hamdan Al Maktoum**
17 **THE THRUSTER,** b g Elmaamul (USA)—Moon Spin **Mr John Wallis**
18 **TREASURE CHEST (IRE),** b g Last Tycoon—Sought Out (IRE) **Lord Weinstock**

TWO-YEAR-OLDS

19 B c Alzao (USA)—Ah Ya Zein (Artaius (USA)) **Sheikh Ahmed Al Maktoum**
20 B f 23/4 Machiavellian (USA)—Air Distingue (USA) (Sir Ivor) **Sheikh Mohammed**
21 **ASAALA (USA),** ch f 24/4 Slew O'Gold (USA)—Alghuzaylah (Habitat) **Mr Hamdan Al Maktoum**
22 B c 8/3 Danehill (USA)—Ausherra (USA) (Diesis) **Sheikh Ahmed Al Maktoum**
23 **AZIHAAM (USA),** ch f 2/3 Cozzene (USA)—Tatwij (USA) (Topsider (USA)) **Mr Hamdan Al Maktoum**
24 B f 13/5 Salse (USA)—Basha (USA) (Chief's Crown (USA)) **Sheikh Mohammed**

MR M. P. TREGONING—continued

25 B c 9/3 Indian Ridge—Cambrel (IRE) (Soviet Star (USA)) **Sheikh Mohammed**
26 ELHIDA (IRE), ch f 23/5 Mujtahid (USA)—Nouvelle Star (AUS) (Luskin Star (AUS)) **Mr Hamdan Al Maktoum**
27 ELHILMEYA (IRE), b f 24/4 Unfuwain (USA)—Awayed (USA) (Sir Ivor) **Mr Hamdan Al Maktoum**
28 B f 2/3 Forty Niner (USA)—Eternal Reve (USA) (Diesis) **Sheikh Mohammed**
29 B c 10/2 Darshaan—Garconniere (Gay Mecene (USA)) **Sheikh Ahmed Al Maktoum**
30 IONIAN SECRET, b f 30/4 Mystiko (USA)—Hearten (Hittite Glory) **The Emotional Partnership**
31 ISTIKBAL (USA), b f 9/5 Kingmambo (USA)—Tafrah (IRE) (Sadler's Wells (USA)) **Mr Hamdan Al Maktoum**
32 ISTINTAJ (USA), b br c 2/5 Nureyev (USA)—Mathkurh (USA) (Riverman (USA)) **Mr Hamdan Al Maktoum**
33 KAFI (USA), b c 7/4 Gulch (USA)—Nonoalca (FR) (Nonoalco (USA)) **Mr Hamdan Al Maktoum**
34 MAGHAARB, ch f 28/2 Machiavellian (USA)—Fida (IRE) (Persian Heights) **Mr Hamdan Al Maktoum**
35 B br f 7/2 Riverman (USA)—Manwah (USA) (Lyphard (USA)) **Mr Hamdan Al Maktoum**
36 MARASEM, b f 17/2 Cadeaux Genereux—Balaabel (USA) (Sadler's Wells (USA)) **Mr Hamdan Al Maktoum**
37 B c 22/1 Fairy King (USA)—Moonshine Lake (Kris) **Sheikh Ahmed Al Maktoum**
38 MUQTARB (IRE), ch c 2/4 Cadeaux Genereux—Jasarah (IRE) (Green Desert (USA)) **Mr Hamdan Al Maktoum**
39 NAFITH, ch c 8/3 Elmaamul (USA)—Wanisa (USA) (Topsider (USA)) **Mr Hamdan Al Maktoum**
40 Gr f 25/1 Shirley Heights—Papago (IRE) (Sadler's Wells (USA)) **Sheikh Mohammed**
41 B f 21/4 Rainbow Quest (USA)—Pelf (USA) (Al Nasr (FR)) **Sheikh Mohammed**
42 B f 2/4 Darshaan—Percy's Lass (Blakeney) **Sheikh Mohammed**
43 QANDIL (USA), ch c 20/5 Riverman (USA)—Confirmed Affair (USA) (Affirmed (USA)) **Mr Hamdan Al Maktoum**
44 Ch c 17/4 Rudimentary (USA)—Raffle (Balidar) **Sheikh Ahmed Al Maktoum**
45 B c 23/2 Mujtahid (USA)—Reem Albaraari (Sadler's Wells (USA)) **Sheikh Ahmed Al Maktoum**
46 B c 30/3 Alleged (USA)—Reine des Iles (USA) (Nureyev (USA)) **Sheikh Mohammed**
47 RESALAH, ch f 20/3 Zafonic (USA)—Ghzaalh (USA) (Northern Dancer) **Mr Hamdan Al Maktoum**
48 Ch f 1/2 Kris—Reveuse du Soir (Vision (USA)) **Sheikh Ahmed Al Maktoum**
49 B f 30/4 Lion Cavern (USA)—Safa (Shirley Heights) **Sheikh Ahmed Al Maktoum**
50 TAANIS (USA), b f 25/1 Dayjur (USA)—Ra'a (USA) (Diesis) **Mr Hamdan Al Maktoum**
51 TABAREEH (IRE), b c 3/2 Marju (IRE)—Rosia Bay (High Top) **Mr Hamdan Al Maktoum**
52 THAWABET, ch c 22/1 Unfuwain (USA)—Raaqiyya (USA) (Blushing Groom (FR)) **Mr Hamdan Al Maktoum**
53 THURAYYA, ch f 16/3 Nashwan (USA)—Elfaslah (IRE) (Green Desert (USA)) **Mr Hamdan Al Maktoum**
54 B br c 18/4 Red Ransom (USA)—Woodja (USA) (Woodman (USA)) **Mr Hamdan Al Maktoum**
55 ZABAAD (USA), b f 4/3 Kingmambo (USA)—Skeeb (USA) (Topsider (USA)) **Mr Hamdan Al Maktoum**

Other Owners: The Viscountess Allendale, Mrs Hugh Dalgety, Major W. R. Hern, Mrs W. R. Hern, Mr E. J. Olympitis, Mr E. B. Parker.

Jockey (Flat): R Hills.

580 MR J. C. TUCK, Didmarton

Postal: **Manor Farm, Oldbury-On-The-Hill, Didmarton, Badminton, Avon, GL9 1EA.**
Phone: **(01454) 238236 FAX (01454) 238488**

1 AT LIBERTY (IRE), 6, b h Danehill (USA)—Music of The Night (USA) **Mr J. R. Tuck**
2 CAPE HENRY, 11, b g Dubassoff (USA)—Cape Mandalin **The Bull Inn Racing Club**
3 COOL CAT (IRE), 7, b g Cataldi—Arctic Sue **Mumm Partnership**
4 HOT 'N SAUCY, 6, b m El Conquistador—Hot 'n Scopey **The Ruby Red Partnership**
5 JACK (IRE), 6, br g Be My Native (USA)—Martialette **Mr J. Hatherell**
6 LEGAL ROMANCE, 5, b m El Conquistador—Legal Aid **Mr Peter Hill**
7 ONE OR TWO, 4, b g Derrylin—Silent Dancer **The Bull Inn Racing Club**
8 QUAKER WALTZ, 8, br m Faustus (USA)—Silent Dancer **The Bull Inn Racing Club**
9 RHYTHM AND BOOZE (IRE), 8, gr h Orchestra—Maple Gold **Dr John Heathcock**
10 RIO'S KING (IRE), 6, b g King's Ride—Rio Dulce **The Gasgoigne Brookes Partnership**
11 THE BREWER, 6, ch g Dunbeath (USA)—Bell Cord **Roger Horler Partnership**

MR J. C. TUCK—continued

THREE-YEAR-OLDS

12 Ch c Keen—Silent Dancer **Mrs J. R. Tuck**

Other Owners: Mrs H. B. Blazey, Mr N. Brookes, Mr D. A. Gascoigne, Mr T. Green, Mr Martin Smith, Mr Paul Stanley, Mr G. S. Tuck.

Jockeys (NH): R Bellamy, Simon McNeill (10-0, w.a.).

581 MR F. G. TUCKER, Wedmore

Postal: **Mudgley Hill Farm, Mudgley, Wedmore, Somerset, BS28 4TZ.**
Phone: **(01934) 712684**

1 **DUNNICKS COUNTRY,** 8, ch m Town And Country—Celtic Beauty **Mr F. G. Tucker**
2 **DUNNICKS DOLITTLE,** 5, b g Sulaafah (USA)—Field Chance **Mr F. G. Tucker**
3 **DUNNICKS TOWN,** 6, b g Town And Country—Country Magic **Mr F. G. Tucker**
4 **DUNNICKS VIEW,** 9, b g Sula Bula—Country Magic **Mr F. G. Tucker**
5 **DUNNICKS WELL,** 9, ch g Sula Bula—Celtic Beauty **Mr F. G. Tucker**

582 MR ANDREW TURNELL, Wantage

Postal: **Orchard Stables, East Hendred, Wantage, Oxfordshire, OX12 8JP.**
Phone: **(01235) 833297 FAX (01235) 832827 MOBILE (0802) 468400**

1 **CATHERINE'S WAY (IRE),** 6, b g Mandalus—Sharp Approach **Mr R. K. Carvill**
2 **CELANDINE,** 5, b m Warning—Silly Bold **Dr John Hollowood**
3 **CLAIRE'S DANCER (IRE),** 5, b g Classic Music (USA)—Midnight Patrol **Mrs Claire Hollowood**
4 **GENERAL FLIGHT,** 4, b g Governor General—Tarka **Top Flight Racing**
5 **GIVENTIME,** 10, ch g Bustino—Duck Soup **Mr L. G. Kimber**
6 **GLENDOE (IRE),** 7, b br g Lord Americo—Jazz Bavard **Mr K. C. B. Mackenzie & Mr L. G. Kimber**
7 **GO CAHOOTS (USA),** 5, gr g Sunshine Forever (USA)—Puss In Cahoots (USA) **Marisa Bartoli & John Moreton**
8 **HARRIGALE MOSS (IRE),** 5, b g Strong Gale—Donegal Moss **Mr A. Stennett & Mrs J. M. Stennett**
9 **HAWAIIAN SAM (IRE),** 8, b g Hawaiian Return (USA)—Thomastown Girl **Mr Robert K. Russell**
10 **HIGHLAND JACK,** 8, ch g Nearly A Hand—Highland Path **Karen Gibbons & Breda Cardiff**
11 **JUST WILLIAM,** 6, b g Nicholas Bill—Rugamour **Mr B. Higham**
12 **LORINS GOLD,** 8, ch g Rich Charlie—Woolcana **Mrs M. R. Taylor**
13 **MANVER (IRE),** 6, b g Mandalus—Verenda **Mrs Christopher Hanbury**
14 **MYSTIC COURT (IRE),** 7, br g Mister Lord (USA)—Magic Money **Court Jesters Partnership 3**
15 **NEGATIVE EQUITY,** 6, ch g Be My Chief (USA)—Rather Romantic (CAN) **Mr D. E. McDowell**
16 **NEWS FLASH (IRE),** 6, b g Strong Gale—Gale Flash **Mrs M. R. Taylor**
17 **NO LIGHT,** 11, gr g Celio Rufo—Lady Templar
18 **PETITE IBNR (IRE),** 7, b m Phardante (FR)—Kilcronat Tune **Mr R. K. Carvill**
19 **RUN WITH THE TIDE,** 5, b g Henbit (USA)—Littoral **Mr H. Stephen Smith & Mr J. P. Cavanagh**
20 **SNOWSHILL HARVEST (IRE),** 7, b g Strong Gale—Slave-Lady **Mr H. Stephen Smith**
21 **SOCIETY GUEST,** 12, ch g High Line—Welcome Break **Robinson Webster (Holdings) Ltd**
22 **THE PALADIN,** 8, b g Nearly A Hand—Romany Serenade **Mr R. K. Carvill**
23 **TOO PLUSH,** 9, b g Kaytu—Plush **Mrs C. C. Williams**
24 **TREE CREEPER (IRE),** 6, b g King's Ride—Lispatrick Lass **Mrs C. C. Williams**
25 **TROUVAILLE (IRE),** 7, b g King's Ride—Dream Run **Stainless Threaded Fasteners Ltd**
26 **VERITY VALENTINE (IRE),** 5, b m King's Ride—More Than Words **Mr A. Stennett & Mrs J. M. Stennett**
27 **WHISPERING COURT (IRE),** 8, ch g Avocat—Wind Over Spain **Court Jesters Partnership 2**

THREE-YEAR-OLDS

28 **ACADEMY (IRE),** ch g Archway (IRE)—Dream Academy **Blenheim Thoroughbred Racing**
29 Gr f Thatching—All Ashore **Blenheim Thoroughbred Racing**

MR ANDREW TURNELL—continued

30 **DISTINCT FLYER (IRE)**, gr c Distinctly North (USA)—Sabev (USA) **Blenheim Thoroughbred Racing**
31 **RHAPSODY IN BLUE (IRE)**, b c Magical Strike (USA)—Palace Blue (IRE) **The Eternal Optimists**

Other Owners: Miss Carolyn A. B. Allsopp, Mr R. F. Bailey, Mrs M. I. Barton, Mrs Heather Chittem, Mr Robert Deighton, Mr A. J. Dixon, Mrs J. C. Greenland, Mrs Jenny Gregory, Mr C. Keene, Mrs M. T. Killoughery, Mr P. G. Killoughery, Mr J. S. Lammiman, Dr M. M. Ogilvy, Mr M. Palmer, Mr Peter Sims, Mr D. A. Speirs, Mr J. B. Stent, Mr Michael G. T. Stokes, Mr N. A. Woodcock.

Jockeys (NH): L Harvey (10-0), S McNeill (10-0).

Conditional: M Griffiths (9-7), C Rae (9-7).

Amateur: Mr J B Diment (9-7).

583 MR D. C. TURNER, Plymouth

Postal: **Higher Collard Farm, Wotter, Plymouth, Devon, PL7 5HU.**
Phone: **(01752) 839231**

1 **FABBL APPROVED**, 6, br g Newski (USA)—What An Experiance **Mrs M. E. Turner**
2 **PC'S CRUISER (IRE)**, 6, b g Homo Sapien—Ivy Holme **Mrs M. E. Turner**
3 **WALK IN THE WOODS**, 11, b m Elegant Air—Red Roses (FR) **Mrs M. E. Turner**

Jockey (NH): R Greene.

Lady Rider: Mrs A Hand (10-0).

584 MR W. G. M. TURNER, Sherborne

Postal: **Sigwells Farm, Sigwells, Corton Denham, Sherborne, Dorset, DT9 4LN.**
Phone: **CORTON DENHAM (01963) 220523 FAX (01963) 220046**

1 **ABSOLUTE PROOF**, 5, b m Interrex (CAN)—Kellyem **Queenstown Partnership**
2 **AERIAL VIEW**, 7, br g Sulaafah (USA)—Flying Portion **Mr E. Goody**
3 **BALIOS (IRE)**, 5, b g Be My Guest (USA)—Clifden Bottoms **B. & T. Racing Club**
4 **BLUE CALVINE**, 4, b g Silver Kite (USA)—Calvanne Miss **Mr C. J. Hill**
5 **DOUBLE FIRST (IRE)**, 4, b f Royal Academy (USA)—Top Knot **Mr Paul Green**
6 **DRUM BATTLE**, 6, ch g Bold Arrangement—Cannon Boy (USA) **Mr David Chown**
7 **GEORGETOWN GIRL**, 6, b m Town And Country—Laura Grey **Mrs H. Fullerton**
8 **GINNY WOSSERNAME**, 4, br f Prince Sabo—Leprechaun Lady **Mr R. A. Cary**
9 **IMPALA**, 4, ch g Interrex (CAN)—Raleigh Gazelle **Mrs C. A. Scott**
10 **ITS GRAND**, 9, b g Sula Bula—Light of Zion **Mrs Deborah Potter**
11 **JUST SIDIUM**, 4, b f Nicholas (USA)—Frimley Dancer **Mr C. J. Hill**
12 **KRABLOONIK (FR)**, 4, b g Bering—Key Role **Mrs Deborah Potter**
13 **MA VIELLE POUQUE (IRE)**, 4, ch f Fayruz—Aussie Aisle (IRE) **Mr O. J. Stokes**
14 **MEDFORD**, 8, b g Pablond—Music Meadow **Mr P. F. Coombes**
15 **MEMBERS WELCOME (IRE)**, 5, b g Eve's Error—Manuale Del Utente **Avon & West Racing Club Ltd**
16 **MILLIE'S LATEST**, 5, b m Latest Model—Millie Gras **Miss J. Hodgkinson**
17 **MOST VITAL**, 7, b g Vital Season—Flavirostris **Major R. J. Thorman**
18 **MOVE WITH EDES**, 6, b g Tragic Role (USA)—Good Time Girl **W. Ede & Co Ltd**
19 **MYSTIC STRAND**, 5, b m Lugana Beach—Tantra **Mr David P. Bell**

MR W. G. M. TURNER—continued

20 **NAZZARO,** 9, b g Town And Country—Groundsel **Mr A. Morrish**
21 **PATRITA PARK,** 4, br f Flying Tyke—Bellinote (FR) **Park Racing Partnership**
22 **PERSISTENCE PAYS,** 4, b g Rolfe (USA)—Nicaline **Mr E. Goody**
23 **RAHEEN (USA),** 5, b h Danzig (USA)—Belle de Jour (USA) **Mr Basheer Kielany**
24 **RE ROI (IRE),** 6, b g Roi Danzig (USA)—Requena **Mr A. R. Brown**
25 **RUSTY REEL,** 8, ch g Scottish Reel—Blakeney Heights **Mr R. Hill**
26 **SLIPPERY FIN,** 6, b m Slip Anchor—Finyska (FR) **Woodmarsh Racing**
27 **SOUTHERN CHIEF,** 4, b g Be My Chief (USA)—Southern Sky **Mr Bill Brown**
28 **SURPRISE EVENT,** 4, b g Tragic Role (USA)—Eleckydo **H. G. Carnell & Son Ltd**
29 **THE FRISKY FARMER,** 5, b g Emarati (USA)—Farceuse **Mr G. Bush**
30 **TRUE VISION,** 4, ch f Interrex (CAN)—Lysithea **Mr Richard Hedditch**
31 **WEATHER WISE,** 6, b g Town And Country—Sunshine Gal **Mr David Chown**

THREE-YEAR-OLDS

32 **BALI-STAR,** b g Alnasr Alwasheek—Baligay **Mr H. G. Carnell**
33 **CAPTAIN BRADY (IRE),** ch g Soviet Lad (USA)—Eight Mile Rock **Johayro Investments**
34 **CATFOOT LANE,** b f Batshoof—T Catty (USA) **Mr T. Lightbowne**
35 **COMPASSIONATE,** b g Seymour Hicks (FR)—Snow Child **Mr E. Goody**
36 **GREEN DOLPHIN,** gr f Greensmith—Jane Herring **Mrs C. A. Scott**
37 **INCH PERFECT,** b g Inchinor—Scarlet Veil **Diamond Racing Ltd**
38 **JILVARRA,** b f Desert Splendour—Charlotte Daughter **Mr R. Navarra**
39 **JUST FOR TINA,** b f Presidium—Mushy Boff **Mr C. J. Hill**
40 **VERDANT EXPRESS,** b f Greensmith—Ballynora **Mr R. Scott**

TWO-YEAR-OLDS

41 **BEEANTEE,** b f Gran Alba (USA)—Superb Lady **B & T Racing Club**
42 Br c Interrex (CAN)—Chieftess **Mr T. Lightbowne**
43 Ch f Pharly (FR)—Cryptal **Mr A. R. Brown**
44 **DALLIMORE BANKES,** b g Keen—Run For Love **Mr T. Lightbowne**
45 **ELLIE MAY,** b f Distant Relative—Nigel's Dream **Mr A. Pyer & B. Sandford**
46 B f Emarati (USA)—Jadebelle **Mr W. G. M. Turner**
47 B f Dilum (USA)—Karonga **W. Ede & Co Ltd**
48 **KING FOLEY,** b c Petong—Salacious **Foley Steelstock**
49 B f Interrex (CAN)—Nicaline **Mr E. Goody**
50 B c Dilum (USA)—Southern Sky **Mr W. Brown & Mr A. Wilkinson**
51 **SWANEE,** b f King's Signet (USA)—Balgownie
52 **TONY TIE,** b c Ardkinglass—Queen of The Quorn **Johayro Investments**

Other Owners: Mr G. L. Barker, Mr M. A. Barrett, Mr G. F. Beazley, Mr David Bousfield, Mr Frank Brady, Mr James P. Brown, Mr J. H. Bush, Mr William Campbell, Mr J. G. Charlton, Miss Dianna Crewe, Mrs Aileen J. K. Croft, Mr J. P. Duffy, Mr Charles Fenby, Fivehead Service Station Ltd., Mrs L. P. Green, Mr Michael Harman, Mrs Susan Hearn, Mr Alan Hirst. Ms J. A. Hodges, Mrs A. F. Horsington, Mr Daniel S. W. Hubbard. Mr Adrian Huett, Mr T. Jarvis, Mr C. C. Lowe, Mr Peter MacKenzie, Mr Edward Matthews, Mr Peter Maunder, Mr T. McComish, Mr P. Nabavi, Mr Mossie O'Connell, Miss Corinne J. Overton, Mr P. Parkin, Mr G. Parkinson, Mr A. Poole, Mrs C. L. Rivenaes, Mr A. C. Roberts. Mr G. H. Robson, Mr Desmond Ruddy, Mr P. L. Scott, Mrs A. G. Sims, Mr A. G. Sims, Mr F. H. Smith, Mr Tony J. Smith, Mr J. Sprake, Mrs K. P. Steemson, Mrs M. S. Teversham, Mr Donald C. Tucker, Mr Stephen Twohig, Mr William Wallace, Mr L. H. Wareham, Mrs L. Wayne, Mrs D. A. Wetherall, Mr R. A. Wilkins, Mr Philip Williams.

Jockey (Flat): T Sprake (w.a.).

Jockey (NH): R Dunwoody (w.a.).

Apprentice: Derek McGaffin (7-12).

Conditional: John Gerard Power, Nathan Willmington.

Amateur: Mrs C Price.

585 MR N. A. TWISTON-DAVIES, Cheltenham

Postal: **Grange Hill Farm, Naunton, Cheltenham, Gloucestershire, GL54 3AY,**
Phone: **(01451) 850278 FAX (01451) 850101**

1 **ARCTIC KINSMAN,** 10, gr g Relkino—Arctic Advert **Mrs R. E. Hambro**
2 **BEEFY NOVA,** 6, ch g Ra Nova—Cherry Sip **Mrs S. Tainton**
3 **BEN EIGER (IRE),** 6, ch g Good Thyne (USA)—Priscilla's Pride **Major W. D. Gibson & Martin Gibson**
4 **BINGLEY BANK (IRE),** 6, br g Mandalus—Royal Reliance **Mrs J. Mould**
5 **BORAZON (USA),** 4, ch g Lyphard (USA)—Berceau (USA) **Mr Matt Archer & Miss Jean Broadhurst**
6 **BOSUNS MATE,** 5, ch g Yachtsman (USA)—Langton Lass **Mr Alan Parker**
7 **CAIUS MARIUS,** 6, ch g Roman Warrior—Haile Lady **Miss M. Stockdale**
8 **CAMELOT KNIGHT,** 12, br g King's Ride—Jeanette Marie **Mr Michael Gates**
9 **CAMP BANK,** 8, b g Strong Gale—Rambling Gold **Mrs J. Mould**
10 **CAUGHT NAPPING (IRE),** 5, b g Supreme Leader—Martiness **The Caught Napping Partnership**
11 **CHIEF RAGER,** 9, ch g Relkino—Metaxa **Mr James Cheetham**
12 **CLARE MAN (IRE),** 10, b g Remainder Man—Bell Walks Rose **Mr M. P. Wareing**
13 **COSY RIDE (IRE),** 6, b g King's Ride—Fortysumthin (IRE) **D. J. Equine Supplies Ltd**
14 **DAMP COURSE (IRE),** 5, ch g Montelimar (USA)—Running Tide **Mr A. M. Armitage**
15 **DOM BELTRANO (FR),** 6, b g Dom Pasquini (FR)—Famous Horse (FR) **Mr Carl Wright**
16 **EAGER BEAVER,** 6, gr g Petoski—Strathdearn **The Mutley Crew**
17 **EARTH SUMMIT,** 10, b g Celtic Cone—Win Green Hill **The Summit Partnership**
18 **FLAPJACK LAD,** 9, b g Oats—Reperage (USA) **Mr H. B. Shouler**
19 **FRANTIC TAN (IRE),** 6, ch g Zaffaran (USA)—Brownskin **The Bunkers Hill Mob**
20 **FREDDIE MUCK,** 8, b g Idiot's Delight—Muckertoo **Mrs C. Twiston-Davies**
21 **FRENCH BUCK (IRE),** 8, br g Phardante (FR)—Flying Silver **Mrs C. M. Scott**
22 **GANPATI (IRE),** 7, ch m Over The River (FR)—Icy Lou **The Oriental Partnership**
23 **GATFLAX (IRE),** 6, b g Supreme Leader—Polly's Slipper **Mr Giles Clarke**
24 **GLEVUM,** 6, gr m Town And Country—Peggy Wig **Mrs J. K. Powell**
25 **HAILE DERRING,** 8, br g Derring Rose—Haile Lady **Mrs V. Stockdale**
26 **HAND WOVEN,** 6, b g Rambo Dancer (CAN)—Lifestyle **Mr Matt Archer & Miss Jean Broadhurst**
27 **HURRICANE HANKS,** 9, br g Strong Gale—Hester Ann **Mr Simon Keswick**
28 **JACK DOYLE (IRE),** 7, ch g Be My Native (USA)—Sister Ida **Drain Logistics**
29 **JALAPENO (IRE),** 7, b g Supreme Leader—Bartlemy Hostess **Mr Alan Parker**
30 **KERAWI,** 5, b g Warning—Kerali **Mr Matt Archer & Miss Jean Broadhurst**
31 **KING'S ROAD (IRE),** 5, b g King's Ride—Live Aid **Mrs Nicholas Jones**
32 **LUGGSY,** 6, b g Ardross—Caoimhe **Mr John Duggan**
33 **MADAM MUCK,** 7, ch m Gunner B—Muckertoo **The Co-optimists**
34 **MADAM'S WALK,** 8, ch m Ardross—Emily Kent **Mrs J. Mould**
35 **MAHLER,** 8, b g Uncle Pokey—Dovey **English Badminton Partnership**
36 **MAJOR TWIST (IRE),** 4, b g Dancing Dissident (USA)—Kafsa (IRE) **Mr F. J. Mills & Mr W. Mills**
37 **MISTER RM,** 6, b g Dominion—La Cabrilla **Mr F. J. Mills & Mr W. Mills**
38 **MISTINGUETT (IRE),** 6, b m Doyoun—Sidama (FR) **Mr John Duggan**
39 **MOORISH,** 8, b g Dominion—Remoosh **Mr Adrian Fitzpatrick**
40 **OCEAN HAWK (USA),** 6, b g Hawkster (USA)—Society Sunrise (USA) **Mr Matt Archer & Miss Jean Broadhurst**
41 **OXBRIDGE LADY,** 7, b m Impecunious—White African **The Hollow Bottom Partnership**
42 **PAT BUCKLEY,** 7, b g Buckley—Raheny **Mrs K. L. Urquhart**
43 **PERCY PARKEEPER,** 5, b g Teenoso (USA)—True Clown **Mr & Mrs Peter Orton**
44 **PIMBERLEY PLACE (IRE),** 10, b g Spanish Place (USA)—Pimberley Shades **Mr A. J. Cresser**
45 **QUEEN OF SPADES (IRE),** 8, b br m Strong Gale—Affordthe Queen **Mrs R. Vaughan**
46 **QUEEN'S CHARTER,** 5, b m Welsh Captain—Sussex Queen **Mr Matt Archer & Miss Jean Broadhurst**
47 **RACKETBALL,** 5, ch g Green Adventure (USA)—Hylton Road **Mrs S. Tainton**
48 **ROCKCLIFFE GOSSIP,** 6, ch g Phardante (FR)—Clonmello **Mr Simon Keswick**
49 **ROMANCER (IRE),** 7, br g Caerleon (USA)—Courtesane (USA) **Mr Matt Archer & Miss Jean Broadhurst**
50 **SAMMORELLO (IRE),** 7, b g Mandalus—Cherry Park **Mrs S. A. MacEchern**
51 **SAN GIORGIO,** 9, b g Lighter—Gold Willow **Mr Peter Kelsall**
52 **SHORE PARTY (IRE),** 6, b g Strong Gale—Ariannrun **Mrs J. Mould**
53 **SISTER DEE,** 5, b m Henbit (USA)—Sister Delaney **Mr Jim Edmunds**
54 **SNOWSHILL SHAKER,** 9, b g Son of Shaka—Knight Hunter **Mr Austin P. Knight**
55 **SPEEDWELL PRINCE (IRE),** 8, ch g Henbit (USA)—Eternal Fire **The Bar Fixtures Partnership**
56 **SPRING DOUBLE (IRE),** 7, br g Seclude (USA)—Solar Jet **Mrs Lorna Berryman**

MR N. A. TWISTON-DAVIES—continued

57 **STAR MARKET,** 8, b g Celestial Storm (USA)—Think Ahead **Mrs P. Joynes**
58 **STEEPLES LAD (IRE),** 5, b g Brush Aside (USA)—Awbeg Lady **Mrs Lorna Berryman**
59 **STORMY SESSION,** 8, b g Celestial Storm (USA)—No Jazz **Mr Christopher Haycock**
60 **SWING QUARTET (IRE),** 8, b br m Orchestra—Sweetly Stung **Mr T. Gold Blyth**
61 **TEXAN BABY (BEL),** 9, b g Baby Turk—Texan Rose (FR) **Mr C. B. Sanderson**
62 **THE CROOKED OAK,** 6, ch g Fearless Action (USA)—Life Goes On **Mr Andy Mavrou**
63 **THE PROMS (IRE),** 7, b g Orchestra—Girseach **Mrs J. Mould**
64 **TIPPING TIM,** 13, b g King's Ride—Jeanarie **Mrs J. Mould**
65 **TOMPETOO (IRE),** 7, ch g Roselier (FR)—Express Course **Tom Pettifer Ltd**
66 **TWO TO TANGO (IRE),** 5, ch m Anshan—Marie de Sologne **Mr F. J. Mills & Mr W. Mills**
67 **UPGRADE,** 4, b g Be My Guest (USA)—Cantanta **Mr Matt Archer & Miss Jean Broadhurst**
68 **WHISTLING RUFUS (IRE),** 6, gr g Celio Rufo—Aryumad **The Aryumad Partnership**
69 **WINNETKA GAL (IRE),** 6, br m Phardante (FR)—Asigh Glen **Mrs Joan L. Egan**
70 **WISLEY WARRIOR,** 7, b g Derring Rose—Miss Topem **The Wisley Golf Partnership**
71 **WISLEY WONDER (IRE),** 8, ch g Phardante (FR)—Priscilla's Pride **The Wisley Golf Partnership**
72 **WOLDSMAN,** 8, b g Tout Ensemble—Savanna Lady VII **Mr R. B. Slatter**
73 **YOUNG HUSTLER,** 11, ch g Import—Davett **Mr Gavin MacEchern**
74 **ZANDER,** 6, ch g Mr Fluorocarbon—Frieda's Joy **Mr John Duggan**

Other Owners: Mr Michael J. Arnold, Mr M. G. Bailey, Mr Ronnie Beevor, Mr Malcolm Berryman, Mr A. Brush, Mr Chris Coley, Mrs A. J. Davies, Mr Huw Davies, Dr John Disney, Mr J. W. Downer, Mrs Karen Duggan, Mr Ian Dunbar, Mr P. H. Earl, Mr Philip Freedman, Mr John French, Mr Ricky George, Mr A. L. D. Gill, Mr R. L. C. Hartley, Mr L. Hellstenius, Mr P. G. Horrocks, Mr P. John Huins, Mr D. Jones, Mr Jack Joseph, Mr B. Keswick, Mr David Langdon, Mr B. J. Lee, Mr Andy Lloyd, Mr K. G. Manley, Mr Denis Milne, Mr G. C. Mordaunt, Mr H. Mould, Mr H. K. Muir, Mr J. O'Gorman, Mr T. H. Ounsley, Mr Howard Parker, Mr Nigel Payne, Mr R. G. Perry, Mr Nick Ponting, Mr Timothy J. Pope, Mr B. M. Powell, Cheltenham Racing Ltd., Mr R. D. Russell, Mr G. W. Sanders, Mrs Valerie Sanderson, Mr C. M. P. Scott, Mrs S. A. Scott, Mrs Marilyn Scudamore, Mr R. Sims, Mr M. G. Smith, Mr Audley Twiston-Davies, Mr P. Wade, Mrs Giles Weaver, Mrs E. J. Wilson, Mr D. J. Wintle, Mr Carl Wright, Mr Andrew P. Wyer, Mr S. M. Yassukovich.

Jockeys (NH): T P Jenks (10-0), C Llewellyn (10-0), C Maude (10-0).

Conditional: J Goldstein, M Keithley (9-7).

Amateur: Mr M Rimell (10-0).

586 MR J. R. UPSON, Towcester

Postal: **Stonewell House, Banbury Lane, Fosters Booth, Towcester, Northamptonshire, NN12 8LG.**
Phone: **(01327) 860043 FAX (01327) 860238**

1 **BENNA BEULA,** 6, b g Arctic Lord—Kathleen Callaghan **Mrs E. Ellis**
2 **BOWLES PATROL (IRE),** 6, gr g Roselier (FR)—Another Dud **The Three Horseshoes Sporting Club**
3 **CATS RUN (IRE),** 10, ch g Deep Run—Zelamere **Mrs Ann Key**
4 **CHATTER BOX,** 6, ch m Backchat (USA)—Vulgan's Bella **The Fourways Partnership**
5 **COME ON EILISH (IRE),** 5, b g Stetchworth (USA)—Salty Sea **The Three Horseshoes Sporting Club**
6 **EAN MOR,** 7, b m Royal Vulcan—Pegs Promise **Mrs D. Upson**
7 **GHOSTLY APPARITION,** 5, gr g Gods Solution—Tawny **Mrs D. Upson**
8 **LUCKY MASTER (IRE),** 6, b g Roselier (FR)—Golden Chestnut **Mrs Ann Key**
9 **OVER ZEALOUS (IRE),** 6, ch g Over The River (FR)—Chatty Di **Middleham Park Racing X**
10 **POLO PONY (IRE),** 6, b g The Noble Player (USA)—Mangan Lane **The Champagne Guzzlers**
11 **REACH THE CLOUDS (IRE),** 6, b g Lord Americo—Dusky Stream **Middleham Park Racing IX**
12 **REFLEX HAMMER,** 7, b g Precious Metal—Khotso **Middleham Park Racing VII**
13 **RIVER CHALLENGE (IRE),** 7, ch g Over The River (FR)—Floppy Disk **Middleham Park Racing III**

MR J. R. UPSON—continued

14 **WILD HADEER,** 4, ch g Hadeer—Wild Moon (USA) **Mr M. Chapman**
15 **YOUNG RADICAL (IRE),** 6, b g Radical—Fountain Blue **Mr N. Jones**

Other Owners: Mrs P. Elsbury, Mrs Gill Forsyth, Mr Frank Fountain, Mr J. D. Horgan, Mr R. H. Mynott, Mr T. S. Palin, Mrs D. Sanders, Mr R. G. Smith, Mr Sidney J. Smith, Mrs R. E. Tate, Mr M. Tucker, Mr J. A. Upson, Mr C. Wallis, Sir Nicholas Wilson.

Jockey (NH): Robbie Supple (10-0).

Conditional: Claire Pierrot (9-7).

587 MR M. D. I. USHER, Wantage

Postal: **Manor Farm Racing Stables, Kingston Lisle, Wantage, Oxfordshire, OX12 9QL.**
Phone: **OFFICE (01367) 820881 FAX (01367) 820883 MOBILE (0831) 873531**

1 **AMNESTY BAY,** 6, b m Thatching—Sanctuary Cove **Shirval Partners**
2 **BA SERENDIPITY,** 5, b m Teenoso (USA)—Lynda-B **Mr Derek Broad**
3 **BAYIN (USA),** 9, b g Caro—Regatela (USA) **Mr Trevor Barker**
4 **COASTGUARDS HERO,** 5, ch g Chilibang—Aldwick Colonnade **Coastguards Estate Agent of Bognor Regis**
5 **IMPERIAL GLEN (IRE),** 4, b f Imperial Frontier (USA)—Tribute To Viqueen **Mr M. Hopkins**
6 **KEEPSAKE (IRE),** 4, b f Distinctly North (USA)—Souveniers **Mr Trevor Barker**
7 **REMAADI SUN,** 6, gr g Cadeaux Genereux—Catch The Sun **Mr Trevor Barker**
8 **RING THE CHIEF,** 6, b g Chief Singer—Lomond Ring **Mr G. A. Summers**
9 **ROCK THE BARNEY (IRE),** 9, ch h Coquelin (USA)—Lady Loire **Mrs Satu Marks**
10 **ROCKY WATERS (USA),** 9, b br g Rocky Marriage (USA)—Running Melody **Mr Philip Saunders**
11 **SCARLET CRESCENT,** 4, b f Midyan (USA)—Scarlet Veil **Midweek Racing**
12 6, B h Portogon—Silver Water **Mr F. D. Usher**
13 **SOAKING,** 8, b g Dowsing (USA)—Moaning Low **Mr Philip Saunders**
14 **SPIRAL FLYER (IRE),** 5, b br m Contract Law (USA)—Souveniers **Mr G. A. Summers**
15 **WHATEVER'S RIGHT (IRE),** 9, b g Doulab (USA)—Souveniers **Mr M. S. C. Thurgood**
16 **ZERMATT (IRE),** 8, b h Sadler's Wells (USA)—Chamonis (USA) **Mrs M. P. Pearson**

THREE-YEAR-OLDS

17 **HEIRESS OF MEATH (IRE),** ch f Imperial Frontier (USA)—Rich Heiress (IRE) **Dr Ian R. Shenkin**
18 **MRS PICKLES,** gr f Northern Park (USA)—Able Mabel **Midweek Racing**
19 **RIVER FRONTIER (IRE),** b f Imperial Frontier (USA)—River Low (IRE) **Dr Ian R. Shenkin**
20 **ROYAL BLUE,** ch c Ron's Victory (USA)—Angels Are Blue **The Ridgeway Partnership**
21 **SILENT PRIDE (IRE),** ch f Pips Pride—Suppression **Miss D. G. Kerr**

TWO-YEAR-OLDS

22 B f 7/5 Minshaanshu Amad—Lahin (Rainbow Quest (USA)) **Mrs E. Gauvain**
23 Ch f 22/3 Formidable (USA)—La Spagna (Aragon) **Mr M. D. I. Usher**
24 B c 14/4 Warrshan (USA)—Shirley's Touch (Touching Wood (USA)) **Mr M. D. I. Usher**

Other Owners: Mr T. Barker, Mr I. E. Chant, Mr Bryan Fry, Mrs S. P. Fry, Mr K. Walton, Mr Carl West-Meads, Mr P. Winfrow.

Lady Rider: Mrs Ann Usher (7-7).

588 MR K. VINCENT, Reigate

Postal: **Heathfield Park Stables, Reigate Heath, Reigate, Surrey, RH2 8QR.**

1 **INCITUS,** 4, br g Green-Fingered—Miss Tenaville **Mr Kage Vincent**
2 **PEACE INITIATIVE,** 6, b g Hadeer—Rostova **Mr Kage Vincent**
3 **RAVUS,** 8, gr g Pragmatic—Craftsmans Oats **Mr Kage Vincent**
4 **RED BEAN,** 10, ch g Ginger Boy—Pharona **Mr Kage Vincent**
5 **SIR TENNASON,** 6, b g Sir Patrick—Miss Tenaville **Mr Kage Vincent**

589 MRS L. A. M. WADHAM, Newmarket

Postal: **The Trainer's House, Moulton Paddocks, Newmarket, Suffolk, CB8 7PJ.**
Phone: **(01638) 662411 (01638) 668821 FAX**

1 **ROBBEN ISLAND (USA),** 4, b br g Pleasant Colony (USA)—Rambushka (USA) **Mr J. J. W. Wadham**
2 5, B g Makbul—Shirley Grove **Mr J. J. W. Wadham**

Other Owners: Mr P. J. Gaynor, Mrs T. Gaynor.

Jockey (NH): J F Titley.

590 MR N. WAGGOTT, Spennymoor

Postal: **Ingledene, Vyners Close, Merrington Lane, Spennymoor, Co. Durham, DL16 7HB.**
Phone: **(01388) 819012**

1 **AMARELLA (IRE),** 4, ch f Soviet Lad (USA)—Eight Mile Rock **Mrs J. Waggott**
2 **BELIEVE IT,** 9, b g Bellypha—Hasty Key (USA) **Mrs J. Waggott**
3 6, B m Ala Hounak—Church Brae **Mr N. Waggott**
4 5, Ch g Highlands—Friendly Wonder **Mr N. Waggott**
5 **KING LEAPRECHAUN,** 6, b g King's Holt—Lucky Delay **Mrs J. Waggott**
6 **POLAR WIND,** 9, ch g El Gran Senor (USA)—Tundra Goose **Mr N. Waggott**
7 **SALTIMBANCO,** 4, ch c Green Forest (USA)—Tea And Scandals (USA) **Mr N. Waggott**
8 **SETTING SUN,** 5, ch h Generous (IRE)—Suntrap (USA) **Mrs J. Waggott**
9 **ZAAMAIN (IRE),** 4, b g Night Shift (USA)—Stylish Girl (USA) **Mr N. Waggott**

THREE-YEAR-OLDS

10 **FRED'S IN THE KNOW,** ch g Interrex (CAN)—Lady Vynz **Mrs J. Waggott**

Amateur: Mr N Waggott Jnr (11-0).

Lady Rider: Miss Tracy Waggott (9-7).

591 MR J. S. WAINWRIGHT, Malton

Postal: **Hanging Hill Farm, Kennythorpe, Malton, North Yorkshire, YO17 9LA.**
Phone: **(01653) 658537 MOBILE (0498) 778070**

1 **BALLARD LADY (IRE),** 6, ch m Ballad Rock—First Blush **Mrs P. Wake**
2 **MAJAL (IRE),** 9, b g Caerleon (USA)—Park Special **Mrs P. Wake**
3 **OCEAN BREEZE,** 4, ch g Most Welcome—Sea Power **Miss N. Bridge**
4 **PANOORAS LORD (IRE),** 4, b g Topanoora—Ladyship **Mr G. R. Brett**

MR J. S. WAINWRIGHT—continued

5 **THALEROS,** 8, b g Green Desert (USA)—Graecia Magna (USA) **Mr M. Gleason**
6 **YOUNG BEN (IRE),** 6, ch g Fayruz—Jive **Mr F. Wood**

THREE-YEAR-OLDS

7 **DIBOLA,** ch g Dilum (USA)—Bella Bambola (IRE) **Mr S. Pedersen**
8 **JOLI FILLE,** b f Merdon Melody—Thabeh **Joli Fille Partnership**
9 **LADYOFDISTINCTION (IRE),** b f Distinctly North (USA)—Lady Anna Livia **Mr L. Mason**
10 **LAST WALTZ,** b f La Grange Music—First Footer **Mr G. R. Brett**
11 **PETARA (IRE),** ch c Petardia—Romangoddess (IRE) **Mr J. H. Pickard**
12 **SEALED BY FATE (IRE),** b g Mac's Imp (USA)—Fairy Don **B Selective Partnership**
13 **TOWNVILLE CEE CEE,** b f Anshan—Holy Day **Townville C. C. Racing Club**

TWO-YEAR-OLDS

14 B g 15/3 Northern Elegance—Denby Wood **Mr A. Longbottom**
15 **MIDRUSH (IRE),** b f 22/3 Polish Patriot (USA)—Midushi (USA) **Mr J. H. Pickard**
16 **PERUGIA LADY (IRE),** ch f 16/5 Perugino (USA)—Love Hurts (IRE) **Mr N. F. Strange**
17 B f 18/4 Midhish—Tara View (IRE) **Mr B. Ross**

Other Owners: Mr D. M. Booth, Mrs Anne-Denise Craven, Mr Dennis L. Dunbar, Miss R. K. Dunbar, Miss V. Foster, Mr W. D. Green, Mr Neil Harrison, Mr Rowland Hill, Ms D. A. Hillier, Mr N. Honeyman, Mr George R. W. Nicholls.

Jockeys (Flat): L Charnock (7-10), D McKeown (8-3), G Parkin (8-4).

Conditional: P Midgley (10-6).

Amateur: Mr K Green (10-0).

592 MR ROBERT B. WALEY-COHEN, Banbury

Postal: **Upton Viva, Banbury, Oxon, OX15 6HT.**
Phone: **OFFICE (0171) 244 6022 HOME (01295) 670242**

1 **HENRIETTA HOWARD (IRE),** 8, b m King's Ride—Knockaville **Mr Robert Waley-Cohen**
2 **JUPITER PROBE (IRE),** 7, br g Phardante (FR)—Bramble Hill **Mr Robert Waley-Cohen**

593 MR C. F. WALL, Newmarket

Postal: **Induna Stables, Fordham Road, Newmarket, Suffolk, CB8 7AQ.**
Phone: **HOME (01638) 668896 OFFICE (01638) 661999 FAX (01638) 667279**

1 **ADMIRALS FLAME (IRE),** 7, b g Doulab (USA)—Fan The Flame **Mrs C. A. Wall**
2 **ADMIRALS SECRET (USA),** 9, ch g Secreto (USA)—Noble Mistress (USA) **Mrs C. A. Wall**
3 **ALMASI (IRE),** 6, b m Petorius—Best Niece **The Equema Partnership**
4 **LEADING SPIRIT (IRE),** 6, b g Fairy King (USA)—Shopping (FR) **Induna Racing Partners Two**
5 **MIDNIGHT ESCAPE,** 5, b g Aragon—Executive Lady **Mr Mervyn Ayers**
6 **MISS KALAGLOW,** 4, b f Kalaglow—Dame du Moulin **Mrs C. A. Wall**
7 **MR SPEAKER (IRE),** 5, ch g Statoblest—Casting Vote (USA) **Mr David Allen**
8 **SALLY GREEN (IRE),** 4, b f Common Grounds—Redwood Hut **Mr K. V. Stenborg**
9 **SUNNY ISLE,** 4, b f Cadeaux Genereux—Highsplasher (USA) **Mr S. Fustok**
10 **TONIGHT'S PRIZE (IRE),** 4, b g Night Shift (USA)—Bestow **Mr Shunya Seki**
11 **TRIPLE HIGH,** 4, b f Reprimand—Rambadale **The Triple S Partnership**

MR C. F. WALL—continued

THREE-YEAR-OLDS

12 **BENS GIFT,** ch f Keen—Monstrosa **Mrs E. M. Bousquet-Payne**
13 **BOW BELLS,** b f Absalom—Dancing Chimes **Mrs R. M. S. Neave**
14 **CARINTHIA (IRE),** br f Tirol—Hot Lavender (CAN) **Hintlesham Racing**
15 **FACE-OFF,** b f Aragon—Rock Face **Mr N. Ahamad**
16 **FIFTH EMERALD,** b f Formidable (USA)—Glossary **Mr M. Ng**
17 **JOCASTA,** b f Warning—Breed Reference **Mr C. J. A. Hughes**
18 **MASAMADAS,** ch c Elmaamul (USA)—Beau's Delight (USA) **Mr M. Tilbrook**
19 **MISALLIANCE,** ch f Elmaamul (USA)—Cabaret Artiste **The Lively Partners**
20 **PRESTISSIMO,** b f Alzao (USA)—Cottonwood **Sir Stanley and Lady Grinstead**
21 **SUMMER DAY BLUES (IRE),** b f Petorius—Atmospheric Blues (IRE) **Mr David Crichton-Watt**
22 **SUNSTREAK,** ch c Primo Dominie—Florentynna Bay **Mr Walter Grubmuller**
23 **SWEET SORROW (IRE),** b f Lahib (USA)—So Long Boys (FR) **Mrs Yoshiko Allan**
24 **SWING ALONG,** ch f Alhijaz—So It Goes **Mr W. G. Bovill**
25 **TIGULLIO (IRE),** b c Rainbows For Life (CAN)—L'Americaine (USA) **Mr Ettore Landi**

TWO-YEAR-OLDS

26 B f 10/4 Polish Patriot (USA)—Alongside (Slip Anchor) **Tansri Azmi Wan Hanzah**
27 **BABET (IRE),** b f 30/4 Mujadil (USA)—Baby's Smile (Shirley Heights) **The Boardroom Syndicate**
28 **BARNACLA (IRE),** ch f 25/2 Bluebird (USA)—Reticent Bride (IRE) (Shy Groom (USA)) **Mr Javier Aznar**
29 **BLACK SILK,** b c 26/3 Zafonic (USA)—Mademoiselle Chloe (Night Shift (USA)) **Mr S. Fustok**
30 **BLIND TRUST (IRE),** b c 3/3 Mtoto—Ancestry (Persepolis (FR)) **Mr N. Ahamad**
31 Br f 9/3 Rock City—Blue Player (Jaazeiro (USA)) **Framlingham Racing Partners**
32 B f 18/2 Chaddleworth (IRE)—Breed Reference (Reference Point) **The Boadicea Partners**
33 **DAY STAR,** b f 14/3 Dayjur (USA)—Krisalya (Kris) **Mr A. E. Oppenheimer**
34 **FAITH AGAIN (IRE),** b f 3/3 Namaqualand (USA)—Intricacy (Formidable (USA)) **Prudence Lady Salt**
35 B c 24/3 Shalford (IRE)—Fille Dansante (IRE) (Dancing Dissident (USA)) **Mr Kim Koon Lau**
36 B f 16/1 Royal Academy (USA)—Laugharne (Known Fact (USA)) **Sir Stanley & Lady Grinstead**
37 B f 9/4 Be My Chief (USA)—Megdale (IRE) (Waajib) **Sir Stanley & Lady Grinstead**
38 **NATURAL PEARL,** gr f 27/4 Petong—Petriele (Mummy's Pet) **Hintlesham Racing**
39 **RICH PLAIN (IRE),** b g 21/3 Roi Danzig (USA)—Winter Tern (USA) (Arctic Tern (USA)) **The Boardroom Syndicate**
40 **ROMAN CANDLE (IRE),** b c 14/4 Sabrehill (USA)—Penny Banger (IRE) (Pennine Walk) **Sir William Stuttaford**
41 **SPINNING STAR,** ch f 20/2 Arazi (USA)—Queen Midas (Glint of Gold) **Mr S. Fustok**
42 **STREET WALKER (IRE),** b f 24/2 Dolphin Street (FR)—Foolish Dame (USA) (Foolish Pleasure (USA)) **The Boardroom Syndicate**
43 **UNDETERRED,** ch c 16/4 Zafonic (USA)—Mint Crisp (IRE) (Green Desert (USA)) **Mr S. Fustok**
44 B f 21/4 Night Shift (USA)—Vanya (Busted) **Mr Javier Aznar**
45 **ZOFFI,** b f 7/4 Most Welcome—Highsplasher (USA) (Bucksplasher (USA)) **Mr S. Fustok**

Other Owners: Mr S. Atkin, Mr T. Bater, Mr W. J. Bridge, Mr P. Brook, Lady Caroline Crawshaw, Mrs J. E. Dobie, Mr R. Fraiser, Mr J. Gosling, Mr P. Gosling, Mr P. Gregory, Mr J. Grimsey, Mrs Jill Kerr-Smiley, Mr A. J. Neal, Mr C. N. Roberts, Mr Kieran D. Scott, Mr Pierpont Scott, Mr John E. Sims, Mr R. A. Spence, Mrs R. A. Sunnucks, Mr G. M. Thompson, Mrs J. F. Toms, Mrs C. J. Walker, Mr J. H. Wall, Mr R. Wayman.

Apprentice: M Doe.

Amateur: Miss Heather Webster.

594 MR T. R. WALL, Church Stretton

Postal: **Harton Manor, Harton, Church Stretton, Shropshire, SY6 7DL.**
Phone: **(01694) 724144 FAX (01694) 724144**

1 **ALDINGTON CHAPPLE,** 10, b g Creetown—Aldington Miss **Mr M. Kiernan**
2 4, B f Warrshan (USA)—Aldwick Colonnade **Mr R. Cave**
3 **ASTRAL INVASION (USA),** 7, ch g Risen Star (USA)—Santiki **Ed Weetman, Reynolds and Dean**

MR T. R. WALL—continued

4 **BELLE DANCER,** 4, b f Rambo Dancer (CAN)—Warning Bell **Mrs S. J. Edwards**
5 **DORMSTON BOYO,** 8, b g Sula Bula—March At Dawn **Mr D. B. Roberts**
6 **GREAT WOLF,** 5, b g Little Wolf—Proudway **Mr F. E. Phillips**
7 **LITTLE KENNY,** 5, b m Warning—Tarvie **Vizard Racing**
8 **TAP ON TOOTSIE,** 6, b m Faustus (USA)—My Tootsie **Mr R. Cowper**
9 **TIGER BRIGHT,** 9, b h Seymour Hicks (FR)—Commander Alice **Miss G. L. D. Hardy**
10 **WEET AND SEE,** 4, b g Lochnager—Simply Style **Ed Weetman (Haulage & Storage) Ltd**
11 **WEET EES GIRL (IRE),** 4, ro f Common Grounds—Kastiliya **Ed Weetman (Haulage & Storage) Ltd**
12 **YOUNG BENSON,** 6, b g Zalazl (USA)—Impala Lass **Mr E. A. Lee**

THREE-YEAR-OLDS

13 **RISKNOWT GETNOWT,** b g Ron's Victory (USA)—Scottish Tina **Vizard Racing**

Other Owners: Mr Derek Dean, Mrs P. Joynes, Mr E. Moore, Mr S. H. Pickering, Mr A. J. Pope, Mr J. H. Reynolds, Mr M. J. Talbot, Mr Keith Warrington, Mrs G. A. Weetman, Mr David M. Williams.

595 MRS H. L. WALTON, Grantham

Postal: **The Dairy, Laughtons Farm, Brandon Road, Hougham, Grantham, Lincolnshire, NG32 2AG.**
Phone: **(01400) 251152 (0589) 609654 MOBILE**

1 **ARIF (IRE),** 6, b g Try My Best (USA)—Sable Royale (USA) **Mrs Jenny Carrington**
2 **DOMINOS RING (IRE),** 9, b g Auction Ring (USA)—Domino's Nurse **Mrs Jenny Carrington**
3 **FUTURE HEALTH,** 8, b g Royal Vulcan—Jupiter's Gem **Mr A. E. Walton**
4 4, B f Ardross—Jupiter's Gem **Mr Richard Halling**
5 **SEA PENNANT,** 4, br f Adbass (USA)—Doubtfire **Mr R. Thompson**
6 **SLOE BRANDY,** 8, b m Hotfoot—Emblazon **Mrs Jenny Carrington**

THREE-YEAR-OLDS

7 Ch g Risk Me (FR)—Farinara **Mr A. E. Walton**

Other Owners: Mr H. A. Depass.

Amateur: Mr A Walton (9-7).

596 MR P. T. WALWYN, Lambourn

Postal: **Windsor House, Lambourn, Hungerford, Berkshire, RG17 8NR.**
Phone: **LAMBOURN (01488) 71347 FAX (01488) 72664**

1 **BEN GUNN,** 6, b g Faustus (USA)—Pirate Maid **Mr Michael White & Mrs P. T. Walwyn**
2 **HATTAB (IRE),** 4, b c Marju (IRE)—Funun (USA) **Mr Hamdan Al Maktoum**
3 **LABEQ (IRE),** 4, b c Lycius (USA)—Ahbab (IRE) **Mr Hamdan Al Maktoum**
4 **TOM MORGAN,** 7, b g Faustus (USA)—Pirate Maid **Mr Michael White & Mrs P. T. Walwyn**

THREE-YEAR-OLDS

5 **ABUHAIL (USA),** br c Silver Hawk (USA)—Bank Key (USA) **Mr Hamdan Al Maktoum**
6 **ALRABYAH (IRE),** br c Brief Truce (USA)—Bean Siamsa **Mr Hamdan Al Maktoum**
7 **DONT MUCK ABOUT,** b g Mukaddamah (USA)— **Windsor House Racing**
8 **EAST WINDS,** ch g Suave Dancer (USA)—Dominio (IRE) **Major & Mrs R. B. Kennard & Partners**
9 **FILFILAH,** ch f Cadeaux Genereux—El Rabab (USA) **Mr Hamdan Al Maktoum**
10 **HADAYIK,** b f Unfuwain (USA)—Almarai (USA) **Mr Hamdan Al Maktoum**
11 **HADITH,** ch c Nashwan (USA)—Azyaa **Mr Hamdan Al Maktoum**
12 **JUNGLE STORY (IRE),** b g Alzao (USA)—Jungle Jezebel **Major & Mrs R. B. Kennard & Partners**

MR P. T. WALWYN—continued

13 **MAJAARI,** b br c Marju (IRE)—Ahbab (IRE) **Mr Hamdan Al Maktoum**
14 **NADWAH (USA),** b f Shadeed (USA)—Tadwin **Mr Hamdan Al Maktoum**
15 **OARE KITE,** b f Batshoof—Portvasco **Mrs Henry Keswick**
16 **REGAL REVOLUTION,** br f Hamas (IRE)—True Queen (USA) **S. Slack, C. Colquhoun, & Mrs Walwyn.**
17 **ROBERTY BOB (IRE),** ch g Bob Back (USA)—Inesdela **Mr P. J. H. Wills**
18 **ROBIN GOODFELLOW,** b c Fairy King (USA)—La Tuerta **Mr Michael Gough**
19 **RUBAMMA,** b c Kris—Idle Gossip (USA) **Mrs P. T. Walwyn**
20 **SAINT ALBERT,** ch g Keen—Thimbalina **Mrs P. T. Walwyn**
21 **SHAN'T,** ch c Shalford (IRE)—Silent Girl **Windsor House Racing**
22 **YANABI (USA),** b f Silver Hawk (USA)—Halholah (USA) **Mr Hamdan Al Maktoum**

TWO-YEAR-OLDS

23 Ch f 5/4 Persian Bold—Adjamiya (USA) (Shahrastani) **Mr Barry Ross**
24 **ALNAJASHEE,** b c 8/2 Generous (IRE)—Tahdid (Mtoto) **Mr Hamdan Al Maktoum**
25 **AL NAKHLAH (USA),** b f 9/3 Sheikh Albadou—Magic Slipper (Habitat) **Mr Hamdan Al Maktoum**
26 **ASEEL (USA),** b c 15/3 Hansel (USA)—Mafatin (IRE) (Sadler's Wells (USA)) **Mr Hamdan Al Maktoum**
27 **AWWALIYA,** b f 28/3 Distant Relative—El Rabab (USA) (Roberto (USA)) **Mr Hamdan Al Maktoum**
28 **EL NAFIS (USA),** b f 14/3 Kingmambo (USA)—Ghashtah (USA) (Nijinsky (CAN)) **Mr Hamdan Al Maktoum**
29 B c 4/4 Robellino (USA)—Future Options (Lomond (USA)) **Mrs R. Bingley**
30 **GHUROOB (IRE),** ch f 27/1 Arazi (USA)—Tablah (USA) (Silver Hawk (USA)) **Mr Hamdan Al Maktoum**
31 B c 21/3 Deploy—Gong (Bustino) **Mr A. D. G Oldrey**
32 **HADRIAN (IRE),** b c 19/3 Hamas (IRE)—Queen Warrior (Daring March) **Mr C. J. Spence & Mrs P. T. Walwyn**
33 **HIBAAT,** ch c 11/3 Zafonic (USA)—Realisatrice (USA) (Raja Baba (USA)) **Mr Hamdan Al Maktoum**
34 **HOUGOUMONT,** b g 6/2 Formidable (USA)—Sure Victory (Stalker)
35 **INTIMAA (IRE),** b f 20/5 Caerleon (USA)—Nahilah (Habitat) **Mr Hamdan Al Maktoum**
36 **JUANITA,** b f 3/5 Be My Chief (USA)—Dominio (IRE) (Dominion) **Major & Mrs R. B. Kennard & Partners**
37 B c 12/3 Ardkinglass—Mia Filia (Formidable (USA))
38 **MUNDAHISH (IRE),** b c 28/3 Marju (IRE)—Wakayi (Persian Bold) **Mr Hamdan Al Maktoum**
39 **OARE LINNET,** ch f 5/5 Polish Precedent—Portvasco (Sharpo) **Mrs Henry Keswick**
40 **ODYSSEY,** b c 22/1 Slip Anchor—Circe (Main Reef) **Mr A. D. G. Oldrey**
41 **RAINBOW ROMEO (IRE),** br c 11/2 Rainbows For Life—Splendid Chance (Random Shot) **Mr Eric Perry**
42 **YA-AIN,** b c 18/3 Warning—Ahbab (IRE) (Ajdal (USA)) **Mr Hamdan A Maktoum**

Late Naming

ORDER, b c Deploy — Gong (Bustino)

Other Owners: Mr George Hartigan, Mrs Brian Maynard, Mr R. J. McCreery, Mr S. F. Oldrey, Mrs D. C. Samworth, Mr M. G. St Quinton, Mr N. H. T. Wrigley.

Jockeys (Flat): P Eddery (8-4, w.a.), R Hills (8-0).

Lady Riders: Marchioness Of Blandford (9-5), Miss Susannah Samworth (8-10).

597 MR M. WANE, Richmond

Postal: **Barn House Racing Stables, Langdale, Melsonby, Richmond, North Yorkshire, DL10 5PW.**
Phone: **(01325) 718046 MOBILE (0468) 962622**

1 **AXEMAN (IRE),** 6, b g Reprimand—Minnie Tudor **Mr John Barton**
2 **BRIGHT DESERT,** 5, b g Green Desert (USA)—Smarten Up **Mr William Graham**
3 **DESERT CAT (IRE),** 5, b g Green Desert (USA)—Mahabba (USA) **Mrs Linda Miller**
4 **DIAMOND CROWN (IRE),** 7, ch g Kris—State Treasure (USA) **Mr J. M. Pickup**
5 **EUROLINK WINDSONG (IRE),** 4, ch f Polish Patriot (USA)—Delvecchia **Mr William Graham**
6 **MEN OF WICKENBY,** 4, b c Shirley Heights—Radiant Bride (USA) **Mr J. P. Slattery**

MR M. WANE—continued

7 **MICHANDRA BOY,** 5, b g Skyliner—Magdalene (IRE) **Mrs Margaret G. Robson**
8 **MILLESIME (IRE),** 6, ch g Glow (USA)—Persian Myth **Mrs H. H. Wane**
9 **MOONLIGHT VENTURE,** 6, b g Jupiter Island—Moonlight Bay **Mr R. Smalley**
10 **NAISSANT,** 5, b m Shaadi (USA)—Nophe (USA) **Mr William Graham**
11 **PRIDE OF PENDLE,** 9, ro m Grey Desire—Pendle's Secret **Mrs Linda Miller**
12 **PRINCE DOME (IRE),** 4, ch g Salt Dome (USA)—Blazing Glory (IRE) **Mr G. W. Jones**
13 **ROYAL DOME (IRE),** 6, b g Salt Dome (USA)—Brook's Dilemma **Mr G. W. Jones**
14 **SKYERS FLYER (IRE),** 4, b br f Magical Wonder (USA)—Siwana (IRE) **Mrs Linda Miller**
15 **TAKE NOTICE,** 5, b h Warning—Metair **Mr J. P. Slattery**
16 **TEN PAST SIX,** 6, ch g Kris—Tashinsky (USA) **Mr James S. Kennerley, Miss Jenny Hall**
17 **TERTIUM (IRE),** 6, b g Nordico (USA)—Nouniya **Mr John Barton**
18 **WESTERN VENTURE (IRE),** 5, ch g Two Timing (USA)—Star Gazing (IRE) **Mr William Graham**

TWO-YEAR-OLDS

19 B f 29/2 Mon Tresor—Lady Itatiba (BEL) (King of Macedon) **Mr James S. Kennerley**
20 B c 15/3 Safawan—Mrs Feathers (Pyjama Hunt) **Mrs H. H. Wane**
21 Ch f 8/5 Weldnaas (USA)—Shadha (Shirley Heights) **Mrs H. H. Wane**

Other Owners: Mr B. R. Bradbury, Mr Greg Gregory, Mr R. D. Marston, Mrs Karen S. Pratt, Mr B. J. Rae, Mr G. Stokes, Mrs H. Wane.

598 MRS V. C. WARD, Grantham

Postal: **Aisby House, Aisby, Grantham, Lincolnshire, NG32 3NF.**
Phone: **(01529) 455260**

1 **CANADIAN FANTASY,** 4, b g Lear Fan (USA)—Florinda (CAN) **Mrs R. F. Key & Mrs V. C. Ward**
2 **CAVIL,** 6, b g Reprimand—Lagta **Mr David Ashbrook**
3 **CITY HALL (IRE),** 4, gr c Generous (IRE)—City Fortress **Mrs R. F. Key & Mrs V. C. Ward**
4 **COUP DE VENT,** 8, ch g Viking (USA)—Callistro **Mrs V. C. Ward**
5 **CYPRESS AVENUE (IRE),** 6, b g Law Society (USA)—Flying Diva **Mr K. R. Gray**
6 **DOCTOR DUNKLIN (USA),** 9, gr g Family Doctor (USA)—Mis Jenifer's Idea (USA) **Mrs V. C. Ward**
7 **FLORENTINO (IRE),** 5, b g Machiavellian (USA)—Helens Dreamgirl **Mr David Ashbrook & Mrs V. C. Ward**
8 **FORMIDABLE PARTNER,** 5, b g Formidable (USA)—Brush Away **Mrs R. F. Key & Mrs V. C. Ward**
9 **GREEN CRUSADER,** 7, b g Green Desert (USA)—Hysterical **Mrs R. F. Key & Mrs V. C. Ward**
10 **IONIO (USA),** 7, ch g Silver Hawk (USA)—Private View (USA) **Mrs R. F. Key & Mrs V. C. Ward**
11 **KENALAN LAD,** 8, b g Pitpan—Hollomoore **Mrs Sally Thornton**
12 **MISTY CAY (IRE),** 4, b f Mujadil (USA)—Quai des Brumes (USA) **Mrs V. C. Ward**
13 **NIGHT WINK (USA),** 6, ch g Rahy (USA)—Lady In White **Mr Andrew Johnson & Mr Alan Kidd**
14 **SOLOMAN SPRINGS (USA),** 8, ch g Wajima (USA)—Malilla (CHI) **Mrs R. F. Key & Mrs V. C. Ward**

599 MRS BARBARA WARING, Welford-on-Avon

Postal: **Rumer Farm Stud and Stables, Long Marston Road, Welford-on-Avon, Warwickshire, CV37 8AF.**
Phone: **MOBILE (0860) 491636**

1 **ABSOLUTELYSTUNNING,** 5, br m Aragon—Dramatic Mood **J. McDonnell, V. Feerick, H. Shapter**
2 **AMILLIONMEMORIES,** 8, br g Macmillion—March Memories **P. Jones, M. Lambert, Elizabeth Burns**
3 **BRONHALLOW,** 5, b g Belmez (USA)—Grey Twig **Feerick, Davies, Parker, Piper & Cleak**
4 **LADY OF GLENDOWAN,** 5, b m Teenoso (USA)—Mearlin **Mr M. Mitchell**
5 **LILLY THE FILLY,** 7, br m Macmillion—March Memories **Mr E. Chivers**
6 **TOMMY COOPER,** 7, br g Macmillion—My Charade **Griffin, Davies, Wilton, Cleak**

MRS BARBARA WARING—continued

TWO-YEAR-OLDS

7 B f 28/4 Rainbows For Life—Debach Delight **McDonnell, Shapter, Cleak & Andrews**

Other Owners: Mr Mike Burns, Mr Harry Chisman, Mr D. Clark, Mr A. G. Gibbs, Mr C. R. Griffin, Mr D. E. Jones, Mr R. J. Simmons, Mrs Anne Strawson.

Jockeys (Flat): A Clark, T Quinn (w.a.), W Ryan.

Jockeys (NH): E Byrne (10-0), P Holley (9-7).

600 MR L. WARING, Wellington

Postal: **Southays Farm, Wrangway, Wellington, Somerset, TA21 9QG.**
Phone: **(01823) 662660**

1 **BOLT OF GOLD,** 10, b m Glint of Gold—Habutai **Mrs J. Waring**
2 **ROSIE-B,** 8, b m Gunner B—Saucy Mop **Mrs J. Waring**

Conditional: M Griffiths (9-7).

601 MR MIKE WARING, Wolverhampton

Postal: **Dunstall Park Stables, Gorsebrook Road, Wolverhampton, West Midlands, WV6 OPE.**
Phone: **(01902) 421421 FAX (01902) 421621 MOBILE (0831) 740218**

1 5, B m Arzanni—Another Molly **Mr M. Waring**
2 **BAPSFORD,** 4, b g Shalford (IRE)—Bap's Miracle **Dunstall Park Centre**
3 **CERTAIN WAY (IRE),** 8, ch g Sure Blade (USA)—Ruffling Point **Dunstall Park Centre**
4 **LASER LIGHT LADY,** 6, b m Tragic Role (USA)—Raina Perera **Dunstall Park Centre**
5 **NICKER,** 4, b g Nicholas (USA)—Glimmer **Dunstall Park Centre**
6 **NITEOWL RAIDER (IRE),** 5, ch g Standaan (FR)—Havana Moon **Dunstall Park Centre**
7 **PERISH THE THOUGHT,** 8, b g Remezzo—Pretty Fast **Foley Steelstock**
8 4, Ch f Commanche Run—Rustica Silk **Mr M. Waring**
9 4, Gr f Arzanni—That's Show Biz **Mr M. Waring**

THREE-YEAR-OLDS

10 **GORGEOUS,** b f Prince Sabo—Crackerjill **Dunstall Park Centre**
11 Ch g Safawan—Return To Romance **Dunstall Park Centre**

Other Owners: Valley Paddocks Racing.

602 MISS S. WATERMAN, Dorchester

Postal: **Melbury Bubb Cottage, Nr Evershot, Dorchester, Dorset, DT2 0NQ.**

1 **SEE MINNOW,** 5, b m Riverwise (USA)--Shepani **Miss S. Waterman**
2 **SEE PROSPERITY,** 6, b g Impecunious—Shepani **Miss S. Waterman**

Jockey (NH): D Salter (9-7).

Conditional: N Willmington.

Lady Rider: Miss S E Waterman (9-5).

603 MR T. R. WATSON, Winchcombe

Postal: **Slade Barn Farm, Pinnock, Winchcombe, Gloucestershire, GL54 5AX.**
Phone: **(01242) 603915**

1 **CUILLIN CAPER,** 6, b m Scottish Reel—That Space **Manor Farm Stud (Rutland)**
2 **DESERT LYNX (IRE),** 5, b m Green Desert (USA)—Sweeping **Mrs R. Ralli**
3 **MICK'S TYCOON (IRE),** 10, b g Last Tycoon—Ladytown **Mr Robin C. B. Brett**
4 **PUSHKA FAIR,** 7, b g Salse (USA)—Orient **Manor Farm Stud (Rutland)**
5 **ROCKAROUNDTHECLOCK,** 4, b g Rock City—Times **Mr Alan A. Wright**
6 **RUN TIGER (IRE),** 5, ch m Commanche Run—Snuggle **Kanlet Ltd**
7 **SAWLAJAN (USA),** 7, ch h Woodman (USA)—Crafty Satin (USA) **Miss S. Hoare**
8 **SAXIFRAGA,** 5, ch g Scottish Reel—Buck's Bloom **Manor Farm Stud (Rutland)**
9 **SEARCHLIGHT (IRE),** 10, ch g Seymour Hicks (FR)—Night Caller **Mr Alan A. Wright**

THREE-YEAR-OLDS

10 B f Always Fair (USA)—Lady Anchor **Newitt and Co Ltd**
11 B f Rudimentary (USA)—Morica **Newitt and Co Ltd**
12 B f Young Senor (USA)—Muznah **Newitt and Co Ltd**

TWO-YEAR-OLDS

13 Ch f 31/3 Prince Sabo—Canoodle (Warpath) **Newitt and Co Ltd**
14 B f 10/2 Simply Great (FR)—Empty Purse (Pennine Walk) **Newitt and Co Ltd**
15 Ch f 13/2 Tina's Pet—Fiddling (Music Boy) **Kanlet Ltd**
16 B f 18/4 Clantime—Orient (Bay Express) **Countess of Lonsdale**
17 B f 19/3 Magic Ring (IRE)—Shirl (Shirley Heights) **Newitt and Co Ltd**
18 Gr f 6/6 Mystiko (USA)—Singalong Lass (Bold Lad (IRE)) **Kanlet Ltd**

Other Owners: Mr G. H. Dodsworth, Mr R. T. Watson, Mrs R. T. Watson, Mrs I. Webb.

604 MR H. J. M. WEBB, Faringdon

Postal: **Peartree Farmhouse, Great Coxwell, Faringdon, Oxfordshire, SN7 7NG.**
Phone: **(01367) 240173 FAX (01367) 242765**

1 **BUY MY PLY,** 5, b g Ballacashtal (CAN)—Miss Inigo **Mr H. J. M. Webb**
2 **TRYMYPLY,** 6, b g Green Adventure (USA)—Miss Inigo **Mr H. J. M. Webb**

THREE-YEAR-OLDS

3 B g Newski (USA)—Miss Inigo **Mr H. J. M. Webb**

605 MR P. R. WEBBER, Banbury

Postal: **Cropredy Lawn, Cropredy, Banbury, Oxfordshire, OX17 1DR.**
Phone: **(01295) 750226 FAX (01295) 758482 MOBILE (0836) 232465**

1 **ARDROM,** 6, ch m Ardross—Drom Lady **Mr F. J. Haggas**
2 **ARTIC GROUND (IRE),** 6, b g Lord Americo—Frozen Ground **Mr C. W. Booth**
3 **BOLD LEAP,** 6, b g Bold Owl—Thabeh **Two Generations Partnership**
4 **BRAZIL OR BUST (IRE),** 7, b g Bustino—Coffee **Mrs C. A. Waters**
5 **BRUSH ME UP (IRE),** 6, b br g Brush Aside (USA)—Eimers Pet **Mrs C. A. Waters**
6 **CARLITO BRIGANTE,** 6, b g Robellino (USA)—Norpella **Mr R. A. H. Perkins**
7 **CAVALRY,** 4, b f Infantry—Moore Stylish **Mr D. A. Beaumont**
8 **CREDO IS KING (IRE),** 8, b g Le Moss—Merendas Sister **Mr G. L. Porter**
9 5, Ch g Over The River (FR)—Daisy Owen **Random Partnership**
10 **ELLIEWELLIEWOO,** 5, b m Syrtos—Ruby's Vision **Mr David Wade-Jones**
11 **ERIN ALLEY (IRE),** 5, ch g Be My Native (USA)—Cousin Flo **L & P Partnership**

MR P. R. WEBBER—continued

12 **FARU,** 6, b h Mtoto—Fade **Jebel Ali Racing Stables**
13 **FLYING BOOTS,** 5, b g Doc Marten—Flying Mistress **Lady Lyell**
14 **FLYING INSTRUCTOR,** 8, gr g Neltino—Flying Mistress **Lady Lyell**
15 **GLEMOT (IRE),** 10, br g Strong Gale—Lady Nethertown **Mr Dennis Yardy**
16 **GLEN GRANT,** 6, ch g Royal Match—Rowan Ville **Mrs D. Holman**
17 **GLOBAL SEARCH (FR),** 4, b g Green Dancer (USA)—Merry Quest (USA) **Elite Racing Club**
18 **GOOD TIME DANCER,** 6, ch m Good Times (ITY)—Linpac Mapleleaf **Good Time Band**
19 **GORDON,** 7, b g Governor General—Red Spider **Mrs C. N. Pitt**
20 **GUILDER,** 4, b g Groom Dancer (USA)—Guillem (USA) **Economic Security**
21 **JACOB'S WIFE,** 8, gr m Baron Blakeney—Vido **The Black Sheep Flock**
22 **JOHN DRUMM,** 7, gr g Alias Smith (USA)—Girl of Shiraz **Mr Andrew Jenkins**
23 **JUNGLI (IRE),** 5, b g Be My Native (USA)—Simple Mind **Mrs P. Starkey**
24 **KAYGEBE (IRE),** 5, b g Moscow Society (USA)—Golden Mela **Mr R. W. Barnett**
25 **LAND AFAR,** 11, b g Dominion—Jouvencelle **Mr T. J. Ford**
26 **LEWESDON MANOR,** 7, b g Broadsword (USA)—Lewesdon View **Mr J. G. Phillips**
27 **LIMITED LIABILITY,** 8, b g Bustino—Fine Asset **Miss Elizabeth Aldous**
28 **LITTLE RED SPIDER,** 5, b m Bustino—Red Spider **Mr Andrew Jenkins**
29 **MARYTAVY,** 4, b f Lycius (USA)—Rose Parade **Mr Bernard Hathaway**
30 **NORDIC CREST (IRE),** 4, b g Danehill (USA)—Feather Glen **The Silver Cod Partnership**
31 **OUR GHILLIE,** 5, ch g Gildoran—Lizzie The Twig **Mrs P. L. Aldersey**
32 **PADDY CLYDE (IRE),** 5, b g Royal Fountain—Thats Irish **Mr John Breslin**
33 **PENROSE LAD (NZ),** 8, b g Captain Jason (NZ)—Salimah (NZ) **Mrs C. N. Weatherby**
34 **PERCY CROW (IRE),** 5, ch g Persian Heights—Slightly Latin **Mrs Susan P. Davis**
35 **QUICK BOWLER (IRE),** 6, b g Bowling Pin—Fortina Lass **Racegoers Club Owners Group (1996)**
36 **RIPARIUS (USA),** 7, b g Riverman (USA)—Sweet Simone (FR) **Mrs David Blackburn**
37 **ROAD RACER (IRE),** 5, br g Scenic—Rally **Mrs Anthony West**
38 **SCOTTISH BAMBI,** 10, ch g Scottish Reel—Bambolona **Mr William J. Kelly**
39 **SEATTLE ALLEY (USA),** 5, b g Seattle Dancer (USA)—Alyanaabi (USA) **L & P Partnership**
40 **SHARP PEARL,** 5, ch g Sharpo—Silent Pearl (USA) **Mr Dennis Yardy**
41 **SIDANORA (IRE),** 8, ch g Montekin—Lady of Eilat **Mr Dennis Yardy**
42 **SIR LUNCHALOT (IRE),** 5, b g Homo Sapien—Halpin **The Random Partnership**
43 **SNOWDON LILY,** 7, br m Town And Country—Welsh Flower **Mrs P. Starkey**
44 **ST MELLION FAIRWAY (IRE),** 9, b g Mandalus—Kilbricken Bay **St Mellion Estates Ltd**
45 **TAKE THE CATCH,** 5, br m Relief Pitcher—Take The Veil **Mr D. R. Stoddart**
46 **TAPPETO,** 6, b g Liboi (USA)—Persian Carpet (FR) **Mrs David Blackburn**
47 **TORN SILK,** 4, b g Top Ville—Cut Velvet (USA) **Lady Bamford**
48 **WHAT'S YOUR STORY (IRE),** 9, ch g The Parson—Lolos Run VII **Mr Jerry Wright**

THREE-YEAR-OLDS

49 **FORMER LOVE (USA),** b f Dynaformer (USA)—Love And Legend (USA) **Mr Brereton C. Jones**

Other Owners: Mr M. P. Aldersey, Mr Philip F. Banks, Mrs D. Barnett, Mrs D. A. Beaumont, Mr A. J. Best, Mr A. Bond, Mr P. M. Burrell, Mr Michael Coghlan, Mr C. D. Coltart, Mr J. S. Dale, Mrs A. J. Davies, Mr P. A. Deal, Mr M. Duff, Mr John W. Egan, Mr Peter Garnett, Mr C. A. Gidman, Miss L. M. Gold, Mrs Mary Grant, Mr Richard Hall, Mrs Mary Hartop, Mr V. Kilkenny, Prof David Lipsey, Mr I. Magee, Mr Rory McGrath, Mrs C. M. Meyrick, Mr G. C. Myddelton, Mr J. G. O'Neill, Mrs J. K. Powell, Mr W. L. Simmons, Mrs I. M. Steinmann, Mr J. D. Steinmann, Mrs J. Taylor, Mr Vernon Taylor, Mrs D. J. Tellwright, Mrs M. Thomlinson, Mrs John Webber, Wellesbourne Property Ltd, Mr P. W. A. Westerman, Mrs R. Wilson.

Jockeys (Flat): K Fallon (w.a.), Dane O'Neill.

Jockeys (NH): J McCarthy (10-0), J Osborne, A Thornton (10-3).

Amateur: Mr P Scott (9-10).

606 MR M. J. WEEDEN, Weymouth

Postal: **Highfield, Fleet, Weymouth, Dorset, DT3 4EB.**

1 **ABSALOM'S LADY,** 10, gr m Absalom—High Point Lady (CAN) **Mr Peter R. Bolton**
2 **CASTERBRIDGE,** 6, ch g Nearly A Hand—G W Supermare **Mr Peter R. Bolton**
3 **CHANTILLY LADY,** 5, ch m Rising—Ladiz **Mr Peter R. Bolton**
4 4, B g Teamster—G W Supermare **Mr Peter R. Bolton**
5 **HAPPY GO LUCKY,** 4, ch f Teamster—Meritsu (IRE) **Mr Peter R. Bolton**
6 **JAZZ DUKE,** 5, ch g Rising—Gone **Mr Peter R. Bolton**
7 **PERFECT PAL (IRE),** 7, ch g Mulhollande (USA)—Gone **Mr Peter R. Bolton**

THREE-YEAR-OLDS

8 **ROYAL SIGNET,** ch f King's Signet (USA)—Ladiz **Mr Peter R. Bolton**

607 MR C. V. WEEDON, Chiddingfold

Postal: **Robins Farm, Fisher Lane, Chiddingfold, Surrey, GU8 4TB.**
Phone: **(0831) 115009 (01428) 683344**

1 **CHECKS AND STRIPES (IRE),** 7, ch g Electric—Dream Toi **Mr David Knox**
2 **FOEHN GALE (IRE),** 7, b m Strong Gale—Woodford Princess **Mr David Knox**
3 **FOREST FEATHER (IRE),** 10, b g Arapahos (FR)—Mistress Boreen **Mr David Knox**
4 **HEDGEHOPPER (IRE),** 10, b g Henbit (USA)—Selham **Mr David Knox**
5 4, B g Arctic Lord—Just Hannah **Mr John Hobbs & Mr Barry Young**
6 **LUNO,** 4, gr c Petong—Teacher's Game **Simulex Ltd**
7 **MIRACLE MAN,** 10, b g Kemal (FR)—Knockeevan Girl **Mr Patrick Evans**
8 **MISS MOONSTONE,** 5, gr m Neltino—Kopjes **Mrs J. M. Jeyes**
9 **MISTER GENEROSITY (IRE),** 7, b g King's Ride—Brownstown Lady **Mr Colin Weedon**
10 **NIGHT ESCAPADE (IRE),** 6, b m Be My Native (USA)—Right Dark **Mr Alf Chadwick**
11 **STORMTRACKER (IRE),** 9, br g Strong Gale—Stay As You Are **Mr Tim Davis**
12 **SWEETLISAJANE (IRE),** 7, b m Strong Gale—Royal Secret **Mr Alf Chadwick**
13 **YOUNG ARDROSS,** 7, b g Ardross—Celtic Silk **Atlantic Foods Ltd**

Other Owners: Mr B. Connolly, Mrs Susan Gay, Mrs A. D. Gray, Mr Colin D. Hale, Mr R. D. Hammond, Mr C. J. Jackson, Mr Richard Lockwood, Mr John Marsh, Mrs Stephanie Marsh, Mr M. Polycarpou, Mr N. R. Robinson, Mr Tony Rooth, Mr R. N. Scott, Mr A. H. Stannard.

608 MR P. WEGMANN, Gloucester

Postal: **Maisemore Park, The Rudge, Maisemore, Gloucester, GL2 8HX.**
Phone: **(01452) 301332 FAX (01452) 505002**

1 **ARKLOW KING (IRE),** 6, br g King's Ride—Lantern Lass **Mr P. Wegmann**
2 **CAPTAIN MORRIS,** 6, b g Sadeem (USA)—Green Blossom **Mr P. Wegmann**
3 **CAPTAIN STOCKFORD,** 11, b g Grey Ghost—Stubbin Moor **Mr P. Wegmann**
4 **KURDISTAN (IRE),** 8, ch g Persian Heights—Late Sally **Mr P. Wegmann**
5 **STRONG GLEN (IRE),** 10, br g Strong Gale—Merry And Bright **Mr P. Wegmann**
6 **SWISS SILVER,** 5, ch g Pragmatic—Jaunty Slave **Mr P. Wegmann**
7 **TAFZAL,** 7, br g Afzal—Taffidale **Mr P. Wegmann**
8 **TAFZALETTE,** 6, ch m Afzal—Taffidale **Mr P. Wegmann**

609 MR D. K. WELD M.V.B. M.R.C.V.S., The Curragh

Postal: **Rosewell House, The Curragh, Co. Kildare, Irish Republic.**
Phone: **353-45-441273/441476 FAX 353-45-441119**

1 **DANCE DESIGN**, 5, b m Sadler's Wells (USA)—Elegance In Design **Satish Sanan**
2 **GATES (USA)**, 5, ch g Jade Hunter—Royal Herat **Joseph King**
3 **GORDI (USA)**, 5, ch g Theatrical—Royal Alydar **Allen Paulson**
4 **IRON COUNTY XMAS (USA)**, 4, b g Cox's Ridge (USA)—Christmas Bonus (USA) **Iron County Farms Inc**
5 **LADY SHANNON (USA)**, 4, gr f Mr Prospector (USA)—Flowing **Mrs B. Maxwell Moran**
6 **MORE'S THE PITY**, 4, ch g Cadeaux Genereux—What A Pity **M. Moore**
7 **MOVING ON UP**, 4, b g Salse—Thundercloud **M. H. Burke**
8 **SENSE OF HONOUR (USA)**, 4, ch f Be My Guest (USA)—Well Supported (USA) **Mrs C. L. Weld**
9 **STAGE AFFAIR (USA)**, 4, b br c Theatrical—Wooing **Michael J. Smurfit**
10 **TARRY FLYNN (IRE)**, 4, br g Kenmare (FR)—Danzig Lass (USA) **Mrs C. L. Weld**
11 **TRADE DISPUTE (IRE)**, 6, ro g Ela-Mana-Mou—Safety Feature **Mrs Gaynor Watt**
12 **ZANKLE (USA)**, 5, b g Opening Verse—Capre **Michael J. Smurfit**

THREE-YEAR-OLDS

13 **ALLEGEDLY YOURS (USA)**, b f Alleged (USA)—Indigo Rose (USA) **Iron County Farms Inc**
14 **ALTHIB (IRE)**, ch g Wolfhound (USA)—Sure Enough (IRE) **Mr T. McManus**
15 **AMHARCLANN (USA)**, ch f Theatrical—Lizad (USA) **Michael J. Smurfit**
16 **BRIEF DECLINE (IRE)**, b c Alzao (USA)—Uncertain Affair **Moyglare Stud Farm**
17 **CAVALLINA (USA)**, b f Theatrical—Sedulous **Thomas McDonagh**
18 **CLEVER CONSUL (IRE)**, b c Acatenango (GER)—Kelvedon **Mr J. F. O'Malley**
19 **CULTURAL ROLE**, ch f Night Shift (USA)—Bright Spells **Moyglare Stud Farm**
20 **ELJAMIL (IRE)**, b c Night Shift (USA)—Gwydion (USA) **Hamdan Al Maktoum**
21 **EMBERS OF FAME (IRE)**, b f Sadler's Wells (USA)—Love For Poetry **Moyglare Stud Farm**
22 **FEARSOME FACTOR (USA)**, b c Alleged (USA)—Spark of Success (USA) **Moyglare Stud Farm**
23 **FOREVER YOUNG**, gr c Indian Ridge—Crodelle **Moyglare Stud Farm**
24 **FRANCIS BAY (USA)**, b c Alleged (USA)—Montage (USA) **Michael Watt**
25 **GREY CISEAUX (IRE)**, gr g Mujtahid—Inisfail **Mr G. Olivero**
26 **GREY LIGHTNING (IRE)**, gr g Brief Truce (USA)—Phazania **J. Kessell**
27 **GUAPO (USA)**, b br c Alleged (USA)—Joy Returned (USA) **Iron County Farms Inc**
28 **GUTNICK (USA)**, b br c Theatrical—Ohsomellow **Geoff Case**
29 **HAMASAH (USA)**, b f Irish River (FR)—In The Habit (USA) **Hamdan Al Maktoum**
30 **HARDA ARDA (USA)**, ch f Nureyev (USA)—Ask The Wind **Mr Wafic Said**
31 **HAWAS (IRE)**, ch f Mujtahid (USA)—Alyakkh **Hamdan Al Maktoum**
32 **HIBERNIAN RHAPSODY (IRE)**, b c Darshaan—Elegance In Design **Moyglare Stud Farm**
33 **HUBLE (USA)**, gr g Theatrical—Al's Charm **Allen Paulson**
34 **INDINOLLA (USA)**, ch f Theatrical—Ottomwa **Mrs C. L. Weld**
35 **INSPIRING STORY (USA)**, b c Woodman (USA)—Looking Brill **Moyglare Stud Farm**
36 **JEANNE D'ARC**, gr f Highest Honor (FR)—Fight Right (FR) **Mrs C. L. Weld**
37 **KEY PROVIDER (USA)**, b c Be My Guest (USA)—Certain Supremacy (USA) **Moyglare Stud Farm**
38 **LEAVE ME ALONE (IRE)**, b f Nashwan (USA)—Perfect Welcome **Moyglare Stud Farm**
39 **MAGICAL SHOT**, b g Magic Ring (IRE)—Final Shot **Mrs D. K. Weld & Mrs C. Kinane**
40 **MAKE NO MISTAKE (IRE)**, b c Darshaan—Respectfully (USA) **Moyglare Stud Farm**
41 **OBVIOUS APPEAL (IRE)**, b f Danehill (USA)—Croglin Water **Moyglare Stud Farm**
42 **PEERLESS MOTION (IRE)**, b c Caerleon (USA)—Final Figure (USA) **Moyglare Stud Farm**
43 **QUEEN OF SILK (IRE)**, b f Brief Truce (USA)—Danzig Lass (USA) **Bruce McAllistair**
44 **RAJJAAF**, ch c Unfuwain (USA)—Forest Lair **Hamdan Al Maktoum**
45 **RAZIK (CAN)**, b c Dayjur (USA)—Sirona (CAN) **Hamdan Al Maktoum**
46 **SANS PRIX (FR)**, b f Caerleon (USA)—Sans Condition **Mrs A. J. F. O'Reilly**
47 **SCREEN IDOL (IRE)**, b f Sadler's Wells (USA)—Spring To Light (USA) **Moyglare Stud Farm**
48 **SHYAM (USA)**, b br f Shadeed (USA)—Checking It Twice **Iron County Farms Inc**
49 **SILVERADO (IRE)**, gr g Indian Ridge—Tajarib **Mrs A. J. F. O'Reilly**
50 **SIMULACRUM (USA)**, ch g Zilzal (USA)—Exactly Like You (usa) **Michael J. Smurfit**
51 **SPRING EASY (IRE)**, b f Alzao (USA)—High Spirited **Mrs J. Magnier**
52 **STAR OF TRAMP (IRE)**, b c Theatrical—Search For Spring (IRE) **Kevin Doyle**
53 **STYLE PARADE (USA)**, b f Diesis—Longing To Dance (USA) **Moyglare Stud Farm**
54 **TAIL OF THE STORM (USA)**, b c Storm Bird (CAN)—Croquetallie (USA) **Glenwood Farm**

MR D. K. WELD M.V.B. M.R.C.V.S.—continued

55 THE THIRD CURATE (IRE), b c Fairy King (USA)—Lassalia **Moyglare Stud Farm**
56 TITUS (USA), b c Theatrical—Sauna (AUS) **Allen Paulson**
57 TWO-TWENTY-TWO (IRE), b c Fairy King (USA)—Easy To Copy (USA) **Moyglare Stud Farm**
58 UNTOLD STORY (USA), b c Theatrical—Committed Miss (USA) **Moyglare Stud Farm**
59 VAGRANT (FR), ch g Nashwan (USA)—Valverda (USA) **Mrs A. J. F. O'Reilly**
60 VINKA (USA), ch f Strawberry Road (AUS)—Cockney Lass **Allen Paulson**
61 WALL ST STATION (USA), b c Wall Street Dancer (USA)—Shout (USA) **John Gunther**
62 ZAFAN (IRE), ch c Zafonic (USA)—Anjuli **Mrs Sean Collins**

TWO-YEAR-OLDS

63 Ch f 24/3 Indian Ridge—Across The Ice (USA) (General Holme (USA)) **Michael J. Smurfit**
64 AICIA (IRE), b f 19/4 Fairy King (USA)—Aisla (USA) (Miswaki (USA)) **Mrs A. J. F. O'Reilly**
65 ALBARAKAT (USA), b f 30/1 Riverman (USA)—Surging (USA) (Fappiano (USA)) **Hamdan Al Maktoum**
66 ALL TO EASY, b f 22/4 Alzao (USA)—Easy To Copy (USA) (Affirmed (USA)) **Moyglare Stud Farm**
67 ANTHEM OF LOVE (USA), ch f 9/4 Silver Hawk (USA)—Missing Love (Thatching) **Moyglare Stud Farm**
68 BASHASHAH (IRE), b f 30/1 Kris—Alyakkh (IRE) (Sadler's Wells (USA)) **Hamdan Al Maktoum**
69 Gr c 13/2 Cadeaux Genereux—Beautiful France (IRE) (Sadler's Wells (USA)) **Moyglare Stud Farm**
70 BETWEEN THE WINDS (USA), ch f 21/4 Diesis—Welcome Proposal (Be My Guest (USA)) **Moyglare Stud Farm**
71 BLEND OF PACE (IRE), b f 3/2 Sadler's Wells (USA)—Trusted Partner (USA) (Affirmed (USA)) **Moyglare Stud Farm**
72 BRIEF LULLABY (IRE), ch f 16/5 Brief Truce (USA)—Temporary Lull (USA) (Super Concorde (USA)) **Moyglare Stud Farm**
73 B f 4/3 Turtle Island (IRE)—Clear Procedure (USA) (The Minstrel (CAN)) **Mrs A. J. F. O'Reilly**
74 Ch c Jade Hunter (USA)—Cockney Lass (Camden Town) **Lord Philip Harris**
75 COSTUME DRAMA (USA), b f 12/2 Alleged (USA)—Comfort And Style (Be My Guest (USA)) **Moyglare Stud Farm**
76 B c 30/3 Be My Guest (USA)—Danzig Lass (USA) (Danzig (USA)) **Mrs C. L. Weld**
77 FADHEL (USA), b c 25/2 Zilzal (USA)—Nice Life (USA) (Sportin' Life (USA)) **Hamdan Al Maktoum**
78 B f 15/5 Mujadil (USA)—First Nadia (Auction Ring (USA)) **Michael J. Smurfit**
79 GENEROUS CHARMER (IRE), b f 8/3 Selkirk (USA)—Uncertain Affair (IRE) (Darshaan) **Moyglare Stud Farm**
80 GRAND AMBITION (USA), b c 1/3 Lear Fan (USA)—Longing To Dance (USA) (Nureyev (USA)) **Moyglare Stud Farm**
81 B f 22/3 Fairy King (USA)—Guanhumara (Caerleon (USA)) **Mrs A. J. F. O'Reilly**
82 HADEB, b f 1/4 Unfuwain (USA)—Mahrah (USA) (Vaguely Noble) **Hamdan Al Maktoum**
83 HALYCON, b c 29/2 Be My Chief (USA)—Countess Olivia (Prince Tenderfoot (USA)) **Peter Wetzel**
84 B c 25/4 Diesis—Happy Gal (FR) (Habitat) **Peter Wetzel**
85 HEROE'S RETURN (IRE), ch c 22/4 Brief Truce (USA)—Offshore Boom (Be My Guest (USA)) **Moyglare Stud Farm**
86 Ch c 21/1 Diesis—High Sevens (Master Willie) **Hamdan Al Maktoum**
87 HIP POCKET (IRE), b c 20/4 Ela-Mana-Mou—Ebony And Ivory (IRE) (Bob Back (USA)) **Michael Watt**
88 IMMOVABLE OPTION (IRE), b c 3/5 Fairy King (USA)—Perfect Welcome (Taufan (USA)) **Moyglare Stud Farm**
89 INTRICATE WEBB (IRE), b c 6/4 Warning—In Anticipation (IRE) (Sadler's Wells (USA)) **Moyglare Stud Farm**
90 LA SERINA (IRE), b f 19/4 Royal Academy (USA)—Hi Bettina (Henbit (USA)) **Thomas McDonagh**
91 B c 8/3 Turtle Island (IRE)—Last Affaire (IRE) (Roi Danzig (USA)) **Mrs A. J. F. O'Reilly**
92 B c 21/4 Green Dancer (USA)—Latest Creation (USA) (Affirmed (USA)) **Moyglare Stud Farm**
93 MAJOR FORCE (USA), b c 6/2 Woodman (USA)—Ready For Action (USA) (Riverman (USA)) **Moyglare Stud Farm**
94 MARCHING ORDERS (IRE), b c 7/6 Nashwan (USA)—Minstrels Folly (USA) (The Minstrel (CAN)) **Moyglare Stud Farm**
95 B f 23/4 Barathea (IRE)—Morcote (IRE) (Magical Wonder (USA)) **Michael J. Smurfit**
96 MUS-IF, b c 2/2 Lahib (USA)—Navajo Love Song (IRE) (Dancing Brave (USA)) **Hamdan Al Maktoum**
97 B c 30/3 College Chapel—Na-Ammah (IRE) (Ela-Mana-Mou) **Lord Philip Harris**
98 B f 11/3 Diesis—Overseas Romance (USA) (Assert) **Moyglare Stud Farm**
99 Ch c 5/2 Perugino (USA)—Perfect Chance (Petorius) **Mr A. McManus**
100 POWER AND PANACHE (USA), b c 7/5 Nureyev (USA)—Clear Issue (USA) (Riverman (USA)) **Moyglare Stud Farm**
101 QUITE REGAL (IRE), b c 10/2 Sadler's Wells (USA)—Spring To Light (USA) (Blushing Groom (FR)) **Moyglare Stud Farm**
102 ROYAL COMMAND (IRE), b c 21/5 Green Desert (USA)—Elegance In Design (Habitat) **Moyglare Stud Farm**

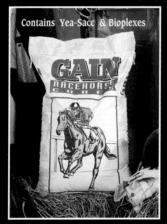

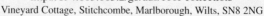

MR D. K. WELD M.V.B. M.R.C.V.S.—continued

103 B c 12/3 Be My Guest (USA)—Sanndila (IRE) (Lashkari) **Michael J. Smurfit**
104 SEASONAL STYLE (IRE), ch f 12/3 Generous (IRE)—
Just Society (USA) (Devil's Bag (USA)) **Moyglare Stud Farm**
105 B c 22/3 Mujadil (USA)—Skinity (Rarity) **Mr Yao**
106 Ch f Miswaki (USA)—Slam Bid (USA) (Forli (ARG)) **Mrs A. J. F. O'Reilly**
107 SOUTH OF HEAVEN (IRE), b f 28/4 Fairy King (USA)—
Epicure's Garden (USA) (Affirmed (USA)) **Moyglare Stud Farm**
108 B br c 5/2 Green Dancer (USA)—Subtle Expression (USA) (Slew O' Gold (USA)) **Michael J. Smurfit**
109 SUPREME CERTAINTY (IRE), b c 11/5 Night Shift (USA)—
Certain Supremacy (USA) (Alydar (USA)) **Moyglare Stud Farm**
110 TACOBARRY (USA), ch c 17/4 Northern Baby (CAN)—Camisha (IRE) (Shernazar) **Michael J. Smurfit**
111 TAJ (FR), b c 15/4 Zafonic (USA)—Numuthej (USA) (Nureyev (USA)) **Hamdan Al Maktoum**
112 Ch c 27/5 Zilzal (USA)—Tesio's Love (USA) (Tom Rolfe) **Mrs A. J. F. O'Reilly**
113 B c 29/3 Brief Truce (USA)—Too Shy (FR) (Top Ville) **Mr C. McHale**
114 TOUCH OF TRUTH (USA), ch f 11/4 Storm Cat (USA)—Grenzen (USA) (Grenfall (USA)) **Moyglare Stud Farm**
115 B f 11/2 Royal Academy (USA)—Trojan Crown (IRE) (Trojan Fen) **Michael J. Smurfit**
116 UPBEAT LEADER (USA), ch c 14/2 Gulch (USA)—
Well Supported (USA) (Key To The Mint (USA)) **Moyglare Stud Farm**
117 WIMBLEDON, b c 12/2 Second Set (IRE)—Rarely Irish (USA) (Irish Tower (USA)) **Prince Fahd Salman**
118 WITH A PRAYER, b f 27/4 Caerleon (USA)—Love For Poetry (Lord Gayle (USA)) **Moyglare Stud Farm**
119 Ch c 27/3 Magic Ring (IRE)—Zinzi (Song) **Lord Philip Harris**

Jockeys (Flat): M J Kinane (8-4), P Shanahan (8-3), P J Smullen (8-3).

610 MR L. WELLS, Billingshurst

Postal: **Pallingham Manor Farm, Wisborough Green, Billingshurst, West Sussex, RH14 0EZ.**
Phone: **HOME (01403) 700679 OFFICE (01403) 700119 FAX (01403) 700899**

1 AUDACTER (IRE), 5, b g Strong Gale—Sue's A Lady **Mrs Carrie Zetter-Wells**
2 BAT OUT OF HELL (IRE), 7, b g Orchestra—One Way Passage **Mrs Carrie Zetter-Wells**
3 B FIFTY TWO (IRE), 7, b g Mandalus—Hyde's Pride **Mrs Carrie Zetter-Wells**
4 BONNIE ONE TWENTY, 7, b m Le Solaret (FR)—Update Gal **Mrs Carrie Zetter-Wells**
5 4, Br g Phardante (FR)—Cathy's Girl **Mrs Carrie Zetter-Wells**
6 CHARLIE CHARLIE, 7, b g Emarati (USA)—Hound Song **Mr A. G. Russell & J. Missin**
7 COUGAR RUN (IRE), 7, b br g Commanche Run—Orra Beg **Mrs Carrie Zetter-Wells**
8 GLOBAL DANCER, 7, b g Night Shift (USA)—Early Call **Double The Pleasure**
9 HARROW WAY (IRE), 8, b g Strong Gale—Merry Miss **Mr David Gower**
10 JAZZY REFRAIN (IRE), 8, b m Jareer (USA)—Gay Refrain **Mr Paul Zetter**
11 KOPAIN, 8, b g Idiot's Delight—Saroan Meed **Stuart-Parsons, Watson, Burr, Finni**
12 LITTLE BUCK (IRE), 10, b g Buckskin (FR)—Little Quince **Mrs Carrie Zetter-Wells**
13 MAIDSTONE MONARCH (IRE), 5, b br g King's Ride—Curragh Breeze **F. G. Wilson**
14 MYSTIC LEGEND (IRE), 6, gr g Standaan (FR)—Mandy Girl **Mrs Elizabeth Sinclair**
15 MY TERN (IRE), 4, b f Glacial Storm (USA)—My Duchess **Mr P. C. Dutton**
16 NIGHT-MARE (IRE), 5, br m Creative Plan (USA)—Fancy Ride **Mrs Carrie Zetter-Wells**
17 OLD ARCHIVES (IRE), 9, b g Rousillon (USA)—Museum Ball (USA) **Mr Paul Zetter**
18 ROCK 'N ROLL STAR (IRE), 6, b g Zaffaran (USA)—Silver Rose **Mrs Carrie Zetter-Wells**
19 SULTAN OF SWING, 9, b g Idiot's Delight—Tropical Swing **Mrs Carrie Zetter-Wells**
20 5, B g Southern Music—Tyqueen **Mrs Carrie Zetter-Wells**

Other Owners: Mrs S. Burr, Ms Finni Robertson, Mr Ben Overton, Mr K. Stuart-Parsons, Mr H. A. D. Warner, Mrs Karen Watson.

Conditional: Lee Moulson (9-1).

Amateurs: Mr Neil Mackenzie-Ross (9-7), Mr Darren Page (10-0).

Lady Rider: Ms Gisella Gibson (9-7).

611 MR E. WEYMES, Middleham

Postal: **Ashgill, Coverham, Leyburn, North Yorkshire, DL8 4TJ.**
Phone: **(01969) 640229**

1 **ARDOUR GLOWING,** 4, b f Ardross—Albaciyna **Mr P. S. Willcocks**
2 **IMPULSIVE AIR (IRE),** 6, b g Try My Best (USA)—Tracy's Sundown **Mr T. A. Scothern**
3 **MURRAY GREY,** 4, gr f Be My Chief (USA)—Couleur de Rose **Mrs P. M. Weymes**
4 **MYSTIQUE AIR (IRE),** 4, b f Mujadil (USA)—Romany Pageant **Mr T. A. Scothern**
5 **QUICK MARCH,** 5, b m Daring March—Cabaletta **Mr J. Weymes**
6 **RAIVUE,** 4, ch g Beveled (USA)—Halka **Mrs A. Birkett**
7 **SING AND DANCE,** 5, b m Rambo Dancer (CAN)—Musical Princess **Mrs N. Napier**
8 **SPECIAL-K,** 6, br m Treasure Kay—Lissi Gori (FR) **Mr G. Falshaw**
9 **WOODETTO (IRE),** 4, b g Maledetto (IRE)—Wood Kay (IRE) **Mrs P. M. Weymes**

THREE-YEAR-OLDS

10 **ARCTIC AIR,** br f Polar Falcon (USA)—Breadcrumb **Mr T. A. Scothern**
11 **CROSBY DON,** b g Alhijaz—Evening Star **Mr D. Raper**
12 **MUSICAL SOCKS,** b f Rambo Dancer (CAN)—Musical Princess **Mrs N. Napier**
13 **OPTIMISTIC AIR (IRE),** b f Sabrehill (USA)—Silent Movie **Mr T. A. Scothern**
14 **QUIZ MASTER,** ch g Superpower—Ask Away **Mrs R. L. Heaton**
15 **STRATEGIC AIR,** ch g Anshan—Kimboltan Katie **Mr T. A. Scothern**

TWO-YEAR-OLDS

16 B c 28/3 Dolphin Street (FR)—Centinela (Caerleon (USA)) **Mr T. A. Scothern**
17 **DESERT MUSIC,** b f 12/3 Ardkinglass—Musical Princess (Cavo Doro) **Mrs N. Napier**
18 B f 8/3 Ezzoud (IRE)—Jhansi Ki Rani (USA) (Far North (CAN)) **Mr T. A. Scothern**
19 **LUNE LASS,** br f 10/3 Cyrano de Bergerac—Oubeck (Mummy's Game) **Mrs A. Birkett**
20 **MAGIC MOMENT,** b f 10/3 Magic Ring (IRE)—Epithet (Mill Reef (USA)) **Mr T. A. Scothern**
21 **MILDON (IRE),** ch c 30/4 Dolphin Street (FR)—Lycia (Targowice (USA)) **Mr D. Raper**

Other Owners: Mr M. Lee, Mrs E. Palamountain, Mr P. L. Pickford, Mr R. N. Wellock.

Amateur: Mr J Weymes (10-4).

612 MR J. R. H. WHARTON, Melton Mowbray

Postal: **Racecourse Farm Stables, Bescaby, Waltham-On-Wolds, Leics. LE14 4AB.**
Phone: **OFFICE 01664 464334 MOBILE 0370 893092 HOME 01664 69868 01476 870092**

1 4, Ch c Minster Son—Another Treat **Mr G. W. Turner**
2 **BALI TENDER,** 7, ch g Balidar—Highest Tender **Mr W. Wharton**
3 **BOLD WELCOME,** 4, ch g Most Welcome—Song's Best **Mr J. M. Berry**
4 **BROTHER HARRY,** 6, ch g Rakaposhi King—Magic **Mr W. Wharton**
5 **DALWHINNIE,** 5, b m Persian Bold—Land Line **Ibra Racing Company**
6 **FAYM (IRE),** 4, b f Fayruz—Lorme **Mr John Wharton**
7 **FIRST GOLD,** 9, gr g Absalom—Cindys Gold **Mr K. D. Standen**
8 **GUY'S GAMBLE,** 5, ch g Mazilier (USA)—Deep Blue Sea **Parkers of Peterborough Plc**
9 **JOSEPH'S WINE,** 9, b g Smile (USA)—Femme Gendarme (USA) **Wetherby Racing Bureau Ltd**
10 **KOTA,** 5, b g Kris—Lady Be Mine (USA) **Mr P. W. Lambert**
11 **MINIHARNA,** 5, gr m Bedford (USA)—Shankhouse Girl **Mrs A. H. Robinson**
12 **POPLIN,** 7, b m Derrylin—Poppy's Pride **Mrs M. Mann**
13 **POPPY'S DREAM,** 8, b m Dreams To Reality (USA)—Poppy's Pride **Mr John Wharton**
14 **REKKAN,** 4, gr g Minster Son—Laura Lager **Mrs V. Craggs**
15 **TOULSTON LADY (IRE),** 6, b m Handsome Sailor—Rainbow Lady **Hickling and Squires Limited**

MR J. R. H. WHARTON—continued

THREE-YEAR-OLDS

16 **ANGIE MINOR,** b f Mazilier (USA)—Angelica Park **Parkers of Peterborough Plc**
17 **HAPPY DAYS AGAIN (IRE),** b f Elbio—Tacheo **Mrs S. M. Moore**
18 **KILLARNEY JAZZ,** b c Alhijaz—Killarney Belle (USA) **M. P. Burke Developments Limited**
19 Gr f Timeless Times (USA)—Laura Lager **Mrs V. Craggs**
20 **PRECISELY (IRE),** b g Petorius—Indigent (IRE) **Mrs S. M. Moore**
21 **SANDY SHORE,** b f Lugana Beach—City Link Lass **Mr J. Rose**
22 **SON OF SKELTON,** ch g Minster Son—Skelton **Mr G. W. Turner**
23 **WELCOME SUNSET,** b c Most Welcome—Deanta In Eirinn **Mr John R. Goddard**

TWO-YEAR-OLDS

24 B f 11/3 Pip's Pride—Baby Brew (Green God)
25 B f 24/4 Up And At 'Em—Sashi Woo (Rusticaro (FR))

Other Owners: Mrs L. J. Berry, Mr Brian Hall, Miss Wendy Hall, Mr T. A. Hughes, Mrs A. C. Lambert, Mr R. M. Micklethwait, Mr John Steel.

613 MR E. A. WHEELER, Pangbourne

Postal: **Coombe Park Stables, Whitchurch on Thames, Pangbourne, Oxfordshire, RG8 7QT.**
Phone: **(01189) 841317 FAX (01189) 841316 MOBILE (0976) 748217**

1 **ANOTHER BATCHWORTH,** 6, b m Beveled (USA)—Batchworth Dancer **Mr M. V. Kirby, Mr C. O'Toole**
2 **BOLD START LADY,** 5, b m Nicholas Bill—La Comedienne **Bold Start Partnership**
3 **CROSS TALK (IRE),** 6, b g Darshaan—Liaison (USA) **Diamant Precision Engineering Ltd**
4 **DANCING MYSTERY,** 4, b g Beveled (USA)—Batchworth Dancer **Austin Stroud & Co Ltd**
5 **DARK MENACE,** 6, br g Beveled (USA)—Sweet And Sure **Benham Racing**
6 **DELIGHT OF DAWN,** 6, b m Never So Bold—Vogos Angel **Diamant Precision Engineering Ltd**
7 **GET TOUGH,** 5, b g Petong—Mrs Waddilove **Mr Michael Merridew**
8 **MALIBU MAN,** 6, ch g Ballacashtal (CAN)—National Time (USA) **Church Racing Partnership**
9 **MISTER RAIDER,** 6, ch g Ballacashtal (CAN)—Martian Melody **Raiders Partnership**
10 **NAILS TAILS,** 5, b g Efisio—Northern Dynasty **Mr M. F. Kentish**
11 **WITHESWAAY LADY,** 5, ch m Ballacashtal (CAN)—Rose of Peace **Miss L. Baker**

THREE-YEAR-OLDS

12 **BATCHWORTH BELLE,** b f Interrex (CAN)—Treasurebound **Mrs Diana Price**
13 **CALL ME VERA,** ch f Beveled (USA)—Cee Beat **Austin Stroud & Co Ltd**
14 **FIERCELY GINGER,** ch c Interrex (CAN)—Broadway Stomp (USA) **The Ferry Boat Syndicate**
15 **LEVEL HEADED,** b f Beveled (USA)—Snowline **Mr C. Harrison**
16 **MASTER REX,** ch g Interrex (CAN)—Whose Lady (USA) **Mr Andrew Shenston**
17 **STREAKER,** gr f Petong—Northern Dynasty **Mr M. F. Kentish**
18 **TOP MAITE,** ch c Komaite (USA)—Top Yard **Mr G. Smith**

TWO-YEAR-OLDS

19 **BATCHWORTH PARK,** b g 11/4 Beveled (USA)—Batchworth Dancer (Romulus) **Mrs Diana Price**
20 B f 29/4 Minshaashu Amad (USA)—Cee Beat (Bairn (USA)) **Austin Stroud & Co Ltd**
21 B f 24/4 Superlative—Champion Girl (Blazing Saddles (AUS)) **Mr G. Witherford**
22 B c 26/4 Whiittingham (IRE)—Davemma (Tachypous) **Mr G. Smith**
23 B f 7/4 Alnasr Alwasheek—Dewberry (Bay Express) **Mr & Mrs S. Stafford**
24 **EBONY BEAVER (IRE),** b br f 25/4 Petardia—Conditional Sale (IRE) (Petorius) **Beaver Computer Supplies**
25 **GOOD ENOUGH GIRL,** b f 2/5 Mac's Imp (USA)—Marton Maid (Silly Season) **Goodenough Removals**
26 B f 5/1 Minshaashu Amad (USA)—Heavenly State (Enchantment) **Mrs Gail Gaisford**
27 B c 2/4 Minshaashu Amad (USA)—Kilmeena Glen (Beveled (USA)) **Mrs J. A. Cleary**
28 **NORTHWING,** b c 10/4 Minshaashu Amad (USA)—Kicking Bird (Bowl Owl) **Mrs D. Brierton**
29 Br c 16/3 Prince Des Coeurs—Pink N' Perky (Tickled Pink) **Hilo Deliveries**
30 B c 26/4 Emarati (USA)—Pink Pumpkin (Tickled Pink) **Mrs J. A. Cleary**
31 B c 16/5 Seven Hearts—Priory Bay (Petong) **Mrs J. A. Cleary**

MR E. A. WHEELER—continued

32 B c 15/5 Efisio—Southern Dynasty (Gunner B) **Mr M. F. Kentish**
33 Ch f 10/5 Alnasr Alwasheek—Superfrost (Tickled Pink) **Mrs J. A. Cleary**

Other Owners: Mr A. Austin, Mr L. Bennett, Mr A. J. Deaner, Miss E. J. Denton, Mr R. C. Denton, Mr Tony Gammon, Mr P. Gill, Mr D. Jackson, Mr S. Jones, Mr John Kavanagh, Mr Noel McLoughlin, Mrs Elaine Merridew, Mr G. Montgomery, Mr C. Mortimer, Mr T. Ryan, Mr S. Tippins, Mr G. G. White.

Jockey (Flat): A Daly (7-10).

Apprentices: S Carson (7-8), B O'Leary (7-12).

Lady Rider: Ms S Deburiatte (9-0).

614 MR A. C. WHILLANS, Hawick

Postal: **Esker House, Newmill-On-Slitrig, Hawick, TD9 9UQ.**
Phone: **(01450) 376642**

1 BORDER COUNTRY, 6, ch g Town And Country—Queen Beyan **Mr Ian R. Flannigan**
2 CONTRAFIRE (IRE), 6, b g Contract Law (USA)—Fiery Song **Mr John J. Elliot**
3 DISTINCT (IRE), 5, b g Distinctly North (USA)—Shy Jinks **Mr G. Whitehead**
4 ELEANOR MAY, 5, b br m Crofthall—Melaura Belle **Mrs L. M. Whillans**
5 ESCOBAR (IRE), 5, br g Cyrano de Bergerac—Gale Force Seven **Mrs L. Johnstone**
6 FAME AND FANTASY (IRE), 7, b m Waajib—Birchwood **Mr G. Harrow**
7 GOSPEL SONG, 6, ch g King Among Kings—Market Blues **Mr Chas N. Whillans**
8 HOBKIRK, 9, b g Niniski (USA)—Banda Sea **Mr W. Amos**
9 MAJOR BELL, 10, br g Silly Prices—Melaura Belle **Mr A. C. Whillans**
10 MINELLA MASTER (IRE), 9, b g The Parson—Shores of Tripoli **Mr I. Campbell**
11 MUFFLED MIST, 7, b m Ayyabaan—Keep Fighting **Mr W. Amos**
12 PALACEGATE KING, 9, ch g King Among Kings—Market Blues **Mr Chas N. Whillans**
13 SUPREME SOVIET, 8, ch g Presidium—Sylvan Song **Mr I. Campbell & Partners**
14 THORTERDYKES LASS (IRE), 5, b m Zaffaran (USA)—Majestic Run **Mr John J. Elliot**

Other Owners: Mrs D. J. Bell, Mr C. Bird, Mr J. T. Blacklock, Mr Ian T. Middlemiss, Mr M. Richardson, Mr A. Robson, Mrs Murray Scott, Mr A. Stewart, Miss Jennifer Taylor, Mr E. Waugh, Mrs John Whyte.

615 MR R. M. WHITAKER, Leeds

Postal: **Hellwood Farm, Hellwood Lane, Scarcroft, Leeds, West Yorkshire, LS14 3BP.**
Phone: **(0113) 2892265 FAX (0113) 2893680**

1 AIR BRIDGE, 6, b g Kind of Hush—Spanish Beauty **Mr N. W. A. Bannister**
2 FAIRY RING (IRE), 4, b f Fairy King (USA)—Emmuska (USA) **Mr R. M. Whitaker**
3 JAY-OWE-TWO (IRE), 4, b g Distinctly North (USA)—Fiery Song **Mr R. M. Whitaker**
4 JUST DISSIDENT (IRE), 6, b g Dancing Dissident (USA)—Betty Bun **Mrs C. A. Hodgetts**
5 LAGO DI VARANO, 6, b g Clantime—On The Record **The PBT Group**
6 MELBOURNE PRINCESS, 4, ch f Primo Dominie—Lurking **Country Lane Partnership**
7 5, Ch g Lord Bud—Mistral Magic **Mr R. M. Whitaker**
8 OUR MAIN MAN, 8, ch g Superlative—Ophrys **Mr Christopher Cooke**
9 REDSTELLA (USA), 9, ch g Theatrical—Orange Squash **Mr R. M. Whitaker**
10 SILK COTTAGE, 6, b g Superpower—Flute Royale **Mr Christopher Cooke**
11 STYLE DANCER (IRE), 4, b g Dancing Dissident (USA)—Showing Style **Mrs C. A. Hodgetts**
12 TINKLERS FOLLY, 6, ch g Bairn (USA)—Lucky Straw **Mr William Hattersley**

MR R. M. WHITAKER—continued

THREE-YEAR-OLDS

13 **BARON LAZLO,** b g Sizzling Melody—Mrs Skinner **Mrs N. Anna Fisher**
14 Ch c Imp Society (USA)—Lewista **Mr R. M. Whitaker**
15 **MECCA PRINCE (IRE),** ch c Shalford (IRE)—Fashion Parade **Mecca Social Clubs**
16 **MECCA PRINCESS,** ch f Weldnaas (USA)—Parfait Amour **Mr R. M. Whitaker**

TWO-YEAR-OLDS

17 Ch f 17/2 Ardkinglass—Jarrettelle **Mr R. M. Whitaker**
18 B c 14/5 Warrshan (USA)—Keen Melody (USA) **Mr R. M. Whitaker**
19 B c 15/3 Ardkinglass—Ling Lane **Mr R. M. Whitaker**
20 **LUANSHYA,** b f 30/4 First Trump—Blues Indigo **The PBT Group**
21 B c 17/5 Rudimentary (USA)—Parfait Amour **Mr R. M. Whitaker**
22 **PETRA NOVA,** ch f 17/5 First Trump—Spinner **Mr R. M. Whitaker**
23 **ROLE MODEL,** br f 15/4 Tragic Role (USA)—Emerald Gulf (IRE) **Mr R. M. Whitaker**
24 B c 1/4 Grand Lodge (USA)—Scaravie (IRE) **Mr R. M. Whitaker**
25 B f 3/4 Clantime—Yankeedoodledancer **Mrs E. Whitaker**

Other Owners: Mr T. L. Adams, Mr D. Bass, Mr D. I. Buckley, Mr Derek D. Clee, Mrs Jean P. Clee, Mr B. Creber, Mr A. J. Gibbons, Mr G. Gillie, Mr G. F. Pemberton, Mr D. Rastrick, Mr Paul A. Rhodes, Mrs Julia Richmond, Mr S. H. Robertshaw, Miss Sara Jane Rodgers, Mrs Margaret Schofield, Mr Allan Simpson, Mrs Juliet Thompson, Mr J. M. Waring, Mr S. R. Whitaker, Mr T. C. Whitaker, Mr C. Michael Wilson.

Amateurs: Mr Peter Breward (9-7), Mr Simon Richard Whitaker (11-7).

616 MISS P. M. WHITTLE, Ledbury

Postal: **Arkle Cottage, Hope End Stables, Hope End, Ledbury, Herefordshire, HR8 1JQ.**
Phone: **(01531) 635899**

1 **A VERSE TO ORDER,** 7, b g Rymer—Born Bossy **Mr T. N. Bailey**
2 **BE IN SPACE,** 7, b m Gunner B—Spaced Out **Mr T. N. Bailey**
3 **BORO HILL (IRE),** 9, ch g Arapahos (FR)—Marbles **Mr Roger Allsop**
4 **COLWALL,** 7, b g Derring Rose—Katebird **Mrs Yvonne Allsop**
5 **COOLEST BY PHAR (IRE),** 6, ch g Phardante (FR)—Gemma's Fridge **Mr W. E. Donohue**
6 **DERRING RULER,** 8, b g Derring Rose—Born Bossy **Mrs K. Lloyd**
7 **MADAM POLLY,** 6, b m Buckley—Vonnage **Mrs Yvonne Allsop**
8 **PERCY BRAITHWAITE (IRE),** 6, b g Kahyasi—Nasseem (FR) **Glass Pig Racing Syndicate**
9 **RUSTY FLAME,** 5, ch g Rustingo—Amethea **Mrs P. Collins & Sir D. Bailey**
10 4, Gr ro f Arzanni—Vonnage **Mrs Yvonne Allsop**
11 **WINTER ROSE,** 7, br g Derring Rose—Eleri **Glass Pig Racing Syndicate**

Other Owners: Mr R. S. Herbert, Mr J. T. Jones, Mr R. F. Jones, Mrs W. D. Smith, Mr N. A. Whittle, Mrs M. R. Winwood.

Conditional: Kevin Hibbert (9-7).

617 MR J. W. WHYTE, Beccles

Postal: **Becks Green Farm, Becks Green Lane, Ilketshall St Andrew, Beccles, Suffolk, NR34 8NB.**
Phone: **(01986) 781221 FAX 781406**

1 **CULRAIN,** 7, b g Hadeer—La Vie En Primrose **Mr John Whyte**
2 **DECISIVE SPICE,** 9, ch g Vital Season—Opt Out **Mr John Whyte**
3 **GOOD OLD CHIPS,** 11, b g Oats—Etoile de Lune **Mr John Whyte**

MR J. W. WHYTE—continued

4 **LIFE OF BRIAN (IRE)**, 7, b g Meneval (USA)—Miss de Jager **Mr John Whyte**
5 **SALISONG**, 9, gr g Song—Sylvanecte (FR) **Mr John Whyte**
6 **STONE ISLAND**, 5, b g Rambo Dancer (CAN)—Single Gal **Mr John Whyte**

Other Owners: Mrs John Whyte.

Amateurs: Mr Matthew Gingell (10-7), Mr Rupert Wakeley (9-12).

618 MR M. J. WILKINSON, Banbury

Postal: **Trafford Bridge, Edgcote, Banbury, Oxfordshire, OX17 1AG.**
Phone: **CHIPPING WARDEN (01295) 660713 CAR (0836) 613330 FAX (01295) 660767**

1 **BARONCELLI**, 8, ch g Baron Blakeney—Toumanova **The Gardians**
2 **BENDOR MARK**, 9, b g Lighter—Montana **Mr C. J. Courage**
3 **BONNIFER (IRE)**, 9, ch g Royal And Regal (USA)—Piper's Lady (CAN) **Towcester Members Race Club**
4 **CARTOUCHE**, 4, gr g Terimon—Emblazon **Mr D. C. Broomfield**
5 **CHEF COMEDIEN (IRE)**, 8, ch g Commanche Run—Clipper Queen **John Nicholls (Banbury) Ltd**
6 **CLASSIC MODEL**, 7, ro g High Line—Fast Car (FR) **The Roan Racing Syndicate**
7 **DISTINCTIVE (IRE)**, 9, ch g Orchestra—Zimuletta **Mr Jeremy Hancock**
8 **FORESTRY**, 4, b g Highest Honor (FR)—Arboretum (IRE) **Mr A. D. Steven**
9 **FOURTH IN LINE (IRE)**, 10, b g Horage—Littoral **John Nicholls (Banbury) Ltd**
10 **HIGHFIELD GENT (IRE)**, 5, gr g Nestor—Tim's Brief **Mr Eric S. Birks**
11 **HULK (AUS)**, 7, gr g Zamoff (NZ)—Eelouette (AUS) **Mr D. Bazin**
12 **LATE RELATION**, 5, ch m Brotherly (USA)—Youaretoolate **Mr J. Colston**
13 **MANOLITO (IRE)**, 4, b g Mandalus—Las-Cancellas **Mr J. P. Hancock**
14 **MISTER DRUM (IRE)**, 9, gr g Aristocracy—Pollyfaster **Mr Malcolm Batchelor**
15 **MOONSPELL**, 4, b f Batshoof—Shimmer **The Diamond Seven Partnership**
16 **NATIVE BUCK (IRE)**, 5, ch g Be My Native (USA)—Buckskins Chat **One Over Par Partnership**
17 **PRINTEMPS (USA)**, 11, b g Roberto (USA)—Golden Lamb (USA) **Mr J. Colston**
18 **RICHDALE**, 4, ch g Rich Charlie—Taffidale **Mr B. L. Lay**
19 **SEABROOK LAD**, 7, b g Derrylin—Moll **Seabrook Partners**
20 **THREE WEEKS**, 5, ch g Formidable (USA)—Zilda (FR) **Mr M. J. Wilkinson**
21 5, Ch m North Col—Toumanova **Mr C. J. Courage**
22 4, B c North Col—Veritate **Mr J. A. G. Wilkinson**
23 **WONTCOSTALOTBUT**, 4, b f Nicholas Bill—Brave Maiden **Wontcostalot Partnership**

Other Owners: Mr D. Ancil, Mrs Delyth Batchelor, Mr A. D. Chorlton, Mrs D. J. Chorlton, Mr A. A. Clifford, Mr R. L. Clifford, Mrs E. R. Courage, Mr R. Cox, Mr P. J. Cunningham, Sue Ellis, Mrs Jeremy Hancock, Mr G. O. Harper, Mr G. F. Haynes, Mrs A. Kemp, Mrs W. Morrell, Mr R. Neal, Mr A. Nicholls, Mr S. Pack, Mrs V. Pharaon, Mr D. Price, Mr D. J. Price, Mrs P. N. Roberts, Mr & Mrs D. Seed, Mr Tom F. A. Thomas, Mr J. Tredwell, Annemarie Wood.

Conditional: G Bazin (10-0), D Painter (9-7).

619 MR D. L. WILLIAMS, Newbury

Postal: **Hillside Stud, Great Shefford, Nr Hungerford, Berkshire, RG17 7DL.**
Phone: **HOME/YARD 01488 638636 FAX 638121 MOBILE 0421 351572/792351**

1 **AMBER VALLEY (USA)**, 7, ch g Bering—Olatha (USA) **Berkshire Commercial Components Ltd**
2 **ASPECTO LAD (IRE)**, 4, ch g Imp Society (USA)—Thatcherite **Mr R. J. Matthews**
3 **BARTON SCAMP**, 6, ch g Sadeem (USA)—Hachimitsu **Miss B. W. Palmer**
4 **HERMES HARVEST**, 10, b g Oats—Swift Messenger **Miss B. W. Palmer**
5 **MAPLE DANCER**, 12, b g Viking (USA)—New York Rose **Dr Ian Shenkin**
6 **MOSS-BEAU**, 6, b g Le Moss—Beau St **Mr Jimmy Hamilton**

MR D. L. WILLIAMS—continued

7 **ONE WORD (IRE)**, 6, b g Nordance (USA)—Purple Rain **Berkshire Commercial Components Ltd**
8 4, B f Rolfe (USA)—Pokey's Belle **Miss B. W. Palmer**
9 **ROYAL CEILIDH (IRE)**, 5, b m Prince Rupert (FR)—Isa **Mr G. C. Farr**
10 **SLIGHTLY OLIVER (IRE)**, 4, b g Silver Kite (USA)—Red Note **Mr P. F. Moore**
11 4, Ch g Rolfe (USA)—Swift Messenger **Mr D. L. Williams**
12 **SYMBOL OF SUCCESS (IRE)**, 7, b g Red Sunset—Simbella **N. O. T. Racing Syndicate**
13 **THATCHAM ISLAND**, 5, ch m Jupiter Island—Floreal **Berkshire Commercial Components Ltd**
14 **TOSKANO**, 6, b g Salse (USA)—Kukri **Berkshire Commercial Components Ltd**
15 **WELSH HARVEST**, 6, b g Weld—Swift Messenger **Mr D. L. Williams**
16 **WESTERN CHIEF (IRE)**, 4, b c Caerleon (USA)—Go Honey Go **Miss B. W. Palmer**
17 **ZAMBRANO (USA)**, 6, ch g Strawberry Road (AUS)—Cloudy Day Sunny (USA) **Mr & Mrs M. McCabe**

THREE-YEAR-OLDS

18 **MERCH RHYD-Y-GRUG**, b f Sabrehill (USA)—Al Washl (USA) **Mouse Racing**
19 Ch f Faustus (USA)—Pokey's Belle **Miss B. W. Palmer**

TWO-YEAR-OLDS

20 Br c Tragic Role—Ketti **berkshire Commercial Components Ltd**
21 Ch c Weld—Swift Messenger

Other Owners: Lt A. G. E. Bate (Royal Horse Artillery), Mr Steve Boddy, Mr F. A. Bonsal, Mr C. Brace, Mr Gareth Cheshire, Mr Bob Kinsley, Laugh A Minute Racing Club, Mrs Pamela Moore, Not Racing, Mr D. L. Williams, Mrs Paula Williams, Mr M. G. Wooldridge.

Amateur: Mr Seamus Durack (9-0).

Lady Rider: Miss Sally Duckett (9-0).

620 MR IAN WILLIAMS, Alvechurch

Postal: **Hob Hill Farm, Seafield Lane, Alvechurch, Worcestershire, B48 9HP.**
Phone: **(01564) 822392 FAX (01564) 822392 MOBILE (0468) 663516**

1 **ALARICO (FR)**, 5, ch g Kadrou (FR)—Calabria (FR) **Hayman and Turton**
2 **AUBURN BOY**, 11, ch g Sexton Blake—Milan Union **Mr Ian Williams**
3 **BABA AU RHUM (IRE)**, 6, b g Baba Karam—Spring About **Mr & Mrs John Poynton**
4 **CLONTOURA (IRE)**, 10, b g Salluceva—Clara Novello **Mr & Mrs John Poynton**
5 **DARK ORCHARD (IRE)**, 7, b g Black Minstrel—Ballyheda's Love **Mr T. J. Parrott**
6 **DASHARAN (IRE)**, 5, b h Shahrastani (USA)—Delsy (FR) **Mr & Mrs John Poynton**
7 **GRANGE COURT (IRE)**, 8, b g Bassa Selim (FR)—Tetlin (FR) **DSM (Demolition Services (Midlands) Ltd)**
8 **GREATEST FRIEND (IRE)**, 5, b m Mandalus—Miss Ranova **New Equine Wear Partnership**
9 **HIT THE BID (IRE)**, 7, b g Buckskin (FR)—Dont Call Me Lady **Mr Peter Bonner**
10 **IN THE GENES**, 4, b g Syrtos—Ruby's Vision **The Mirror Punters Club**
11 **JEVINGTON (IRE)**, 6, b g Mandalus—Hyde's Pride **M. F. C. A. Ltd**
12 **JULTARA (IRE)**, 9, ch g Strong Statement (USA)—La Bise **Mr Roger Barby**
13 **KNIGHTSBRIDGE BRED**, 4, b f Montelimar (USA)—Shahdjat (IRE) **Knightsbridge BC**
14 **LATCHFORD (IRE)**, 6, ch g Carlingford Castle—Comeragh Princess **Ten Strong Racing**
15 **LETTYFAK (FR)**, 4, br c Akarad (FR)—Lettyfana (USA) **Mr & Mrs John Poynton**
16 5, B m Un Desperado—Mar Del Plata **Pell-Mell Partners**
17 **MAZILEO**, 5, b g Mazilier (USA)—Embroglio (USA) **Mrs H. Parrott**
18 **MR BOJANGLES (IRE)**, 7, b g Orchestra—Lavarna Lady **Mrs D. Lousada**
19 **MR JAMBOREE**, 12, b g Martinmas—Miss Reliant **Mrs D. Lousada**
20 **OBLITERATE (IRE)**, 6, b g Jolly Jake (NZ)—Bradawn **Mr & Mrs John Poynton**
21 **PATRINGTON BOY**, 5, b g Sayf El Arab (USA)—Gunnard **Mr Frank Murphy**
22 **POLLY UMRIGAR (IRE)**, 7, b br g Phardante (FR)—Flashey Blond **Mr & Mrs John Poynton**
23 **SPICETRESS**, 4, gr f Chilibang—Foreign Mistress **M. F. C. A. Ltd**
24 **SUPER SHARP (NZ)**, 10, ch g Brilliant Invader (AUS)—Aspen Annie (NZ) **Malcolm & Sue Penny**
25 **TARA-BROGAN**, 5, b g Jupiter Island—Princess Semele **DSM (Demolition Services (Midlands) Ltd)**

MR IAN WILLIAMS—continued

26 THE BREWMASTER (IRE), 6, ch g Torus—Bonne Bouche **Mr John Poynton & Mr Jim Brewer**
27 WINSFORD HILL, 7, ch g Nearly A Hand—Gay Ticket **The May Be Partnership**
28 WINSTON RUN, 6, ch g Derrylin—Craftsmans Made **Mrs Nichola J. Mathias**

THREE-YEAR-OLDS

29 DRAGON BOY, b c Bustino—Safe House **Mrs Nichola J. Mathias**
30 OPERETTA (FR), b f Lashkari—Lyric Opera **Mr & Mrs John Poynton**
31 TORY BOY, b c Deploy—Mukhayyalah **Mrs Nichola J. Mathias**

Other Owners: Ms Barbara Ashby-Jones, Mr J. C. Collett, Miss S. E. Cook, Mr Martin Cruddace, Mr Alan C. Elliot, Mr C. D. Harrison, Mr V. A. Harrison, Mrs E. Hayman, Mr P. S. Hayman, Mr Patrick Kelly, Mr Mohammed Saed Samii, Mr M. F. Sheasby, Mr B. C. Thomas, Mr R. J. Turton, Mr S. F. Turton.

Jockeys (NH): D Bridgwater, A P McCoy (w.a.).

Conditional: Eugene Husband (9-10), Barry McGann (9-7).

Lady Rider: Miss L Pope (9-7).

621 MR L. J. WILLIAMS, Newport, Gwent

Postal: **Upper Grange, St. Brides Netherwent, Magor, Newport, Gwent, NP6 3AT.**
Phone: **(01633) 880605**

1 BALINGER BOY, 8, b g Balinger—Young Gipsy **Mr L. J. Williams**
2 CELESTIAL STREAM, 11, ch g Paddy's Stream—Starlight Beauty **Mr L. J. Williams**
3 DARK DELIGHT, 7, br m Idiot's Delight—Starlight Beauty **Mr L. J. Williams**
4 TWILIGHT TOM, 9, ro g Pragmatic—Starlight Beauty **Mr L. J. Williams**

622 MR R. J. R. WILLIAMS, Newmarket

Postal: **Hurworth House Stables, Fordham Road, Newmarket, Suffolk, CB8 7AA.**
Phone: **Office: (01638) 663218 Home:(01638) 665819 Fax: (01638) 660145**

1 ICE AGE, 4, gr c Chilibang—Mazarine Blue **Mr Harry Ormesher**
2 MISS VITA (USA), 4, b f Alleged (USA)—Torrid Tango (USA) **Entente Cordiale**
3 PIZZICATO, 4, b f Statoblest—Musianica **Mr Richard I. Morris Jr**
4 RADAR O'REILLY, 4, b g Almoojid—Travel Bye **Mr Harry Ormesher**
5 REVOLUTION, 4, b c Suave Dancer (USA)—Sunny Flower (FR) **Entente Cordiale**

THREE-YEAR-OLDS

6 PRODIGAL SON (IRE), b c Waajib—Nouveau Lady (IRE) **Mr Richard I. Morris Jr**
7 THE ARTFUL DODGER, b g Alhijaz—Madam Millie **Equinimity**

TWO-YEAR-OLDS

8 FATHER MULCAHY, b c 17/3 Safawan—Constant Delight (Never So Bold) **Mr Harry Ormesher**
9 Ch c 24/3 Northern Park (USA)—Miss Trilli (Ardoon) **Northern Park Partnership**
10 B f 1/4 Mujadil (USA)—Nurse Jo (USA) (J O Tobin (USA)) **Clayton Bigley Partnership**

Other Owners: Mr Richard Abbott, Mr Chris Barker, Mr Colin G. R. Booth, Mr Brian Chandler, Mr P. E. T. Chandler, Mr Andy Cole, Mr Gerry Crean, Mr John Holden, Mr Jonathan Kinge, Miss Angie Nichol, Mr Hugh O'Neil, Mr Brian Page, Mr N. Payne, Mr Mark Pritchard, Mr Tony Rowland, Mr Peter Tudball.

Jockeys (Flat): D Biggs, R Cochrane.

623 MR S. C. WILLIAMS, Newmarket

Postal: **133 Tulyar Walk, Newmarket, Suffolk, CB8 7AX.**
Phone: **YARD (01638) 663984 HOME & FAX (01638) 560143**

1 **ALAGNA,** 4, b f Unfuwain (USA)—Spica (USA) **Mr W. J. de Ruiter**
2 **ALLIED ACADEMY,** 4, ch g Royal Academy (USA)—Tsungani **Allied Calibrations Limited**
3 **COLLEGE PRINCESS,** 4, b f Anshan—Tinkers Fairy **College Farm Thoroughbreds**
4 **CONCER ARALL,** 4, ch g Ron's Victory (USA)—Drudwen **Mr E. J. Lloyd**
5 **CONCER UN,** 6, ch g Lord Bud—Drudwen **Mr E. J. Lloyd**
6 **LITTLE ACORN,** 4, b g Unfuwain (USA)—Plaything **Mr Alasdair Simpson**
7 4, Ch g Keen—Loredana **Mr D. A. Shekells**
8 **SELMESTON (IRE),** 6, b g Double Schwartz—Baracuda (FR) **Mr Chris Wright**
9 **SIEGE PERILOUS (IRE),** 5, b g Taufan (USA)—Carado **Mr S. Demanuele**
10 **THAT MAN AGAIN,** 6, ch g Prince Sabo—Milne's Way **J. T. Duffy & R. E. Duffy**
11 **WHO'S THAT MAN,** 4, gr c Mystiko (USA)—Milne's Way **Mr M. Jameson And Mr John T. Duffy**

THREE-YEAR-OLDS

12 **BRAVE MAPLE,** b c Petong—Hazy Kay (IRE) **The Cherry Pickers Syndicate**
13 **CARADOC,** ch c Bustino—Hathaway **Mr John D. Hurd**
14 **CEINWEN,** ch f Keen—Drudwen **Mr E. J. Lloyd**
15 **COLLEGE ROSE,** b f Prince Sabo—Tinkers Fairy **P. & C. Dunnett & G. Allessi**
16 **COUPLED,** ch f Wolfhound (USA)—Twice A Gool (USA) **Mr James Miller**
17 **FAST FRANC (IRE),** ch g Paris House—Elle Va Bon **Mr J. W. Lovitt**
18 **FERGHANA MA,** br f Mtoto—Justine (GER) **Dr Klaus E. Rohde**
19 **HOBART JUNCTION (IRE),** ch c Classic Secret (USA)—Art Duo **Tom Ford & Tony Regan**
20 **JARRAYAN,** ch f Machiavellian (USA)—Badrah (USA) **The Cherry Pickers Syndicate**
21 **LA FAZENDA,** b f Warning—Teresa (SPA) **Livingstone Tradings**
22 **MISS SABRENA,** b f Sabrehill (USA)—Tebre (USA) **Livingstone Tradings**
23 **RAZOR,** b c Warning—Smarten Up **Ivyclose Ltd**
24 **REDSWAN,** ch g Risk Me (FR)—Bocas Rose **Mr P. Geoghan**
25 **SWANMORE LADY (IRE),** b f Forzando—Steffi **Mr A. G. Axton**
26 **SWEET SERENATA,** gr f Keen—Serenata **Rib & Co**

TWO-YEAR-OLDS

27 **AWINITA,** b f 30/1 Prince Sabo—Tsungani **Mr I. A. Southcott**
28 Gr f 14/4 Mystiko (USA)—Eladale (IRE) **Mr A. J. Simpson**
29 **EVENING CHANCE,** ch f 27/3 Mystiko (USA)—Serenata **Mr B. Jamieson**
30 **FORTUNE COOKIE,** ch f 17/1 Selkirk (USA)—Lucky Round **Dr St John & Mrs Sherry Collyer**
31 **GOLD LODGE,** ch c 27/1 Grand Lodge—Glimmering Girl (USA) **Livingstone Tradings**
32 Gr c 15/2 Shareef Dancer (USA)—Highest Ever (FR) **Mr M. North & Mr R. Baldwin**
33 B c 21/3 Cyrano de Bergerac—Rose Ciel (IRE) **Mr Chris Wright**
34 **SLIP OF THE TONGUE,** b f 18/4 Slip Anchor—Plaything **Mr A. J. Simpson**
35 **SUAVE FRANKIE,** ch c 15/1 Suave Dancer (USA)—Francia **Mr D. Burge & Mr B. W. Wyatt**
36 Ch f 18/3 Unfuwain (USA)—Sylvatica **Mr W. J. de Ruiter**
37 **TOPACIO,** b c 10/5 Saddlers' Hall (IRE)—Teresa (USA) **Livingstone Tradings**

Other Owners: Mr T. Baldwin, Mr E. Carter, Mr M. Christofi, Mrs D. Garrett, Mr D. Heeney, Lloyd Brothers, Mr J. W. Orbell, Mr M. Peacock, Mr P. J. C. Simmonite, Skeltools Ltd, Mrs Marion E. Southcott, Mrs A. Stacey.

Jockey (Flat): Kevin Darley (w.a.).

Apprentice: D Williams (7-3).

624 MRS S. D. WILLIAMS, South Molton

Postal: **Hilltown Farm, Mariansleigh, South Molton, Devon, EX36 4NS.**
Phone: **BISHOPS NYMPTON (01769) 550291 FAX (01769) 550291**

1 **AMBLESIDE (IRE),** 7, b g Kambalda—Noellespir **Mr B. M. Yin**
2 **BEANO SCRIPT,** 5, b g Prince Sabo—Souadah (USA) **Mr A. Fitzgerald**
3 **BOMBA CHARGER,** 6, b g Prince of Peace—Lady Guinevere **Mr M. B. Ogle**
4 **CENTO (IRE),** 5, b g Shernazar—Callianire **Mr B. M. Yin**
5 **COUNTRYMASTER,** 9, b g Scottish Reel—Rhinestone **Mr Chris Brasher**
6 **INDIAN LEGEND (IRE),** 5, br m Phardante (FR)—Let's Compromise **F. W. & E. P. Ridge**
7 **LAUREN'S TREASURE (IRE),** 7, b g Satco (FR)—Fern Glen **Miss H. J. Flower**
8 **MASTER RASTUS,** 5, b g Neltino—Blakeney Sound **Mr W. Peto**
9 **SON OF COURAGE,** 5, bl g Straight Knight—Fort Courage **Mr M. Smale**
10 **SOUTHERNHAY BOY,** 7, b g Minster Son—Lady Andrea **Mr D. C. Coard**

Other Owners: Mr J. M. Barlow, Mr M. P. Fear, Mr S. A. Jones, Mr Eric Le Ruez, Mrs K. Oseman, Mrs S. J. Stovold.

Jockey (NH): S McNeill (10-0).

625 MISS V. M. WILLIAMS, Hereford

Postal: **Aramstone, Kings Caple, Hereford, HR1 4TU.**
Phone: **& FAX (01432) 840646 MOBILE (0370) 627108**

1 **BACK ON THE LASH (IRE),** 6, b g Supreme Leader—Avida Dancer **Liverpool Low-Life Racing Club**
2 **BALLY CLOVER,** 11, ch g Deep Run—Miss de Jager **Mr James Williams**
3 **BELAMI,** 5, b g Bold Fox—Solbella **Mr Colin Hadley**
4 **BICYCLE THIEF (IRE),** 5, ch g Archway (IRE)—Push Bike **Mr B. Moore**
5 **BIGSOUND (IRE),** 6, b g Little Bighorn—Lightfoot Lady **F. Lynch**
6 **BLUE CHIP (IRE),** 5, b m Executive Perk—Blue Jama **Mr J. M. Boodle**
7 **BOOTS MADDEN (IRE),** 8, b g The Parson—Little Welly **Mr L. J. A. Phipps**
8 **BOWL OF GOLD,** 5, ch m Gildoran—Bishop's Bow **Suivi Partnership**
9 **CAREYSVILLE (IRE),** 7, b g Carmelite House (USA)—Kavali **Mr Geoffrey Johnson**
10 **CELTIC ABBEY,** 10, b g Celtic Cone—Cagaleena **Mr G. J. Powell**
11 **C'EST MOI LAUREL (FR),** 4, b g Rose Laurel—Tadjmine (FR) **Mr Robert Ogden**
12 **COPERS COPE LAD (IRE),** 5, b g Montelimar (USA)—Golden Privet (IRE) **Sceptre House Golf Society**
13 **DEVONSHIRE (IRE),** 5, b br g King's Ride—Lispatrick Lass **Mr Robert Ogden**
14 **EFFECTUAL,** 5, b g Efisio—Moharabuiee **Mr B. C. Dice**
15 **EVERYTHING'S ROSY,** 6, b m Ardross—Give Me Credit **R. E. M. Partnership**
16 **FED ON OATS,** 10, b g Oats—Fedelm **Mr John Kottler**
17 **FERRIS (IRE),** 5, br g Homo Sapien—Jane Pitt **Mr P. Tompsett**
18 **FORTRIA ROSIE DAWN,** 8, b m Derring Rose—Fortria **Mr M. J. Fenn**
19 **GLAISDALE (IRE),** 9, b g Lomond (USA)—Glass Slipper **Mrs Ann Key**
20 **GUIDO (IRE),** 7, b g Supreme Leader—Cool Amanda **Mr P. Tompsett**
21 **GULLIBLE GUY,** 6, b g Domynsky—Halmaseta **Mr G. A. Roberts**
22 **HENRY CONE,** 9, br g Celtic Cone—Misty Sunset **Mrs David J. Barrington**
23 **IMPERIAL VINTAGE (IRE),** 8, ch g Aristocracy—Monasootha **Mr David M. Williams**
24 **KNIGHTSBRIDGE LAD (IRE),** 6, ch g Be My Native (USA)—Solo Guest **Knightsbridge BC**
25 **KNIGHTSBRIDGE PERK (IRE),** 6, b g Executive Perk—Wayward Beauty **Knightsbridge BC**
26 **KNIGHTSBRIDGE SCOT,** 7, ch g Scottish Reel—Marie Galante (FR) **Knightsbridge BC**
27 **LADY MARLOW,** 4, b f Arzanni—Another Molly **Mr B. Moore**
28 **LADY REBECCA,** 6, b m Rolfe (USA)—Needwood Fortune **Kinnersley Optimists**
29 **LEOTARD,** 11, b g Lyphard's Special (USA)—Tondbad **Mrs P. A. H. Hartley**
30 **LIMIT THE DAMAGE (USA),** 6, ch g Elmaamul (USA)—Kraemey (USA) **Mr Frank Murphy**
31 **MARTELL BOY (NZ),** 11, b g Princes Gate—Amorae (NZ) **Mr David G. Jones**
32 **MASTER CHET (IRE),** 8, b g Callernish—C C Meade **Mr Irvin S. Naylor**
33 **MISTER SANDROVITCH (IRE),** 5, b g Be My Native (USA)—Salufair **Mr P. Sandrovitch**

MISS V. M. WILLIAMS—continued

34 **MOSKVA (IRE),** 5, b g Strong Gale—Ballyhoura Lady **Chris & Antonia Deuters**
35 **MUSIC PLEASE,** 6, ch g Music Boy—Ask Mama **D. J. Equine Supplies Ltd**
36 **NORDANCE PRINCE (IRE),** 7, b g Nordance (USA)—Shirleys Princess **Pinks Gym**
37 **OSOSHOT,** 5, b g Teenoso (USA)—Duckdown **Mrs Jeanne Horton**
38 **OUR DAWNY,** 5, b m Gunner B—Mossy Morning **Mrs J. M. F. Dibben**
39 **PENNYWISE,** 5, br m Lepanto (GER)—Stubbin Moor **Mr George Stainton**
40 **POLAR FLIGHT,** 4, br g Polar Falcon (USA)—Fine Honey (USA) **Mr B. M. Collins**
41 **PRUSSIAN STEEL (IRE),** 7, gr g Torus—Lady Barnaby **Chris & Antonia Deuters**
42 **RAPHAEL BODINE (IRE),** 9, b g Crash Course—Noelbonne Femme **Mr Howard Parker**
43 **RIDING CROP (IRE),** 8, b g King's Ride—Vintage Harvest **Mr K. Hill**
44 **ROSENCRANTZ (IRE),** 6, b g Sadler's Wells (USA)—Rosananti **Mrs I. Phillips**
45 **SHIRLEY VENTURE,** 5, b m Be My Chief (USA)—Our Shirley **M. F. C. A. Ltd**
46 **SILK VESTMENTS,** 6, b m Rakaposhi King—Preachers Popsy **Mrs J. H. F. Dibben**
47 **SPARKLING CONE,** 9, gr g Celtic Cone—Sparkling Time (USA) **Mrs M. Horton**
48 **SPEARHEAD AGAIN (IRE),** 9, b g Strong Gale—Affordthe Queen **Mr Len Jakeman**
50 **WHIRLAWHILE (USA),** 4, b g Silver Hawk (USA)—My Turbulent Beau (USA) **Cheltenham Racing Ltd**
51 **WILMOTT'S FANCY,** 6, b m Buckley—Misty Sunset **Mrs J. K. Peutherer**
52 **YOUNG ARCHIE (IRE),** 5, b g Yashgan—Fatal Hesitation **Birch Hall Racing Partners**

Other Owners: Mr M. Checketts, Mr Bob Clarke, Mr H. B. B. Clowes, Sally Lady Codrington, Mr David Currie, Miss J. Davies, Mr Roger F. Downes, Mr Christopher J. Fell, Mr W. J. Fenn, Mr Roger Gifford, Mr P. A. H. Hartley, Mr J. A. Hassall, Mr Ray Horton, Mr D. Jinks, Mrs M. E. Jones, Mr H. Kaye, Mr Michael A. Knight, Mr A. M. Morley, Mr Alan Parker, Mr Peter Pink, Mrs J. Redvers, Mrs Maureen J. Russell, Mr E. C. Stephens, Mr Steve Stuart, Mr P. M. S. Tham, Mrs Michele Varmen, Miss V. M. Williams.

Jockey (NH): N Williamson (w.a.).

Conditional: S Kelly (9-7).

626 MR A. J. WILSON, Cheltenham

Postal: **Glenfall Stables, Ham, Charlton Kings, Cheltenham, Gloucestershire, GL52 6NH.**
Phone: **(01242) 244713 OR (01242) 226319**

1 **BUCKHEART,** 8, b g Buckley—Florista **Mrs T. D. Pilkington**
2 **BUCKS REEF,** 6, b g Buckley—Coral Delight **Mr John Astbury**
3 **JUNGLE KING (NZ),** 9, ch g Kings Island—Jungle Licence (AUS) **Mr A. M. Darlington**
4 **KINO'S CROSS,** 9, b g Relkino—Coral Delight **Mr N. V. Harvey**
5 4, Ch f Fearless Action (USA)—Kitchi Koo **Mrs M. J. Wilson**
6 **ROYAL PIPER (NZ),** 11, b g Piperhill—Blue Ice (NZ) **Mr A. M. Darlington**
7 **SURPRISE CITY,** 7, b g Wonderful Surprise—Better Try Again **Mr Tim Leadbeater**
8 **WOT NO GIN,** 9, b g Broadsword (USA)—Lawnswood Miss **The Up and Running Partnership**
9 **YOUNG TYCOON (NZ),** 7, br g Young Runaway—Spare Money (NZ) **Mr A. M. Darlington**

Other Owners: Mr D. G. Blagden.

627 CAPT J. H. WILSON, Preston

Postal: **Moor Farm, Sollom, Tarleton, Preston, Lancashire, PR4 6HR.**
Phone: **(01772) 812780 FAX (01772) 815744**

1 **AMY LEIGH (IRE),** 5, b m Imperial Frontier (USA)—Hollyberry (IRE) **Mr J. P. Hacking**
2 **BEACH BUOY (IRE),** 4, ch g Orchestra—Seapoint **Mrs C. J. Black**
3 **JIMJAREER (IRE),** 5, br g Jareer (USA)—Onthecomet **Mrs G. S. Rees**

CAPT J. H. WILSON—continued

4 **KATIE KOMAITE,** 5, b m Komaite (USA)—City To City **Red Rose Partnership**
5 **KOMASTA,** 4, b g Komaite (USA)—Sky Fighter **Mr F. Cunliffe**
6 **NKAPEN ROCKS (SPA),** 5, b g Risk Me (FR)—Debutina Park **Lady Lilford**
7 **SHOWGIRL,** 4, ch f Handsome Sailor—Early Doors **Andy Partnership**

THREE-YEAR-OLDS

8 **BENROCK (IRE),** ch g Ballad Rock—Madame Champvert (IRE) **Mr J. P. Hacking**
9 **DOUBLE APPEAL (IRE),** b f Waajib—Leaping Salmon **Mr J. Thompson**
10 **PICCOLO CATIVO,** b f Komaite (USA)—Malcesine (IRE) **Mr J. W. Gittins**
11 **PIPIJI (IRE),** gr f Pip's Pride—Blue Alicia **Mr A. N. Brooke Rankin**
12 Br f Profilic—Rather Gorgeous **Mr T. Murray**

TWO-YEAR-OLDS

13 Ch f 26/3 Timeless Times (USA)—Busted Love (Busted) **Mr A Rhodes**
14 B f 24/1 Distant Relative—Red Rosein (Red Sunset) **Mr J. W. Gittins**

Other Owners: Mr S. Aspinall, Mr P. Bamford, Mr M. Binns, Miss J. Bond, Mrs Lynn Campion, Mr T. W. Coombs, Mr A. C. Findlay, Mr Mike Keating, Times Of Wigan, Mr P. W. Phillips, Mr Michael M. Taylor.

Apprentice: Angela Hartley (7-7).

Lady Rider: Mrs G S Rees (8-10).

628 MISS S. J. WILTON, Stoke-on-Trent

Postal: **Round Meadow Racing Stables, Rownal Road, Wetley Rocks, Stoke-on-Trent, Staffordshire, ST9 0BP.**

Phone: **HOME 0782 550861 OFFICE 0782 550115 FAX 0782 550158 MOBILE 0831 659666**

1 **ALAN BALL,** 12, b g Broadsword (USA)—Keshoon **Mr John Pointon**
2 **ANDY'S BIRTHDAY (IRE),** 7, ch g King Luthier—Clonroche Abendego **John Pointon and Sons**
3 **BLATANT OUTBURST,** 8, b g War Hero—Miss Metro **John Pointon and Sons**
4 **BOURBON COUNTY (IRE),** 8, ch g The Parson—Money Spinner **John Pointon and Sons**
5 **BRER FOX (IRE),** 9, b g Orchestra—Winter Fox **John Pointon & Sons**
6 **CRIME CRACKER,** 7, b m Broadsword (USA)—Burley Hill Lass **Mr Martin Pointon**
7 **DANCING AT LAHARN (IRE),** 8, b g Euphemism—Beau Lady **John Pointon & Sons**
8 **DANCING RANGER,** 7, b g Broadsword (USA)—Elegant Nell **John Pointon & Sons**
9 **GOING GREY,** 8, gr g Little Wolf—Lion And Lamb **John Pointon & Sons**
10 **GOOD CAUSE,** 14, ch h Kris—Goodwin Sands (USA) **Mr John Pointon**
11 **JARAAB,** 7, b g Sure Blade (USA)—Ostora (USA) **John Pointon and Sons**
12 **MEADOW DANCER,** 7, ch m Broadsword (USA)—Lion And Lamb **John Pointon & Sons**
13 **MOUNTAIN HALL (IRE),** 8, b g Buckskin (FR)—Arctic Lucy **John Pointon and Sons**
14 **MUSTN'T GRUMBLE (IRE),** 8, b g Orchestra—Gentle Heiress **John Pointon & Sons**
15 **NIGHT HARMONY (IRE),** 5, ch h Digamist (USA)—Quaver **John Pointon and Sons**
16 **PEARL ANNIVERSARY (IRE),** 5, ch g Priolo (USA)—Tony Award (USA) **John Pointon and Sons**
17 **TRANELCO,** 7, b g Arkan—Warbury Dell **John Pointon and Sons**

Other Owners: Mr Paul Adams, Mr Carl Pointon, Mrs S. A. Pointon, Mr Mike Worthington.

Jockey (NH): T Eley (10-0).

Conditional: D Vicary (9-10).

629 MR P. L. WINKWORTH, Godalming

Postal: **Merton Place Stud, Dunsfold, Surrey, GU8 4NP.**
Phone: **(01483) 200211 FAX (01483) 200878**

1 **ADDED DIMENSION (IRE)**, 7, b g Top Ville—Lassalia **Mr N. A. Dunger**
2 **BALLYHARRY (IRE)**, 8, b g Phardante (FR)—Oakville Lady **Mr D. R. Obank**
3 **CEANNAIRE (IRE)**, 8, b g Supreme Leader—Hunter's Pet **Mr P. Winkworth**
4 **COSMIC STAR**, 8, gr m Siberian Express (USA)—Miss Bunty **Mr P. Winkworth**
5 **DUNSFOLD DAZZLER**, 6, b m Phardante (FR)—Rositary (FR) **Mr P. Winkworth**
6 **DUNSFOLD DOLLY**, 5, b m Strong Gale—Rositary (FR) **The Dunsfold Dollies**
7 **GAMBIT**, 5, b g Henbit (USA)—Merton Mistress **Mrs Tishy Williams**
8 **MIDNIGHT WATCH (USA)**, 4, b c Capote (USA)—Midnight Air (USA) **Mr P. Winkworth**
9 **MUSEUM (IRE)**, 7, b g Tate Gallery (USA)—Go Anywhere **R. D. Barber & R. J. B. Blake**
10 **NUMBER CRUNCHER**, 13, ch g Orchestra—I'm No Saint **Mr P. Winkworth**
11 **PULKERRY (IRE)**, 8, ch g King Luthier—Kylemore Abbey **Mrs Olive Jackson**
12 **THE CARROT MAN**, 10, ch g True Song—Minor Furlong **Mrs Jill Winkworth**
13 **WILD RICE**, 6, b g Green Desert (USA)—On Show **Mr N. A. Dunger**

Other Owners: Mr Robert Belcher, Mrs Abby Bellan, Mrs Rosie Brough, Mrs Stephanie Cuthbert, Mrs Cax Du Pon, Mrs Jo Farrant, Mrs Mie Hacking, Mrs Judy Martin-Jenkins, Mrs Janey Masters, Mrs Roe Orange, Mrs Fiona Stafford-Taylor, Mrs Sarah Ter Haar, Mrs Anne Timberlake, Mr David A. Turnbull, Mr C. C. Turner, Mr Matthew Turner, Mrs Sabby Watson, Mrs Uschi Williams, Mrs Tessa Winkworth.

Jockeys (NH): L Aspell, P Hide (w.a.).

Conditional: X Aizpuru (w.a.).

Amateur: Mr O McPhail (w.a.).

630 MR R. S. WOOD, York

Postal: **Manor Farm, Nawton, York, YO6 5RD.**

1 **BLAZING HOLLY**, 6, br m Holly Buoy—Stuart's Gem **Mr R. S. Wood**
2 **GEM OF HOLLY**, 5, b m Holly Buoy—Stuart's Gem **Mr R. S. Wood**

631 MR R. D. E. WOODHOUSE, York

Postal: **Teal House, Greets Farm, Welburn, York, YO6 7EJ.**
Phone: **WHITWELL ON THE HILL (01653618) 637**

1 **ADVANCED STEEL**, 5, b g Roscoe Blake—Minstrel Sally **Patrick Burling Developments Ltd**
2 **BOSTON MAN**, 7, b g True Song—Tempest Girl **Mr M. K. Oldham**
3 **CITY GENT**, 4, b g Primitive Rising (USA)—Classy Lassy **Mr Harry Atkinson**
4 **DONNYBROOK (IRE)**, 5, ch g Riot Helmet—Evening Bun **Mr R. Smith (York)**
5 4, B g Rakaposhi King—Fedelm **Mr M. K. Oldham**
6 **FRANKIE**, 4, b g Shalford (IRE)—Twilight Secret **Mr S. Crowther**
7 **GLASSHOUSE**, 4, b c Thatching—Isle of Glass (USA) **Miss C. Foster**
8 **GRANGEWAY**, 4, b f La Grange Music—My Always **Mr R. D. E. Woodhouse**
9 **HITCHHIKER**, 4, b g Picea—Lady Lax **Miss J. M. Slater**
10 **HUTCEL LOCH**, 7, b m Lochnager—Errema **Mr C. A. Booth**
11 **LOOKING GOOD**, 5, ch m Derrylin—Burling Moss **Mrs S. L. Bard**
12 **MASTER BOSTON (IRE)**, 10, gr g Soughaan (USA)—Ballinoe Lass **Mr M. K. Oldham**
13 **OWTABEATIM (IRE)**, 4, ch g Alphabatim (USA)—Mossey Tune **Mr I. Bray**

MR R. D. E. WOODHOUSE—continued

14 **PHARARE (IRE),** 8, ch g Phardante (FR)—Shakie Lady **Mr C. F. Colquhoun**
15 **THEGREYOSS,** 5, gr g Sulaafah (USA)—Miss Bluebell **The Welburn Racing Society**
16 **TIGHAM,** 4, b g Tigani-Harpham—Starlight **Mr J. C. Owen**

Other Owners: Mr N. E. R. Brown, Mrs C. M. Clarke, Mr T. C. Dewhirst, Mr D. J. Hall, Mr D. W. Hoggard, Mr W. H. Jackson, Mrs Cheryl L. Owen, Mrs G. Robinson, Mr D. W. Thompson, Mr R. S. Wood.

Jockeys (NH): W Dwan (10-0), N Williamson (10-0).

632 MR S. WOODMAN, Chichester

Postal: **Parkers Stables, 8 Pook Lane, East Lavant, Chichester, West Sussex, PO18 0AU.**
Phone: **OFFICE (01243) 527136**

1 **BEN BOWDEN,** 5, br g Sharrood (USA)—Elegant Rose **Mrs N. F. Maltby**
2 **CREDON,** 10, b g Sunyboy—Credo's Daughter **Fusilier Racing**
3 **KING CREDO,** 13, b g Kinglet—Credo's Daughter
4 **NIGHT FLARE (FR),** 6, ch g Night Shift (USA)—Gold Flair **Mrs Fiona Gordon**
5 **NIGHT IN A MILLION,** 7, br g Night Shift (USA)—Ridalia **Leith Hill Chasers**
6 **SHANUKE (IRE),** 6, b m Contract Law (USA)—Auntie Ponny **Mr R. Howitt**
7 **SILVERY,** 4, gr f Petong—Petit Peu (IRE) **Mrs N. F. Maltby**

THREE-YEAR-OLDS

8 **LITTLE TUMBLER (IRE),** b f Cyrano de Bergerac—Glass Minnow (IRE) **Mrs W. Edgar**

Other Owners: Mr Ton Atkins, Miss Susan Jameson, Mrs G. S. Knight, Mr Andrew Lee, Mr Brian Plaistowe, Mr Roy F. Reeve, Mr P. D. Savill, Ms Fiona Slomovic, Mr James Wilkinson, Mrs Sally Woodman, Mrs June Young.

Jockeys (NH): R Dunwoody (w.a.), A Maguire (w.a.).

633 MRS A. M. WOODROW, High Wycombe

Postal: **Crookswood Stud Farm, Horsleys Green, High Wycombe, Buckinghamshire, HP14 3XB.**
Phone: **(01494) 482557**

1 **MUALLAF (IRE),** 6, b g Unfuwain (USA)—Honourable Sheba (USA) **Mrs Ann Woodrow & Mr J. G. Woodrow**
2 **NIGHT FANCY,** 10, ch g Night Shift (USA)—Smooth Siren (USA) **Mrs Ann Woodrow & Mr J. G. Woodrow**
3 **PEGMARINE (USA),** 15, b g Text (USA)—Symbionese (USA) **Mrs Ann Woodrow & Mr J. G. Woodrow**

Jockey (NH): J A McCarthy (10-0).

Conditional: Gerry Hogan (10-0).

634 MR S. P. C. WOODS, Newmarket

Postal: **La Grange Stables, Snailwell Road, Newmarket, Suffolk, CB8 7DP.**
Phone: **(01638) 561844 FAX (01638) 561352**

1 **ANCHOR VENTURE,** 5, b g Slip Anchor—Ski Michaela (USA) **Dr Frank S. B. Chao**
2 **ANOTHER TIME,** 6, ch g Clantime—Another Move **Mr D. Sullivan**
3 **CANTON VENTURE,** 6, ch g Arctic Tern (USA)—Ski Michaela (USA) **Dr Frank S. B. Chao**
4 **DIVINITY,** 4, ch f Lycius (USA)—Heavenly Abode (FR) **Mr Ian M. Deane**
5 **GEORGIA VENTURE,** 4, b f Shirley Heights—Georgica (USA) **Dr Frank S. B. Chao**
6 **GREEN CARD (USA),** 4, br c Green Dancer (USA)—Dunkellin (USA) **Mr P. K. L. Chu**
7 **MY LEARNED FRIEND,** 7, b g Broken Hearted—Circe **Mrs J Roberts**

MR S. P. C. WOODS—continued

8 POINTELLE, 4, b f Sharpo—Clymene **Mrs J. Roberts**
9 POLAR CHAMP, 5, b g Polar Falcon (USA)—Ceramic (USA) **Mr P. K. L. Chu**
10 RAISE A PRINCE (FR), 5, b g Machiavellian (USA)—Enfant d'Amour (USA) **Mr George Tong**
11 SHAMANIC, 6, b g Fairy King (USA)—Annie Albright (USA) **Aston House Stud**
12 SUMMER QUEEN, 4, b f Robellino (USA)—Carolside **Mr Arashan Ali**
13 TRANS SIBERIA, 7, gr g Siberian Express (USA)—Olivian **Mr S. P. C. Woods**
14 UKRAINE VENTURE, 4, b f Slip Anchor—Sherkraine **Dr Frank S. B. Chao**

THREE-YEAR-OLDS

15 BANKER DWERRY (FR), b c Unfuwain (USA)—Tartique Twist (USA) **Dr Frank S. B. Chao**
16 BENJAMIN FRANK, b g Tragic Role (USA)—Flower Princess **Mr Benjamin Lam**
17 BIRTHDAY VENTURE, b f Soviet Star (USA)—Maestrale **Dr Frank S. B. Chao**
18 CHUSHAN VENTURE, b f Pursuit of Love—Relatively Sharp **Dr Frank S. B. Chao**
19 B g Soviet Star (USA)—Devon Defender **Mr Robert Russell**
20 DITHER, br g Dilum (USA)—Peacock Feather **Mrs Jan Smith**
21 LITTLE INDIAN, ch c Little Missouri (USA)—Both Sides Now (USA) **Mr G. V. Wright**
22 LONGWOOD LADY, b f Rudimentary (USA)—Brown Velvet **Longwood Partnership**
23 MISTER BENJAMIN (IRE), b g Polish Patriot (USA)—Frau Ahuyentante (ARG) **Mrs Julie Choy**
24 POLO VENTURE, ch g Polar Falcon (USA)—Ceramic (USA) **Dr Frank S. B. Chao**
25 PURSUIT VENTURE, b f Pursuit of Love—Our Shirley **Dr Frank S. B. Chao**
26 REINE CERISE, b f Shareef Dancer (USA)—Sakura Queen (IRE) **Mr Ian M. Deane**
27 SLIP VENTURE, b c Slip Anchor—Sherkraine **Dr Frank S. B. Chao**
28 WHISTLE TEST, gr g Kris—Cut Velvet (USA) **Mr D. Sullivan**
29 WUXI VENTURE, b g Wolfhound (USA)—Push A Button **Dr Frank S. B. Chao**

TWO-YEAR-OLDS

30 AUTUMN STONE (IRE), b f 17/3 Bigstone (IRE)—Open Date (IRE) (Thatching) **Mr Mark Johnson**
31 B c 28/2 Polar Falcon (USA)—Briggsmaid (Elegant Air) **Mr Dennis Yardy**
32 B c 30/1 Primo Dominie—Carolside (Music Maestro) **Mr Arashan Ali**
33 B f 7/5 Pursuit of Love—Ceramic (USA) (Raja Baba (USA)) **Dr Frank S. B. Chao**
34 Ch c 1/4 Unfuwain (USA)—City of Angels (Woodman (USA)) **Dr Frank S. B. Chao**
35 COME WHAT MAY (IRE), ch f 1/3 Common Grounds—Poplina (USA) (Roberto (USA)) **Storm Again Syndicate**
36 Ch c 21/4 Star de Naskra (USA)—Dance Troupe (USA) (Native Charger (USA)) **Mr P. K. L. Chu**
37 B c 17/3 Pursuit of Love—Georgica (USA) (Raise A Native) **Dr Frank S. B. Chao**
38 HIGH TATRA (IRE), b c 27/4 Polish Patriot (USA)—Bouffant (High Top) **Mr W. J. P. Jackson & Mr Rex Norton**
39 B c 29/2 Salse (USA)—Ivory Moment (USA) (Sir Ivor)
40 LEAVE IT TO ME, b f 18/3 College Chapel—Enaam (Shirley Heights) **Mr Joe Sanchez**
41 Gr c 4/5 Mystiko (USA)—Marathia (Blushing Scribe (USA))
42 B c 29/3 Polar Falcon (USA)—Our Shirley (Shirley Heights) **Dr Frank S. B. Chao**
43 Ch c 4/4 Polar Falcon (USA)—Phoneix Venture (IRE) (Thatching) **Dr Frank S. B. Chao**
44 Ch c 31/3 Wolfhound (USA)—Relatively Sharp (Sharpen Up)
45 B c 4/3 Be My Chief (USA)—Saffron Crocus (Shareef Dancer (USA))
46 B c 5/3 Unfuwain (USA)—Sherkraine (Shergar) **Dr Frank S. B. Chao**
47 B c 4/4 River Special (USA)—Stanwich Miss (USA) (Advocator) **Mr Edward Chen**
48 Ch c 2/4 River Special (USA)—Stubborn Star (USA) (Star Choice (USA)) **Sentinel Bloodstock**
49 Ch c 8/2 Deploy—Tasseled (USA) (Tate Gallery (USA)) **Dr Frank S. B. Chao**
50 THATCHROYAL (IRE), ch c 24/2 Thatching—Wish You Were Here (USA) (Secretariat (USA)) **Mr G. V. Wright**
51 TOMOE GOZEN (IRE), b f 11/2 Brief Truce (USA)—Deelish (IRE) (Caerleon (USA)) **Mr Mike Simpson**
52 TRANSITION (IRE), b c 12/4 Brief Truce (USA)—Six Penny Express (Bay Express) **Broadgate III Partnership**
53 Ch f 11/4 Keen—Turtle Dove (Gyr (USA)) **One Dream Partnership**

Other Owners: Mr John Davies (Stonehill), Mr John Fullick, Mr Mike Perkins, Mr D. G. Raffel, Mr John B. Sunley, Mr Dwayne Woods, Mr R. V. Wright.

Jockey (NH): P Hide (10-0, w.a.).

Amateur: K Santana (9-7).

Lady Rider: Mrs L Woods (9-0).

635 MR G. WOODWARD, Newark

Postal: **The Barns, Southwell Racecourse, Rolleston, Newark, Nottinghamshire, NG25 0TS.**
Phone: **Tel: (01636) 816717 Mobile: (0973) 982793 Fax: (01636) 816717**

1 **BATALEUR,** 5, b g Midyan (USA)—Tinkerbird **Mr Michael Worth**
2 **GREEN BOPPER (USA),** 5, b g Green Dancer (USA)—Wayage (USA) **Mr G. Woodward**
3 **LISALEEN WREN (IRE),** 9, br g The Parson—Kitty Wren **Miss C. S. Padgett**
4 **LORD NASKRA (USA),** 9, b g Naskra (USA)—Corvallis (USA) **Mr J. Pownall**
5 **MIDDAY COWBOY (USA),** 5, b g Houston (USA)—Perfect Isn't Easy (USA) **Wetherby Racing Bureau 29**

THREE-YEAR-OLDS

6 **ATLANTA,** b f Rock City—Olympic Run **Mr J. Pownall**
7 **NEWRYMAN,** ch g Statoblest—With Love **Mr A. M. McArdle**
8 **SCOLD,** gr f Reprimand—Hopea (USA) **Mr A.M. McArdle**
9 **SHE'S SURREAL,** b f Superpower—Petomania **Mr G. Woodward**
10 **TYPHOON GINGER (IRE),** ch f Archway (IRE)—Pallas Viking **Mr G. Woodward**

Other Owners: Mr Andrew Bates, Mr Andrew Lloyd, Mr M. S. Moule, Trentvalley Riding Centre.

Jockeys (Flat): G Carter (8-0, w.a), L Newton (8-0).

Jockey (NH): D Verco (10-0).

636 MISS J. WORMALL, Ibstock

Postal: **Ibstock Grange, Ibstock, Leicester, LE67 6LN.**
Phone: **(01530) 260224 MOBILE (0374) 641132**

1 **DERRING FLOSS,** 8, b m Derring Rose—Win Green Hill **Mrs R. Wormall**
2 **JAFFA,** 6, ch g Kind of Hush—Sip of Orange **Mrs R. Wormall**
3 **NORTHERN STAR,** 7, ch g Ardross—Daisy Star **Mrs R. Wormall**

637 MR GEOFFREY WRAGG, Newmarket

Postal: **Abington Place, Bury Road, Newmarket, Suffolk, CB8 7BT.**
Phone: **OFFICE (01638) 662328 FAX (01638) 663576**

1 **ARCADIAN HEIGHTS,** 10, b g Shirley Heights—Miss Longchamp **Mr J. L. C. Pearce**
2 **BARROW CREEK,** 4, ch c Cadeaux Genereux—Breadcrumb **Baron G. von Ullmann**
3 **CROSSILLION,** 10, b g Rousillon (USA)—Croda Rossa (ITY) **Mr G. Wragg**
4 **DANTESQUE (IRE),** 5, b h Danehill (USA)—I Want My Say (USA) **Mollers Racing**
5 **FABLED LIGHT (IRE),** 4, b c Alzao (USA)—Fabled Lifestyle **Mollers Racing**
6 **FINAL TRIAL (IRE),** 4, b c Last Tycoon—Perfect Alibi **Mollers Racing**
7 **FLINT KNAPPER,** 4, ch c Kris—Circe's Isle **Mr A. E. Oppenheimer**
8 **GERMANO,** 5, b h Generous (IRE)—Gay Fantastic **Baron G. von Ullmann**
9 **HENRY ISLAND (IRE),** 5, ch h Sharp Victor (USA)—Monterana **Mr H. H. Morriss**
10 **IBLIS (IRE),** 6, b g Danehill (USA)—In Unison **Mr G. Wragg**
11 **MAWINGO (IRE),** 5, b h Taufan (USA)—Tappen Zee **Mrs Claude Lilley**
12 **MOTET,** 4, b c Mtoto—Guest Artiste **Mr A. E. Oppenheimer**
13 **MUCH COMMENDED,** 4, b f Most Welcome—Glowing With Pride **Mr A. E. Oppenheimer**
14 **SALFORD LAD,** 4, b c Don't Forget Me—Adjusting (IRE) **Mr A. J. Thompson**
15 **SASURU,** 5, b h Most Welcome—Sassalya **Mr A. E. Oppenheimer**
16 **TATIKA,** 8, ch g Tate Gallery (USA)—Independentia **Mr G. Wragg**
17 **THE FARAWAY TREE,** 4, b f Suave Dancer (USA)—Sassalya **Mr A. E. Oppenheimer**
18 **THE PRINCE,** 4, b c Machiavellian (USA)—Mohican Girl **Mr I. R. MacNicol**

MR GEOFFREY WRAGG—continued

THREE-YEAR-OLDS

19 **AOIFE (IRE)**, ch f Thatching—Aunt Hester (IRE) **Kaniz Bloodstock Investments Ltd**
20 **BELSAZAR (USA)**, b c Miswaki (USA)—Blushing Redhead (USA) **Baron G. von Ullmann**
21 **CORAL SEEKER**, ch c Rainbow Quest (USA)—Miss Kuta Beach **Mr J. L. C. Pearce**
22 **DAYMER (IRE)**, ch c Deploy—Rose Cordial (USA) **Mollers Racing**
23 **EFODOS**, ch f Pursuit of Love—Sariza **Mr L. Marinopoulos**
24 **FOREST CALL**, ch f Wolfhound (USA)—Balnaha **Mr A. E. Oppenheimer**
25 **GLOBAL WARNING**, b c Warning—Reprocolor **Lancen Farm Partnership**
26 **GOLDEN LYRIC (IRE)**, ch c Lycius (USA)—Adjala **Mollers Racing**
27 **GULLAND**, b c Unfuwain (USA)—Spin **Mollers Racing**
28 **KIMBERLEY**, b c Shareef Dancer (USA)—Willowbank **Mrs John Van Geest**
29 **MARGONE (USA)**, b br f Dayjur (USA)—Whispered Secret (CAN) **Gestut Schlenderhan**
30 **MISS RIVIERA STAR**, ch f Generous (IRE)—Miss Beaulieu **Mr J. L. C. Pearce**
31 **MISS THE POINT (USA)**, ch c Miswaki (USA)—Engagingly (USA) **Mr P. D. Savill**
32 **NOBLE CYRANO**, ch c Generous (IRE)—Miss Bergerac **Mr J. L. C. Pearce**
33 **RIDGEWAY (IRE)**, b c Indian Ridge—Regal Promise **Mollers Racing**
34 **SCONCED (USA)**, ch c Affirmed (USA)—Quaff (USA) **Mrs H. H. Morriss**
35 **SIXPENCE**, b f Saddlers' Hall (IRE)—Half A Dozen (USA) **Cheveley Park Stud**
36 **THERE BE DEMONS (USA)**, b c Devil's Bag (USA)—Krisalya **Mr A. E. Oppenheimer**
37 **TRUSCOTT (IRE)**, ch c Thatching—Remember Mulvilla **Mollers Racing**
38 **VEROCITY (FR)**, b g Groom Dancer (USA)—Villella **Mr John A. Newton**
39 **WATER'S EDGE**, b f Saddlers' Hall (IRE)—Irish Impulse (USA) **Cheveley Park Stud**

TWO-YEAR-OLDS

40 **BALISADA**, ch f 10/2 Kris—Balnaha (Lomond (USA)) **Mr A. E. Oppenheimer**
41 **CASSANDRA GO (IRE)**, gr f 3/4 Indian Ridge—Rahaam (USA) (Secreto (USA)) **Mr A. E. Oppenheimer**
42 **CHAMBRE SEPAREE (USA)**, ro f 31/3 Cozzene (USA)—Ice House (Northfields (USA)) **Miss K. Rausing**
43 **CHIEF REBEL (USA)**, b c 3/2 Chief's Crown (USA)—
Robellino Miss (USA) (Robellino (USA)) **Eclipse Partnership**
44 **DESDEMONA (IRE)**, b f 10/3 Lahib (USA)—Tragic Point (IRE) (Tragic Role (USA)) **Cheveley Park Stud**
45 **DOWNLAND (IRE)**, b c 18/2 Common Grounds—Boldabsa (Persian Bold) **Mollers Racing**
46 **FRAPPE (IRE)**, b f 24/2 Inchinor—Glatisant (Rainbow Quest (USA)) **Mr A. E. Oppenheimer**
47 **GALLERY GOD (FR)**, ch c 28/2 In The Wings—El Fabulous (FR) (Fabulous Dancer (USA)) **Mr Takashi Watanabe**
48 **ISLAND HOUSE (IRE)**, ch c 19/2 Grand Lodge (USA)—Fortitude (IRE) (Last Tycoon) **Mollers Racing**
49 **ISLE AU HAUT (IRE)**, b f 31/3 Indian Ridge—Monterana (Sallust) **Mrs H. H. Morriss**
50 **KITTIWAKE**, b f 15/3 Barathea (IRE)—Gull Nook (Mill Reef (USA)) **Gestut Schlenderhan**
51 **LAMZENA (IRE)**, b f 14/3 Fairy King (USA)—Ezana (Ela-Mana-Mou) **Mr Roy Bracher**
52 **LOLETTE**, b f 27/4 Arazi (USA)—Wild Pavane (Dancing Brave (USA)) **Mr A. E. Oppenheimer**
53 **MISS AMANPURI**, b f 22/2 Alzao (USA)—Miss Rinjani (Shirley Heights) **Mr J. L. C. Pearce**
54 **MRS SIDDONS (IRE)**, ch f 9/5 Royal Academy (USA)—White Water (FR) (Pharly (FR)) **Mrs Rebecca Philipps**
55 **OKLAHOMA**, br f 22/3 Shareef Dancer (USA)—Ranimer (Relko) **Mrs Rebecca Philipps**
56 **OUTCRY**, b f 23/1 Caerleon (USA)—In Full Cry (USA) (Seattle Slew (USA)) **Mr A. E. Oppenheimer**
57 **PASSE PASSE (USA)**, b f 18/2 Lear Fan (USA)—
Madame L'Enjoleur (USA) (L'Enjoleur (CAN)) **Mr A. E. Oppenheimer**
58 **REPEAT WARNING**, b f 24/4 Warning—Reprocolor (Jimmy Reppin) **Lancen Farm Partnership**
59 **SALFORD FLYER**, b c 9/3 Pharly (FR)—Edge of Darkness (Vaigly Great) **Mr A. J. Thompson**
60 **SELIANA**, b f 22/1 Unfuwain (USA)—Anafi (Slip Anchor) **Mr L. Marinopoulos**
61 **SLOANE**, ch c 3/5 Machiavellian (USA)—Gussy Marlowe (Final Straw) **Mrs John Van Geest**
62 **SOSSUS VLEI**, b c 24/2 Inchinor—Sassalya (Sassafras (FR)) **Mr A. E. Oppenheimer**
63 **SWALLOW FLIGHT (IRE)**, b br c 20/4 Bluebird (USA)—Mirage (Red Sunset) **Mollers Racing**
64 **TALARIA (IRE)**, ch f 24/3 Petardia—Million At Dawn (IRE) (Fayruz) **Mrs Claude Lilley**
65 **TALIBAN (IRE)**, b c 30/4 Bigstone (IRE)—Aunt Hester (IRE) (Caerleon (USA)) **Mollers Racing**
66 **TRIG POINT**, b f 16/3 Rudimentary (USA)—Beacon Hill (Bustino) **Cheveley Park Stud**
67 **TURNTABLE (IRE)**, b f 25/1 Dolphin Street (FR)—Sharp Circle (IRE) (Sure Blade (USA)) **Cheveley Park Stud**
68 **TWENTY FIRST**, ch f 11/2 Inchinor—Picnicing (Good Times (ITY)) **Bloomsbury Stud**
69 **VENETIAN PEARL (IRE)**, ch f 12/4 Generous (IRE)—Veronica (Persian Bold) **Baron G. von Ullmann**

Other Owners: Mrs A. Barrow, Mr Simon Broke, Mr A. R. G. Cane, Mr N. J. Charrington, Mr R. H. Cowell, Mr D. W. Dennis, Lady De Ramsey, Mr C. Hellyer, Mr S. J. Richmond-Watson, Mr Gerard Strahan, Baroness Karin Von Ullmann.

Jockeys (Flat): M Hills (8-4), G E H Milligan (7-11).

638 MR G. H. YARDLEY, Malvern

Postal: **Upper Woodsfield Farm, Newland, Malvern, Worcestershire, WR13 5AQ.**
Phone: **WORCESTER (01905) 830245**

1 **CLASSIC COLOURS (USA),** 5, ch g Blushing John (USA)—All Agleam (USA) **Mr Philip Jones**
2 **HO-JOE (IRE),** 8, b g Burslem—Walkyria **Mr S. Ho**
3 **IRISH KINSMAN,** 5, b g Distant Relative—Inesdela **Mr M. P. Aldersey**
4 **RIVER WYE (IRE),** 6, b g Jareer (USA)—Sun Gift **Mr S. Ho**
5 **SCHOLAR GREEN,** 6, b g Green Adventure (USA)—Quelle Chemise **Mr Philip Jones**
6 **TOP SCHOLAR,** 6, b m Derrylin—Herald The Dawn **Mr M. P. Aldersey**
7 **ZANDALEE,** 9, gr m Lucky Wednesday—Starkist **Mr J. T. Long**

Jockey (Flat): Russell Price (8-0).

Jockey (NH): V Slattery.

Lady Rider: Miss A Yardley (8-0).

639 MR W. G. YOUNG, Carluke

Postal: **Overton Farm, Crossford, Carluke, Lanarkshire, ML8 5QF.**
Phone: **(01555) 860226**

1 **GOOD PROFIT,** 9, ch g Meadowbrook—Night Profit **Mr W. G. Young**
2 **MEADOWLECK,** 9, b m Meadowbrook—Leckywil **Mr W. G. Young**
3 **SINGING PROFIT,** 6, b m Gold Song—Gold Profit **Mr W. G. Young**
4 **SOUND PROFIT,** 10, ch m Scallywag—Night Profit **Mr W. G. Young**

ADDITIONAL TEAMS

640 MRS MYRIAM BOLLACK-BADEL, Lamorlaye

Postal: **20 Rue Blanche, 60260 Lamorlaye, France.**
Phone: **(33) 03 44 21 49 66 FAX (33) 03 44 21 33 67 MOBILE(33) 06 07 89 17 37**

ALWAYS EARNEST (USA), 10, b g Alleged—Nettie Cometti **Scuderia Mirabella**
APRIL BLOSSOM (FR), 6, ch m Sarhoob—Martha Spanks **Mr Cecil Motschmann**
BIMBOLA (FR), 4, b f Bikala—Agnes Lily **Mr Tullio Attias**
CUCUTIKA, 4, b f Formidable—Cupira **Stall Formidable**
PERIODE BLEUE, 4, ch f Pistolet Bleu—Nuit de Lune **Mr G. Halphen**
THEATRE KING, 4, b c Old Vic—Draft Board **Mr J. C. Smith**

THREE-YEAR-OLDS

CHINE, b f Inchinor—Tweedling **Francoise de Chatelperron**
FRENCH PARTNER (USA), b c Seattle Song—Cloelia **Mrs Myriam Bollack-Badel**
HARLEM SNOW (FR), b c Subotica—Hokey Pokey **Mr Cecil Motschmann**
HATA (GER), b f Surumu—Hankaretta **Stall Formidable**
HEBDOMEROS (FR), b g Arctic Tern—Miss Gaylord **Catherine Niederhauser**
KRASAVITSA (FR), ch f Dancing Spree—Kiss Me Kate **Mr Cecil Motschmann**
LIMATA (GER), b f Big Shuffle—Liborina **Stall Formidable**
LION'S SHARE, b g Lion Cavern—Periquito **Mr J. C. Smith**
MANDERA (GER), b f Surumu—Marching Sara **Stall Formidable**
MARQUANTE (IRE), b f Brief Truce—Festive Season **Marion Goodbody**
NEW LOOK (FR), b f Baylis—Alight **Catherine Niederhauser**
SAYEL, ch f Elmaamul—Sayulita **Mr G. Halphen**
SILVER LUNE, b f Priolo—Selune **Jacques Herold**
SIR XAVIER (FR), b c Always Fair—Seasonal Pleasure **Mr Tullio Attias**

MRS MYRIAM BOLLACK-BADEL—continued

TWO-YEAR-OLDS

ATHEE, b f Hamas—Incharder **Mr G. Halphen**
AUBERGADE (FR), b f Kaldoun—Anna Edes **Francoise de Chatelperron**
NEVER MORE (FR), b c Sanglamore—Neraida **Mr J. C. Smith**
ROCADE (IRE), b f Barathea—Royal Climber **Scuderia Mirabella**

641 MISS H. DAY, Taunton

Postal: **Pyleigh Court Farm, Lydeard St Lawrence, Taunton, Somerset, TA4 3QZ,**
Phone: **(01984) 667229 FAX (01984) 667428**

CALLERMINE, 9, ch m Callernish—Lady Vulmid **Miss H. Day**
LADY CALLERNISH, 8, b m Callernish—Lady Vulmid **Miss H. Day**
LIGHTER LORD, 7, b g Lighter—Lady Vulmid **Miss H. Day**
NORA FOGHERTY, 7, b m Idiot's Delight—Kathleen Callaghan **Miss H. Day**
WATERROW, 10, br m Idiot's Delight—Waterside **Miss H. Day**

642 MR P. HUGHES, Bagenalstown

Postal: **Fenniscourt, Bagenalstown, Co. Carlow, Ireland.**
Phone: **(0503) 21250/21882**

ACES AND EIGHTS (IRE), 8, b g Phardante (FR)—No Battle **P. Hughes**
7, Br m Satco (FR)—Andonova **P. Hughes**
BEAL NA BLATH (IRE), 4, b f Un Desperado (FR)—Grainne Mac Cool **P. Hughes**
BE MY TRUMP (IRE), 6, b m Be My Native (USA)—Flashing Digit **P. Hughes**
CLUB COUPE (IRE), 6, b g John French—Grainne Mac Cool **P. Hughes**
COIN MACHINE (IRE), 9, b g Seclude (USA)—Penny Levy **P. Hughes**
5, B g Un Desperado (FR)—Cool Rose Lady **P. Hughes**
4, Br f Buckskin (FR)—First Nadia **P. McManemy**
GREY TO GO (IRE), 4, gr f Fat-Taak—Bean Fhionn
4, B g Un Desperado (FR)—Istris Abu **P. Hughes**
JAZZ KING, 5, gr g Kalaglow—Sabrine **M. Scully**
LAWZ (IRE), 4, b g Lahib (USA)—Sea Port **D. O'Rourke**
MANTLES PRINCE, 4, ch g Emarati (USA)—Miami Mouse **R. McSharry**
MEN OF NINETYEIGHT (IRE), 6, b g King's Ride—Penny Holder **P. Hughes**
MUMARIS (USA), 4, b br g Capote (USA)—Barakat **P. C. Byrne**
5, B m Un Desperado (FR)—Node
5, B m King's Ride—Penny Holder **P. Hughes**
5, B g King's Ride—Penny Maes **P. Hughes**
POLENKA (IRE), 4, ch f Polish Precedent (USA)—Amana River (USA) **S. Hughes**
QUINZE, 5, b g Charmer—Quaranta **P. C. Byrne**
RUTABAGA (IRE), 9, b g Mazaad—Quartette Royale **P. Hughes**
SAVU SEA (IRE), 4, b f Slip Anchor—Soemba **M. Doran**
SOUND ORCHESTRA (IRE), 7, b g Orchestra—Northern Dandy **P. Hughes**
VA DESPERADO (IRE), 8, b g Un Desperado (FR)—Tasskeen (FR) **P. Hughes**

TWO-YEAR-OLDS

B c 18/4 Mukaddamah (USA)—Diabola (USA) **P. Hughes**

Jockeys (NH): R Dunwoody (w.a.), K P Gaule (9-7).

Conditional: R C Foster (9-7).

Amateurs: Mr P A Farrell (10-0), Mr T R Hughes (9-7).

Lady Rider: Miss L E Anderson.

643 MR T. KERSEY, Rotherham

Postal: **Bleak House Stable, 16 Packman Road, West Melton, Rotherham, South Yorkshire, S63 6AH**
Phone: **(0709) 873166**

AVARICE, 12, ch h Persian Bold—Parsimony **Mr T. Kersey**
BOLD AMBITION, 11, br g Ela-Mana-Mou—Queen of The Dance **Mr M. E. Taylor**
CAN'T WAIT (IRE), 8, b g Phardante (FR)—Battle Again **Mr T. Kersey**
FEATHERSTONE ROVER, 7, br g Hotfoot—Melting Snows **Mr T. Kersey**
HUMARA (IRE), 6, b m Astronef—Estivalia **Mr T. Kersey**
LITTLE TORMENT, 9, b g Jalmood (USA)—Head First **Mr T. Kersey**
LOMOND LASSIE (USA), 5, b m Lomond (USA)—Herbivorous (USA) **Mr M. E. Taylor**
MEDIA STAR, 13, ch m Star Appeal—Linduna **Mr T. Kersey**
NASHOON (IRE), 9, b g Nashamaa—Nistona **Mr M. E. Taylor**
NEWMARKET SAUSAGE, 17, ch g Owen Dudley—Manoeuvre **Mr T. Kersey**
THE COTTONWOOL KID, 6, b g Blakeney—Relatively Smart **Mrs S. E. Cooper**

Other Owners: Mrs S. E. Cooper, Mrs Christine Halsall, Mr M. E. Taylor.

Jockey (NH): Susan Kersey (9-10).

Apprentice: Sharon Kersey (8-0).

Amateurs: Mr T Kersey (11-0), Miss Julie Middleton (9-0).

644 MR MICHAEL KETTLE, Blewbury

Postal: **Whiteshoot Stables, Woodway Road, Blewbury, Oxon, OX11 9EZ.**
Phone: **HOME/FAX (01235) 851161 OFFICE/FAX (01235) 851735 MOBILE (0411) 321813**

DAHABIAH, 4, ch f Soviet Star (USA)—Queen Midas **Umm Qarn Racing**
HAZAAF (USA), 9, ch h Woodman (USA)—Solo Disco (USA) **Mr J. D. Eggleton**

TWO-YEAR-OLDS

B f 27/3 Alnasr Alwasheek—Belle Danseuse (Bellypha)
BONNIE DUNDEE, br f 21/5 Rock City—Shy Dolly (Cajun) **Mr J. Graham**
CALCAVELLA, b f 13/3 Pursuit of Love—Brightside (IRE) (Last Tycoon) **Pillar To Post Racing (2)**
B c 12/3 Petardia—Comfrey Glen (Glenstal (USA))
CORVINO, b c 30/4 Tragic Role (USA)—Clare Island (Connaught) **Pillar To Post Racing (3)**
MIRACULOUS GUEST, b f 6/2 Be My Guest (USA)—Mystery Ship (Decoy Boy)
ON THE BLACK (IRE), b c 5/5 Petardia—Salonniere (FR) (Bikala) **Pillar To Post Racing**
SINGING THE BLUES, b f 23/2 Bonny Scot (IRE)—Don't Smile (Sizzling Melody) **Umm Qarn Racing**

Other Owners: Mr P. Bartholomew, Mr A. Cousins, Mrs C. Kettle, Mr B. Simpson.

Jockey (Flat): Tim Sprake (7-13).

645 MRS F. E. WHITE, Chelmsford

Postal: **The Lodge, Nipsells Farm, Nipsells Chase, Mayland, Chelmsford, Essex, CM3 6EJ.**
Phone: **(01621) 742161 FAX (01621) 742161 MOBILE (0410) 081808 (0850) 209368**

LITTLE DUCHESS (IRE), 6, b m Roselier (FR)—Croghan Valley **Mr W. White**
STEEL FOUNTAIN (IRE), 6, b m Royal Fountain—Louemma **Mr W. White**
WELSH ELOQUENCE, 5, b m Welsh Captain—Eloquence **Mr W. White**

Lady Rider: Miss S White (9-7).

INDEX TO HORSES

The Figure before the name of the horse refers to the number of the team in which it appears and **The Figure after** the horse supplies a ready reference to each animal. Horses are indexed strictly alphabetically, e.g. THE CARROT MAN appears in the T's, MR BUSBY in the MR's, ST MELLION DRIVE in the ST's etc.

LOCATION OF TRAINING QUARTERS

References show squares as on map
IN SEVERAL CASES THE NEAREST MAIN CENTRE IS SHOWN TO LOCATE SITUATION OF STABLES

Adam, James R., Gordon B3
Akbary, H., Newmarket E6
Akehurst, J., Epsom F5
Alder, D. S., Belford B4
Allan, A. R., Cornhill-on-Tweed B3
Allen, C. N., Newmarket E6
Allen, J. S., Alcester E4
Alner, R. H., Blandford G4
Alston, E. J., Preston D3
Arbuthnot, D., Compton F4
Armson, R. J., Melbourne E4
Armstrong, R. W., Newmarket E6
Arnold, J. R., Upper Lambourn F4
Avison, Mrs P. M. A.., York C4
Ayliffe, N. G., Minehead F2
Aynsley, J. W. F., Morpeth C4

Bailey, A., Tarporley D3
Bailey, K. C., Upper Lambourn F4
Baker, R. J., Tiverton G2
Balding, G. B., Andover F4
Balding, I. A., Kingsclere F4
Balding, J., Doncaster D4
Barclay, Mrs A., Moreton-In-Marsh E4
Banks, J. E., Newmarket E6
Barclay, J., Leslie A3
Barker, D. W., Richmond C4
Barlow, Sir J., Nantwich D3
Barnes, M. A., Penrith C3
Barr, R. E., Middlesbrough C5
Barratt, L. J., Oswestry E2
Barron, T. D., Thirsk C4
Barrow, A. K., Bridgwater F3
Bartlett, R. A. Airdrie B2
Barwell, C. R., Tiverton G2
Bastiman, R., Wetherby D4
Baugh, B. P. J., Audley E3
Beaumont, P., Brandsby C5
Bell, M. L. W., Newmarket E6
Bell, S. B., Driffield C5
Bennett, C. J., Dymock F4
Bennett, J. A., Wantage F4
Benstead, C. J., Epsom F5
Berry, J., Cockerham C3
de P. Berry, J. C., Newmarket E6
Berry, N., Upper Lambourn F4
Best, J. R., Maidstone F6
Bethell, J. D., Middleham C4
Bethell, W. A., Hull D5
Bevan, E. G., Hereford E3
Bevan, P. J., Uttoxeter E4
Bickerton, Mrs P. F., Market Drayton E3
Billinge, J. N. R., Cupar A3
Birkett, J. J., Workington C2
Bishop, K., Bridgwater F3
Black, Mrs C. J., Oswestry E3
Blackmore, A. G., Hertford F6
Blanshard, M. T. W., Upper Lambourn F4
Bolton, M. J., Shrewton F6
Booth, Charles B., Flaxton D5
Bosley, M. R., Wantage F4
Bousfield, B., Brough C3
Bower, Miss L. J., Alresford F4
Bowlby, Mrs A. J., Wantage F4
Bowring, S. R., Edwinstowe E4
Bradburne, Mrs S. C., Cupar A3
Bradley, J. M., Chepstow F3
Bradley, P., Forsbrook E4
Bradstock, M. F., Wantage F4
Bravery, G. C., Newmarket E6
Brazington, R. G., Redmarley F3
Brennan, O., Worksop D5
Brewis, Miss Rhona, Belford B4
Bridger, J. J., Liphook G5
Bridgwater, K. S., Lapworth E4
Brisbourne, W. M., Baschurch E3
Brittain, C. E., Newmarket E6
Brittain, M. A., Warthill D4
Brooks, C. P. E., Lambourn F4
Brookshaw, S. A., Shrewsbury E3
Brotherton, R., Pershore E3
Brown, I. R., Leominster E3
Brown, Mrs J., Malton C5
Brown, J. L., Llanwrda E2
Broyd, Miss A. E., Crickhowell F3
Buckler, R. H., Bridport G3
Buckley, Mrs J. R., Caistor D6
Buckley, M., South Molton F2
Burchell D., Ebbw Vale F3
Burke, K. R., Wantage F4
Butler, G., Faringdon F4
Butler, P., Lewes G6
Bycroft, N., Brandsby C5

Caldwell, T. H., Warrington D3
Callaghan, N. A., Newmarket E6

Calver, P., Ripon C4
Camacho, Miss J. A., Malton C5
Cambidge, B. R., Bishopswood E3
Campbell, I., Newmarket E6
Campion, A. M., Tunworth F5
Candy, Henry D., Wantage F4
Carey, D. N., Raglan F3
Caro, D. J., Ledbury F3
Carr, T. J., Saltburn-by-Sea C5
Carroll, A. W., Worcester E3
Carter, O. J., Ottery St. Mary G3
Casey, W. T., Dorking F5
Cecil, H. R. A., Newmarket E6
Cecil, Mrs J., Newmarket E6
Chadwick, S. G., Hayton C3
Chamberlain, A. J., Swindon F4
Chamberlain, N., West Auckland C4
Chamings, P. R., Tadley F4
Champion, R., Newmarket E6
Chance, N. T., Lambourn F4
Channon, M., Upper Lambourn F4
Chapman, D. W., York C4
Chapman, M. C., Market Rasen E5
Chappell, Major D. N., Pulborough G5
Chapple-Hyam, P. W., Marlborough F4
Charles-Jones, G. F. H., Wantage F4
Charlton, J. I. A., Stocksfield B3
Charlton, R. J., Beckhampton F4
Cheesbrough, P., Bishop Auckland C4
Chesney, Dr. D., Dorchester G3
Clark, S. B., Sutton-on-the-Forest D4
Clarke, P. C., Hailsham G6
Clement, T. T., Newmarket E6
Clutterbuck, K. F., Royston E6
Cockburn, R. G., Carlisle C3
Cole, H. T., Taunton G3
Cole, P. F. I., Whatcombe F4
Cole, S. N., Tiverton G2
Comerford, K. C., Aylesbury F5
Connell, Lady, Brackley E5
Coton, F., Nottingham E4
Cottrell, L. G., Cullompton G2
Cowell, R. M. H., Newmarket E6
Craggs, R., Sedgefield C4
Craze, Miss J. F., York C4
Cresswell, J. K. S., Oakamoor E4
Cullinan, J., Aylesbury F5
Cumani, L. M., Newmarket E6
Cundell, P. D., Newbury F4
Cunningham-Brown, K., Stockbridge F4
Curley, B. J., Newmarket E6
Curtis, J. W. P., Driffield F4
Curtis, R., Lambourn F4
Cuthbert, T. A. K., Carlisle C3
Cyzer, C., Horsham F5

Dace, L. A., Storrington G5
Dalton, J. N., Shifnal E3
Dalton, P. T., Burton-on-Trent E4
Davies, G. W. J., Abergavenny F3
Davis, Miss L. V., Wolverhampton E3
Davison, Miss Z. C., Woldingham F5
Day, Miss H., Taunton G3
De Haan, B., Lambourn F4
Dean, Richard, Maidstone F6
Dennis, W. W., Bude G1
Dicken, A. R., Dunbar B4
Dickin, R., Stratford-on-Avon E4
Dixon, J. E., Carlisle C3
Dodds, John P., Alnwick B4
Dods, M. J. K., Darlington C4
Donnell, T. W., Swadlincote E4
Dow, S. L., Epsom F5
Drewe, C. J., Didcot F4
Du Plessis, Miss J. M., Saltash G1
Dunlop, E. A. L., Newmarket E6
Dunlop, J. L., Arundel G5
Dunn, A. J. K., Minehead F2
Dutfield, P. N., Seaton G2
Dwyer, C. A., Newmarket E6

Earle, S. A., Marlborough F4
Easterby, M. W., Sheriff Hutton C4
Easterby, T. D., Malton C5
Eccles, P., Lambourn F4
Eckley, B. J., Brecon F2
Eckley, Malcolm W., Ludlow E3
Edwards, G. F., Minehead F2
Edwards, Miss S., Pulborough G5
Egerton, C. R., Chaddleworth F4
Elliott, E. A., Rushyford C4
Ellison, B., Lanchester C4
Elsworth, D. R. C., Whitsbury G4
England, Miss E. M. V., Rugby E4
Enright, G. P., Lewes G6
Etherington, T. J., Malton C5
Eustace, J. M. P., Newmarket E6
Evans, J. T., Bromyard E3
Evans, Mrs M., Haverfordwest F1
Evans, P. D., Welshpool E2
Eyre, J. L., Hambleton C4

Fahey, R. A., Malton C5
Fairhurst, C. W., Middleham C4
Fanshawe, J. R., Newmarket E6
Farrell, P., Taunton G3
Felgate, P. S., Melton Mowbray E5
Fetherson-Godley, M. J., East Ilsley F4
Ffrench Davis, D. J. S., Upper Lambourn F4
FitzGerald, J. G., Malton C5
Flower, R. M., Jevington G6
Forbes, A. L., Uttoxeter E4
Forster, D. M., Darlington C4
Forster, Capt. T. A., Ludlow E3
Foster, A. G., Lambourn F4
Fox, J. C., Marlborough F4
Frost, R. G., Buckfastleigh G2

Gandolfo, D. R., Wantage F4
Gaselee, N. A., Upper Lambourn F4
Gee, B., Worksop D5
George, T. R., Slad F3
Gifford, J. T., Findon G5
Gilligan, P. L., Newmarket E6
Glover, J. A., Worksop D5
Goess-Saurau, Countess, Marlborough F4
Goldie, J. S., Glasgow B2
Goldie, R. H., Kilmarnock B1
Gollings, S., Louth D6
Goodfellow, Mrs A. C. D., Earlston B3

Gosden, J. H. M., Newmarket E6
Graham, Mrs H. O., Jedburgh B3
Graham, N. A., Newmarket E6
Grant, C., Billingham C4
Grassick, L. P., Cheltenham F4
Gray, F., Haywards Heath G5
Greathead, T. R., Chipping Norton E4
Greenway, V. G., Taunton G3
Griffiths, S. G., Carmarthen F2
Grissell, D. M., Brightling F6
Gubby, B., Bagshot F5
Guest, R., Newmarket E6

Haggas, W. J., Newmarket E6
Haine, Mrs D., Newmarket E6
Haldane, J. S., Mindrum B4
Hall, L. Montague, Tadworth F5
Hall, Miss S. E., Middleham C4
Ham, G. A., Axbridge F3
Hammond, M. D., Middleham C4
Hannon, R., Marlborough F4
Harris, J. L., Melton Mowbray E5
Harris, P. W., Berkhamsted F5
Harvey, A. H., Bishop's Stortford F6
Haslam, Patrick, Middleham C4
Hawke, N. J., Chard G3
Haydn Jones, D., Pontypridd F3
Haynes, H. E., Swindon F4
Haynes, J. C., Kendal C3
Haynes, M. J., Epsom F5
Hayward, P. A., Netheravon F4
Heaton-Ellis, M. J. B., Wroughton F4
Hedger, P. R., Chichester G5
Hemsley, C. J., Witney F4
Henderson, N. J., Lambourn F4
Henderson, Mrs R. G., Okehampton G2
Herries, Lady, Littlehampton G5
Hetherton, J., Malton C5
Hiatt, P. W., Banbury E4
Hicks, Mrs C. M., Naunton F4
Hills, B. W., Lambourn F4
Hills, J. W., Lambourn F4
Hoad, R. P. C., Lewes G6
Hobbs, A. G., Kingsbridge G2
Hobbs, P. J., Minehead F2
Hodges, R. J., Somerton F3
Hollingsworth, A. F., Feckenham E4
Hollinshead, R., Upper Longdon E4
Horgan, C., Pulborough G5
Horner-Harker, Mrs S. L., Yarm C5
Howe, H. S., Tiverton G2
Howling, P., Newmarket E6
Hubbard, G. A., Woodbridge E6
Hubbuck, J. S., Hexham C3
Hughes, J. R., Ludlow E3
Huntingdon, Lord, West Ilsley F4

Incisa, Don E., Middleham C4
Ingram, R., Epsom F5

Jackson, C. F. C. Malvern E3
Jackson, F. S., Lowdham D5
James, E. L. J. D., Hungerford F4
Jarvis, A. P., Aston Upthorpe F4
Jarvis, M. A., Newmarket E6
Jarvis, W., Newmarket E6
Jefferson, J. M., Malton C5
Jenkins, J. R. W., Royston E6
Jenks, W. P., Bridgnorth E3
Jessop, A. E. M., Chelmsford F6
Jestin, F., Wigton C2
Jewell, Mrs L. C., Sutton Valence F6
Johnsey, Miss C., Chepstow F3
Johnson, Mrs A. E., Newmarket E6
Johnson, J. H., Crook C4
Johnson, P. R., Cannock E4
Johnson, R. W., Newcastle-upon-Tyne C4
Johnson, Mrs S. M., Madley F3
Johnson Houghton, G. F., Newmarket E6
Johnson Houghton, R. F., Didcot F4
Johnston, M. S., Middleham C4
Jones, A. P., Eastbury F4
Jones, Bob, Newmarket E6
Jones, C. H., Cheltenham F4
Jones, G. Elwyn, Lampeter E2
Jones, Mrs M. A., Lambourn F4
Jones, P. J., Marlborough F4
Jones, T. M., Guildford F5
Jordan, F. T. J., Leominster E3
Jordan, Mrs J., Yarm C5
Joseph, J., Amersham F5
Juckes, R. T., Abberley E3

Kavanagh, H. M., Bodenham E3
Keddy, T., Alfrick E3
Kelleway, A., Newmarket E6
Kelleway, Miss G. M., Whitcombe G4
Kelly, G. P., Sheriff Hutton C4
Kemp, W. T., Duns B3
Kettlewell, S. E., Middleham C4
King, J. S., Swindon F4
Kinsey, T. R., Ashton D3
Kirby, F., Northallerton C4
Kirby, J., Wantage F4
Knight, Miss H. C., Wantage F4
Knight, S. G., Taunton G3

Lamb, D. A., Seahouses B4
Lamb, Mrs K. M., Seahouses B4
Lamyman, Mrs S., Lincoln D5
Leadbetter, S. J., Berwick-upon-Tweed B4
Ledger, R. R., Sittingbourne F6
Lee, R., Presteigne E3
Leigh, J. P., Gainsborough D5
Lewis, G., Epsom F5
Littmoden, N. P., Wolverhampton E3
Livermore, R. E. A., Usk F2
Llewellyn, B. J., Bargoed F2
Lloyd, F., Bangor-on-Dee E3
Lloyd-James, L. R., Malton C5
Lockwood, A., Malton C5
Loder, D. R., Newmarket E6
Long, J. E., Woldingham F5
Lungo, L., Carrutherstown B2

Macauley, N. J., Melton Mowbray E5
Mackie, W. J. W., Church Broughton E4
Mactaggart, A. B., Hawick B3
Madgwick, M. J., Denmead, ... G4
Mahdi, K., Newmarket E6

Makin, P. J., Marlborough F4
Mann, C. J., Upper Lambourn F4
Margarson, G. G., Newmarket..............................E6
Marks, D., Upper Lambourn..................................F4
Marshall, Mrs L. A., Morpeth B4
Marvin, R. F., Southwell D5
Mason, N. B., Brancepeth................................... C4
McAuliffe, K., Lambourn......................................F4
McCain, D., Cholmondeley D3
McConnochie, J. C., Stratford-on-Avon E4
McCourt, G. M., Wantage F4
McGhin, R., Exning..E6
McGovern, T. P., Lewes G6
McInnes-Skinner, Mrs C., Melton Mowbray E5
McKellar, R., Carluke..B3
McKenzie-Coles, W. G., Taunton.........................F3
McKeown, W. J., Newcastle C4
McKie, Mrs V., Twyford..F5
McMahon, B. A., Tamworth..................................F5
McMath, B. J., Newmarket...................................E6
McMillan, M. D., Bibury..F4
Meade, M., Malmesbury.......................................F4
Meagher, M. G., Ormskirk D3
Meehan, B. J., Upper Lambourn..........................F4
Mellor, S., Swindon...F4
Milligan, Miss M. K., Middleham C4
Millman, B. R., Cullompton.................................. G3
Mills, T. G., Epsom F5
Mitchell, C. W., Dorchester.................................. G3
Mitchell, N. R., Dorchester G3
Mitchell, Pat, Newmarket.....................................E6
Mitchell, Philip, Epsom...F5
Mobley, Miss H., Brackley E5
Moffatt, D., Cartmel... C2
Monteith, P., Rosewell B3
Moore, G. L., Brighton... G5
Moore, G. M., Middleham.................................... C4
Moore, J. S., Hungerford F4
Morgan, B. C., Burton-on-Trent............................E4
Morgan, K. A., Melton Mowbray E5
Morlock, C. P. H., Wantage F4
Morris, David, Newmarket E6
Morris, Derrick, Epsom F5
Morrison, H., East Ilsley F4
Moscrop, Mrs E., Seaton Burn.............................B4
Muggeridge, M. P., Newbury F4
Muir, W., Lambourn F4
Mulholland, A. B., Hambleton C4
Mullineaux, M., Tarporley D3
Mullins, J. W., Amesbury F4
Murphy, F., Leyburn.. C4
Murphy, P. G., Bristol...F3
Murray-Smith, D. J. G., Market Harborough.........E5
Murtagh, F. P., Carlisle C3
Musson, W. J., Newmarket E6

Naughton, Mrs A. M., Richmond......................... C4
Naughton, T. J., Epsom.......................................F5
Neville, J., Newport, Gwent F3
Nicholls, D., Thirsk.. C4
Nicholls, P. F., Shepton Mallet.............................F3
Nicholson, D., Temple Guiting.............................F4
Nixon, G. R. S., Selkirk..B3
Nock, Mrs S., Stow-on-the-Wold F4
Nolan, D. A., Wishaw B2
Norton, J., Barnsley.. D4
Noseda, J. J., Newmarket E6

O'Brien, D. C., Tonbridge.....................................F6
Odell, Mrs S. M., Chipping Norton........................F4
Old, J. A. B., Wroughton.......................................F4
Oldroyd, G. R., York C4
Oliver, J. K. M., Hawick B3
O'Neill, J. J., Penrith C3
O'Neill, O., Cheltenham F4
Orde-Powlett, H., Leyburn C4
O'Reilly, J. F. P., Barnsley D4
O'Shea, J. G. M., Westbury-on-Severn..................F3
Owen, E. H., Denbigh.. D2

Palling, B., Cowbridge..F2
Park, I., Stockton-on-Tees C5
Parker, C., Lockerbie...B2
Parkes, J. E., Malton C5
Payne, J. R., Dulverton..F2
Payne, J. W., Newmarket E6
Peacock, R. E., Malmesbury.................................F3
Pearce, B. A., Lingfield..F6
Pearce, J., Newmarket E6
Peill, M. A., Thirsk... C4
Perratt, Miss L. A., Ayr.. B1
Perrett, Mrs A. J., Pulborough G5
Phillips, R. T., Lambourn......................................F4
Pilkington, Mrs T. D., Stow-on-the-Wold F4
Pipe, M., Wellington G3
Pitman, Mrs J., Upper Lambourn F4
Pitman, M. A. Upper Lambourn............................F4
Pittendrigh, S. I., South Wylam B4
Plater, Ms L. C., Newcastle-upon-Tyne C4
Pocock, R. E., Bridgwater.....................................F3
Polglase, M. J., Newmarket..................................E6
Popham, C. L., Taunton.......................................F3
Poulton, J. C., Lewes G6
Poulton, J. R., Lewes G6
Preece, W. G., Telford...E3
Prescott, Sir M., Newmarket................................E6
Price, C. J., Leominster.......................................E3
Price, R. J. Hereford E3
Pritchard, P. A., Shipston-on-Stour F4
Pritchard, Dr. P. L. J., Purton...............................F3
Purdy, P. D., Bridgwater......................................F3

Quinn, J. J., Malton C5
Quinn, M., Wantage...F4

Ramsden, Mrs J. R., Thirsk C4
Ratcliffe, C. I., Welburn C5
Raw, W., Richmond C4
Reed, W. G. Hexham... C3
Reveley, Mrs G. R., Saltburn............................... C5
Rich, P. M., Llangovan...F3
Richards, G., Pontypridd F3
Richards, G. W., Greystoke C3
Richards, Mrs L., Chichester G5
Richardson, Mrs S. L., Cheltenham.....................F4
Ritchens, P. C., Tidworth......................................F4
Robeson, Mrs P., Newport Pagnell E5
Roe, C. G., Chalford..F3
Rothwell, B. S., Malton.. C5
Rowe, R., Pulborough G5

Rowland, Miss M. E., Lower Blidworth D5
Russell, Miss L. V., Kinross A3
Ryall, B. J. M., Yeovil G3
Ryan, M. J., Newmarket E6

Sanders, Miss B., Epsom F5
Saunders, M. S., Wells F3
Scargill, Dr. J. D., Newmarket E6
Scriven, B., Taunton F3
Scrivens, Mrs J., Tiverton G2
Shaw, D., Newark D5
Sheehan, J. J., Findon G5
Sheppard, M. I., Ledbury E3
Sherwood, O. M. C., Upper Lambourn F4
Siddall, Miss L. C., Tadcaster D4
Simpson, R., Wendover F5
Slack, Mrs D. E., Appleby C3
Sly, Mrs P. M., Peterborough E5
Smart, B., Lambourn F4
Smith, Alfred, Beverley D5
Smith, A. D., Westward Ho F2
Smith, C., Wellingore D5
Smith, Denys, Bishop Auckland C4
Smith, J. P., Rugeley E4
Smith, Julian S., Tirley F4
Smith, N. A., Upton Snodsbury E3
Smith, Ralph J., Northleach F4
Smith, Mrs S. J., Bingley D4
Smyth-Osbourne, J. G., Towcester E5
Snook, L. A., Sturminster Newton G3
Soane, V. St John, Hungerford F4
Sowersby, M. E., York D5
Spearing, J. L., Severn Stoke E3
Spicer, R. C., Spalding E6
Stephens, Miss V. A., Taunton F3
Stewart, A. C., Newmarket E6
Stokell, Miss A., Claverdon E4
Storey, F. S., Carlisle C3
Storey, Mrs J. M., Kelso B3
Storey, W., Consett C4
Stoute, M., Newmarket E6
Streeter, A. P., Uttoxeter E4
Stubbs, Mrs L., Marlborough F4
Supple, K. R., Wrotham F6
Swinbank, Mrs A., Richmond C4
Swindlehurst, D. G., Carlisle C3

Tate, T. P., Tadcaster D4
Taylor, Mrs L. C., Chipping Warden E5
Thom, D. T., Newmarket E6
Thomas, Mrs D., Bridgend F2
Thompson, Ronald, Doncaster D4
Thomson, A. M., Greenlaw B4
Thomson, Mrs D., Milnathort A2
Thomson, N. B., Shaftesbury G3
Thomson, R. W., Hawick B3
Thorner, G. E., Wantage F4
Thornton, C. W., Middleham C4
Tinning, W. H., York C4
Todhunter, D. M., Ulverston C3
Toller, J. A. R., Whitsbury G4
Tompkins, M. H., Newmarket E6
Townsley, Mrs P. Laxton, Godalming F5
Tregoning, M. P., Lambourn F4
Tuck, J. C., Didmarton F3
Tucker, F. G., Wedmore F3
Turnell, A., Wantage F4
Turner, D. C., Plymouth G2
Turner, W. G. M., Sherborne F3
Twiston-Davies, N. A., Cheltenham F4

Upson, J. R., Towcester E5
Usher, M. D. I., Wantage F4

Vincent, K., Reigate F5

Wadham, Mrs L. A. M., Newmarket E6
Waggott, N., Spennymoor C4
Wainwright, J. S., Malton C5
Waley-Cohen, Robert B., Banbury E4
Wall, C. F., Newmarket E6
Wall, T. R., Church Stretton E3
Walton, Mrs H. L., Grantham E5
Walwyn, P. T., Lambourn F4
Wane, M., Richmond C4
Ward, Mrs V. C., Grantham E5
Waring, Mrs B., Welford-on-Avon E4
Waring, L., Wellington G3
Waring, M., Wolverhampton E3
Waterman, Miss S., Dorchester G3
Watson, T. R., Winchcombe F3
Webb, H. J. M., Faringdon F4
Webber, P. R., Banbury E4
Weeden, M. J., Weymouth G3
Weedon, C. V., Chiddingfold G5
Wegmann, P., Gloucester F4
Wells, L., Billingshurst F5
Weymes, E., Middleham C4
Wharton, J. R. H., Melton Mowbray E5
Wheeler, E. A., Pangbourne F4
Whillans, A. C., Hawick B3
Whitaker, R. M., Leeds D4
Whittle, Mrs P. M., Ledbury E3
Whyte, J. W., Beccles E7
Wilkinson, M. J., Banbury E4
Williams, D. L., Newbury F4
Williams, I., Alvechurch E4
Williams, L. J., Newport, Gwent F3
Williams, R. J. R., Newmarket E6
Williams, S. C., Newmarket E6
Williams, Mrs S. D., South Molton G2
Williams, Miss V. M., Hereford E3
Wilson, A. J., Cheltenham F4
Wilson, Capt. J. H., Preston D3
Wilton, Miss S. J., Stoke-on-Trent E3
Winkworth, P. L., Godalming F5
Wood, R. S., York C4
Woodhouse, R. D. E., York C4
Woodman, S., Chichester G5
Woodrow, Mrs A. M., High Wycombe F5
Woods, S. P. C., Newmarket E6
Woodward, G., Newark D5
Wormall, Miss J., Ibstock E4
Wragg, G., Newmarket E6

Yardley, G. H., Malvern E3
Young, W. G., Carluke B2

TRAINERS' VAT NUMBERS

TRAINER	REG NUMBER
James R. Adam	634749611
Jonathan Akehurst	563964796
J. S. Allen	660853133
D. W. P. Arbuthnot	314895146
R. J. Armson	684042534
R. W. Armstrong	334139375
J. R. Arnold	614780342
J. W. F. Aynsley	621192373
K. C. Bailey	314664563
R. J. Baker	469685478
I. A. Balding	199094119
J. Balding	457758887
J. E. Banks	571150172
Mrs A. Barclay	640970535
D. W. Barker	633223080
Sir John K. Barlow, Bt	159545139
M. A. Barnes	621400401
L. J. Barratt	594448986
A. K. Barrow	129915054
C. R. Barwell	585986658
J. A. Bennett	641874914
C. J. Benstead	209580263
J. Berry	334882733
J. C. De P. Berry	638100758
W. A. Bethell	599140408
E. G. Bevan	133511704
P. J. Bevan	411111236
K. Bishop	379411236
Mrs C. J. Black	489077101
A. G. Blackmore	632284255
M. T. W. Blanshard	314339869
Charles B. Booth	313503014
J. R. Bosley	194382340
Mrs A. J. Bowlby	569925283
S. R. Bowring	509278724
Mrs S. C. Bradburne	561323270
J. M. Bradley	274664333
P. Bradley	368164627
M. F. Bradstock	491470535
Mrs S. A. Bramall	481800354
G. C. Bravery	571294237
Owen Brennan	117561673
J. J. Bridger	704253271
C. E. Brittain	102592304
M. A. Brittain	599146977
Miss A. E. Broyd	615563149
R. H. Buckler	398770975
David Burchell	540651465
N. Bycroft	171213794
T. H. Caldwell	643608242
N. A. Callaghan	102933011
B. R. Cambidge	159314164
I. Campbell	345422666
A. M. Campion	587879646
W. T. Casey	485999065
Mrs J. Cecil	571088141
S. G. Chadwick	621156867
R. Champion, M.B.E.	200286217
M. Channon	189661117
David W. Chapman	168959983
M. C. Chapman	344208574
Major D. N. Chappell	614533657
P. W. Chapple-Hyam	639328024
J. I. A. Charlton	176290937
P. Cheesbrough	258834717
K. F. Clutterbuck	636738704
H. T. Cole	130398972
P. F. I. Cole	314293378
S. N. Cole	121061826
L. G. Cottrell	140877853
R. Craggs	602268958
J. Cullinan	694657575
P. D. Cundell	614824055
Charles Cyzer	193494821
P. T. Dalton	616881224
B. De Haan	314859934
M. J. K. Dods	257933133
S. L. Dow	413544574
C. J. Drewe	362659921
Miss J. M. Du Plessis	643455339
P. N. Dutfield	634367727
C. A. Dwyer	638198012
M. W. Easterby	169069725
Malcolm W. Eckley	133976644
C. R. Egerton	569752780
D. R. C. Elsworth	355785023
G. P. Enright	435943923
J. M. P. Eustace	521219779
P. D. Evans	489174986
J. L. Eyre	567150241
R. A. Fahey	598892254
C. W. Fairhurst	602285861
J. R. Fanshawe	521042309
P. S. Felgate	309389434
M. J. Fetherston-Godley	314028695
D. J. S. Ffrench-Davis	614877712
J. G. FitzGerald	167445835
Capt T. A. Forster	198928487
R. G. Frost	464882116
N. A. Gaselee	200779676
J. T. Gifford	192834929
J. A. Glover	570900256
J. S. Goldie	556428423
J. H. M. Gosden	637815906
Mrs H. O. Graham	693940885
N. A. Graham	521298456
C. Grant	633646239
Frederick Gray	620739940
D. M. Grissell	192342270
R. Guest	521042211
W. J. Haggas	442932451
Mrs D. Haine	344518947
J. S. Haldane	271440773
Miss S. E. Hall	602277467
G. A. Ham	469736784
M. D. Hammond	546958392
R. Hannon	188397010
J. L. Harris	117472769
Peter W. Harris	301872384
Patrick Haslam	199936189
J. C. Haynes	621426962
M. J. Haynes	211231925
M. J. B. Heaton-Ellis	576278007
P. R. Hedger	503611295
N. J. Henderson	314065590
Mrs R. G. Henderson	631215678
Lady Herries	321820494
J. Hetherton	598972355
P. W. Hiatt	119746644
Mrs C. M. Hicks	700846652
B. W. Hills	385437325
J. W. Hills	569940094
A. G. Hobbs	679438280
P. J. Hobbs	357220859
R. J. Hodges	379438207
R. Hollinshead	100714234

Name	VAT Number
G. A. Hubbard	637802135
Lord Huntingdon	390634151
Don E. Incisa	602257083
A. P. Jarvis	569954274
M. A. Jarvis	344445361
W. Jarvis	410611119
J. M. Jefferson	347619039
J. R. W. Jenkins	321802888
W. P. Jenks	632098837
Mrs L. C. Jewell	619190534
John H. Johnson	532645354
R. F. Johnson Houghton	199189886
A. P. Jones	537596404
T. M. Jones	211537989
J. Joseph	578594081
R. T. Juckes	275450647
Miss G. M. Kelleway	634657324
W. T. Kemp	202759770
S. E. Kettlewell	441582653
Miss H. C. Knight	200516720
G. Lewis	210700431
N. P. Littmoden	687860277
B. J. Llewellyn	615583533
F. Lloyd	625050964
L. R. Lloyd-James	599176181
D. R. Loder	571447728
W. J. W. Mackie	390480447
K. Mahdi	688315693
P. J. Makin	194790518
C. J. Mann	614848525
D. Marks	199926095
N. B. Mason	177004279
K. McAuliffe	614826833
J. C. McConnochie	589597255
T. P. McGovern	620849049
Mrs C. McInnes Skinner	115347979
W. J. McKeown	621277361
Mrs V. McKie	581014370
Martyn Meade	576029426
B. J. Meehan	614603958
S. Mellor	199598571
Miss M. K. Milligan	633271164
B. R. Millman	570248055
T. G. Mills	564116061
N. R. Mitchell	570325361
Pat Mitchell	192511569
Philip Mitchell	210994078
D. Moffatt	378696576
G. L. Moore	190606467
G. M. Moore	602113509
J. S. Moore	541696036
H. Morrison	614830161
M. P. Muggeridge	568603025
William R. Muir	569863572
J. W. Mullins	504372669
F. Murphy	634496811
D. J. G. Murray Smith	392016367
F. P. Murtagh	686608000
W. J. Musson	213080024
James Neville	542870732
P. F. Nicholls	600891753
John Norton	364180067
D. C. O'Brien	619365913
J. J. O'Neill	257253650
O. O'Neill	275553829
J. G. M. O'Shea	655355815
J. A. B. Old	501801302
J. K. M. Oliver	270373273
J. E. Parkes	391888005
J. W. Payne	521068184
R. E. Peacock	160348383
J. Pearce	443013104
R. T. Phillips	614622855
Mrs T. D. Pilkington	618259426
M. C. Pipe	130961289
M. A. Pitman	614846825
M. J. Polglase	637800631
C. L. Popham	131287782
Sir Mark Prescott Bt	102416525
P. A. Pritchard	377100172
P. D. Purdy	529855403
Mick Quinn	585354413
Mrs J. R. Ramsden	444381746
W. G. Reed	621184371
Mrs G. R. Reveley	391822439
P. M. Rich	655867779
Graham Richards	615535939
Mrs P. Robeson	608630448
B. S. Rothwell	599172585
R. Rowe	397611812
Miss L. V. Russell	663751812
B. J. M. Ryall	186378909
M. J. Ryan	285407345
Miss B. Sanders	448745510
J. J. Sheehan	237456547
O. M. C. Sherwood	363042676
Miss L. C. Siddall	431044695
Mrs P. M. Sly	486255319
B. Smart	450209482
Alfred Smith	168216456
Denys Smith	258094929
Mrs S. J. Smith	180903566
J. G. Smyth-Osbourne	670402953
L. A. Snook	634363543
J. L. Spearing	275942326
A. C. Stewart	428074648
Miss Ann Stokell	687860179
W. Storey	177757509
Mrs A. Swinbank	546764019
T. P. Tate	313539865
Mrs L. C. Taylor	623648926
D. T. Thom	103696770
Mrs Dorothy Thomson	561441459
R. W. Thomson	300614125
M. H. Tompkins	334108488
J. C. Tuck	618276525
F. G. Tucker	131549581
W. G. M. Turner	453883518
J. R. Upson	623653839
Robert B. Waley-Cohen	623686426
C. F. Wall	496701221
P. T. Walwyn	200416627
Mrs V. C. Ward	690281136
C. V. Weedon	212347206
P. Wegmann	681808804
E. Weymes	258248241
A. C. Whillans	663893882
R. M. Whitaker	170674459
J. W. Whyte	410521022
M. J. Wilkinson	443798217
D. L. Williams	551337849
Mrs S. D. Williams	631020504
A. J. Wilson	286154441
R. S. Wood	313587459
R. D. E. Woodhouse	332320311
S. P. C. Woods	571402465
Geoffrey Wragg	102855589

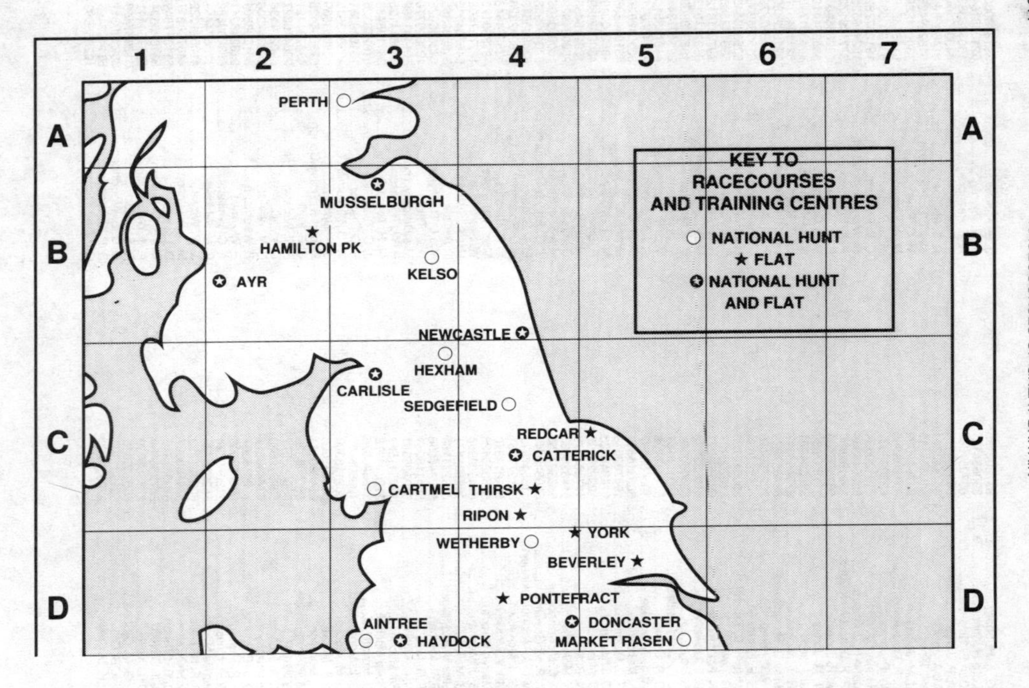
1
2
3
4
5
6
7
A
B
C
D
KEY TO RACECOURSES AND TRAINING CENTRES
NATIONAL HUNT
FLAT
NATIONAL HUNT AND FLAT
PERTH
MUSSELBURGH
HAMILTON PK
AYR
KELSO
NEWCASTLE
HEXHAM
CARLISLE
SEDGEFIELD
REDCAR
CATTERICK
CARTMEL
THIRSK
RIPON
WETHERBY
YORK
BEVERLEY
PONTEFRACT
AINTREE
HAYDOCK
DONCASTER
MARKET RASEN

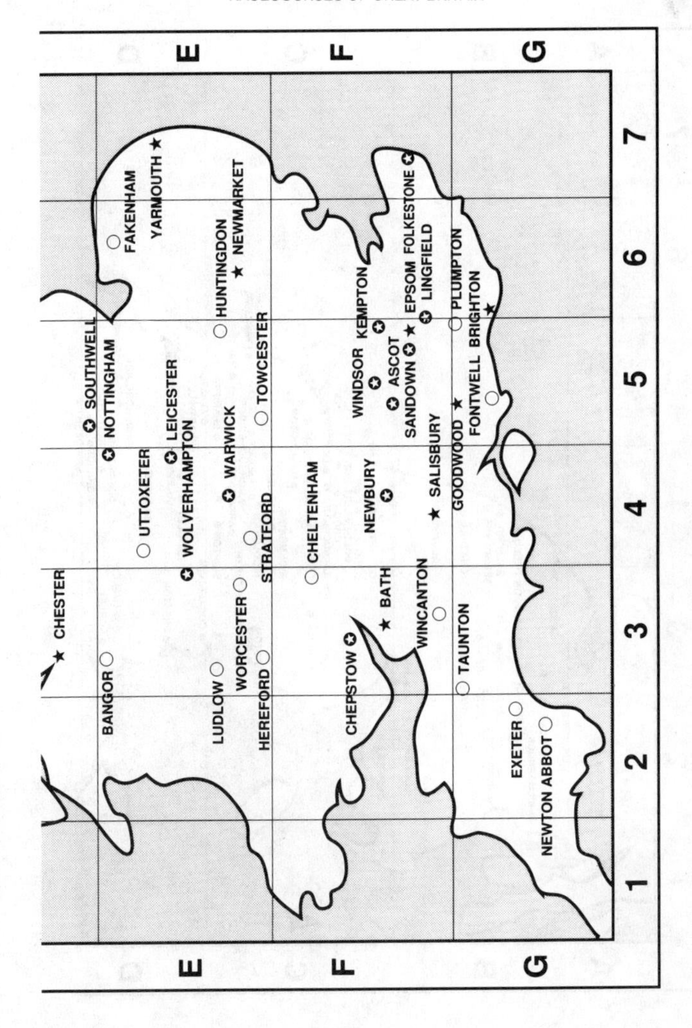
E
F
G
1
2
3
4
5
6
7
CHESTER
BANGOR
SOUTHWELL
NOTTINGHAM
FAKENHAM
YARMOUTH
UTTOXETER
LEICESTER
WOLVERHAMPTON
WARWICK
HUNTINGDON
NEWMARKET
LUDLOW
WORCESTER
HEREFORD
STRATFORD
TOWCESTER
CHELTENHAM
CHEPSTOW
BATH
NEWBURY
WINDSOR
KEMPTON
ASCOT
SANDOWN
EPSOM
FOLKESTONE
LINGFIELD
SALISBURY
WINCANTON
GOODWOOD
FONTWELL
BRIGHTON
PLUMPTON
TAUNTON
EXETER
NEWTON ABBOT

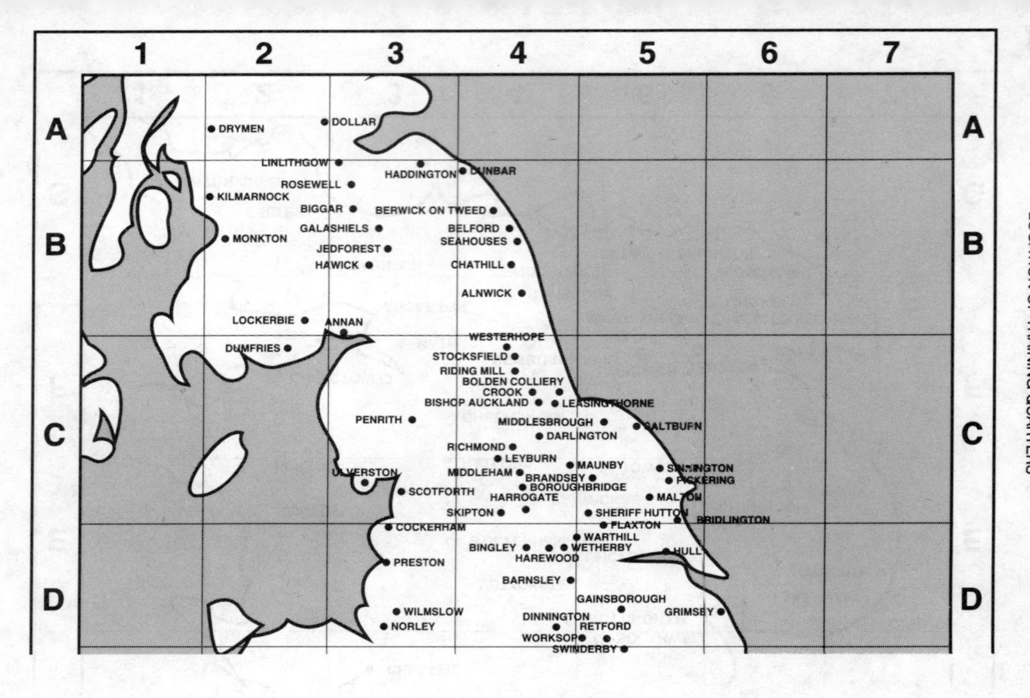
1
2
3
4
5
6
7
A
B
C
D
DRYMEN
DOLLAR
LINLITHGOW
HADDINGTON
DUNBAR
ROSEWELL
KILMARNOCK
BIGGAR
BERWICK ON TWEED
GALASHIELS
BELFORD
MONKTON
SEAHOUSES
JEDFOREST
HAWICK
CHATHILL
ALNWICK
LOCKERBIE
ANNAN
WESTERHOPE
DUMFRIES
STOCKSFIELD
RIDING MILL
BOLDEN COLLIERY
CROOK
BISHOP AUCKLAND
LEASINGTHORNE
PENRITH
MIDDLESBROUGH
SALTBURN
DARLINGTON
RICHMOND
LEYBURN
MAUNBY
MIDDLEHAM
ULVERSTON
BRANDSBY
PICKERING
BOROUGHBRIDGE
SCOTFORTH
HARROGATE
MALTON
SKIPTON
SHERIFF HUTTON
BRIDLINGTON
COCKERHAM
FLAXTON
WARTHILL
BINGLEY
WETHERBY
HULL
HAREWOOD
PRESTON
BARNSLEY
GAINSBOROUGH
WILMSLOW
GRIMSBY
DINNINGTON
NORLEY
RETFORD
WORKSOP
SWINDERBY

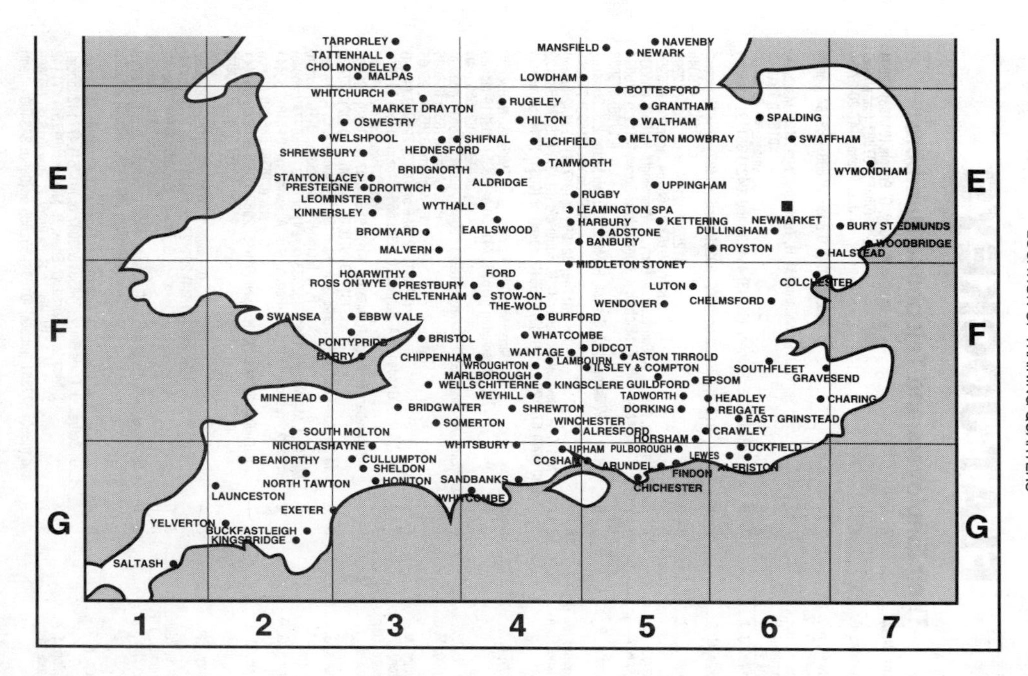
E
F
G
1
2
3
4
5
6
7
TARPORLEY
TATTENHALL
CHOLMONDELEY
MALPAS
WHITCHURCH
MARKET DRAYTON
OSWESTRY
WELSHPOOL
SHREWSBURY
HEDNESFORD
BRIDGNORTH
STANTON LACEY
PRESTEIGNE
DROITWICH
LEOMINSTER
KINNERSLEY
WYTHALL
BROMYARD
MALVERN
HOARWITHY
ROSS ON WYE
PRESTBURY
CHELTENHAM
FORD
STOW-ON-THE-WOLD
EARLSWOOD
MANSFIELD
LOWDHAM
RUGELEY
HILTON
SHIFNAL
LICHFIELD
ALDRIDGE
TAMWORTH
NEWARK
NAVENBY
BOTTESFORD
GRANTHAM
WALTHAM
MELTON MOWBRAY
UPPINGHAM
RUGBY
LEAMINGTON SPA
HARBURY
KETTERING
ADSTONE
BANBURY
MIDDLETON STONEY
SPALDING
SWAFFHAM
WYMONDHAM
NEWMARKET
DULLINGHAM
ROYSTON
BURY ST EDMUNDS
WOODBRIDGE
HALSTEAD
COLCHESTER
CHELMSFORD
LUTON
WENDOVER
SWANSEA
PONTYPRIDD
BARRY
EBBW VALE
BRISTOL
CHIPPENHAM
WROUGHTON
MARLBOROUGH
WELLS
CHITTERNE
BURFORD
WHATCOMBE
WANTAGE
LAMBOURN
DIDCOT
ASTON TIRROLD
ILSLEY & COMPTON
KINGSCLERE
GUILDFORD
EPSOM
SOUTHFLEET
GRAVESEND
CHARING
WEYHILL
SHREWTON
WINCHESTER
ALRESFORD
TADWORTH
DORKING
HEADLEY
REIGATE
EAST GRINSTEAD
CRAWLEY
UCKFIELD
HORSHAM
PULBOROUGH
LEWES
ALFRISTON
FINDON
ARUNDEL
CHICHESTER
UPHAM
COSHAM
MINEHEAD
BRIDGWATER
SOMERTON
WHITSBURY
SANDBANKS
WHITCOMBE
SOUTH MOLTON
NICHOLASHAYNE
CULLUMPTON
SHELDON
HONITON
BEANORTHY
NORTH TAWTON
LAUNCESTON
EXETER
BUCKFASTLEIGH
KINGSBRIDGE
YELVERTON
SALTASH

FLAT JOCKEYS

Their Employers and Telephone Numbers

Jockey	st	lb	Employers and Telephone Numbers
Adams, N. M.	7	10	A. K. Barrow, N. Berry, G. Enright (01488) 72004 or (0836) 787881 (car phone)
Asmussen, C.	8	3	J. E. Pease 1-47-20-07-50
Bardwell, G.	7	10	J. Pearce, D. C. O'Brien (01638) 668484 (agent)
Batteate, D. M.	8	1	
Biggs, D. D.	7	13	R. J. R. Williams, M. H. Tompkins, Mrs. N. J. Macauley (01638) 731216
Bloomfield, P.	8	4	
Boeuf, D.	8	0	D. Smaga, 44 57 14 03
Bramhill, J. A.,	7	5	J. S. Goldie, R. E. Peacock (01543) 454390 and (0421) 381191 (mobile)
Carlisle, N. A.	7	8	(01832) 280132 or (0860) 392889 and (01432) 274613 (agent) or (0589) 439345
Carroll, J.	8	2	(01253) 812299 or (01253) 812299
Carter, G. A.	7	10	J. Berry (01638) 668484 (agent) or 665950
Charnock, L.	7	10	P. Haslam, Miss J. A. Camacho, J. Berry, J. Wainwright (01653) 695004
Clark, A. S.	8	2	M Heaton-Ellis, P. Mitchell, K. Cunningham-Brown (01222) 615594 or (01798) 873028
Cochrane, R.	8	6	R. J. R. Williams, J. D. Scargill, F. Murphy, B. McMath, J. J. Sheehan, A. P. Jones (01638) 743045
Connorton, N. B.	8	2	(01748) 824059 or (01751) 477142 (agent)
Culhane, P. A.	8	2	Mrs G. R. Reveley, R. Fahey, C. B. Booth c/o (01937) 836171/582122 or (01977) 675129 and (0748) 825640 (agent) or (0831) 201425 (mobile)
Darley, K.	8	1	J. Berry, Mrs G. R. Reveley, S. C. Williams, N. Bycroft, T. J. Etherington (01638) 741060 or (0836) 789919 (agent) or (0860) 926556 (car)
Day, N. P.	8	2	D. Morris, R. Jones, G. C. Bravery (01638) 666431, (0831) 336611 (mobile)
Deering, M.	7	10	P. Wigham (01653) 696065 P. Wigham (01653) 696065
Demuro, M.	7	10	(01353) 723588 or (0370) 725019 (agent)
Dettori, L.	8	4	J. Gosden, I. A. Balding (01638) 666431 and (0850) 011811
Doleuze, O.	7	3	Mrs C. Head 344 21 49 58
Doyle, B.	8	1	B. Meehan, N. Berry, R. Millman, (01638) 664347 or (0836) 296860 and (01793) 870606 (agent) or (0402) 277425
Drowne, S.	8	0	M. Heaton-Ellis, D. Elsworth, G. A. Ham, M. S. Saunders, C. A. Dwyer, P. G. Murphy, G. B. Balding, J. R. Poulton, Mrs N. J. Macauley (01761) 453555 (agent) or (0831) 865974 (mobile)
Duffield, G. P.	8	2	Sir Mark Prescott, Miss L. A. Perratt, Mrs. A. Swinbank (01748) 950444 and (01638) 666350 (agent)
Dwyer, M. J.	7	7	I. Balding, W. Muir, C. N. Allen (01635) 298210 and (01638) 561441 or (0370) 270820 (agent)
Eddery, Pat	8	4	G. Lewis, P. Walwyn, (01844) 290282 or (01844) 201427 and (01385) 317979 (agent)
Eddery, Paul	8	0	G. Lewis, (01884) 201427 (agent)
Edmunds, J. P.	8	0	J. Balding (01302) 719734
Egan, J. F.	8	0	P. D. Evans, J. C. De Berry, N. T. Chance, Mrs. L. Stubbs (0802) 276798 and (01638) 561441 or (0370) 270820
Fallon, K. F.	8	4	H. R. A. Cecil, E. J. Alston, J. L. Eyre, J. G. Fitzgerald, D. Smith, L. G. Cottrell, J. C. de Berry (01653) 693087 or (01751) 477142 (agent)
Fanning, J. K.	7	12	Miss L. A Perratt, D. Shaw, R. McKellar (01751) 477142
Fenton, M.,	8	2	M. L. W. Bell, J. C. de Berry, C. Roe (01638) 660669 and (0850) 377301 (mobile) (01638) 552666 or (0860) 343400 (agent)

Name	st	lb	Trainers / Contact
Ffrench, R.	7	12	(L. Cumani) (01638) 561450 (agent)
Fortune, J. J.	8	6	Mrs J. R. Ramsden, S. Kettlewell, B. A. McMahon, J. J. Quinn (01279) 725831 or (01638) 561450 (agent) or (01638) 743756
Garth, A.,	7	10	(W. M. Brisbourne) (01543) 490298
Gibson, Dale	7	12	(01937) 842642 or (0831) 103354 (mobile) and (01531) 631593 or (0860) 370359 (agent)
Greaves, Miss A.	8	1	D. Nicholls (01845) 501470 or (0498) 575747
Grenet, F.	8	7	P. Bary 44-21-44-10
Guillot, S.			P. Bary
Halliday, V.	8	4	(0402) 561784 (mobile) and (01977) 557167 (agent) or (0378) 647520 (mobile)
Harrison, D.	7	12	(01638) 666350
Hills, M.	8	4	G. Wragg, J. W. Hills (01284) 850805
Hills, R.	8	1	J. W. Hills, P. Walwyn, R. Armstrong (01284) 850805 or (01638) 570389 and (0860) 235151 (agent)
Hind, G.	8	0	P. S. Felgate (01638) 741060 or (0836) 789919 (mobile)
Hodgson, K.	8	5	G. R. Oldroyd, C. B. Booth (01653) 691536
Hogan, D.	8	4	J. M. Oxx (045) 521858
Holland, D. P.	8	2	(01403) 275150 or (0831) 282788 (agent) (0850) 300449 (agent's mobile)
Hughes, B. R.	8	0	D. T. Hughes (045) 21490 or (088) 594701
Hughes, R. D.	8	8	R. Hannon, (01672) 810328 or (01638) 561450 (agent)
Johnson, E.	7	9	B. McMath (01638) 720960 or (0831) 345360 (mobile)
Kennedy, N.	7	7	B. Ellison, J. Hetherton (01751) 477142 (agent)
Kinane, M. J.	8	4	D. K. Weld (045) 21739 or (088) 567770
Lappin, R.	8	1	J. L. Eyre (01845) 597481 (01969) 622477
Long, Miss L. G.	8	3	J. E. Long (01273) 621346
Lord, W.	8	1	(01638) 669846
Lowe, J. J.	7	10	H. Cecil (01638) 577469 and (01761) 453555 (agent) or (0831) 865974 (mobile)
Lucas, T.	8	5	M. W. Easterby (01757) 288270 and (0370) 812011 (mobile)
Mackay, A.	7	10	R. Brotherton, I. Campbell (01761) 453555 (agent) or (0831) 865974 (mobile)
Marshall, J.	7	7	M. Hammond (0969) 640228 or (0969) 24238
Martinez, J. L.	8	2	(01353) 723588 and mobile (0370) 725019 (agent)
McGlone, A.	7	11	H. Cecil, R. Ingram (01638) 731367 or (0836) 628159 or (01903) 264336 (agent)
McKeown, D.	8	4	C. W. Thornton, J. S. Wainwright, R. Bastiman (01977) 681247
McLaughlin, J.	8	7	(01638) 668115
McLaughin, T. G.	8	4	R. F. Marvin (01638) 660214
Milligan, G.	7	11	G. Wragg (01638) 660229 and (01323) 509086 (agent)
Morris, A.	8	0	J. R. Poulton, (0883) 344893 or (0372) 271526
Morris, Mrs C. L.	8	2	G. L. Moore, M. Channon (01793) 710469
Mosse, G.			A. De Royer-Dupre
Munro, A.	7	12	(0763) 289370 or (0850) 338815 (mobile) or (0536) 412144 or (0831) 630363 (agent's mobile)
Murtagh, J. P.	8	5	J. Oxx (087) 586617 or (045) 522460
Newton, L.	7	13	B. A. McMahon (01353) 723588 and (0802) 167255 or (0411) 133533
Norton, F.	7	10	(01761) 453555 (agent) or (0831) 865974 (mobile)
Nutter, C.	8	4	(01638) 668153
O'Connor, W.	8	5	M. Kauntze, R. Hannon (045) 32877 and (0370) 518735 (mobile)
O'Donohoe, D.	7	13	(01638) 660758
O'Gorman, Miss E.	8	4	W. A. O'Gorman c/o (01638) 663330
O'Neill, Dane.	8	0	R. Hannon, R. Dickin, P. R. Webber (01635) 247532

Name	st	lb	Contact
O'Reilly, J. F. P.	7	10	(0977) 648229
O'Shea, D. G.	7	10	W. Musson (01638) 578001 or (0836) 618318
Parkin, G.	8	4	M. W. Easterby, J. S. Wainwright (01347) 878368
Perham, R.	8	4	R. Hannon, N. Berry, A. J. Chamberlain (01367) 820129 or (0836) 521636 or (01889) 582638 (agent)
Price, R. W.	7	11	R. Brotherton, R. Armstrong (01761) 453555 (agent) or (0831) 865974 (mobile)
Quinn, J. A.	7	10	Dr J. D. Scargill, S. Gollings, N. Bycroft, Mrs. A. E. Johnson, (01638) 665454, (01638) 730445 or (0860) 883330 (mobile) or (01751) 477142 (agent)
Quinn, T. R.	8	2	Mr Fahd Salman's horses (owner), D. Elsworth, P. Cole, R. Dickin, J. Akehurst, D. Arbuthnot, T. Mills (01488) 648091 or (0831) 821100 (mobile)
Reid, J.	8	6	P. Chapple-Hyam, W. Muir, D. Haydn-Jones, R. Johnson-Houghton, T. Mills (036 782) 0214
Rimmer, Mark	8	4	(01638) 800487 and (01432) 274613 (agent)
Roberts, M.	8	0	A. Stewart (01529) 414874 (agent) or (0468) 481599 (mobile)
Roche, C.	8	4	J. Bolger (045) 21464 or (088) 557078
Rutter, C.	7	10	P. Cole, T. Donnelly, M. R. Bosley (01235) 751614 or (01531) 631593 and (0860) 370359 (agent)
Ryan, W.	8	2	H. Cecil (01638) 741060 or (01638) 660758 (agent)
Sanders, S.	8	3	Sir Mark Prescott, J. Toller, J. Akehurst, Miss B. Sanders (0181) 3971367 and (01638) 666350 (agent)
Shanahan, P.	8	3	D. K. Weld, C. Collins (088) 566560
Slattery, J. V.	8	6	R. J. Baker, O O'Neill (01242) 820907 or (0831) 545789
Smith, D. V.	7	13	(045) 33811
Smullen, P. J.	8	3	J. Oxx, D. K. Weld, T. Stack (087) 523636 and (0405) 37305 or (087) 601818 (agent)
Sprake, T. J.	7	11	W. Turner, A. Foster, R. Millman, B. Palling, A. P. Jones, K. Cunningham-Brown (01793) 870606 (agent)
Stack, J. J.	8	4	B. Smart, T. T. Clement (01638) 666091 and (0860) 329555 or (0468) 012667
Street, R.	7	7	P. Hayward (01488) 71412 and 71548
Supple, W.	8	0	(045) 22583 or (088) 582645
Swinburn, W. R.	8	6	(01440) 820277 and (0411) 477778 (agent)
Tate, J.,	7	10	(01638) 660758 (agent)
Tebbutt, M.	8	4	B. Meehan (01638) 730356 and (0802) 913758
Tinkler, Mrs K.	7	10	Don Enrico Incisa (01653) 658245
Urbina, O.	8	6	L. Cumani (01353) 723588 or (0370) 725019 (agent)
Varley, N.	7	10	D. A. Nolan (01761) 453555 and (0831) 865974 (mobile)
Weaver, J.	8	4	P. Haslam, Miss S. E. Hall, D. J. Ffrench Davis (0181) 4715477 and (0836) 230335 (agent)
Webster, S. G.	8	9	Mrs N. J. Macauley, Miss J. F. Craze (01904) 608458 and (0585) 683359
Whitworth, S.	8	4	H. S. Howe, D. W. Arbuthnot, N. P. Littmoden, Mrs L. Stubbs (01638) 578001 and (0850) 157198 (0672) 40961 or (0793) 870606 (agent)
Wigham, M.	8	2	R. Jones, J. Pearce, S. Mellor (01638) 560507 or (0831) 456426 (mobile) or (0827) 66105
Williams, S. D.	8	4	N. A. Smith (01623) 823579 and (0589) 950832 or (0378) 269618 (agent)
Williams, T.	7	12	J. L. Eyre, B. J. Llewellyn, J. S. Goldie (01635) 247532 or (01635) 247532 (agent)
Wright, D. T.	7	3	(0829) 760762 or (0831) 865974 (agent)

APPRENTICES

Name	st	lb	Trainer	Contact
Adamson, C. N.	7	3		(0793) 791113 and (0733) 261274 (agent)
Ahern, E.,	7	2	Mr M. J. Grassick	c/o (045) 434483
Appleby, Miss V.,	7	13	Mr T. D. Barron	c/o (01845) 587435
Axon, K.,	7	3	Mr J. S. Moore	c/o (01488) 648822
Baird, M.	7	7	Mr K. Mahdi	c/o (01638) 603193
Baker, Miss K. A.,	7	7	Mr M. T. W. Blanshard	(01488) 71091
Bales, Miss C.,	7	13	Miss J. F. Craze	(01904) 608305
Barsby, Miss A.	7	6	Mr H. Akbary	c/o (0467) 407804
Bastiman, H. J.	8	11	Mr R. Bastiman	(01423) 359397
Black, M.	8	2	Mr T. Stack	(062) 54129
Bond, A.			Mr A. Bailey	c/o (01829)760762
Bone, Miss C.	8	4	Mr G. L. Moore	(01273) 620405
Bosley,J.	7	3	Mr A. Bailey	c/o (01829)760762
Boyle, F. J.,	7	12	Mr B. A. McMahon	
Bradley, P.	7	3	Mr J. Berry	c/o (01524) 791179 and (01524) 792854 (agent) or (0467) 677948 (mobile)
Brisland, R.	7	7	Mr G. L. Moore	(01273) 620405
Buckley, S.	7	12	Mr L. Eyre	c/o (01845) 597481
Burchell, D. G.,	7	3	Mr D. C. O'Brien	(01892) 824123
Carson, S.	7	8	Mr E. A. Wheeler	c/o (01189) 841317
Clarke, P	7	13	Mr J. W. Hills	(01488) 73144 (01353) 723588 or (0370) 725019 (agent)
Clarke, S.	7	7	Mr R. Hollinshead	(01543) 490298
Cleary, P.	7	10	Mr M. Channon	(01488) 71149
Cody-Butler, R.	7	7	Mr P. Chapple-Hyam	c/o (01672) 514901
Cogan, C.	7	10	Lord Huntingdon	(01635) 281747
Cook, Miss Aimee,	7	13	Lord Huntingdon	(01635) 281747
Copp, S.	8	3	Mrs M. Reveley	c/o (01287) 652301
Cornally, J.	8	0	Mr M. J. Haynes	c/o (01372) 722664
Cox, Miss Charlotte,	7	12	Mr G. Charles-Jones	(01235) 767713
Daly, A.,	7	12	Mr M. Heaton-Ellis	(01793) 815009
Denby, D.	8	0	Mr G. Lewis	c/o (01372) 277662
Dickerson, S.	7	10	Mr J. W. Hills	(01488) 73144
Dobbs, P. J.,	7	12	Mr R. Hannon	(01264) 850254
Doe, P.	7	3	Mr S. Dow	(01432) 274613 (agent)
Eddery, A. M.	7	11	Mr M. Channon	(01488) 71149
Egan, D.	6	12	Mr R. Fahey	c/o (01653) 628001
Farmer, R.	7	10	Mr M. A. Brittain	c/o (01759) 371472
Faulkner, G.	8	8	Mr D. R. Loder	(01353) 723588 and (0370) 725019 (agent) or (01638) 730618
Fessey, P. J.	7	7	Mr J. Berry	(01524) 792854 and (01524) 792854 (agent) or (0467) 677948 (mobile)
Finnamore, S. D.	7	12	Mr M. W. Easterby	(01347) 878368
Fowle, J.	7	3	Mr M. Heaton-Ellis	c/o (01793) 815009 and (01761) 453555 (agent) or (0831) 865974 (mobile)
Fredericks, P.,	7	12	Mr S. Kettlewell	c/o (01969) 640411 or (01638) 561450 (agent)
Gallagher, G. H.,	7	9		(01264) 850254
Gannon, Miss C.	7	2	Mr J. Oxx	c/o (045) 521310
Goode, P. L	7	12	Mr P. Haslam	(01969) 624351
Gotobed, J. L.	8	4	Mr C. Dwyer	c/o (01638) 667857
Grantham, I.	7	7	Mr M. S. Johnston	(01969) 622237

Name	st	lb	Trainer	Telephone
Griffiths, D.	8	4	Mr P. J. Makin	c/o (01672) 512973
Hackett. Miss L.,	7	3	Mr T. G. Mills	c/o (01372) 377209
Hall, A.	8	7	Mr A. W. Carroll	c/o (01653) 793459
Hammond, M.	8	5	Mr C. N. Allen	(01638) 667870
Hannon, G.,	8	0	Mr B. Meehan	(01488) 73656 or (01488) 73636
Harfield, M. W.	7	13	Mr L. M. Hall	c/o (01737) 814847 and 370911
Harrison, S. Cogan,	7	0	Lord Huntingdon	(01635) 281747
Hart, Miss K.	7	5	Mr T. D. Barron	c/o (01845) 587435 or (01353) 723588 or (0370) 725019 (agent)
Hartley, Miss A.	7	7	Capt J. Wilson	c/o (01772) 812780
Hartley, Miss S.,	8	0	Mr S. A. Earle	c/o (01793) 861157
Havlin, R.	8	2	Mr P. Chapple-Hyam	(0850) 829449 and (01793) 813992 or (0402) 277425 (agent)
Hayden, A.,	7	12	Mr R. Hollinshead	(01543) 490298
Henry, M. P.	7	8	Mr J. Hills	(01488) 73144 and (01736) 793224 (agent)
Hudson, I.	8	8	Mr R. E. Peacock	c/o (01666) 577238
Hunnam, Miss Jo	7	10	Mr W. J. Haggas	c/o (01977) 557167
Jackson, Miss S.	7	9	Mr H. Candy	c/o (01367) 820276
Jones, Miss G.	7	10	Mr R. W. Jones	(01440) 820342
Joyce, Miss E.	7	10	Mr M. Quinn	
Kinsella, D.	6	7	Mr M. J. Grassick	c/o (045) 434483
Lake, R.	8	0	Mr G. B. Balding	c/o (01264) 772278
Lavelle, K.	7	2	Mr J. Oxx	c/o (045) 521310
Lowther, C.	7	12	Mr J. Berry	c/o (01524) 791179 and (01524) 792854 (agent) or (0467) 677948 (mobile)
Lund, Miss C.	7	10	Sir Mark Prescott	c/o (01638) 662117
Lynch, F.,	7	13	Mr R. Hollinshead	(01543) 490298
Masterson, Miss L.	8	7	Mr I. A. Balding	c/o (01635) 298210
McCabe, P. A.	8	3	Mr M. J. Ryan	c/o (001638) 664172
McCarthy, A.	7	3	Mr P. D. Evans	c/o (01938) 570288 and (01296) 625716 (agent) or (0378) 269618 (mobile)
McCauley, J.	7	3	Miss L. Perratt	(01292) 266232
McGaffin, D.	8	0	Mr W. Turner	(01963) 220523
Melrose, S.	7	1	Mr J. K. Oliver	c/o (01450) 870216
Mernagh, D.	7	3	Mr M. Brittain	c/o (01759) 371472 and (0467) 834337
Mitchell, Miss S.	8	5	Mr D. Gandolfo	(01672) 5408631 and (0468) 122587 (mobile)
Moffatt, Darren	7	4	Mr D. Moffatt	(0498) 621645 (mobile)
Mullen, R.	7	7	Mr M. Bell	c/o (01638) 666567
Mundy, P.	7	8	Mr R. Dickin	(01789) 450052
Murphy, Miss J.,	7	10	Mrs J. Jordan	(01642) 701061
Murphy, P. P.	7	11	Mr J. S. Moore	(01488) 648720 and (01761) 453555 (agent) or (0831) 865974 (mobile)
Newman, L.	7	3	Mr R. Hannon	(01264) 850254
Nicholls, A.	7	5	Mr B. W. Hills	(01488) 71548
Nosworthy, Miss C. C.,	7	12	Mr N. A. Callaghan	
O'Connor, B. M.	7	12	Mr M. J. Grassick	c/o (045) 434483
O'Keefe, Miss S.	8	3	Mr J. Oxx	c/o (045) 521310
O'Leary, B.	7	12	Mr E. A. Wheeler	c/o (01189) 841317
O'Neill, David. W.	7	10	Mr P. Cole	c/o (01488) 638 433
O'Neill, L. Miss,	8	0	Mr J. Oxx	c/o (045) 521310
Olley, S. W.	8	11	Mr J. J. O'Neill	c/o (01768) 484555
Parkin, K.	7	10	Mr C. E. Brittain	c/o (01638) 664347
Parsons, K.	7	5	Mr R. J. Charlton	c/o (01672) 539533
Pierrepont, K.	8	2	Mr N. P. Littmoden	c/o (01902) 688558
Pollard, N.	7	3		
Polli, A.	7	5	Mr L. Cumani	c/o (01638) 665432 and (01353) 723588 or (0370) 725019 (agent) and (0802) 167255

Name	Weight		Trainer	Telephone
Power, I.	7	0	Mr J. Oxx	c/o (045) 521310
Quinn, P.,	7	0	Mr R. Hollinshead	(01543) 490298
Rock, D.	6	10	Mr M. J. Grassick	c/o (045) 434483
Roberts, Paul	8	2	Mr J. Berry	c/o (01524) 791179 and (01524) 792854 (agent) or (0467) 677948 (mobile)
Shea, P. C.	8	2	Mr W. Musson	c/o (01638) 663371
Siddall, T.	8	3	Miss L. Siddall	c/o (01977) 557167
Sked, K.	7	7	Mr M. Johnston	c/o (01969) 22237
Smith, B.	7	7	Mr H. Candy	c/o (01367) 820276
Smith, J. D.	8	0	Mr B. W. Hills	(01488) 71548
Smith, R.	7	12	Mr R. Hannon	(01264) 850254
Somers, Miss Lisa,	7	13	Mr P. N. Dutfield	(01297) 553560
Sparkes, G.	7	5	Mr L. Cumani	c/o (01638) 665432
Stack, E.	8	0	Mr F. Flood	c/o (045) 403136
Stamp, D.	6	0	Mr J. C. Hayden	c/o (045) 481598
Stringer, P.			Mr N. Meade	c/o (046) 54197
Strudholme, R.	8	12		(01235) 764456
Sweeney D.F.,	7	7		(0378) 269618 (agent)
Teague, C.	8	4	Mr S. R. Bowring	c/o (01623) 822451
Tynan, F.	8	7	Mr G. B. Balding	c/o (01264) 772278
Wade, P.	8	0	Mr D. T. Hughes	c/o (045) 521490
West, Miss C.	8	0	Mrs J.R. Ramsden	(01845) 587226
Whelan, A. W. E.	8	3	Miss G. M. Kelleway	(01305) 257353
Wilkinson, Jason	8	5	Mr W. Muir	(01488) 73098
Williams, D.	7	3	Mr S.C.Williams	(01638)663984
Winston, R. F.	7	7	Mr R. Fahey	(01653) 628001
Worden, Miss Melanie,	7	10	Mr E. J. Alston	(01772) 612120
Wright, Miss N.	7	5	Mr H. Candy	c/o (01367) 820276
Young, D. L.	7	5	Mr L. Cumani	c/o (01638) 665432

Owners names are shown against their horses where this information is available. In the case of Partnerships and Syndicates, the nominated owner is given alongside the horse with other owners listed below the team.

N.H. JOCKEYS

Weights, Phone Numbers, Stables

* Jockeys shown with an asterisk hold a "conditional" licence or a claiming licence. They are entitled to claim 7lb until they have won 15 races; thereafter 5lb until they have won 30 races; thereafter 3lb until they have won 55 races.
†Restricted to Conditional Jockeys Races and National Hunt Flat Races only.

Ahern, M., 10-0 ....(01488) 73605
*Aizpuru, X., 9-7... (R. Dickin) (01789) 450052 and (01531) 631593 (agent)
*Aspell, L., 10-0... (J. Gifford) (01903) 893323 and (0468) 910522 (mobile)

*Bastiman, H., 9-7,. (R. Bastiman) (01423) 359397
*Batchelor, M., 9-7. (G. L. Moore) (01273) 620405 and (01273) 477120 (agent)
*Bates, A., 9-9, ...(G. B. Balding, W. Muir) (01264) 772278 and (01761) 453555 (agent) or (0831) 865974 (mobile)
*Bazin, G., 10-0. (M. J. Wilkinson) (01295) 750711
Bellamy, R. J., 10-0................ (J. C. McConnochie, J. C. Tuck, P. A. Pritchard) (01451) 810563 or (0836) 241458 or (01531) 631593 (agent)
Bentley, D. B., 9-7 .... (L. Plater, M. A. Peill, M. D. Hammond) (01989) 768974 and (01323) 509086 (agent)
Bentley, N. A., 9-11 ....(Miss S. Hall, G. M. Moore) (01969) 623054 or (0860) 199440 (mobile) and (01347) 810825 (agent)
*Berry, M., 10-0, ...(C. Brooks) (01488) 72077 and (01242) 700225 (agent)
*Brace, G., 9-7 ....(C. Brooks) (01488) 72077
Bradley, G. J., 10-2........... (C. Brooks, D. Elsworth) (01235) 751533 or mobile (0850) 350200 or agent (01337) 761369
*Brennan, M. A., 9-10..................... (J. G. O'Shea) (01527) 522480
Brennan, M. J., 10-0...(O. Brennan) (01636) 73878 or (0585) 884942 (mobile)
Bridgwater, D., 10-0, (J. L. Spearing, K. Bridgwater, G. M. McCourt) (01386) 584597 or (0831) 635817 (Mobile) and (01536) 485433 (agent)
Burchell, D. J., 10-0.. (D. Burchell) (01495) 302551 or (0836) 329290 (car)
Burke, J. H., 10-0 .... (D. Lamb) (0665) 720260
*Burke, R., 9-7 .... (J. R. Fowler (046 22361)
*Burns, R., 9-7.. (G. W. Richards) (01768) 892291 (agent) and (0374) 161202
Burrough, S., 10-2.......(G. Ham) (0860) 869374 or (01823) 324618 and (01784) 241126 (agent)
*Burrows, O. J., 9-9(J. Gifford) (01903) 261799 and (0468) 962913
Byrne, D. C., 10-0........ (Mrs M. Jones, F.J. Jordan) (01653) 600461 (home) or (0836) 278374 (agent)

Cahill, G., 9-7 ....(01287) 652000 and (01374) 161202 (agent)
*Callaghan, E. G., 9-10... (J. H. Johnson, B. Ellison, Mrs. J. Brown) (01653) 600461
Callaghan, J.G., 10-0 (G. M. Moore, C. W. Fairhurst) (01969) 622504 and (01751) 477142
Carberry, Paul, 10-0..... (F. Murphy, J. G. Fitzgerald, D. Todhunter, J. H. Johnson) (0181) 4715477 (agent) or (0836) 230335
Cash, B., 10-0 .... (A. L. Moore) (045) 876292
*Clarke, B. J., 10-0(F. T. J. Jordan) (01568) 760281
Clarke, M. J., 9-10.......................(01306) 631565
Clifford, B., 10-0 .... (G. B. Balding, A. Foster) (01984) 40239 and (0374) 620549 or (01235) 921250 agent (0860) 234342 (mobile)
Cooper L. P., 9-7..... (J. J. O'Neill) (01768) 484555
Cotter, C., 9-0........(D. T. Hughes, E. M. O'Sullivan) (045) 521490 and (0862) 316203 (mobile)
*Creech, D. P., 9-7........(G. Foster) (01488) 73765
Culloty, J., 9-7.............(Miss H. Knight, R. Dickin, J. C. Poulton, J. J. Sheehan) (01452) 760482 (agent)
*Cummings, L., 9-7(P. F. Nicholls) (01749) 860656
Curran, Sean, 9-12 (M. Muggeridge) (01488) 72222 and (0374) 146169 (mobile)
Cuthbert, Miss C., 9-0............... (T. A. K. Cuthbert) c/o (01228) 60822

Dascombe, T. G., 10-0.................(01636) 816719 and (01761) 453555 (agent) or (0831) 865974 (mobile)
Dicken, A., 10-6...............................(01372) 728781 or (01323) 509086
Dobbin, A., 10-0 ....(G. Richards, P. Monteith, F. Murtagh, B. Ellison, J. H. Johnson) (01768) 863495 (home) and (01768) 892291 (agent) or (0374) 161202
Donnelly, J., 10-0 ....(Capt. D. Swan) (0505) 42306
*Dowling W. J., 9-7..... (L. Lungo) (01387) 840361
*Dunne, M., 9-7, ...(01488) 72409
Dunwoody, T. R., 10-2.................(01367) 243111 or (0836) 502290 (car) and (01536) 485433 (agent)
*Durham, C., 9-10... (M. Pipe) c/o (01884) 840715
Dwan, W. J., 10-0 ....(R. Woodhouse, F. Kirby) (01653) 691539 and (01653) 697171

*Ede, A. C., 9-7 (M. D. Hammond) (01969) 640228 and (01768) 892291 (agent)
Eley, T., 10-0 .... (A. Streeter, Miss S. Wilton, T. Donnelly) (01283) 734083 and (mobile) (0411) 165106 and (01889) 568919
Elkins, R., 9-12 .... (G. Hubbard)
†Elsworth, D., 9-7 (Mrs S. J. Smith) (01274) 564930

Farrant, R., 10-0 .... (Mrs J. Pitman, P. G. Murphy, J. M. Bradley, B. Palling) (01367) 24480 (0850) 730733 (mobile)
Fenton, B., 10-0 .... (G. Balding, C. Barwell, J. R. Hughes) (01737) 761369 (agent) or (0860) 234342
*Finnegan, D., 9-7 ... (N. T. Chance) (01488) 73436
FitzGerald, M. A., 10-2 (N. Henderson, W. T. Casey, S. Gollings, G. F. Edwards, H. E. Haynes, J. G. O'Shea) (01367) 243208 or (0850) 742004 (mobile) or (01737) 761369 (agent)
*Fleming, L., 9-0 .... (F. Flood) (045) 403333
Flood, F. J. 9-9 .... (F. Flood) (045) 403136
Foster, M. R., 10-0 ..... (P. Haslam, C. W. Thornton, Mrs. A. M. Naughton, Miss L. V. Russell, F. Murphy) (01969) 624588 and (01525) 383633 (agent)
*Fowler, S., 10-2 .... (N. Babbage)
Fox, S., 10-0 (J. C. Fox, G. B. Balding, P. C. Ritchens) (01980) 670964 and (0468) 737575 (mobile)
Frost, J. D., 10-4 .... (R. Frost) (01364) 642267 or (01962) 772271 (agent)

Gallagher, D. T., 10-0 .... (M. Heaton-Ellis, D. Murray-Smith, C. Brooks, M. Blanshard, W. T. Casey, N. B. Mason, J. L. Harris) (01488) 73330 or (01337) 761369 (agent)
*Gallagher, G. R. P., 10-0 .... (J. E. Long) (01883) 348250
*Garritty, A. 9-7 .... (R. Rowe) (01903) 742871
Garritty, R. J., 10-4 .... (Mrs. L. Ramsden, M. D. Hammond, T. D. Easterby, T. Tate) (01653) 600221 or (01751) 477142 (agent)
Gaule, K. P., 9-7 ...... (G. Hubbard) (01440) 821133 and (0836) 618318 (agent)
*Goldstein, J., 9-7 .... (N. A. Twiston-Davies) (0370) 970759
*Graham, S., 9-7 .... (G. C. Roe) (01453)885487
*Grattan, B. D., 9-7 (P. Beaumont) (01347) 888208
*Greatrex, W. 9-7 .... (J. Gifford) (01903) 261799 and (0468) 218506 (mobile)
Greene, R. J., 10-0 .... (K. Bishop, D. C. Turner) (01323) 509086 (agent)
*Griffiths, M. J., 9-7.... (A. Turnell) (01235) 833297 and (01235) 763242 (agent) or (0585) 101540
Guest, R. C., 10-0... (Mrs S. J. Smith, N. B. Mason, J. P. Dodds) (01274) 564930 and (0830) 883303 (car) or (01932) 243913 (agent)

*Hagger, T.,9-7 . (N. Henderson) c/o (01488)72259 and ((01628) 770766 (agent) or (0378) 357905
*Hambidge, Miss K. R., 9-0 .... (M. Bradstock) (01235) 760780
*Handley, M. J., 9-7 (C.P. Morlock) (01367) 820510
*Hannity, N., 9-7 ... (G. M. Moore) (01969) 623823
Harding, B. P., 9-7 (G. W. Richards) (01768) 483912 (home) and (01768) 892291 (agent) or (0374) 161202
Harvey, L. J., 10-0 .... (A. Turnell, R. Brotherton, B. C. Morgan, J. Bennett, A. J. Chamberlain) (01235) 751608 or (0831) 399633 and (01225) 834059 (agent)
*Hearn, S., 9-7 . (Mrs. M. A. Jones) (01488) 73135
*Henley, P., 10-0..... (J. S. Moore) (01488) 648822 and (01737) 761369 (agent) or (0860) 234342
*Herrington, M., 9-7 .... (Mrs M. Reveley) (01287) 654243
Hide, P. E., 10-0 .... (J. Gifford, S. P. Woods) (01903) 877323 or (0468) 233324
*Hobson, R., 9-7 ..... (G. McCourt) (01235) 764456
*Hodges, R. J., 9-9 (F. T. J. Jordan) (01287) 610955 or (01751) 477142 (agent)
*Hogan, G., 9-12 .... (D. Nicholson, Miss E. M. Rowland, J. R. Hughes, Mrs. A. M. Woodrow, A P Jones) (01367) 242866 or (01386) 584209 and (01737) 761369 (agent)
*Hogg, T., 10-0 ..... (G. M. Moore) (01969) 623823
Holley, P., 10-0 ...... (D. Elsworth) (01725) 518271 and (0860) 483083 (mobile) or (01761) 453555 (agent) and (0831) 865974 (mobile)
*Honour, C. E., 9-7 .. (O. Sherwood) (01488) 71411
*Horrocks, N., 9-7 .... (M. D. Hammond) (01969) 640228 and (01768) 892291 (agent)
Hourigan, M., 9-7 .... (0932) 243913 (0860) 234342 (agent)
*Huet, J., 9-7 .... (M. Pipe) c/o (01884) 840715
Hughes, R., 10-0 .... (01638) 561450
*Husband, E., 9-10 .... (I. Williams, P. Hiatt) (01564) 822392 and ((01623) 661730 (agent) or (0973) 601881

Irvine, A. J., 9-10 .... (Miss Z. C. Davison) (01883) 331114

*Jardine, I., 9-7 .... (P. Monteith) (0131) 4402309 and (01524) 792854 (agent)
Jenks, T. P., 10-0 .... (W. Jenks, P. R. Chamings, D. McCain, N. Twiston-Davies) (01451) 870686 and (01628) 770766 or (0378) 357905 (mobile)
*Jewett, D. J., 9-6 ... (J. J. O'Neill) (01768) 484555
Johnson, K., 10-0 .... (S. Bell) (01388) 721813 or (0374) 131121 (mobile)
Johnson, R., 10-0 .... (D. Nicholson, S. E. Kettlewell, N. T. Chance, Mrs S. Johnson, T. George, R. Lee) (0452) 760482 and (01737) 761369 (agent)

*Kavanagh, D. J., 9-7 . (T. George) (01452) 814267 and (01235) 821250 (agent) and (0831) 547233
Kavanagh, J. R., 10-0 .... (N. Henderson, Mrs. L. C. Jewell, C. Morlock) (01367) 243968 or (0831) 376837 or (0860) 234342 or (01932) 243913 (agent)
*Keenan, J., 9-7 ...... (J. S. Moore) (01488) 648822
*Keighley, M. H., 9-7 .... (N. Twiston-Davies) (01451) 850278
*Kelly. K., 9-0 .... (D. T. Hughes) (045) 521490

*Kelly, S. P. 9-7 .... (Miss V. M. Williams) c/o (01432) 840646
*Keniry, F., 9-7......(G. B. Balding) (01264) 772278
Kent, T. J., 10-0 ....(01638) 721811 or (01638) 560634 and (01440) 821133 (agent)

Lawrence, I. R., 9-7(M. R. Bosley) (01635) 201554 (0836) 211479 (mobile)
Leahy, D., 10-0... (Mrs L. C. Jewell) (0831) 323736 or (01367) 820214 (agent)
*Leahy, F. T., 9-7 .... (J. Fitzgerald, M. Meagher) (01751) 477148
*Lee, G. M., 9-7 ....(Mrs M. Reveley) (01751) 77142 (agent)
Leech, J. P., 10-0.......... (R. Curtis) (01488) 73763 and (01488) 73007 (office)
Llewellyn, C., 10-0.................... (N. Twiston-Davies, R. Brotherton, W. Brisbourne, N. Gaselee, B. De Haan, B. Smart, B. J. McMath, J. Old) (0836) 783223 (mobile) or (01934) 641658 agent
Long, Miss Leesa, 9-7 .... (Mrs M. Long) (01273) 621346
Lower, J. A., 10-4 .... (M. Pipe) Wellington (01823) 473580
*Lynn, N. R., 9-7(S. A. Brookshaw) (01743) 709227
Lyons, G., 10-2 ....(Miss M. Rowland, R. T. Juckes, B. P. Baugh, R. Hollinshead) (01543) 876740 or (0831) 330265 (mobile)

*Magee, J., 9-11 ......(C. Mann) c/o (01488) 73118 and (01628) 770766 (agent) or (0370) 262686
Maguire, A., 10-0... (D. Nicholson) (01737) 761369 and (01737) 768821 or (0860) 234342 (agent)
Marston, W. J., 10-0....(L. P. Grassick, Mrs. P. Sly, Mrs V. McKie) (01451) 821553 or (0831) 664745 (agent)
*Massey, R. I., 9-11(D. Nicholson, R. C. Brazington, W. Brisbourne, K. A. Morgan) (01386) 584 209/219 and (01235) 821250 (agent)
Maude, C. G., 10-0(S. Earle, W. G. McKenzie-Coles, N. A. Twiston-Davies) (01386) 854841 or (0831) 094601 or (01793) 870606 (agent)
McCarthy, J. A., 10-0..... (O. Sherwood, C. Egerton, P. R. Webber, A. H. Harvey, D. Marks) (01488) 73139 (agent) or (0860) 905017
*McCormack, C., 9-7...(M. Todhunter, W. T. Kemp, B. Ellison, J. C. Haynes) (01287) 652000
McCoy, A. P., 10-0........(M. Pipe) (01264) 772278 and (01737) 761369 (agent)
*McDermott, J., 10-0(R. Buckler) (01308) 488 502
McDougall, S. J., 10-0 ....(01361) 850242 and (0378) 700924 (mobile)
*McGann, B., 9-7 ......(I. Williams) (01564) 822392 or (01242) 700225 (agent)
*McGovern, S., 9-5..(M. Cunningham) (046) 24281
*McGrath, R., 9-7......... (J. J. O'Neill, W. T. Kemp, J. S. Goldie) (01768) 454555
McLaughlin, J. F. S., 10-0....................... (R. Harris) (01638) 668115
McLoughlin, P. J., 9-7................(Mrs A. Woodrow) (01737) 761369 (agent) or (01296) 622058

McNeill, S. R., 10-0 ....(C. Brooks, A. P. Jones, A. Turnell, L. G. Cottrell, J. C. McConnochie, J. C. Tuck, D. Ffrench-Davis, Mrs S. D. Williams) (01488) 648861 or (0831) 107468
*Melrose, S., 9-7...........(R. Allan) (01890) 820581
*Midgley, P. T., 10-4 .... (M. W. Easterby, J. S. Wainwright, Miss M. Rowland, G. P. Kelly) (01347) 878368 and (0860) 233041 (agent)
Mitchell, Miss S., 9-7 .. (D. Gandolfo, N. R. Mitchell, W. G. Mckenzie-Coles, Mrs. L. C. Jewell, A. K. Barrow) (01672) 5408631 and (0468) 122587 (mobile)
*Moffatt, D. J., 10-4 .... (D. Moffatt, G. M. McCourt) (01539) 536689 or (0467) 367282 (mobile)
*Mogford, J., 9-7.....................(Capt. T. A. Forster) (01584) 875036
Moloney, M. J., 10-0 .... (J. Berry, J. Birkett) (01768) 892291
†Mooney, M. F.,9-7, ...(Mrs. D. Haine) (01638) 665514
Morris, Derrick, 10-0... (D. Morris) (01372) 725592
*Mortimer, T. J. 9-7.......................(K. S. Bridgwater) (01564) 782895
*Moulson, L., 9-1 ......(01403) 700766 and 700911
*Murphy, T. C., 9-10 ....(N. Henderson) c/o (01488) 72259
Murphy, T. J., 9-7...........................(P. F. Nicholls) (01235) 821250 and (0831) 547233

*Naughton, M. H.(Mrs M. Reveley) (01287) 654243
*Newton, M. J., 9-7.................(L. R. Lloyd-James) c/o (01653) 698568
Niven, P., 10-4 (Mrs G. R. Reveley, Miss L. Perratt, D. Todhunter, Miss J. C. Camacho, S. E. Kettlewell) (01751) 477142 (agent) or (0860) 260999 (car)

*O'Connor, T. A., 9-7 (R. G. Frost) (01364) 642267
O'Dwyer, C. 10-0.................................(A. L. Moore, M. Morris) (0188555) 692
O'Hara, L., 10-0 (Miss L. Perratt, Mrs. D. Thomson, J. Birkett) (01759) 371586 (agent) or (0860) 596031 (mobile) and (01228) 512318
*O'Shea, S. M., 9-7 ....(N. M. Babbage) (01242) 242699
*Oliver, H. J., 9-7 .... (O O'Neill) (01242) 673275 and 676194
Osborne, J. A., 10-0 ...... (O. Sherwood, P. Mitchell, I. Balding, C. Egerton) (01488) 73139 or (0860) 533422 (car)
O'Sullivan, D. K., 10-4........ (K. Cunningham-Brown, R. Rowe) (01736) 793224 or (0374) 725718 (mobile) or (01903) 742871 (agent)
*O'Sullivan, D. W., 9-7...... (A. Moore) (045) 76292

†Painter, D., 9-7 (M. J. Wilkinson) (01295) 750711
Parker, D., 10-0........ (C. Parker, Mrs. D. Thomson, B. Ellison, J. C. Haynes, R. W. Thomson, R. McKellar) (01576) 510232
Pears, O., 10-0.................................(0850) 514068
*Parkhouse, J., 9-9.................................. (R. Curtis) (01488) 73007 (office)

†Pierrot, Miss Claire., 9-7 ....(J. Upson) (01327) 860043
*Pike, I. W., 9-7 ....(R. Lee) (01544) 267672
†Pitcher, L., 9-7.................... (J. S. King, J. Neville) (01633) 680978
Porritt, S., 9-7................................(01969) 473950
Powell, B. G., 9-7(R. Buckler, A. K. Barrow, D. Carey, A. Chamberlain, M. Heaton-Ellis, A. M. Campion, B. Meehan, S. Earle, Mrs. A. J. Bowlby, J. C. De Berry, G. Thorner, R. Dickin) (01793) 782286 or (0860) 314745 and (01793) 522359 (agent)
*Power, J. G., 9-7 ......(W. Turner) (01963) 220523
*Prior, J., 10-0 ....(D. Burchell) (01495) 302551
Procter, A. R., 9-7 ....(0454) 250814 and (0831) 865974 (agent)

*Rae, C., 9-7.............. (A. Turnell) (01235) 833297 (01793) 870606 (agent)
*Rafter, C., 9-7.............(C. Brooks) (01488) 72077

Ranger, M., 10-0 .... (C. Smith) (01526) 833245
Reed, W. T., 10-6 .... (W. G. Reed, M. Dods, J. Glover) (01347) 810825 and (01434) 344016 (agent)
*Reid, D., 9-7. (Miss L.V. Russell) (01577) 862482 or (0467) 872723 and (01382) 477334
Richards, M. R., 10-0 ....(O. Sherwood, Mrs L. Richards, W. Muir, P. Hedger, Miss B. Sanders) (01243) 574882 or (0973) 198435 (mobile)
Roche, A., 9-12....... (J. J. O'Neill) (01768) 484555
*Rossiter, N., ...(01440) 821133 and (0836) 618318 (agent)
*Ryan, G. F. 9-9 (Mrs S. J. Smith) (01274) 564930
Ryan, J. B. 10-0...............................(01932) 243913 or (0860) 234342 (agent) and (04100) 39925
*Ryan, S., 9-7 ....(T. D. Easterby)

*Salter, D., 9-9......... (B. Millman) (01823) 681054 or (01884) 266620 agent
*Scales, M. N., 9-7..(N. T. Chance) (01488) 73436
*Scholes, A. P., 9-7........................(J. G. O'Shea) c/o (01594) 516201
*Shenkin, g., 9-10 .. (A. G. Hobbs) (01548) 550553
Sharratt, M., 10-0 .... (N. A. Smith) (01905) 616350 and (0973) 669067 (mobile)
Shortt, J., 10-0 .... (Mrs. J. Harrington) (045) 85336 or (088) 530672
*Siddall, T., 9-7 .... (Miss L. Siddall, J. Hetherton) (01977) 557167
*Slattery, D. M.,9-13 .... (Miss K. George)
Slattery, J. V., 10-0..........(O. O'Neill, G. H. Yardley, R. J. Baker) (01242) 820907 or (0831) 545789
Smith, A. S., 10-0.................(K. Morgan, J. Glover, J. H. Johnson, W. Bethell, D. Shaw) (0166478) 711/488 or (0831) 272910
Smith, C. N., 10-0.... (Mrs G. R. Reveley, T. J. Carr, S. Bell) (01287) 639312
*Smith, M., 9-7 (J. G. O'Shea) c/o (01594) 516201
Smith, V., 10-0 ....(01638) 668972 or (0860) 386108 (mobile)

Stokell, Miss Ann., 9-7................. (M. Barraclough) (092684) 3332
Storey, B., 10-0 ...... (F. Storey, Mrs. A. Goodfellow, C. Parker, J. Charlton, D. M. Forster, J. K. Oliver, D. Nolan, R. W. Thomson, M. A. Barnes) (01228) 75376 or (0860) 432881 (mobile)
*Supple, G., 9-7 ....(M. Pipe, S. N. Cole, B. Scriven, K. Bishop) c/o (01884) 840715 and (0467) 790947
Supple, J. A., 9-11..................(Mrs. A. Swinbank, Mrs A. Naughton) (01325) 718173 and (0374) 699540 (agent)
Supple, R. J., 9-7 ....(J. Upson, P. Beaumont, F. Murtagh, T. J. Etherington, N. Bycroft, Miss A. Stokell) (01628) 770766 (agent) (01845) 578883 and (0850) 120134 (mobile)
*Suthern, L., 9-7..................(N. A. Twiston-Davies) (01386) 858279
Swan, C. F. 9-7........(Capt. D. Swan) (0505) 42410 or (088) 573194

*Taylor, S. D., 9-7 ....(J. Wade, J. S. Goldie, R. E. Barr) (01768) 881152
*Thomas, D., 9-07................ (Mrs. J. R. Ramsden)
Thorner, Miss C., 9-10 .... (G. Thorner) (01235) 763003
Thornton, A. R., 10-3....... (P. R. Webber, K. Bailey, Miss L. V. Russell, T. J. Etherington, R. Alner, G. F. Johnson-Houghton, J. C. McConnochie, J. C. Poulton, R. Dickin) (01488) 73155 or (0831) 102065 (mobile)
*Thornton, R. A., 10-0 ....(D. Nicholson, G. A. Ham, S. Gollings, H. E. Haynes) (01386) 584209 and (01737) 761369 (agent) or (0860) 234342
Titley, J. F., 10-0 ....(Miss H. C. Knight, Mrs. D. Haine) (01367) 243968 and (0802) 212978
*Todd, A. W., 9-0. (R. Thompson) (01302) 845904
Tormey, G., 10-0 ....(P. J. Hobbs, J. C. De Berry, Miss A. Stokell) (01452) 760482 (agent)
Treacy, T. P. 9-7............ (P. Mullins) (0503) 75121 and (087) 505298 (mobile)
*Turner, D. I., 9-7 ....(J. Mullins)

Upton, Guy, 10-2 .... (B. Meehan, A. P. Jones) (01488) 681853 or (0385) 307872 (car) or (01225) 834059 (agent)

†Vicarey, D., 9-10.......................(Miss S. J. Wilton) (01782) 550861
†Vickers, L.J., 9-7 ....(N. Henderson) c/o (01488) 72259
Verco, D. I., 10-0...........................(G. Woodward) (01203) 317150 and (0966) 396874

*Webb, C. 9-9 ....(S. Mellor, R. E. Peacock) (01242) 251697 and (0973) 911294 or (01793) 522359 (agent)
*Webb, D., 9-7..............................(01287) 652000
*Wilkinson, R. D. J., 10-0 .... (Mrs S. Smith) (01274) 564930

Williamson, N., 10-0 .... (K. Bailey, C. Egerton, Miss V. M. Williams) (01488) 648437 or (0831) 343434 (mobile) or (01737) 761369 (agent)
*Wilmington, N., 9-7 (R. Alner) c/o (01258) 817271
Worthington, W. M., 10-0............ (M. C. Chapman, R. F. Marvin) (01455) 619206 or (0673) 843663

Wyer, L. A., 10-0......... (T. D. Easterby, J. J. Quinn, R. Fahey, T. J. Etherington) (01653) 628877 or (0831) 218288 (mobile) or (01751) 477142 (agent)
Wynne, S., 10-0...................... (Capt. T. A. Forster, J. C. McConnochie, W. M. Brisbourne) (01584) 872834 and (0468) 113062 (mobile)

AMATEUR RIDERS

Riding weights and telephone numbers.

Alers-Hankey, D., 10-0, ... c/o (01285) 861347
Allen, Miss L. 9-7, ... c/o (01733) 211575
Allison, Miss J. K., 9-5, ... (01488) 73656
or (01488) 73636
Appleby, M., 10-7, ... (01488) 73007 (office)
Armson, R. J., 10-7, ... (01332) 865293
or (0468) 996072 (moible)
Armytage, M. D., 10-3, ... (01367) 87637
or (0860) 507447 (car)

Babington, E., 9-7, ... (01264) 772278
or (01264) 771298
Balding, A., 11-0, ... (01264) 772278
and (01635) 298210
Barlow, T. D. B., 11-0, ...(01270) 524057
Barraclough, Miss S., 9-7, ... (071) 3818829
or (0831) 576806
Barrett, R., 9-4, ... (01733) 893453
and (0589) 163191 (mobile) or (01638) 660605
Barry, T. J., 10-7, ... (01748) 822803
Bastiman, Miss R., 9-7, ... (01423) 359397
Beedles, A., 10-0, ...(01672) 514428
Billinge, J. N. R., 11-7, ...(01344) 655180
Blackwell, S., 10-00, ...(01495) 302551
Blyth, R., ...(0181) 6806814
Bonner, C., 9-7, ... c/o (01969) 624238
and (0498) 674496 (mobile)
Bosley, Miss Sarah Jane, 9-0, ... (01367) 820115
or (0378) 938040 (mobile) and (0367) 242224
Bradburne, Miss Lorna, 9-4, ...(01337) 810325
and (0468) 216941 (mobile)
Bradburne, M., 10-2,....................(01337) 810325
and (0370) 624268 (mobile)
Breward, P., 9-7, ... (0113) 2892265
Bridger, D., 10-0, ... c/o (01428) 722528
Bridger, Miss Madeleine, 9-0, c/o (01428) 722528
Brookshaw, Miss Heidi, 9-6, ... (01743) 709227
Brown, A., 9-7, ... (01327) 860654
Brown, Miss M. J., 8-12, ... c/o (01743) 741536
Buckley, R., 10-0, ...(01372) 273729
Burke, P. J., ... 018259310
Burkett, Miss Z., 9-7, ...
Burnell, W., 10-0, ...(01423) 359175
Burton, R. 10-0, ...c/o (01451) 822431
Butler, Mrs E. L., 8-7, ...(01273) 477254
Byrne, E., 9-7, ... c/o (01488) 71483
Byrne J. P., 9-0, ... c/o (045) 403206

Cahill, Mrs S. M., 7-12, ... (0483) 38297
Cambidge, J. R., 10-0, ... c/o (0195276) 249
Carrol, M., ... (0191) 3736277
Carson, Melanie, 8-5, ... (01388) 603317
Carter, Miss D., 9-0, ... c/o (01698) 381829
Chapman, N., 10-0, ... (01673) 843663
Charles-Jones, A. S., 10-0, ... (01993) 823265
Clark, R., 10-7, ...(01347) 810700
Clark, Miss R. A., 9-10, ... (01347) 810700
or car (0850) 837123
Close, P. L., 8-12, ... (01638) 730480
Collins, Miss Tracey, ... (045) 41239
Colville, Miss S., ... (0181) 6806814
Comerford, S. J.,9-0, ... c/o (01844)3520904
Comerford, T. J., 9-7, ... (01287) 652000
Coogan, V. L., 10-2, ... (01353) 721673
Coombe, Miss M. S., 9-0, ... (01305) 782218
and (01305) 761745
Coonan, R.F., 10-0, ... (01488) 73436
Cooper, R. F.,10-0, ... c/o (01844)3520904
Cowdrey, Mrs Maxine, 8-10, ... (01903) 871367
or (01903) 871460
Crowley, F., ... (051) 375726
Crowley, J., 9-0, ... (01935)840003
Cuff. T., 10-0, ...(01372) 361929
Cunningham, Miss Tara, 9-0, ... (046) 31672
Cuthbert, Miss Helen, 9-0, ... (01228) 560822

Dalton, A. N., 10-12, ... (0195 271) 656
and (01989) 62250
Darby, J., 10-2, ... (01372) 377209
Davidson, J. T., 9-7, ... (01576) 510232
Deburiatte, Miss S. T., 9-0, ... (01672) 541484
Delahunt, J., 10-10, ... (01292) 266232
Dempsey, A., 10-0, ... (045) 521490
and (0882) 728835 (mobile)
Deniel, Miss A. J., 9-7, ... (01653) 600461
or (01653) 618594
Dennis, T., 10-5, ...(01288) 352849
Dennis, D., 10-3, ... (01288) 352849
Dewhurst, J., 10-0, ... (01734) 451222
Diment, J. B., 9-7, ... (01235) 833297
and (01235) 812095 (home)
Dolan, B., 9-10, ... c/o (045) 403206
Donnelly, G., 10-4, ... (045) 76292
Doumen, T., 9-0, ... (00 33) 44214501
Doyle, Miss E., 9-4, ... (01969) 622289
Duckett, Miss Sally, 9-7, ... (0531) 890644
Dudley, Anne, 8-9, ... (01993) 878551
and (01993) 878279
Dunbar, C., 10-7, ... (01555) 892356
Dunwoody, Mrs C., 8-7, ... (01235) 59287
Durack, S., 9-7, ... (01984) 640435
and (01488) 638636
Durman, Miss S. J., 8-7, ... (01264) 850218
Dyson, Miss C., 9-7, ... (01653) 793459

Ellis, Miss K., 8-7, ... (03643) 457
Elliot, G., 9-9, ... c/o (01884) 840715
Ellwood, O., 10-0, ... (01276) 61179
Elsey, Miss A. F., 8-12,, ... (01653) 693149
Embiricos, Miss A. E., 10-6, ... (01638) 660048

Enright, Mrs M., 8-7, ... (01273) 479183
Ephgrave, H., (01481) 63412 and (0449) 81163412
Evans, A., 10-0, ... (01938) 570288
Evans, Miss C., ... (01789) 205277

Farrant, A., 10-12, ... (098987) 343
Fearon, W., 9-0, ... c/o (01347) 888641
Feilden, Miss J., 8-7, ... (01638) 577470
Fenton, P., 10-0, ... (052) 56156
Findlay, S., 9-7, ... (01273) 693049
Fitzgerald, Martin, ... (01594) 516201
Fitzgerald, M. P., 10-0, ... (063) 90676
Flynn, P., 9-7, ... (01984) 640419
Flynn, Miss R. E., 9-9, ... c/o 01638) 661508
Folkes, Miss Emma, 8-7, ... (01488) 73605
and (0410) 855227 (mobile)
Foustok, Miss I., 8-2, ... c/o (01638) 668503
Ford, Mrs Carrie, 9-0, ... (01829) 760095
and (0421) 623905
Ford, Richard 10-7, ... (01829) 760095
or (0421) 623905
Forristal, R., 9-7, ... c/o (01488) 71483
Forster, Miss Sandra, 10-0, ... (01450) 870281
Foster, B., 10-2, ... (01664) 464711
Foustok, Miss Iky, 8-4, ... (01638) 570211
or (0973) 855778
Frith, M., 9-10, ... (0385) 565301

Galpin, Mrs J., 9-0, ... (01398) 351333
Garley, Miss E., 9-0, ... (01296) 655255
Gatehouse, Miss E. B., 9-0, ... (01572) 737586
(evenings) (01572) 822399
Gee, M. P., 10-0, ... (01909) 731101
Gibson, B. S., 9-7, ... (01387) 840361
Gibson, Miss Gisella., 9-7, ... (01403) 700766
and 700911
Gingell, M. J., 10-7, ... (01223) 441418
Goble, K., 9-0, ... (01372) 271526
Gollins, Mrs. J. M., 9-0, ... (01507) 343204
Grant, B., 10-0, ... (01296) 655255
Grassick, J. R., 9-7, ... (01242) 603124
and (0976) 779623 (mobile)
Green, K., 10-0, ... (01653) 658349
Guest, R. B., 9-0, ... (0468) 978766

Haigh, Miss V., 9-0, ... (01302) 852396
Hale, R. A., 9-7, ... (01768) 892291
Hand, Miss A., 10-0, ... (01822) 820512
Hammond, Mrs. A. J., 8-12, ... (01969) 640228
Hannaford, Miss C., 9-7, (01903) 893031
Harding, Hon. Miss D., 9-7, ... (0171) 3794787
and (0836) 762403 (mobile)
Harford, G. J., 10-3, ... c/o(046) 34102/31672
Harney, D., 10-7, ... (01235) 764456
Harrison, Miss J., 9-0, ... (01476) 860090
Hartrey, M. T., ... (051) 375726
Hayden, M., ... (045) 897438
Haynes, Miss F., 9-5, ... (01793) 762437
or (0831) 400395 (car)
Haynes, Miss Y., 9-4, ... (01372) 722664
Henderson, Mrs R. G., 10-0, ... (01837) 52914
Henderson, W. J., 10-0, ... (01837) 52914
Hennessy, S. P., 10-0, ... (062) 54129

Higgins Miss S., 8-12, ... (01488) 638433
or (01562) 851497
Hills, C. B., 9-7, ... (01488)71548
Holdsworth, A., 9-7, ... (01364) 642267
Howe, S., 9-10, ... (01388) 834636
Hutsby, F., 10-0, ... c/o (01386) 584209/219

Ingram, Mrs. S., 9-7, ... (01372) 748505

Jacobs, A., 9-7, ... (01638) 660048
James, Miss E., 9-7, ... (1885) 483535
James, E. L., 10-0, ... (01488) 72637
Jefford, L., 10-0, ... (01884) 35839
Johnson, Peter, 10-9, ... (0191) 2674464
Johnson-Houghton, Miss E. A., 9-7, (01488) 73144
Jones, Diana Jane, 9-0, ... (01691) 648559
and (01440) 820342
Jones, Miss E., 8-9, ... (01495) 302551
and (01823) 665156 or (01685) 843467
Jones, Miss I. D. W., 9-3, ... (01691) 659720
Jones, Miss K., 9-7, ... c/o (01749) 841011
Juckes, J., 10-0, ... (01388) 834636

Kauntze, Miss S., 9-3, ... (010) 3538350440
or (010) 3536607121
Kelleway, Miss S., 8-0, ... (01638) 664292
Kendal, Miss B., 9-7, ... (01524) 791179
and (01524) 792854 (agent)
or (0467) 677948 (mobile)
Kendellen, B.,9-7, ... (01488) 72409
Kelly, P. M., ... (045) 521106
Kerswell, Miss S., 9-9, ... (017684) 84555
Keswick, M., 9-7, ...(0190) 468337
Keuthen, Miss M.,9-0, ... (01845) 587435
Kimber, Dr. A., 10-0, ... c/o (01844)3520904
Kinane, A., 9-7, ... c/o (01903) 742871
Kinnane, B., 10-0, ... (062) 54129

Lake, G., 9-0, (01829) 720352 and (0836) 780879
Lamb, Miss S., 9-7, ... (01665) 720251
and (0385) 220724 (mobile)
Latham, R., 10-0, ... (01635) 281745
Lawrence, J., 9-7, ... (01273) 890124
Le Brocq, Mrs J., 8-7, ... (01534) 481461
Lightbody, M., ...(01292) 266232
Llewellyn, J. L., 10-5, ... (01685) 841259
or (01685) 844827
Long, Miss Leesa, 9-7, ... (01273) 890244
Lukaniuk, V., 9-0, ... (01842) 812340
Macintosh, Miss Lois, 8-7, ... (01273) 477124
Mackley, M., 10-4, ... (01949) 842293
and (01242) 700225 (agent)
Mancini, M. W., 10-0, ... (01789) 415607
Mannish, M., 9-7, ... (0181) 340 5315
Marchioness of Blandford, 9-5, ... (01608) 677558
Markham, G., 10-0, ... (01969) 623823
Marks, Miss A. K., 9-7, ... (01488) 71767
Marshall, Miss V., 8-5, ... (01488) 71632
or (0374) 946120
McAllister, P. M., 9-7, ... (01279) 461546 (work)
and (01279) 757154 (home)
McCabe, Miss A., 9-0, ... (01488) 73436
McEntee, C., 9-10, ... (01638) 663512

McHale, Mrs D., 8-8, ... (01264) 850854
McKenzie-Ross, R., 9-7, ... (01403) 700911
McPhail, O., 9-7, ... c/o (01386) 584209/219
and (01452) 760482 (agent)
Mitchell, Miss H. 8-12, ... (01372) 273729
Mitchell, N., 11-3, ... (01300) 348739
Mongan, I., 8-4, ... (01273) 620405
Moore, Miss A., 10-0, ... c/o (045)76292
Moore, Mrs Jayne, 8-0, ... (01273) 620106
Moore, J. D., 10-0, ... c/o (01258) 817271
Moore, Miss K., 8-7, ... (01476) 860090
Moore, Mrs. S. J., 8-0, ... (01488) 648822
Moran, N., 10-0, ... (01725) 518889
Morris, Mrs M., 9-0, ... (01623) 822714
Morshead, Mrs A. L., 8-12, ... (01347) 888273
(01347) 888208
Moscrop, G.R., 10-7, ... (0191) 2362145
Mulhall, C. A., 10-2, ... (01904) 691510
and (0589) 809395
Mullins, T., 10-11, (0503) 75121 and (088) 555531
Mullins, W. P., 11-0, ... (0503) 21786
and (088) 564940
Murphy, P., 10-0, ... (01969) 622038

Naylor, Dr J. R. J., 10-7, ... c/o (01980) 621059
Newey-Vincent, Miss S., 9-7, ... (01264) 772278

Olding, Miss D., 10-4, ... (01388) 834636
Olivefalk, Miss M. L., 9-7, ... (0505) 42306
O'Meara, J., 9-0, ... (0505) 42221
O'Ryan, K. R., 10-0, ... (01488) 73118
and (01628) 770766 (agent) or (0370) 262686
O'Sullivan William, 10-7, ... (022) 47116
O'Sullivan, Brendan, 10-7, ... (022) 47116
O'Sullivan, Miss Fiona, 9-7, ... (022) 47116
O'Sullivan, Miss M., ... (01488) 71703
Orde-Powlett, Harry A. N., 10-0, .. (01969) 623679
Orde-Powlett, W. Ben, 10-0, ... (01969) 623679
Owen, J., 9-7, ... c/o (01844)3520904

Page, D., 10-0, ... (01403) 700766 and 700911
Parker, A., 10-0, ... (01576) 300238
or (01576) 5105232
Peacock, Mrs C., 9-4, ... (01952) 728037
or (01666) 577238
Pearce, Lydia., 8-7, ... (01638) 664669
Perrett, Mrs A., 9-3, ... (01798) 874894
(0410) 075970 (mobile)
Phillips, P., 10-5, ... (01488)638620
Phizachlea, Miss S., 8-7, ... (01827) 830376
Pope, Miss I., 9-7, ...
Potts, Miss S., 10-4, ... (01782) 721636
Poulton, Mrs C., 9-7, ... (01273) 302486
Preston, Miss L., 10-0, ... (01325) 718173
Price, Mrs. C. J., 8-9, ... (01963) 220523
Prior, S., 10-7, ... (01829) 271522
Pritchard, J., 10-12, ... (01926) 632391
or (0531) 634461
Pritchard, Dr P. L. J., 9-11, ... (01453) 811989
Purdy, Miss A. J., 9-2, ... (0797) 0803706
or (01823) 451632

Ramsden, Miss E., 8-7, ... c/o (01845) 587226
Rees, Mrs G., 8-10, ... (01772) 812780
Rees, J., 9-10, ... (01235) 833297
and (01235) 821518
Richards, G., 9-0, ... (01495) 302638
Richards, Miss N.,8-7, ... (01633) 680978
Rimell, M., 10-7, ... (01451) 30417
Roberts, Miss V., 9-7, ... (01242) 700225 (agent)
Robinson, D. T., 9-7, ... (01507) 363525
Robinson, Major S., ... c/o (01980) 626344
Robson, A. W., 10-9, ... (01668) 213416
Robson, Miss P, 9-0, ... (01830) 530241

Samworth, Miss S., 8-10, ... (01235) 751507
Sansome, A. D., 10-12, ... (01327) 262918
Santana, K., 9-2, ... (0181) 6516482
and (0374) 495515 or (01638) 561844
Saunders, B., ... (01949) 60671
Saunders, Mrs J. A., 9-0, ... (060124) 739
Saville, J. M., 10-0, ... (01274) 564930
Scott, P., 10-4, ... (01295) 758218
or (01295) 750226
Sharratt, Miss S., 10-2, ... (01543) 490197
Shaw, D. B., 9-7, ... (01829)760762
Shiels, R., 11-4, ... (01835) 854060
Spearing, Miss C. M., 9-0, ... (01789) 772639
Spearing, Miss T. S., 9-0, ... (01789) 772639
Stack, J. A., 9-10, ... (062) 54129
Stephens, Miss V. A., 9-7, ... (01984) 667427
Stokell, Miss A., 9-7, ... (01926) 842464
Storey, C., 10-2, ... (069 77) 3810
Stringer, Mrs. A., 9-0, ...
Sunderland, Mrs. K., 8-7, ... (01295) 758686
Swan, Miss N., 9-7, ... (0505) 42457
Swiers, S. J., 10-7, ... (01423) 324155
Swindlehurst, D., 10-4, ... (01228) 74376
and (01228) 74289
Sykes, Miss A. 9-7, ... (01588) 638451
and (01989) 730314

Tizzard, J.C. L., 10-0, ... (0976) 778657
and (01805) 623156 or (01749) 860656
Townsley, Miss C., 9-0, ... (01483) 200849
or (0836) 205579 (mobile)
Townsley, Miss L., 10-0, ... (01483) 200849
Townsley, P., 11-0, ... (01483) 200849
Townson, J. G., 10-10, ... (01638) 660696
and (0374) 824308) (mobile)
Tyler-Morris, J., 8-12, ... (01902) 688558

Usher, Mrs A., 7-7, ... (01793) 791115

Verdon, T., 9-10, ... (01534) 483296
Vigors, C., 10-10, ... (01488) 72561
and (01638) 665146 or (0402) 106220 (mobile)
Vollaro, Miss Lucy, 8-7, ...

Waggot, N. Jnr., 11-0, ... (01388) 819012
Waggot, Miss T., 9-7, ... (01388) 819012
Wakley, R., 9-12, ... (01488) 648603
Wall, Breeda, 8-0, ... (045) 521490
Walton, A., 9-7, ... (01400) 251152
and (0589) 609654
Waters, T., 10-0, ... (01634) 668088

Watson, C., 8-11, ... (01455) 274609
Weatherley, G., 10-0, (01903) 872226 or 741796
Webster, Miss H., 8-7, (01638) 668115 or 661999
Wells, Miss A., 8-7, ...
Wenyon, w., 9-12, ... (01759) 373007
Wharf, P. Wharf., 9-7, ... (01565) 777275
Wheate, K., 9-7, ... (01308) 488210
Whitaker, S. R., 11-7, ... (0113) 2892341
White, R., 10-10, ... (01984) 640532
White, Miss S., 9-7, ... (01621) 742161
and (0850) 209368
Widger, R., 10-7, ... (01984) 640419
Williams, Mrs. C., 9-0, ... (01969) 623271
Wilson, C. R., 10-12, ... (01325) 374595
Wintle, A., 10-7, ... (01452) 760377
and (01452) 760482 (agent)
Woods, Mrs. L. J., 9-0, ... (01638) 662063
Wormall, Miss J., 9-0, ... (01530) 260224
Wright, Miss S., 9-0, ... (01623) 794831
Wylie, R., 10-0, , ...

Yardley, Miss A., 8-0, ... (01905) 830245
Young, J., 10-7, ... (01548) 550805

If an entry is incorrect or has been omitted, please notify the editor by January 8th, 1999.

This will ensure it appears correctly in the 1999 edition.

RACECOURSES OF GREAT BRITAIN

AINTREE (N.H)

(Grand National Course) - Triangular, 2m 2f (16) 494y run-in with elbow. Perfectly flat. A severe test for both horse and rider, putting a premium on jumping ability, fitness and courage, although some of the fences were recently modified.
(Mildmay Course) - Rectangular, 1m 4f (8) 260y run-in. A very fast course with sharp bends.
Address: Aintree Racecourse, Aintree, Liverpool, L9 5AS Tel: (0151) 523 2600 Fax: (0151) 530 1512
E-mail: aintree@races.u-net.com Internet: http://www.demon.co.uk/racenews/aintree
Clerk of the Course: Mr C. H. Barnett, Aintree Racecourse, Aintree, Liverpool L9 5AS. Tel: (0151) 523 2600.
Photography: By prior permission only from Aintree Racecourse.
176 boxes allocated in strict rotation. A new Stable Lads' Hostel was opened for the 1995 Grand National meeting and facilities are available on the course for up to 100 stable staff.
By Car: North of the City, near the junction of the M57 and M58 with the A59 (Preston).
By Rail: Aintree Station is adjacent to the Stands, from Liverpool Central.
By Air: Liverpool (Speke) Airport is 10 miles. Helicopter landing facility by prior arrangement.
Leading Trainers (since 1991): D. Nicholson 22-98 (22.5%), **M. C. Pipe** 19-141 (13.5%), **G. Richards** 12-71 (16.9%).
Leading Jockeys (since 1991): R. Dunwoody 14-113 (12.0%), **A. P. McCoy** 10-31 (32.0%), **N. Williamson** 10-56 (17.0%).

ASCOT(R.H)

A triangular course of 1m 6f 34y. The course goes downhill from the mile and a half start for three furlongs into Swinley Bottom (the lowest part of the track): it soon joins the Old Mile (which starts on a chute) and is then uphill with a straight run-in of two and a half furlongs, the last 100y being level. The straight mile (Royal Hunt Cup Course) is downhill from the start, rises to the five furlong gate and then falls slightly to the junction of the courses. The whole course is of a galloping nature with easy turns but is nevertheless a testing one, especially on soft going.
Address: Ascot Racecourse, Ascot, Berkshire SL5 7JN Tel: (01344) 22211 Fax: (01344) 24978
E-mail: AscotatITL.Net Internet: http://www.sportinglife.co.uk/ascot/

Clerk of the Course and Secretary: Mr A. N. Cheyne, Ascot Racecourse, Ascot, Berkshire SL5 7JN. Tel: (01344) 22211.
Racecourse Director: Mr D. Erskine-Crum
Going Reports: (01344) 874567/ (0585) 505407 (Mobile)
Free, shavings, straw or paper.
By Car: West of the town on the A329. Easy access from the M3 (Junc 3) and the M4 (Junc 6). Car parking adjoining the course and Ascot Heath. Contact the Secretary, Ascot Authority. Tel: (01344) 876456.
By Rail: Regular service from Waterloo to Ascot (500y from the racecourse).
By Air: Helicopter landing facility at the course. London (Heathrow) Airport 15 miles, White Waltam Airfield 12 miles.
Leading Trainers (since 1991): J. L. Dunlop 35-208 (16.8%), **J. H. M. Gosden** 32-194 (16.5%), **M. R. Stoute** 31-252 (12.3%).
Leading Jockeys (since 1991): L. Dettori 53-352 (15.0%), **Pat Eddery** 46-345 (13.0%), **J. Reid** 35-329 (10.0%).

ASCOT (N.H)

Triangular, 1m 6f (10) 240y run-in mostly uphill. A galloping course with an uphill finish, Ascot provides a real test of stamina. The fences are stiff and sound jumping is essential, especially for novices.
Address: Ascot Racecourse, Ascot, Berkshire SL5 7JN Tel: (01344) 22211 Fax: (01344) 24978
E-mail: AscotatITL.Net Internet: http://www.sportinglife.co.uk/ascot/
Clerk of the Course and Secretary: Mr A. N. Cheyne, Ascot Racecourse, Ascot, Berkshire SL5 7JN. Tel: (01344) 22211.
Racecourse Director: Mr D. Erskine-Crum
Going Reports: (01344) 874567/ (0585) 505407 (Mobile)
Stabling: Free, shavings, straw or paper.
By Car: West of the town on the A329. Easy access from the M3 (Junc 3) and the M4 (Junc 6). Car parking adjoining the course and Ascot Heath. Contact the Secretary, Ascot Authority. Tel: (01344) 876456.
By Rail: Regular service from Waterloo to Ascot (500y from the racecourse).
By Air: Helicopter landing facility at the course. London (Heathrow) Airport 15 miles, White Waltam Airfield 12 miles.
Leading Trainers (since 1991): M. C. Pipe 28-121 (23.1%), **N. A. Twiston-Davies** 23-146 (15.8%), **D. Nicholson** 22-100 (22.0%).
Leading Jockeys (since 1991): J. Osborne 37-149 (24.0%), **R. Dunwoody** 29-182 (15.0%), **A. P. McCoy** 24-85 (28.0%).

AYR (L.H)

A wide, relatively flat oval track of just over 1m 4f. An extension to the back straight provides a 1m 3f course with a sweeping turn at the top of the track tojoin the straight course four furlongs from the winning post. The straight six furlongs falls slightly for some three and a half furlongs and then rises slightly. In general, this is a very fair galloping course.

Address: Ayr Racecourse, Whitletts Road, Ayr KA8 0JE Tel: (01292) 264179 Fax: (01292) 610140

Internet: www.ayr-racecourse.com

Clerk of the Course and Manager: Mr Mark Kershaw, Racecourse Office, 2 Whitletts Road, Ayr. Tel: (01292) 264179. Mobile: (0850) 464258.

Secretary and Manager: Mr Mark Kershaw, address as above.

Free stabling and accommodation for lads and lasses. Tel: (01292) 264179.

By Car: East of the town on the A758. Free parking for buses and cars.

By Rail: Ayr Station (trains on the half hour from Glasgow Central). Journey time 55 minutes. Buses and taxis also to the course.

By Air: Prestwick International Airport (10 minutes by car). Glasgow Airport (1 hour).

Leading Trainers (since 1991): B. W. Hills 30-81 (37.0%), **M. Johnston** 27-203 (13.3%), **Mrs M. Reveley** 26-152 (17.1%).

Leading Jockeys (since 1991): K. Darley 57-275 (20.0%), **J. Weaver** 29-175 (16.0%), **D. Holland** 26-110 (23.0%).

AYR (N.H)

Oval, 1m 4f (9) 210y run-in. Relatively flat and one of the fastest tracks in Great Britain. It is a well-drained course and the ground rarely becomes testing. Suits the long-striding galloper.

Address: Ayr Racecourse, Whitletts Road, Ayr KA8 0JE Tel: (01292) 264179 Fax: (01292) 610140

Internet: www.ayr-racecourse.com

Clerk of the Course and Manager: Mr Mark Kershaw, Racecourse Office, 2 Whitletts Road, Ayr. Tel: (01292) 264179. Mobile: (0850) 464258.

Secretary and Manager: Mr Mark Kershaw, address as above.

Free stabling and accommodation for lads and lasses. Tel: (01292) 264179.

By Car: East of the town on the A758. Free parking for buses and cars.

By Rail: Ayr Station (trains on the half hour from Glasgow Central). Journey time 55 minutes. Buses and taxis also to the course.

By Air: Prestwick International Airport (10 minutes by car). Glasgow Airport (1 hour).

Leading Trainers (since 1991): G. Richards 68-336 (20.2%), **Mrs M. Reveley** 57-230 (24.8%), **J. J. O'Neill** 29-166 (17.5%).

Leading Jockeys (since 1991): P. Niven 50-215 (23.0%), **A. Dobbin** 39-198 (19.0%), **B. Storey** 38-260 (14.0%).

BANGOR-ON-DEE (N.H)

Circular, 1m 4f (9) 325y run-in. Apart from some `ridge and furrow', this is a flat course notable for three sharp bends, especially the paddock turn. Suits handy, speedy sorts and is ideal for front-runners.
Address: Bangor-On-Dee Racecourse, Bangor-On-Dee, nr Wrexham, Clwyd LL13 0DA Tel: (01978) 780323
Clerk of the Course: B. R. Davies, Shepherds Meadow, Eaton Bishop, Hereford, HR2 9UA. Tel: (01981) 250052 (Office), (01981) 580260 (Home), (01831) 602207 (Car).
Secretary and Manager: P. W. Ockleston, Chorlton Hall, Malpas, Cheshire, SY14 7ET. Tel: (01948) 860122 (Office), (01978) 780323 (Racedays).
85 stables, allotted on arrival. Shavings (straw on request). Applications to the Manager.
By Car: 5 miles South-East of Wrexham, off the B5069.
By Rail: Wrexham Station (bus or taxi to the course).
By Air: Helicopters may land by prior arrangement with Clerk of the Course at entirely their own risk.
Leading Trainers (since 1991): M. C. Pipe 46-154 (29.9%). **G. Richards** 39-188 (20.7%), **N. A. Twiston-Davies** 21-106 (19.8%).
Leading Jockeys (since 1991): R. Dunwoody 32-110 (29.0%), **A. Maguire** 18-88 (20.0%), **D. Bridgwater** 15-79 (18.0%).

BATH (L.H)

An oval track of 1m 4f 25y with 1m 3f 144y, 1m 2f 46y and 1m 5y starts set on chutes from the back straight and an uphill run-in of four furlongs, which bends to the left. There is no straight course but an extension provides for races of five furlongs and of 5f 167y, which run generally uphill and left-handed to a distinct left-handed curve about a furlong from the winning post.
Address: The Racecourse, Lansdown, Bath Tel: Office: (01291) 622260 Racedays: (01225) 424609
Clerk of the Course: Mr R. D. Farrant, Tylers Farm, Gravel Hill Road, Yate, Bristol BS17 5BN. Tel: (01454) 313186.
Secretary & Club Secretary: Miss S. J. Wilcox, Hopkins Farm, Lower Tysoe, Warwick CV35 0BN Tel/Fax: (01295) 688030
Free stabling and accommodation for lads and lasses. Tel: (01225) 444274
By Car: 2 miles North-West of the City (M4 Junc 18) at Lansdown. Unlimited free car and coach parking space immediately behind the stands. Special bus services operate from Bath to the racecourse.
By Rail: Bath Station (from Paddington), regular bus service from Bath to the course (3 miles).
By Air: Bristol or Colerne Airports. (no landing facilities at the course).
Leading Trainers (since 1991): P. F. I. Cole 25-156 (16.0%), **I. A. Balding** 24-138 (17.4%), **R. Charlton** 22-65 (33.9%).
Leading Jockeys (since 1991): Pat Eddery 38-148 (25.0%), **T. Quinn** 35-217 (16.0%), **J. Reid** 30-185 (16.0%).

BEVERLEY (R.H)

An oval course of 1m 3f set on two levels. A chute to the back straight provides a mile and a quarter course, which has a straight run of some five furlongs to a steep downhill bend into the home turn and an uphill run-in of two and a half furlongs. The five furlong course, which rises throughout with a distinct jink after a furlong and a slight bend to the right at halfway, provides a severe test for juveniles at the start of the season. The downhill turn into the straight and the short run-in prevent this from being an entirely galloping track.

Address: Beverley Race Co. Ltd., York Road, Beverley, Yorkshire HU17 9QZ Tel: (01482) 867488/882645
Fax: (01482) 863892

Clerk of the Course and Manager: Mr J. G. Cleverly, F.R.I.C.S., The Grandstand, York Road, Beverley. Tel: (01944) 768203 (evenings), (01482) 867488/882645 (Course Office). Course foreman - Home (01430) 810409, Mobile (0585 678186). Free.

By Car: 7 miles from the M62 (Junc 38) off the A1035. Free car parking opposite the course. Owners and Trainers use a separate enclosure.

By Rail: Beverley Station (Hull-Scarborough line). Occasional bus service to the course (1 mile).

By Air: Helicopter landings by prior arrangement. Light aircraft landing facilities at Linley Hill, Leven airport.

Leading Trainers (since 1991): J. Berry 35-214 (16.4%), **M. Johnston** 32-176 (18.2%), **Mrs M. Reveley** 26-160 (16.3%).

Leading Jockeys (since 1991): K. Darley 76-366 (20.0%), **K. Fallon** 28-249 (11.0%), **J. Weaver** 25-182 (13.0%).

BRIGHTON (L.H)

The course forms a horseshoe of 1m 4f round with easy turns and a run-in of three and a half furlongs. The first three furlongs are slightly uphill. Then there is a gentle descent and rise to about four furlongs from home. From there the ground falls steeply until about two furlongs out; then a sharp rise with the last 100y level. This sharp track, reminiscent of Epsom with its pronounced gradients, is unsuitable for big, long-striding animals, but it suits sharp sorts and is something of a specialists' course.

Address: Brighton Racecourse, Brighton, Sussex BN2 2XZ Tel: (01273) 603580
Fax: (01273) 673267
E-mail: 1016111.141@compuserve.com

Clerk of the Course: Mr G. R. Stickels, Lingfield Park 1991 Ltd., Lingfield, Surrey RH7 6PQ. Tel: (01342) 834800 or (01273) 603580 (racedays).
Managers: Lingfield 1991 Ltd., address as above.
Stabling and accommodation available on request. Tel: (01273) 682912

By Car: East of the town on the A27 (Lewes Road). There is a car park adjoining the course.

By Rail: Brighton Station (from Victoria on the hour, London Bridge or Portsmouth). Special bus service to the course from the station (approx 2 miles) and to the sea front.

By Air: No racecourse facilities.

Leading Trainers (since 1991): R. Hannon 62-329 (18.8%), **G. L. Moore** 29-210 (13.8%), **L. M. Cumani** 25-75 (33.3%).
Leading Jockeys (since 1991): T. Quinn 68-325 (20.0%), **J. Reid** 33-236 (13.0%), **M. Roberts** 31-145 (21.0%).

CARLISLE (R.H)

A pear-shaped, undulating course of 1m 5f with an extension for a mile and a half start and a straight uphill run-in of three and a half furlongs. The six furlong course (which includes the five furlong) starts on a chute, bears right for the first furlong and a half and again at the turn into the straight. The rise to the winning post, although it begins to level out from `the distance', makes it a stiff test of stamina.
Address: Carlisle Racecourse, Durdar Road, Carlisle CA2 4TS Tel: (01228) 22973 Fax: (01228) 591827
Clerk of the Course: Mr J. E. Fenwicke-Clennell, Chapel House, Arkholme, Carnforth, Lancs LA6 1AX. Tel: (01524) 221633 ,Mobile: (0860) 737729.
Secretary & Club Secretary: Mrs Ann Bliss, Brackenridge, Brackenthwaite, Wigton, Cumbria, CA7 8AS. Tel: (01693) 42634.
Stabling and accommodation available on request. Please phone Head Groundsman on (01228) 46188, or Stable Office on (01228) 49489 by 5pm day before racing.
By Car: 2 miles south of the town (Durdar Road). Easy access from the M6 (Junc 42). The car park is free (adjacent to the course). Trackside car parking £3 (except Saturdays & Bank Holidays £5).
By Rail: Carlisle Station (2 miles from the course).
By Air: Helicopter landing facility by prior arrangement.
Leading Trainers (since 1991): J. Berry 32-176 (18.2%), **Mrs M. Reveley** 23-99 (23.2%), **M. Johnston** 19-102 (18.6%).
Leading Jockeys (since 1991): K. Darley 32-175 (18.0%), **G. Duffield** 24-118 (20.0%), **K. Fallon** 22-132 (16.0%).

CARLISLE (N.H)

Pear-shaped, 1m 5f (9) 300y run-in uphill. Undulating and a stiff test of stamina, ideally suited to the long-striding thorough stayer. Three mile chases start on a chute, and the first fence is only jumped once. Ground tends to be either very fast or very soft.
Address: Carlisle Racecourse, Durdar Road, Carlisle CA2 4TS Tel: (01228) 22973 Fax: (01228) 591827
Clerk of the Course: Mr J. E. Fenwicke-Clennell, Chapel House, Arkholme, Carnforth, Lancs LA6 1AX. Tel: (01524) 221633, Mobile: (0860) 737729.
Secretary & Club Secretary: Mrs Ann Bliss, Brackenridge, Brackenthwaite, Wigton, Cumbria, CA7 8AS. Tel: (01693) 42634.
Stabling and accommodation available on request. Please phone Head Groundsman on (01228) 46188, or Stable Office on (01228) 49489 by 5pm day before racing.
By Car: 2 miles south of the town (Durdar Road). Easy access from the M6 (Junc 42). The car park is free (adjacent to the course). Trackside car parking £3 (except Saturdays & Bank Holidays £5).
By Rail: Carlisle Station (2 miles from the course).
By Air: Helicopter landing facility by prior arrangement.
Leading Trainers (since 1991): G. Richards 48-259 (18.5%), **Mrs M. Reveley** 40-138 (29.0%), **C. Parker** 22-184 (12.0%).
Leading Jockeys (since 1991): P. Niven 42-159 (26.0%), **B. Storey** 34-251 (13.0%), **A. Dobbin** 29-159 (18.0%).

CARTMEL (N.H)

Oval, 1m 1f (6) 800y run-in. Almost perfectly flat but very sharp, with the longest run-in in the country, approximately half a mile. The fences are stiff but fair.
Address: Cartmel Racecourse, Cartmel, nr Grange-Over-Sands, Cumbria LA11 6QF
Tel: (01539) 536340
Fax: (01539) 536004
Clerk of the Course: Mr C. H. Barnett, Aintree Racecourse, Aintree, Liverpool L9 5AS. Tel: (0151) 523 2600.
Number of boxes and accommodation for lads ands lasses is limited. Prior booking is advisable. Apply to Mr J. Moorhouse, Cloggerbeck House, Cartmel. Tel: (01539) 536494.
By Car: 1 mile West of the town, 2 miles off the B5277 (Grange-Haverthwaite road). M36 (Junc 36).
By Rail: Cark and Cartmel Station (21/2 miles) (Carnforth-Barrow line).
By Air: Light aircraft facilities available at Cark Airport (4 miles from the course). Helicopter landing facility at the course, by prior arrangement only.
Leading Trainers (since 1991): G. Richards 21-66 (31.8%), **J. White** 14-57 (24.6%), **M. C. Chapman** 11-87 (12.6%).
Leading Jockeys (since 1991): A. Dobbin 12-33 (36.0%), **P. Niven** 12-35 (34.0%), **Richard Guest** 10-20 (50.0%).

CATTERICK (L.H)

An oval, undulating course of 1m 180y with two chutes, one for seven furlong and another for five furlong starts, and a straight run-in of three furlongs. The five furlong course is downhill throughout, sharply at first, and jinks left-handed at the junction of the courses. The seven furlong track joins the round course at the six furlong gate and is slightly downhill to the home turn. This sharp track is entirely unsuitable for long-striding gallopers and is often a specialists' track for both horse and jockey.
Address: The Racecourse, Catterick Bridge, Richmond, North Yorkshire DL10 7PE
Tel: (01748) 811478
Fax: (01748) 811082
Clerk of the Course: (Flat) Mr James Sanderson, c/o The Racecourse, Catterick Bridge, Richmond, North Yorkshire DL10 7PE. (Jumps) Mr S. C. Enderby, The Riding, Hexham, Northumberland NE46 4PF. Tel: (01434) 606881 (Office). Fax: (01434) 605814.
Secretary: International Racecourse Management Ltd., c/o The Racecourse, Catterick Bridge, Richmond, North Yorkshire DL10 7PE. Tel: (01748) 811478. Fax: (01748) 811082.
Stabling: Boxes are allotted on arrival. Contact Mr Adrian Swingler, Racecourse Lodge, Catterick. Tel: (01748) 811478.
By Car: The course is adjacent to the A1, 1 mile North-West of the town on the A6136. There is a free car park.
By Rail: Darlington Station (special buses to course - 14 mile journey).
Leading Trainers (since 1991): J. Berry 42-291 (14.4%), **B. W. Hills** 32-81 (39.5%), **Mrs M. Reveley** 29-152 (19.1%).
Leading Jockeys (since 1991): K. Darley 45-233 (19.0%), **J. Carroll** 38-231(16.0%), **J. Fortune** 23-170 (13.0%).

DONCASTER (N.H)

onical, 2m (11) 247y run-in. A very fair, flat track ideally suited to the long-striding
alloper. The quality of the fences has improved in recent years, and are not as easy
they used to be.
ldress: Doncaster Racecourse, Grand Stand, Leger Way, Doncaster DN2 6BB
l: (01302) 320066
x: (01302) 323271 E-mail: info@britishracing.com Internet: www.britishracing.com
rk of the Course (NH): Major C. L. Moore, Doncaster Racecourse Grandstand,
er Way, Doncaster.
ef Executive: Mr J. Sanderson, International Racecourse Management Ltd.,
ndstand, Leger Way, Doncaster DN2 6BB. Tel: (01302) 320066. Fax: (01673)
434 (Office).
stabling and accommodation.
ar: East of the town, off the A638 (M18 Junc 3 & 4). Club members car park
rved. Large public car park free and adjacent to the course.
ail: Doncaster Central Station (from King's Cross). Special bus service from the
n (1 mile).
r: Helicopter landing facility by prior arrangement only.
g Trainers (since 1991): Mrs M. Reveley 25-116 (21.6%), **D. Nicholson** 14-62 (22.6%),
tzGerald 14-98 (14.3%).
g Jockeys (since 1991): P. Niven 20-85 (23.0%), **L. Wyer** 11-63 (17.0%),
erry 10-29 (34.0%).

EPSOM (L.H)

e Derby start at the top of the Downs, the course climbs steadily for the first
ending four furlongs, then levels out for nearly two furlongs before falling
round the bend to Tattenham Corner and into the straight. This is of less than
ngs and ends with a fairish rise of just over a furlong to the winning post. The
Suburban course and the Epsom Mile are, respectively, the last 1m 2f 15y
ast 1m 110y of the Derby course. The five furlong course (Egmont Course) is
straight and, running sharply downhill to the junction with the round course,
est in the world. The Derby course is a unique test for the thoroughbred, the
fast early pace demanding stamina, and the bends and gradients calling for
action. Well-balanced, medium-sized, handy sorts seem to do best over
gs.
United Racecourses Ltd., Racecourse Paddock, Epsom, Surrey KT18 5NJ
2) 726311
e Course & General Manager: Mr A. J. Cooper, The Racecourse, Epsom
rrey KT18 5LQ. Tel: (01372) 726311, Mobile (0374) 230850
g and accommodation. Tel (01372) 725794
niles South of the town on the B290 (M25 Junc 8 & 9). For full car park
apply to: The Club Secretary, Epsom Grandstand, Epsom Downs, Surrey
Tel: (01372) 726311.
som, Epsom Downs or Tattenham Corner Stations (trains from London
erloo, Victoria). Regular bus services run to the course from Epsom and
erground Station.

CATTERICK (N.H)

Oval, 1m 1f (9) 240y run-in. Undulating, sharp track that favours the handy, front-running sort, rather than the long-striding galloper.
Address: The Racecourse, Catterick Bridge, Richmond, North Yorkshire DL10 7PE
Tel: (01748) 811478
Fax: (01748) 811082
Clerk of the Course: (Flat) Mr James Sanderson, c/o The Racecourse, Catterick Bridge, Richmond, North Yorkshire DL10 7PE. (Jumps) Mr S. C. Enderby, The Riding, Hexham, Northumberland NE46 4PF. Tel: (01434) 606881 (Office). Fax: (01434) 605814.
Secretary: International Racecourse Management Ltd., c/o The Racecourse, Catterick Bridge, Richmond, North Yorkshire DL10 7PE. Tel: (01748) 811478. Fax: (01748) 811082.
Stabling: Boxes are allotted on arrival. Contact Mr Adrian Swingler, Racecourse Lodge, Catterick. Tel: (01748) 811478.
By Car: The course is adjacent to the A1, 1 mile North-West of the town on the A6136. There is a free car park.
By Rail: Darlington Station (special buses to course - 14 mile journey).
Leading Trainers (since 1991): Mrs M. Reveley 37-163 (22.7%), **M. D. Hammond** 18-163 (11.0%), **J. G. FitzGerald** 18-95 (19.0%).
Leading Jockeys (since 1991): P. Niven 33-135 (24.0%), **B. Storey** 21-206 (10.0%), **R. Garritty** 19-125 (15.0%).

CHELTENHAM (N.H)

(Old Course) - Oval, 1m 4f (9) 350y run-in. A testing, undulating track with stiff fences. The ability to stay is essential as the going can get heavy in wet weather.
(New Course) - Oval, 1m 5f (10) 220y run-in. Undulating, stiff fences, testing course, uphill for the final half-mile.
(Park Course) - Oval, 1m 5f (9) 220y uphill run-in. Not as testing as the other two courses and designed to put less strain on the horses' legs in early and late-season.
Clerk of the Course: Major P. W. F. Arkwright, Shirley Farm, Little Wolford, Shipston-on-Stour, Warwickshire. Tel: (01608) 684460.
Address: Cheltenham Racecourse, Prestbury Park, Cheltenham, Gloucestershire GL50 4SH Tel (01242) 513014
Fax: (01242) 224227 Internet: http://www.cheltenham.co.uk
Club Secretary: Mrs R. Hammond, address and phone as Managing Director.
Managing Director: E. W. Gillespie, The Racecourse, Prestbury Park, Cheltenham, Gloucestershire. Tel: (01242) 513014.
Ample stabling and accommodation for lads. Apply to the Stable Manager (01242) 513014.
By Car: 11/2 miles North of the town on the A435. M5 (Junc 10 or 11).
By Rail: Cheltenham (Lansdowne) Station. Buses and taxis to course.
By Air: Helicopter landing site to the North-East of the stands.
Leading Trainers (Park) (since 1991): M. C. Pipe 10-32 (31.3%), **K. C. Bailey** 7-26 (26.9%), **Mrs J. Pitman** 4-7 (57.1%)
Leading Jockeys (Park) (since 1991): R. Dunwoody 5-33 (15.0%), **W. Marston** 4-14 (28.0%), **A. Maguire** 3-23 (13.0%).
Leading Trainers (Old & New) (since 1991): M. C. Pipe 57-415 (13.7%), **D. Nicholson** 56-288 (19.4%), **N. A. Twiston-Davies** 31-261 (11.9%).
Leading Jockeys (Old & New) (since 1991): R. Dunwoody 56-294 (19.0%), **J. Osborne** 35-215 (16.0%), **A. Maguire** 28-187 (14.0%).

CHEPSTOW (L.H)

An oval, undulating course, about 2m in circumference with a straight run-in of five furlongs, which extends to make a straight mile. All races of up to a mile are run on the latter, which is downhill to the five furlong start and then rises sharply for two and a half furlongs before levelling out to the winning post. The changing gradients prevent this from being a really galloping track.
Address: Chepstow Racecourse, Chepstow, Gwent NP6 5YH Tel: (01291) 622260 Fax: (01291) 625550
Clerk of the Course and Manager: Mr R. Farrant, Tylers Farm, Gravel Hill Road, Yate, nr Bristol BS17 5BN. Tel: (01291) 622260 (Office). (01454) 313186 (Home). (01850) 888380 (Mobile). Fax: (01291) 625550.
Secretary: G. C. Francis, 17 Welsh Street, Chepstow, Gwent NP6 5YH.
109 boxes, allotted on arrival. Limited accommodation for lads and lasses. Apply: (01291) 623414.
By Car: 1 mile North-West of the town on the A466. (1 mile from Junc 22 of the M4 (Severn Bridge)). There is a Free public car park opposite the Stands entrance.
By Rail: Chepstow Station (from Paddington, change at Gloucester or Newport). The course is 1 mile from station.
By Air: Helicopter landing facility in the centre of the course.
Leading Trainers (since 1991): R. Hannon 26-199 (13.1%), **H. R. A. Cecil** 15-47 (31.9%), **L. M. Cumani** 12-22 (54.6%).
Leading Jockeys (since 1991): J. Reid 19-123 (15.0%), **L. Dettori** 15-56 (26.0%), **T. Sprake** 14-112 (12.0%).

CHEPSTOW (N.H)

Oval, 2m (11) 240y run-in. Many changing gradients, five fences in the home straight. Favours the long-striding front-runner, but stamina is important.
Address: Chepstow Racecourse, Chepstow, Gwent NP6 5YH Tel: (01291) 622260 Fax: (01291) 625550
Clerk of the Course and Manager: Mr R. Farrant, Tylers Farm, Gravel Hill Road, Yate, nr Bristol BS17 5BN. Tel: (01291) 622260 (Office). (01454) 313186 (Home). (01850) 888380 (Mobile). Fax: (01291) 625550.
Secretary: G. C. Francis, 17 Welsh Street, Chepstow, Gwent NP6 5YH.
109 boxes, allotted on arrival. Limited accommodation for lads and lasses. Apply: (01291) 623414.
By Car: 1 mile North-West of the town on the A466. (1 mile from Junc 22 of the M4 (Severn Bridge)). There is a Free public car park opposite the Stands entrance.
By Rail: Chepstow Station (from Paddington, change at Gloucester or Newport). The course is 1 mile from station.
By Air: Helicopter landing facility in the centre of the course.
Leading Trainers (since 1991): M. C. Pipe 91-355 (25.6%), **P. J. Hobbs** 33-140 (23.6%), **N. A. Twiston-Davies** 29-163 (17.8%).
Leading Jockeys (since 1991): R. Dunwoody 42-176 (23.0%), **A. P. McCoy** 29-109 (26.0%), **D. Bridgwater** 20-98 (20.0%).

CHESTER (L.H)

A perfectly flat, circular course, 1m 73y in circumference, with a sharp bend to a straight run-in of 230y. Long distance events are an extreme test of stamina, but fo middle-distance races and sprints, the course greatly favours a sharp-actioned ho Horses with previous winning form on this track are worthy of note.
Address: The Racecourse, Chester CH1 2LY Tel: (01244) 323170 Fax: (01244 344971
Clerk of the Course: Mr C. H. Barnett, Aintree Racecourse, Aintree, Liverpool L 5AS. Tel: (0151) 523 2600 or (01244) 323170 (racedays).
Racecourse Manager: Mr R. Walls
Secretary: Kidsons Impey, Steam Mill, Chester.CH3 5AN Tel: (01244) 327171
Free stabling (175 boxes) and accommodation.
By Car: The course is near the centre of the city on the A548 (Queensferry R The Owners and Trainers car park is adjacent to the County Stand. There is car park in the centre of the course.
By Rail: Chester Station (3/4 mile from the course). Services from Euston, Paddington and Northgate.
By Air: Hawarden Airport (2 miles).
Leading Trainers (since 1991): A. Bailey 24-211 (11.4%), **M. R. Stoute** 24-100 (24.0% **B. W. Hills** 23-113 (20.4%).
Leading Jockeys (since 1991): Pat Eddery 28-111 (25.0%), **K. Darley** 19-109 (17.0% **K. Fallon** 18-135 (13.0%).

DONCASTER (L.H)

A pear-shaped track, about 1m 7f 110y in circumference with a distinc the mile marker. There is a level run-in of four and a half furlongs, ext straight mile, which tapers from a width of 88ft at the five-furlong pole winning post. A round mile joins the straight course at a tangent. This track is suitable for strongly-built stayers and calls for stamina and c
Address: Doncaster Racecourse, Grand Stand, Leger Way, Donca Tel: (01302) 320066
Fax: (01302) 323271 E-mail: info@britishracing.com Internet: ww
Chief Executive & Clerk of Course (Flat): Mr J. Sanderson, Inter Racecourse Management Ltd., Grandstand, Leger Way, Doncaste (01302) 320066. Fax: (01673) 843434 (Office).
Free stabling and accommodation.
By Car: East of the town, off the A638 (M18 Junc 3 & 4). Club m reserved. Large public car park free and adjacent to the course.
By Rail: Doncaster Central Station (from King's Cross). Special station (1 mile).
By Air: Helicopter landing facility by prior arrangement only.
Leading Trainers (since 1991): J. H. M. Gosden 51-227 (22.5%), **B. W H. R. A. Cecil** 40-158 (25.3%).
Leading Jockeys (since 1991): Pat Eddery 53-282 (18.0%), **K. Darley L. Dettori** 43-288 (14.0%).

By Air: London (Heathrow) and London (Gatwick) are both within 20 miles of the course. Heliport (Derby Meeting only) apply to Hascombe Aviation. Tel: (01279) 680291.

Leading Trainers (since 1991): R. Hannon 20-197 (10.2%), **Lord Huntingdon** 14-37 (37.8%), **M. R. Stoute** 12-79 (15.2%).

Leading Jockeys (since 1991): M. Roberts 24-125 (19.0%), **Pat Eddery** 24-154 (15.0%), **J. Reid** 19-125 (15.0%).

EXETER (N.H)

Oval, 2m (11) 300y run-in uphill. Undulating with a home straight of half a mile. A good test of stamina, suiting the handy, well-balanced sort. Has separate summer and winter courses, with different lay-outs of fences.

Address: Exeter Racecourse, Kennford, nr Exeter, Devon EX6 7XS Tel: (01392) 832599 Fax: (01392) 833454

Clerk of the Course and Manager: N. G. P. Ansell, Pillhead House, Bideford, EX39 4NF (01237) 472574 Racecourse. (01392) 832599. Fax (01392) 833454.

28 boxes at Kennford (2 miles from the course) allotted on arrival; 69 loose boxes on the course. Sleeping accommodation and canteen for both lads and lasses. Apply to Mrs J. Browning. Tel: (01392) 832816.

By Car: The course is at Haldon, 5 miles South-West of Exeter on the A38 (Plymouth) road, 2 miles East of Chudleigh.

By Rail: Exeter (St Davids) Station.

Leading Trainers (since 1991): M. C. Pipe 129-460 (28.0%), **P. J. Hobbs** 44-221 (19.9%), **Miss H. C. Knight** 42-144 (29.2%).

Leading Jockeys (since 1991): R. Dunwoody 43-169 (25.0%), **A. P. McCoy** 27-128 (21.0%), **J. Frost** 27-190 (14.0%).

FAKENHAM (N.H)

Square, 1m (6) 200y run-in. On the turn almost throughout and undulating, suiting the handy front-runner. The going rarely becomes heavy.

Address: The Racecourse, Fakenham, Norfolk NR21 7NY Tel: (01328) 862388 Fax: (01328) 855908

Clerk of the Course: Mr Godfrey Tabiner, 37 Hornbeam Road, Newbold Verdon, Leicestershire. LE9 9NT Tel: (01455) 823834.

Racecourse Manager: Mr P. B. Firth, The Racecourse, Fakenham, Norfolk. NR21 7NY Tel: (01328) 862388

76 boxes allotted in rotation. Tel: (01328) 862388.

By Car: 1 mile South of the town on the B1146 (East Dereham) road.

By Rail: Norwich Station (26 miles) (Liverpool Street line), King's Lynn (22 miles) (Liverpool Street).

By Air: Helicopter landing facility in the centre of the course.

Leading Trainers (since 1991): O. Brennan 15-44 (34.1%), **J. R. Jenkins** 12-66 (18.2%), **M. J. Ryan** 10-31 (32.3%).

Leading Jockeys (since 1991): M. Brennan 13-52 (25.0%), **A. Maguire** 7-27 (25.0%), **R. Dunwoody** 6-19 (31.0%).

FOLKESTONE (R.H)

A circuit of 1m 3f, somewhat undulating, with a straight run-in of two and a half furlongs. Five and six furlong races start on an extension which joins the round course about three furlongs from the line and has a slight rise over the final furlong. Despite its gentle turns and its width, Folkestone can not be described as a galloping track.
Address: Folkestone Racecourse, Westenhanger, Hythe, Kent CT21 4HX Tel (01303) 266407 Fax: (01303) 260185 E-mail: 1016111.141@compuserve.com
Clerk of the Course: Mr G. R. Stickels, Lingfield Park 1991 Ltd., Lingfield, Surrey RH7 6PQ. Tel: (01342) 834800/ Mobile: (0973) 737006 or (01303) 266407 (racedays) or (01303) 873114 (home). Assistant Clerk of the Course: Mr F. I. W. Cameron, Lingfield Park 1991 Ltd., Lingfield, Surrey.
90 boxes allotted in rotation. Advance notice required for overnight accommodation, before 12 noon on the day prior to racing.
By Car: 6 miles West of town at Westenhanger. Easy access from Junc 11 of the M20. Car park adjoins stands. (Free, except course enclosure £4).
By Rail: Westenhanger Station adjoins course. Trains from Charing Cross.
By Air: Helicopter landing facility by prior arrangement.
Leading Trainers (since 1991): R. Hannon 31-212 (14.6%), **J. Pearce** 22-87 (25.3%), **J. L. Dunlop** 19-70 (27.1%).
Leading Jockeys (since 1991): Paul Eddery 29-162 (17.0%), **T. Quinn** 29-204 (14.0%), **G. Duffield** 24-156 (15.0%).

FOLKESTONE (N.H)

Oval, 1m 3f (8) chases 220y run-in, hurdles 250y run-in. An undulating course with easy fences, not particularly suitable for the long-striding galloper.
Address: Folkestone Racecourse, Westenhanger, Hythe, Kent CT21 4HX Tel (01303) 266407 Fax: (01303) 260185 E-mail: 1016111.141@compuserve.com
Clerk of the Course: Mr G. R. Stickels, Lingfield Park 1991 Ltd., Lingfield, Surrey RH7 6PQ. Tel: (01342) 834800/ Mobile: (0973) 737006 or (01303) 266407 (racedays) or (01303) 873114 (home). Assistant Clerk of the Course: Mr F. I. W. Cameron, Lingfield Park 1991 Ltd., Lingfield, Surrey.
90 boxes allotted in rotation. Advance notice required for overnight accommodation, before 12 noon on the day prior to racing.
By Car: 6 miles West of town at Westenhanger. Easy access from Junc 11 of the M20. Car park adjoins stands. (Free, except course enclosure £4).
By Rail: Westenhanger Station adjoins course. Trains from Charing Cross.
By Air: Helicopter landing facility by prior arrangement.
Leading Trainers (since 1991): J. T. Gifford 23-114 (20.2%), **R. Rowe** 16-84 (19.1%), **D. M. Grissell** 15-89 (16.9%).
Leading Jockeys (since 1991): A. Maguire 12-70 (17.0%), **M. A. Fitzgerald** 10-48 (20.0%), **P. Hide** 9-51 (17.0%).

FONTWELL (N.H)

2m (7) 230y run-in with left-hand bend close home. The figure-of-eight chase course suits handy types and is something of a specialists' track. The hurdle course is oval, one mile round with nine hurdles per two and a quarter miles.

Address: Fontwell Park Racecourse, nr Arundel, West Sussex BN18 0SX Tel: (01243) 543645 Fax: (01444) 450990

Clerk of the Course: Mr G. R. Stickels, Lingfield Park 1991 Ltd., Lingfield, Surrey RH7 6PQ. Tel: (01342) 834800/ Mobile: (0973) 737006 or (01303) 873114 (home).

Assistant Clerk of the Course: Mr P. D. Deacon Tel: Office (01342) 834800

77 boxes. Limited accommodation for 16 lads and 3 girls only. If arriving the day before the meeting, contact: Mr R. Mant. Tel: (01243) 543335.

By Car: South of village at the junction of the A29 (Bognor) and A27 (Brighton-Chichester) roads.

By Rail: Barnham Station (2 miles). Brighton-Portsmouth line (access via London Victoria).

By Air: Helicopter landing facility by prior arrangement with the Clerk of the Course.

Leading Trainers (since 1991) J. T. Gifford 41-221 (18.6%), **M. C. Pipe** 38-129 (29.5%), **P. J. Hobbs** 28-94 (29.8%).

Leading Jockeys (since 1991): A. Maguire 35-190 (18.0%), **A. P. McCoy** 25-103 (24.0%) **P. Hide** 24-117 (20.0%).

GOODWOOD (R.H)

Set on the edge of the Downs, a straight six furlongs with a triangular loop on one side provides a variety of courses with the possibility of re-entering just above or below the five furlong gate. The Cup Course of about two and a half miles starts on a chute adjacent to the five furlong start and, running the reverse way of the course, turns left after about four furlongs and returns to the straight five furlong run-in by the top bend. The Stakes Course is the last 2m 3f, the Bentinck Course the last 1m 6f and the Gratwicke Course the last 1m 4f of the Cup Course. The Craven Course is 1m 2f, starting in almost the same spot as the Gratwicke Course but running in the reverse direction and returning to the five furlong run-in by the top bend. The Old Mile and seven furlong courses start on the Cup Course and join the five furlong course on the lower bend. The five and six furlong (Stewards' Cup) courses are perfectly straight, the first furlong of the latter being uphill and then slightly undulating to the finish. The sharp bends and downhill gradients suit the handy, well-balanced, neat-actioned sort over middle-distances and are against the big, long-striding horse.

Address: Goodwood Racecourse Ltd., Goodwood, Chichester, West Sussex PO18 0PX Tel: (01243) 755022

Fax: (01243) 755025 Internet: http://www.demon.co.uk/racenews/goodwood

Clerk of the Course and General Manager: Mr R. N. Fabricius, Goodwood Racecourse Limited, Chichester, Sussex. Tel: (01243) 779922, Fax 01243 778686.

Free stabling and accommodation for runners (110 well equipped boxes at Goodwood House). Subsidised canteen and recreational facilities.Tel: (01243) 774107 or (01243 774157) or Mobile (0860) 951375

By Car: 6 miles North of Chichester between the A286 & A285. There is a car park adjacent to the course. Ample free car and coach parking.

By Rail: Chichester Station (from Victoria or London Bridge). Regular bus service to the course (6 miles).
By Air: Helicopter landing facility by prior arrangement with Stephenson Aviation. Tel: (01243) 779222. Goodwood Airport 2 miles (taxi to the course).
Leading Trainers (since 1991): R. Hannon 57-540 (10.6%), **P. F. I. Cole** 39-197 (19.8%), **J. H. M. Gosden** 36-188 (19.2%).
Leading Jockeys (since 1991): Pat Eddery 60-308 (19.0%), **J. Reid** 54-357 (15.0%), **T. Quinn** 54-400 (13.0%).

HAMILTON (R.H)

A straight six furlongs with a pear-shaped loop course of 1m 5f from a start in front of the stands and a run-in of five and a half furlongs. The turns are easy on the loop. The track is undulating with a dip (which can be very testing in wet weather) about three furlongs out and then rises to level out for the last 150y. A course where judgement and experience can make a considerable difference. Races are usually run at a true gallop here and form can be relied upon.
Address: Hamilton Park Racecourse, Bothwell Road, Hamilton, Lanarkshire ML3 0DW Tel: (01698) 283806
Fax: (01698) 286621
Clerk of the Course: Mr W. G. Farnsworth, The Racecourse, Bothwell Road, Hamilton ML3 0DW (01698) 283806. Fax: (01698) 286621.
Chief Executive and Secretary: Miss H. Dudgeon, The Racecourse, Bothwell Road, Hamilton ML5 0DW. Tel: (01698) 283806. Fax: (01698) 286621.
Head Groundsman: Mobile (0850) 609037
Free stabling (120 boxes) and accommodation on request. Tel: (01698) 284892.
By Car: Off the A74 on the B7071 (Hamilton-Bothwell road). (M74 Junc 5). Free parking for cars and buses.
By Rail: Hamilton West Station (1 mile).
By Air: Glasgow Airport (20 miles).
Leading Trainers (since 1991): J. Berry 74-400 (18.5%), **M. Johnston** 47-269 (17.5%), **Mrs M. Reveley** 43-220 (19.6%).
Leading Jockeys (since 1991): K. Darley 59-321 (18.0%), **J. Carroll** 53-320 (16.0%), **J. Weaver** 52-199 (26.0%).

HAYDOCK (L.H)

An almost flat, oval track, 1m 5f round, with a run-in of four and a half furlongs and a straight six furlong course. The 1m 4f gate is set on a short chute. This course, which is of a galloping nature, suits the long-striding horse. On rain-affected turf, the going down the stands' rail in the straight is often faster and horses have often won races by being brought over to that side.
Address: Haydock Park Racecourse, Newton-le-Willows, Merseyside WA12 0HQ
Tel: (01942) 725963
Fax: (01942) 270879
Clerk of the Course: Major P. W. F. Arkwright, Shirley Farm, Little Wolford, Shipston-on-Stour, Warwickshire. Tel: (01608) 684460.

Manager: Mr R. Thomas, Haydock Park Racecourse Company Limited, Newton-le-Willows, Merseyside WA12 0HQ. Tel: (01942) 725963.
Secretary: Mr G. Proctor, Haydock Park Racecourse, Newton-le-Willows, Merseyside WA12 0HQ. Tel: (01942) 725963
Applications to be made to the Racecourse for stabling and accommodation.
By Car: The course is on the A49 near Junc 23 of the M6.
By Rail: Newton-le-Willows Station (Manchester-Liverpool line) is 21/2 miles from the course. Earlstown 3 miles from the course. Warrington Bank Quay and Wigan are on the London to Carlisle/ Glasgow line.
By Air: Landing facilities in the centre of the course for helicopters and planes not exceeding 10,000lbs laden weight. Apply to the Sales Office.
Leading Trainers (since 1991): J. H. M. Gosden 38-149 (25.5%), **J. L. Dunlop** 36-161 (22.4%), **B. W. Hills** 28-127 (22.1%).
Leading Jockeys (since 1991): W. Ryan 34-171 (19.0%), **Pat Eddery** 34-126 (26.0%), **J. Carroll** 31-306 (10.0%).

HAYDOCK (N.H)

Oval, 1m 5f (10) 440y run-in. Flat, galloping chase course with stiff drop fences. The hurdle track, which is sharp, is inside the chase course and has some tight bends.
Address: Haydock Park Racecourse, Newton-le-Willows, Merseyside WA12 0HQ
Tel: (01942) 725963
Fax: (01942) 270879
Clerk of the Course: Major P. W. F. Arkwright, Shirley Farm, Little Wolford, Shipston-on-Stour, Warwickshire. Tel: (01608) 684460.
Manager: Mr R. Thomas, Haydock Park Racecourse Company Limited, Newton-le-Willows, Merseyside WA12 0HQ. Tel: (01942) 725963.
Secretary: Mr G. Proctor, Haydock Park Racecourse, Newton-le-Willows, Merseyside WA12 0HQ. Tel: (01942) 725963
Applications to be made to the Racecourse for stabling and accommodation.
By Car: The course is on the A49 near Junc 23 of the M6.
By Rail: Newton-le-Willows Station (Manchester-Liverpool line) is 21/2 miles from the course. Earlstown 3 miles from the course. Warrington Bank Quay and Wigan are on the London to Carlisle/ Glasgow line.
By Air: Landing facilities in the centre of the course for helicopters and planes not exceeding 10,000lbs laden weight. Apply to the Sales Office.
Leading Trainers (since 1991): G. Richards 53-175 (30.3%), **M. C. Pipe** 50-206 (24.3%), **N. A. Twiston-Davies** 20-91 (22.0%).
Leading Jockeys (since 1991): R. Dunwoody 29-101 (28.0%), **A. Maguire** 15-67 (22.0%), **P. Niven** 15-100 (15.0%).

HEREFORD (N.H)

Square, 1m 4f (9) 300y run-in. The turns, apart from the final one which is on falling ground, are easily negotiated, placing the emphasis on speed rather than stamina. A handy position round the home turn is vital, as winners rarely come from behind. The hurdle track is on the outside of the chase course. The fences have a reputation of being pretty stiff, but at the same time fair.

Address: Hereford Racecourse, Roman Road, Holmer, Hereford HR4 9 QU Tel: (01981) 250436 (Office) (01432) 273560 (Course) Fax: (01981) 250192 (Office) (01432) 352807 (Course)

Clerk of the Course and Secretary: J. Williams, F.R.I.C.S., Shepherds Meadow, Eaton Bishop, Hereford. Tel: (01981) 250436 (Office). (01432) 273560.

90 boxes allocated on arrival. Apply to the Stabling Manager, The Racecourse House, Roman Road, Holmer, Hereford. Tel: (01432) 273560.

By Car: 1 mile North West of the City off the A49 (Leominster) road.

By Rail: Hereford Station (1 mile from the course).

By Air: Helicopter landing facility in the centre of the course by arrangement with the Clerk of the Course, and entirely at own risk.

Leading Trainers M. C. Pipe 58-193 (30.1%), **N. A. Twiston-Davies** 40-149 (26.9%), **K. C. Bailey** 24-128 (18.8%).

Leading Jockeys (since 1991): D. Bridgwater 29-138 (21.0%), **A. P. McCoy** 25-88 (28.0%), **C. Llewellyn** 25-107 (23.0%).

HEXHAM (N.H)

Oval, 1m 4f (10) 220y run-in. An undulating course that becomes very testing when the ground is soft, it has easy fences and a stiff uphill climb to the finishing straight, which is on a separate spur.

Address: Hexham Racecourse, The Riding, Hexham, Northumberland NE46 4PF Tel: (01434) 606881 (Non-racedays) (01434) 603112 (racedays) Internet: leoz@pipex.dial.com

Clerk of the Course and Manager: S. C. Enderby, The Riding, Hexham. Tel: (01434) 606881 (Racecourse Office), (01434) 603738 (Course). Fax: (01434) 605814.

70 boxes allocated in rotation.

By Car: 11/2 miles South-West of the town off the B6305.

By Rail: Hexham Station (Newcastle-Carlisle line). Free bus to the course. A free bus is available from Hexham Station.

By Air: Helicopter landing facility in centre of course (by special arrangement only).

Leading Trainers (since 1991): G. Richards 36-142 (25.4%), **L. Lungo** 30-121 (24.8%), **G. M. Moore** 24-124 (19.4%).

Leading Jockeys (since 1991): P. Niven 31-144 (21.0%), **A. Dobbin** 28-127 (22.0%), **T. Reed** 28-158 (17.0%).

HUNTINGDON (N.H)

Oval, 1m 4f (9) 200y run-in. Perfectly flat, galloping track with a tricky open ditch in front of the stands. The two fences in the home straight can cause problems for novice chasers. Suits front runners.
Address: The Racecourse, Brampton, Huntingdon, Cambridgeshire PE18 8NN Tel: (01480) 454610
Fax: (01480) 455275
Clerk of the Course: H. P. C. Bevan, The Old House, Little Everdon, Daventry, Northants NN11 3BG. Tel: (01327) 361266.
Manager: Adam Waterworth.
100 boxes available. Allotted on arrival.
By Car: The course is situated at Brampton, 2 miles West of Huntingdon on the A14. Easy access from the A1 (1/2 mile from the course).
By Rail: Huntingdon Station. Buses and taxis to course.
By Air: Helicopter landing facility by prior arrangement.
Leading Trainers (since 1991): K. C. Bailey 31-98 (31.6%), **J. T. Gifford** 26-129 (20.2%), **D. Nicholson** 24-94 (25.5%).
Leading Jockeys (since 1991): R. Dunwoody 31-161 (19.0%), **A. Maguire** 24-147 (16.0%), **P. Hide** 18-73 (24.0%).

KELSO (N.H)

Oval, 1m 3f (9) 440y run-in uphill. Rather undulating with two downhill fences opposite the stands, Kelso suits the nippy, front-running sort, though the uphill run to the finish helps the true stayer. The hurdle course is smaller and very sharp with a tight turn away from the stands.
Address: Kelso Racecourse, Kelso, Roxburghshire Tel: (01228) 22973 (Office) (01573) 224767 (Racedays)
Fax: (01228) 591827
Clerk of the Course: Mr J. E. Fenwicke-Clennell, Toft Way, Sharperton, Morpeth, Northumberland NE65 7AE. Tel: (01669) 650369. Fax: (01669) 650339.
Secretary: Mr Richard M. Landale, c/o Sale & Partners, 18-20 Glendale Road, Wooler, Northumberland NE71 6DW. Tel: (01668) 281611. Fax: (01668) 281113
Racecourse: (01573) 224767. Groundsman's Mobile: (0374) 172527
81 boxes allotted in rotation. Reservations for stabling and accommodation for lads and lasses at the racecourse. Please phone Head Groundsman Tel: (01573) 224767/ Mobile: (0374) 172527 or Racecourse stables: (01573) 224822 by 5pm the day before racing.
By Car: 1 mile North of the town, off the B6461.
By Rail: Berwick-upon-Tweed Station. 23 mile bus journey to Kelso.
Leading Trainers (since 1991): Mrs M. Reveley 59-194 (30.4%), **G. Richards** 42-180 (23.3%), **M. D. Hammond** 32-156 (20.5%).
Leading Jockeys (since 1991): P. Niven 66-193 (34.0%), **B. Storey** 38-243 (15.0%), **A. Dobbin** 32-179 (17.0%).

KEMPTON (R.H)

A 1m 5f triangular course with a three and a half furlong straight run-in. The 1m 2f Jubilee Course starts on an extension to the round course and sprint races are run over a separate diagonal course. Kempton is a perfectly flat track which can not be described as either sharp or galloping.

Address: Kempton Park Racecourse, Sunbury-on-Thames, Middlesex TW16 5AQ
Tel: (01932) 782292 Fax: (01932) 782044
Internet: http://www.demon.co.uk/.racenews/rht
Clerk of the Course: Mr P. R. McNeile, Kempton Park, Sunbury-on-Thames. Tel: (01932) 782292 Raceday Fax: (01932) 779525.
Racecourse Manager: Mr J. M. Thick
Stabling: 99 boxes, allocated on arrival. Prior booking required for overnight stay. Tel: (01932) 783334
By Car: On the A308 near Junc 1 of the M3. Main car park £2, Silver Ring and centre car park free.
By Rail: Kempton Park Station (from Waterloo).
By Air: London (Heathrow) Airport 6 miles.
Leading Trainers (since 1991): R. Hannon 53-418 (12.7%), **M. R. Stoute** 24-136 (17.7%), **J. L. Dunlop** 24-187 (12.8%).
Leading Jockeys (since 1991): Pat Eddery 62-311 (19.0%), **T. Quinn** 36-309 (11.0%), **J. Reid** 31-243 (12.0%).

KEMPTON (N.H)

Triangular, 1m 5f (10) 175y run-in. Practically flat; sharp course where the long run between the last obstacle on the far side and the first in the home straight switches the emphasis from jumping to speed.

Address: Kempton Park Racecourse, Sunbury-on-Thames, Middlesex TW16 5AQ
Tel: (01932) 782292 Fax: (01932) 782044
Internet: http://www.demon.co.uk/.racenews/rht
Clerk of the Course: Mr P. R. McNeile, Kempton Park, Sunbury-on-Thames. Tel: (01932) 782292 Raceday Fax: (01932) 779525.
General Manager: Mr J. M. Thick
Stabling: 99 boxes, allocated on arrival. Prior booking required for overnight stay. Tel: (01932) 783334
By Car: On the A308 near Junc 1 of the M3. Main car park £2, Silver Ring and centre car park free.
By Rail: Kempton Park Station (from Waterloo).
By Air: London (Heathrow) Airport 6 miles.
Leading Trainers (since 1991): D. Nicholson 27-114 (23.7%), **N. J. Henderson** 26-117 (22.2%), **M. C. Pipe** 21-101 (20.8%).
Leading Jockeys (since 1991): J. Osborne 37-167 (22.0%), **R. Dunwoody** 33-164 (20.0%), **A. Maguire** 28-131 (21.0%).

LEICESTER (R.H)

An oval track of approximately 1m 5f with a straight run-in of five furlongs. Races of a mile and less are run on a dead straight course which joins the round course five furlongs from the finish, the first half being downhill, followed by an ascent gradually levelling off to the winning post. The bends into the straight and after the winning post have been cambered to make a more galloping track.

Address: Leicester Racecourse, Oadby, Leicester LE2 3QH Tel: (01162) 716515

Clerk of the Course: Captain N. E. S. Lees, Westfield House, The Links, Newmarket, Suffolk CB8 0TG Tel: (01638) 663482 or (01284) 386651 (home)

Secretary: D. C. Henson, Leicester Racecourse Co. Ltd., The Racecourse, Leicester. Tel: (0116) 2716515 or (01604) 30757.

Stabling: 109 boxes,allocated on arrival. Accommodation for one attendant per horse only. Canteen opens at 7.30a.m. Tel: (0116) 271 2115

By Car: The course is 21/2 miles South-East of the City on the A6 (M1, Junc 21). The car park is free.

By Rail: Leicester Station (from St Pancras) is 21/2 miles.

By Air: Helicopter landing facility in the centre of the course.

Leading Trainers (since 1991): R. Hannon 40-269 (14.9%), **J. L. Dunlop** 33-177 (18.6%), **H. R. A. Cecil** 33-128 (25.8%).

Leading Jockeys (since 1991): L. Dettori 54-248 (21.0%), **Pat Eddery** 49-218 (22.0%), **T. Quinn** 29-240 (12.0%).

LEICESTER (N.H)

Rectangular, 1m 6f (10) 250y run-in uphill. An undulating course with an elbow 150y from the finish, Leicester can demand a high degree of stamina, for the going can become extremely heavy and the last three furlongs are uphill.

Address: Leicester Racecourse, Oadby, Leicester LE2 4AL Tel: (01162) 716515

Clerk of the Course: Captain N. E. S. Lees, Westfield House, The Links, Newmarket, Suffolk CB8 0TG Tel: (01638) 663482 or (01284) 386651 (home).

Secretary: D. C. Henson, Leicester Racecourse Co. Ltd., The Racecourse, Leicester. Tel: (0116) 2716515 or (01604) 30757.

Stabling: 109 boxes,allocated on arrival. Accommodation for one attendant per horse only. Canteen opens at 7.30a.m. Tel: (0116) 271 2115

By Car: The course is 21/2 miles South-East of the City on the A6 (M1, Junc 21). The car park is free.

By Rail: Leicester Station (from St Pancras) is 21/2 miles.

By Air: Helicopter landing facility in the centre of the course.

Leading Trainers (since 1991): M. C. Pipe 37-129 (28.7%), **D. Nicholson** 18-81 (22.2%), **Mrs J. Pitman** 18-90 (20.0%).

Leading Jockeys (since 1991): A. Maguire 14-78 (17.0%), **A. P. McCoy** 12-46 (26.0%), **R. Dunwoody** 12-68 (17.0%).

LINGFIELD (L.H)

A 7f 140y straight course with a downhill gradient for about five furlongs, a slight rise and then a gradual fall to the winning post. The round turf course joins the straight at the four furlong post and then follows round the outside of the All-Weather tracks to the summit of a slight hill before turning downhill into the straight. The Derby Trial Course (1m 3f 106y) is very similar to the Epsom Derby Course and provides a good test for the Classic. The re-alignment of the turf course to accomodate the All-Weather tracks has made the turn out of the back straight much less pronounced. However, most of the characteristics remain. The Equitrack course favours the keen, free-running, sharp-actioned horse, particularly so in sprints, which are run on the turn.

Address: Lingfield Park Racecourse, Lingfield, Surrey RH7 6PQ Tel: (01342) 834800 Fax: (01342) 832833
E-mail: 1016111.141@compuserve.com

Clerk of the Course: Mr G. R. Stickels, Lingfield Park Racecourse, Surrey RH7 6PQ (01342) 834800/ Mobile (0973) 737006. Assistant Clerks of the Course Mr P. D. Deacon & Mr F. I. W. Cameron (address as above),
200 boxes. For details of accommodation apply to the Manager, Mr W. Sutton (01342) 834800. Advance notice for overnight accommodation required before 12 noon on the day before racing.

By Car: South-East of the town off the A22 (M25 Junc 6). Ample free parking. Reserved car park £3.

By Rail: Lingfield Station (regular services from London Bridge and Victoria). 1/2m walk to the course.

By Air: London (Gatwick) Airport 10 miles. Helicopter landing facility south of wind-sock.

Leading Trainers Turf (since 1991): R. Hannon 38-308 (12.3%), **J. L. Dunlop** 19-143 (13.3%), **H. R. A. Cecil** 19-59 (32.2%).

Leading Jockeys Turf (since 1991): T. Quinn 31-227 (13.0%), **R. Cochrane** 30-167 (17.0%), **J. Reid** 27-182 (14.0%).

Leading Trainers All-Weather (since 1991): G. L. Moore 71-502 (14.1%), **M. Johnston** 62-320 (19.4%), **R. J. O'Sullivan** 60-405 (14.8%).

Leading Jockeys All-Weather (since 1991): J. Weaver 80-348 (22.0%), **L. Dettori** 74-282 (26.0%), **D. Biggs** 61-588 (10.0%).

LINGFIELD (N.H)

Conical, 1m 5f (10) 200y run-in. Severely undulating with a tight downhill turn into the straight, the chase course suits front runners and those of doubtful resolution.

Address: Lingfield Park Racecourse, Lingfield, Surrey RH7 6PQ Tel: (01342) 834800 Fax: (01342) 832833
E-mail: 1016111.141@compuserve.com

Clerk of the Course: Mr G. R. Stickels, Lingfield Park Racecourse, Surrey RH7 6PQ (01342) 834800/ Mobile (0973) 737006. Assistant Clerks of the Course Mr P. D. Deacon & Mr F. I. W. Cameron (address as above), 200 boxes. For details of accommodation apply to the Manager, Mr W. Sutton (01342) 834800. Advance notice for overnight accommodation required before 12 noon on the day before racing.

By Car: South-East of the town off the A22 (M25 Junc 6). Ample free parking. Reserved car park £3.
By Rail: Lingfield Station (regular services from London Bridge and Victoria). 1/2m walk to the course.
By Air: London (Gatwick) Airport 10 miles. Helicopter landing facility south of wind-sock.
Leading Trainers (since 1991): J. T. Gifford 15-87 (17.2%), **Andrew Turnell** 14-49 (28.6%), **M. C. Pipe** 14-70 (20.0%).
Leading Jockeys (since 1991): A. Maguire 25-111 (22.0%), **R. Dunwoody** 17-81 (20.0%), \ **D. O'Sullivan** 14-113 (12.0%).

LUDLOW (N.H)

Oval, 1m 4f (9) 185y run-in. The chase course is flat and has quite sharp bends into and out of the home straight, although long-striding horses never seem to have any difficulties. The hurdle course is on the outside of the chase track and is not so sharp.
Address: Ludlow Race Club Ltd, The Racecourse, Bromfield, Ludlow, Shropshire SY8 2BT Tel: (01584) 856221/269 (Racedays) (01981) 250052 (Non-racedays) Fax: (01584) 856217 (Racedays) (01981) 250192 (Non-racedays)
Secretary & Clerk of the Course: B. R. Davies. Tel: (01981) 580260 (Home), (01981) 250052 (Office), (01831) 602207 (Car), (01584) 856221 (racedays).
Registered Office: Shepherds Meadow, Eaton Bishop, Hereford HR2 9UA. Fax: (01891) 250192.
Free and allocated on arrival. 100 stables, mainly shavings with a limited number of paper and straw.
By Car: The course is situated at Bromfield, 2 miles North of Ludlow on the A49.
By Rail: Ludlow Station (Hereford-Shrewsbury line) 2 miles.
By Air: Helicopter landing facility in the centre of the course by arrangement with the Clerk of the Course and entirely at own risk.
Leading Trainers (since 1991): M. C. Pipe 38-143 (26.6%), **D. Nicholson** 32-126 (25.4%), **K. C. Bailey** 25-117 (21.4%).
Leading Jockeys (since 1991): R. Dunwoody 24-79 (30.0%), **A. Maguire** 21-109 (19.0%), **N. Williamson** 18-107 (16.0%).

MARKET RASEN (N.H)

Oval, 1m 2f (8) 250y run-in. A sharp, undulating course with a long run to the straight, Market Rasen favours the handy, front-running type. The fences are not as easy as they used to be.
Address: Market Rasen Racecourse, Legsby Road, Market Rasen, Lincolnshire LN8 3EA Tel: (01673) 843434
Fax: (01673) 844532
Clerk of the Course & Manager: Major C. L. Moore, The Racecourse, Legsby Road, Market Rasen LN8 3EA. Tel: (01673) 843434, Fax (01673) 844532.
99 boxes at the course, allocated on arrival. Accommodation for lads and lasses is by reservation only.

By Car: The town is just off A46, and the racecourse is one mile East of the town on the A631. Free car parks and racecards.
By Rail: Market Rasen Station 1 mile (King's Cross - Cleethorpes line).
By Air: Helicopter landing facility by prior arrangement only.
Leading Trainers (since 1991): Mrs M. Reveley 37-147 (25.2%), **J. G. FitzGerald** 29-153 (19.0%), **M. C. Pipe** 28-105 (26.7%).
Leading Jockeys (since 1991): P. Niven 30-160 (18.0%), **L. Wyer** 26-136 (19.0%), **A. S. Smith** 23-180 (12.0%).

MUSSELBURGH (R.H)

An oval of 1m 2f, with sharp bends and a straight, slightly undulating run-in of four furlongs. An extension provides a five furlong course, which bears slightly left and makes a distinct right-hand inclination after a furlong. Edinburgh is virtually flat but, with the turns being very sharp, handiness and manoeuvrability are at a premium.
Address: Musselburgh Racecourse, Linkfield Road, Musselburgh, East Lothian Tel: (0131) 665 2859 (Racecourse)
(01292) 264179 (Non-racedays) Fax: (0131) 653 2083
Clerk of the Course: Mr M. Kershaw, Racecourse Office, 2 Whitletts Road, Ayr. Tel: (01292) 264179 (Office). (0131) 665 2859 (Race days), (0850) 464258 (Mobile).
Secretary/Manager: Mr M. Kershaw
Free stabling. Accommodation for one night in B & B provided. Tel: (0131) 665 4955
By Car: The course is situated at Musselburgh, 5 miles East of Edinburgh on the A1. Car park, adjoining course, free for buses and cars.
By Rail: Waverley Station (Edinburgh). Local Rail service to Musselburgh.
By Air: Edinburgh (Turnhouse) Airport 30 minutes by car.
Leading Trainers (since 1991): J. Berry 58-281 (20.6%), **M. Johnston** 22-150 (14.7%), **Mrs M. Reveley** 17-125 (13.6%).
Leading Jockeys (since 1991): K. Darley 51-244 (20.0%), **J. Carroll** 44-249 (17.0%), **J. Weaver** 35-160 (21.0%).

MUSSELBURGH (N.H)

Rectangular, 1m 3f (8) 150y run-in (variable). A virtually flat track with sharp turns, suiting the handy, front-running sort. Edinburgh drains well.
Address: Musselburgh Racecourse, Linkfield Road, Musselburgh, East Lothian Tel: (0131) 665 2859 (Racecourse)
(01292) 264179 (Non-racedays) Fax: (0131) 653 2083
Clerk of the Course: Mr M. Kershaw, Racecourse Office, 2 Whitletts Road, Ayr. Tel: (01292) 264179 (Office). (0131) 665 2859 (Race days), (0850) 464258 (Mobile).
Secretary/Manager: Mr M. Kershaw
Free stabling. Accommodation for one night in B & B provided. Tel: (0131) 665 4955
By Car: The course is situated at Musselburgh, 5 miles East of Edinburgh on the A1. Car park, adjoining course, free for buses and cars.
By Rail: Waverley Station (Edinburgh). Local Rail service to Musselburgh.
By Air: Edinburgh (Turnhouse) Airport 30 minutes by car.
Leading Trainers (since 1991): M. D. Hammond 40-185 (21.6%), **Howard Johnson** 28-139 (20.1%), **P. Monteith** 22-114 (19.3%).
Leading Jockeys (since 1991): B. Storey 26-188 (13.0%), **A. Dobbin** 17-116 (14.0%), **P. Niven** 16-90 (17.0%).

NEWBURY (L.H)

An oval track of about 1m 7f, 80 feet wide with a slightly undulating straight mile. The round mile and 7f 60y starts are set on a chute from the round course and both join the straight about five furlongs from the finish. Newbury is a good, galloping track, which is efficiently watered during dry periods.
Address: The Racecourse, Newbury, Berkshire RG14 7NZ Tel: (01635) 40015 or (01635) 550354
Clerk of the Course: R. N. J. Pridham, 109 Greenham Road, Newbury, Berkshire RG14 7JE. Tel: (01635) 49511 or Racecourse Office (01635) 40015.
Chief Executive, Secretary and Club Secretary: Major General J. D. G. Pank, C.B.
Free stabling (127 boxes) and accommodation for lads and lasses.
By Car: East of the town off the A34 (M4, Junc 12 or 13). Car park, adjoining enclosures, free, except Southmead £2
By Rail: Newbury Racecourse Station, adjoins course.
By Air: Light Aircraft landing strip East/West. 830 metres by 30 metres wide. Helicopter landing facilities.
Leading Trainers (since 1991): R. Hannon 48-659 (7.3%), **P. W. Chapple-Hyam** 47-209 (22.5%), **J. H. M. Gosden** 47-202 (23.3%).
Leading Jockeys (since 1991): J. Reid 65-395 (16.0%), **L. Dettori** 64-323 (19.0%), **Pat Eddery** 57-393 (14.0%).

NEWBURY (N.H)

Oval, 1m 6f (11) 255y run-in. Slightly undulating, wide and galloping in nature. The fences are stiff and sound jumping is essential. One of the fairest tracks in the country.
Address: The Racecourse, Newbury, Berkshire RG14 7NZ Tel: (01635) 40015 or (01635) 550354
Clerk of the Course: R. N. J. Pridham, 109 Greenham Road, Newbury, Berkshire RG14 7JE. Tel: (01635) 49511 or Racecourse Office (01635) 40015.
Chief Executive, Secretary and Club Secretary: Major General J. D. G. Pank, C.B.
Free stabling (127 boxes) and accommodation for lads and lasses.
By Car: East of the town off the A34 (M4, Junc 12 or 13). Car park, adjoining enclosures, free, except Southmead £2
By Rail: Newbury Racecourse Station, adjoins course.
By Air: Light Aircraft landing strip East/West. 830 metres by 30 metres wide. Helicopter landing facilities.
Leading Trainers (since 1991): D. Nicholson 35-164 (21.3%), **N. J. Henderson** 35-180 (19.4%), **M. C. Pipe** 29-139 (20.9%).
Leading Jockeys (since 1991): J. Osborne 55-215 (25.0%), **R. Dunwoody** 50-208 (24.0%), **A. Maguire** 25-147 (17.0%).

NEWCASTLE (L.H)

An oval course of 1m 6f with a chute to provide a 1m 2f start and a straight run-in of four furlongs, gradually rising until levelling off in the final 100y. The run-in extends to allow a straight mile, which is against the collar all the way. Newcastle is a galloping track with the final climb making it a test of stamina and is not one for short runners.
Address: High Gosforth Park, Newcastle-Upon-Tyne NE3 5HP Tel: (0191) 236 2020
Clerk of the Course: Mr David McAllister c/o High Gosforth Park Ltd, High Gosforth Park, Newcastle-upon-Tyne. NE3 5HP. Tel: (0191) 236 2020.
Company Secretary & Club Secretary: Mr J. C. Tulip
Free. It is essential to book accommodation in advance. Apply to the Manager. Tel: (0191) 217 0060 the day before racing, or the Racecourse Office otherwise.
By Car: 4 miles North of the city on the A6125 (near the A1). Car and coach park free.
By Rail: Newcastle Central Station (from King's Cross), a free bus service operates from South Gosforth and Regent Centre Metro Station.
By Air: Helicopter landing facility by prior arrangement. The Airport is 4 miles from the course.
Leading Trainers (since 1991): J. Berry 31-227 (13.7%), **M. Johnston** 29-201 (14.4%), **Mrs M. Reveley** 29-231 (12.6%).
Leading Jockeys (since 1991): K. Darley 41-307 (13.0%), **J. Carroll** 31-238 (13.0%), **J. Weaver** 26-141 (18.0%).

NEWCASTLE (N.H)

Oval, 1m 6f (11) 220y run-in. A gradually rising home straight of four furlongs makes this galloping track a true test of stamina, especially as the ground can become very heavy. The fences are rather stiff.
Address: High Gosforth Park, Newcastle-Upon-Tyne NE3 5HP Tel: (0191) 236 2020
Clerk of the Course: Mr David McAllister c/o High Gosforth Park Ltd, High Gosforth Park, Newcastle-upon-Tyne. NE3 5HP. Tel: (0191) 236 2020.
Company Secretary & Club Secretary: Mr J. C. Tulip
Free. It is essential to book accommodation in advance. Apply to the Manager. Tel: (0191) 217 0060 the day before racing, or the Racecourse Office otherwise.
By Car: 4 miles North of the city on the A6125 (near the A1). Car and coach park free.
By Rail: Newcastle Central Station (from King's Cross), a free bus service operates from South Gosforth and Regent Centre Metro Station.
By Air: Helicopter landing facility by prior arrangement. The Airport is 4 miles from the course.
Leading Trainers (since 1991): Mrs M. Reveley 54-213 (25.4%), **Howard Johnson** 21-179 (12.4%), **M. W. Easterby** 18-79 (22.8%).
Leading Jockeys (since 1991): P. Niven 54-192 (28.0%), **B. Storey** 23-196 (11.0%), **A. Dobbin** 19-138 (13.0%).

NEWMARKET (R.H)

(Rowley Mile Course) - There is a straight course of ten furlongs with slight undulations as far as `The Bushes', about two furlongs from the finish. From that point it is downhill for a furlong to `The Dip', the final furlong being uphill. The Cesarewitch course starts on the Beacon Course, which turns right into the straight. The ten furlong straight is a wide, galloping track ideal for long-striding horses.
(July Course) - All races up to a mile inclusive are run on the straight Bunbury Mile, which has a steadily increasing downhill gradient after two furlongs, the final furlong being uphill. Races further than a mile start on the Cesarewitch course and turn right into the straight mile. Like the Rowley Mile course, this is a wide, galloping track.
Address: Newmarket Racecourse, Newmarket, Suffolk CB8 0TG Tel: (01638) 663482 (Main Office) (01638) 662524 (Rowley) (01638) 662752 (July) Fax: (01638) 663044
Clerk of the Course: Captain N. E. S. Lees, Westfield House, The Links, Newmarket. Tel: (01638) 663482.
Manager/Assistant Clerk of the Course: Mr C. R. Kennedy
Stabling: Free accommodation available at the Links Stables (100 boxes). Tel: (01638) 662200
By Car: South-West of the town on the A1304 London Road (M11 Junc 9). Free car parking at the rear of the enclosure. Members car park £1 all days; Free courtesy bus service from Newmarket Station, Bus Station and High Street, commencing 90 minutes prior to the first race, and return trips up to 60 minutes after the last race.
By Rail: Infrequent rail service to Newmarket Station from Cambridge (Liverpool Street) or direct bus service from Cambridge (13 mile journey).
By Air: Landing facilities for light aircraft and helicopters on racedays at both racecourses. See Flight Guide. Cambridge Airport 11 miles.
Leading Trainers Rowley (since 1991): H. R. A. Cecil 60-275 (21.8%), **J. H. M. Gosden** 44-296 (14.9%), **B. W. Hills** 40-346 (11.6%).
Leading Jockeys Rowley (since 1991): Pat Eddery 92-465 (19.0%), **L. Dettori** 74-504 (14.0%), **W. R. Swinburn** 40-281 (14.0%).
Leading Trainers July (since 1991): R. Hannon 39-317 (12.3%), **H. R. A. Cecil** 37-153 (24.2%), **J. H. M. Gosden** 33-190 (17.4%).
Leading Jockeys July (since 1991): Pat Eddery 62-299 (20.0%), **L. Dettori** 55-292 (18.0%), **M. Roberts** 30-224 (13.0%).

NEWTON ABBOT (N.H)

Oval, 1m 2f (7) 300y run-in. Flat with two tight bends and a water jump situated three fences from home. The nippy, agile sort is favoured. The run-in can be very short on the hurdle course.
Address: Newton Abbot Races Ltd., Kingsteignton Road, Newton Abbot, Devon TQ12 3AF Tel: (01626) 53235 or
(01626) 775285 Fax: (01626) 336972
Clerk of the Course: Mr M. J. Trickey, The Racecourse, Kingsteignton Road, Newton Abbot. Tel: (01626) 53235 or (01374) 620717 (Mobile) or (01598) 740203 (Home).
General Manager: Pat Masterson. Tel: (01626) 53235/ Mobile (0378) 463207.
100 boxes, allocated on arrival.

By Car: North of the town on the A380. Torquay 6 miles, Exeter 17 miles.
By Rail: Newton Abbot Station (from Paddington) 3/4 mile. Buses and taxis operate to and from the course.
By Air: Helicopter landing pad in the centre of the course.
Leading Trainers (since 1991): M. C. Pipe 156-575 (27.1%), **P. J. Hobbs** 68-246 (27.6%), **P. F. Nicholls** 44-181 (24.3%).
Leading Jockeys (since 1991): R. Dunwoody 68-225 (30.0%), **A. P. McCoy** 62-185 (33.0%), **D. Bridgwater** 28-135 (20.0%).

NOTTINGHAM (L.H)

A galloping oval track with a straight run-in of about five furlongs, from which a chute provides a straight six furlongs. The turns on this flat course are easy.
Address: Nottingham Racecourse, Colwick Park, Nottingham NG2 4BE Tel: (0115) 958 0620 Fax: (0115) 958 4515
Clerk of the Course: Major C. Moore, Hamilton House, Toft-next-Newton, Market Rasen, Lincolnshire LN8 3NE. Tel: (01673) 878575.
Racecourse Manager: Mrs Jan Lloyd, The racecourse Office, Colwick Park, Nottingham. Tel: (0115) 958 0620
Secretary: R. Goodman, Prestbury Park, Cheltenham, Gloucestershire GL50 4SH. Tel: (01242) 513014.
Free. 120 boxes allotted on arrival. New hostel for lads and lasses. Tel (0115) 950 1198
By Car: 2 miles East of the City on the B686. The car park is free. Silver Ring Picnic Car Park £12 (admits car and four occupants).
By Rail: Nottingham (Midland) Station. Regular bus service to course (2 miles).
By Air: Helicopter landing facility in the centre of the course.
Leading Trainers (since 1991): H. R. A. Cecil 36-104 (34.6%), **J. L. Dunlop** 31-185 (16.8%), **P. F. I. Cole** 18-112 (16.1%).
Leading Jockeys (since 1991): L. Dettori 37-196 (18.0%), **Pat Eddery** 31-140 (22.0%), **W. Ryan** 28-224 (12.0%).

PERTH (N.H)

Rectangular, 1m 2f (8) 283y run-in. A flat, easy track with sweeping turns. Not a course for the long-striding galloper. An efficient watering system ensures that the ground rarely gets hard.
Address: Perth Racecourse, Scone Palace Park, Perth PH2 6BB Tel (01738) 551597 Fax: (01738) 552439
Internet: http://www.perth.org.uk/perth.races.htm
Clerk of the Course: Mr S. R. Morshead, Racecourse Office, 2 Whitletts Road, Ayr. Tel: (01292) 264179 (Office), (01655) 750277 (Home)/ Mobile (0860) 210777.
Secretary: Miss I. J. C. Grant, Penrose Hill, Moffat, Dumfriesshire. Tel: (01683) 220131. Racedays (01738) 551597.
100 boxes and accommodation for lads and lasses. Apply to the Secretary. Stables Tel: (01738) 21604 (racedays only).
By Car: 4 miles North of the town off the A93.
By Rail: Perth Station (from Dundee) 4 miles. There are buses to the course.
By Air: Scone Airport (33/4 miles). Edinburgh Airport 45 minutes.

Leading Trainers (since 1991): M. D. Hammond 36-146 (24.7%), **G. Richards** 36-177 (20.3%), **Mrs M. Reveley** 32-80 (40.0%).
Leading Jockeys (since 1991): P. Niven 41-119 (34.0%), **A. Dobbin** 21-95 (22.0%), **B. Storey** 20-188 (10.0%).

PLUMPTON (N.H)

Oval, 1m 1f (7) 200y run-in uphill. A tight, undulating circuit with an uphill finish, Plumpton favours the handy, fast jumper. The ground often gets heavy, as the course is based on clay soil.
Address: Plumpton Racecourse Ltd., Plumpton, Sussex Tel: (01273) 890383 (Racedays) (01444) 441211 (Non-racedays) Fax: (01444) 450990
Clerk of the Course: Mr C. E. Griggs, 11 Boltro Road, Haywards Heath, Sussex, RH16 1BP. Tel: (01444) 441111, Fax: (01444) 450990.
75 boxes allocated in rotation. Advance notice is required for overnight arrival. Tel: (01273) 890383/ Fax: (01444) 450990.
By Car: 2 miles North of the village off the B2116.
By Rail: Plumpton Station (from Victoria) adjoins course.
By Air: Helicopter landing facility by prior arrangement with the Clerk of the Course.
Leading Trainers (since 1991): M. C. Pipe 34-80 (42.5%), **R. Rowe** 20-123 (16.3%), **J. R. Jenkins** 20-130 (15.4%).
Leading Jockeys (since 1991): A. Maguire 48-183 (26.0%), **A. P. McCoy** 30-84 (35.0%), **R. Dunwoody** 27-129 (20.0%).

PONTEFRACT (L.H)

An oval, undulating course of 2m 133y with two sharp bends and a straight run-in of only two furlongs. There is a steep ascent over the last three furlongs. The undulations make it unsuitable for a long-striding horse, although a degree of stamina is called for. There have been a number of course specialists at Pontefract.
Address: Pontefract Park Race Co. Ltd., The Park, Pontefract, West Yorkshire Tel: (01977) 703224 (Admin Office)
(01977) 702210 (Racedays) Fax: (01977) 600577 (Admin Office) (01977) 702210 (Racedays)
Clerk of the Course and Secretary: Mr J. Norman Gundill, 33 Ropergate, Pontefract, West Yorkshire. WF8 1LE
Tel: (01977) 703224 (Office), (01977) 620649 (Home), (01977) 702210 (racedays only).
Stabling and accommodation must be reserved (116 boxes). They will be allocated on a first come-first served basis. Tel: (01977 702323)
By Car: 1 mile North of the town on the A639. Junc 32 of M62. Free car park adjacent to the course.
By Rail: Pontefract Station (Baghill), 11/2 miles from the course. Regular bus service from Leeds.
By Air: Helicopters by arrangement only. (Nearest airfield: Doncaster, Sherburn-in-Elmet, Yeadon (Leeds/Bradford).
Leading Trainers (since 1991): Mrs J. R. Ramsden 49-301 (16.3%), **Mrs M. Reveley** 29-189 (15.3%), **H. R. A. Cecil** 20-50 (40.0%).
Leading Jockeys (since 1991): K. Fallon 47-267 (17.0%), **K. Darley** 38-320 (11.0%), **L. Dettori** 33-162 (20.0%).

REDCAR (L.H)

A perfectly flat, narrow, oval course of two miles with a straight run-in of five furlongs, which extends backwards to make a straight mile. Despite two very tight bends into and out of the back straight, Redcar is an excellent galloping course.

Address: Redcar Racecourse, Redcar, Cleveland TS10 2BY Tel: (01642) 484068 Fax: (01642) 488272

Clerk of the Course: Mr J. E. Gundill, Redcar Racecourse, Redcar, Cleveland. TS10 2BY Tel: Mobile (0370) 613049.

Racecourse Office; The Racecourse, Redcar, Cleveland TS10 2BY. Tel: (01642) 484068.

Groundsman; Mr J. Berry, The Racecourse, Redcar, Cleveland. Tel: (01642) 489861 (Stables on racedays only (01642) 484254).

By Car: In town off the A1085. Free parking adjoining the course for buses and cars.

By Rail: Redcar Station (1/4 mile from the course).

By Air: (None). Landing facilities at Turners Arms Farm (600y runway) Yearby, Cleveland. 2 miles South of the racecourse - transport available. Teeside airport (18 miles west of Redcar).

Leading Trainers (since 1991): Mrs M. Reveley 67-520 (12.9%), **J. H. M. Gosden** 27-105 (25.7%), **J. Berry** 25-241 (10.4%).

Leading Jockeys (since 1991): K. Darley 79-406 (19.0%), **K. Fallon** 31-212 (14.0%), **J. Carroll** 25-222 (11.0%).

RIPON (R.H)

An oval course of 1m 5f, joined to a straight six furlongs by a tightish bend at the five furlong point. The straight course is slightly on the ascent except for a shallow dip at the `distance' and, in general, this is a rather sharp track, a course where experience can be decisive.

Address: Ripon Racecourse, Boroughbridge Road, Ripon, North Yorkshire HG4 1UG Tel: (01765) 602156

Fax: (01765) 690018 E-mail: mail@hutchbutch.demon.co.uk

Clerk of the Course: Mr J. M. Hutchinson, 77 North Street, Ripon HG4 1DS. Tel: (01765) 602156, evenings (01845) 567378, Mobile (0860) 679904. Non-racedays: Admin. Office, 77, North Street, Ripon HG4 1DS. Tel: (01765) 602156. Fax (01765) 690018. Racedays: The Racecourse, Boroughbridge Road, Ripon HG4 3UG. Tel: (01765) 603696.

Trainers requiring stabling (104 boxes available) are requested to contact Mr P. Bateson, The Racecourse, Ripon prior to 11a.m. the day before racing. Tel: (01765) 603696.

By Car: The course is situated 2 miles South-East of the city, on the B6265. There is ample free parking for cars and coaches. For reservations apply to the Secretary.

By Rail: Harrogate Station (11 miles), or Thirsk (15 miles). Bus services to Ripon.

By Air: Helicopters only on the course. Otherwise Leeds/Bradford airport.

Leading Trainers (since 1991): H. R. A. Cecil 30-70 (42.9%), **J. Berry** 28-207 (13.5%), **M. Johnston** 27-161 (16.8%).

Leading Jockeys (since 1991): K. Darley 45-245 (18.0%), **J. Weaver** 25-125 (20.0%), **W. Ryan** 24-112 (21.0%).

SALISBURY (R.H)

The course consists of a loop with an arm of about four furlongs for the finish of all races. Contests of up to a mile are almost straight except for a slight right-hand bend at halfway. On the 1m 6f course, horses start opposite the stands, turn to the left around the loop and re-enter the straight at the seven furlong starting gate. The last half-mile is uphill, providing a stiff test of stamina.
Address: Salisbury Racecourse, Netherhampton, Salisbury, Wiltshire SP2 8PN Tel: (01722) 326461
Fax: (01722) 412710
Clerk of the Course: Mr R. I. Renton, Salisbury Racecourse, Netherhampton, Salisbury, Wiltshire SP2 8PN.
Secretary: The Bibury Club, Salisbury Racecourse, Netherhampton, Salisbury, Wiltshire. Tel: (01722) 326461.
Free stabling (112 boxes) and accommodation for lads and lasses, apply to the Stabling Manager (01722) 327327.
By Car: 3 miles South-West of the city on the A3094 at Netherhampton. Free car park adjoins the course.
By Rail: Salisbury Station is 31/2 miles (from Waterloo). Bus service to the course.
By Air: Helicopter landing facility near the ten furlong start.
Leading Trainers (since 1991): R. Hannon 66-518 (12.7%), **P. F. I. Cole** 25-146 (17.1%), **J. L. Dunlop** 25-185 (13.5%).
Leading Jockeys (since 1991): Pat Eddery 34-174 (19.0%), **L. Dettori** 32-148 (21.0%), **T. Quinn** 31-214 (14.0%).

SANDOWN (R.H)

An oval course of 1m 5f with a straight run-in of four furlongs. The ground is almost level until entering the straight, where it rises to the winning post. Five furlong contests are run on a separate straight course which cuts diagonally across the inside of the main circuit and is uphill all the way. The track suits long-striding horses and is a real test of stamina.
Address: Sandown Park Racecourse, Esher, Surrey KT10 9AJ Tel: (01372) 463072
Fax: (01372) 470427
Clerk of the Course: Mr A. J. Cooper, Sandown Park, Esher, Surrey. Tel: (01372) 463072 Mobile (0374) 230850.
Club Secretary: Racing Manager: Mr S. H. Wallis, Address and Tel as above.
Managing Director: Mrs S. C. Ellen.
Free stabling (108 boxes) and accommodation for lads and lasses. tel: (01372) 463511
By Car: 4 miles South-West of Kingston-on-Thames, on the A307 (M25 Junc 10). The members' car park in More Lane £2. All other car parking is free.
By Rail: Esher Station (from Waterloo) adjoins the course.
By Air: London (Heathrow) Airport 12 miles.
Leading Trainers (since 1991): R. Hannon 53-475 (11.2%), **M. R. Stoute** 36-228 (15.8%), **J. H. M. Gosden** 30-160 (18.8%).
Leading Jockeys (since 1991): Pat Eddery 81-411 (19.0%), **L. Dettori** 60-315 (19.0%), **M. Roberts** 46-307 (14.0%).

SANDOWN (N.H)

Oval, 1m 5f (11) 220y run-in uphill. Features seven fences on the back straight, the last three (Railway Fences) are very close together and can often decide the outcome of races. The stiff uphill climb to the finish puts the emphasis very much on stamina, but accurate-jumping, free-running sorts are also favoured. Hurdle races are run on the Flat course.

Address: Sandown Park Racecourse, Esher, Surrey KT10 9AJ Tel: (01372) 463072 Fax: (01372) 470427

Clerk of the Course: Mr A. J. Cooper, Sandown Park, Esher, Surrey. Tel: (01372) 463072 Mobile (0374) 230850.

Club Secretary: Racing Manager: Mr S. H. Wallis, Address and Tel as above.

Managing Director: Mrs S. C. Ellen.

Free stabling (108 boxes) and accommodation for lads and lasses. tel: (01372) 463511

By Car: 4 miles South-West of Kingston-on-Thames, on the A307 (M25 Junc 10). The members' car park in More Lane £2. All other car parking is free.

By Rail: Esher Station (from Waterloo) adjoins the course.

By Air: London (Heathrow) Airport 12 miles.

Leading Trainers (since 1991): D. Nicholson 36-124 (29.0%), **J. T. Gifford** 35-224 (15.6%), **M. C. Pipe** 18-105 (17.1%).

Leading Jockeys (since 1991): R. Dunwoody 46-185 (24.0%), **J. Osborne** 28-155 (18.0%), **A. Maguire** 26-127 (20.0%).

SEDGEFIELD (N.H)

Oval, 1m 2f (8) 200y run-in: Hurdles 200y run-in. Undulating with fairly tight turns. and does not suit the big, long-striding horse.

Address: Sedgefield Racecourse, Sedgefield, Stockton-on-Tees, Cleveland TS21 2HW Tel: (01740) 621925 (Office) (01740) 620366 (Racedays) Fax: (01740) 620663

Clerk of the Course: J. G. Cleverly, F.R.I.C.S., Grandstand, York Road, Beverley, North Humberside HU17 8QZ. Tel: (01944) 768203 (Home), (01482) 867488 (Office).

Secretary: A. Brown, The Bungalow, Sedgefield Racecourse, Sedgefield, Stockton-on-Tees, Cleveland TS21 2HW. Tel: (01740) 621925.

Course Foreman: Sedgefield (01740) 22629 or 20366 (race days only).

115 boxes filled in rotation. No forage.

By Car: 3/4 mile South-West of the town, near the junction of the A689 (Bishop Auckland) and the A177 (Durham) roads. The car park is free.

By Rail: Darlington Station (9 miles). Durham Station (12 miles).

By Air: Helicopter landing facility in car park area by prior arrangement only.

Leading Trainers (since 1991): Mrs M. Reveley 103-368 (28.0%), **G. M. Moore** 36-214 (16.8%), **Howard Johnson** 31-245 (12.7%).

Leading Jockeys (since 1991): P. Niven 83-276 (30.0%), **L. Wyer** 31-158 (19.0%), **A. Maguire** 21-96 (21.0%).

SOUTHWELL (L.H)

The All-Weather Fibresand track consists of an oval circuit, 1m 2f in circumference, with a three furlong straight and a spur to provide a five furlong straight All-Weather track. The turf tracks are on the inside of the All-Weather track. A sharp, flat circuit, Southwell suits the keen, front-running sort.

Address: Southwell Racecourse, Rolleston, Newark, Nottinghamshire NG25 0TS
Tel: (01636) 814481
Fax: (01636) 812271

Clerk of the Course: Mr A. J. Bealby, The Rookery, Bragborough Hall, Braunston, Daventry, Northamptonshire NN11 7HA. Tel: (01788) 891795. Fax: (01636) 812271.

110 boxes at the course. Applications for staff and horse accommodation to be booked by noon the day before racing on (01636) 814481

By Car: The course is situated at Rolleston, 3 miles South of Southwell, 5 miles from Newark.

By Rail: Rolleston Station (Nottingham-Newark line) adjoins the course.

Leading Trainers (since 1991): D. W. Chapman 76-761 (10.0%), **M. Johnston** 59-314 (18.8%), **T. D. Barron** 59-370 (16.0%).

Leading Jockeys (since 1991): J. Quinn 55-768 (7.0%), **J. Weaver** 54-307 (17.0%), **Dean McKeown** 54-521 (10.0%).

SOUTHWELL (N.H)

Oval, 1m 1f (7) 220y run-in. A tight, flat track with a short run-in, admirably suited to front-runners.

Address: Southwell Racecourse, Rolleston, Newark, Nottinghamshire NG25 0TS
Tel: (01636) 814481
Fax: (01636) 812271

Clerk of the Course: Mr A. J. Bealby, The Rookery, Bragborough Hall, Braunston, Daventry, Northamptonshire NN11 7HA. Tel: (01788) 891795. Fax: (01636) 812271.

110 boxes at the course. Applications for staff and horse accommodation to be booked by noon the day before racing on (01636) 814481

By Car: The course is situated at Rolleston, 3 miles South of Southwell, 5 miles from Newark.

By Rail: Rolleston Station (Nottingham-Newark line) adjoins the course.

Leading Trainers (since 1991): K. C. Bailey 16-69 (23.2%), **Mrs M. Reveley** 15-39 (38.5%), **J. G. M. O'Shea** 15-60 (25.0%).

Leading Jockeys (since 1991): S. Wynne 27-149 (18.0%), **A. Maguire** 24-84 (28.0%), **R. Dunwoody** 24-79 (30.0%).

STRATFORD-ON-AVON (N.H)

Triangular, 1m 2f (8) 200y run-in. Virtually flat with two tight bends, and quite a short home straight. A sharp and turning course, Stratford-on-Avon suits the well-balanced, handy sort.
Address: Stratford Racecourse, Luddington Road, Stratford-upon-Avon, Warwickshire CV37 9SE
Tel; (01789) 267949 Fax: (01789) 415850
Clerk of the Course: James H. Sanderson Esq, Catterick Racecourse, Catterick Bridge, Richmond, N. Yorks, DL10 7PE. Tel: (01748) 811478. (01789) 267949 (Racedays), Fax: (01748) 811082.
Club Secretary: Mrs J. M. Dunstan, Rickstaddles, Snitterfield, Stratford-on-Avon, Warwickshire. Tel: (01789) 731322.
Company Secretary and Racecourse Manager: Mrs A. L. N. Gale, The Racecourse, Luddington Road, Stratford-on-Avon, Warwickshire. Tel: (01789) 267949.
92 boxes available. Allotted on arrival. Advance notice must be given for overnighters. Tel: (01789) 267949.
By Car: 1 mile from the town centre, off the A429 (Evesham road).
By Rail: Stratford-on-Avon Station (from Birmingham New Street or Leamington Spa) 1 mile.
By Air: Helicopter landing facility by prior arrangement.
Leading Trainers (since 1991): M. C. Pipe 46-176 (26.1%), **D. Nicholson** 23-110 (20.9%), **N. A. Twiston-Davies** 20-103 (19.4%).
Leading Jockeys (since 1991): A. Maguire 33-131 (25.0%), **R. Dunwoody** 26-146 (17.0%), **A. P. McCoy** 25-119 (21.0%).

TAUNTON (N.H)

Elongated oval, 1m 2f (8) 150y run-in uphill. Sharp turns, especially after the winning post, with a steady climb from the home bend. Suits the handy sort.
Address: Taunton Racecourse, Orchard Portman, Taunton, Somerset TA3 7BL Tel: (01823) 337172 (Office)
Fax: (01823) 325881
Clerk of the Course: Mr M. Trickey, The Racecourse, Taunton, Somerset TA3 7BL. Tel: (01823) 337172 or (01598) 740203 (Home).
Approx. 100 boxes. Allotted on arrival. Advance bookings for long journeys. Apply to the Stable Manager, c/o The Racecourse (01823) 337172 or (01823) 331195.
By Car: 2 miles South of the town on the B3170 (Honiton) road (M5 Junc 25). Free car park for Members. The public car parks are free or £3 on course.
By Rail: Taunton Station 21/2 miles. There are buses and taxis to course.
Leading Trainers (since 1991): M. C. Pipe 82-365 (22.5%), **P. J. Hobbs** 34-175 (19.4%), **R. J. Hodges** 34-318 (10.7%).
Leading Jockeys (since 1991): A. P. McCoy 22-110 (20.0%), **M. A. Fitzgerald** 19-147 (12.0%), **D. Bridgwater** 17-116 (14.0%).

THIRSK (L.H)

An oval track of 1m 2f, with fairly tight turns and an undulating run-in of four furlongs. Races of five and six furlongs start on a straight, more undulating two furlong extension of the run-in. Though the turns on the round course are comparatively easy, the track is somewhat sharp. The going seldom rides heavy.

Address: Thirsk Racecourse, Station Road, Thirsk, North Yorkshire YO7 1QL Tel: (01845) 522276 Fax: (01845) 525353

Managing Director/Company Director & Clerk of the Course: Mr Christopher Tetley, The Racecourse, Station Road, Thirsk, North Yorkshire YO7 1QL. Tel: (01845) 522276.

Registered Office: Thirsk Racecourse Limited, The Racecourse, Station Road, Thirsk, North Yorkshire YO7 1QL. Tel: (01845) 522276. Fax: (01845) 525353.

For stabling and accommodation apply to, The Racecourse, Station Road, Thirsk, North Yorkshire. Tel: (01845) 522276 or (01845) 522096 (racedays).

By Car: West of the town on the A61. Free car park adjacent to the course for buses and cars.

By Rail: Thirsk Station (from King's Cross). 1/2 mile from the course.

By Air: Helicopters only, landing on the hockey pitch. Prior arrangement required.Tel: Racecourse (01845) 522276. Fixed wing aircraft can land at RAF Leeming. Tel: (01677) 423041. Light aircraft at Bagby. Tel: (01845) 597385 or (01845) 537555.

Leading Trainers (since 1991): M. Johnston 23-136 (16.9%), **J. Berry** 22-198 (11.1%), **T. D. Barron** 19-174 (10.9%).

Leading Jockeys (since 1991): G. Duffield 35-147 (23.0%), **J. Weaver** 29-125 (23.0%), **K. Darley** 25-219 (11.0%).

TOWCESTER (N.H)

Square, 1m 6f (10) 200y run-in uphill. The final six furlongs are uphill. One of the most testing tracks in the country with the emphasis purely on stamina.

Address: The Racecourse, Easton Neston, Towcester, Northants NN12 7HS Tel: (01327) 353414

Fax: (01327) 358534 Internet: http;//www.demon.co.uk/racenews/towcester

Clerk of the Course and Manager: Hugo Bevan, The Old House, Little Everdon, Daventry, Northamptonshire NN11 3BG. Tel: (01327) 361266.

Secretary: M. Chapman, Towcester Racecourse, Towcester, Northamptonshire NN12 7HS. Tel: (01327) 353414.

75 boxes available and allotted on arrival.

By Car: 1 mile South-East of the town on the A5 (Milton Keynes road). M1 (Junc 15) (from the South), M1 (Junc 16) (from the North).

By Rail: Northampton Station (Euston) 9 miles, buses to Towcester; or Milton Keynes (Euston) 12 miles, taxis available.

Leading Trainers (since 1991): D. Nicholson 36-101 (35.6%), **O. Brennan** 28-163 (17.2%), **K. C. Bailey** 20-99 (20.2%).

Leading Jockeys (since 1991): R. Dunwoody 28-131 (21.0%), **M. Brennan** 26-143 (18.0%), **A. Maguire** 25-104 (24.0%).

UTTOXETER (N.H)

Oval, 1m 2f (8) 170y run-in. Few undulations, easy bends and fences and a flat home straight of over half a mile. Suits front-runners, especially on the two mile hurdle course.
Address; The Racecourse, Wood Lane, Uttoxeter, Staffordshire ST14 8BD Tel: (01889) 562561 Fax: (01889) 562786
Clerk of the Course and Manager: Major D. McAllister, The Racecourse, Wood Lane, Uttoxeter. Tel: (01889) 562561.
90 boxes, allotted on arrival. Tel: (01889) 562561.
By Car: South-East of the town off the B5017 (Marchington Road).
By Rail: Uttoxeter Station (Crewe-Derby line) adjoins the course.
Leading Trainers (since 1991): M. C. Pipe 71-239 (29.7%), **N. A. Twiston-Davies** 31-151 (20.5%), **K. C. Bailey** 30-174 (17.2%)
Leading Jockeys (since 1991): R. Dunwoody 51-228 (22.0%), **J. Osborne** 36-130 (27.0%), **N. Williamson** 29-182 (15.0%).

WARWICK (L.H)

A nearly circular track, 1m 6f 32y in circumference, with a distinct rise and fall levelling off a mile from home, and a run-in of about two and a half furlongs. The five furlong course has a left-hand elbow at the junction with the round course. The mile course, straight for the first five furlongs, then turns into the home straight. This sharp track favours handiness and speed rather than staying power.
Address: Warwick Racecourse, Hampton Street, Warwick CV34 6HN Tel: (01926) 491553 Fax: (01926) 403223
Clerk of the Course and Racecourse Manager: Miss Lisa Rowe, Warwick Racecourse, Hampton Street, Warwick CV34 6HN. Tel: (01926) 491553. Fax (01926) 403223.
Raceday Clerk of the Course: Mr A. J. P. Waterworth
112 boxes allocated on arrival or by reservation (01526) 493803.
By Car: West of the town on the B4095 adjacent to Junc 15 of the M40. Free parking (except the Members' Car Park, £5 to Daily Club Members).
By Rail: Warwick or Leamington Spa Station.
Leading Trainers (since 1991): P. F. I. Cole 19-121 (15.7%), **J. Berry** 19-137 (13.9%), **G. Lewis** 15-74 (20.3%).
Leading Jockeys (since 1991): T. Quinn22-147 (14.0%), **J. Reid** 22-124 (17.0%), **Pat Eddery** 20-61 (32.0%).

WARWICK (N.H)

Circular, 1m 6f (10) 240y run-in. Undulating with tight bends, five quick fences in the back straight and a short home straight, Warwick favours handiness and speed rather than stamina.
Address: Warwick Racecourse, Hampton Street, Warwick CV34 6HN Tel: (01926) 491553 Fax: (01926) 403223
Racecourse Manager: Miss Lisa Rowe, Warwick Racecourse, Hampton Street, Warwick CV34 6HN. Tel: (01926) 491553. Fax (01926) 403223.
Clerk of the Course and Racecourse Manager: Miss Lisa Rowe, Warwick Racecourse, Hampton Street, Warwick CV34 6HN. Tel: (01926) 491553. Fax (01926) 403223.
Raceday Clerk of the Course: Mr A. J. P. Waterworth
112 boxes allocated on arrival or by reservation (01526) 493803.
By Car: West of the town on the B4095 adjacent to Junc 15 of the M40. Free parking (except the Members' Car Park, £5 to Daily Club Members).
By Rail: Warwick or Leamington Spa Station.
Leading Trainers (since 1991): M. C. Pipe 50-190 (26.3%), **D. Nicholson** 34-163 (20.9%), **Mrs J. Pitman** 23-126 (18.3%).
Leading Jockeys (since 1991): R. Dunwoody 41-121 (33.0%), **J. Osborne** 22-115 (19.0%), **A. Maguire** 21-107 (19.0%).

WETHERBY (N.H)

Oval, 1m 4f (9) 200y run-in slightly uphill. A flat, very fair course which suits the long-striding galloper.
Address; The Racecourse, York Road, Wetherby, West Yorkshire LS22 5EJ Tel; (01937) 582035
Fax; (01937) 580565
Clerk of the Course: C. M. Tetley, The Racecourse, Wetherby. Tel: (01937) 582035
Secretary: Miss A. Dalby The Racecourse, Wetherby. Tel: (01937) 582035.
98 boxes allocated on arrival. Accommodation for lads and lasses.
By Car: East of the town off the B1224 (York Road). Adjacent to the A1. Excellent bus and coach facilities. Car park free.
By Rail: Leeds Station 12 miles. Buses to Wetherby.
Leading Trainers (since 1991): Mrs M. Reveley 69-267 (25.8%), **G. Richards** 36-184 (19.6%), **J. G. FitzGerald** 28-160 (17.5%).
Leading Jockeys (since 1991): P. Niven 63-263 (23.0%), **L. Wyer** 53-224 (23.0%), **A. Maguire** 26-114 (22.0%).

WINCANTON (N.H)

Rectangular, 1m 3f (9) 200y run-in. Good galloping course where the going rarely becomes heavy. The home straight is mainly downhill.

Address: Wincanton Racecourse, Wincanton, Somerset BA9 8BJ Tel; (01963) 32344 Fax: (01963) 34668

Clerk of the Course and Manager: R. I. Renton, Wincanton Racecourse, Wincanton, Somerset BA9 8BJ. Tel: (01963) 32344. Fax: (01963) 34668.

92 boxes allocated on arrival, overnight accommodation must be booked in advance. Apply to the Stable Manager, Wincanton Racecourse. Tel: (01963) 32344.

By Car: 1 mile North of the town on the B3081.

By Rail: Gillingham Station (from Waterloo) or Castle Cary Station (from Paddington). Buses and taxis to the course.

By Air: Helicopter landing area is situated in the centre of the course.

Leading Trainers (since 1991): M. C. Pipe 59-225 (26.2%), **P. F. Nicholls** 32-171 (18.7%), **Mrs J. Pitman** 25-103 (24.3%).

Leading Jockeys (since 1991): R. Dunwoody 39-185 (21.0%), **J. Osborne** 18-93 (19.0%), **A. P. McCoy** 17-91 (18.0%).

WINDSOR (Fig. 8)

In the form of a figure eight, Windsor has a circuit of 1m 4f 110y. Although both left and right-hand turns are met in races of a mile and a half, only right-hand turns occur in races up to 1m 70y. The five furlong course bends slightly to the right approaching halfway but is otherwise straight. The track is perfectly flat and its sharpness is largely offset by the long run-in.

Address: Royal Windsor Racecourse, Maidenhead Road, Windsor, Berkshire SL4 5JJ Tel: (01753) 864076
Fax: (01753) 830156

Clerk of the Course and Director: Hugo Bevan, The Old House, Little Everdon, Daventry, Northamptonshire. Tel: (01327) 361266

Racecourse Manager: Mrs S. DIngle, The Racecourse, Windsor, Berkshire. Tel: (01753) 865234 or (01753) 864726; Stables (01753) 865350.

Reservation required for overnight stay and accommodation only. Tel: (01753) 865234.

By Car: North of the town on the A308 (M4 Junc 6). Car parks adjoin the course (£1, £1.50, £2).

By Rail: Windsor Central Station (from Paddington) or Windsor & Eton Riverside Station (from Waterloo).

By Air: London (Heathrow) Airport 15 minutes by car via the M4. Also White Waltham Airport (West London Aero Club) 15 minutes.

Leading Trainers (since 1991): R. Hannon 62-377 (16.5%), **H. R. A. Cecil** 18-54 (33.3%), **P. F. I. Cole** 15-114 (13.2%).

Leading Jockeys (since 1991): Pat Eddery 66-292 (22.0%), **J. Reid** 37-229 (16.0%), **L. Dettori** 37-181 (20.0%).

WINDSOR (N.H)

1m 4f (7) 200y run-in. Perfectly flat but sharp figure-of-eight course, suited to front runners and those of doubtful stamina.

Address: Royal Windsor Racecourse, Maidenhead Road, Windsor, Berkshire SL4 5JJ Tel: (01753) 864076
Fax: (01753) 830156

Clerk of the Course and Director: Hugo Bevan, The Old House, Little Everdon, Daventry, Northamtponshire. Tel: (01327) 361266

Racecourse Manager: Mrs S. DIngle, The Racecourse, Windsor, Berkshire. Tel: (01753) 865234 or (01753) 864726; Stables (01753) 865350.

Reservation required for overnight stay and accommodation only. Tel: (01753) 865234.

By Car: North of the town on the A308 (M4 Junc 6). Car parks adjoin the course (£1, £1.50, £2).

By Rail: Windsor Central Station (from Paddington) or Windsor & Eton Riverside Station (from Waterloo).

By Air: London (Heathrow) Airport 15 minutes by car via the M4. Also White Waltham Airport (West London Aero Club) 15 minutes.

Leading Trainers (since 1991): K. C. Bailey 21-88 (23.9%), **Miss H. C. Knight** 15-79 (19.0%), **N. J. Henderson** 15-84 (17.9%).

Leading Jockeys (since 1991): M. A. Fitzgerald 12-63 (19.0%), **M. Richards** 12-121 (9.0%), **N. Williamson** 12-80 (15.0%).

WOLVERHAMPTON (L.H)

An oval circuit, a mile in circumference with a run-in of 380y. The Fibresand surface consists of a blended mixture of silica sand and synthetic fibres set in a re-enforced sub-base.A turf track for hurdles and chases is situated on the outside of the All-Weather track.

Address: Wolverhampton Racecourse, Dunstall Park, Gorsebrook Road, Wolverhampton WV6 0PE
Tel: (01902) 421421 Fax: (01902) 716626

Clerk of the Course: Mr A. J. Bealby, The Rookery, Bragborough Hall, Braunston, Daventry, Northamptonshire NN11 7HA. Tel: (01788) 891795.

74 boxes allotted on arrival. Applications for lads and lasses, and overnight stables must be made to Racecourse by noon on the day before racing. Tel: (01902) 24481. Fax (01902) 716626

By Car: 1 mile North of town on the A449 (M54 Junc 2 or M6 Junc 12). Car parking free of charge.

By Rail: Wolverhampton Station (from Euston) 1 mile.

By Air: Halfpenny Green Airport 8 miles.

Leading Trainers (since 1991): R. Hollinshead 63-690 (9.1%), **J. Berry** 53-381 (13.9%), **M. Johnston** 52-250 (20.8%).

Leading Jockeys (since 1991): J. Weaver 59-288 (20.0%), **G. Carter** 44-286 (15.0%), **S. Sanders** 40-358 (11.0%).

WOLVERHAMPTON (N.H)

Jump racing was scheduled to start at Wolverhampton until December 26th, 1995, but has suffered from abandonment of racing at all scheduled meetings so far.

Address: Wolverhampton Racecourse, Dunstall Park, Gorsebrook Road, Wolverhampton WV6 0PE

Tel: (01902) 421421 Fax: (01902) 716626

Clerk of the Course: Mr A. J. Bealby, The Rookery, Bragborough Hall, Braunston, Daventry, Northamptonshire NN11 7HA. Tel: (01788) 891795.

74 boxes allotted on arrival. Applications for lads and lasses, and overnight stables must be made to Racecourse by noon on the day before racing. Tel: (01902) 24481. Fax (01902) 716626

By Car: 1 mile North of town on the A449 (M54 Junc 2 or M6 Junc 12). Car parking free of charge.

By Rail: Wolverhampton Station (from Euston) 1 mile.

By Air: Halfpenny Green Airport 8 miles.

Leading Trainers (since 1991): D. Nicholson 12-40 (30.0%), **M. C. Pipe** 12-41 (29.3%), **Miss H. C. Knight** 8-29 (27.6%).

Leading Jockeys (since 1991): R. Dunwoody 15-63 (23.0%), **J. Osborne** 13-41 (31.0%), **M. A. Fitzgerald** 5-14 (35.0%).

WORCESTER (N.H)

Elongated oval, 1m 5f (9) 220y run-in. Flat with easy turns, Worcester is a very fair, galloping track.

Address; Worcester Racecourse, Pitchcroft, Worcester WR1 3EJ Tel: (01905) 21338 (Racedays) (01905) 25364 (Non-racedays) Fax: (01905) 617563

Clerk of the Course: Hugo Bevan, The Old House, Little Everdon, Daventry, Northamptonshire NN11 3BG. Tel: (01327) 361266.

Manager: S. Brice, The Racecourse, Worcester. Tel: (01905) 25364 or (01684) 62033.

108 boxes allotted on arrival. Overnight accommodation for lads and lasses in Worcester.

By Car: West of the city off the A449 (Kidderminster road) (M5 Junc 8).

By Rail: Foregate Street Station, Worcester (from Paddington) 3/4 mile.

By Air: Helicopter landing facility in the centre of the course, by prior arrangement only.

Leading Trainers (since 1991): M. C. Pipe 78-238 (32.8%), **D. Nicholson** 41-158 (26.0%), **P. J. Hobbs** 38-194 (19.6%).

Leading Jockeys (since 1991): R. Dunwoody 50-308 (16.0%), **A. P. McCoy** 49-171 (28.0%), **A. Maguire** 45-234 (19.0%).

YARMOUTH (L.H)

An oblong course of about 1m 4f with a slight fall to a run-in of five furlongs. The straight mile joins the round course at the run-in and is perfectly level. The five, six and seven furlong courses form part of the straight mile.

Address: The Racecourse, Jellicoe Road, Great Yarmouth, Norfolk NR30 4AU Tel: (01493) 842527
Fax: (01493) 843254

Clerk of the Course: Mr D. C. Henson, F.R.I.C.S., 2 Lower Mounts, Northampton NN1 3DE. Tel: (01604) 30757. Fax: (01604) 30758.

Manager: Mr David Thompson, The Racecourse, Jellicoe Road, Great Yarmouth, Norfolk NR30 4AU. Tel: (01493) 842527 Fax: (01493) 843254.

Stabling allocated on arrival. Tel: (01493) 855651.

By Car: 1 mile East of town centre (well sign-posted from A47 & A12). Large car park adjoining course £1.

By Rail: Great Yarmouth Station (1 mile). Bus service to the course.

By Air: Helicopter landing facilities available 300y from the course at North Denes Airfield. Tel: (01493) 851500. Fixed wing aircraft landing facilities are available at a private airfield in Ludham. Prior permission is required through Mr R. Collins. Tel: (01493) 843211. Fax: (01493) 859555.

Leading Trainers (since 1991): H. R. A. Cecil 38-146 (26.0%), **C. E. Brittain** 29-239 (12.1%), **M. R. Stoute** 27-145 (18.6%).

Leading Jockeys (since 1991): R. Hills 45-212 (21.0%), **L. Dettori** 40-190 (21.0%), **M. Roberts** 39-221 (17.0%).

YORK (L.H)

From the two mile start at the bottom of the Knavesmire, this wide, U-shaped course runs parallel with the Tadcaster Road for five furlongs before bending left to pass under Knavesmire Wood and join the straight six furlongs round a sweeping turn in front of the five furlong gate. A new two furlong extension, set at a tangent, also joins the round course here and caters for seven furlong events. A fair, galloping course which calls for stamina and courage, especially in the wet weather when the going can be very testing. Because of the watering system, when the going is soft, much better ground can be found by racing wide in the back straight.

Address: The Racecourse, York YO2 1EX Tel: (01904) 620911 Fax: (01904) 611071

Manager, Clerk of the Course and Secretary: Mr J. L. Smith F.C.A., The Racecourse, York YO2 1EX. Tel: (01904) 620911. Fax: (01904) 611071.

Stabling: 200 boxes available. Tel: (Racedays) (01904) 706317

By Car: 1 mile South-East of the city on the A1036. Car parking bookings can be made prior to race meetings (except August) for reserved car park (£2 (inc. VAT) per day). All other parking is free.

By Rail: 11/2 miles York Station (from King's Cross). Special bus service from station to the course.

By Air: Light aircraft and helicopter landing facilities available at Rufforth aerodrome (5,000ft tarmac runway). £20 landing fee-transport arranged to course.
Leeds/Bradford airport (25 miles).

Leading Trainers (since 1991); J. H. M. Gosden 39-168 (23.2%), **H. R. A. Cecil** 37-153 (24.2%), **M. R. Stoute** 36-204 (17.7%).

Leading Jockeys (since 1991): L. Dettori 56-292 (19.0%), **Pat Eddery** 56-314 (17.0%), **M. Roberts** 37-237 (15.0%).

RACEFORM STANDARD TIMES

The following represent the standard true-run race times for the various distances and courses brought to 9st.

ASCOT

5f....................1/0.2s
6f....................1/14s
7f....................1/27.7s
1m (str)....................1/40s
1m (rnd)....................1/40.8s
1¼m....................2/5.3s
1½m....................2/30.8s
2m 45yds....................3/27s
2½m....................4/17s
2¾m 34yds....................4/50s

AYR

5f....................56.8s
6f....................1/9.8s
7f....................1/25s
1m....................1/37.4s
1m 1f....................1/48.5s
1¼m....................2/5.8s
1¼m 192yds....................2/14.6s
1m 5f 13yds....................2/46s
1m 7f....................3/10.7s
2m 1f 105yds....................3/40s

BATH

5f 11yds....................1/0.5s
5f 161yds....................1/9.5s
1m 5yds....................1/38s
1¼m 46yds....................2/6s
1m 3f 144yds....................2/25.6s
1m 5f 22yds....................2/45.7s
2m 1f 34yds....................3/41.4s

BEVERLEY

5f....................1/1.8s
7f 100yds....................1/31.4s
1m 100yds....................1/44s
1m 1f 207yds....................2/3.1s
1m 3f 216yds....................2/33s
2m 35yds....................3/30.5s

BRIGHTON

5f 59yds....................60s
5f 213yds....................1/7.2s
6f 209yds....................1/20s
7f 214yds....................1/31.5s
1m 1f 209yds....................1/58.3s
1m 3f 196yds....................2/26.7s

CARLISLE

5f....................59.8s
5f 207yds....................1/11.8s
6f 206yds....................1/25.7s
7f 214yds....................1/37s
1½m....................2/29s
1¾m 32yds....................3/5s
2m 1f 52yds....................3/37s

CATTERICK

5f....................57.5s
5f 212yds....................1/10.9s
7f....................1/23.6s
1m 3f 214yds....................2/32.5s
1m 4f 44yds....................2/34s
1m 5f 175yds....................2/57.5s
1m 7f 177yds....................3/23s

CHEPSTOW

5f 16yds....................57s
6f 16yds....................1/9s
7f 16yds....................1/19s
1m 14yds....................1/31.2s
1¼m 36yds....................2/5.6s
1½m 23yds....................2/32.4s
2m 49yds....................3/28s
2¼m....................3/49s
2m 2f 33yds....................3/52s

CHESTER

5f 16yds....................1/0.2s
6f 18yds....................1/13.3s
7f 2yds....................1/25.2s
7f 122yds....................1/31s
1¼m 75yds....................2/8.7s
1m 3f 79yds....................2/23.6s
1½m 66yds....................2/36.2s
1m 5f 89yds....................2/50s
1m 7f 195yds....................3/22.9s
2¼m 147yds....................4/5m

DONCASTER

5f	58.9s
5f 140yds	1/6.6s
6f	1/12.1s
7f	1/24.5s
1m (str)	1/37.7s
1m (rnd)	1/38.4s
1¼m 60yds	2/7.8s
1½m	2/30s
1¾m 132yds	3/2.6s
2m 110yds	3/30s
2¼m	3/52s

EPSOM

5f	54.5s
6f	1/7.5s
7f	1/20.3s
1m 114yds	1/42s
1¼m 18yds	2/4s
1½m 10yds	2/34.5s

FOLKESTONE

5f	57.9s
6f	1/10.2s
6f 189yds	1/21.4s
1m 1f 149yds	1/57.7s
1½m	3/31.2s
1m 7f 92yds	3/18s
2m 93yds	3/29s

GOODWOOD

5f	56.7s
6f	1/9.8s
7f	1/24.8s
1m	1/37.2s
1m 1f	1/53s
1¼m	2/7.1s
1½m	2/34s
1¾m	2/59s
2m	3/24s
2½m	4/15s

HAMILTON

5f 4yds	58s
6f 5yds	1/8.7s
1m 65yds	1/42.6s
1m 1f 36yds	1/52s
1m 3f 16yds	2/16.2s
1½m 17yds	2/29.4s
1m 5f 9yds	2/42.5s

HAYDOCK

5f	59.5s
6f	1/11.7s
7f 30yds	1/28s
1m 30yds	1/40.6s
1¼m 120yds	2/11s
1m 3f 200yds	2/29.4s
1¾m	2/58.2s
2m 45yds	3/27.2s

KEMPTON

5f	59.1s
6f	1/11.2s
7f (rnd)	1/23.5s
7f (Jubilee)	1/24.5s
1m (rnd)	1/36.5s
1m (Jubilee)	1/37.7s
1m 1f (rnd)	1/50.6s
1¼m (Jubilee)	2/03.5s
1m 3f 30yds	2/18.8s
1½m	2/29.4s
1¾m 92y	3/3s
2m	3/24.6s

LEICESTER

5f 2yds	58.8s
5f 218yds	1/10.4s
7f 9yds	1/22.6s
1m 8yds	1/35s
1m 1f 218yds	2/3.2s
1m 3f 183yds	2/28s

LINGFIELD (TURF)

5f	57s
6f	1/9s
7f	1/21.2s
7f 140yds	1/29s
1m 1f	1/51s
1¼m	2/5.2s
1m 3f 106yds	2/24.7s
1¾m	2/59s
2m	3/24s

LINGFIELD (AWT)

5f	58.4s
6f	1/11.4s
7f	1/24.2s
1m	1/37.4s
1¼m	2/4.5s
1½m	2/30s
1m 5f	2/42s
2m	3/21s

MUSSELBURGH

5f....57.7s
7f 30yds....1/26s
1m 16yds....1/38.5s
1m 3f 32yds....2/19.7s
1½m 31yds....2/32.2s
1¾m....2/56.6s
2m....3/23s

NEWBURY

5f 34yds....1/0.2s
6f 8yds....1/11.8s
7f (str)....1/24.1s
7f 64yds (rnd)....1/27.6s
1m (str)....1/38s
1m 7yds (rnd)....1/36s
1m 1f....1/50.3s
1¼m 6yds....2/4s
1m 3f 5yds....2/17.2s
1½m 5yds....2/30s
1m 5f 61yds....2/45.5s
2m....3/24.2s

NEWCASTLE

5f....59.2s
6f....1/12.5s
7f....1/25.2s
1m (rnd)....1/39s
1m 3yds (str)....1/38.6s
1m 1f 9yds....1/52.3s
1¼m 32yds....2/6.7s
1½m 93yds....2/37.5s
2m 19yds....3/25.5s

NEWMARKET (ROWLEY MILE COURSE)

5f....58.7s
6f....1/11.8s
7f....1/24.5s
1m....1/37.3s
1m 1f....1/50.5s
1¼m....2/4.7s
1½m....2/30.5s
1¾m....2/56s
2m....3/23.3s
2¼m....3/50.4s

(JULY COURSE)

5f....58.3s
6f....1/12s
7f....1/25s
1m....1/37.5s
1m 1f....1/50.5s
1¼m....2/3.6s
1½m....2/28.8s
1¾m 175yds....3/8s
2m 24yds....3/23s

NOTTINGHAM

5f 13yds....58.9s
6f 15yds....1/11.5s
1m 54yds....1/41.3s
1m 1f 213yds....2/2.5s
1¾m 15yds....2/57.5s
2m 9yds....3/22.4s
2m 1f 188yds....3/49.5s

PONTEFRACT

5f....1/2s
6f....1/15.4s
1m 4yds....1/42.4s
1¼m 6yds....2/8.9s
1½m 8yds....2/34.3s
2m 1f 22yds....3/39.5s
2m 1f 216yds....3/52s
2m 5f 122yds....4/42.5s

REDCAR

5f....57.5s
6f....1/10.2s
7f....1/23.5s
1m....1/35s
1m 1f....1/50.7s
1¼m....2/3.6s
1m 3f....2/17s
1m 5f 135yds....2/52s
1¾m 19yds....2/59.3s
2m 4yds....3/25s

RIPON

5f....58s
6f....1/10.5s
1m....1/38.1s
1m 1f....1/51s
1¼m....2/3.5s
1½m 60yds....2/33.5s
2m....3/25s

SALISBURY

5f....60s
6f....1/13s
6f 212yds....1/26s
1m....1/39.7s
1m 1f 209yds....2/05.3s
1½m....2/31s
1¾m....3/0s

SANDOWN

5f 6yds....1/0.7s
7f 16yds....1/28.6s
1m 14yds....1/41.2s
1m 1f....1/53.1s
1¼m 7yds....2/06.7s
1m 3f 91yds....2/22.5s
1¾m....2/58.9s
2m 78yds....3/32s

SOUTHWELL (AWT)

5f....57s
6f....1/13.5s
7f....1/26.5s
1m....1/39.8s
1m 3f....2/22s
1½m....2/35s
1¾m....3/0s
2m....3/31s

THIRSK

5f....58s
6f....1/9.7s
7f....1/24.3s
1m....1/36.5s
1½m....2/30s
2m....3/23s

WARWICK

5f....58s
6f....1/12s
7f....1/24.2s
1m....1/36.4s
1¼m 169yds....2/14.3s
1½m 115yds....2/38.5s
1¾m 194yds....3/10s
2m 20yds....3/25s

WINDSOR

5f 10yds....59.7s
5f 217yds....1/11s
1m 67yds....1/42.2s
1¼m 7yds....2/4.9s
1m 3f 135yds....2/25.3s

WOLVERHAMPTON (AWT)

5f....58.3s
6f....1/11s
7f....1/24.7s
1m 100yds....1/45s
1m 1f 79yds....1/55.5s
1½m....2/32.5s
1¾m 166yds....3/7.4s
2m 46yds....3/27s

YARMOUTH

5f 43yds....1/0.7s
6f 3yds....1/10.9s
7f 3yds....1/23.6s
1m 3yds....1/35.5s
1¼m 21yds....2/2.7s
1m 3f 101yds....2/20s
1¾m 17yds....2/56.7s
2m....3/23.5s
2m 2f 51yds....3/54.6s

YORK

5f....57.7s
6f....1/10.5s
6f 214yds....1/23.3s
7f 202yds....1/38s
1m 205yds....1/48.1s
1¼m 85yds....2/9s
1m 3f 195yds....2/27.8s
1m 5f 194yds....2/54.2s
1m 7f 195yds....3/20s

RACEFORM RECORD TIMES

As recorded by "Raceform" since 1936.

ASCOT

DISTANCE	TIME	AGE	WT	GOING	HORSE	DATE
5f	59.1 secs	3	8-8	Firm	Orient	Jun 21, 1986
5f	59.72 secs	2	8-8	Firm	Lyric Fantasy (IRE)	Jun 17, 1992
6f	1m 12.53	4	9-4	Firm	Shalford (IRE)	Jun 17, 1992
6f	1m 13.63	2	8-8	Firm	Minstrella (USA)	Jun 19, 1986
7f	1m 25.94	3	9-1	Firm	Prince Ferdinand	Jun 17, 1992
7f	1m 27.25	2	8-11	Fast	Celtic Swing	Oct 8, 1994
1m(Rnd)	1m 38.58	3	9-0	Good to firm	Ridgewood Pearl	Jun 21, 1995
1m(Rnd)	1m 40.92	2	8-7	Fast	Untold	Spt 26, 1985
1m(St)	1m 38.07	4	7-8	Firm	Colour Sergeant	Jun 17, 1992
1m 2f	2m 2.76	4	9-3	Good to firm	First Island (IRE)	Jun 18, 1996
1m 4f	2m 26.95	5	8-9	Firm	Stanerra	Jun 17, 1983
2m 45y	3m 25.29	3	9-3	Firm	Landowner (IRE)	Jun 17, 1992
2m 4f	4m 15.67	5	9-0	Firm	Royal Gait (disq)	Jun 16, 1988
2m 6f 34y	4m 51.32	4	8-8	Firm	Otabari	Jun 20, 1986

AYR

DISTANCE	TIME	AGE	WT	GOING	HORSE	DATE
5f	57.2 secs	4	9-5	Fast	Sir Joey (USA)	Spt 16, 1993
5f	57.62 secs	2	8-6	Good to firm	Conspiracy	Spt 19, 1996
6f	68.98 secs	7	8-8	Fast	Sobering Thoughts	Spt 10, 1993
6f	69.73 secs	2	7-10	Good	Sir Bert	Spt 17, 1969
7f	1m 24.97	5	7-11	Firm	Sir Arthur Hobbs	Jun 19, 1992
7f	1m 25.71	2	9-0	Fast	Jazeel (USA)	Spt 16, 1993
1m	1m 36.0	4	7-13	Firm	Sufi	Spt 16, 1959
1m	1m 39.21	2	9-0	Firm	Kribensis	Spt 17, 1986
1m 1f	1m 53.46	3	11-2	Good to firm	Epic Stand	Jly 19, 1997
1m 2f	2m 5.2	8	10-0	Fast	Knock Knock	Spt 18, 1993
1m 2f 192y	2m 13.31	4	9-0	Good	Azzaam (USA)	Spt 18, 1991
1m 5f 13y	2m 45.81	4	9-7	Fast	Eden's Close	Spt 18, 1993
1m 7f	3m 13.16	3	9-4	Good	Romany Rye	Spt 19, 1991
2m 1f 105y	3m 45.0	4	6-13	Good	Curry	Spt 16, 1955

BATH

DISTANCE	TIME	AGE	WT	GOING	HORSE	DATE
5f 11y	60.1 secs	4	9-9	Good to firm	To The Roof (IRE)	May 11, 1996
5f 11y	60.8 secs	2	8-11	Fast	Cheyenne Spirit	Aug 9, 1994
5f 161y	68.1 secs	6	9-0	Firm	Madraco	May 22, 1989
5f 161y	1m 10.0	2	8-13	Fast	Morocco (IRE)	Jly 22, 1991
1m 5y	1m 38.2	4	9-9	Firm	Air Commodore (IRE)	Jly 1, 1995
1m 5y	1m 40.3	2	8-12	Good to firm	Khassah	Spt 9, 1996
1m 2f 46y	2m 6.5	4	9-4	Firm	Farmost	Jly 23, 1997
1m 3f 144y	2m 25.9	4	9-2	Firm	Alriffa	May 13, 1995
1m 5f 22y	2m 47.3	4	10-0	Firm	Flown	Aug 13, 1991
2m 1f 34y	3m 43.9	6	7-9	Fast	Patroclus	Jly 10, 1991

BEVERLEY

DISTANCE	TIME	AGE	WT	GOING	HORSE	DATE
5f	60.3 secs	4	9-11	Firm	Eager Deva	Apr 25, 1991
5f	61.3 secs	2	9-0	Good to firm	Jhazi	Spt 18, 1996
7f 100y	1m 29.4	3	7-8	Firm	Who's Tef (IRE)	Jly 30, 1991
7f 100y	1m 30.9	2	9-0	Firm	Majal (IRE)	Jly 30, 1991
1m 100y	1m 42.3	3	8-4	Firm	Legal Case	Jun 14, 1989
1m 100y	1m 43.3	2	9-0	Firm	Arden	Spt 24, 1986
1m 1f 207y	2m 0.65	4	11-7	Good to firm	Ooh Ah Cantona	Jly 8, 1995
1m 3f 216y	2m 30.6	3	8-1	Hard	Coinage	Jun 18, 1986
2m 35y	3m 29.3	4	9-2	Good to firm	Rushen Raider	Aug 14, 1996

BRIGHTON

DISTANCE	TIME	AGE	WT	GOING	HORSE	DATE
5f 59y	59.4 secs	3	8-9	Firm	Play Hever Golf	May 27, 1993
5f 59y	60.1 secs	2	9-0	Firm	Bid For Blue	May 6, 1993
5f 213y	67.3 secs	3	8-9	Firm	Third Party	Jun 3, 1997
5f 213y	68.1 secs	2	8-9	Firm	Song Mist (IRE)	Jly 16, 1996
6f 209y	1m 19.4	4	9-3	Firm	Sawaki	Spt 4, 1991
6f 209y	1m 19.9	2	8-11	Hard	Rain Burst	Spt 15, 1988
7f 214y	1m 30.9	5	8-12	Hard	Chase The Door	Jly 26, 1990
7f 214y	1m 32.8	2	9-7	Firm	Asian Pete	Oct 3, 1989
1m 1f 209y	1m 57.2	3	9-0	Firm	Get The Message	Apr 30, 1984
1m 3f 196y	2m 25.8	4	8-2	Firm	New Zealand	Jly 4, 1985

CARLISLE

DISTANCE	TIME	AGE	WT	GOING	HORSE	DATE
5f	59.4 secs	7	8-8	Hard	Serious Hurry	Aug 21, 1995
5f	60.2 secs	2	8-9	Hard	Metal Boys	Jun 1, 1989
5f 207y	1m 11.8	6	8-13	Firm	Night Patrol	Aug 27, 1970
5f 207y	1m 12.9	2	8-9	Hard	Parfait Amour	Spt 10, 1991
6f 206y	1m 25.4	4	9-1	Firm	Move With Edes	Jly 6, 1996
6f 206y	1m 26.6	2	9-4	Hard	Sense Of Priority	Spt 10, 1991
7f 214y	1m 37.3	5	7-12	Hard	Thatched (IRE)	Aug 21, 1995
7f 214y	1m 44.6	2	8-8	Firm	Blue Garter	Spt 9, 1980
1m 4f	2m 28.8	3	8-5	Firm	Desert Frolic (IRE)	Jun 27, 1996
1m 6f 32y	3m 2.2	6	8-10	Firm	Explosive Speed (USA)	May 26, 1994

CATTERICK

DISTANCE	TIME	AGE	WT	GOING	HORSE	DATE
5f	57.1 secs	4	8-7	Fast	Kabcast	Jly 7, 1989
5f	57.7 secs	2	9-0	Fast	Verde Alitalia (IRE)	Spt 21, 1991
5f 212y	1m 10.4	3	8-8	Firm	Triad Treble	May 31, 1984
5f 212y	1m 11.4	2	9-4	Firm	Captain Nick	Jly 11, 1978
7f	1m 23.0	4	7-12	Firm	Royal Ziska	Jun 9, 1973
7f	1m 24.1	2	8-11	Firm	Lindas Fantasy	Spt 18, 1982
1m 3f 214y	2m 34.1	5	9-10	Good to firm	Keep Your Distance	Oct 13, 1995
1m 5f 175y	2m 54.8	3	8-5	Firm	Geryon	May 31, 1984
1m 7f 177y	3m 20.8	4	7-11	Firm	Bean Boy	Jly 8, 1982

CHEPSTOW

DISTANCE	TIME	AGE	WT	GOING	HORSE	DATE
5f 16y	56.8 secs	3	8-4	Firm	Torbay Express	Spt 15, 1979
5f 16y	57.6 secs	2	8-11	Firm	Micro Love	Jly 8, 1986
6f 16y	68.8 secs	4	8-6	Fast	African Rex (FR)	May 12, 1987
6f 16y	69.4 secs	2	9-0	Fast	Royal Fi Fi (USA)	Spt 9, 1989
7f 16y	1m 19.9	3	9-10	Firm	Prince Titian	Aug 29, 1978
7f 16y	1m 20.8	2	9-0	Good to firm	Royal Amaretto	Spt 12, 1996
1m 14y	1m 31.8	6	9-6	Firm	Traditional Miss	Jun 27, 1981
1m 14y	1m 33.1	2	8-11	Good to firm	Ski Academy (IRE)	Aug 28, 1995
1m 2f 36y	2m 4.1	5	8-9	Hard	Leonidas (USA)	Jly 5, 1983
1m 4f 23y	2m 31.0	7	9-6	Hard	Maintop	Aug 27, 1984
2m 49y	3m 27.7	4	9-0	Fast	Wizzard Artist	Jly 1, 1989
2m 2f	4m 0.2	8	9-1	Good to firm	Tamarpour (USA)	Jly 4, 1995

CHESTER

DISTANCE	TIME	AGE	WT	GOING	HORSE	DATE
5f 16y	59.2 secs	3	10-0	Firm	Althrey Don	Jly 10, 1964
5f 16y	60.4 secs	2	8-11	Firm	Cynara	May 3, 1960
6f 18y	1m 12.78	6	9-2	Good	Stack Rock	Jun 23, 1993
6f 18y	1m 13.4	2	9-3	Good	Stung	Jly 27, 1968
7f 2y	1m 25.27	3	9-3	Fast	Mizaaya	May 7, 1992
7f 2y	1m 26.28	2	8-4	Fast	By Hand	Aug 31, 1991
7f 122y	1m 32.0	6	8-5	Firm	Cee-Jay-Ay	May 6, 1993
7f 122y	1m 35.0	2	9-0	Firm	Double Value	Spt 1, 1972
1m 2f 75y	2m 7.98	3	8-10	Firm	Beneficial	May 10, 1993
1m 3f 79y	2m 23.71	3	8-11	Fast	Braiswick	May 10, 1989
1m 4f 66y	2m 34.21	3	8-11	Fast	Old Vic	May 9, 1989
1m 5f 89y	2m 45.43	5	8-11	Firm	Rakaposhi King	May 7, 1987
1m 7f 195y	3m 24.53	7	7-11	Good to firm	Moonlight Quest	Jly 30, 1995
2m 2f 147y	4m 3.35	5	8-8	Good to firm	Top Cees	May 10, 1995

DONCASTER

DISTANCE	TIME	AGE	WT	GOING	HORSE	DATE
5f	58.05 secs	4	9-2	Good to firm	Bollin Joanne	Spt 10, 1997
5f	58.4 secs	2	9-5	Firm	Sing Sing	Spt 11, 1959
5f 140y	66.2 secs	3	9-2	Good	Welsh Abbot	Spt 12, 1958
5f 140y	68.0 secs	2	8-10	Good	Crown Flatts	Oct 25, 1947
6f	69.74 secs	3	8-9	Good to firm	Iltimas (USA)	Jly 26, 1995
6f	1m 11.2	2	8-11	Firm	Paddy's Sister	Spt 9, 1959
7f	1m 22.6	3	9-4	Hard	Pinolli	Jun 3, 1963
7f	1m 23.21	2	8-10	Good to firm	Bahhare (USA)	Spt 13, 1996
1m(St)	1m 36.71	3	8-10	Good to firm	Mushahid (USA)	Jly 17, 1996
1m(St)	1m 37.52	2	9-5	Good to firm	Lend A Hand	Spt 11, 1997
1m(Rnd)	1m 35.34	3	9-0	Fast	Gneiss (USA)	May 2, 1994
1m(Rnd)	1m 37.49	2	9-0	Good to firm	Midnight Line (USA)	Spt 11, 1997
1m 2f 60y	2m 5.48	3	8-8	Good to firm	Carlito Brigante	Jly 26, 1995
1m 2f 60y	2m 13.47	2	8-8	Good	Yard Bird	Nov 6, 1981
1m 4f	2m 29.72	3	8-6	Good to firm	Busy Flight	Spt 13, 1996
1m 6f 132y	3m 2.22	3	8-3	Firm	Brier Creek (USA)	Spt 10, 1992
2m 110y	3m 34.44	4	9-12	Fast	Farsi	Jun 12, 1992
2m 2f	3m 52.17	4	9-0	Good to firm	Canon Can (USA)	Spt 11, 1997

EPSOM

DISTANCE	TIME	AGE	WT	GOING	HORSE	DATE
5f	53.6 secs	4	9-5	Firm	Indigenous	Jun 2, 1960
5f	55.02 secs	2	8-9	Good	Prince Aslia	Jun 9, 1995
6f	67.91 secs	5	7-7	Firm	Moor Lane	Jun 7, 1973
6f	67.85 secs	2	8-11	Fast	Showbrook (IRE)	Jun 5, 1991
7f	1m 20.15	4	8-7	Firm	Capistrano	Jun 7, 1972
7f	1m 22.17	2	8-9	Fast	Shamrock Fair (IRE)	Aug 30, 1994
1m 114y	1m 40.75	3	8-6	Fast	Sylva Honda	Jun 5, 1991
1m 114y	1m 42.8	2	8-5	Fast	Nightstalker	Aug 30, 1988
1m 2f 18y	2m 3.5	5	7-13	Good	Crossbow (unofficial)	Jun 7, 1967
1m 4f 10y	2m 32.31	3	9-0	Firm	Lammtarra (USA)	Jun 10, 1995

FOLKESTONE

DISTANCE	TIME	AGE	WT	GOING	HORSE	DATE
5f	58.7 secs	6	10-0	Firm	Friendly Brave (USA)	Jun 28, 1996
5f	58.5 secs	2	9-2	Good to firm	Pivotal	Nov 6, 1995
6f	1m 10.4	3	8-9	Firm	Spotted Eagle	Apr 23, 1996
6f	1m 11.0	2	7-13	Hard	Fashion Model	Aug 31, 1970
6f 189y	1m 21.3	3	8-9	Firm	Cielamour (USA)	Aug 9, 1988
6f 189y	1m 23.7	2	8-11	Good to firm	Hen Harrier	Jly 3, 1996
1m 1f 149y	1m 57.8	4	8-11	Firm	Lord Raffles	Jun 2, 1980
1m 4f	2m 33.3	4	8-8	Hard	Snow Blizzard	Jun 30, 1992
1m 7f 92y	3m 23.1	3	9-11	Firm	Mata Askari	Spt 12, 1991
2m 93y	3m 32.5	6	7-13	Firm	North West	Jly 21, 1981

GOODWOOD

DISTANCE	TIME	AGE	WT	GOING	HORSE	DATE
5f	56.25 secs	4	9-5	Good to firm	Hever Golf Rose	Jly 25, 1995
5f	57.53 secs	2	8-12	Fast	Poets Cove	Aug 3, 1990
6f	69.58 secs	4	8-3	Firm	For the Present	Jly 30, 1994
6f	1m 10.08	2	9-7	Good to firm	April The Eighth	Jly 25, 1995
7f	1m 23.88	3	8-7	Good to firm	Brief Glimpse (IRE)	Jly 25, 1995
7f	1m 25.97	2	8-11	Fast	Maroof (USA)	Jly 30, 1992
1m	1m 35.71	3	8-13	Firm	Distant View (USA)	Jly 27, 1994
1m	1m 38.94	2	9-0	Good to firm	Mutawwaj (IRE)	Spt 24, 1997
1m 1f	1m 52.81	3	9-6	Firm	Vena (IRE)	Jly 27, 1995
1m 2f	2m 4.96	3	8-6	Firm	Kartajana	Aug 4, 1990
1m 4f	2m 31.57	3	8-10	Firm	Presenting	Jly 25, 1995
1m 6f	2m 58.8	3	8-10	Firm	Secret Waters	Aug 2, 1990
2m	3m 23.57	4	9-5	Firm	Tioman Island	Jly 28, 1994
2m 4f	4m 11.75	3	7-10	Firm	Lucky Moon	Aug 2, 1990

HAMILTON

DISTANCE	TIME	AGE	WT	GOING	HORSE	DATE
5f 4y	58.0 secs	5	8-6	Firm	Golden Sleigh	Spt 6, 1972
5f 4y	58.0 secs	2	7-8	Firm	Fair Dandy	Spt 25, 1972
6f 5y	69.3 secs	4	8-7	Firm	Marcus Game	Jly 11, 1974
6f 5y	1m 10.1	2	7-5	Hard	Yoohoo	Spt 8, 1976
1m 65y	1m 42.7	6	7-7	Firm	Cranley	Spt 25, 1972
1m 65y	1m 45.8	2	8-11	Firm	Hopeful Subject	Spt 24, 1973
1m 1f 36y	1m 54.2	3	8-2	Hard	Fairman	Aug 20, 1976
1m 3f 16y	2m 20.5	3	9-3	Firm	Wang Feihoong	Jly 21, 1983
1m 4f 17y	2m 32.0	4	7-4	Firm	Fine Point	Aug 24, 1981
1m 5f 9y	2m 45.2	6	9-6	Firm	Mentalasanythin	Jun 14, 1995

HAYDOCK

DISTANCE	TIME	AGE	WT	GOING	HORSE	DATE
5f	58.9 secs	3	7-5	Firm	Fish and Chips	Jun 6, 1970
5f	59.2 secs	2	9-4	Firm	Money For Nothing	Aug 12, 1964
6f	69.92 secs	4	9-0	Good to firm	Iktamal (USA)	Spt 7, 1996
6f	1m 11.63	2	8-11	Good to firm	Tamnia	Jly 8, 1995
7f 30y	1m 27.21	4	9-4	Firm	Indian King	Jun 5, 1982
7f 30y	1m 29.4	2	9-0	Good to firm	Apprehension	Spt 7, 1996
1m 30y	1m 40.2	4	8-10	Good to firm	Moving Arrow	Aug 5, 1995
1m 30y	1m 40.69	2	8-12	Good to firm	Besiege	Spt 7, 1996
1m 2f 120y	2m 8.53	3	8-7	Good to firm	Fahal (USA)	Aug 5, 1995
1m 3f 200y	2m 26.4	5	8-2	Firm	New Member	Jly 4, 1970
1m 6f	2m 59.9	4	9-10	Good	Soloman's Dancer	Aug 6, 1994
2m 45y	3m 27.09	4	8-13	Firm	Prince of Peace	May 26, 1984

KEMPTON

DISTANCE	TIME	AGE	WT	GOING	HORSE	DATE
5f	57.42 secs	4	9-3	Good to firm	Almaty (IRE)	May 31, 1997
5f	58.3 secs	2	9-7	Firm	Schweppeshire Lad	Jun 3, 1978
6f	1m 10.04	7	7-10	Firm	Jokist	Apr 6, 1990
6f	1m 10.8	2	8-10	Good	Zabara	Spt 22, 1951
7f(Rnd)	1m 23.59	3	9-2	Good to firm	Wild Rice	Aug 2, 1995
7f(Rnd)	1m 27.52	2	8-6	Good	Duke of Ragusa	Spt 1, 1972
7f (Jub)	1m 23.63	3	9-0	Good to firm	Shaheen (USA)	May 31, 1997
7f (Jub)	1m 24.78	2	9-0	Good to firm	Canons Park	Jun 28, 1995
1m(Jub)	1m 35.39	3	8-12	Good to firm	Private Line (USA)	Jun 28, 1995
1m(Jub)	1m 38.78	2	9-0	Good to firm	Taverner Society (IRE)	Spt 22, 1997
1m(Rnd)	1m 35.81	4	9-1	Firm	County Broker	May 23, 1984
1m(Rnd)	1m 43.4	2	7-0	Good	Fascinating	Nov 3, 1956
1m 1f	1m 50.56	3	8-12	Fast	Sky Conqueror (USA)	Jun 29, 1988
1m 2f	1m 59.53	4	9-6	Firm	Batshoof	Apr 6, 1990
1m 3f 30y	2m 16.2	4	9-2	Firm	Shernazar	Spt 6, 1985
1m 4f	2m 30.18	6	8-5	Firm	Going Going	Spt 7, 1985
1m 6f 92y	3m 6.59	4	9-8	Good	Renzo	Spt 21, 1997
2m	3m 26.53	4	9-10	Good to firm	Latahaab (USA)	May 27, 1995

LEICESTER

DISTANCE	TIME	AGE	WT	GOING	HORSE	DATE
5f 2y	58.2 secs	4	9-5	Fast	Lucky Parkes	Spt 6, 1994
5f 2y	58.4 secs	2	9-0	Firm	Cutting Blade	Jun 9, 1986
5f 218y	69.4 secs	3	8-12	Fast	Lakeland Beauty	May 29, 1990
5f 218y	1m 10.1	2	9-0	Firm	Thordis	Oct 24, 1995
7f 9y	1m 20.8	3	8-7	Firm	Flower Bowl	Jun 9, 1986
7f 9y	1m 22.9	2	9-2	Good to firm	Rabi (IRE)	Spt 22, 1997
1m 8y	1m 33.8	3	9-0	Good to firm	Clifton Fox	May 29, 1995
1m 8y	1m 34.6	2	8-9	Firm	Lady Carla	Oct 24, 1995
1m 1f 218y	2m 2.4	3	8-11	Firm	Effigy	Nov 4, 1985
1m 1f 218y	2m 5.3	2	9-1	Good to firm	Windsor Castle	Oct 14, 1996
1m 3f 183y	2m 27.9	3	8-12	Firm	Al Widyan (IRE)	Oct 23, 1995

LINGFIELD (Turf)

DISTANCE	TIME	AGE	WT	GOING	HORSE	DATE
5f	56.24 secs	3	9-1	Fast	Eveningperformance	Jly 25, 1994
5f	57.25 secs	2	8-9	Fast	Quiz Time	Aug 6, 1994
6f	68.2 secs	6	9-10	Firm	Al Amead	Jly 2, 1986
6f	68.6 secs	2	9-3	Firm	The Ritz	Jun 11, 1965
7f	1m 20.2	8	7-10	Hard	Polar Jest	Aug 19, 1955
7f	1m 21.34	2	7-6	Firm	Mandav	Oct 3, 1980
7f 140y	1m 26.73	3	8-6	Fast	Hiaam (USA)	Jly 11, 1987
7f 140y	1m 29.93	2	8-12	Firm	Rather Warm	Nov 7, 1978
1m 1f	1m 52.4	4	9-2	Good to firm	Quandary (USA)	Jly 15, 1995
1m 2f	2m 5.79	3	9-3	Firm	Aromatic	Jly 14, 1990
1m 3f 106y	2m 23.95	3	8-5	Firm	Night-Shirt	Jly 14, 1990
1m 6f	3m 2.7	4	9-3	Good to firm	Ballynakelly	Jly 13, 1996
2m	3m 28.96	3	9-0	Firm	Lothian	Spt 20, 1990

LINGFIELD (AWT)

DISTANCE	TIME	AGE	WT	GOING	HORSE	DATE
5f	58.01 secs	4	8-5	Standard	Little Saboteur	Feb 20, 1993
5f	59.11 secs	2	9-2	Standard	Fruitana (IRE)	Nov 7, 1996
6f	1m 10.58	4	9-4	Standard	J Cheever Loophole	Nov 23, 1989
6f	1m 11.65	2	9-7	Standard	Time's Arrow (IRE)	Jly 10, 1992
7f	1m 22.99	3	9-3	Standard	Confronter	Jly 18, 1992
7f	1m 24.0	2	8-12	Standard	Scottish Castle	Nov 2, 1990
1m	1m 36.32	5	9-5	Standard	Vanroy	Nov 30, 1989
1m	1m 36.5	2	9-5	Standard	San Pier Niceto	Nov 30, 1989
1m 2f	2m 2.93	4	9-3	Standard	Rapporteur	Nov 2, 1990
1m 2f	2m 7.5	2	8-11	Standard	Star Fighter	Nov 26, 1994
1m 4f	2m 29.3	4	8-6	Standard	Puff Puff	Nov 8, 1990
1m 5f	2m 43.82	3	8-9	Standard	Ela Man Howa	Nov 26, 1994
2m	3m 20.09	3	9-0	Standard	Yenoora (IRE)	Aug 8, 1992

MUSSELBURGH

DISTANCE	TIME	AGE	WT	GOING	HORSE	DATE
5f	57.4 secs	4	7-2	Firm	Palm Court Joe	Jly 4, 1977
5f	57.5 secs	2	8-2	Firm	Arasong	May 16, 1994
7f 15y	1m 26.0	6	9-0	Firm	Show of Hands	Apr 19, 1982
7f 15y	1m 27.5	2	9-1	Fast	Mubdi (USA)	Oct 6, 1986
1m 16y	1m 38.3	4	8-13	Firm	Churchillian	Jly 11, 1977
1m 16y	1m 40.9	2	8-11	Fast	Trompe d'Oeil	Oct 6, 1986
1m 3f 32y	2m 19.7	3	8-10	Firm	Old Court	Jly 4, 1977
1m 4f 31y	2m 32.2	5	7-9	Good	Glengrigor	Apr 15, 1946
1m 7f 16y	3m 10.4	3	8-0	Good	Cunningham	Spt 21, 1953

NEWBURY

DISTANCE	TIME	AGE	WT	GOING	HORSE	DATE
5f 34y	59.77 secs	4	9-4	Good to firm	Struggler	Spt 20, 1996
5f 34y	60.52 secs	2	8-7	Good to firm	Lord Kintyre	Jly 19, 1997
6f 8y	1m 10.71	5	9-3	Good to firm	Jayannpee	Jly 20, 1996
6f 8y	1m 11.49	2	8-6	Good to firm	Crystal Crossing (IRE)	Jly 20, 1996
7f	1m 23.84	5	9-3	Good to firm	Celestial Key (USA)	Jun 15, 1995
7f	1m 24.13	2	8-13	Good to firm	Imperial President	Jly 20, 1996
7f 64y(Rnd)	1m 26.13	4	9-12	Good to firm	Green Perfume (USA)	Jly 19, 1996
7f 64y(Rnd)	1m 28.81	2	8-10	Fast	Duty Time	Aug 14, 1993
1m	1m 35.76	4	9-0	Fast	Emperor Jones (USA)	May 13, 1994
1m	1m 38.96	2	8-10	Good to firm	King Sound	Spt 20, 1996
1m 7y(Rnd)	1m 34.91	3	8-9	Fast	Philidor	May 16, 1992
1m 7y(Rnd)	1m 37.29	2	8-11	Firm	Master Willie	Oct 1, 1979
1m 1f	1m 49.65	3	8-0	Good to firm	Holtye (IRE)	May 21, 1995
1m 2f 6y	2m 1.29	3	8-7	Fast	Wall Street (USA)	Jly 20, 1996
1m 3f 5y	2m 17.51	4	9-0	Fast	Hateel	May 19, 1990
1m 4f 5y	2m 29.2	4	8-9	Hard	Vidi Vici	Jun 21, 1951
1m 5f 61y	2m 44.9	5	10-0	Good to firm	Mystic Hill	Jly 20, 1996
2m	3m 25.42	8	9-12	Good to firm	Moonlight Quest	Jly 19, 1996

NEWCASTLE

DISTANCE	TIME	AGE	WT	GOING	HORSE	DATE
5f	58.0 secs	4	9-2	Fast	Princess Oberon (IRE)	Jly 23, 1994
5f	58.83 secs	2	9-0	Firm	Atlantic Viking (IRE)	Jun 4, 1997
6f	1m 11.21	3	9-2	Good	Tadwin	Jun 30, 1990
6f	1m 12.67	2	9-0	Firm	Sundance Kid (USA)	Oct 3, 1989
7f	1m 23.53	3	8-5	Firm	Beaudelaire (USA)	Jly 23, 1983
7f	1m 25.1	2	9-0	Good to firm	Multitone	Aug 4, 1996
1m(Rnd)	1m 38.96	3	8-12	Firm	Jacamar	Jly 27, 1989
1m(Rnd)	1m 39.97	2	9-0	Firm	Laxey Bay	Oct 3, 1989
1m 3y(St)	1m 39.9	3	9-0	Good	Epic Stand	May 22, 1997
1m 3y(St)	1m 38.8	2	8-6	Good	The Fly	Aug 26, 1996
1m 1f 9y	1m 52.3	3	6-3	Good	Ferniehurst	Jun 23, 1936
1m 2f 32y	2m 6.59	3	8-11	Fast	Missionary Ridge	Jun 29, 1990
1m 4f 93y	2m 37.3	5	8-12	Firm	Retender (USA)	Jun 25, 1994
2m 19y	3m 22.0	4	7-12	Good	Nectar II	Jun 23, 1937

NEWMARKET (Rowley)

DISTANCE	TIME	AGE	WT	GOING	HORSE	DATE
5f	56.81 secs	6	9-2	Fast	Lochsong	Apr 30, 1994
5f	58.78 secs	2	8-13	Good	Clifton Charlie	Oct 4, 1990
6f	1m 10.25	4	9-8	Good to firm	Lake Coniston (IRE)	Apr 18, 1995
6f	1m 10.14	2	9-0	Good	Lycius (USA)	Oct 4, 1990
7f	1m 22.24	4	9-5	Fast	Perfolia (USA)	Oct 18, 1991
7f	1m 23.45	2	9-0	Fast	Dr Devious (IRE)	Oct 18, 1991
1m	1m 35.08	3	9-0	Fast	Mister Baileys	Apr 30, 1994
1m	1m 36.74	2	9-0	Fast	Bold Pursuit (IRE)	Oct 18, 1991
1m 1f	1m 47.45	3	8-3	Firm	Sin Timon	Oct 1, 1977
1m 2f	2m 1.04	3	8-10	Good	Palace Music (USA)	Oct 20, 1984
1m 2f	2m 4.65	2	9-4	Good	Highland Chieftain	Nov 2, 1985
1m 4f	2m 27.67	3	8-5	Fast	Kiveton Kabooz	Oct 17, 1991
1m 6f	2m 54.34	5	8-6	Fast	Tudor Island	Spt 30, 1994
2m	3m 19.51	5	9-5	Good to firm	Grey Shot	Oct 4, 1997

NEWMARKET (July)

DISTANCE	TIME	AGE	WT	GOING	HORSE	DATE
5f	58.12 secs	4	8-11	Firm	Sweet Magic	Jly 22, 1995
5f	58.52 secs	2	8-10	Good	Seductress	Jly 10, 1990
6f	69.82 secs	4	9-6	Good	Cadeaux Genereux	Jly 13, 1989
6f	1m 10.61	2	8-10	Fast	Mujtahid (USA)	Jly 11, 1990
7f	1m 23.56	3	8-12	Good	Inchinor	Jun 26, 1993
7f	1m 24.46	2	8-11	Good to firm	Ruznama (USA)	Aug 25, 1995
1m	1m 36.8	4	9-7	Hard	Pink Flower	Jun 6, 1944
1m	1m 39.01	2	8-11	Good to firm	Traceability	Aug 25, 1995
1m 2f	2m 2.31	4	9-1	Fast	Vallance	Aug 1, 1992
1m 4f	2m 26.7	3	8-1	Fast	Desert Team (USA)	Jly 6, 1993
1m 6f 175y	3m 6.07	3	8-10	Fast	Spring to Action	Jly 8, 1993
2m 24y	3m 24.32	5	10-0	Fast	Jack Button	Aug 5, 1994

NOTTINGHAM

DISTANCE	TIME	AGE	WT	GOING	HORSE	DATE
5f 13y	58.4 secs	6	8-8	Good	Minstrel King	Mar 29, 1960
5f 13y	57.9 secs	2	8-9	Firm	Hoh Magic	May 13, 1994
6f 15y	1m 10.0	4	9-2	Firm	Ajanac	Aug 8, 1988
6f 15y	1m 11.4	2	8-11	Firm	Jameelapi (USA)	Aug 8, 1983
1m 54y	1m 39.6	4	8-2	Fast	Blake's Treasure	Spt 2, 1991
1m 54y	1m 40.8	2	9-0	Fast	King's Loch (IRE)	Spt 3, 1991
1m 1f 213y	2m 2.3	3	8-8	Firm	Ayaabi	Jly 21, 1984
1m 1f 213y	2m 5.6	2	9-0	Firm	Al Salite	Oct 28, 1985
1m 6f 15y	2m 57.8	3	8-10	Firm	Buster Jo	Oct 1, 1985
2m 9y	3m 24.0	5	7-7	Firm	Fet	Oct 5, 1936

PONTEFRACT

DISTANCE	TIME	AGE	WT	GOING	HORSE	DATE
5f	61.1 secs	5	7-7	Hard	Regal Bingo	Spt 29, 1971
5f	61.4 secs	2	8-9	Fast	Breakaway	Aug 6, 1987
6f	1m 12.6	3	7-13	Firm	Merry One	Aug 29, 1970
6f	1m 14.0	2	9-3	Firm	Fawzi	Spt 6, 1983
1m 4y	1m 41.4	5	8-12	Firm	Nevison's Lad	May 14, 1965
1m 4y	1m 42.8	2	9-13	Firm	Star Spray	Spt 6, 1983
1m 2f 6y	2m 6.2	4	7-8	Hard	Happy Hector	Jly 9, 1979
1m 2f 6y	2m 13.0	2	9-0	Good to firm	Warbrook	Oct 2, 1995
1m 4f 8y	2m 34.3	4	8-9	Hard	Ezra	Jun 23, 1975
2m 1f 22y	3m 42.1	3	9-2	Firm	Night Eye (USA)	Spt 6, 1983
2m 1f 216y	3m 51.1	3	8-8	Firm	Kudz (USA)	Spt 9, 1986
2m 5f 122y	4m 47.8	4	8-4	Firm	Physical (USA)	May 14, 1984

REDCAR

DISTANCE	TIME	AGE	WT	GOING	HORSE	DATE
5f	56.5 secs	3	9-7	Firm	Nazela	Aug 10, 1990
5f	56.9 secs	2	9-0	Firm	Mister Joel	Oct 24, 1995
6f	68.6 secs	3	9-2	Fast	Sizzling Saga (IRE)	Jun 21, 1991
6f	69.5 secs	2	9-7	Firm	Times of Times	Oct 24, 1995
7f	1m 21.0	3	9-1	Firm	Empty Quarter	Oct 3, 1995
7f	1m 21.9	2	8-11	Firm	Nagwa	Spt 27, 1975
1m	1m 33.1	3	9-5	Firm	Night Wink (USA)	Oct 24, 1995
1m	1m 36.7	2	8-8	Fast	Carbonate	Spt 15, 1987
1m 1f	1m 48.5	5	8-12	Firm	Mellottie	Jly 25, 1990
1m 1f	1m 53.8	2	9-0	Good	Double Trigger (IRE)	Spt 25, 1993
1m 2f	2m 1.5	5	9-3	Firm	Inaad	May 29, 1989
1m 3f	2m 17.0	3	8-9	Firm	Photo Call	Aug 7, 1990
1m 5f 135y	2m 54.6	6	9-10	Firm	Brodessa	Jun 20, 1992
1m 6f 19y	2m 59.9	3	8-6	Firm	Trainglot	Jly 25, 1990
2m 4y	3m 24.9	3	9-3	Fast	Subsonic (IRE)	Oct 8, 1991

RIPON

DISTANCE	TIME	AGE	WT	GOING	HORSE	DATE
5f	57.6 secs	5	8-10	Good	Broadstairs Beauty (IRE)	May21,1995
5f	57.8 secs	2	8-8	Firm	Super Rocky	Aug 5,1991
6f	69.8 secs	5	7-0	Firm	Quoit	Jly 23,1966
6f	1m 10.9	2	8-11	Good	Kahir Almaydan (IRE)	Aug28,1995
1m	1m 37.0	4	7-10	Firm	Crown Witness	Aug25,1980
1m	1m 41.2	2	7-2	Good	Roanstreak	Spt 5,1970
1m 1f	1m 50.5	3	9-2	Good to firm	Bold Words (CAN)	Apr 9,1997
1m 2f	2m 2.7	3	9-4	Firm	Swift Sword	Jly 20,1991
1m 4f 60y	2m 32.2	6	8-7	Firm	Cholo	Spt 27,1941
2m	3m 26.2	5	9-6	Good to firm	Nigels Lad (IRE)	May28,1997

SALISBURY

DISTANCE	TIME	AGE	WT	GOING	HORSE	DATE
5f	59.4 secs	3	8-11	Firm	Bellsabanging	May 5, 1993
5f	59.8 secs	2	8-5	Good to firm	Tarf (USA)	Aug 17, 1995
6f	1m 11.54	4	8-7	Fast	Prince Sky	Jun 25, 1986
6f	1m 12.41	2	9-1	Fast	Basma (USA)	Spt 6, 1991
6f 212y	1m 24.98	3	9-7	Firm	High Summer	Spt 5, 1996
6f 212y	1m 25.97	2	9-0	Firm	More Royal (USA)	Jun 29, 1995
1m	1m 38.94	5	8-10	Firm	Weaver Bird	Jun 29, 1995
1m	1m 43.86	2	9-3	Firm	Carocrest	Spt 1, 1983
1m 1f 209y	2m 4.46	4	7-7	Fast	Kala Nashan	Jun 25, 1986
1m 4f	2m 32.08	3	8-9	Good	Chief Contender (IRE)	May 5, 1996
1m 6f	2m 58.01	4	10-0	Fast	Dancing Affair	Aug 16, 1984

SANDOWN

DISTANCE	TIME	AGE	WT	GOING	HORSE	DATE
5f 6y	58.82 secs	6	8-9	Good to firm	Palacegate Touch	Spt 17, 1996
5f 6y	59.48 secs	2	9-3	Firm	Times Time	Jly 22, 1982
7f 16y	1m 26.36	3	9-0	Firm	Mawsuff	Jun 14, 1986
7f 16y	1m 27.87	2	8-12	Good to firm	Red Camellia	Jly 25, 1996
1m 14y	1m 39.08	3	8-8	Firm	Linda's Fantasy	Aug 19, 1983
1m 14y	1m 41.14	2	8-11	Fast	Reference Point	Spt 23, 1986
1m 1f	1m 54.01	3	9-7	Firm	Al Shafa	Jun 15, 1996
1m 1f	1m 57.62	2	9-0	Good to firm	Night Watch (USA)	Aug 30, 1995
1m 2f 7y	2m 2.14	4	8-11	Firm	Kalaglow	May 31, 1982
1m 3f 91y	2m 21.61	4	8-3	Fast	Aylesfield	Jly 7, 1984
1m 6f	2m 58.85	3	9-2	Fast	Sun of Spring	Aug 11, 1993
2m 78y	3m 29.93	6	9-2	Firm	Sadeem (USA)	May 29, 1989

SOUTHWELL

DISTANCE	TIME	AGE	WT	GOING	HORSE	DATE
5f	57.7 secs	3	9-6	Standard	Case Law	Aug 15, 1990
5f	58.9 secs	2	8-9	Standard	Nor-Do-I	Nov 29, 1996
6f	1m 13.3	3	9-2	Standard	Rambo Express	Dec 18, 1990
6f	1m 13.9	2	9-0	Standard	Superstrike	Jly 31, 1991
7f	1m 26.8	5	8-4	Standard	Amenable	Dec 13, 1990
7f	1m 27.0	2	8-4	Standard	Rejoice (IRE)	Nov 30, 1990
1m	1m 17.0	4	9-12	Standard	Bella Parkes	Mar 3, 1995
1m	1m 38.0	2	8-9	Standard	Alpha Rascal	Nov 13, 1990
1m 3f	2m 21.5	4	9-7	Standard	Tempering	Dec 5, 1990
1m 4f	2m 34.1	4	9-12	Standard	Fast Chick	Nov 8, 1989
1m 6f	3m 1.6	3	7-7	Standard	Qualitair Aviator	Dec 1, 1989
2m	3m 37.8	4	9-12	Standard	Megan's Flight	Dec 6, 1989

THIRSK

DISTANCE	TIME	AGE	WT	GOING	HORSE	DATE
5f	56.9 secs	4	8-6	Firm	Singing Star	Aug 3, 1990
5f	57.4 secs	2	9-1	Firm	Nifty Fifty (IRE)	Jly 19, 1991
6f	69.4 secs	4	10-0	Firm	Tiler (IRE)	Jly 26, 1996
6f	69.2 secs	2	9-6	Good to firm	Westcourt Magic	Aug 25, 1995
7f	1m 22.6	5	6-11	Firm	Tuanwun	May 29, 1970
7f	1m 24.6	2	8-12	Firm	Man of Harlech	Aug 2, 1975
1m	1m 34.8	4	8-13	Firm	Yearsley	May 5, 1990
1m	1m 38.5	2	8-9	Good to firm	Ivan Luis (FR)	Spt 7, 1996
1m 4f	2m 30.0	4	8-2	Firm	Casting Vote	Aug 1, 1964
2m	3m 22.3	3	8-11	Firm	Tomaschek (USA)	Jly 17, 1981

WARWICK

DISTANCE	TIME	AGE	WT	GOING	HORSE	DATE
5f	57.8 secs	5	9-4	Fast	Another Episode (IRE)	Aug 29, 1994
5f	58.6 secs	2	8-11	Firm	Olympic Spirit	Jun 10, 1996
6f	1m 11.8	4	9-5	Firm	Pride of Kilmallock	Jly 1, 1960
6f	1m 12.1	2	7-7	Firm	Sum Mede	Jly 14, 1989
7f	1m 23.5	4	9-2	Good to firm	Russian Music	Mar 31, 1997
7f	1m 24.8	2	9-4	Firm	Nocino	Jly 28, 1979
1m	1m 36.0	3	9-0	Firm	Academic World (USA)	Aug 25, 1975
1m	1m 37.5	2	9-3	Firm	Perfect Stranger	Oct 14, 1986
1m 2f 169y	2m 13.2	3	8-8	Firm	Classic Tale	Jly 7, 1987
1m 4f 115y	2m 37.2	5	8-12	Hard	Noirmont Buoy	Jun 19, 1967
1m 6f 194y	3m 8.9	4	9-1	Firm	Chucklestone	Jly 7, 1987
2m 20y	3m 25.8	4	9-7	Fast	Sanamar (disq)	Aug 29, 1988

WINDSOR

DISTANCE	TIME	AGE	WT	GOING	HORSE	DATE
5f 10y	59.2 secs	3	9-7	Fast	La Tuerta	Jly 15, 1985
5f 10y	58.9 secs	2	9-0	Firm	Strictly Private	Jly 22, 1974
5f 217y	1m 10.1	3	8-4	Firm	Sweet Relief	Spt 11, 1978
5f 217y	69.0 secs	2	8-7	Fast	Options Open	Jly 25, 1994
1m 67y	1m 41.5	4	7-2	Firm	Blowing Bubbles	Jly 16, 1984
1m 2f 7y	2m 3.0	3	9-1	Firm	Moomba Masquerade	May 19, 1980
1m 3f 135y	2m 21.5	3	9-2	Firm	Double Florin (USA)	May 19, 1980

Teams which have arrived too late for inclusion in Horses In Training 1998 will be published in the Raceform Update.

WOLVERHAMPTON

DISTANCE	TIME	AGE	WT	GOING	HORSE	DATE
5f	60.5 secs	7	8-7	Standard	Sir Tasker	Jan 4, 1995
5f	62.3 secs	2	8-10	Standard	Imperial Garden (IRE)	Aug 31, 1996
6f	1m 13.2	7	9-8	Standard	Sea-Deer	Aug 31, 1996
6f	1m 14.4	2	9-0	Standard	Trailblazer	Nov 2, 1996
7f	1m 27.3	4	10-0	Standard	Rocketeer	Jan 4, 1995
7f	1m 28.5	2	8-9	Standard	Mudflap	Aug 17, 1996
1m	2m 38.4	5	8-13	Standard	Johns Act (USA)	Mar 8, 1995
1m 100y	1m 48.6	3	9-0	Standard	Contrafire (IRE)	Jan 4, 1995
1m 100y	1m 50.6	2	9-0	Standard	Upper Grosvenor	Dec 27, 1993
1m 1f 79y	1m 59.3	12	9-6	Standard	Aitch N'Bee	Jan 4, 1995
1m 4f	2m 38.4	3	8-2	Standard	New Inn	Nov 26, 1994
1m 6f 166y	3m 11.3	4	8-11	Standard	Noufari (FR)	Jan 4, 1995
2m 46y	3m 39.3	4	9-6	Standard	Secret Serenade	Jan 18, 1995

YARMOUTH

DISTANCE	TIME	AGE	WT	GOING	HORSE	DATE
5f 43y	60.2 secs	3	8-11	Fast	Charm Bird	Spt 15, 1988
5f 43y	60.9 secs	2	8-8	Firm	Aberbevine	Jun 14, 1967
6f 3y	1m 10.1	3	8-10	Good to firm	Proud Native	Aug 10, 1997
6f 3y	1m 10.4	2	9-0	Fast	Lanchester	Aug 15, 1988
7f 3y	1m 22.2	3	8-7	Fast	Cielamour (USA)	Spt 15, 1988
7f 3y	1m 22.2	2	9-0	Fast	Warrshan (USA)	Spt 14, 1988
1m 3y	1m 34.6	3	8-11	Firm	Bonne Etoile	Jun 27, 1995
1m 3y	1m 34.4	2	8-11	Fast	Alderney	Spt 14, 1988
1m 2f 21y	2m 3.5	3	8-7	Firm	Supreme Sound	Spt 17, 1997
1m 3f 101y	2m 23.0	3	8-9	Firm	Rahil (IRE)	Jly 1, 1993
1m 6f 17y	2m 57.8	3	8-2	Fast	Barakat	Jly 24, 1990
2m	3m 28.9	3	8-13	Firm	Dawn Summit	May 28, 1997
2m 2f 51y	3m 57.2	3	9-8	Firm	Motet	Spt 18, 1997

YORK

DISTANCE	TIME	AGE	WT	GOING	HORSE	DATE
5f	56.16 secs	3	9-3	Fast	Dayjur (USA)	Aug 23, 1990
5f	57.39 secs	2	7-8	Firm	Lyric Fantasy (USA)	Aug 20, 1992
6f	68.82 secs	4	9-4	Fast	Shalford (IRE)	May 14, 1992
6f	69.59 secs	2	9-0	Good	Indiscreet (CAN)	Aug 22, 1996
6f 214y	1m 21.77	3	8-4	Good	Ruznama (USA)	Aug 22, 1996
6f 214y	1m 22.98	2	8-10	Fast	Options Open	Aug 16, 1994
7f 202y	1m 34.81	4	8-10	Good	Concer Un	Aug 22, 1996
7f 202y	1m 37.43	2	9-0	Good	Prince of My Heart	Oct 4, 1995
1m 205y	1m 48.89	6	8-4	Fast	No Comebacks	Jun 10, 1994
1m 205y	1m 52.43	2	8-1	Firm	Oral Evidence	Oct 6, 1988
1m 2f 85y	2m 6.18	3	9-0	Firm	Erhaab (USA)	May 11, 1994
1m 3f 195y	2m 25.79	3	9-0	Fast	Diminuendo (USA)	Aug 16, 1988
1m 5f 194y	2m 52.77	4	9-0	Good to firm	Classic Cliche (IRE)	May 16, 1996
1m 7f 195y	3m 18.49	3	8-0	Fast	Dam Busters (USA)	Aug 16, 1988

FLAT SPEED FIGURES 1997

The following list, based on Raceform Standard Times, shows speed figures of 30 and upwards, returned on British and selected Irish and French tracks. All the ratings are given at 9st. after allowances for going and distance behind winners. Additional information in parentheses following the Speed Figure shows the distance of the race in furlongs, course, state of going and the date on which the figure was recorded. Going abbreviations are: Hd (hard), F (firm), Gf (good-to-firm), Gs (good-to-soft); G (good), S (soft), Hy (heavy).

Aardwolf 38 (22f,Asc,S,Jun 20)
Abajany 60 (8f,San,GF,Spt 16)
Able Player (USA) 31 (12f,Crl,G,Jun 25)
Able Sheriff 49 (5f,Pon,GF,Apr 22)
Aboo Hom 39 (13½f,Chs,G,Spt 24)
Abou Zouz (USA) 45 (7f,Nwm,S,Jun 28)
A Breeze 41 (7f,Don,GF,Mar 22)
Absolute Liberty (USA) 38 (10f,Lin,G,Jun 24)
Absolutely Fayre 32 (8f,Pon,GF,Jun 9)
Absolutelystunning 36 (10f,Not,GF,Apr 11)
Absolute Utopia (USA) 50 (10f,Sal,G,Oct 1)
Abtaal 38 (8f,War,G,May 5)
Academy House (IRE) 37 (20f,Asc,G,Jun 17)
Academy Star 44 (10f,Goo,G,Spt 13)
Acharne 80 (8f,San,GF,Apr 25)
Action Jackson 48 (10f,Bri,F,Aug 16)
Admirals Flame (IRE) 49 (8f,Nwm,G,Jun 7)
Admirals Secret (USA) 40 (12f,Fol,S,Jun 27)
Advance East 30 (12 1/2f,War,G,Jun 24)
Aerleon Pete (IRE) 53 (12f,Hay,G,Spt 26)
Afaan (IRE) 68 (5f,Red,G,Nov 4)
Aficionado (IRE) 38 (8f,Not,GF,Apr 11)
Afon Alwen 54 (12f,Bri,F,Jly 28)
African-Pard (IRE) 57 (10f,Chp,G,Aug 25)
Agent Mulder 31 (8f,Sal,GF,May 15)
Agony Aunt 45 (10f,Rip,G,Aug 30)
Ailleacht (USA) 46 (5f,Cur,G,Jly 13)
Air Express (IRE) 94 (8f,Asc,G,Jun 17)
Air Quest 60 (14f,Goo,GS,May 21)
Ajayib (USA) 51 (11f,Ayr,S,Oct 13)
Ajcombe (IRE) 49 (16f,Goo,GF,Spt 25)
Akalim 51 (7f,Chp,G,Spt 11)
Akdariya (IRE) 53 (12f,Asc,G,Jun 19)
Al Abraq (IRE) 54 (8f,San,GF,May 27)
Alaflak (IRE) 45 (10f,Bat,F,Jly 23)
Alakdar (CAN) 37 (10f,Don,GS,Jun 28)
Alamein (USA) 66 (7f,Yar,G,Jly 16)
Alamode 30 (5f,Don,G,May 24)
Alarico (FR) 33 (14f,San,GF,Jly 30)
Alarme Belle 46 (7f,Leo,S,Nov 9)
Alarmist 54 (10f,Goo,GF,Jun 12)
Al Azhar 75 (12f,Don,S,Nov 8)
Albaha (USA) 62 (12f,Thi,G,Aug 2)
Albert The Bear 69 (7f,Lin,GF,Aug 17)
Alcalali (USA) 53 (12f,Yor,G,Aug 20)
Alekos (USA) 41 (10f,Lon,,Jun 22)
Alezal 57 (8f,Asc,G,Jun 17)
Alfahaal (IRE) 56 (8f,Lei,S,Oct 13)
Alfredo Alfredo (USA) 38 (10f,Not,GF,Apr 11)
Alhaarth (IRE) 96 (10f,Lon,G,Oct 4)
Alhawa (USA) 68 (8f,San,GF,Apr 25)
Alhosaam 54 (16f,Chs,G,Spt 24)
Alifandango (IRE) 44 (9f,Goo,GF,Jly 30)
Alikhlas 47 (7f,San,GF,Spt 16)
Ali-Royal (IRE) 86 (9f,Nwm,G,Apr 16)
Aliya (IRE) 59 (15f,Lon,G,Oct 4)
Allied Forces (USA) 90 (8f,Asc,G,Spt 27)
Allinson's Mate (IRE) 55 (7f,Don,G,Jun 7)
All Is Fair 51 (7f,Nwm,GF,Oct 3)
All On 41 (16f,Nwc,G,Aug 6)
Allstars Express 36 (10f,Fol,F,Apr 10)
All The Colours (IRE) 37 (16f,Leo,S,Nov 9)
Almasi (IRE) 79 (6f,Ayr,G,Spt 20)
Al Masroor (USA) 60 (7f,San,GF,Jly 30)
Almaty (IRE) 76 (5f,Don,GF,Spt 10)
Almond Rock 77 (7 1/2f,Chs,S,Aug 30)
Almost Skint (IRE) 38 (7f,Leo,G,Apr 19)
Al Muallim (USA) 66 (6f,Lin,GF,Aug 17)
Almuhimm (USA) 56 (7f,Asc,G,Aug 1)
Almuhtaram 43 (12f,Bri,F,Jun 3)
Almushtarak (IRE) 94 (8 1/2f,Eps,G,Jun 7)
Alphabet 60 (8f,Wnd,G,Aug 23)
Alpine Hideaway (IRE) 63 (8f,Nwm,GF,May 31)
Alpine Panther (IRE) 52 (11f,Ayr,GS,Spt 18)
Alpine Time (IRE) 58 (7f,San,G,May 26)
Al Reet (IRE) 41 (7f,Don,GS,Jun 28)
Alsahib (USA) 52 (8f,Nwb,S,May 18)
Al's Alibi 57 (12f,Hay,S,Mar 29)
Alumisiyah (USA) 70 (6f,Hay,S,Oct 15)
Always Alight 64 (6f,Ayr,G,Spt 20)
Always Earnest (USA) 93 (20f,Lon,G,Oct 4)
Always Grace 34 (6f,Fol,GF,Jun 4)

Always Happy 39 (8f,Bri,F,May 23)
Always Loyal (USA) 94 (9f,Lon,GF,Oct 5)
Always On My Mind 66 (6f,Nwm,GF,Nov 1)
Amadour (IRE) 40 (11 1/2f,Wnd,GF,Jun 2)
Amazing Bay 52 (5f,Nwm,G,May 3)
Amber Fort 67 (8f,Nwb,G,Jun 12)
Ambidextrous (IRE) 47 (10 1/2f,Hay,G,Jly 5)
American Whisper 48 (10f,Don,G,Oct 24)
Amiarge 37 (16f,Rip,GF,May 28)
Amid Albadu (USA) 83 (8 1/2f,Eps,G,Jun 7)
Among Men (USA) 89 (7f,Asc,GF,Jun 18)
Amrak Ajeeb (IRE) 82 (9f,Nwm,G,Apr 16)
Amron 52 (6f,Crl,G,Apr 25)
Amyas (IRE) 88 (10 1/2f,Yor,G,Aug 20)
Anak-Ku 63 (10f,Chp,GF,Aug 3)
Anchored In Love 34 (7f,Goo,GS,May 21)
Anchorena 36 (16f,Rip,GF,May 28)
Anchor Venture 45 (10f,Pon,GF,Jun 9)
Ancient Quest 59 (11 1/2f,Wnd,GS,Jun 30)
Andreyev (IRE) 65 (7f,Nwm,G,Apr 16)
Anetta 32 (7f,Cat,GF,Spt 20)
Aneysar (IRE) 67 (9f,Lon,S,May 15)
Angel Chimes 55 (9f,Nwm,GF,Oct 4)
Angel Face (USA) 56 (11f,War,GF,Apr 12)
Angus-G 73 (12f,Nwm,G,Apr 16)
Anjou 43 (14f,Yar,F,Oct 29)
Annaba (IRE) 53 (12 1/2f,Lon,G,Oct 4)
Anna Thea (IRE) 83 (10 1/2f,Cha,S,Jun 8)
Anno Luce 62 (14 1/2f,Don,GF,Spt 10)
Annus Mirabilis (FR) 91 (10f,Wnd,G,Aug 23)
Anokato 50 (5f,Goo,G,Spt 24)
Anonym (IRE) 44 (7f,Yor,G,Jly 12)
Anotheranniversary 75 (5f,Nwm,G,Jly 19)
Another Batchworth 44 (5f,Red,GF,Oct 18)
Another Episode (IRE) 40 (5f,Ayr,S,Oct 14)
Another Night (IRE) 62 (10f,Don,GF,Spt 10)
Another Nightmare (IRE) 35 (5f,Ham,S,Jly 1)
Another Time 75 (9f,Nwb,GF,Jly 19)
Ansellman 75 (5f,Asc,Hy,Oct 11)
Antapoura (IRE) 41 (16f,Leo,S,Nov 9)
Antarctic Storm 55 (8f,Nwm,G,Oct 18)
Antithesis (IRE) 32 (5f,Rip,GF,Apr 17)
Antonia's Choice 34 (6f,Lin,GF,Aug 17)
Antonias Melody 49 (6f,Nwm,G,May 3)
Anyar Reem 60 (10f,Don,GS,Jun 29)
Apache Star 65 (8f,Nwm,G,Oct 18)
Apollo Red 66 (7f,Lin,GF,May 31)
Apprehension 74 (10f,Don,G,May 24)
Aquatic Queen 38 (6f,Fol,GF,Aug 5)
Aquavita 39 (12f,Bri,F,May 29)
Arabian King 48 (12f,Cha,G,Jun 1)
Arabian Story 96 (10f,Nwb,GF,Jly 19)
Araboybill 39 (12f,Chp,G,Aug 25)
Arcady 48 (20f,Asc,G,Jun 17)
Arcatura 31 (10f,Not,G,May 9)
Archello (IRE) 46 (5f,Bev,GF,Jun 5)
Arco Colora 45 (10f,Goo,G,Spt 13)
Arctic Fancy (USA) 60 (14f,Yor,GS,Jun 13)
Arctic Owl 63 (12f,Asc,GF,Spt 28)
Arctiid (USA) 52 (10f,Kem,G,May 24)
Ardarroch Prince 41 (10f,Ayr,GF,May 30)
Ardent 42 (8f,Lei,S,Oct 13)
Arethusa 61 (6f,Bat,Hy,May 11)
Arian Spirit (IRE) 34 (15f,Ayr,GF,Aug 9)
Arif (IRE) 38 (14f,Not,S,Jly 5)
Arletty 34 (11f,Kem,GF,Spt 22)
Arnie (IRE) 30 (6f,Goo,S,Jun 20)
Arriving 53 (10f,Nwb,GF,Spt 18)
Arruhan (IRE) 65 (7f,Nwc,GF,Oct 1)
Arterxerxes 69 (7f,Yar,GF,Aug 21)
Artful Dane (IRE) 67 (8f,Goo,GS,Jun 20)
Artic Courier 72 (12f,Eps,G,Spt 5)
Arzani (USA) 48 (12 1/2f,War,GF,Jly 19)
Asas 46 (10f,Lin,GF,May 31)
Asef Alhind 65 (7f,San,GF,Jly 23)
Ashby Hill (IRE) 63 (10f,Nwm,G,May 2)
Ashkernazy (IRE) 36 (5f,Wnd,GF,Jly 14)
Ashley Park (IRE) 55 (10f,Cur,GS,Aug 16)
As-Is 32 (12f,Lei,GF,May 27)
Askern 47 (10 1/2f,Hay,GF,Aug 8)
Assailable 51 (8f,Nwm,G,May 4)
Assured Gamble 58 (16f,Asc,GF,Jun 18)
Astarabad (USA) 80 (10f,Lon,G,Oct 4)
Astrac (IRE) 63 (6f,Hay,S,May 5)
Astral Invader (IRE) 45 (7f,Lei,GF,Mar 27)
Atlantic Desire (IRE) 68 (10f,Goo,GF,Aug 1)
Atlantic Mist 38 (12f,Kem,G,May 5)
At Large (IRE) 62 (6f,Not,GF,Oct 4)
At Liberty (IRE) 50 (12f,Bri,F,May 23)
Atnab (USA) 39 (7f,Kem,GF,May 31)
Attarikh (IRE) 35 (8f,Bat,G,Spt 8)
Attitre (FR) 67 (10f,Nwm,G,May 4)
Attitude 58 (8f,Lei,GF,Oct 5)
Augustan 54 (10f,Pon,GF,Aug 7)
Aunty Jane 78 (8f,Asc,S,Jly 26)
Aurelian 32 (14f,Red,F,Aug 23)
Autumn Cover 61 (8f,Kem,G,May 5)
Autumn Time (IRE) 32 (12f,Nwm,G,Apr 15)
Averring (USA) 55 (7f,Cur,G,Oct 4)
Averti (IRE) 99 (6f,Asc,GF,Spt 27)
Awad (USA) 78 (12f,Hpk,F,Nov 8)
Awassi (IRE) 38 (6f,Don,G,Jly 31)
Awesome Wells (IRE) 59 (11 1/2f,Lin,G,Spt 9)
Azizzi 73 (6f,Ayr,G,Spt 20)
Azores 54 (9f,San,GS,Aug 29)
Azra (IRE) 46 (7f,Cur,S,Spt 20)
Aztec Flyer (USA) 40 (16f,Not,GF,Aug 6)

Baba Au Rhum (IRE) 54 (8f,Goo,GF,Jly 29)
Babsy Babe 49 (6f,Rip,GF,Aug 4)
Baby Jane 36 (11f,Ham,S,Jun 25)
Bacchus 63 (6f,Nwm,GS,Jly 18)

Bachelors Pad 46 (7f,Nwm,GF,Oct 3)
Backhander (IRE) 37 (7f,Lei,GF,Mar 27)
Back Row 48 (12f,Nwm,GF,Oct 31)
Badenoch (IRE) 41 (12f,Chp,G,May 26)
Badge of Fame (IRE) 52 (14f,Yor,S,Spt 3)
Badlesmere (USA) 55 (8f,Kem,G,May 5)
Bahamian Beauty (USA) 51 (5f,Yor,G,Aug 20)
Bahamian Bounty 51 (6f,Nwm,G,Jly 10)
Bahamian Knight (CAN) 66 (12f,Don,GF,Spt 12)
Bahamian Sunshine (USA) 69 (12f,Goo,GF,Aug 1)
Bahhare (USA) 88 (8f,Asc,G,Spt 27)
Bajan Rose 57 (5f,Sal,GS,Jun 25)
Baked Alaska 55 (7f,Nwm,G,Apr 15)
Bakers Daughter 51 (10f,Wnd,GF,Jly 28)
Balalaika 97 (9f,Lon,GF,Oct 5)
Balance of Power 31 (7f,Eps,GS,Jly 9)
Bali Paradise (USA) 69 (10f,Nwb,GS,Spt 20)
Bali-Pet 31 (7f,Cat,GF,May 31)
Ballard Lady (IRE) 32 (7f,Hay,GS,Jly 3)
Ball Gown 66 (10 1/2f,Yor,G,May 14)
Ballpoint 50 (12f,Cat,G,Apr 23)
Ballymote 62 (5f,Cat,G,Apr 23)
Bally Souza (IRE) 61 (12f,Hay,GF,Aug 8)
Banbury (USA) 52 (7f,Hay,S,Mar 29)
Band on the Run 70 (8f,Yor,G,Jly 11)
Banzhaf (USA) 60 (7f,Bri,F,Spt 28)
Barba Papa (IRE) 70 (10f,Goo,GF,Aug 1)
Barbason 62 (7f,Bri,F,Spt 28)
Bardon Hill Boy (IRE) 63 (10f,San,GF,Jly 24)
Barings (FR) 66 (11f,Lon,G,Apr 6)
Baritone 48 (8f,Rip,GF,Apr 17)
Barnburgh Boy 57 (8f,Pon,GF,Oct 6)
Barnum Sands 69 (10f,Kem,G,Spt 21)
Baron Ferdinand 58 (10f,Nwm,GF,Oct 31)
Barrack Yard 44 (7f,Don,G,May 6)
Barranak (IRE) 51 (5f,Lin,S,Jun 28)
Barrel of Hope 35 (8f,Don,GF,Mar 21)
Barresbo 40 (8f,Edi,GF,May 31)
Barrier Ridge 54 (8f,Thi,F,Jun 2)
Bartex (FR) 69 (8f,Cha,S,May 12)
Bashful Brave 35 (5f,Rip,GF,Aug 4)
Basman (IRE) 63 (12f,Eps,G,Spt 5)
Basse Besogne (IRE) 70 (8f,Dea,G,Aug 3)
Batabanoo 40 (16f,Not,GF,Spt 15)
Bataleur 43 (6f,Crl,G,Apr 25)
Bathe In Light (USA) 45 (12f,Bri,GF,Spt 3)
Batoutoftheblue 31 (16f,Nwc,G,Aug 6)
Batsman 34 (6f,Wnd,G,Jly 7)
Battleship Bruce 31 (8f,Wnd,GS,Jun 30)
Baubigny (USA) 37 (8f,Not,G,Apr 29)
Bayford Thrust 48 (6f,Lin,G,Jun 24)
Bayin (USA) 53 (6f,Nwb,GF,May 28)
Bay of Islands 69 (10f,Nwm,G,May 2)
Beach Buoy (IRE) 38 (9f,Rip,GF,Jly 19)
Beacon Silver 40 (10f,San,GF,Spt 16)
Beano Script 45 (8f,Edi,G,Jun 16)
Bear Hug 46 (10f,Lin,S,May 10)
Bea's Ruby (IRE) 56 (7f,Chs,S,May 7)
Beauchamp Jade 70 (13f,Nwb,GS,Spt 20)
Beauchamp King 72 (8f,Asc,G,Jun 17)
Beauchamp Lion 34 (14f,Red,F,Aug 23)
Beaumont (IRE) 63 (14f,Not,G,Oct 30)
Beautiful Fire (IRE) 33 (8f,Leo,G,Apr 19)
Beau Venture (USA) 58 (5f,Goo,G,Spt 24)
Bedazzle 35 (8f,Rip,G,Jun 18)
Bedouin Honda 45 (10f,Nwm,G,Apr 15)
Bedouin Prince (USA) 42 (12f,Bri,F,Apr 21)
Bee Health Boy 55 (6f,Red,G,Jun 20)
Begorrat (IRE) 46 (11f,Ayr,S,Oct 14)
Behaviour 80 (9f,Nwm,G,Apr 16)
Behind The Scenes 39 (9f,Goo,G,May 22)
Bel Canto (IRE) 36 (10f,San,GF,Spt 16)
Bellagrana 32 (12f,Bri,F,Oct 1)
Bellara 40 (14f,Hay,S,May 5)
Bellas Gate Boy 43 (7f,Lin,GF,May 31)
Belle Bijou 32 (13f,Ham,G,Aug 13)
Bello (ARG) 62 (10f,Lon,G,Oct 4)
Belmarita (IRE) 58 (12f,Nwm,GF,Oct 2)
Benatom (USA) 77 (14f,Goo,GF,Jly 29)
Bend Wavy (IRE) 41 (8f,Don,GS,Nov 8)
Ben Gunn 65 (8f,Nwm,G,Jly 8)
Benjamins Law 43 (10f,Pon,G,Jly 8)
Benny The Dip (USA) 91 (12f,Eps,G,Jun 7)
Bentico 35 (8f,Wnd,GS,Jun 30)
Benzoe (IRE) 62 (6f,Yor,G,Aug 19)
Bequeath 75 (10f,Don,GF,Jun 7)
Berlin Blue 53 (14 1/2f,Don,GF,Spt 10)
Beryllium 45 (9f,San,GS,Aug 29)
Besiege 43 (12f,Lei,G,Oct 27)
Best Before Dawn (IRE) 75 (6f,Asc,GS,Jun 20)
Best of All (IRE) 63 (8f,Edi,GS,Jun 30)
Be True 37 (12f,Bri,GF,Oct 23)
Better Offer (IRE) 73 (12f,Asc,GF,Spt 28)
Bevier 32 (8f,Lei,GF,Oct 5)
Be Warned 44 (7f,Nwc,GF,Mar 31)
Bewitching Lady 32 (11 1/2f,Yar,GF,Spt 16)
Beyond Calculation (USA) 51 (7f,Thi,G,Jly 25)
Bianca Nera 43 (8f,Nwm,G,May 4)
Big Ander (SPA) 40 (15f,Lon,G,Oct 4)
Big Ben 35 (7f,Nwm,GF,Aug 9)
Big Sky Chester (USA) 87 (12f,Hpk,F,Nov 8)
Big Target (IRE) 38 (10f,Bat,GS,May 19)
Bijou d'Inde 91 (8f,Asc,G,Spt 27)
Bilko 38 (6f,Kem,G,Mar 29)
Billy Bushwacker 69 (10f,Don,GF,Spt 10)
Billy Nomaite 36 (8f,Thi,F,Jun 2)
Bimsey (IRE) 70 (14f,San,GF,Jly 16)
Bina Gardens 54 (10f,Chp,G,Spt 11)
Bin Rosie 81 (8f,Nwb,GS,Spt 20)
Bint Albaadiya (USA) 75 (6f,Nwm,S,Jun 27)
Bintang Timor (USA) 41 (6f,Nwm,GF,Apr 17)

Bint Baladee 63 (12f,Eps,G,Jun 6)
Bint Shihama (USA) 51 (7f,Yar,G,Jly 16)
Birchwood Sun 42 (7f,Lei,GS,Oct 14)
Bishops Court 82 (5f,Asc,S,Jun 21)
Bit on the Side (IRE) 66 (12f,Eps,G,Aug 10)
Blane Water (USA) 46 (7f,Nwm,G,Jly 8)
Blatant Outburst 30 (14f,Not,GF,Apr 21)
Blaze of Song 36 (10f,Lei,G,Oct 28)
Blazer's Baby 30 (7f,Kem,GF,May 31)
Blazing Imp (USA) 45 (5f,Edi,GS,Jun 23)
Blenheim Terrace 43 (12f,Edi,GF,Spt 15)
Blessed Spirit 68 (8f,Nwm,G,Jly 19)
Blessingindisguise 81 (6f,Yor,G,Aug 19)
Blewbury Hill (IRE) 61 (7f,Kem,GF,May 31)
Blockade (USA) 43 (10f,Not,GF,Jun 9)
Blood Orange 31 (6f,Nwm,GF,Apr 17)
Blooming Amazing 49 (10f,Red,GF,Oct 18)
Blot 39 (8f,San,GF,Jly 24)
Blowing Away (IRE) 38 (7f,Yar,F,Spt 17)
Bluebell Miss 38 (10f,Yar,G,Jly 16)
Blue Duster (USA) 69 (6f,Asc,G,Jun 19)
Blue Flyer (IRE) 56 (7f,Yar,GF,Aug 21)
Blue Goblin (USA) 71 (6f,Asc,G,Jun 19)
Blue Imperial (FR) 46 (8f,Bat,F,Jly 23)
Blue Iris 67 (6f,Bat,Hy,May 11)
Blue Lamp (USA) 33 (5f,Rip,GF,Aug 16)
Blue Ridge 54 (5f,Lin,GS,Aug 28)
Blue River (IRE) 69 (10 1/2f,Yor,G,May 13)
Blues Queen 47 (6f,Hay,G,Jly 5)
Blueygreen 51 (7f,Yar,G,Jly 16)
Blurred (IRE) 40 (10f,Nwm,G,May 2)
Boater 52 (8f,Thi,GS,May 17)
Bold Becky 33 (8f,Bat,GF,May 30)
Bold Brief 38 (5f,Crl,G,Jly 5)
Bold Buster 66 (11f,Ayr,GS,Spt 18)
Bold Demand 58 (12f,Eps,G,Jun 7)
Bold Effort (FR) 77 (5f,Dea,G,Aug 3)
Bold Elect 40 (20f,Goo,GF,Jly 30)
Bold Faith 41 (8f,Not,G,Nov 3)
Bold Gayle 30 (5f,Not,GF,Mar 31)
Bold Oriental (IRE) 60 (10f,Nwm,GF,Jly 9)
Bold Spring (IRE) 42 (6f,Nwm,G,Jun 7)
Bold Tina (IRE) 44 (7f,Bri,GF,Spt 3)
Bold Top 45 (10f,Pon,GF,Jun 9)
Bold Tycoon (IRE) 36 (7f,Cur,GS,Jun 28)
Bold Words (CAN) 83 (8f,San,GF,May 26)
Bolino Star (IRE) 68 (16f,Leo,S,Nov 9)
Bolivar (IRE) 59 (16f,Asc,S,Jun 21)
Bollero (IRE) 39 (7 1/2f,Bev,GF,Jly 15)
Bollin Dorothy 42 (7f,Cat,GF,Aug 15)
Bollin Frank 49 (8f,Rip,GF,Aug 25)
Bollin Harry 56 (6f,Red,G,Jun 20)
Bollin Joanne 92 (6f,Asc,GS,Jun 20)
Bollin Terry 51 (8f,Nwc,F,Jun 4)
Bolshoi (IRE) 85 (5f,Asc,GS,Jun 20)
Bombazine (IRE) 54 (12f,Asc,Hy,Oct 11)
Bonanza Peak (USA) 61 (10f,Pon,GS,Oct 20)
Bonapartiste (FR) 78 (15f,Lon,G,Oct 4)
Bon Guest (IRE) 31 (8f,Not,GF,Jly 19)
Bon Luck (IRE) 46 (7f,Fol,GF,Apr 22)
Bonnie Lassie 35 (9f,Ayr,S,Oct 13)
Boojum 48 (8f,Nwm,GF,Nov 1)
Book At Bedtime (IRE) 64 (14 1/2f,Don,GF,Spt 10)
Bookcase 37 (11f,War,GF,Apr 12)
Border Falcon 30 (8f,Nwb,GF,Apr 19)
Borgia (GER) 87 (12f,Hpk,F,Nov 8)
Bosra Sham (USA) 95 (10f,Asc,G,Jun 17)
Boss Lady (IRE) 45 (10 1/2f,Hay,S,Oct 15)
Bowcliffe 52 (8f,Red,GF,Oct 28)
Bowcliffe Court (IRE) 63 (16 1/2f,San,GS,Jly 5)
Bowcliffe Grange (IRE) 44 (5f,Thi,GF,Aug 22)
Bowden Rose 71 (6f,Not,GF,Jly 30)
Bowled Over 54 (12f,Nwm,G,Apr 16)
Bowlers Boy 59 (6f,Rip,G,Aug 30)
Bramble Bear 45 (6f,Kem,GF,Spt 22)
Brambles Way 41 (10f,Nwc,GF,Oct 22)
Brand New Dance 52 (14f,San,GF,Aug 14)
Brandon Jack 41 (10f,San,GF,Jly 24)
Brandon Magic 73 (14f,Yor,GS,Jun 13)
Brandonville 52 (7f,Hay,GS,Jly 3)
Brave Edge 85 (5f,Dea,G,Aug 3)
Brave Envoy 43 (8f,Lei,S,Oct 13)
Braveheart (IRE) 55 (7f,Nwm,GF,Nov 1)
Brave Kris (IRE) 56 (8f,Asc,S,Jun 21)
Brave Montgomerie 48 (9f,Ayr,G,Jun 20)
Break the Rules 73 (10f,Don,GF,Mar 20)
Brecon 36 (13f,Bat,G,Spt 8)
Brecongill Lad 53 (6f,Cat,G,Jun 6)
Breezed Well 35 (8f,Chp,G,Aug 3)
Bridie's Pride 38 (18f,Chp,GS,Jly 5)
Brigand (IRE) 65 (8f,Nwb,S,Spt 19)
Brighstone 54 (10f,Eps,GS,Jly 9)
Brighter Byfaah (IRE) 38 (17f,Bat,F,Jly 23)
Bright Fountain (IRE) 30 (9f,San,GS,Aug 29)
Bright Heritage (IRE) 60 (8f,Wnd,G,Aug 23)
Bright Water 77 (12f,Goo,GF,Aug 1)
Brilliance (FR) 88 (10 1/2f,Cha,S,Jun 8)
Brilliant Red 81 (8f,Goo,GS,Jun 29)
Briska (IRE) 30 (8f,Kem,GF,Spt 22)
Broad River (USA) 46 (7f,Goo,G,May 20)
Broadstairs Beauty (IRE) 59 (6f,Lei,G,Oct 27)
Broctune Gold 65 (7f,Crl,G,Apr 25)
Brodessa 45 (14f,Not,GF,Jly 19)
Broken Rites (IRE) 31 (16f,Leo,S,Nov 9)
Broughtons Error 36 (7f,Nwm,G,May 16)
Broughton's Pride (IRE) 42 (8f,Ham,S,May 4)
Broughtons Turmoil 65 (8f,Asc,GF,Apr 30)
Brutal Fantasy (IRE) 65 (5f,Cat,G,Apr 23)
Brynkir 31 (8f,Not,G,Apr 29)
Bubble Wings (FR) 59 (10f,Chp,G,Spt 11)
Bubbly 59 (7f,Bri,F,Spt 28)
Buck's Boy (USA) 88 (12f,Hpk,F,Nov 8)

Buddy Marvel (IRE) 45 (10f,Leo,YS,May 11)
Bulington (FR) 69 (10 1/2f,Lon,S,Apr 27)
Bulsara 31 (10f,Bev,GF,Jun 5)
Burden Of Proof (IRE) 57 (6f,Asc,G,Jun 19)
Burning (USA) 61 (11 1/2f,Yar,G,Jly 16)
Burning Truth (USA) 52 (8f,San,GS,Apr 26)
Burn Out 51 (20f,Asc,G,Jun 17)
Burnt Offering 43 (14f,San,GF,May 27)
Burundi (IRE) 39 (10 1/2f,Hay,G,Jly 5)
Bushwhacker 41 (7f,Hay,GS,Jly 3)
Busy Flight 91 (12f,Lon,GF,Oct 5)
Butrinto 49 (6f,Nwm,GS,Jly 18)
Byzantium 56 (8f,Kem,G,May 24)

Cadeaux Cher 54 (6f,Red,G,Nov 4)
Cadeaux Tryst 82 (8f,Asc,GF,Jun 18)
Ca'd'oro 57 (8f,Don,GS,Nov 8)
Caerfilly Dancer 55 (5f,Asc,S,Jun 21)
Caiseal Ros (IRE) 47 (10f,Leo,G,Apr 19)
Calamander (IRE) 44 (8f,Wnd,GF,Jly 14)
Calder King 41 (9f,Ham,S,Apr 2)
Calendula 56 (10f,Lei,G,Oct 28)
Calypso Grant (IRE) 71 (10f,Goo,GF,Aug 1)
Calypso Lady (IRE) 36 (8f,War,GF,Oct 7)
Cambridge Ball (IRE) 30 (10f,Yar,F,Jun 11)
Camionneur (IRE) 51 (5f,Thi,GF,Aug 22)
Campaign 36 (14f,Not,G,Nov 3)
Campaspe 52 (12f,Rip,GF,Aug 4)
Camp David (GER) 47 (20f,Asc,G,Jun 19)
Camporese (IRE) 65 (12f,Hay,G,Jly 5)
Canadian Fantasy 38 (9f,Ham,S,Jly 1)
Can Can Lady 60 (8f,Nwc,G,May 5)
Candereli (IRE) 42 (10f,Leo,YS,May 11)
Canon Can (USA) 82 (18f,Nwm,G,Oct 18)
Canovas Heart 75 (5f,Yor,G,Oct 8)
Cantina 38 (7f,Cat,GF,Spt 20)
Canton Venture 50 (12f,Thi,G,Jun 17)
Canyon Creek (IRE) 42 (8f,Don,GF,Mar 20)
Cape Cross (IRE) 80 (8f,Goo,GF,Aug 2)
Cape Pigeon (USA) 36 (8f,Sal,GS,Jun 25)
Capilano Princess 72 (10f,Don,G,Jly 30)
Cap Juluca (IRE) 97 (8 1/2f,Eps,G,Jun 7)
Capsoff (IRE) 42 (11 1/2f,Yar,GS,Jly 2)
Captain Carat 45 (5f,Cat,GF,May 30)
Captain Carparts 32 (7f,Cat,G,Apr 23)
Captain Collins (IRE) 78 (7f,Asc,GF,Jun 18)
Captain Horatius (IRE) 64 (10f,Goo,G,May 22)
Captain Jack 61 (18f,Nwm,G,Oct 18)
Captain Scott (IRE) 56 (8f,Yor,G,May 15)
Captain's Guest (IRE) 67 (15f,Nwm,G,Jly 19)
Captain Sinbad 35 (5f,War,GF,Apr 12)
Carati 33 (6f,Yar,GF,Jly 22)
Carburton 55 (10f,Wnd,GF,Jun 9)
Caribbean Star 60 (7f,San,GF,Spt 17)
Carisbrooke 48 (12f,Rip,GF,Aug 25)
Carlisle Bay (IRE) 37 (9f,Cur,S,Spt 21)

Carlton (IRE) 48 (8f,Nwc,G,May 22)
Carlys Quest 40 (8f,Sal,GF,May 15)
Carmine Lake (IRE) 67 (5f,Don,GF,Spt 10)
Carnelly (IRE) 48 (12f,Leo,G,Jly 19)
Carol's Dream (USA) 34 (11f,War,GF,Apr 12)
Carranita (IRE) 91 (6f,Nwm,G,Apr 15)
Carreamia 33 (6f,Don,GS,Jun 28)
Casey Tibbs (IRE) 58 (10f,Leo,G,Apr 19)
Cashmere Lady 67 (8f,Red,F,Aug 23)
Cashmirie 35 (10f,Bev,G,Jly 29)
Castel Rosselo 53 (7f,Thi,G,Jun 17)
Castle Courageous 56 (16f,Goo,G,Jun 12)
Casual Water (IRE) 52 (12 1/2f,War,GF,Jun 9)
Catalan Opening (NZ) 90 (7f,Stn,GF,Dec 14)
Catchable 61 (12f,Don,GF,Spt 12)
Catchment 34 (10f,Goo,G,Spt 13)
Catch The Blues (IRE) 79 (6f,Asc,G,Jun 19)
Cathedral (IRE) 74 (5f,Lin,GS,Aug 28)
Catienus (USA) 80 (10f,Cur,GS,Aug 16)
Cats Bottom 36 (8f,Bat,G,Jun 28)
Cauda Equina 48 (6f,Nwb,GF,Jly 18)
Caudillo (IRE) 49 (6f,Sal,S,Jun 26)
Caution 53 (6f,Not,GF,Oct 4)
Caviar Royale (IRE) 59 (10 1/2f,Yor,G,May 13)
Cayman Kai (IRE) 92 (6f,Nwm,G,Apr 15)
Cedez le Passage (FR) 54 (12f,Eps,G,Apr 23)
Cee-Jay-Ay 42 (8f,War,F,Jun 4)
Cee-N-K (IRE) 52 (8f,Red,GF,Oct 18)
Celandine 45 (7f,Cat,GF,Spt 20)
Celebrant 30 (10f,Lei,GF,Spt 9)
Celebration Cake (IRE) 48 (8f,Ayr,G,Spt 20)
Celeric 95 (20f,Lon,G,Oct 4)
Celestial Choir 75 (12f,Don,GF,Spt 12)
Celestial Key (USA) 60 (8f,Asc,GF,Jun 18)
Censor 47 (12f,Thi,G,Aug 2)
Centre Stalls (IRE) 94 (8f,Yor,G,May 14)
Chabrol (CAN) 49 (14f,Not,GF,Apr 11)
Chadwell Hall 47 (6f,Not,GF,Apr 8)
Chairmans Choice 42 (9f,Goo,GF,Jly 31)
Chairmans Daughter 36 (16 1/2f,Fol,GF,Aug 19)
Chai-Yo 62 (8f,Asc,Hy,Oct 10)
Champagne Prince 80 (10f,Nwm,G,May 2)
Champagne Warrior (IRE) 31 (12f,Rip,GF,Apr 9)
Change For A Buck (USA) 45 (7f,Nwm,G,Apr 16)
Chania (IRE) 57 (9f,Cur,S,Spt 21)
Charity Crusader 32 (12f,Bev,GF,Apr 5)
Charlie Sillett 66 (6f,Chs,S,Jun 25)
Charlotte Corday 80 (10 1/2f,Yor,G,May 14)
Charlton Imp (USA) 32 (8f,Chp,GF,Jly 11)
Charming Admiral (IRE) 44 (14f,Not,G,Nov 3)
Charnwood Jack (USA) 48 (10f,Lei,F,Apr 3)
C-Harry (IRE) 52 (6f,Chs,GF,Jun 4)
Charter 52 (16f,Rip,GF,May 28)
Chasetown Flyer (USA) 42 (8f,Wnd,GF,Jun 16)
Chateauherault (IRE) 32 (13f,Ham,G,Aug 13)
Chatham Island 40 (15f,Nwm,GS,Jun 11)

Chauncy Lane (IRE) 37 (10f,Cur,GS,May 25)
Check The Band (USA) 70 (5f,Asc,GS,Jun 20)
Cheek To Cheek 41 (12f,Bri,F,Jly 28)
Chemcast 52 (5f,Rip,G,Jun 19)
Cherokee Flight 46 (10f,Lei,GF,Spt 9)
Cherry Blossom (IRE) 35 (6f,Nwm,GF,Apr 17)
Chewit 62 (8f,Nwm,GF,Nov 1)
Chickawicka (IRE) 68 (7f,Nwm,G,Apr 16)
Chief Bearhart (CAN) 95 (12f,Hpk,F,Nov 8)
Chief Contender (IRE) 95 (20f,Lon,G,Oct 4)
Chief Monarch 55 (10f,Don,GF,Spt 13)
Chief's Song 32 (16f,Goo,GF,Spt 25)
Children's Choice (IRE) 45 (14f,Not,GF,Oct 4)
Chili Concerto 54 (5f,Wnd,S,May 19)
Chinaberry 43 (7f,Goo,GS,May 21)
China Girl (IRE) 44 (6f,Eps,G,Aug 10)
China Red (USA) 52 (8f,Not,GF,Apr 11)
Chinour (IRE) 35 (8f,War,GF,Apr 12)
Chris's Lad 57 (12f,Nwm,G,Jun 7)
Churchill's Shadow (IRE) 32 (6f,Bat,G,Spt 8)
Cim Bom Bom (IRE) 62 (5f,Pon,GF,Jly 18)
Cinema Paradiso 57 (8 1/2f,Eps,G,Jun 6)
Circle of Magic 32 (8f,Lei,G,Jly 23)
Cirino (USA) 72 (9f,Cha,G,Jun 1)
Ciro's Pearl (IRE) 57 (12f,Asc,G,Jun 19)
Ciste (IRE) 32 (8f,Leo,YS,May 11)
Cittern 42 (16f,Nwc,G,Aug 6)
City Gambler 55 (8f,Lei,G,Aug 11)
City Hall (IRE) 57 (16f,Not,S,Oct 15)
Civil Liberty 51 (12f,Asc,Hy,Oct 10)
Clan Ben (IRE) 75 (10f,Nwm,G,May 3)
Clan Chief 69 (6f,Eps,G,Jun 7)
Classical Dance (IRE) 31 (11f,Ham,G,Aug 13)
Classic Ballet (FR) 50 (12f,Edi,GF,Spt 15)
Classic Beauty (IRE) 49 (10f,Bev,GF,Apr 24)
Classic Cliche (IRE) 89 (16f,Goo,GF,Jly 31)
Classic Colours (USA) 39 (10f,Pon,GS,Oct 20)
Classic Dame (FR) 43 (12f,Fol,GF,Aug 19)
Classic Fan (USA) 32 (10f,Wnd,G,Aug 4)
Classic Find (USA) 59 (12f,Nwm,G,Apr 16)
Classic Flyer (IRE) 55 (12f,Edi,GF,Spt 15)
Classic Jenny (IRE) 41 (10f,Wnd,GF,Jun 16)
Classic Leader 52 (6f,Chp,GF,Jun 13)
Classic Line 44 (14f,Not,G,Oct 30)
Classic Parisian (IRE) 40 (10f,Bat,GF,Jly 17)
Classic Park 63 (8f,Asc,GF,Jun 18)
Classy Chief 31 (10f,Fol,F,Apr 10)
Clerio 39 (8f,Cur,S,Spt 7)
Clerkenwell (USA) 66 (11f,Nwb,GF,Spt 18)
Clever Caption (IRE) 61 (5f,Nwm,G,May 3)
Cliburnel News (IRE) 40 (16f,Not,GF,Spt 15)
Clinking 32 (14f,Yar,F,Oct 29)
Clodora (FR) 97 (9f,Lon,GF,Oct 5)
Cloudings (IRE) 59 (10 1/2f,Lon,S,May 11)
Cloud Inspector (IRE) 64 (20f,Goo,GF,Jly 30)
Clouds Hill (FR) 45 (8f,Goo,GF,Jly 29)
Clued Up 46 (8f,Chp,GS,Jly 1)
Clytha Hill Lad 42 (8f,Hay,GF,Aug 15)
Coastal Bluff 83 (6f,Goo,GF,Aug 2)
Coastguards Hero 30 (7f,San,GF,Jly 30)
Coble 39 (8f,Nwm,G,May 4)
Coh Sho No 46 (15 1/2f,Fol,F,Apr 10)
Cointosser (IRE) 34 (8f,Sal,F,Jly 18)
Cois Na Farraige (IRE) 30 (13f,Ham,GS,Apr 10)
Cold Steel 40 (8f,Nwm,GS,Jly 18)
College Night (IRE) 32 (6f,Bri,GF,May 6)
College Princess 30 (5f,Red,GF,Jly 19)
Collier Bay 45 (16f,Hay,S,Mar 29)
Colour Code 73 (10f,Ayr,GF,May 30)
Colour Counsellor 31 (10f,Bri,F,Aug 16)
Colway Ritz 57 (7f,Red,F,Aug 10)
Comanche Companion 52 (8f,Nwm,GS,Oct 16)
Come Together 38 (10f,Nwb,GF,Spt 18)
Commanche Court (IRE) 67 (16f,Leo,S,Nov 9)
Compass Pointer 39 (14f,Hay,GS,May 24)
Compatibility (IRE) 53 (6f,Hay,G,Jly 5)
Compromise (IRE) 42 (7f,War,GF,May 24)
Compton Place 72 (5f,Asc,GS,Jun 20)
Concer Un 73 (7f,Nwm,G,Apr 16)
Confronter 48 (8f,Goo,GF,Jly 29)
Connemara (IRE) 65 (6f,Nwm,GF,May 31)
Conon Falls (IRE) 53 (10f,Goo,G,May 20)
Consort 72 (8f,Nwm,GS,Oct 16)
Conspicuous (IRE) 66 (10f,Eps,G,Jun 7)
Conspiracy 53 (7f,Nwm,G,Jly 8)
Contentment (IRE) 45 (10f,Wnd,GF,Jun 16)
Contrarie 35 (16f,Not,S,Oct 15)
Cool Edge (IRE) 64 (7f,Cur,G,Apr 12)
Copper Shell 32 (10f,Bat,GF,Apr 29)
Cordate (IRE) 41 (8f,Kem,G,May 24)
Coretta (IRE) 48 (12f,Asc,GF,Spt 28)
Corniche Quest (IRE) 56 (6f,Not,G,May 23)
Corradini 62 (16 1/2f,San,GF,May 26)
Cosmic Prince (IRE) 59 (8f,War,GF,Apr 12)
Cottage Prince (IRE) 36 (12f,Cat,G,Jun 6)
Count Tony 41 (10f,Yar,GF,Aug 21)
Courageous Knight 31 (14f,Sal,GF,Aug 1)
Courbaril 42 (14f,Sal,GF,Aug 1)
Court Express 47 (6f,Crl,GF,Jun 25)
Court House 31 (6f,Pon,GF,Oct 6)
Courtship 56 (8f,Pon,GF,Apr 22)
Craigary 39 (12f,Ham,G,Aug 2)
Craigievar 72 (7f,Hay,S,May 5)
Crazy Chief 44 (9f,Nwb,GS,Oct 25)
Credit Squeeze 35 (12f,Bat,G,Aug 12)
Cretan Gift 90 (6f,Asc,GF,Spt 27)
Crimson Tide (IRE) 76 (9f,Nwm,GF,Apr 17)
Crissem (IRE) 44 (7f,Cat,GF,Spt 20)
Croeso Cynnes 39 (6f,Chp,GS,Aug 3)
Crofters Ceilidh 76 (5f,Yor,GS,Jun 13)
Croft Pool 84 (5f,Asc,GS,Jun 20)
Cross The Border 66 (5f,Thi,GF,Aug 22)

Crowded Avenue 71 (5f,Asc,GF,Spt 28)
Crown Court (USA) 73 (8f,Asc,GF,Jun 18)
Crown of Light 76 (12f,Eps,G,Jun 6)
Crown of Thorns (USA) 44 (8f,San,GF,Jly 24)
Crumpton Hill (IRE) 87 (7f,Asc,GF,Spt 27)
Cryhavoc 57 (6f,Goo,GS,Spt 13)
Crystal Crossing (IRE) 36 (6f,Nwm,GF,May 31)
Crystal Falls (IRE) 48 (12f,Thi,G,Jun 17)
Crystal Gold 66 (10 1/2f,Hay,GF,Jun 7)
Crystal Hearted 63 (8f,Not,GF,Apr 11)
Crystal Heights (FR) 47 (7f,Bri,F,Jly 15)
Cuban Nights (USA) 40 (15 1/2f,Fol,GF,Apr 22)
Cuban Reef 43 (10f,Pon,GF,Aug 7)
Cuesta Rey (USA) 35 (8 1/2f,Eps,G,Spt 5)
Cuff Link (IRE) 60 (16f,Nwb,GF,Spt 18)
Cugina 53 (10f,San,S,Aug 30)
Curzon Street 49 (12f,Bri,GF,Spt 3)
Cybertechnology 65 (8f,Nwm,GS,Oct 16)
Cyrano's Lad (IRE) 86 (6f,Yor,G,May 13)
Cyrian (IRE) 54 (14f,Yor,G,Aug 19)
Czarna (IRE) 39 (8f,Bri,F,Apr 21)

Daawe (USA) 70 (6f,Red,G,Jun 20)
Dahiyah (USA) 41 (7f,Lei,GF,Mar 27)
Daira 45 (12 1/2f,Nwc,G,Jly 28)
Dalliance (IRE) 62 (9f,San,GF,Jun 14)
Dalwhinnie 40 (12f,Nwm,GS,Jun 11)
Damancher 57 (10f,Cur,GS,May 25)
Dame Kiri (FR) 58 (12 1/2f,Lon,G,Oct 4)
Dame Laura (IRE) 80 (6f,Asc,GF,Spt 27)
Dance Design (IRE) 75 (10f,Cur,GS,May 25)
Dance Parade (USA) 52 (7f,Nwb,GF,Apr 18)
Dance So Suite 86 (12f,Eps,G,Spt 5)
Dances With Dreams 82 (8f,Lon,S,May 11)
Dances With Hooves 35 (10f,San,GF,Jly 30)
Dancethenightaway 81 (5f,Asc,Hy,Oct 11)
Dancing Cavalier 59 (14f,Not,GF,Apr 11)
Dancing Cormorant 30 (11f,Ham,S,Jly 1)
Dancing Drop 70 (7f,San,G,May 26)
Dancing Feather 31 (12f,Chp,GF,Jun 13)
Dancing Image 77 (7f,Goo,GS,May 22)
Dancing Lawyer 39 (7f,Lin,GF,May 31)
Dancing Mystery 38 (6f,Bat,G,Spt 8)
Dancing Queen (IRE) 30 (10f,Yar,GF,Jly 28)
Dande Flyer 51 (5f,Fol,G,Mar 26)
Danegold (IRE) 41 (10f,Chp,G,Spt 11)
Danehill Dancer (IRE) 68 (6f,Yor,G,May 15)
Daneskaya 85 (8f,Dea,G,Aug 3)
Danesman (IRE) 32 (13f,Nwb,GS,Spt 20)
Danetime (IRE) 82 (6f,Goo,GF,Aug 2)
Dangerous Diva (IRE) 56 (7f,Nwm,G,Oct 18)
Danish Rhapsody (IRE) 72 (9f,Goo,G,Spt 12)
Dannistar 32 (11f,War,F,May 5)
Dantesque (IRE) 79 (12f,Don,GF,Spt 12)
Danzas 47 (10f,Bat,F,Jly 23)
Darapour (IRE) 54 (13f,Nwb,GS,Spt 20)
Darashandeh (IRE) 80 (10 1/2f,Cha,S,Jun 8)
Daraydan (IRE) 41 (22f,Asc,S,Jun 20)
Darazari (IRE) 68 (12f,Cha,S,Jun 8)
Darb Alola (USA) 51 (5f,Asc,S,Jun 21)
Darcy 49 (9f,Rip,GS,May 18)
Darien 38 (13f,Bat,G,Spt 8)
Daring Destiny 61 (6f,Nwm,G,May 4)
Dark Age (IRE) 46 (11 1/2f,Wnd,GF,Jun 9)
Dark Green (USA) 52 (12f,Goo,G,Jun 13)
Dark Menace 36 (7f,Bri,F,Jun 3)
Dark Mile (USA) 64 (6f,Hay,S,Oct 15)
Darnaway 49 (7f,Lin,G,Spt 9)
Dashing Blue 86 (6f,Goo,GF,Aug 2)
Dashing Dancer (IRE) 37 (6f,Pon,GF,Apr 22)
Dauphin (IRE) 43 (12f,Nwm,GF,Oct 2)
Davids Revenge 36 (6f,Wnd,G,Jly 7)
Davis Rock 44 (6f,Lin,GF,Jly 11)
Davoski 56 (10 1/2f,Hay,GF,Aug 15)
Dawam Allail (IRE) 50 (8f,War,S,Jly 4)
Daylami (IRE) 86 (8f,Asc,G,Jun 17)
Daylight Dreams 37 (8f,Lin,GF,Jly 26)
Dayville (USA) 49 (7f,War,GF,Jly 19)
Dazzle 91 (6f,Asc,GF,Spt 27)
Dead Aim (IRE) 50 (10 1/2f,Hay,GS,Spt 5)
Deadline Time (IRE) 31 (11f,Ayr,S,Oct 14)
Deadly Dudley (IRE) 58 (7f,Nwm,G,Oct 18)
Debutante Days 59 (12 1/2f,Nwc,G,Jly 28)
Decorated Hero 93 (8f,Hpk,F,Nov 8)
Dee Pee Tee Cee (IRE) 55 (8f,Red,F,Aug 23)
Deep Finesse 73 (5f,Asc,GS,Jun 20)
Deeply Vale (IRE) 48 (7f,Yor,S,Spt 4)
Deep Water (USA) 55 (10f,Nwm,GF,Oct 3)
Deerly 32 (6f,Chp,G,May 26)
Defined Feature (IRE) 58 (7f,Yar,GF,Aug 21)
Degree 44 (8f,Edi,G,Jun 16)
Delight of Dawn 46 (7f,Cat,GF,Spt 20)
Delilah (IRE) 65 (12f,Asc,Hy,Oct 11)
Dellua (IRE) 53 (9f,Ayr,S,Oct 13)
Delta Soleil (USA) 67 (6f,Red,G,Jun 20)
Democrat 30 (7f,Lei,S,Oct 13)
Denbrae (IRE) 49 (6f,Wnd,GS,Jun 30)
Densben 35 (7f,Crl,F,May 29)
Denton Lad 45 (6f,Rip,G,Apr 26)
Depreciate 53 (6f,Pon,GS,Spt 2)
Desert Beauty (IRE) 64 (8f,Nwm,GF,Nov 1)
Desert Cat (IRE) 39 (7f,Crl,G,Apr 25)
Desert Dunes 51 (15f,Nwm,GS,Jun 11)
Desert Fighter 58 (10f,Don,GF,Mar 20)
Desert Horizon 74 (10f,Goo,GF,Aug 1)
Desert King (IRE) 85 (8f,Asc,G,Jun 17)
Desert Lynx (IRE) 49 (6f,Not,GF,Jly 30)
Desert Mountain (IRE) 43 (12f,Don,GF,Mar 22)
Desert Story (IRE) 78 (10f,Lon,G,Oct 4)
Desert Time 46 (8f,San,GF,Jun 14)
Desert Track 74 (8f,Red,GF,Oct 18)
Devilish Charm (USA) 45 (14f,Red,GF,Oct 18)

Diamond Crown (IRE) 38 (10f,Pon,GF,Jun 9)
Dick Turpin (USA) 54 (10f,Goo,G,Spt 13)
Dictation (USA) 60 (7f,Thi,G,May 16)
Diego 54 (16f,Asc,S,Jun 21)
Diffident (FR) 70 (6f,Yor,G,May 15)
Diminutive (USA) 39 (10f,Yar,F,Spt 17)
Dirab 50 (16f,Nwc,G,Aug 6)
Disallowed (IRE) 34 (10f,Not,GF,Spt 23)
Dispol Diamond 44 (7f,Red,F,May 1)
Dispol Gem 62 (8f,Rip,G,Jly 7)
Distinctive Dream (IRE) 67 (6f,Not,GF,Oct 4)
Divide And Rule 41 (5f,Chs,S,May 6)
Divina Luna 66 (7f,War,GF,Jly 19)
Divine Miss-P 47 (5f,War,GS,Aug 25)
Divinity 30 (10f,San,GF,Apr 25)
Dizzy Tilly 48 (12f,Nwm,GF,Oct 31)
Docklands Carriage (IRE) 38 (6f,Cat,GF,May 30)
Docklands Limo 56 (14f,Yor,G,Aug 20)
Doc Ryan's 49 (12f,Edi,GS,Nov 6)
Doctor Bravious (IRE) 54 (8f,Asc,GF,Apr 30)
Dokos (USA) 59 (8f,Don,GS,May 5)
Domappel 57 (14f,Red,GF,May 26)
Dominant Air 70 (6f,Kem,GF,Spt 22)
Dominant Duchess 50 (14f,Goo,GF,Aug 2)
Dominelle 32 (5f,Crl,F,May 29)
Domino Flyer 60 (10f,Nwc,G,Mar 25)
Dona Filipa 32 (5f,Red,G,Nov 4)
Don Pepe 52 (6f,Yar,F,Jun 11)
Don Sebastian 39 (8 1/2f,Eps,S,Jly 2)
Don't Care (IRE) 60 (7f,Nwc,GF,Mar 31)
Don't Worry Me (IRE) 94 (5f,Asc,GS,Jun 20)
Don't Worry Mike 30 (7f,Crl,GF,Aug 4)
Dormy Three 30 (10f,Lei,GS,Apr 26)
Double Action 75 (6f,Ayr,G,Spt 20)
Double Alleged (USA) 59 (12f,Nwm,GS,Oct 16)
Double Bounce 69 (6f,Not,G,Spt 28)
Double Eclipse (IRE) 89 (16f,Nwm,GF,Oct 4)
Double Eight (IRE) 41 (12f,Cat,GF,Spt 20)
Double Espresso (IRE) 53 (12f,Eps,G,Spt 5)
Double Flight 40 (9f,Ham,GS,Jun 18)
Double Gold 33 (10f,Nwb,GF,May 28)
Double-J (IRE) 52 (6f,Nwc,F,Jun 4)
Double March 32 (6f,Lei,G,Oct 27)
Double Matt (IRE) 38 (6f,Lei,G,Jly 17)
Double Oscar (IRE) 67 (5f,Crl,F,Aug 27)
Double Splendour (IRE) 78 (6f,Yor,G,May 13)
Double Trigger (IRE) 92 (20f,Lon,G,Oct 4)
Dovebrace 44 (6f,Hay,S,Oct 15)
Dovedon Star 61 (12f,Lei,S,Oct 13)
Doyella (IRE) 52 (10f,Chp,GS,Jly 1)
Dragonada (USA) 74 (8f,Goo,GF,Aug 2)
Dramatic Moment 39 (10f,Goo,GS,Jun 20)
Dream of Nurmi 52 (12f,Goo,GF,Jly 30)
Dreams End 77 (9f,Nwm,G,Apr 16)
Drift 42 (12f,Bri,F,Oct 1)
Drive Assured 31 (12f,Lei,GS,Apr 26)
Dr Johnson (USA) 69 (10f,Cur,GS,May 25)
Dr Martens (IRE) 43 (8f,Nwm,G,Jly 19)
Dr Massini (IRE) 49 (10f,Kem,GF,Mar 31)
Duello 60 (8f,Nwb,S,May 18)
Duke Valentino 47 (7 1/2f,Bev,S,Jun 11)
Dukhan (USA) 42 (10f,Lei,GF,Spt 9)
Dulcinea 41 (7f,Kem,GF,May 31)
Dummer Golf Time 51 (7f,Yor,S,Spt 4)
Dunabrattin 33 (14f,Not,G,Nov 3)
Duncombe Hall 30 (15 1/2f,Fol,F,Spt 26)
Dundel (IRE) 53 (9f,Goo,GF,Aug 22)
Duraid (IRE) 57 (8f,Hay,G,Spt 26)
Durgams First (IRE) 53 (12f,Nwm,GF,Oct 2)
Durham 59 (16f,Goo,GF,Spt 25)
Dushyantor (USA) 83 (12f,Eps,G,Spt 5)
Dust Dancer 48 (10f,Sal,GF,Aug 13)
Dyhim Diamond (IRE) 82 (5f,Dea,G,Aug 3)

Eager To Please 37 (7f,War,GF,Jun 9)
Eagle Canyon (IRE) 44 (12 1/2f,Nwc,G,May 22)
Eagle Dancer 59 (10f,Lin,S,May 10)
Eastern Prophets 66 (5f,San,GF,Apr 25)
Easycall 81 (5f,Asc,GS,Jun 20)
Easy Dollar 96 (6f,Nwm,G,Apr 15)
Easy Song (USA) 45 (10f,Yar,F,Spt 17)
Ebadiyla (IRE) 76 (12f,Lon,GF,Oct 5)
Edan Heights 65 (10f,Nwm,G,May 2)
Eden Rock (GER) 76 (8f,Lon,GF,Oct 5)
Edipo Re 45 (12f,Lei,G,Oct 27)
Ed's Folly (IRE) 44 (7f,Lei,GS,Oct 14)
Effectual 67 (10f,Kem,G,May 24)
Effervescence 36 (7f,San,GF,Spt 17)
Egoli (USA) 60 (8f,Lei,GF,Oct 5)
Eider Hill 31 (8f,Nwb,S,Spt 19)
Ela-Aristokrati (IRE) 77 (12f,Asc,G,Jun 20)
El Angelo (USA) 83 (8f,Hpk,F,Nov 8)
Ela-Yie-Mou (IRE) 35 (14 1/2f,Kem,G,Spt 10)
Elbaaha 67 (12f,Don,GF,Spt 12)
Election Day (IRE) 81 (16f,Goo,GF,Jly 31)
Elegant Dance 30 (8f,Kem,G,May 5)
Elegant Warning (IRE) 68 (7f,Nwm,G,Apr 15)
Eleos 47 (10 1/2f,Lon,S,May 11)
Elfland (IRE) 73 (7f,Nwm,GS,Jun 20)
Elite Hope (USA) 30 (7f,San,G,May 26)
Ella Lamees 32 (6f,Wnd,GF,Jly 21)
Ellens Lad (IRE) 54 (5f,Wnd,S,May 19)
Ellway Lady (IRE) 37 (12f,Bri,F,Oct 1)
Elly Fleetfoot (IRE) 43 (12f,Chp,G,May 26)
Elnadim (USA) 105 (6f,Asc,GF,Spt 27)
El Opera (IRE) 47 (6f,Nwm,GF,May 31)
Embroidered 30 (6f,Bat,G,Aug 7)
Embryonic (IRE) 51 (17f,Pon,GF,Apr 22)
Emerging Market 77 (7f,Nwm,G,Apr 16)
Energy Man 34 (8f,Edi,GF,May 2)
English Invader 40 (12f,Nwm,G,Apr 16)
Enlisted (IRE) 32 (10f,Red,GS,Jly 26)

Entice (FR) 92 (9f,Lon,GF,Oct 5)
Entrepreneur 92 (8f,Nwm,G,May 3)
Epic Stand 63 (8f,Nwm,G,Oct 18)
Eponine 39 (14f,Yar,F,Jun 11)
Epworth 49 (10f,Nwc,Hy,Jun 28)
Erlking (IRE) 45 (12f,Chp,G,Aug 25)
Ertlon 64 (7f,Yar,GF,May 28)
Erupt 43 (6f,Sal,GF,Jly 12)
Es Go 33 (12f,Bri,F,Oct 1)
Eshtiaal (USA) 71 (10f,Pon,GF,Spt 25)
Eskimo Nel (IRE) 60 (12f,Hay,S,Mar 29)
Esperto 33 (10f,Fol,G,Jly 9)
Essayeffsee 45 (12f,Edi,GF,Jly 18)
Eternal Joy 39 (8f,Cur,G,Jly 13)
Eternity 35 (12f,Nwm,GF,Oct 31)
Ethbaat (USA) 35 (8f,War,GF,Apr 12)
Etoile (FR) 75 (12f,Eps,G,Jun 6)
Etterby Park (USA) 62 (16f,Chs,G,Spt 24)
Eurobox Boy 60 (8f,San,G,Aug 13)
Eurolink Profile 49 (7f,Lin,GF,Jly 12)
Euro Sceptic (IRE) 38 (8 1/2f,Bev,GF,Spt 17)
Eva Luna (USA) 65 (12f,Lei,G,Jun 14)
Eveningperformance 77 (5f,Nwb,GF,Spt 18)
Even Top (IRE) 77 (10f,Wnd,G,Aug 23)
Everglades (IRE) 60 (6f,Goo,G,May 20)
Evezio Rufo 30 (11f,War,F,May 5)
Evidently (IRE) 30 (8f,Nwb,S,Spt 19)
Exactly (IRE) 46 (16f,Cat,GF,Spt 20)
Executive Design 52 (14f,Hay,S,May 5)
Expialiodoocius 34 (11f,War,GF,Jun 9)
Express Gift 43 (14f,Hay,GS,May 24)
Express Girl 37 (5f,Rip,GS,May 18)

Fabled Light (IRE) 40 (10 1/2f,Chs,S,May 6)
Fabulous Mtoto 40 (14f,Sal,GF,Aug 1)
Fahris (IRE) 83 (9f,Nwm,GF,Apr 17)
Fahs (USA) 66 (10f,Don,GF,Spt 13)
Fairhonor (FR) 75 (15 1/2f,Lon,S,May 18)
Fairly Sure (IRE) 37 (7f,Bri,F,Spt 28)
Fairy Knight 49 (10f,Wnd,GF,Jun 2)
Fairy Prince (IRE) 53 (6f,Don,G,Jly 31)
Faith Alone 60 (6f,Yar,GS,Jly 3)
Faithful Son (USA) 88 (8f,Asc,G,Spt 27)
Falak (USA) 82 (10f,Don,G,May 24)
Falls O'Moness (IRE) 43 (9f,Ayr,GS,Spt 19)
Fame Again 52 (7f,Don,G,May 6)
Family Man 66 (8f,Nwm,GF,May 31)
Family Tradition (IRE) 49 (14f,Cur,S,Spt 20)
Fancy A Fortune (IRE) 46 (7f,Thi,G,Aug 1)
Fancy Design (IRE) 32 (8f,San,G,Aug 13)
Fantail 65 (10f,Nwm,GF,Oct 3)
Fantastic Fellow (USA) 77 (8f,Hpk,F,Nov 8)
Fantastic Flame (IRE) 50 (10f,Ayr,GS,Spt 19)
Far Ahead 66 (14f,Hay,GF,Aug 9)
Farasan (IRE) 77 (9f,Nwm,G,Apr 16)
Faraway Lass 66 (6f,Goo,GF,Aug 2)
Farewell My Love (IRE) 39 (6f,Wnd,S,May 12)
Farfields Prince 41 (11f,Ayr,GS,Spt 18)
Farhan (USA) 31 (10f,Pon,GF,Jun 3)
Farhana 70 (6f,Yor,G,May 15)
Faringdon Future 47 (8f,San,GF,Spt 16)
Farley Green 37 (6f,Wnd,GF,Jly 28)
Farley Mount 42 (8f,Lei,G,May 26)
Farmost 65 (10f,Bat,F,Jly 23)
Farringdon Hill 56 (11 1/2f,Wnd,GF,Aug 11)
Fatal Baraari 33 (8f,San,GF,Jly 24)
Fatefully (USA) 76 (10f,Nwm,GF,Oct 4)
Father Dan (IRE) 54 (10f,Bri,F,Aug 16)
Father Sky 65 (16f,Goo,GF,Spt 25)
Fayik 44 (6f,Nwm,GF,Aug 9)
Faym (IRE) 37 (8f,Lei,G,Aug 11)
Featherstone Lane 47 (5f,Nwc,F,Jun 4)
Feel A Line 47 (7f,Yar,GS,Jly 2)
Fern's Governor 53 (10f,Nwm,G,May 2)
Ferny Hill (IRE) 65 (12f,Don,GF,Spt 12)
Fiametta 49 (8f,Asc,Hy,Oct 10)
Field of Vision (IRE) 30 (14f,Cat,G,Mar 26)
Fieldridge 51 (17f,Bat,Hy,May 11)
Fier Danseur (FR) 53 (12f,Cha,G,Jun 1)
Fife Major (USA) 40 (12f,Bri,F,Oct 1)
Fighting Times 43 (10f,Nwc,GF,Oct 22)
Fiji 45 (10f,Chp,GF,Jly 25)
Filial (IRE) 51 (10f,Red,F,Spt 26)
Filmore West 41 (12f,Don,G,Oct 25)
Final Stab (IRE) 52 (8f,San,G,Aug 13)
Final Stage (IRE) 35 (10f,Nwm,G,Apr 15)
Final Warning 30 (8f,Not,GF,Apr 8)
Finarts Bay 32 (7f,Kem,G,Spt 21)
Fine Fellow (IRE) 58 (8f,Lon,G,Apr 20)
Finisterre (IRE) 35 (6f,Pon,GF,Apr 22)
Finsbury Flyer (IRE) 44 (8f,San,GF,May 27)
Fionn de Cool (IRE) 47 (8f,San,GS,Jly 4)
First Chance (IRE) 47 (8f,San,GF,Spt 16)
First Gold 40 (7f,Crl,GS,May 9)
First Island (IRE) 88 (8f,San,GF,Apr 25)
First Maite 63 (6f,Hay,S,Oct 15)
First Principle 51 (6f,Bat,G,Spt 8)
Fisiostar 41 (6f,Nwc,GF,Aug 3)
Flag Down (CAN) 93 (12f,Hpk,F,Nov 8)
Flag Fen (USA) 53 (8f,Rip,GS,May 18)
Flagship 49 (10f,San,GF,Spt 16)
Flamboyance (USA) 64 (7f,Asc,GF,Spt 27)
Flashtalkin' Flood 44 (8f,Not,S,Jun 23)
Fleeting Glimpse 66 (10f,Lon,S,May 18)
Fleet River (USA) 38 (8 1/2f,Eps,G,Spt 5)
Fletcher 65 (15f,Nwm,GF,Jly 10)
Flint Knapper 72 (10f,Nwm,GF,Spt 30)
Flirting Around (USA) 62 (16f,Asc,GF,Jun 18)
Floating Charge 35 (7f,Lin,G,Spt 9)
Florentino (IRE) 55 (12f,Bri,F,May 23)
Flowing Fortune 46 (10f,Goo,GF,Jun 12)
Flying Colours (IRE) 32 (7f,Goo,GS,May 21)

Flying Harold 37 (5f,Goo,GF,Jun 6)
Flying North (IRE) 72 (10f,Bev,S,Jun 11)
Flying Pennant (IRE) 50 (7f,Lin,GF,May 31)
Fly To The Stars 83 (8f,Asc,G,Jun 17)
Flyway (FR) 67 (12f,Cha,S,Jun 8)
Foist 48 (7f,Thi,GF,Apr 18)
Fond Embrace 55 (5f,Chp,GS,Jly 1)
Fonteyn 35 (6f,Fol,G,Jly 9)
Fooled You (USA) 31 (8f,Rip,GF,Apr 9)
Foot Battalion (IRE) 58 (10 1/2f,Hay,GF,Jun 7)
Forcing Bid 31 (6f,Fol,G,Oct 21)
Foreign Rule (IRE) 37 (12 1/2f,War,GF,Jun 9)
Forest Buck (USA) 65 (10f,Nwm,G,May 3)
Forest Fantasy 44 (8f,Not,GF,Aug 6)
Forest Robin 49 (10f,Don,GF,Mar 20)
Forgie (IRE) 63 (16f,Chs,G,Spt 24)
Forgotten Times (USA) 46 (6f,Wnd,G,Jly 7)
For the Present 63 (6f,Red,G,Jun 20)
Fort Knox (IRE) 34 (7f,Bri,F,Jun 3)
Fortunes Course (IRE) 40 (17f,Bat,Hy,May 11)
For Your Eyes Only 71 (8f,Nwm,G,Oct 18)
Forza Figlio 75 (10f,Nwm,G,May 3)
Forzair 40 (12f,Edi,GF,Jly 18)
Foundry Lane 65 (14f,Yor,S,Spt 3)
Fourdaned (IRE) 48 (10f,Don,GF,Mar 20)
Foxes Tail 32 (8f,Rip,GF,Apr 17)
Fragrant Mix (FR) 75 (11f,Lon,G,Apr 6)
Frederick James 42 (7f,Red,G,Jun 20)
Fredrik The Fierce (IRE) 35 (5f,Chs,S,May 6)
Free As A Bird 37 (7f,Yar,F,Jun 5)
Freedom Chance (IRE) 51 (12f,Bri,F,Jly 28)
Freequent 75 (10 1/2f,Yor,G,Aug 20)
Free To Speak (IRE) 44 (10f,Cur,GS,May 25)
French Ballerina (IRE) 56 (14f,Leo,G,May 28)
French Ginger 31 (8f,Rip,GF,Aug 26)
French Grit (IRE) 54 (6f,Pon,GF,Jun 9)
French Ivy (USA) 54 (16f,Rip,GF,May 28)
French Mist 39 (14f,Yar,G,Jun 23)
Fresh Fruit Daily 53 (10f,Not,GF,Apr 21)
Friendly Brave (USA) 45 (5f,Wnd,G,Aug 4)
Frozen Sea (USA) 46 (12f,Eps,G,Apr 23)
Fuenji (FR) 64 (8f,Dea,G,Aug 3)
Fullopep 34 (12f,Cat,GF,Jly 16)
Fun Galore (USA) 56 (7f,Goo,GF,Aug 1)
Furnish 40 (5f,Ayr,G,Jun 21)
Further Flight 79 (16f,Nwm,GF,Oct 4)
Further Outlook (USA) 57 (8f,Asc,G,Jun 17)
Fur Will Fly 44 (6f,Sal,GF,May 4)
Future Perfect 71 (10f,Goo,GF,Aug 1)

Gadge 60 (7f,Goo,GS,May 22)
Gadroon 35 (9f,Ayr,S,Oct 13)
Gaelic Storm 66 (5f,Eps,G,Aug 25)
Gain Line (USA) 45 (7f,Yar,GF,May 28)
Galapino 55 (16f,Asc,G,Spt 27)
Galine 60 (6f,Nwm,G,May 3)
Game Ploy (POL) 89 (10 1/2f,Yor,G,Aug 20)
Ganga (IRE) 69 (10f,Red,GF,Oct 18)
Garnock Valley 65 (6f,Thi,GS,May 17)
Garolo (FR) 59 (16f,Asc,GF,Apr 30)
Garuda (IRE) 52 (10f,Nwm,G,Apr 15)
Gates (USA) 38 (8f,Asc,GF,Jun 18)
Gay Breeze 37 (6f,Yar,F,Spt 18)
Gazelle Royale (FR) 77 (12f,Eps,G,Jun 6)
Gee Bee Boy 34 (10f,Red,GF,Oct 28)
Gee Bee Dream 56 (7f,Nwc,Hy,Jun 28)
Geimhriuil (IRE) 61 (7f,Hay,GS,May 24)
General Academy (IRE) 75 (8f,San,GF,May 26)
General Assembly (IRE) 76 (12f,Nwm,G,May 4)
General Glow 32 (12f,Edi,GF,Jly 18)
General Haven 57 (11f,War,F,May 5)
General Monty 42 (8f,Thi,F,Jun 2)
General Mouktar 47 (14f,Hay,GS,May 24)
General Sir Peter (IRE) 39 (5f,Chp,G,Spt 11)
Generosa 51 (16f,Leo,S,Nov 9)
Generous Gift 69 (10f,Goo,GF,Aug 1)
Generous Lady 40 (16f,Leo,S,Nov 9)
Generous Libra 70 (8f,Nwb,GS,May 16)
Genevra (IRE) 86 (9f,Lon,GF,Oct 5)
Gentilesse 40 (10f,Lin,S,May 10)
Genuine John (IRE) 55 (7 1/2f,Bev,GF,Apr 5)
Georgia Venture 59 (14 1/2f,Don,GF,Spt 10)
Geri (USA) 94 (8f,Hpk,F,Nov 8)
Germano 99 (10f,Nwb,GF,Jly 19)
Get A Life 36 (12f,Edi,G,Jly 7)
Get The Point 47 (8f,Rip,GF,Apr 17)
Ghalib (IRE) 68 (8f,Asc,Hy,Oct 10)
Gharib (USA) 48 (5f,Bev,GF,Spt 17)
Ghataas 70 (11f,Ayr,G,Spt 20)
Ghillies Ball 47 (12f,Asc,G,Aug 1)
Gift Token 64 (10f,Nwb,GF,Spt 18)
Giko 41 (7f,Kem,GF,May 31)
Gi La High 54 (6f,Not,GF,Spt 15)
Gilling Dancer (IRE) 32 (8f,Rip,GF,May 28)
Ginger Rogers 38 (16f,Not,GF,Spt 15)
Ginzbourg 60 (10f,Don,G,Jly 30)
Gipsy Princess 40 (7f,Cat,GF,Spt 20)
Give Me A Ring (IRE) 79 (8f,San,GF,Apr 25)
Gladys Althorpe (IRE) 36 (8f,Thi,G,Jly 25)
Glen Ogil 33 (9f,Nwm,GF,Oct 31)
Glen Parker (IRE) 67 (8f,Wnd,G,Aug 23)
Globe Runner 39 (12f,Ham,GF,Aug 18)
Glow Forum 52 (12f,Nwm,GF,Oct 31)
Go Britannia 73 (20f,Goo,GF,Jly 30)
Godmersham Park 48 (8f,Not,G,May 17)
Go For Salt (USA) 47 (10f,Bat,G,Jly 7)
Go Hence 42 (12f,Bev,G,Jly 29)
Going For Broke 35 (10f,Bev,GF,Apr 24)
Gold Blade 59 (9f,Ayr,GF,Jly 19)
Gold Desire 54 (10 1/2f,Yor,S,Spt 4)
Gold Edge 44 (5f,Ayr,S,Oct 14)
Golden Ace (IRE) 51 (10 1/2f,Yor,S,Spt 4)

Golden Arches (FR) 85 (10 1/2f,Cha,S,Jun 8)
Golden Hadeer 38 (15f,War,G,Jun 24)
Golden Hello 35 (12f,Don,GF,Spt 12)
Golden Melody 30 (16f,Not,S,Oct 8)
Golden Pound (USA) 63 (6f,Eps,S,Jly 2)
Golden Saddle (USA) 32 (10f,Bri,F,Jly 16)
Golden Thunderbolt (FR) 47 (12f,Bev,GF,Jun 5)
Golden Touch (USA) 43 (11f,War,F,May 5)
Gold Lance (USA) 48 (8f,Goo,G,Spt 12)
Gold Millenium (IRE) 36 (8f,Kem,G,May 24)
Gold Spats (USA) 81 (8f,Goo,G,May 20)
Gone for a Burton (IRE) 52 (10f,Don,G,Oct 25)
Gone Savage 67 (5f,San,GF,Apr 25)
Goodbye Gatemen (IRE) 45 (6f,Bri,F,Jun 3)
Good Reputation 35 (9f,Goo,G,May 22)
Good To Talk 38 (5f,Edi,GS,Jun 23)
Gordi (USA) 64 (12f,Leo,G,Jly 19)
Goretski (IRE) 61 (5f,Bev,GS,Aug 13)
Gothenberg (IRE) 85 (8f,San,GF,Apr 25)
Graceful Lass 60 (12f,Chp,GF,Jly 11)
Gracie Lady (IRE) 57 (10f,Lon,S,May 18)
Grand Chapeau (IRE) 54 (6f,Pon,GS,Spt 2)
Grand Cru 39 (16 1/2f,San,GS,Jly 5)
Grand Lad (IRE) 56 (6f,Lei,F,Apr 3)
Grand Musica 62 (8f,Nwm,GS,Oct 16)
Grand Ovation (IRE) 31 (8f,Kem,G,May 24)
Grand Splendour 58 (10f,Bev,GF,Jun 5)
Granny's Pet 67 (6f,Hay,G,Jly 5)
Grapeshot (USA) 72 (8f,Nwm,GF,Apr 17)
Grapevine (IRE) 41 (11 1/2f,Chs,S,May 7)
Grate Times 46 (7f,Thi,F,Jun 2)
Great Child 62 (8f,Nwm,GF,Oct 3)
Great Easeby (IRE) 39 (18f,Nwm,G,Oct 18)
Greatest 40 (7f,Lei,GS,Oct 14)
Great Oration (IRE) 37 (17f,Pon,GF,Aug 17)
Greek Palace (IRE) 49 (8f,Nwb,GF,Apr 19)
Greenaway Bay (USA) 56 (10f,Don,G,May 24)
Green Card (USA) 74 (8f,Kem,G,May 24)
Green Jewel 57 (9f,Goo,G,Jun 12)
Green Lady (IRE) 73 (8f,Dea,G,Aug 3)
Green Power 58 (8f,Rip,G,Jun 19)
Greenstead (USA) 48 (12f,Don,G,Oct 25)
Gresatre 38 (7f,Nwm,G,Aug 22)
Gretel 44 (8f,Goo,G,May 22)
Grey Again 33 (7f,Cat,GF,Spt 20)
Grey Kingdom 58 (7f,Yor,S,Spt 4)
Grey Shot 93 (16f,Nwm,GF,Oct 4)
Grey Way (USA) 78 (10f,Goo,GF,Aug 2)
Grief (IRE) 71 (10f,San,S,Aug 30)
Grooms Gold (IRE) 39 (8f,Not,G,Nov 3)
Groom's Gordon (FR) 65 (7f,Asc,GF,Jun 18)
Groucho (USA) 40 (10f,Nwm,G,Apr 15)
Ground Game 56 (12f,Asc,GF,Jun 18)
Grovefair Venture 30 (8f,Nwm,G,Jly 19)
Guesstimation (USA) 49 (10f,Bri,GF,Aug 27)
Guest Alliance (IRE) 32 (15 1/2f,Fol,GF,Apr 22)
Gulf Harbour (IRE) 36 (10 1/2f,Chs,S,May 6)
Gulf Shaadi 79 (8f,Nwm,G,Oct 18)
Gulliver 59 (8f,Thi,F,Jun 2)
Gumair (USA) 37 (14f,Not,GF,Jun 9)
Gunners Glory 39 (7f,Nwm,G,Aug 22)
Gwespyr 42 (7f,Bri,F,May 29)
Gymcrak Flyer 51 (7f,Red,G,May 12)
Gymcrak Premiere 54 (8f,Red,GF,Oct 28)
Gymcrak Tiger (IRE) 33 (14f,Not,GF,Apr 21)

Hachiyah (IRE) 57 (10f,Eps,GS,Jly 9)
Hadawah (USA) 36 (8f,Sal,GF,May 15)
Hadidi 34 (12f,Cat,GF,Jly 16)
Hajr (IRE) 58 (8f,Goo,GF,Jly 29)
Half Tone 49 (5f,Goo,G,Spt 24)
Hal Hoo Yaroom 39 (12f,Eps,G,Spt 5)
Halmanerror 39 (7f,Lei,GS,Oct 14)
Halowing (USA) 57 (7f,Cat,S,Oct 17)
Hal's Pal 77 (8f,Asc,GF,Jun 18)
Haltarra (USA) 73 (10f,Kem,G,Spt 21)
Hanan (USA) 31 (6f,Nwm,GF,Aug 9)
Hanbitooh (USA) 34 (15 1/2f,Fol,F,Apr 10)
Handaza (IRE) 49 (9f,Cur,S,Spt 21)
Handsome Ridge 77 (8f,Asc,G,Jun 17)
Hannah's Usher 31 (7f,Lin,GF,Jun 14)
Hannalou (FR) 32 (8f,Bri,F,May 29)
Happy Go Lucky 55 (10f,Nwb,GF,Spt 18)
Happy Minstral (USA) 45 (12f,Goo,GF,Jly 30)
Harbour Dues 92 (12f,Eps,G,Jun 7)
Hard to Figure 77 (6f,Ayr,G,Spt 20)
Hardy Dancer 64 (10f,Kem,GF,Mar 31)
Harlequin Walk (IRE) 36 (10f,Bri,F,Oct 1)
Harmony Hall 42 (14f,Sal,GF,Aug 21)
Haroldon (IRE) 54 (10f,Wnd,G,Jly 7)
Harry's Treat 33 (8f,Edi,S,Mar 27)
Harry Wolton 89 (10 1/2f,Yor,G,Aug 20)
Harvey White (IRE) 38 (11f,War,GF,Oct 7)
Hasta la Vista 39 (16f,Thi,GF,Aug 11)
Hattaafeh (IRE) 40 (16f,Kem,G,Mar 29)
Hattab (IRE) 79 (6f,Nwb,GF,Jly 19)
Havago 43 (7f,San,G,May 26)
Hawait (IRE) 67 (8f,Don,GF,Spt 13)
Hawker Hunter (USA) 68 (12f,Don,GF,Jun 7)
Hawkish (USA) 34 (10f,Bev,GF,Jun 5)
Hawksbill Henry (USA) 34 (6f,Nwm,GF,Aug 9)
Hawksley Hill (IRE) 83 (8f,Yor,G,Aug 21)
Hayes Way (IRE) 56 (8f,Nwm,G,Jly 19)
Hazard a Guess (IRE) 74 (10f,Kem,GF,Mar 31)
Heart Full of Soul 39 (10f,Lei,GF,Spt 22)
Heart of Armor 59 (12f,Hay,GF,Aug 8)
Heart of Gold (IRE) 61 (12 1/2f,Nwc,G,Jun 27)
Heathyards Rock 52 (12f,Nwm,G,Jun 7)
Heavenly Calm (USA) 72 (15f,Lon,G,Oct 4)
Heavenly Miss (IRE) 43 (6f,Wnd,S,May 12)
Heavenly Ray (USA) 59 (8f,Nwm,GF,Nov 1)
Heaven's Command 74 (8f,Dea,G,Aug 3)

Heighth of Fame 38 (12f,Crl,G,Jun 25)
Height of Heights (IRE) 61 (14f,Sal,GF,Aug 1)
Helicon (IRE) 55 (10f,San,GF,Jly 16)
Helios 49 (8f,Chp,GS,Jly 1)
Helissio (FR) 99 (10½f,Lon,S,Apr 27)
Hello Mister 79 (6f,Nwb,GF,Jly 19)
Helmsman (USA) 80 (8f,Hpk,F,Nov 8)
Hen Harrier 62 (8f,Rip,GF,Apr 17)
Henley (USA) 60 (10f,Don,G,Jly 30)
Henry's Mother 44 (8f,Kem,G,May 5)
Henry The Fifth 51 (10f,Nwm,G,May 3)
Herbshan Dancer 31 (11½f,Wnd,S,Jun 23)
Here Comes a Star 41 (5f,Nwc,F,Jun 4)
Here Comes Herbie 42 (16f,Nwm,GF,Aug 8)
Here's To Howie (USA) 33 (8f,Not,GS,Oct 8)
Heritage 71 (12f,Nwm,GS,Oct 16)
Heron Island (IRE) 72 (20f,Asc,G,Jun 19)
Herr Trigger 55 (12f,Goo,GF,Aug 22)
He's Got Wings (IRE) 40 (13f,Ham,GS,Apr 10)
Hever Golf Charmer 34 (8f,Edi,G,Jun 16)
Hever Golf Glory 66 (8f,Cha,S,May 12)
Hever Golf Magic (IRE) 34 (6f,Fol,GF,Apr 22)
Hever Golf Mover 38 (6f,Not,GF,Spt 15)
Hever Golf Rocket 49 (6f,Lin,GF,Aug 17)
Hever Golf Rose 90 (5f,Asc,GS,Jun 20)
Hever Golf Star 42 (5f,Fol,GF,Apr 10)
Hidden Meadow 90 (7f,Yor,G,Aug 21)
Highborn (IRE) 78 (7f,Nwm,GS,Jun 20)
High Domain (IRE) 46 (5f,Sal,GF,Jun 11)
Highfield Fizz 34 (18f,Pon,GS,Oct 20)
High Five (IRE) 35 (17f,Bat,Hy,May 11)
Highflying 48 (16f,Rip,GF,May 28)
High Intrigue (IRE) 43 (14f,San,GF,Jly 24)
High Low (USA) 37 (11f,Ham,GS,Jly 4)
Highly Prized 41 (12f,Sal,GF,May 4)
Highly Respected (IRE) 31 (7½f,Chs,S,May 6)
High On Life 41 (12f,Bev,G,Jly 29)
High Premium 74 (9f,Yor,GS,Jun 14)
High Spirits (IRE) 54 (8f,Nwm,G,Oct 18)
Hill Farm Blues 46 (10f,Bat,G,Jly 7)
Hill Farm Dancer 34 (12f,Bat,GF,Apr 29)
Hillswick 37 (16f,Goo,GF,Spt 25)
Hiltons Executive (IRE) 32 (5f,Rip,GF,Aug 16)
Hi Mujtahid (IRE) 31 (7f,Crl,GF,Aug 4)
Hi Nod 68 (8f,Asc,S,Jly 26)
Hirasah (IRE) 54 (8f,San,G,Aug 13)
Hisar (IRE) 52 (10f,Pon,GF,Spt 25)
Hoh Express 69 (14f,Goo,GF,Jly 29)
Hoh Flyer (USA) 34 (11f,Red,GF,May 26)
Hoh Returns (IRE) 54 (5f,Nwb,GF,Apr 18)
Holloway Melody 30 (8f,Lei,G,Oct 27)
Homestead 35 (8f,Not,G,Nov 3)
Honourable 62 (12f,Yor,S,Spt 4)
Hoofprints (IRE) 36 (12f,Fol,GF,Aug 19)
Hopesay 37 (6f,Red,F,Spt 26)
Hornbeam 79 (7f,Asc,GF,Jun 18)
House of Dreams 33 (9f,Red,GF,Oct 7)
Howaida (IRE) 51 (7f,San,GF,Spt 16)
How Long 76 (7f,Nwm,G,Apr 16)
Hulal 43 (7f,Cat,S,Jly 3)
Hullbank 43 (16f,Bev,GF,Jun 4)
Humourless 66 (12f,Asc,GF,Jun 18)
Hunters of Brora (IRE) 73 (9f,Nwm,GF,Oct 4)
Hurricane State (USA) 56 (8½f,Eps,G,Jun 7)
Hurtleberry (IRE) 66 (8f,Goo,GS,May 21)
Husun (USA) 37 (6f,Lin,GF,Jun 14)
Hype Energy 36 (5f,War,GS,Aug 25)
Hype Superior (IRE) 30 (5f,Bev,Hy,Jly 5)

Iamus 76 (8f,Nwc,G,Jly 26)
Ibin St James 46 (10f,Rip,GF,Apr 9)
Iblis (IRE) 71 (8f,Lei,G,May 26)
I Can't Remember 52 (7½f,Chs,S,May 6)
Ice Age 47 (5f,Lei,G,Aug 20)
Icy Guest (USA) 36 (7f,Nwb,S,May 18)
Idrica 62 (12f,Hay,GF,Aug 8)
Iechyd-Da (IRE) 52 (10½f,Hay,S,Mar 29)
Ihtiyati (USA) 79 (10f,Don,GF,Spt 13)
Ijtinab 46 (7f,San,GF,Jly 23)
Ikatania 51 (12f,Goo,G,Jun 12)
Ikhtisar (USA) 35 (12f,Chp,GF,Jun 13)
Ile de Librate 31 (10f,Goo,G,Spt 13)
Ile Distinct (IRE) 50 (10f,Not,GF,Spt 15)
Illusion 64 (10½f,Yor,G,Aug 20)
Il Principe (IRE) 41 (16f,Cat,GF,Spt 20)
Impala 42 (8½f,Eps,S,Jly 2)
Imperial Scholar (IRE) 61 (7f,Nwm,G,Apr 15)
Imp Express (IRE) 34 (5f,Thi,GF,Aug 22)
Impish (IRE) 31 (5f,Ham,S,May 8)
Imposing Time 37 (5f,War,GF,Jly 19)
Impulsif (USA) 48 (7f,Lin,GF,Jly 12)
Impulsive Air (IRE) 56 (8f,Rip,G,Jly 7)
Imroz (USA) 70 (7f,Yor,G,Aug 21)
I'm Still Here 36 (6f,Ham,S,Apr 2)
Inchacooley (IRE) 38 (8f,Leo,GS,Aug 4)
Inchcailloch (IRE) 61 (20f,Asc,G,Jun 17)
Inclination 44 (8f,Lei,G,Aug 11)
In Command (IRE) 71 (8f,Asc,G,Jun 17)
Indian Relative 52 (6f,Lin,GF,May 31)
Indian Rocket 74 (6f,Asc,G,Jun 19)
Indian Spark 63 (6f,Sal,GF,May 4)
Indigo Dawn 34 (16f,Nwc,G,Aug 6)
Indiscreet (CAN) 45 (7f,Asc,GF,Jun 18)
Indium 45 (10f,Bat,GF,Apr 29)
Infatuation 74 (10f,Red,GF,Oct 18)
Influence Pedler 33 (14f,Not,G,Oct 30)
In Good Nick 39 (7½f,Bev,G,May 10)
Inimitable 38 (12f,Don,G,Jly 16)
In Question 43 (11f,War,GF,Jun 9)
Insatiable (IRE) 89 (8f,San,GF,May 26)
Insider Trader 45 (5f,Ham,G,Jun 11)
Interdream 47 (9f,Kem,G,Aug 20)

In The Genes 41 (10f,Lei,G,Oct 28)
In the Money (IRE) 31 (12f,Lei,GF,Mar 27)
Intiaash (IRE) 62 (5f,Bat,GF,Apr 29)
Intikhab (USA) 73 (8f,Thi,GS,May 17)
Intisab 70 (7f,San,G,May 26)
Invermark 66 (12f,Don,S,Nov 8)
Invest Wisely 38 (18f,Don,GF,Mar 21)
Invocation 30 (6f,Goo,S,Jun 20)
Irish Accord (USA) 62 (7f,Yor,G,Jly 12)
Irish Light (USA) 53 (8f,Nwm,GF,Nov 1)
Irsal 46 (14f,San,GF,Aug 14)
Irtifa 35 (7f,Kem,GF,May 31)
Isitoff 62 (11 1/2f,Wnd,G,Aug 4)
Island Lore (IRE) 53 (7f,Nwb,GF,Apr 18)
Island Sanctuary (IRE) 49 (12f,Hay,G,Spt 21)
Isle of Man (USA) 63 (10f,Don,G,May 24)
Ismaros 54 (10f,San,GF,Jly 16)
Italian Symphony (IRE) 30 (7f,Fol,G,Oct 21)
Ithaki (IRE) 61 (12f,Cha,G,Jun 1)
Ivan Luis (FR) 68 (12f,Goo,GF,Jly 29)
Ivor's Deed 41 (6f,Cat,G,Apr 23)
Ivor's Flutter 52 (18f,Nwm,G,Oct 18)
Ivory Dawn 52 (5f,Nwm,S,Jun 27)
Ivory's Grab Hire 49 (7f,Yar,GF,Jly 22)

Jack Doyle (IRE) 36 (10f,Ayr,GF,May 30)
Jack Flush (IRE) 40 (8f,Thi,GS,May 17)
Jack The Lad (IRE) 46 (10 1/2f,Yor,GS,Jun 14)
Jafn 56 (8f,Asc,Hy,Oct 10)
Jalb (IRE) 47 (8f,Nwc,G,May 5)
Jamaican Flight (USA) 55 (16f,Rip,GF,Aug 26)
Jameel Asmar 61 (9f,Yor,GS,Jun 14)
Jamrat Jumairah (IRE) 57 (8f,Don,G,Jly 31)
Jaseur (USA) 70 (16f,Asc,G,Spt 27)
Jaunty Jack 64 (10f,Eps,G,Jun 6)
Java Red (IRE) 39 (10f,Red,G,Nov 4)
Java Shrine (USA) 44 (8f,Chp,GF,Jly 11)
Jawah (IRE) 60 (14f,Not,G,Oct 30)
Jawhari 56 (8f,Lin,GF,Jly 10)
Jayannpee 96 (6f,Goo,G,May 20)
Jay-Owe-Two (IRE) 64 (8f,Nwm,GS,Oct 16)
Jazz King 67 (14f,Goo,GF,Jly 29)
Jazz Track (IRE) 48 (12f,Rip,GF,Aug 25)
J B Quick 33 (10f,Pon,G,Jly 8)
Jean Pierre 45 (10f,Pon,GF,Apr 16)
Jedi Knight 60 (8f,Red,GF,Oct 28)
Jeffrey Anotherred 68 (7 1/2f,Chs,S,May 6)
Jennelle 60 (6f,Nwm,S,Jun 27)
Jibereen 50 (8f,Nwm,G,Jly 19)
Jilly Woo 31 (8 1/2f,Eps,G,Spt 5)
Jiyush 78 (16f,Nwm,GF,Oct 4)
Johan Cruyff 61 (10f,Cur,GS,Jun 6)
Johayro 48 (7f,Red,GF,Oct 28)
John Emms (IRE) 49 (6f,Fol,GF,Apr 22)
Johnny Staccato 49 (6f,Nwb,GF,Jly 19)
John O'Dreams 33 (5f,Bat,GF,Apr 29)

Joli's Son 36 (10f,Lin,S,May 10)
Jo Maximus 49 (7f,Don,G,Jun 7)
Jo Mell 92 (7f,Asc,GF,Spt 27)
Jona Holley 44 (8f,San,GF,May 27)
Jorrocks (USA) 60 (7f,Goo,GF,Aug 1)
Jubilee Scholar (IRE) 30 (7f,Fol,GF,Jly 14)
Jucea 37 (6f,Lei,GF,Oct 5)
Jude 30 (12f,Chp,GF,Jun 13)
Judicial Supremacy 56 (8f,Goo,GS,May 21)
Juggler 41 (10f,Don,G,Oct 25)
Jukebox Jive 30 (10f,Pon,G,Jly 8)
Junikay (IRE) 38 (12f,Fol,G,Oct 21)
Jupiter (IRE) 46 (6f,Not,GF,Apr 11)
Just Alex (IRE) 32 (10f,Asc,G,Jly 25)
Just Bob 61 (5f,Nwc,GF,Oct 1)
Just Dissident (IRE) 46 (5f,Pon,GF,Jly 18)
Just Grand (IRE) 48 (12f,Chp,GF,Jly 11)
Justinianus (IRE) 46 (7f,Bri,F,Spt 28)
Just Loui 55 (6f,Lin,S,May 10)
Just Nick 61 (8f,Asc,G,Jun 17)
Just Visiting 47 (6f,Hay,G,Jly 5)
Juvenilia (IRE) 30 (7f,Yar,F,Jun 5)
Juwwi 52 (7f,Nwm,G,Apr 16)

Kadeena 41 (8f,Nwc,F,Jun 4)
Kafaf (USA) 50 (7f,Yar,G,Jly 16)
Kafil (USA) 40 (8f,War,S,Jly 4)
Kahal 85 (7f,Asc,GF,Jun 18)
Kailey Goddess (USA) 37 (7f,San,GF,Jly 30)
Kailey Senor (USA) 61 (8f,San,GS,Jly 4)
Kaiser Kache (IRE) 46 (7f,Kem,GF,May 31)
Kala Sunrise 67 (8f,Nwm,G,Oct 18)
Kaldou Star 80 (8f,Lon,GF,Oct 5)
Kaliana (IRE) 77 (12f,Yor,G,Aug 21)
Kalimat 46 (7f,Crl,F,Aug 27)
Kalimisik (FR) 54 (10 1/2f,Lon,S,May 11)
Kalinini (USA) 38 (8f,Yar,GS,Jly 2)
Kalinka (IRE) 64 (9f,Goo,GF,Jly 30)
Kamanev (IRE) 40 (10f,Wnd,GF,Jly 14)
Kamin (USA) 54 (8f,San,GF,Spt 16)
Kammtarra (USA) 83 (8 1/2f,Eps,G,Jun 7)
Karakia (IRE) 34 (8f,Wnd,GF,Jly 28)
Karawan 40 (7f,Sal,GF,Aug 1)
Karinska 48 (7f,Yar,GF,Aug 10)
Karisma (IRE) 44 (13f,Ham,GS,Apr 10)
Kashwan (SPA) 63 (10 1/2f,Lon,G,Apr 20)
Kass Alhawa 52 (8f,Not,G,Oct 8)
Kassana (IRE) 57 (12 1/2f,Lon,G,Oct 4)
Kathryn's Pet 48 (10f,Pon,GF,Apr 16)
Katie Komaite 36 (8f,Not,G,Nov 3)
Kawa-Ib (IRE) 40 (7f,Hay,G,Spt 26)
Kayf Tara 51 (10f,Asc,G,Jly 25)
Kayvee 79 (7f,Asc,GF,Spt 27)
Kaziranga (USA) 42 (10f,Rip,G,Aug 30)
Kedwick (IRE) 38 (10f,Goo,GS,Jun 20)
Keen Dancer 40 (8f,Bat,G,May 19)

Keep Battling 33 (12f,Edi,G,Jun 16)
Keepsake (IRE) 31 (16f,Not,S,Oct 8)
Kemo Sabo 60 (7f,Crl,G,Apr 25)
Kenmist 77 (8f,Asc,GF,Spt 27)
Kennemara Star (IRE) 68 (8f,Nwm,G,Jly 8)
Kentucky Fall (FR) 56 (6f,Yar,GF,Aug 21)
Kernof (IRE) 51 (12f,Edi,GF,Jly 18)
Keroub (FR) 69 (11f,Lon,G,Apr 6)
Keston Pond (IRE) 49 (7f,Nwc,GF,Mar 31)
Kewarra 70 (10f,Nwm,GF,Oct 3)
Keyboogie (USA) 44 (8f,San,G,Aug 13)
Key to My Heart (IRE) 70 (10 1/2f,Yor,G,Jly 12)
Khafaaq 61 (7f,Hay,GS,Jly 3)
Khalik (IRE) 47 (7f,Goo,G,Jun 12)
Khassah 62 (8f,Asc,GF,Jun 18)
Khawafi 56 (10f,Goo,GF,Jun 12)
Khayali (IRE) 60 (10f,Nwm,G,Aug 2)
Khazinat El Dar (USA) 37 (8f,San,S,Aug 30)
Kid Ory 34 (7f,Thi,GF,Apr 18)
Kilcullen Lad (IRE) 55 (5f,Yar,GF,Spt 16)
Kildee Lad 52 (6f,Eps,GS,Jun 25)
Kilernan 37 (12f,Thi,G,Aug 2)
Kilma (USA) 64 (14f,Nwm,GS,Oct 17)
Kilnamartyra Girl 30 (12f,Edi,G,Jly 7)
Kilshanny 37 (10f,Goo,G,Jun 13)
Kilvine 43 (7f,San,GF,Jly 30)
Kind of Light 51 (6f,Goo,GS,Spt 13)
King Alex 89 (10f,Cur,GS,Aug 16)
King Athelstan (USA) 47 (8f,War,G,May 5)
Kingchip Boy 54 (8 1/2f,Eps,G,Apr 23)
Kingdom Pearl 33 (12f,Edi,GS,Nov 6)
Kingfisher Mill (USA) 81 (12f,Asc,G,Spt 27)
King Kato 50 (12f,Asc,S,Jly 26)
King of Peru 78 (6f,Asc,GS,Jun 20)
King of Tunes (FR) 67 (8f,Asc,GF,Apr 30)
King Parrot (IRE) 31 (8f,Sal,F,Jly 18)
Kings Assembly 51 (10f,Chp,G,Spt 11)
Kings Harmony (IRE) 50 (7f,Bri,F,Apr 21)
King Sound 74 (12f,Asc,G,Spt 27)
King Uno 36 (7f,Red,GF,Oct 7)
Kinnescash (IRE) 54 (10 1/2f,Hay,G,Jly 5)
Kintavi 43 (12f,Lei,G,May 26)
Kira 75 (6f,Eps,G,Jun 7)
Kirkwall 76 (9f,Cha,G,Jun 1)
Kirov Protege (IRE) 34 (12f,Bri,F,Spt 28)
Kissel 37 (7f,Cat,S,Jly 3)
Kistena (FR) 53 (5f,Lon,GF,Oct 5)
Klondike Charger (USA) 35 (10f,Red,GF,May 27)
Knave 32 (8f,Edi,S,Mar 27)
Knave's Ash (USA) 50 (7f,Nwc,G,Aug 25)
Knobbleeneeze 66 (7f,Goo,GS,May 22)
Knotty Hill 55 (6f,Lei,GS,Apr 26)
Koathary (USA) 58 (8f,Nwb,S,May 18)
Komi 74 (8f,Asc,G,Jun 17)
Komlucky 55 (7f,Thi,G,May 16)
Kool Kat Katie (IRE) 82 (10f,Nwm,GF,Oct 4)
Koraloona (IRE) 48 (11 1/2f,Wnd,G,Aug 4)
Kota 47 (12f,Lei,F,Apr 3)
Kram 37 (5f,Yor,G,Oct 8)
Kristal Breeze 41 (12f,Fol,G,Jly 9)
Kristal Bridge 30 (10f,Wnd,GF,Jly 14)
Krosno 45 (11 1/2f,Lin,GF,Aug 2)
Krystal Max (IRE) 31 (6f,Kem,G,May 24)
Kuala Lipis (USA) 80 (10 1/2f,Yor,G,Aug 20)
Kulepopsie (IRE) 32 (12 1/2f,Nwc,GF,Aug 6)
Kumait (USA) 54 (8f,Don,G,Jly 31)
Kutta 67 (12f,Nwm,G,May 2)
Kyle Rhea 56 (11 1/2f,Chs,S,May 7)

Labeq (IRE) 49 (10f,Nwm,GF,Aug 23)
La Blue (GER) 98 (9f,Lon,GF,Oct 5)
La Brief 37 (16f,Nwc,G,Mar 25)
Lachesis 30 (6f,Rip,G,Aug 30)
La Curamalal (IRE) 37 (10f,San,GF,Apr 25)
La Dolce Vita 50 (7f,Red,F,Aug 10)
Lady Arpel (IRE) 31 (14f,Leo,G,May 28)
Lady Assassin (IRE) 30 (5f,Leo,G,Spt 13)
Lady Carla 57 (12f,Asc,G,Jun 20)
Lady Caroline Lamb (IRE) 48 (5f,Cat,GF,Aug 5)
Lady Diesis (USA) 54 (6f,Pon,S,Jun 30)
Lady of The Lake 48 (16f,Bev,GS,Aug 14)
Lady Sheriff 68 (5f,Eps,G,Aug 25)
Lago Di Varano 66 (5f,Yor,G,May 14)
Laguna Bay (IRE) 40 (10f,Goo,GF,Aug 23)
Lalindi (IRE) 44 (10f,Fol,F,Apr 10)
Lallans (IRE) 69 (14f,Goo,GF,Jly 29)
Lamarita 58 (5f,Nwm,S,Jun 27)
La Modiste 72 (8f,Nwb,GS,Spt 20)
Lamorna 43 (7f,Cat,GF,Spt 20)
La Nana (FR) 87 (10 1/2f,Cha,S,Jun 8)
Lancashire Legend 35 (6f,Bri,F,May 23)
Landlord 33 (15f,War,GF,May 24)
La Petite Fusee 67 (6f,Lin,S,May 10)
Lapu-Lapu 45 (10f,Nwc,GF,Oct 22)
Largesse 53 (12f,Hay,G,Spt 21)
Last Chance 31 (7f,Yar,GF,Jly 28)
Last Laugh (IRE) 48 (12f,Bat,GF,Apr 29)
Last Second (IRE) 72 (10f,Goo,GF,Aug 2)
Latalomne (USA) 61 (8f,Not,GF,Apr 8)
Latvian 45 (12f,Edi,GS,Jun 23)
Laurel Delight 48 (5f,Eps,G,Jun 7)
Laurel Seeker (USA) 37 (11 1/2f,Lin,F,Oct 3)
Lavender Della (IRE) 49 (12 1/2f,War,G,Jun 24)
La Volta 41 (6f,Not,GF,Spt 15)
Lawahik 71 (10f,Don,G,May 24)
Law Commission 76 (8f,Goo,G,May 20)
Law Dancer (IRE) 42 (10f,San,GF,Spt 16)
Lawz (IRE) 41 (8 1/2f,Eps,G,Spt 5)
Lay The Blame 54 (8f,Rip,GF,May 28)
Leading Note (USA) 48 (11 1/2f,Yar,G,Jly 16)
Leading Princess (IRE) 40 (5f,Ham,S,May 4)
Lear Jet (USA) 50 (12f,Fol,GF,Aug 19)

Le Destin (FR) 85 (10 1/2f,Lon,S,Apr 27)
Ledgendry Line 63 (12f,Don,G,May 24)
Legal Issue (IRE) 48 (7 1/2f,Bev,GF,Jun 4)
Legendary Lover (IRE) 43 (10 1/2f,Hay,GS,Spt 5)
Legend Maker (IRE) 40 (13 1/2f,Dea,G,Aug 3)
Le Grand Gousier (USA) 36 (11 1/2f,Yar,GF,Spt 16)
Leif the Lucky (USA) 48 (10f,Don,GS,Jun 29)
Lennox Lewis 31 (5f,Cat,GF,Jly 23)
Leonard Quercus (FR) 87 (20f,Lon,G,Oct 4)
Levelled 58 (6f,Kem,GF,Spt 22)
Leviticus (IRE) 41 (10f,Bev,Hy,Jly 5)
Liathach 31 (14f,Not,S,Jly 5)
Lidanna 37 (5f,Leo,G,Jun 2)
Life of Riley 53 (12f,Nwm,GS,Jun 20)
Liffre (IRE) 58 (14f,Yor,G,Aug 19)
Light Programme 60 (10f,Nwm,GF,Jly 9)
Light Reflections 40 (12f,Bat,G,May 11)
Lila Pedigo (IRE) 33 (10f,Bev,GF,Apr 5)
Lillibella 32 (5f,Pon,GF,Spt 25)
Lilli Claire 65 (8f,Goo,G,May 22)
Lil's Boy (USA) 45 (7f,Cur,G,May 3)
Lime Street Blues (IRE) 39 (8f,War,GF,May 24)
Limni (USA) 48 (8f,Nwb,S,Spt 19)
Lindrick Lady (IRE) 46 (10f,Bev,Hy,Jly 4)
Linoise (FR) 81 (5f,Dea,G,Aug 3)
Lionize (USA) 55 (8f,Lei,G,Oct 28)
Liquid Gold (IRE) 51 (8f,Don,G,Jly 16)
Listed Account (USA) 56 (6f,Nwm,GS,Jly 18)
Literary 57 (8f,Lei,S,Oct 13)
Literary Society (USA) 61 (5f,Yar,GF,Spt 16)
Little Acorn 49 (14f,San,GF,Jly 24)
Little Pilgrim 37 (7f,Fol,GF,Jly 14)
Littlestone Rocket 34 (5f,Fol,G,Jly 9)
Livius (IRE) 40 (10f,Bat,G,Jly 7)
Lochangel 85 (6f,Asc,GF,Spt 27)
Loch-Hurn Lady 34 (5f,Cat,G,Mar 26)
Loch Patrick 65 (7f,Nwb,GF,Aug 16)
Loch Style 33 (7f,Cat,G,Mar 26)
Lomberto 65 (10f,Nwb,GS,Spt 20)
London Lights 49 (11f,Kem,GF,Mar 31)
London News (SAF) 77 (10f,Asc,G,Jun 17)
London's Heart (USA) 30 (10f,Lei,F,Apr 3)
Lonely Heart 60 (10f,Goo,GF,Aug 22)
Lonely Leader (IRE) 85 (8f,Kem,G,May 5)
Longwick Lad 47 (5f,Thi,GF,May 3)
Lookingforarainbow (IRE) 54 (10f,Kem,GF,Mar 31)
Lookout 36 (10f,Don,GS,Jun 28)
Look Who's Calling (IRE) 54 (7f,Hay,GS,May 24)
Lord Advocate 45 (13f,Ham,G,Jun 11)
Lord Cromby (IRE) 85 (10f,Lon,G,Oct 4)
Lord Discord 40 (10f,Rip,GF,Aug 25)
Lord Eurolink (IRE) 65 (8f,Asc,S,Jun 21)
Lord Hastie (USA) 39 (13f,Ham,GS,Apr 10)
Lord High Admiral (CAN) 73 (5f,Sal,GS,Spt 4)
Lord Jim (IRE) 59 (16f,Asc,GF,Apr 30)
Lord Oberon (IRE) 32 (8f,Goo,G,Spt 24)
Lord of Men 71 (10f,San,GF,Jly 16)
Lord Olivier (IRE) 68 (6f,Eps,G,Apr 23)
Lord Sky 43 (5f,Ham,S,May 4)
Lorins Gold 31 (8f,War,F,Jun 4)
Lough Erne 30 (6f,Red,G,Nov 4)
Loup Sauvage (USA) 76 (10f,Nwm,G,Oct 18)
Love Has No Pride (USA) 49 (9f,Kem,G,May 5)
Love Me Do (USA) 41 (11f,Ham,GS,Jly 4)
Love Venture 32 (8f,Not,GF,Jly 30)
Loveyoumillions (IRE) 45 (10f,Don,GF,Mar 20)
Loving And Giving 49 (6f,Nwb,GF,Jly 18)
Lucayan Beach 36 (6f,Nwb,G,Oct 24)
Lucayan Prince (USA) 70 (6f,Asc,G,Jun 19)
Lucky Archer 45 (8f,War,GF,Oct 7)
Lucky Begonia (IRE) 37 (8f,Not,G,Jun 18)
Lucky Coin (USA) 93 (8f,Hpk,F,Nov 8)
Lucky Dip 42 (5f,Bat,GF,May 30)
Ludo 38 (12f,Bat,GF,Jun 14)
Lunar Mist 51 (6f,Lei,G,May 26)
Lunasa (IRE) 43 (16f,Leo,S,Nov 9)
Lunch Party 30 (7f,Yar,F,Spt 17)
Luso 99 (12f,Stn,GF,Dec 14)
Lycility (IRE) 46 (10f,Pon,GF,Spt 25)
Lynton Lad 55 (8f,Not,G,Jun 18)
Lysandros (IRE) 40 (10f,San,GF,Spt 16)

Macaribo 35 (8f,Pon,GF,Oct 6)
Macgillycuddy (IRE) 37 (5f,Sal,GS,Jun 25)
Machiavelli 38 (12f,Nwb,GF,Aug 16)
Mac Oates 32 (8f,Goo,G,Spt 24)
Madame Chinnery 50 (11 1/2f,San,GF,May 27)
Madison Mist 31 (8f,Not,GF,Apr 11)
Madison Welcome (IRE) 46 (11f,Ham,GS,Jly 4)
Madly Sharp 68 (7f,Nwm,G,Apr 16)
Mad Militant (IRE) 51 (11 1/2f,Wnd,GF,Aug 11)
Maftool 60 (8f,Asc,S,Jun 21)
Maftun (USA) 35 (12f,Rip,GF,Apr 9)
Magellan (USA) 83 (8f,Hpk,F,Nov 8)
Magellano (USA) 60 (12f,Lon,S,May 15)
Magical Cliche (USA) 39 (8f,Leo,YS,May 11)
Magic Combination (IRE) 50 (11 1/2f,San,GS,Jly 4)
Magic Lahr (GER) 43 (8f,Bat,G,Aug 12)
Magic Lake 34 (6f,Not,GF,Spt 15)
Magic Mill (IRE) 63 (8f,Red,GF,Oct 28)
Maiden Castle 43 (10 1/2f,Yor,G,May 15)
Maid of Camelot 61 (10f,Nwc,G,Aug 25)
Maiteamia 37 (5f,Nwc,GF,Mar 31)
Majal (IRE) 37 (12f,Cat,G,Jun 6)
Majesty (IRE) 52 (10f,Goo,GF,Aug 22)
Major Change 77 (10f,Eps,G,Jun 7)
Majorien 73 (12f,Hpk,F,Nov 8)
Make Ready 40 (5f,Lei,G,Aug 20)
Malabi (USA) 43 (6f,Lin,GF,Jun 14)
Maladerie (IRE) 46 (7f,Red,GF,Oct 7)

Male-Ana-Mou (IRE) 77 (12f,Eps,G,Spt 5)
Malibu Man 57 (5f,Lin,GF,Jly 10)
Mallia 60 (6f,Nwm,G,May 3)
Mamalik (USA) 76 (9f,Cha,G,Jun 1)
Manaloj (USA) 32 (10f,Nwm,G,May 3)
Manazil (IRE) 58 (10f,Nwm,GF,Jly 9)
Mandilak (USA) 58 (12f,Goo,GF,Jly 30)
Manful 63 (12f,Edi,G,Jun 16)
Mangus (IRE) 52 (5f,Chs,S,May 6)
Man Howa (IRE) 59 (6f,Hay,S,May 5)
Manikato (USA) 36 (7f,Fol,GF,Apr 22)
Manileno 40 (12f,Bri,F,May 29)
Mannenberg (IRE) 73 (10f,Lon,G,Oct 4)
Manolo (FR) 52 (5f,Pon,GF,Apr 22)
Mantles Prince 59 (12f,Asc,Hy,Oct 10)
Manuetti (IRE) 35 (10f,Eps,S,Jly 2)
Mapengo 33 (12f,Chp,G,Aug 25)
Maple Bay (IRE) 39 (8f,Nwc,GF,Oct 1)
Maradata (IRE) 38 (10 1/2f,Hay,GF,Aug 15)
Maradi (IRE) 42 (10f,Lin,GF,May 31)
Maralinga (IRE) 60 (10 1/2f,Chs,GF,Jly 11)
Mara River 62 (9f,Goo,GF,Jly 30)
Marathon (USA) 79 (8f,Lon,GF,Oct 5)
Marathon Maid 49 (14f,Yor,G,Aug 19)
March Crusader 66 (6f,Goo,GS,Spt 13)
Marchman 36 (10f,Bri,F,Jun 3)
March Star (IRE) 45 (6f,Yar,F,Spt 17)
Mardi Gras (IRE) 40 (10 1/2f,Hay,S,Mar 29)
Mardrew 49 (10f,Nwm,GF,Spt 30)
Marengo 51 (6f,Eps,GS,Jun 25)
Marie Dora (FR) 49 (8f,Kem,G,May 24)
Marilaya (IRE) 55 (10f,Nwm,GF,Jly 9)
Marino Street 46 (5f,Crl,F,Jun 12)
Marjaana (IRE) 66 (7 1/2f,Bev,GS,Aug 13)
Marjorie Rose (IRE) 40 (5f,Ham,S,Jly 1)
Marl 57 (6f,Goo,GS,May 21)
Maroulla (IRE) 32 (9f,Kem,GF,May 31)
Maroussie (FR) 46 (13 1/2f,Dea,G,Aug 3)
Marozia (USA) 38 (8f,Yar,G,Oct 22)
Marsad (IRE) 41 (6f,Wnd,S,May 12)
Marsayas (IRE) 38 (16f,Cat,GF,May 31)
Marsh Marigold 36 (12f,Cat,GF,Jly 16)
Marsul (USA) 50 (12f,Hay,G,Spt 26)
Mary Cornwallis 55 (6f,Nwm,GF,Aug 9)
Marylebone (IRE) 46 (5f,Bev,GF,Apr 11)
Mary Magdalene 55 (6f,Hay,G,Spt 21)
Masharik (IRE) 55 (12f,Yor,G,Aug 21)
Mashhaer (USA) 48 (7f,Goo,GF,Aug 2)
Massyar Seventeen 37 (8f,San,GF,Jly 30)
Master Beveled 65 (8f,Nwb,S,May 18)
Master Boots 64 (7f,Nwm,GF,Jly 10)
Master Charter 50 (8f,Nwc,G,Jun 27)
Master Foley 33 (6f,Not,GF,Apr 11)
Master M-E-N (IRE) 50 (8 1/2f,Eps,G,Apr 23)
Master Millfield (IRE) 38 (11f,War,F,May 5)
Master of Passion 50 (5f,Lin,S,Jun 28)
Masterpiece 40 (6f,Nwm,GF,Apr 17)
Master Planner 53 (6f,Nwm,G,May 3)
Matoaka 43 (7f,Eps,G,Spt 5)
Matthias Mystique 37 (16 1/2f,Fol,GF,Jun 4)
Mattimeo (IRE) 78 (10f,Nwm,GF,Spt 30)
Mawared (IRE) 68 (18f,Nwm,G,Oct 18)
Mawingo (IRE) 63 (8f,Rip,GF,Aug 25)
Mayflower 32 (8f,Lei,S,Oct 13)
May King Mayhem 35 (15f,War,GF,Jly 12)
Maylane 75 (10f,Nwm,GF,Jly 9)
Maypole (IRE) 43 (7f,Hay,G,Spt 26)
May Queen Megan 48 (8f,War,GF,Oct 7)
Mazeed (IRE) 37 (7f,Bri,F,Spt 28)
Mazilla 32 (11f,War,GF,Jun 9)
Mazurek 55 (14f,San,GF,Jly 16)
Mbulwa 41 (8f,Thi,GF,Aug 11)
Mcgillycuddy Reeks (IRE) 57 (10f,Rip,G,Aug 30)
Medaaly 52 (10 1/2f,Yor,G,May 14)
Medaille Militaire 71 (10f,Goo,G,May 22)
Media Star (USA) 70 (14f,Goo,GF,Jly 29)
Medieval Lady 51 (9f,Nwm,G,May 2)
Meg's Memory (IRE) 37 (12f,Chp,GF,Jly 11)
Meilleur (IRE) 42 (12f,Bat,G,Spt 8)
Meliksah (IRE) 67 (5f,Nwm,G,Jly 19)
Mellors (IRE) 30 (6f,Bri,F,Apr 11)
Melodica 43 (14f,San,GF,Jly 24)
Mels Baby (IRE) 65 (10f,Don,GF,Mar 20)
Memorise (USA) 68 (12f,Don,GF,Spt 12)
Mengaab (USA) 62 (12f,Goo,GF,Aug 22)
Mentalasanythin 57 (11f,Ham,G,Aug 2)
Meranti 46 (6f,Not,GF,Apr 8)
Merciless Cop 48 (9f,San,GS,Aug 29)
Merit (IRE) 53 (16 1/2f,Don,S,Nov 8)
Merrily 34 (6f,Cat,G,Apr 23)
Mersey Beat 65 (10f,Nwm,GF,Jly 9)
Meshhed (USA) 69 (7f,Nwb,GF,Aug 16)
Messina (IRE) 43 (10f,San,GF,Spt 16)
Metastasio 44 (16f,Leo,S,Nov 9)
Meteor Strike (USA) 52 (10f,Don,GF,Spt 10)
Mezzoramio 42 (7f,Yar,F,Spt 17)
Middle East 49 (6f,Not,S,Oct 15)
Midnight Escape 79 (5f,Hay,GF,Aug 9)
Midnight Shift (IRE) 54 (6f,Lei,G,Oct 27)
Midnight Watch (USA) 44 (8f,Lei,G,Oct 28)
Midyan Blue (IRE) 57 (12f,Hay,S,Mar 29)
Midyan Call 70 (8f,Nwm,GF,Oct 3)
Midyan Queen 41 (7f,Crl,F,Aug 27)
Mighty Phantom (USA) 51 (11 1/2f,Wnd,G,Aug 4)
Migwar 47 (10f,Nwb,GS,Spt 20)
Mihriz (IRE) 44 (9f,Nwm,GF,Oct 4)
Mijas 37 (5f,Lin,G,May 9)
Mike's Double (IRE) 47 (7f,Nwm,G,Aug 22)
Mile High 63 (5f,Not,GF,Mar 31)
Miletrian Refurb (IRE) 36 (5f,Fol,G,Mar 26)
Military (USA) 60 (10f,Nwm,G,Aug 2)
Mill End Boy 34 (5f,Bev,GF,Jun 5)

Millesime (IRE) 42 (6f,Cat,G,Apr 23)
Millroy (USA) 39 (8f,Don,GF,Mar 22)
Milly of The Vally 54 (14f,Goo,GF,Aug 2)
Miltonfield 68 (20f,Asc,G,Jun 17)
Mimosa 47 (8f,Asc,GF,Apr 30)
Mind Games 68 (5f,Yor,G,Aug 21)
Mindrace 51 (5f,Wnd,GF,Jly 14)
Minersville (USA) 34 (9f,Ayr,G,Jun 20)
Mingling Glances (USA) 42 (10f,Cur,GS,Jun 6)
Ministerial Model (IRE) 40 (7f,Cur,GS,Jun 28)
Miracle Kid (USA) 43 (10f,Don,GF,Mar 20)
Mislemani (IRE) 41 (8f,Bat,G,Jun 28)
Missfortuna 43 (11f,Kem,GF,Spt 22)
Missile Toe (IRE) 32 (8f,San,GF,Jun 14)
Miss Riviera 63 (8f,Goo,G,May 22)
Miss Riviera Rose 36 (10f,Pon,GF,Apr 22)
Miss Sancerre 61 (7f,Nwm,G,Apr 15)
Mister Aspecto (IRE) 45 (12f,Bev,G,Jly 29)
Mister Jolson 66 (6f,Fol,G,Oct 21)
Mister Pink 54 (10f,Nwm,GF,Apr 17)
Mister Raider 33 (5f,Wnd,GF,Aug 18)
Mister Westsound 34 (6f,Ham,G,Aug 13)
Misty Point 42 (8f,Kem,G,May 24)
Misty Rain 43 (10f,Rip,GF,Aug 25)
Mithak (USA) 66 (14f,Nwm,GS,Oct 17)
Mithali 80 (10f,Don,GF,Spt 10)
Mo-Addab (IRE) 63 (8f,Don,GS,Jun 29)
Mohaajir (USA) 57 (14f,Leo,GS,Aug 4)
Mohawk River (IRE) 75 (10f,Nwm,G,Aug 2)
Monaassib 99 (6f,Asc,GF,Spt 27)
Monaco (IRE) 45 (7f,Goo,G,Jun 12)
Monaco Gold (IRE) 51 (12f,Ham,S,Jun 25)
Monarch's Pursuit 30 (12f,Edi,G,Aug 28)
Mon Bruce 51 (5f,Nwc,GF,Oct 22)
Mongol Warrior (USA) 74 (15^{1}/2f,Lon,S,May 18)
Monis (IRE) 30 (10f,Not,GF,Jun 9)
Monitor 54 (10f,Rip,GF,Aug 4)
Mono Lady (IRE) 61 (12f,Bri,GF,Spt 3)
Mons 73 (12f,Nwm,G,May 2)
Monte Cavo 46 (10f,Nwm,G,Aug 1)
Montecristo 61 (14f,Not,G,Nov 3)
Montendre 64 (6f,Bat,G,Spt 8)
Montfort (USA) 65 (12f,Yor,GS,Jun 13)
Montone (IRE) 36 (8f,War,GF,May 24)
Montrestar 42 (5f,Nwm,GF,Aug 23)
Monument 50 (10f,Chp,G,Spt 11)
Monza (USA) 73 (10^{1}/2f,Yor,G,May 14)
Moonax (IRE) 55 (20f,Asc,G,Jun 19)
Moon Blast 65 (12f,Eps,G,Spt 5)
Moon Colony 59 (14f,Not,S,Oct 15)
Moon Fairy 37 (7f,Yar,F,Jun 11)
Moonlight Paradise (USA) 54 (8f,Asc,GF,Jun 18)
Moonshine Girl (USA) 59 (7f,Eps,G,Jun 7)
Moonshiner (USA) 58 (7f,Hay,G,Spt 26)
Moon Song 30 (7f,Yar,F,Jun 5)
Moon Strike (FR) 74 (5f,Hay,GF,Aug 9)
Moran 32 (10f,Wnd,GF,Jly 14)
Morocco (IRE) 48 (7f,Sal,GF,Jun 11)
Mosconi (IRE) 32 (7f,Cur,G,Apr 12)
Moscow Mist (IRE) 60 (8f,Red,GF,Oct 28)
Most Respectful 32 (7f,Crl,G,Apr 25)
Motet 57 (18f,Yar,F,Spt 18)
Mouche 55 (6f,Nwc,GF,Oct 22)
Mountaineer (IRE) 32 (14f,Not,GF,Oct 4)
Mountgate 55 (7f,Nwm,G,May 16)
Mount Genius (USA) 36 (8f,Thi,F,Jun 2)
Mount Holly (USA) 64 (8f,Don,GS,Nov 8)
Mousehole 59 (5f,Rip,G,Jun 19)
Mousse Glacee (FR) 91 (10^{1}/2f,Cha,S,Jun 8)
Move Smartly (IRE) 40 (7f,Red,F,May 1)
Move With Edes 37 (7f,Crl,G,Jly 5)
Moving Arrow 66 (8f,Hay,GF,Jun 7)
Moving Out 36 (16f,Not,GF,Spt 15)
Mowelga 32 (10f,Nwb,G,Oct 24)
Mowjood (USA) 36 (10f,Not,GF,Aug 6)
Mowlaie 42 (10^{1}/2f,Hay,GF,Jun 6)
Mozambique (IRE) 43 (7f,Kem,G,Spt 21)
Mr Bergerac (IRE) 76 (6f,Ayr,G,Spt 20)
Mr Bombastique (IRE) 51 (10^{1}/2f,Yor,G,May 13)
Mr Browning (USA) 56 (12f,Bri,F,Jun 3)
Mr Cube (IRE) 42 (8f,War,GF,May 24)
Mr Fortywinks (IRE) 39 (11f,Ayr,GS,Spt 18)
Mr Frosty 51 (6f,Lin,S,May 10)
Mr Lightfoot (IRE) 64 (9f,Cur,S,Spt 21)
Mr Majica 46 (6f,Bat,G,Spt 8)
Mr Paradise (IRE) 55 (8f,San,GF,Spt 16)
Mr Rough 43 (8f,Nwb,G,Jun 12)
Mrs Miniver (USA) 68 (10f,Nwm,GF,Oct 4)
Mr Speaker (IRE) 42 (7f,Chp,G,Spt 11)
Mr Sponge (USA) 62 (8f,Nwb,GS,Spt 20)
Mr Teigh 55 (7f,Nwm,GF,Oct 4)
Mr Wild (USA) 59 (12f,Kem,G,May 5)
Muara Bay 34 (10f,Bri,F,Oct 1)
Mubariz (IRE) 36 (7f,Lei,GF,Mar 27)
Muchea 93 (6f,Asc,GF,Spt 27)
Muhandam (IRE) 51 (6f,Don,GS,Jun 28)
Muhassil (IRE) 42 (10f,Pon,GF,Spt 25)
Muhtafel 49 (8f,Not,GF,Jly 19)
Mujova (IRE) 57 (7f,Hay,G,Spt 27)
Mukaddar (USA) 60 (8f,San,GS,Jly 5)
Mukhatab 46 (9f,Red,GF,Oct 7)
Mukhlles (USA) 57 (8f,Bat,G,Aug 12)
Mullagh Hill Lad (IRE) 42 (6f,Bat,G,Jun 28)
Mullitover 53 (7f,Nwm,G,May 16)
Multicoloured (IRE) 64 (12f,Don,GF,Spt 12)
Multi Franchise 34 (7f,Bri,F,Jly 15)
Mumaris (USA) 37 (8f,Not,GF,Apr 8)
Mungo Park 56 (5f,Nwc,GF,Oct 22)
Municipal Girl (IRE) 30 (6f,Cat,GF,May 30)
Murchan Tyne (IRE) 32 (13f,Bat,G,Spt 8)
Murphy's Gold (IRE) 43 (8f,War,GF,May 24)
Murron Wallace 33 (8f,Bat,G,Spt 8)

Musalsal (IRE) 77 (10 1/2f,Yor,G,May 14)
Muscadel 53 (12 1/2f,Lon,G,Oct 4)
Muscatana 35 (7f,Red,GF,Oct 7)
Musharak 57 (7f,Kem,G,Spt 21)
Musical Dancer (USA) 56 (10f,Nwm,G,May 2)
Musical Pursuit 62 (8f,Nwb,GS,Spt 20)
Music Gold (IRE) 73 (5f,Nwm,G,Jly 19)
Musick House (IRE) 65 (8f,Yor,G,May 14)
Mutabari (USA) 40 (8f,Not,G,Oct 30)
Mutadarra (IRE) 59 (10f,Nwm,GF,Spt 30)
Mutahadeth 30 (8f,Nwm,GF,Aug 9)
Mutasawwar 44 (6f,Sal,GF,May 4)
My Abbey 40 (5f,Hay,G,Jly 4)
My Beloved (IRE) 38 (8f,Nwm,GS,Jly 18)
My Best Valentine 85 (6f,Asc,GF,Spt 27)
Mybotye 53 (7f,Chp,G,Spt 11)
My Branch 61 (7f,Nwm,S,Jun 28)
My Emma 85 (12f,Lon,GF,Oct 5)
My Godson 37 (7 1/2f,Bev,GF,Jly 21)
My Handsome Prince 41 (8f,Rip,GF,Jly 19)
My Learned Friend 61 (13f,Nwb,GF,Jly 19)
My Lewicia (IRE) 66 (10f,Nwc,GF,Aug 3)
My Melody Parkes 72 (6f,Nwm,G,Apr 15)
Myrmidon 51 (5f,Asc,S,Jun 21)
Myrtlebank 54 (12f,Eps,G,Spt 5)
Myrtle Quest 66 (8f,Kem,GF,Spt 22)
Mystical 48 (6f,Lei,GF,Spt 22)
Mystic Quest (IRE) 35 (12f,Lei,GF,May 27)
Mystic Ridge 41 (8f,Nwb,GF,Apr 19)
Mystique Air (IRE) 40 (7f,Yor,S,Spt 4)
Myttons Mistake 66 (8f,Lei,G,Oct 27)
My Valentina 54 (10f,Nwb,GF,Spt 18)

Nabhaan (IRE) 85 (12f,Nwm,G,May 4)
Naissant 44 (6f,Not,GF,Spt 15)
Naivasha 33 (8f,Edi,G,Jly 7)
Najm Mubeen (IRE) 80 (10f,Nwm,G,May 3)
Nambucca 41 (10f,Don,GF,Mar 21)
Naninja (USA) 78 (8f,Hpk,F,Nov 8)
Nanton Point (USA) 62 (20f,Asc,G,Jun 17)
Nant Y Gamer (FR) 46 (7f,Nwm,G,Aug 22)
Napier Star 30 (5f,Wnd,GF,Jly 14)
Napoleon Star (IRE) 38 (6f,Cat,G,Jun 6)
Napoli Express (FR) 58 (11f,Lon,G,Apr 6)
Natalia Bay (IRE) 61 (8f,Kem,G,May 24)
Native Rhythm (IRE) 31 (7f,Chp,G,Spt 11)
Natural Eight (IRE) 49 (10f,Nwm,G,Apr 15)
Natural Key 60 (7f,Lin,F,Apr 4)
Nature Dancer 36 (10f,Rip,GF,Aug 4)
Naughty Pistol (USA) 46 (7f,Thi,GF,Apr 18)
Naval Games 50 (12f,Nwm,GF,Oct 2)
Nawasib (IRE) 38 (10f,Goo,GS,Jun 27)
Ned's Bonanza 36 (5f,Crl,F,May 29)
Needle Gun (IRE) 55 (10f,San,GS,Apr 26)
Needle Match 58 (7f,Crl,F,Aug 27)
Needwood Epic 33 (12f,Bev,G,Aug 23)
Nellie North 38 (5f,Wnd,GF,Jly 14)
Neronian (IRE) 40 (9f,Ayr,G,Jun 20)
Nervous Rex 39 (6f,Lei,GF,Spt 22)
Neuwest (USA) 70 (7f,Nwm,GF,Aug 9)
Never Think Twice 52 (6f,Wnd,GS,Jun 30)
Newbridge Boy 35 (10f,Red,G,Nov 4)
New Century (USA) 62 (7f,Nwm,G,Apr 16)
New Frontier (IRE) 68 (15f,Lon,G,Oct 4)
New Inn 36 (12f,Asc,Hy,Oct 10)
Newlands Corner 50 (6f,Lei,G,Jun 14)
Newport Knight 54 (12f,Eps,G,Apr 23)
Nichol Fifty 44 (12f,Chs,GF,Jly 11)
Nicker 33 (6f,Bri,F,Jly 16)
Nick of Time 37 (15 1/2f,Fol,S,Jly 2)
Nicola's Princess 35 (12f,Chs,GF,Jly 11)
Nifty Norman 62 (5f,Bev,Hy,May 11)
Nigel's Lad (IRE) 73 (16f,Rip,GF,May 28)
Nightbird (IRE) 76 (7f,Asc,GF,Jun 18)
Night Chorus 50 (8f,Not,G,Apr 29)
Night City 61 (11f,Ayr,G,Spt 20)
Night Dance 67 (7 1/2f,Bev,GF,Apr 11)
Night Express 40 (5f,Rip,GF,Aug 16)
Night Flight 49 (6f,Nwc,F,Jun 4)
Night Harmony (IRE) 42 (6f,Bat,GS,May 19)
Nightingale Song 42 (6f,Bat,G,Spt 8)
Nightlark (IRE) 53 (10f,Nwb,GF,Spt 18)
Night Mirage (USA) 48 (10 1/2f,Hay,GS,Spt 5)
Night of Glass 53 (7f,Cat,S,Oct 17)
Night Watch (USA) 64 (10f,San,GS,Jly 5)
Night Wink (USA) 51 (10f,Bri,GF,Aug 27)
Nigrasine 75 (6f,Hay,G,Jly 5)
Nile Valley (IRE) 33 (17f,Bat,GF,May 30)
Nineacres 58 (6f,Hay,S,May 5)
Ninth Symphony 35 (8f,Rip,GF,May 28)
Nkapen Rocks (SPA) 48 (8f,Rip,G,Jly 7)
Nobalino 52 (5f,Red,G,Nov 4)
Nobby Barnes 34 (9f,Yor,S,Spt 3)
Nobel Lad 40 (8 1/2f,Bev,GF,Apr 24)
Nobility (IRE) 45 (8f,Cur,GS,Aug 16)
Noble Dane (IRE) 47 (10f,Nwb,GF,Spt 18)
Noble Hero 31 (12f,Bri,F,May 29)
No Cliches 59 (8f,Pon,GF,Jly 18)
Noeprob (USA) 48 (8f,Bat,G,May 19)
No Extras (IRE) 71 (6f,Goo,GS,Spt 13)
No Grousing (IRE) 37 (8f,Rip,G,Jun 18)
Noisette 78 (8f,Asc,GF,Spt 27)
Nominator Lad 49 (7f,Hay,G,Spt 27)
Nomore Mr Niceguy 69 (8f,Asc,G,Jun 17)
No More Pressure (IRE) 55 (8f,Nwm,GS,Oct 16)
Nononito (FR) 78 (15 1/2f,Lon,S,May 18)
Non Vintage (IRE) 32 (12f,Nwm,G,Jun 7)
Nopalea 47 (5f,Edi,G,Jun 16)
Nordansk 44 (16f,Goo,GF,Spt 25)
Nordic Breeze (IRE) 54 (8f,Chp,GS,Jly 1)
Nordic Crest (IRE) 45 (12f,Pon,GF,Jun 3)
Nordinex (IRE) 39 (7f,San,GF,Spt 16)

Nor-Do-I 48 (7f,Hay,G,Spt 27)
Norman Conquest (USA) 39 (10f,Goo,G,Spt 13)
Nornax Lad (USA) 30 (13f,Bat,G,Jly 7)
Northern Angel (IRE) 53 (8f,Lin,GF,Jly 10)
Northern Blessing 52 (8f,Not,GF,Spt 23)
Northern Drums 60 (12f,Don,GF,Mar 22)
Northern Fan (IRE) 42 (7f,Lei,GF,Mar 27)
Northern Flash 40 (8f,Nwc,Hy,Jun 28)
Northern Fleet 53 (20f,Asc,G,Jun 17)
Northern Judge 34 (6f,War,F,May 5)
Northern Motto 43 (12f,Don,GF,Jun 7)
Northern Sun 54 (9f,Kem,G,Mar 29)
Northern Touch 32 (12f,Bev,G,Jly 29)
North Reef (IRE) 49 (10f,Lei,GS,Oct 14)
Nosey Native 49 (11f,Ham,GS,Jly 4)
No Slouch (IRE) 50 (9f,Cur,S,Spt 21)
Not Forgotten (USA) 45 (12f,Nwm,G,Apr 15)
Nothing Doing (IRE) 36 (11^{1}/2f,Wnd,GF,Jly 21)
Nothin' Leica Dane (AUS) 74 (12f,Lon,GF,Oct 5)
Noufari (FR) 51 (14f,Hay,GF,Aug 9)
Nwaamis (USA) 78 (8f,Asc,G,Jun 17)

Oatey 40 (6f,Don,G,Jun 7)
Obelos (USA) 46 (10f,Lei,GF,Spt 9)
Oberons Boy (IRE) 37 (12f,Edi,GF,Jly 18)
Oberon's Dart (IRE) 39 (6f,Yar,GS,Jly 3)
Occam (IRE) 37 (8f,Not,GF,Spt 23)
Occupandiste (IRE) 96 (7f,Lon,,Jun 22)
Ocean Park 48 (11f,War,GF,Apr 12)
Ocean Ridge (USA) 73 (8f,Dea,G,Aug 3)
Ochos Rios (IRE) 49 (7f,Don,G,May 6)
Ocker (IRE) 42 (7f,Lei,GS,Oct 14)
Octavia Hill 43 (7f,Bri,F,Jly 15)
Off The Rails 33 (12f,Fol,F,Spt 26)
Oggi 76 (6f,Asc,GS,Jun 20)
Oh Nellie (USA) 72 (7f,Nwm,G,Apr 15)
Ohnonotagain 35 (6f,Cat,GF,May 31)
Old Rouvel (USA) 64 (16f,Nwm,GF,Oct 4)
Olivo (IRE) 45 (7f,Goo,G,Jun 12)
Olympic Majesty (FR) 55 (10f,Cur,GS,Jun 6)
Omaha City (IRE) 77 (7f,Asc,GF,Spt 27)
Once More for Luck (IRE) 40 (12f,Nwm,GF,Oct 2)
One For Baileys 51 (15f,Nwm,GF,Jly 10)
Onefourseven 58 (20f,Goo,GF,Jly 30)
Oneknight With You 32 (7f,War,F,May 5)
One Life To Live (IRE) 43 (9f,Ham,GS,Jun 18)
One So Wonderful 82 (10f,Nwm,GF,Oct 4)
On Fair Stage (IRE) 50 (12f,Leo,G,Jly 19)
On The Green 31 (7f,Yar,GF,Jly 28)
Oops Pettie 72 (10f,Don,G,Nov 7)
Opalette 56 (10f,Pon,G,May 23)
Opaque 60 (14f,Yor,S,Spt 3)
Open Affair 48 (12f,Bri,F,May 29)
Open Credit 48 (6f,Ham,G,Spt 29)
Opening Range 31 (6f,Yar,F,Spt 18)
Opera Buff (IRE) 62 (12f,Bri,GF,Oct 23)
Ops Smile (USA) 83 (12f,Hpk,F,Nov 8)
Opulent 43 (10f,Nwc,G,Jun 27)
Orange Grouse (IRE) 48 (7f,Leo,S,Nov 9)
Orange Place (IRE) 70 (8f,Goo,GS,May 21)
Orchestra Stall 70 (16f,Asc,GF,Apr 30)
Ordained 51 (12f,Nwm,GF,Oct 31)
Orford Ness (FR) 60 (8f,Cha,G,Jun 1)
Oriane 42 (7f,Leo,S,Nov 9)
Oriel Lad 31 (7^{1}/2f,Bev,GF,Jun 4)
Oriental Express 93 (9f,Stn,GF,Dec 14)
Oriole 43 (7f,Red,F,Aug 10)
Orontes (USA) 47 (7f,San,G,May 26)
Orsay 64 (8f,Nwm,GF,May 31)
Ortelius 33 (8f,Goo,GS,May 21)
Oscar (IRE) 73 (12f,Cha,G,Jun 1)
Oscar Schindler (IRE) 98 (12f,Lon,GF,Oct 5)
Osomental 40 (5f,Yor,GS,Jun 13)
Otaiti (IRE) 52 (13^{1}/2f,Dea,G,Aug 3)
Our People 53 (9f,Lin,S,May 10)
Our Way 40 (9f,San,GF,Jun 14)
Out Line 50 (6f,Lin,GF,Jly 11)
Out of Sight (IRE) 54 (8f,Yor,G,May 15)
Out on a Promise (IRE) 46 (12f,Crl,G,Jly 5)
Outset (IRE) 47 (14f,Red,GF,Oct 18)
Out West (USA) 54 (8f,Goo,G,May 22)
Over To You (USA) 61 (10f,Nwm,G,May 2)
Oxbane 39 (6f,Yar,F,Spt 18)

Padauk 42 (15^{1}/2f,Fol,F,Spt 26)
Paddy Lad (IRE) 50 (6f,Sal,GF,May 4)
Paddy's Rice 42 (8f,Bri,F,May 29)
Pageboy 37 (6f,Not,GF,Jly 30)
Paint It Black 38 (8f,Thi,F,Jun 2)
Palacegate Jack (IRE) 56 (5f,Edi,GF,Jly 18)
Palacegate Touch 58 (5f,Cat,S,Oct 17)
Palacoona (GER) 45 (9f,Lon,S,Apr 27)
Palaemon 42 (16f,Goo,GF,Spt 25)
Palamon (USA) 61 (12f,Eps,G,Apr 23)
Palatial Style 68 (10f,Don,GF,Spt 10)
Paldost 30 (6f,Ham,GF,Jly 11)
Palio Sky 57 (12f,Goo,GF,Jly 29)
Palisade (USA) 36 (6f,Yar,F,Spt 17)
Pallium (IRE) 37 (5f,Ayr,S,Oct 14)
Palme D'Or (IRE) 81 (10^{1}/2f,Cha,S,Jun 8)
Palo Blanco 56 (7f,Goo,GS,Jun 20)
Panama City (USA) 78 (9f,Nwm,GF,Apr 17)
Panther (IRE) 47 (5f,Hay,G,Jly 4)
Papering (IRE) 84 (10^{1}/2f,Yor,G,May 14)
Papita (IRE) 35 (6f,Nwm,GF,Apr 17)
Papua 65 (12f,Nwm,GS,Oct 16)
Paradise Navy 61 (14f,Yar,GF,Aug 21)
Pardan 34 (6f,Cat,G,Spt 27)
Paris Babe 47 (6f,Eps,GS,Jly 9)
Party Romance (USA) 72 (10f,Don,GF,Spt 10)
Pas De Reponse (USA) 63 (8f,Nwm,G,May 4)
Passage Creeping (IRE) 42 (10f,Lin,GF,Jun 14)

Passi d'Orlando (IRE) 72 (10f,Don,G,May 24)
Passiflora 37 (7f,San,G,May 26)
Passing Strangers (USA) 52 (10f,Pon,GS,Oct 20)
Passionatti 50 (5f,Cat,S,Oct 17)
Passion For Life 53 (6f,Don,GF,Mar 22)
Pasternak 79 (9f,Nwm,GF,Oct 4)
Pater Noster (USA) 66 (8f,San,GF,Apr 25)
Patina 31 (6f,Lei,G,Jun 14)
Patriot Games (IRE) 53 (10f,San,S,Aug 30)
Patsy Grimes 77 (5f,Hay,G,Spt 27)
Pay Homage 55 (12f,Chp,GF,Aug 3)
Pearl Dawn (IRE) 39 (5f,Lin,G,May 17)
Peartree House (IRE) 75 (7f,Asc,GF,Jun 18)
Pegasus Bay 39 (8f,Bat,G,Aug 12)
Peintre Celebre (USA) 100 (12f,Lon,GF,Oct 5)
Pekay 56 (10f,Red,GF,Oct 18)
Pelham (IRE) 66 (8f,Nwm,GF,Apr 17)
Pendolino (IRE) 36 (10f,Pon,GF,Apr 16)
Pengamon 54 (7f,Nwm,G,Apr 16)
Penlop 48 (8f,Lei,S,Oct 13)
Pennys From Heaven 51 (11 1/2f,Wnd,S,May 19)
Pennywell 42 (8f,Not,G,Apr 29)
Pension Fund 47 (12f,Yor,G,Aug 21)
Pentad (USA) 70 (15f,Lon,G,Oct 4)
Peppers (IRE) 51 (12f,Bat,F,Jly 23)
Peppiatt 60 (7f,Lin,GF,Jly 12)
Percy Isle (IRE) 58 (14f,San,GF,Jly 16)
Perfect Brave 43 (5f,Hay,G,Jly 4)
Perfect Pal (IRE) 58 (7f,San,GF,Jly 30)
Perfect Paradigm (IRE) 54 (12f,Chs,S,May 7)
Perfect Poppy 41 (7f,Nwm,G,May 16)
Pericles 59 (8f,Red,F,Aug 23)
Perilous Plight 43 (7f,Fol,G,Mar 26)
Perryston View 81 (6f,Ayr,G,Spt 20)
Persevere 39 (6f,Bat,G,Spt 8)
Persian Blue 40 (12f,Sal,GF,Aug 13)
Persian Butterfly 33 (11 1/2f,Wnd,GF,Jun 9)
Persian Fayre 63 (8f,Nwm,GF,Nov 1)
Persian Punch (IRE) 94 (20f,Lon,G,Oct 4)
Peter Perfect 30 (7f,San,GF,Jly 30)
Petite Danseuse 45 (6f,Lei,GF,Spt 22)
Petoskin 46 (12f,Bri,F,Apr 21)
Petraco (IRE) 45 (5f,War,GF,Mar 31)
Pharaoh's Joy 45 (5f,Lin,GF,May 24)
Philanthrop (FR) 77 (15 1/2f,Lon,S,May 18)
Philistar 66 (8 1/2f,Eps,G,Jun 6)
Philmist 49 (11f,Ayr,GS,Spt 18)
Phonetic 66 (8f,Nwb,S,May 18)
Phylida 33 (8f,Nwm,GS,Jly 18)
Pickens (USA) 39 (10f,Don,G,Oct 25)
Pietro Bembo (IRE) 49 (12f,Nwm,G,Aug 2)
Pike Creek (USA) 65 (15f,Nwm,GS,Jun 11)
Pilsudski (IRE) 101 (12f,Lon,GF,Oct 5)
Pinchincha (FR) 57 (10f,Pon,GF,Spt 25)
Pine Ridge Lad (IRE) 36 (8f,Ham,G,Spt 29)
Pinfloron (USA) 79 (8f,Hpk,F,Nov 8)
Piquant 36 (7f,Don,G,May 24)
Pistol (IRE) 54 (12f,Fol,F,Spt 26)
Pizzicato 43 (5f,Bri,F,Jly 16)
Plaisir d'Amour (IRE) 70 (6f,Yor,G,Aug 19)
Plan For Profit (IRE) 58 (9f,Goo,GF,Jly 31)
Plaza De Toros (USA) 47 (10f,Leo,YS,May 11)
Pleading 57 (7f,Lin,G,Spt 9)
Pleasureland (IRE) 47 (20f,Asc,G,Jun 17)
Pleasure Time 56 (5f,Lei,G,Aug 20)
Pleasure Trick (USA) 35 (8f,Pon,GF,Jly 18)
Plum First 43 (6f,Pon,GS,Spt 2)
Poddington 46 (10f,Don,GF,Jun 7)
Pointelle 36 (7f,Kem,GF,May 31)
Pointer 48 (5f,Chp,G,Spt 11)
Poker-B (IRE) 38 (5f,Leo,G,Spt 13)
Poker School (IRE) 33 (10f,San,S,Aug 30)
Polar Champ 58 (10 1/2f,Hay,GF,Aug 8)
Polar Eclipse 39 (7f,Nwm,GF,Nov 1)
Polar Flight 59 (10 1/2f,Yor,G,May 13)
Polarize 30 (8f,Thi,G,Jly 25)
Polar Prince (IRE) 101 (8 1/2f,Eps,G,Jun 7)
Polar Prospect 53 (10f,Nwm,GF,Spt 30)
Polenista 43 (10f,Goo,GF,Jun 12)
Polenka (IRE) 39 (7f,Cat,GF,Spt 20)
Polish Rhythm (IRE) 57 (8f,Kem,GF,Spt 22)
Polish Romance (USA) 55 (6f,Nwm,GS,Jly 18)
Polish Warrior (IRE) 55 (5f,Asc,S,Jun 21)
Polly Golightly 54 (5f,Cat,S,Oct 17)
Polly Peculiar 36 (8f,War,GF,May 24)
Polonaise Prince (USA) 36 (12f,Bat,G,Spt 8)
Polska Princess (GER) 34 (10f,Chp,GS,Jly 1)
Poltarf (USA) 40 (14f,Hay,G,Spt 26)
Polyphony (USA) 40 (15f,Nwm,GS,Jun 11)
Pomona 71 (8f,Wnd,G,Aug 23)
Portite Sophie 37 (10f,Bev,GF,Apr 24)
Portuguese Lil 43 (8 1/2f,Bev,GF,Jun 5)
Poseidon 69 (12f,Goo,GF,Jly 29)
Posidonas 99 (12f,Stn,GF,Dec 14)
Poteen (USA) 88 (8f,Nwm,G,May 3)
Power Game 47 (8f,Edi,GF,May 31)
Pradesh 39 (10f,Nwm,GF,Jly 9)
Praeditus 39 (7f,Lin,GF,Jly 12)
Prairie Falcon (IRE) 60 (12f,Asc,G,Jun 19)
Prairie Minstrel (USA) 32 (8f,Bat,G,Aug 12)
Predappio 98 (12f,Lon,GF,Oct 5)
Premier 34 (8f,Lei,GF,Oct 5)
Premier Bay 71 (10 1/2f,Yor,GS,Jun 14)
Premier Dance 35 (12f,Fol,S,Jun 27)
Premier Generation (IRE) 53 (10f,Lei,GS,Apr 26)
Premier Night 66 (14 1/2f,Don,GF,Spt 10)
Premium Gift 33 (5f,Bev,G,Jun 11)
Prends Ca (IRE) 77 (6f,Hay,G,Spt 21)
Present Arms (USA) 70 (10 1/2f,Yor,G,Aug 20)
Present Chance 51 (7f,Yor,G,Jly 12)
Present Generation 65 (6f,Fol,GF,Aug 5)
Present Situation 48 (8 1/2f,Eps,GS,Aug 25)

Press On Nicky 38 (8f,Bat,GS,May 11)
Pride of Brixton 40 (5f,Cat,S,Oct 17)
Pride of Hayling (IRE) 37 (6f,Fol,GF,Aug 19)
Pride of Pendle 59 (8f,Yor,G,Jly 11)
Priena (IRE) 66 (8f,Asc,GF,Spt 27)
Prima Silk 66 (6f,Lei,G,Jun 14)
Prima Verde 50 (7 1/2f,Bev,S,Jun 11)
Prime Light 58 (8f,Pon,GF,Jly 18)
Prime Partner 34 (8f,Rip,G,Jun 18)
Primo Lara 66 (7f,Nwm,GF,Oct 4)
Prince Alex (IRE) 45 (12f,Nwm,G,Aug 2)
Prince Babar 81 (6f,Asc,GS,Jun 20)
Prince Danzig (IRE) 46 (12f,Nwm,G,Apr 16)
Prince de Loir 51 (8f,Nwm,GS,Jly 18)
Prince Dome (IRE) 65 (5f,Asc,S,Jun 21)
Prince Kinsky 62 (12f,Eps,G,Apr 23)
Princely Sound 37 (6f,Nwm,G,Aug 22)
Prince of Andros (USA) 71 (10f,Goo,G,May 22)
Prince of Denial 74 (8f,Nwb,GS,Spt 20)
Prince of India 56 (7f,Don,G,Oct 25)
Prince of My Heart 90 (10 1/2f,Yor,G,Aug 20)
Prince of Parkes 39 (5f,Edi,GS,Jun 23)
Princess Danielle 53 (11 1/2f,Wnd,G,Aug 4)
Princess Efisio 48 (8f,Not,G,Jun 18)
Princess of Hearts 36 (8f,Not,GF,Apr 11)
Princess Topaz 58 (16f,Asc,G,Spt 27)
Prince Zando 39 (6f,Fol,GF,Apr 22)
Principal Boy (IRE) 39 (9f,Ham,GS,Jun 18)
Priolo Prima 58 (10f,Lei,GS,Oct 14)
Private Fixture (IRE) 45 (12f,Bri,F,May 29)
Proper Blue (USA) 68 (10f,Goo,G,May 22)
Prospector's Cove 49 (10f,Wnd,G,Jly 7)
Prospero 58 (17f,Bat,GF,Spt 29)
Protocol (IRE) 46 (11 1/2f,San,GF,May 27)
Proud Monk 42 (8f,Goo,GS,Jun 20)
Proud Native (IRE) 64 (6f,Ayr,G,Spt 20)
Prussian Blue (USA) 75 (15 1/2f,Lon,S,May 18)
Psicossis 56 (12f,Chp,G,May 26)
Public Purse (USA) 65 (16f,Asc,GF,Jun 18)
Puce 75 (14 1/2f,Don,GF,Spt 10)
Punkah (USA) 45 (10f,Not,GF,Apr 11)
Purchasing Power (IRE) 52 (7f,Nwm,G,May 16)
Purist 55 (10f,Nwm,G,Apr 15)
Purple Fling 64 (6f,Rip,G,Aug 30)
Purple Splash 79 (14f,Yor,GS,Jun 13)
Pusey Street Girl 31 (6f,Lei,GS,Apr 26)
Puteri Wentworth 46 (12f,Edi,GS,Nov 6)
Putra (USA) 34 (8f,Nwm,G,May 3)
Puzzlement 36 (9f,Kem,G,Mar 29)

Q Factor 63 (8f,Nwb,S,May 18)
Que Belle (USA) 84 (12f,Lon,GF,Oct 5)
Queen Maud (IRE) 81 (10 1/2f,Cha,S,Jun 8)
Queen of Shannon (IRE) 44 (7f,Chp,G,Spt 11)
Queens Consul (IRE) 69 (7 1/2f,Chs,S,Aug 30)
Queen's Insignia (USA) 46 (8f,Wnd,GS,Jun 30)
Queen's Pageant 38 (7f,Nwm,S,Jun 28)
Quest For Best (USA) 35 (10f,San,GF,Apr 25)
Quezon City 31 (11f,Red,GF,May 26)
Quibbling 37 (8f,Nwm,G,Aug 2)
Quiet Arch (IRE) 49 (10f,Kem,G,May 24)
Quiet Venture 43 (10f,Lei,GF,Spt 9)
Quilling 47 (8f,Crl,F,Jun 25)
Quws 68 (9f,Cur,S,Spt 21)

Raaha 58 (7f,Lin,GF,Aug 17)
Racing Heart 34 (8f,Lei,G,Aug 11)
Radiancy (IRE) 55 (7f,Chs,S,May 7)
Raed 44 (7f,Don,G,Jly 31)
Raffles Rooster 57 (12f,Yor,GS,Jun 14)
Raheen (USA) 69 (7f,Thi,GF,May 3)
Rainbow Rain (USA) 52 (6f,Nwm,G,Jun 7)
Raindancing (IRE) 41 (9f,Goo,GF,Jly 30)
Raindeer Quest 39 (10f,Nwc,GF,Oct 22)
Rainwatch 65 (12f,Hay,S,Oct 15)
Raise A Prince (FR) 56 (10f,Nwm,G,May 2)
Raivue 66 (10f,Don,GF,Spt 10)
Raiyoun (IRE) 46 (10f,Cur,G,May 3)
Rajpoute (FR) 79 (12f,Hpk,F,Nov 8)
Rakis (IRE) 71 (7f,Lin,F,Apr 4)
Ralitsa (IRE) 30 (12f,Edi,GF,Jly 18)
Rambling Bear 93 (6f,Nwm,G,Apr 15)
Rambold 40 (6f,Yar,F,Jun 11)
Rambo Waltzer 59 (7f,Thi,GF,Apr 18)
Ramike (IRE) 47 (16 1/2f,San,GS,Jly 5)
Ramooz (USA) 83 (8f,Asc,GF,Jun 18)
Ramsey Hope 52 (5f,Crl,F,Jun 12)
Random Kindness 54 (12f,Bri,GF,Oct 23)
Rapier 64 (8f,Asc,G,Jun 17)
Rare Talent 40 (10f,Rip,GF,Aug 16)
Rasayel (USA) 60 (10f,Not,GF,Apr 21)
Rash Gift 38 (10f,Lin,G,Jun 24)
Rashik 57 (8f,Nwb,GF,Apr 19)
Rasin (IRE) 41 (10f,Leo,G,Apr 19)
Rate Cut (USA) 57 (10 1/2f,Lon,G,Apr 20)
Rawi 39 (6f,Nwc,GF,Aug 3)
Rayouni (IRE) 81 (10f,Cur,GS,Aug 16)
Reaganesque (USA) 36 (12f,Chp,GF,Aug 3)
Real Estate 48 (11 1/2f,Wnd,S,Jun 23)
Realt Dhun Eibhir 35 (7f,Cur,GS,Jun 28)
Reams of Verse (USA) 82 (10f,Nwm,GF,Oct 4)
Rebecca Sharp 89 (8f,Asc,G,Spt 27)
Rebel County (IRE) 54 (9f,Yor,GS,Jun 14)
Rechullin 51 (7f,Nwm,G,Jly 8)
Recourse (USA) 45 (10f,Nwm,G,Apr 15)
Redbridge (USA) 39 (11f,Nwb,GF,Apr 18)
Red Camellia 82 (8f,Lon,S,May 11)
Red Guard 52 (8f,Lin,GF,Jly 10)
Red Raja 53 (16f,Goo,GF,Spt 25)
Red Robbo (CAN) 73 (8f,Asc,GF,Jun 18)
Redwing 61 (8f,Asc,G,Jun 17)
Referendum (IRE) 65 (7f,Nwm,G,Apr 16)

Refuse To Lose 52 (7f,San,GF,Spt 16)
Regait 42 (16f,Nwm,GF,Jly 9)
Regal Eagle 31 (16f,Bev,GF,Jun 4)
Regal Patrol 50 (9f,Lin,S,May 10)
Regal Reprimand 48 (10f,Chp,G,Spt 11)
Regal Splendour (CAN) 36 (8f,Goo,GS,May 21)
Regal Thunder (USA) 45 (10f,Nwm,GF,Jly 9)
Reggie Buck (USA) 44 (8f,Nwm,G,Apr 16)
Rehaab 40 (8f,Yar,GF,Aug 6)
Reimei 40 (14f,Sal,GF,Aug 21)
Reine Wells (IRE) 63 (12f,Asc,Hy,Oct 11)
Reinhardt (IRE) 32 (5f,Bev,GF,Jun 5)
Remaadi Sun 75 (12f,Eps,G,Spt 5)
Renata's Prince (IRE) 48 (8f,San,GS,Jly 4)
Rennyholme 39 (5f,Bev,GF,Jly 15)
Renown 55 (12f,Bri,F,May 23)
Renzo (IRE) 77 (16f,Asc,G,Spt 27)
Repertory 66 (5f,Asc,Hy,Oct 11)
Resist the Force (USA) 50 (6f,Nwm,G,Aug 1)
Resounder (USA) 51 (7f,Asc,GF,Apr 30)
Restless Spirit (USA) 61 (6f,Hay,G,Jly 5)
Restructure (IRE) 78 (7f,Nwb,GF,Jly 18)
Return of Amin 63 (7f,Nwm,G,Oct 18)
Reunion (IRE) 74 (7f,Nwm,G,Apr 15)
Revoque (IRE) 91 (8f,Nwm,G,May 3)
Reward 42 (8f,Kem,G,May 24)
Rex Mundi 60 (11f,Ayr,GS,Spt 18)
Rhapsody In White (IRE) 51 (10f,Goo,G,Jun 13)
Rheinbold 54 (12f,Thi,G,Aug 2)
Ricardo 57 (10f,Goo,GF,Aug 22)
Riccarton 38 (10f,Not,GF,Spt 23)
Rich Glow 46 (5f,Hay,G,Jly 4)
Rich Ground 65 (7f,Nwm,G,Apr 16)
Rich In Love (IRE) 62 (7f,Yar,GF,Aug 10)
Rickenbacker (IRE) 49 (9f,Ham,G,Jun 11)
Ricky Ticky Tavie (USA) 55 (7f,Red,F,Spt 26)
Ridaiyma (IRE) 64 (12f,Asc,GF,Spt 28)
Rififi 62 (6f,Nwm,GS,Oct 17)
Right Man 51 (16 1/2f,San,GS,Jly 5)
Right Tune 59 (8f,Don,G,Jly 30)
Right Wing (IRE) 67 (8f,Asc,S,Jun 21)
Righty Ho 47 (10f,Bri,GF,Spt 3)
Ring the Chief 31 (10f,Wnd,GF,Jly 28)
Rising Dough (IRE) 46 (10f,Eps,GS,Jly 9)
Rising Spray 55 (12f,Bat,G,Aug 12)
Risky Rose 34 (14f,Cat,GF,May 30)
River Bay (USA) 80 (10 1/2f,Lon,S,Apr 27)
River North (IRE) 52 (12f,Lei,G,Jun 14)
River of Fortune (IRE) 30 (7f,War,F,May 5)
River Pilot 50 (10f,Nwm,GF,Jly 9)
River Run (IRE) 37 (10f,Pon,GF,Jun 9)
Rivers Magic 32 (11 1/2f,Wnd,GF,Jly 14)
River's Source (USA) 55 (10f,Don,G,Jly 30)
River Tern 51 (5f,Wnd,G,Aug 4)
River Usk 55 (11f,Ayr,G,Spt 20)
Riyadian 70 (9f,Ham,G,Jun 11)
Road Racer (IRE) 44 (10f,Bev,G,Jly 29)
Robban Hendi (USA) 45 (10f,Pon,GF,Jun 3)
Robellion 37 (5f,San,GF,Spt 17)
Rochea 31 (8f,Lei,G,Jly 23)
Rockcracker (IRE) 40 (6f,Fol,GF,Jun 4)
Rock Falcon (IRE) 56 (7f,Nwc,GF,Oct 1)
Rockforce 66 (10 1/2f,Chs,S,May 6)
Rock Island Line (IRE) 62 (8f,Nwc,G,May 22)
Rock Symphony 47 (7f,War,GF,Jly 19)
Rock The Barney (IRE) 37 (10f,San,GF,Spt 16)
Rocky Dance (FR) 52 (8f,Lei,G,Aug 11)
Rocky Oasis (USA) 69 (10f,Nwm,GS,Oct 16)
Roffey Spinney (IRE) 57 (6f,Fol,G,Oct 21)
Roi du Nord (FR) 36 (10f,Not,GF,Spt 15)
Roisin Clover 39 (12f,Kem,GF,May 31)
Rokeby Bowl 76 (12f,Nwm,G,May 4)
Romanov (IRE) 84 (12f,Eps,G,Jun 7)
Roman Reel (USA) 44 (12f,Bri,F,Apr 21)
Romios (IRE) 80 (10f,Kem,GF,Mar 31)
Ron's Round 39 (10f,Lei,GF,Spt 22)
Rosabella 44 (12 1/2f,Lon,G,Oct 4)
Rosa Royale 30 (8f,Lei,GF,Spt 22)
Roseate Lodge 30 (7f,Crl,G,Jun 26)
Roseate Wood (FR) 87 (5f,Dea,G,Aug 3)
Rose Carnival 31 (10 1/2f,Hay,GS,Spt 5)
Rose of Glenn 37 (14f,Not,GF,Jly 19)
Rossel (USA) 42 (13f,Ham,S,May 4)
Rosy Outlook (USA) 57 (6f,Nwm,G,Jun 7)
Rotor Man (IRE) 43 (7f,San,G,May 26)
Roufontaine 72 (12f,Chp,G,May 26)
Round Robin (IRE) 46 (7 1/2f,Bev,GS,May 20)
Roving Minstrel 62 (8f,Don,GF,Mar 22)
Royal Acclaim 32 (11 1/2f,Lin,F,Oct 3)
Royal Affinity (IRE) 32 (5f,Cur,G,Jly 13)
Royal Amaretto (IRE) 78 (10f,Nwb,GF,Jly 19)
Royal Applause 86 (6f,Asc,G,Jun 19)
Royal Aty (IRE) 54 (6f,Asc,GS,Jun 20)
Royal Castle (IRE) 58 (14f,Nwm,GS,Oct 17)
Royal Ceilidh (IRE) 54 (8f,Thi,GF,May 3)
Royal Circus 30 (13f,Bat,G,Jly 7)
Royal Court (IRE) 78 (12f,Asc,G,Jun 20)
Royal Crown (IRE) 58 (12f,Bat,G,Jun 28)
Royal Crusade (USA) 37 (8f,San,G,Aug 13)
Royal Diversion (IRE) 56 (12f,Nwm,GF,Oct 2)
Royal Dome (IRE) 57 (6f,Lei,G,Oct 27)
Royale Figurine (IRE) 77 (6f,Bat,Hy,May 11)
Royale Finale (IRE) 38 (8f,Nwb,GF,Apr 19)
Royale Rose (FR) 33 (8f,San,GF,Spt 17)
Royal Expression 55 (12f,Ham,S,Jun 25)
Royal Mark (IRE) 67 (7f,Nwc,G,Aug 6)
Royal Philosopher 51 (8f,San,GF,Apr 25)
Royal Result (USA) 55 (7f,Nwm,GF,Oct 4)
Royal Roulette 30 (10f,Fol,G,Oct 21)
Royal Scimitar (USA) 66 (12f,Nwm,G,May 4)
Royal Seaton 62 (10f,Kem,GF,Mar 31)
Royal South (IRE) 44 (7f,Thi,GF,May 3)

Roy Boy 44 (7f,Lin,GF,Jun 14)
Rude Awakening 42 (7f,Don,GF,Mar 22)
Rudimental 72 (10f,Don,GF,Spt 10)
Rudi's Pet (IRE) 69 (6f,Ayr,G,Spt 20)
Rufalda (IRE) 50 (12f,Bri,GF,Spt 3)
Rumbustious 33 (8f,Lei,G,Aug 11)
Rum Lad 46 (6f,Not,GF,Oct 4)
Runic Symbol 33 (10f,Bri,GF,Aug 27)
Running Free (IRE) 31 (12f,Bri,F,Jly 24)
Running Green 54 (8f,Edi,S,Mar 27)
Running Stag (USA) 74 (8f,Goo,GF,Aug 2)
Runs in the Family 48 (5f,War,G,Jun 24)
Rushcutter Bay 61 (6f,Not,G,Spt 28)
Rusk 50 (12f,Nwm,S,Jun 27)
Russian Music 90 (7f,Asc,GF,Spt 27)
Russian Revival (USA) 98 (6f,Asc,GF,Spt 27)
Russian Rose (IRE) 56 (16f,Nwm,GF,Jly 9)
Rutland Chantry (USA) 54 (10f,Pon,GS,Oct 20)
Ryafan (USA) 87 (10 1/2f,Cha,S,Jun 8)
Rymer's Rascal 49 (7f,Yor,S,Spt 4)

Saafeya (IRE) 70 (10f,Don,GF,Spt 10)
Sabadilla (USA) 76 (12f,Don,S,Nov 8)
Sabina 54 (5f,San,G,Apr 26)
Sabot 60 (7f,Nwm,G,May 16)
Sacho (IRE) 64 (11f,Ayr,G,Spt 20)
Sacrament 52 (14f,Yor,G,May 15)
Saddlers' Hope 53 (10f,Bat,GF,Jly 17)
Sadlers Home (IRE) 43 (14f,Leo,GS,Aug 4)
Safey Ana (USA) 58 (7f,Yar,GF,May 28)
Saffron Rose 46 (8f,Not,G,Apr 29)
Safio 65 (7f,Nwm,GF,Nov 1)
Sagebrush Roller 45 (10f,Don,GS,Jun 29)
Saguaro 59 (7f,Lei,S,Oct 13)
Saibhreas (IRE) 34 (10f,Leo,G,Apr 19)
Saifan 74 (8f,Nwb,GS,Spt 20)
Saint Express 70 (6f,Red,G,Jun 20)
Salamah 58 (10f,Don,G,May 24)
Sally Green (IRE) 44 (5f,Nwm,G,Oct 2)
Sally Slade 50 (5f,War,G,Jun 24)
Salmon Ladder (USA) 55 (10f,Wnd,GF,Aug 18)
Salsee Lad 33 (14f,San,GF,Aug 14)
Salska 51 (14f,Not,G,Oct 30)
Saltando (IRE) 47 (7f,Nwm,G,May 16)
Salty Behaviour (IRE) 42 (6f,Pon,GF,Oct 6)
Salty Jack (IRE) 43 (6f,Nwm,GF,Nov 1)
Samapour (IRE) 48 (10 1/2f,Lon,G,Apr 20)
Samara (IRE) 96 (9f,Lon,GF,Oct 5)
Samara Song 53 (7f,Chp,G,Spt 11)
Sambac (USA) 39 (7f,Nwm,G,May 4)
Samraan (USA) 76 (16f,Goo,GF,Jly 31)
Sam Rockett 52 (12f,Chp,G,Aug 25)
Samsung Spirit 47 (6f,Rip,GF,Aug 25)
Samuel Scott 45 (14f,Not,GF,Apr 21)
Samwar 55 (5f,Chs,S,Aug 30)
Sandabar 59 (7f,Goo,GS,May 22)
Sandbaggedagain 43 (12f,Yor,GS,Jun 13)
Sandblaster 34 (8f,Edi,GS,Jun 30)
Sand Cay (USA) 34 (7f,Sal,GS,Jun 25)
Sandicliffe (USA) 48 (7f,Yar,F,Spt 17)
Sandmoor Chambray 86 (10 1/2f,Yor,G,Aug 20)
Sandmoor Denim 45 (8f,Rip,GS,May 18)
Sandstone (IRE) 61 (8f,Not,GF,Apr 11)
Sandy Floss (IRE) 59 (16f,Goo,GF,Spt 25)
Sandystones 30 (9f,Goo,G,May 22)
Santillana (USA) 70 (10f,Nwm,GS,Oct 16)
Sapphire Son (IRE) 41 (12f,Bri,F,Jly 24)
Sarasota Storm 33 (15f,War,GF,Jly 12)
Saratoga Red (USA) 34 (8f,Lei,S,Oct 13)
Sarayir (USA) 62 (10f,Nwc,G,Aug 25)
Sarbaron (IRE) 34 (12f,Nwm,G,Aug 2)
Sarmatian (USA) 47 (9f,Ham,GF,Jly 11)
Saseedo (USA) 55 (7f,Nwm,G,Apr 16)
Sasuru 66 (10f,San,GS,Apr 26)
Satin Stone (USA) 64 (7f,Kem,GF,May 31)
Sausalito Bay 75 (15f,Lon,G,Oct 4)
Savona (IRE) 34 (6f,Wnd,S,May 12)
Saxon Bay 39 (6f,Chp,GF,Jun 13)
Sayyaramix (FR) 42 (6f,Kem,GF,Mar 31)
Scaraben 52 (8f,Lei,GF,Jun 2)
Scarlet Crescent 37 (8f,Bat,GF,Jly 17)
Scarrots 49 (12f,Nwm,G,Aug 2)
Scathebury 48 (8f,Edi,GF,Apr 14)
Scattergun 46 (10f,Nwb,S,May 17)
Scenicris (IRE) 46 (7 1/2f,Bev,GF,Apr 5)
Sceptre Lady (IRE) 44 (7f,Nwb,GF,Apr 18)
Schnozzle (IRE) 40 (12 1/2f,War,G,Jun 24)
Scissor Ridge 43 (6f,Nwb,GF,Aug 15)
Scoss 39 (10f,Nwm,S,Jun 27)
Scottish Bambi 41 (10f,Lei,GF,Spt 9)
Sea Dane 55 (6f,Kem,GF,Mar 31)
Sea Danzig 51 (6f,Nwb,GF,May 28)
Sea-Deer 70 (6f,Nwm,G,May 3)
Sea Freedom 56 (14f,Nwm,G,May 16)
Seattle Alley (USA) 52 (10f,Sal,G,Oct 1)
Seattle Art (USA) 36 (12f,Nwm,GS,Jun 11)
Seattle Swing 46 (10f,Chp,G,Spt 11)
Sea Victor 62 (16f,Asc,G,Spt 27)
Secret Aly (CAN) 76 (10f,Kem,GF,Mar 31)
Secret Ballot (IRE) 52 (12f,Lei,S,Oct 13)
Secret Combe (IRE) 41 (7f,Kem,GF,May 31)
Secret Service (IRE) 60 (14f,Hay,GS,May 24)
Secret Spring (FR) 63 (9f,Nwm,GF,Oct 4)
Sedbergh (USA) 54 (14f,Red,GF,May 26)
Seebe (USA) 84 (8f,Lon,S,May 11)
Sekari 64 (8f,Not,GF,Apr 11)
Selberry 43 (10f,Don,GF,Mar 20)
Select Choice (IRE) 37 (7f,Cat,G,Apr 23)
Selfish 53 (8f,Kem,G,May 5)
Selhurstpark Flyer (IRE) 88 (6f,Asc,GS,Jun 20)
Sellette (IRE) 58 (10 1/2f,Hay,GF,Jun 7)
Selmeston (IRE) 33 (16f,Not,S,Oct 15)

Sendoro (IRE) 71 (11f,Lon,G,Apr 6)
Senorita Matilda (USA) 45 (6f,Lin,GF,Jly 11)
Sense of Priority 33 (7f,Cat,G,Mar 26)
Serape 43 (7f,Thi,GF,Apr 19)
Serendipity (FR) 51 (10f,Sal,G,Oct 1)
Serenity 59 (7f,Nwm,GF,Oct 3)
Sergeyev (IRE) 46 (7f,Lei,GS,Apr 26)
Serious Trust 40 (14f,Sal,GF,Aug 21)
Serpentara 41 (10f,Lei,GF,Spt 9)
Severity 47 (7f,Yar,G,Jly 16)
Shabanaz 36 (11 1/2f,Wnd,GF,Jun 9)
Shades of Love 41 (6f,Pon,GF,Jly 18)
Shadiann (IRE) 56 (12f,Bat,G,Jun 28)
Shadirwan (IRE) 59 (17f,Bat,F,Jly 23)
Shadoof 60 (10f,Don,GF,Spt 13)
Shadow Jury 51 (6f,War,F,May 5)
Shaffishayes 53 (12f,Yor,GS,Jun 14)
Shaft of Light 85 (12f,Eps,GS,Aug 25)
Shahboor (USA) 35 (14f,Yar,GF,Aug 6)
Shaheen (USA) 73 (8f,Nwb,GS,May 16)
Shahik (USA) 43 (10f,Wnd,GF,Jly 21)
Shaka 70 (11f,Lon,G,Apr 6)
Shalaal (USA) 63 (7f,Lei,S,Oct 13)
Shalateeno 63 (12f,Eps,G,Spt 5)
Shalstayholy (IRE) 57 (5f,Don,GF,Spt 12)
Shamanic 63 (7f,Nwc,GF,Oct 1)
Shamikh 34 (8f,Nwm,G,May 3)
Shantarskie (IRE) 41 (5f,Bev,GF,Spt 17)
Shantou (USA) 71 (12f,Asc,S,Jly 26)
Sharaf Kabeer 55 (12f,Lei,G,Jun 14)
Sharbadarid (IRE) 60 (10f,Rip,GF,Aug 25)
Share Delight (IRE) 54 (8f,Yor,G,May 15)
Sharemono (USA) 30 (8f,Leo,G,Apr 19)
Shark (IRE) 36 (8f,Rip,GF,Jly 19)
Sharkiyah (IRE) 41 (7f,Nwm,G,Apr 16)
Sharp Consul (IRE) 75 (10f,Nwm,G,May 2)
Sharp Deed (IRE) 38 (8 1/2f,Bev,GF,Jly 15)
Sharp Hat 64 (6f,Yor,GS,Jun 14)
Sharp Imp 49 (7f,Sal,GF,Jun 11)
Sharp 'n' Shady 47 (7f,Don,GS,Jun 28)
Sharp 'n Smart 58 (7f,Fol,G,Mar 26)
Sharpo Wassl 52 (7f,Yar,GF,Jly 28)
Sharp Pearl 68 (5f,Nwm,GF,Aug 23)
Sharp Rebuff 67 (7f,Nwb,GF,May 28)
Sharp Return 33 (7f,Fol,G,Oct 21)
Sharp Shuffle (IRE) 66 (9f,Goo,GF,Jly 31)
Sharp Stock 45 (5f,Goo,GS,May 22)
Sharp Temper 51 (8f,Asc,G,Jun 17)
Sharpwitted 34 (7f,Yar,F,Jun 11)
Shashi (IRE) 41 (7f,Lin,GF,Jun 14)
Shaska 67 (10f,Nwb,GF,Spt 18)
Shavinsky 33 (6f,Not,G,May 23)
Shawaf (USA) 52 (7f,Nwm,G,Apr 15)
Shawm 67 (8f,Hay,G,Spt 21)
Shaya 46 (10f,Asc,G,Jly 25)
Sheep Stealer 47 (10f,Wnd,G,Aug 4)
Sheer Danzig (IRE) 76 (12f,Don,GF,Mar 22)
Sheer Face 62 (8f,San,GF,Spt 16)
Sheilas Dream 33 (11 1/2f,Wnd,GF,Jly 14)
Shell Ginger (IRE) 43 (10f,Cur,GS,May 25)
Sheltering Sky (IRE) 65 (7f,Nwb,GF,Jly 18)
Sheraz (IRE) 33 (7f,Nwc,G,May 5)
Sherqy (IRE) 47 (12 1/2f,Nwc,GF,Aug 6)
Shift Again (IRE) 37 (14f,Not,GF,Oct 4)
Shifting Moon 43 (10f,Bat,F,Jly 23)
Shii-Take 73 (8f,Nwm,G,May 3)
Shinerolla 61 (8f,Nwm,G,Oct 18)
Shining Cloud 51 (6f,Nwm,G,May 3)
Shining Dancer 54 (14f,San,GF,Jly 16)
Shining Example 57 (9f,Goo,G,Jun 13)
Shinko King (IRE) 77 (7f,Stn,GF,Dec 14)
Shirley Sue 58 (20f,Goo,GF,Jly 30)
Shirley Venture 55 (15 1/2f,Fol,GF,Apr 22)
Shock Value (IRE) 65 (7f,Yar,G,Jly 16)
Shontaine 46 (8f,Ham,G,Spt 29)
Shooting Light (IRE) 56 (14f,San,S,Aug 30)
Shooting Star (IRE) 34 (10f,Goo,G,Spt 13)
Shouk 48 (10 1/2f,Hay,S,May 5)
Shoumatara (USA) 41 (7f,Bri,F,Jun 3)
Showboat 52 (7f,Nwm,G,May 4)
Show Faith (IRE) 42 (9f,Goo,GF,Aug 23)
Siberian Mystic 31 (12f,Sal,GF,Aug 13)
Siege Perilous (IRE) 52 (16 1/2f,San,GS,Aug 29)
Signs And Wonders 44 (7f,San,G,May 26)
Sihafi (USA) 35 (7 1/2f,Bev,GF,Jun 4)
Silankka 36 (10f,Bat,G,Jly 7)
Silca Key Silca 66 (6f,Lin,G,Jun 24)
Silence in Court (IRE) 55 (14 1/2f,Don,G,Oct 24)
Silence Reigns 66 (12f,Goo,GF,Jly 29)
Silently 72 (14f,San,GF,Jly 16)
Silent Miracle (IRE) 53 (5f,Nwm,GF,Aug 23)
Silent Valley 32 (10f,Don,GF,Spt 10)
Silk Cottage 39 (5f,Edi,GF,Jly 18)
Silk St John 65 (8f,Kem,G,Spt 21)
Silverani (IRE) 85 (10f,Nwm,GF,Oct 3)
Silver Groom (IRE) 66 (10f,Kem,GF,Mar 31)
Silver Harrow 48 (8f,Bat,G,Spt 8)
Silvering (FR) 41 (7f,Yor,G,Aug 21)
Silver Kristal 48 (7f,Goo,GF,Aug 1)
Silver Lining 45 (7f,Lei,G,Jly 17)
Silver Patriarch (IRE) 91 (12f,Eps,G,Jun 7)
Silver Purse 38 (6f,Nwm,G.Jun 7)
Silver Secret 39 (8f,Lei,G,Aug 11)
Silver Whirl (USA) 49 (10f,Nwb,GF,Spt 18)
Silver Wonder (USA) 35 (12f,Nwm,G,May 16)
Silvery 50 (10f,Goo,G,Spt 13)
Silvretta (IRE) 40 (11 1/2f,Wnd,G,Aug 4)
Simple Logic 35 (7f,Lin,G,Aug 9)
Sing And Dance 32 (10f,Nwc,G,Mar 25)
Single Empire (IRE) 57 (12f,Nwm,G,May 3)
Singspiel (IRE) 90 (10 1/2f,Yor,G,Aug 19)
Sing With the Band 32 (6f,Not,GF,Apr 8)

Sioux 39 (12f,Hay,G,Spt 21)
Siouxrouge 30 (7f,Bri,GF,May 6)
Sipowitz 37 (18f,Pon,GS,Oct 20)
Sir Arthur Hobbs 43 (8f,Thi,F,Jun 2)
Sirinndi (IRE) 36 (16f,Cur,GS,Oct 4)
Sir Joey (USA) 68 (6f,Nwm,G,May 3)
Sir Ricky (USA) 51 (12f,Bat,G,Spt 8)
Sir Talbot 56 (9f,San,GF,Jun 14)
Sir Tasker 35 (6f,Cat,GF,Jly 16)
Sis Garden 48 (8f,Wnd,G,Aug 23)
Six Clerks (IRE) 34 (12f,Cat,GF,May 30)
Six Zero (FR) 58 (12f,Lon,S,May 15)
Siyadah (USA) 68 (10f,Nwm,G,May 4)
Sizzling 40 (6f,Bri,F,Apr 11)
Sky Commander (USA) 56 (10f,Nwm,S,Jun 27)
Sky Dome (IRE) 58 (8f,Don,GF,Mar 22)
Skyers Flyer (IRE) 48 (6f,Cat,G,Jun 6)
Slasher Jack (IRE) 52 (12f,Edi,GS,Nov 6)
Sleepless 48 (7f,Nwb,S,May 17)
Sleepytime (IRE) 73 (8f,Nwm,G,May 4)
Slip Jig (IRE) 57 (12f,Chs,GF,Jly 11)
Slipstream 43 (10f,Nwm,G,Apr 15)
Slipstream Star 30 (9f,Ham,G,Spt 29)
Smarter Charter 66 (7 1/2f,Bev,GF,Apr 11)
Smart Guest 33 (7f,Lei,G,Jly 17)
Smart Kid (IRE) 54 (6f,Sal,GF,May 4)
Smart Play (USA) 56 (11 1/2f,San,GF,Jly 16)
Smart Spirit (IRE) 54 (8f,Nwc,G,May 5)
Smokey From Caplaw 55 (8f,Red,GF,Oct 28)
Snap Crackle Pop (IRE) 38 (5f,San,G,Apr 26)
Snow Kid 74 (6f,Don,S,Nov 8)
Snow Partridge (USA) 53 (12f,Chp,GF,Jly 11)
Snow Princess (IRE) 71 (14 1/2f,Don,GF,Spt 10)
Snowy Mantle 30 (10f,Nwm,G,Aug 1)
Society Rose 42 (10 1/2f,Yor,G,May 13)
Soda Pop (IRE) 48 (12f,Bri,F,Jly 24)
Soden (IRE) 30 (10f,Not,GF,Spt 15)
Sofyaan (USA) 62 (12f,Nwm,GS,Jun 20)
So Intrepid (IRE) 69 (6f,Ayr,G,Spt 20)
Solar Storm 68 (8f,Ayr,G,Spt 20)
Soldier Cove (USA) 45 (8f,Edi,S,Mar 27)
Solfegietto 43 (7f,Red,GS,Jly 26)
Solo Mio (IRE) 78 (12f,Nwm,GS,Oct 16)
Somerton Boy (IRE) 59 (8f,Don,G,Jly 16)
Somerton Reef 41 (7f,Leo,S,Nov 9)
Song Mist (IRE) 49 (7f,Bri,F,Spt 28)
Song of Freedom 72 (10f,Don,GF,Spt 13)
Song of Skye 62 (7f,San,GF,Jly 23)
Song Of The Sword 58 (12f,Hay,S,Mar 29)
Songsheet 58 (5f,Chp,G,Spt 11)
Soojama (IRE) 48 (14f,Nwm,G,May 16)
Sooty Tern 55 (8f,Bat,F,Jly 23)
Sophomore 46 (9f,Goo,G,Jun 12)
Sotonian (HOL) 33 (5f,Not,G,May 17)
Sound Appeal 32 (10f,Sal,S,Jun 26)
Sound the Trumpet (IRE) 39 (7f,Fol,G,Mar 26)
Souperficial 34 (6f,Ham,S,Jly 1)
South China Sea 42 (7f,Nwm,G,Aug 22)
Southerly Wind 57 (8f,Pon,GF,Aug 17)
Southern Dominion 42 (5f,Ayr,S,Oct 14)
Sovereign Crest (IRE) 42 (12f,Bri,F,Jly 24)
Sovereign Page (USA) 44 (11f,War,F,Jun 4)
Sovereigns Court 53 (8f,Not,S,Oct 15)
Soviet Leader 65 (6f,Ayr,G,Spt 20)
Soviet Line (IRE) 81 (8f,Hpk,F,Nov 8)
Soviet State (USA) 76 (6f,Nwb,GF,Jly 19)
Space Race 57 (10f,Bat,F,Jly 23)
Spaniards Close 42 (6f,Bat,G,Aug 7)
Spaniard's Mount 32 (8f,Yar,GS,Jly 3)
Spanish Knot (USA) 49 (7f,Thi,F,Jun 2)
Spanish Verdict 41 (8f,Red,G,May 12)
Sparky 46 (12f,Edi,GF,Spt 15)
Spartan Girl (IRE) 38 (10f,Eps,S,Jly 2)
Spartan Heartbeat 64 (14f,Not,G,Oct 30)
Special-K 42 (8f,Rip,GF,Jly 19)
Speculator (IRE) 60 (8 1/2f,Eps,G,Aug 10)
Speedball (IRE) 73 (7f,Asc,GF,Spt 27)
Speedboat (USA) 37 (7f,Red,F,Spt 26)
Speedfriend (GER) 36 (12f,Cha,G,Jun 1)
Speed On 75 (5f,Nwm,G,Jly 19)
Speedy Classic (USA) 51 (7f,Chp,GF,Jly 25)
Spender 60 (6f,Bat,GF,Jun 14)
Spick And Span 38 (11f,Ayr,GS,Spt 18)
Spinning World (USA) 98 (8f,Hpk,F,Nov 8)
Spirito Libro (USA) 61 (10 1/2f,Yor,G,May 14)
Spotted Eagle 53 (6f,Red,G,May 12)
Spring Marathon (USA) 35 (20f,Asc,G,Jun 17)
Spy Knoll 50 (13 1/2f,Chs,G,Spt 24)
Squared Away 36 (8f,War,GF,May 24)
Square Mile Miss (IRE) 30 (8f,Pon,GF,Apr 16)
Squeak 95 (9f,Lon,GF,Oct 5)
Squire Corrie 77 (5f,Cat,S,Oct 17)
Stackattack (IRE) 65 (7 1/2f,Bev,GS,Aug 13)
Stage Affair (USA) 51 (14f,Cur,S,Spt 20)
Stahr 35 (12f,Fol,GF,Jly 14)
Stakis Casinos Boy (IRE) 50 (12f,Pon,GF,Jun 3)
Stalled (IRE) 44 (11f,Ham,GS,Jly 4)
Standown 42 (6f,Red,G,May 12)
Stand Tall 63 (6f,Hay,G,Spt 21)
Stanton Harcourt (USA) 71 (8f,Nwm,GF,Nov 1)
Starborough 96 (8f,Asc,G,Jun 17)
Star Entry 42 (10f,Fol,G,Oct 21)
Star Gambit (USA) 38 (8f,Nwb,S,Spt 19)
Star Invader 43 (7f,Lei,S,Oct 13)
Star Manager (USA) 77 (8f,San,GF,Apr 25)
Star of Ring (IRE) 54 (7f,Thi,GF,Apr 19)
Star Precision 67 (12f,Chp,G,May 26)
Star Profile (IRE) 68 (8f,Lon,S,May 11)
Star Rage (IRE) 72 (16f,Asc,G,Spt 27)
Star Selection 65 (11f,Ayr,G,Spt 20)
Star Talent (USA) 78 (8 1/2f,Eps,G,Jun 6)
Star Turn (IRE) 51 (8f,Lei,S,Oct 13)

Statajack (IRE) 56 (12f,Chp,G,Aug 25)
State Approval 47 (11 1/2f,Wnd,GF,Jun 2)
State Fair 71 (15f,Nwm,GF,Jly 10)
State of Caution 55 (6f,Hay,G,Spt 21)
Statoyork 56 (7f,Lin,F,Apr 4)
St Blaine (CAN) 50 (7f,Fol,S,Jun 27)
Steamroller Stanly 64 (12f,Don,GF,Spt 12)
Stellar Line (USA) 51 (8f,Rip,GF,May 28)
Stephensons Rocket 41 (6f,Not,GF,Apr 21)
Step N Go (IRE) 45 (10f,Pon,G,May 23)
Step On Degas 43 (8f,Goo,G,Spt 12)
Steward (FR) 80 (12f,Lon,GF,Oct 5)
Stilett (IRE) 46 (8f,Nwm,GF,Jly 10)
St Lawrence (CAN) 39 (14f,Yor,S,Spt 3)
Stolen Kiss (IRE) 46 (5f,Bev,GF,Jly 15)
Stonecutter 39 (15 1/2f,Fol,F,Apr 10)
Stoned Imaculate (IRE) 38 (16f,Not,GF,Spt 23)
Stone Flower (USA) 61 (10f,Don,GF,Spt 10)
Stone Ridge (IRE) 74 (8f,San,GF,Apr 25)
Stoppes Brow 66 (7f,Nwb,GF,May 28)
Stormless 50 (10f,Nwc,GF,Oct 22)
Stormy Story (USA) 34 (10f,Wnd,G,Aug 4)
Story Line 67 (16f,Asc,G,Spt 27)
Storyteller (IRE) 32 (6f,Red,F,Spt 26)
Stowaway 79 (10f,Don,G,May 24)
St Radegund 52 (7f,Goo,GS,May 21)
Strategic Choice (USA) 75 (10 1/2f,Lon,S,Apr 27)
Strathmore Clear 56 (8f,War,GF,Apr 12)
Strat's Quest 43 (6f,Wnd,S,May 12)
Strawberry Roan (IRE) 50 (8f,Leo,YS,May 11)
Strazo (IRE) 78 (9f,Nwb,GF,Jly 19)
Street General 57 (12f,Nwm,G,Apr 15)
Stretarez (FR) 78 (15 1/2f,Lon,S,May 18)
Struggler 88 (5f,Dea,G,Aug 3)
Stuffed 48 (5f,Yor,G,May 14)
Sturgeon (IRE) 48 (10f,Wnd,G,Aug 4)
Style Dancer (IRE) 53 (7f,Hay,G,Spt 27)
Stylish Ways (IRE) 43 (7f,Cat,S,Oct 17)
Sualtach (IRE) 63 (8f,Red,GF,Oct 28)
Sublime Beauty (USA) 63 (10f,Cur,GS,May 25)
Such Boldness 33 (12f,Eps,GS,Jly 9)
Sudest (IRE) 45 (12f,Bat,GF,Jun 14)
Suedoro 32 (5f,Ham,GF,Jly 11)
Sue Me (IRE) 48 (5f,Nwc,GF,Oct 22)
Sue's Return 69 (8f,Goo,GF,Jly 29)
Suez Tornado (IRE) 67 (8f,Nwm,G,Jly 8)
Suga Hawk (IRE) 54 (12f,Chs,GF,Jly 11)
Sugarfoot 66 (8f,Asc,S,Jun 21)
Sugar Mill 73 (12f,Hay,S,Mar 29)
Suile Mor 36 (8f,Chp,GS,Jly 1)
Suite Factors 41 (6f,Bat,G,Spt 8)
Suivez 32 (10 1/2f,Hay,G,Jly 5)
Summer Dance 63 (10f,Nwb,GF,Spt 18)
Summerhill Special (IRE) 62 (11f,Ayr,GS,Spt 18)
Summerosa (USA) 49 (7f,Hay,GS,Jly 3)
Summer Queen 43 (7f,Nwm,G,Apr 15)
Sun Alert (USA) 40 (12f,Yor,GS,Jun 13)
Sunbeam Dance (USA) 68 (11f,Nwb,GF,Spt 18)
Sun Mark (IRE) 49 (12f,Ham,S,Jun 25)
Sunny Isle 45 (10 1/2f,Hay,S,Oct 15)
Sunny Lane (AUS) 89 (12f,Stn,GF,Dec 14)
Sun of Spring 52 (11f,Ham,GS,Jly 4)
Sunset Reigns (IRE) 38 (5f,Cur,G,Jly 13)
Superbelle 30 (11 1/2f,Yar,GF,Spt 16)
Super Benz 48 (7f,Thi,G,May 16)
Superbit 58 (5f,Hay,G,Jly 4)
Supercal 76 (8f,Dea,G,Aug 3)
Superior Force 41 (8f,Goo,GS,May 21)
Superior Premium 77 (6f,Ayr,G,Spt 20)
Superlao (BEL) 34 (5f,War,GF,Jly 19)
Super Monarch 52 (8f,Nwm,G,May 4)
Superpride 45 (7f,Ayr,S,May 21)
Super Scravels 35 (7f,Fol,GF,Jly 14)
Super Serenade 30 (10f,Bri,GF,Spt 3)
Supply And Demand 78 (10f,Goo,GF,Aug 1)
Supreme Sound 46 (10f,Bri,F,Spt 28)
Supreme Thought 50 (6f,Sal,GS,Aug 8)
Supremism 38 (8f,Nwm,GF,May 31)
Surf City 48 (7f,Cat,GF,May 31)
Surgeon 65 (12f,Cha,S,Jun 8)
Surprise Mission 70 (5f,Asc,Hy,Oct 11)
Surtsey 36 (10f,Lei,F,Apr 3)
Sushi Bar (IRE) 31 (12f,Ham,G,Spt 1)
Swain (IRE) 97 (12f,Lon,GF,Oct 5)
Swan At Whalley 51 (5f,Chs,S,Aug 30)
Swan Hunter 58 (14f,Hay,GS,May 24)
Swan Island 37 (8f,Bat,GF,Spt 29)
Sweet Contralto 61 (9f,Goo,GF,Aug 22)
Sweet Fortune (USA) 47 (8f,Kem,G,Spt 21)
Sweet Glow (FR) 33 (14f,Not,GF,Apr 11)
Sweet Magic 51 (5f,Goo,G,Spt 24)
Sweet Mate 37 (6f,Not,G,May 9)
Sweetness Herself 73 (16f,Nwc,Hy,Jun 28)
Sweet Wilhelmina 62 (8f,Nwb,GS,Spt 20)
Swift 48 (8f,Nwm,G,Aug 2)
Swift Gulliver (IRE) 89 (6f,Asc,GF,Spt 27)
Swift Sovereign 34 (7f,Hay,GS,May 24)
Swiftway 38 (10f,Don,GF,Mar 21)
Swinging The Blues (IRE) 40 (8f,Goo,G,Spt 12)
Swing West (USA) 40 (8f,Kem,G,May 24)
Swino 54 (5f,Red,GF,Oct 18)
Swiss Law 73 (8f,Asc,G,Jun 17)
Sword Arm 60 (8f,Bat,GF,Jly 17)
Swynford Dream 56 (5f,Yor,G,May 14)
Sycamore Boy (USA) 33 (8f,Hay,G,Spt 21)
Sycamore Lodge (IRE) 43 (6f,Rip,G,Aug 30)
Sylvan Dancer (IRE) 44 (6f,Sal,GS,Aug 8)
Sylvan Princess 59 (8f,Asc,GF,Apr 30)
Sylva Paradise (IRE) 92 (6f,Nwm,G,Apr 15)
Symboli Kildare (IRE) 41 (5f,Cur,G,Jly 13)
Symonds Inn 69 (12f,Eps,G,Jun 7)

Tabasco Jazz 36 (7f,Thi,GF,May 3)
Taberann (IRE) 51 (10f,Ayr,S,Oct 14)
Tadeo 81 (5f,Nwm,G,Jly 19)
Tael of Silver 35 (7f,Cat,GF,Spt 20)
Taffs Well 61 (7f,San,GF,Spt 17)
Tailwind 34 (6f,Crl,GF,Jun 25)
Taipan (IRE) 62 (10f,Cur,GS,May 25)
Tajar (USA) 33 (10f,San,GF,Spt 16)
Tajrebah (USA) 46 (7f,Lin,GF,Jun 14)
Takhlid (USA) 62 (7f,Fol,GF,Jun 4)
Talib (USA) 32 (8f,Yar,F,Spt 18)
Tallulah Belle 57 (10f,Bev,GF,Apr 24)
Tal-Y-Llyn (IRE) 44 (7f,Nwb,S,May 18)
Tamarpour (USA) 50 (20f,Asc,G,Jun 17)
Tamayaz (CAN) 68 (10 1/2f,Hay,GF,Aug 9)
Tamure (IRE) 62 (12f,Don,S,Nov 8)
Tanaasa (IRE) 62 (11 1/2f,Lin,S,May 10)
Tango King 42 (12f,Pon,GF,Jun 3)
Tangshan (CAN) 35 (8f,Bat,GF,May 30)
Taoiste 54 (5f,San,GF,Jly 16)
Tappeto 50 (14f,San,G,Aug 13)
Taragona 32 (7 1/2f,Bev,S,Jun 11)
Tarator (USA) 79 (15 1/2f,Lon,S,Apr 27)
Tarry 49 (12f,Nwm,GF,Oct 31)
Tarski 39 (9f,Yor,S,Spt 4)
Tart (FR) 44 (12f,Fol,G,Jly 9)
Tart and a Half 59 (5f,Rip,G,Jun 19)
Tarxien 49 (12f,Lei,S,Oct 13)
Tashiriya (IRE) 46 (9f,Lon,S,Apr 27)
Tasik Chini (USA) 35 (12 1/2f,War,GF,Jun 9)
Tassili (IRE) 50 (8 1/2f,Bev,GF,Jun 5)
Taswib (USA) 47 (10f,Lei,F,Apr 3)
Tatika 55 (8f,Nwb,G,Jun 12)
Taufan Boy 51 (14f,Not,GF,Oct 4)
Taufan's Melody 85 (12f,Asc,GF,Spt 28)
Taunt 80 (12f,Don,S,Nov 8)
Tawafek (USA) 55 (16f,Asc,G,Spt 27)
Tayovullin (IRE) 31 (7f,Lei,G,Jly 23)
Tayseer (USA) 68 (7f,Asc,GF,Jun 18)
Tea Party (USA) 40 (7f,Goo,GS,Jun 20)
Tear White (IRE) 49 (5f,Goo,G,Spt 24)
Technicolour (IRE) 31 (11 1/2f,San,GF,Jly 16)
Tedburrow 87 (5f,Asc,GF,Spt 28)
Telemania (IRE) 64 (8f,Goo,GF,Jly 29)
Tellion 34 (12f,Fol,GF,Jly 14)
Teme Valley 54 (11 1/2f,Lin,G,Spt 9)
Tempting Prospect 47 (12f,Asc,GF,Spt 28)
Temptress 61 (10 1/2f,Yor,G,May 14)
Ten Past Six 46 (10f,Rip,G,Apr 26)
Tenuous 88 (9f,Lon,GF,Oct 5)
Teofilio (IRE) 71 (8f,Asc,G,Jun 17)
Terdad (USA) 51 (8f,Red,G,Jun 21)
Tertium (IRE) 66 (7f,Nwc,Hy,Jun 28)
Tessajoe 65 (12f,Cat,GF,Spt 20)
Test The Water (IRE) 43 (7 1/2f,Chs,S,May 6)
Texas Cowgirl (IRE) 41 (6f,Fol,GF,Jun 4)
Tezaab 33 (8f,Lei,G,Jly 23)
Thaljanah (IRE) 67 (14f,Yor,GS,Jun 13)
Thatched (IRE) 42 (7 1/2f,Bev,GF,Jly 21)
Thatchmaster (IRE) 59 (10f,Goo,GF,Aug 23)
That Man Again 67 (5f,Nwc,GF,Oct 1)
Theano (IRE) 58 (8f,Nwm,GF,Jly 9)
Theatreworld (IRE) 53 (16f,Cur,GS,Oct 4)
The Barnsley Belle (IRE) 30 (7f,Don,GS,Jun 28)
The Bower (IRE) 35 (8f,Cur,GS,Jun 27)
The Butterwick Kid 45 (12f,Edi,G,Jun 16)
The Dilettanti (USA) 83 (10f,Nwm,G,May 3)
The Executor 53 (10f,Goo,GF,Aug 23)
The Faraway Tree 73 (12f,Yor,G,Aug 21)
The Fly 76 (12f,Eps,G,Jun 7)
The Flying Phantom 44 (14f,Yar,GF,Aug 6)
The Frisky Farmer 44 (7f,Thi,G,May 16)
The Fugative 52 (5f,Fol,G,Jly 9)
The Gay Fox 62 (6f,Ayr,G,Spt 20)
The Green Grey 38 (8f,Bat,GF,Spt 29)
The Happy Fox (IRE) 47 (6f,Pon,G,Jly 8)
The In-Laws (IRE) 65 (10f,Red,GF,Oct 18)
The Lambton Worm 46 (6f,Nwc,Hy,Jun 28)
Theme Arena 42 (16f,Not,S,Oct 15)
The Negotiator 30 (7f,Kem,GF,Mar 31)
The Prince 66 (8f,Kem,G,Spt 21)
The Puzzler (IRE) 65 (5f,Nwm,GS,Oct 16)
Therhea (IRE) 68 (8f,Asc,GF,Spt 28)
The Roundsills 31 (12f,Cat,GF,Jly 16)
The Stager (IRE) 42 (8f,War,GF,Oct 7)
The Wad 46 (5f,War,GS,Aug 25)
The West (USA) 42 (7f,Nwb,GF,Apr 19)
The Wyandotte Inn 37 (7 1/2f,Bev,GF,Apr 24)
Thick as Thieves 33 (6f,Cat,G,Apr 23)
Third Party 41 (6f,Bri,F,Jun 3)
Thisonesforalice 35 (11f,Ayr,GF,Jly 14)
Thornby Park 61 (16f,Asc,G,Spt 27)
Three Arch Bridge 58 (8f,Rip,GF,May 28)
Three Cheers (IRE) 80 (15f,Lon,G,Oct 4)
Three For A Pound 46 (7f,Cat,S,Jly 3)
Thunderheart 38 (13f,Ham,G,Jun 11)
Thwaab 51 (6f,Lin,GF,May 31)
Tiger Lake 41 (12f,Asc,Hy,Oct 10)
Tigrello 65 (8f,Asc,G,Jun 17)
Tikopia 56 (12f,Goo,GF,Aug 22)
Tiler (IRE) 68 (6f,Ayr,G,Spt 20)
Time Allowed 72 (12f,Nwm,G,May 2)
Time Can Tell 39 (8f,Lei,G,Aug 20)
Time for Action (IRE) 69 (10f,Don,G,Oct 25)
Time For Tea (IRE) 32 (6f,War,F,May 5)
Time of Night (USA) 43 (8f,Not,G,May 23)
Time To Tango 42 (5f,Red,F,May 1)
Tinker Amelia 36 (6f,Cur,S,Oct 18)
Tinker Osmaston 54 (5f,San,GS,Aug 29)
Tinklers Folly 38 (10f,Pon,GF,Jun 9)
Tipperary Sunset (IRE) 50 (8f,Don,GS,Nov 8)
Tipsy Creek (USA) 67 (5f,Nwb,GF,Spt 18)

Tissue of Lies (USA) 46 (13f,Ham,GS,Jun 18)
Tithcar 46 (5f,Edi,GF,Aug 20)
Titta Ruffo 64 (10f,Nwm,GF,Oct 3)
Titus Livius (FR) 96 (5f,Asc,GS,Jun 20)
Toi Toi (IRE) 49 (10f,Chp,GS,Jly 1)
Token Gesture (IRE) 65 (10f,Cur,GS,May 25)
Tomba 78 (6f,Nwc,Hy,Jun 28)
Tommy Tempest 30 (5f,Wnd,GF,Jly 14)
Tommy Tortoise 41 (14f,Yar,G,Jun 23)
Tom Tailor (GER) 44 (12f,Lei,S,Oct 13)
Tonight's Prize (IRE) 51 (10f,San,GF,Spt 16)
Tonka 51 (10f,Not,G,May 9)
Tonnerre 54 (10½f,Yor,S,Spt 4)
Top 32 (12f,Thi,G,Aug 1)
Topatori (IRE) 45 (10f,Ayr,GS,Spt 19)
Top Banana 67 (6f,Nwm,G,May 3)
Top Cees 72 (14f,Goo,GF,Jly 29)
Top Jem 49 (10f,Nwc,Hy,Jun 28)
Top of The Form (IRE) 49 (5f,Chs,G,Spt 24)
Top Shelf 36 (10f,Yar,F,Jun 11)
Topton (IRE) 62 (6f,Fol,G,Oct 21)
Torch Vert (IRE) 53 (17f,Bat,GF,Spt 29)
Toronto 32 (5f,Edi,GF,May 31)
Totem Dancer 59 (12f,Ham,G,Spt 29)
To the Roof (IRE) 90 (6f,Asc,GS,Jun 20)
Tough Act 55 (10f,Goo,G,Spt 13)
Tough Leader 51 (7½f,Bev,GF,Apr 24)
Toujours Riviera 64 (8f,Nwm,G,Jly 8)
Tout A Coup (IRE) 48 (10f,Cur,GS,Jun 28)
Traceability 59 (10f,San,GF,Jly 30)
Trading Aces 46 (7f,War,F,May 5)
Tramline 70 (15f,Nwm,GS,Jun 11)
Transom (USA) 70 (20f,Goo,GF,Jly 30)
Travelmate 44 (12f,Nwm,GS,Jun 20)
Treasure Touch (IRE) 57 (6f,Not,GF,Apr 11)
Tregaron (USA) 84 (7f,Asc,GF,Spt 27)
Tremplin (USA) 55 (10½f,Hay,G,Jly 5)
Tribal Moon (IRE) 36 (10f,Wnd,GF,Jun 16)
Tribal Peace (IRE) 49 (9f,Goo,GF,Jly 31)
Trilby 47 (13f,Ham,GS,Jun 18)
Triple Hay 69 (6f,Goo,GF,Aug 2)
Triple Leap 34 (10½f,Hay,G,Spt 21)
Trojan Hero (SAF) 58 (8f,Lei,GF,Jun 2)
Trojan Risk 49 (10f,Goo,GS,Jun 20)
Trojan Sea (USA) 43 (10½f,Lon,S,Apr 27)
Trooper 33 (12f,Fol,GF,Jly 14)
Tropical Beach 51 (5f,Crl,G,Jly 5)
True Glory (IRE) 51 (10f,Don,GS,Jun 28)
Trying Times (IRE) 42 (11f,Ayr,GF,Jly 14)
Tsarnista 57 (8f,Goo,G,May 22)
Tudor Island 48 (14f,San,GF,Jly 16)
Tulipa (USA) 70 (12f,Hay,G,Jly 5)
Tulsa (IRE) 48 (8f,Lei,S,Oct 13)
Tumbleweed Pearl 49 (7f,Asc,GF,Jun 18)
Tumbleweed Ridge 78 (7f,Yar,G,Jly 16)
Turgenev (IRE) 68 (14f,Yor,S,Spt 3)
Turnpole (IRE) 66 (16f,Chs,G,Spt 24)
Tuscan Dawn 59 (5f,Lin,GF,Jly 10)
Twice as Sharp 70 (5f,Nwb,GF,Aug 16)
Twilight Sleep (USA) 52 (12f,Chs,GF,Jly 11)
Twin Creeks 50 (7f,San,GF,Spt 17)
Twin Time 43 (8f,Not,GF,Aug 6)
Two On The Bridge 34 (6f,Thi,G,Jun 17)
Two Socks 49 (12f,Bat,G,Aug 12)
Tycooness (IRE) 54 (14f,Not,G,Oct 30)
Tycoon Girl (IRE) 54 (7f,War,F,May 5)
Tycoon Tina 31 (9f,Ayr,S,Oct 13)
Tycoon Todd (USA) 60 (8f,Nwm,G,May 3)
Tykeyvor (IRE) 69 (14½f,Don,GF,Spt 10)
Tymeera 47 (6f,War,F,May 5)
Typhoon Eight (IRE) 56 (10f,San,GF,May 26)
Tyrolean Dream (IRE) 52 (12f,Lei,S,Oct 13)

Ukraine Venture 57 (10f,San,GF,Apr 25)
Ultimate Smoothie 52 (14f,Hay,GF,Aug 9)
Ultra Beet 37 (5f,Crl,G,Jly 5)
Ultra Boy 54 (8f,Rip,GF,May 28)
Unchanged 55 (15½f,Fol,F,Spt 26)
Uncle Doug 35 (16f,Cat,GF,Spt 20)
Unconditional Love (IRE) 77 (8½f,Eps,G,Jun 6)
Undercover Agent (IRE) 59 (7f,War,F,May 5)
Union Town (IRE) 73 (10½f,Yor,GS,Jun 14)
U-No-Harry (IRE) 42 (5f,Chs,GF,Jun 4)
Unshaken 32 (7f,Nwm,GS,Jun 20)
Up in Flames (IRE) 35 (8f,Not,G,Jun 18)
Upper Mount Clair 41 (15f,War,GF,Apr 12)
Urgent Reply (USA) 42 (10f,Lin,S,May 10)
Urgent Swift 70 (12f,Goo,GF,Aug 22)
Ursa Major 38 (7f,Goo,GS,Spt 13)
Utmost Zeal (USA) 41 (8f,Bat,G,May 19)

Vagabond Chanteuse 67 (10f,Nwm,G,May 4)
Vain Tempest 51 (12f,Hay,G,Spt 21)
Valagalore 52 (14f,Hay,GF,Aug 9)
Valedictory 80 (12f,Nwm,G,May 4)
Val's Prince (USA) 98 (9f,Stn,GF,Dec 14)
Vanadium Ore 38 (10f,Red,G,Nov 4)
Vanborough Lad 31 (8f,Wnd,GS,Jun 30)
Van Chino 39 (7f,Lei,S,Oct 13)
Van Gurp 63 (7f,Chs,GF,Jun 4)
Vanishing Trick (USA) 56 (9f,Goo,GF,Jly 30)
Varnishing Day (IRE) 36 (7f,Nwm,GF,Aug 9)
Varxi (FR) 65 (9f,Lon,S,May 15)
Vasari (IRE) 50 (5f,Chs,S,May 6)
Vax Star 30 (5f,Nwc,G,Jly 26)
Veiled Threat (IRE) 89 (9f,Lon,GF,Oct 5)
Veni Vidi Vici (IRE) 53 (8f,Kem,GF,Spt 22)
Venture Capitalist 68 (6f,Yor,G,Aug 19)
Verdi (IRE) 39 (6f,Sal,GF,May 4)
Vereva (IRE) 93 (10½f,Cha,S,Jun 8)
Verglas (IRE) 52 (12f,Cur,GS,Jun 29)
Veridian 66 (12f,Don,G,May 24)

Vernoy (USA) 89 (7f,Lon,,Jun 22)
Veronica Franco 46 (12f,Nwm,GF,Oct 31)
Versatility 30 (10f,Red,G,Nov 4)
Vertical Speed (FR) 51 (14½f,Don,GF,Spt 13)
Via Verbano (IRE) 67 (10f,Cur,GS,Aug 16)
Viburnum 34 (14f,Not,S,Oct 15)
Vicious Circle 42 (10f,Pon,GF,Jun 3)
Vicki Romara 44 (12f,Thi,GS,May 17)
Victory Team (IRE) 59 (7f,Nwb,G,Oct 24)
Village Native (FR) 42 (5f,Goo,GS,May 22)
Villarica (IRE) 37 (7½f,Chs,GF,Jly 11)
Vintage Escape (IRE) 32 (7f,Cur,GS,Jun 28)
V I P Charlie 35 (6f,Wnd,G,Jly 7)
Virtual Reality 69 (10f,Nwm,G,May 2)
Viscoumtess Brave (IRE) 32 (10f,Nwb,G,Jun 12)
Visionary (FR) 81 (10f,Lon,G,Oct 4)
Viva Verdi (IRE) 43 (8f,Not,GF,Aug 6)
Vivo (IRE) 34 (8f,Cur,GS,Jun 27)
Voila Premiere (IRE) 54 (12f,Don,G,May 24)
Vola Via (USA) 64 (11f,War,GF,Apr 12)
Volley (IRE) 64 (7f,War,GF,Jly 19)
Voyagers Quest (USA) 67 (10f,San,GS,Apr 26)
Vrennan 32 (10½f,Hay,GS,May 24)

Waders Dream (IRE) 32 (7f,Crl,F,Aug 27)
Wafir (IRE) 72 (10f,Don,GF,Spt 13)
Wahiba Sands 75 (12f,Don,GF,Spt 12)
Waikiki Beach (USA) 54 (8f,Chp,G,Aug 3)
Waiting Game (IRE) 51 (9f,Rip,GF,Apr 9)
Wakeel (USA) 70 (12f,Eps,G,Aug 10)
Walkabout 36 (14f,Nwm,GF,May 31)
Walk the Beat 52 (7f,Don,G,May 24)
Warbler 74 (15f,Lon,G,Oct 4)
Wardara 38 (5f,Lon,S,May 11)
Warm Spell 46 (10f,Pon,G,Jly 8)
Warning Express 35 (6f,Fol,G,Oct 21)
Warningford 50 (8f,Don,G,Jly 31)
Warning Reef 48 (17f,Pon,GF,Apr 22)
Warning Time 87 (6f,Asc,GS,Jun 20)
Warren Knight 36 (9f,Goo,G,Jun 13)
Warring 33 (7f,War,F,May 5)
Warrior King (IRE) 41 (8f,Lei,S,Oct 13)
Wasp Ranger (USA) 70 (7f,Eps,G,Jun 7)
Watch Me (IRE) 31 (5f,Bat,GF,Apr 29)
Watch The Fire 57 (6f,Not,GF,Spt 15)
Water Flower 46 (12f,Nwm,GF,Oct 2)
Waterspout (USA) 30 (10f,Red,GF,Oct 18)
Waterwave (USA) 51 (10f,Ayr,S,Oct 14)
Wathbat Nashwan 53 (10½f,Hay,G,Jly 5)
Waypoint 77 (7f,Nwb,GF,Jly 18)
Wee Dram 35 (7f,Nwm,G,Apr 15)
Weet-A-Minute (IRE) 77 (7f,Yor,G,Aug 21)
Weet Ees Girl (IRE) 31 (5f,Cat,G,Apr 23)
Weetman's Weigh (IRE) 69 (7f,Thi,F,Jun 2)
Welcome Heights 45 (7f,Chp,G,Spt 11)
Welcome Home 32 (7f,Sal,GS,Jun 25)
Wellaki (USA) 48 (10½f,Yor,G,Oct 8)
Well Armed (IRE) 34 (10f,Nwc,GF,May 5)
Wellcome Inn 31 (14f,Red,F,Aug 23)
Well Drawn 37 (7f,Chp,GF,Jly 25)
Wellspring (IRE) 64 (6f,Nwm,S,Jun 27)
Well Warned 50 (7f,Red,GF,Oct 7)
Welsh Mill (IRE) 65 (14f,Hay,S,May 5)
Welsh Mountain 34 (8f,Yar,GF,Aug 6)
Welsh Queen (IRE) 40 (8f,Leo,YS,May 11)
Welton Arsenal 70 (8f,Kem,G,May 5)
Welville 38 (7f,Hay,S,May 5)
Wentbridge Lad (IRE) 48 (10f,Bri,F,Aug 16)
Wesley's Lad (IRE) 34 (14f,Not,S,Jly 5)
Westcourt Magic 77 (5f,Chs,S,Aug 30)
Western General 47 (9f,Ham,S,Jly 1)
Western Hour (USA) 34 (10f,Nwb,G,Jun 12)
Western Sonata (IRE) 34 (8f,Don,G,May 6)
West Humble 51 (7f,Lin,G,May 10)
Westminster (IRE) 52 (10f,Wnd,GF,Jly 28)
What A Fuss 44 (11½f,Yar,G,Jly 16)
Whatever's Right (IRE) 52 (10f,Wnd,GF,Jly 28)
What Happened Was 41 (8f,Nwm,G,Jly 8)
Whenby (USA) 90 (7f,Lon,,Jun 22)
Whirlawhile (USA) 35 (10f,Bat,GS,May 19)
Whispering Dawn 47 (10f,Bat,GF,Jly 17)
Whitechapel (USA) 69 (12f,Asc,Hy,Oct 10)
White Emir 71 (6f,Nwb,GF,May 28)
White Plains (IRE) 62 (12f,Eps,G,Apr 23)
White Settler 52 (7f,Sal,GF,Jun 11)
Whitewater Affair 82 (12f,Yor,G,Aug 20)
Whitley Grange Boy 42 (10f,Nwc,G,Mar 25)
Whittle Rock 47 (8f,Pon,G,May 23)
Whizz Kid 32 (5f,Bat,GF,Apr 29)
Who's That Man 34 (10f,Bri,F,Jly 16)
Wijara (IRE) 61 (11½f,Wnd,G,Aug 23)
Wilawander 66 (12f,Don,GF,Mar 22)
Wilcuma 72 (10f,Kem,G,Spt 21)
Wild Event (USA) 80 (8f,Hpk,F,Nov 8)
Wild Palm 51 (7f,Goo,GS,May 22)
Wild Rice 53 (7f,Nwm,G,Apr 16)
Wild Rita 66 (12f,Eps,G,Apr 23)
Wild Sky (IRE) 60 (7f,Nwm,GF,Nov 1)
Wildwood Flower 79 (6f,Ayr,G,Spt 20)
Wilkins 48 (16f,Goo,GF,Spt 25)
Will Do 48 (6f,Not,GF,Apr 8)
William's Well 43 (5f,Crl,G,Jun 26)
Willie Conquer 71 (12f,Don,S,Nov 8)
Willow Dale (IRE) 61 (6f,Eps,S,Jly 2)
Will To Win 36 (5f,Chp,G,Spt 11)
Will You Dance 40 (12f,Hay,GF,Aug 8)
Wind Cheetah (USA) 63 (7f,Asc,GF,Jun 18)
Windrush Boy 42 (5f,War,GF,Jly 19)
Windrush Holly 33 (10f,Wnd,GF,Jun 2)
Windsor Castle 69 (16f,Asc,GF,Jun 18)
Windswept (IRE) 33 (8f,Wnd,G,Aug 23)
Windy Treat (USA) 42 (7f,Nwm,GF,Aug 9)

Winged Hussar 58 (16f,Leo,S,Nov 9)
Winnebago 40 (13f,Ham,G,Aug 13)
Winsome Wooster 56 (7f,San,GF,Jly 30)
Winston 38 (8f,Ham,G,Spt 29)
Winter Garden 74 (15f,Nwm,GF,Jly 10)
Winter Romance 75 (8f,Yor,G,May 14)
Winter Scout (USA) 43 (7f,Crl,G,Jly 5)
Wishing Stone (USA) 64 (10f,Nwb,GF,Spt 18)
Witchfinder (USA) 45 (8f,Lei,S,Oct 13)
Witching Hour (IRE) 49 (8f,Asc,GF,Apr 30)
With A Will 30 (8f,Chp,G,Aug 3)
With Fire (USA) 57 (12f,Lon,S,May 15)
Without Friends (IRE) 32 (6f,Bri,F,Apr 11)
Wixim (USA) 94 (9f,Stn,GF,Dec 14)
Wizard King 90 (7f,Nwc,G,Jly 26)
Wolf Mountain 53 (6f,Yar,GF,Aug 10)
Woodbeck 57 (8f,Don,G,Jly 30)
Woodren (USA) 57 (12f,Hay,G,Jly 5)
Woody's Boy (IRE) 40 (11^{1}/2f,Wnd,G,Aug 4)
World Premier 83 (6f,Yor,G,May 13)
Worldwide Elsie (USA) 47 (10f,Bev,GF,Apr 24)
Wot No Fax 44 (12f,Eps,G,Apr 23)
Wray (IRE) 30 (10f,Cur,G,May 3)

Xenophon of Cunaxa (IRE) 40 (7f,Nwm,S,Jun 28)
Xylem (USA) 58 (8f,Nwc,GF,Oct 1)

Yabint El Sultan 67 (10f,Nwb,GF,Spt 18)
Yak Alfaraj 36 (12f,Chp,G,May 26)
Yalaietanee 64 (7f,Nwb,GF,Apr 19)
Yalta (IRE) 70 (8f,Kem,G,Spt 21)
Ya Malak 88 (5f,Eps,G,Jun 7)
Yarob (IRE) 45 (10f,Eps,G,Spt 5)
Yashmak (USA) 75 (12f,Eps,G,Jun 6)
Yavlensky (IRE) 43 (10f,San,GS,Apr 26)
Yeast 37 (8f,Don,GF,Mar 20)
Yeoman Oliver 46 (8f,Not,G,Nov 3)
Yet Again 42 (12f,Chp,GF,Aug 3)
Yokohama (USA) 72 (12f,Lon,GF,Oct 5)
Yorkie George 74 (7f,Yar,G,Jly 16)
Yorkshire (IRE) 64 (10^{1}/2f,Yor,G,May 14)
Youdontsay 70 (6f,Lin,S,May 10)
Young Ben (IRE) 30 (5f,Cat,GF,Jly 23)
Young Bigwig (IRE) 63 (6f,Hay,G,Spt 21)
Young Duke (IRE) 31 (8f,Sal,GS,Jun 25)
Young Precedent 57 (7f,Nwb,GF,Aug 16)
Your Most Welcome 51 (10f,Wnd,GF,Jly 28)
Yours In Sport 30 (8f,Rip,GF,Apr 9)
Yxenery (IRE) 56 (10f,Lon,S,May 18)

Zaahir (IRE) 32 (7f,Don,GF,Mar 21)
Zafarabad (IRE) 56 (10f,Leo,G,Apr 19)
Zafarelli 33 (15^{1}/2f,Fol,S,Jly 2)
Zahran (IRE) 30 (7f,Fol,GF,May 28)
Za-Im 64 (6f,Nwb,GF,Jly 19)
Zaima (IRE) 66 (7f,Goo,G,May 20)
Zalitzine (USA) 54 (9f,Nwb,GS,Oct 25)
Zamalek (USA) 39 (8f,San,G,Aug 13)
Zamindar (USA) 86 (8f,Nwm,G,May 3)
Zankle (USA) 66 (9f,Nwm,GF,Oct 4)
Zaralaska 89 (10f,Goo,GF,Jly 29)
Zaretski 47 (7f,Nwm,GF,Oct 4)
Zelda Zonk 65 (7f,Red,G,May 12)
Zenith Rose (FR) 59 (10^{1}/2f,Lon,S,May 11)
Zermatt (IRE) 43 (9f,Nwb,GF,Jly 19)
Zerpour (IRE) 60 (12f,Don,G,Oct 25)
Zidac 55 (10f,Lin,GF,Jun 14)
Ziggy's Dancer (USA) 64 (6f,Ayr,G,Spt 20)
Zinzari (FR) 49 (10f,Pon,GF,Jun 3)
Zoom Up (IRE) 69 (10f,Nwm,GF,Spt 30)
Zorba 54 (9f,Ayr,S,Oct 13)
Zorro 30 (10f,Yar,F,Jun 5)
Zugudi 64 (10f,Nwm,GS,Oct 16)
Zuhair 72 (6f,Kem,G,May 24)
Zurs (IRE) 55 (7f,Nwm,G,Apr 16)

THREE YEAR-OLDS AND UPWARDS - Sand

Absolute Liberty (USA) 51 (8^{1}/2f,Wol,Std,Aug 8)
Acharne 36 (10f,Lin,Std,Nov 25)
Advance Repro 37 (6f,Sou,Std,Apr 1)
Afaan (IRE) 48 (6f,Sou,Std,Mar 17)
African-Pard (IRE) 34 (11f,Sou,Std,Feb 17)
Agent 32 (7f,Lin,Std,Feb 20)
Ahliyat (USA) 33 (8^{1}/2f,Wol,Std,Dec 26)
Ajina (USA) 86 (9f,Hpk,Fst,Nov 8)
Alarico (FR) 48 (10f,Lin,Std,Jan 28)
Albaha (USA) 49 (12f,Wol,Std,Mar 5)
Alfahaal (IRE) 37 (8f,Lin,Std,Nov 25)
Al Helal 35 (12f,Lin,Std,Jan 23)
Aljaz 38 (5f,Wol,Std,Nov 29)
All In Leather 34 (9^{1}/2f,Wol,Std,Aug 8)
All On 54 (12f,Wol,Std,May 11)
Alpine Hideaway (IRE) 52 (7f,Sou,Std,Jly 10)
Al Reet (IRE) 42 (6f,Sou,Std,Jun 19)
Alsahib (USA) 58 (12f,Wol,Std,Nov 29)
Always Happy 36 (12f,Lin,Std,Jan 30)
Amadour (IRE) 51 (12f,Lin,Std,Feb 25)
Ambidextrous (IRE) 32 (12f,Wol,Std,Feb 12)
Amico 33 (10f,Lin,Std,Mar 1)
Amington Lass 31 (5f,Wol,Slw,Jan 4)
Amy Leigh (IRE) 38 (5f,Wol,Slw,Jan 4)
Anak-Ku 52 (10f,Lin,Std,Apr 4)
Anchor Venture 42 (10f,Lin,Std,May 14)
Angel Face (USA) 57 (9^{1}/2f,Wol,Std,Mar 15)

Anita's Contessa (IRE) 40 (6f,Sou,Std,Jan 10)
Anjou 35 (16f,Lin,Std,Nov 25)
Anokato 43 (5f,Lin,Std,Nov 6)
Anonym (IRE) 54 (8 1/2f,Wol,Std,May 30)
Another Batchworth 37 (5f,Lin,Std,Nov 6)
Another Monk (IRE) 39 (12f,Lin,Std,Nov 28)
Another Nightmare (IRE) 30 (6f,Wol,Std,Mar 5)
Ansellman 46 (5f,Wol,Std,Mar 8)
Antonias Melody 63 (6f,Sou,Std,Feb 14)
Anyar Reem 56 (11f,Sou,Std,Jun 19)
Apollo Red 51 (6f,Lin,Std,Apr 4)
Arcatura 30 (10f,Lin,Std,Jan 11)
Arctic Thunder (USA) 55 (12f,Wol,Std,Nov 29)
Arian Spirit (IRE) 32 (16f,Wol,Std,Jly 25)
Around Fore Alliss 44 (8f,Lin,Std,Jun 21)
Arzani (USA) 40 (10f,Lin,Std,Jan 2)
Ashgore 30 (6f,Sou,Std,Jan 13)
As-Is 30 (12f,Lin,Std,Feb 27)
Aspecto Lad (IRE) 34 (8f,Sou,Std,Jan 13)
Assume (USA) 32 (8f,Lin,Std,Mar 24)
Astrac (IRE) 57 (7f,Wol,Std,Nov 1)
At Liberty (IRE) 51 (12f,Lin,Std,Mar 27)
Awesome Power 38 (10f,Lin,Std,Jan 2)
Awesome Venture 56 (6f,Sou,Std,Jan 13)
Aztec Flyer (USA) 30 (16f,Lin,Std,Nov 25)

Baaheth (USA) 34 (8f,Lin,Std,Jan 14)
Baby Jane 30 (8 1/2f,Wol,Std,Mar 8)
Backview 30 (12f,Wol,Std,Feb 21)
Bagshot 46 (8f,Lin,Std,Feb 27)
Bailieborough Boy (IRE) 33 (8 1/2f,Wol,Std,Feb 19)
Bakers Daughter 30 (10f,Lin,Std,Feb 25)
Ballard Lady (IRE) 34 (7f,Sou,Std,Feb 3)
Banzhaf (USA) 70 (8f,Lin,Std,May 9)
Bapsford 38 (9 1/2f,Wol,Std,Dec 6)
Barbara's Jewel 45 (12f,Wol,Std,May 11)
Barbason 54 (7f,Lin,Std,Nov 18)
Bardon Hill Boy (IRE) 48 (9 1/2f,Wol,Std,Jan 29)
Barrack Yard 39 (6f,Wol,Std,Apr 12)
Barrel of Hope 51 (7f,Lin,Std,Jan 28)
Bashful Brave 45 (5f,Sou,Std,Spt 8)
Batabanoo 31 (12f,Sou,Std,Apr 28)
Batoutoftheblue 38 (15f,Wol,Std,Spt 30)
Beauman 31 (9 1/2f,Wol,Slw,Jan 4)
Beaumont (IRE) 37 (15f,Wol,Std,Jan 8)
Bedouin Honda 31 (10f,Lin,Std,Nov 18)
Bedouin Prince (USA) 33 (13f,Lin,Std,Jun 28)
Behrens (USA) 56 (10f,Hpk,Fst,Nov 8)
Ben Gunn 34 (10f,Lin,Std,Jan 2)
Benjamins Law 47 (8f,Sou,Std,Apr 28)
Bentico 61 (8f,Lin,Std,Jun 24)
Bernard Seven (IRE) 43 (8f,Lin,Std,Feb 18)
Besweetome 36 (8f,Lin,Std,Feb 22)
Bet On Sunshine (USA) 97 (6f,Hpk,Fst,Nov 8)
Be Warned 38 (8 1/2f,Wol,Std,Oct 18)
Beyond Calculation (USA) 31 (6f,Wol,Std,Spt 20)
Big Bang 32 (8 1/2f,Wol,Std,Feb 26)
Big Ben 50 (7f,Lin,Std,Jun 28)
Biya (IRE) 35 (10f,Lin,Std,Jan 30)
Blooming Amazing 36 (8f,Sou,Std,Dec 8)
Blue Flyer (IRE) 64 (7f,Lin,Std,Jan 18)
Blues Magic (IRE) 31 (5f,Lin,Std,Feb 22)
Blues Queen 32 (5f,Sou,Std,Spt 8)
Blushing Desert 39 (7f,Lin,Std,Nov 6)
Blushing Grenadier (IRE) 33 (8f,Lin,Std,Feb 22)
Boffy (IRE) 39 (5f,Wol,Slw,Jan 4)
Bogan (IRE) 39 (7f,Lin,Std,Aug 28)
Bogart 31 (7f,Wol,Std,Feb 19)
Bold Aristocrat (IRE) 55 (6f,Sou,Std,Jun 19)
Bold Effort (FR) 73 (5f,Wol,Std,Mar 8)
Bold Frontier 60 (5f,Wol,Std,Mar 8)
Bold Street (IRE) 32 (6f,Sou,Std,Jly 21)
Bongo 33 (8 1/2f,Wol,Std,Dec 26)
Bon Guest (IRE) 35 (9 1/2f,Wol,Std,Jly 11)
Bonne Ville 32 (12f,Wol,Std,Nov 1)
Bon Secret (IRE) 47 (8 1/2f,Wol,Std,Jan 8)
Bowled Over 30 (8f,Lin,Std,Nov 25)
Brand New Dance 37 (12f,Wol,Std,Apr 12)
Brecon 41 (16f,Lin,Std,Nov 10)
Brilliant Red 57 (10f,Lin,Std,Feb 11)
Broadstairs Beauty (IRE) 60 (6f,Sou,Std,Jan 27)
Broughtons Formula 44 (16f,Lin,Std,Feb 11)
Broughton's Pride (IRE) 40 (7f,Sou,Std,Feb 24)
Broughtons Turmoil 40 (8 1/2f,Wol,Std,Jun 21)
Brutal Fantasy (IRE) 46 (6f,Sou,Std,Jan 3)
Burundi (IRE) 38 (11f,Sou,Std,Nov 17)

Calendula 41 (10f,Lin,Std,May 9)
Canadian Fantasy 39 (9 1/2f,Wol,Std,Jun 18)
Canary Falcon 31 (15f,Wol,Slw,Jan 4)
Can Can Charlie 33 (10f,Lin,Std,Jan 9)
Canton Venture 66 (12f,Lin,Std,May 14)
Captain Carat 35 (6f,Sou,Std,Jan 20)
Captain Scott (IRE) 35 (8f,Sou,Std,Mar 17)
Captain's Day 43 (10f,Lin,Std,Feb 25)
Carmine Lake (IRE) 56 (6f,Hpk,Fst,Nov 8)
Carol Again 34 (11f,Sou,Std,Feb 17)
Carol's Dream (USA) 33 (12f,Sou,Std,Apr 28)
Cartouche 33 (8f,Sou,Std,Apr 28)
Cashmere Lady 62 (8 1/2f,Wol,Std,Jun 21)
Castle Ashby Jack 34 (6f,Lin,Std,May 14)
Castles Burning (USA) 49 (8f,Lin,Std,Mar 24)
Castle Secret 40 (16f,Wol,Std,Jly 25)
Caudillo (IRE) 38 (8 1/2f,Wol,Std,Mar 8)
Ceanothus (IRE) 32 (12f,Wol,Std,Aug 16)
Cedez le Passage (FR) 31 (9 1/2f,Wol,Std,Jan 8)
Celestial Choir 47 (9 1/2f,Wol,Std,Jan 8)
Centre Stalls (IRE) 33 (9 1/2f,Wol,Std,Dec 6)
Certain Magic 32 (15f,Wol,Std,Oct 6)
Chadleigh Lane (USA) 51 (9 1/2f,Wol,Std,Mar 15)
Chadwell Hall 62 (5f,Sou,Std,Apr 1)

Chairmans Choice 38 (10f,Lin,Std,Nov 28)
Chaluz 41 (7f,Sou,Std,Nov 14)
Champagne Warrior (IRE) 43 (11f,Sou,Std,Jun 19)
Charnwood Jack (USA) 46 (12f,Wol,Std,Dec 6)
Chemcast 43 (5f,Wol,Std,Jan 22)
Cherokee Flight 45 (9½f,Wol,Std,Aug 16)
Chewit 79 (8½f,Wol,Std,Nov 15)
Chilling 33 (5f,Wol,Std,Feb 26)
China Castle 67 (12f,Wol,Std,Feb 19)
Chipstead Bay (IRE) 41 (7f,Lin,Std,Dec 10)
Churchill's Shadow (IRE) 32 (7f,Lin,Std,Nov 28)
Cim Bom Bom (IRE) 64 (7f,Wol,Std,Feb 12)
Circled (USA) 41 (12f,Sou,Std,Jan 10)
Classic Ballet (FR) 49 (12f,Wol,Std,Oct 18)
Classic Find (USA) 49 (10f,Lin,Std,Dec 2)
Classy Chief 30 (13f,Lin,Std,Feb 13)
Clear Mandate (USA) 57 (9f,Hpk,Fst,Nov 8)
Coleridge 38 (16f,Lin,Std,Mar 4)
Colins Choice 37 (8½f,Wol,Std,Aug 16)
Colosse 30 (13f,Lin,Std,Feb 8)
Concer Arall 39 (8½f,Wol,Std,Nov 1)
Concer Un 48 (8½f,Wol,Std,Jun 21)
Confide (USA) 87 (6f,Hpk,Fst,Nov 8)
Confronter 39 (10f,Lin,Std,Nov 25)
Corinchili 34 (5f,Sou,Std,May 8)
Cossack Count 43 (7f,Lin,Std,Dec 19)
Cotteir Chief (IRE) 63 (12f,Wol,Std,Apr 8)
Count Tony 38 (10f,Lin,Std,Jly 11)
Crafty Friend (USA) 51 (6f,Hpk,Fst,Nov 8)
Cretan Gift 86 (6f,Sou,Std,Feb 28)
Crystal Gold 38 (9½f,Wol,Std,May 11)
Curzon Street 39 (10f,Lin,Std,Nov 13)
Cyrian (IRE) 43 (8½f,Wol,Std,Mar 8)
Czarna (IRE) 31 (12f,Lin,Std,Feb 18)

Daawe (USA) 65 (5f,Sou,Std,Apr 1)
Dahiyah (USA) 34 (7f,Sou,Std,Jan 13)
Daintree (IRE) 30 (7f,Lin,Std,Nov 10)
Dalliance (IRE) 67 (9½f,Wol,Std,Jun 7)
Dances With Hooves 39 (10f,Lin,Std,Jan 16)
Dancing-Alone 32 (12f,Sou,Std,Feb 10)
Dancing Mystery 44 (6f,Sou,Std,Oct 20)
Dancing Sioux 44 (8½f,Wol,Std,May 30)
Dande Flyer 41 (5f,Wol,Std,Jan 8)
Danka 44 (12f,Lin,Std,Nov 28)
Daring Flight (USA) 30 (8½f,Wol,Std,Feb 26)
Dark Waters (IRE) 33 (16f,Lin,Std,Aug 2)
Daryabad (IRE) 36 (7f,Lin,Std,Jan 4)
Davis Rock 39 (8f,Sou,Std,Dec 18)
Davoski 40 (10f,Lin,Std,Apr 4)
Dawalib (USA) 45 (7f,Lin,Std,Feb 8)
Dawam Allail (IRE) 42 (9½f,Wol,Std,May 24)
Deeply Vale (IRE) 44 (7f,Sou,Std,Aug 15)
Defined Feature (IRE) 41 (7f,Wol,Std,Feb 26)
Delrob 37 (6f,Sou,Std,Feb 14)
Delta Soleil (USA) 46 (8f,Lin,Std,Nov 10)
Democrat 64 (8f,Sou,Std,Dec 8)
Deputy Commander (USA) 86 (10f,Hpk,Fst,Nov 8)
Desert Calm (IRE) 30 (8f,Lin,Std,Feb 18)
Desert Invader (IRE) 49 (7f,Sou,Std,Jan 6)
Dictation (USA) 32 (6f,Sou,Std,Feb 24)
Digpast (IRE) 50 (10f,Lin,Std,Mar 4)
Dirab 38 (12f,Sou,Std,Mar 14)
Dominant Air 39 (6f,Wol,Std,Jan 29)
Domino Flyer 36 (8f,Sou,Std,Jan 10)
Don Sebastian 47 (9½f,Wol,Std,Feb 12)
Don't Drop Bombs (USA) 38 (12f,Lin,Std,Nov 28)
Don't Worry Mike 46 (8½f,Wol,Std,Nov 1)
Double Espresso (IRE) 30 (10f,Lin,Std,Jan 7)
Double March 31 (10f,Lin,Std,Jan 9)
Double-O 50 (6f,Wol,Std,Dec 26)
Double Oscar (IRE) 48 (6f,Wol,Std,Oct 18)
Double Rush (IRE) 41 (10f,Lin,Std,May 24)
Dovebrace 32 (7f,Lin,Std,Dec 2)
Dowty (USA) 89 (10f,Hpk,Fst,Nov 8)
Dragonjoy 45 (8½f,Wol,Std,Apr 8)
Dream Carrier (IRE) 37 (7f,Sou,Std,Feb 24)
Dr Edgar 41 (12f,Wol,Std,Mar 15)
Duello 31 (8½f,Wol,Std,Apr 12)
Duke Valentino 62 (7f,Lin,Std,Jan 23)
Dummer Golf Time 42 (7f,Lin,Std,Nov 18)
Durham 39 (16f,Lin,Std,Nov 10)
Dust 31 (8f,Sou,Std,Nov 17)

Eager To Please 34 (7f,Lin,Std,Jan 2)
Eagle Dancer 49 (9½f,Wol,Std,May 24)
Eastern Prophets 52 (6f,Wol,Std,Dec 26)
Eastleigh 37 (8f,Lin,Std,Mar 13)
Edan Heights 31 (14f,Sou,Std,Nov 24)
Effectual 53 (8½f,Wol,Std,Apr 12)
Effervescence 52 (7f,Lin,Std,Jan 2)
Ela Man Howa 39 (12f,Lin,Std,Jan 18)
Elite Hope (USA) 59 (7f,Wol,Slw,Jan 4)
Elmhurst (USA) 99 (6f,Hpk,Fst,Nov 8)
El Nido 35 (12f,Sou,Std,Jan 24)
Elton Ledger (IRE) 57 (6f,Sou,Std,Jan 13)
Enchanting Eve 41 (7f,Lin,Std,Dec 10)
English Invader 51 (13f,Lin,Std,Mar 4)
Enlisted (IRE) 47 (10f,Lin,,Dec 10)
Ertlon 59 (8f,Lin,Std,May 14)
Escena (USA) 79 (9f,Hpk,Fst,Nov 8)
Ethbaat (USA) 51 (9½f,Wol,Std,Mar 15)
Etterby Park (USA) 36 (12f,Wol,Std,Apr 8)
Eurobox Boy 32 (10f,Lin,Std,Dec 2)
Euro Forum 36 (15f,Wol,Std,Oct 6)
Eurolink the Lad 32 (9½f,Wol,Std,Apr 26)
Everset (FR) 47 (8½f,Wol,Std,May 30)
Exotic Wood (USA) 91 (6f,Hpk,Fst,Nov 8)
Explosive Power 41 (9½f,Wol,Slw,Jan 4)

Failed To Hit 46 (8 1/2f,Wol,Std,Jly 25)
Fairy Knight 42 (10f,Lin,Std,Mar 4)
Farley Mount 35 (10f,Lin,Std,Apr 4)
Farmost 73 (9 1/2f,Wol,Std,Dec 6)
Father Dan (IRE) 45 (8f,Lin,Std,Feb 11)
Fayik 53 (6f,Sou,Std,Nov 24)
Faym (IRE) 37 (7f,Wol,Std,Apr 8)
Featherstone Lane 49 (5f,Sou,Std,Spt 8)
Fife Major (USA) 41 (7f,Wol,Std,Jly 11)
Filial (IRE) 58 (12f,Wol,Std,Nov 1)
First Maite 52 (5f,Wol,Std,Apr 26)
Flag Fen (USA) 31 (8f,Sou,Std,Feb 28)
Flagstaff (USA) 31 (8 1/2f,Wol,Std,Feb 21)
Foot Battalion (IRE) 48 (8 1/2f,Wol,Std,Mar 5)
Forcing Bid 62 (6f,Wol,Std,Nov 15)
Forest Boy 40 (9 1/2f,Wol,Std,Jan 4)
Forgotten Times (USA) 43 (6f,Lin,Std,Feb 25)
Fort Knox (IRE) 40 (7f,Lin,Std,Jan 4)
Fourdaned (IRE) 30 (12f,Lin,Std,Nov 28)
Fresh Fruit Daily 42 (12f,Wol,Std,May 11)
Friendly Brave (USA) 37 (6f,Lin,Std,Apr 4)

Gablesea 37 (7f,Sou,Std,Nov 14)
Gadge 43 (6f,Wol,Std,Oct 4)
Gad Yakoun 32 (7f,Wol,Slw,Jan 4)
Galapino 48 (8 1/2f,Wol,Std,Jan 8)
General Haven 56 (12f,Lin,Std,May 14)
General Sir Peter (IRE) 42 (5f,Wol,Std,Apr 12)
Genuine John (IRE) 44 (8f,Sou,Std,Jan 24)
Giko 45 (8f,Sou,Std,Nov 24)
Gi La High 49 (5f,Wol,Std,Mar 5)
Glide Path (USA) 35 (12f,Lin,Std,Nov 28)
Globetrotter (IRE) 60 (9 1/2f,Wol,Std,Feb 19)
Glow Forum 53 (12f,Wol,Std,Oct 4)
Godmersham Park 41 (8f,Sou,Std,Nov 24)
Going For Broke 33 (8 1/2f,Wol,Std,May 24)
Gold Blade 47 (13f,Lin,Std,Mar 4)
Golden Hadeer 46 (15f,Wol,Std,Jan 8)
Golden Pound (USA) 35 (6f,Wol,Std,Oct 18)
Golden Touch (USA) 34 (9 1/2f,Wol,Std,Jan 8)
Goodbye Gatemen (IRE) 50 (7f,Lin,Std,May 14)
Goodwood Lass (IRE) 32 (12f,Wol,Std,Jun 18)
Goretski (IRE) 50 (5f,Sou,Std,Jun 6)
Grand Cru 31 (12f,Sou,Std,Apr 28)
Grand Hotel (IRE) 32 (9 1/2f,Wol,Std,Aug 16)
Greatest 55 (7f,Lin,Std,Feb 25)
Greenspan (IRE) 55 (12f,Wol,Std,Nov 1)
Gresatre 49 (6f,Sou,Std,Mar 3)
Grooms Gold (IRE) 39 (8f,Sou,Std,Nov 17)
Ground Game 51 (12f,Wol,Std,May 24)
Grovefair Lad (IRE) 30 (12f,Wol,Std,Dec 6)
Guesstimation (USA) 37 (11f,Sou,Std,Dec 8)
Guest Alliance (IRE) 47 (16f,Lin,Std,Feb 11)
Gulf Shaadi 55 (8f,Sou,Std,Jan 13)

Hal's Pal 77 (8 1/2f,Wol,Std,Apr 12)
Hannah's Usher 51 (6f,Wol,Std,Nov 1)
Happy Medium (IRE) 30 (11f,Sou,Std,Mar 3)
Harmony In Red 31 (7f,Lin,Std,Feb 6)
Haroldon (IRE) 30 (10f,Lin,Std,Spt 9)
Harpoon Louie (USA) 38 (8f,Lin,Std,Dec 2)
Hattaafeh (IRE) 52 (16f,Lin,Std,Feb 22)
Hatta Sunshine (USA) 36 (8f,Lin,Std,Jan 23)
Hawaii Storm (FR) 42 (7f,Lin,Std,Jan 21)
Haydn James (USA) 41 (9 1/2f,Wol,Std,Dec 6)
Hayes Way (IRE) 36 (8f,Lin,Std,Feb 6)
Hazel 37 (9 1/2f,Wol,Std,Jan 11)
Heathyards Lady (USA) 34 (8 1/2f,Wol,Std,Oct 18)
Heighth of Fame 58 (13f,Lin,Std,Mar 4)
Henry the Hawk 39 (5f,Sou,Std,Spt 8)
Hesabull (USA) 98 (6f,Hpk,Fst,Nov 8)
Hever Golf Charger (IRE) 34 (7f,Lin,Std,Feb 15)
Hever Golf Eagle 34 (10f,Lin,Std,Feb 25)
Hidden Lake (USA) 50 (9f,Hpk,Fst,Nov 8)
Hill Farm Dancer 52 (9 1/2f,Wol,Std,Feb 26)
Hoh Majestic (IRE) 40 (6f,Sou,Std,May 19)
Holders Hill (IRE) 36 (8f,Sou,Std,Jun 19)
Honor Glide (USA) 37 (10f,Hpk,Fst,Nov 8)
Hurtleberry (IRE) 54 (7f,Lin,Std,Jan 28)

Iamus 50 (7f,Sou,Std,Mar 3)
Iblis (IRE) 67 (7f,Sou,Std,Mar 3)
Ice Age 37 (5f,Wol,Std,Nov 29)
Icy Guest (USA) 43 (7f,Sou,Std,Jly 21)
Illuminate 31 (12f,Lin,Std,Feb 6)
Il Trastevere (FR) 31 (12f,Lin,Std,Jan 4)
Imperial Garden (IRE) 33 (5f,Lin,Std,Jan 23)
Impulsif (USA) 44 (8f,Lin,Std,Nov 10)
Indigo Dawn 43 (16f,Lin,Std,Dec 10)
Infamous (USA) 31 (9 1/2f,Wol,Std,Jan 29)
In Good Faith 39 (8f,Sou,Std,Jan 6)
In the Money (IRE) 45 (12f,Lin,Std,Feb 18)
Intiaash (IRE) 44 (7f,Sou,Std,Jly 10)
Invocation 52 (8f,Lin,Std,Feb 18)
Island Sanctuary (IRE) 34 (8f,Sou,Std,Apr 28)
Italian Symphony (IRE) 50 (6f,Wol,Std,Nov 1)
Itsinthepost 52 (7f,Wol,Std,Jly 11)
Ivor's Deed 35 (7f,Lin,Std,Nov 13)
Ivory's Grab Hire 34 (5f,Lin,Std,Feb 20)

Jewel Princess (USA) 30 (9f,Hpk,Fst,Nov 8)
Jibereen 63 (7f,Sou,Std,Jan 13)
Jigsaw Boy 36 (7f,Sou,Std,May 12)
Johnnie the Joker 58 (8 1/2f,Wol,Std,Jun 27)
Jolly Jackson 34 (8 1/2f,Wol,Std,Feb 26)
Jo Maximus 42 (7f,Lin,Std,Jan 4)
Jona Holley 40 (8f,Sou,Std,Oct 20)
Joseph's Wine (IRE) 61 (8f,Sou,Std,Dec 18)
Juggler 37 (7f,Lin,Std,May 14)
Just Dissident (IRE) 30 (5f,Lin,Std,Dec 22)
Justinianus (IRE) 37 (6f,Lin,Std,Feb 20)
Just Loui 41 (7f,Lin,Std,Jun 28)

Kafil (USA) 48 (10f,Lin,,Dec 10)
Kailey Senor (USA) 47 (10f,Lin,Std,Dec 2)
Kalamata 39 (12f,Sou,Std,Feb 10)
Kalar 52 (5f,Wol,Std,Mar 8)
Kalimat 45 (8f,Sou,Std,Jly 10)
Keen Companion 30 (10f,Lin,Std,Jly 26)
Ki Chi Saga (USA) 47 (8f,Lin,Std,Mar 27)
Kildee Lad 35 (6f,Lin,Std,Apr 4)
Kilnamartyra Girl 30 (12f,Sou,Std,Jan 24)
Kingchip Boy 48 (8f,Sou,Std,Feb 14)
Kira 52 (5f,Wol,Std,Mar 8)
Klipspinger 43 (6f,Sou,Std,Jan 1)
Knotty Hill 67 (7f,Sou,Std,Mar 3)
Komasta 35 (8 1/2f,Wol,Slw,Jan 4)
Kriscliffe 42 (10f,Lin,Std,Mar 24)
Kristopher 33 (8f,Lin,Std,Jun 21)
Krystal Max (IRE) 46 (6f,Wol,Std,Jan 8)
Kuala Lipis (USA) 67 (8 1/2f,Wol,Std,Mar 8)

Labudd (USA) 39 (12f,Lin,Std,Jan 16)
La Dolce Vita 43 (7f,Sou,Std,Mar 3)
Lady Sheriff 52 (5f,Sou,Std,May 8)
Lady Silk 35 (7f,Sou,Std,Feb 3)
La Modiste 47 (10f,Lin,Std,Jly 11)
Lancashire Legend 57 (7f,Lin,Std,Jan 16)
La Petite Fusee 37 (7f,Lin,Std,Dec 10)
Laurel Seeker (USA) 32 (12f,Lin,Std,Dec 19)
Law Dancer (IRE) 43 (8f,Lin,Std,Jun 24)
Lawn Lothario 41 (12f,Wol,Std,Mar 1)
Leading Spirit (IRE) 66 (12f,Wol,Std,Feb 19)
Legal Issue (IRE) 46 (8f,Sou,Std,Nov 24)
Leigh Crofter 50 (6f,Sou,Std,Jan 10)
Lennox Lewis 36 (5f,Sou,Std,Spt 8)
Le Sport 48 (8f,Sou,Std,Jan 31)
Lift Boy (USA) 42 (7f,Lin,Std,Feb 15)
Lionize (USA) 73 (8 1/2f,Wol,Std,Dec 26)
Liquid Gold (IRE) 53 (8f,Sou,Std,Aug 15)
Little Ibnr 53 (6f,Sou,Std,Jan 13)
Live Project (IRE) 45 (8f,Lin,Std,Mar 4)
Loch Bering (USA) 55 (9 1/2f,Wol,Std,Dec 6)
Loch Style 52 (8 1/2f,Wol,Std,Jan 8)
Lord Sky 45 (5f,Lin,Std,Mar 27)
Lucky Begonia (IRE) 50 (12f,Wol,Std,Nov 21)
Lucky Revenge 34 (6f,Sou,Std,Jan 27)
Lucy of Arabia (IRE) 37 (6f,Sou,Std,Mar 3)

Madrina 43 (5f,Wol,Std,Feb 19)
Maftun (USA) 38 (12f,Sou,Std,Feb 28)
Magazine Gap 30 (8f,Lin,Std,Jun 24)
Magic Fizz 30 (6f,Wol,Std,Apr 26)
Magic Mill (IRE) 62 (10f,Lin,Std,Nov 6)
Major Change 58 (12f,Wol,Std,Mar 5)
Malibu Man 55 (6f,Wol,Std,Spt 30)
Mallia 51 (6f,Wol,Std,Dec 13)
Manful 42 (12f,Lin,Std,Nov 28)
Mangus (IRE) 38 (5f,Wol,Std,Feb 12)
Manikato (USA) 33 (7f,Lin,Std,Nov 6)
Mansab (USA) 65 (6f,Sou,Std,Feb 7)
Maradata (IRE) 39 (9 1/2f,Wol,Std,Jan 22)
Mardrew 37 (8f,Sou,Std,Jan 13)
Marjorie Rose (IRE) 36 (6f,Sou,Std,Feb 14)
Marozia (USA) 35 (7f,Lin,Std,Nov 6)
Mary Cornwallis 30 (6f,Lin,Std,Nov 28)
Massyar Seventeen 46 (10f,Lin,Std,Dec 2)
Master Beveled 53 (10f,Lin,Std,Jan 14)
Master Boots 61 (7f,Sou,Std,Jly 26)
Master Foley 32 (5f,Wol,Std,Jly 25)
Master Millfield (IRE) 34 (12f,Wol,Std,Oct 4)
Master of Passion 39 (5f,Wol,Std,Jan 8)
Matthias Mystique 39 (16f,Lin,Std,Feb 13)
Ma Vielle Pouque (IRE) 46 (5f,Sou,Std,Spt 8)
Mazeed (IRE) 41 (9 1/2f,Wol,Std,Dec 6)
Meilleur (IRE) 31 (16f,Lin,Std,Dec 10)
Mellors (IRE) 40 (7f,Lin,Std,Feb 8)
Mels Baby (IRE) 38 (7f,Sou,Std,Feb 24)
Mendoza 35 (8f,Lin,Std,Mar 24)
Men's Exclusive (USA) 89 (6f,Hpk,Fst,Nov 8)
Mentalasanythin 37 (9 1/2f,Wol,Std,Apr 26)
Merciless Cop 35 (9 1/2f,Wol,Std,Jun 18)
Mercury (IRE) 38 (12f,Wol,Std,Nov 21)
Mersey Beat 30 (10f,Lin,Std,Mar 1)
Michael Venture 38 (10f,Lin,Std,Jly 26)
Middle East 55 (6f,Sou,Std,Nov 24)
Mijas 54 (5f,Lin,Std,Jan 14)
Mike's Double (IRE) 54 (6f,Wol,Std,Oct 4)
Millroy (USA) 53 (8 1/2f,Wol,Std,Jan 22)
Milos 41 (7f,Lin,Std,Jan 9)
Mimosa 36 (10f,Lin,Std,Mar 4)
Minister's Melody (USA) 61 (9f,Hpk,Fst,Nov 8)
Mister Aspecto (IRE) 55 (12f,Wol,Std,Oct 4)
Mizyan (IRE) 42 (16f,Wol,Std,Jly 25)
Molly Music 45 (8 1/2f,Wol,Std,Oct 18)
Mon Bruce 54 (5f,Sou,Std,Spt 8)
Mono Lady (IRE) 57 (10f,Lin,Std,May 9)
Montecristo 63 (12f,Wol,Std,Nov 21)
Montone (IRE) 50 (12f,Lin,Std,Jan 18)
Moonraking 43 (12f,Wol,Std,Dec 13)
More Than You Know (IRE) 33 (12f,Lin,Std,Jan 25)
Mozambique (IRE) 39 (6f,Sou,Std,Oct 20)
Mr Bergerac (IRE) 47 (6f,Wol,Std,Oct 18)
Mr Fortywinks (IRE) 53 (12f,Wol,Std,Nov 21)
Mr Frosty 44 (7f,Lin,Std,Feb 1)
Mr Majica 33 (8f,Lin,Std,Dec 12)
Mr Nevermind (IRE) 58 (8f,Lin,Std,Feb 8)
Mr Paradise (IRE) 39 (7f,Sou,Std,Dec 18)
Mr Sponge (USA) 35 (7f,Wol,Std,Nov 1)
Mullagh Hill Lad (IRE) 36 (5f,Sou,Std,Jun 13)
Mutahadeth 36 (8f,Sou,Std,Jun 19)
Mutasawwar 37 (7f,Wol,Std,Nov 21)
Mybotye 32 (7f,Wol,Std,Nov 21)
Mystery Matthias 30 (6f,Lin,Std,Feb 25)

Mystic Quest (IRE) 36 (12f,Lin,Std,Oct 27)
Mystic Strand 30 (12f,Sou,Std,Jly 26)
Mythical 50 (8f,Sou,Std,Spt 8)
Myttons Mistake 41 (8f,Lin,Std,Nov 25)

Nakhal 38 (10f,Lin,Std,Jan 2)
Nant Y Gamer (FR) 48 (7f,Lin,Std,Nov 18)
Napier Star 50 (5f,Wol,Std,May 24)
Napoleon Star (IRE) 31 (6f,Sou,Std,Feb 24)
Nashaat (USA) 37 (8f,Lin,Std,Jan 23)
Naughty Pistol (USA) 46 (6f,Sou,Std,Jan 27)
Naval Games 41 (12f,Wol,Std,Nov 21)
Needle Match 53 (6f,Sou,Std,Mar 17)
Needwood Epic 34 (15f,Wol,Std,Oct 6)
Never Think Twice 46 (7f,Lin,Std,Jan 4)
Newbridge Boy 31 (10f,Lin,Std,Nov 13)
New Century (USA) 80 (8 1/2f,Wol,Std,Mar 8)
Newlands Corner 44 (6f,Sou,Std,Aug 15)
Night City 63 (12f,Lin,Std,Nov 6)
Night Express 42 (7f,Wol,Std,Jun 7)
Nightingale Song 38 (5f,Wol,Std,Feb 12)
Night Mirage (USA) 40 (9 1/2f,Wol,Std,Dec 13)
Night Wink (USA) 47 (10f,Lin,Std,Feb 18)
Nikita's Star (IRE) 59 (12f,Wol,Std,Feb 19)
Nineacres 38 (6f,Wol,Std,Nov 1)
Nobalino 45 (5f,Wol,Std,Nov 29)
No Grousing (IRE) 37 (7f,Wol,Std,Nov 21)
Nomore Mr Niceguy 45 (8 1/2f,Wol,Std,Jan 22)
Nordic Breeze (IRE) 42 (8f,Sou,Std,Jan 10)
Nordinex (IRE) 34 (8f,Lin,Std,Feb 18)
Nor-Do-I 59 (8 1/2f,Wol,Std,Aug 8)
Northern Accord 31 (8 1/2f,Wol,Std,Nov 1)
Northern Afleet (USA) 74 (6f,Hpk,Fst,Nov 8)
Northern Angel (IRE) 52 (8 1/2f,Wol,Std,Nov 15)
Northern Fan (IRE) 37 (9 1/2f,Wol,Std,Mar 5)
Northern Motto 42 (12f,Wol,Std,Feb 12)
No Speeches (IRE) 37 (10f,Lin,Std,Mar 24)
No Submission (USA) 33 (11f,Sou,Std,Feb 17)
Noufari (FR) 49 (15f,Wol,Std,Jan 8)

Oberons Boy (IRE) 44 (8f,Lin,Std,Jan 7)
Oberon's Dart (IRE) 55 (7f,Sou,Std,Aug 15)
Once More for Luck (IRE) 43 (12f,Sou,Std,Feb 17)
Oneforthelditch (USA) 52 (9 1/2f,Wol,Std,Dec 13)
Onefourseven 35 (15f,Wol,Std,Spt 30)
One Off the Rail (USA) 38 (12f,Lin,Std,Mar 27)
Oneoftheoldones 34 (8f,Sou,Std,Jan 13)
Opera Buff (IRE) 54 (12f,Wol,Std,Oct 4)
Orange Place (IRE) 33 (8f,Sou,Std,Spt 8)
Ordained 32 (12f,Wol,Std,Dec 13)
Other Club 36 (8 1/2f,Wol,Std,Dec 26)
Our Eddie 30 (10f,Lin,Std,Jan 2)
Our People 30 (8f,Sou,Std,Aug 15)
Our Shadee (USA) 32 (8f,Lin,Std,Jan 16)
Outstayed Welcome 30 (16f,Lin,Std,Mar 4)

Padauk 35 (16f,Lin,Std,Nov 10)
Pageboy 37 (6f,Lin,Std,Feb 11)
Paint It Black 32 (6f,Sou,Std,Jan 27)
Palacegate Jack (IRE) 62 (5f,Sou,Std,Spt 8)
Palacegate Touch 56 (7f,Lin,Std,Nov 6)
Palisander (IRE) 43 (10f,Lin,Std,Nov 6)
Palo Blanco 46 (6f,Sou,Std,Nov 24)
Paradise Navy 40 (15f,Wol,Std,Oct 6)
Pas De Reponse (USA) 50 (6f,Hpk,Fst,Nov 8)
Passionatti 33 (5f,Sou,Std,Spt 8)
Pater Noster (USA) 61 (9 1/2f,Wol,Std,Feb 26)
Patina 30 (8 1/2f,Wol,Std,Dec 26)
Pegasus Bay 45 (10f,Lin,Std,Nov 6)
Pengamon 66 (8f,Lin,Std,May 9)
Pennywell 42 (8f,Lin,Std,Jun 14)
People Direct 35 (8 1/2f,Wol,Std,Jun 21)
Perfect Brave 32 (5f,Wol,Std,Apr 12)
Pericles 61 (7f,Wol,Std,Oct 4)
Perilous Plight 39 (8f,Lin,Std,Mar 4)
Perpetual Light 45 (9 1/2f,Wol,Std,Dec 6)
Persian Conquest (IRE) 37 (12f,Lin,Std,Jan 21)
Persuasion 41 (12f,Lin,Std,Jan 25)
Petite Danseuse 31 (7f,Lin,Std,Nov 28)
Petoskin 54 (16f,Lin,Std,Feb 22)
Pharaoh's Joy 34 (6f,Wol,Std,Nov 1)
Pharly Dancer 32 (12f,Sou,Std,Apr 28)
Philmist 44 (12f,Lin,Std,Nov 28)
Phoenix Princess 47 (8 1/2f,Wol,Std,Oct 18)
Pinchincha (FR) 42 (9 1/2f,Wol,Std,Feb 19)
Pine Ridge Lad (IRE) 30 (8f,Lin,Std,Dec 4)
Piquant 39 (8f,Lin,Std,Feb 27)
Plan For Profit (IRE) 57 (8f,Lin,Std,Nov 10)
Pleasure Trick (USA) 34 (7f,Sou,Std,Jan 6)
Plum First 32 (7f,Sou,Std,Jan 6)
Pointe Fine (FR) 33 (12f,Wol,Std,Aug 16)
Polar Champ 55 (12f,Wol,Std,Oct 4)
Polyphony (USA) 34 (12f,Wol,Std,Apr 12)
Premier Dance 47 (12f,Wol,Std,Nov 29)
Premier Generation (IRE) 48 (11f,Sou,Std,Dec 8)
Presentiment 39 (8 1/2f,Wol,Std,Nov 1)
Present Situation 46 (8f,Lin,Std,Feb 8)
Pride of Brixton 39 (6f,Wol,Std,Spt 30)
Prima Silk 61 (6f,Sou,Std,Jan 27)
Prime Light 48 (8f,Lin,Std,May 9)
Primo Lara 43 (7f,Wol,Std,Dec 6)
Prince Danzig (IRE) 65 (12f,Wol,Std,Feb 19)
Princely Sound 57 (6f,Lin,Std,Feb 11)
Prince of Denial 49 (9 1/2f,Wol,Std,Dec 6)
Princess Efisio 43 (7f,Sou,Std,Jun 6)
Private Audience (USA) 62 (12f,Lin,Std,Nov 28)
Private Fixture (IRE) 55 (11f,Sou,Std,Jun 19)
Prophets Honour 45 (9 1/2f,Wol,Std,Jan 11)
Protocol (IRE) 37 (10f,Lin,Std,Apr 4)
Proud Monk 33 (7f,Sou,Std,Dec 18)
Punkah (USA) 44 (10f,Lin,Std,Feb 18)
Purple Fling 35 (7f,Lin,Std,Mar 13)

Puzzlement 58 (9^1/2f,Wol,Std,Dec 6)

Qualitair Pride 34 (12f,Sou,Std,Jan 24)
Queenfisher 30 (8f,Lin,Std,Jan 18)
Queen of All Birds (IRE) 41 (8f,Lin,Std,Feb 8)
Queens Consul (IRE) 31 (8^1/2f,Wol,Std,Apr 8)
Queen's Pageant 54 (8^1/2f,Wol,Std,Dec 26)
Quiet Arch (IRE) 45 (10f,Lin,Std,Jan 14)

Radu Cool (USA) 77 (9f,Hpk,Fst,Nov 8)
Raed 38 (11f,Sou,Std,Dec 8)
Raffles Rooster 39 (12f,Wol,Std,Apr 8)
Raindeer Quest 33 (12f,Sou,Std,Jan 24)
Raise A Prince (FR) 59 (12f,Wol,Std,Nov 29)
Rakis (IRE) 62 (7f,Wol,Std,Feb 12)
Rambo Waltzer 63 (8^1/2f,Wol,Std,Mar 8)
Ramsey Hope 53 (5f,Lin,Std,Feb 27)
Random Kindness 64 (12f,Wol,Std,Nov 29)
Rasayel (USA) 46 (12f,Lin,Std,Jan 18)
Rawi 35 (7f,Lin,Std,Jan 21)
Redoubtable (USA) 48 (6f,Wol,Std,Dec 26)
Red Phantom (IRE) 42 (12f,Wol,Std,Dec 26)
Regal Splendour (CAN) 50 (8f,Lin,Std,Feb 4)
Rehaab 38 (10f,Lin,Std,Nov 10)
Renown 40 (10f,Lin,Std,Feb 6)
Resist the Force (USA) 50 (8f,Lin,Std,Jun 14)
Rex Mundi 52 (12f,Wol,Std,Oct 6)
Richter Scale (USA) 41 (6f,Hpk,Fst,Nov 8)
Rififi 56 (5f,Lin,Std,Feb 20)
Ring the Chief 30 (7f,Sou,Std,Feb 24)
River Captain (USA) 42 (11f,Sou,Std,Mar 3)
River Keen (IRE) 62 (12f,Sou,Std,Mar 17)
River Seine (FR) 31 (7f,Lin,Std,Jan 21)
Road Racer (IRE) 37 (11f,Sou,Std,Feb 17)
Robbo 42 (15f,Wol,Std,Oct 6)
Robellion 57 (8f,Lin,Std,Feb 18)
Robo Magic (USA) 56 (6f,Lin,Std,Feb 11)
Rock Island Line (IRE) 31 (7f,Wol,Std,Oct 4)
Roffey Spinney (IRE) 43 (5f,Lin,Std,Feb 22)
Roman Reel (USA) 56 (8f,Lin,Std,Mar 13)
Rood Music 54 (15f,Wol,Std,Jan 8)
Roufontaine 47 (12f,Lin,Std,Dec 4)
Royal Action 53 (10f,Lin,Std,Mar 1)
Royal Aty (IRE) 43 (8f,Lin,Std,Jan 9)
Royal Carlton (IRE) 58 (8f,Lin,Std,Mar 4)
Royal Cascade (IRE) 31 (6f,Wol,Std,Feb 12)
Royal Legend 30 (11f,Sou,Std,May 19)
Royal Roulette 37 (12f,Lin,Std,Nov 28)
Running Stag (USA) 70 (9^1/2f,Wol,Std,Dec 6)
Russian Music 60 (9^1/2f,Wol,Std,Dec 6)
Rutland Chantry (USA) 45 (9^1/2f,Wol,Std,Spt 30)

Sabot 62 (8^1/2f,Wol,Std,Mar 8)
Safa Dancer 30 (9^1/2f,Wol,Std,May 24)
Safecracker 36 (12f,Wol,Std,Oct 6)
Safio 36 (5f,Wol,Std,Mar 8)
Saifan 35 (8^1/2f,Wol,Std,Nov 15)
Sailormaite 43 (8f,Sou,Std,Aug 15)
Sally Slade 45 (5f,Lin,Std,Jan 14)
Salty Behaviour (IRE) 44 (8f,Lin,Std,Dec 10)
Salty Jack (IRE) 59 (7f,Lin,Std,Dec 10)
Sapphire Son (IRE) 31 (12f,Lin,Std,Jan 23)
Saratoga Red (USA) 46 (7f,Lin,Std,Nov 6)
Savinio (USA) 65 (10f,Hpk,Fst,Nov 8)
Scissor Ridge 52 (7f,Lin,Std,Jan 23)
Sea Danzig 56 (10f,Lin,Std,Nov 6)
Sea-Deer 37 (6f,Wol,Std,Nov 21)
Sea Devil 43 (6f,Sou,Std,Feb 24)
Sea God 38 (12f,Sou,Std,Jan 24)
Sea Spouse 45 (8f,Sou,Std,Jan 31)
Sea Victor 37 (11f,Sou,Std,Jan 6)
Sea Ya Maite 56 (8^1/2f,Wol,Std,Oct 18)
Second Colours (USA) 70 (12f,Wol,Std,Feb 19)
Secret Aly (CAN) 50 (10f,Lin,Std,Feb 18)
Sedbergh (USA) 37 (14f,Sou,Std,Apr 1)
Selberry 45 (8^1/2f,Wol,Std,Jan 22)
Sense of Priority 49 (6f,Sou,Std,Jan 20)
Shades of Love 42 (7f,Sou,Std,Dec 18)
Shadow Jury 47 (6f,Sou,Std,Feb 7)
Shaffishayes 43 (8^1/2f,Wol,Std,Apr 8)
Shahik (USA) 30 (12f,Lin,Std,Nov 28)
Shakiyr (FR) 32 (14f,Sou,Std,Dec 8)
Shalaal (USA) 35 (8f,Sou,Std,Dec 8)
Shalstayholy (IRE) 32 (7f,Lin,Std,Feb 13)
Shanghai Lil 35 (10f,Lin,Std,Apr 4)
Sharp Cat (USA) 82 (9f,Hpk,Fst,Nov 8)
Sharp Imp 38 (6f,Lin,Std,Jan 4)
Sharp 'n Smart 40 (7f,Lin,Std,Jan 16)
Sharp Shuffle (IRE) 53 (8f,Lin,Std,Nov 10)
Shashi (IRE) 34 (6f,Sou,Std,Jan 27)
Sheraz (IRE) 36 (10f,Lin,Std,Jan 30)
Shinerolla 66 (8^1/2f,Wol,Std,Mar 8)
Shontaine 36 (7f,Lin,Std,Jan 9)
Shuttlecock 32 (11f,Sou,Std,Feb 17)
Signs And Wonders 40 (10f,Lin,Std,Aug 2)
Sihafi (USA) 45 (6f,Lin,Std,Feb 13)
Silca Key Silca 49 (7f,Wol,Std,Oct 6)
Silk Cottage 49 (5f,Sou,Std,Spt 8)
Silk St John 56 (8f,Sou,Std,Dec 8)
Sing With the Band 52 (5f,Wol,Std,Feb 19)
Siouxrouge 50 (6f,Wol,Std,Jan 22)
Sir Joey (USA) 51 (7f,Wol,Std,Nov 1)
Sis Garden 48 (7f,Wol,Std,Apr 26)
Skelton Sovereign (IRE) 42 (12f,Wol,Std,Dec 13)
Skip Away (USA) 100 (10f,Hpk,Fst,Nov 8)
Sky Commander (USA) 55 (7f,Lin,Std,May 14)
Slip Jig (IRE) 48 (12f,Lin,Std,Jan 4)
Smart Boy (IRE) 41 (10f,Lin,,Dec 10)
Smart Guest 31 (7f,Wol,Std,May 24)
Smart Kid (IRE) 30 (7f,Wol,Std,Oct 6)
Snow Kid 53 (7f,Wol,Std,Jun 7)
Soaking 52 (8f,Lin,Std,Jan 16)

Soda 39 (6f,Sou,Std,Mar 3)
Soden (IRE) 47 (10f,Lin,Std,Aug 2)
Soldier Cove (USA) 41 (9 1/2f,Wol,Std,Mar 5)
Soojama (IRE) 35 (12f,Lin,Std,Feb 18)
Sooty Tern 38 (8f,Lin,Std,Jan 7)
South Eastern Fred 58 (9 1/2f,Wol,Std,Jan 29)
Soviet King (IRE) 32 (12f,Wol,Std,Feb 12)
Spaniards Close 63 (5f,Sou,Std,Spt 8)
Spaniard's Mount 39 (7f,Lin,Std,Feb 6)
Sparkling Edge 30 (5f,Lin,Std,Jan 23)
Sparky 48 (9 1/2f,Wol,Std,Jly 25)
Speedy Classic (USA) 55 (6f,Lin,Std,Mar 1)
Spencer's Revenge 41 (8f,Lin,Std,Feb 11)
Spender 58 (5f,Lin,Std,Mar 27)
Square Deal (FR) 46 (8 1/2f,Wol,Std,Apr 8)
Squire Corrie 52 (6f,Lin,Std,Feb 13)
Squire's Occasion (CAN) 52 (12f,Lin,Std,Jan 18)
Stalled (IRE) 35 (16f,Wol,Std,Jly 25)
Stand Tall 62 (7f,Sou,Std,Mar 3)
Star Rage (IRE) 38 (12f,Wol,Std,Jan 15)
Star Talent (USA) 62 (7f,Lin,Std,Jan 16)
Star Turn (IRE) 37 (7f,Lin,Std,Aug 28)
Statajack (IRE) 60 (12f,Lin,Std,Nov 6)
State Approval 62 (12f,Wol,Std,Jun 21)
State of Caution 69 (7f,Sou,Std,Mar 3)
Statistician 39 (7f,Lin,Std,Jan 9)
Steal 'Em 39 (6f,Wol,Std,Mar 5)
Steamroller Stanly 66 (10f,Lin,Std,Feb 11)
Stellar Line (USA) 37 (10f,Lin,Std,Feb 25)
Step On Degas 45 (7f,Lin,Std,Jan 4)
Stolen Kiss (IRE) 48 (6f,Sou,Std,Jun 19)
Stoppes Brow 58 (8f,Lin,Std,May 14)
Stretching (IRE) 38 (11f,Sou,Std,Mar 3)
Suez Tornado (IRE) 46 (8 1/2f,Wol,Std,Mar 8)
Suga Hawk (IRE) 46 (11f,Sou,Std,Feb 17)
Superapparos 30 (5f,Sou,Std,Spt 8)
Superbelle 36 (10f,Lin,Std,Feb 15)
Super High 69 (9 1/2f,Wol,Std,Jan 8)
Superior Force 38 (8f,Lin,Std,Jan 18)
Super Rocky 30 (5f,Sou,Std,Spt 8)
Supreme Star (USA) 40 (13f,Lin,Std,Jan 30)
Surf City 31 (7f,Sou,Std,Jan 27)
Swan Hunter 65 (12f,Wol,Std,Dec 6)
Swan Island 33 (6f,Sou,Std,Apr 28)
Sweet Mate 35 (6f,Sou,Std,May 19)
Sweet Supposin (IRE) 54 (8f,Lin,Std,May 9)
Sweet Wilhelmina 47 (7f,Lin,Std,Feb 22)
Swift 31 (8 1/2f,Wol,Std,Mar 1)
Swinging Sixties (IRE) 32 (13f,Lin,Std,Mar 4)
Sword Arm 31 (8 1/2f,Wol,Std,Mar 5)
Swynford Dream 34 (5f,Sou,Std,Dec 8)
Sylvan Dancer (IRE) 31 (6f,Sou,Std,Nov 24)

Taiki Blizzard (USA) 62 (10f,Hpk,Fst,Nov 8)
Tailwind 34 (6f,Sou,Std,Jly 10)
Takhlid (USA) 49 (8f,Sou,Std,Apr 28)
Tallulah Belle 46 (9 1/2f,Wol,Std,Jan 11)
Tart (FR) 39 (12f,Wol,Std,Oct 18)
Tatika 60 (8f,Lin,Std,Mar 1)
Tawafek (USA) 41 (10f,Lin,Std,Jan 2)
Tayovullin (IRE) 34 (7f,Sou,Std,Apr 1)
Tear White (IRE) 38 (5f,Lin,Std,Dec 2)
Tellion 40 (9 1/2f,Wol,Std,May 24)
Terdad (USA) 37 (11f,Sou,Std,Mar 3)
Thai Morning 81 (8 1/2f,Wol,Std,Mar 8)
That Man Again 47 (6f,Wol,Std,Nov 15)
Theatre Magic 54 (7f,Wol,Std,Apr 26)
The Barnsley Belle (IRE) 41 (7f,Sou,Std,Nov 14)
The Executor 42 (8 1/2f,Wol,Std,Jly 25)
The Frisky Farmer 34 (7f,Lin,Std,Jan 9)
The Happy Fox (IRE) 55 (6f,Wol,Std,Oct 18)
The Institute Boy 38 (6f,Lin,Std,Jan 25)
The Wyandotte Inn 42 (6f,Sou,Std,Mar 14)
Thick as Thieves 32 (5f,Lin,Std,Feb 6)
Thordis 53 (6f,Wol,Std,Oct 4)
Threadneedle (USA) 50 (9 1/2f,Wol,Std,Dec 13)
Three Arch Bridge 48 (8f,Sou,Std,Feb 10)
Three Weeks 38 (9 1/2f,Wol,Slw,Jan 4)
Time Can Tell 44 (9 1/2f,Wol,Std,Feb 19)
Time of Night (USA) 31 (7f,Sou,Std,Dec 18)
Time To Fly 39 (6f,Sou,Std,Jly 21)
Tissue of Lies (USA) 48 (8f,Lin,Std,Nov 10)
Toi Toi (IRE) 36 (12f,Wol,Std,Dec 6)
Touch Gold (USA) 37 (10f,Hpk,Fst,Nov 8)
Touch'n'go 36 (10f,Lin,Std,Mar 1)
Toujours Riviera 49 (9 1/2f,Wol,Std,Dec 13)
Track Gal (USA) 54 (6f,Hpk,Fst,Nov 8)
Trading Aces 42 (7f,Wol,Std,Apr 8)
Trafalger (USA) 59 (6f,Hpk,Fst,Nov 8)
Treasure Touch (IRE) 45 (6f,Sou,Std,Feb 3)
Tribal Peace (IRE) 46 (10f,Lin,Std,Jan 9)
Trojan Hero (SAF) 45 (7f,Lin,Std,Nov 28)
Truly Bay 38 (7f,Sou,Std,Feb 24)
Tuigamala 39 (8f,Lin,Std,Mar 4)
Tumbleweed Ridge 37 (7f,Wol,Std,Mar 29)
Tuscan Dawn 38 (5f,Lin,Std,Mar 27)
Twilight Sleep (USA) 36 (12f,Wol,Std,Jun 27)
Twin Creeks 67 (8f,Lin,Std,Nov 10)

Ultra Beet 53 (6f,Wol,Std,Jan 8)
Unconditional Love (IRE) 52 (10f,Lin,Std,Nov 25)
Up in Flames (IRE) 32 (9 1/2f,Wol,Std,Dec 6)
Ursa Major 36 (10f,Lin,,Dec 10)

Venice Beach 38 (8 1/2f,Wol,Std,Mar 5)
Venture Connect 40 (9 1/2f,Wol,Std,Feb 12)
Victory Team (IRE) 36 (8f,Lin,Std,Dec 12)
Village Native (FR) 48 (5f,Wol,Std,Aug 8)
Villarica (IRE) 52 (8 1/2f,Wol,Std,Nov 1)
V I P Charlie 42 (6f,Sou,Std,Feb 10)
Vrennan 60 (12f,Lin,Std,Nov 28)

Waikiki Beach (USA) 55 (8 1/2f,Wol,Std,May 30)
Walk the Beat 46 (6f,Sou,Std,Jan 20)
Waypoint 47 (6f,Wol,Std,Oct 18)
Weet And See 37 (8 1/2f,Wol,Std,Mar 8)
Weetman's Weigh (IRE) 31 (7f,Wol,Std,Mar 29)
Welcome Heights 42 (10f,Lin,Std,Dec 2)
Wentbridge Lad (IRE) 30 (8 1/2f,Wol,Std,May 30)
Western Sonata (IRE) 41 (10f,Lin,Std,May 24)
What A Fuss 36 (7f,Wol,Std,Jan 29)
Whatever's Right (IRE) 36 (8f,Lin,Std,Jan 23)
Whiskey Wisdom (CAN) 84 (10f,Hpk,Fst,Nov 8)
Whispered Melody 47 (7f,Lin,Std,Nov 18)
Whispering Dawn 36 (9 1/2f,Wol,Std,Mar 1)
Whitelock Quest 32 (8 1/2f,Wol,Std,Apr 8)
White Plains (IRE) 78 (10f,Lin,,Dec 10)
Whitley Grange Boy 37 (14f,Sou,Std,Nov 14)
Wildfire (SWI) 39 (9 1/2f,Wol,Std,Aug 16)
Wildmoor 36 (12f,Wol,Std,Dec 13)
Wild Palm 41 (7f,Wol,Std,Jly 11)
Will Do 37 (6f,Lin,Std,Jan 2)
Will To Win 32 (6f,Wol,Std,Mar 8)
Witchfinder (USA) 34 (7f,Lin,Std,Nov 18)
Without Friends (IRE) 31 (7f,Lin,Std,Jun 28)
Worldwide Elsie (USA) 37 (10f,Lin,Std,May 9)
Wottashambles 50 (16f,Lin,Std,Feb 11)

Xenophon of Cunaxa (IRE) 32 (9 1/2f,Wol,Std,Dec 26)

Yacht 31 (12f,Lin,Std,Nov 6)
Yeoman Oliver 50 (8f,Sou,Std,Jan 24)
Yet Again 45 (12f,Lin,Std,Jan 2)
Young Annabel (USA) 34 (7f,Sou,Std,May 12)

Zacaroon 32 (12f,Lin,Std,Jan 16)
Zahid (USA) 33 (10f,Lin,Std,Feb 25)
Zain Dancer 34 (6f,Sou,Std,Jly 21)
Zalotto (IRE) 50 (8f,Sou,Std,Nov 24)
Zamalek (USA) 33 (10f,Lin,Std,Jan 30)
Zatopek 36 (12f,Sou,Std,Feb 24)
Zermatt (IRE) 38 (9 1/2f,Wol,Std,Oct 4)
Ziggy's Dancer (USA) 52 (6f,Wol,Std,Oct 18)
Zorba 35 (9 1/2f,Wol,Std,Spt 30)
Zuhair 54 (6f,Wol,Std,May 1)
Zurs (IRE) 46 (8 1/2f,Wol,Std,Mar 8)

TWO YEAR-OLDS - Turf

Aberkeen 32 (6f,Nwc,GF,Aug 3)
Abreeze (USA) 53 (7f,San,GF,Spt 16)
Absalom's Lad 31 (7f,Bri,GF,Oct 23)
Absolutly Sparklin 44 (7f,Lei,GS,Oct 14)
Abuhail (USA) 40 (8f,San,S,Aug 30)
Abusamrah (USA) 36 (6f,Nwm,GF,Oct 31)
Acebo Lyons (IRE) 41 (7f,Nwb,GS,Oct 25)
Achilles 46 (8f,Yor,S,Oct 8)
Acid Test 32 (7f,Nwb,GF,Aug 16)
Adjutant 34 (6f,Hay,GF,Aug 15)
Admire 32 (8f,Chp,GS,Aug 25)
After Eight 32 (6f,Red,GF,Oct 28)
After The Rain 44 (8f,Nwc,G,Aug 25)
Aganon 35 (6f,Nwb,GS,Spt 20)
Air Attache (USA) 38 (7f,Nwm,G,Aug 22)
Aix En Provence (USA) 56 (7f,Nwm,GF,Oct 3)
Ajig Dancer 40 (6f,Nwb,S,May 17)
Akarita (IRE) 31 (7f,Hay,Hy,Oct 15)
Albarahin (USA) 53 (8f,Nwm,GF,Oct 31)
Alboostan 56 (8f,Goo,G,Spt 12)
Alborada 48 (7f,Cur,GS,Oct 4)
Alcayde 38 (7f,Hay,G,Spt 27)
Alconleigh 58 (6f,Rip,GS,May 18)
Al-Fateh (IRE) 40 (7f,Don,G,Nov 7)
Alfiglia 47 (5f,Asc,G,Jun 20)
Alharir (USA) 49 (8f,Don,GF,Spt 11)
Alignment (IRE) 30 (7f,San,GF,Aug 14)
Al Mabrook (IRE) 39 (6f,Nwm,G,Aug 2)
Almandab (IRE) 50 (8f,Not,G,Oct 30)
Almutawakel 69 (8f,Asc,GF,Spt 28)
Alpen Wolf (IRE) 32 (5f,Wnd,S,May 12)
Al's Fella (IRE) 31 (5f,Wnd,S,May 19)
Altibr (USA) 57 (7f,Lei,G,Oct 27)
Always Lucky 30 (5f,Fol,F,Spt 26)
Amabel (USA) 51 (7f,Nwb,GS,Oct 25)
Ambitious 35 (6f,Fol,G,Spt 2)
Andy Dufresne 66 (9f,Leo,S,Nov 9)
Anemos (IRE) 39 (7f,Don,G,Nov 7)
Angel Hill 44 (6f,Don,GF,Spt 13)
Angelina 37 (6f,Fol,G,Spt 2)
Angstrom (IRE) 41 (8f,Don,G,Nov 7)
Anita At Dawn (IRE) 33 (6f,Not,S,Jun 23)
Anna Palariva (IRE) 47 (8f,Lon,GF,Oct 5)
Another Fantasy (IRE) 50 (6f,Asc,S,Jly 26)
Anstand 39 (5f,Red,GF,Oct 28)
Anvil (USA) 43 (7f,Asc,G,Jun 19)
Apache Red (IRE) 40 (7f,Nwm,GF,Spt 30)
Arawak Cay (IRE) 46 (5f,Asc,G,Jun 19)
Arbenig (IRE) 33 (6f,Red,GF,Oct 28)
Arctic Star 37 (7f,Nwb,GS,Oct 25)
Arian Da 55 (5f,Fol,F,Spt 26)
Ariant (USA) 32 (6f,Nwb,GF,Jly 18)
Arjan (IRE) 45 (5f,Cat,S,Oct 17)
Arkadian Hero (USA) 69 (6f,Rip,GF,Aug 25)
Arm And A Leg (IRE) 36 (7f,Nwm,GS,Oct 16)
Arpeggio 32 (6f,Nwm,GF,May 31)
Asad 38 (7f,Yar,F,Oct 29)
Asakir 43 (10f,Lei,S,Oct 13)
Ascot Cyclone (USA) 53 (6 1/2f,Don,GF,Spt 10)

Asfurah (USA) 57 (6f,Nwm,G,Jly 8)
Ashraakat (USA) 57 (8f,Lon,GF,Oct 5)
Astrapi 57 (6f,Asc,GF,Spt 27)
Astrologer 48 (6f,Nwb,GS,Spt 20)
Asyaad (USA) 30 (6f,Cat,GF,Spt 20)
Atlanta 42 (6f,Nwb,GS,Spt 20)
Atlantic Viking (IRE) 52 (5f,Nwm,GF,Oct 31)
Attractive Crown (USA) 31 (7f,Cur,GS,Oct 4)
Atuf (USA) 65 (6f,Asc,GF,Spt 27)
Aurigny 51 (5f,Asc,G,Jun 20)

Baajil 47 (6f,Nwm,GF,Oct 31)
Baby Grand (IRE) 46 (5f,Ayr,GS,Spt 18)
Bahamian Melody (USA) 42 (6f,Lin,G,Spt 9)
Bahr 57 (7f,Nwb,GF,Aug 15)
Balaclava (IRE) 34 (7f,Kem,G,Aug 20)
Balaitini (IRE) 30 (7f,Lin,G,Spt 9)
Balanita (IRE) 40 (7f,Bri,GF,Oct 23)
Baltic State (USA) 52 (6f,Yar,F,Jun 5)
Bandbox (IRE) 49 (6f,Lei,G,Oct 28)
Banningham Blade 49 (5f,San,GF,May 27)
Barrelbio (IRE) 32 (5f,Edi,GS,Nov 6)
Batswing 42 (7f,Asc,Hy,Oct 11)
Bawsian 37 (8f,Red,G,Nov 4)
Bayleaf 41 (5f,Don,GF,Spt 13)
Bay Prince (IRE) 50 (5f,Yor,G,Aug 20)
Bedevilled 43 (6f,Lei,G,Oct 28)
Behold 36 (7f,Yar,GS,Jly 3)
Belladera (IRE) 45 (6f,Nwm,G,Jly 8)
Belle de Nuit (IRE) 50 (7f,Nwm,GF,Spt 30)
Bellow (IRE) 36 (7f,Nwm,GF,Jly 9)
Bemsha Swing (IRE) 52 (6f,Nwm,GF,Aug 23)
Be My Wish 38 (5f,Nwb,GF,Jly 19)
Beneventus 36 (7f,San,GF,Spt 16)
Benin (USA) 42 (7f,Lei,GF,Oct 5)
Ben Rinnes 42 (6f,Wnd,S,Jun 23)
Bergen (IRE) 32 (6f,Pon,GF,Jly 18)
Bering Gifts (IRE) 45 (8f,Nwm,GS,Oct 16)
Bermuda Boy 54 (6f,Sal,GF,Aug 21)
Bernardo Bellotto (IRE) 40 (6f,Eps,G,Aug 10)
Best of Our Days 40 (5f,Red,GF,Oct 28)
Bettron 53 (7f,Nwb,GS,Oct 25)
Beware 44 (6f,Nwm,G,Jly 19)
Bintang (IRE) 73 (6f,Yor,G,Aug 21)
Blakeset 59 (6f,Nwm,GF,Oct 4)
Bliss (IRE) 39 (5f,Nwm,G,Oct 2)
Blue Desert 44 (8f,Not,G,Oct 8)
Blue Gentian (USA) 44 (7f,Nwb,S,Spt 19)
Blue Kite 49 (6f,Don,GF,Spt 13)
Blueprint (IRE) 33 (8f,Nwb,S,Spt 19)
Blueridge Dancer (IRE) 47 (6f,Nwm,G,Jly 9)
Blue Shadow 32 (6f,Wnd,G,Aug 23)
Bluewain Lady 30 (7f,San,GF,Aug 14)
Blue Zola (IRE) 33 (8f,Nwm,GF,Nov 1)
Blundell Lane (IRE) 60 (6f,Red,GF,Oct 28)
Bobbydazzle 38 (8f,Nwc,G,Aug 25)
Bodfaridistinction (IRE) 55 (5f,Chs,Hy,May 8)
Bodyguard 43 (5f,Asc,G,Jun 19)
Bold Edge 61 (6f,Nwb,GF,Jly 19)
Bold Fact (USA) 66 (6f,Asc,G,Jun 17)
Bold King 30 (6f,Chp,GS,Jly 5)
Bolero Kid 44 (7 1/2f,Bev,GS,Aug 14)
Borani 54 (8f,Goo,G,Spt 13)
Border Arrow 58 (8f,Nwm,GS,Oct 16)
Bound To Please 38 (5f,Wnd,GF,Jly 21)
Braganza (USA) 30 (5f,Lin,F,Oct 3)
Branston Berry (IRE) 60 (6f,Hay,G,Spt 26)
Brave Reward (USA) 54 (7f,Lei,GS,Oct 14)
Brimming 39 (7f,Yar,F,Spt 17)
Brimstone (IRE) 35 (6f,Bat,G,Aug 12)
Bristol Channel 39 (7f,Nwb,GS,Oct 25)
Broughtons Mill 32 (6f,Nwm,G,Jly 19)
Browning 31 (6f,Nwb,GS,Spt 20)
Bullion 40 (7f,Nwb,GS,Spt 19)
Burnt Yates (IRE) 49 (7f,Chs,G,Spt 24)
Buzz 30 (5f,Rip,G,Aug 30)

Caernarfon Bay (IRE) 31 (6f,Nwb,G,Oct 24)
Calchas (IRE) 58 (7 1/2f,Bev,GF,Jly 21)
Call To Order 49 (5f,San,GF,Spt 17)
Campari (IRE) 30 (8f,Pon,GF,Spt 25)
Canadian Puzzler (USA) 45 (8f,Nwm,GS,Oct 17)
Cape Verdi (IRE) 72 (6f,Yor,G,Aug 21)
Capital Prince (FR) 40 (7f,Yar,G,Oct 22)
Capri 32 (8f,Not,G,Oct 30)
Captain Logan (IRE) 38 (7f,Yar,G,Oct 22)
Captain Tim 44 (7f,Yar,G,Oct 22)
Carambo 30 (5f,Thi,G,May 17)
Carbon 37 (7f,Yor,G,Aug 19)
Carinthia (IRE) 36 (6f,Wnd,G,Aug 23)
Carol Singer (USA) 36 (5f,Ayr,GS,Spt 18)
Carrowkeel (IRE) 63 (7f,Don,GF,Spt 12)
Carry The Flag 43 (8f,War,GF,Oct 7)
Casino King (IRE) 54 (7f,Asc,GF,Spt 28)
Catch The Rainbow 33 (7f,San,S,Aug 30)
Caversfield 40 (7f,Lei,G,Oct 27)
Cease Fire (IRE) 42 (6f,Sal,GF,Aug 21)
Celtic Cavalier (IRE) 45 (7f,San,GS,Aug 29)
Celtic Cross 42 (6f,Nwb,GF,Aug 15)
Celtic Pageant 51 (7f,Lei,GS,Oct 14)
Central Committee (IRE) 41 (7 1/2f,Bev,GF,Spt 17)
Central Park (IRE) 70 (7f,Asc,G,Jun 19)
Centre Court 35 (5f,Wnd,G,Jly 7)
Cerisette (IRE) 36 (7f,Lin,GF,Jly 12)
Chattan 53 (7f,Yar,G,Oct 22)
Chenille (IRE) 63 (9f,Leo,S,Nov 9)
Chester House (USA) 61 (7f,Yor,G,Aug 19)
Chieftain (IRE) 38 (5f,Lin,G,Aug 9)
Chief Whip (USA) 38 (6f,Goo,G,Spt 25)
Child Prodigy (IRE) 40 (5f,Asc,GF,Jun 18)
Chim Chiminey 42 (8f,Yor,S,Oct 8)
Chinaider (IRE) 43 (6f,Yor,G,Aug 20)
Chips (IRE) 54 (5f,Wnd,S,May 12)

Chist (USA) 41 (7f,Red,G,Nov 4)
Chocolate (IRE) 44 (7f,Yar,GF,Spt 16)
Chrysalis 35 (5f,Bri,GF,May 6)
Circus 37 (7f,Nwm,GF,Spt 30)
City Honours (USA) 69 (8f,Asc,GF,Spt 28)
Clapham Common (IRE) 43 (8f,Pon,GS,Oct 20)
Classic Manoeuvre (USA) 54 (7f,Asc,G,Jun 19)
Classy Cleo (IRE) 47 (5f,Hay,Hy,Oct 15)
Clef of Silver 46 (6f,Nwm,G,Aug 2)
Cloak of Darkness (IRE) 32 (7f,San,GF,Spt 16)
Close Shave 39 (7f,Yar,G,Oct 22)
Close Up (IRE) 41 (8f,Hay,S,Oct 15)
Cloudberry 48 (6f,Ayr,GS,Spt 19)
Cloud Castle 30 (7f,Nwm,GS,Oct 17)
Colleville 38 (7f,Lei,G,Aug 11)
Commander Charlie 38 (7f,San,GF,Jly 16)
Composition 32 (6f,Goo,G,Jun 13)
Compradore 44 (5f,Nwb,GF,May 28)
Conectis (IRE) 49 (6f,Nwm,G,Jly 8)
Confirmation 39 (7f,Ayr,GS,Spt 19)
Connoisseur Bay (USA) 50 (7f,Nwm,G,Oct 2)
Contrary Mary 47 (5f,Lin,GF,May 31)
Cool Prospect 33 (5f,Rip,GF,Aug 26)
Cool Secret 50 (6f,Hay,G,Spt 26)
Corniche (IRE) 46 (8f,Ayr,G,Spt 20)
Cortachy Castle (IRE) 62 (5f,Asc,G,Jun 20)
Cosmic Countess (IRE) 30 (6f,Bri,F,Spt 28)
Country Garden 37 (8f,Nwc,G,Aug 25)
Courageous (IRE) 45 (6f,Asc,Hy,Oct 10)
Court Lane (USA) 52 (6f,Nwm,GF,Oct 4)
Craigsteel 68 (8f,Asc,GF,Spt 28)
Crazee Mental 58 (6f,Nwm,GF,Spt 30)
Critical Air 32 (6f,Fol,G,Oct 21)
Cruinn A Bhord 46 (7f,Nwm,GF,Nov 1)
Crystal Wind (IRE) 57 (9f,Leo,S,Nov 9)
Cumbrian Cadet 43 (6f,Yor,G,Aug 20)
Cumbrian Caruso 51 (6f,Pon,S,Jun 30)
Czar Wars 32 (7f,War,GS,Aug 25)

Da Boss 39 (7f,San,GS,Jly 5)
Daggers Drawn (USA) 75 (7f,Don,GF,Spt 12)
Dance Trick (USA) 54 (6f,Eps,G,Jun 6)
Dancing Icon (IRE) 35 (5f,Hay,GF,Aug 9)
Dancing Phantom 36 (8f,Lin,GS,Aug 28)
Danyross (IRE) 50 (6f,Nwm,G,Jly 8)
Daring Derek (USA) 37 (6f,Lin,F,Oct 3)
Dark Moondancer 42 (7f,Hay,Hy,Oct 15)
Dashing Chief (IRE) 63 (10f,Nwm,GF,Nov 1)
Daunting Lady (IRE) 64 (5f,Chs,S,May 6)
Daymarti (IRE) 74 (15f,Lon,G,Oct 4)
Days of Grace 31 (5f,Nwm,G,Apr 16)
Dazilyn Lady (USA) 55 (6f,Yor,G,Aug 21)
Decisive Action (USA) 46 (8f,Not,S,Oct 15)
Deep Space (IRE) 33 (6f,Asc,S,Jly 26)
Defiance 37 (6f,Eps,G,Aug 10)
Dekelsmary 32 (6f,Lei,GF,Spt 22)
Deki (USA) 45 (7 1/2f,Bev,GS,Aug 14)
Delciana (IRE) 30 (6f,Lei,GF,Spt 22)
Demolition Jo 54 (6f,Nwm,GS,Oct 16)
Dernier Croise (FR) 34 (5f,Fol,G,Spt 2)
Derryquin 44 (8f,Don,G,Nov 7)
Desert Drama (IRE) 57 (8f,Lon,GF,Oct 5)
Desert Lady (IRE) 37 (5f,Don,GS,Jun 28)
Desert Prince (IRE) 67 (6f,Asc,G,Jun 17)
Designer (USA) 58 (6f,Nwm,G,Oct 2)
Deterrent 46 (6f,Don,G,Oct 25)
Deva Lady 35 (6f,Yor,G,Aug 20)
Diamond White 48 (6f,Nwm,G,Aug 2)
Dil 33 (5f,Hay,GS,Spt 5)
Diligence (IRE) 66 (5f,Goo,GS,May 20)
Dilkusha (IRE) 33 (6f,Nwm,GS,Oct 17)
Dim Ots 39 (5f,Bat,GS,May 19)
Distant Mirage (IRE) 54 (8f,Nwb,GS,Oct 25)
Dixie Dynamo (USA) 37 (6f,Cur,GS,Jun 29)
D'Marti 37 (6f,Red,GS,Jly 26)
Docksider (USA) 70 (7f,Don,GF,Spt 12)
Dodo (IRE) 40 (6f,Asc,G,Aug 1)
Dog Watch 44 (7f,Red,G,Nov 4)
Doomna (IRE) 35 (7f,Goo,GF,Jly 31)
Doraid (IRE) 45 (7f,Hay,G,Spt 27)
Double Brandy 48 (6f,Lei,G,Oct 28)
Double Edged 42 (8f,Don,GS,Nov 8)
Dover Soul 30 (6f,Sal,GF,Aug 21)
Dower House 37 (8f,Yar,F,Spt 18)
Dr Fong (USA) 60 (8f,Asc,S,Oct 11)
Duck Row (USA) 53 (8f,Nwb,S,Spt 19)
Due South 53 (8f,Nwc,G,Aug 25)
Dutch Lad 35 (8f,Nwm,GS,Oct 17)

Eagle's Cross (USA) 31 (8f,Nwm,GS,Oct 16)
Eastern Lyric 42 (5f,Nwb,GS,Spt 20)
Eastern Purple (IRE) 51 (5f,Ayr,GS,Spt 18)
Easter Ogil (IRE) 38 (6f,Cat,S,Oct 16)
Eco Friendly 43 (8f,Don,GS,Nov 8)
Edwardian 30 (8f,Not,S,Oct 15)
Elakik 44 (8f,Yar,G,Oct 22)
Elanaaka 33 (7 1/2f,Bev,GF,Spt 17)
Eleonora d'Arborea 45 (6f,Red,GS,Jly 26)
Eleventh Duke (IRE) 50 (5f,Fol,G,Spt 2)
Elhabub 53 (6f,Nwc,GF,Oct 1)
Eljjanah (USA) 30 (7f,Red,GF,Jly 19)
Ella (IRE) 50 (5f,Asc,Hy,Oct 11)
Ellenbrook (IRE) 32 (5f,Red,F,Spt 26)
Eloquent 51 (7f,San,GF,Jly 24)
Elshamms 55 (7f,Nwm,G,Oct 18)
Elsurur (USA) 39 (7f,Nwm,G,Oct 18)
Embassy 77 (6f,Asc,S,Jly 26)
Emmajoun 32 (6f,Fol,G,Spt 2)
Emperor Naheem (IRE) 42 (5f,Nwb,GS,Spt 20)
Empirical (USA) 32 (6f,Lei,G,Oct 27)
Enchant 36 (6f,Nwm,GF,Oct 4)
Epsom Cyclone (USA) 33 (6f,Nwb,GS,Spt 20)
Equity Princess 54 (8f,Asc,S,Oct 11)

Erro Codigo 33 (6f,Red,GF,Aug 9)
Escudo (IRE) 46 (5f,Fol,F,Spt 26)
Euro Venture 34 (5f,Don,G,May 5)
Evander (IRE) 51 (8f,Nwb,GS,Oct 25)
Evening World (FR) 43 (8f,Nwb,S,Spt 19)
Exbourne's Wish (USA) 45 (6f,Nwm,GF,Oct 4)
Exclusive 59 (8f,Asc,GF,Spt 28)
Exit To Somewhere (IRE) 37 (7 1/2f,Bev,G,Jly 29)
Expect To Shine 51 (7f,Nwm,G,Oct 18)

Face-Off 30 (7f,Lin,F,Oct 3)
Facile Tigre 32 (5f,Nwb,GS,Spt 20)
Fa-Eq (IRE) 48 (6f,Nwb,G,Oct 24)
Fairy Flight (IRE) 34 (6f,Cur,S,Spt 7)
Fairy Rock (IRE) 30 (6f,Lei,G,Oct 27)
Fakhr (USA) 34 (7f,Sal,GF,Jly 12)
Fantasy Island (IRE) 46 (7f,Nwm,G,Aug 22)
Far Removed (IRE) 47 (6f,Don,GF,Spt 13)
Fast Franc (IRE) 33 (5f,Fol,S,Jun 27)
Fast Tempo (IRE) 36 (5f,Wnd,GS,Jun 30)
Fayrana (IRE) 42 (7f,Goo,GF,Aug 2)
Festival Song (USA) 33 (6f,Cur,GS,Jun 29)
Ffestiniog (IRE) 50 (7f,Nwb,GS,Oct 25)
Fiamma (IRE) 48 (7f,Nwm,G,Oct 18)
Fields of Omagh (USA) 30 (7f,Don,G,Nov 7)
Filey Brigg 71 (6f,Asc,S,Jly 26)
Filfilah 57 (6f,Asc,S,Jly 26)
Final Tango 52 (7f,Red,GF,Oct 18)
Fire Goddess 32 (6f,Asc,S,Jun 21)
First Village (IRE) 40 (5f,Hay,G,Spt 21)
Fiveo'clock Shadow (IRE) 40 (5f,Bri,GF,May 6)
Five of Spades (IRE) 51 (6f,Not,G,Nov 3)
Fizzed 48 (6f,Ayr,GS,Spt 19)
Flame Tower (IRE) 37 (6f,Fol,G,Oct 21)
Flame Violet (IRE) 45 (7f,Cur,S,Spt 7)
Flaming Ember (IRE) 49 (6f,Eps,G,Jun 6)
Flawless 61 (7f,Nwm,GF,Oct 4)
Fleetwood (IRE) 53 (7f,Hay,G,Spt 21)
Flight 34 (6f,Yar,GF,Aug 21)
Florazi 56 (7f,Don,G,Oct 25)
Flow By 32 (7f,Nwm,GF,Aug 8)
Flower O'Cannie (IRE) 46 (7 1/2f,Bev,Hy,Jly 5)
Flying Bold (IRE) 37 (7f,Nwb,GS,Oct 25)
Folklore 54 (5f,Rip,GF,Aug 26)
Forest Treasure (IRE) 57 (6f,Asc,S,Jly 26)
Former Love (USA) 37 (7f,Lei,G,Oct 27)
Forum 47 (6f,Nwm,G,Jly 8)
Free As The Wind (IRE) 33 (8f,Not,G,Oct 30)
Freedom Quest (IRE) 33 (7f,Chs,G,Spt 24)
Free Option (IRE) 44 (7f,Red,G,Nov 4)
Friar Tuck 57 (6f,Ham,G,Spt 29)
Friendly Warning (FR) 47 (6f,Nwm,G,Aug 2)
Frond 54 (7f,Nwc,GF,Oct 22)
Fruits of Love (USA) 57 (7f,Nwb,GF,Aug 15)
Fundance 36 (6f,Not,G,Spt 28)

Gandoura (USA) 34 (6f,Nwb,GF,Aug 15)
General Monck 32 (8f,Not,G,Oct 30)
Generosity 35 (7f,Goo,GF,Aug 1)
Generous Embrace 32 (6f,Lin,Std,Aug 28)
Genoa 37 (7f,Nwm,GF,Nov 1)
Ghali (USA) 46 (7f,Asc,GF,Spt 28)
Gipsy Moth 55 (5f,Hay,GF,Aug 15)
Giveaway 41 (8f,Hay,S,Oct 15)
Glass River 40 (5f,Red,GF,Oct 28)
Glorosia (FR) 64 (8f,Asc,GF,Spt 28)
Glory of Grosvenor (IRE) 41 (8f,Nwb,S,Spt 19)
Going Places 39 (5f,Nwm,G,Apr 16)
Golden Dice (USA) 55 (7f,Don,GF,Spt 10)
Golden Fortune 43 (7f,Nwm,GF,Spt 30)
Golden Hawk (USA) 41 (8f,Kem,GF,Spt 22)
Golden Mirage (IRE) 47 (5f,Wnd,S,May 12)
Golden Reprimand (IRE) 40 (6f,Nwm,GS,Oct 17)
Golden Strategy (IRE) 38 (5f,Wnd,GF,Jly 21)
Goodwood Cavalier 32 (7f,Lei,GS,Oct 14)
Grace Browning 30 (6f,War,GF,Oct 7)
Grand Slam (IRE) 36 (7f,Nwb,GF,Spt 18)
Grazia 58 (6f,Nwm,GF,Oct 4)
Great Dane (IRE) 35 (7f,Yar,F,Oct 29)
Greek Dance (IRE) 36 (7f,Kem,G,Spt 10)
Greenbrook 39 (7f,San,S,Aug 30)
Guaranteed 40 (7f,Chs,GS,Aug 29)
Guildhall 34 (8f,Yor,S,Oct 8)
Gulland 59 (8f,Pon,GS,Oct 20)
Gurkha 41 (6f,Yor,S,Spt 4)
Gypsy Passion (IRE) 49 (7f,Red,G,Nov 4)

Haami (USA) 63 (7f,Nwm,GF,Oct 3)
Hadayik 48 (8f,Don,GF,Spt 11)
Hadid (USA) 47 (5f,Nwb,GF,May 28)
Hadith 31 (8f,Bri,GF,Oct 23)
Hakeem (IRE) 54 (6f,Nwm,GF,Oct 4)
Half-Hitch (USA) 30 (6f,Thi,G,Jly 25)
Halmahera (IRE) 84 (5f,Asc,Hy,Oct 11)
Hanzanar (IRE) 35 (8f,Cur,S,Oct 18)
Happy Days 39 (6f,Yor,G,May 15)
Happy Days Again (IRE) 46 (6f,Nwm,G,Aug 2)
Happy Wanderer 31 (5f,Red,GF,Oct 28)
Harbour Master (FR) 71 (6f,Asc,G,Jun 17)
Harmonic Way 43 (7f,Lei,GS,Oct 14)
Have Merci 46 (9f,Leo,S,Nov 9)
Hayil (USA) 61 (6f,Nwm,G,Oct 2)
Headhunter (IRE) 46 (7f,Nwm,GF,Spt 30)
Heavenly Abstone 50 (6f,Chs,GF,Aug 3)
Heed My Warning (IRE) 50 (7f,Cur,S,Spt 7)
Heeremandi (IRE) 51 (6f,Nwm,GF,Spt 30)
Herminius (IRE) 41 (8f,Red,GF,Oct 18)
Hickory (IRE) 37 (6f,Asc,G,Jun 17)
High And Low 43 (7f,Don,G,Nov 7)
High Carry 47 (5f,Nwm,G,Oct 2)
High-Rise (IRE) 43 (7f,Don,G,Nov 7)
High Sheriff (IRE) 48 (7f,War,GF,Jly 19)
Highwayman (IRE) 35 (7f,Yar,F,Spt 17)
Hill Magic 45 (6f,Nwb,GF,Jly 19)

Himself (USA) 33 (8f,Lei,G,Oct 28)
Hirst Bridge (IRE) 39 (5f,Thi,G,May 17)
Hoh Chi Min 59 (6f,Ayr,GS,Spt 19)
Hoh Justice 37 (5f,San,GF,Spt 17)
Ho Leng (IRE) 45 (6f,Red,GF,Oct 18)
Hollow Haze (USA) 45 (7f,Nwb,S,Spt 19)
Holy Wine (USA) 35 (8f,Lin,G,Spt 9)
Honest Borderer 34 (7f,Nwm,G,Oct 2)
Honey Storm (IRE) 34 (7f,Lin,G,Spt 9)
Hopping Higgins (IRE) 50 (6f,Leo,GS,Aug 10)
Housekeeper (IRE) 37 (7f,Lin,G,Oct 27)
Howies Choice (IRE) 30 (5f,Cat,G,Spt 27)
Hujoom (IRE) 52 (6f,Ayr,G,Spt 20)
Huntswood 35 (5f,Fol,GF,Aug 5)

Iceband (USA) 55 (6f,Nwm,G,Jly 19)
I Cried For You (IRE) 33 (5f,Not,GF,Oct 4)
Ikhteyaar (USA) 51 (6f,Kem,G,Spt 10)
Impressionist (IRE) 62 (7f,Nwm,G,Oct 18)
Impulsive Decision (IRE) 41 (6f,Fol,G,Oct 21)
Inchalong 44 (6f,Not,G,Nov 3)
Inchtina 33 (7f,Kem,GF,Spt 22)
Indian Missile 48 (7f,Asc,Hy,Oct 10)
Indimaaj 32 ($7\frac{1}{2}$f,Bev,G,Jly 29)
Iris May 36 (6f,Ham,S,Jun 25)
Iron Mountain (IRE) 30 (10f,Not,GF,Spt 23)
Islamabad 43 (5f,Wnd,GF,Jun 2)
Isle De France (USA) 59 (8f,Lon,GF,Oct 5)
Its All Relative 51 (5f,Ayr,GS,Spt 18)
Ivory's Joy 40 (5f,Nwb,GS,Spt 20)

Jaazim (USA) 38 (8f,Not,S,Oct 15)
Jackerin (IRE) 43 (5f,Hay,GF,Aug 15)
Jacmar (IRE) 60 (6f,Ham,G,Spt 29)
Jay Gee (IRE) 56 (6f,Nwm,G,Aug 2)
Jazz Club (USA) 45 (7f,Yor,G,Aug 19)
Jewel (IRE) 31 (5f,Nwm,G,Apr 16)
Jibe (USA) 63 (8f,Asc,GF,Spt 28)
Jila (IRE) 43 (7f,Yar,G,Oct 22)
Jilted (IRE) 39 (6f,Nwm,GF,Oct 4)
Jimmy Too 57 (6f,Nwb,GS,Spt 20)
Jocasta 30 (6f,Nwm,GS,Oct 17)
Joint Regent (USA) 34 (7f,Nwm,G,Oct 2)
Julies Jewel (IRE) 34 (6f,Not,G,Spt 28)
Jungle Story (IRE) 31 (7f,Cat,G,Spt 27)
Junior Muffin (IRE) 37 (5f,San,G,Spt 16)
Just Another Time 39 (6f,Fol,F,Spt 26)
Just In Time 46 (7f,Goo,GF,Aug 1)

Kahtan 35 (8f,Don,GF,Spt 12)
Kameez (IRE) 38 (7f,Nwc,GF,Oct 22)
Karakorum (IRE) 38 (7f,Cur,S,Spt 7)
Kathies Pet 40 (6f,Fol,G,Oct 21)
Kawafil (IRE) 44 (8f,Bat,G,Spt 8)
Kennet 47 (6f,Kem,G,Spt 21)
Kettlesing (IRE) 41 (5f,Not,GF,Oct 4)
Khalas 36 (7f,Nwc,G,Aug 25)
Kheyrah (USA) 66 (6f,Hay,G,Spt 26)
Khumba Mela (IRE) 57 (8f,Lon,GF,Oct 5)
Kilcora (IRE) 39 (5f,Chs,S,May 6)
Kilimanjaro 69 (8f,Asc,GF,Spt 28)
Kim's Brave 60 (10f,Nwm,GF,Nov 1)
King Darius (IRE) 41 (7f,Goo,GF,Aug 2)
King Of Kings (IRE) 60 (7f,Cur,GS,Aug 16)
Kings Arrow (IRE) 38 (7f,Lei,GS,Oct 14)
Kitza (IRE) 40 (6f,Cur,S,Spt 7)
Komistar 57 (8f,Nwb,GS,Oct 25)
Krisamba 47 (7f,Lei,GS,Oct 14)
Krispy Knight 45 (6f,Nwm,GF,Jly 25)

Lady Alexander (IRE) 44 (7f,Cur,S,Spt 7)
Lady Charlotte 32 (6f,Bat,GF,Spt 29)
Lady In Waiting 63 (6f,Yor,GS,Jun 13)
Lady Moll 40 (5f,Rip,G,Apr 26)
La-Faah (IRE) 49 (7f,Asc,Hy,Oct 11)
Lakeland Pride (IRE) 32 (6f,Yor,G,May 15)
Land of Dreams 57 (6f,Rip,GF,Aug 25)
La Nuit Rose (FR) 38 (7f,Lei,S,Oct 13)
Last Christmas 49 (7f,Hay,G,Spt 27)
Late Night Out 53 (6f,Not,G,Oct 30)
La Tiziana 31 (7f,Cat,S,Oct 16)
Law Library (IRE) 48 (6f,Cur,S,Spt 7)
Lea Grande 53 (7f,Nwm,GF,Nov 1)
Lear Spear (USA) 35 (7f,Kem,G,Spt 10)
Legal Lark (IRE) 41 (6f,Fol,F,Spt 26)
Legend of Love 34 (6f,Hay,GF,Aug 15)
Leggera (IRE) 48 (7f,Nwb,GS,Oct 25)
Legs Be Frendly (IRE) 51 (5f,Lin,G,Oct 27)
Lend A Hand 58 (8f,Don,GF,Spt 11)
Leofric 35 (6f,Lin,G,Spt 9)
Lets Be Fair 40 (5f,Ham,G,Aug 2)
Lido (IRE) 50 (7f,Don,G,Oct 25)
Lift The Offer (IRE) 33 (7f,Lei,G,Jly 23)
Light Step (USA) 35 (7f,Don,GS,Jun 28)
Likely Story (IRE) 56 (6f,Ayr,GS,Spt 19)
Lincolnshire (USA) 33 (5f,Sal,GF,May 15)
Linden Heights 56 (6f,Nwm,G,Jly 9)
Little Indian 61 (7f,San,GS,Aug 29)
Little Miss Huff (IRE) 34 (7f,War,GS,Aug 25)
Lobuche (IRE) 31 (5f,Bri,GF,May 6)
Loch Laird 39 (5f,Lin,F,Apr 4)
Lone Piper 36 (7f,Yar,GS,Jly 3)
Lonesome Dude (CAN) 53 (7f,Lei,G,Oct 27)
Long Bond (IRE) 34 ($7\frac{1}{2}$f,Bev,GF,Spt 17)
Long Siege (IRE) 32 (6f,Nwm,G,Jly 9)
Lord Kintyre 71 (5f,Asc,Hy,Oct 11)
Lord Lieutenant 38 (5f,Bev,GF,Spt 17)
Lord Smith 53 (7f,Nwm,GF,Jly 25)
Lord Warford 34 (7f,Hay,G,Spt 27)
Love Academy 40 (6f,Nwc,GF,Oct 22)
Love Kiss (IRE) 31 (8f,Don,G,Nov 7)
Lovers Knot 53 (7f,Nwm,GF,Nov 1)
Loving Claim (USA) 62 (8f,Lon,GF,Oct 5)
Lucayan Indian (IRE) 58 (6f,Nwc,GF,Oct 1)

Lucky Double 32 (7f,Sal,G,Oct 1)
Lucky Myst 31 (7f,War,GF,Jly 19)

Madjamila (IRE) 40 (7f,Lin,G,Oct 27)
Magical 41 (6f,Rip,GF,Aug 25)
Magical Minty (IRE) 34 (7f,Cur,GS,Aug 30)
Magic of Aloha (IRE) 40 (7f,Nwm,GF,Spt 30)
Mahboob (IRE) 58 (7f,Don,GF,Spt 10)
Main Street 33 (6f,Wnd,G,Aug 23)
Majaari 43 (6f,Kem,G,Spt 10)
Mantles Pride 55 (5f,Fol,F,Spt 26)
Mantles Star 54 (7f,Goo,GF,Aug 2)
Mantusis (IRE) 45 (8f,Kem,GF,Spt 22)
Marie Loup (FR) 57 (6f,Asc,GF,Spt 27)
Marigot Bay (IRE) 32 (6f,Cur,S,Spt 7)
Mark of Prophet (IRE) 31 (7f,War,GF,Oct 7)
Marksman (IRE) 53 (6f,Nwm,GS,Jun 20)
Marran (IRE) 47 (7f,Bri,F,Spt 28)
Marske Machine 33 (7f,San,S,Aug 30)
Marton Moss (SWE) 45 (6f,Rip,GF,Aug 25)
Mary Jane 42 (5f,Red,GF,Oct 28)
Mashab 36 (7f,Lei,GS,Oct 14)
Masha-Il (IRE) 32 (6f,Don,G,Nov 7)
Master Mac (USA) 36 (6f,Lin,GF,Jly 12)
Mawsoof 41 (8f,Not,G,Spt 28)
Mazboon (USA) 44 (7f,Yar,GS,Jly 3)
Means Business (IRE) 35 (5f,Lin,GF,Jly 26)
Mempari (IRE) 47 (7f,Cur,S,Spt 7)
Meniatarra (USA) 32 (7f,Nwm,GF,Nov 1)
Merciless 38 (8f,Don,G,Oct 24)
Merlin's Ring 57 (7f,Goo,GF,Aug 2)
Middle Temple 40 (8f,Yar,G,Oct 22)
Midnight Line (USA) 67 (8f,Don,GF,Spt 11)
Midsummer Night (IRE) 36 (5f,Nwm,G,Oct 2)
Mighty Sure (IRE) 39 (5f,Red,F,Spt 26)
Mihnah (IRE) 42 (6f,Yor,S,Oct 8)
Mijana (IRE) 61 (6f,Rip,GF,Aug 25)
Milligan (FR) 56 (9f,Lon,G,Oct 4)
Millitrix 37 (7f,Nwb,S,Spt 19)
Minivet 38 (7f,Nwm,G,Oct 2)
Miquelon 38 (8f,,Yar,G,Oct 22)
Misalliance 32 (7f,Nwc,GF,Oct 1)
Misbah (USA) 56 (7f,Yar,G,Oct 22)
Mishraak (IRE) 48 (5f,Fol,G,Spt 2)
Miss Bussell 30 (7f,Nwm,GF,Nov 1)
Missed The Cut (IRE) 30 (5f,Fol,F,Spt 26)
Miss Money Spider (IRE) 31 (6f,Asc,Hy,Oct 10)
Miss Zafonic (FR) 72 (6f,Asc,S,Jly 26)
Mister Bankes 30 (5f,Wnd,GS,Jun 30)
Mister Rambo 49 (6f,Nwb,G,Oct 24)
Mitch Passi (IRE) 37 (6f,Cat,S,Oct 16)
Mohawk (IRE) 37 (7f,Lin,F,Oct 3)
Mondschein 51 (7f,Red,GF,Oct 18)
Monsajem (USA) 39 (8f,Nwm,GS,Oct 17)
Montano (USA) 45 (7f,Bri,GF,Oct 23)
Monte Lemos (IRE) 67 (6f,Nwm,GF,Oct 4)

Moonlight Flit 34 (7 1/2f,Bev,GF,Spt 17)
Moontabeh 34 (5f,Lin,S,Jun 28)
Moothyeb (USA) 35 (6f,Yar,F,Jun 5)
Mountain Song 34 (8f,Cur,S,Spt 21)
Mowbray (USA) 36 (7f,Kem,G,Aug 20)
Mr Cahill (USA) 39 (7f,Yar,GF,Aug 6)
Mrs Malaprop 47 (5f,Cat,G,Spt 27)
Mubrik (IRE) 44 (7f,Nwb,GF,Spt 18)
Mudalal (USA) 39 (7f,Lei,G,Oct 27)
Mudeer 73 (8f,Don,G,Oct 25)
Mugello 57 (6f,Nwb,GF,Jly 19)
Muhaba (USA) 49 (8f,Hay,G,Spt 27)
Muhtathir 65 (7f,San,GS,Jly 4)
Mulahen 44 (7f,Lei,GS,Oct 14)
Mushraaf 50 (7f,Don,GF,Spt 10)
Musical Twist (USA) 53 (6f,Nwb,GF,Aug 15)
Mustique Dream 32 (6f,Bat,GF,Jly 17)
Mutamam 71 (8f,Don,G,Oct 25)
Mutawwaj (IRE) 57 (7f,Yor,G,Aug 19)
Mystagogue 30 (7f,War,GF,Jly 19)
Mysterious Ecology 32 (8f,Kem,GF,Spt 22)
Mysticism 41 (5f,Nwb,GF,Jly 19)

Nadwah (USA) 71 (6f,Yor,G,Aug 21)
Name of Love (IRE) 66 (7f,Nwm,GF,Oct 4)
Nanoushka (IRE) 53 (7f,Nwm,GF,Oct 4)
Narrogin (USA) 37 (8f,Lei,GF,Oct 5)
Naskhi 42 (8f,Pon,GF,Spt 25)
Natalis (IRE) 42 (7f,Cur,GS,Aug 30)
Naughty Blue (USA) 50 (7f,Yar,F,Spt 17)
Nautical Star 41 (7f,San,GS,Jly 5)
Naviasky (IRE) 35 (7f,Don,G,Oct 25)
Next Round (IRE) 41 (7f,San,GF,Jly 24)
Night Flyer 45 (7f,Bri,F,Spt 28)
Night Owl 32 (6f,Kem,G,Spt 10)
Night Rule 58 (10f,Nwm,GF,Nov 1)
Night Shot 55 (6f,Don,GF,Spt 13)
Niki (IRE) 56 (6f,Asc,GF,Spt 27)
Noble Demand (USA) 48 (8f,Nwm,GS,Oct 17)
Noemie (FR) 46 (8f,Lon,GF,Oct 5)
North Ofthe Border 37 (7f,Lei,G,Oct 27)
Nuclear Debate (USA) 59 (6f,Nwm,GS,Oct 16)
Nuit d'Or (IRE) 32 (7f,Hay,G,Spt 27)
Nunthorpe 38 (6f,Pon,GF,Spt 25)

Oberon's Mistral 31 (8f,Lei,GF,Spt 9)
Obsessed 38 (7f,San,GF,Jly 24)
Occhi Verdi (IRE) 37 (7f,Nwm,GF,Spt 30)
Odette 37 (5f,Cat,S,Oct 17)
Oh Hebe (IRE) 30 (5f,Bat,G,Aug 12)
O' Higgins (IRE) 35 (8f,Red,GF,Oct 18)
Oh So Easy 38 (5f,San,GF,Spt 17)
O'Kelly (DEN) 39 (7f,Chs,GS,Aug 29)
Ok John (IRE) 31 (5f,Fol,F,Spt 26)
Olive The Twist (USA) 30 (7f,Don,G,Nov 7)
One Singer 51 (5f,Red,G,May 12)
One To Go (IRE) 32 (6f,Red,GF,Oct 28)

Only For Gold 44 (5f,Bev,GF,Jun 5)
Only In Dreams 30 (7f,Lei,S,Oct 13)
Opera King (USA) 33 (7f,Don,G,Jly 30)
Opposition Leader 40 (7f,War,G,Jun 24)
Optimistic 43 (8f,Don,GF,Spt 11)
Oriel Girl 32 (5f,Edi,GF,Aug 20)
Ouaisne 44 (5f,Red,G,Jun 20)
Out Like Magic 34 (6f,Pon,S,Jun 30)
Outsourcing (USA) 35 (7f,San,GF,Jly 16)

Pacifica 47 (5f,Nwm,G,Apr 16)
Panama House 37 (7f,Thi,GF,Aug 11)
Pantar (IRE) 43 (7f,Nwm,GF,Spt 30)
Parisian Lady (IRE) 41 (6f,Sal,GF,Jly 12)
Particular Friend 32 (7f,Nwm,GS,Jly 18)
Pas de Memoires (IRE) 37 (8f,Red,G,Nov 4)
Pass The Rest (IRE) 39 (7f,Hay,Hy,Oct 15)
Patsy Culsyth 42 (5f,Ayr,GS,Spt 18)
Pay On Red (USA) 37 (7f,Asc,Hy,Oct 10)
Peak Path (IRE) 37 (7f,San,GF,Spt 16)
Pegnitz (USA) 59 (7f,Asc,GF,Spt 28)
Pelagos (FR) 35 (7f,Nwb,GF,Spt 18)
Percy-P 39 (5f,Sal,GF,May 15)
Perfect Peach 40 (5f,Bev,GS,Aug 13)
Persiano 47 (6f,Nwm,GS,Oct 16)
Persian Venture 39 (7f,San,S,Aug 30)
Petara (IRE) 33 (6f,Rip,GS,May 18)
Petarga 38 (5f,Nwb,GF,Jly 19)
Peter's Imp (IRE) 54 (6f,Hay,G,Spt 26)
Phone Alex (IRE) 38 (5f,San,GF,Apr 25)
Photogenic 38 (7f,Nwm,GF,Spt 30)
Pierpoint (IRE) 39 (6f,Ham,G,Spt 29)
Plan-B 35 (8f,Yar,F,Spt 18)
Plasir Des Yeux (FR) 58 (8f,Lon,GF,Oct 5)
Pleasuredancer (USA) 34 (7f,Lei,GF,Oct 5)
Poetto 32 (6f,Goo,GF,Aug 22)
Polo Venture 32 (8f,Pon,GS,Oct 20)
Poly Blue (IRE) 53 (6f,Nwb,GS,Spt 20)
Pontoon 53 (7f,Nwm,GF,Nov 1)
Pool Music 56 (5f,San,GF,May 27)
Positive Air 36 (6f,Not,GF,Spt 15)
Praetorian Gold 36 (6f,Not,G,Spt 28)
Premium Princess 50 (6f,Red,GF,Oct 28)
Premium Pursuit 45 (6f,Ayr,G,Spt 20)
Premium Quest 33 (8f,Pon,GS,Oct 20)
Priceless 31 (8f,Goo,G,Spt 12)
Pride of Place (IRE) 34 (7f,Lin,G,Spt 9)
Primavera 32 (7f,War,GF,Jly 19)
Prime Hand 32 (5f,Rip,G,Jly 7)
Prince Ashleigh 31 (7f,Cat,S,Oct 17)
Prince Foley 40 (5f,Bev,GF,Jun 5)
Princely Heir (IRE) 59 (6f,Leo,GS,Aug 10)
Princess Natalie 38 (6f,Nwm,GF,Oct 4)
Priors Moor 34 (8f,Goo,G,Spt 13)
Prix Star 30 (5f,Crl,GS,May 9)
Prolix 70 (8f,Asc,GF,Spt 28)
Prompt Delivery (USA) 44 (6f,Pon,GF,Spt 25)
Prose (IRE) 57 (6f,Rip,GS,May 18)
Publisher (USA) 32 (8f,Yar,F,Oct 29)
Pure Coincidence 66 (5f,Hay,G,Spt 21)
Pure Nobility (IRE) 46 (7f,Lei,G,Oct 27)
Pursuit Venture 32 (7f,Lin,G,Oct 27)
Putuna 45 (7f,Nwm,GF,Spt 30)

Qilin (IRE) 61 (6f,Nwm,GF,Oct 4)
Quel Senor (FR) 63 (9f,Lon,G,Oct 4)
Quiet Assurance (USA) 58 (8f,Don,G,Oct 25)
Quintus (USA) 40 (7f,Nwb,GF,Jly 19)
Quite Happy (IRE) 40 (5f,Red,GF,Oct 28)
Quiver Tree 30 (6f,Nwm,G,Jly 19)
Quiz Master 41 (5f,Red,GF,Oct 28)
Quiz Show 34 (6f,Not,GF,Spt 15)

Rabah 56 (8f,Nwm,GF,Oct 31)
Rabi (IRE) 66 (7f,Lei,GF,Spt 22)
Radar (IRE) 43 (7f,Bri,GF,Oct 23)
Rainbow High 32 (7f,Hay,Hy,Oct 15)
Rainbow Ways 44 (8f,Nwm,GS,Oct 16)
Raise A King 70 (6f,Nwm,GF,Oct 4)
Rambling Rose 53 (8f,Not,GF,Spt 23)
Ranna 42 (7f,Red,GF,Oct 18)
Rapid Reliance 32 (5f,San,G,Spt 16)
Ra Ra Rasputin 32 (6f,Don,GF,Spt 13)
Rare Indigo 48 (5f,Lin,G,Oct 27)
Ratiyya (IRE) 35 (7f,Yar,GF,Spt 16)
Ray of Sunshine (IRE) 33 (7f,Thi,GF,Aug 11)
Ray's Folly (IRE) 48 (7f,San,GS,Jly 5)
Razor 42 (7f,Nwm,GF,Spt 30)
Really Done It Now (IRE) 31 (5f,War,GF,Jun 9)
Reap Rewards 36 (5f,Bev,GF,Jun 5)
Rebalza (IRE) 33 (7f,Nwc,GF,Aug 6)
Recognition 44 (6f,Fol,G,Spt 2)
Red Leggings 38 (7f,War,GF,Oct 7)
Red Pepper (IRE) 31 (5f,Fol,F,Spt 26)
Red Sky Charlie 33 (7f,Nwb,GF,Spt 18)
Refined (IRE) 52 (5f,Cat,S,Oct 16)
Regalo 45 (5f,Lin,G,Oct 27)
Regal Patriarch (IRE) 30 (8f,Nwm,GS,Oct 16)
Regal Revolution 75 (6f,Ayr,GS,Spt 19)
Rejected 40 (5f,Hay,GF,Jun 7)
Remarkable Style (USA) 38 (7f,Cur,S,Spt 7)
Requestor 37 (6f,Rip,GF,Aug 26)
Respond 34 (7f,Nwb,GS,Oct 25)
Rhein Hill (IRE) 31 (7f,War,GF,Oct 7)
Rich Choice 52 (6f,Red,GF,Oct 28)
Rico Suave (IRE) 37 (8f,Goo,G,Spt 25)
Ridgeway (IRE) 34 (7f,Nwm,GF,Spt 30)
Riley 31 (7f,Bri,F,Spt 28)
Ring Dancer 55 (6f,Not,G,Oct 30)
Ringleader 38 (8f,Nwm,GF,Nov 1)
Risada (IRE) 30 (8f,Lin,GS,Aug 28)
Risque Lady 65 (5f,Hay,G,Spt 21)
Rita's Rock Ape 36 (5f,Not,GF,Oct 4)
Ritual 30 (7f,Lei,GS,Oct 14)

Robeena 39 (6f,Hay,G,Jly 5)
Robin Goodfellow 45 (6f,Cat,S,Oct 16)
Roborant 34 (7f,Lei,G,Jly 23)
Rodinia (USA) 34 (5f,Sal,GF,May 15)
Roi Brisbane 49 (6f,Nwc,GF,Oct 1)
Roi de Danse 32 (6f,Kem,G,Aug 20)
Ron's Pet 31 (5f,Hay,S,May 5)
Rosewood Lady (IRE) 30 (6f,Wnd,G,Aug 23)
Royal Bounty (IRE) 39 (7 1/2f,Bev,G,Aug 23)
Royal Dream 43 (6f,Chs,GF,Aug 3)
Royal Ground (IRE) 44 (8f,Goo,G,Spt 13)
Royal Rights 34 (6f,Yar,G,Jly 16)
Royal Shyness 55 (6f,Nwm,GF,Spt 30)
Rubamma 33 (7f,Cat,S,Oct 17)
Rusty Babe (IRE) 44 (5f,Bev,GF,Jun 5)
Ruzen (IRE) 32 (5f,Lei,GS,Apr 26)
Ryefield 35 (6f,Nwc,GF,Oct 22)

Sabhaan 31 (6f,Goo,G,Spt 12)
Sacchetti (IRE) 30 (5f,Lin,F,Oct 3)
Sada 33 (6f,Red,GF,Oct 7)
Sadian 30 (8f,Lin,GS,Aug 28)
Saeedah 31 (7f,Lei,G,Aug 11)
Saffron Lane (IRE) 46 (7f,Nwb,GF,Aug 16)
Saints Be Praised (USA) 51 (7f,Asc,G,Jun 19)
Salamanca 49 (5f,Lin,G,Aug 9)
Salsette 30 (6f,Chs,GS,Aug 29)
Sandside 41 (5f,Chs,S,Jun 25)
Sandy Shore 32 (6f,Not,S,Jun 23)
Sans Rivale 31 (5f,Edi,G,Aug 28)
Sapphire Ring 69 (6f,Ayr,GS,Spt 19)
Sarah Stokes (IRE) 38 (6f,Not,G,Oct 30)
Saralea (FR) 49 (8f,Lon,GF,Oct 5)
Saratoga Springs (CAN) 73 (8f,Don,G,Oct 25)
Sassy Lady (IRE) 32 (6f,Nwm,GF,Oct 4)
Scent of Success (USA) 40 (7f,Asc,Hy,Oct 10)
Sconced (USA) 31 (7f,Yar,G,Oct 22)
Scorned (GER) 54 (7f,Don,G,Nov 7)
Sea Magic (IRE) 51 (7f,Don,G,Oct 25)
Season Of Love (FR) 45 (9f,Lon,G,Oct 4)
Second Empire (IRE) 69 (8f,Lon,G,Spt 14)
Secret Archive 45 (7f,Goo,GF,Aug 1)
Selkirk Rose (IRE) 42 (6f,Ayr,GS,Spt 19)
Sense of Wonder 43 (6f,Not,G,Nov 3)
Sensory 44 (7f,Nwb,G,Oct 24)
Setteen 56 (7f,Asc,G,Jly 25)
Shadow of Doubt (IRE) 54 (6f,Asc,G,Jun 17)
Shahtoush (IRE) 49 (7f,Cur,S,Spt 7)
Shalford's Honour (IRE) 58 (5f,Hay,G,Spt 21)
Shanillo 31 (7f,Nwb,GF,Spt 18)
Sharp Cracker (IRE) 45 (7f,Nwc,GF,Aug 6)
Sharp Play 65 (8f,Asc,GF,Spt 28)
Shart (IRE) 44 (6f,Nwm,GS,Oct 17)
Shaveling 37 (7f,Red,G,Nov 4)
Shawdon 62 (5f,Nwm,G,Oct 2)
Shegardi 64 (5f,Goo,GS,May 20)
Sherganzar 38 (6f,Lei,G,Oct 28)
Shfoug (USA) 61 (6f,Asc,GF,Spt 27)
Shimaal 52 (7f,Nwm,G,Aug 22)
Shmoose (IRE) 57 (6f,Nwb,GF,Aug 15)
Shudder 48 (6f,Nwm,GF,Nov 1)
Shuhrah (USA) 60 (7f,Nwm,GF,Oct 4)
Sick As A Parrot 40 (8f,Yar,G,Oct 22)
Sideman (IRE) 37 (5f,Leo,YS,May 11)
Signatory 46 (7f,Bri,GF,Oct 23)
Silca Key Service 37 (6f,Goo,GF,Aug 2)
Silent Pride (IRE) 30 (5f,San,GF,Apr 25)
Silent Tribute (IRE) 57 (8f,Lon,GF,Oct 5)
Silic (FR) 74 (9f,Lon,G,Oct 4)
Silken Dalliance 36 (6f,Lei,G,Oct 28)
Silver Rhapsody (USA) 35 (8f,Don,G,Oct 24)
Silversmith (FR) 37 (6f,Lin,GF,Aug 17)
Silvertown 37 (7f,San,GF,Jly 23)
Sinon (IRE) 62 (10f,Nwm,GF,Nov 1)
Sixpence 38 (6f,Nwm,GF,Oct 4)
Sky Red 31 (6f,Nwm,GF,Oct 4)
Sky Rocket 47 (6f,Don,GF,Spt 13)
Smart Squall (USA) 54 (7f,Asc,Hy,Oct 10)
Smooth Sailing 47 (6f,Kem,G,May 24)
Social Charter (USA) 52 (7f,Lei,GS,Oct 14)
Socket Set 67 (6f,Asc,S,Jly 26)
Soft Touch (IRE) 34 (7f,Lin,G,Spt 9)
Solo Spirit 38 (6f,Lei,G,Oct 27)
Somayda (IRE) 34 (7f,Nwb,GF,Aug 16)
Son of Skelton 33 (7 1/2f,Bev,Hy,Jly 5)
Soviet Bureau (IRE) 42 (7f,Sal,GF,Aug 13)
Spanish Fern (USA) 53 (7f,Nwm,GF,Nov 1)
Speaker's Chair 33 (7f,Nwb,GF,Aug 15)
Special Quest (FR) 74 (9f,Lon,G,Oct 4)
Special Treat 53 (6f,Yor,G,Oct 8)
Speedfit Too (IRE) 56 (6f,Nwm,GF,Aug 23)
Splendid Isolation (USA) 45 (6f,Nwm,GF,Oct 31)
Spree Rose 31 (7f,War,GF,Oct 7)
Spring Fever 33 (6f,Nwm,GF,Oct 31)
Star 55 (5f,Hay,G,Spt 21)
Starmaker (IRE) 42 (7 1/2f,Bev,Hy,Jly 5)
Star of Grosvenor (IRE) 37 (7f,Nwm,GF,Spt 30)
Stately Princess 31 (6f,Nwm,G,Aug 2)
Statua (IRE) 59 (6f,Yor,G,Aug 21)
Stayingalive (USA) 46 (6f,Nwm,G,Jly 8)
St Helensfield 63 (10f,Nwm,GF,Nov 1)
St Lucia (IRE) 38 (6f,Nwb,GS,Spt 20)
Stone of Destiny 54 (7f,Nwb,GF,Aug 16)
Stop Out 39 (7f,Nwm,GF,Aug 9)
Storm Fromthe East 43 (6f,Kem,G,Spt 21)
Storm River (USA) 37 (8f,Hay,G,Spt 27)
Striding King 31 (5f,Sal,GF,May 15)
Success And Glory (IRE) 58 (8f,Goo,G,Spt 13)
Suivez La Trace 40 (5f,Pon,S,Jun 30)
Summer Deal (USA) 48 (7f,Nwc,GF,Oct 22)
Sunley Seeker 39 (7f,Nwb,GS,Spt 19)
Super Geil 34 (5f,Lin,G,Oct 27)

Super Sonic Sonia (IRE) 55 (9f,Leo,S,Nov 9)
Supreme Angel 50 (5f,Hay,Hy,Oct 15)
Surprised 36 (5f,Cat,G,Spt 27)
Surveyor 66 (6f,Kem,G,Spt 21)
Susun Kelapa (USA) 40 (7f,Cur,GS,Oct 4)
Swanmore Lady (IRE) 37 (5f,Red,F,Spt 26)
Sweet Reward 38 (6f,Pon,S,Jun 30)
Sweet Sorrow (IRE) 36 (6f,Nwb,GF,Aug 15)
Swift Alliance 48 (6f,Asc,G,Jun 17)
Swing Along 40 (6f,Nwm,GS,Oct 17)
Swing Sister 43 (7f,Lei,GS,Oct 14)

Taalluf (USA) 39 (6f,Not,GF,Jly 19)
Tabasco (IRE) 49 (6f,Asc,GF,Spt 27)
Tadwiga 57 (7f,Nwm,G,Oct 18)
Tajasur (IRE) 40 (6f,Don,GS,Jun 29)
Tajawuz 45 (7f,Nwc,GF,Oct 22)
Tajmil (IRE) 32 (6f,Goo,G,Jun 13)
Takarian (IRE) 31 (7f,Leo,GS,Oct 27)
Tamarisk (IRE) 69 (7f,Nwm,GF,Spt 30)
Tarascon (IRE) 50 (7f,Cur,S,Spt 7)
Tarashaan 34 (10f,Not,GF,Spt 23)
Tartan Lass 30 (7f,Nwm,GF,Nov 1)
Tattinger 40 (6f,Kem,G,Spt 10)
Taverner Society (IRE) 49 (8f,Kem,GF,Spt 22)
Teapot Row (IRE) 71 (8f,Asc,GF,Spt 28)
Tempus Fugit 49 (5f,Wnd,GS,Jun 30)
Ten Bob (IRE) 34 (8f,Edi,GS,Nov 6)
Tenbyssimo (IRE) 54 (8f,Lon,G,Spt 14)
Tensile (IRE) 32 (8f,Chp,G,Aug 25)
Teroom 32 (7f,Yar,G,Oct 22)
Territory (IRE) 45 (5f,Not,S,Oct 8)
Thanksgiving (IRE) 67 (6f,Ayr,GS,Spt 19)
The Blues Academy (IRE) 30 (6f,Nwc,GF,Oct 22)
The Boy John (USA) 39 (5f,Nwb,GS,Spt 20)
The Downtown Fox 52 (6f,Nwm,GS,Oct 16)
The Gene Genie 63 (10f,Nwm,GF,Nov 1)
The Glow-Worm (IRE) 57 (8f,Nwm,GS,Oct 17)
The Groveller 38 (6f,Chs,S,Aug 30)
The Hobby Lobby (IRE) 34 (6f,Wnd,G,Aug 23)
The King Of Cloyne (USA) 40 (7f,Cur,GS,Aug 30)
The Limping Cat (IRE) 32 (5f,Yor,G,Aug 20)
Thelonius (IRE) 34 (7f,War,GS,Aug 25)
The Rich Man (IRE) 46 (6f,Pon,S,Jun 30)
Thief Of Hearts (IRE) 76 (9f,Lon,G,Oct 4)
Third Cousin (IRE) 43 (6f,Not,G,Nov 3)
Three Star Rated (IRE) 45 (5f,Edi,GF,Spt 15)
Tightrope 43 (8f,Lei,GF,Oct 5)
Timbervati (USA) 38 (7f,Yar,G,Oct 22)
Timekeeper (USA) 38 (7f,Yar,GS,Jly 3)
Tippitt Boy 54 (5f,Don,GF,Spt 13)
Titan 33 (7f,Asc,Hy,Oct 10)
Titanic (IRE) 54 (5f,Lin,G,Oct 27)
Title Bid (USA) 43 (6f,Cat,GF,Spt 20)
Toblersong 45 (6f,Eps,S,Jly 2)
Tom Dougal 31 (7f,Nwm,GS,Oct 16)
Torianna (USA) 31 (5f,Red,F,Aug 23)
Torrent 35 (6f,Goo,G,Spt 25)
Tracking 62 (7f,Don,G,Jly 31)
Trans Island 60 (7f,Nwb,GF,Jly 19)
Transylvania 34 (6f,Nwb,GF,Aug 15)
Treasure Chest (IRE) 44 (8f,Goo,G,Spt 13)
Trident (USA) 43 (7f,San,GF,Jly 23)
Trigger Happy (IRE) 61 (10f,Nwm,GF,Nov 1)
Tullich Refrain 30 (5f,Wnd,GF,Jly 21)
Tumblweed Prospect 56 (6f,Nwb,GS,Spt 20)
Tuning 52 (8f,Not,GF,Spt 23)
Tussle 54 (6f,Asc,Hy,Oct 10)
Two Williams 41 (5f,Bev,Hy,Jly 4)

Up At The Top (IRE) 43 (6f,Fol,G,Spt 2)
Uplifting 39 (6f,Nwb,G,Oct 24)

Vice Presidential 40 (6f,Ayr,G,Spt 20)
Victory Note (USA) 66 (6f,Nwb,GF,Jly 19)
Vignette (USA) 43 (6f,Hay,GF,Aug 15)
Viola Royale (IRE) 38 (7f,Cur,GS,Oct 4)
Virtuous 51 (8f,Don,GF,Spt 11)
Vocation (IRE) 35 (7f,Lin,G,Spt 9)
Volontiers (FR) 43 (7f,Don,G,Nov 7)
Voodoo Saint (USA) 42 (7f,Don,GF,Spt 10)

Wadi 31 (8f,Not,S,Oct 15)
Wait'n'see 44 (5f,Crl,F,Jun 12)
Wales 61 (8f,Goo,G,Spt 13)
Wathbat Lion 32 (7f,Nwb,GF,Aug 16)
Wave Rock 31 (8f,Not,G,Spt 28)
Way Out Yonder 36 (6f,Nwm,GF,May 31)
Wenda (IRE) 65 (6f,Asc,GF,Spt 27)
Whisky Mack (IRE) 36 (6f,Lei,G,Jly 17)
Who Nose (IRE) 37 (7f,Nwm,GF,Oct 3)
Wigging 32 (6f,Not,GF,Spt 23)
Winona (IRE) 43 (7f,Cur,GS,Oct 4)
Winsa (USA) 34 (8f,Don,G,Oct 24)
Winsome George 51 (6f,Rip,GS,May 18)
Wiston Cheese (USA) 55 (6f,Asc,Hy,Oct 10)
Wolfhunt 33 (5f,Wnd,GS,Jun 30)
Woodland Melody (USA) 51 (7f,San,GF,Jly 24)
Wrekin Pilot 56 (7f,Nwb,GF,Jly 19)
Wuxi Venture 48 (7f,Nwm,GF,Oct 3)

Xaar 84 (7f,Nwm,G,Oct 18)

Yanabi (USA) 33 (6f,Goo,GF,Jly 29)
Yorkies Boy 61 (5f,Nwb,GS,Spt 20)
Young Ibnr (IRE) 38 (5f,Chs,S,May 6)
Young Josh 39 (6f,Goo,G,Spt 25)

Zaya 32 (7f,Don,G,Oct 24)
Zelanda (IRE) 58 (6f,Yor,G,Aug 21)
Zero Three Fifteen (IRE) 30 (7f,War,GS,Aug 25)
Zizi (IRE) 41 (6 1/2f,Don,GF,Spt 10)
Zydeco (IRE) 40 (7f,War,GF,Oct 7)

TWO YEAR-OLDS - Sand

Arbenig (IRE) 40 (6f,Wol,Std,Oct 4)
Bawsian 34 (8f,Lin,Std,Nov 18)
Beautiful Pleasure (USA) 34 (8 1/2f,Hpk,Fst,Nov 8)
Beechwood Quest (IRE) 30 (5f,Sou,Std,Jly 10)
Blue Kite 45 (5f,Wol,Std,Spt 30)
Bound To Please 41 (6f,Wol,Std,Oct 4)
Calchas (IRE) 39 (6f,Wol,Std,Jun 18).
Cantonese (USA) 42 (7f,Wol,Std,Nov 15)
Carambo 50 (7f,Wol,Std,Oct 6)
Career Collection (USA) 57 (8 1/2f,Hpk,Fst,Nov 8)
Carrielle (USA) 37 (8 1/2f,Hpk,Fst,Nov 8)
Classy Cleo (IRE) 52 (5f,Lin,Std,Nov 28)
Confirmation 48 (7f,Sou,Std,Spt 8)
Countess Diana (USA) 73 (8 1/2f,Hpk,Fst,Nov 8)
Critical Air 35 (6f,Wol,Std,Oct 4)
Dawson's Legacy (USA) 72 (8 1/2f,Hpk,Fst,Nov 8)
Diamond Drill (USA) 41 (7f,Lin,Std,Dec 10)
Diamond On The Run (USA) 38 (8 1/2f,Hpk,Fst,Nov 8)
Double Edged 37 (8f,Sou,Std,Nov 24)
Double Honor (USA) 64 (8 1/2f,Hpk,Fst,Nov 8)
Emperor's Gold 31 (8 1/2f,Wol,Std,Nov 1)
Favorite Trick (USA) 82 (8 1/2f,Hpk,Fst,Nov 8)
Flight 32 (8f,Lin,Std,Dec 19)
Freedom Quest (IRE) 41 (7f,Wol,Std,Nov 15)
Genius (IRE) 31 (8 1/2f,Wol,Std,Nov 29)
Gralmano (IRE) 50 (8 1/2f,Wol,Std,Nov 29)
Guaranteed 31 (7f,Wol,Std,Aug 16)
Hanuman Highway (IRE) 38 (8f,Lin,Std,Dec 19)
Happy Days Again (IRE) 30 (5f,Sou,Std,Jun 19)
Happy Wanderer 35 (6f,Wol,Std,Oct 4)
Johnbill (USA) 70 (8 1/2f,Hpk,Fst,Nov 8)
Just Another Time 38 (5f,Lin,Std,Dec 19)
Kirby's Song (CAN) 45 (8 1/2f,Hpk,Fst,Nov 8)
Lift The Offer (IRE) 39 (8f,Lin,Std,Nov 18)
Long Island 30 (6f,Wol,Std,Nov 1)
Love Again 39 (5f,Wol,Std,Spt 30)
Love Lock (USA) 34 (8 1/2f,Hpk,Fst,Nov 8)
Main Street 31 (6f,Wol,Std,Nov 1)
Mareeba 34 (8 1/2f,Wol,Std,Nov 29)
Marie J (USA) 46 (8 1/2f,Hpk,Fst,Nov 8)
Masamadas 35 (8f,Sou,Std,Nov 24)
Montano (USA) 36 (6f,Lin,Std,Nov 10)
Naked Oat 34 (7f,Sou,Std,Dec 18)
Nationalore (USA) 71 (8 1/2f,Hpk,Fst,Nov 8)
Night Vigil (IRE) 33 (8f,Lin,Std,Nov 13)
One Singer 50 (7f,Wol,Std,Oct 6)
Pas de Memoires (IRE) 44 (7f,Sou,Std,Nov 14)
Pedro (IRE) 42 (7f,Wol,Std,Oct 6)
Poetto 30 (5f,Wol,Std,Oct 4)
Press Ahead 30 (6f,Wol,Std,Oct 4)
Primaly (CAN) 50 (8 1/2f,Hpk,Fst,Nov 8)
Primary Colours 44 (7f,Sou,Std,Dec 18)
Private Seal 33 (5f,Lin,Std,Dec 19)
Prompt Delivery (USA) 30 (7f,Wol,Std,Aug 16)
Ra Ra Rasputin 37 (6f,Wol,Std,Aug 16)
Rare Indigo 38 (5f,Wol,Std,Oct 4)
Respond 33 (8f,Lin,Std,Dec 10)
Roi Brisbane 42 (6f,Wol,Std,Nov 1)
Rubamma 31 (8 1/2f,Wol,Std,Nov 29)
Russian Romeo (IRE) 30 (6f,Sou,Std,Nov 17)
Santa Faye (IRE) 42 (6f,Sou,Std,Oct 20)
Shegardi 35 (5f,Lin,Std,Nov 10)
Silken Dalliance 40 (6f,Wol,Std,Oct 4)
Snappy Times 31 (5f,Sou,Std,Spt 8)
Socket Set 35 (5f,Sou,Std,Jun 19)
Souvenir Copy (USA) 70 (8 1/2f,Hpk,Fst,Nov 8)
Stage Whisper 34 (8 1/2f,Wol,Std,Dec 13)
Super Geil 31 (5f,Sou,Std,Spt 8)
The Groveller 32 (7f,Wol,Std,Aug 16)
Third Cousin (IRE) 44 (6f,Wol,Std,Oct 4)
Time Limit (USA) 60 (8 1/2f,Hpk,Fst,Nov 8)
Vista Alegre 35 (5f,Lin,Std,Nov 10)
Vivid Angel (USA) 43 (8 1/2f,Hpk,Fst,Nov 8)
Wolfhunt 35 (6f,Wol,Std,Dec 6)

Teams which have arrived too late for inclusion in Horses In Training 1998 will be published in the Raceform Update.

RACEFORM FASTEST PERFORMERS

5f - 6f

1. Elnadim (USA)....................105
2. Monaassib 99
3. Averti (IRE) 99
4. Elmhurst 99
5. Russian Revival (USA) 98
6. Hesabull..............................98
7. Bet On Sunshine 97
8. Easy Dollar 96
9. Titus Livius.........................96
10. Jayannpee 96
11. Don't Worry Me (IRE) 94
12. Rambling Bear 93
13. Muchea..............................93
14. Sylva Paradise (IRE) 92
15. Cayman Kai (IRE)..............92
16. Bollin Joanne 92
17. Carranita (IRE) 91
18. Dazzle.................................91
19. Exotic Wood 91
20. Cretan Gift..........................90

7f - 9f

1. Polar Prince (IRE)..............101
2. Spinning World (USA) 98
3. La Blue (GER) 98
4. Val's Prince.........................98
5. Cap Juluca (IRE) 97
6. Balalaika 97
7. Clodora 97
8. Starborough.........................96
9. Samara (IRE).......................96
10. Alhaarth (IRE)....................96
11. Occupandiste (IRE) 96
12. Squeak 95
13. Wixim (USA) 94
14. Air Express (IRE)................94
15. Centre Stalls (IRE).............94
16. Always Loyal (USA)............94
17. Almushtarak (IRE) 94
18. Geri......................................94
19. Decorated Hero 93
20. Lucky Coin..........................93

10f - 12f

1. Pilsudski (IRE) 101
2. Peintre Celebre (USA).......100
3. Skip Away 100
4. Germano...............................99
5. Helissio 99
6. Luso......................................99
7. Posidonas.............................99
8. Predappio 98
9. Oscar Schindler 98
10. Swain (IRE) 97
11. Arabian Story......................96
12. Bosra Sham (USA).............95
13. Chief Bearhart (CAN) 95
14. Vereva (IRE).......................93
15. Flag Down (CAN) 93
16. Harbour Dues 92
17. Benny The Dip (USA) 91
18. Silver Patriarch (IRE).........91
19. Mousse Glacee..................91
20. Busy Flight..........................91

13f and upwards

1. Celeric 95
2. Chief Contender (IRE) 95
3. Persian Punch (IRE)..........94
4. Grey Shot 93
5. Always Earnest (USA) 93

6. Double Trigger (IRE) 92
7. Classic Cliche (IRE)...........89
8. Double Eclipse (IRE) 89
9. Leonard Quercus..............87
10. Canon Can (USA)..............82
11. Election Day (IRE) 81
12. Three Cheers (IRE) 80
13. Shaft of Light 80
14. Tarator (USA) 79
15. Further Flight 79
16. Purple Splash 79
17. Jiyush 78
18. Stretarez 78
19. Nononito 78
20. Bonapartiste 78

TWO-YEAR-OLDS
5f - 6f

1. Halmahera (IRE)................84
2. Embassy...............................77
3. Regal Revolution 75
4. Bintang (IRE) 73
5. Cape Verdi (IRE) 72
6. Miss Zafonic (FR) 72
7. Filey Brigg...........................71
8. Nadwah (USA)....................71
9. Lord Kintyre 71
10. Harbour Master (FR) 71
11. Raise A King.......................70
12. Sapphire Ring....................69
13. Arkadian Hero (USA).........69
14. Desert Prince (IRE) 67
15. Socket Set 67
16. Monte Lemos (IRE) 67
17. Thanksgiving (IRE) 67
18. Diligence (IRE) 66
19. Bold Fact (USA).................66
20. Victory Note (USA) 66

7f and upwards

1. Xaar 84
2. Favorite Trick......................82
3. Thief Of Hearts (IRE).........76
4. Daggers Drawn (USA).......75
5. Special Quest 74
6. Daymarti (IRE)...................74
7. Silic 74
8. Saratoga Springs (CAN)....73
9. Mudeer 73
10. Countess Diana 73
11. Dawson's Legacy 72
12. Teapot Row (IRE).............71
13. Mutamam..........................71
14. Nationalore 71
15. Central Park (IRE) 70
16. Docksider (USA)...............70
17. Prolix..................................70
18. Souvenir Copy 70
19. Johnbill 70
20. Almutawakel 69

Owners names are shown against their horses where this information is available. In the case of Partnerships and Syndicates, the nominated owner is given alongside the horse with other owners listed below the team.

DATES OF PRINCIPAL RACES

(Subject to alteration)

JANUARY

MILDMAY CAZALET MEMORIAL CHASE (Sandown)	Sat.	10
TOLWORTH HURDLE (Sandown)	Sat.	10
NEWTON CHASE (Haydock)	Sat.	10
THE LADBROKE (Leopardstown)	Sat.	10
PML LIGHTNING NOVICES' CHASE (Ascot)	Sat.	17
VICTOR CHANDLER CHASE (Ascot)	Sat.	17
DIPPER NOVICES' CHASE (Newcastle)	Sat.	17
SCOTTISH BORDERS NATIONAL (Kelso)	Fri.	23
MOREBATTLE HURDLE (Kelso)	Fri.	23
BIC RAZOR LANZAROTE HANDICAP HURDLE (Kempton)	Sat.	24
PETER MARSH CHASE (Haydock)	Sat.	24
HAYDOCK PARK CHAMPION HURDLE TRIAL (Haydock)	Sat.	24
PREMIER LONG DISTANCE HURDLE (Haydock)	Sat.	24
AIG IRISH CHAMPION HURDLE (Leopardstown)	Sun.	25
BURGER KING THYESTES CHASE (Gowran Park)	Thu.	29
CLEEVE HURDLE (Cheltenham)	Sat.	31
PILLAR PROPERTY INVESTMENTS CHASE (Cheltenham)	Sat.	31
PERTEMPS GREAT YORKSHIRE HANDICAP CHASE (Doncaster)	Sat.	31
TOM DREAPER HANDICAP CHASE (Fairyhouse)	Sat.	31

FEBRUARY

AGFA DIAMOND CHASE (Sandown)	Sat.	7
HENNESSY GOLD CUP (Leopardstown)	Sun.	8
PREMIERE 'NH' AUCTION NOVICES' HURDLE (Wincanton)	Thur.	12
TOTE GOLD TROPHY HURDLE (Newbury)	Sat.	14
MITSUBISHI SHOGUN GAME SPIRIT CHASE (Newbury)	Sat.	14
PERSIAN WAR PATTERN HURDLE (Chepstow)	Sat.	21
TOTE EIDER CHASE (Newcastle)	Sat.	21
AXIMSTER 100 KINGWELL PATTERN HURDLE (Wincanton)	Thur.	26
JIM FORD CHASE (Wincanton)	Thur.	26
HENNESSY COGNAC HURDLE (Kelso)	Fri.	27
RACING POST CHASE (Kempton)	Sat.	28
RENDLESHAM HURDLE (Kempton)	Sat.	28
GREENALLS GRAND NATIONAL TRIAL CHASE (Haydock)	Sat.	28

MARCH

SUNDERLANDS IMPERIAL CUP (Sandown)	Sat.	14
LINCOLN TRIAL (Wolverhampton)	Sat.	14
SMURFIT CHAMPION HURDLE (Cheltenham)	Tue.	17
CITROEN SUPREME NOVICE HURDLE (Cheltenham)	Tue.	17
GUINNESS ARKLE CHALLENGE TROPHY CHASE (Cheltenham)	Tue.	17
SUN ALLIANCE CHASE (Cheltenham)	Wed.	18
SUN ALLIANCE HURDLE (Cheltenham)	Wed.	18
QUEEN MOTHER CHAMPION CHASE (Cheltenham)	Wed.	18
CORAL CUP HURDLE (Cheltenham)	Wed.	18
TOTE CHELTENHAM GOLD CUP CHASE (Cheltenham)	Thur.	19
ELITE RACING CLUB TRIUMPH HURDLE (Cheltenham)	Thur.	19
BONUSPRINT STAYERS HURDLE (Cheltenham)	Thur.	19
MARSTONS PEDIGREE MIDLANDS GRAND NATIONAL (Uttoxeter)	Sat.	21
WINTER DERBY (AW) (Lingfield)	Sat.	21
LINCOLN HANDICAP (Doncaster)	Sat.	28
DUBAI WORLD CUP (Nad Al Sheba)	Sat.	28
IRISH LINCOLNSHIRE (The Curragh)	Sun.	29

APRIL

MARTELL CUP CHASE (Aintree) .... Thur. 2
JOHN HUGHES TROPHY (Aintree) .... Thur. 2
MUMM MELLING CHASE (Aintree) .... Fri. 3
MARTELL FOXHUNTERS CHASE (Aintree) .... Fri. 3
MARTELL AINTREE HURDLE (Aintree) .... Sat. 4
MARTELL GRAND NATIONAL CHASE (Aintree) .... Sat. 4
GLADNESS STAKES (The Curragh) .... Sun. 5
LETHEBY & CHRISTOPHER LONG DISTANCE HURDLE (Ascot) .... Wed. 8
MILCARS EASTER STAKES (Kempton) .... Sat. 11
MILCARS MASAKA STAKES (Kempton) .... Sat. 11
FIELD MARSHALL STAKES (Haydock) .... Sat. 11
CORAL ROSEBERY HANDICAP (Kempton) .... Mon. 13
JAMESON IRISH GRAND NATIONAL (Fairyhouse) .... Mon. 13
POWER GOLD CUP CHASE (Fairyhouse) .... Tue. 14
SHADWELL STUD NELL GWYN STAKES (Newmarket) .... Tue. 14
ABERNANT STAKES (Newmarket) .... Tue. 14
EBF NH NOVICES' RACE FINAL HURDLE (Cheltenham) .... Wed. 15
FAUCETS SILVER TROPHY CHASE (Cheltenham) .... Wed. 15
DAN MOORE HANDICAP CHASE (Fairyhouse) .... Wed. 15
NGK SPARK PLUGS EUROPEAN FREE HANDICAP (Newmarket) .... Wed. 15
EARL OF SEFTON STAKES (Newmarket) .... Wed. 15
CITY INDEX CRAVEN STAKES (Newmarket) .... Thur. 16
FEILDEN STAKES (Newmarket) .... Thur. 16
DUBAI DUTY FRED DARLING STAKES (Newbury) .... Fri. 17
JOHN PORTER STAKES (Newbury) .... Sat. 18
GREENHAM STAKES (Newbury) .... Sat. 18
LADBROKE SPRING CUP (Newbury) .... Sat. 18
STAKIS CASINOS SCOTTISH NATIONAL (Ayr) .... Sat. 18
DAILY MAIL SCOTTISH CHALLENGE CUP (Ayr) .... Sat. 18
SANDOWN MILE (Sandown) .... Fri. 24
GORDON RICHARDS EBF STAKES (Sandown) .... Sat. 25
WHITBREAD GOLD CUP CHASE (Sandown) .... Sat. 25
THRESHER CLASSIC TRIAL (Sandown) .... Sat. 25
COUNTRY PRIDE CHAMPION NOVICE HURDLE (Punchestown) .... Tue. 28
BMW HANDICAP CHASE (Punchestown) .... Tue. 28
HEINEKEN GOLD CUP (Punchestown) .... Wed. 29
INSULPAK VICTORIA CUP (Ascot) .... Wed. 29
INSULPAK SAGARO STAKES (Ascot) .... Wed. 29
MURPHYS IRISH STOUT CHAMPION HURDLE (Punchestown) .... Thur. 30

MAY

KUWAIT GREEN RIDGE NEWMARKET STAKES (Newmarket) .... Fri. 1
SAGITTA JOCKEY CLUB STAKES (Newmarket) .... Fri. 1
CROWTHER HOMES SWINTON HURDLE (Haydock) .... Sat. 2
CROWTHER HOMES SPRING TROPHY (Haydock) .... Sat. 2
SAGITTA 2000 GUINEAS STAKES (Newmarket) .... Sat. 2
PALACE HOUSE STAKES (Newmarket) .... Sat. 2
LADBROKE HANDICAP (Newmarket) .... Sat. 2
TETRARCH STAKES (The Curragh) .... Sat. 2
KENTUCKY DERBY (Churchill Downs) .... Sat. 2
SAGITTA 1000 GUINEAS STAKES (Newmarket) .... Sun. 3
R. L. DAVISON PRETTY POLLY STAKES (Newmarket) .... Sun. 3
JUBILEE HANDICAP (Kempton) .... Mon. 4
CHESTER VASE (Chester) .... Tue. 5
CHESTER CUP (Chester) .... Wed. 6
SHADWELL STUD CHESHIRE OAKS (Chester) .... Wed. 6
ORMONDE STAKES (Chester) .... Thur. 7
DEE STAKES (Chester) .... Thur. 7

DERBY TRIAL (Lingfield) ... Sat. 9
OAKS TRIAL (Lingfield) ... Sat. 9
DUBAI POULE D'ESSAI DES POULICHES (Longchamp) ... Sun. 10
DUBAI POULE D'ESSAI DES POULAINS (Longchamp) ... Sun. 10
PRIX LUPIN (Longchamp) ... Sun. 10
TATTERSALLS MUSIDORA STAKES (York) ... Tue. 12
DANTE STAKES (York) ... Wed. 13
YORKSHIRE CUP (York) ... Thur. 14
DUKE OF YORK STAKES (York) ... Thur. 14
KING CHARLES II STAKES (Newmarket) ... Fri. 15
VODAFONE FILLIES TRIAL STAKES (Newbury) ... Fri. 15
JUDDMONTE LOCKINGE STAKES (Newbury) ... Fri. 15
PREAKNESS STAKES (Pimlico) ... Sat. 16
PREDOMINATE STAKES (Goodwood) ... Tue. 19
TRIPLEPRINT LUPE STAKES (Goodwood) ... Wed. 20
RUINART CHAMPAGNE FESTIVAL STAKES (Goodwood) ... Thur. 21
CRAWLEY WARREN HERON STAKES (Kempton) ... Sat. 23
LEAHURST SANDY LANE STAKES (Haydock) ... Sat. 23
TOTE CREDIT SILVER BOWL (Haydock) ... Sat. 23
AIRLIE/COOLMORE IRISH 1000 GUINEAS (The Curragh) ... Sat. 23
IRISH 2000 GUINEAS (The Curragh) ... Sun. 24
TRIPLEPRINT TEMPLE STAKES (Sandown) ... Mon. 25
BONUSPRINT HENRY II STAKES (Sandown) ... Mon. 25
ZETLAND GOLD CUP (Redcar) ... Mon. 25
BRIGADIER GERARD STAKES (Sandown) ... Tue. 26
NATIONAL STAKES (Sandown) ... Tue. 26
LEISURE STAKES (Lingfield) ... Sat. 30
CORAL SPRINT HANDICAP (Newmarket) ... Sat. 30
PRIX DU JOCKEY CLUB (Chantilly) ... Sun. 31

JUNE

GALLINULE STAKES (The Curragh) ... Fri. 5
VODAFONE OAKS STAKES (Epsom) ... Fri. 5
VODAFONE CORONATION CUP (Epsom) ... Fri. 5
VODAFONE DERBY STAKES (Epsom) ... Sat. 6
VODAFONE DIOMED STAKES (Epsom) ... Sat. 6
JOHN OF GAUNT STAKES (Haydock) ... Sat. 6
BELMONT STAKES (Belmont Park) ... Sat. 6
PRIX DE DIANE (Chantilly) ... Sun. 7
BALLYMACOLL STUD STAKES (Newbury) ... Thur. 11
WILLIAM HILL TROPHY (York) ... Sat. 13
ST. JAMES'S PALACE STAKES (Royal Ascot) ... Tue. 16
PRINCE OF WALES'S STAKES (Royal Ascot) ... Tue. 16
COVENTRY STAKES (Royal Ascot) ... Tue. 16
CORONATION STAKES (Royal Ascot) ... Wed. 17
JERSEY STAKES (Royal Ascot) ... Wed. 17
QUEENS VASE STAKES (Royal Ascot) ... Wed. 17
QUEEN MARY STAKES (Royal Ascot) ... Wed. 17
ROYAL HUNT CUP HANDICAP (Royal Ascot) ... Wed. 17
GOLD CUP (Royal Ascot) ... Thur. 18
CORK AND ORRERY STAKES (Royal Ascot) ... Thur. 18
RIBBLESDALE STAKES (Royal Ascot) ... Thur. 18
NORFOLK STAKES (Royal Ascot) ... Thur. 18
HARDWICKE STAKES (Royal Ascot) ... Fri. 19
KINGS STAND STAKES (Royal Ascot) ... Fri. 19
WOKINGHAM HANDICAP (Royal Ascot) ... Fri. 19
KING EDWARD VII STAKES (Royal Ascot) ... Fri. 19
LADBROKE HANDICAP (Ascot) ... Sat. 20
GOFFS £100,000 CHALLENGE (The Curragh) ... Fri. 26
NORTHERN ROCK GOSFORTH PARK CUP HANDICAP (Newcastle) ... Fri. 26

NEWCASTLE BROWN ALE NORTHUMBERLAND PLATE (Newcastle) .... Sat. 27
VAN GEEST CRITERION STAKES (Newmarket) .... Sat. 27
NGK SPARK PLUGS FRED ARCHER STAKES (Newmarket) .... Sat. 27
INDEPENDENT NEWSPAPERS PRETTY POLLY STAKES (The Curragh) .... Sat. 27
BUDWEISER IRISH DERBY (The Curragh) .... Sun. 28

JULY

HONG KONG JOCKEY CLUB TROPHY (Sandown) .... Fri. 3
CORAL-ECLIPSE STAKES (Sandown) .... Sat. 4
JULY TROPHY (Haydock) .... Sat. 4
LANCASHIRE OAKS (Haydock) .... Sat. 4
OLD NEWTON CUP (Haydock) .... Sat. 4
PRINCESS OF WALES'S STAKES (Newmarket) .... Tue. 7
HEIDSIECK CHAMPAGNE CHERRY HINTON STAKES (Newmarket) .... Tue. 7
FALMOUTH STAKES (Newmarket) .... Wed. 8
JULY STAKES (Newmarket) .... Wed. 8
DUKE OF CAMBRIDGE HANDICAP (Newmarket) .... Wed. 8
LADBROKE BUNBURY CUP (Newmarket) .... Thur. 9
DARLEY JULY CUP (Newmarket) .... Thur. 9
BAHRAIN TROPHY (Newmarket) .... Thur. 9
JOHN SMITH'S MAGNET CUP (York) .... Sat. 11
DAILY MAIL CLASSIFIED SILVER TROPHY (Lingfield) .... Sat. 11
KILDANGAN STUD IRISH OAKS (The Curragh) .... Sun. 12
FOOD BROKERS ANIMAL TRUST TROPHY (Newmarket) .... Sat. 18
TENNENTS SCOTTISH CLASSIC (Ayr) .... Mon. 20
BEESWING STAKES (Newcastle) .... Sat. 25
THE KING GEORGE VI AND QUEEN ELIZABETH DIAMOND STAKES (Ascot) .... Sat. 25
PRINCESS MARGARET STAKES (Ascot) .... Sat. 25
MELD STAKES (The Curragh) .... Sat. 25
GROSVENOR CASINO CUP (Goodwood) .... Tue. 28
WESTMINSTER TAXI INSURANCE GORDON STAKES (Goodwood) .... Tue. 28
KING GEORGE STAKES (Goodwood) .... Tue. 28
SUSSEX STAKES (Goodwood) .... Wed. 29
TOTE GOLD TROPHY STAKES (Goodwood) .... Wed. 29
MARRIOTT HOTELS GOODWOOD STAKES (Goodwood) .... Wed. 29
LANSON CHAMPAGNE VINTAGE STAKES (Goodwood) .... Wed. 29
DIGITAL GALWAY PLATE (Galway) .... Wed. 29
OAK TREE STAKES (Goodwood) .... Thur. 30
GOODWOOD CUP (Goodwood) .... Thur. 30
SALOMON BROTHERS RICHMOND STAKES (Goodwood) .... Thur. 30
WILLIAM HILL GOLDEN MILE (Goodwood) .... Thur. 30
JOCKEY CLUB OF KENYA MOLECOMB STAKES (Goodwood) .... Fri. 31
GLORIOUS STAKES (Goodwood) .... Fri. 31
VOLVO CONTRACTS GLOBETROTTER STAKES (Goodwood) .... Fri. 31

AUGUST

VODAFONE NASSAU STAKES (Goodwood) .... Sat. 1
VODAC STEWARDS CUP (Goodwood) .... Sat. 1
ROSE OF LANCASTER STAKES (Haydock) .... Sat. 8
SWEET SOLERA STAKES (Newmarket) .... Sat. 8
HEINZ 57 PHOENIX STAKES (Leopardstown) .... Sun. 9
HUNGERFORD STAKES (Newbury) .... Fri. 14
WASHINGTON SINGER STAKES (Newbury) .... Fri. 14
GEOFFREY FREER STAKES (Newbury) .... Sat. 15
SWETTENHAM STUD ST HUGH'S STAKES (Newbury) .... Sat. 15
WILLIAM HILL GREAT ST. WILFRID HANDICAP (Ripon) .... Sat. 15
RIDGEWOOD PEARL DESMOND STAKES (The Curragh) .... Sat. 15
JUDDMONTE INTERNATIONAL STAKES (York) .... Tue. 18
GREAT VOLTIGEUR STAKES (York) .... Tue. 18
YORKSHIRE OAKS (York) .... Wed. 19

TOTE EBOR HANDICAP (York) .... Wed. 19
GIMCRACK STAKES (York) .... Wed. 19
NUNTHORPE STAKES (York) .... Thur. 20
STAKIS CASINO LOWTHER STAKES (York) .... Thur. 20
SOLARIO STAKES (Sandown) .... Fri. 21
WETHERBYS DASH (Wolverhampton) .... Sat. 22
HOPEFUL STAKES (Newmarket) .... Fri. 28
CROWSON PRESTIGE STAKES (Goodwood) .... Fri. 28
TRIPLEPRINT CELEBRATION MILE (Goodwood) .... Sat. 29
SPORT ON 5 MARCH STAKES (Goodwood) .... Sat. 29
TATTERSALLS BREEDERS STAKES (The Curragh) .... Sat. 29
MOET AND CHANDON SILVER MAGNUM STAKES (Epsom) .... Mon. 31
NEWCASTLE EXHIBITION ALE BLAYDON RACE (Newcastle) .... Mon. 31
PERTEMPS VIRGINIA RATED STAKES (Newcastle) .... Mon. 31
CHAMPION 2-Y-O TROPHY (Ripon) .... Mon. 31

SEPTEMBER

SEPTEMBER STAKES (Epsom) .... Sat. 5
SPRINT CUP (Haydock) .... Sat. 5
MOYGLARE STUD STAKES (The Curragh) .... Sun. 6
PARK HILL STAKES (Doncaster) .... Wed. 9
TOTE PORTLAND HANDICAP (Doncaster) .... Wed. 9
GNE RAILWAY DONCASTER CUP (Doncaster) .... Thur. 10
BRITAIN'S RAILWAY PARK STAKES (Doncaster) .... Thur. 10
MAY HILL STAKES (Doncaster) .... Thur. 10
LAURENT-PERRIER CHAMPAGNE STAKES (Doncaster) .... Fri. 11
SCHRODER INVESTMENT MANAGEMENT STAKES (Goodwood) .... Fri. 11
BELLWAY HOMES STARDOM STAKES (Goodwood) .... Fri. 11
CHAMPION STAKES (Leopardstown) .... Sat. 12
FLYING CHILDERS STAKES (Doncaster) .... Sat. 12
ST LEGER STAKES (Doncaster) .... Sat. 12
SHADWELL ESTATES FIRTH OF CLYDE STAKES (Ayr) .... Fri. 18
LADBROKE AYR GOLD CUP (Ayr) .... Sat. 19
BONUSPRINT MILL REEF STAKES (Newbury) .... Sat. 19
TOTE AUTUMN CUP (Newbury) .... Sat. 19
COURAGE STAKES (Newbury) .... Sat. 19
JEFFERSON SMURFIT MEMORIAL ST. LEGER (The Curragh) .... Sat. 19
THE AGA KHAN STUDS NATIONAL STAKES (The Curragh) .... Sun. 20
ROA FOUNDATION STAKES (Goodwood) .... Wed. 23
GUINNESS KERRY NATIONAL (Listowel) .... Wed. 23
CHARLTON HUNT SUPREME STAKES (Goodwood) .... Thur. 24
QUEEN ELIZABETH II STAKES (Ascot) .... Sat. 26
CUMBERALND LODGE STAKES (Ascot) .... Sat. 26
TOTE FESTIVAL HANDICAP (Ascot) .... Sat. 26
RACAL DIADEM STAKES (Ascot) .... Sat. 26
FILLIES MILE (Ascot) .... Sun. 27
GTECH ROYAL LODGE STAKES (Ascot) .... Sun. 27
TOTE SUNDAY SPECIAL HANDICAP (Ascot) .... Sun. 27
MAIL ON SUNDAY MILE HANDICAP FINAL (Ascot) .... Sun. 27
TATTERSALLS HOUGHTON SALES STAKES (Newmarket) .... Tue. 29
SHADWELL STUD CHEVELEY PARK STAKES (Newmarket) .... Tue. 29

OCTOBER

JRA NAKAYAMA ROUS STAKES (Newmarket) .... Thur. 1
MIDDLE PARK STAKES (Newmarket) .... Thur. 1
RACING POST GODOLPHIN STAKES (Newmarket) .... Fri. 2
SOMERVILLE TATTERSALL STAKES (Newmarket) .... Fri. 2
JOCKEY CLUB CUP (Newmarket) .... Sat. 3
SUN CHARIOT STAKES (Newmarket) .... Sat. 3
TOTE CAMBRIDGESHIRE HANDICAP (Newmarket) .... Sat. 3

IRISH CESAREWITCH (The Curragh) .... Sat. 3
PRIX DE L'ARC DE TRIOMPHE (Longchamp) .... Sun. 4
BONUSPRINT OCTOBER STAKES (Ascot) .... Fri. 9
PRINCESS ROYAL STAKES (Ascot) .... Sat. 10
WILLMOTT DIXON. CORNWALLIS STAKES (Ascot) .... Sat. 10
EAST COAST ROCKINGHAM STAKES (York) .... Sat. 10
CORAL SPRINT TROPHY (York) .... Sat. 10
DARLEY STAKES (Newmarket) .... Fri. 16
BEDFORD LODGE HOTEL BENTINCK STAKES (Newmarket) .... Fri. 16
CHALLENGE STAKES (Newmarket) .... Sat. 17
DEWHURST STAKES (Newmarket) .... Sat. 17
OWEN BROWN ROCKFEL STAKES (Newmarket) .... Sat. 17
DUBAI CHAMPION STAKES (Newmarket) .... Sat. 17
TOTE CESAREWITCH HANDICAP (Newmarket) .... Sat. 17
COMCAST TEESSIDE TWO-YEAR-OLD TROPHY (Redcar) .... Sat. 17
CHARISMA GOLD CUP (Kempton) .... Sat. 17
JUDDMONTE BERESFORD STAKES (The Curragh) .... Sat. 17
VODAFONE HORRIS HILL STAKES (Newbury) .... Fri. 23
PERPETUAL ST. SIMON STAKES (Newbury) .... Sat. 24
RADLEY STAKES (Newbury) .... Sat. 24
RACING POST TROPHY (Doncaster) .... Sat. 24
DESERT ORCHID S. W. PATTERN CHASE (Wincanton) .... Sun. 25
LADBROKE AUTUMN HANDICAP (Newmarket) .... Sat. 31
ZETLAND STAKES (Newmarket) .... Sat. 31
CHARLIE HALL CHASE (Wetherby) .... Sat. 31

NOVEMBER

FOSTERS MELBOURNE CUP (Flemington) .... Tue. 3
WILLIAM HILL HALDON GOLD CUP CHASE (Exeter) .... Tue. 3
GAMEKEEPERS HANDICAP CHASE (Haydock) .... Thu. 5
BADGER BEER CHASE (Wincanton) .... Sat. 7
TANGLEFOOT ELITE HURDLE (Wincanton) .... Sat. 7
TOTE SILVER TROPHY (Chepstow) .... Sat. 7
TOTE CREDIT NOVEMBER HANDICAP (Doncaster) .... Sat. 7
BREEDERS' CUP (Churchill Downs) .... Sat. 7
SPORTING INDEX CROSS COUNTRY CHASE (Cheltenham) .... Fri. 13
MURPHY'S GOLD CUP CHASE (Cheltenham) .... Sat. 14
MURPHY'S DRAUGHTFLOW HURDLE (Cheltenham) .... Sat. 14
SEAN GRAHAM MOTHERWELL CHASE (Ayr) .... Sun. 15
EDWARD HANMER HANDICAP CHASE (Haydock) .... Wed. 18
COOPERS & LYBRAND HURDLE (Ascot) .... Fri. 20
FIRST NATIONAL BANK GOLD CUP CHASE (Ascot) .... Sat. 21
BECHER CHASE (Aintree) .... Sat. 21
PETERBOROUGH CHASE (Huntingdon) .... Sat. 21
HENNESSY COGNAC GOLD CUP CHASE (Newbury) .... Sat. 28
GERRY FEILDEN HURDLE (Newbury) .... Sat. 28
LONG DISTANCE HURDLE (Newbury) .... Sat. 28
TIM MOLONY CHASE (Haydock) .... Sat. 28
NEWCASTLE B. SOCIETY FIGHTING FIFTH HURDLE (Newcastle) .... Sat. 28
JAPAN CUP (Tokyo) .... Sun. 29
HATTONS GRACE HURDLE (Fairyhouse) .... Sun. 29
ROYAL BOND NOVICE HURDLE (Fairyhouse) .... Sun. 29
DRINMORE CHASE (Fairyhouse) .... Sun. 29

DECEMBER

MITSUBISHI SHOGUN TINGLE CREEK CHASE (Sandown) .... Sat. 5
WILLIAM HILL HANDICAP HURDLE (Sandown) .... Sat. 5
CORAL REHEARSAL CHASE (Chepstow) .... Sat. 5
WULFRUN STAKES (Wolverhamtpon) .... Sat. 5
LAMBERT FENCHURCH NOVICES' CHASE (Lingfeild) .... Sat. 12

SUMMIT NOVICES' HURDLE (Lingfield)........Sat. 12
TOMMY WHITTLE CHASE (Haydock)........Sat. 12
TRIPLEPRINT GOLD CUP (Cheltenham)........Sat. 12
BONUSPRINT BULA HURDLE (Cheltenham)........Sat. 12
BETTERWARE CUP CHASE (Ascot)........Sat. 19
LONG WALK HURDLE (Ascot)........Sat. 19
PERTEMPS KING GEORGE VI CHASE (Kempton)........Sat. 26
ROWLAND MEYRICK HANDICAP CHASE (Wetherby)........Sat. 26
DENNYS CHASE (Leopardstown)........Sat. 26
PADDY POWER CHASE (Leopardstown)........Sun. 27
CASTLEFORD CHASE (Wetherby)........Mon. 28
PERTEMPS CHRISTMAS HURDLE (Kempton)........Mon. 28
CORAL WELSH NATIONAL (Chepstow)........Mon. 28
ERICSSON CHASE (Leopardstown)........Mon. 28

THE VODAFONE DERBY STAKES (CLASS A)
EPSOM, SATURDAY, JUNE 6th

HORSE	TRAINER
Abiyan (IRE)	A. de Royer-Dupre, France
Absolutly Sparklin	L. M. Cumani
Abuhail (USA)	P. T. Walwyn
Abulijood (IRE)	B. Hanbury
Abusamrah (USA)	R. W. Armstrong
Act Defiant (USA)	P. F. I. Cole
Adjutant	B. J. Meehan
Afarad (IRE)	J. Oxx, Ireland
Afraah (IRE)	Saeed bin Suroor, UAE
Aim High	M. R. Stoute
Air Attache (USA)	G. Lewis
Akasian (IRE)	
Al-Fateh (IRE)	J. L. Dunlop
Albarahin (USA)	Saeed bin Suroor, UAE
Alfarabi (USA)	Saeed bin Suroor, UAE
Aliabad (IRE)	M. R. Stoute
Alleged Aggressor (USA)	A. P. O'Brien, Ireland
Alliteration	A. Fabre, France
Almandab (IRE)	J. H. M. Gosden
Almazhar (IRE)	E. A. L. Dunlop
Almohad	
Almutawakel	Saeed bin Suroor, UAE
Altitude (IRE)	Sir Mark Prescott
Ambiguous	D. R. Loder
Ambition	A. Fabre, France
Anemos (IRE)	M. A. Jarvis
Annadawi	E. A. L. Dunlop
Asakir	Saeed bin Suroor, UAE
Aware	P. Bary, France
Azurose	C. E. Brittain
Baajil	L. M. Cumani
Baffin Bay	H. R. A. Cecil
Balizac (IRE)	A. Fabre, France
Banaan	L. M. Cumani
Banker Dwerry (FR)	S. P. C. Woods
Battle Cry	L. M. Cumani
Battle Warning	H. Candy
Bayyadi (IRE)	J. Oxx, Ireland
Behrajan (IRE)	
Beneventus	J. L. Dunlop
Benin (USA)	H. R. A. Cecil
Bequia	A. Fabre, France
Berkeley Square (IRE)	A. P. O'Brien, Ireland
Bersaglio	W. Jarvis
Best Quest	J. H. M. Gosden
Beware	R. W. Armstrong
Beyond Reach	
Bianconi (USA)	A. P. O'Brien, Ireland
Bien Costaud	E. Lellouche, France
Bin Arazi	M. Johnston
Boldini (IRE)	A. P. O'Brien, Ireland
Bombastic	B. W. Hills
Border Arrow	I. A. Balding
Boreas	L. M. Cumani
Born Winner	H. R. A. Cecil
Bourbon Street (USA)	L. M. Cumani
Brave Charger (USA)	Saeed bin Suroor, UAE
Brave Reward (USA)	M. R. Stoute
Brave Ruler (IRE)	A. P. O'Brien, Ireland
Brilliancy (USA)	A. Fabre, France
Brimming	H. R. A. Cecil
Bullet	W. J. Haggas
Burhan (USA)	Saeed bin Suroor, UAE
Bushman's River (USA)	P. Bary, France
Cadillac Jukebox (USA)	J. W. Hills
Caernarfon Bay (IRE)	P. F. I. Cole
Cage Aux Folles (IRE)	J. W. Hills
Capital Prince (FR)	Saeed bin Suroor, UAE
Capri	H. R. A. Cecil
Captain Melleray (IRE)	A. P. O'Brien, Ireland
Carry The Flag	P. F. I. Cole
Casino Captive (USA)	P. W. Chapple-Hyam
Catamaran	J. H. M. Gosden
Cellini	L. M. Cumani
Celtic Cavalier (IRE)	A. P. O'Brien, Ireland
Central Park (IRE)	P. F. I. Cole
Chapel Lane (IRE)	A. C. Stewart
Chateau Royal (USA)	A. P. O'Brien, Ireland
Chieftain (IRE)	N. A. Callaghan
Chief Whip (USA)	L. M. Cumani
Chrysolite (IRE)	B. W. Hills
Circe's Symbol	A. Fabre, France
Circus	C. E. Brittain
Citrus Express (SWE)	P. Mooney
City Honours (USA)	P. W. Chapple-Hyam
Cloclo (IRE)	E. Lellouche, France
Coconut Creek (IRE)	A. P. O'Brien, Ireland
Colorado Prince (USA)	
Compere	A. Fabre, France
Connoisseur Bay (USA)	P. W. Chapple-Hyam
Cool Vibes	J. Pearce
Copeland	
Copernicus	P. F. I. Cole
Coral Seeker	G. Wragg
Corniche (IRE)	P. F. I. Cole
Courageous (IRE)	P. F. I. Cole
Courteous	P. F. I. Cole
Court Shareef	R. Dickin
Craigsteel	H. R. A. Cecil
Creon	L. M. Cumani
Crescendo (FR)	
Croco Rouge (IRE)	P. Bary, France
Dabus	H. R. A. Cecil
Daisy Fay	
Dalayil (IRE)	Saeed bin Suroor, UAE
Darialann (IRE)	A. de Royer-Dupre, France
Dark Shell (IRE)	M. R. Stoute
Daryapour (IRE)	A. de Royer-Dupre, France
Dashing Chief (IRE)	M. A. Jarvis
Dashing Knight (IRE)	D. R. Loder
Daymarti (IRE)	A. de Royer-Dupre, France
Decisive Action (USA)	P. F. I. Cole
Denarius (USA)	J. H. M. Gosden
Desert Tycoon (IRE)	J. H. M. Gosden
Desired	
Detroit City (FR)	J. E. Hammond, France
Diligence (IRE)	P. F. I. Cole
Divvinayshan (IRE)	R. W. Armstrong
Dixit (USA)	Mrs C. Head, France
Dmowski	A. C. Stewart
Dolfikar (IRE)	A. de Royer-Dupre, France
Doraid (IRE)	J. H. M. Gosden
Double Account (FR)	Mrs C. Head, France
Double Blade	M. Johnston
Dower House	W. Jarvis
Dream Well (FR)	P. Bary, France
Dr Watson	L. M. Cumani
Dual Purpose (IRE)	Noel Furlong, Ireland
Duck Row (USA)	J. A. R. Toller
Dushanbe (IRE)	L. M. Cumani
Dynamism (FR)	H. R. A. Cecil
Eagle's Cross (USA)	R. Charlton
Eaton Square (USA)	H. R. A. Cecil
Echelle Musicale	E. A. L. Dunlop
Eco Friendly	B. W. Hills
Ei Ei	B. W. Hills

Elaando	J. E. Pease, France
Elhayq (IRE)	J. L. Dunlop
Emerald Heights	J. R. Fanshawe
Eminence Grise (IRE)	H. R. A. Cecil
Enborne	H. R. A. Cecil
Enzeli (IRE)	J. Oxx, Ireland
Equity	L. M. Cumani
Estuary (USA)	A. Fabre, France
Ethereal	D. R. Loder
Etisalat (IRE)	R. W. Armstrong
Extravaganza	P. F. I. Cole
Extrovert (IRE)	G. Lewis
Fa-Eq (IRE)	Saeed bin Suroor, UAE
Fakhr (USA)	J. L. Dunlop
Falcon Crest	N. A. Callaghan
Family Crest (IRE)	A. P. O'Brien, Ireland
Fantastic Quest (IRE)	Mrs C. Head, France
Fantasy Island (IRE)	Saeed bin Suroor, UAE
Fearsome Factor (USA)	D. K. Weld, Ireland
Fisherman's Cove (USA)	A. P. O'Brien, Ireland
Flag Connection (USA)	Mrs C. Head, France
Fleetwood (IRE)	H. R. A. Cecil
Flying Kiss (IRE)	Saeed bin Suroor, UAE
Forever Young	D. K. Weld, Ireland
Francis Bay (USA)	D. K. Weld, Ireland
French Wood (USA)	B. Hanbury
Fruits of Love (USA)	M. Johnston
Full Spate	R. Charlton
Gatecrasher	J. R. Fanshawe
Gedy Red (USA)	H. R. A. Cecil
Generosity	P. F. I. Cole
Generous Rosi	D. R. Loder
Generous Terms	H. Candy
Generous Ways	E. A. L. Dunlop
Giveaway	H. R. A. Cecil
Giverney (IRE)	A. Fabre, France
Gleaming Hill (USA)	M. R. Stoute
Glenmead	A. C. Stewart
Glissando (IRE)	A. Fabre, France
Global Warning	G. Wragg
Glory of Grosvenor (IRE)	P. W. Chapple-Hyam
Glory of Love	J. Hetherton
Golden Chimes (USA)	Charles O'Brien, Ireland
Golden Dancer (IRE)	
Golden Hawk (USA)	P. F. I. Cole
Golden Lyric (IRE)	G. Wragg
Gondola (IRE)	J. H. M. Gosden
Greek Dance (IRE)	M. R. Stoute
Grimshaw (USA)	H. R. A. Cecil
Gulland	G. Wragg
Gwynfi	
Haami (USA)	J. L. Dunlop
Hadith	P. T. Walwyn
Hanzanar (IRE)	J. Oxx, Ireland
Harbour Master (FR)	A. P. O'Brien, Ireland
Hariymi (IRE)	J. Oxx, Ireland
Harmony	L. M. Cumani
Hawadeth	M. P. Tregoning
Hibernian Rhapsody (IRE)	D. K. Weld, Ireland
Highlands (FR)	A. Fabre, France
High-Rise (IRE)	L. M. Cumani
High Noon	L. M. Cumani
High Tension (USA)	P. F. I. Cole
Highwayman (IRE)	M. R. Stoute
Himrani (IRE)	J. Oxx, Ireland
Himself (USA)	H. R. A. Cecil
Hudood (USA)	Saeed bin Suroor, UAE
Hunt Hill (IRE)	Sir Mark Prescott
Impressionist (IRE)	A. P. O'Brien, Ireland
In Arcadia	A. Fabre, France
Incentive	J. H. M. Gosden
Incepta	B. W. Hills
Indimaaj	J. L. Dunlop
Inner Light	L. M. Cumani
Innovative Step (USA)	D. K. Weld, Ireland
Inspiring Story (USA)	D. K. Weld, Ireland
Ireland's Eye (IRE)	M. Johnston
Jaazim (USA)	M. R. Stoute
Jabal Hadeed (IRE)	M. A. Jarvis
Jazil	J. H. M. Gosden
Jeehaad (USA)	Saeed bin Suroor, UAE
Jila (IRE)	R. W. Armstrong
Joint Regent (USA)	B. W. Hills
Kabool	
Kadir	M. P. Tregoning
Kagoshima (IRE)	L. M. Cumani
Kahtan	J. L. Dunlop
Kaid (IRE)	E. A. L. Dunlop
Karasi (IRE)	M. R. Stoute
Kasid (IRE)	D. K. Weld, Ireland
Kassiyan (IRE)	A. de Royer-Dupre, France
Katiyar (IRE)	J. Oxx, Ireland
Khaliandak (IRE)	J. Oxx, Ireland
Khatani (IRE)	J. Oxx, Ireland
Kilimanjaro	M. R. Stoute
King of Kings (IRE)	A. P. O'Brien, Ireland
Kirilov (IRE)	R. W. Armstrong
Knife Edge (USA)	M. R. Stoute
Krispy Knight	J. W. Hills
Kumatour	L. M. Cumani
Laffah (USA)	J. H. M. Gosden
Land A Hand (USA)	
Landing Light (IRE)	R. Charlton
Landing Slot (USA)	D. K. Weld, Ireland
La Nuit Rose (FR)	Saeed bin Suroor, UAE
Last Christmas	B. W. Hills
Last Mango (IRE)	D. R. Loder
Laurentide (USA)	H. R. A. Cecil
Leap To Glory (USA)	D. R. Loder
Legal Lunch (USA)	P. W. Harris
Lightning Star (USA)	A. P. O'Brien, Ireland
Liniyan (IRE)	L. M. Cumani
Long Siege (IRE)	D. R. Loder
Look And Learn (FR)	N. Clement, France
Love Academy	M. Johnston
Love Blushes (IRE)	M. Johnston
Love Kiss (IRE)	M. Johnston
Loyal Deed (USA)	J. Oxx, Ireland
Loyal Toast (USA)	L. M. Cumani
Madrid	M. R. Stoute
Mahboob (IRE)	
Majestic Hills	J. L. Dunlop
Make No Mistake (IRE)	D. K. Weld, Ireland
Malsoon (USA)	N. Clement, France
Maltayar (IRE)	L. M. Cumani
Mane Frame	H. Morrison
Manhattan Island	
Man of Courage	E. A. L. Dunlop
Mardani (IRE)	J. Oxx, Ireland
Maridpour (IRE)	M. R. Stoute
Marillac	D. R. Loder
Marksman (IRE)	L. M. Cumani
Mark Time	M. H. Tompkins
Marran (IRE)	J. L. Dunlop
Masali (IRE)	A. de Royer-Dupre, France
Masarkal (IRE)	J. Oxx, Ireland
Massenet (IRE)	J. H. M. Gosden
Maverick (FR)	A. Fabre, France
Mazboon (USA)	E. A. L. Dunlop
Measureless	J. R. Arnold
Meaux (IRE)	C. E. Brittain
Medieval (IRE)	J. E. Pease, France
Meniatarra (USA)	Saeed bin Suroor, UAE
Methmoon (IRE)	Saeed bin Suroor, UAE
Midnight Guest (IRE)	L. M. Cumani
Mijana (IRE)	J. H. M. Gosden
Miller (FR)	A. Fabre, France
Mi Picasso (IRE)	
Mirror Mirror (IRE)	Noel Furlong, Ireland
Misbah (USA)	B. Hanbury

Mister Eric	R. Gibson, France
Monsajem (USA)	E. A. L. Dunlop
Moon Quest	R. Charlton
Moratorium (USA)	H. R. A. Cecil
Mornington	J. Noseda
Mr Hamad	B. Hanbury
Mufeed	M. Johnston
Muftin (IRE)	K. Prendergast, Ireland
Muhaba (USA)	Saeed bin Suroor, UAE
Muhib (USA)	M. R. Stoute
Munaza (USA)	R. W. Armstrong
Munif (USA)	B. Hanbury
Mutafarij (USA)	E. A. L. Dunlop
Mutamam	A. C. Stewart
Mutawwaj (IRE)	Saeed bin Suroor, UAE
My Career	E. A. L. Dunlop
Nasanice (IRE)	Saeed bin Suroor, UAE
Nautical Star	J. W. Hills
Nedawi	Saeed bin Suroor, UAE
Negus	
Night Image	B. Hanbury
Night Magic	B. Hanbury
Night People	W. Jarvis
Night Rule	B. Hanbury
Nobelist	A. Fabre, France
Northern Major (USA)	M. R. Stoute
Note Musicale	
Nousayri (IRE)	L. M. Cumani
Octave	A. Fabre, France
One Dinar (FR)	J. H. M. Gosden
Opera King (USA)	Saeed bin Suroor, UAE
Opera Queen (USA)	E. A. L. Dunlop
Otaarid (IRE)	B. Hanbury
Otavalo (IRE)	Mrs C. Head, France
Outsourcing (USA)	P. F. I. Cole
Pagan	L. M. Cumani
Paganini	H. R. A. Cecil
Pairumani Star (IRE)	J. L. Dunlop
Palais (IRE)	M. R. Stoute
Palasari (IRE)	A. de Royer-Dupre, France
Palmetto Bay (IRE)	M. R. Stoute
Pantar (IRE)	I. A. Balding
Paper Tiger (USA)	R. Charlton
Peak Path (IRE)	M. R. Stoute
Peerless Motion (IRE)	D. K. Weld, Ireland
Pegnitz (USA)	C. E. Brittain
Pelfre	A. Fabre, France
Pendoggett (USA)	D. R. C. Elsworth
Perellina (IRE)	S. Wattel, France
Pinmix (FR)	A. Fabre, France
Plan-B	J. H. M. Gosden
Playacting (USA)	J. Oxx, Ireland
Play Safe	B. W. Hills
Power Corrupts (IRE)	Noel Furlong, Ireland
Pozarica	Saeed bin Suroor, UAE
Precipice	D. R. Loder
Prehistoric (USA)	A. Fabre, France
Premium Rate (USA)	E. A. L. Dunlop
Princer (CAN)	V. Caruso, Italy
Proudy (IRE)	S. Wattel, France
Pure Nobility (IRE)	B. W. Hills
Quevilly	J. Oxx, Ireland
Quiet Assurance (USA)	E. A. L. Dunlop
Quintus (USA)	P. F. I. Cole
Rabah	J. L. Dunlop
Rabi (IRE)	E. A. L. Dunlop
Rainald (USA)	J. H. M. Gosden
Rainbow High	B. W. Hills
Rainbow Ways	B. W. Hills
Rainmaker	M. A. Jarvis
Rainshack	
Rainstorm	J. H. M. Gosden
Rajati (USA)	Mrs J. Cecil
Rajjaaf	D. K. Weld, Ireland
Ramon Vega	L. M. Cumani
Ray of Hope (USA)	I. A. Balding
Real Dedication	G. Woodward
Red Bordeaux	B. W. Hills
Regal Patriarch (IRE)	J. L. Dunlop
Regent	Sir Mark Prescott
Res Judicata	J. E. Pease, France
Rivelino (IRE)	A. P. O'Brien, Ireland
Roman King (IRE)	J. H. M. Gosden
Room To Improve (IRE)	
Royal Request (IRE)	Saeed bin Suroor, UAE
Rubamma	P. T. Walwyn
Sadian	H. R. A. Cecil
Sadler's Secret (IRE)	Mrs C. Head, France
Safi	Major W. R. Hern
Sagamix (FR)	A. Fabre, France
Saints Be Praised (USA)	R. Akehurst
Salvage	
Saratoga Springs (CAN)	A. P. O'Brien, Ireland
Sayarshan (FR)	A. Fabre, France
Sea Wave (IRE)	Saeed bin Suroor, UAE
Second Empire (IRE)	A. P. O'Brien, Ireland
Secrecy	P. F. I. Cole
Secret Saver (USA)	M. R. Stoute
Senanjar (IRE)	A. de Royer-Dupre, France
Sentry Duty	W. J. Haggas
Sestino (IRE)	Mrs C. Head, France
Shaatir	N. Clement, France
Shah of Persia (IRE)	J. Oxx, Ireland
Shaiydari (IRE)	L. M. Cumani
Shamawan (IRE)	L. M. Cumani
Shamsiyani (IRE)	A. de Royer-Dupre, France
Shart (IRE)	J. H. M. Gosden
Shedari (IRE)	
Shimaal	Saeed bin Suroor, UAE
Shmoose (IRE)	Saeed bin Suroor, UAE
Shogun (IRE)	J. H. M. Gosden
Sideman (IRE)	A. P. O'Brien, Ireland
Silent Warning	Sir Mark Prescott
Silver Sabre (USA)	E. A. L. Dunlop
Singer Sargent (USA)	M. R. Stoute
Sir Eric (FR)	R. Gibson, France
Sky Rocket	M. R. Stoute
Social Charter (USA)	P. W. Chapple-Hyam
Social Graces (IRE)	D. K. Weld, Ireland
Somayda (IRE)	J. L. Dunlop
Sombero	J. E. Hammond, France
Sottvus (IRE)	L. M. Cumani
Soviet Bureau (IRE)	Miss Gay Kelleway
Speaker's Chair	R. Charlton
Special Quest (FR)	Mrs C. Head, France
Spindrift (IRE)	L. M. Cumani
Stanott (IRE)	L. M. Cumani
Star of Tramp (IRE)	D. K. Weld, Ireland
Sternsinger (USA)	H. R. A. Cecil
Stero Heights (IRE)	E. A. L. Dunlop
Stingray (IRE)	M. Johnston
Stylish Flight (USA)	E. A. L. Dunlop
Sugar Dance	M. J. Heaton-Ellis
Sunshine Street (USA)	N. Meade, Ireland
Sure Dancer (USA)	P. F. I. Cole
Sweet Victory	J. C. Rouget, France
Sylphides (ITY)	R. Akehurst
Taakid (USA)	K. Prendergast, Ireland
Takarian (IRE)	J. Oxx, Ireland
Taleban	L. M. Cumani
Tarakan (IRE)	L. M. Cumani
Tarasi (IRE)	J. Oxx, Ireland
Tarbazan (IRE)	A. de Royer-Dupre, France
Tassle (IRE)	A. Fabre, France
Teapot Row (IRE)	J. A. R. Toller
Temper Lad (USA)	J. H. M. Gosden
Tensile (IRE)	L. M. Cumani
Teroom	A. C. Stewart
Terrazzo (USA)	R. Charlton
The Card King (IRE)	A. Fabre, France

The Glow-Worm (IRE)	B. W. Hills	Vrin (IRE)	L. M. Cumani
There Be Demons (USA)	G. Wragg	Waiting Knight (USA)	B. Hanbury
The Third Curate (IRE)	D. K. Weld, Ireland	Wajori (USA)	J. H. M. Gosden
Thief of Hearts (IRE)	A. Fabre, France	Wales	P. F. I. Cole
Think Snow	J. H. M. Gosden	Walpole	D. R. Loder
Thrashing	C. E. Brittain	Waterberg (IRE)	A. Fabre, France
Tiger Haven (IRE)	A. P. O'Brien, Ireland	Watership Dance	H. R. A. Cecil
Tightrope	Sir Mark Prescott	Watkins	F. Murphy
Time Loss	H. Candy	Wave Racer	B. Hanbury
Titanic (IRE)	J. H. M. Gosden	Way Out Yonder	B. W. Hills
Tomaszewski (FR)	P. W. Harris	Welcoming	J. H. M. Gosden
Tornado Prince (IRE)	N. A. Callaghan	Wemyss Quest	H. R. A. Cecil
Tory Boy	I. P. Williams	Wend's Day (IRE)	P. F. I. Cole
Trans Island	I. A. Balding	Which Hand	C. Laffon-Parias, France
Travelling Clock	B. A. McMahon	Whistle Stop (USA)	C. E. Brittain
Treasure Mountain (USA)	P. F. I. Cole	White Scissors (USA)	H. R. A. Cecil
Trident (USA)	M. R. Stoute	Wild Tempo (FR)	P. Nataf, France
Triple Blade (USA)	N. Clement, France	Winning Saint (IRE)	M. H. Tompkins
Tutankhamun	M. R. Stoute	Zaha (IRE)	R. W. Armstrong
Twickenham (USA)	H. R. A. Cecil	Zalal (IRE)	L. M. Cumani
Two-Twenty-Two (IRE)	D. K. Weld, Ireland	Zariyar (IRE)	
Uhuru Peak (FR)	J. E. Hammond, France	Zool	B. Hanbury
Undaunted (IRE)	J. S. Bolger, Ireland	Zydeco (IRE)	M. C. Pipe
Untold Story (USA)	D. K. Weld, Ireland	ex Lady Gerard	L. M. Cumani
Uranus Quercus (FR)	F. Doumen, France	ex Polkadot Bikini (IRE)	
Vagrant (FR)	D. K. Weld, Ireland	ex Queen of The Court (USA)	D. J. S. ffrench Davis
Varapour (IRE)	A. de Royer-Dupre, France	ex Reine des Iles (USA)	Charles O'Brien, Ireland
Victory Note (USA)	P. W. Chapple-Hyam	ex Saraday	K. Prendergast, Ireland

EUROPEAN FREE HANDICAP

NEWMARKET, CRAVEN MEETING 1998 (ON THE DEWHURST STAKES COURSE) WEDNESDAY, APRIL 15th

The NGK Spark Plugs European Free Handicap (Class A) (Listed race) with £30,000 added for two-years old only of 1997 (including all two-years-old in the 1997 International Classification), to run as three-years-old; lowest weight 7st 10lb; highest weight 9st 7lb. Penalty for winner after December 31, 1997, 5lb.

SEVEN FURLONGS.

Rating		st	lb	SF
127	Xaar (GB)	9	7	77
119	Second Empire (IRE)	8	13	70
118	Central Park (IRE)	8	12	72
	Daggers Drawn (USA)	8	12	77
	Embassy (GB)	8	12	79
116	Charge d'Affaires (GB)	8	10	–
	Lend A Hand (GB)	8	10	62
	Saratoga Springs (CAN)	8	10	77
115	Mudeer (GB)	8	9	78
	Tamarisk (IRE)	8	9	74
114	Hayil (USA)	8	8	67
	Muhtathir (GB)	8	8	71
	Princely Heir (IRE)	8	8	65
113	Crazee Mental (GB)	8	7	75
	Loving Claim (USA)	8	7	69
	Mutamam (GB)	8	7	78
112	Arkadian Hero (USA)	8	6	77
	Bold Fact (USA)	8	6	74
	Carrowkeel (IRE)	8	6	71
	Docksider (USA)	8	6	78
	Midnight Line (USA)	8	6	75
	Thief of Hearts (IRE)	8	6	84
111	Alboostan (GB)	8	5	65
	Designer (USA)	8	5	67
	Glorosia (FR)	8	5	73
	Halmahera (IRE)	8	5	93
	Harbour Master (FR)	8	5	80
	King of Kings (IRE)	8	5	69
	Little Indian (GB)	8	5	70
	Special Quest (FR)	8	5	83
110	Asakir (GB)	8	4	53
	Asfurah (USA)	8	4	67
	Daymarti (IRE)	8	4	84
	Desert Prince (IRE)	8	4	77
	El Maimoun (GB)	8	4	–
	Impressionist (IRE)	8	4	72
	Isle de France (USA)	8	4	69
	Jimmy Too (GB)	8	4	67
	Lord Kintyre (GB)	8	4	81
	Merlin's Ring (GB)	8	4	67
	Name of Love (IRE)	8	4	76
	Royal Shyness (GB)	8	4	65
	Tarascon (IRE)	8	4	60
	Teapot Row (IRE)	8	4	81
	Tracking (GB)	8	4	72
	Woodland Melody (USA)	8	4	61
109	Baltic State (USA)	8	3	63
	Cape Verdi (IRE)	8	3	83
	Croco Rouge (IRE)	8	3	–
	Heed My Warning (IRE)	8	3	61
	Jibe (USA)	8	3	74
	Mijana (IRE)	8	3	72
	Risk Material (IRE)	8	3	–
	Silic (FR)	8	3	85
108	Anna Palariva (IRE)	8	2	59
	Bodyguard (GB)	8	2	55
	Chester House (USA)	8	2	73
	City Honours (USA)	8	2	81
	Haami (USA)	8	2	75
	La-Faah (IRE)	8	2	61
	Nadwah (USA)	8	2	83
	Pinmix (FR)	8	2	–
	Plaisir Des Yeux (FR)	8	2	70
	Pool Music (GB)	8	2	68
	Prolix (GB)	8	2	82
	Regal Revolution	8	2	87
	Shahtoush (IRE)	8	2	61
	Speedfit Too (IRE)	8	2	68
	Tippitt Boy (GB)	8	2	66
107	Alborada (GB)	8	1	61
	Almutawakel (GB)	8	1	82
	Arawak Cay (IRE)	8	1	59
	Ashraakat (USA)	8	1	70
	Celtic Cavalier (IRE)	8	1	58
	Desert Drama (IRE)	8	1	70
	Fairly Grey (FR)	8	1	–
	Fruits of Love (USA)	8	1	70
	Greenlander (GB)	8	1	–
	Gulland (GB)	8	1	72
	Heeremandi (IRE)	8	1	64
	Khumba Mela (IRE)	8	1	70
	Kilimanjaro (GB)	8	1	82
	Lady In Waiting (GB)	8	1	76
	Linden Heights (GB)	8	1	69
	Mantles Star (GB)	8	1	67
	Mempari (IRE)	8	1	60
	Mountain Song (GB)	8	1	47
	Scenery (IRE)	8	1	–

Rating	Horse	st	lb		
	Silent Tribute (IRE)	8	1	....	70
	Tenbyssimo (IRE)	8	1	....	67
	Trans Island (GB)	8	1	....	73
	Wren (IRE)	8	1	....	–
	Zalaiyka (FR)	8	1	....	71
106	Bahr (GB)	8	0	....	71
	Bintang (IRE)	8	0	....	87
	Craigsteel (GB)	8	0	....	82
	Eco Friendly (GB)	8	0	....	57
	Exclusive (GB)	8	0	....	73
	Flawless (GB)	8	0	....	75
	Gold Away (IRE)	8	0	....	–
	Hopping Higgins (IRE)	8	0	....	64
	Lady Alexander (IRE)	8	0	....	58
	Land of Dreams (GB)	8	0	....	71
	Pegnitz (USA)	8	0	....	73
	Victory Note (USA)	8	0	....	80
105	Dr Fong (USA)	7	13	....	75
	Flame Violet (IRE)	7	13	....	60
	Insight (FR)	7	13	....	–
	Mowbray (USA)	7	13	....	51
	Roi Gironde (IRE)	7	13	....	–
	Sharp Domino (GB)	7	13	....	–
	Shuhrah (USA)	7	13	....	75

THREE-YEAR-OLDS OF 1997

A classification for three-year-olds trained in Great Britain, which ran during 1997 and have been allotted a rating of not less than 105 (7st 7 lb).

$1\frac{3}{4}$m plus

Rating		st	lb
113	Windsor Castle (GB)	8	1
107	Three Cheers (IRE)	7	9
106	Palio Sky (GB)	7	8
106	Winter Garden (GB)	7	8
105	Book At Bedtime (IRE)	7	7
106	Silence Reigns (GB)	7	8
105	Monza (USA)	7	7
105	Musical Dancer (USA)	7	7
105	Rainwatch (GB)	7	7
105	Tanaasa (IRE)	7	7

1m 3f plus

Rating	Horse	st	lb
123	Silver Patriarch (IRE)	8	11
119	Stowaway (GB)	8	7
118	Kingfisher Mill (USA)	8	6
117	Reams of Verse (USA)	8	5
115	Panama City (USA)	8	3
115	Romanov (IRE)	8	3
114	Falak (USA)	8	2
113	Crown of Light (GB)	8	1
113	Ivan Luis (FR)	8	1
113	Kaliana (IRE)	8	1
112	Etoile (FR)	8	0
112	Maylane (GB)	8	0
110	King Sound (GB)	7	12
109	Single Empire (IRE)	7	11
109	Poseidon (GB)	7	11
108	Apprehension (GB)	7	10
108	Nicole Pharly (GB)	7	10
107	Haltarra (USA)	7	9
107	Memorise (USA)	7	9
106	Attitre (FR)	7	8
106	Badlesmere (USA)	7	8
106	Ghataas (GB)	7	8
106	Palio Sky (GB)	7	8
106	Shaya (GB)	7	8

$9\frac{1}{2}$f plus

Rating	Horse	st	lb
126	Benny The Dip (USA)	9	0
122	Bahhare (USA)	8	10
122	Ryafan (USA)	8	10
118	Yashmak (USA)	8	6
117	Reams of Verse (USA)	8	5
116	Kool Kat Katie (IRE)	8	4
116	One So Wonderful (GB)	8	4
115	Romanov (IRE)	8	3
114	Crystal Hearted (GB)	8	2
113	Handsome Ridge (GB)	8	1
113	Voyagers Quest (USA)	8	1
112	Squeak (GB)	8	0
111	Entice (FR)	7	13
111	Musalsal (IRE)	7	13
110	Catienus (USA)	7	12
110	Grapeshot (USA)	7	12
109	Dust Dancer (GB)	7	11
109	Royal Amaretto (IRE)	7	11
107	Amid Albadu (USA)	7	9
107	Green Card (USA)	7	9
107	Haltarra (USA)	7	9
107	Sandstone (IRE)	7	9
106	Jaunty Jack (GB)	7	8
105	Monza (USA)	7	7

7f plus

Rating	Horse	st	lb
124	Entrepreneur (GB)	8	12
122	Revoque (IRE)	8	10
122	Starborough (GB)	8	10
120	Air Express (IRE)	8	8
120	Sleepytime (IRE)	8	8
119	Poteen (USA)	8	7
118	Among Men (USA)	8	6
118	Cape Cross (IRE)	8	6
117	Fahris (IRE)	8	5
116	Rebecca Sharp (GB)	8	4
115	Crimson Tide (IRE)	8	3
115	Faithful Son (USA)	8	3
115	Hidden Meadow (GB)	8	3
115	Ocean Ridge (USA)	8	3
114	Desert Story (IRE)	8	2
114	Fantastic Fellow (USA)	8	2
114	Kahal (GB)	8	2
114	Mamalik (USA)	8	2
114	Seebe (USA)	8	2
114	Yalaietanee (GB)	8	2
112	Oh Nellie (USA)	8	0
112	Red Camellia (GB)	8	0
112	Reunion (IRE)	8	0
111	Dances With Dreams (GB)	7	13
111	Fly To The Stars (GB)	7	13
111	Intikhab (USA)	7	13
110	Catienus (USA)	7	12
110	Dazzle (GB)	7	12
110	The Fly (GB)	7	12
110	Grapeshot (USA)	7	12
109	Bold Words (CAN)	7	11
109	Dance Parade (USA)	7	11
108	Andreyev (IRE)	7	10
107	Amid Albadu (USA)	7	9
107	Elegant Warning (IRE)	7	9
107	In Command (IRE)	7	9
107	Khassah (GB)	7	9
107	Supercal (GB)	7	9
107	Swiss Law (GB)	7	9
106	Rich Ground (GB)	7	8
106	Royal Aty (IRE)	7	8
106	Well Warned (GB)	7	8
105	Barnum Sands (GB)	7	7
105	Shii-Take (GB)	7	7
105	Soviet State (USA)	7	7
105	Wind Cheetah (USA)	7	7

5f plus

Rating	Horse	st	lb
121	Compton Place (GB)	8	9
121	Elnadim (USA)	8	9
117	Carmine Lake (IRE)	8	5
117	Danetime (IRE)	8	5
116	Tomba (GB)	8	4
114	Indian Rocket (GB)	8	2
111	Deep Finesse (GB)	7	13
111	Muchea (GB)	7	13
111	Snow Kid (GB)	7	13
110	Blue Goblin (USA)	7	12
110	Nightbird (IRE)	7	12
109	Bahamian Bounty (GB)	7	11
109	Deadly Dudley (IRE)	7	11
108	Bint Albaadiya (USA)	7	10
108	Cathedral (IRE)	7	10
107	Easycall (GB)	7	9
107	Lochangel (GB)	7	9
105	Grand Lad (IRE)	7	7

FOUR-YEAR-OLDS AND UP OF 1997

A classification for four-year-olds and upwards trained in Great Britain, which ran during 1997 and have been allotted a rating of not less than 105 (7st 7 lb).

1¾m plus

Rating	Horse	Age	st	lb
121	Classic Cliche (IRE)	5	8	9
119	Celeric (GB)	5	8	7
119	Orchestra Stall (GB)	5	8	7
118	Double Trigger (IRE)	6	8	6
116	Election Day (IRE)	5	8	4
115	Double Eclipse (IRE)	5	8	3
113	Chief Contender (IRE)	4	8	1
113	Persian Punch (IRE)	4	8	1
112	Canon Can (USA)	4	8	0
112	Clerkenwell (USA)	4	8	0
112	Grey Shot (GB)	5	8	0
112	Samraan (USA)	4	8	0
111	Eva Luna (USA)	5	7	13
111	Heron Island (IRE)	4	7	13
111	Kutta (GB)	5	7	13
110	Corradini (GB)	5	7	12

110	Further Flight (GB)	1	7	12
108	Snow Princess (IRE)	5	7	10
107	Jiyush (GB)	4	7	9
107	Wilawander (GB)	4	7	9

1m 3f plus

129	Swain (IRE)	5	9	3
125	Shantou (USA)	4	8	13
124	Predappio (GB)	4	8	12
120	Luso (GB)	5	8	8
117	Annus Mirabilis (FR)	5	8	5
117	Dushyantor (USA)	4	8	5
117	Mons (GB)	4	8	5
117	My Emma (GB)	4	8	5
117	Posidonas (GB)	5	8	5
116	Busy Flight (GB)	4	8	4
115	Needle Gun (IRE)	7	8	3
115	Strategic Choice (USA)	6	8	3
114	Time Allowed (GB)	4	8	2
114	Whitewater Affair (GB)	4	8	2
113	Harbour Dues (GB)	4	8	1
112	Annaba (IRE)	4	8	0
111	Arabian Story (GB)	4	7	13
111	Eva Luna (USA)	5	7	13
111	Kutta (GB)	5	7	13
111	Royal Court (IRE)	4	7	13
110	Ela-Aristokrati (IRE)	5	7	12
110	Further Flight	11	7	12
110	Salmon Ladder (USA)	5	7	12
110	Tamure (IRE)	5	7	12
110	Taufan's Melody (GB)	6	7	12
110	Salmon Ladder (USA)	5	7	12
110	Tamure (IRE)	5	7	12
110	Taufan's Melody (GB)	6	7	12
109	Camporese (IRE)	4	7	11
109	Tulipa (USA)	4	7	11
108	Bright Water (GB)	4	7	10
105	Anno Luce (GB)	4	7	7
105	Nabhaan (IRE)	4	7	7

$9\frac{1}{2}$f plus

134	Pilsudski (IRE)	5	9	8
132	Singspiel (IRE)	5	9	6
131	Bosra Sham (USA)	4	9	5
121	Alhaarth (IRE)	4	8	9
120	Allied Forces (USA)	4	8	8
120	Taipan (IRE)	5	8	8
116	Tamayaz (CAN)	5	8	4
115	London News (SAF)	5	8	3
114	Germano (GB)	4	8	2
114	Kammtarra (USA)	4	8	2
112	King Alex (GB)	4	8	0
112	Lord of Men (GB)	4	8	0
112	Zaralaska (GB)	6	8	0
111	Arabian Story (GB)	4	7	13
111	Even Top (IRE)	4	7	13
110	Santillana (USA)	4	7	12
109	Cap Juluca (IRE)	5	7	11
109	Dr Massini (IRE)	4	7	11
109	Freequent (GB)	4	7	11
108	Multicoloured (IRE)	4	7	10
108	Prince of Andros (USA)	7	7	10
107	Bequeath (GB)	5	7	9
106	Acharne (GB)	4	7	8
106	Grey Way (USA)	4	7	8
105	Danish Rhapsody (IRE)	4	7	7
105	Fatefully (USA)	4	7	7
105	Forest Buck (USA)	4	7	7
105	Helicon (IRE)	4	7	7
105	Medaille Militaire (GB)	5	7	7
105	Sandmoor Chambray (GB)	6	7	7

7f plus

123	Ali-Royal (IRE)	4	8	11
123	First Island (IRE)	5	8	11
120	Allied Forces (USA)	4	8	8
119	Sasuru (GB)	4	8	7
119	Wizard King (GB)	6	8	7
118	Decorated Hero (GB)	5	8	6
118	Wixim (USA)	4	8	6
117	Gothenberg (IRE)	4	8	5
116	Lucayan Prince	4	8	4
116	River Keen (IRE)	5	8	4
115	Centre Stalls (IRE)	4	8	3
115	Russian Revival (USA)	4	8	3
114	Bijou d'Inde (GB)	4	8	2
113	Polar Prince (IRE)	4	8	1
111	Bin Rosie (GB)	5	7	13
111	Cool Edge (IRE)	6	7	13
111	Even Top (IRE)	4	7	13
110	Almushtarak (IRE)	4	7	12
110	Nwaamis (USA)	5	7	12
109	Cap Juluca (IRE)	5	7	11
108	Restructure (IRE)	5	7	10
107	Amrak Ajeeb (IRE)	5	7	9
107	Ramooz (USA)	4	7	9
106	Acharne (GB)	4	7	8
106	Cadeaux Tryst (GB)	5	7	8
106	Hawksley Hill (IRE)	4	7	8
106	Samara (IRE)	4	7	8
105	How Long (GB)	4	7	7
105	Jo Mell (GB)	4	7	7
105	Neuwest (USA)	5	7	7

5f plus

121	Royal Applause (GB)	4	8	9
116	Lucayan Prince	4	8	4
115	Coastal Bluff (GB)	5	8	3
115	Ya Malak (GB)	6	8	3
114	Averti (IRE)	6	8	2
114	Monaassib (GB)	6	8	2
113	My Best Valentine (GB)	7	8	1
112	Cyrano's Lad (IRE)	8	8	0
111	Almaty (IRE)	4	7	13
111	Diffident (FR)	5	7	13
110	Dashing Blue (GB)	4	7	12
110	Farhana (GB)	4	7	12
110	Struggler (GB)	5	7	12
110	Tedburrow (GB)	5	7	12
109	Croft Pool (GB)	6	7	11
109	Danehill Dancer (IRE)	4	7	11
108	Hever Golf Rose (GB)	6	7	10
108	Midnight Escape (GB)	4	7	10
108	Eveningperformance (GB)	6	7	10
108	Hever Golf Rose (GB)	6	7	10
108	Midnight Escape (GB)	4	7	10
108	Rambling Bear (GB)	4	7	10
107	Bollin Joanne (GB)	4	7	9
107	Brave Edge (GB)	6	7	9
107	Cretan Gift (GB)	6	7	9
106	Bolshoi (IRE)	5	7	8
106	Easy Dollar (GB)	5	7	8
106	Mind Games (GB)	5	7	8
106	Royale Figurine (IRE)	6	7	8
105	How Long (GB)	4	7	7
105	To The Roof (IRE)	5	7	7

IRISH CLASSIFICATIONS

TWO-YEAR-OLDS OF 1997

For two-year-olds only that ran in 1997 and are assessed by handicappers Ciaran Kennelly and Dermot MacDermott at a rating of 100 (7st 2lb) or more relative to the International Classifications. Horses trained abroad are included if they won, or achieved their rating, in Ireland.

Rating		st	lb
119	Second Empire (IRE)	8	7
116	Saratoga Springs (CAN)	8	4
114	Princely Heir (IRE)	8	2
111	Harbour Master (FR)	7	13
111	King of Kings	7	13
110	Asfurah (USA)	7	12
110	Impressionist (IRE)	7	12
110	Tarascon (IRE)	7	12
109	Heed My Warning (IRE)	7	11
109	Risk Material (IRE)	7	11
108	Shahtoush (IRE)	7	10
107	Alborada (GB)	7	9
107	Celtic Cavalier (IRE)	7	9
107	Fruits Of Love (USA)	7	9
107	Heeremandi (IRE)	7	9
107	Mempari (IRE)	7	9
107	Mountain Song (GB)	7	9
106	Hopping Higgins (IRE)	7	8
106	Lady Alexander (IRE)	7	8
105	Flame Violet (IRE)	7	7
105	Mowbray (USA)	7	7
104	Boldini (IRE)	7	6
104	Natalis (IRE)	7	6
104	Sharp Play (GB)	7	6
103	Danyross (IRE)	7	5
103	Winona (IRE)	7	5
102	Andy Dufresne (GB)	7	4
102	Hoh Chi Min (GB)	7	4
102	Magical Minty (IRE)	7	4
102	Sideman (IRE)	7	4
102	The King of Cloyne (USA)	7	4
101	Remarkable Style (USA)	7	3
101	Takarian (IRE)	7	3
100	Hanzanar (IRE)	7	2
100	Kincara Palace (IRE)	7	2

IRISH CLASSIFICATIONS

THREE-YEAR-OLDS OF 1997

For horses rated 100 (7st 2lb) or more relative to the 1997 International Classification, which were trained in Ireland in 1997. Horses trained abroad are included if they won, or achieved their rating in Ireland.

1¾m plus

		st	lb
117	Ebadiyla (IRE)	8	5
102	Buddy Marvel (IRE)	7	4
100	Aliya (IRE)	7	2
105	Zafarabad (IRE)	7	7
104	Olympic Majesty (FR)	7	6
103	Darroozett (GB)	7	5

1m 3f plus

		st	lb
124	Desert King (IRE)	8	12
121	Dr Johnson (IRE)	8	9
121	Loup Sauvage (USA)	8	9
120	Ebadiyla (IRE)	8	8
115	Yashmak (USA)	8	3
114	Brilliance (FR)	8	2
111	Johan Cruyff (GB)	7	13
109	Token Gesture (IRE)	7	11
105	Family Tradition (IRE)	7	7
101	Akdariya (IRE)	7	3
100	Aliya (IRE)	7	2
100	Bakkar (IRE)	7	2
100	Khairabar (IRE)	7	2
100	Spirit of Tara (IRE)	7	2

9f plus

		st	lb
128	Desert King (IRE)	9	2
112	Rayouni (IRE)	8	0
111	Johan Cruyff (GB)	7	13
111	Mingling Glances (USA)	7	13
110	Catienus (USA)	7	12
109	Ashley Park (IRE)	7	11
108	Caiseal Ros (IRE)	7	10
108	Casey Tibbs (USA)	7	10
106	Stage Affair (USA)	7	8

7f plus

		st	lb
122	Desert King (IRE)	8	10
116	Verglas (IRE)	8	4
112	Classic Park (GB)	8	0
110	Strawberry Roan (IRE)	7	12
110	Swift Gulliver (IRE)	7	12
109	Quws (GB)	7	11
107	Clerio (GB)	7	9
107	Nobility (IRE)	7	9
106	Rich Ground (GB)	7	8
105	Azra (IRE)	7	7
105	Dangerous Diva (IRE)	7	7
105	Supercal (GB)	7	7
103	Lil's Boy (USA)	7	5
103	Mr Lightfoot (IRE)	7	5
102	Almost Skint (IRE)	7	4
102	Crown Regent (IRE)	7	4
100	Alarme Belle (GB)	7	2
100	Chania (IRE)	7	2
100	Orange Jasmine (IRE)	7	2
100	Via Verbano (IRE)	7	2

5f plus

		st	lb
106	Check The Band (USA)	7	8
106	Swift Gulliver (IRE)	7	8
104	Grass Roots	7	6

IRISH CLASSIFICATIONS

FOUR-YEAR-OLDS AND UPWARDS

For horses rated 100 (7st 2lb) or more relative to the 1997 International Classification, which were trained in Ireland in 1997. Horses trained abroad are included if they won or achieved their rating in Ireland.

Rating		Age	st	lb
	1¾m plus			
117	Oscar Schindler (IRE)	5	8	5
113	Persian Punch (IRE)	4	8	1
110	Orchestra Stall (GB)	5	7	12
107	French Ballerina (IRE)	4	7	9
107	Whitewater Affair (GB)	4	7	9
100	Damancher (GB)	5	7	2
100	Gordi (USA)	4	7	2
	1m 3f plus			
124	Oscar Schindler (IRE)	5	8	12
104	Lafitte The Pirate (GB)	4	7	6
104	Mohaajir (USA)	6	7	6
100	Munif (IRE)	5	7	2
100	Vivo (IRE)	4	7	2
	9f plus			
134	Pilsudski (IRE)	5	9	8
119	Oscar Schindler (IRE)	5	8	7
115	Dance Design (IRE)	4	8	3
112	King Alex (GB)	4	8	0
108	Raiyoun (IRE)	4	7	10
	7f plus			
119	Alhaarth (IRE)	4	8	7
119	Wizard King (GB)	6	8	7
117	Gothenberg (IRE)	4	8	5
115	Burden of Proof (IRE)	5	8	3
111	Cool Edge (IRE)	6	7	13
107	Ramooz (USA)	4	7	9
101	Orange Grouse (IRE)	4	7	3
100	Tout A'Coup (IRE)	4	7	2
	5f plus			
115	Burden of Proof (IRE)	5	8	3
115	Lucayan Prince (USA)	4	8	3
111	Catch The Blues (IRE)	4	7	13
109	Theano (IRE)	4	7	11
108	Midnight Escape (GB)	4	7	10
106	Bolshoi (IRE)	5	7	8
105	Ailleacht (USA)	5	7	7
104	Ger's Royale (IRE)	6	7	6
103	Cretan Gift (GB)	6	7	5
101	Best Before Dawn (IRE)	6	7	3

If an entry is incorrect or has been omitted, please notify the editor by January 8th, 1999. This will ensure it appears correctly in the 1999 edition.

INTERNATIONAL CLASSIFICATION

For three-year-olds only, which during 1997 have run or been trained in Europe, Japan or North America, or have in races open to outside competition been assessed jointly by international classification committee handicappers and North American rating committee racing officials at a rating of 105 (7st 7lb) or above. In the case of North American horses, the minimum is 110.

1¾m plus

Rating		st	lb	Trained
115	Vertical Speed (FR)	8	3	FR
113	Windsor Castle (GB)	8	1	GB
111	Ungaro (GER)	7	13	GER
107	New Frontier (IRE)	7	9	FR
107	Three Cheers (IRE)	7	9	GB
106	Asolo (GER)	7	8	GER
106	Palio Sky (GB)	7	8	GB
106	Winter Garden (GB)	7	8	GB
105	Book At Bedtime (IRE)	7	7	GB
105	Ithaca (GB)	7	7	FR
105	Kaldoun Choice (FR)	7	7	FR

1m 3f plus

Rating		st	lb	Trained
137	Peintre Celebre (USA)	9	11	FR
126	Touch Gold (USA)	9	0	USA
125	Silver Charm (USA)	8	13	USA
124	Free House (USA)	8	12	USA
123	Silver Patriarch (IRE)	8	11	GB
121	Borgia (GER)	8	9	GER
121	Caitano (GB)	8	9	IRE
121	Dr Johnson (USA)	8	9	IRE
120	Ebadiyla (IRE)	8	8	IRE
120	Oscar (IRE)	8	8	FR
120	Silk Justice (JPN)	8	8	JPN
119	Astarabad (USA)	8	7	FR
119	Stowaway (GB)	8	7	GB
118	Kingfisher Mill (USA)	8	6	GB
118	Que Belle (CAN)	8	6	GER
117	Baroon (GB)	8	5	GER
117	Reams of Verse (USA)	8	5	GB
116	Queen Maud (IRE)	8	4	FR
116	Rajpoute (FR)	8	4	FR/USA
115	Magellano (USA)	8	3	FR
115	Panama City (USA)	8	3	GB/USA
115	Romanov (IRE)	8	3	GB
114	Brilliance (FR)	8	2	FR
114	Falak (USA)	8	2	GB
114	Gazelle Royale (FR)	8	2	FR
114	Shaka (GB)	8	2	FR
113	Crown of Light (GB)	8	1	GB
113	Fragrant Mix (IRE)	8	1	FR
113	Happy Change (GER)	8	1	GER
113	Ivan Luis (FR)	8	1	GB
113	Kaliana (IRE)	8	1	GB
113	Mejiro Dober (JPN)	8	1	JPN
112	Ajano (GER)	8	0	GER
112	Don't Worry (GER)	8	0	GER
112	Etoile (FR)	8	0	GB
112	Majorien (GB)	8	0	FR
112	Maylane (GB)	8	0	GB
111	Alekos (USA)	7	13	FR
111	Johan Cruyff (GB)	7	13	IRE/HK
110	King Sound (GB)	7	12	GB
109	Single Empire (IRE)	7	11	GB
109	Token Gesture (IRE)	7	11	IRE
109	Poseidon (GB)	7	11	GB
108	Apprehension (GB)	7	10	GB
108	Dame Kiri (FR)	7	10	FR
108	Nicole Pharly (GB)	7	10	GB
107	Fier Danseur (FR)	7	9	FR
107	Haltarra (USA)	7	9	GB
107	Legend Maker (IRE)	7	9	FR
107	Memorise (USA)	7	9	GB
107	New Frontier (IRE)	7	9	FR
107	Silver Fun (FR)	7	9	FR

107	War Declaration (IRE)	7	9	ITY
106	Attitre (FR)	7	8	GB
106	Badlesmere (USA)	7	8	GB
106	Ghataas (GB)	7	8	GB
106	Kassana (IRE)	7	8	FR
106	Palio Sky (GB)	7	8	GB
106	Shaya (GB)	7	8	GB
106	Silence Reigns (GB)	7	8	GB
105	Family Tradition (IRE)	7	7	IRE
105	Honey Colour (IRE)	7	7	ITY
105	Kaldoun Choice (FR)	7	7	FR
105	Monza (USA)	7	7	GB
105	Musical Dancer (USA)	7	7	GB
105	Rainwatch (GB)	7	7	GB
105	Tanaasa (IRE)	7	7	GB

9½f plus

128	Desert King (IRE)	9	2	IRE
126	Benny The Dip (USA)	9	0	GB
125	Loup Sauvage (USA)	8	13	FR
125	Silver Charm (USA)	8	13	USA
124	Captain Bodgit (USA)	8	12	USA
124	Free House (USA)	8	12	USA
122	Bahhare (USA)	8	10	GB
122	Behrens (USA)	8	10	USA
122	Deputy Commander (USA)	8	10	USA
122	Runup The Colors (USA)	8	10	USA
122	Ryafan (USA)	8	10	GB/USA
118	Honor Glide (USA)	8	6	USA
118	Yashmak (USA)	8	6	GB
117	Reams of Verse (USA)	8	5	GB
116	Ithaki (IRE)	8	4	FR
116	Kirkwall (GB)	8	4	FR
116	Kool Kat Katie (IRE)	8	4	GB
116	Mousse Glacee (FR)	8	4	FR
116	One So Wonderful (GB)	8	4	GB
116	Precocity (USA)	8	4	USA
116	Rajpoute (FR)	8	4	FR
115	Always Loyal (USA)	8	3	FR
115	Romanov (IRE)	8	3	GB
115	Wild Rush (USA)	8	3	USA
114	Crystal Hearted (GB)	8	2	GB
114	Lord Cromby (IRE)	8	2	USA/FR
114	Shaka (GB)	8	2	FR
113	Eden Rock (GER)	8	1	GER
113	Handsome Ridge (GB)	8	1	GB
113	Voyagers Quest (USA)	8	1	GB
113	Worldly Ways (GB)	8	1	USA
112	Rayouni (IRE)	8	0	IRE
112	Squeak (GB)	8	0	GB
111	Entice (FR)	7	13	GB
111	Johan Cruyff (GB)	7	13	IRE
111	Mr Groush (USA)	7	13	USA
111	Musalsal (IRE)	7	13	GB
110	Catienus (USA)	7	12	GB
110	Cloudings (IRE)	7	12	FR
110	Grapeshot (USA)	7	12	GB
110	La Nana (FR)	7	12	FR
109	Arabian King (FR)	7	11	FR
109	Ashley Park (IRE)	7	11	IRE
109	Dust Dancer (GB)	7	11	GB
109	Kashwan (SPA)	7	11	FR
109	Lomita (GER)	7	11	GER
109	Royal Amaretto (IRE)	7	11	GB
109	Zenith Rose (FR)	7	11	FR
108	Bedside Story (GB)	7	10	ITY
108	Caiseal Ros (IRE)	7	10	IRE
108	Casey Tibbs (IRE)	7	10	IRE/USA
108	March Groom (USA)	7	10	HUN/GER
108	Palme d'Or (IRE)	7	10	FR
107	Amid Albadu (USA)	7	9	GB
107	Anna Thea (IRE)	7	9	GER
107	Green Card (USA)	7	9	GB
107	Haltarra (USA)	7	9	GB
107	Sandstone (IRE)	7	9	GB
106	Jaunty Jack (GB)	7	8	GB
106	Keep Playing (FR)	7	8	FR
106	Stage Affair (USA)	7	8	IRE
106	Tenuous (GB)	7	8	FR
105	Keroub (FR)	7	7	FR
105	Monza (USA)	7	7	GB
105	Rate Cut (USA)	7	7	FR
105	Zafarabad (IRE)	7	7	IRE

7f plus

Rating	Horse	st	lb	Country
126	Touch Gold (USA)	9	0	USA
124	Entrepreneur (GB)	8	12	GB
124	Free House (USA)	8	12	USA
123	Ajina (USA)	8	11	USA
123	Sharp Cat (USA)	8	11	USA
122	Behrens (USA)	8	10	USA
122	Daylami (IRE)	8	10	FR
122	Glitter Woman (USA)	8	10	USA
122	Revoque (IRE)	8	10	GB
122	Starborough (GB)	8	10	GB
121	Blushing K D (USA)	8	9	USA
120	Air Express (IRE)	8	8	GB
120	Sleepytime (IRE)	8	8	GB
119	Poteen (USA)	8	7	GB
119	Taiki Shuttle (USA)	8	7	JPN
118	Among Men (USA)	8	6	GB
118	Anet (USA)	8	6	USA
118	Cape Cross (IRE)	8	6	GB
118	Dixie Flag (USA)	8	6	USA
118	Pulpit (USA)	8	6	USA
118	Tomisue's Delight (USA)	8	6	USA
118	Zamindar (USA)	8	6	FR
117	Accelerator (USA)	8	5	USA
117	Awesome Again (CAN)	8	5	USA
117	Fahris (IRE)	8	5	GB
117	Subordination (USA)	8	5	USA
116	Auntie Mame (USA)	8	4	USA
116	Concerto (USA)	8	4	USA
116	Crypto Star (USA)	8	4	USA
116	Famous Digger (USA)	8	4	USA
116	Lasting Approval (USA)	8	4	USA
116	Rebecca Sharp (GB)	8	4	GB
116	Verglas (IRE)	8	4	IRE
115	Always Loyal (USA)	8	3	FR
115	Arthur L (USA)	8	3	USA
115	Blazing Sword (USA)	8	3	USA
115	Crimson Tide (IRE)	8	3	GB
115	Faithful Son (USA)	8	3	GB
115	Frisk Me Now (USA)	8	3	USA
115	Golden Arches (FR)	8	3	FR/USA
115	Hidden Meadow (GB)	8	3	GB
115	Ocean Ridge (USA)	8	3	GB
115	Phantom On Tour (USA)	8	3	USA
115	River Squall (USA)	8	3	USA
115	Rob 'n Gin (USA)	8	3	USA
115	Starry Dreamer (USA)	8	3	USA
115	Wild Rush (USA)	8	3	USA
114	Brave Act (GB)	8	2	USA
114	Desert Story (IRE)	8	2	GB
114	Fantastic Fellow (USA)	8	2	GB/USA
114	Freeport Flight (USA)	8	2	USA
114	Hello (IRE)	8	2	USA
114	Holzmeister (USA)	8	2	USA
114	Kahal (GB)	8	2	GB
114	Kaldou Star (GB)	8	2	FR
114	Mamalik (USA)	8	2	GB
114	Marathon (USA)	8	2	FR
114	Pacificbounty (USA)	8	2	USA
114	Seebe (USA)	8	2	GB
114	See You Soon (FR)	8	2	FR/USA
114	Visionary (FR)	8	2	FR
114	Yalaietanee (GB)	8	2	GB
113	Minister's Melody (USA)	8	1	USA
113	Neuilly (USA)	8	1	FR
113	Ordway (USA)	8	1	USA
113	Richter Scale (USA)	8	1	USA
113	Royal Indy (USA)	8	1	USA
113	Skybound (USA)	8	1	CAN
113	Steel Ruhlr (USA)	8	1	USA
113	Tekken (IRE)	8	1	USA
113	Witchful Thinking (USA)	8	1	USA
113	Worldly Ways (GB)	8	1	USA
112	Aneysar (IRE)	8	0	FR
112	Ascutney (USA)	8	0	USA
112	Banker's Gold (USA)	8	0	USA
111	Classic Park (GB)	8	0	IRE
112	Fine Fellow (IRE)	8	0	FR
112	Funontherun (USA)	8	0	USA
112	Kyoei March (JPN)	8	0	JPN
112	Leo's Gypsy Dancer (USA)	8	0	USA
112	Nombre Premier (GB)	8	0	FR
112	Oh Nellie (USA)	8	0	GB
112	Queen of Money (USA)	8	0	USA

112	Red Camellia (GB)	8	0	GB
112	Reunion (IRE)	8	0	GB
112	Salt It (USA)	8	0	USA
112	Speed World (USA)	8	0	JPN
112	Thesaurus (USA)	8	0	USA
112	Wild Wonder (USA)	8	0	USA
111	Acceptable (USA)	7	13	USA
111	Anklet (USA)	7	13	USA
111	Cash Deposit (USA)	7	13	CAN
111	Celtic Warrior (USA)	7	13	USA
111	Clodora (FR)	7	13	FR
111	Dances With Dreams (GB)	7	13	GB
111	Early Colony (USA)	7	13	USA
111	Fly To The Stars (GB)	7	13	GB
111	Inexcessivelygood (USA)	7	13	USA
111	Intikhab (USA)	7	13	GB
111	Is Tirol (IRE)	7	13	GER
111	Jack Flash (USA)	7	13	USA
111	Mingling Glances (USA)	7	13	IRE/USA
111	P T Indy (USA)	7	13	USA
111	Royal Strand (IRE)	7	13	USA
111	Shammy Davis (USA)	7	13	USA
111	Swearingen (USA)	7	13	USA
111	Unite's Big Red (USA)	7	13	USA
111	Zede (USA)	7	13	USA
110	Baleno (GER)	7	12	GER
110	Catienus (USA)	7	12	GB
110	Cryptocloser (CAN)	7	12	CAN
110	Dazzle (GB)	7	12	GB
110	The Fly (GB)	7	12	GB
110	Glitman (USA)	7	12	USA
110	Grapeshot (USA)	7	12	GB
110	Jim And Tonic (FR)	7	12	FR
110	Keos (USA)	7	12	FR
110	Leestown (USA)	7	12	USA
110	Really Happy (USA)	7	12	USA
110	Smokin Mel (USA)	7	12	USA
110	Sonja's Faith (IRE)	7	12	USA
110	Statesmanship (USA)	7	12	USA
110	Stolen Gold (USA)	7	12	USA
110	Strawberry Roan (IRE)	7	12	IRE
110	Swift Gulliver (IRE)	7	12	IRE
110	Two Smart (USA)	7	12	USA
110	Varxi (FR)	7	12	FR
109	Bold Words (CAN)	7	11	GB
109	Cirino (USA)	7	11	FR
109	Dance Parade (USA)	7	11	GB
109	Heaven's Command (GB)	7	11	FR/USA
109	Night Player (IRE)	7	11	FR
109	Quws (GB)	7	11	IRE
108	Andreyev (IRE)	7	10	GB
108	Blasket Island (IRE)	7	10	FR
107	Amid Albadu (USA)	7	9	GB
107	Clerio (GB)	7	9	FR
107	Elegant Warning (IRE)	7	9	GB
107	In Command (IRE)	7	9	GB
107	Khassah (GB)	7	9	GB
107	Nobility (IRE)	7	9	IRE
107	Orford Ness (GB)	7	9	FR
107	Risiat (IRE)	7	9	ITY
107	Sensitivity (USA)	7	9	FR
107	Such Charisma (CAN)	7	9	FR
107	Supercal (GB)	7	9	GB
107	Swiss Law (GB)	7	9	GB
106	Basse Besogne (IRE)	7	8	FR
106	Inkatha (FR)	7	8	FR/USA
106	Kepster (USA)	7	8	FR
106	Rich Ground (GB)	7	8	GB
106	Royal Aty (IRE)	7	8	GB
106	Veiled Threat (IRE)	7	8	FR
106	Well Warned (GB)	7	8	GB
105	Azra (IRE)	7	7	IRE
105	Barnum Sands (GB)	7	7	GB
105	Dangerous Diva (IRE)	7	7	IRE
105	Green Lady (IRE)	7	7	FR
105	Mateyev (USA)	7	7	FR
105	Shii-Take (GB)	7	7	GB
105	Soviet State (USA)	7	7	GB
105	Vernoy (USA)	7	7	FR
105	Wind Cheetah (USA)	7	7	GB

5f plus

121	Compton Place (GB)	8	9	GB
121	Elnadim (USA)	8	9	GB

		st	lb	
120	Fabulously Fast (USA)	8	8	USA
120	Smoke Glacken (USA)	8	8	USA
117	Carmine Lake (IRE)	8	5	GB
117	Danetime (IRE)	8	5	GB
117	Lord Grillo (ARG)	8	5	USA
117	Tale of The Cat (USA)	8	5	USA
116	Kelly Kip (USA)	8	4	USA
116	Tomba (GB)	8	4	GB
115	Ain't Bluffing (USA)	8	3	USA
115	Pas de Reponse (USA)	8	3	FR
114	Indian Rocket (GB)	8	2	GB
114	Pearl City (USA)	8	2	USA
113	Alyssum (USA)	8	1	USA
113	Confide (USA)	8	1	USA
113	Partner's Hero (USA)	8	1	USA
112	Crown Ambassador (USA)	8	0	USA
112	Nombre Premier (GB)	8	0	FR
112	Star of Goshen (USA)	8	0	USA
111	Deep Finesse (GB)	7	13	GB
111	Dyhim Diamond (IRE)	7	13	FR
111	Latin Dancer (USA)	7	13	USA
111	Muchea (GB)	7	13	GB
111	Snow Kid (GB)	7	13	GB
110	Aldiza (USA)	7	12	USA
110	Blue Goblin (USA)	7	12	GB
110	Capture The Gold (USA)	7	12	USA
110	Move (USA)	7	12	USA
110	Nightbird (IRE)	7	12	GB
110	Oro De Mexico (USA)	7	12	USA
110	Swiss Yodeler (USA)	7	12	USA
110	Thisnearlywasmine (USA)	7	12	USA
110	Trafalger (USA)	7	12	USA
110	Valid Affect (USA)	7	12	USA
110	Washington Color (USA)	7	12	JPN
109	Bahamian Bounty (GB)	7	11	GB
109	Deadly Dudley (IRE)	7	11	GB
108	Bint Albaadiya (USA)	7	10	GB
108	Cathedral (IRE)	7	10	GB
107	Easycall (GB)	7	9	GB
107	Lochangel (GB)	7	9	GB
106	Check The Band (USA)	7	8	IRE
106	Clever Caption (IRE)	7	8	FR
105	Grand Lad (IRE)	7	7	GB

INTERNATIONAL CLASSIFICATION

A classification for four-year-olds and upwards, which during 1997 have run or been trained in Europe, Japan or North America, or have in races open to outside competition been assessed jointly by international classification committee handicappers and North American rating committee racing officials at a rating of 105 (7st 7lb) or above. In the case of North American horses, the minimum is 110.

1¾m plus

		age	st	lb	
124	Might And Power (NZ)	4	8	12	AUS
121	Classic Cliche (IRE)	5	8	9	GB
120	Doriemus (NZ)	7	8	8	AUS
119	Celeric (GB)	5	8	7	GB
119	Marlin (USA)	4	8	7	USA
119	Orchestra Stall (GB)	5	8	7	GB
118	Double Trigger (IRE)	6	8	6	GB
118	Sakura Laurel (JPN)	6	8	6	JPN
117	Sunshack (GB)	6	8	5	USA
116	Election Day (IRE)	5	8	4	GB
115	Double Eclipse (IRE)	5	8	3	GB
113	African Dancer (USA)	5	8	1	USA
113	Chief Contender (IRE)	4	8	1	GB
113	Markham (AUS)	4	8	1	AUS
113	Persian Punch (IRE)	4	8	1	GB
112	Canon Can (USA)	4	8	0	GB
112	Clerkenwell (USA)	4	8	0	GB

112 Grey Shot (GB) .... 5 8 0 GB
112 Samraan (USA)............... 4 8 0 GB
111 Eva Luna (USA) .... 5 7 13 GB
111 Heron Island (IRE)........... 4 7 13 GB
111 Kutta (GB) .... 5 7 13 GB
110 Camp David (GER).......... 7 7 12 GER
110 Corradini (GB)................ 5 7 12 GB
110 Further Flight (GB).......... 11 7 12 GB
110 Key To My Heart (IRE) .... 7 7 12 GB
110 Philanthrop (FR)............. 5 7 12 FR
110 Stretarez (FR) .... 4 7 12 FR
110 Tarator (USA) .... 4 7 12 FR
109 Always Earnest (USA)..... 9 7 11 FR
108 Nononito (FR) .... 6 7 10 FR
108 Snow Princess (IRE)....... 5 7 10 GB
108 Upper Class (GER).......... 4 7 10 GER
107 French Ballerina (IRE)...... 4 7 9 IRE
107 Jiyush (GB) .... 4 7 9 GB
107 Oliviero (FR) .... 4 7 9 FR
107 Wilawander (GB)............. 4 7 9 GB
106 Arbatax (IRE) .... 4 7 8 FR
106 Eurynome (GER).............. 4 7 8 FR
106 Sacrament (GB).............. 6 7 8 FR
105 Fairhonor (FR) .... 4 7 7 FR

1m 3f plus

129 Swain (IRE)..................... 5 9 3 GB
125 Shantou (USA)................. 4 8 13 GB
124 Oscar Schindler (IRE)...... 5 8 12 IRE
124 Predappio (GB)............... 4 8 12 GB
123 Chief Bearhart (CAN)....... 4 8 11 CAN
122 Influent (CAN) .... 6 8 10 USA
122 Val's Prince (USA) .... 5 8 10 USA
121 Bubble Gum Fellow (JPN) 4 8 9 JPN
120 Luso (GB)........................ 5 8 8 GB
119 Air Groove (JPN)............ 4 8 7 JPN
119 Down The Aisle (USA)..... 4 8 7 USA
119 Flag Down (CAN) .... 7 8 7 USA
119 Marvelous Sunday (JPN) 5 8 7 JPN
119 Windsharp (USA) .... 6 8 7 USA
118 Ops Smile (USA)............. 5 8 6 USA
118 River Bay (USA)............. 4 8 6 FR/USA
118 Tsukuba Symphony (GB) 4 8 6 JPN
117 Annus Mirabilis (FR) .... 5 8 5 GB
117 Dushyantor (USA).......... 4 8 5 GB
117 Mons (GB)...................... 4 8 5 GB
117 My Emma (GB).............. 4 8 5 GB
117 Posidonas (GB) .... 5 8 5 GB
117 Sunshack (GB)............... 6 8 5 USA
116 Busy Flight (GB)............. 4 8 4 GB
116 Dowty (USA) .... 5 8 4 USA
116 Lassigny (USA).............. 6 8 4 USA
116 Le Destin (FR) .... 4 8 4 FR
116 Taiki Blizzard (USA) .... 6 8 4 JPN
115 Golden Pond (IRE) .... 4 8 3 USA
115 Needle Gun (IRE) .... 7 8 3 GB
115 Strategic Choice (USA) ... 6 8 3 GB
114 Flyway (FR) .... 4 8 2 FR/USA
114 Peckinpah's Soul (FR)..... 5 8 2 USA
114 Rosen Kavalier (JPN) ...... 4 8 2 JPN
114 Time Allowed (GB).......... 4 8 2 GB
114 Whitewater Affair (GB) .... 4 8 2 GB
113 Bon Point (GB)............... 7 8 1 USA
113 Buck's Boy (USA) .... 4 8 1 USA
113 Harbour Dues (GB) .... 4 8 1 GB
113 Lakeshore Road (USA).... 4 8 1 USA
113 Protektor (GER) .... 8 8 1 GER
113 Seaborg (ARG) .... 6 8 1 USA
113 Wurftaube (GER)............ 4 8 1 GER
113 Yokohama (USA) .... 6 8 1 FR
112 Annaba (IRE).................. 4 8 0 GB
112 Big Sky Chester (CAN) .... 5 8 0 USA
112 Dance Partner (JPN) ...... 5 8 0 JPN
112 Mongol Warrior (USA)..... 4 8 0 GB
112 Papering (IRE) .... 4 8 0 GB
112 Prussian Blue (USA)........ 5 8 0 USA
112 Riyadian (GB) .... 5 8 0 GB
112 Shanawi (IRE)................ 5 8 0 USA
112 Surgeon (GB)................. 4 8 0 FR
111 Arabian Story (GB).......... 4 7 13 GB
111 Cymbala (FR) .... 4 7 13 USA
111 Eva Luna (USA) .... 5 7 13 GB
111 Fahim (GB)..................... 4 7 13 USA

111 Kutta (GB) 5 7 13 GB
111 Narrabeth (IRE) 4 7 13 GER
111 Nothin' Leica Dane (AUS) 5 7 13 FR
111 Royal Court (IRE) 4 7 13 GB
111 Royal Touch (JPN) 4 7 13 JPN
111 Snake Eyes (USA) 7 7 13 USA
111 Surako (GER) 4 7 13 GER
111 Yutosei (JPN) 7 7 13 JPN
110 Chorwon (USA) 4 7 12 USA
110 Darazari (IRE) 4 7 12 FR
110 Desert Waves (CAN) 7 7 12 CAN
110 Ela-Aristokrati (IRE) 5 7 12 GB
110 Fortitude (USA) 4 7 12 USA
110 Embraceable You (FR) 4 7 12 USA
110 Further Flight 11 7 12 GB
110 Salmon Ladder (USA) 5 7 12 GB
110 Sentimental Moi (USA) 7 7 12 USA
110 Steward (FR) 4 7 12 FR
110 Tamure (IRE) 5 7 12 GB
110 Taufan's Melody (GB) 6 7 12 GB
110 Winsox (USA) 6 7 12 USA
109 Camporese (IRE) 4 7 11 GB
109 Toto Le Moko (IRE) 4 7 11 ITY
109 Tulipa (USA) 4 7 11 GB
108 Bright Water (GB) 4 7 10 GB
108 Coral Reef (ITY) 4 7 10 ITY
108 For Valour (USA) 4 7 10 FR
108 Pacajas (GER) 5 7 10 GER
108 Try Again (GER) 6 7 10 GER
107 De Quest (GB) 5 7 9 FR
107 Otaiti (IRE) 4 7 9 FR
106 Tarawa (IRE) 5 7 8 ITY
105 Anno Luce (GB) 4 7 7 GB
105 Concepcion (GER) 7 7 7 GER
105 Nabhaan (IRE) 4 7 7 GB
105 Trait De Genie (FR) 5 7 7 FR

9½f plus

134 Pilsudski (IRE) 5 9 8 GB
132 Singspiel (IRE) 5 9 6 GB
131 Bosra Sham (USA) 4 9 5 GB
131 Gentlemen (ARG) 5 9 5 USA
127 Skip Away (USA) 4 9 1 USA
126 Helissio (FR) 4 9 0 FR
126 Siphon (BRZ) 6 9 0 USA
125 Windsharp (USA) 6 8 13 USA
123 Marlin (USA) 4 8 11 USA
123 Sandpit (BRZ) 8 8 11 USA
121 Maxzene (USA) 4 8 9 USA
121 Memories of Silver (USA) 4 8 9 USA
121 Alhaarth (IRE) 4 8 9 GB
120 Allied Forces (USA) 4 8 8 GB
120 Always A Classic (CAN) 4 8 8 CAN
120 Oxalagu (GER) 5 8 8 GER
120 Percutant (GB) 6 8 8 USA
120 Taipan (IRE) 5 8 8 GB
119 Awad (USA) 7 8 7 USA
119 Different (ARG) 5 8 7 USA
119 Rainbow Dancer (FR) 6 8 7 USA
118 Ops Smile (USA) 5 8 6 USA
117 Crafty Friend (USA) 4 8 5 USA
117 Fanjica (IRE) 5 8 5 USA
117 Luna Wells (IRE) 4 8 5 USA
117 Sunshack (GB) 6 8 5 USA
117 Whiskey Wisdom (CAN) 4 8 5 USA
117 Yokama (USA) 4 8 5 USA
116 Ampulla (USA) 6 8 4 USA
116 Dowty (USA) 5 8 4 USA
116 Lassigny (USA) 6 8 4 USA
116 Le Destin (FR) 4 8 4 FR
116 Tamayaz (CAN) 5 8 4 UAE/GB
115 Artan (IRE) 5 8 3 GER
115 Baroud d'Honneur (FR) 4 8 3 FR
115 Clear Mandate (USA) 5 8 3 USA
115 Dance Design (IRE) 4 8 3 IRE
115 London News (SAF) 5 8 3 SAF/GB
115 Lord Jain (ARG) 5 8 3 USA
114 Devil River Peek (USA) 5 8 2 GER
114 Germano (GB) 4 8 2 GB
114 Hokuto Vega (JPN) 7 8 2 JPN
114 Kammtarra (USA) 4 8 2 UAE/GB
114 Mt Sassafras (CAN) 5 8 2 CAN
114 Same Old Wish (USA) 7 8 2 USA
114 Talloires (USA) 7 8 2 USA

113 Diplomatic Jet (USA) ...... 5 8 1 USA
112 B A Valentine (USA) .... 4 8 0 USA
112 Bulington (FR) .... 5 8 0 FR
112 King Alex (GB) .... 4 8 0 GB
112 Lord of Men (GB)........... 4 8 0 GB
112 River Deep (USA)............ 6 8 0 USA
112 Storm Trooper (USA) ...... 4 8 0 USA
112 Zaralaska (GB) .... 6 8 0 GB
111 Arabian Story (GB).......... 4 7 13 GB
111 Cairo Express (USA) .... 5 7 13 USA
111 Chequer (USA)............... 5 7 13 USA
111 Dorec (IRE) .... 7 7 13 UAE
111 Even Top (IRE)............... 4 7 13 GB
111 Instant Friendship (USA).. 4 7 13 USA
111 Narrabeth (IRE).............. 4 7 13 GER
111 Royal Touch (JPN).......... 4 7 13 JPN
111 Tamhid (USA)................. 4 7 13 UAE/USA
111 Tocopilla (ARG) .... 7 7 13 USA
111 Wings Bash (IRE)............ 5 7 13 USA
111 Yutosei (JPN) .... 7 7 13 JPN
110 The Barking Shark (USA) 4 7 12 USA
110 Dreamer (USA) .... 5 7 12 USA
110 Golden Larch (USA)........ 6 7 12 USA
110 L'Annee Folle (FR) .... 4 7 12 FR
110 Santillana (USA).............. 4 7 12 GB
110 Taxi de Nuit (USA) .... 5 7 12 ITY
110 Two Ninety Jones (USA) 6 7 12 USA
110 Victory Speech (USA) ..... 4 7 12 USA
109 Cap Juluca (IRE)............. 5 7 11 GB
109 Dr Massini (IRE) .... 4 7 11 GB
109 Freequent (GB) .... 4 7 11 GB
109 Zero Problemo (IRE) .... 4 7 11 GER
108 Coral Reef (ITY) .... 4 7 10 ITY
108 Multicoloured (IRE) .... 4 7 10 GB
108 Prince of Andros (USA)... 7 7 10 GB
108 Raiyoun (IRE) .... 4 7 10 IRE
108 Songline (SWE).............. 4 7 10 SWE
108 Triano (GER).................. 4 7 10 GER
107 Bequeath (GB) .... 5 7 9 GB
107 Nero Zilzal (USA) .... 4 7 9 FR
107 Ravier (ITY) .... 6 7 9 ITY
107 Supreme Commander (FR) 4 7 9 ITY
106 Acharne (GB).................. 4 7 8 GB
106 Bon Jovi (GER) .... 4 7 8 GER
106 Grey Way (USA) .... 4 7 8 GB
106 Lorado (GB).................... 6 7 8 GER
106 Milford Track (IRE).......... 4 7 8 FR
106 Tarawa (IRE).................. 5 7 8 ITY
105 Concepcion (GER) .... 7 7 7 GER
105 Danish Rhapsody (IRE) ... 4 7 7 GB
105 Fatefully (USA)................ 4 7 7 GB
105 Forest Buck (USA) .... 4 7 7 GB
105 Helicon (IRE) .... 4 7 7 GB
105 Hondero (GER) .... 7 7 7 GER
105 Medaille Militaire (GB)..... 5 7 7 GB
105 Sandmoor Chambray (GB) 6 7 7 GB
105 Turning Wheel (USA)....... 4 7 7 FR

7f plus

127 Formal Gold (CAN).......... 4 9 1 USA
126 Alphabet Soup (USA) ...... 6 9 0 USA
126 Jewel Princess (USA) ..... 5 9 0 USA
126 Spinning World (USA) ..... 4 9 0 FR
124 Hidden Lake (USA) .... 4 8 12 USA
124 Louis Quatorze (USA)...... 4 8 12 USA
123 Ali-Royal (IRE)................ 4 8 11 GB
123 First Island (IRE) .... 5 8 11 GB
122 Halo America (USA)........ 7 8 10 USA
122 Occupandiste (IRE) .... 4 8 10 FR
122 Twice The Vice (USA) ..... 6 8 10 USA
121 Langfuhr (CAN)............... 5 8 9 CAN
121 Will's Way (USA) .... 4 8 9 USA
120 Allied Forces (USA)......... 4 8 8 GB
120 Always A Classic (CAN).. 4 8 8 CAN
120 Donna Viola (GB) .... 5 8 8 USA
120 Geri (USA)...................... 5 8 8 USA
120 Isitingood (USA) .... 6 8 8 USA
120 Marlin (USA)................... 4 8 8 USA
119 Catalan Opening (NZ) ...... 5 8 7 AUS
119 Different (ARG) .... 5 8 7 USA
119 Sasuru (GB).................... 4 8 7 GB
119 Wizard King (GB) .... 6 8 7 GB
118 Benchmark (USA) .... 6 8 6 USA
118 Decorated Hero (GB)....... 5 8 6 GB

118 Feasibility Study (USA).... 5 8 6 USA
118 Flat Fleet Feet (USA) .... 4 8 6 USA
118 Lucky Coin (USA) .... 4 8 6 USA
118 Wixim (USA).................. 4 8 6 GB
117 Atticus (USA)................. 5 8 5 USA
117 Crafty Friend (USA)......... 4 8 5 USA
117 Escena (USA) .... 4 8 5 USA
117 Gothenberg (IRE) .... 4 8 5 GB
116 Alpride (IRE).................. 6 8 4 USA
116 Kiridashi (CAN).............. 5 8 4 CAN
116 Lucayan Prince.............. 4 8 4 GB
116 River Keen (IRE) .... 5 8 4 GB/USA
116 Taiki Blizzard (USA) .... 6 8 4 JPN
116 Tejano Run (USA) .... 5 8 4 USA
115 Belle's Flag (USA).......... 4 8 3 USA
115 Burden of Proof (IRE)...... 5 8 3 IRE
115 Centre Stalls (IRE).......... 4 8 3 GB
115 Clear Mandate (USA) ...... 5 8 3 USA
115 Crown Attorney (CAN)..... 4 8 3 USA
115 Expelled (USA)............... 5 8 3 USA
115 Genuine (JPN) .... 5 8 3 JPN
115 Helmsman (USA)............ 5 8 3 USA
115 Labeeb (GB) .... 5 8 3 USA
115 Montjoy (USA)............... 5 8 3 USA
115 Ok By Me (CAN) .... 4 8 3 USA
115 Rainbow Blues (IRE) .... 4 8 3 USA
115 Rare Blend (USA)........... 4 8 3 USA
115 Real Connection (USA).... 6 8 3 USA
115 Russian Revival (USA) .... 4 8 3 GB
115 Sharp Appeal (USA)........ 4 8 3 USA
115 Top Rung (USA) .... 6 8 3 USA
115 Wild Event (USA) .... 4 8 3 USA
114 Basqueian (CAN) .... 6 8 2 USA
114 Bijou d'Inde (GB) .... 4 8 2 GB
114 City By Night (USA) .... 4 8 2 USA
114 Devil River Peek (USA).... 5 8 2 GER
114 Devil's Cup (USA)........... 4 8 2 USA
114 Devious Course (USA) .... 5 8 2 USA
114 El Angelo (USA).............. 5 8 2 USA
114 Listening (USA) .... 4 8 2 USA
114 Mecke (USA)................... 5 8 2 USA
114 Media Nox (GB) .... 4 8 2 USA
114 Power Flame (GER) .... 4 8 2 GER
114 Same Old Wish (USA)..... 7 8 2 USA
114 Simon du Desert (FR) ..... 4 8 2 FR
114 Smooth Runner (USA)..... 6 8 2 USA
114 Soviet Line (IRE)............ 7 8 2 UAE/USA
114 Talloires (USA) .... 7 8 2 USA
114 Trail City (USA).............. 4 8 2 USA
114 Waky Nao (GB)............... 4 8 2 GER
113 Boyce (USA)................... 6 8 1 USA
113 Kingdom Found (USA) .... 7 8 1 USA
113 La Blue (GER)................ 4 8 1 GER
113 Magellan (USA).............. 4 8 1 USA
113 Pinfloron (FR) .... 5 8 1 USA
113 Polar Prince (IRE) .... 4 8 1 GB
113 Red Roses Story (FR)..... 5 8 1 USA
113 Romy (USA) .... 6 8 1 USA
113 Sixieme Sens (USA)........ 5 8 1 USA
113 Toda Una Dama (ARG).... 4 8 1 USA
113 Western Winter (USA)..... 5 8 1 USA
112 Antespend (USA) .... 4 8 0 USA
112 Auriette (IRE)................. 5 8 0 USA
112 B A Valentine (USA)........ 4 8 0 USA
112 Blushing Heiress (USA)... 5 8 0 USA
112 Brave Note (IRE)............ 6 8 0 USA
112 Daneskaya (GB).............. 4 8 0 FR
112 De Puntillas (GB) .... 5 8 0 USA
112 Inner City (IRE) .... 8 8 0 USA
112 Irish Wings (IRE)............ 5 8 0 USA
112 Mufattish (USA) .... 4 8 0 USA
112 Naskra Colors (USA)....... 5 8 0 USA
112 Radu Cool (USA) .... 5 8 0 USA
112 Rumpipumpy (GB).......... 4 8 0 USA
112 Savinio (USA) .... 7 8 0 USA
112 Semoran (USA).............. 4 8 0 USA
112 Shemozzle (IRE) .... 4 8 0 USA
112 Stephanotis (CAN) .... 4 8 0 CAN
112 Top Glory (FR)................ 4 8 0 USA
112 Traces of Gold (USA)...... 5 8 0 USA
112 Wavy Run (IRE) .... 6 8 0 USA
111 Accento (GB).................. 4 7 13 GER
111 A Magicman (FR)............ 5 7 13 USA
111 Ambivalent (USA) .... 4 7 13 USA

Rating	Horse	Age	st	lb	Country
111	Announce (USA)	5	7	13	USA
111	Bin Rosie (GB)	5	7	13	GB
111	Careless Heiress (USA)	4	7	13	USA
111	Cat's Cradle (USA)	5	7	13	USA
111	Colcon (USA)	4	7	13	USA
111	Connecting Terms (USA)	4	7	13	USA
111	Cool Edge (IRE)	6	7	13	GB
111	Da Bull (USA)	5	7	13	USA
111	Distorted Humor (USA)	4	7	13	USA
111	Even Top (IRE)	4	7	13	GB
111	Grafin (USA)	6	7	13	USA
111	Green Means Go (USA)	5	7	13	USA
111	Kalatos (GER)	5	7	13	GER
111	Kierkegaard (GB)	4	7	13	ITY
111	Martiniquais (IRE)	4	7	13	FR/USA
111	Mister Fire Eyes (IRE)	5	7	13	USA
111	Ormsby (USA)	5	7	13	USA
111	Pacific Fleet (USA)	5	7	13	USA
111	Palliser Bay (USA)	5	7	13	USA
111	Refinado Tom (ARG)	4	7	13	USA
111	Shin Kaiun (JPN)	5	7	13	JPN
111	Slicious (GB)	5	7	13	USA
111	Snake Eyes (USA)	7	7	13	USA
111	Surachai (USA)	4	7	13	USA
111	Wheatly Special (USA)	4	7	13	USA
111	Wings Bash (IRE)	5	7	13	USA
110	Almushtarak (IRE)	4	7	12	GB
110	Beboppin Baby (USA)	4	7	12	USA
110	Best Tie Up (JPN)	5	7	12	JPN
110	Fortitude (USA)	4	7	12	USA
110	Full And Fancy (USA)	5	7	12	USA
110	Ghostly Moves (USA)	5	7	12	USA
110	Mighty Forum (GB)	6	7	12	USA
110	Nwaamis (USA)	5	7	12	GB
110	Oriental Express (IRE)	4	7	12	HK
110	Powder Bowl (USA)	5	7	12	USA
110	Rakida B (USA)	6	7	12	USA
110	Ready To Order (USA)	4	7	12	USA
110	Region (USA)	8	7	12	USA
110	River Flyer (USA)	6	7	12	USA
110	Romarin (BRZ)	7	7	12	USA
110	Royal Suzuka (IRE)	4	7	12	JPN
110	Shoop (USA)	6	7	12	USA
110	Taxi de Nuit (USA)	5	7	12	ITY
110	Three Fanfares (USA)	4	7	12	USA
110	Tychonic (GB)	7	7	12	USA
110	Via Lombardia (IRE)	5	7	12	USA
110	Western Echo (USA)	5	7	12	USA
109	Cap Juluca (IRE)	5	7	11	GB
109	Zero Problemo (IRE)	4	7	11	GER
108	Balalaika (GB)	4	7	10	GB
108	Morigi (GB)	6	7	10	ITY
108	Restructure (IRE)	5	7	10	GB
107	Amrak Ajeeb (IRE)	5	7	9	GB
107	Grey Risk (FR)	4	7	9	FR
107	Perim (FR)	4	7	9	FR
107	Ramooz (USA)	4	7	9	GB
107	Robins (IRE)	5	7	9	ITY
106	Acharne (GB)	4	7	8	GB
106	Battle Dore (USA)	4	7	8	FR
106	Cadeaux Tryst (GB)	5	7	8	GB
106	Hawksley Hill (IRE)	4	7	8	GB/USA
106	Parfait Glace (FR)	5	7	8	FR
106	Precious Ring (USA)	4	7	8	FR
106	Samara (IRE)	4	7	8	GB
106	Sinyar (IRE)	5	7	8	GER
106	Trojan Sea (USA)	6	7	8	FR
105	Alamo Bay (USA)	4	7	7	FR
105	How Long (GB)	4	7	7	GB
105	Jo Mell (GB)	4	7	7	GB
105	Neuwest (USA)	5	7	7	GB

5f plus

Rating	Horse	Age	st	lb	Country
121	Royal Applause (GB)	4	8	9	GB
120	Elmhurst (USA)	7	8	8	USA
120	Langfuhr (USA)	5	8	8	USA
119	Hesabull (USA)	4	8	7	USA
119	Victor Cooley (CAN)	4	8	7	CAN
118	Bet On Sunshine (USA)	5	8	6	USA
117	Crafty Friend (USA)	4	8	5	USA
117	Miss Golden Circle (USA)	5	8	5	USA
117	Unbridled's Song (USA)	4	8	5	USA
116	Northern Afleet (USA)	4	8	4	USA
115	Burden of Proof (IRE)	5	8	3	IRE
115	Coastal Bluff (GB)	5	8	3	GB

115	Men's Exclusive (USA)....	4	8	3 USA
115	Punch Line (USA)	7	8	3 USA
115	Royal Haven (USA)	5	8	3 USA
115	Score A Birdie (USA)	6	8	3 USA
115	Ya Malak (GB)	6	8	3 GB
114	Averti (IRE).....................	6	8	2 GB
114	Boundless Moment (USA)	5	8	2 USA
114	First Intent (USA)	8	8	2 USA
114	Kistena (FR)	4	8	2 FR
114	Lakota Brave (USA).........	8	8	2 USA
114	Monaassib (GB)..............	6	8	2 GB
114	Toga Toga Toga (USA)....	5	8	2 USA
114	Track Gal (USA)..............	6	8	2 USA
113	Advancing Star (USA)	4	8	1 USA
113	Capote Belle (USA)	4	8	1 USA
113	Chip (USA)	4	8	1 USA
113	Diligence (USA)	4	8	1 USA
113	Exotic Wood (USA)	5	8	1 SA
113	High Stakes Player (USA)	5	8	1 USA
113	J J'sdream (USA)	4	8	1 USA
113	My Best Valentine (GB) ...	7	8	1 GB
113	Shinko King (IRE)............	6	8	1 JPN
113	Ski Dancer (USA)............	5	8	1 USA
113	Sugino Hayakaze (USA) ..	4	8	1 JPN
113	Titus Livius (FR)	4	8	1 FR
113	Western Fame (USA)	5	8	1 USA
112	Cat Be Nimble (USA).......	5	8	0 USA
112	Cyrano's Lad (IRE)..........	8	8	0 GB
112	Dancin Renee (USA)	5	8	0 USA
112	Frisco View (USA)............	4	8	0 USA
112	Gold Land (USA)..............	6	8	0 USA
112	Morris Code (USA)..........	5	8	0 USA
112	Sandtrap (USA)...............	4	8	0 USA
111	Almaty (IRE)	4	7	13 GB
111	Appealing Skier (USA).....	4	7	13 USA
111	Ashboro (CAN)	4	7	13 CAN
111	Avenue of Gold (USA)	4	7	13 USA
111	Catch The Blues (IRE)	5	7	13 IRE
111	Cold Execution (USA)......	6	7	13 USA
111	Diffident (FR)	5	7	13 GB
111	Don't Worry Me (IRE)......	5	7	13 FR
111	Lottsa Talc (USA)	7	7	13 USA
111	Stalwart Member (USA) ..	4	7	13 USA
111	Top Secret (USA)...........	4	7	13 USA
111	Why Change (USA)	4	7	13 USA
110	Criollito (ARG)	6	7	12 USA
110	Dashing Blue (GB)	4	7	12 GB
110	The Exeter Man (USA).....	5	7	12 USA
110	Farhana (GB)	4	7	12 GB
110	Global Player (GB)	4	7	12 GER
110	Madame Pandit (USA).....	4	7	12 USA
110	Phone The Doctor (USA)	5	7	12 USA
110	Political Whit (USA)	4	7	12 USA
110	Raw Gold (USA)	4	7	12 USA
110	Score Quick (USA)..........	5	7	12 USA
110	Struggler (GB)	5	7	12 GB
110	Tedburrow (GB)	5	7	12 GB
110	Top Account (USA)	5	7	12 USA
110	Tres Paraiso (USA)	5	7	12 USA
110	Vivace (USA)	4	7	12 USA
110	Wise Dusty (USA)	6	7	12 USA
109	Armando Carpio (GB)......	4	7	11 ITY
109	Croft Pool (GB)	6	7	11 GB
109	Danehill Dancer (IRE)	4	7	11 GB
109	Theano (IRE)..................	4	7	11 IRE
108	Eveningperformance (GB)	6	7	10 GB
108	Hever Golf Rose (GB)......	6	7	10 GB
108	Midnight Escape (GB)	4	7	10 GB
108	Rambling Bear (GB)	4	7	10 GB
108	Wardara (GB).................	5	7	10 FR
107	Bollin Joanne (GB)	4	7	9 GB
107	Brave Edge (GB)	6	7	9 GB
107	Cretan Gift (GB)	6	7	9 GB
107	Linoise (FR)....................	5	7	9 FR
106	Bolshoi (IRE)	5	7	8 GB
106	Easy Dollar (GB)	5	7	8 GB
106	Hakiki (IRE)	5	7	8 NOR
106	Late Parade (IRE)...........	6	7	8 ITY
106	Mind Games (GB)	5	7	8 GB
106	Roseate Wood (FR)	4	7	8 GER
106	Royale Figurine (IRE)	6	7	8 GB
106	Winning Smile (FR).........	7	7	8 FR
105	Ailleacht (USA)	5	7	7 IRE
105	How Long (GB)..............	4	7	7 GB
105	Munaaji (USA)	6	7	7 GER
105	To The Roof (IRE)..........	5	7	7 GB

GODOLPHIN HORSES IN INTERNATIONAL CLASSIFICATIONS

OLDER HORSES

Horse	Breeding	Rating
Swain	Nashwan (USA)-Love Smitten (CAN)	**129**
Predappio	Polish Precedent (USA)-Khalafiya	**124**
Alhaarth	Unfuwain (USA)-Irish Valley (USA)	**121**
Classic Cliche	Salse (USA)-Pato	**121**
Allied Forces	Miswaki (USA)-Mangala (USA)	**120**
Annus Mirabilis	Warning-Anna Petrovna (FR)	**117**
Tamayaz (in UAE)	Gone West (USA)-Minstrelsy (USA)	**116**
Kammtarra (in UAE)	Zilzal (USA)-Snow Bride (USA)	**114**
Diffident	Nureyev (USA)-Shy Princess (USA)	**111**
Tulipa	Alleged (USA)-Black Tulip (FR)	**109**
Helicon	Nashwan (USA)-Hebba (USA)	**105**

THREE-YEAR-OLDS

Horse	Breeding	Rating
Daylami	Doyoun-Daltawa (IRE)	**122**
Starborough	Soviet Star (USA)-Flamenco Wave (USA)	**122**
Stowaway	Slip Anchor-On Credit (USA)	**119**
Cape Cross	Green Desert (USA)-Park Appeal	**118**
Faithful Son	Zilzal (USA)-Carduel (USA)	**115**
Ocean Ridge	Storm Bird (CAN)-Polar Bird (IRE)	**115**
Kahal	Machiavellian (USA)-Just A Mirage	**114**
Desert Story	Green Desert (USA)-Aliysa	**114**
Yalaietanee	Sadler's Wells (USA)-Vaigly Star	**114**
Crown Of Light	Mtoto-Russian Countess (USA)	**113**
Maylane	Mtoto-Possessive Dancer	**112**
Entice	Selkirk (USA)-Loure (USA)	**111**
Fly To The Stars	Bluebird (USA)-Rise And Fall	**111**
Blue Goblin	Trempolino (USA)-Blue Daisy (USA)	**110**
Cloudings	Sadler's Wells (USA)-Ispahan	**110**
King Sound	Caerleon (USA)-Flood (USA)	**110**
Nightbird	Night Shift (USA)-Pippas Song	**110**
Bahamian Bounty	Cadeaux Genereux-Clarentia	**109**
Haltarra	Zilzal (USA)-Snow Bride (USA)	**107**

GODOLPHIN HORSES IN INTERNATIONAL CLASSIFICATIONS

TWO-YEAR-OLDS

Horse	Breeding	Rating
Central Park	In The Wings-Park Special	118
Embassy	Cadeaux Genereux-Pass The Peace	118
Mudeer	Warning-Colorvista	115
Asakir	Nashwan (USA)-Yakul (USA)	110
Asfurah	Dayjur (USA)-Mathkurh (USA)	110
Woodland Melody	Woodman (USA)-Eloquent Minister (USA)	110
Cape Verdi	Caerleon (USA)-Afrique Bleu Azur (USA)	109
City Honours	Darshaan-Ikebana (IRE)	108
Almutawakel	Machiavellian (USA)-Elfaslah (IRE)	107
Bintang	Soviet Star (USA)-Brush Away	106
Shuhrah	Danzig (USA)-Sajjaya (USA)	105

HIGH–PRICED YEARLINGS OF 1997 AT TATTERSALLS' SALES

The following yearlings realised 80,000 guineas and over at Tattersalls' Sales in 1997:-

Name and Breeding	Vendor	Purchaser	Gns
B.c. Sadler's Wells (USA) — Crystal Spray	Watership Down Stud	Mr D. O'Byrne	625,000
B.c. Sadler's Wells (USA) — Darara	Watership Down Stud	Godolphin Mgt. Co.	500,000
Etizaaz (USA) B.f. Diesis — Alamosa	Kirtlington Stud	Shadwell Estate Co.	500,000
B.f. Sadler's Wells (USA) — Cocotte	Barronstown Stud, Ireland	German Intl. B/S	480,000
Ch.f. Rainbow Quest (USA) — Bella Colora	Meon Valley Stud	B.B.A. (UK)	470,000
Gr.c. Nureyev (USA) — Ancient Regime (USA)	Ted Voute, Agent	Addison Racing Inc.	460,000
Ch.c. Zafonic (USA) — Princess Accord (USA)	Cheveley Park Stud	Godolphin Mgt. Co.	440,000
Ch.f. Woodman (USA) — Toujours Elle (USA)	Haras Du Quesnay, France	Shadwell Estate Co.	430,000
Raucous Lad B.c. Warning — Someone Special	Meon Valley Stud	Gainsborough Stud Mgt.	420,000
B.c. Warning — Sistabelle	Meon Valley Stud	B.B.A. (UK)	420,000
Ch.c. Woodman (USA) — Crockadore (USA)	Ballylinch Stud, Ireland	Darley Stud Mgt.	400,000
Impresario B.c. Sadler's Wells (USA) — Exclusive Order (USA)	Cheveley Park Stud	B.B.A. (UK)	375,000
Pop Queen Ch.f. Nashwan (USA) — Pick Of The Pops	Meon Valley Stud	C.B.A.	370,000
Gr.f. Rainbow Quest (USA) — Alruccaba	Airlie Stud, Ireland	Godolphin Mgt. Co.	360,000
B.f. Danehill (USA) — Purchasepaperchase	Barronstown Stud, Ireland	Mr D. O'Byrne	330,000
Yeoman's Point (IRE) B.c. Sadler's Wells (USA) — Truly Bound (USA)	Ashtown House Stud, Ire	Mr D. O'Byrne	320,000
B.c. Sadler's Wells (USA) — Guess Again (GER)	Ted Voute, Agent	B.B.A. (UK)	310,000
Kittiwake B.f. Barathea (IRE) — Gull Nook	Low House Stud	German Intl. B/S	300,000
B.c. Sadler's Wells (USA) — Sequel (IRE)	Camas Park Stud, Ireland	Darley Stud Mgt.	300,000
Alfath (USA) Ch.c. Diesis — Lady Express (IRE)	John Troy, Agent	Shadwell Estate Co.	280,000
Ipso Facto (IRE) B/Br.c. Sunday Silence (USA) — Lingerie	Camas Park Stud, Ireland	Mr Guy Armengol	280,000
Brightest Star B.f. Unfuwain (USA) — Shirley Superstar	Meon Valley Stud	German Intl. B/S	280,000
B.c. Zafonic (USA) — Lady Blackfoot	Brick Kiln Stud	Darley Stud Mgt.	265,000
B.f. Sadler's Wells (USA) — Military Tune (IRE)	Raffin Stud	Addison Racing Inc.	260,000
B.c. Zafonic (USA) — Rappa Tap Tap (FR)	Meon Valley Stud	T'bred Corp.	260,000
B.c. Green Desert (USA) — Hyabella	Meon Valley Stud	John Magnier	250,000
Tayil (IRE) B.c. Caerleon (USA) — Desert Bluebell	Tullamaine Castle Stud, Ire	Shadwell Estate Co.	250,000
Urban Ocean (USA) Ch.c. Bering — Urban Sea (USA)	Camas Park Stud, Ireland	Mr J. P. Deroubaix	230,000
Canaletto B.c. Royal Academy (USA) — Diavolina (USA)	The Marston Stud	B.B.A. (UK)	225,000
Ch.c. Woodman (USA) — Dance Play	John Troy, Agent	Shadwell Estate Co.	220,000
Mayo B.c. Nashwan (USA) — Nuryana	Hascombe Stud	Mr R. O'Ryan	220,000
Spanish Lady (IRE) B.f. Bering — Belle Arrivee	Biddestone Stud	Mr J. Dunlop	220,000
Br.f. Warning — Valika	Cheveley Park Stud	C. Gordon-Watson	220,000
B/Br.c. Nureyev (USA) — Aviara (USA)	Kirtlington Stud	Horse France	215,000
Devil's Imp (IRE) Ch.f. Cadeaux Genereux — High Spirited	Airlie Stud, Ireland	Gainsborough Stud Mgt.	210,000
B.c. Midyan (USA) — Panache Arabelle	Meon Valley Stud	Darley Stud Mgt.	210,000
B.f. Unfuwain (USA) — Armorique (IRE)	Camas Park Stud, Ireland	Equine Invest. Consul	205,000
Ch.c. Zafonic (USA) — Connecting Link (USA)	Ted Voute, Agent	Shadai Farm	205,000
Cassandra Go (IRE) Gr.f. Indian Ridge — Rahaam (USA)	Corduff Stud, Ireland	Mr Trevor C. Stewart	200,000

Norwegian Wood (IRE) Ch.c. Woodman (USA) — Kotama (USA)	Lynn Lodge Stud, Ireland	Peter Doyle B/S	200,000
B.c. Be My Guest (USA) — Marseillaise	Ashtown House Stud, Ire	Hugo Merry B/S	200,000
Gr.f. Caerleon (USA) — Passamaquoddy (USA)	Genesis Green Stud	London T'Bred Services	200,000
Turaath (IRE) B.c. Sadler's Wells (USA) — Diamond Field (USA)	Lynn Lodge Stud, Ireland	Shadwell Estate Co.	200,000
Raise A Grand (IRE) Ch.c. Grand Lodge (USA) — Atyaaf (USA)	Chippenham Lodge Stud	Mr Gordon Smyth	190,000
B.c. Sadler's Wells (USA) — Twine	Barronstown Stud, Ireland	Michael Stoute Ltd.	190,000
Taliban (IRE) B.c. Bigstone (IRE) — Aunt Hester (IRE)	Round Hill Stud, Ireland	John Ferguson B/S	180,000
Ch.f. Rainbow Quest (USA) — Hatton Gardens	Crimbourne Stud	Addison Racing Inc.	180,000
B.c. Green Desert (USA) — Rensaler (USA)	Cheveley Park Stud	Shadai Farm	180,000
Ch.c. Indian Ridge — Elaine's Honour (USA)	Mount Coote Stud, Ireland	Juno Intl.	175,000
Esteraad Ch.f. Cadeaux Genereux — Eclipsing (IRE)	Ted Voute, Agent	Shadwell Estate Co.	170,000
Kuster B.c. Indian Ridge — Ustka	Round Hill Stud, Ireland	Mrs A. Skiffington	170,000
Ch.c. Affirmed (USA) — Norma (USA)	Corduff Stud, Ireland	Newgate Stud Co.	170,000
Red Sea B.c. Barathea (IRE) — Up Anchor (IRE)	Lavington Stud	Mr Guy Armengol	170,000
Minnesota B.c. Danehill (USA) — Santi Sana	Floors Stud	Hugo Merry B/S	170,000
Gr.c. Sabrehill (USA) — Butsova	Middle Park Stud, as Agent	Newgate Stud Co.	160,000
Healing Hands Br.f. Zafonic (USA) — One Life (USA)	Crimbourne Stud	Gainsborough Stud Mgt.	160,000
B.c. Barathea (IRE) — Kithanga (IRE)	Cotswold Stud	P.F.I. Cole Ltd.	160,000
B.c. Caerleon (USA) — Petticoat Lane	Landscape Stud, Ireland	C. Gordon-Watson	160,000
B.c. Darshaan — Pont-Aven	Knocktoran Stud, Ireland	Darley Stud Mgt.	160,000
B.f. Barathea (IRE) — Tribal Rite	Britton House Stud	C. Gordon-Watson	160,000
Ch.c. Trempolino (USA) — Air De Noblesse (USA)	Barnane Stud, Ireland	Newgate Stud Co.	150,000
B.f. Indian Ridge — Benedicite	Overbury Stud	John Ferguson B/S	150,000
Fiumincino (IRE) B.c. Barathea (IRE) — Lacovia (USA)	Knocktoran Stud, Ireland	Addison Racing Inc.	150,000
Mazaya (IRE) B.f. Sadler's Wells (USA) — Sharaniya (USA)	Barronstown Stud, Ireland	Shadwell Estate Co.	150,000
B.c. Dehere (USA) — Pirouette	Thomastown Castle, Ire	Shadai Farm	150,000
Ch.c. Indian Ridge — Spring Daffodil	Islanmore Stud, Ireland	John Ferguson B/S	150,000
Sumood B.f. Rainbow Quest (USA) — Bella Ballerina	Meon Valley Stud	Shadwell Estate Co.	150,000
B.c. Bluebird (USA) — Triode (USA)	Ted Voute, Agent	John Ferguson B/S	150,000
B.c. Robellino (USA) — Greenvera (USA)	Bloomsbury Stud	C. Gordon-Watson	145,000
B.c. Shirley Heights — Historiette	Kirtlington Stud	Darley Stud Mgt.	145,000
B.f. Sadler's Wells (USA) — Kareena	Barronstown Stud, Ireland	B.B.A. (Ireland)	145,000
Houston Time (USA) Ch.c. Rahy (USA) — Band (USA)	Ted Voute, Agent	C. Gordon-Watson	140,000
B.c. Barathea (IRE) — Fern	Ted Voute, Agent	Addison Racing Inc.	140,000
B.f. Alleged (USA) — Gazayil (USA)	Camas Park Stud, Ireland	Shadwell Estate Co.	140,000
Gold Academy (IRE) B.c. Royal Academy (USA) — Soha (USA)	Glenvale Stud, Ireland	Peter Doyle B/S	140,000
B.c. Royal Academy (USA) — Lady Donna	Ashtown House Stud, Ire	Mr D. O'Byrne	140,000
Marnor (USA) B.c. Diesis — Love's Reward	Haras Des Capucines, Fr.	Mr M. W. Easterby	140,000
B.c. Sadler's Wells (USA) — Penza	Airlie Stud, Ireland	Mr D. O'Byrne	140,000
Pretty Woman (IRE) B.f. Alzao (USA) — Simply Gorgeous	Camas Park Stud, Ireland	Belgrave B/S Ltd.	140,000
Ch.c. Irish River (FR) — Rosyphard (USA)	John Troy, Agent	P.F.I. Cole Ltd.	140,000
B.c. Sadler's Wells (USA) — Natuschka	Tally Ho Stud, Ireland	Mr F. Barry	135,000
Treasury Ch.f. Generous (IRE) — Atlantic Flyer (USA)	Barouche Stud Ltd.	Cheveley Park Stud	135,000
B.c. Danehill (USA) — Always Friendly	Lavington Stud	Horse France	130,000
Crystal Magician Ch.c. Cadeaux Genereux — Miss Temerity	Bloomsbury Stud	Gainsborough Stud Mgt.	130,000

Mafaatin (IRE) Ch.f. Royal Academy (USA) — Aquitaine (USA)	Landscape Stud, Ireland	Shadwell Estate Co.	130,000
Ch.f. Woodman (USA) — Qena (USA)	Ted Voute, Agent	Mossborough Stud Co.	130,000
Ch.f. Bluebird (USA) — Scammony (IRE)	Maryville Stud, Ireland	Peter Doyle B/S	130,000
B.f. Alleged (USA) — Steal The Thunder (CAN)	Ted Voute, Agent	London T'bred Services	130,000
Gr.c. Rainbow Quest (USA) — Heavenly Cause (USA)	Ted Voute, Agent	J S Company Ltd.	125,000
Ch.c. Generous (IRE) — Idyllic (USA)	Camas Park Stud, Ireland	Hugo Merry B/S	125,000
Abla B.f. Robellino (USA) — Sans Blague (USA)	Floors Stud	Shadwell Estate Co.	125,000
Date B.c. Cadeaux Genereux — Faribole (IRE)	Cotswold Stud	C. Gordon-Watson	120,000
Miss Shena (USA) B.f. Gulch (USA) — Fire And Shade (USA)	Cotswold Stud	C. Gordon-Watson	120,000
Baker Street B.c. Dolphin Street (FR) — Joli's Girl	Camas Park Stud, Ireland	Mr D. O'Byrne	120,000
Moon Shot Gr.c. Pistolet Bleu (IRE) — La Luna (USA)	Corduff Stud, Ireland	Sir Mark Prescott	120,000
Mukhtaal B.c. Machiavellian (USA) — On The House (FR)	Hascombe Stud	Shadwell Estate Co.	120,000
Ch.f. Kris — Reveuse Du Soir	Woodcote Stud	Darley Stud Mgt.	120,000
Tissifer B.c. Polish Precedent (USA) — Ingozi	Hascombe Stud	Mr M. W. Easterby	120,000
B.c. Dolphin Street (FR) — Biraya	Yeomanstown Stud, Ireland	John Ferguson B/S	115,000
First Magnitude (IRE) Ch.c. Arazi (USA) — Crystal Cup (USA)	Haras Des Capucines, Fr.	Mr Guy Armengol	115,000
Rimatara Ch.c. Selkirk (USA) — Humble Pie	Overbury Stud	Mr I. A. Balding	115,000
Bilbaino (USA) B.c. Dehere (USA) — La Polonaise (USA)	The Grove Stud	Brian Grassick B/S	115,000
B.c. Cadeaux Genereux — On Tiptoes	Limestone Stud	Darley Stud Mgt.	115,000
B.c. In The Wings — Bogus John (CAN)	Northmore Stud	John Ferguson	110,000
Caerau Ch.f. Nashwan (USA) — Charming Life	Yeomanstown Lodge Stud	B.B.A. (UK)	110,000
Ch.c. Diesis – Dream Play (USA)	Airlie Stud, Ireland	Darley Stud Mgt.	110,000
B.c. Northern Flagship (USA) — Key Bid (USA)	Camas Park Stud, Ireland	Cheerine Stud	110,000
Time Mill B.c. Shirley Heights — Not Before Time (IRE)	Ted Voute, Agent	B.B.A. (Ireland)	110,000
Surprise Encounter Ch.c. Cadeaux Genereux — Scandalette	Lanwades & Staffordstown Studs	C. Gordon-Watson	110,000
B.c. Gulch (USA) — So Cozy (USA)	Cotswold Stud	Chantilly Bloodstock	110,000
B.c. Be My Chief (USA) — Countess Olivia	Ballymoney Park Stud, Ire	Newmarket Intl.	105,000
B.c. Saddlers' Hall (IRE) — Full Orchestra	Cheveley Park Stud	Darley Stud Mgt.	105,000
Gr.c. Salse (USA) — High Matinee	Camas Park Stud, Ireland	C. Gordon-Watson	105,000
B.c. Lear Fan (USA) — Ladanum (USA)	Bruno Deberdt, Agent	Bluegrass B/S Agcy	105,000
B.c. Indian Ridge — Above Water (IRE)	John Osborne, Agent	John Warren B/S	100,000
B.c. Zilzal (USA) — Allegedly (USA)	Kim Nardelli, Agent	C. Gordon-Watson	100,000
B.c. Machiavellian (USA) — Al Yazi (USA)	Ashtown House Stud, Ire	C.B.A.	100,000
B.f. Red Ransom (USA) — Asdaf (USA)	Ted Voute, Agent	Darley Stud Mgt.	100,000
Indigo Bay (IRE) B.c. Royal Academy (USA) — Cape Heights	Knocktoran Stud, Ireland	Mr A. Stewart	100,000
B/Br.c. Quest For Fame — Committed Miss (USA)	Ashtown House Stud, Ire	Cheerine Stud	100,000
Br.c. Sadler's Wells (USA) — Dwell (USA)	Westerlands Stud	Darley Stud Mgt.	100,000
Ch.c. Woodman (USA) — Easy 'N Gold (USA)	Ted Voute, Agent	Mr Nick de Meric	100,000
B.c. Sabrehill (USA) — Flower Arrangement	Manor House Stud	Darley Stud Mgt.	100,000
Ch.c. Diesis — High Sevens	Trickledown Stud	Shadwell Estate Co.	100,000
B.c. Zafonic (USA) — June Moon (IRE)	Ted Voute, Agent	C.B.A.	100,000
B.c. Danehill (USA) — Karawasha (IRE)	Camas Park Stud, Ireland	C.B.A.	100,000
Rain God B.c. Rainbow Quest (USA) — Mystic Goddess (USA)	Cheveley Park Stud	B.B.A. (UK)	100,000
B.c. Zafonic (USA) — Overcast (IRE)	Old Mill Stud	Darley Stud Mgt.	100,000
Snoozy B.f. Cadeaux Genereux — Quiet Week-End	Highclere Stud	John Warren B/S	100,000

Castara Beach (IRE) B.f. Danehill (USA) — Sea Harrier	Ted Voute, Agent	Mr D. O'Byrne	100,000
B.f. Danzig (USA) — Some Romance (USA)	Ted Voute, Agent	B.B.A. (Ireland)	100,000
Waterstone (USA) B.c. Riverman (USA) — Lovealoch (IRE)	Ted Voute, Agent	Kern/Lillingston Ass.	100,000
Worship (USA) Ch.f. Irish River (FR) — Pedestal	Bloomsbury Stud	C. Gordon-Watson	100,000
B.c. Fairy King (USA) — Raymouna (IRE)	Camas Park Stud, Ireland	John Ferguson B/S	98,000
B.f. Kris — Idle Gossip (USA)	John Troy, Agent	Killeen Castle Stud	95,000
Ch.c. Indian Ridge — Mercy Bien (IRE)	Piper's Hill Stud, Ireland	C. Gordon-Watson	95,000
Sarangani B.c. Polish Precedent (USA) — Height of Folly	Ted Voute, Agent	Mr I. A. Balding	94,000
B.c. Caerleon (USA) — Random Chance	Thomastown Castle, Ire	North Hills Mgt.	94,000
Ch.c. Nashwan (USA) — Total Chic (USA)	Abbeville & Meadowcourt Studs	Peter Doyle B/S	94,000
B/Br.f. Woodman (USA) — Book Collector (USA)	Ashtown House Stud, Ire	London T'bred Services	90,000
B.f. Danehill (USA) — Carmelized (CAN)	Devonia Stud	Peter Doyle B/S	90,000
Inkberry Ch.f. Cadeaux Genereux — Chatterberry	Buckhurst Stud	Mr D. O'Byrne	90,000
B.c. Darshaan — Garconniere	Mount Coote Stud, Ireland	Darley Stud Mgt.	90,000
Ch.f. Woodman (USA) — Jaana	Warren Park Stud	John Walsh B/S	90,000
King Midas B.c. Bluebird (USA) — Ellebanna	Furnace Mill Stud	C. Gordon-Watson	90,000
Ch.f. Lion Cavern (USA) — Mariakova (USA)	Raffin Stud	Addison Racing Inc.	90,000
B.c. Farma Way (USA) — Ottomwa (USA)	Ashtown House Stud, Ire	Mr Mike Ryan	90,000
Ch.c. Arazi (USA) — Pushy	Bloomsbury Stud	Umm Qarn Mgt. Co.	90,000
Sossus Vlei B.c. Inchinor — Sassalya	Hascombe Stud	Horse France	90,000
B.c. Kingmambo (USA) — Moivouloirtoi (USA)	Haras Du Quesnay, France	Asian B/S Services	88,000
Sharp Stepper B.f. Selkirk (USA) — Awtaar (USA)	Minster Stud	Mr J. Gosden	88,000
Deal Fair B.c. Grand Lodge (USA) — Darshay (FR)	Watership Down Stud	German Intl. B/S	85,000
Ch.f. Bluebird (USA) — Eastern Shore	Floors Stud	John Ferguson B/S	85,000
Fairy Queen (IRE) B.f. Fairy King (USA) — Dedicated Lady (IRE)	Yeomanstown Lodge Stud	C. Gordon-Watson	85,000
Cops (IRE) Ch.c. Grand Lodge (USA) — Gentle Guest (IRE)	Rathbarry Stud, Ireland	C. Gordon-Watson	85,000
Upon A Wish B/Br.c. Alzao (USA) — Imprecise	Floors Stud	C. Gordon-Watson	85,000
Br.c. Doyoun — Loure (USA)	Mellon Stud, Ireland	C.B.A.	85,000
B.f. Rainbow Quest (USA) — Music And Dance (USA)	Barronstown Stud, Ireland	Equine Invest. Consul	85,000
B.f. Rahy (USA) — No More Ironing (USA)	Mellon Stud, Ireland	B.B.A. (Ireland)	85,000
Sheer Viking (IRE) B.c. Danehill (USA) — Schlefalora	Thomastown Castle, Ire	John Ferguson B/S	85,000
B.c. Perugino (USA) — Almost Heaven	Ashtown House Stud, Ire	Cheerine Stud	84,000
B.c. Hermitage (USA) — Bourbon Miss (USA)	Corduff Stud, Ireland	Mrs A. Skiffington	82,000
B.f. Cadeaux Genereux — Colorvista	Meon Valley Stud	Bullard B/S	80,000
B.c. Warning – Dancing Prize (IRE)	Cheveley Park Stud	Emerald B/S	80,000
Ch.f. Nashwan (USA) — Devil's Needle (USA)	Ted Voute, Agent	Mr Mike Ryan	80,000
B.c. Generous (IRE) — Famosa	John Troy, Agent	B.B.A. (UK)	80,000
Cajole (IRE) Ch.f. Barathea (IRE) — Frendly Persuasion	Rathbarry Stud, Ire (Agent)	Mrs A. Skiffington	80,000
Jig (IRE) B.f. Catrail (USA) — River Jig (USA)	Ted Voute, Agent	Newgate Stud Co.	80,000
B.f. Shirley Heights — Manhattan Sunset (USA)	Old Mill Stud	Mr William Haggas	80,000
Nulli Secundus B.c. Polar Falcon (USA) — Exclusive Virtue (USA)	Cheveley Park Stud	B.B.A. (UK)	80,000
Sagittarius B.c. Sadler's Wells (USA) — Ste Nitouche (FR)	Wattlefield Hall Stud	Walter Nilsen	80,000
B.f. Sadler's Wells (USA) — Salvora (USA)	Camas Park Stud, Ireland	Darley Stud Mgt.	80,000
B.c. Salse (USA) — Stardyn	Pine Ridge Farm Ltd.	Darley Stud Mgt.	80,000
B.c. Brief Truce (USA) — Too Shy (FR)	Bellewstown Farm Stud, Ire	Mr D. K. Weld	80,000
Venetian Pearl (IRE) Ch.f. Generous (IRE) — Veronica	Woodcote Stud	German Intl. B/S	80,000

HIGH – PRICED YEARLINGS OF 1997 AT GOFFS' SALES

The following yearlings realised 98,000 Irish guineas and over at Goffs' Irish National Yearling sales in 1997:-

Name and Breeding	Vendor	Purchaser	Ire Gns
B.c. Sadler's Wells (USA) — Or Vision (USA)	Camas Park Stud	D. L. O'Byrne	1,200,000
Ch.f. Barathea (IRE) — Welsh Love	Kilcarn Stud	John Ferguson Bloodstock	950,000
Ch.c. Nashwan (USA) — Whakilyric (USA)	Camas Park Stud	Darley Stud Management	900,000
High King (IRE) B.c. Fairy King (USA) — Ploy	Kilcarn Stud	D. L. O'Byrne	650,000
Oath (IRE) B.c. Fairy King (USA) — Sheer Audacity	Iverk House Stud	The Thoroughbred Corp.	450,000
Peajay (USA) B.c. Dehere (USA) — Petroleuse	Ashtown House Stud	M. W. Easterby	395,000
Ch.f. Be My Guest (USA) — Secretary Bird (IRE)	Airlie Stud	D. L. O'Byrne	350,000
Entikaa (IRE) B.c. Sadler's Wells (USA) — Miranisa	Ashtown House Stud	Shadwell Estate	340,000
Tchaikovsky (IRE) Br.c. Caerleon (USA) — Bold Flawless (USA)	Irish National Stud	D. L. O'Byrne	340,000
Ch.c. Grand Lodge (USA) — Guest Room (IRE)	Kilcarn Stud	Darley Stud Management	310,000
B.f. Green Desert (USA) — Old Domesday Book	Loughbrown Stud	Kern Lillingston Assocs.	300,000
B.c. Storm Bird (CAN) — Croquetallie (USA)	Camas Park Stud	Addison Racing Inc.	300,000
Shaftesbury (IRE) B.c. Sadler's Wells (USA) — Surmise (USA)	Camas Park Stud	Newmarket International	275,000
Tolmezzo (IRE) B.c. Fairy King (USA) — Olbia	Kildaragh Stud	German International BA	270,000
Coliseum (IRE) B.c. Sadler's Wells (USA) — Gravieres (FR)	Ballylinch Stud	D. L. O'Byrne	260,000
Bright Hope (IRE) B.f. Danehill (USA) — Crystal Cross (USA)	Triermore Stud	Peter Harris	250,000
B.c. Fairy King (USA) — Exotic Bride (USA)	Barronstown Stud	H. F. for Too Late B/S	250,000
B.c. Catrail (USA) —Menominee	Irish National Stud	The Thoroughbred Corp.	210,000
Ch.f. Irish River (FR) — Spit Curl (USA)	Staffordstown	John Gosden Esq.	210,000
B.c. Rainbow Quest (USA) – Alexandrie (USA)	Camas Park Stud	Silky Green Inc.	210,000
B.c. Catrail (USA) — Quiche	Triermore Stud	Darley Stud Management	200,000
Doonaree (IRE) B.c. Sadler's Wells (USA) — Rosananti	Barronstown Stud	R. J. O'Ryan, Esq	200,000
Ch.c. Indian Ridge — Shih Ching (USA)	Mountain View Stud	Darley Stud Management	200,000
Valnerina (IRE) Br.f. Caerleon (USA) — Lady Capulet (USA)	Camas Park Stud	BBA (Ire) Ltd.	195,000
B.c. Perugino (USA) — Love With Honey	Yeomanstown Stud	Mr Clive Brittain	180,000
Ch.c. Kingmambo (USA) — Danse Royale (IRE)	Kilcarn Stud	D. L. O'Byrne	180,000
B.f. Bigstone (IRE) — Final Decision	Lisieux Stud (agent)	John Gosden, Esq.	160,000
B.c. Waajib — Maimiti	Thomastown Castle	D. L. O'Byrne	160,000
B.f. Fairy King (USA) — Belle Passe	Derrygrath Stud	Darley Stud Management	160,000
Tarfaa (IRE) B.c. Night Shift (USA) — Robinia (USA)	Ballylinch Stud (agent)	Shadwell Estate Co.	155,000
Musketeer (IRE) B.c. Danehill (USA) — Helvellyn (USA)	Abbeville & Meadowcourt Studs	D. L. O'Byrne	150,000
Ch.c. Caerleon (USA) — Jaljuli	Ballylinch Stud	John Ferguson B/S	150,000
B.c. Barathea (IRE) — Overcall	Eyrefield Lodge Stud	Ivan Allan Esq.	150,000
B.c. Barathea (IRE) — Atlantic Dream (USA)	Redpender Stud	D. L. O'Byrne	150,000
B.c. Royal Academy (USA) — Brecon Beacons (IRE)	Ashtown House Stud	Silky Green Inc.	150,000
B.f. Gone West (USA) — Dear Dorothy (USA)	Haras des Capucines	BBA (Ire) Ltd.	140,000
White Truffle (USA) Ch.f. Dehere (USA) — Familiar (USA)	Kildaragh Stud	Belgrave Bloodstock	135,000
La Serina (IRE) B.f. Royal Academy (USA) — Hi Bettina	Kilcarn Stud	Mr Thomas McDonogh	130,000
B.f. Sadler's Wells (USA) — Katie McLain (USA)	Pipers Hill Stud	Mr John Walsh	130,000

Fadhel (USA) B.c. Zilzal (USA) — Nice Life (USA)	Yeomanstown Stud (agent)	Shadwell Estate Co. Ltd	130,000
Indian Bazaar (IRE) Ch.c. Indian Ridge — Bazaar Promise	Mountain View Stud	Sir Mark Prescott	130,000
B.f. Sadler's Wells (USA) — Delage	Ballysheehan Stud	Darley Stud Management	130,000
Ch.c. Bigstone (IRE)— Petite Liqueurelle (IRE)	Ashtown House Stud	Horse France SA	125,000
B/Br.c. El Gran Senor (USA) — Warm The Sauce (USA)	Ashtown House Stud	Silky Green Inc.	125,000
B.f. Alzao (USA) — Gold Tear (USA)	Forenaghts Stud	The Thoroughbred Corp.	120,000
B.c. Barathea (IRE) — Hanzala (FR)	Landscape Stud (agent)	Darley Stud Management	120,000
Freetown (IRE) B.c. Shirley Heights — Pageantry	Barronstown Stud	Newgate Stud Company	120,000
B.c. Catrail (USA) — Sabaah (USA)	Irish National Stud	Silky Green Inc.	120,000
Ch.c. Royal Academy (USA) — Smaoineamh	Redmondstown Stud	Silky Green Inc.	120,000
B.c. Sadler's Wells (USA) — Societe Royale	Lynn Lodge Stud	D. L. O'Byrne	120,000
Ch.c. College Chapel — Foolish Fun	Glenvale Stud	Horse France SA	115,000
Gr.f. Sadler's Wells (USA) — Modiyna	Barronstown Stud	Darley Stud Management	115,000
Downland (IRE) B.c. Common Grounds — Boldabsa	Yeomanstown Stud	John Ferguson Bloodstock	115,000
Br.c. Hamas (IRE) — Kafsa (IRE)	Rathasker Stud	The Thoroughbred Corp.	110,000
Stanley Wigfield (USA) B.c. Woodman (USA) — Las Meninas	Camas Park Stud	R. O'Ryan, Esq.	110,000
B.c. Perugino (USA) — Regal Society (IRE)	Kildare Stud	James Delahooke, Esq.	110,000
King Oberon (IRE) B.c. Fairy King (USA) — Annenberg	Croom House Stud	John Warren	110,000
Rainbow Stage (USA) B.f. Lear Fan (USA) — Certain Flair	Airlie Stud	BBA (Ire) Ltd	110,000
B.f. Fairy King (USA) — More Fizz	Glenvale Stud	G. Troeller/G. Kelleway	110,000
B.c. Indian Ridge — Martinova	Castledillon Stud	K. Nishiura	105,000
B.c. Zafonic (USA) — New Europe	Yeomanstown Stud	Horse France SA	100,000
B.f. Grand Lodge (USA) — Style Of Life (USA)	Pipers Hill Stud	Roger Charlton, Esq.	100,000
Ch.c. El Gran Senor (USA) — Chateau Dancer (USA)	Ashtown House Stud	BBA (Ire) Ltd.	100,000
Moon Dragon (IRE) B.c. Sadler's Wells (USA) — Moonsilk	Newborough Stud	C. Gordon-Watson	98,000

WINNERS OF GREAT RACES

LINCOLN HANDICAP

Doncaster—1m

Year	Winner	Runners
1977	Blustery 5-7-11	26
1978	Captains Wings 5-7-10	25
1979	Fair Season 5-8-10	23
1980	King's Ride 4-8-12	18
1981	Saher 5-8-12	19
1982	Kings Glory 4-8-3	26
1983	Mighty Fly 4-8-4	26
1984	Saving Mercy 4-8-9	26
1985	Cataldi 4-9-10	26
1986	K-Battery 5-8-4	25
1987	Star of a Gunner 7-8-8	25
1988	Cuvee Charlie 4-8-1	25
1989	Fact Finder 5-7-9	25
1990	Evichstar 6-7-12	24
1991	Amenable 6-8-1	25
1992	High Low 4-8-0	24
1993	High Premium 5-8-8	24
1994	Our Rita 5-8-5	24
1995	Roving Minstrel 4-8-3	23
1996	Stone Ridge 4-8-7	24
1997	Kuala Lipis 4-8-6	24

GREENHAM STAKES (3y)

Newbury—7f

Year	Winner	Runners
1977	He Loves Me 8-10	11
1978	Derrylin 8-10	11
1979	Kris 9-0	9
1980	Final Straw 9-0	9
1981	Another Realm 9-0	6
1982	Cajun 9-0	5
1983	Wassl 9-0	5
1984	Creag-an-Sgor 9-0	8
1985	Bairn 9-0	6
1986	Faustus 9-0	9
1987	Risk Me 9-0	8
1988	Zelphi 9-0	7
1989	Zayyani 9-0	12
1990	Rock City 9-0	6
1991	Bog Trotter 9-0	7
1992	Lion Cavern 9-0	8
1993	Inchinor 9-0	7
1994	Turtle Island 9-0	8
1995	Celtic Swing 9-0	9
1996	Danehill Dancer 9-0	8
1997	Yalaietanee 9-0	6

JOHN PORTER STAKES

Newbury—1m 4f 5yds

Year	Winner	Runners
1977	Decent Fellow 4-8-9	11
1978	Orchestra 4-9-0	10
1979	Icelandic 4-8-11	12
1980	Niniski 4-9-0	16
1981	Pelerin 4-8-8	9
1982	Glint of Gold 4-9-0	11
1983	Diamond Shoal 4-8-8	8
1984	Gay Lemur 4-8-8	13
1985	Jupiter Island 6-8-8	14
1986	Lemhill 4-8-8	8
1987	Rakaposhi King 5-8-10	12
1988	Alwasmi 4-8-10	8
1989	Unfuwain 4-8-13	7
1990	Brush Aside 4-8-10	11
1991	Rock Hopper 4-8-10	10
1992	Saddlers' Hall 4-8-13	11
1993	Linpac West 7-8-12	7
1994	Right Win 4-9-3	10
1995	Strategic Choice 4-8-11	10
1996	Spout 4-8-8	9
1997	Whitewater Affair 4-8-8	13

EUROPEAN FREE HANDICAP (3y)

Newmarket—7f

Year	Winner	Runners
1977	Mrs McArdy 8-0	19
1978	Remainder Man 7-10	12
1979	Lyric Dance 8-10	14
1980	Moorestyle 8-10	13
1981	Motavato 8-13	13
1982	Match Winner 9-4	13
1983	Boom Town Charlie 8-11	8
1984	Cutting Wind 8-8	17
1985	Over The Ocean 8-11	11
1986	Green Desert 9-7	8
1987	Noble Minstrel 9-7	11
1988	Lapierre 9-1	9
1989	Danehill 9-1	9
1990	Anshan 9-7	10
1991	Mystiko 9-2	11
1992	Pursuit of Love 9-1	9
1993	So Factual 9-6	7
1994	Bluegrass Prince 8-13	10
1995	Diffident 9-5	12
1996	Cayman Kai 9-7	8
1997	Hidden Meadow 9-3	11

CRAVEN STAKES (3y)

Newmarket—1m

Year	Winner	Runners
1977	Limone 8-10	9
1978	Admiral's Launch 8-10	10
1979	Lyphard's Wish 8-7	3
1980	Tyrnavos 8-7	9
1981	Kind of Hush 8-7	9
1982	Silver Hawk 8-7	9
1983	Muscatite 8-7	5
1984	Lear Fan 8-12	5
1985	Shadeed 8-7	6
1986	Dancing Brave 8-7	11
1987	Ajdal 9-0	6
1988	Doyoun 8-9	5
1989	Shaadi 8-9	5
1990	Tirol 8-12	6
1991	Marju 8-9	8
1992	Alnasr Alwasheek 8-9	8
1993	Emperor Jones 8-9	9
1994	King's Theatre 9-0	10

1995 Painter's Row 8-12 5
1996 Beauchamp King 9-0 5
1997 Desert Story 8-12 8

CLASSIC TRIAL (3y)
Sandown—1m 2f 7yds

1977 Artaius 8-9 5
1978 Whitstead 8-11 8
1979 Troy 8-7 5
1980 Henbit 8-7 6
1981 Shergar 8-7 9
1982 Peacetime 8-7 11
1983 Gordian 8-7 7
1984 Alphabatim 9-0 8
1985 Damister 8-7 4
1986 Shahrastani 8-7 4
1987 Gulf King 8-12 8
1988 Galitzin 8-7 5
1989 Old Vic 8-8 3
1990 Defensive Play 8-11 6
1991 Hailsham 8-11 5
1992 Pollen Count 8-11 10
1993 True Hero 8-11 6
1994 Linney Head 8-10 9
1995 Pentire 8-10 8
1996 Santillana 8-10 9
1997 Voyagers Quest 8-12 6

VICTORIA CUP
Ascot—7f

1977 Duke Ellington 4-9-1 16
1978 Private Line 5-8-13 16
1979 The Adrianstan 4-8-6 18
1980 Kampala 4-9-3 16
1981 Columnist 4-9-13 14
1982 Indian King 4-9-3 13
1983 Abandoned
1984 Mummy's Pleasure 5-8-9 13
1985 Tremblant 4-8-5 22
1986 Ready Wit 5-7-13 14
1987 Fusilier 5-7-9 20
1988 Wing Park 4-9-1 16
1989 Top Dream 4-9-1 23
1990 Lomax 4-9-3 19
1991 Sky Cloud 5-7-11 14
1992 Band on the Run 5-9-0 21
1993 Tender Moment 5-7-7 22
1994 Face North 6-8-1 25
1995 Jawaal 5-8-6 25
1996 Yeast 4-8-9 24
1997 Tregaron 6-8-13 25

JUBILEE HANDICAP
Kempton—1m

1977 Lord Helpus 4-9-5 16
1978 Sunday Guest 4-8-12 14
1979 Smartset 4-7-0 12
1980 Blue Refrain 4-9-5 10
1981 Greenwood Star 4-9-2 10
1982 Tugoflove 6-8-3 12
1983 Elmar 4-8-10 12
1984 Larionov 4-9-11 11
1985 Portogon 7-7-11 11
1986 Pennine Walk 4-9-11 23
1987 Turfah 4-8-12 15
1988 Just A Flutter 4-9-3 11
1989 Electric Lady 4-9-8 14
1990 Langtry Lady 4-8-3 12
1991 St Ninian 5-9-3 12
1992 Venus Observed 4-9-1 12
1993 Pay Homage 5-9-1 13
1994 Caleman 5-8-12 14
1995 Desert Green 6-9-4 11
1996 Desert Green 7-9-6 13
1997 Autumn Cover 5-8-3 16

JOCKEY CLUB STAKES
Newmarket—1m 4f

1977 Oats 4-9-1 11
1978 Classic Example 4-9-5 7
1979 Obraztsovy 4-8-11 9
1980 More Light 4-8-11 8
1981 Master Willie 4-8-12 6
1982 Ardross 6-8-12 6
1983 Electric 4-8-10 11
1984 Gay Lemur 4-8-7 6
1985 Kirmann 4-8-7 8
1986 Phardante 4-8-7 3
1987 Phardante 5-8-12 7
1988 Almaarad 5-8-10 4
1989 Unfuwain 4-8-10 6
1990 Roseate Tern 4-8-9 7
1991 Rock Hopper 4-8-7 8
1992 Sapience 6-8-12 9
1993 Zinaad 4-8-9 8
1994 Silver Wisp 5-8-9 8
1995 Only Royale 6-8-11 7
1996 Riyadian 4-8-9 9
1997 Time Allowed 4-8-6 10

CHESTER VASE (3y)
Chester—1m 4f 66yds

1977 Hot Grove 8-12 6
1978 Icelandic 8-12 4
1979 Cracaval 8-8 6
1980 Henbit 8-12 5
1981 Shergar 8-12 10
1982 Super Sunrise 8-12 8
1983 Abandoned
1984 Kaytu 8-8 7
1985 Law Society 8-12 5
1986 Nomrood 8-12 7
1987 Dry Dock 8-11 8
1988 Unfuwain 8-11 4
1989 Old Vic 8-11 5
1990 Belmez 8-11 3
1991 Toulon 8-11 5
1992 Twist and Turn 8-11 5
1993 Armiger 8-11 6
1994 Broadway Flyer 8-10 6
1995 Luso 8-10 7
1996 High Baroque 8-10 6
1997 Panama City 8-10 5

CHESTER CUP
Chester—2m 2f 147yds

1977 Sea Pigeon 7-8-8 15
1978 Sea Pigeon 8-9-7 13
1979 Charlotte's Choice 4-8-4 13
1980 Arapahos 5-9-5 10
1981 Donegal Prince 5-8-4 15
1982 Dawn Johnny 5-8-8 16
1983 Abandoned
1984 Contester 4-8-2 9
1985 Morgans Choice 8-7-11 16
1986 Western Dancer 5-9-0 22
1987 Just David 4-9-8 13
1988 Old Hubert 7-7-8 17
1989 Grey Salute 6-8-7 14
1990 Travelling Light 4-9-1 16
1991 Star Player 5-8-10 16
1992 Welshman 6-7-8 16
1993 Rodeo Star 7-7-13 18
1994 Doyce 5-7-10....17
1995 Top Cees 5-8-8....18
1996 Merit 4-7-10 18
1997 Top Cees 7-8-11 12

ORMONDE STAKES
Chester—1m 5f 89yds

1977 Oats 4-9-0 8
1978 Crow 5-9-0 7
1979 Remainder Man 4-8-10 4
1980 Niniski 4-9-4 10
1981 Pelerin 4-9-4 5
1982 Six Mile Bottom 4-8-10 6
1983 Abandoned
1984 Teenoso 4-9-4 5
1985 Seismic Wave 4-8-10 8
1986 Brunico 4-8-10 8
1987 Rakaposhi King 5-8-11 5
1988 Mr Pintips 4-8-11 6
1989 Mountain Kingdom 5-8-11 3
1990 Braashee 4-8-11 6
1991 Per Quod 6-8-11 7
1992 Saddlers' Hall 4-9-2 7
1993 Shambo 6-9-2....5
1994 Shambo 7-9-2....8
1995 Zilzal Zamaan 4-8-11....4
1996 Oscar Schindler 4-8-11 7
1997 Royal Court 4-8-11 7

OAKS TRIAL (3y fillies)
Lingfield—1m 3f 106yds

1977 Lucent 9-0 5
1978 Suni 9-0 9
1979 Reprocolor 9-0 7
1980 Gift Wrapped 9-0 7
1981 Leap Lively 9-0 7
1982 Tants 9-0 9
1983 Give Thanks 9-0 12
1984 Out of Shot 9-0 7
1985 Kiliniski 8-9 11
1986 Mill on the Floss 8-9 8
1987 Port Helene 8-9 8
1988 Bahamian 8-9 7
1989 Aliysa 8-9 5
1990 Rafha 9-1 5
1991 Ausherra 8-9 7
1992 User Friendly 8-9 5
1993 Oakmead 8-9 6
1994 Munnaya 8-8....8
1995 Asterita 8-8....5
1996 Lady Carla 8-8 4
1997 Crown of Light 8-8 5

DERBY TRIAL (3y)
Lingfield—1m 3f 106yds

1977 Caporello 9-0 8
1978 Whitstead 9-0 6
1979 Milford 9-0 8
1980 Ginistrelli 9-0 7
1981 Riberetto 9-0 8
1982 Jalmood 9-0 6
1983 Teenoso 9-0 11
1984 Alphabatim 9-0 5
1985 Slip Anchor 9-0 8
1986 Mashkour 9-0 6
1987 Legal Bid 9-0 8
1988 Kahyasi 9-0 8
1989 Cacoethes 9-0 7
1990 Rock Hopper 9-0 5
1991 Corrupt 9-0 8
1992 Assessor 9-0 7
1993 Bob's Return 9-0....8
1994 Hawker's News 8-7....6
1995 Munwar 8-7 7
1996 Mystic Knight 8-7....6
1997 Silver Patriarch 8-7....5

CORAL HANDICAP (3y)
(formerly Holsten Diat Pils Handicap)
Newmarket—6f

1981 Sharp Venita 7-3 12
1982 Admirals Princess 9-2 13
1983 Bold Secret 8-6....10
1984 Lovers Bid 7-3 14
1985 Zanata 8-4 12
1986 Latch Spring 7-10 14
1987 Bel Byou 8-4....15
1988 Cadeaux Genereux 8-0....16
1989 Didicoy 8-12....11
1990 Case Law 9-7....11
1991 Arturian 8-3....13
1992 Splice 8-4....13
1993 True Precision 7-10....15
1994 Tabook 9-5 13
1995 Perryston View 8-11....12
1996 Atraf 9-7 13
1997 Blue Goblin 8-13 12

MUSIDORA STAKES (3y fillies)
York—1m 2f 85yds

1977 Triple First 9-0 9
1978 Princess of Man 9-0....9
1979 Rimosa's Pet 9-0 10
1980 Bireme 9-0....9

1981 Condessa 9-0 ... 5
1982 Last Feather 9-0 ... 5
1983 Give Thanks 9-0 ... 8
1984 Optimistic Lass 9-0 ... 9
1985 Fatah Flare 9-0 ... 9
1986 Rejuvenate 8-11 ... 7
1987 Indian Skimmer 8-8 ... 3
1988 Diminuendo 8-11 ... 6
1989 Snow Bride 8-8 ... 6
1990 In The Groove 8-8 ... 5
1991 Gussy Marlowe 8-8 ... 5
1992 All At Sea 8-8 ... 5
1993 Marillette 8-10 ... 5
1994 Hawajiss 8-10 ... 7
1995 Pure Grain 8-10 ... 5
1996 Magnificient Style 8-8 ... 5
1997 Reams of Verse 8-11 ... 10

DANTE STAKES (3y)

York—1m 2f 85yds

1977 Lucky Sovereign 9-0 ... 15
1978 Shirley Heights 9-0 ... 9
1979 Lyphard's Wish 9-0 ... 14
1980 Hello Gorgeous 9-0 ... 8
1981 Beldale Flutter 9-0 ... 6
1982 Simply Great 9-0 ... 6
1983 Hot Touch 9-0 ... 9
1984 Claude Monet 9-0 ... 15
1985 Damister 9-0 ... 5
1986 Shahrastani 9-0 ... 7
1987 Reference Point 9-0 ... 8
1988 Red Glow 9-0 ... 7
1989 Torjoun 9-0 ... 7
1990 Sanglamore 9-0 ... 7
1991 Environment Friend 9-0 ... 8
1992 Alnasr Alwasheek 9-0 ... 7
1993 Tenby 9-0 ... 5
1994 Erhaab 9-0 ... 9
1995 Classic Cliche 8-11 ... 8
1996 Glory of Dancer 8-11 ... 7
1997 Benny The Dip 8-11 ... 9

YORKSHIRE CUP

York—1m 5f 194yds

1977 Bright Finish 4-8-10 ... 7
1978 Smuggler 5-8-10 ... 7
1979 Pragmatic 4-8-7 ... 10
1980 Noble Saint 4-9-1 ... 8
1981 Ardross 5-8-12 ... 6
1982 Ardross 6-9-1 ... 6
1983 Line Slinger 4-8-4 ... 10
1984 Band 4-8-10 ... 9
1985 Ilium 4-8-7 ... 10
1986 Eastern Mystic 4-8-9 ... 7
1987 Verd-Antique 4-8-9 ... 7
1988 Moon Madness 5-9-0 ... 8
1989 Mountain Kingdom 5-8-9 ... 6
1990 Braashee 4-8-9 ... 6
1991 Arzanni 4-8-9 ... 7
1992 Rock Hopper 5-8-13 ... 8
1993 Assessor 4-9-0 ... 8
1994 Key To My Heart 4-8-9 ... 7
1995 Moonax 4-9-0 ... 7
1996 Classic Cliche 4-9-0 ... 5
1997 Celeric 5-8-9 ... 9

DUKE OF YORK STAKES

York—6f

1977 Boldboy 7-9-12 ... 13
1978 Private Line 5-9-4 ... 16
1979 Thatching 4-9-0 ... 9
1980 Flash N'Thunder 3-8-1 ... 7
1981 King of Spain 5-9-0 ... 10
1982 Jester 3-8-2 ... 11
1983 Vorvados 6-9-0 ... 11
1984 Gabitat 6-9-4 ... 10
1985 Chapel Cottage 4-8-11 ... 10
1986 Grey Desire 6-9-0 ... 10
1987 Handsome Sailor 4-9-0 ... 9
1988 Handsome Sailor 5-9-8 ... 13
1989 Indian Ridge 4-9-4 ... 10
1990 Lugana Beach 4-9-4 ... 7
1991 Green Line Express 5-9-4 ... 11
1992 Shalford 4-9-4 ... 9
1993 Hamas 4-9-0 ... 10
1994 Owington 3-8-9 ... 11
1995 Lake Coniston 4-9-4 ... 7
1996 Venture Capitalist 7-9-0 ... 12
1997 Royal Applause 4-9-0 ... 10

LOCKINGE STAKES

Newbury—1m

1977 Relkino 4-9-0 ... 9
1978 Don 4-9-4 ... 10
1979 Young Generation 3-8-4 ... 10
1980 Kris 4-9-7 ... 7
1981 Belmont Bay 4-9-0 ... 6
1982 Motavato 4-9-0 ... 7
1983 Noalcoholic 6-9-4 ... 10
1984 Cormorant Wood 4-9-5 ... 6
1985 Prismatic 3-7-13 ... 11
1986 Scottish Reel 4-9-1 ... 8
1987 Then Again 4-9-4 ... 9
1988 Broken Hearted 4-9-4 ... 5
1989 Most Welcome 5-9-1 ... 4
1990 Safawan 4-9-0 ... 6
1991 Polar Falcon 4-9-0 ... 4
1992 Selkirk 4-9-5 ... 10
1993 Swing Low 4-9-0 ... 10
1994 Emperor Jones 4-9-0 ... 11
1995 Soviet Line 5-9-0 ... 5
1996 Soviet Line 6-9-0 ... 7
1997 First Island 5-9-0 ... 10

TOTE CREDIT SILVER BOWL (3y)

(Cecil Frail Handicap before 1986)

Haydock—1m 30yds

1977 Owen Jones 7-9 ... 11
1978 Fair Top 7-10 ... 11
1979 Bold Owl 8-1 ... 10
1980 Greenwood Star 7-7 ... 13
1981 Silver Season 9-5 ... 12

1982 Spanish Pool 9-6 12
1983 Schuss 8-5 10
1984 Incisive 7-9 10
1985 Trucidator 9-7 11
1986 Al Bashaama 7-10 13
1987 Mohamed Abdu 7-8 8
1988 Jamarj 9-7 15
1989 Safawan 8-11 13
1990 Cashtal Dazzler 7-7 8
1991 Takaddum 9-3 13
1992 Sharpitor 9-0 11
1993 Moorish 8-2 13
1994 Dance Turn 9-0 12
1995 Sonic Boy 9-7 9
1996 Winter Romance 9-0 10
1997 Alezal 9-1 6

HENRY II STAKES
Sandown—2m 78yds

1978 Smuggler 5-9-0 6
1979 Buckskin 6-9-3 6
1980 Billion 6-8-8 8
1981 No race
1982 Ardross 6-9-3 5
1983 Ore 5-8-11 7
1984 Harly 4-8-11 5
1985 Destroyer 4-8-8 8
1986 Longboat 5-8-11 10
1987 Saronicos 4-8-10 7
1988 Primitive Rising 4-8-10 9
1989 Sadeem 6-9-2 8
1990 Teamster 4-8-13 6
1991 Top of The World 4-8-10 7
1992 Drum Taps 6-9-4 8
1993 Brier Creek 4-8-10 8
1994 My Patriarch 4-8-10 9
1995 Double Trigger 4-8-13 7
1996 Double Trigger 5-9-5 5
1997 Persian Punch 4-8-10 7

PREDOMINATE STAKES (3y)
Goodwood—1m 2f

1977 Royal Blend 8-11 6
1978 English Harbour 8-11 9
1979 Troy 9-0 4
1980 Prince Bee 8-6 8
1981 No race
1982 Peacetime 9-0 9
1983 Morcon 8-6 6
1984 Ilium 8-6 12
1985 Lanfranco 9-0 8
1986 Allez Milord 8-12 8
1987 Ibn Bey 8-12 9
1988 Minster Son 9-1 7
1989 Warrshan 8-12 8
1990 Razeen 8-12 6
1991 Man From Eldorado 8-12 8
1992 Jeune 8-12 9
1993 Geisway 8-12 6
1994 Opera Score 8-8 5
1995 Pentire 9-0 6
1996 Don Micheletto 8-8 9
1997 Grapeshot 8-11 6

LUPE STAKES (3y)
Goodwood—1m 2f

1977 Western Star 8-8 5
1978 Cistus 8-8 7
1979 Britannias Rule 8-3 5
1980 Vielle 8-8 8
1981 Golden Bowl 8-8 4
1982 Height of Fashion 8-11 4
1983 Current Raiser 8-3 8
1984 Miss Beaulieu 8-8 15
1985 Bella Colora 8-11 6
1986 Tralthee 8-11 6
1987 Scimitarra 8-11 16
1988 Miss Boniface 8-11 4
1989 Lady Shipley 8-11 7
1990 Moon Cactus 9-3 7
1991 Fragrant Hill 8-11 9
1992 Oumaldaaya 8-11 6
1993 Gisarne 8-11 7
1994 Bulaxie 9-0 6
1995 Subya 8-11 9
1996 Whitewater Affair 8-8 9
1997 Maid of Camelot 8-8 7

TEMPLE STAKES
Sandown—5f 6yds

1977 Vilgora 5-9-0 6
1978 *Oscilight 3-8-2 ....
*Smarten Up 3-8-2 15
1979 Double Form 4-8-11 12
1980 Sharpo 3-8-2 10
1981 Abandoned
1982 Mummy's Game 3-8-2 13
1983 Fearless Lad 4-9-8 11
1984 Petorius 3-8-6 9
1985 Never So Bold 5-9-5 6
1986 Double Schwartz 5-9-3 10
1987 Treasure Kay 4-9-3 9
1988 Handsome Sailor 5-9-3 10
1989 Dancing Dissident 3-8-8 6
1990 Dayjur 3-8-8 8
1991 Elbio 4-9-3 8
1992 Snaadee 5-9-3 9
1993 Paris House 4-9-7 10
1994 Lochsong 6-9-7 9
1995 Mind Games 3-8-8 5
1996 Mind Games 4-9-7 9
1997 Croft Pool 6-9-3 10

BRIGADIER GERARD STAKES
Sandown—1m 2f 7yds

1977 Jellaby 4-8-8 9
1978 Gunner B 5-8-11 8
1979 Jellaby 6-8-11 7
1980 Gregorian 4-8-11 3
1981 Abandoned
1982 Kalaglow 4-8-11 8
1983 Stanerra 5-8-5 10
1984 Adonijah 4-8-8 9
1985 Commanche Run 4-9-3 5
1986 Bedtime 6-8-10 7
1987 Mtoto 4-8-10 8

1988 Highland Chieftain 5-9-1 7
1989 Hibernian Gold 4-8-10 6
1990 Husyan 4-8-10 6
1991 Stagecraft 4-8-10 11
1992 Opera House 4-9-1 3
1993 Red Bishop 5-8-10 5
1994 Chatoyant 4-8-10 14
1995 Alriffa 4-8-10 7
1996 Pilsudski 4-8-10 11
1997 Bosra Sham 4-9-0 6

LEISURE STAKES
Lingfield—6f

1978 Gypsy Dancer 3-8-7 6
1979 Absalom 4-9-10 7
1980 The Pug 3-8-3 6
1981 Runnett 4-9-10 7
1982 Sylvan Barbarosa 3-8-3 8
1983 Solimile 3-8-6 7
1984 Habibti 4-9-3 8
1985 Alpine Strings 4-9-4 7
1986 Hallgate 3-8-3 9
1987 Mister Majestic 3-8-3 11
1988 Gallic League 3-8-3 8
1989 Restore 6-9-0 12
1990 Sharp N'Early 4-9-0 8
1991 Polish Patriot 3-8-5 15
1992 Central City 3-7-13 8
1993 Pips Pride 3-8-4 9
1994 Hard to Figure 8-9-0 8
1995 Roger The Butler 5-9-0 9
1996 Rambling Bear 3-8-10 10
1997 Cyrano's Lad 8-9-0 7

DIOMED STAKES
Epsom—1m 114yds

1977 Gunner B 4-9-6 6
1978 Ovac 5-9-9 9
1979 Spring In Deepsea 4-9-4 11
1980 Hardgreen 4-9-3 5
1981 Saher 5-9-6 6
1982 Prima Voce 3-8-3 8
1983 Lofty 3-8-3 6
1984 Adonijah 4-9-9 7
1985 Scottish Reel 3-8-7 7
1986 Pennine Walk 4-9-9 10
1987 Lauries Warrior 3-8-6 10
1988 Waajib 5-9-9 8
1989 Shining Steel 3-8-7 8
1990 Eton Lad 3-8-6 9
1991 Sylva Honda 3-8-6 11
1992 Zaahi 3-8-5 9
1993 Enharmonic 6-9-7 8
1994 Bluegrass Prince 3-8-6 11
1995 Mr Martini 5-9-4 7
1996 Blomberg 4-9-4 8
1997 Polar Prince 4-9-4 9

CORONATION CUP
Epsom—1m 4f 10yds

1977 Exceller 4-9-0 6
1978 Crow 5-9-0 5
1979 Ile de Bourbon 4-9-0 4
1980 Sea Chimes 4-9-0 4
1981 Master Willie 4-9-0 5
1982 Easter Sun 5-9-0 8
1983 Be My Native 4-9-0 6
1984 Time Charter 5-8-11 6
1985 Rainbow Quest 4-9-0 7
1986 Saint Estephe 4-9-0 10
1987 Triptych 5-8-11 5
1988 Triptych 6-8-11 4
1989 Sheriff's Star 4-9-0 9
1990 In The Wings 4-9-0 6
1991 In The Groove 4-8-11 7
1992 Saddlers' Hall 4-9-0 9
1993 Opera House 5-9-0 8
1994 Apple Tree 5-9-0 11
1995 Sunshack 4-9-0 7
1996 Swain 4-9-0 4
1997 Singspiel 5-9-0 5

JOHN OF GAUNT STAKES
Haydock—7f 30yds

1977 Gwent 4-9-5 4
1978 Persian Bold 3-8-10 10
1979 Borzoi 3-8-0 4
1980 Hard Fought 3-8-0 8
1981 Last Fandango 4-9-4 7
1982 Indian King 4-9-4 7
1983 Abandoned
1984 Mr Meeka 3-8-3 13
1985 Sarab 4-9-4 8
1986 Firm Landing 3-8-0 11
1987 Linda's Magic 3-8-4 5
1988 Wantage Park 4-8-9 9
1989 Weldnaas 3-8-7 13
1990 Palace Street 3-8-3 7
1991 Swordsmith 4-8-12 8
1992 Norton Challenger 5-9-4 8
1993 Celestial Key 3-8-2 4
1994 Eurolink Thunder 4-9-5 8
1995 Mutakddim 4-8-12 8
1996 Inzar 4-9-5 9
1997 Decorated Hero 5-9-3 4

WILLIAM HILL TROPHY (HANDICAP) (3y)
York—6f

1977 Mofida 8-13 10
1978 Emperor's Shadow 7-11 14
1979 Eagle Boy 7-8 17
1980 Optimate 8-0 13
1981 Marking Time 7-9 9
1982 Cyrils Choice 9-1 8
1983 Autumn Sunset 7-8 17
1984 Ashley Rocket 7-4 16
1985 Si Signor 8-9 12
1986 *Governor General 8-12 ....
*Sew High 7-7 12
1987 Dowsing 7-10 15
1988 Cadeaux Genereux 8-5 10
1989 Sure Gold 8-11 10
1990 Katzakeena 8-10 10

1991 Sheikh Albadou 9-3 15
1992 Orthorhombus 9-2 11
1993 Aradanza 9-2 13
1994 Encore M'Lady 7-11 14
1995 Bold Effort 3-8-8 15
1996 Polish Spring 3-8-6 14
1997 Return of Amin 3-7-7 19

QUEEN ANNE STAKES

Ascot—1m

1977 Jellaby 4-9-8 8
1978 Radetzky 5-9-5 10
1979 Baptism 3-8-5 9
1980 Blue Refrain 4-9-8 11
1981 Belmont Bay 4-9-11 10
1982 Mr Fluorocarbon 3-8-6 10
1983 Valiyar 4-9-5 10
1984 Trojan Fen 3-8-5 6
1985 Rousillon 4-9-5 8
1986 Pennine Walk 4-9-2 9
1987 Then Again 4-9-5 6
1988 Waajib 5-9-2 5
1989 Warning 4-9-8 7
1990 Markofdistinction 4-9-5 9
1991 Sikeston 5-9-8 11
1992 Lahib 4-9-2 9
1993 Alflora 4-9-2 9
1994 Barathea 4-9-8 10
1995 Nicolotte 4-9-2 7
1996 Charnwood Forest 4-9-2 9
1997 Allied Forces 4-9-5 11

PRINCE OF WALES'S STAKES

Ascot—1m 2f

1977 Lucky Wednesday 4-9-1 5
1978 Gunner B 5-9-1 6
1979 Crimson Beau 4-9-1 7
1980 Ela-Mana-Mou 4-9-4 10
1981 Hard Fought 4-9-4 9
1982 Kind of Hush 4-9-1 7
1983 Stanerra 5-8-12 11
1984 Morcon 4-9-1 5
1985 Bob Back 4-9-7 4
1986 English Spring 4-8-12 9
1987 Mtoto 4-9-4 10
1988 Mtoto 5-9-8 4
1989 Two Timing 3-8-4 8
1990 Batshoof 4-9-5 8
1991 Stagecraft 4-9-3 6
1992 Perpendicular 4-9-3 11
1993 Placerville 3-8-4 11
1994 Muhtarram 5-9-7 11
1995 Muhtarram 6-9-8 6
1996 First Island 4-9-3 12
1997 Bosra Sham 4-9-5 6

ST JAMES'S PALACE STAKES (3y)

Ascot—1m

1977 Don 9-0 7
1978 Jaazeiro 9-0 8
1979 Kris 9-0 5
1980 Posse 9-0 8
1981 To-Agori-Mou 9-0 8
1982 Dara Monarch 9-0 9
1983 Horage 9-0 7
1984 Chief Singer 9-0 8
1985 Bairn 9-0 8
1986 Sure Blade 9-0 7
1987 Half a Year 9-0 5
1988 Persian Heights 9-0 7
1989 Shaadi 9-0 5
1990 Shavian 9-0 8
1991 Marju 9-0 7
1992 Brief Truce 9-0 8
1993 Kingmambo 9-0 4
1994 Grand Lodge 9-0 9
1995 Bahri 9-0 9
1996 Bijou D'Inde 9-0 9
1997 Starborough 9-0 8

COVENTRY STAKES (2y)

Ascot—6f

1977 Solinus 8-11 17
1978 Lake City 8-11 20
1979 Varingo 8-11 18
1980 Recitation 8-11 13
1981 Red Sunset 8-11 16
1982 Horage 8-11 8
1983 Chief Singer 8-11 14
1984 Primo Dominie 8-11 8
1985 Sure Blade 8-11 12
1986 Cutting Blade 8-11 19
1987 Always Fair 8-13 13
1988 High Estate 8-13 9
1989 Rock City 8-13 16
1990 Mac's Imp 8-13 13
1991 Dilum 8-13 14
1992 Petardia 8-13 12
1993 Stonehatch 8-13 6
1994 Sri Pekan 8-13 16
1995 Royal Applause 8-12 13
1996 Verglas 8-12 15
1997 Harbour Master 8-12 15

KING EDWARD VII STAKES (3y)

Ascot—1m 4f

1977 Classic Example 8-10 10
1978 Ile de Bourbon 8-6 10
1979 Ela-Mana-Mou 8-6 9
1980 Light Cavalry 8-6 10
1981 Bustomi 8-6 10
1982 Open Day 8-6 11
1983 Shareef Dancer 8-6 7
1984 Head for Heights 8-6 10
1985 Lanfranco 8-6 10
1986 Bonhomie 8-8 13
1987 Love the Groom 8-8 8
1988 Sheriff's Star 8-8 8
1989 Cacoethes 8-8 6
1990 Private Tender 8-8 8
1991 Saddlers' Hall 8-8 9
1992 Beyton 8-8 12
1993 Beneficial 8-8 8
1994 Fover 8-8 8

1995 Pentire 8-8 8
1996 Amfortas 8-8 7
1997 Kingfisher Mill 8-8 5

JERSEY STAKES (3y)
Ascot—7f

1977 Etienne Gerard 8-10 13
1978 Camden Town 8-10 17
1979 Blue Refrain 9-2 17
1980 Hard Fought 9-2 13
1981 Rasa Penang 8-10 20
1982 Merlins Charm 8-7 21
1983 Tecorno 8-6 13
1984 Miss Silca Key 8-7 16
1985 Pennine Walk 8-10 19
1986 Cliveden 8-10 20
1987 Midyan 9-1 13
1988 Indian Ridge 8-10 12
1989 Zilzal 8-10 12
1990 Sally Rous 8-7 15
1991 Satin Flower 8-7 14
1992 Prince Ferdinand 9-1 12
1993 Ardkinglass 9-1 15
1994 *Gneiss 8-10
*River Deep 8-10 21
1995 Sergeyev 8-10 16
1996 Lucayan Prince 8-10 16
1997 Among Men 8-13 20

QUEEN MARY STAKES (2y fillies)
Ascot—5f

1977 Amaranda 8-8 13
1978 Greenland Park 8-8 21
1979 Abeer 8-8 14
1980 Pushy 8-8 17
1981 Fly Baby 8-8 11
1982 Widaad 8-8 16
1983 Night of Wind 8-8 15
1984 Hi-Tech Girl 8-8 17
1985 Gwydion 8-8 14
1986 Forest Flower 8-8 13
1987 Princess Athena 8-8 15
1988 Gloriella 8-8 12
1989 Dead Certain 8-8 13
1990 On Tiptoes 8-8 12
1991 Marling 8-8 14
1992 Lyric Fantasy 8-8 13
1993 Risky 8-8 11
1994 Gay Gallanta 8-8 16
1995 Blue Duster 8-8 12
1996 Dance Parade 8-8 13
1997 Nadwah 8-8 18

CORONATION STAKES (3y fillies)
Ascot—1m

1977 Orchestration 9-0 10
1978 Sutton Place 8-8 14
1979 One In A Millon 9-4 13
1980 Cairn Rouge 9-4 8
1981 Tolmi 9-0 10
1982 Chalon 9-0 8
1983 Flame of Tara 9-0 6
1984 Katies 9-4 10
1985 Al Bahathri 9-4 7
1986 Sonic Lady 9-4 7
1987 Milligram 9-0 6
1988 Magic of Life 9-0 8
1989 Golden Opinion 9-0 12
1990 Chimes of Freedom 9-0 7
1991 Kooyonga 9-0 8
1992 Marling 9-0 7
1993 Gold Splash 9-0 5
1994 Kissing Cousin 9-0 10
1995 Ridgewood Pearl 9-0 10
1996 Shake The Yoke 9-0 7
1997 Rebecca Sharp 9-0 6

ROYAL HUNT CUP
Ascot—1m

1977 My Hussar 5-8-10 15
1978 Fear Naught 4-8-0 19
1979 Pipedreamer 4-8-5 24
1980 Tender Heart 4-9-0 22
1981 Teamwork 4-8-6 20
1982 Buzzards Bay 4-8-12 20
1983 Mighty Fly 4-9-3 31
1984 Hawkley 4-8-6 18
1985 Come on the Blues 6-8-2 27
1986 Patriach 4-7-12 32
1987 Vague Shot 4-9-5 25
1988 Governorship 4-9-6 26
1989 True Panache 4-9-4 27
1990 Pontenuovo 5-7-7 32
1991 Eurolink The Lad 4-8-9 29
1992 Colour Sergeant 4-7-8 31
1993 Imperial Ballet 4-8-12 30
1994 Face North 6-8-3 32
1995 Realities 5-9-10 32
1996 Yeast 4-8-6 31
1997 Red Robbo 4-8-6 32

QUEENS VASE
Ascot—2m 45yds

1977 Millionaire 3-8-5 14
1978 Le Moss 3-8-0 12
1979 Buttress 3-8-5 13
1980 Toondra 3-8-0 14
1981 Ore 3-8-0 13
1982 Evzon 4-9-3 14
1983 Santella Man 4-9-8 17
1984 Baynoun 3-8-0 11
1985 Wassl Merbayeh 3-8-0 10
1986 Stavordale 3-7-10 13
1987 Arden 3-8-9 9
1988 Green Adventure 8-9 14
1989 Weld 8-9 11
1990 River God 8-11 11
1991 Jendali 8-11 14
1992 Landowner 8-11 11
1993 Infrasonic 8-11 8
1994 Silver Wedge 8-11 12
1995 Stelvio 8-11 11
1996 Gordi 8-11 14
1997 Windsor Castle 8-11 11

CORK AND ORRERY STAKES
Ascot—6f

1977 He Loves Me 3-8-4 15
1978 Sweet Mint 4-8-8 12
1979 Thatching 4-9-0 17
1980 Kearney 3-8-0 20
1981 The Quiet Bidder 3-8-2 16
1982 Indian King 4-9-0 18
1983 Sylvan Barbarosa 4-8-10 17
1984 Committed 4-8-7 15
1985 Dafayna 3-7-11 12
1986 Sperry 3-8-0 10
1987 Big Shuffle 3-8-4 11
1988 Posada 3-7-12 14
1989 Danehill 3-8-0 12
1990 Great Commotion 4-9-0 17
1991 Polish Patriot 3-8-2 16
1992 Shalford 4-9-4 17
1993 College Chapel 3-8-10 19
1994 Owington 3-8-10 17
1995 So Factual 5-8-13 11
1996 Atraf 3-8-6 17
1997 Royal Applause 4-9-3 23

NORFOLK STAKES (2y)
Ascot—5f

1977 Emboss 8-11 5
1978 Schweppeshire Lad 8-11 8
1979 Romeo Romani 8-11 10
1980 Chummy's Special 8-11 6
1981 Day Is Done 8-11 8
1982 Brondesbury 8-11 5
1983 Precocious 8-11 5
1984 Magic Mirror 8-11 4
1985 Marouble 8-11 10
1986 Sizzling Melody 8-11 6
1987 Colmore Row 8-13 8
1988 Superpower 8-13 10
1989 Petillante 8-8 6
1990 Line Engaged 8-13 9
1991 Magic Ring 8-13 9
1992 Niche 8-8 9
1993 Turtle Island 8-13 8
1994 Mind Games 8-13 6
1995 Lucky Lionel 8-12 9
1996 Tipsy Creek 8-12 10
1997 Tippitt Boy 8-12 6

GOLD CUP
Ascot—2m 4f

1977 Sagaro 6-9-0 6
1978 Shangamuzo 5-9-0 10
1979 Le Moss 4-9-0 6
1980 Le Moss 5-9-0 8
1981 Ardross 5-9-0 4
1982 Ardross 6-9-0 5
1983 Little Wolf 5-9-0 12
1984 Gildoran 4-9-0 9
1985 Gildoran 5-9-0 12
1986 Longboat 5-9-0 11
1987 Paean 4-9-0 8
1988 Sadeem 5-9-0 13
1989 Sadeem 6-9-0 8
1990 Ashal 4-9-0 11
1991 Indian Queen 6-8-13 12
1992 Drum Taps 6-9-2 6
1993 Drum Taps 7-9-2 10
1994 Arcadian Heights 6-9-2 9
1995 Double Trigger 4-9-0 7
1996 Classic Cliche 4-9-0 7
1997 Celeric 5-9-2 13

RIBBLESDALE STAKES (3y fillies)
Ascot—1m 4f

1977 Nanticious 8-10 9
1978 Relfo 8-10 12
1979 Expansive 8-7 7
1980 Shoot A Line 8-11 9
1981 Strigida 8-7 9
1982 Dish Dash 8-7 10
1983 High Hawk 8-7 14
1984 Ballinderry 8-7 9
1985 Sally Brown 8-7 10
1986 Gull Nook 8-8 12
1987 Queen Midas 8-8 6
1988 Miss Boniface 8-8 11
1989 Alydaress 8-9 6
1990 Hellenic 8-8 11
1991 Third Watch 8-8 14
1992 Armarama 8-8 8
1993 Thawakib 8-8 8
1994 Bolas 8-8 9
1995 Phantom Gold 8-8 7
1996 Tulipa 8-8 10
1997 Yashmak 8-8 9

HARDWICKE STAKES
Ascot—1m 4f

1977 Meneval 4-9-0 7
1978 Montcontour 4-8-12 8
1979 Obraztsovy 4-8-9 6
1980 Scorpio 4-9-0 7
1981 Pelerin 4-8-12 9
1982 Critique 4-8-9 8
1983 Stanerra 5-8-9 10
1984 Khairpour 5-8-12 7
1985 Jupiter Island 6-8-9 4
1986 Dihistan 4-8-9 10
1987 Orban 4-8-9 4
1988 Almaarad 5-8-12 8
1989 Assatis 4-8-9 4
1990 Assatis 5-9-0 7
1991 Rock Hopper 4-8-12 9
1992 Rock Hopper 5-8-12 5
1993 Jeune 4-8-9 5
1994 Bobzao 5-8-9 11
1995 Beauchamp Hero 5-8-9 6
1996 Oscar Schindler 4-8-9 8
1997 Predappio 4-8-12 10

WOKINGHAM STAKES
Ascot—6f

1977 Calibina 5-8-5 13

1978 Equal Opportunity 4-7-12 24
1979 Lord Rochford 4-8-8 28
1980 Queen's Pride 4-7-13 29
1981 Great Eastern 4-9-8 29
1982 Battle Hymn 3-7-7 24
1983 Melindra 4-7-5 27
1984 Petong 4-9-6 28
1985 Time Machine 4-7-12 30
1986 Touch of Grey 3-8-8 28
1987 Bel Byou 3-8-3 29
1988 Powder Blue 6-8-5 30
1989 Mac's Fighter 4-9-12 27
1990 Knight of Mercy 4-8-6 28
1991 Amigo Menor 5-8-7 29
1992 Red Rosein 6-8-1 29
1993 Nagida 4-8-7 30
1994 Venture Capitalist 5-8-12 30
1995 Astrac 4-8-7 30
1996 Emerging Market 4-8-13 29
1997 Selhurstpark Flyer 6-8-9 30

KING'S STAND STAKES
Ascot—5f

1977 Godswalk 3-8-9 11
1978 Solinus 3-8-9 8
1979 Double Form 4-9-3 13
1980 African Song 3-8-9 14
1981 Marwell 3-8-6 12
1982 Fearless Lad 3-8-9 14
1983 Sayf El Arab 3-8-9 16
1984 Habibti 4-9-0 11
1985 Never So Bold 5-9-3 15
1986 Last Tycoon 3-8-9 14
1987 Bluebird 3-8-9 12
1988 Chilibang 4-9-3 8
1989 Indian Ridge 4-9-3 15
1990 Dayjur 3-8-10 15
1991 Elbio 4-9-3 10
1992 Sheikh Albadou 4-9-3 10
1993 Elbio 6-9-3 8
1994 Lochsong 6-9-0 8
1995 Piccolo 4-9-6 10
1996 Pivotal 3-8-10 17
1997 Don't Worry Me 5-8-13 18

NORTHUMBERLAND PLATE
Newcastle—2m 19yds

1977 Tug of War 4-8-7 15
1978 Tug of War 5-9-2 10
1979 Totowah 5-8-2 11
1980 Mon's Beau 5-7-7 15
1981 Dawn Johnny 4-8-6 18
1982 Abandoned
1983 Weavers Pin 6-8-8 14
1984 Karadar 6-9-10 19
1985 Trade Line 4-7-10 13
1986 Sneak Preview 6-8-12 15
1987 Treasure Hunter 8-7-7 20
1988 Stavordale 5-9-2 10
1989 Orpheus 3-7-7 12
1990 Al Maheb 4-8-11 12
1991 Tamarpour 4-7-7 14
1992 Witness Box 5-9-9 13
1993 Highflying 7-7-11 18
1994 Quick Ransom 6-8-8 20
1995 Bold Gait 4-9-10 17
1996 Celeric 4-9-4 13
1997 Windsor Castle 3-8-10 18

VAN GEEST CRITERION STAKES
Newmarket—7f

1981 Dalsaan 4-9-7 8
1982 Noalcoholic 5-9-7 14
1983 Thug 3-8-10 12
1984 Grey Desire 4-9-7 11
1985 Capricorn Belle 4-9-9 12
1986 Mister Wonderful 3-8-5 14
1987 Linda's Magic 3-8-2 5
1988 Cadeaux Genereux 3-8-5 5
1989 Zilzal 3-8-10 4
1990 Rock City 3-9-1 7
1991 La Grange Music 4-9-2 12
1992 Toussaud 3-8-4 7
1993 Inchinor 3-8-12 10
1994 Hill Hopper 3-8-4 6
1995 Pipe Major 3-8-8 8
1996 Gabr 6-9-10 9
1997 Ramooz 4-9-2 9

FOSTER'S SILVER CUP
(formerly Sun Page 3 Silver Cup)
York—1m 7f 195yds

NB: Race distance changed in 1994 to 1m 5f 194yds

1985 Skaramanga 3-8-6 4
1986 Rakaposhi King 4-8-12 6
1987 Lemhill 5-9-4 6
1988 Waterfield 4-8-12 6
1989 Ibn Bey 5-9-5 3
1990 Wajna 3-7-11 4
1991 Great Marquess 4-9-8 7
1992 Tyrone Bridge 6-9-6 7
1993 Brandon Prince 5-8-7 4
1994 Castle Courageous 7-9-5 7
1995 Saxon Maid 4-9-5 5
1996 Celeric 4-9-7 5
1997 Benatom 4-8-7 7

ECLIPSE STAKES
Sandown—1m 2f 7yds

1977 Artaius 3-8-8 10
1978 Gunner B 5-9-7 9
1979 Dickens Hill 3-8-8 7
1980 Ela-Mana-Mou 4-9-7 6
1981 Master Willie 4-9-7 7
1982 Kalaglow 4-9-7 9
1983 Solford 3-8-8 9
1984 Sadler's Wells 3-8-8 9
1985 Pebbles 4-9-4 4
1986 Dancing Brave 3-8-8 8
1987 Mtoto 4-9-7 8
1988 Mtoto 5-9-7 8

1989 Nashwan 3-8-8 6
1990 Elmaamul 3-8-10 7
1991 Environment Friend 3-8-10 7
1992 Kooyonga 4-9-4 12
1993 Opera House 5-9-7....................8
1994 Ezzoud 5-9-7 8
1995 Halling 4-9-7....................8
1996 Halling 5-9-7....................7
1997 Pilsudski 5-9-7....................5

OLD NEWTON CUP
Haydock—1m 3f 200yds

1977 Mint 3-7-7 11
1978 Move Off 5-9-4 12
1979 St Briavels 5-9-3 7
1980 Shady Nook 5-9-5....................10
1981 Dogberry 3-7-5 8
1982 Valentinian 4-10-3....................10
1983 Regal Steel 5-8-2 9
1984 Bishop's Ring 3-8-6 6
1985 Clanrallier 5-8-3 10
1986 Rakaposhi King 4-9-7....................10
1987 Pipsted 3-8-0....................9
1988 Roushayd 4-9-10....................9
1989 Nickle Plated 4-9-7....................16
1990 Hateel 4-9-6....................9
1991 Libk 3-8-11....................12
1992 Matador 5-9-2....................9
1993 Glide Path 4-8-2....................11
1994 Glide Path 5-8-10....................11
1995 Lombardic 4-8-12....................10
1996 Key To My Heart 6-10-0....................8
1997 Zaralaska 6-9-8....................16

LANCASHIRE OAKS (fillies and mares)
Before 1991 3-year-old fillies only
Haydock—1m 3f 200yds

1977 Busaca 8-11 5
1978 Princess Eboli 9-1 9
1979 Reprocolor 9-1....................5
1980 Vielle 8-11 6
1981 Rhein Bridge 8-11 7
1982 Sing Softly 8-11 8
1983 Give Thanks 9-1 13
1984 Sandy Island 8-11 9
1985 Graecia Magna 8-11....................8
1986 Park Express 8-11....................9
1987 Three Tails 9-1 6
1988 Andaleeb 8-9 8
1989 Roseate Tern 8-9 8
1990 Pharian 8-9....................4
1991 Patricia 3-8-4....................11
1992 Niodini 3-8-4....................11
1993 Rainbow Lake 3-8-4....................8
1994 State Crystal 3-8-4....................8
1995 Fanjica 3-8-4....................5
1996 Spout 4-9-6 10
1997 Squeak 3-8-4 8

CHERRY HINTON STAKES (2y)
Newmarket—6f

1977 Turkish Treasure 8-10....................9
1978 Devon Ditty 8-13....................13
1979 Mrs Penny 8-7 10
1980 Nasseem 8-10 11
1981 Travel On 8-10 10
1982 Crime of Passion 8-10....................8
1983 Chapel Cottage 8-10....................9
1984 Top Socialite 8-10....................8
1985 Storm Star 8-10....................12
1986 Forest Flower 9-0 10
1987 Diminuendo 8-9 9
1988 Kerrera 8-9 9
1989 Chimes of Freedom 8-9....................8
1990 Chicarica 8-12 8
1991 Musicale 8-9....................6
1992 Sayyedati 8-9....................7
1993 Lemon Souffle 8-9....................8
1994 Red Carnival 8-9 7
1995 Applaud 8-9....................8
1996 Dazzle 8-9....................9
1997 Asfurah 8-9....................12

BUNBURY HANDICAP
Newmarket—7f

1977 Kintore 5-8-0 8
1978 Greenhill God 4-8-5....................11
1979 Pipedreamer 4-9-3....................14
1980 Steeple Bell 4-7-9....................14
1981 Captain Nick 5-9-13 11
1982 Paterno 4-9-1....................14
1983 Mummy's Pleasure 4-9-3 19
1984 Mummy's Pleasure 5-8-12 17
1985 Tremblant 4-8-12....................18
1986 Patriach 4-9-1....................16
1987 Individualist 4-8-5 15
1988 Pinctada 6-8-3....................16
1989 Baldomero 4-7-7 18
1990 Fedoria 4-8-3 19
1991 Savoyard 3-9-0 17
1992 Consigliere 4-9-1 20
1993 En Attendant 5-9-4 27
1994 En Attendant 6-9-12....................20
1995 Cadeaux Tryst 3-9-1....................19
1996 Crumpton Hill 4-8-12....................16
1997 Tumbleweed Ridge 4-9-6 20

PRINCESS OF WALES'S STAKES
Newmarket—1m 4f

1977 Lord Helpus 4-9-2....................8
1978 Pollerton 4-9-2....................4
1979 Milford 3-8-2....................6
1980 Nicholas Bill 5-9-2....................9
1981 Light Cavalry 4-9-9....................8
1982 Height of Fashion 3-7-11....................4
1983 Quilted 3-8-0....................11
1984 Head for Heights 3-8-6....................9
1985 Petoski 3-8-0....................5
1986 Shardari 4-9-0....................6
1987 Celestial Storm 4-9-0 9
1988 Unfuwain 3-8-0....................5
1989 Carroll House 4-9-5....................5
1990 Sapience 4-9-0 7
1991 Rock Hopper 4-9-3 6

1992 Saddlers' Hall 4-9-5 4
1993 Desert Team 3-8-1 7
1994 Wagon Master 4-9-0 12
1995 Beauchamp Hero 5-9-5 9
1996 Posidonas 4-9-7 8
1997 Shantou 4-9-7 7

FALMOUTH STAKES (fillies)
Newmarket—1m

1977 River Dane 3-8-5 6
1978 Cistus 3-8-2 10
1979 Rose Above 4-8-10 7
1980 Stumped 3-7-12 9
1981 Star Pastures 3-8-3 10
1982 Chalon 3-8-11 7
1983 Royal Heroine 3-8-5 8
1984 Meis El-Reem 3-8-5 5
1985 Al Bahathri 3-8-11 9
1986 Sonic Lady 8-11 8
1987 Sonic Lady 4-9-10 4
1988 Inchmurrin 3-8-6 7
1989 Magic Gleam 3-8-6 6
1990 Chimes of Freedom 3-8-12 5
1991 Only Yours 3-8-6 6
1992 Gussy Marlowe 4-9-1 7
1993 Niche 3-8-6 11
1994 Lemon Souffle 3-8-6 6
1995 Caramba 3-8-6 5
1996 Sensation 3-8-6 9
1997 Ryafan 3-8-6 7

JULY STAKES (2y)
Newmarket—6f

1977 Royal Harmony 8-10 4
1978 Main Reef 8-13 6
1979 Final Straw 8-10 7
1980 Age Quod Agis 8-10 3
1981 End of the Line 8-10 11
1982 Horage 9-2 7
1983 Superlative 8-10 6
1984 Primo Dominie 9-1 7
1985 Green Desert 8-10 8
1986 Mansooj 8-10 8
1987 Sanquirico 8-10 7
1988 Always Valiant 8-10 4
1989 Rock City 9-1 4
1990 Mujtahid 8-10 4
1991 Showbrook 8-10 4
1992 Wharf 8-10 6
1993 First Trump 8-10 6
1994 Fallow 8-10 6
1995 Tagula 8-10 9
1996 Rich Ground 8-10 9
1997 Bold Fact 8-10 8

JULY CUP
Newmarket—6f

1977 Gentilhombre 4-9-6 8
1978 Solinus 3-8-11 14
1979 Thatching 4-9-6 11
1980 Moorestyle 3-8-11 14
1981 Marwell 3-8-8 14
1982 Sharpo 5-9-6 16
1983 Habibti 3-8-8 15
1984 Chief Singer 3-8-11 9
1985 Never So Bold 5-9-6 9
1986 Green Desert 3-8-11 5
1987 Ajdal 3-8-11 11
1988 Soviet Star 4-9-6 9
1989 Cadeaux Genereux 4-9-6 11
1990 Royal Academy 3-8-13 9
1991 Polish Patriot 3-8-13 8
1992 Mr Brooks 5-9-6 8
1993 Hamas 4-9-6 12
1994 Owington 3-8-13 9
1995 Lake Coniston 4-9-6 9
1996 Anabaa 4-9-5 10
1997 Compton Place 3-8-13 9

MAGNET CUP
York—1m 2f 85yds

1977 Air Trooper 4-9-6 8
1978 Town and Country 4-8-13 9
1979 Tesoro Mio 4-8-3 9
1980 Fine Sun 3-7-8 12
1981 Amyndas 3-8-5 11
1982 Buzzards Bay 4-9-8 6
1983 Bedtime 3-7-9 9
1984 Straight Man 3-8-11 9
1985 Chaumiere 4-9-7 12
1986 Chaumiere 5-9-5 11
1987 *Brave Dancer 3-8-8 ....
*Wolsey 3-8-6 9
1988 Bashful Boy 3-8-2 16
1989 Icona 3-9-8 10
1990 Eradicate 5-9-4 19
1991 Halkopous 5-7-3 12
1992 Mr Confusion 4-8-3 17
1993 Baron Ferdinand 3-8-9 13
1994 Cezanne 5-9-12 16
1995 Naked Welcome 3-8-4 16
1996 Wilcuma 5-9-2 17
1997 Pasternak 4-8-3 21

PRINCESS MARGARET STAKES (2y)
Ascot—6f

1977 Sarissa 9-1 7
1978 Devon Ditty 9-1 4
1979 Luck of the Draw 8-12 4
1980 Tolmi 8-12 7
1981 Circus Ring 8-12 9
1982 Royal Heroine 8-12 6
1983 Desirable 8-12 4
1984 Al Bahathri 8-12 9
1985 Kingscote 8-12 11
1986 Hiaam 8-8 6
1987 Bluebook 8-8 6
1988 Muhbubh 8-8 6
1989 Pharaoh's Delight 8-8 6
1990 Cloche d'Or 8-8 4
1991 Bezelle 8-8 10
1992 Marina Park 8-11 6
1993 A Smooth One 8-8 7

1994 Tajannub 8-8....8
1995 Blue Duster 9-0....7
1996 Seebe 8-9....8
1997 Embassy 8-9....7

BEESWING STAKES
Newcastle—7f

1977 In Haste 3-8-5....9
1978 John de Coombe 3-8-5....7
1979 Jeroboam 3-8-5....3
1980 Kampala 4-9-6....7
1981 Milk of the Barley 4-9-0....6
1982 Silly Steven 3-8-5....8
1983 Beaudelaire 3-8-5....7
1984 Major Don 4-9-3....7
1985 Sarab 4-9-6....7
1986 Hadeer 4-9-0....9
1987 Farajullah 4-9-1....8
1988 Salse 3-8-9....6
1989 Great Commotion 3-8-6....4
1990 Savahra Sound 5-9-6....6
1991 Bold Russian 4-9-0....7
1992 Casteddu 3-8-7....7
1993 Eurolink Thunder 3-8-7....9
1994 Gabr 4-9-0....10
1995 Shahid 3-8-7....7
1996 Iktamal 4-9-0....9
1997 Wizard King 6-9-4....8

STEWARDS' CUP
Goodwood—6f

1977 Calibina 5-8-5....24
1978 Ahonoora 3-8-0....23
1979 Standaan 3-7-10....16
1980 Repetitious 3-7-2....28
1981 Crews Hill 5-9-9....30
1982 Soba 3-8-4....30
1983 Autumn Sunset 3-8-2....23
1984 Petong 4-9-10....26
1985 Al Trui 5-8-1....28
1986 Green Ruby 5-8-12....24
1987 Madraco 4-7-2....30
1988 Rotherfield Greys 6-8-8....28
1989 Very Adjacent 4-7-4....22
1990 Knight of Mercy 4-9-0....30
1991 Notley 4-8-7....29
1992 Lochsong 4-8-0....30
1993 King's Signet 4-9-10....29
1994 For The Present 4-8-3....26
1995 Shikari's Son 8-8-13....27
1996 Coastal Bluff 4-9-5....30
1997 Danetime 3-8-10....30

GORDON STAKES (3y)
Goodwood—1m 4f

1977 Pollerton 8-10....4
1978 Sexton Blake 8-10....5
1979 More Light 8-10....6
1980 Prince Bee 8-10....6
1981 Bustomi 9-2....5
1982 Electric 8-13....6
1983 John French 8-10....6
1984 Commanche Run 8-10....8
1985 Kazaroun 8-10....5
1986 Allez Milord 8-10....5
1987 Love the Groom 9-2....6
1988 Minster Son 8-10....5
1989 Warrshan 8-10....4
1990 Karinga Bay 8-10....6
1991 Stylish Senor 8-10....3
1992 Bonny Scot 8-10....6
1993 Right Win 8-10....8
1994 Broadway Flyer 8-13....9
1995 Presenting 8-10....7
1996 St Mawes 8-10....12
1997 Stowaway 8-10....10

OAK TREE STAKES
Goodwood—7f

1980 Trevita 3-8-5....10
1981 Star Pastures 3-8-11....6
1982 Chalon 3-9-0....5
1983 Fenny Rough 3-8-7....6
1984 Brocade 3-8-5....10
1985 Ever Genial 3-8-5....6
1986 Royal Loft 3-8-7....12
1987 Gayane 3-8-10....6
1988 Ohsomellow 3-8-10....7
1989 Kerita 3-8-7....6
1990 Alidiva 3-8-9....9
1991 Himiko 3-8-7....8
1992 Storm Dove 3-8-7....9
1993 Moon Over Miami 3-8-7....11
1994 Blue Siren 3-8-10....10
1995 Brief Glimpse 3-8-7....10
1996 Thrilling Day 3-8-13....14
1997 Dazzle 3-8-7....8

SUSSEX STAKES
Goodwood—1m

1977 Artaius 3-8-10....11
1978 Jaazeiro 3-8-10....6
1979 Kris 3-8-10....7
1980 Posse 3-8-10....9
1981 Kings Lake 3-8-10....9
1982 On the House 3-8-7....13
1983 Noalcoholic 6-9-7....11
1984 Chief Singer 3-8-10....5
1985 Rousillon 4-9-7....10
1986 Sonic Lady 3-8-7....5
1987 Soviet Star 3-8-10....7
1988 Warning 3-8-10....9
1989 Zilzal 3-8-10....8
1990 Distant Relative 4-9-7....7
1991 Second Set 3-8-13....8
1992 Marling 3-8-10....8
1993 Bigstone 3-8-13....10
1994 Distant View 3-8-13....9
1995 Sayyedati 5-9-4....6
1996 First Island 4-9-7....10
1997 Ali-Royal 4-9-7....9

RICHMOND STAKES (2y)
Goodwood—6f

1977 Persian Bold 8-11 5
1978 Young Generation 8-11 5
1979 Castle Green 8-11 5
1980 Another Realm 8-11 10
1981 Tender King 8-11 7
1982 Gallant Special 8-11 4
1983 Godstone 8-11 9
1984 Primo Dominie 8-11 6
1985 Nomination 8-11 10
1986 Rich Charlie 8-11 8
1987 Warning 8-11 7
1988 Heart of Arabia 9-0 6
1989 Contract Law 8-11 5
1990 Mac's Imp 8-11 7
1991 Dilum 8-11 4
1992 Son Pardo 8-11 6
1993 First Trump 8-11 5
1994 Sri Pekan 8-11 6
1995 Polaris Flight 8-11 6
1996 Easycall 8-11 7
1997 Daggers Drawn 8-11 6

KING GEORGE STAKES
Goodwood—5f

1977 Scarcely Blessed 3-8-2 9
1978 Music Maestro 3-9-1 7
1979 Ahonoora 4-9-3 7
1980 Valeriga 4-9-6 9
1981 King of Spain 5-9-8 8
1982 Tina's Pet 4-9-0 12
1983 Soba 4-9-0 14
1984 Anita's Prince 3-8-8 13
1985 Primo Dominie 3-8-13 11
1986 Double Schwartz 5-9-5 14
1987 Singing Steven 3-8-13 9
1988 Silver Fling 3-8-5 13
1989 Statoblest 3-8-8 13
1990 Argentum 3-9-0 14
1991 Title Roll 3-8-7 15
1992 Freddie Lloyd 3-9-0 11
1993 Lochsong 5-8-11 11
1994 Lochsong 6-9-7 15
1995 Hever Golf Rose 4-9-5 11
1996 Rambling Bear 3-8-10 14
1997 Averti 6-9-0 15

SCHWEPPES HANDICAP
Goodwood—1m

1987 Waajib 4-9-10 20
1988 Strike Force 3-8-6 21
1989 Safawan 3-8-0 14
1990 March Bird 5-7-8 16
1991 Sky Cloud 5-8-7 15
1992 Little Bean 3-8-2 21
1993 Philidor 4-8-4 19
1994 Fraam 5-9-9 13
1995 Khayrapour 5-7-13 21
1996 Moscow Mist 5-7-10 18
1997 Fly to The Stars 3-9-6 20

GOODWOOD CUP
Goodwood—2m

1977 Grey Baron 4-9-3 8
1978 Tug of War 5-9-0 5
1979 Le Moss 4-9-7 5
1980 Le Moss 5-9-7 5
1981 Ardross 5-9-7 6
1982 Heighlin 6-9-0 8
1983 Little Wolf 5-9-7 7
1984 Gildoran 4-9-7 4
1985 Valuable Witness 5-9-0 7
1986 Longboat 5-9-7 5
1987 Sergeyevich 3-7-10 5
1988 Sadeem 5-9-7 6
1989 Mazzacano 4-9-0 5
1990 Lucky Moon 3-7-10 6
1991 Further Flight 5-9-0 10
1992 Further Flight 6-9-5 11
1993 Sonus 4-9-3 9
1994 Tioman Island 4-9-5 15
1995 Double Trigger 4-9-5 9
1996 Grey Shot 4-9-0 7
1997 Double Trigger 6-9-0 10

GLOBETROTTER HANDICAP (3y)
(Formerly Extel Handicap and News of the World Handicap before 1970)
Goodwood—1m 2f

1977 Ad Lib Ra 9-0 14
1978 Crimson Beau 8-2 7
1979 Lindoro 9-0 8
1980 Karamita 7-7 10
1981 Indian Trail 8-3 9
1982 Busaco 9-1 10
1983 Millfontaine 8-13 12
1984 Free Guest 8-6 15
1985 Fish 'N' Chips 8-3 13
1986 Chinoiserie 8-11 13
1987 Broken Hearted 9-3 13
1988 Kazaviyna 7-10 14
1989 Biennial 9-2 8
1990 Kawtuban 9-2 8
1991 Green Danube 8-2 16
1992 Party Cited 9-4 18
1993 Western Cape 8-12 18
1994 Frustration 8-6 10
1995 Jalfrezi 7-10 14
1996 Fahim 8-13 14
1997 Future Perfect 8-9 18

SCHRODERS GLORIOUS STAKES
Goodwood—1m 4f

1979 Bohemian Grove 3-8-3 5
1980 Water Mill 3-8-2 7
1981 Capstan 3-7-1 5
1982 Capstan 4-9-1 4
1983 Seymour Hicks 3-8-5 7
1984 Longboat 3-8-2 6
1985 Shernazar 4-9-1 9
1986 Nisnas 3-8-2 8
1987 Knockando 3-8-5 9

1988 Maksud 3-8-2 4
1989 Knoosh 3-8-5 3
1990 Hajade 3-8-6 4
1991 Fly Away Soon 3-8-3 5
1992 Spinning 5-9-2 6
1993 Usaidit 4-8-7 12
1994 Duke of Eurolink 5-8-8 8
1995 Midnight Legend 4-9-7 7
1996 Salmon Ladder 4-9-5 9
1997 Bahamian Sunshine 6-8-7 7

MOLECOMB STAKES (2y)

Goodwood—5f

1977 Hatta 8-10 7
1978 Greenland Park 9-4 6
1979 Keep Off 8-10 6
1980 Marwell 8-10 7
1981 Prowess Prince 8-10 6
1982 Kafu 8-10 4
1983 Precocious 9-0 7
1984 Absent Chimes 8-10 8
1985 Hotbee 8-7 9
1986 Gemini Fire 8-12 6
1987 Classic Ruler 8-12 7
1988 Almost Blue 8-12 13
1989 Haunting Beauty 8-7 10
1990 Poets Cove 8-12 4
1991 Sahara Star 8-7 7
1992 Millyant 8-7 11
1993 Risky 8-12 5
1994 Hoh Magic 8-10 7
1995 Almaty 9-3 7
1996 Carmine Lake 8-7 7
1997 Lady Alexander 8-12 13

NASSAU STAKES (fillies)

Goodwood—1m 2f

1977 Triple First 3-8-5 8
1978 Cistus 3-8-5 7
1979 Connaught Bridge 3-8-5 10
1980 Vielle 3-8-5 7
1981 Go Leasing 3-8-8 11
1982 Dancing Rocks 3-8-5 11
1983 Acclimatise 3-8-5 6
1984 Optimistic Lass 3-8-8 5
1985 Free Guest 4-9-8 11
1986 Park Express 3-8-8 7
1987 Nom de Plume 3-8-7 5
1988 Ela Romara 3-8-6 7
1989 Mamaluna 3-8-6 5
1990 Kartajana 3-8-6 6
1991 Ruby Tiger 4-9-4 6
1992 Ruby Tiger 5-9-1 7
1993 Lyphard's Delta 3-8-6 9
1994 Hawajiss 3-8-6 9
1995 Caramba 3-8-9 6
1996 Last Second 3-8-6 8
1997 Ryafan 3-8-9 7

HUNGERFORD STAKES

Newbury—7f 64yds

1977 He Loves Me 3-8-11 10
1978 Tannenberg 3-8-6 10
1979 Skyliner 4-9-0 13
1980 Kampala 4-9-0 8
1981 Dalsaan 4-9-0 10
1982 Pas de Seul 3-8-9 10
1983 Salieri 3-8-11 10
1984 Prego 4-9-0 8
1985 Ever Genial 3-8-6 12
1986 Hadeer 4-9-3 11
1987 Abuzz 3-8-3 8
1988 Salse 3-8-9 11
1989 Distant Relative 3-8-11 7
1990 Norwich 3-8-9 7
1991 Only Yours 3-8-11 9
1992 Mojave 3-8-8 10
1993 Inchinor 3-8-11 13
1994 *Young Ern 4-9-3
*Pollen Count 5-9-0 12
1995 Harayir 3-8-13 9
1996 Bin Rosie 4-9-0 8
1997 Decorated Hero 5-9-0 10

GEOFFREY FREER STAKES

Newbury—1m 5f 61yds

1977 Valinsky 3-8-4 5
1978 Ile de Bourbon 3-8-9 7
1979 Niniski 3-8-1 7
1980 Nicholas Bill 5-9-5 5
1981 Ardross 5-9-8 4
1982 Ardross 6-9-8 4
1983 Khairpour 4-9-0 7
1984 Baynoun 3-8-5 5
1985 Shernazar 4-9-0 5
1986 Bakharoff 3-8-3 6
1987 Moon Madness 4-9-8 4
1988 Top Class 3-8-3 6
1989 Ibn Bey 5-9-8 6
1990 Charmer 5-9-2 5
1991 Drum Taps 5-9-5 7
1992 Shambo 5-9-3 4
1993 Azzilfi 3-8-5 5
1994 Red Route 3-8-5 6
1995 Presenting 3-8-5 6
1996 Phantom Gold 4-9-3 7
1997 Dushyantor 4-9-6 4

SOLARIO STAKES (2y)

Sandown—7f 16yds

1977 Bolak 8-11 9
1978 Lyphard's Wish 9-1 6
1979 Rankin 9-4 4
1980 To-Agori-Mou 9-0 4
1981 No race
1982 The Fort 9-0 6
1983 Falstaff 9-0 4
1984 Oh So Sharp 8-8 9
1985 Bold Arrangement 9-0 5
1986 Shining Water 8-8 11
1987 Sanquirico 9-0 4

1988 High Estate 9-0 6
1989 Be My Chief 9-0 3
1990 Radwell 8-11 9
1991 Chicmond 8-11 7
1992 White Crown 8-11 9
1993 Island Magic 8-11 3
1994 Lovely Millie 8-9 7
1995 Alhaarth 9-2 4
1996 Brave Act 8-11 7
1997 Little Indian 8-11 5

JUDDMONTE INTERNATIONAL STAKES

(Benson & Hedges Gold Cup before 1986)
York—1m 2f 85yds

1977 Relkino 4-9-6 8
1978 Hawaiian Sound 3-8-10 10
1979 Troy 3-8-10 10
1980 Master Willie 3-8-10 12
1981 Beldale Flutter 3-8-10 9
1982 Assert 3-8-10 7
1983 Caerleon 3-8-10 9
1984 Cormorant Wood 4-9-3 9
1985 Commanche Run 4-9-6 6
1986 Shardari 4-9-6 12
1987 Triptych 5-9-3 10
1988 Shady Heights 4-9-6 6
1989 Ile De Chypre 4-9-6 7
1990 In The Groove 3-8-9 9
1991 Terimon 5-9-6 6
1992 Rodrigo de Triano 3-8-12 12
1993 Ezzoud 4-9-6 11
1994 Ezzoud 5-9-6 8
1995 Halling 4-9-6 6
1996 Halling 5-9-5 6
1997 Singspiel 5-9-5 4

GREAT VOLTIGEUR STAKES (3y)

York—1m 3f 195yds

1977 Alleged 8-11 7
1978 Whitstead 8-7 8
1979 Noble Saint 8-7 5
1980 Prince Bee 8-7 5
1981 Glint of Gold 9-0 6
1982 Electric 8-7 7
1983 Seymour Hicks 8-7 5
1984 Rainbow Quest 8-7 7
1985 Damister 8-11 4
1986 Nisnas 8-7 7
1987 Reference Point 9-0 3
1988 Sheriff's Star 8-12 4
1989 Zalazl 8-9 3
1990 Belmez 9-0 5
1991 Corrupt 8-9 7
1992 Bonny Scot 8-9 6
1993 Bob's Return 8-9 9
1994 Sacrament 8-9 7
1995 Pentire 8-12 4
1996 Dushyantor 8-9 6
1997 Stowaway 8-9 5

YORKSHIRE OAKS (fillies and mares)

Before 1991 3-year-old fillies only
York—1m 3f 195yds

1977 Busaca 9-0 8
1978 Fair Salinia 9-0 10
1979 Connaught Bridge 9-0 5
1980 Shoot a Line 9-0 7
1981 Condessa 9-0 11
1982 Awaasif 9-0 7
1983 Sun Princess 9-0 6
1984 Circus Plume 9-0 5
1985 Sally Brown 9-0 7
1986 Untold 9-0 11
1987 Bint Pasha 9-0 9
1988 Diminuendo 9-0 6
1989 Roseate Tern 9-0 5
1990 Hellenic 9-0 6
1991 Magnificent Star 3-8-11 7
1992 User Friendly 3-8-11 8
1993 Only Royale 4-9-7 8
1994 Only Royale 5-9-7 7
1995 Pure Grain 3-8-8 8
1996 Key Change 3-8-8 9
1997 My Emma 4-9-4 8

EBOR HANDICAP

York—1m 5f 194yds

1977 Move Off 4-8-1 14
1978 Totowah 4-8-1 22
1979 Sea Pigeon 9-10-0 17
1980 Shaftesbury 4-8-5 16
1981 Protection Racket 3-8-1 22
1982 Another Sam 5-9-2 15
1983 Jupiter Island 4-9-0 16
1984 Crazy 3-8-13 14
1985 Western Dancer 4-8-6 19
1986 Primary 3-8-7 22
1987 Daarkom 4-9-3 15
1988 Kneller 3-8-1 21
1989 Sapience 3-8-4 18
1990 Further Flight 4-8-8 22
1991 Deposki 5-7-3 22
1992 Quick Ransom 4-8-3 22
1993 Sarawat 5-8-2 21
1994 Hasten To Add 4-9-3 21
1995 Sanmartino 3-7-11 21
1996 Clerkenwell 3-7-11 21
1997 Far Ahead 5-8-0 21

GIMCRACK STAKES (2y)

York—6f

1977 Tumbledownwind 9-0 5
1978 Stanford 9-0 11
1979 Sonnen Gold 9-0 7
1980 Bel Bolide 9-0 9
1981 Full Extent 9-0 8
1982 Horage 9-0 7
1983 Precocious 9-0 6
1984 Doulab 9-0 8
1985 Stalker 9-0 6
1986 Wiganthorpe 9-0 11
1987 Reprimand 9-0 6

1988 Sharp N' Early 9-0 8
1989 Rock City 9-3 5
1990 Mujtahid 9-3 5
1991 River Falls 9-0 5
1992 Splendent 9-0 8
1993 Turtle Island 9-5 8
1994 Chilly Billy 9-0 11
1995 Royal Applause 9-0 5
1996 Abou Zouz 8-11 9
1997 Carrowkeel 8-11 7

NUNTHORPE STAKES

York—5f

1977 Haveroid 3-9-2 8
1978 Solinus 3-9-2 9
1979 Ahonoora 4-9-6 9
1980 Sharpo 3-9-2 11
1981 Sharpo 4-9-0 9
1982 Sharpo 5-9-0 11
1983 Habibti 3-8-7 10
1984 Committed 4-8-11 8
1985 Never So Bold 5-9-0 7
1986 Last Tycoon 3-9-2 8
1987 Ajdal 3-9-2 11
1988 Handsome Sailor 5-9-6 12
1989 Cadeaux Genereux 4-9-6 11
1990 Dayjur 3-9-3 9
1991 Sheikh Albadou 3-9-3 9
1992 Lyric Fantasy 2-7-8 11
1993 Lochsong 5-9-3 11
1994 Piccolo 3-9-3 10
1995 So Factual 5-9-6 8
1996 Pivotal 3-9-7 8
1997 *Ya Malak 6-9-9
*Coastal Bluff 5-9-9 15

BRADFORD AND BINGLEY HANDICAP

(Rose of York Handicap before 1983)
York—7f 202yds

1977 Chukaroo 5-7-11 10
1978 Petronisi 4-8-1 15
1979 Piaffer 4-8-6 9
1980 Miner's Lamp 3-8-7 12
1981 Silver Season 3-9-0 9
1982 Indian Trail 4-8-8 11
1983 Mauritzfontein 4-7-11 14
1984 King of Clubs 3-8-12 17
1985 Lucky Ring 3-8-3 14
1986 Digger's Rest 3-9-4 14
1987 Prince Rupert 3-8-8 12
1988 Kingsfold Flame 5-8-5 15
1989 Known Ranger 3-9-4 16
1990 You Missed Me 4-9-2 17
1991 Pontenuovo 6-9-9 16
1992 Doulab's Image 5-8-11 22
1993 Dawning Street 5-8-13 15
1994 Lap of Luxury 5-8-7 13
1995 Cap Juluca 3-8-11 15
1996 Concer Un 4-8-10 18
1997 Concer Un 5-8-7 14

LOWTHER STAKES (2y fillies)

York—6f

1977 Enstone Spark 8-11 9
1978 Devon Ditty 9-0 11
1979 Mrs Penny 9-0 8
1980 Kittyhawk 8-8 5
1981 Circus Ring 8-11 8
1982 Habibti 8-11 8
1983 Prickle 8-11 9
1984 Al Bahathri 8-11 10
1985 Kingscote 8-11 7
1986 Polonia 9-0 9
1987 Ela Romara 8-11 5
1988 Miss Demure 8-11 9
1989 Dead Certain 9-0 6
1990 Only Yours 8-11 9
1991 Culture Vulture 8-11 4
1992 Niche 9-0 6
1993 Velvet Moon 8-11 9
1994 Harayir 8-11 6
1995 Dance Sequence 8-11 9
1996 Bianca Nera 8-11 9
1997 Cape Verdi 8-11 9

PRESTIGE STAKES (2y)

(Formerly Waterford Candelabra Stakes)
Goodwood—7f

1981 Stratospheric 8-6 6
1982 Flamenco 8-9 9
1983 Shoot Clear 8-9 8
1984 Bella Colora 8-6 6
1985 Asteroid Field 8-6 6
1986 Invited Guest 8-7 6
1987 Obeah 8-9 6
1988 Life at the Top 8-12 7
1989 Moon Cactus 8-12 7
1990 Jaffa Line 8-9 5
1991 Musicale 9-0 5
1992 Love of Silver 8-9 7
1993 Glatisant 8-9 6
1994 Pure Grain 8-9 9
1995 Bint Shadayid 8-9 6
1996 Red Camellia 8-12 5
1997 Midnight Line 8-9 6

CELEBRATION MILE

(Formerly Waterford Crystal Mile)
Goodwood—1m

1977 Be My Guest 3-8-7 6
1978 Captain James 4-8-13 5
1979 Kris 3-8-12 8
1980 Known Fact 3-8-12 6
1981 To-Agori-Mou 3-8-12 6
1982 Sandhurst Prince 3-8-5 8
1983 Montekin 4-8-13 6
1984 Rousillon 3-8-6 5
1985 Abandoned
1986 Then Again 3-8-7 8
1987 Milligram 3-8-7 4

1988 Prince Rupert 4-9-3 6
1989 Distant Relative 3-8-12 5
1990 Shavian 3-9-0 5
1991 Bold Russian 4-9-0 5
1992 Selkirk 4-9-3 7
1993 Swing Low 4-9-3 6
1994 Mehthaaf 3-8-11 6
1995 Harayir 3-8-12 6
1996 Mark of Esteem 3-9-1 7
1997 Among Men 3-8-9 4

SPRINT CUP
Haydock—6f

1977 Boldboy 7-9-8 7
1978 Absalom 3-9-6 14
1979 Double Form 4-9-8 7
1980 Moorestyle 3-8-12 8
1981 Runnett 4-9-3 6
1982 Indian King 4-9-3 9
1983 Habibti 3-8-9 6
1984 Petong 4-9-3 9
1985 Orojoya 3-8-12 8
1986 Green Desert 3-8-12 8
1987 Ajdal 3-9-0 8
1988 Dowsing 4-9-2 10
1989 Danehill 3-9-5 9
1990 Dayjur 3-9-6 9
1991 Polar Falcon 4-9-9 6
1992 Sheikh Albadou 4-9-9 8
1993 Wolfhound 4-9-9 7
1994 Lavinia Fontana 5-8-9 8
1995 Cherokee Rose 4-8-11 6
1996 Iktamal 4-9-0 11
1997 Royal Applause 4-9-0 9

SEPTEMBER STAKES
Kempton—1m 3f 30yds

1979 Cracaval 3-8-10 7
1980 More Light 4-9-2 7
1981 Kind of Hush 3-8-4 11
1982 Critique 4-9-2 7
1983 Lyphard's Special 3-8-4 6
1984 Bedtime 4-9-0 8
1985 Shernazar 4-9-2 5
1986 Dihistan 4-9-2 7
1987 Knockando 3-8-4 8
1988 Percy's Lass 4-8-11 8
1989 Assatis 4-9-5 5
1990 Lord of the Field 3-8-6 6
1991 Young Buster 3-8-6 5
1992 Jeune 3-8-6 5
1993 Spartan Shareef 4-9-3 9
1994 Wagon Master 4-9-5 5
1995 Burooj 5-9-0 7
1996 Sacrament 5-9-5 7
1997 Maylane 3-8-5 (Run at Epsom) 6

MAY HILL STAKES (2y)
Doncaster—1m

1981 Height of Fashion 8-9 4
1982 Bright Crocus 8-7 8
1983 Satinette 8-6 9
1984 Ever Genial 8-6 7
1985 Midway Lady 8-6 6
1986 Laluche 8-9 10
1987 Intimate Guest 8-8 6
1988 Tessla 8-8 11
1989 Rafha 8-8 5
1990 Majmu 8-8 7
1991 Midnight Air 8-8 13
1992 Marillette 8-8 12
1993 Hawajiss 8-8 5
1994 Mamlakah 8-8 11
1995 Solar Crystal 8-9 11
1996 Reams of Verse 8-9 11
1997 Midnight Line 9-0 9

PORTLAND HANDICAP
Doncaster—5f 140yds

1977 Jon George 3-7-12 12
1978 Goldhills Pride 4-8-10 13
1979 Oh Simmie 4-7-0 21
1980 Swelter 4-8-2 20
1981 Touch Boy 5-8-11 21
1982 Vorvados 5-8-13 14
1983 Out of Hand 4-7-3 15
1984 Dawn's Delight 6-7-8 22
1985 Lochtillum 6-8-1 17
1986 Felipe Toro 3-8-2 23
1987 Dawn's Delight 9-8-13 23
1988 Roman Prose 3-9-3 22
1989 Craft Express 3-8-9 22
1990 Love Legend 5-8-7 21
1991 Sarcita 3-8-6 21
1992 Lochsong 4-8-12 22
1993 Amron 6-9-0 18
1994 Hello Mister 3-8-10 22
1995 Hello Mister 4-8-7 22
1996 Musical Season 4-8-5 21
1997 Dashing Blue 4-9-12 22

PARK HILL STAKES (fillies and mares)
Before 1991 3-year-old fillies only
Doncaster—1m 6f 132yds

1977 Royal Hive 9-0 3
1978 Idle Waters 9-0 10
1979 Quay Line 9-0 5
1980 Shoot a Line 9-0 6
1981 Alma Ata 9-0 13
1982 Swiftfoot 9-0 6
1983 High Hawk 9-0 7
1984 Borushka 9-0 13
1985 I Want To Be 9-0 7
1986 Rejuvenate 8-9 12
1987 Trampship 8-9 5
1988 Casey 8-9 9
1989 Lucky Song 8-10 4
1990 Madame Dubois 8-9 8
1991 Patricia 3-8-8 11
1992 Niodini 3-8-5 12
1993 Anna of Saxony 4-9-3 9
1994 Coigach 3-8-5 8
1995 Noble Rose 4-9-3 8
1996 Eva Luna 4-9-3 6
1997 Book at Bedtime 3-8-5 7

BRITAIN'S FASTEST RAILWAY PARK STAKES

(formerly Kiveton Park Stakes)
Doncaster—1m

1978 Green Girl 3-8-4 12
1979 Tap on Wood 3-9-3 7
1980 Known Fact 3-9-3 4
1981 Kittyhawk 3-8-5 6
1982 The Quiet Bidder 4-9-10 9
1983 Annie Edge 3-8-4 8
1984 Sarab 3-8-13 10
1985 Lucky Ring 3-8-13 8
1986 Hadeer 4-9-4 12
1987 Guest Performer 3-8-4 12
1988 Salse 3-8-11 6
1989 Gold Seam 3-8-7 6
1990 Green Line Express 4-9-0 10
1991 Bog Trotter 3-9-0 12
1992 Pursuit of Love 3-9-3 10
1993 Swing Low 4-9-7 6
1994 Soviet Line 4-9-0 9
1995 Bishop of Cashel 3-8-9 8
1996 Bishop of Cashel 4-9-4 8
1997 Almushtarak 4-9-0 8

DONCASTER CUP

Doncaster—2m 2f

1977 Shangamuzo 4-8-12 5
1978 Buckskin 5-9-2 6
1979 Le Moss 4-9-2 5
1980 Le Moss 5-9-2 5
1981 Protection Racket 3-7-6 4
1982 Ardross 6-9-2 8
1983 Karadar 5-8-5 8
1984 Wagoner 4-8-5 4
1985 Spicy Story 4-8-9 8
1986 Longboat 5-9-6 4
1987 Buckley 4-8-13 8
1988 Kneller 3-8-4 4
1989 Weld 3-8-0 3
1990 Al Maheb 4-9-5 10
1991 Great Marquess 4-9-3 8
1992 Further Flight 6-9-3 5
1993 Assessor 4-9-7 5
1994 Arcadian Heights 6-9-7 9
1995 Double Trigger 4-9-7 6
1996 Double Trigger 5-9-7 6
1997 Canon Can 4-9-0 5

CHAMPAGNE STAKES (2y)

Doncaster—7f

1977 Sexton Blake 9-0 6
1978 R. B. Chesne 9-0 7
1979 Final Straw 9-0 9
1980 Gielgud 9-0 10
1981 Achieved 9-0 8
1982 Gorytus 9-0 5
1983 Lear Fan 9-0 4
1984 Young Runaway 9-0 6
1985 Sure Blade 9-0 5
1986 Don't Forget Me 9-0 9
1987 Warning 9-0 4
1988 Prince of Dance 8-11 7
1989 Abandoned
1990 Bog Trotter 8-11 5
1991 Rodrigo de Triano 8-11 5
1992 Petardia 9-0 9
1993 Unblest 8-11 4
1994 Sri Pekan 9-0 7
1995 Alhaarth 9-0 3
1996 Bahhare 8-10 4
1997 Daggers Drawn 9-0 5

FLYING CHILDERS STAKES (2y)

(Norfolk Stakes before 1973)
Doncaster—5f

1977 Music Maestro 9-0 8
1978 Devon Ditty 8-11 7
1979 Abeer 8-11 6
1980 Marwell 8-11 6
1981 Peterhof 9-0 7
1982 Kafu 9-0 5
1983 Superlative 9-0 10
1984 Prince Sabo 9-0 6
1985 Green Desert 9-0 8
1986 Sizzling Melody 9-0 6
1987 Gallic League 8-11 7
1988 Shuttlecock Corner 8-11 8
1989 Abandoned
1990 Distinctly North 8-11 6
1991 Paris House 8-11 5
1992 Poker Chip 8-6 7
1993 Imperial Bailiwick 8-6 8
1994 Raah Algharb 8-11 8
1995 Cayman Kai 8-12 8
1996 Easycall 9-3 7
1997 Land of Dreams 8-7 7

AYR GOLD CUP

Ayr—6f

1977 Jon George 3-8-4 25
1978 Vaigly Great 3-9-6 24
1979 Primula Boy 4-7-7 22
1980 Sparkling Boy 3-9-2 24
1981 First Movement 3-7-10 21
1982 Famous Star 3-7-7 14
1983 Polly's Brother 5-8-3 28
1984 Able Albert 4-8-6 29
1985 Camps Heath 4-7-9 25
1986 Green Ruby 5-8-11 29
1987 Not So Silly 3-7-10 29
1988 So Careful 5-7-7 29
1989 Joveworth 6-8-0 29
1990 Final Shot 3-8-2 29
1991 Sarcita 3-8-10 28
1992 Lochsong 4-9-0 28
1993 Hard To Figure 7-9-6 29
1994 Daring Destiny 3-8-0 29
1995 Royale Figurine 4-8-9 29
1996 Coastal Bluff 4-9-10 28
1997 Wildwood Flower 4-9-3 29

SELECT STAKES
(Formerly Valdoe Stakes)
Goodwood—1m 2f

Year	Winner	Runners
1977	Balmerino 5-9-9	9
1978	Gunner B 5-9-9	3
1979	Bolide (at Sandown) 3-7-13	6
1980	Welsh Chanter 4-9-3	6
1981	Prince Bee 4-9-9	4
1982	Peacetime 3-8-10	6
1983	Morcon 3-8-7	6
1984	Bob Back 3-8-5	5
1985	Iroko 3-8-4	8
1986	Dancing Brave 3-8-13	6
1987	Most Welcome 3-8-6	6
1988	Mtoto 5-9-9	5
1989	Legal Case 3-8-6	5
1990	Missionary Ridge 3-8-12	5
1991	Filia Ardross 5-8-11	6
1992	Knifebox 4-9-0	10
1993	Knifebox 5-9-3	6
1994	Alderbrook 5-9-0	7
1995	Triarius 5-9-0	6
1996	Singspiel 4-9-3	4
1997	Fahris 3-8-7	5

COURAGE HANDICAP
(Peter Hastings Handicap before 1985)
Newbury—1m 2f 6yds

Year	Winner	Runners
1977	April 3-8-3	11
1978	Pam's Gleam 5-8-0	8
1979	Effulgence 4-9-4	7
1980	Etching 3-8-5	9
1981	Atlantic Boy 4-9-4	8
1982	Oratavo 4-7-13	13
1983	Mauritzfontein 4-8-2	9
1984	Miss Saint-Cloud 3-8-8	7
1985	Leading Star 3-8-13	15
1986	Power Bender 4-8-1	13
1987	Shabib 3-8-4	9
1988	Ile de Chypre 3-9-3	16
1989	Monastery 3-8-4	16
1990	Lord of Tusmore 3-8-2	10
1991	Palatial Style 4-9-7	11
1992	Montpelier Boy 4-8-0	14
1993	Lindon Lime 3-8-5	14
1994	Green Crusader 3-8-1	8
1995	Kutta 3-9-5	20
1996	Game Ploy 4-8-5	17
1997	Sharp Consul 5-8-7	15

MILL REEF STAKES (2y)
Newbury—6f 8yds

Year	Winner	Runners
1977	Formidable 8-11	6
1978	King of Spain 8-11	8
1979	Lord Seymour 8-11	7
1980	Sweet Monday 8-11	7
1981	Hays 8-11	8
1982	Salieri 8-11	5
1983	Vacarme 8-11	7
1984	Local Suitor 8-11	12
1985	Luqman 8-11	9
1986	Forest Flower 8-8	9
1987	Magic of Life 8-6	5
1988	Russian Bond 8-11	4
1989	Welney 8-11	7
1990	Time Gentlemen 8-11	7
1991	Showbrook 9-1	5
1992	Forest Wind 8-11	7
1993	Polish Laughter 8-11	5
1994	Princely Hush 8-11	9
1995	Kahir Almaydan 8-12	6
1996	Indian Rocket 8-12	10
1997	Arkadian Hero 8-12	7

AUTUMN CUP (Handicap)
Newbury—1m 5f 61yds

Year	Winner	Runners
1977	Nearly a Hand 3-8-4	12
1978	Piccadilly Line 5-8-12	8
1979	Greatham House 3-9-1	13
1980	Castle Keep 3-9-1	10
1981	Telsmoss 5-8-4	10
1982	Fitzpatrick 3-8-6	14
1983	Jupiter Island 4-9-8	16
1984	First Bout 3-7-7	13
1985	Eastern Mystic 3-9-4	16
1986	Broken Wave 3-8-3	13
1987	Aim To Please 3-8-2	14
1988	Green Adventure 3-9-10	17
1989	Braashee 3-9-5	16
1990	First Victory 4-9-6	12
1991	Talos 3-8-8	14
1992	Castoret 6-7-13	18
1993	Castoret 7-9-12	20
1994	Warm Spell 4-8-5	16
1995	Whitechapel 7-9-0	23
1996	Kutta 4-10-0	12
1997	Darapour 3-8-11	13

CUMBERLAND LODGE STAKES
Ascot—1m 4f

Year	Winner	Runners
1977	Orange Bay 5-9-7	6
1978	Fordham 3-8-2	5
1979	Main Reef 3-8-5	6
1980	Fingal's Cave 3-8-3	5
1981	Critique 3-8-5	8
1982	Lafontaine 5-9-0	7
1983	Band 3-8-5	8
1984	Bedtime 4-9-3	7
1985	Shardari 3-8-6	5
1986	Kazaroun 4-9-3	4
1987	Moon Madness 4-9-7	5
1988	Assatis 3-8-5	6
1989	Tralos 4-9-0	4
1990	Ile de Nisky 4-9-0	7
1991	Drum Taps 5-9-5	5
1992	Opera House 4-9-5	5
1993	Prince of Andros 3-8-6	6
1994	Wagon Master 4-9-5	6
1995	Riyadian 3-8-6	8
1996	Wall Street 3-8-6	7
1997	Kingfisher Mill 3-8-11	8

THE FILLIES MILE (2y fillies)

Ascot—1m

1977 Cherry Hinton 9-1 8
1978 Formulate 9-1 9
1979 Quick as Lightning 8-12 9
1980 Leap Lively 8-12 7
1981 Height of Fashion 9-2 8
1982 Acclimatise 8-9 8
1983 Nepula 8-9 8
1984 Oh So Sharp 8-10 8
1985 Untold 8-7 9
1986 Invited Guest 9-0 12
1987 Diminuendo 8-13 7
1988 Tessla 8-13 8
1989 Silk Slippers 8-10 8
1990 Shamshir 8-10 12
1991 Culture Vulture 8-10 7
1992 Ivanka 8-10 8
1993 Fairy Heights 8-10 11
1994 Aqaarid 8-10 9
1995 Bosra Sham 8-10 6
1996 Reams of Verse 8-10 8
1997 Glorosia 8-10 8

DIADEM STAKES

Ascot—6f

1977 Gentilhombre 4-9-7 6
1978 Creetown 6-9-7 14
1979 Absalom 4-9-7 6
1980 Sovereign Rose 3-9-0 9
1981 Moorestyle 4-9-7 10
1982 Indian King 4-9-7 12
1983 Salieri 3-9-3 12
1984 Never So Bold 4-9-7 9
1985 Al Sylah 3-8-9 8
1986 Hallgate 3-8-12 12
1987 Dowsing 3-8-12 17
1988 Cadeaux Genereux 3-8-12 13
1989 Chummy's Favourite 4-9-2 11
1990 Ron's Victory 3-8-11 14
1991 Shalford 3-8-11 16
1992 Wolfhound 3-8-11 11
1993 Catrail 3-8-11 9
1994 Lake Coniston 3-8-11 11
1995 Cool Jazz 4-9-0 15
1996 Diffident 4-9-0 12
1997 Elnadim 3-8-12 14

QUEEN ELIZABETH II STAKES

Ascot—1m

1977 Trusted 4-9-0 7
1978 Homing 3-8-7 11
1979 Kris 3-9-0 7
1980 Known Fact 3-9-0 7
1981 To-Agori-Mou 3-9-0 6
1982 Buzzards Bay 4-9-0 10
1983 Sackford 3-8-7 9
1984 Teleprompter 4-9-0 6
1985 Shadeed 3-9-0 7
1986 Sure Blade 3-8-11 7
1987 Milligram 3-8-8 5
1988 Warning 3-8-11 8
1989 Zilzal 3-8-11 5
1990 Markofdistinction 4-9-4 10
1991 Selkirk 3-9-0 9
1992 Lahib 4-9-4 9
1993 Bigstone 3-9-0 9
1994 Maroof 4-9-4 9
1995 Bahri 3-8-11 6
1996 Mark of Esteem 3-8-11 7
1997 Air Express 3-8-11 9

ROYAL LODGE STAKES (2y)

Ascot—1m

1977 Shirley Heights 8-11 8
1978 Ela-Mana-Mou 8-11 8
1979 Hello Gorgeous 8-11 4
1980 Robellino 8-11 8
1981 Norwick 8-11 9
1982 Dunbeath 8-11 9
1983 Gold and Ivory 8-11 5
1984 Reach 8-11 8
1985 Bonhomie 8-11 7
1986 Bengal Fire 8-11 9
1987 Sanquirico 8-13 10
1988 High Estate 8-13 5
1989 Digression 8-10 9
1990 Mujaazif 8-10 8
1991 Made of Gold 8-10 8
1992 Desert Secret 8-10 10
1993 Mister Baileys 8-10 9
1994 Eltish 8-10 8
1995 Mons 8-11 8
1996 Benny The Dip 8-11 8
1997 Teapot Row 8-11 8

CHEVELEY PARK STAKES (2y fillies)

Newmarket—6f

1977 Sookera 8-11 10
1978 Devon Ditty 8-11 7
1979 Mrs Penny 8-11 12
1980 Marwell 8-11 8
1981 Woodstream 8-11 13
1982 Ma Biche 8-11 9
1983 Desirable 8-11 12
1984 Park Appeal 8-11 13
1985 Embla 8-11 14
1986 Forest Flower 8-11 5
1987 Ravinella 8-11 8
1988 Pass the Peace 8-11 7
1989 Dead Certain 8-11 11
1990 Capricciosa 8-11 11
1991 Marling 8-11 9
1992 Sayyedati 8-11 4
1993 Prophecy 8-11 6
1994 Gay Gallanta 8-11 10
1995 Blue Duster 8-11 5
1996 Pas de Reponse 8-11 8
1997 Embassy 8-11 8

MIDDLE PARK STAKES (2y)
Newmarket—6f

1977	Formidable 9-0	7
1978	Junius 9-0	10
1979	Known Fact 9-0	7
1980	Mattaboy 9-0	9
1981	Cajun 9-0	13
1982	Diesis 9-0	6
1983	Creag-an-Sgor 9-0	9
1984	Bassenthwaite 9-0	8
1985	Stalker 9-0	6
1986	Mister Majestic 9-0	7
1987	Gallic League 9-0	5
1988	Mon Tresor 9-0	6
1989	Balla Cove 9-0	6
1990	Lycius 9-0	9
1991	Rodrigo de Triano 9-0	6
1992	Zieten 9-0	6
1993	First Trump 9-0	8
1994	Fard 9-0	10
1995	Royal Applause 8-11	5
1996	Bahamian Bounty 8-11	11
1997	Hayil 8-11	8

SUN CHARIOT STAKES (fillies and mares)
Before 1974: 3-year-old fillies only.
Newmarket—1m 2f

1977	Triple First 3-9-0	7
1978	Swiss Maid 3-8-7	9
1979	Topsy 3-8-7	8
1980	Snow 3-8-7	7
1981	Home on the Range 3-8-6	10
1982	Time Charter 3-9-0	10
1983	Cormorant Wood 3-8-5	9
1984	Free Guest 3-8-4	8
1985	Free Guest 4-9-4	5
1986	Dusty Dollar 3-8-7	7
1987	Infamy 3-8-7	6
1988	Indian Skimmer 4-9-6	6
1989	Braiswick 3-8-7	9
1990	Kartajana 3-8-11	7
1991	Ristna 3-8-8	5
1992	Red Slippers 3-8-8	7
1993	Talented 3-8-8	7
1994	La Confederation 3-8-8	7
1995	Warning Shadows 3-8-8	7
1996	Last Second 3-8-11	9
1997	One So Wonderful 3-8-8	8

CAMBRIDGESHIRE
Newmarket—1m 1f

1977	Sin Timon 3-8-3	27
1978	Baronet 6-9-0	18
1979	Smartset 4-8-8	24
1980	Baronet 8-9-3	19
1981	Braughing 4-8-4	28
1982	Century City 3-9-6	29
1983	Sagamore 4-7-8	30
1984	Leysh 3-8-7	34
1985	Tremblant 4-9-8	31
1986	Dallas 3-9-6	31
1987	Balthus 4-8-1	31
1988	Quinlan Terry 3-8-5	29
1989	Rambo's Hall 4-8-6	34
1990	Risen Moon 3-8-9	40
1991	Mellottie 6-9-1	29
1992	Rambo's Hall 7-9-3	30
1993	Penny Drops 4-7-13	33
1994	Halling 3-8-8	30
1995	Cap Juluca 3-9-10	39
1996	Clifton Fox 4-8-2	38
1997	Pasternak 4-9-1	36

JOCKEY CLUB CUP
Newmarket—2m

1977	Grey Baron 4-9-3	5
1978	Buckskin 5-9-7	6
1979	Nicholas Bill 4-8-11	8
1980	Ardross 4-9-5	5
1981	Centroline 3-8-4	9
1982	Little Wolf 4-9-5	8
1983	Karadar 5-9-3	5
1984	Old Country 5-9-7	4
1985	Tale Quale 3-8-4	10
1986	Valuable Witness 6-9-5	4
1987	Buckley 4-9-3	11
1988	Kneller 3-8-7	5
1989	Weld 3-8-7	3
1990	Great Marquess 3-8-3	7
1991	Further Flight 5-9-3	6
1992	Further Flight 6-9-3	4
1993	Further Flight 7-9-3	6
1994	Further Flight 8-9-3	5
1995	Further Flight 9-9-3	8
1996	Celeric 4-9-0	8
1997	Grey Shot 5-9-5	7

SUPREME STAKES
Goodwood—7f

1987	Asteroid Field 4-8-6	10
1988	Fair Judgement 4-8-12	8
1989	Kerita 3-8-5	8
1990	Anshan 3-8-9	6
1991	Osario 4-8-12	13
1992	Hazaam 3-8-9	7
1993	Abandoned	
1994	Soviet Line 4-9-2	9
1995	Inzar 3-8-8	10
1996	Tagula 3-8-9	9
1997	Decorated Hero 5-9-2	6

PRINCESS ROYAL STAKES
Ascot—1m 4f

1977	Aloft 3-8-9	11
1978	Trillionaire 3-8-6	6
1979	Alia 3-8-3	11
1980	Karamita 3-8-7	8
1981	Flighting 3-8-3	11
1982	Believer 3-8-3	14
1983	Sylph 3-8-3	11
1984	One Way Street 3-8-7	11
1985	Free Guest 4-9-7	15
1986	Tashtiya 3-8-9	6

1987 Abandoned
1988 Banket 3-8-6 8
1989 Snow Bride 3-8-11 10
1990 Narwala 3-8-6 7
1991 Always Friendly 3-8-6 8
1992 Cunning 3-8-9 9
1993 Abandoned
1994 Dancing Bloom 4-9-0 7
1995 Labibeh 3-8-6 5
1996 Time Allowed 3-8-7 11
1997 Delilah 3-8-7 7

CORNWALLIS STAKES (2y)

Ascot—5f

1977 Absalom 9-0 8
1978 Greenland Park 8-11 7
1979 Hanu 9-0 8
1980 Pushy 8-11 7
1981 My Lover 9-0 7
1982 Tatibah 9-0 9
1983 Petorius 9-0 14
1984 Doulab 9-0 11
1985 Hallgate 9-0 13
1986 Singing Steven 8-11 9
1987 Abandoned
1988 Hadif 8-13 13
1989 Argentum 8-13 9
1990 Mujadil 8-13 11
1991 Magic Ring 9-2 11
1992 Up And At 'Em 8-13 13
1993 Abandoned
1994 Millstream 8-11 7
1995 Mubhij 8-12 7
1996 Easycall 9-4 11
1997 Halmahera 8-12 13

DEWHURST STAKES (2y)

Newmarket—7f

1977 Try My Best 9-0 7
1978 Tromos 9-0 6
1979 Monteverdi 9-0 6
1980 Storm Bird 9-0 5
1981 Wind and Wuthering 9-0 9
1982 Diesis 9-0 4
1983 El Gran Senor 9-0 10
1984 Kala Dancer 9-0 11
1985 Huntingdale 9-0 8
1986 Ajdal 9-0 5
1987 Abandoned
1988 *Prince of Dance 9-0
*Scenic 9-0 6
1989 Dashing Blade 9-0 7
1990 Generous 9-0 8
1991 Dr Devious 9-0 9
1992 Zafonic 9-0 11
1993 Grand Lodge 9-0 10
1994 Pennekamp 9-0 7
1995 Alhaarth 9-0 4
1996 In Command 9-0 8
1997 Xaar 9-0 7

ROCKFEL STAKES (2y)

Newmarket—7f

1981 Top Hope 8-8 8
1982 Saving Mercy 8-7 7
1983 Mahogany 8-8 13
1984 Kashi Lagoon 8-5 9
1985 Tralthee 8-6 9
1986 At Risk 8-9 13
1987 Abandoned
1988 Musical Bliss 8-8 9
1989 Negligent 8-8 12
1990 Crystal Gazing 8-8 6
1991 Musicale 8-11 6
1992 Yawl 8-8 7
1993 Relatively Special 8-8 9
1994 Germane 8-8 8
1995 Bint Salsabil 8-12 8
1996 Moonlight Paradise 8-12 6
1997 Name of Love 8-12 12

CHALLENGE STAKES

Newmarket—7f

1977 Boldboy 7-9-6 8
1978 Spence Bay 3-9-2 12
1979 Kris 3-9-2 7
1980 Moorestyle 3-9-2 6
1981 Moorestyle 4-9-6 7
1982 Noalcoholic 5-9-6 8
1983 Salieri 3-9-2 10
1984 Brocade 3-8-13 7
1985 Efisio 3-9-2 8
1986 Lucky Ring 4-9-0 12
1987 Asteroid Field 4-8-11 7
1988 Salse 3-8-10 8
1989 Distant Relative 3-8-13 6
1990 Sally Rous 3-8-8 8
1991 Mystiko 3-9-0 7
1992 Selkirk 4-9-3 8
1993 Catrail 3-8-11 7
1994 Zieten 4-9-0 8
1995 Harayir 3-8-12 8
1996 Charnwood Forest 4-9-4 8
1997 Kahal 3-8-12 12

REDCAR TWO-YEAR-OLD TROPHY (2y)

Redcar—6f

1989 Osario 8-4 25
1990 Chipaya 8-5 19
1991 Casteddu 8-1 25
1992 Pips Pride 8-5 24
1993 Cape Merino 7-7 26
1994 Maid For Walking 7-13 26
1995 Blue Iris 8-2 26
1996 Proud Native 8-7 25
1997 Grazia 8-2 26

CHAMPION STAKES

Newmarket—1m 2f

1977 Flying Water 4-9-0 8
1978 Swiss Maid 3-8-7 10
1979 Northern Baby 3-8-10 14

1980 Cairn Rouge 3-8-7 13
1981 Vayrann 3-8-10 16
1982 Time Charter 3-8-7 14
1983 Cormorant Wood 3-8-7 19
1984 Palace Music 3-8-10 15
1985 Pebbles 4-9-0 10
1986 Triptych 4-9-0 11
1987 Triptych 5-9-0 11
1988 Indian Skimmer 4-9-0 5
1989 Legal Case 3-8-10 11
1990 In The Groove 3-8-9 10
1991 Tel Quel 3-8-12 12
1992 Rodrigo de Triano 3-8-12 10
1993 Hatoof 4-9-0 12
1994 Dernier Empereur 4-9-4 8
1995 Spectrum 3-8-10 8
1996 Bosra Sham 3-8-8 6
1997 Pilsudski 5-9-2 7

CESAREWITCH
Newmarket—2m 2f

1977 Assured 4-8-4 11
1978 Centurion 3-9-8 17
1979 Sir Michael 3-7-8 11
1980 Popsi's Joy 5-8-6 27
1981 Halsbury 3-8-4 30
1982 Mountain Lodge 3-7-10 28
1983 Bajan Sunshine 4-8-8 28
1984 Tom Sharp 4-7-5 26
1985 Kayudee 5-8-1 21
1986 Orange Hill 4-7-9 25
1987 Private Audition 5-7-9 28
1988 Nomadic Way 3-7-9 24
1989 Double Dutch 5-9-10 22
1990 Trainglot 3-7-12 25
1991 Go South 7-7-11 22
1992 Vintage Crop 5-9-6 24
1993 Aahsaylad 7-8-12 31
1994 Captain's Guest 4-9-9 32
1995 Old Red 5-7-11 21
1996 Inchcailloch 7-7-3 26
1997 Turnpole 6-7-10 31

HORRIS HILL STAKES (2y)
Newbury—7f 64yds

1977 *Derrylin 9-0 ....
*Persian Bold 9-0 12
1978 Kris 9-0 9
1979 Super Asset 9-0 4
1980 Kalaglow 9-0 10
1981 Montekin 9-0 8
1982 Abandoned
1983 Elegant Air 9-0 7
1984 Efisio 9-0 5
1985 Celtic Heir 9-0 12
1986 Naheez 9-0 7
1987 Glacial Storm 8-12 9
1988 Gouriev 8-12 8
1989 Tirol 8-12 8
1990 Sapieha 8-12 9
1991 Lion Cavern 8-12 7
1992 Beggarman Thief 8-12 11
1993 Tatami 8-12 8
1994 Painter's Row 8-12 10
1995 Tumbleweed Ridge 8-9 9
1996 Desert Story 8-9 8
1997 La-Faah 8-9 8

ST SIMON STAKES
Newbury—1m 4f 5yds

1977 Hot Grove 3-8-10 11
1978 Obraztsovy 3-8-7 6
1979 Main Reef 3-8-10 7
1980 Shining Finish 3-8-7 9
1981 Little Wolf 3-8-7 7
1982 Abandoned
1983 Jupiter Island 4-9-0 11
1984 Gay Lemur 4-9-6 11
1985 Shardari 3-8-10 8
1986 Jupiter Island 7-8-9 9
1987 Lake Erie 4-9-0 11
1988 Upend 3-8-4 9
1989 Sesame 4-8-11 11
1990 Down The Flag 3-8-7 8
1991 Further Flight 5-9-3 11
1992 Up Anchor 3-8-4 8
1993 Kithanga 3-8-4 11
1994 Persian Brave 4-9-0 9
1995 Phantom Gold 3-8-9 12
1996 Salmon Ladder 4-9-0 12
1997 Kaliana 3-8-4 10

RACING POST TROPHY (2y)
(Formerly Observer Gold Cup and The Futurity Stakes)
Doncaster—1m

1977 Dactylographer 9-0 12
1978 Sandy Creek 9-0 11
1979 Hello Gorgeous 9-0 7
1980 Beldale Flutter 9-0 7
1981 Count Pahlen 9-0 13
1982 Dunbeath 9-0 8
1983 Alphabatim 9-0 9
1984 Lanfranco 9-0 10
1985 Bakharoff 9-0 9
1986 Reference Point 9-0 10
1987 Emmson 9-0 6
1988 Al Hareb 9-0 8
1989 Be My Chief 9-0 (Run at Newcastle) 5
1990 Peter Davies 9-0 4
1991 Seattle Rhyme 9-0 8
1992 Armiger 9-0 10
1993 King's Theatre 9-0 9
1994 Celtic Swing 9-0 8
1995 Beauchamp King 9-0 4
1996 Medaaly 9-0 9
1997 Saratoga Springs 9-0 8

NOVEMBER HANDICAP
Doncaster—1m 4f

1977 Sailcloth 3-7-7 20
1978 Eastern Spring 4-7-10 21
1979 Morse Code 4-8-3 14
1980 Path of Peace 4-8-5 22

1981 Lafontaine 4-8-7 20
1982 *Double Shuffle 3-9-0 ....
*Turkoman 3-8-7 17
1983 Asir 3-8-7 25
1984 Abu Kadra 3-8-12 23
1985 Bold Rex 3-8-7 24
1986 Beijing 3-8-4 25
1987 Swingit Gunner 6-8-11 25
1988 Young Benz 4-8-4 22
1989 Firelight Fiesta 4-9-8 19
1990 Azzaam 3-9-8 24
1991 Hieroglyphic 3-8-13 22
1992 Turgenev 3-9-0 25
1993 Quick Ransom 5-8-10 25
1994 Saxon Maid 3-8-9 24
1995 Snow Princess 3-8-2 18
1996 Clifton Fox 4-8-10 22
1997 Sabadilla 3-7-8 24

Winners of Principal Races in Ireland

IRISH 2000 GUINEAS (3y)
The Curragh—1m

1977 Pampapaul 9-0 21
1978 Jaazeiro 9-0 12
1979 Dickens Hill 9-0 9
1980 Nikoli 9-0 13
1981 Kings Lake 9-0 13
1982 Dara Monarch 9-0 14
1983 Wassl 9-0 10
1984 Sadler's Wells 9-0 9
1985 Triptych 8-11 16
1986 Flash of Steel 9-0 6
1987 Don't Forget Me 9-0 8
1988 Prince of Birds 9-0 14
1989 Shaadi 9-0 12
1990 Tirol 9-0 9
1991 Fourstars Allstar 9-0 12
1992 Rodrigo de Triano 9-0 6
1993 Barathea 9-0 11
1994 Turtle Island 9-0 9
1995 Spectrum 9-0 9
1996 Spinning World 9-0 10
1997 Desert King 9-0 12

IRISH 1000 GUINEAS (3y fillies)
The Curragh—1m

1977 Lady Capulet 9-0 14
1978 More So 9-0 17
1979 Godetia 9-0 12
1980 Cairn Rouge 9-0 18
1981 Arctique Royale 9-0 15
1982 Prince's Polly 9-0 24
1983 L'Attrayante 9-0 18
1984 Katies 9-0 23
1985 Al Bahathri 9-0 15
1986 Sonic Lady 9-0 19
1987 Forest Flower 9-0 11
1988 Trusted Partner 9-0 16
1989 Ensconse 9-0 13
1990 In The Groove 9-0 12
1991 Kooyonga 9-0 12
1992 Marling 9-0 9
1993 Nicer 9-0 14
1994 Mehthaaf 9-0 10
1995 Ridgewood Pearl 9-0 10
1996 Matiya 9-0 12
1997 Classic Park 9-0 10

IRISH DERBY (3y)
The Curragh—1m 4f

1977 The Minstrel 9-0 15
1978 Shirley Heights 9-0 11
1979 Troy 9-0 9
1980 Tyrnavos 9-0 13
1981 Shergar 9-0 12
1982 Assert 9-0 10
1983 Shareef Dancer 9-0 12
1984 El Gran Senor 9-0 8
1985 Law Society 9-0 13
1986 Shahrastani 9-0 11
1987 Sir Harry Lewis 9-0 8
1988 Kahyasi 9-0 11
1989 Old Vic 9-0 8
1990 Salsabil 8-11 9
1991 Generous 9-0 6
1992 St Jovite 9-0 11
1993 Commander in Chief 9-0 11
1994 Balanchine 8-11 9
1995 Winged Love 9-0 13
1996 Zagreb 9-0 13
1997 Desert King 9-0 10

IRISH OAKS (3y fillies)
The Curragh—1m 4f

1977 Olwyn 9-0 8
1978 Fair Salinia 9-0 12
1979 Godetia 9-0 13
1980 Shoot A Line 9-0 8
1981 Blue Wind 9-0 10
1982 Swiftfoot 9-0 10
1983 Give Thanks 9-0 12
1984 Princess Pati 9-0 11
1985 Helen Street 9-0 9
1986 Colorspin 9-0 8
1987 Unite 9-0 8
1988 *Diminuendo 9-0
*Melodist 9-0 9
1989 Alydaress 9-0 5
1990 Knight's Baroness 9-0 10
1991 Possessive Dancer 9-0 10
1992 User Friendly 9-0 9
1993 Wemyss Bight 9-0 11
1994 Bolas 9-0 10
1995 Pure Grain 9-0 10
1996 Dance Design 9-0 6
1997 Ebadiyla 9-0 11

HEINZ '57' PHOENIX STAKES (2y)
Leopardstown—6f

1977 Perla 8-11 ... 6
1978 Kilijaro 8-11 ... 9
1979 Smokey Lady 8-11 ... 10
1980 Swan Princess 8-11 ... 10
1981 Achieved 9-0 ... 7
1982 Sweet Emma 8-11 ... 11
1983 King Persian 9-0 ... 13
1984 Aviance 8-11 ... 8
1985 Roaring Riva 9-0 ... 13
1986 Minstrella 8-11 ... 10
1987 Digamist 9-0 ... 12
1988 Superpower 9-0 ... 12
1989 Pharaoh's Delight 8-11 ... 10
1990 Mac's Imp 9-0 ... 13
1991 Bradawn Breever 9-0 ... 9
1992 Pips Pride 9-0 ... 9
1993 Turtle Island 9-0 ... 9
1994 Eva Luna 8-11 ... 10
1995 Danehill Dancer 9-0 ... 10
1996 Mantovani 9-0 ... 9
1997 Princely Heir 9-0 ... 9

IRISH CHAMPION STAKES
Leopardstown—1m 2f
(Phoenix Champion Stakes before 1991)

1984 Sadler's Wells 3-8-11 ... 12
1985 Commanche Run 4-9-6 ... 11
1986 Park Express 3-8-8 ... 13
1987 Triptych 5-9-3 ... 12
1988 Indian Skimmer 4-9-3 ... 9
1989 Carroll House 4-9-6 ... 9
1990 Elmaamul 3-8-11 ... 8
1991 Suave Dancer 3-8-11 ... 7
1992 Dr Devious 3-8-11 ... 8
1993 Muhtarram 4-9-4 ... 10
1994 Cezanne 5-9-4 ... 8
1995 Pentire 3-8-11 ... 8
1996 Timarida 4-9-1 ... 6
1997 Pilsudski 5-9-4 ... 7

IRISH CAMBRIDGESHIRE
The Curragh—1m (Hcap)

1977 Poacher's Moon 4-10-0 ... 22
1978 Loyal Son 4-7-13 ... 22
1979 Habituate 3-9-3 ... 19
1980 I'm Ready 3-8-3 ... 24
1981 Majestic Nurse 6-8-3 ... 18
1982 Majestic Star 5-9-5 ... 14
1983 Persian Royale 3-7-13 ... 25
1984 Chammsky 5-9-4 ... 21
1985 National Form 4-9-9 ... 24
1986 Any Song 3-9-1 ... 26
1987 Silius 4-7-10 ... 24
1988 Ben's Pearl 3-7-9 ... 30
1989 Smoggy Spray 5-8-10 ... 17
1990 Jonjas Chudleigh 3-9-10 ... 22
1991 Must Hurry 4-8-0 ... 12
1992 Khizarabad 3-8-3 ... 16
1993 Wandering Thoughts 4-8-2 ... 18
1994 Saibot 5-9-0 ... 18
1995 The Bower 6-7-8 ... 15
1996 Raiyoun 3-9-8 ... 16
1997 Quws 3-9-2 ... 11

MOYGLARE STUD STAKES (2y fillies)
The Curragh—7f

1977 Ridaness 8-12 ... 9
1978 Phil's Fancy 8-11 ... 9
1979 Daness 8-11 ... 6
1980 Arctique Royale 8-11 ... 14
1981 Woodstream 8-11 ... 14
1982 Habibti 8-11 ... 15
1983 Gala Event 8-11 ... 20
1984 Park Appeal 8-11 ... 13
1985 Gayle Gal 8-11 ... 15
1986 Minstrella 8-11 ... 8
1987 Flutter Away 8-11 ... 11
1988 Flamenco Wave 8-11 ... 11
1989 Chimes of Freedom 8-11 ... 7
1990 Capricciosa 8-11 ... 8
1991 Twafeaj 8-11 ... 8
1992 Sayyedati 8-11 ... 8
1993 Lemon Souffle 8-11 ... 11
1994 Belle Genius 8-11 ... 8
1995 Priory Belle 8-11 ... 13
1996 Bianca Nera 8-11 ... 10
1997 Tarascon 8-12 ... 12

NATIONAL STAKES (2y)
The Curragh—8f
(7f up to 1996)

1977 Diamonds Are Trump 9-0 ... 9
1978 Tap on Wood 9-0 ... 10
1979 Monteverdi 9-0 ... 15
1980 Storm Bird 9-0 ... 10
1981 Day Is Done 9-0 ... 11
1982 Glenstal 9-0 ... 9
1983 El Gran Senor 9-0 ... 8
1984 Law Society 9-0 ... 9
1985 Tate Gallery 9-0 ... 9
1986 Lockton 9-0 ... 9
1987 Caerwent 9-0 ... 6
1988 Classic Fame 9-0 ... 12
1989 Dashing Blade 9-0 ... 10
1990 Heart of Darkness 9-0 ... 8
1991 El Prado 9-0 ... 5
1992 Fatherland 9-0 ... 5
1993 Manntari 9-0 ... 6
1994 Definite Article 9-0 ... 5
1995 Danehill Dancer 9-0 ... 7
1996 Desert King 9-0 ... 10
1997 King of Kings 9-0 ... 9

IRISH ST LEGER
Before 1983: 3-year-olds only
The Curragh—1m 6f

1977 Transworld 9-0 ... 9
1978 M-Lolshan 9-0 ... 8
1979 Niniski 9-0 ... 10
1980 Gonzales 9-0 ... 8
1981 Protection Racket 9-0 ... 7
1982 Touching Wood 9-0 ... 10

Year	Winner	Runners
1983	Mountain Lodge 4-9-4	10
1984	Opale 4-9-4	9
1985	Leading Counsel 3-8-12	12
1986	Authaal 3-8-12	6
1987	Eurobird 8-9	8
1988	Dark Lomond 3-8-9	13
1989	Petite Ile 3-8-9	10
1990	Ibn Bey 6-9-8	12
1991	Turgeon 5-9-8	10
1992	Mashaallah 4-9-8	9
1993	Vintage Crop 6-9-8	8
1994	Vintage Crop 7-9-8	8
1995	Strategic Choice 4-9-8	7
1996	Oscar Schindler 4-9-8	9
1997	Oscar Schindler 5-9-8	7

IRISH CESAREWITCH

The Curragh—2m (Hcap)

Year	Winner	Runners
1977	Cill Dara 5-9-6	28
1978	Chateau Royal 3-8-8	23
1979	Jack of Trumps 7-8-13	23
1980	Potato Merchant 5-7-8	20
1981	The Neurologist 3-9-3	30
1982	Five Nations 5-8-2	29
1983	Five Nations 6-7-11	20
1984	Jean-Claude 3-7-11	24
1985	Ravaro 5-9-12	30
1986	Orient Rose 3-8-12	23
1987	Try a Brandy 5-8-4	29
1988	Midsummer Gamble 7-8-12	26
1989	Marlion 8-7-8	18
1990	Chirkpar 3-7-4	19
1991	Aiybak 5-7-1	16
1992	Sinntara 3-7-7	17
1993	Cliveden Gail 4-9-3	23
1994	Elupa 3-7-10	22
1995	Montelado 8-8-9	14
1996	Miltonfield 7-8-6	26
1997	Winged Hussar 4-8-9	20

Winners of Principal Races in France

PRIX GANAY

Longchamp—1m 2f 110yds

Year	Winner	Runners
1977	Arctic Tern 4-9-2	12
1978	Trillion 4-8-13	8
1979	Frere Basile 4-9-2	8
1980	Le Marmot 4-9-2	6
1981	Argument 4-9-2	9
1982	Bikala 4-9-2	10
1983	Lancastrian 6-9-2	7
1984	Romildo 4-9-2	8
1985	Sagace 5-9-2	7
1986	Baillamont 4-9-2	10
1987	Triptych 5-8-13	10
1988	Saint Andrews 4-9-2	5
1989	Saint Andrews 5-9-2	7
1990	Creator 4-9-2	10
1991	Kartajana 4-8-13	7
1992	Subotica 4-9-2	7
1993	Vert Amande 5-9-2	8
1994	Marildo 7-9-2	8
1995	Pelder 5-9-2	10
1996	Valanour 4-9-2	10
1997	Helissio 4-9-2	8

POULE D'ESSAI DES POULAINS (3y)

Longchamp—1m

Year	Winner	Runners
1977	Blushing Groom 9-2	6
1978	Nishapour 9-2	14
1979	Irish River 9-2	4
1980	In Fijar 9-2	13
1981	Recitation 9-2	10
1982	Melyno 9-2	9
1983	L'Emigrant 9-2	10
1984	Siberian Express 9-2	14
1985	No Pass No Sale 9-2	9
1986	Fast Topaze 9-2	8
1987	Soviet Star 9-2	14
1988	Blushing John 9-2	10
1989	Kendor 9-2	10
1990	Linamix 9-2	7
1991	Hector Protector 9-2	6
1992	Shanghai 9-2	9
1993	Kingmambo 9-2	10
1994	Green Tune 9-2	7
1995	Vettori 9-2	8
1996	Ashkalani 9-2	10
1997	Daylami 9-2	6

POULE D'ESSAI DES POULICHES (3y)

Longchamp—1m

Year	Winner	Runners
1977	Madelia 9-2	8
1978	Dancing Maid 9-2	10
1979	Three Troikas 9-2	7
1980	Aryenne 9-2	6
1981	Ukraine Girl 9-2	10
1982	River Lady 9-2	9
1983	L'Attrayante 9-2	10
1984	Masarika 9-2	11
1985	Silvermine 9-2	10
1986	Baiser Vole 9-2	8
1987	Miesque 9-2	8
1988	Ravinella 9-2	8
1989	Pearl Bracelet 9-2	16
1990	Houseproud 9-2	14
1991	Danseuse du Soir 9-2	9
1992	Culture Vulture 9-2	9
1993	Madeleine's Dream 9-2	8
1994	East of the Moon 9-2	8
1995	Matiara 9-2	16
1996	Ta Rib 9-0	9
1997	Always Loyal 9-0	7

PRIX LUPIN (3y)
Longchamp—1m 2f 110yds

1977 Pharly 9-2 11
1978 Acamas 9-2 11
1979 Top Ville 9-2 9
1980 Belgio 9-2 13
1981 No Lute 9-2 9
1982 Persepolis 9-2 10
1983 L'Emigrant 9-2 7
1984 Dahar 9-2 7
1985 Metal Precieux 9-2 8
1986 Fast Topaze 9-2 7
1987 Groom Dancer 9-2 7
1988 Exactly Sharp 9-2 9
1989 Galetto 9-2 6
1990 Epervier Bleu 9-2 7
1991 Cudas 9-2 7
1992 Johann Quatz 9-2 7
1993 Hernando 9-2 5
1994 Celtic Arms 9-2 8
1995 Flemensfirth 9-2 6
1996 Helissio 9-2 5
1997 Cloudings 9-2 5

PRIX SAINT-ALARY (3y fillies)
Longchamp—1m 2f

1977 Madelia 8-11 6
1978 Reine de Saba 9-2 10
1979 Three Troikas 9-2 7
1980 Paranete 9-2 8
1981 Tootens 9-2 10
1982 Harbour 9-2 8
1983 Smuggly 9-2 8
1984 Grise Mine 9-2 11
1985 Fitnah 9-2 10
1986 Lacovia 9-2 9
1987 Indian Skimmer 9-2 9
1988 Riviere d'Or 9-2 8
1989 Behera 9-2 7
1990 Air de Rein 9-2 9
1991 Treble 9-2 6
1992 Rosefinch 9-2 11
1993 Intrepidity 9-2 7
1994 Moonlight Dance 9-2 6
1995 Muncie 9-2 5
1996 Luna Wells 9-0 6
1997 Brilliance 9-0 7

PRIX JEAN PRAT (3y)
Chantilly—1m 1f 55yds

1977 Lightning 9-2 8
1978 Dom Racine 9-2 11
1979 Young Generation 9-2 7
1980 Night Alert 9-2 12
1981 Cresta Rider 9-2 9
1982 Melyno 9-2 5
1983 Ginger Brink 9-2 10
1984 Mendez 9-2 6
1985 Baillamont 9-2 8
1986 Magical Wonder 9-2 9
1987 Risk Me 9-2 9
1988 Lapierre 9-2 8
1989 Local Talent 9-2 6
1990 Priolo 9-2 6
1991 Sillery 9-2 7
1992 Kitwood 9-2 5
1993 Le Balafre 9-2 8
1994 Millkom 9-2 6
1995 Torrential 9-2 7
1996 Le Triton 9-2 6
1997 Starborough 9-2 5

PRIX D'ISPAHAN
(now run at Longchamp)
Chantilly—1m 1f 55yds

1977 Lightning 3-8-9 6
1978 Carwhite 4-9-6 10
1979 Irish River 3-8-9 8
1980 Nadjar 4-9-6 10
1981 The Wonder 3-8-9 11
1982 Al Nasr 4-9-6 6
1983 Crystal Glitters 3-8-9 12
1984 Crystal Glitters 4-9-7 8
1985 Sagace 5-9-6 7
1986 Baillamont 4-9-6 8
1987 Highest Honor 4-9-2 6
1988 Miesque 4-8-13 6
1989 Indian Skimmer 5-8-13 6
1990 Creator 4-9-2 9
1991 Sanglamore 4-9-2 7
1992 Zoman 5-9-2 11
1993 Arcangues 5-9-2 7
1994 Bigstone 4-9-2 7
1995 Green Tune 4-9-2 9
1996 Halling 5-9-2 4
1997 Sasuru 4-9-2 6

PRIX DU JOCKEY-CLUB (3y)
Chantilly—1m 4f

1977 Crystal Palace 9-2 14
1978 Acamas 9-2 20
1979 Top Ville 9-2 11
1980 Policeman 9-2 14
1981 Bikala 9-2 12
1982 Assert 9-2 14
1983 Caerleon 9-2 12
1984 Darshaan 9-2 17
1985 Mouktar 9-2 11
1986 Bering 9-2 13
1987 Natroun 9-2 17
1988 Hours After 9-2 16
1989 Old Vic 9-2 12
1990 Sanglamore 9-2 12
1991 Suave Dancer 9-2 7
1992 Polytain 9-2 17
1993 Hernando 9-2 11
1994 Celtic Arms 9-2 15
1995 Celtic Swing 9-2 11
1996 Ragmar 9-2 15
1997 Peintre Celebre 9-2 14

PRIX DE DIANE (3y fillies)
Chantilly—1m 2½f

1977 Madelia 9-2....13
1978 Reine de Saba 9-2....17
1979 Dunette 9-2....12
1980 Mrs Penny 9-2....14
1981 Madam Gay 9-2....14
1982 Harbour 9-2....14
1983 Escaline 9-2....17
1984 Northern Trick 9-2....15
1985 Lypharita 9-2....10
1986 Lacovia 9-2....14
1987 Indian Skimmer 9-2....11
1988 Resless Kara 9-2....16
1989 Lady in Silver 9-2....14
1990 Rafha 9-2....14
1991 Caerlina 9-2....13
1992 Jolypha 9-2....12
1993 Shemaka 9-2....14
1994 East of the Moon 9-2....9
1995 Carling 9-2....12
1996 Sil Sila 9-0....12
1997 Vereva 9-0....12

GRAND PRIX DE PARIS (3y)
Longchamp—1m 2f
(1m 7f up to 1986)

1977 Funny Hobby 8-11....11
1978 Galiani 8-11....14
1979 Soleil Noir 8-11....7
1980 Valiant Heart 8-11....14
1981 Glint of Gold 8-11....11
1982 Le Nain Jaune 8-11....11
1983 Yawa 8-11....7
1984 At Talaq 8-12....11
1985 Sumayr 8-11....7
1986 Swink 8-11....9
1987 Risk Me 9-2....9
1988 Fijar Tango 9-2....10
1989 Dancehall 9-2....8
1990 Saumarez 9-2....8
1991 Subotica 9-2....9
1992 Homme de Loi 9-2....10
1993 Fort Wood 9-2....9
1994 Millkom 9-2....12
1995 Valanour 9-2....10
1996 Grape Tree Road 9-2....10
1997 Peintre Celebre 9-2....7

GRAND PRIX DE SAINT-CLOUD
Saint-Cloud—1m 4f

1977 Exceller 4-9-8....10
1978 Guadanini 4-9-8....9
1979 Gay Mecene 4-9-8....13
1980 *Dunette 4-9-5
*Shakapour 3-8-9....9
1981 Akarad 3-8-9....10
1982 Glint of Gold 4-9-8....9
1983 Diamond Shoal 4-9-8....9
1984 Teenoso 4-9-9....11
1985 Strawberry Road 6-9-8....7
1986 Acatenango 4-9-8....9
1987 Moon Madness 4-9-8....6
1988 Village Star 5-9-8....10
1989 Sheriff's Star 4-9-8....6
1990 In The Wings 4-9-8....8
1991 Epervier Bleu 4-9-8....12
1992 Pistolet Bleu 4-9-8....7
1993 User Friendly 4-9-5....8
1994 Apple Tree 5-9-8....8
1995 Carnegie 4-9-8....8
1996 Helissio 3-8-8....9
1997 Helissio 4-9-9....4

PRIX JACQUES LE MAROIS
Deauville—1m

1977 Flying Water 4-8-12....7
1978 Kenmare 3-8-8....10
1979 Irish River 3-8-8....8
1980 Nadjar 4-9-2....9
1981 Northjet 4-9-2....11
1982 The Wonder 4-9-2....9
1983 Luth Enchantee 3-8-7....10
1984 Lear Fan 3-8-9....10
1985 Vin de France 3-8-9....11
1986 Lirung 4-9-2....12
1987 Miesque 3-8-6....9
1988 Miesque 4-8-13....6
1989 Polish Precedent 3-8-9....10
1990 Priolo 3-8-9....10
1991 Hector Protector 3-8-9....10
1992 Exit to Nowhere 4-9-4....14
1993 Sayyedati 3-8-8....8
1994 East of the Moon 3-8-8....9
1995 Miss Satamixa 3-8-8....9
1996 Spinning World 3-8-11....9
1997 Spinning World 4-9-4....6

PRIX MORNY (2y)
Deauville—6f

1977 Super Concorde 8-11....10
1978 Irish River 8-11....11
1979 Princess Lida 8-11....10
1980 Ancient Regime 8-8....7
1981 Green Forest 8-11....5
1982 Deep Roots 8-11....6
1983 Siberian Express 8-11....7
1984 Seven Springs 8-8....7
1985 Regal State 8-8....11
1986 Sakura Reiko 8-8....8
1987 First Waltz 8-8....8
1988 Tersa 8-8....8
1989 Machiavellian 8-11....7
1990 Hector Protector 8-11....12
1991 Arazi 8-11....4
1992 Zafonic 8-11....10
1993 Coup de Genie 8-8....8
1994 Hoh Magic 8-10....6
1995 Tagula 9-0....8
1996 Bahamian Bounty 9-0....5
1997 Charge d'Affaires 8-13....7

PRIX DU MOULIN DE LONGCHAMP
Longchamp—1m

1977 Pharly 3-8-11 7
1978 Sanedtki 4-8-13 10
1979 Irish River 3-8-11 8
1980 Kilijaro 4-8-13 11
1981 Northjet 4-9-2 12
1982 Green Forest 3-8-11 9
1983 Luth Enchantee 3-8-8 8
1984 Mendez 3-8-11 7
1985 Rousillon 4-9-2 12
1986 Sonic Lady 3-8-8 14
1987 Miesque 3-8-8 7
1988 Soviet Star 4-9-2 7
1989 Polish Precedent 3-8-11 11
1990 Distant Relative 4-9-2 6
1991 Priolo 4-9-2 12
1992 All At Sea 3-8-8 10
1993 Kingmambo 3-8-11 11
1994 Ski Paradise 4-8-13 7
1995 Ridgewood Pearl 3-8-8 8
1996 Ashkalani 3-8-11 9
1997 Spinning World 4-9-2 9

PRIX DE LA SALAMANDRE (2y)
Longchamp—7f

1977 John de Coombe 8-11 8
1978 Irish River 8-11 6
1979 Princesse Lida 8-8 7
1980 Miswaki 8-11 5
1981 Green Forest 8-11 5
1982 *Deep Roots 8-11 ....
*Maximova 8-8 6
1983 Seattle Song 8-11 5
1984 Noblequest 8-11 7
1985 Baiser Vole 8-8 10
1986 Miesque 8-8 10
1987 Common Grounds 8-11 6
1988 Oczy Czarnie 8-8 9
1989 Machiavellian 8-11 6
1990 Hector Protector 8-11 7
1991 Arazi 8-11 8
1992 Zafonic 8-11 6
1993 Coup de Genie 8-8 6
1994 Pennekamp 8-11 8
1995 Lord of Men 8-11 7
1996 Revoque 9-0 5
1997 Xaar 9-0 8

PRIX VERMEILLE (3y fillies)
Longchamp—1m 4f

1977 Kamicia 9-2 18
1978 Dancing Maid 9-2 12
1979 Three Troikas 9-2 13
1980 Mrs Penny 9-2 12
1981 April Run 9-2 10
1982 All Along 9-2 13
1983 Sharaya 9-2 12
1984 Northern Trick 9-2 10
1985 Walensee 9-2 13
1986 Darara 9-2 8
1987 Bint Pasha 9-2 12
1988 Indian Rose 9-2 8
1989 Young Mother 9-2 7
1990 Salsabil 9-2 9
1991 Magic Night 9-2 14
1992 Jolypha 9-2 10
1993 Intrepidity 9-2 8
1994 Sierra Madre 9-2 9
1995 Carling 9-2 10
1996 My Emma 9-0 10
1997 Queen Maud 9-0 9

PRIX DU CADRAN
Longchamp—2m 4f

1977 Buckskin 4-9-2 5
1978 Buckskin 5-9-2 9
1979 El Badr 4-9-2 5
1980 Shafaraz 7-9-2 6
1981 Gold River 4-8-13 6
1982 El Badr 7-9-2 5
1983 Karkour 5-9-2 6
1984 Neustrien 5-9-2 6
1985 Balitou 6-9-2 7
1986 Air de Cour 4-9-2 6
1987 Royal Gait 4-9-2 9
1988 Yaka 5-9-2 5
1989 Trebrook 5-9-2 3
1990 Mercalle 4-8-13 6
1991 Victoire Bleue 4-8-13 7
1992 Sought Out 4-8-13 7
1993 Assessor 4-9-2 11
1994 Molesnes 4-8-13 8
1995 Always Earnest 7-9-2 6
1996 Nononito 5-9-2 10
1997 Chief Contender 4-9-2 7

PRIX DE L'ABBAYE DE LONGCHAMP
Longchamp—5f

1977 Gentilhombre 4-9-11 11
1978 Sigy 2-8-5 7
1979 Double Form 4-9-11 13
1980 Moorestyle 3-9-11 9
1981 Marwell 3-9-8 10
1982 Sharpo 5-9-11 13
1983 Habibti 3-9-7 8
1984 Committed 4-9-7 12
1985 Committed 5-9-7 12
1986 Double Schwartz 5-9-11 13
1987 Polonia 3-9-7 9
1988 Handsome Sailor 5-9-11 10
1989 Silver Fling 4-9-7 16
1990 Dayjur 3-9-11 6
1991 Keen Hunter 4-9-11 14
1992 Mr Brooks 5-9-11 9
1993 Lochsong 5-9-8 11
1994 Lochsong 6-9-7 10
1995 Hever Golf Rose 4-9-7 12
1996 Kistena 3-9-8 10
1997 Carmine Lake 3-9-8 12

PRIX MARCEL BOUSSAC (2y fillies)

Longchamp—1m
(Criterium des Pouliches before 1980)

1977 Tarona 8-9 14
1978 Pitasia 8-9 8
1979 Aryenne 8-9 13
1980 Tropicaro 8-9 10
1981 Play It Safe 8-9 8
1982 Goodbye Shelley 8-9 11
1983 Almeira 8-9 7
1984 Triptych 8-9 9
1985 Midway Lady 8-9 15
1986 Miesque 8-9 11
1987 Ashayer 8-9 12
1988 Mary Linoa 8-9 11
1989 Salsabil 8-9 15
1990 Shadayid 8-9 9
1991 Culture Vulture 8-11 14
1992 Gold Splash 8-11 11
1993 Sierra Madre 8-11 8
1994 Macoumba 8-11 6
1995 Miss Tahiti 8-11 11
1996 Ryafan 8-11 13
1997 Loving Claim 8-12 10

GRAND CRITERIUM (2y)

Longchamp—1m

1977 Super Concorde 8-11 13
1978 Irish River 8-11 12
1979 Dragon 8-11 8
1980 Recitation 8-11 11
1981 Green Forest 8-11 10
1982 Saint Cyrien 8-11 8
1983 Treizieme 8-8 9
1984 Alydar's Best 8-8 6
1985 Femme Elite 8-8 11
1986 Danishkada 8-8 8
1987 Fijar Tango 8-11 6
1988 Kendor 8-11 9
1989 Jade Robbery 8-11 8
1990 Hector Protector 8-11 5
1991 Arazi 8-11 6
1992 Tenby 8-11 11
1993 Lost World 8-11 7
1994 Goldmark 8-11 4
1995 Loup Solitaire 8-11 7
1996 Revoque 9-0 9
1997 Second Empire 9-0 5

PRIX DE LA FORET

Longchamp—7f

1977 Sanedtki 3-9-7 10
1978 Sanedtki 4-9-8 10
1979 Producer 3-9-7 14
1980 Moorestyle 3-9-11 9
1981 Moorestyle 4-9-12 9
1982 Pas de Seul 3-9-11 9
1983 Ma Biche 3-9-7 8
1984 Procida 3-9-11 10
1985 Brocade 4-9-8 14
1986 Sarab 5-9-12 16
1987 Soviet Star 3-9-11 14
1988 Salse 3-9-11 13
1989 Gabina 4-9-11 8
1990 Septieme Ciel 3-9-12 10
1991 Danseuse du Soir 3-9-6 7
1992 Wolfhound 3-9-10 8
1993 Dolphin Street 3-9-10 5
1994 Bigstone 4-9-11 12
1995 Poplar Bluff 3-9-0 10
1996 A Magicman 4-9-2 11
1997 Occupandiste 4-8-13 10

PRIX ROYAL-OAK

Longchamp—1m 7f 110yds
Before 1979: 3-year-olds only

1977 Rex Magna 3-9-2 13
1978 Brave Johnny 3-9-2 8
1979 Niniski 3-8-11 9
1980 Gold River 3-8-8 13
1981 Ardross 5-9-3 7
1982 Denel 3-8-11 13
1983 Old Country 4-9-3 14
1984 Agent Double 3-8-11 11
1985 Mersey 3-8-8 12
1986 El Cuite 3-8-11 10
1987 Royal Gait 4-9-3 11
1988 Star Lift 4-9-3 16
1989 Top Sunrise 4-9-3 9
1990 *Braashee 4-9-3 ....
*Indian Queen 5-9-0 11
1991 Turgeon 5-9-3 8
1992 Assessor 3-8-11 12
1993 Raintrap 3-8-11 8
1994 Moonax 3-8-11 7
1995 Sunshack 4-9-4 7
1996 Red Roses Story 4-9-1 5
1997 Ebadiyla 3-8-7 11

CRITERIUM DE SAINT-CLOUD (2y)

Saint-Cloud—1m 2f

1977 Tarek 8-9 7
1978 Callio 8-11 11
1979 Providential 8-9 13
1980 The Wonder 8-13 10
1981 Bon Sang 9-0 14
1982 Escaline 8-6 12
1983 Darshaan 8-9 12
1984 Mouktar 8-9 14
1985 Fast Topaze 8-9 13
1986 Magistros 8-11 15
1987 Waki River 8-11 9
1988 Miserden 8-11 10
1989 Intimiste 8-11 10
1990 Pistolet Bleu 8-11 9
1991 Glaieul 8-11 9
1992 Marchand de Sable 8-11 8
1993 Sunshack 8-11 7
1994 Poliglote 9-0 9
1995 Polaris Flight 9-0 5
1996 Shaka 9-0 10
1997 Special Quest 9-0 7

Winners of Principal National Hunt Races

MURPHY'S GOLD CUP (HANDICAP CHASE)
formerly Mackeson Gold Cup
Cheltenham 2m 4f 110y

1986	Very Promising	8-11-13	11
1987	Beau Ranger	9-10-12	14
1988	Pegwell Bay	7-11-02	13
1989	Joint Sovereignty	9-10-04	15
1990	Multum In Parvo	7-11-02	13
1991	Another Coral	8-10-01	15
1992	Tipping Tim	7-10-10	16
1993	Bradbury Star	8-11-08	15
1994	Bradbury Star	9-11-11	14
1995	Dublin Flyer	9-11-08	12
1996	Challenger du Luc	6-10-02	12
1997	Senor El Betrutti	8-10-00	9

FIRST NATIONAL BANK GOLD CUP (HANDICAP CHASE)
formerly H & T WALKER GOLD CUP
Ascot 2m 4f

1986	Church Warden	7-10-07	6
1987	Weather The Storm	7-11-00	11
1988	Saffron Lord	6-11-03	5
1989	Man O'Magic	8-11-05	11
1990	Blazing Walker	6-11-06	5
1991	Kings Fountain	8-11-01	8
1992	Deep Sensation	7-11-02	10
1993	*Abandoned due to frost*		
1994	Raymylette	7-11-10	11
1995	Sound Man	7-12-00	5
1996	Strong Promise	5-10-05	8
1997	Simply Dashing	6-11-10	11

HENNESSY COGNAC GOLD CUP (HANDICAP CHASE)
Newbury 3m 2f 110y

1986	Broadheath	9-10-05	15
1987	Playschool	9-10-08	12
1988	Strands Of Gold	9-10-00	12
1989	Ghofar	6-10-02	8
1990	Arctic Call	7-11-00	13
1991	Chatam	7-10-06	15
1992	Sibton Abbey	7-10-00	13
1993	Cogent	9-10-01	9
1994	One Man	6-10-00	16
1995	Couldnt Be Better	8-10-08	11
1996	Coome Hill	7-10-00	11
1997	Suny Bay	8-11-08	14

TRIPLEPRINT GOLD CUP (HANDICAP CHASE)
Cheltenham 2m 4f

1986	Oregon Trail	6-10-07	6
1987	Bishop's Yarn	8-10-07	5
1988	Pegwell Bay	7-10-13	10
1989	Clever Folly	9-10-04	6
1990	*Abandoned due to snow*		
1991	Kings Fountain	8-11-10	8
1992	Another Coral	9-11-04	10
1993	Fragrant Dawn	9-10-02	11
1994	Dublin Flyer	8-10-02	11
1995	*Abandoned due to frost*		
1996	Addington Boy	8-11-10	10
1997	Senor El Betrutti	8-11-03	9

PERTEMPS CHRISTMAS HURDLE
Kempton 2m

1986	Nohalmdun	5-11-03	7
1987	Osric	4-11-03	8
1988	Kribensis	4-11-03	7
1989	Kribensis	5-11-03	8
1990	Fidway	5-11-07	8
1991	Gran Alba	5-11-07	7
1992	Mighty Mogul	5-11-07	8
1993	Muse	6-11-07	5
1994	Absaloms's Lady	6-11-02	6
1995	*Abandoned due to frost*		
1996	*Abandoned due to frost*		
1997	Kerawi	4-11-07	5

PERTEMPS KING GEORGE VI CHASE
Kempton 3m

1986	Desert Orchid	7-11-10	8
1987	Nupsala (FR)	8-11-10	9
1988	Desert Orchid	9-11-10	5
1989	Desert Orchid	10-11-10	6
1990	Desert Orchid	11-11-10	9
1991	The Fellow (FR)	6-11-10	8
1992	The Fellow (FR)	7-11-10	8
1993	Barton Bank	7-11-10	10
1994	Algan (FR)	6-11-10	9
1995	*One Man	8-11-10	11
1996	One Man	8-11-10	5
1997	See More Business	7-11-10	8

(*Run at Sandown Jan 6th 1996)

CORAL WELSH NATIONAL (HANDICAP CHASE)
Chepstow 3m 6f
1986-1994 Run in December

1986	Stearsby	7-11-05	17
1987	Playschool	9-10-11	13
1988	Bonanza Boy	7-10-01	12
1989	Bonanza Boy	8-11-11	12
1990	Cool Ground	11-10-0	9
1991	Carvill's Hill	9-11-12	17
1992	Run For Free	8-10-09	11
1993	Riverside Boy	10-10-0	8
1994	*Master Oats	8-11-06	8
1995	*Abandoned due to frost*		
1996	*Abandoned due to frost*		
1997	Earth Summit	9-10-13	14

*Run at Newbury

LADBROKE HANDICAP HURDLE
run as Irish Sweeps Hurdle until 1986
Leopardstown 2m

1986	Bonalma	6-10-13	22
1987	Barnbrook Again	6-11-08	22
1988	Roark	6-11-11	15
1989	Redundant Pal	6-10-00	17
1990	Redundant Pal	7-11-05	27
1991	The Illiad	10-10-13	17
1992	How's The Boss	6-10-02	20
1993	Glencloud	5 10-13	25
1994	Atone	7 10-08	25
1995	Anusha	5-10-02	17
1996	Dance Beat	5-09-12	22
1997	Master Tribe	7-10-04	23

VICTOR CHANDLER (HANDICAP CHASE)
Ascot 2m

1987	*Abandoned due to frost*		
1988	*Abandoned due to fog*		
1989	Desert Orchid	10-12-00	5
1990	Blitzkreig	8-10-04	5
1991	Meikleour	11-10-00	10
1992	Waterloo Boy	9-11-10	5
1993	Sybillin	7-10-10	11
1994	*Viking Flagship	7-10-10	4
1995	Martha's Son	8-10-09	8
1996	Big Matt	9-10-04	11
1997	**Ask Tom	8-10-10	8

(* Run at Warwick)
(**Run at Kempton Jan 18th)

AGFA DIAMOND HANDICAP CHASE
Sandown 3m 110y

1986	Burrough Hill Lad	10-12-00	6
1987	Desert Orchid	8-11-10	6
1988	Charter Party	10-10-11	11
1989	Desert Orchid	10-12-00	4
1990	*Abandoned due to waterlogging*		
1991	Desert Orchid	12-12-00	4
1992	Espy	9-10-07	9
1993	Country Member	8-10-07	3
1994	Second Schedual	9-10-07	5
1995	Deep Bramble	8-11-10	11
1996	Amtrak Express	9-10-07	3
1997	Dextra Dove	10-11-02	6

TOTE GOLD TROPHY (HANDICAP HURDLE)
Newbury 2m 110y

1986	*Abandoned due to snow*		
1987	Neblin	8-10-00	21
1988	Jamesmead	7-10-00	19
1989	Grey Salute	6-11-05	10
1990	Deep Sensation	5-11-03	17
1991	*Abandoned due to frost*		
1992	Rodeo Star	6-10-10	15
1993	King Credo	8-10-00	16
1994	Large Action	6-10-08	11
1995	Mysilv	5-10-08	8
1996	Squire Silk	7-10-12	18
1997	Make a Stand	6-11-07	18

HENNESSY COGNAC GOLD CUP
Leopardstown 3m

1988	Playschool	10-12-00	5
1989	Carvill's Hill	7-12-00	9
1990	Nick The Brief	8-12-00	6
1991	Nick The Brief	9-12-00	6
1992	Carvill's Hill	10-12-00	10
1993	Jodami	8-12-00	7
1994	Jodami	9-12-00	6
1995	Jodami	10-12-00	6
1996	Imperial Call	7-12-00	8
1997	Danoli	9-12-00	8

RACING POST HANDICAP CHASE
Kempton 3m

1988	Rhyme 'n' Reason	9-10-11	12
1989	Bonanza Boy	8-11-01	11
1990	Desert Orchid	11-12-03	8
1991	Docklands Express	9-10-07	9
1992	Docklands Express		
1993	Zeta's Lad	10-10-10	12

1994	Antonin	6-10-04	16
1995	Val D'Alene	8-11-02	9
1996	Rough Quest	10-10-08	9
1997	Mudahim	11-10-02	9

SUNDERLANDS IMPERIAL CUP (HANDICAP) HURDLE
Sandown 2m 110y

1986	Insular	6-9-10	19
1987	Inlander	6-10-03	23
1988	Sprowston Boy	5-10-11	15
1989	Travel Mystery	6-10-08	8
1990	Moody Man	5-10-13	15
1991	Precious Boy	5-10-06	13
1992	King Credo	7-10-04	10
1993	Olympian	6-10-00	15
1994	Precious Boy	8-11-07	13
1995	Collier Bay	5-10-02	10
1996	Amancio	5-10-08	11
1997	Carlito Brigante	5-10-00	18

GUINNESS ARKLE CHALLENGE TROPHY (NOVICES) CHASE
Cheltenham 2m

1986	Oregon Trail	6-11-08	14
1987	Gala's Image	7-11-08	19
1988	Danish Flight	9-11-08	12
1989	Waterloo Boy	6-11-08	14
1990	Comandante	8-11-08	14
1991	Remittance Man	7-11-08	14
1992	Young Pokey	7-11-08	11
1993	Travado	7-11-08	8
1994	Nakir	6-11-08	11
1995	Klairon Davis	6-11-08	11
1996	Ventana Canyon	7-11-08	16
1997	Or Royal	6-11-08	9

SMURFIT CHAMPION HURDLE
Cheltenham 2m 110y

1986	See You Then	6-12-00	23
1987	See You Then	7-12-00	18
1988	Celtic Shot	6-12-00	21
1989	Beech Road	7-12-00	15
1990	Kribensis	6-12-00	19
1991	Morley Street	7-12-00	24
1992	Royal Gait	9-12-00	16
1993	Granville Again	7-12-00	18
1994	Flakey Dove	8-11-09	15
1995	Alderbrook	6-12-00	14
1996	Collier Bay	6-12-00	16
1997	Make a Stand	6-12-00	17

QUEEN MOTHER CHAMPION CHASE
Cheltenham 2m

1986	Buck House	8-12-00	11
1987	Pearlyman	8-12-00	8
1988	Pearlyman	9-12-00	8
1989	Barnbrook Again	8-12-00	8
1990	Barnbrook Again	9-12-00	9
1991	Katabatic	8-12-00	7
1992	Remittance Man	8-12-00	6
1993	Deep Sensation	8-12-00	9
1994	Viking Flagship	7-12-00	8
1995	Viking Flagship	8-12-00	10
1996	Klairon Davis	7-12-00	7
1997	Martha's Son	10-12-00	6

ROYAL SUNALLIANCE NOVICES' CHASE
Cheltenham 3m

1986	Cross Master	9-11-04	30
1987	Kildimo	7-11-04	18
1988	The West Awake	7-11-04	14
1989	Envopak Token	8-11-04	15
1990	Garrison Savannah	7-11-04	9
1991	Rolling Ball	8-11-04	20
1992	Miinnehoma	9-11-04	18
1993	Young Hustler	6-11-04	8
1994	Monsieur Le Cure	8-11-04	18
1995	Brief Gale	8-10-13	13
1996	Nahthen Lad	7-11-04	12
1997	Hanakham	8-11-04	14

ELITE RACING CLUB TRIUMPH HURDLE (4-y-o)
formerly Daily Express Triumph Hurdle
Cheltenham 2m 1f

1986	Solar Cloud	11-00	28
1987	Alone Success	11-00	29
1988	Kribensis	11-00	26
1989	Ikdam	11-00	27
1990	Rare Holiday	11-00	30
1991	Oh So Risky	11-00	27
1992	Duke Of Monmouth	11-00	30
1993	Shawiya	10-09	25
1994	Mysilv	10-09	28
1995	Kissair	11-00	26
1996	Paddy's Return	11-00	29
1997	Commanche Court	11-00	28

TOTE CHELTENHAM GOLD CUP (CHASE)
Cheltenham 3m 2f 110y

1986	Dawn Run	8-11-09	11
1987	The Thinker	9-12-00	12
1988	Charter Party	10-12-00	15
1989	Desert Orchid	10-12-00	13
1990	Norton's Coin	9-12-00	12
1991	Garrison Savannah	8-12-00	14
1992	Cool Ground	10-12-00	8
1993	Jodami	8-12-00	16
1994	The Fellow	9-12-00	15
1995	Master Oats	9-12-00	15
1996	Imperial Call	7-12-00	10
1997	Mr Mulligan	9-12-00	14

MARTELL CUP CHASE
Aintree 3m 1f

1986	Beau Ranger	8-11-05	4
1987	Wayward Lad	12-11-05	6
1988	Desert Orchid	9-11-05	4
1989	Yahoo	8-11-05	8
1990	Toby Tobias	8-11-09	5
1991	Aquilifer	11-11-05	5
1992	Kings Fountain	9-11-09	8
1993	Docklands Express	11-11-05	4
1994	Docklands Express	12-11-05	4
1995	Merry Gale	7-11-09	6
1996	Scotton Banks	7-11-05	6
1997	Barton Bank	11-11-05	5

GLENLIVET ANNIVERSARY HURDLE (4-y-o)
Aintree 2m 110y

1986	Dark Raven	11-00	16
1987	Aldino	11-00	13
1988	Royal Illusion	11-00	14
1989	Vayrua	11-00	9
1990	Sybillin	11-00	18
1991	Montpelier Lad	11-05	14
1992	Salwan	11-00	13
1993	Titled Dancer	10-09	8
1994	Tropical Lake	10-09	12
1995	Stompin	11-00	18
1996	Zabadi	11-00	11
1997	Quakers Field	11-00	12

MUMM MELLING CHASE
Aintree 2m 4f

1991	Blazing Walker	7-11-10	7
1992	Remittance Man	8-11-10	4
1993	Deep Sensation	8-11-10	4
1994	Katabatic	11-11-10	5
1995	Viking Flagship	8-11-10	6
1996	Viking Flagship	9-11-10	4
1997	Martha's Son	10-11-10	4

MARTELL AINTREE CHASE (LIMITED HANDICAP)
Aintree 2m

1986	Kathies Lad	9-10-13	6
1987	Sea Merchant	10-10-07	9
1988	Prideaux Boy	10-10-07	13
1989	Feroda	8-10-07	9
1990	Nohalmdun	9-10-07	12
1991	Blitzkreig	8-10-13	11
1992	Katabatic	9-12-00	4
1993	Boutzdaroff	11-10-07	6
1994	Uncle Ernie	9-10-08	8
1995	Coulton	8-11-08	12
1996	Arctic Kinsman	8-11-00	10
1997	Down the Fell	8-10-07	10

MARTELL AINTREE HURDLE
Aintree 2m 4f

1985	Bajan Sunshine	6-11-06	7
1986	Aonoch	7-11-09	9
1987	Aonoch	8-11-09	7
1988	Celtic Chief	5-11-06	9
1989	Beech Road	7-11-09	12
1990	Morley Street	6-11-06	6
1991	Morley Street	7-11-07	9
1992	Morley Street	8-11-07	6
1993	Morley Street	9-11-07	6
1994	Danoli	6-11-07	9
1995	Danoli	7-11-07	6
1996	Urubande	6-11-07	8
1997	Bimsey	7-11-07	7

STAKIS SCOTTISH GRAND NATIONAL (HANDICAP CHASE)
Ayr 4m 1f

1986	Hardy Lad	9-10-00	24
1987	Little Polveir	9-10-00	11
1988	Mighty Mark	9-10-04	17
1989	Roll-A-Joint	11-10-00	11
1990	Four Trix	9-10-00	28
1991	Killone Abbey	8-10-00	18
1992	Captain Dibble	7-11-00	21
1993	Run For Free	9-11-10	21
1994	Earth Summit	6-10-00	22
1995	Willsford	12-10-12	22
1996	Moorcroft Boy	11-10-02	20
1997	Belmont King	9-11-10	17

WHITBREAD GOLD CUP (HANDICAP CHASE)
Sandown 3m 5f 110y

1986	Plundering	9-10-06	16
1987	Lean Ar Aghaidh	10- 9-10	9
1988	Desert Orchid	9-11-11	12
1989	Brown Windsor	7-10-00	18
1990	Mr Frisk	11-10-05	13
1991	*Docklands Express	9-10-03	10
1992	Topsham Bay	9-10-01	11
1993	**Topsham Bay	10-10-01	13
1994	Ushers Island	8-10-00	12
1995	Cache Fleur	9-10-01	14
1996	Life of a Lord	10-11-10	17
1997	Harwell Lad	8-10-0	9

(*Cahervillahow 7-11-02 disqualified from 1st)
(** Givus A Buck 10-10-00 disqualified from 1st)

CROWTHER HOMES SWINTON (HANDICAP HURDLE)
Haydock 2m

1986	Prideaux Boy	8-11-02	20
1987	Inlander	6-10-08	8
1988	Past Glories	5-11-09	23
1989	State Jester	6-10-00	18
1990	Sybillin	4-10-01	14
1991	Winnie The Witch	7-10-02	12
1992	Bitofabanter	5-11-11	22
1993	Spinning	6-11-00	17
1994	Dreams End	6-11-04	18
1995	Chief Minister	6-11-06	13
1996	Tragic Hero	4-10-09	19
1997	Dreams End	9-11-11	19

1000 GUINEAS STAKES (3y fillies) Newmarket—1 mile

Year	Owner	Winner and Price	Jockey	Trainer	Second	Third	Ran	Time
1960	Mrs H Jackson's	Never Too Late (8/11)	R Poincelet	E Pollet	Lady in Trouble	Running Blue	14	1 39.89
1961	Mrs S Costello's	Sweet Solera (4/1)	W Rickaby	R Day	Ambergris	Indian Melody	14	1 38.14
1962	R More O' Ferrall's	Abermaid (100/6)	W Williamson	H Wragg	Display	West Side Story	14	1 39.36
1963	Mrs P Widener's	Hula Dancer (1/2)	R Poincelet	E Pollet	Spree	Royal Cypher	12	1 42.34
1964	Beatrice, Lady Granard's	Pourparler (11/2)	G Bougoure	P J Prendergast	Gwen	*Royal Danseuse *Petite Gina	18	1 38.82
1965	L Holliday's	Night Off (9/2)	W Williamson	W Wharton	Yami	Mabel	16	1 45.43
1966	Mrs J Mills's	Glad Rags (100/6)	P Cook	V O'Brien	Berkeley Springs	Miliza	21	1 40.30
1967	R Boucher's	Fleet (11/2)	G Moore	N Murless	St Pauli Girl	Lacquer	16	1 44.76
1968	Mrs N Murless's	Caergwrle (4/1)	A Barclay	N Murless	Photo Flash	Sovereign	14	1 40.38
1969	R Moller's	Full Dress (7/1)	R Hutchinson	H Wragg	Hecuba	Motionless	13	1 44.53
1970	Jean, Lady Ashcombe's	Humble Duty (3/1)	L Piggott	P Walwyn	Gleam	Black Satin	12	1 42.13
1971	F Hue-Williams's	Altesse Royale (25/1)	Y Saint Martin	N Murless	Super Honey	Catherine Wheel	10	1 40.90
1972	Mrs R Stanley's	Waterloo (8/1)	E Hide	J W Watts	Marisela	Rose Dubarry	18	1 39.49
1973	G Pope's	Mysterious (11/1)	G Lewis	N Murless	Jacinth	Shellshock	14	1 42.12
1974	The Queen's	Highclere (12/1)	J Mercer	R Hern	Polygamy	Mrs Twiggyw'kle	15	1 40.32
1975	Mrs D O' Kelly's	Nocturnal Spree (14/1)	J Roe	S Murless	Girl Friend	Joking Apart	16	1 41.65
1976	D Wildenstein's	Flying Water (2/1)	Y Saint Martin	A Penna	Konafa	Kesar Queen	25	1 37.83
1977	Mrs E Kettlewell's	Mrs McArdy (16/1)	E Hide	M W Easterby	Freeze the Secret	Sanedtki	18	1 40.07
1978	R Bonnycastle's	Enstone Spark (35/1)	E Johnson	B Hills	Fair Salinia	Seraphima	16	1 41.56
1979	Helena Springfield Ltd's	One in a Million (evens)	J Mercer	H Cecil	Abbeydale	Yanuka	17	1 43.06
1980	O Phipps's	Quick as Lightning (12/1)	B Rouse	J Dunlop	Our Home	Mrs Penny	23	1 41.89
1981	H Joel's	Fairy Footsteps (6/4)	L Piggott	H Cecil	Tolmi	Go Leasing	14	1 40.43
1982	Sir P Oppenheimer's	On The House (33/1)	J Reid	H Wragg	Time Charter	Dione	15	1 40.45
1983	Maktoum Al-Maktoum's	Ma Biche (5/2)	F Head	Mme C Head	Favoridge	Habibti	18	1 41.71
1984	M Lemos's	Pebbles (8/1)	P Robinson	C Brittain	Meis El-Reem	Desirable	15	1 38.18
1985	Sheikh Mohammed's	Oh So Sharp (2/1)	S Cauthen	H Cecil	Al Bahathri	Bella Colora	17	1 36.85
1986	H Ranier's	Midway Lady (10/1)	R Cochrane	B Hanbury	Maysoon	Sonic Lady	15	1 41.54
1987	S Niarchos's	Miesque (15/8)	F Head	F Boutin	Milligram	Interval	14	1 38.48
1988	E Aland's	Ravinella (4/5)	G W Moore	Mme C Head	Dabaweyaa	Diminuendo	12	1 40.88
1989	Sheikh Mohammed's	Musical Bliss (7/2)	W R Swinburn	M Stoute	Kerrera	Aldbourne	7	1 42.69
1990	Hamdan Al-Maktoum's	Salsabil (6/4)	W Carson	J Dunlop	Heart of Joy	Negligent	10	1 38.06
1991	Hamdan Al-Maktoum's	Shadayid (4/6)	W Carson	J Dunlop	Kooyonga	Crystal Gazing	14	1 38.18
1992	Maktoum Al-Maktoum's	Hatoof (5/1)	W R Swinburn	Mme C Head	Marling	Kenbu	14	1 39.45
1993	Mohamed Obaida's	Sayyedati (4/1)	W R Swinburn	C Brittain	Niche	Ajfan	12	1 37.34
1994	R Sangster's	Las Meninas (12/1)	J Reid	T Stack	Balanchine	Coup de Genie	15	1 36.71
1995	Hamdan Al-Maktoum's	Harayir (5/1)	R Hills	Major W R Hern	Aqaarid	Moonshell	14	1 36.72
1996	Wafic Said's	Bosra Sham (10/11)	Pat Eddery	H Cecil	Matiya	Bint Shadayid	13	1 37.75
1997	Greenbay Stables Ltd's	Sleepytime (5/1)	K Fallon	H Cecil	Oh Nellie	Dazzle	15	1 37.66

2000 GUINEAS STAKES (3y) Newmarket—1 mile

Year	Owner	Winner and Price	Jockey	Trainer	Second	Third	Ran	Time
1960	R Webster's	Martial (18/1)	R Hutchinson	P J Prendergast	Venture	Auroy	17	1 38.33
1961	T Yuill's	Rockavon (66/1)	N Stirk	G Boyd	Prince Tudor	Time Greine	22	1 39.46
1962	G Glover's	Privy Councillor (100/6)	W Rickaby	T Waugh	Romulus	Prince Poppa	19	1 38.74
1963	Miss M Sheriffe's	Only for Life (33/1)	J Lindley	J Tree	Ionian	Corpora	21	1 45.00
1964	Mrs H. Jackson's	Baldric (20/1)	W Pyers	E Fellows	Faberge	Balustrade	27	1 38.44
1965	W Harvey's	Niksar (100/8)	D Keith	W Nightingall	Silly Season	Present	22	1 43.31
1966	P Butler's	Kashmir (7/1)	J Lindley	M Bartholomew	Great Nephew	Celtic Song	25	1 40.63
1967	H Joel's	Royal Palace (100/30)	G Moore	N Murless	Taj Dewan	Missile	18	1 39.37
1968	R Guest's	Sir Ivor (11/8)	L Piggott	V O'Brien	Petingo	Jimmy Reppin	10	1 39.26
1969	J Brown's	Right Tack (15/2)	G Lewis	J Sutcliffe	Tower Walk	Welsh Pageant	13	1 41.65
1970	C Engelhard's	Nijinsky (4/7)	L Piggott	V O'Brien	Yellow God	Roi Soleil	14	1 41.54
1971	Mrs J Hislop's	Brigadier Gerard (11/2)	J Mercer	R Hern	Mill Reef	My Swallow	6	1 39.20
1972	Sir J Thorn's	High Top (85/40)	W Carson	B Van Cutsem	Roberto	Sun Prince	12	1 40.82
1973	Mrs B Davis's	Mon Fils (50/1)	F Durr	R Hannon	Noble Decree	Sharp Edge	18	1 42.97
1974	Mme M Berger's	Nonoalco (19/2)	Y Saint Martin	F Boutin	Giacometti	Apalachee	12	1 39.53
1975	C d'Alessio's	Bolkonski (33/1)	G Dettori	H Cecil	Grundy	Dominion	24	1 39.53
1976	C d'Alessio's	Wollow (evens)	G Dettori	H Cecil	Vitiges	Thieving Demon	17	1 38.09
1977	N Schibbye's	Nebbiolo (20/1)	G Curran	K Prendergast	Tachypous	The Minstrel	18	1 38.54
1978	J Hayter's	Roland Gardens (28/1)	F Durr	D Sasse	Remainder Man	Weth Nan	19	1 47.33
1979	A Shead's	Tap On Wood (20/1)	S Cauthen	B Hills	Kris	Young Generation	20	1 43.60
1980	K Abdulla's (Nureyev fin first disqualified)	Known Fact (14/1)	W Carson	J Tree	Posse	Night Alert	14	1 40.46
1981	Mrs A Muinos's	To-Agori-Mou (5/2)	G Starkey	G Harwood	Mattaboy	Bel Bolide	19	1 41.43
1982	G Oldham's	Zino (8/1)	F Head	F Boutin	Wind and Wuthering	Tender King	26	1 37.13
1983	R Sangster's	Lomond (9/1)	Pat Eddery	V O'Brien	Tolomeo	Muscatite	16	1 43.87
1984	R Sangster's	El Gran Senor (15/8)	Pat Eddery	V O'Brien	Chief Singer	Lear Fan	9	1 37.41
1985	Maktoum Al Maktoum's	Shadeed (4/5)	L Piggott	M Stoute	Bairn	Supreme Leader	14	1 37.41
1986	K Abdulla's	Dancing Brave (15/8)	G Starkey	G Harwood	Green Desert	Huntingdale	15	1 40.00
1987	J Horgan's	Don't Forget Me (9/1)	W Carson	R Hannon	Bellotto	Midyan	13	1 36.74
1988	H H Aga Khan's	Doyoun (4/5)	W R Swinburn	M Stoute	Charmer	Bellefella	9	1 41.73
1989	Hamdan Al-Maktoum's	Nashwan (3/1)	W Carson	R Hern	Exbourne	Danehill	14	1 36.44
1990	John Horgan's	Tirol (9/1)	M Kinane	R Hannon	Machiavellian	Anshan	14	1 35.84
1991	Lady Beaverbrook's	Mystiko (13/2)	M Roberts	C Brittain	Lycius	Ganges	14	1 37.83
1992	R Sangster's	Rodrigo de Triano (6/1)	L Piggott	P Chapple-Hyam	Lucky Lindy	Pursuit of Love	16	1 38.37
1993	K Abdulla's	Zafonic (5/6)	Pat Eddery	A Fabre	Barathea	Bin Ajwaad	14	1 35.32
1994	G R Bailey Ltd's	Mister Baileys (16/1)	J Weaver	M Johnston	Grand Lodge	Colonel Collins	23	1 35.08
1995	Sheikh Mohammed's	Pennekamp (9/2)	T Jarnet	A Fabre	Celtic Swing	Bahri	11	1 35.16
1996	Godolphin's	Mark of Esteem (8/1)	L Dettori	S bin Suroor	Even Top	Bijou D'Inde	13	1 37.59
1997	M Tabor & Mrs J. Magnier's	Entrepreneur (11/2)	M Kinane	M Stoute	Revoque	Poteen	16	1 35.64

DERBY STAKES (3y) Epsom—1 mile 4 furlongs 10 yards

Year	Owner	Winner and Price	Jockey	Trainer	Second	Third	Ran	Time
1959	Sir H de Trafford's	Parthia (10/1)	W Carr	C B-Rochfort	Fidalgo	Shantung	20	2 36.00
1960	Sir V Sassoon's	St Paddy (7/1)	L Piggott	N Murless	Alcaeus	Kythnos	17	2 35.80
1961	Mrs A. Plesch's	Psidium (66/1)	R Poincelet	H Wragg	Dicta Drake	Pardao	28	2 36.40
1962	R Guest's	Larkspur (22/1)	N Sellwood	V O'Brien	Arcor	Le Cantilien	26	2 37.60
1963	F Dupre's	Relko (5/1)	Y Saint Martin	F Mathet	Merchant Venturer	Ragusa	26	2 39.40
1964	J Ismay's	Santa Claus (15/8)	A Breasley	M Rogers	Indiana	Dillettante	17	2 41.98
1965	J Ternynck's	Sea-Bird (7/4)	P. Glennon	E Pollet	Meadow Court	I Say	22	2 38.41
1966	Lady Z Wernher's	Charlottown (5/1)	A Breasley	G Smyth	Pretendre	Black Prince	25	2 37.63
1967	H Joel's	Royal Palace (7/4)	G Moore	N Murless	Ribocco	Dart Board	22	2 38.36
1968	R Guest's	Sir Ivor (4/5)	L Piggott	V O'Brien	Connaught	Mount Athos	13	2 38.73
1969	A Budgett's	Blakeney (15/2)	E Johnson	A Budgett	Shoemaker	Prince Regent	26	2 40.30
1970	C Engelhard's	Nijinsky (11/8)	L Piggott	V O'Brien	Gyr	Stintino	11	2 34.68
1971	P Mellon's	Mill Reef (100/30)	G Lewis	I Balding	Linden Tree	Irish Ball	21	2 37.14
1972	J Galbreath's	Roberto (3/1)	L Piggott	V O'Brien	Rheingold	Pentland Firth	22	2 36.09
1973	A Budgett's	Morston (25/1)	E Hide	A Budgett	Cavo Doro	Freefoot	25	2 35.92
1974	Mrs N. Phillips's	Snow Knight (50/1)	B Taylor	P Nelson	Imperial Prince	Giacometti	18	2 35.04
1975	Dr C Vittadini's	Grundy (5/1)	Pat Eddery	P Walwyn	Nobiliary	Hunza Dancer	18	2 35.35
1976	N B Hunt's	Empery (10/1)	L Piggott	M Zilber	Relkino	Oats	23	2 35.69
1977	R Sangster's	The Minstrel (5/1)	L Piggott	V O'Brien	Hot Grove	Blushing Groom	22	2 36.44
1978	Lord Halifax's	Shirley Heights (8/1)	G Starkey	J Dunlop	Hawaiian Sound	Remainder Man	25	2 35.30
1979	Sir M Sobell's	Troy (6/1)	W Carson	R Hern	Dickens Hill	Northern Baby	23	2 36.59
1980	Mrs A Plesch's	Henbit (7/1)	W Carson	R Hern	Master Willie	Rankin	24	2 34.77
1981	H H Aga Khan's	Shergar (10/11)	W Swinburn	M Stoute	Glint of Gold	Scintillating Air	18	2 44.21
1982	R Sangster's	Golden Fleece (3/1)	Pat Eddery	V O'Brien	Touching Wood	Silver Hawk	18	2 34.27
1983	E Moller's	Teenoso (9/2)	L Piggott	G Wragg	Carlingford Castle	Shearwalk	21	2 49.07
1984	L Miglitti's	Secreto (14/1)	C Roche	D O'Brien	El Gran Senor	Mighty Flutter	17	2 39.12
1985	Lord H. de Walden's	Slip Anchor (9/4)	S Cauthen	H Cecil	Law Society	Damister	14	2 36.23
1986	H H Aga Khan's	Shahrastani (11/2)	W Swinburn	M Stoute	Dancing Brave	Mashkour	17	2 37.13
1987	L Freedman's	Reference Point (6/4)	S Cauthen	H Cecil	Most Welcome	Bellotto	19	2 33.90
1988	H H Aga Khan's	Kahyasi (11/1)	R Cochrane	L Cumani	Glacial Storm	Doyoun	14	2 33.84
1989	Hamdan Al-Maktoum's	Nashwan (5/4)	W Carson	R Hern	Terimon	Cacoethes	12	2 34.90
1990	K Abdulla's	Quest For Fame (7/1)	Pat Eddery	R Charlton	Blue Stag	Elmaamul	18	2 37.26
1991	F Salman's	Generous (9/1)	A Munro	P Cole	Marju	Star of Gdansk	13	2 34.00
1992	Sidney H Craig's	Dr Devious (8/1)	J Reid	P Chapple-Hyam	St Jovite	Silver Wisp	18	2 36.19
1993	K Abdulla's	Commander in Chief (15/2)	M Kinane	H Cecil	Blue Judge	Blues Traveller	16	2 34.51
1994	Hamdan Al-Maktoum's	Erhaab (7/2)	W Carson	J Dunlop	King's Theatre	Colonel Collins	25	2 34.16
1995	Saeed Maktoum Al Maktoum's	Lammtarra (14/1)	W Swinburn	S Bin Suroor	Tamure	Presenting	15	2 32.31
1996	K Dasmal's	Shaamit (12/1)	M Hills	W Haggas	Dushyantor	Shantou	20	2 35.05
1997	L Knight's	Benny The Dip (11/1)	W Ryan	J Gosden	Silver Patriarch	Romanov	13	2 35.77

OAKS STAKES (3y fillies) Epsom—1 mile 4 furlongs 10 yards

Year	Owner	Winner and Price	Jockey	Trainer	Second	Third	Ran	Time
1965	J C Brady's	Long Look (100/7)	J Purtell	V O'Brien	Mabel	Ruby's Princess	18	2 39.56
1966	C Clore's	Valoris (11/10)	L Piggott	V O'Brien	Berkeley Springs	Varinia	13	2 39.35
1967	Countess M Batthyany's	Pia (100/7)	E Hide	W Elsey	St Pauli Girl	Ludham	12	2 38.34
1968	H Berlin's	La Lagune (11/8)	G Thiboeuf	F Boutin	Glad One	Pandora Bay	14	2 41.66
1969	Lord Rosebery's	Sleeping Partner (100/6)	J Gorton	D Smith	Frontier Goddess	Myastrid	15	2 39.94
1970	Mrs S Joel's	Lupe (100/30)	A Barclay	N Murless	State Pension	Arctic Wave	16	2 41.46
1971	F Hue-Williams's	Altesse Royale (6/4)	G Lewis	N Murless	Maina	La Manille	11	2 36.95
1972	C St George's	Ginevra (8/1)	A Murray	R Price	Regal Exception	Arkadina	17	2 39.35
1973	G Pope's	Mysterious (13/8)	G Lewis	N Murless	Where You Lead	Aureoletta	10	2 36.31
1974	L Freedman's	Polygamy (3/1)	Pat Eddery	P Walwyn	Furioso	Matuta	15	2 39.39
1975	J Morrison's	Juliette Marny (12/1)	L Piggott	J Tree	Val's Girl	Moonlight Night	12	2 39.10
1976	D Wildenstein's	Pawneese (6/5)	Y Saint Martin	A Penna	Roses for the Star	African Dancer	14	2 35.25
1977	The Queen's	Dunfermline (6/1)	W Carson	R Hern	Freeze the Secret	Vaguely Deb	13	2 36.53
1978	S Hanson's	Fair Salinia (8/1)	G Starkey	M Stoute	Dancing Maid	Suni	15	2 36.82
1979	J Morrison's	Scintillate (20/1)	Pat Eddery	J Tree	Bonnie Isle	Britannia's Rule	14	2 43.74
1980	R Hollingsworth's	Bireme (9/2)	W Carson	R Hern	Vielle	The Dancer	11	2 34.33
1981	Mrs B Firestone's	Blue Wind (3/1)	L Piggott	D Weld	Madam Gay	Leap Lively	12	2 40.93
1982	R Barnett's	Time Charter (12/1)	W Newnes	H Candy	Slightly Dangerous	Last Feather	13	2 34.21
1983	Sir M Sobell's	Sun Princess (6/1)	W Carson	R Hern	Acclimatise	New Coins	15	2 40.98
1984	Sir R McAlpine's	Circus Plume (4/1)	L Piggott	J Dunlop	Media Luna	Poquito Queen	15	2 38.97
1985	Sheikh Mohammed's	Oh So Sharp (6/4)	S Cauthen	H Cecil	Triptych	Dubian	12	2 41.37
1986	H Ranier's	Midway Lady (15/8)	R Cochrane	B Hanbury	Untold	Maysoon	15	2 35.60
1987	Sheikh Mohammed's	Unite (11/1)	W R Swinburn	M Stoute	Bourbon Girl	Three Tails	11	2 38.17
1988	Sheikh Mohammed's	Diminuendo (7/4)	S Cauthen	H Cecil	Sudden Love	Animatrice	11	2 35.02
1989	Sheikh Mohammed's	Snow Bride (13/2)	S Cauthen	H Cecil	Roseate Tern	Mamaluna	9	2 34.22
	(Aliysa finished first but was disqualified)							
1990	Hamdan Al-Maktoum's	Salsabil (2/1)	W Carson	J Dunlop	Game Plan	Knight's Baroness	8	2 38.70
1991	Maktoum Al-Maktoum's	Jet Ski Lady (50/1)	C Roche	J Bolger	Shamshir	Shadayid	9	2 37.30
1992	W J Gredley's	User Friendly (5/1)	G Duffield	C Brittain	All At Sea	Pearl Angel	7	2 39.77
1993	Sheikh Mohammed's	Intrepidity (5/1)	M Roberts	A Fabre	Royal Ballerina	Oakmead	14	2 34.19
1994	Godolphin's	Balanchine (6/1)	L Dettori	H Ibrahim	Wind In Her Hair	Hawajiss	10	2 40.37
1995	Maktoum Al Maktoum/ Godolphin's	Moonshell (3/1)	L Dettori	S Bin Suroor	Dance A Dream	Pure Grain	10	2 35.44
1996	Wafic Said's	Lady Carla (100/30)	Pat Eddery	H Cecil	Pricket	Mezzogiorno	11	2 35.55
1997	K Abdulla's	Reams of Verse (5/6)	K Fallon	H Cecil	Gazelle Royale	Crown of Light	12	2 35.59

ST LEGER STAKES (3y) Doncaster—1 mile 6 furlongs 132 yards

Year	Owner	Winner and Price	Jockey	Trainer	Second	Third	Ran	Time
1959	W Hill's	Cantelo (100/7)	E Hide	C Elsey	Fidalgo	Pindari	11	3 4.60
1960	Sir V Sassoon's	St Paddy (4/6)	L Piggott	N Murless	Die Hard	Vienna	9	3 13.20
1961	Mrs V Lilley's	Aurelius (9/2)	L Piggott	N Murless	Bounteous	Dicta Drake	13	3 6.60
1962	L Holliday's	Hethersett (100/8)	W Carr	R Hern	Monterrico	Miralgo	15	3 10.80
1963	J Mullion's	Ragusa (2/5)	G Bougoure	P J Prendergast	Star Moss	Fighting Ship	7	3 5.40
1964	C Engelhard's	Indiana (100/7)	J Lindley	J Watts	Patti	Soderini	15	3 5.40
1965	J Astor's	Provoke (28/1)	J Mercer	R Hern	Meadow Court	Solstice	11	3 18.60
1966	R Sigtia's	Sodium (7/1)	F Durr	G Todd	Charlottown	David Jack	9	3 9.80
1967	C Engelhard's	Ribocco (7/2)	L Piggott	R Houghton	Hopeful Venture	Ruysdael	9	3 5.40
1968	C Engelhard's	Ribero (100/30)	L Piggott	R Houghton	Canterbury	Cold Storage	8	3 19.80
1969	G Oldham's	Intermezzo (7/1)	R Hutchinson	H Wragg	Ribofilio	Prince Consort	11	3 11.80
1970	C Engelhard's	Nijinsky (2/7)	L Piggott	V O'Brien	Meadowville	Politico	9	3 6.40
1971	Mrs J Rogerson's	Athens Wood (5/2)	L Piggott	H T Jones	Homeric	Falkland	8	3 14.90
1972	O Phipps's	Boucher (3/1)	L Piggott	V O'Brien	Our Mirage	Ginevra	7	3 28.71
1973	W Behrens's	Peleid (28/1)	F Durr	W Elsey	Buoy	Duke of Ragusa	13	3 8.21
1974	Lady Beaverbrook's	Bustino (11/10)	J Mercer	R Hern	Giacometti	Riboson	10	3 9.02
1975	C St George's	Bruni (9/1)	A Murray	R Price	King Pellinore	Libra's Rib	12	3 9.02
1976	D Wildenstein's	Crow (6/1)	Y Saint-Martin	A Penna	Secret Man	Scallywag	15	3 13.17
1977	The Queen's	Dunfermline (10/1)	W Carson	R Hern	Alleged	Classic Example	13	3 5.17
1978	M Lemos's	Julio Mariner (28/1)	E Hide	C Brittain	Le Moss	M-Lolshan	14	3 4.94
1979	A Rolland's	Son of Love (20/1)	A Lequeux	R Collet	Soleil Noir	Niniski	17	3 9.02
1980	H Joel's	Light Cavalry (3/1)	J Mercer	H Cecil	Water Mill	World Leader	7	3 11.48
1981	Sir J Astor's	Cut Above (28/1)	J Mercer	R Hern	Glint of Gold	Bustomi	7	3 11.60
1982	Maktoum Al Maktoum's	Touching Wood (7/1)	P Cook	H T Jones	Zilos	Diamond Shoal	15	3 3.53
1983	Sir M Sobell's	Sun Princess (11/8)	W Carson	R Hern	Esprit du Nord	Carlingford Castle	10	3 16.65
1984	I Allan's	Commanche Run (7/4)	L Piggott	L Cumani	Baynoun	Alphabatim	11	3 9.93
1985	Sheikh Mohammed's	Oh So Sharp (8/11)	S Cauthen	H Cecil	Phardante	Lanfranco	6	3 7.13
1986	Duchess of Norfolk's	Moon Madness (9/2)	Pat Eddery	J Dunlop	Celestial Storm	Untold	8	3 5.03
1987	L Freedman's	Reference Point (4/11)	S Cauthen	H Cecil	Mountain Kingdom	Dry Dock	7	3 5.91
1988	Lady Beaverbrook's	Minster Son (15/2)	W Carson	N A Graham	Diminuendo	Sheriff's Star	6	3 6.80
1989	C St George's (Run at Ayr)	Michelozzo (6/4)	S Cauthen	H Cecil	Sapience	Roseate Tern	8	3 20.72
1990	M Arbib's	Snurge (7/2)	T Quinn	P Cole	Hellenic	River God	8	3 8.78
1991	K Abdulla's	Toulon (5/2)	Pat Eddery	A Fabre	Saddlers' Hall	Micheletti	10	3 3.12
1992	W J Gredley's	User Friendly (7/4)	G Duffield	C Brittain	Sonus	Bonny Scot	7	3 5.48
1993	Mrs G A E Smith's	Bob's Return (3/1)	P Robinson	M Tompkins	Armiger	Edbaysaan	9	3 7.85
1994	Sheikh Mohammed's	Moonax (40/1)	Pat Eddery	B Hills	Broadway Flyer	Double Trigger	8	3 4.19
1995	Godolphin's	Classic Cliche (100/30)	L Dettori	S Bin Suroor	Minds Music	Istidaad	10	3 9.74
1996	Sheikh Mohammed's	Shantou (8/1)	L Dettori	J Gosden	Dushyantor	Samraan	11	3 5.10
1997	P Winfield's	Silver Patriarch (5/4)	Pat Eddery	J Dunlop	Vertical Speed	The Fly	10	3 6.92

KING GEORGE VI AND QUEEN ELIZABETH STAKES
Ascot—1 mile 4 furlongs

Year	Owner	Winner and Price	Jockey	Trainer	Second	Third	Ran	Time
1961	Mme E Couturie's	Right Royal 3-8-7 (6/4)	R Poincelet	E Pollet	St Paddy	Rockavon	4	2 40.34
1962	F Dupre's	Match 4-9-7 (9/2)	Y Saint Martin	F Mathet	Aurelius	Arctic Storm	11	2 32.02
1963	J Mullion's	Ragusa 3-8-7 (4/1)	G Bougoure	P J Prendergast	Miralgo	Tarqogan	10	2 33.80
1964	Mrs H Jackson's	Nasram 4-9-7 (100/7)	W Pyers	E Fellows	Santa Claus	Royal Avenue	4	2 33.15
1965	G Bell's	Meadow Court 3-8-7 (6/5)	L Piggott	P J Prendergast	Soderini	Oncidium	12	2 33.27
1966	J Hornung's	Aunt Edith 4-9-4 (7/2)	L Piggott	N Murless	Sodium	Prominer	5	2 35.06
1967	S Joel's	Busted 4-9-7 (4/1)	G Moore	N Murless	Salvo	Ribocco	9	2 33.64
1968	H Joel's	Royal Palace 4-9-7 (7/4)	A Barclay	N Murless	Felicio	Topyo	7	2 33.22
1969	Duke of Devonshire's	Park Top 5-9-4 (9/4)	L Piggott	B van Cutsem	Crozier	Hogarth	9	2 32.46
1970	C Engelhard's	Nijinsky 3-8-7 (40/85)	L Piggott	V O'Brien	Blakeney	Crepellana	6	2 36.16
1971	P Mellon's	Mill Reef 3-8-7 (8/13)	G Lewis	I Balding	Ortis	Acclimatization	10	2 32.56
1972	Mrs J Hislop's	Brigadier Gerard 4-9-7 (8/13)	J Mercer	R Hern	Parnell	Riverman	9	2 32.91
1973	N B Hunt's	Dahlia 3-8-4 (10/1)	W Pyers	M Zilber	Rheingold	Our Mirage	12	2 30.43
1974	N B Hunt's	Dahlia 4-9-4 (15/8)	L Piggott	M Zilber	Highclere	Dankaro	10	2 33.03
1975	Dr C Vittadini's	Grundy 3-8-7 (4/5)	P Eddery	P Walwyn	Bustino	Dahlia	11	2 26.98
1976	D Wildenstein's	Pawneese 3-8-5 (9/4)	Y Saint Martin	A Penna	Bruni	Orange Bay	10	2 29.36
1977	R Sangster's	The Minstrel 3-8-8 (7/4)	L Piggott	V O'Brien	Orange Bay	Exceller	11	2 30.48
1978	D McCall's	Ile de Bourbon 3-8-8 (12/1)	J Reid	F Houghton	Hawaiian Sound	Montcontour	14	2 30.53
1979	Sir M Sobell's	Troy 3-8-8 (2/5)	W Carson	R Hern	Gay Mecene	Ela-Mana-Mou	7	2 33.75
1980	S Weinstock's	Ela-Mana-Mou 4-9-7 (11/4)	W Carson	R Hern	Mrs Penny	Gregorian	10	2 35.39
1981	H H Aga Khan's	Shergar 3-8-8 (2/5)	W Swinburn	M Stoute	Madam Gay	Fingals Cave	7	2 35.40
1982	A Ward's	Kalaglow 4-9-7 (13-2)	G Starkey	G Harwood	Assert	Glint of Gold	9	2 31.58
1983	R Barnett's	Time Charter 4-9-4 (5/1)	J Mercer	H Candy	Diamond Shoal	Sun Princess	9	2 30.78
1984	E Moller's	Teenoso 4-9-7 (13/2)	L Piggott	G Wragg	Sadler's Wells	Tolomeo	13	2 27.95
1985	Lady Beaverbrook's	Petoski 3-8-8 (12/1)	W Carson	R Hern	Oh So Sharp	Rainbow Quest	12	2 27.61
1986	K Abdulla's	Dancing Brave 3-8-8 (6/4)	Pat Eddery	G Harwood	Shardari	Triptych	9	2 29.49
1987	L Freedman's	Reference Point 3-8-8 (11/10)	S Cauthen	H Cecil	Celestial Storm	Triptych	9	2 34.63
1988	Sheikh Ahmed Al Maktoum	Mtoto 5-9-7 (4/1)	M Roberts	A C Stewart	Unfuwain	Tony Bin	10	2 37.33
1989	Hamdan Al-Maktoum's	Nashwan 3-8-8 (2/9)	W Carson	R Hern	Cacoethes	Top Class	7	2 32.27
1990	Sheikh Mohammed's	Belmez 3-8-9 (15/2)	M Kinane	H Cecil	Old Vic	Assatis	11	2 30.76
1991	F Salman's	Generous 3-8-9 (4/6)	A Munro	P Cole	Sanglamore	Rock Hopper	9	2 28.99
1992	Mrs V K Payson's	St Jovite 3-8-9 (4/5)	S Craine	J Bolger	Saddlers' Hall	Opera House	8	2 30.85
1993	Sheikh Mohammed's	Opera House 5-9-7 (8/1)	M Roberts	M Stoute	White Muzzle	Commander in Chief	10	2 33.94
1994	Sheikh Mohammed's	King's Theatre 3-8-9 (12/1)	M Kinane	H Cecil	White Muzzle	Wagon Master	12	2 28.92
1995	Saeed Maktoum Al Maktoum's	Lammtarra 3-8-9 (9/4)	L Dettori	S Bin Suroor	Pentire	Strategic Choice	7	2 31.01
1996	Mollers Racing's	Pentire 4-9-7 (100/30)	M Hills	G Wragg	Classic Cliche	Shaamit	8	2 28.11
1997	Godolphin's	Swain 5-9-7 (16/1)	J Reid	S Bin Suroor	Pilsudski	Helissio	8	2 36.45

PRIX DE L'ARC DE TRIOMPHE Longchamp—1 mile 4 furlongs

Year	Owner	Winner and Price	Jockey	Trainer	Second	Third	Ran	Time
1959	Aly Khan's	Saint Crespin 3-8-10 (17/1)	G Moore	A Head	Midnight Sun	Le Loup Garou	25	2 33.30
1960	H Aubert's	Puissant Chef 3-8-10 (14/1)	M Garcia	C Bartholomew	Hautain	Point d'Amour	17	2 43.90
1961	E Verga's	Molvedo 3-8-10 (18/10)	E Camici	A Maggi	Right Royal	Misti	19	2 38.40
1962	Mme C del Ducca's	Soltikoff 3-8-10 (40/1)	M Depalmas	R Pelat	Monade	Val de Loir	24	2 30.90
1963	Baron G de Rothschild's	Exbury 4-9-6 (36/10)	J Deforge	G Watson	Le Mesnil	Misti	15	2 34.90
1964	R Ellsworth's	Prince Royal 3-8-10 (16/1)	R Poincelet	G Bridgland	Santa Claus	La Bamba	22	2 35.50
1965	J Ternynck's	Sea-Bird 3-8-10 (6/5)	P Glennon	E Pollet	Reliance	Diatome	20	2 35.50
1966	W Burmann's	Bon Mot 3-8-10 (53/10)	F Head	W Head	Sigebert	Lionel	24	2 39.80
1967	Mme S Volterra's	Topyo 3-8-10 (82/1)	W Pyers	M Bartholomew	Salvo	Ribocco	30	2 38.20
1968	Mrs W Franklyn's	Vaguely Noble 3-8-10 (5/2)	W Williamson	E Pollet	Sir Ivor	Carmarthen	17	2 35.20
1969	S McGrath's	Levmoss 4-9-6 (52/1)	W Williamson	S McGrath	Park Top	Grandier	24	2 29.00
1970	A Plesch's	Sassafras 3-8-10 (19/1)	Y Saint Martin	F Mathet	Nijinsky	Miss Dan	15	2 29.70
1971	P Mellon's	Mill Reef 3-8-10 (7/10)	G Lewis	I Balding	Pistol Packer	Cambrizzia	18	2 28.30
1972	Countess M Batthyany's	San San 3-8-7 (37/2)	F Head	A Penna	Rescousse	Homeric	19	2 28.30
1973	H Zeisel's	Rheingold 4-9-6 (77/10)	L Piggott	B Hills	Allez France	Hard to Beat	27	2 35.80
1974	D Wildenstein's	Allez France 4-9-3 (1/2)	Y Saint Martin	A Penna	Comtesse de Loir	Margouillat	20	2 36.90
1975	W Zeitelhack's	Star Appeal 5-9-6 (119/1)	G Starkey	T Grieper	On My Way	Comtesse de Loir	24	2 33.60
1976	J Wertheimer's	Ivanjica 4-9-1 (71/10)	F Head	A Head	Crow	Youth	20	2 39.40
1977	R Sangster's	Alleged 3-8-11 (38/10)	L Piggott	V O'Brien	Balmerino	Crystal Palace	26	2 30.60
1978	R Sangster's	Alleged 4-9-4 (7/5)	L Piggott	V O'Brien	Trillion	Dancing Maid	18	2 36.10
1979	Mme G Head's	Three Troikas 3-8-8 (88/10)	F Head	Mme C Head	Le Marmot	Troy	22	2 28.90
1980	R Sangster's	Detroit 3-8-8 (67/10)	Pat Eddery	O Douieb	Argument	Ela-Mana-Mou	20	2 28.00
1981	J Wertheimer's	Gold River 4-9-1 (53/1)	G W Moore	A Head	Bikala	April Run	24	2 35.20
1982	H H Aga Khan's	Akiyda 3-8-8 (43/4)	Y Saint Martin	F. Mathet	Ardross	Awaasif	17	2 37.00
1983	D Wildenstein's	All Along 4-9-1 (173/10)	W Swinburn	P Biancone	Sun Princess	Luth Enchantee	26	2 28.10
1984	D Wildenstein's	Sagace 4-9-4 (29/10)	Y Saint Martin	P Biancone	Northern Trick	All Along	22	2 39.10
1985	K Abdulla's	Rainbow Quest 4-9-4 (71/10)	Pat Eddery	J Tree	Sagace	Kozana	15	2 29.50
1986	K Abdulla's	Dancing Brave 3-8-11 (11/10)	Pat Eddery	G Harwood	Bering	Triptych	15	2 27.70
1987	P de Moussac's	Trempolino 3-8-11 (20/1)	Pat Eddery	A Fabre	Tony Bin	Triptych	11	2 26.30
1988	Mrs V Gaucci del Bono's	Tony Bin 5-9-4 (14/1)	J Reid	L Camici	Mtoto	Boyatino	24	2 27.30
1989	A Balzarini's	Carroll House 4-9-4 (19/1)	M Kinane	M Jarvis	Behera	Saint Andrews	19	2 30.80
1990	B McNall's	Saumarez 3-8-11 (15/1)	G Mosse	N Clement	Epervier Bleu	Snurge	21	2 29.80
1991	H Chalhoub's	Suave Dancer 3-8-11 (37/10)	C Asmussen	J Hammond	Magic Night	Pistolet Bleu	14	2 31.40
1992	O Lecerf's	Subotica 4-9-4 (88/10)	T Jarnet	A Fabre	User Friendly	Vert Amande	18	2 39.00
1993	D Tsui's	Urban Sea 4-9-1 (37/1)	E Saint Martin	J Lesbordes	White Muzzle	Opera House	23	2 37.90
1994	Sheikh Mohammed's	Carnegie 3-8-11 (3/1)	T Jarnet	A Fabre	Hernando	Apple Tree	20	2 31.10
1995	Saeed Maktoum Al Maktoum's	Lammtarra 3-8-11 (2/1)	L Dettori	S Bin Suroor	Freedom Cry	Swain	16	2 31.80
1996	E Sarasola's	Helissio 3-8-11 (18/10)	O Peslier	E Lellouche	Pilsudski	Oscar Schindler	16	2 29.90
1997	D Wildenstein's	Peintre Celebre 3-8-11 (22/10)	O Peslier	A Fabre	Pilsudski	Borgia	18	2 24.60

GRAND NATIONAL STEEPLECHASE (Aintree)—4m 4f

Year	Winner and Price	Age & Weight	Jockey	Second	Third	Ran	Time
1958	Mr What (18-1)	8 10 6	A Freeman	Tiberetta	Green Drill	31	10 1.20
1959	Oxo (8-1)	8 10 13	M Scudamore	Wyndburgh	Mr What	34	9 37.20
1960	Merryman II (13-2)	9 10 12	G Scott	Badanloch	Clear Profit	26	9 26.20
1961	Nicolaus Silver (28-1)	9 10 1	H Beasley	Merryman II	O'Malley Point	35	9 22.60
1962	Kilmore (28-1)	12 10 4	F T Winter	Wyndburgh	Mr What	32	9 50.00
1963	Ayala (66-1)	9 10 0	P Buckley	Carrickbeg	Hawa's Song	47	9 35.80
1964	Team Spirit (18-1)	12 10 3	G W Robinson	Purple Silk	Peacetown	33	9 47.00
1965	Jay Trump (100-8)	8 11 5	Mr C Smith, jun	Freddie	Mr Jones	47	9 30.60
1966	Anglo (50-1)	8 10 0	T Norman	Freddie	Forest Prince	47	9 52.80
1967	Foinavon (100-1)	9 10 0	J Buckingham	Honey End	Red Alligator	44	9 49.60
1968	Red Alligator (100-7)	9 10 0	B Fletcher	Moidore's Token	Different Class	45	9 28.60
1969	Highland Wedding (100-9)	12 10 4	E Harty	Steel Bridge	Rondetto	30	9 30.80
1970	Gay Trip (15-1)	8 11 5	P Taaffe	Vulture	Miss Hunter	28	9 38.00
1971	Specify (28-1)	9 10 13	J Cook	Black Secret	Astbury	38	9 34.20
1972	Well To Do (14-1)	9 10 1	G Thorner	Gay Trip	Black Secret	42	10 8.40
1973	Red Rum (9-1)	8 10 5	B Fletcher	Crisp	L'Escargot	38	9 1.90
1974	Red Rum (11-1)	9 12 0	B Fletcher	L'Escargot	Charles Dickens	42	9 20.30
1975	L'Escargot (13-2)	12 11 3	T Carberry	Red Rum	Spanish Steps	31	9 31.10
1976	Rag Trade (14-1)	10 10 12	J Burke	Red Rum	Eyecatcher	32	9 20.90
1977	Red Rum (9-1)	12 11 8	T Stack	Churchtown Boy	Eyecatcher	42	9 30.30
1978	Lucius (14-1)	9 10 9	B R Davies	Sebastian V	Drumroan	37	9 33.90
1979	Rubstic (25-1)	10 10 0	M Barnes	Zongalero	Rough & Tumble	34	9 52.90
1980	Ben Nevis (40-1)	12 10 12	Mr C Fenwick	Rough & Tumble	The Pilgarlic	30	10 17.40
1981	Aldaniti (10-1)	11 10 13	R Champion	Spartan Missile	Royal Mail	39	9 47.20
1982	Grittar (7-1)	9 11 5	E Saunders	Hard Outlook	Loving Words	39	9 12.60
1983	Corbiere (13-1)	8 11 4	B de Haan	Greasepaint	Yer Man	41	9 47.04
1984	Hallo Dandy (13-1)	10 10 2	N Doughty	Greasepaint	Corbiere	40	9 21.04
1985	Last Suspect (50-1)	11 10 5	H Davies	Mr Snugfit	Corbiere	40	9 42.70
1986	West Tip (15-2)	9 10 11	R Dunwoody	Young Driver	Classified	40	9 33.00
1987	Maori Venture (28-1)	11 10 13	S C Knight	The Tsarevich	Lean Ar Aghaidh	40	9 19.30
1988	Rhyme n'Reason (10-1)	9 11 0	B Powell	Durham Edition	Monanore	40	9 53.50
1989	Little Polveir (28-1)	12 10 3	J Frost	West Tip	The Thinker	40	10 6.80
1990	Mr Frisk (16-1)	11 10 6	Mr M Armytage	Durham Edition	Rinus	38	8 47.80
1991	Seagram (12-1)	11 10 6	N Hawke	Garrison Savannah	Auntie Dot	40	9 29.90
1992	Party Politics (14-1)	8 10 7	C Llewellyn	Romany King	Laura's Beau	40	9 6.30
1993	Race Void						
1994	Miinnehoma (16-1)	11 10 8	R Dunwoody	Just So	Moorcroft Boy	36	10 18.80
1995	Royal Athlete (40-1)	12 10 6	J Titley	Party Politics	Over The Deel	35	9 4.00
1996	Rough Quest (7-1)	10 10 7	M Fitzgerald	Encore Un Peu	Superior Finish	27	9 0.80
1997	Lord Gyllene (14-1)	9 10 0	A Dobbin	Suny Bay	Camelot Knight	36	9 5.80

1997 TWO-YEAR-OLD RATINGS

Compiled by Walter Glynn (Raceform Private Handicapper)

To find the top rated horse in each race, add one point for each pound carried below 9st, or subtract one point for each pound carried above 9st. The figure in parenthesis is an all-weather rating.

Abandonment (IRE) .88
Abbatiale (FR) 75
Aberkeen 82
Above Board 63
Abreeze (USA)..........94
Absalom's Lad 63
Absentee...................50
Absoluta (IRE) 83
Absolutly Sparklin ...92
Abu Camp.................46
Abuhail (USA).........101
Abusamrah (USA)....79
Academy (IRE) 60
Acebo Lyons (IRE)...85
Achilles 90
Acid Test..................72
Act Defiant (USA).....81
Act of Folly 59
Adeste Fideles..65 (61)
Adjutant 73
Admire 74
Adrenalin 54
Aegean Dawn 71
African Nugget (IRE)38
After Dawn (IRE) 61
After Eight.........59 (60)
After The Rain 84
Agami (USA).............40
Aganon 71
Air Attache (USA).....76
Aisling Beag (IRE)....61
Aislo (IRE).................84
Aix En Provence (USA)
.................................103
Ajig Dancer...............93
Akarita (IRE) 72
Alarming Motown.....57
Albarahin (USA) 91
Alberich (IRE)...........80
Albinella (IRE) 73
Alboostan 107
Alborada 101
Albrighton.................55
Alcayde 72
Alconleigh 93
Aldwych Arrow (IRE)67
Al-Fateh (IRE) 84
Alfiglia.......................87
Algaleb 34 (70)
Algebra 57 (49)
Alharir (USA) 92
Alignment (IRE)........89
Aljjawarih (USA).....107
Allasella (IRE)...........67
Allaton (IRE) 59
Alleged Aggressor (USA)
..................................80
Allegedly Yours (USA)
..................................74
Allgrit (USA) 74
Alliteration 80
All Made Up (USA) ...70
Allmaites...................72
All Our Blessings (IRE)
..................................30
Al Mabrook (IRE)......80
Almandab (IRE)........96
Almazhar (IRE) 52
Almurooj 53
Almutawakel..........105
Alonzo (IRE) 92
Alpen Wolf (IRE).......71
Alpha Whisky (GER) 73
Alrabyah (IRE)..........55
Al's Fella (IRE) ..74 (52)
Althib (IRE) 76
Altibr (USA) 101
Altitude (IRE)...........61
Always Crowded (USA)
..................................77
Always Lucky....65 (76)
Always True (USA)...76
Always Trying 46
Alzahra......................56
Amabel (USA)..........95
Amazonian 52 (46)
Amber Regent...45 (52)
Ambiguous 56
Ambitious 69
Ameena (USA)..........67
American Cousin58 (58)
Amiasapphire...........31
Amington Girl...........48
Amravati (IRE)..........96
Andalish....................47
Anditz (IRE) 51
Andoya......................90
Andoya (FR) 90
Andy Dufresne 105
Anemos (IRE) 73
Angel Hill 78
Angelina....................58
Angelique 51
Angry Albert.............46
Angstrom (IRE) 92
Anita At Dawn (IRE).80
Anita Marie (IRE)......35
Anka Lady.................45
Anna..........................64
Anna Palariva (IRE)..83
Anniemitchellslass ..44
Announcing Peace ..56
................................(36)
Another Fantasy (IRE).
...............................102
Another Wyn-Bank ..50
Anstand 65
Antonia's Double 71
Antonio Joli.......49 (21)
Antrim Coast 81
Anvil (USA)...............76
Apache Red (IRE).....92
Apple Sauce 53
Appyabo 70 (64)
April Project (IRE)....56
Aquarela 69
Arab Gold 68
Arawak Cay (IRE).....96
Arbenig (IRE) 68 (77)

Arcane Star (IRE)71 (35)
Arctic Air....................76
Arctic Star..................71
Are Yer There 48
Argumentative...........51
Arian Da.....................83
Ariant (USA) 85
Arjan (IRE) 75
Arkadian Hero (USA)...
..................................104
Arm And A Leg (IRE)71
Arnaqueur (USA)......88
Arpeggio 79
Arry Martin.................65
Asad 89
Asakir.........................97
Asbestaswecan.........57
Ascot Cyclone (USA)...
....................................92
Asfurah (USA) 101
Ashjajon.....................38
Ashraakat (USA) 94
Asinbox (IRE) 51
Aspen (IRE) 69
Aspirant Dancer 52
Asprilla (IRE) 41
Asset Manager 73
Astrapi 83
Astrologer..................86
Asyaad (USA)............74
Atlanta 77 (77)
Atlantic Viking (IRE) 97
Attractive Crown (USA)
...................................88
Atuf (USA)..................86
Aunt Sadie 69
Aurigny 91
Averham Star....32 (42)
Aviva Lady (IRE)47 (10)
Azulino (IRE) 55
Baajil 90
Babanina....................71
Baby Grand (IRE).....95
Baby Spice 34
Baby's Tiara (IRE)....64
Badila (IRE)...............80
Baffin Bay 91
Bahamian Melody (USA)
...................................75
Bahr............................97
Bala 64
Balaclava (IRE).........72
Balaitini (IRE) 76
Balance The Books..83
Balanita (IRE)....67 (60)
Bali Dance.........65 (65)
Balla d'Aire (IRE)......74
Ballasilla...........59 (61)
Balla Sola (IRE) 97
Ballet Rambert 73
Ballyellery (IRE) 84
Ballykissann.............64
Ballyvelig Lady (IRE)45
Baltic State (USA) 99
Bamford Castle (IRE)...
...................................76
Banahoe Boy............50
Banakat (IRE) 55
Bandbox (IRE)..........84
Banker Dwerry (FR).90
Bank On Him.....43 (51)
Banningham Blade ..94
Bardonecchia (ITY)..95
Barrelbio (IRE)..........64
Basic Style 50 (35)
Batchworth Belle 39
..................................(74)
Batswing...................80
Battle Warning 37
Bawsian............72 (72)
Bayleaf.......................87
Baylham....................67
Bay of Delight...........54
Bay Prince (IRE).......95
Bay Watch (IRE) 49
Bayyadi (IRE)............55
Beacon Blaze 57
Beauchamp Magic ...58
Beau Vienna 45
Be Crafty (USA)........84
Bedevilled.................78
Beebeep (IRE) 62
Beechwood Quest (IRE)
........................59 (75)
Behold.......................80
Beldarian (IRE) 75
Belladera (IRE) 84
Bella With A Zee (IRE).
...................................60
Belle de Montfort 38
Belle de Nuit (IRE)....85
Bellow (IRE).............78
Bemsha Swing (IRE)....
.................................101
Be My Girl 56
Be My Wish...............78
Beneventus 77
Benin (USA)..............89
Benjamin Frank........41
Ben Rinnes...............84
Bergen (IRE).............86
Bering Gifts (IRE).....82
Berkeley Square (IRE)
...................................64
Bermuda Boy 91
Bermuda Triangle (IRE)
........................57 (44)
Bernardo Bellotto (IRE)
.........................78 (72)
Best Attempt 37
Best of Our Days......66
.................................(62)
Best Quest................59
Bettron 87
Beware 84
Bhutan (IRE).............59
Bianconi (USA).........71
Bidding Ace..............54
Billionaire 39
Billy Owl (IRE) 50
Bintang (IRE)..........107
Bint Kaldoun (IRE)...74
Bint Nadia 57
Bird Of Prey (IRE) 71
Bismarck (IRE) 79
Black Jet...........30 (61)
Black Pidgeon (IRE).67
Black Rock City........59
Blakeset 83
Blanche The Almond...
.........................48 (11)
Blarney Park 56 (26)
Blazing Billy 46
Bless 'im 75
Bliss (IRE).................74
Blitz.......................35 (5)
Blu Carillon (IRE) ...106
Blue Anchor 55
Blueberry 66
Blue Dawn (IRE).......69
Blue Desert 65 (63)
Blue Gentian (USA)..84
Blue Kite...........81 (74)

Blue Marine (GER)...83
Blue Monk (IRE).......75
Blue Music (IRE)......61
Blueprint (IRE)..........80
Blueridge Dancer (IRE) 96
Blue Shadow.....67 (74)
Bluewain Lady..........89
Blue Zola (IRE)..72 (66)
Blundell Lane (IRE)..76
Blushing Victoria.....76 ....(47)
Boat Strand (IRE).....87
Bobbydazzle............78
Boccolino 36
Bodfaridistinction (IRE) 77
Bodfari Pride (IRE)...68
Bodyguard.............103
Bold Edge................98
Bold Fact (USA) 102
Boldini (IRE)...........103
Bold King..................70
Bold Legacy (IRE)....57 ....(57)
Bold Raparee (IRE)..98
Bolero Kid.........86 (64)
Bollin Ann.................56
Bollin Ethos..............30
Bollinger Rose (IRE) 65 ....(51)
Bolshaya...................54
Bomb Alaska............62
Bombastic 83
Bombay Mix (IRE)....79
Bon Sizzle.................54
Borani 75
Border Arrow............95
Boreas Hill (IRE).......36
Boulevard Rouge (USA) 78 (58)
Bound To Please78 (78)
Bow Bells..........59 (50)
Bow Peep (IRE).65 (46)
Bradbury Falls (IRE) 56
Braganza (USA)........74
Brandon Frank.........79
Branston Berry (IRE)79 ....(55)
Brave Maple..............53
Brave Noble (USA)...84
Brave Reward (USA)87
Break For Peace (IRE). 37
Breakin Even.....52 (21)
Bridge 61
Brief Fling (IRE)........50
Brief Journey (IRE)..58
Brief Sentiment (IRE)... 89
Briery Mec.........53 (23)
Brimming.................76
Brimstone (IRE)........81
Bristol Channel........84
Broken Promise (IRE).. 74
Bronzino 68
Brookhouse Lady (IRE) 60
Brooksie 55
Broughtons Mill 58
Browning...........58 (52)
Bryony Brind (IRE)...48
Buddy And Soda (IRE) 68
Bullion......................82
Burgan (IRE)............77
Burning Love...........45
Burnt Yates (IRE).....72
Buzz 88
Buzzing (IRE)...........43
Buzz The Agent........50
Cadillac Jukebox (USA) 54
Cadmax (IRE) 48
Caernarfon Bay (IRE)69
Cage Aux Folles (IRE) 73
Caheredmond Girl (IRE) 59
Cairo Lady (IRE).......43
Calchas (IRE)....93 (88)
Caledonian Express 68
Calliram.....................62
Call Me Vera 54
Call To Order............91
Campari (IRE)...........67
Campione (IRE)........50
Campo Catino (IRE).83
Canadian Puzzler (USA) 78
Candy Twist.............49
Canonize (IRE) 80
Cantonese (USA) .....68 ....(85)
Canzona (IRE) 72
Cape Hope.........67 (68)
Cape Verdi (IRE).......99
Capital Prince (FR)...75
Caplaw Skeen...........49
Capri..........................79
Captain Bliss.....64 (44)
Captain Brady (IRE).63 ....(59)
Captain Jones (IRE).61 ....(20)
Captain Logan (IRE) 79
Captain McCloy (USA). 63
Captain Tim 79
Captivating (IRE)......67
Captive Fact (USA)..40
Caradoc............70 (31)
Carambo...........69 (86)
Caraway 44
Carbon 87
Careful Timing..........72
Caribbean Monarch (IRE) 41
Carinthia (IRE)..........71
Carlasanta (IRE).......52
Carnabrae (IRE)........75
Carol Grimes 64
Caroline's Pet (IRE) .46
Carol Singer (USA)..73 ....(52)
Carouse 65
Carrick View (IRE)....49
Carrowkeel (IRE)....101
Carry The Flag..........91
Carver Doone 39
Carver John..............34
Casa Rosa 42
Casati (IRE)..............71
Casino Ace (IRE)77 (68)
Casino King (IRE) 90
Cast A Spell.............45
Castle Friend............55
Castleross 87
Casual Magic............33
Catch The Dragon (IRE) 78
Catch The Rainbow .61

Dixie Crossroads 55
Dixie d'Oats..............57
Dixie Dynamo (USA) 94
Diya (IRE)..................83
D'Marti.......................76
Doating (IRE)............79
Dockland Executive .30
Docklands Dispatch (IRE)...................62 (63)
Docksider (USA) 108
Dodo (IRE) 84
Dog Watch 84
Donegal Sean....47 (29)
Donna's Double 51
Doodle.......................41
Doomna (IRE)...........82
Dooze (IRE)...............47
Doraid (IRE).............79
Dorton Grange..47 (19)
Dot............................54
Double Appeal (IRE) 38 ....(42)
Double Blade............82
Double Brandy 83
Double Classic (USA).. 70
Double Edged...82 (74)
Double Power...........63
Dougs Dream (IRE)..44 ....(16)
Dove Orchid (IRE)....81
Dover Soul 67 (22)
Dower House..........101
Downclose Duchess 46
Dragon Boy 57
Dragon Triumph (IRE) 89
Dress Design (IRE) ..88
Dr Fong (USA)..........95
Dry Lightning 60
Dublivia.....................41
Duck Row (USA) 100
Dudeen (IRE)............64
Dudley Allen.............39
Due South.................93
Dulcileme (GER).......84
Durar 69
Durgams Delight (IRE). 54 (38)
Durham Flyer............71
Dutch Lad 73

Eager Hero................42
Eagle's Cross (USA) 84
Early Fin (IRE) 72
Early Memory (USA) 48
Eastern Glory (USA) 50
Eastern Lyric............75
Eastern Purple (IRE) 89
Easter Ogil (IRE) 76
Eastwell Hall.............55
Eastwell Minstrel......65
E B Treasure.............31
Eco Friendly 99
Eddie Rombo............49
Edna's Gift (IRE)57 (62)
Edwardian.................85
Ei Ei 81
Eiffel Tiger (IRE).......53
Elabellou (IRE)..47 (47)
Elakik 83
Elanaaka 78
Elba Magic (IRE).......63
Elbarree (IRE)...........50
Electric Isle (IRE) 64
Eleonora d'Arborea .84
Eleventh Duke (IRE).89
El Gabor (IRE) 63
Elhabub.....................83
Elhayq (IRE)..............81
Eliza Acton 74
Eljamil (IRE)..............90
Eljjanah (USA)..........71
Ella (IRE)...................85
Ella Falls (IRE) ..67 (28)
Ellenber 55 (51)
Ellenbrook (IRE)74 (65)
Elleysanta..........64 (45)
Ellway Prince............64
El Maimoun.............101
Elmortero Derufino (IRE) 84
Eloquent 94
Elsaayoura (IRE)......52
Elshamms.................95
Elsinore (IRE)...........68
Elsurur (USA)...........84
Embassy 106
Embody.....................74
Emerald Heights 76
Emerald Project (IRE) 94
Eminent 67 (67)

Emmajoun 66
Emperor Naheem (IRE) 80
Emperor's Gold 60 (64)
Empire Gold (USA) ..76
Empire Park..............74
Empire State (IRE) ...65
Empirical (USA)........75
Enchant.....................66
English Lady (IRE)...65
En Retard (IRE) 84
Epsom Cyclone (USA) 60
Equity Princess........89
Erro Codigo..............65
Escudo (IRE) 81
Espresso...................59
Essandess (IRE)53 (56)
Esse 51
Estopped (IRE).........56
Ethereal.....................62
Eurofen.............61 (12)
Euro Venture 78
Evander (IRE) 87
Evening Set (GER)...92
Evening World (FR)100
Every Penny 50
Exbourne's Wish (USA) 85
Exclusive 99
Existential (FR).........74
Exit To Somewhere (IRE) 82
Expect To Shine.......91
Eymir (IRE) 88
Fabrice 72
Face-Off 74
Facile Tigre...............78
Facsimile 71
Fa-Eq (IRE) 86
Fair Deal (USA).........75
Fair Game (IRE) 67 (45)
Fair Sonia 64
Fairy Domino 64 (34)
Fairy Flight (IRE)......86
Fairy Rock (IRE).......73
Fakhr (USA).............91
Falkenberg (FR) 65 (63)
Family Crest (IRE)....76
Fantasy Island (IRE) 84
Fantasy Night (IRE)..55

Fanti Dancer (IRE)....75
Farndon Princess 55
Far Removed (IRE)...79
Far-So-La..................31
Fashion Victim 82
Fast Franc (IRE)70 (43)
Fast Tempo (IRE) 74
.................................(35)
Fawning 63
Fayez 54 (48)
Fayrana (IRE)............80
Fearless Brave..56 (20)
Fear Not (IRE)...........55
Feel Free (IRE)..........41
Fender Park (IRE).....37
Fen Warrior...............52
Ferghana Ma 75 (41)
Festival Flyer............62
Festival Song (USA) 98
Fey Rouge (IRE).......43
Ffestiniog (IRE)........94
Fiamma (IRE)............88
Fiddler's Rock (IRE).86
Fields of Omagh (USA)
...................................74
Fifth Emerald 40 (30)
Figawin 69 (59)
Filey Brigg 86
Filfilah 83
Filgrave (IRE) 57 (59)
Final Claim................66
Final Settlement (IRE)..
...................................48
Final Tango...............86
Fire Goddess............65
First Consul (USA)...70
First Dance 70
First Encounter (IRE)84
First Frame 38
First Idea...................47
First Master 74
First Village (IRE).....80
Five Fairies........63 (45)
Fiveo'clock Shadow
(IRE) 78
Five of Spades (IRE) 79
Fizzed.........................84
Flame Tower (IRE) ...59
................................(73)
Flame Violet (IRE) ..109
Flaming Ember (IRE)88

Flash d'Or (IRE) ..47 (9)
Flatley (IRE)..............55
Flawless.....................99
Flaxen Pride (IRE)....62
Fleet Lady (IRE)........46
Fleetwood (IRE)........95
Fleur-de-Lys 42
Flickan 66 (70)
Flicker...............68 (12)
Flight..................77 (77)
Flight For Freedom..66
Flirtina........................43
Floral Park 42
Florazi 90
Flow By 79
Flower O'Cannie (IRE).
...................................85
Flush (FR).................72
Fly By Night (IRE) 79
Flying Bold (IRE)71 (62)
Flying Clouds 47
Flying High (IRE)......48
Flying Singer 65
Folklore......................93
Fontevrault (FR).......75
Foreign Love (USA) .54
Forest Fire (SWE).....46
Forest Treasure (IRE) ..
...................................89
Forget About It (IRE)83
Forgotten Star (IRE).66
Formation Dancer....54
Former Love (USA)..73
Forty Love (IRE)66 (36)
Forum.........................86
Foxie Lady 47
Francesca's Folly.....57
Francois Laboure (IRE)
...................................70
Frankie Fair (IRE).....62
.................................(62)
Frankie Ferrari (IRE) 59
Frankie's Girl (IRE) ..42
Franklin Lakes..........65
Freckles.............32 (55)
Freddie Mac (IRE) 39
Fred's In The Know..38
Free 74
Free As The Wind (IRE)
...................................79
Freedom Quest (IRE)84

...............................(84)
Free Option (IRE).....80
French Connection ..78
French Pride (IRE) ...45
Friar Tuck 90
Friendly Warning (FR) .
...................................77
Frisky (IRE)...............64
Frisky Lady 51 (51)
Fritton (IRE)..............44
Frolicking 72 (30)
Frond.........................84
Frontliner (IRE).........54
Fruits of Love (USA) 97
Full Moon..................32
Fundance 72 (50)
Fung Shui (IRE) 51 (39)
Gaelic Quinie (IRE) ..54
..................................(3)
Gaily Mill 70
Galahad (IRE) 89
Gallaash (USA).........56
Game Bird.................60
Gamine (IRE) 70
Gandoura (USA).......66
Gay Abandon 46
Gay Paree (IRE)........71
Geisha Girl................83
Gem...........................56
General Joey 41
General Klaire 71
General Monck.........79
Generosity................69
Generous Embrace..74
................................(74)
Generous Rosi 63
Generous Terms 63
Genius (IRE)......66 (50)
Genoa........................68
Gentle Thoughts 79
George (IRE).............79
Ghali (USA)...............77
Ghorapani (IRE) 48 (38)
Gifted Bairn (IRE).....31
................................(54)
Gift of Gold........76 (64)
Gildersleve 59
Ginner Morris 62
Gipsy Moth 91
Girlie Set (IRE) ..34 (46)
Giveaway 85

Give Her Sally (IRE) .43
Glamorgan (IRE) 57
Glass River........66 (41)
Gleaming Hill (USA).69
Glenstal Lad......38 (48)
Glitter Princess 73
Global Risk...............36
Globe Raider 47
Glorosia (FR)..........100
Glory of Grosvenor (IRE) 88
Glory of Love...........65
God Knows (IRE) 39
Going Places............70
Gold Away (IRE).......90
Goldbridge (IRE) 64
Goldenacres......54 (32)
Golden Chimes (USA) 86
Golden Dice (USA)...98
Golden Fortune........78
Golden Hawk (USA).81
Golden Lyric (IRE) ...48
Golden Mirage (IRE) 96
Golden Reprimand (IRE) 86
Golden Rule.............74
Golden Spanish (USA) 80
Golden Strategy (IRE) 78
Goldfill..............69 (53)
Goldman (IRE)..........83
Goldmaster 50 (28)
Gold Radiance..........70
Goldstar (IRE)...........55
Goldstorm (IRE) 54
Goldtune...................85
Good Catch (IRE).....85
Good On Yer.............58
Good Reason (IRE)..39
Goodwood Cavalier.86
Gorgeous 36 (33)
Grace Browning.......81
Gralmano (IRE)45 (101)
Grand Estate 75
Grand Slam (IRE) 72
Grazia.......................97
Great Dane (IRE) 86
Great Figile (IRE)......44
Great Lyth Lass (IRE) 65 (21)
Great Melody (IRE)...60
Grecian Prince 57
Greeba 62
Greek Dance (IRE) ...84
Greenbrook.......71 (71)
Green Jacket............78
Greenlander.............95
Grey Ciseaux (IRE) ..80
Grey Lightning (IRE)73
Grinkov (IRE)............56
Grosvenor Miss (IRE) 45
Grosvenor Spirit (IRE). 48
Guaranteed 81 (80)
Guenivite (USA) 41
Guildhall 78
Guilsborough 68
Gulland 102
Gunboat Diplomacy.54
Gunzells (USA).........69
Gurkha 91
Guscott (IRE)............85
Gypsy Hill 78
Gypsy Passion (IRE)85
Haami (USA)...........110
Hadayik....................86
Hadid (USA).............79
Hadith......................82
Hakeem (IRE)...........78
Half A Knicker...62 (33)
Half-Hitch (USA).......86
Hallucination (IRE)...94
Halmahera (IRE).....111
Hanzanar (IRE) 84
Happy (FR)...............73
Happy Days 77
Happy Days Again (IRE) 84 (68)
Happy Heart (FR) 71
Happy Wanderer57 (72)
Harbour Master (FR).... 100
Harda Arda (USA) 58
Harmonic Way..........92
Harnage (IRE)..........61
Hasanat....................84
Hasene (FR).............73
Hastate.....................56
Haunt The Zoo..........63
Have A Break............59
Have Merci................86
Hayburner.................56
Hayil (USA).............103
Hazarama (IRE) 62
Headhunter (IRE) 91
Heathyards Sheik.....75 ....(62)
Heavenly Abstone....80 ....(57)
Heavenly Falls (IRE) 73 ....(22)
Heed My Warning (IRE) 105
Heemanela (IRE) 32
Heeremandi (IRE)...103
Heffo's Army (IRE)...58
Heiress of Meath (IRE). 43
Helenes Hill 36 (18)
Henry The Proud (IRE) 71 (3)
Here On Business (IRE) 58
Herminius (IRE)........80
Hermitage Bay (IRE) 94
Hetra Heights (USA) 52
Heuston Station (IRE).. 81
Hever Golf Machine .63 ....(31)
Hever Golf Passion (IRE) 71
Hevergolf Princess (IRE)..................64 (43)
Hever Golf Ranger ...65
Hey Up Mate (IRE)....69 ....(14)
Hibernian Rhapsody (IRE) 85
Hickory (IRE) 77
Hidden Prospect (IRE). 69
Hiding Place 65
High And Low...........77
High And Mighty 57
Highbury Legend .....38 ....(56)
High Carry 87
High Gain.................72
High Honour (IRE)....70

High Jinks.................57
Highly Pleased (USA) ..
..................................55
High Money.......68 (43)
High Noon.................65
High-Rise (IRE).........87
High Sheriff (IRE).....83
High Tension (USA).75
Highwayman (IRE)...85
Hill Magic..................82
Hillside Rose (IRE)...77
Himself (USA)...........93
Hippocracy...............65
Hirst Bridge (IRE).....83
Hit The Spot (IRE)....58
................................(53)
Hobart Junction (IRE)..
..................................72
Hogaif (IRE)..............70
Hoh Chi Min..............96
Hoh Justice..............74
Hoh Navigator (IRE).74
Ho Leng (IRE).........101
Hollow Haze (USA)...85
Holly Hedge (IRE).....79
Hollywood Paradise
(IRE)..........................91
Holy Smoke..............63
Holy Wine (USA)......77
Hombre.....................72
Home Comforts........61
Honest Borderer......78
Honey Storm (IRE)...80
Honey Suckle...........55
Hopefully..................63
Hopeful Star (IRE)....56
................................(50)
Hope Value........67 (49)
Hopping Higgins (IRE).
..................................99
Hot Spot...................33
Hot Topic (IRE) .31 (29)
Housekeeper (IRE)...85
House On Fire (IRE).50
................................(55)
Howies Choice (IRE)65
Hugger-Mugger........43
Hujoom (IRE)............91
Hunt Hill (IRE)...........48
Huntmore (IRE)........62
Huntswood...............86
Huxleen.....................66
Iceband (USA)..........98
I Cried For You (IRE)67
Ida Lupino (IRE).......40
Ikhteyaar (USA)........95
Il Destino..........59 (72)
Imbackagain (IRE)....40
................................(50)
Imelda (USA)............43
I'm Not Sure......47 (54)
Impaldi (IRE).............75
Imperial Honey (IRE)65
Imperial Prince.........66
Implicitly...........65 (49)
Impressionist (IRE) 105
Impulse (IRE) 66 (56)
Impulsive Decision
(IRE)..................63 (77)
Imshishway (IRE).....83
I'm Tef...............42 (67)
Incepta......................50
Inchahoy...................50
Inchalong..................72
Inchtina.....................80
Indian Missile...........89
Indian Silver.............79
Indimaaj....................77
Indy Knight (IRE)......35
Infinity (IRE).............46
Ingle Boy...................39
Inner Key..................41
Innocent Pleasures
(IRE).........................83
Inn On The Park.......38
Inshallah...................64
Insight (FR).............108
Internal Affair (USA) 61
In The Sun (USA).....65
Intuitive.....................36
Irish Summit (IRE)....79
Iris May.....................74
Irma Dancer (IRE).....45
Iron Mountain (IRE)..70
Isabella......................50
Ishbiliya (IRE)...........78
Islamabad.................90
Island Doy.................68
Island Girl (IRE) 66 (48)
Island Race..............46
Isle De France (USA)95
Italian Rose......61 (35)
Itch.....................75 (24)
Its All Relative..........89
Itsnotyetnamed........51
Ivory Crown (IRE).....51
Ivory Isle (IRE)..........56
Ivory League............69
Ivory's Joy................73
Jaazim (USA)............88
Jackerin (IRE)...........79
Jackerri (IRE)............61
Jackies Webb...........48
Jack-N-Jilly (IRE).....50
................................(52)
Jack Ruby.................49
Jacmar (IRE).............93
Jacobina...................65
Jade Vine (IRE).........55
Jadilian (IRE)............68
Jago.........................47
Jamorin Dancer........82
Jane's A Lady (IRE).50
Jarnail (FR)...............38
Jarrayan...................59
Jasmine Tea.............41
Jato Dancer (IRE).....49
Jay And-A (IRE)........98
Jaybee Silver............53
Jayess Elle...............57
Jay Gee (IRE)............92
Jayir (IRE).................67
Jazz Club (USA).......90
Jazz Singer...............55
Jeanne D'Arc............56
Jet Set Sarah (USA).52
Jewel (IRE)................60
Jibe (USA).................99
Jila (IRE)...................84
Jilted (IRE)................80
Jilvarra...............40 (10)
Jim Dore (IRE)..........69
Jimmy Swift (IRE).....71
Jimmy The Greek (IRE)
..................................95
Jimmy Too.................98
Jocasta.....................76
Jockweiler (IRE)61 (40)
John Bowdler Music39
John Ferneley...........52
Joint Regent (USA)..77
Joleah (IRE)..............76
Joli Fille............53 (38)

Jollyhack 61
Jolly Harbour 48 (43)
Jonas Nightengale...74
Jovine (USA) 78
Juinevera (IRE)....81
Julies Jewel (IRE) 64 (70)
June Bounty (USA)..39
Jungle Story (IRE)....74
Junior Muffin (IRE)...77 (49)
Jus'chillin' (IRE)63 (27)
Just Another Time ...67 (73)
Just As Little (IRE)...41
Just A Stroll....44
Just Deserts 43
Justin Hope 49
Just In Time....80
Just Nobby 41
Just Testing 60 (39)
Just Wondering (IRE) .. 74
Kadir....68
Kahtan....94
Kalagold (IRE) 86
Kameez (IRE)....68
Kananaskis (IRE) 75
Kantone (IRE)....43
Karakorum (IRE) 99
Katah....72
Kate Lane (IRE) 79
Kathies Pet 62
Katie's Cracker .55 (54)
Katies Treat (IRE).....39 (23)
Katy Thomas 55
Katyushka (IRE) 74
Kawafil (IRE)....95
Kayo....71 (57)
Kearneys Arch (IRE) 56
Keen Lady 48 (20)
Kenkan (IRE) 74
Kennet 74 (63)
Kettlesing (IRE) 74
Key Provider (IRE) ...59
Khalas....84
Khatani (IRE) 93
Khattaff (IRE)....73
Kheyrah (USA) 83
Khumba Mela (IRE) 102
Kierans Bridge (IRE)51
Kilbride Blues (IRE) .77
Kilcora (IRE) 80
Kilcullen (IRE) 82
Kilimanjaro 105
Killarney Jazz....58 (55)
Killone Lady (IRE)....79
Killucan King....35
Kimberley 52
Kim's Brave 86
Kincara Palace (IRE).... 101
King Darius (IRE) 79
Kingdom Queen (IRE).. 61
King of Dance....59
King Of Kings (IRE)107
King of The River (USA) 87
King Priam (IRE) 33
Kings Arrow (IRE) 71
Kings Check......54 (54)
King's Colours (USA) .. 35
King's Hussar ...57 (59)
King Slayer 68
· Kinnear (IRE)....77
Kite....55 (33)
Kitoph (IRE)....44
Kitza (IRE)....90
Knife Edge (USA).....52
Kolby....61
Komistar 93
Konker 73
Krisamba 80
Krispy Knight 81
Kustom Kit Kate58 (40)
Laa Jadeed (IRE)......65 (51)
Lady Alexander (IRE)... 101
Lady Almitra......55 (21)
Lady Charlotte....82
Lady Eil....55 (55)
Lady Felix 50
Lady For Life (IRE)...75
Lady From Limerick (IRE) 65
Lady Imza....48 (28)
Lady In Waiting 92
Lady Laphroaig (FR)59
....(58)
Lady Moll 79
Ladyofdistinction (IRE) 44
Lady Of Guadalope (IRE) 30
Lady of The Dance...30
Lady Rachel (IRE) 59
Lady Ralphina 44
Lady Rochelle 44
Lady Rockstar 43
Lady's Heart (IRE)....62
Lady So Bold 50 (29)
Lady Yavanna....74
La-Faah (IRE)....108
Laffah (USA)....65
La Galleria 46
Lakeland Pride (IRE)70
Lake Taal 61
Lake Wobegone (IRE) 31
La Lyonesse 56
Lambs Lane....63
La Mouette (USA).....66
Lamsaat (IRE)....59
Land of Dreams....98
La Nuit Rose (FR).....89
Laramania 62 (59)
La Rochelle (IRE) 66
Lasham....72 (50)
Last Christmas....83
Last Knight (IRE)......61
Last Lap....54 (44)
Last Mecene (FR) 90
Late Night Out 95
Latin Bay....53
Latin Nexus (USA) ...74
La Tiziana 75
Latterly (USA)....69
Laurel Pleasure 69
Lauren's Lad.....69 (61)
Lawful Contract (IRE) 32 (45)
Law Library (IRE) 98
Leafy Isle (IRE) 75
Lea Grande....84
Lear Spear (USA) 83
Leather And Scrim (IRE)....45 (1)
Legal Lark (IRE) 68 (55)
Legal Lunch (USA)...84

Legend of Love........73
Leggera (IRE) 92
Legs Be Frendly (IRE) 89
Lemon Bridge (IRE) .59
Lend A Hand...........119
Leofric 68 (18)
Lesley's Adventure (IRE) 42
L'Estable Fleurie (IRE). 90
Lets Be Fair 91
Lets Clic Together (IRE) 76
Liberte Bell (IRE)59 (29)
Lido (IRE)..................85
Life Sentence....61 (26)
Liffey Ballad (IRE)....71
Liffeydale (IRE).........61
Lift The Offer (IRE)...68 ....(83)
Lightning Star (USA)81
Light Step (USA) 76
Likely Story (IRE).....85
Lilanita 41
Lilian Marks (IRE).....48
Lincolnshire (USA) ..74
Linden Heights.........97
Lindesberg 71
Lineage 48
Linguistic Dancer.....31
Linnetsong........62 (46)
Lionel 95
Lisa Simpson (IRE)..52
Lisa's Pride (IRE).....73
Little Bella (IRE) 70
Little Brave 73
Little Cracker 61 (36)
Little Fizz...........67 (52)
Little Indian............102
Little Miss Huff (IRE)73
Little Risk 44 (32)
Little Tumbler (IRE)..59
Livingstone..............48
Lizop (IRE)...............75
Llanasa 65
Lobuche (IRE) 65
Lochdene (IRE) 69
Loch Laird 73
Lone Piper 92
Lonesome Dude (CAN) 97
Long Bond (IRE) 81
Longbowman....37 (17)
Long Island 67 (67)
Long Siege (IRE)......72
Lookingforlove Del (IRE)..................38 (16)
Lord Kintyre 110
Lord Lieutenant........79
Lord of Love 69
Lord Smith...............89
Lord Warford 68
Loubin Lane 52
Louis Philippe (USA)82
Love Academy 86
Love Again 62 (66)
Love Kiss (IRE) 82
Lovers Knot.............84
Loving Claim (USA) .98
Loyal Deed (USA).....55
Lucayan Indian (IRE)91
Lucky Double 75
Lucky Myst 66
Lucy Glitters (USA)..62
Ludere (IRE)......37 (37)
Lunchtime Girl ..35 (54)
Lutine Bell 39
Lycian (IRE).............49
Maazoom (IRE).........48
Mac Black 98
Macca Luna (IRE).....62
Mach One (FR) 38
Madame Claude (IRE).. 78
Madame Jones (IRE)68
Madjamila (IRE)........84
Madman's Mirage (FR) 50
Maduka (IRE)............92
Maedaley 55 (51)
Maggice............50 (32)
Magical.....................76
Magical Baba (IRE) ..86
Magical Colours (IRE).. 62
Magical Dancer (IRE)59
Magical Minty (IRE)102
Magical Peace (IRE).89
Magic Falls (IRE)54 (46)
Magic Morning 35
Magic of Aloha (IRE)77
Magic Powers...........65
Magic Rainbow.........76
Magic Spring (IRE)...67
Maginot (USA)..........55
Mahab (USA) 69
Mahboob (IRE) 101
Maiella......................52
Mail Shot (IRE) 54
Main Street........68 (68)
Mai Tai (IRE) 64
Majaari 94
Majalis......................74
Majestic Hills 83
Major Ballaby (IRE)..75
Makahu Don........58 (9)
Make Believe.....57 (50)
Make No Mistake (IRE) 90
Malozza.............36 (59)
Maltesse (IRE) 78
Malvadilla (IRE) 57
Mamma's Boy...........73
Mamora Bay (IRE)....70 ....(51)
Mandhar (IRE) 60
Manila Moon (USA)..43
Mannequin (IRE) 69
Mansa Musa (IRE)....70
Mantello 56
Mantles Pride 83
Mantles Star......92 (74)
Mantusis (IRE)..........87
Marahill Lad.............47
March Fourteenth (USA).......................67
Mareeba.............67 (77)
Margaret's Dancer ...52 ....(31)
Margone (USA).........58
Mariana 58
Mari-Ela (IRE) 72
Marie Loup (FR) 78
Marigot Bay (IRE).....94
Marilia (IRE) 77
Mark of Prophet (IRE) 73
Markskeepingfaith (IRE) 64
Marksman (IRE)........77
Marran (IRE) 79
Marske Machine.......65

Marton Moss (SWE) .85
Mary Jane..........68 (54)
Mary Lou (IRE)..53 (49)
Masamadas.......60 (72)
Mashab....................69
Masha-Il (IRE)...........79
Master Caster (IRE)..65
Master Mac (USA)....81
Matata (IRE).............76
Matter Of Trust (IRE)99
Mawsoof...................80
Maytong....................63
Mazboon (USA)........93
Mazurka....................80
Meadgate's Dreamer (IRE)..................49 (15)
Means Business (IRE)...................................62
Meatball (FR)............90
Medina Miss......52 (44)
Mega Project (IRE)...70
Megred......................68
Me Jane (IRE)...........53
Melachrino (IRE)......37
Melette......................65
Memorial (IRE)..55 (57)
Mempari (IRE).........102
Memphis Dancer......49
Meniatarra (USA)......63
Merch Rhyd-Y-Grug.38
Merciless..................88
Mercury Falling.58 (23)
Merlin's Ring..........101
Methmoon (IRE).......63
Michelee............39 (70)
Middle Temple..........79
Midlands Girl (IRE)...36
Midnight Line (USA)...................................105
Midnight Sting..........64
Midsummer Night (IRE)...................................77
Midsummer Romance (IRE)..........................59
Mighty Magic............76
Mighty Sure (IRE).....67
Migrate (USA)...........72
Mihnah (IRE).............85
Mijana (IRE)...........102
Milad (IRE)...............76
Mille Miglia (IRE)......38
Mill End Quest..66 (30)
Millie's Lily (IRE)......77
Milligan (FR).............82
Milling (IRE).............47
Millitrix......................77
Minetta...............80 (54)
Miniver (IRE)............48
Minivet......................81
Minjara......................48
Mi Picasso (IRE).......36
Miquelon...................88
Miracle Ridge (IRE)..71
Mirror Mirror (IRE)....86
Misalliance................71
Misbah (USA)...........91
Mishraak (IRE)..........92
Mislead (IRE)............76
Mismewmew.............56
Miss Beveled.....46 (17)
Miss Brighton (IRE) .75
Miss Bussell.............61
Miss Chiquita (IRE)..75
Miss Dangerous74 (39)
Miss Dilletante..........45
Missed Domino........54
Missed The Cut (IRE)72
Miss Eliminator........62
Miss Emer (IRE).......77
Miss Hit.....................43
Missing The Beat (USA)...................................51
Mission Hills.............66
Miss Main Street (IRE)...................................61
Miss Money Spider (IRE)..................70 (72)
Miss Muffett (IRE)....51...............................(10)
Miss Puci...........62 (29)
Miss Rusty (IRE)......45
Miss Salsa Dancer...73
Miss Scooter.....59 (22)
Miss Shannon (IRE).37
Miss Skye (IRE).65 (45)
Miss Slender............50
Miss Vivien...............75
Miss Zafonic (FR).....87
Mister Bankes..........85
Mister Benjamin (IRE)...........................65 (69)
Mister Bunch............43
Mister Rambo...........87
Mister Tricky.....46 (32)
Misty Moor................71
Mitch Passi (IRE)......86...............................(79)
Mitra (IRE).................92
Mockery....................48
Moet (IRE).................60
Mohawk (IRE)....72 (43)
Mole Creek................62
Momentarily (USA)...55
Mondschein..............85
Monopoly (IRE).59 (57)
Monsajem (USA)......78
Montano (USA) .72 (78)
Monte Lemos (IRE)..91
Moon Gorge..............64
Moonlight Flit...........63
Moonlight Truce (IRE)...................................75
Moonstone (IRE)......72
Moontabeh................85
Moothyeb (USA).......63
Moratorium (USA)....66
Morristown Dancer (IRE)..........................75
Moss Side Monkey...60...............................(27)
Mothers Help............53
Mountain Magic........59
Mountain Song.......105
Moving Princess......64
Mowbray (USA)......104
Moy (IRE)..................55
Mr Cahill (USA).........83
Mr Fund Switch.43 (35)
Mr Kiffups (IRE)........40
Mr Mcken (IRE).........72
Mr Miyagi..................66
Mrs Malaprop...........82
Mrs Middle................66
Mrs Potter (IRE)........86
Mubrik (IRE)..............80
Mudalal (USA)..........83
Mudeer....................113
Muftin (IRE)...............51
Muftuffenuf...............72
Mugello.....................94
Muhaba (USA)........100
Muhib (USA)............79
Muhtathir................105

Muja's Magic (IRE)...59 ...(60)
Muji...63
Mulahen...86
Mumtaaz...76
Munasib (IRE)...72
Murmoon...75
Mushraaf...93
Musical Myth (USA).63
Musical Twist (USA) 85
Musk Lime (USA)...100
Mustique Dream79 (79)
Mutafarij (USA)...76
Mutamam...111
Mutawwaj (IRE)...102
Muyassir (IRE)...63
My Bet...60 (55)
My Lost Love...58 (32)
My Pledge (IRE)...58
Mystagogue...65 (82)
Mysterious Ecology.64
Mysterious Miss (IRE) ...85
Mystery Dream (IRE)66
Mystery Guest (IRE).57
Mystical Rodge...40
Mystical Song...62
Mystic Flight (USA)..57
Mysticism...81
My Tyson (IRE) .66 (66)
My Way (FR)...76
Naayel (IRE)...59
Nadwah (USA)...98
Najjar (USA)...74
Naked Oat...71 (71)
Name of Love (IRE)104
Nanoushka (IRE)...91
Narrogin (USA)...73
Naskhi...79
Natalie's Pet...44
Natalis (IRE)...103
Natayig...38
National Academy (GER)...89
National Wish (USA) 57
Naughty Blue (USA).99
Nautical Star...80
Nautical Warning...68
Naviasky (IRE)...79
Naviglio...47
Nazario (IRE)...61
Near Dunleer (IRE)...64
Nebl...67
Nebuchadnezzar...48
Needwood Spirit...76
Needwood Spitfire...36
Nero's Dancer (IRE).32
Nesala...42
Newala...52 (56)
Newhargen (IRE)...61
Next Round (IRE)...84
Ngaere Princess51 (18)
Night Auction (IRE)..68 ...(56)
Night Flyer...77
Night Over Day...40
Night Owl...76
Night Patrol (IRE)...48
Night People...62
Night Rule...83
Night Scent (IRE)...79
Night Shot...87
Night Vigil (IRE) 65 (73)
Niki (IRE)...77
Nisaba (IRE)...66 (58)
Noble Demand (USA)... ...80
Nobledil (IRE)...89
Noble Patriot...58 (51)
Nocturne (IRE)...33
Noemie (FR)...82
Norcroft Joy...50
Nordic Pirjo...50
Noreastern (IRE)...49
Norski Lad...58
Northern Lass (IRE).47
Northern Royal (IRE)79
North Ofthe Border..83
No Shame...57
Nuclear Debate (USA) ...86
Nuit d'Or (IRE)...66 (51)
Nunthorpe...76
Nuvellino...33 (33)
Oare Kite...66
Oberon's Mistral...78
Obsessed...81
Obvious Appeal (IRE).. ...83
Occhi Verdi (IRE)...78
Ocean Line (IRE)...56
Odette...70
Oh Hebe (IRE)...74
O' Higgins (IRE)...74
Oh Never Again (IRE).. ...72 (70)
Oh So Easy...68
Oisin (IRE)...76
Ok Babe...67 (67)
O'Kelly (DEN)...79
Ok John (IRE)...59 (62)
Olive The Twist (USA). ...74
Ollie's Chuckle (IRE)80
Omar's Odyssey (IRE). ...46 (45)
Ombra di Nube (FR).59
On Call...40
One Dinar (FR)...42
One Singer...92 (86)
One To Go (IRE)...63
Only For Gold...84 (67)
Only In Dreams...79
On The Mat...63
On The Right Side...85
Opening Meet...78
Opening Night...53 (37)
Opera King (USA)...85
Operatic...58 (54)
Opopmil (IRE)...58 (57)
Opportune (GER)...63
Opposition Leader...78
Optimistic...81
Orange Bush (IRE)...56 ...(48)
Oriel Girl...71 (38)
Orient Way (IRE)...62
Orleans (IRE)...45
Ornamental...30 (45)
Orsino...81
Oso Rich...36
Osprey Reef (USA)...85
Ouaisne...97
Our Dad's Lad...44
Our Molly Malone...62
Our Valentine (IRE)..60
Out Like Magic..80 (76)
Out'N'About (IRE)...80
Outsourcing (USA)..85
Outspoken...88
Overture (IRE)...86
Paarl Rock...59
Pabella Bluebird (IRE)

..................................42
Pacifica 79
Paddy Deux 31
Paddy McGoon (USA) 60
Pairumani Star (IRE) 68
Palmetto Bay (IRE)...79
Panama House 81
Pantar (IRE) 80
Paradable (IRE) 85
Paradise Soul (USA) 77
Parisian Lady (IRE)..93
Parlez Moi d'Amour (IRE) 39 (39)
Particular Friend 82
Pas de Memoires (IRE) 72 (91)
Pass The Rest (IRE).80
Patricia Olive (IRE)...58
Patsy Culsyth....69 (16)
Pay On Red (USA)....78
Peaceful Sarah 61
Peak Path (IRE) 78
Pedro (IRE)........68 (78)
Pegnitz (USA).........100
Pelagius (IRE)...........80
Pelagos (FR).............71
Penniless (IRE) .74 (50)
Penny Whistle 61
Penrose (IRE) 77
Percy..................48 (62)
Percy-P 76
Perecapa (IRE)..35 (21)
Perfect Harmony (IRE). 78
Perfect Peach 78
Peridot 45
Persian Fantasia 33
Persian Fortune 55 (59)
Persian Isle (IRE) 65
Persiano....................74
Persian Sabre...........61
Persian Venture 67
Per Tuti (IRE)............83
Petaling (IRE)....56 (51)
Petane (IRE)..............63
Petara (IRE) 66
Petarga......................78
Peter's Imp (IRE)81 (48)
Petite Lady................44
Petite Tache..............34
Petronilla (USA) 89
Petruchio (IRE).........64
Phantom Ring...55 (68)
Phantom Waters 66
Phone Alex (IRE)......72
Photogenic 92
Pianist (IRE)..............70
Piccadilly 69
Piccolo Cativo...47 (52)
Pichon Baron (USA) 62
Pierpoint (IRE)..........78
Pigeon.......................67
Pink Ticket 55 (62)
Pinmix (FR)...............92
Pinochet (USA).........57
Pinsharp (IRE) 36
Pinup 54 (34)
Piped Aboard (IRE)..62
Pipe Music (IRE)53 (51)
Pipes Of Peace (IRE)55
Pippas Pride (IRE)....39
Pip's Addition (IRE) .54 ....(68)
Pips Song (IRE)........77
Pixielated (IRE).........73
Plan-B 82
Plasir Des Yeux (FR)94
Plastered In Paris (IRE) 45
Playgroup 55
Play Safe...................63
Pleasant Dreams......51
Pleasure....................36
Pleasuredancer (USA). 81 (74)
Poetry In Motion (IRE). 59
Poetto 75 (62)
Polish Pilot (IRE)......67 ....(48)
Polo Venture 72 (72)
Polska Modelle (FR).41
Poly Blue (IRE).........80
Ponda Rosa (IRE).....55
Pontoon 84
Pool Music................96
Porcellino (IRE)........39
Porthilly Buoy...52 (28)
Porto Foricos (USA) 67
Positive Air...............78
Praetorian Gold........75
Pre Catelan 59
Precise Direction (IRE) 75
Prediction (IRE)........62
Premium Princess ...66
Premium Pursuit......84
Premium Quest 70
Premium Rate (USA)72
Press Ahead......48 (67)
Pressurise 45
Prevalence................93
Priceless...................91
Priddy Green 49
Pride of Bryn.......51 (9)
Pride of My Heart 83
Pride of Place (IRE)..80
Prilora (IRE)..............48
Prima Facie...............60
Primary Colours58 (81)
Primaticcio (IRE)......41
Primavera 68
Prime Hand...............79
Prime Time Girl 57
Primfaheights...........38
Primordial (FR).........50
Prince Ashleigh 79 (64)
Prince Batshoof 66
Prince Foley 92
Princely Heir (IRE) .104
Princely Spark (IRE) 61
Prince Minata (IRE)..63
Prince Nicholas........44
Prince Of Monaco (IRE) 81
Prince of Salsa 35
Prince Oxley......44 (44)
Princess Londis........67
Princess Natalie 79
Princess Olivia 44
Priolette (IRE)...........54
Priors Moor 62 (51)
Private Seal 70 (68)
Prix Star 76
Prodigal Son (IRE) ...57 ....(59)
Prolix.......................106
Prompt Delivery (USA) 82 (79)
Proof Positive...........66
Prose (IRE)........82 (82)
Prospectheus (USA) 80

Prospectress (USA).64
Prospectus (IRE)......80
Public Figure (IRE)...70
Publisher (USA) 88
Pulsar (FR)................82
Pure Coincidence ....97 ....(77)
Pure Nobility (IRE)...85
Pursuit Venture........76
Putuna......................82
Qilin (IRE) 91
Qismat 30 (69)
Quakeress (IRE).......66
Queen Of Fibres (IRE) 41
Queen Of Silk (IRE)..96
Queen of Tides (IRE)72
Queen Salote............69
Queen Sarabi (IRE)..73
Queen's Hat..............53
Quiet Assurance (USA) 98
Quintrell Downs 61
Quintus (USA)..........83
Quite Happy (IRE) 66
Quiver Tree..............56
Quiz Master 67
Quiz Show 76
Raazi 34 (15)
Rabah.......................94
Rabea (USA).............50
Rabi (IRE).................96
Rachaels North (IRE)69
Radar (IRE) 79
Raffaello (IRE)..........66
Rahika Rose 67
Rainbow High...........76
Rainbow Ways 88
Rainmaker 54 (53)
Rainswept.................70
Raise A King.............94
Rambling Rose.........93
Ranna.......................76
Rapid Eagle (IRE).....58
Rapid Reliance..72 (55)
Ra Ra Rasputin.71 (82)
Rare Indigo........86 (70)
Rathclarin (IRE)........48
Ratiyya (IRE) 72 (46)
Rayik........................81
Ray of Sunshine (IRE). 73
Ray's Folly (IRE) 84
Razor........................79
Reach For A Star......55
Ready Fontaine........38
Really Done It Now (IRE)..................65 (28)
Reap Rewards..........76
Rebalza (IRE)............68
Recognition.............65
Red Brook Lad 40
Red Cascade (IRE)...37
Red Leggings...........75
Red Maple (USA)......67
Red Pepper (IRE) .....73 ....(52)
Red Rabbit...............77
Red Risk...........36 (44)
Red Sky Charlie 69
Redswan 63
Refined (IRE) 93
Regal Arrow.............44
Regalo......................83
Regal Patriarch (IRE)67
Regal Revolution 97
Rejected...................86
Relate 71
Remarkable Style (USA).......................99
Remember Frimley ..33 ....(9)
Repose (IRE) 34
Repton 36
Requestor 83
Respond...........78 (78)
Resume (IRE) 72
Resurrection (IRE) ...61
Retention (IRE).........75
Revenge Is Sweet ....41 ....(31)
Rewardia (IRE)..75 (25)
Rhapsody In Blue (IRE) 38
Rhein Hill (IRE).........73
Rhinefield Beauty (IRE) 58
Ribble Assembly......61
Ribblesdale..............68
Rich Choice 68
Richmond Hill...........57
Rico Suave (IRE)88 (66)
Ridgeway (IRE).........71
Ridgewood Ruby (IRE) 73
Right Cross Jonny (USA).........................31
Right Job (IRE).........75
Riley 72
Ring Dancer.............93
Ringleader.........70 (53)
Ring The Rafters 51
Rio (IRE) 69 (7)
Rioja.........................69
Riot..........................64
Risada (IRE).............77
Rising Mane.............43
Rising of The Moon (IRE) 83
Risk Material (IRE) .109
Risky Girl..................66
Risky Whisky 64 (64)
Risque Lady 96
Rita's Rock Ape 72
Ritual........................63
River Ball (FR)..........98
River Beat (IRE)........50
River Flare (USA).....90
River Frontier (IRE)..50 ....(40)
Robanna 64
Robeena...................78
Robert The Bruce.....34
Roberty Bob (IRE)....51
Robin Goodfellow....83
Robin Lane 68
Roborant..................78
Robsart (IRE)............72
Rockette...................58
Rock From The Sun.51 ....(51)
Rock Sounds............39
Rodinia (USA)...........71
Roi Brisbane 79 (79)
Roi de Danse 72
Roi Gironde (IRE)...101
Roisin Splendour (IRE) 56
Ron's Pet 86
Rose Petal (USA) 50
Rosewood Lady (IRE).. ....64 (51)
Roy 45

Shambles....................40
Shamwari Song........63
Shanillo......................67
Shanko (IRE) 86
Shannon (IRE)...64 (43)
Shannon's Secret (IRE)
....................................65
Shanthi 62 (26)
Shantung (IRE).........71
Shape Shifter (IRE)..70
Sharazad (IRE) 68
Sharera (IRE)............73
Sharpaten (IRE)........70
Sharp Catch (IRE)....98
Sharp Cracker (IRE).77
Sharp Domino 96
Sharp Fellow.....52 (51)
Sharp Monkey...58 (59)
Sharp Play 101
Sharp Shooter (IRE).57
Sharp Steel........45 (26)
Shart (IRE) 90
Shaveling..................73
Shawdon...................97
Shecando (IRE) 57
Shegardi 84 (90)
Sheila-B 57
Shereevagh (IRE).....61
Sherganzar 74
Sherpa (IRE).............58
She's A Gem 49 (50)
She's Wonderful (IRE).
....................................54
Shfoug (USA) 82
Shifting.............73 (40)
Shifty Mouse 40
Shimaal 90
Shindium 52
Shipley Glen 44
Shira-a.......................66
Shmoose (IRE) 89
Shohra Wa Jaah.......66
Short Romance (IRE)...
....................................65
Shotley Marie (IRE)..34
Shudder 97
Shuhrah (USA) 98
Shvera (IRE) 55
Shyam (USA)............45
Sick As A Parrot.......79
Sideman (IRE) 106
Siena (GER).............61
Sighisoara (ITY) 72
Signatory...........75 (45)
Silca Key Service.....71
Silent Pride (IRE)......52
................................(45)
Silent Tribute (IRE) ..93
Silent Warning..........44
Silken Dalliance 65 (77)
Silverado (IRE) 78
Silver Hope (IRE).......54
Silver Joy 38 (23)
Silver Picean (IRE)...35
Silver Rhapsody (USA)
....................................85
Silver Sea (USA).......45
Silversmith (FR) 70
Silver Strand (IRE) ...74
Silver Sun 60
Silvertown.................79
Silvery Halo (USA) ...76
Simlet 70
Simply Gifted............74
Simply Super............81
Sinan (USA)..............67
Sinch 43
Sing For Me (IRE).....70
................................(46)
Sinon (IRE) 86
Sir Cador (IRE) 77
Si Senorita................43
Sixpence 68
Sixth Avenue (IRE)...36
................................(17)
Skatt 57
Skippool Creek (IRE)42
Skyers A Kite............33
Sky Mountain (IRE)..58
Sky Red.....................61
Sky Rocket 99
Sledmere (IRE) 37
Slew Magic (IRE).61 (3)
Slew Of Silver (USA)48
Slightly Sober (IRE).57
Slim Prior 52 (59)
Slipper.......................75
Slippery Slope (IRE) 83
Slip Venture..............63
Smart Beau (USA)....61
Smart Prince.............71
Smart Squall (USA)..99
Smart Venture...30 (31)
Smiling Voter (IRE)..78
................................(54)
Smokeycove (IRE) ...55
Smooth Princess (IRE)
.........................39 (65)
Smooth Sailing.80 (28)
Snappy Times...57 (57)
Snowballs..................72
Soap Stone........42 (28)
Social Charter (USA)94
Society King (IRE)....35
Socket Set 85 (73)
Soeur Ti (FR) 84
Soft Touch (IRE)80 (54)
Solo Song 51
Solo Spirit..................81
Solway Lass (IRE)....53
Somayda (IRE) 69
Somethingbeautiful
(USA)..........................70
Somosierra (IRE)......76
Son of Good Times..33
Son of Skelton..........64
Sopran Dandy (IRE).85
Sopran Londa (IRE) .91
Sorridar.....................60
Southdown Cyrano
(IRE) 41
Southern-Be-George47
Soviet Beam (IRE)....44
Soviet Bureau (IRE).86
Soviet Eight (IRE).....49
Spanish Eyes 41
Spanish Fern (USA).84
Sparkling Secret 32
Speaker's Chair........87
Specialist 75
Special Nash (IRE)...99
Special Quest (FR)...97
Special Treat 92
Speedfit Too (IRE)....97
Speed Hill (IRE)........66
Spice Girl 52
Spirito 49
Spirit of Love (USA).45
................................(31)
Spirit of The Nile (FR)
....................................82
Splendid (IRE) 46
Splendid Isolation

(USA)..........................88
Sporty Spice (IRE) ...42
Spree Rose........57 (57)
Spring Fever.............76
Squabble...................59
Stage Whisper ..67 (75)
Stalwart Legion (IRE)58
Star............................86
Star Begonia.............83
Star Crystal (IRE).....82
Starkey......................97
Starliner (IRE)...........64
Starmaker (IRE)........89
Star of Grosvenor (IRE)
...................................77
Star of The Course
(USA)........................39
Star To The North (IRE)
...................................40
Stately Favour...65 (53)
Stately Princess.......71
Static Power (IRE)....51
Statorhythm......35 (13)
Statua (IRE) 97
Stay Alert (IRE).........68
Stayingalive (USA)...85
St Clair Shores (USA)..
...................................77
Stellissima (IRE).......70
St Enodoc (FR).........64
Stephangeorge.........54
Sterling High (IRE)...56
Sternsinger (USA)....71
St Helensfield...........87
Still Waters 68
Stingray (IRE)...........75
Sting Umbro (ITY)....69
St Lucia (IRE)....65 (13)
Stone Beck 68
Stone of Destiny 93
Stop Out....................93
Stopwatch (IRE).......88
Storm Cry (USA) 75
Storm Fromthe East 84
Storm River (USA) ...87
Stormy Blue (IRE)....52
Strategic Air 59
Stravsea 66 (15)
Street Singer 32
Strictly Rhythm 65
Striding King 68
Strike Hard (IRE)......69
Stylish Academy (IRE).
...................................58
Stylish Storm (USA).48
Success And Glory
(IRE) 93
Suellajoy 68
Suggest.....................70
Suivez La Trace 80 (36)
Sumbawa (IRE).........63
Summer Day Blues
(IRE) 58
Summer Deal (USA).78
................................(82)
Summer River (IRE).45
................................(13)
Summer Scene (IRE)34
Summerseat......42 (68)
Summer Style (IRE) .70
Sun Dancing (IRE) ...46
................................(82)
Sun In The Morning .68
................................(31)
Sunley Seeker...81 (81)
Sun Lion (IRE)..........75
Sunshine Pet (IRE)...44
Sunshine Street (USA)
...................................89
Sunstreak 57
Supacalifragilistk.....60
Superchief 65
Super Geil 72 (57)
Super Passat (IRE)...61
Super Rascal.....52 (68)
Super Snip................57
Super Sonic Sonia
(IRE) 94
Supreme Angel 81
Sure Quest................63
Surpresa Cara 49
Surprised..................71
Surprise Present (IRE).
...................................66
Surveyor 93
Susun Kelapa (USA) 93
Suzy Street (IRE)......75
Swanmore Lady (IRE)..
...........................58 (60)
Swaybus...........52 (18)
Sweet Dreams 71
Sweet Reward 72
Sweet Rosie (IRE) 64
................................(45)
Sweet Senorita 34
Sweet Sorrow (IRE)..78
Swift Alliance 78
Swift Time.................67
Swing Along.............86
Swing Sister 85
Swingtime.................56
Swoosh 72
Sylvan Cloud.....34 (36)
Taakid (USA) 57
Taalluf (USA) 78
Ta Aruf (USA) 79
Tabasco (IRE)...........70
Tadwiga 97
Taispeain (IRE).........95
Tajasur (IRE).............79
Tajawuz.....................75
Taj Mahal (IRE)..38 (50)
Tajmil (IRE)...............72
Takarian (IRE).........103
Take A Risk 61
Take A Turn 79
Take Care (IRE) 61
Talaheart...................42
Taleca Son (IRE) 68
Tales of Bounty (IRE) ..
...................................60
Tamarisk (IRE)........111
Tamburello (IRE)......44
................................(31)
Tamerin Bay 69
Tancred Times 68
Tangerine Flyer.72 (72)
Tanimbar (IRE) 49
Tankersley 54
Tarascon (IRE) 106
Tarashaan.................74
Tarbaan (IRE) 86
Tartan Lass 61 (66)
Tasbok (IRE).............60
Taste of Success 65
Tattinger 84
Taverner Society (IRE)
...................................81
Taylor's Pride...........40
Tazkiya......................56
Teapot Row (IRE)...107
Tearaway 74
Technician (IRE)52 (38)

Technohead (IRE)....89
Teepee (IRE)......56 (40)
Teishebaini (IRE)......96
Telalanjon.................79
Temeraire (USA).......65
Temper Lad (USA) ...47
Tempus Fugit...........84
Ten Bob (IRE)...........91
Tenbyssimo (IRE) 95
Tender Doll (IRE)50 (21)
Tennessee (SWI)......73
Tensile (IRE)............75
Ten Tricks (IRE) 76
Tereyna.....................70
Teroom......................67
Territory (IRE)...........83
Thanksgiving (IRE) ..89
Thanks Keith.....62 (65)
The Ant (IRE)............43
The Artful Dodger 53
Theatre of Dreams...75
The Beat Rolls On
(IRE) 64
The Blues Academy
(IRE) 76
The Boy John (USA) 81
The Cannie Rover 49
Thecomebackking...55
................................(35)
The Downtown Fox..79
The Druidess (IRE)...47
................................(41)
The Fuelologist...57 (5)
The Gene Genie 87
The Glow-Worm (IRE)..
...................................89
The Groveller 81 (81)
The Hobby Lobby (IRE)
...........................68 (37)
The Honorable Lady 67
The Imposter (IRE)...56
The King Of Cloyne
(USA).......................101
The Limping Cat (IRE)
...................................84
Thelonius (IRE) 71
The Magistrate (IRE) 77
Theme Tune.............67
The Realtour............64
There Be Demons
(USA).........................75

The Rich Man (IRE)..86
The Robe 58 (49)
The Thruster 62 (47)
The Woodcock 48
Third Cousin (IRE) ...82
................................(81)
Thistle Park 73
Thomas O'Malley 56
................................(29)
Thorntoun Belle (IRE)..
...................................51
Thrashing 66
Three Angels (IRE)...66
Three Star Rated (IRE).
...................................90
Three Tenners 68
Thumbellina.............41
Thundering Papoose...
...................................36
Tiara 47
Tie Break (IRE)..54 (84)
Tifosi (IRE)...............62
Tiger Haven (IRE).....76
Tightrope...........79 (59)
Tigi 37
Tigullio (IRE).............55
Tilburg 58 (27)
Timbervati (USA)......79
Timekeeper (USA)....83
Timeless Isle (IRE)...86
Time To Hunt...........56
Time To Time 55 (49)
Tindaya 61
Tinerana Law (IRE) ..69
Tinos Island (IRE) 42
Tippitt Boy 100
Titan 76
Titanic (IRE).............94
Title Bid (USA)..........90
Tittle Tattle (IRE) 90
Tiye...........................68
Toblersong 93
Todos Santos (IRE)..59
Tokay 61
Toll's Times.........56 (9)
To Love With Love...81
Tom 54
Tom Dougal.......66 (56)
Topaz 44
Top Floor (IRE).........68
Top Gear (IRE)..........59

Top Maite.................69
Torianna (USA).........78
Tornado Prince (IRE)64
Torrent 79
Torso.........................61
Total Tropix.......54 (36)
To The Skies (USA)..74
Touchanova 54 (52)
Touch of Colour 50
Tough Nell (IRE).......64
Touraneena 59
Townville Cee Cee ...59
Tracking.................101
Trans Island.............91
Transylvania............66
Travelling Clock 39
Treasure Chest (IRE)83
Treasure Island.39 (37)
Treble Term.......65 (49)
Tremonnow 59
Treverrick (IRE)........79
Trident (USA)............85
Trigger Happy (IRE).85
Trinity Reef 64
Trojan Wolf...............52
Trophy Wife (FR)......71
Truth Teller........66 (66)
Tugela (USA) 57
Tui 56 (32)
Tullich Refrain ..64 (13)
Tumbleweed Hero....79
Tumblweed Prospect...
...................................83
Tundra (IRE) 42
Tuning......................82
Turf Moor (IRE).........56
Tussle 95
Tutankhamun 65
Twoforten 64
Two-Twenty-Two (IRE)
...................................82
Two Williams............82
U K Magic (IRE)........61
Uniform.....................55
Uninhibited (IRE)......91
Universal Lady 74
Unknown Quest 39
Un Melodie...............80
Untold Story (USA) ..63
Up At The Top (IRE).65
Uplifting 77

RACEFORM TOP RATED TWO-YEAR-OLDS OF 1997

Horse	Rating
Xaar	127
Lend A Hand	119
Second Empire (IRE)	116
Daggers Drawn (USA)	114
Mudeer	113
Charge D'Affaires	113
Saratoga Springs (CAN)	113
Mutamam	111
Tamarisk (IRE)	111
Central Park (IRE)	111
Halmahera (IRE)	111
Haami (USA)	110
Lord Kintyre	110
Zalaiyka (FR)	109
Zelding (IRE)	109
Risk Material (IRE)	109
Flame Violet (IRE)	109
Insight (FR)	108
La-Faah (IRE)	108
Docksider (USA)	108
Bintang (IRE)	107
Teapot Row (IRE)	107
Alboostan	107
Aljjawarih (USA)	107
King Of Kings (IRE)	107
Wish Me Luck (IRE)	106
Celtic Cavalier (IRE)	106
Prolix	106
Chester House (USA)	106
Tarascon (IRE)	106
Embassy	106
Blu Carillon (IRE)	106
Sideman (IRE)	106
Desert Drama (IRE)	105
Andy Dufresne	105
Kilimanjaro	105
City Honours (USA)	105
Heed My Warning (IRE)	105
Midnight Line (USA)	105
Almutawakel	105
Impressionist (IRE)	105
Mountain Song	105
Muhtathir	105
Desert Prince (IRE)	105

TURF STATISTICS

LEADING FLAT TRAINERS, 1997

(Win and place prizemoney in Britain from 20th March to 8th November)

		Races Won	Stakes £
1.	M. R. Stoute	84	2,140,949
2.	J. H. M. Gosden	91	1,812,411
3.	H. R. A. Cecil	78	1,622,721
4.	J. L. Dunlop	97	1,441,331
5.	S bin Suroor	41	1,175,283
6.	B. W. Hills	78	1,022,465
7.	L. M. Cumani	66	1,013,308
8.	M. Johnston	92	809,506
9.	D. R. Loder	55	774,316
10.	P. F. I. Cole	58	757,472
11.	R. Hannon	85	710,643
12.	P. W. Chapple-Hyam	37	674,005
13.	I. A. Balding	52	611,944
14.	G. Wragg	26	540,684
15.	J. Berry	80	476,194
16.	Sir Mark Prescott	43	453,558
17.	D. Morley	24	443,854
18.	Mrs J. R. Ramsden	44	441,992
19.	B. J. Meehan	54	436,623
20.	C. E. Brittain	19	411,678
21.	T. D. Easterby	33	397,624
22.	R. Charlton	38	385,360
23.	J. L. Eyre	39	340,499
24.	E. A. L. Dunlop	27	335,008
25.	Lady Herries	32	311,143
26.	R. Akehurst	24	307,766
27.	P. W. Harris	34	295,213
28.	A. P. O'Brien,Ireland	3	285,874
29.	M. W. Easterby	46	283,925
30.	Mrs M. Reveley	38	282,013
31.	A. Fabre,France	1	275,444
32.	J. A. R. Toller	14	257,581
33.	W. R. Muir	30	255,795
34.	M. R. Channon	36	254,906
35.	E. J. Alston	21	245,707
36.	Lord Huntingdon	20	240,801
37.	B. Hanbury	26	240,025
38.	Miss Gay Kelleway	41	240,006
39.	D. Nicholls	29	232,697
40.	P. T. Walwyn	31	231,424
41.	M. Bell	30	227,268
42.	N. A. Callaghan	17	225,907
43.	B. A. McMahon	26	210,183
44.	G. L. Moore	34	207,861
45.	G. Lewis	25	202,029
46.	D. R. C. Elsworth	23	200,282
47.	T. D. Barron	25	196,847
48.	R. Guest	23	195,642
49.	Mrs J. Cecil	11	192,867
50.	A. C. Stewart	18	190,972

LEADING FLAT OWNERS, 1997

(Win and place prizemoney in Britain from 20th March to 8th November)

		Races Won	Stakes £
1.	Sheikh Mohammed	87	1,480,859
2.	Mr Hamdan Al Maktoum	85	1,343,877
3.	Mr K. Abdulla	48	1,180,853
4.	Godolphin	40	1,161,199
5.	Maktoum Al Maktoum	55	911,425
6.	Mr Landon Knight	2	743,842
7.	Mr M Tabor & Mrs John Magnier	19	690,138
8.	Lord Weinstock	13	654,208
9.	Mr R. E. Sangster	28	630,871
10.	Mr Peter Winfield	5	494,649
11.	H R H Prince Fahd Salman	27	396,961
12.	Mr A. E. Oppenheimer	19	381,853
13.	Greenbay Stables Ltd	4	293,555
14.	Cheveley Park Stud	32	286,524
15.	Sheikh Ahmed Al Maktoum	24	256,845
16.	Highclere Thoroughbred Racing Ltd	16	248,793
17.	Mr Mohamed Obaida	2	246,337
18.	Lucayan Stud	19	233,510
19.	Mr Wafic Said	10	217,317
20.	H H Aga Khan	14	213,815
21.	Duke of Devonshire	6	201,962
22.	Mr Christopher Spence	4	192,283
23.	Mr P. D. Savill	24	187,903
24.	Mr J. C. Smith	12	179,306
25.	Mr Daniel Wildenstein	0	153,810
26.	Lord Howard de Walden	7	153,327
27.	The Queen	10	146,372
28.	Mr Robert Smith	4	134,322
29.	Fittocks Stud	5	130,501
30.	Mollers Racing	7	125,694
31.	Mr Cyril Humphris	8	117,956
32.	Mr George Strawbridge	7	116,421
33.	Mr Graham Rock	2	113,383
34.	Sheikh Marwan Al Maktoum	3	110,596
35.	Mr R. M. Cyzer	14	110,129
36.	Matthews Breeding and Racing	3	109,606
37.	Cliveden Stud	5	108,774
38.	Mr J. R. Good	8	108,670
39.	Sunpak Potatoes	2	106,071
40.	Mr Chris Hardy	9	105,770
41.	Mr M. Calvert	2	102,973
42.	Miss B. Swire	13	98,326
43.	Mr P. R. C. Morrison	2	92,546
44.	Al Muallim Partnership	9	89,816
45.	Mr D. J. Deer	4	89,052
46.	Mrs J. M. Corbett	5	88,803
47.	C H Newton Jnr Ltd	5	87,679
48.	The Bibby Halliday Partnership	4	87,165

LEADING FLAT JOCKEYS, 1997

(Wins in Britain from 20th March to 8th November)

	Win £	1st	2nd	3rd	Unpl	Total Mts	Per cent	£1 Level stake
K. Fallon	1,845,353	196	137	116	460	909	21.6	+ **118.23**
L. Dettori	1,892,853	173	113	93	388	767	22.6	- 29.07
K. Darley	719,789	128	107	96	509	840	15.2	- 64.18
Pat Eddery	1,288,172	116	87	65	363	631	18.4	- 151.44
J. Reid	1,137,912	110	105	97	511	823	13.4	- 151.28
R. Hills	655,488	85	73	86	281	525	16.2	- 48.08
S. Sanders	613,597	84	98	91	502	775	10.8	- 129.03
M. Hills	852,183	83	64	72	342	561	14.8	- 21.82
J. Weaver	358,769	80	72	62	359	573	14.0	- 91.67
J. Fortune	413,545	78	75	79	443	675	11.6	- 170.27
D. Holland	399,001	77	71	66	390	604	12.8	- 143.18
T. Sprake	325,479	75	65	75	445	660	11.4	- 27.95
R. Ffrench	320,841	73	61	58	403	595	12.3	- 14.57
G. Duffield	422,810	71	68	56	406	601	11.8	- 178.68
T. Quinn	586,304	71	72	86	435	664	10.7	- 215.66
J. F. Egan	215,672	61	63	62	402	588	10.4	- 12.46
Dane O'Neill	273,375	55	63	77	516	711	7.7	- 318.64
Martin Dwyer	194,964	51	60	45	369	525	9.7	- 90.75
A. Culhane	186,247	50	63	37	444	594	8.4	- 224.86
R. Cochrane	383,883	50	64	65	391	570	8.8	- 148.26
G. Carter	265,863	49	53	52	387	541	9.1	- 234.64
W. Ryan	838,630	48	62	64	323	497	9.7	- 247.34
M. Roberts	343,784	48	50	40	342	480	10.0	- 102.42
J. Quinn	225,143	48	60	73	571	752	6.4	- 325.18
C. Lowther	233,839	47	32	36	286	401	11.7	+ **22.40**
J. Carroll	179,201	46	65	71	485	667	6.9	- 294.75
L. Charnock	257,163	43	51	52	416	562	7.7	- 179.12
S. Drowne	172,877	41	40	42	499	622	6.6	- 250.63
Paul Eddery	180,144	40	36	37	383	496	8.1	- 307.58
D. Harrison	166,884	39	39	29	240	347	11.2	- 47.11
P. Fessey	141,606	37	45	33	342	457	8.1	- 230.56
Dean McKeown	189,829	36	29	40	389	494	7.3	- 76.01
A. Clark	129,600	35	50	35	368	488	7.2	- 112.66
M. Fenton	133,657	32	24	37	284	377	8.5	- 122.71
B. Doyle	194,225	31	39	33	188	291	10.7	- 24.66
D. Sweeney	101,579	31	16	24	181	252	12.3	- 22.83
R. Hughes	137,406	30	33	37	157	257	11.7	- 50.46
O. Peslier	872,994	29	11	14	98	152	19.1	+ **98.39**
G. Hind	182,966	29	34	35	223	321	9.0	- 120.76
C. Rutter	156,403	26	37	30	321	414	6.3	- 115.53
S. Whitworth	97,113	26	29	30	247	332	7.8	- 76.25
F. Lynch	94,163	26	33	38	270	367	7.1	- 201.75

NATIONAL HUNT STATISTICS

LEADING JUMP TRAINERS, 1996/97

		Races Won	Stakes £
1.	M. C. Pipe	212	1,399,510
2.	D. Nicholson	100	1,063,552
3.	G. Richards	74	606,828
4.	Mrs M. Reveley	87	463,452
5.	K. C. Bailey	77	436,062
6.	N. A. Twiston-Davies	52	428,815
7.	P. F. Nicholls	56	379,570
8.	P. J. Hobbs	64	363,375
9.	N. J. Henderson	58	360,752
10.	Capt T. A. Forster	36	337,645
11.	O. Sherwood	49	325,327
12.	C. P. E. Brooks	27	315,155
13.	Miss H. C. Knight	47	308,876
14.	J. T. Gifford	41	277,334
15.	S. A. Brookshaw	15	276,654
16.	R. H. Alner	24	266,622
17.	Mrs S. J. Smith	42	265,954
18.	M. D. Hammond	47	255,811
19.	P. Bowen	33	224,044
20.	J. G. FitzGerald	29	205,400

LEADING JUMP OWNERS, 1996/97

		Races Won	Stakes £
1.	Mr Robert Ogden	42	290,762
2.	Mr P. A. Deal	6	256,921
3.	Mr Stanley Clarke	8	253,350
4.	Mr D. A. Johnson	18	227,462
5.	Mr G. A. Hubbard	11	160,382
6.	Michael And Gerry Worcester	3	158,433
7.	Mrs J. Mould	5	142,185
8.	Uplands Bloodstock	6	140,503
9.	Mr J. Hales	5	139,482
10.	Mr P. J. Hartigan	2	130,090
11.	Mr B. T. Stewart-Brown	6	123,170
12.	Mr & Mrs Raymond Anderson Green	16	115,966
13.	Lord Vestey	6	112,995
14.	Martin Pipe Racing Club	25	111,837
15.	Mrs Jill Dennis	5	91,844
16.	Lady Harris	8	91,626
17.	Mr J. P. McManus	2	85,427
18.	Mrs E. A. Murray	4	84,366
19.	Mr P. Bowen	10	80,393
20.	Mrs E. Queally	2	76,587

LEADING JUMP JOCKEYS, 1996/97

	Win £	1st	2nd	3rd	Unpl	Total Mts	Per cent		£1 Level stake
A. P. McCoy	1025946	190	130	78	266	664	28.6	+	**3.28**
J. Osborne	847233	131	82	63	254	530	24.7	+	**64.31**
R. Dunwoody	779999	111	101	70	276	558	19.9	-	134.80
R. Johnson	414173	102	78	91	293	564	18.1	-	24.53
N. Williamson	507958	85	71	66	308	530	16.0	-	53.76
P. Niven	316186	84	57	50	188	379	22.2	-	15.85
M. A. Fitzgerald	315946	82	62	52	248	444	18.5	-	82.69
A. Maguire	367732	81	72	61	183	397	20.4	-	103.76
A. Dobbin	474961	73	52	46	224	395	18.5	-	16.28
D. Bridgwater	255010	69	47	49	224	389	17.7	-	25.52
R. Garritty	221605	62	66	51	176	355	17.5	-	92.63
P. Carberry	240296	61	40	29	120	250	24.4	+	**47.67**
C. Llewellyn	297037	57	42	48	265	412	13.8	+	**17.29**
C. Maude	238007	56	45	38	222	361	15.5	-	96.88
Richard Guest	173088	50	47	41	180	318	15.7	-	51.91
R. Supple	163498	49	39	43	206	337	14.5	-	9.99
B. Storey	225553	48	48	49	253	398	12.1	-	131.14
A. Thornton	117260	38	66	54	295	453	8.4	-	166.84
B. Powell	160261	36	43	49	323	451	8.0	-	248.90
D. Walsh	133471	35	25	26	185	271	12.9	-	85.03
P. Hide	130976	35	39	26	174	274	12.8	-	87.15
B. Fenton	113702	35	55	44	271	405	8.6	-	149.43
G. Bradley	136067	33	40	37	152	262	12.6	-	38.02
J. Culloty	108080	32	22	24	162	240	13.3	-	13.27
Mr R. Thornton	159337	30	41	50	182	303	9.9	-	53.42
C. O'Dwyer	121240	28	23	14	84	149	18.8	-	36.97
T. J. Murphy	112866	28	28	33	192	281	10.0	-	81.97
J. F. Titley	90665	28	22	14	102	166	16.9	-	26.30
S. Wynne	71158	27	33	31	156	247	10.9	-	14.01
M. Foster	85193	27	21	19	145	212	12.7	-	15.22
J. Railton	82972	26	27	26	147	226	11.5	-	63.16
Michael Brennan	77458	26	19	23	158	226	11.5	-	71.55
R. Farrant	213278	26	16	22	104	168	15.5	+	**48.55**
Derek Byrne	87455	26	22	21	124	193	13.5	-	82.34
G. Cahill	60898	24	39	28	192	283	8.5	-	129.91
L. Wyer	82144	23	15	15	100	153	15.0	-	36.97
J. R. Kavanagh	80274	23	33	27	185	268	8.6	-	173.55
L. Aspell	103485	23	29	18	123	193	11.9	+	**25.98**
T. Dascombe	59185	22	28	37	182	269	8.2	-	69.50
M. Richards	75530	22	26	27	158	233	9.4	-	58.15
E. Callaghan	78552	21	21	15	93	150	14.0	+	**7.88**
A. S. Smith	61883	21	39	30	213	303	6.9	-	142.76
G. Tormey	116393	20	14	20	104	158	12.7	+	**3.55**
J. Supple	46893	20	9	12	94	135	14.8	-	28.44
P. Henley	58603	20	33	26	126	205	9.8	-	48.48
D. Gallagher	79026	19	32	26	189	266	7.1	-	134.64
R. Massey	36176	19	9	7	127	162	11.7	-	61.21
D. Morris	62928	19	13	25	104	161	11.8	-	29.98
X. Aizpuru	45693	18	21	11	87	137	13.1	+	**2.28**
W. Marston	60738	18	37	29	271	355	5.1	-	255.98

LEADING TRAINERS ON THE FLAT: 1896 - 1997

1896 A Hayhoe
1897 R Marsh
1898 R Marsh
1899 J Porter
1900 R Marsh
1901 J Huggins
1902 R S Sievier
1903 G Blackwell
1904 P P Gilpin
1905 W T Robinson
1906 Hon G Lambton
1907 A Taylor
1908 C Morton
1909 A Taylor
1910 A Taylor
1911 Hon G Lambton
1912 Hon G Lambton
1913 R Wootton
1914 A Taylor
1915 P P Gilpin
1916 R C Dawson
1917 A Taylor
1918 A Taylor
1919 A Taylor
1920 A Taylor
1921 A Taylor
1922 A Taylor
1923 A Taylor
1924 R C Dawson
1925 A Taylor
1926 F Darling
1927 Frank Butters
1928 Frank Butters
1929 R C Dawson
1930 H S Persse
1931 J Lawson
1932 Frank Butters
1933 F Darling
1934 Frank Butters
1935 Frank Butters
1936 J Lawson
1937 C Boyd-Rochfort
1938 C Boyd-Rochfort
1939 J L Jarvis
1940 F Darling
1941 F Darling
1942 F Darling
1943 W Nightingall
1944 Frank Butters
1945 W Earl
1946 Frank Butters
1947 F Darling
1948 C F N Murless
1949 Frank Butters
1950 C H Semblat
1951 J L Jarvis
1952 M Marsh
1953 J L Jarvis
1954 C Boyd-Rochfort
1955 C Boyd-Rochfort
1956 C F Elsey
1957 C F N Murless
1958 C Boyd-Rochfort
1959 C F N Murless
1960 C F N Murless
1961 C F N Murless
1962 W Hern
1963 P Prendergast
1964 P Prendergast
1965 P Prendergast
1966 M V O'Brien
1967 C F N Murless
1968 C F N Murless
1969 A M Budgett
1970 C F N Murless
1971 I Balding
1972 W Hern
1973 C F N Murless
1974 P Walwyn
1975 P Walwyn
1976 H Cecil
1977 M V O'Brien
1978 H Cecil
1979 H Cecil
1980 W Hern
1981 M Stoute
1982 H Cecil
1983 W Hern
1984 H Cecil
1985 H Cecil
1986 M Stoute
1987 H Cecil
1988 H Cecil
1989 M Stoute
1990 H Cecil
1991 P Cole
1992 R Hannon
1993 H Cecil
1994 M Stoute
1995 J Dunlop
1996 Saeed bin Suroor
1997 M Stoute

CHAMPION JOCKEYS: 1894 - 1997

1894 M Cannon 167
1895 M Cannon 184
1896 M Cannon 164
1897 M Cannon 145
1898 O Madden 161
1899 S Loates 160
1900 L Reiff 143
1901 O Madden 130
1902 W Lane 170
1903 O Madden 154
1904 O Madden 161
1905 E Wheatley 124
1906 W Higgs 149
1907 W Higgs 146
1908 D Maher 139
1909 F Wootton 165
1910 F Wootton 137
1911 F Wootton 187
1912 F Wootton 118
1913 D Maher 115
1914 S Donoghue 129
1915 S Donoghue 62
1916 S Donoghue 43
1917 S Donoghue 42
1918 S Donoghue 66
1919 S Donoghue 129
1920 S Donoghue 143
1921 S Donoghue 141
1922 S Donoghue 102

Year	Jockey	Wins
1923	S Donoghue	89
	C Elliott	89
1924	C Elliott	106
1925	G Richards	118
1926	T Weston	95
1927	G Richards	164
1928	G Richards	148
1929	G Richards	135
1930	F Fox	129
1931	G Richards	145
1932	G Richards	190
1933	G Richards	259
1934	G Richards	212
1935	G Richards	217
1936	G Richards	174
1937	G Richards	216
1938	G Richards	206
1939	G Richards	155
1940	G Richards	68
1941	H Wragg	71
1942	G Richards	67
1943	G Richards	65
1944	G Richards	88
1945	G Richards	104
1946	G Richards	212
1947	G Richards	269
1948	G Richards	224
1949	G Richards	261
1950	G Richards	201
1951	G Richards	227
1952	G Richards	231
1953	G Richards	191
1954	D Smith	129
1955	D Smith	168
1956	D Smith	155
1957	A Breasley	173
1958	D Smith	165
1959	D Smith	157
1960	L Piggott	170
1961	A Breasley	171
1962	A Breasley	179
1963	A Breasley	176
1964	L Piggott	140
1965	L Piggott	160
1966	L Piggott	191
1967	L Piggott	117
1968	L Piggott	139
1969	L Piggott	163
1970	L Piggott	162
1971	L Piggott	162
1972	W Carson	132
1973	W Carson	164
1974	Pat Eddery	148
1975	Pat Eddery	164
1976	Pat Eddery	162
1977	Pat Eddery	176
1978	W Carson	182
1979	J Mercer	164
1980	W Carson	166
1981	L Piggott	179
1982	L Piggott	188
1983	W Carson	159
1984	S Cauthen	130
1985	S Cauthen	195
1986	Pat Eddery	176
1987	S Cauthen	197
1988	Pat Eddery	183
1989	Pat Eddery	171
1990	Pat Eddery	209
1991	Pat Eddery	165
1992	M Roberts	206
1993	Pat Eddery	169
1994	L Dettori	233
1995	L Dettori	211
1996	Pat Eddery	186
1997	K Fallon	202

LEADING OWNERS: 1894 - 1997

1894	Mr H. McCalmont
1895	Ld de Rothschild
1896	Ld de Rothschild
1987	Mr J Gubbins
1898	Ld de Rothschild
1899	Duke of Westminster
1900	H.R.H. The Prince of Wales
1901	Sir G Blundell Maple
1902	Mr R S Sievier
1903	Sir James Miller
1904	Sir James Miller
1905	Col W Hall Walker
1906	Ld Derby (late)
1907	Col W Hall Walker
1908	Mr J B Joel
1909	Mr "Fairie"
1910	Mr "Fairie"
1911	Ld Derby
1912	Mr T Pilkington
1913	Mr J B Joel
1914	Mr J B Joel
1915	Mr L Neumann
1916	Mr E Hulton
1917	Mr "Fairie"
1918	Lady James Douglas
1919	Ld Glanely
1920	Sir Robert Jardine
1921	Mr S B Joel
1922	Ld Woolavington
1923	Ld Derby
1924	H.H. Aga Khan
1925	Ld Astor
1926	Ld Woolavington
1927	Ld Derby
1928	Ld Derby
1929	H.H. Aga Khan
1930	H.H. Aga Khan
1931	Mr J A Dewar
1932	H.H. Aga Khan
1933	Ld Derby
1934	H.H. Aga Khan
1935	H.H. Aga Khan
1936	Ld Astor
1937	H.H. Aga Khan
1938	Ld Derby
1939	Ld Rosebery
1940	Lord Rothermere
1941	Ld Glanely
1942	His Majesty
1943	Miss D Paget
1944	H.H. Aga Khan
1945	Ld Derby
1946	H.H. Aga Khan
1947	H.H. Aga Khan
1948	H.H. Aga Khan
1949	H.H. Aga Khan
1950	M M Boussac
1951	M M Boussac
1952	H. H. Aga Khan
1953	Sir Victor Sassoon
1954	Her Majesty
1955	Lady Zia Wernner
1956	Maj L B Holliday
1957	Her Majesty
1958	Mr J McShain

1959	Prince Aly Khan
1960	Sir Victor Sassoon
1961	Maj L B Holliday
1962	Maj L B Holliday
1963	Mr J R Mullion
1964	Mrs H E Jackson
1965	M J Ternynck
1966	Lady Zia Wernher
1967	Mr H J Joel
1968	Mr Raymond R Guest
1969	Mr D Robinson
1970	Mr C Engelhard
1971	Mr P Mellon
1972	Mrs J Hislop
1973	Mr N B Hunt
1974	Mr N B Hunt
1975	Dr C Vittadini
1976	Mr D Wildenstein
1977	Mr R Sangster
1978	Mr R Sangster
1979	Sir M Sobell
1980	S Weinstock
1981	H.H. Aga Khan
1982	Mr R Sangster
1983	Mr R Sangster
1984	Mr R Sangster
1985	Sheikh Mohammed
1986	Sheikh Mohammed
1987	Sheikh Mohammed
1988	Sheikh Mohammed
1989	Sheikh Mohammed
1990	Mr Hamdan Al-Maktoum
1991	Sheikh Mohammed
1992	Sheikh Mohammed
1993	Sheikh Mohammed
1994	Mr Hamdan Al-Maktoum
1995	Mr Hamdan Al-Maktoum
1996	Godolphin
1997	Sheikh Mohammed

LEADING SIRES: 1894 - 1997

1894	St Simon
1895	St Simon
1896	St Simon
1897	Kendal
1898	Galopin
1899	Orme
1900	St Simon
1901	St Simon
1902	Persimmon
1903	St Frusquin
1904	Gallinule
1905	Gallinule
1906	Persimmon
1907	St Frusquin
1908	Persimmon
1909	Cyllene
1910	Cyllene
1911	Sundridge
1912	Persimmon
1913	Desmond
1914	Polymelus
1915	Polymelus
1916	Polymelus
1917	Bayardo
1918	Bayardo
1919	The Tetrarch
1920	Polymelus
1921	Polymelus
1922	Lemberg
1923	Swynford
1924	Son-in-Law
1925	Phalaris
1926	Hurry On
1927	Buchan
1928	Phalaris
1929	Tetratema
1930	Son-in-Law
1931	Pharos
1932	Gainsborough
1933	Gainsborough
1934	Blandford
1935	Blandford
1936	Fairway
1937	Solario
1938	Blandford
1939	Fairway
1940	Hyperion
1941	Hyperion
1942	Hyperion
1943	Fairway
1944	Fairway
1945	Hyperion
1946	Hyperion
1947	Nearco
1948	Big Game
1949	Nearco
1950	Fair Trial
1951	Nasrullah
1952	Tehran
1953	Chanteur II
1954	Hyperion
1955	Alycidon
1956	Court Martial
1957	Court Martial
1958	Mossborough
1959	Petition
1960	Aureole
1961	Aureole
1962	Never Say Die
1963	Ribot
1964	Chamossaire
1965	Court Harwell
1966	Charlottesville
1967	Ribot
1968	Ribot
1969	Crepello
1970	Northern Dancer
1971	Never Bend
1972	Queen's Hussar
1973	Vaguely Noble
1974	Vaguely Noble
1975	Great Nephew
1976	Wolver Hollow
1977	Northern Dancer
1978	Mill Reef (USA)
1979	Petingo
1980	Pitcairn
1981	Great Nephew
1982	Be My Guest (USA)
1983	Northern Dancer
1984	Northern Dancer
1985	Kris
1986	Nijinsky (CAN)
1987	Mill Reef (USA)
1988	Caerleon (USA)
1989	Blushing Groom (FR)
1990	Sadler's Wells (USA)
1991	Caerleon (USA)
1992	Sadler's Wells (USA)
1993	Sadler's Wells (USA)
1994	Sadler's Wells (USA)
1995	Sadler's Wells (USA)
1996	Sadler's Wells (USA)
1997	Sadler's Wells (USA)

LEADING BREEDERS: 1909 - 1997

1909	Mr "Fairie"
1910	Mr "Fairie"
1911	Ld Derby (late)
1912	Col. W Hall Walker
1913	Mr J B Joel
1914	Mr J B Joel
1915	Mr L Neumann
1916	Mr E Hulton
1917	Mr "Fairie"
1918	Lady James Douglas
1919	Ld Derby
1920	Ld Derby
1921	Mr S B Joel
1922	Ld Derby
1923	Ld Derby
1924	Lady Sykes
1925	Ld Astor
1926	Ld Woolavington
1927	Ld Derby
1928	Ld Derby
1929	Ld Derby
1930	Ld Derby
1931	Ld Dewar
1932	H.H. Aga Khan
1933	Sir Alec Black
1934	H.H. Aga Khan
1935	H.H. Aga Khan
1936	Ld Astor
1937	H.H. Aga Khan
1938	Ld Derby
1939	Ld Rosebery
1940	Mr H E Morriss
1941	Ld Glanely
1942	National Stud
1943	Miss D Paget
1944	Ld Rosebery
1945	Ld Derby
1946	Lt- Col H Boyd-Rochfort
1947	H.H. Aga Khan
1948	H.H. Aga Khan
1949	H.H. Aga Khan
1950	M M Boussac
1951	M M Boussac
1952	H. H. Aga Khan
1953	Mr F Darling
1954	Maj L B Holliday
1955	Someries Stud
1956	Maj L B Holliday
1957	Eve Stud
1958	Mr R Ball
1959	Prince Aly Khan and the late H.H. Aga Khan
1960	Eve Stud Ltd
1961	Eve Stud Ltd
1962	Maj L B Holliday
1963	Mr H F Guggenheim
1964	Bull Run Stud
1965	Mr J Ternynck
1966	Someries Stud
1967	Mr H J Joel
1968	Mill Ridge Farm
1969	Lord Rosebery
1970	Mr E P Taylor
1971	Mr P Mellon
1972	Mr J Hislop
1973	Claiborne Farm
1974	Mr N B Hunt
1975	Overbury Stud
1976	Dayton Ltd
1977	Mr E P Taylor
1978	Cragwood Estates Inc
1979	Ballymacoll Stud
1980	P Clarke
1981	H.H. Aga Khan
1982	Someries Stud
1983	White Lodge Stud
1984	Mr E P Taylor
1985	Dalham Stud Farms
1986	H.H. Aga Khan
1987	Cliveden Stud
1988	H. H. Aga Khan
1989	Mr Hamdan Al-Maktoum
1990	Capt. Macdonald-Buchanan
1991	Barronstown Stud
1992	Swettenham Stud
1993	Juddmonte Farms
1994	Shadwell Farm & Estate Ltd
1995	Shadwell Farm & Estate Ltd
1996	Sheikh Mohammed
1997	Sheikh Mohammed

If an entry is incorrect or has been omitted, please notify the editor by January 8th, 1999. This will ensure it appears correctly in the 1999 edition.

LEADING SIRES OF 1997 IN GREAT BRITAIN AND IRELAND

STALLION	BREEDING	RNRS	WNRS	WINS	WIN MONEY	PLACES	PLACE MONEY	TOTAL
SADLER'S WELLS (1981)	by Northern Dancer	97	51	75	1009625	175	410114	1419738
DANEHILL (1986)	by Danzig	87	39	66	1057935	180	352340	1410275
SILVER HAWK (1979)	by Roberto	28	11	15	735892	68	174000	909892
FAIRY KING (1982)	by Northern Dancer	99	44	68	603213	143	279783	882996
ROYAL ACADEMY (1987)	by Nijinsky	78	34	52	564088	130	254048	818137
POLISH PRECEDENT (1986)	by Danzig	46	14	23	614708	58	179389	794097
IN THE WINGS (1986)	by Sadler's Wells	39	18	28	500820	77	146775	647595
EFISIO (1982)	by Formidable	85	36	71	437339	143	171672	609012
NASHWAN (1986)	by Blushing Groom	45	23	36	476480	67	116766	593247
MACHIAVELLIAN (1987)	by Mr Prospector	33	21	28	301091	74	271688	572779
SOVIET STAR (1984)	by Nureyev	41	14	23	472935	65	97181	570116
GENEROUS (1988)	by Caerleon	53	31	49	444089	80	107789	551878
WARNING (1985)	by Known Fact	85	36	58	355277	145	192760	548037
CADEAUX GENEREUX (1985)	by Young Generation	62	28	50	373597	113	167141	540738
SADDLERS' HALL (1988)	by Sadler's Wells	31	9	12	247447	37	290192	537640
MTOTO (1983)	by Busted	44	19	30	350594	97	183018	533612
NUREYEV (1977)	by Northern Dancer	28	10	16	309601	48	212877	522479
GREEN DESERT (1983)	by Danzig	93	38	51	264838	141	248895	513733
SALSE (1985)	by Topsider	58	18	23	331718	82	180690	512408
WOODMAN (1983)	by Mr Prospector	43	17	26	207754	65	273393	481147

LEADING BRITISH AND IRISH BASED SIRES OF 1997 (GREAT BRITAIN, IRELAND AND OVERSEAS)

STALLION	BREEDING	DOMESTIC WNRS	DOMESTIC WINS	WIN MONEY	OVERSEAS WNRS	OVERSEAS WINS	WIN MONEY	TOTAL
DANEHILL (1986)	by Danzig	39	66	1057935	49	97	1894859	2952794
CAERLEON (1980)	by Nijinsky	36	52	261604	55	103	2444570	2706174
IN THE WINGS (1986)	by Sadler's Wells	18	28	500820	27	44	1808842	2309662
SADLER'S WELLS (1981)	by Northern Dancer	51	75	1009625	57	76	1267484	2277108
FAIRY KING (1982)	by Northern Dancer	44	68	603213	36	63	1485806	2089020
LAST TYCOON (1983)	by Try My Best	20	24	87204	62	114	1736890	1824094
ROYAL ACADEMY (1987)	by Nijinsky	34	52	564088	50	84	1089286	1653375
POLISH PRECEDENT (1986)	by Danzig	14	23	614708	12	16	975855	1590563
GREEN DESERT (1983)	by Danzig	38	51	264838	27	43	1216620	1481458
BE MY GUEST (1974)	by Northern Dancer	14	21	88998	47	90	1019590	1108588
ALZAO (1980)	by Lyphard	39	55	252321	54	96	852807	1105128
SALSE (1985)	by Topsider	18	23	331718	14	24	633114	964832
RAINBOW QUEST (1981)	by Blushing Groom	23	38	164480	25	38	781619	946099
NASHWAN (1986)	by Blushing Groom	23	36	476480	14	27	441781	918261
MACHIAVELLIAN (1987)	by Mr Prospector	21	28	301091	35	54	589014	890105
BLUEBIRD (1984)	by Storm Bird	19	31	263692	56	107	611056	874748
EFISIO (1982)	by Formidable	36	71	437339	20	46	400101	837440
PERSIAN BOLD (1975)	by Bold Lad (IRE)	21	27	107078	38	79	715610	822688
NIGHT SHIFT (1980)	by Northern Dancer	37	42	230437	31	54	582943	813379
MARJU (1988)	by Last Tycoon	16	19	174742	24	48	612604	787345

LEADING TWO-YEAR-OLD SIRES OF 1997 IN GREAT BRITAIN AND IRELAND

STALLION	BREEDING	RNRS	WNRS	WINS	WIN MONEY	PLACES	PLACE MONEY	TOTAL
FAIRY KING (1982)	by Northern Dancer	42	18	26	295880	54	69848	365727
ZAFONIC (1990)	by Gone West	15	9	11	168340	11	24882	193221
CADEAUX GENEREUX (1985)	by Young Generation	15	7	11	150664	15	39001	189665
DANEHILL (1986)	by Danzig	27	12	17	142147	45	46506	188653
DIESIS (1980)	by Sharpen Up	15	9	13	140878	11	36167	177045
SADLER'S WELLS (1981)	by Northern Dancer	10	3	6	158409	16	17811	176220
CAERLEON (1980)	by Nijinsky	25	8	9	80230	27	77466	157696
TIROL (1987)	by Thatching	13	6	10	123536	15	33394	156930
EL GRAN SENOR (1981)	by Northern Dancer	6	3	6	141850	6	13273	155123
DAYJUR (1987)	by Danzig	9	3	6	118667	8	34761	153429
ALZAO (1980)	by Lyphard	38	14	16	79344	55	72759	152102
MUJADIL (1988)	by Storm Bird	26	11	22	90379	57	60387	150766
ROYAL ACADEMY (1987)	by Nijinsky	20	11	15	82828	29	62858	145686
GREEN DESERT (1983)	by Danzig	23	7	10	66260	21	73270	139531
WARNING (1985)	by Known Fact	29	11	16	69743	31	68651	138394
GENEROUS (1988)	by Caerleon	19	7	10	115644	14	13054	128698
NIGHT SHIFT (1980)	by Northern Dancer	46	13	15	89624	56	39016	128640
WAAJIB (1983)	by Try My Best	14	5	6	88866	16	37272	126139
PETARDIA (1990)	by Petong	40	8	13	90202	60	30664	120866
BRIEF TRUCE (1989)	by Irish River	34	9	11	50856	55	68319	119176

LEADING FIRST CROP SIRES OF 1997 IN GREAT BRITAIN AND IRELAND

STALLION	BREEDING	RNRS	WNRS	WINS	WIN MONEY	PLACES	PLACE MONEY	TOTAL
ZAFONIC (1990)	by Gone West	15	9	11	168340	11	24882	193221
PETARDIA (1990)	by Petong	40	8	13	90202	60	30664	120866
BRIEF TRUCE (1989)	by Irish River	34	9	11	50856	55	68319	119176
MAGIC RING (1989)	by Green Desert	23	7	8	35719	39	70124	105843
TENBY (1990)	by Caerleon	14	5	9	51777	21	46638	98415
SECOND SET (1988)	by Alzao	15	6	7	39985	13	34746	74732
MUKADDAMAH (1988)	by Storm Bird	13	4	11	53974	11	5826	59799
HAMAS (1989)	by Danzig	9	4	9	48615	13	9828	58443
LION CAVERN (1989)	by Mr Prospector	23	7	9	30148	27	27257	57404
CASE LAW (1987)	by Ahonoora	8	2	3	20374	12	35408	55782
INCHINOR (1990)	by Ahonoora	13	4	8	29741	25	24368	54109
GREENSMITH (1986)	by Known Fact	6	4	14	43399	11	6923	50321
PARIS HOUSE (1989)	by Petong	19	7	12	37703	16	10622	48326
WOLFHOUND (1989)	by Nureyev	21	5	6	22861	39	25366	48227
PIPS PRIDE (1990)	by Efisio	26	7	7	21353	38	25364	46717
SABREHILL (1990)	by Diesis	21	5	6	32570	9	7222	39791
ARDKINGLASS (1990)	by Green Desert	7	4	6	20496	11	8281	28777
KING'S SIGNET (1989)	by Nureyev	18	5	6	16094	20	10591	26685
EXBOURNE (1986)	by Explodent	4	3	4	16762	8	9619	26381
CASTEDDU (1989)	by Efisio	11	3	5	13660	19	11862	25522

STALLIONS EARNINGS FOR 1997

(includes every stallion who sired a winner on the flat in Great Britain and Ireland in 1997).

STALLIONS	RNRS	STARTS	WNRS	WINS	PLACES	TOTAL
ABSALOM	38	224	9	13	55	73000.87
ADBASS (USA)	6	22	1	2	7	9137.90
ADONIJAH	1	20	1	2	2	5098.00
AFFIRMED (USA)	6	29	1	2	8	29696.73
AHONOORA	2	8	1	1	0	9346.20
AJRAAS (USA)	9	52	1	1	16	10939.87
AKARAD (FR)	6	25	2	3	9	22225.60
AL HAREB (USA)	10	48	1	1	10	12755.04
ALHIJAZ (GB)	18	61	2	3	19	19010.08
ALLEGED (USA)	28	75	5	5	24	93931.16
ALLEGING (USA)	2	29	2	4	8	19660.50
ALMOOJID	7	23	1	1	3	4734.50
AL NASR (FR)	7	25	1	1	8	7275.65
ALNASR ALWASHEEK (GB)	9	40	2	2	10	13636.80
ALWASMI (USA)	3	18	1	3	4	13292.35
ALWUHUSH (USA)	1	6	1	1	4	8922.50
ALYSHEBA (USA)	1	15	1	1	4	6210.15
ALZAO (USA)	105	491	39	55	172	437620.56
ANITA'S PRINCE	20	117	7	7	30	38475.28
ANSHAN	47	229	12	17	68	129688.04
ARAGON	46	311	13	23	50	142586.75
ARAZI (USA)	20	105	9	13	35	91738.60
ARCANE (USA)	8	45	2	2	8	11111.50
ARCHWAY (IRE)	32	181	9	15	58	106180.56
ARCTIC TERN (USA)	6	35	2	3	13	25256.15
ARDKINGLASS (GB)	7	44	4	6	11	28777.20
ARDROSS	4	13	1	2	1	10523.05
ARKAN	1	17	1	2	8	8808.00
ARRASAS (USA)	4	29	1	1	9	6927.85
ASTRONEF	30	129	3	4	20	18831.58
BABA KARAM	2	8	1	2	3	8058.75
BACALAO (USA)	2	25	1	1	6	5409.85
BAIRN (USA)	13	100	6	11	28	70888.95
BALIDAR	3	10	1	2	1	13896.38
BALLACASHTAL (CAN)	12	93	6	10	22	47845.70
BALLAD ROCK	38	241	16	26	60	124486.18
BARRYS GAMBLE	7	35	2	2	8	10340.35
BARRY'S RUN (IRE)	3	27	1	1	11	7316.82
BATSHOOF	35	183	11	13	36	74921.22
BAY EXPRESS	3	25	2	2	8	9995.55
BEDFORD (USA)	1	3	1	1	0	2574.00
BELDALE FLUTTER (USA)	4	24	3	3	6	11749.25
BELLYPHA	1	13	1	1	5	4648.50
BELMEZ (USA)	23	109	3	4	27	50242.85
BELONG TO ME (USA)	1	4	1	1	1	3857.50
BE MY CHIEF (USA)	43	192	10	11	50	63566.98
BE MY GUEST (USA)	43	222	14	21	64	127091.26
BE MY NATIVE (USA)	26	78	3	6	16	34955.48
BERING	19	82	6	8	23	209433.45
BEVELED (USA)	76	550	33	51	150	298297.31
BIKALA	3	11	1	2	0	6443.06
BLACK TIE AFFAIR	2	15	2	3	3	11618.15
BLAKENEY	6	45	2	3	12	12531.00
BLUEBIRD (USA)	49	268	19	31	68	337420.80
BLUSHING JOHN (USA)	6	20	1	1	4	4504.50

STALLIONS	RNRS	STARTS	WNRS	WINS	PLACES	TOTAL
BOB BACK (USA)	18	83	8	11	21	52302.87
BOLD ARRANGEMENT	13	78	3	4	17	22744.45
BOLD OWL	5	36	2	2	9	11852.50
BOLD RUCKUS (USA)	1	5	1	1	3	14543.34
BOREEN (FR)	2	2	1	1	0	0.00
BRIEF TRUCE (USA)	34	128	9	11	55	119175.58
BROAD BRUSH (USA)	1	5	1	1	0	3899.00
BROKEN HEARTED	20	103	7	12	28	117109.51
BRUSH ASIDE (USA)	2	8	1	1	3	3295.80
BURSLEM	3	16	1	1	6	6300.85
BUSTINO	13	61	4	6	16	34527.47
CADEAUX GENEREUX	62	358	28	50	113	540738.02
CAERLEON (USA)	79	317	36	52	126	462194.88
CAHILL ROAD (USA)	3	12	1	1	4	6545.50
CAPOTE (USA)	5	27	2	2	8	17271.35
CARNIVALAY (USA)	2	13	1	1	4	8247.60
CARO	3	20	1	1	1	3876.50
CASE LAW	8	46	2	3	12	55781.95
CASTEDDU (GB)	11	66	3	5	19	25521.99
CASTLE KEEP	3	17	1	1	5	5284.50
CATALDI	6	15	1	1	3	3514.84
CELESTIAL STORM (USA)	4	21	2	3	3	19307.50
CHARMER	16	83	3	5	23	33573.95
CHIEF'S CROWN (USA)	17	67	3	3	24	70308.04
CHIEF SINGER	10	67	4	7	18	44467.22
CHILIBANG	36	243	6	8	47	47705.20
CIGAR	6	52	1	1	12	9477.70
CLANTIME	51	345	14	26	86	227998.90
CLASSIC MUSIC (USA)	29	126	4	5	37	37673.79
CLASSIC SECRET (USA)	17	97	4	7	34	37082.54
CLEVER TRICK (USA)	4	45	2	4	12	22204.40
COMMANCHE RUN	6	18	2	2	6	26143.90
COMMON GROUNDS	68	339	25	32	85	199101.40
CONQUERING HERO (USA)	10	63	4	5	10	22433.42
CONTRACT LAW (USA)	33	204	8	11	43	51085.33
COQUELIN (USA)	3	31	2	3	5	11231.35
COX'S RIDGE (USA)	2	6	1	1	3	5191.80
COZZENE (USA)	7	29	2	3	13	42865.45
CRAFTY PROSPECTOR (USA)	6	22	2	2	9	11980.62
CRICKET BALL (USA)	1	14	1	1	6	7002.85
CROFTHALL	8	48	2	2	10	48327.14
CROWNING HONORS (CAN)	3	26	1	5	7	20672.20
CRYPTOCLEARANCE (USA)	3	3	1	1	0	6775.00
CYRANO DE BERGERAC	48	320	14	25	87	164886.84
DAMISTER (USA)	16	99	8	13	38	117218.66
DANCE OF LIFE (USA)	7	33	2	2	3	12944.10
DANCING BRAVE (USA)	4	12	1	1	4	6060.35
DANCING DISSIDENT (USA)	41	274	14	21	63	196375.61
DANEHILL (USA)	87	483	39	66	180	1410274.87
DANZIG (USA)	30	147	17	25	65	430880.09
DANZIG CONNECTION (USA)	3	27	1	2	9	9882.10
DARING MARCH	8	31	2	2	6	8330.50
DARSHAAN	46	159	18	23	55	212400.04
DASHING BLADE	6	45	2	7	13	94971.77
DAYJUR (USA)	23	90	8	14	32	210851.59
DEEP RUN	2	3	1	1	0	5086.63
DEPLOY	35	141	4	6	33	93292.00
DERRYLIN	2	15	1	1	4	5000.50
DEVIL'S BAG (USA)	4	10	1	1	1	3846.25
DIESIS	43	160	17	22	45	282821.78
DIGAMIST (USA)	20	99	3	6	15	41812.10

STALLIONS	RNRS	STARTS	WNRS	WINS	PLACES	TOTAL
DILUM (USA)	11	41	1	1	9	15364.57
DISTANT RELATIVE	37	249	17	34	86	322318.73
DISTINCTLY NORTH (USA)	77	428	20	33	93	238322.97
DIXIE BRASS (USA)	2	4	1	1	2	8086.64
DIXIELAND BAND (USA)	12	58	8	13	19	82780.22
DOMINION	24	170	8	24	48	202210.06
DOMINION ROYALE	12	88	4	8	27	56685.90
DOMITOR (USA)	1	12	1	4	4	12895.02
DOMYNSKY	7	36	1	2	8	11468.55
DON'T FORGET ME	59	264	16	29	56	157677.36
DOUBLE SCHWARTZ	15	99	7	10	14	48988.70
DOUBLETOUR (USA)	6	23	1	1	6	7953.86
DOULAB (USA)	18	161	7	8	40	43357.77
DOWSING (USA)	25	198	10	16	56	124018.83
DOYOUN	27	72	10	12	27	101877.90
DUNBEATH (USA)	14	74	5	7	23	35366.45
DURGAM (USA)	15	80	3	7	14	27232.74
DYNAFORMER (USA)	4	11	1	1	4	41833.25
EASY GOER (USA)	3	12	2	2	5	8945.65
EFISIO	85	561	36	71	143	609011.81
ELA-MANA-MOU	32	128	11	19	41	215358.77
ELBIO	12	57	3	4	14	17825.62
EL GRAN SENOR (USA)	21	97	10	17	38	288694.68
ELMAAMUL (USA)	27	140	10	12	31	55849.30
EMARATI (USA)	45	296	16	26	88	179035.90
EMPEROR FOUNTAIN	1	12	1	1	4	12257.00
ENVIRONMENT FRIEND (GB)	15	84	5	6	18	74298.83
ERINS ISLE	9	35	3	3	7	15221.53
ESKIMO (USA)	1	1	1	1	0	1648.50
EXACTLY SHARP (USA)	5	36	2	3	10	38378.09
EXBOURNE (USA)	4	22	3	4	8	26380.82
EXECUTIVE MAN	8	35	2	2	6	8675.65
EXHIBITIONER	3	5	1	1	0	3785.00
EXIT TO NOWHERE (USA)	7	20	1	1	5	8524.00
EXPLODENT (USA)	2	20	1	2	6	10120.50
FABULOUS DANCER (USA)	2	17	1	3	9	12346.47
FAIRY KING (USA)	99	463	44	68	143	882995.98
FAUSTUS (USA)	17	79	3	5	15	30256.70
FAYRUZ	47	283	13	15	83	116997.27
FIGHTING FIT (USA)	4	38	2	2	14	10971.55
FLOOSE	1	8	1	1	3	5897.70
FOOLS HOLME (USA)	7	43	4	6	16	27084.80
FORMIDABLE (USA)	40	252	6	7	51	50407.37
FORTY NINER (USA)	5	10	1	1	1	3528.50
FORZANDO	40	296	21	31	86	215891.16
GABITAT	3	25	1	1	9	11837.25
GALETTO (FR)	1	13	1	4	6	36673.95
GEIGER COUNTER (USA)	10	49	5	7	16	35852.26
GENEROUS (IRE)	53	219	31	49	80	551877.92
GILDED TIME (USA)	2	4	1	1	2	4941.25
GILDORAN	10	50	4	6	14	27270.60
GLACIAL STORM (USA)	3	7	1	1	1	257.43
GLOW (USA)	7	19	1	1	5	4356.00
GOLD ALERT (USA)	1	9	1	2	2	6307.90
GOLD CREST (USA)	1	10	1	1	5	5874.85
GOLDEN HEIGHTS	4	14	1	1	2	5988.00
GOLDEN LAHAB (USA)	3	16	1	3	7	19581.50
GONE WEST (USA)	22	83	7	8	30	141941.98
GOOD TIMES (ITY)	7	37	2	3	8	12272.70
GOOFALIK (USA)	1	3	1	1	1	2779.50
GOVERNOR GENERAL	7	29	1	1	2	5136.00

STALLIONS	RNRS	STARTS	WNRS	WINS	PLACES	TOTAL
GREAT COMMOTION (USA)	9	59	4	12	13	70800.36
GREEN DANCER (USA)	18	92	7	11	31	117041.03
GREEN DESERT (USA)	93	423	38	51	141	513732.58
GREEN FOREST (USA)	7	30	1	1	4	10717.82
GREEN RUBY (USA)	6	44	1	1	7	10100.90
GREENSMITH	6	34	4	14	11	50321.38
GREY DAWN II	1	4	1	1	0	2388.25
GREY DESIRE	10	81	3	10	24	71817.50
GROOM DANCER (USA)	20	80	9	10	36	93584.90
GULCH (USA)	13	48	5	7	12	52180.42
GUNNER B	8	48	3	5	12	24693.45
HABITAT	3	20	1	2	3	6666.00
HADEER	22	153	9	15	41	79292.09
HAMAS (IRE)	9	42	4	9	13	58443.45
HANDSOME SAILOR	24	131	4	4	30	34953.25
HANSEL (USA)	6	15	1	1	7	14508.81
HARD FOUGHT	4	61	3	5	20	25249.85
HAWKSTER (USA)	3	12	2	2	5	23228.40
HEIGHTS OF GOLD	1	14	1	1	4	7627.00
HELLO GORGEOUS (USA)	1	2	1	1	1	2760.00
HERALDISTE (USA)	1	18	1	1	2	3848.50
HERMITAGE (USA)	5	18	2	2	5	34712.00
HIGH ESTATE	45	213	12	20	51	120536.48
HIGHEST HONOR (FR)	15	58	4	4	16	69081.31
HIGH KICKER (USA)	9	44	1	1	8	5823.80
HIGH LINE	1	7	1	2	3	7032.25
HIGH TOP	2	9	1	1	1	2712.00
HOLLOW HAND	2	5	1	1	2	2139.84
HOMEBOY	1	12	1	1	3	3200.00
HOMING	2	11	1	1	3	3452.80
HORAGE	8	41	3	4	11	17289.85
HOUSEBUSTER (USA)	3	19	2	4	5	16595.65
HOUSTON (USA)	4	23	1	1	5	6305.50
HUBBLY BUBBLY (USA)	7	51	3	6	13	29523.35
IMPERIAL FALCON (CAN)	2	13	1	2	1	5219.75
IMPERIAL FRONTIER (USA)	45	247	13	21	64	101041.86
IMP SOCIETY (USA)	37	218	13	14	52	70505.81
INCA CHIEF (USA)	19	84	1	1	16	12933.00
INCHINOR (GB)	13	60	4	8	25	54108.50
INDIAN RIDGE	70	346	23	33	112	421338.19
INSAN (USA)	2	8	2	2	1	6105.25
INTERREX (CAN)	30	165	7	14	34	70603.37
IN THE WINGS	39	191	18	28	77	647594.65
IRISH RIVER (FR)	21	86	8	10	31	91934.77
IT'S FREEZING (USA)	1	9	1	2	2	7337.75
JALMOOD (USA)	5	27	1	2	5	9421.10
JAREER (USA)	13	52	1	1	10	6490.55
JEU DE PAILLE (FR)	1	5	1	1	2	3787.13
JUMBO HIRT (USA)	2	14	1	3	3	27858.55
JUPITER ISLAND	7	25	1	1	6	7147.28
KABOUR	4	37	2	5	8	20376.70
KADROU (FR)	1	7	1	1	3	5538.75
KAHYASI	29	110	8	10	33	106827.95
KALAGLOW	14	114	4	15	40	94929.70
KALA SHIKARI	3	27	1	5	9	48397.25
KALDOUN (FR)	4	27	1	1	10	25511.85
K-BATTERY	4	15	2	4	3	13491.75
KEEN	43	185	9	13	26	49839.05
KEFAAH (USA)	20	123	6	10	39	51184.78
KENDOR (FR)	2	19	2	3	8	12629.40
KENMARE (FR)	18	75	9	12	20	73940.26

STALLIONS	RNRS	STARTS	WNRS	WINS	PLACES	TOTAL
KIND OF HUSH	2	30	1	1	4	4561.00
KING OF CLUBS	3	31	2	5	9	20323.06
KING'S RIDE	4	5	2	2	0	2712.87
KING'S SIGNET (USA)	18	80	5	6	20	26685.15
KNESSET (USA)	1	5	1	1	2	3061.88
KNOWN FACT (USA)	12	60	5	10	25	91456.25
KOMAITE (USA)	44	269	16	20	49	91258.55
KRIS	58	292	24	32	86	238133.26
KRIS S (USA)	4	9	3	6	0	73318.75
KYLIAN (USA)	5	26	3	4	9	26142.45
LAHIB (USA)	37	156	14	17	49	115745.42
LANCASTRIAN	1	1	1	1	0	4069.31
LASHKARI	3	18	2	2	4	7149.00
LAST TYCOON	69	282	20	24	85	195559.16
LATEST MODEL	1	12	1	1	4	8056.35
LAW SOCIETY (USA)	34	154	8	14	40	91730.91
LEADING COUNSEL (USA)	1	3	1	2	1	9985.75
LEAD ON TIME (USA)	7	51	2	4	16	16477.18
LEAR FAN (USA)	24	134	10	18	42	305228.10
LEPANTO (GER)	3	11	1	1	7	3877.47
LIBOI (USA)	4	24	2	3	5	13096.25
LIDHAME	2	20	1	1	4	4698.35
LION CAVERN (USA)	23	67	7	9	27	57404.25
LITTLE MISSOURI (USA)	1	5	1	2	2	27737.50
LOCAL TALENT (USA)	2	19	1	2	9	17788.40
LOCHNAGER	14	101	4	4	12	16558.10
LOMOND (USA)	13	74	4	7	18	37031.74
LONGLEAT (USA)	1	12	1	1	7	8652.60
LORD AT WAR (ARG)	3	14	1	2	2	15562.39
LORD BUD	5	28	1	1	5	27319.98
LUCKY WEDNESDAY	1	4	1	1	0	1469.00
LUGANA BEACH	19	117	7	12	29	78737.15
LYCIUS (USA)	36	169	11	18	40	122978.41
LYPHARD (USA)	11	49	4	5	21	100931.84
MACHIAVELLIAN (USA)	33	166	21	28	74	572778.58
MAC'S IMP (USA)	52	323	11	14	69	96683.35
MAELSTROM LAKE	16	83	1	1	24	14759.75
MAGICAL STRIKE (USA)	17	54	3	3	16	16334.77
MAGICAL WONDER (USA)	17	83	6	8	23	42016.17
MAGIC RING (IRE)	23	115	7	8	39	105843.20
MAKBUL	1	7	1	2	5	102972.60
MALEDETTO (IRE)	9	37	1	1	4	5730.50
MANILA (USA)	9	43	4	9	15	45536.85
MANSOOJ	4	38	1	3	8	13089.92
MARJU (IRE)	40	190	16	19	51	219652.26
MARTIN JOHN	3	22	1	1	7	6888.81
MASTERCLASS (USA)	13	61	4	7	12	21601.69
MASTER WILLIE	9	54	2	4	13	33653.90
MAZAAD	12	55	3	5	13	22235.71
MAZILIER (USA)	29	190	11	18	42	81391.72
MERDON MELODY	13	61	2	3	7	13326.04
MICHELOZZO (USA)	1	10	1	2	2	4773.00
MIDYAN (USA)	55	294	17	21	76	161141.60
MINING (USA)	4	28	1	1	5	4055.85
MINSHAANSHU AMAD (USA)	3	29	2	5	10	19396.90
MINSTER SON	9	33	1	2	6	8096.00
MIRAMAR REEF	1	2	1	1	1	3648.52
MISWAKI (USA)	15	61	5	5	10	109858.12
MOMENT OF HOPE (USA)	1	9	1	2	4	6994.00
MONTELIMAR (USA)	4	20	1	1	2	5618.81
MON TRESOR	17	84	3	4	20	26053.57

STALLIONS	RNRS	STARTS	WNRS	WINS	PLACES	TOTAL
MOSCOW SOCIETY (USA)	4	17	1	2	2	4143.46
MOST WELCOME	52	282	20	30	83	263382.73
MR PROSPECTOR (USA)	16	54	10	14	20	108188.59
MTOTO	44	273	19	30	97	533612.47
MUJADIL (USA)	43	293	18	31	92	209675.22
MUJTAHID (USA)	47	247	19	23	73	143387.96
MUKADDAMAH (USA)	13	60	4	11	11	59799.13
MULHOLLANDE (USA)	6	46	2	5	6	16791.10
MUSCATITE	1	12	1	1	1	6019.80
MUSIC BOY	19	101	4	7	24	49004.25
MYSTIKO (USA)	35	200	11	19	48	79672.97
NABEEL DANCER (USA)	5	49	2	3	20	28764.28
NAEVUS (USA)	2	6	2	3	1	12420.01
NALCHIK (USA)	5	41	1	4	7	17400.52
NASHAMAA	14	93	4	7	15	50204.95
NASHWAN (USA)	45	178	23	36	67	593246.70
NESHAD (USA)	3	28	2	7	7	20196.70
NEVER SO BOLD	35	203	6	14	53	121904.42
NEW EXPRESS	1	10	1	2	4	7189.75
NICHOLAS (USA)	19	108	4	7	23	45526.56
NIGHT SHIFT (USA)	99	507	37	42	161	351216.71
NINISKI (USA)	26	98	7	12	23	92977.19
NISHAPOUR (FR)	6	24	3	3	2	11498.80
NOBLE PATRIARCH	16	70	3	3	11	12122.98
THE NOBLE PLAYER (USA)	8	47	4	9	15	40151.28
NOMINATION	29	175	9	18	40	125849.79
NORDANCE (USA)	6	46	1	1	17	35945.57
NORDICO (USA)	44	255	12	22	53	102217.41
NORTHERN BABY (CAN)	6	37	2	4	7	15102.60
NORTHERN FLAGSHIP (USA)	4	18	1	2	4	7470.35
NORTHERN PARK (USA)	9	32	1	1	3	4683.25
NORTHERN STATE (USA)	10	54	2	4	8	17959.50
NORTHERN TEMPEST (USA)	1	8	1	1	1	3204.00
NORTHIAM (USA)	1	7	1	1	4	56941.20
NORTHJET	1	3	1	1	2	3504.38
NORTON CHALLENGER	7	35	2	2	3	5526.10
NORWICK (USA)	3	14	1	1	6	6195.00
NUREYEV (USA)	28	110	10	16	48	522478.59
OGYGIAN (USA)	1	6	1	1	1	2258.00
OLD VIC	30	177	14	21	56	204919.59
OPENING VERSE (USA)	2	9	2	3	3	27465.07
OVAC (ITY)	1	4	1	1	1	86.63
PARIS HOUSE (GB)	19	79	7	12	16	48325.58
PENNINE WALK	19	134	7	12	35	63940.86
PERSIAN BOLD	56	269	21	27	66	159071.29
PERSIAN HEIGHTS	17	86	5	11	24	132461.31
PERSONAL HOPE (USA)	2	8	1	1	2	5014.96
PETARDIA (GB)	40	215	8	13	60	120865.50
PETONG	73	439	18	28	93	169889.18
PETORIUS	42	243	17	26	68	160602.68
PETOSKI	15	85	4	11	21	49177.97
PHARDANTE (FR)	12	22	2	2	2	4073.14
PHARLY (FR)	39	231	12	22	59	257654.25
PIPS PRIDE (GB)	26	110	7	7	38	46716.78
PIRATE ARMY (USA)	1	10	1	1	2	3475.00
PLATINI (GER)	1	5	1	1	0	3385.50
PLUGGED NICKLE (USA)	1	22	1	3	3	6962.40
POLAR FALCON (USA)	47	210	20	32	59	233523.35
POLISH PATRIOT (USA)	39	243	14	33	76	224981.98
POLISH PRECEDENT (USA)	46	185	14	23	58	794096.55
POSEN (USA)	18	70	3	5	18	32426.79

STALLIONS	RNRS	STARTS	WNRS	WINS	PLACES	TOTAL
PRECIOUS METAL	6	14	1	1	0	2430.00
PRECOCIOUS	31	177	5	5	44	38514.03
PRESIDIUM	45	225	10	13	37	90926.85
PRIMO DOMINIE	77	474	28	43	128	299446.12
PRINCE DANIEL (USA)	10	68	4	6	14	30090.03
PRINCE RUPERT (FR)	16	90	6	8	26	44043.58
PRINCE SABO	64	325	17	20	75	197657.97
PRIOLO (USA)	29	146	10	13	49	129979.09
PRIVATE ACCOUNT (USA)	7	27	2	2	14	26461.83
PROJECT MANAGER	38	187	10	18	49	107478.48
PUISSANCE	49	304	17	25	71	134759.89
PURSUIT OF LOVE (GB)	37	168	12	16	76	150431.54
QUEST FOR FAME	4	20	2	3	7	23218.55
QUIET AMERICAN (USA)	1	4	1	1	3	5368.00
RAHY (USA)	8	45	5	7	16	118203.85
RAINBOW QUEST (USA)	56	262	23	38	91	236450.15
RAINBOWS FOR LIFE (CAN)	13	50	1	1	8	8158.48
RAISE A MAN (USA)	1	11	1	2	4	6826.20
RAKAPOSHI KING	3	18	2	3	6	12786.10
RAMBO DANCER (CAN)	60	423	24	36	117	236889.94
RARE PERFORMER (USA)	1	13	1	2	5	9954.45
RED RANSOM (USA)	19	102	11	13	38	174127.37
RED SUNSET	17	110	5	13	31	67827.93
REFERENCE POINT	4	40	1	2	9	12265.75
REPRIMAND	58	359	22	36	100	246959.55
RHOMAN RULE (USA)	3	8	1	1	4	29678.23
RICH CHARLIE	8	96	4	6	21	35654.70
RISING	1	5	1	1	3	3967.82
RISK ME (FR)	92	477	23	37	91	157278.35
RIVER FALLS (GB)	45	233	9	12	40	59593.99
RIVER GOD (USA)	3	33	1	1	4	4886.00
RIVERMAN (USA)	33	120	10	16	41	363996.20
ROBELLINO (USA)	55	299	20	32	81	365882.78
ROCK CITY	39	211	12	14	66	82853.51
ROCK HOPPER	26	122	6	7	32	66491.54
ROI DANZIG (USA)	31	187	13	18	49	124249.79
RON'S VICTORY (USA)	27	131	6	8	32	47186.35
ROSELIER (FR)	7	10	1	2	1	11529.70
ROUSILLON (USA)	12	73	6	10	23	45224.60
ROYAL ACADEMY (USA)	78	416	34	52	130	818136.60
ROYAL VULCAN	1	1	1	1	0	0.00
RUBIANO (USA)	4	22	2	4	7	39397.05
RUDIMENTARY (USA)	32	197	12	13	52	102216.38
RUNAWAY GROOM (CAN)	1	8	1	2	3	15382.75
RUSTICARO (FR)	4	18	2	3	6	11112.78
RYMER	1	17	1	3	5	20128.25
SABREHILL (USA)	21	67	5	6	9	39791.20
SADDLERS' HALL (IRE)	31	129	9	12	37	537639.50
SADLER'S WELLS (USA)	97	426	51	75	175	1419738.19
SAFAWAN	23	134	7	13	24	60859.76
SALEM DRIVE (USA)	2	10	1	1	3	10036.75
SALSE (USA)	58	259	18	23	82	512407.57
SALT DOME (USA)	22	173	11	22	37	105026.59
SANGLAMORE (USA)	16	64	1	1	26	36506.00
SARAB	1	7	1	1	3	4418.90
SARATOGA SIX (USA)	1	12	1	1	4	6133.75
SATCO (FR)	3	14	1	3	4	88725.30
SAUMAREZ	1	5	1	1	3	3954.80
SAVAHRA SOUND	2	26	2	4	15	22856.75
SAYF EL ARAB (USA)	10	65	3	10	11	37495.80
SCALLYWAG	1	10	1	2	4	7209.40

STALLIONS	RNRS	STARTS	WNRS	WINS	PLACES	TOTAL
SCENIC	36	193	9	13	51	93060.22
SCOTTISH REEL	7	28	1	1	9	15809.80
SCRIPT OHIO (USA)	2	8	1	1	5	4119.73
SEATTLE SLEW (USA)	3	8	1	1	4	6990.10
SECOND SET (IRE)	15	52	6	7	13	74731.56
SECRETO (USA)	2	22	2	2	3	14293.10
SEEKING THE GOLD (USA)	9	62	6	11	20	66754.81
SELKIRK (USA)	47	177	19	31	65	291983.23
SHAADI (USA)	13	122	8	22	38	286297.45
SHADEED (USA)	21	99	6	10	32	83349.33
SHAHRASTANI (USA)	11	54	3	5	19	30056.57
SHALFORD (IRE)	57	305	15	28	92	157020.61
SHARDARI	10	30	3	4	6	13499.02
SHAREEF DANCER (USA)	40	210	9	14	61	106980.05
SHARPO	56	325	21	33	86	271837.56
SHARP VICTOR (USA)	14	65	3	5	13	64597.91
SHARROOD (USA)	18	109	8	15	39	182122.58
SHAVIAN	13	114	7	16	25	95242.76
SHEIKH ALBADOU (GB)	13	53	4	5	18	64888.19
SHERNAZAR	20	61	5	9	20	122022.92
SHIRLEY HEIGHTS	55	250	21	28	89	300651.14
SIBERIAN EXPRESS (USA)	13	88	4	4	26	25376.60
SILLY PRICES	4	20	1	1	4	5496.00
SILVER HAWK (USA)	28	143	11	15	68	909892.47
SILVER KITE (USA)	31	184	6	8	42	51543.90
SIMPLY GREAT (FR)	26	118	7	12	32	66784.69
SIMPLY MAJESTIC (USA)	1	8	1	1	5	14238.67
SIZZLING MELODY	20	91	4	6	13	30047.84
SKY CLASSIC (CAN)	5	13	1	1	8	10226.74
SKYLINER	8	21	1	1	1	2735.25
SLEW O' GOLD (USA)	6	34	2	2	14	17051.20
SLIP ANCHOR	57	232	17	27	69	362189.72
SMILE (USA)	1	6	1	3	0	7016.25
SONG	3	30	1	1	3	9339.67
SON OF SHAKA	2	17	1	1	1	4024.00
SOVEREIGN DANCER (USA)	4	21	2	5	3	33049.85
SOVIET LAD (USA)	28	150	7	9	37	48113.47
SOVIET STAR (USA)	41	183	14	23	65	570116.47
STALKER	1	8	1	1	3	11262.37
STANDAAN (FR)	7	21	1	2	3	61740.96
STARRY NIGHT (USA)	1	17	1	2	5	20624.75
STATOBLEST	62	398	26	46	87	232498.59
ST JOVITE (USA)	18	73	6	6	26	48638.95
STORM BIRD (CAN)	16	44	4	5	14	87630.65
STORM CAT (USA)	8	37	5	8	14	47953.04
STRAWBERRY ROAD (AUS)	2	14	1	1	3	3415.25
STRIKE GOLD (USA)	1	7	1	2	3	34279.75
STRONG GALE	3	9	1	1	2	3308.17
SUAVE DANCER (USA)	18	86	6	8	30	76069.47
SUMMER SQUALL (USA)	4	25	2	3	15	27132.83
SUNSHINE FOREVER (USA)	7	29	2	2	14	49616.27
SUPERLATIVE	35	183	10	18	40	83339.50
SUPERPOWER	38	261	8	13	79	79738.20
SUPREME LEADER	5	15	2	4	3	13356.53
SURE BLADE (USA)	14	58	2	5	21	48483.02
SWAN'S ROCK	1	3	1	2	1	12400.99
SWEET MONDAY	1	10	1	1	1	4890.00
SWORD DANCE	1	16	1	3	4	8512.20
SYLVAN EXPRESS	10	67	2	2	19	19179.00
TACHYON PARK	1	7	1	1	1	3886.25
TATE GALLERY (USA)	4	23	3	3	7	15889.70

STALLIONS	RNRS	STARTS	WNRS	WINS	PLACES	TOTAL
TAUFAN (USA)	46	298	16	30	95	234341.77
TEAMSTER	3	13	1	1	2	4338.00
TEENOSO (USA)	14	49	4	4	14	51441.04
TEJANO (USA)	2	25	1	2	6	11947.20
TELSMOSS	1	8	1	3	1	11253.50
TENBY (GB)	14	54	5	9	21	98415.02
TENDER KING	2	22	1	1	2	2537.50
TERIMON	12	61	4	5	14	28031.20
THATCHING	55	346	17	23	97	195075.01
THEATRICAL	16	58	7	10	18	71823.84
THEATRICAL CHARMER	6	19	1	1	3	4672.25
THEN AGAIN	12	86	5	8	17	37544.35
THORN DANCE (USA)	3	21	2	3	4	12027.75
THOWRA (FR)	12	71	1	1	13	10570.75
TIDARO (USA)	4	19	1	5	3	18919.86
TIME FOR A CHANGE (USA)	1	2	1	1	1	4035.70
TIMELESS MOMENT (USA)	2	7	1	1	2	7417.00
TIMELESS TIMES (USA)	40	270	10	17	66	90378.34
TINA'S PET	34	246	10	15	38	73113.75
TIROL	51	287	19	28	75	257396.75
TOCA MADERA	5	37	2	2	10	9963.37
TOPANOORA	10	55	3	5	16	53813.92
TOPSIDER (USA)	4	21	1	1	3	2113.38
TOP VILLE	7	44	3	7	16	36091.13
TOUCH OF GREY	12	77	4	5	15	20381.10
TRAGIC ROLE (USA)	20	94	8	15	23	75177.14
TREASURE KAY	33	197	9	17	39	74845.87
TREMBLANT	4	15	1	1	4	4287.12
TREMPOLINO (USA)	11	44	4	7	11	118375.66
TRY MY BEST (USA)	12	117	7	13	39	113505.17
TWO TIMING (USA)	3	12	1	1	1	2977.00
UNCLE POKEY	1	4	1	1	2	5419.50
UN DESPERADO (FR)	4	13	1	1	3	4018.56
UNFUWAIN (USA)	44	186	16	23	66	248002.93
VAGUE SHOT	4	23	1	2	4	13976.25
VAIGLY GREAT	2	10	1	1	5	5839.20
VALIYAR	3	19	1	1	4	9253.82
VICE REGENT (CAN)	1	6	1	1	0	2427.25
VILLAGE STAR (FR)	3	29	1	2	6	6779.58
VISION (USA)	12	63	4	7	24	30940.72
WAAJIB	55	280	17	25	70	423277.10
WARNING	85	485	36	58	145	548037.09
WARRSHAN (USA)	32	193	9	15	47	65232.65
WASSL	1	18	1	3	7	14103.35
WELDNAAS (USA)	38	211	7	14	48	75202.79
WELL DECORATED (USA)	1	17	1	1	3	3334.65
WELSH CAPTAIN	6	30	1	1	3	4628.20
WELSH TERM	3	15	2	2	5	10175.74
WILD AGAIN (USA)	3	5	1	1	1	3791.25
WITH APPROVAL (CAN)	6	24	1	3	11	15705.07
WOLFHOUND (USA)	21	82	5	6	39	48227.00
WOLVERLIFE	2	10	1	1	2	3151.75
WOODMAN (USA)	43	162	17	26	65	481146.81
ZAFONIC (USA)	15	32	9	11	11	193221.15
ZAYYANI	2	5	1	1	3	35457.81
ZIGGY'S BOY (USA)	2	20	1	1	7	13631.40
ZILZAL (USA)	25	104	13	21	44	253787.45

STATISTICS BY KIND PERMISSION OF WEATHERBYS

JUMP STALLIONS EARNINGS FOR 1996/97

(includes every stallion who sired a winner over jumps in Great Britain and Ireland in 1996/97).

STALLIONS	RNRS	STARTS	WNRS	WINS	PLACES	TOTAL
ABEDNEGO	12	33	3	5	5	20653.41
ABSALOM	24	99	4	7	34	64909.18
ACCORDION	15	60	6	7	17	36258.79
ADBASS (USA)	2	10	2	2	5	9994.70
ADONIJAH	7	36	1	2	10	11053.75
AFFIRMED (USA)	1	5	1	1	2	3266.00
AFZAL	11	33	1	1	9	8808.70
AJDAL (USA)	2	5	2	3	1	11887.00
AJRAAS (USA)	8	33	4	5	9	23731.99
AKARAD (FR)	3	17	2	5	9	27770.60
AL HAREB (USA)	5	20	1	1	5	4934.47
ALIAS SMITH (USA)	26	80	3	7	17	71002.27
ALLEGED (USA)	14	71	6	8	20	50455.27
ALLEGED DASH (USA)	1	8	1	3	5	11536.00
ALLEGING (USA)	3	14	2	6	4	20527.00
ALL HASTE (USA)	2	10	2	2	1	8479.16
AL NASR (FR)	4	31	2	3	11	32131.00
ALPHABATIM (USA)	1	5	1	2	1	6152.06
AL SIRAT (USA)	4	18	1	1	5	8711.45
ALTAYAN	1	3	1	1	0	3051.98
ALWAYS FAIR (USA)	2	6	1	1	2	3107.90
ALYSHEBA (USA)	1	9	1	1	7	7155.50
ALZAO (USA)	33	122	10	15	43	68113.03
AMAZING BUST	12	46	2	2	8	7373.81
AMEN (FR)	1	8	1	2	2	5038.95
AMORISTIC (USA)	1	5	1	2	2	6910.39
ANDRETTI	7	24	1	1	3	3633.78
ANITA'S PRINCE	4	10	1	1	4	5032.31
ANOTHER REALM	2	9	1	1	2	3771.50
ANSHAN	5	18	2	4	6	37191.91
ARAPAHOS (FR)	10	36	1	1	19	11586.83
ARCHITECT (USA)	5	13	1	1	3	3723.88
ARCTIC LORD	26	80	2	3	10	27225.00
ARCTIC TERN (USA)	10	36	3	4	6	13241.22
ARDROSS	50	178	17	28	56	147896.98
ARISTOCRACY	45	174	8	26	37	136458.12
ARKAN	3	13	2	3	4	7768.90
AROKAR (FR)	1	2	1	1	1	2886.14
ARRASAS (USA)	4	11	1	3	1	9158.10
ARZANNI	3	8	1	1	2	2473.50
ASHFORD (USA)	6	26	1	1	6	7099.40
ASHMOLEAN (USA)	1	7	1	1	1	2316.83
ASIR	12	53	3	5	11	17757.92
ASSERT	4	23	4	9	4	26551.80
ATHENS TREASURE	1	9	1	2	4	9553.25
AUCTION RING (USA)	6	17	1	1	5	5505.50
AVOCAT	10	33	1	3	7	28840.71
BACKCHAT (USA)	5	11	1	1	2	3106.00
BAIRN (USA)	15	75	4	10	19	37810.05
BALBOA	3	9	1	2	1	5728.25
BALLACASHTAL (CAN)	22	69	2	2	27	27912.50
BALLIOL	3	16	2	2	3	7171.80
BARACHOIS (CAN)	2	15	1	1	5	3964.00
BARBAROLLI (USA)	3	14	2	2	1	5412.61
BAR DEXTER (USA)	3	14	1	3	4	27037.57

STALLIONS	RNRS	STARTS	WNRS	WINS	PLACES	TOTAL
BARON BLAKENEY	30	100	5	5	31	33488.10
BASSA SELIM (FR)	1	6	1	1	2	2814.43
BAY EXPRESS	1	7	1	1	2	6186.40
BEAU CHARMEUR (FR)	15	57	3	3	15	21374.04
BELDALE FLUTTER (USA)	3	19	2	6	3	25647.24
BELFORT (FR)	10	28	2	4	9	23224.50
BELLYPHA	4	23	1	2	6	10133.90
BELMEZ (USA)	7	29	3	3	8	12303.60
BE MY CHIEF (USA)	13	55	1	5	14	22104.29
BE MY GUEST (USA)	20	76	6	11	20	46061.96
BE MY NATIVE (USA)	84	261	21	29	91	154908.05
BERING	9	34	2	2	15	23993.17
BEVELED (USA)	13	67	6	9	21	51205.68
BIKALA	2	6	1	1	1	3608.60
BISHOP OF ORANGE	2	7	1	2	2	6470.00
BLACK MINSTREL	42	132	5	5	28	28145.74
BLACK TIE AFFAIR	1	7	1	1	3	5327.00
BLAKENEY	20	75	2	3	14	15522.65
BLAKENEY POINT	2	4	1	1	0	8689.00
BLAZING SADDLES (AUS)	1	5	1	1	3	7134.00
BLUEBIRD (USA)	12	47	3	3	9	10406.04
BLUSHING JOHN (USA)	2	11	1	4	3	11211.00
BLUSHING SCRIBE (USA)	2	12	1	2	3	4584.00
BOB BACK (USA)	24	102	7	10	40	79344.94
BOLD ARRANGEMENT	13	73	4	4	22	20476.32
BOLD FOX	3	14	1	4	1	8919.50
BOLD OWL	15	44	1	1	8	5198.30
BOOTSMAN BAINS (GER)	1	3	1	1	0	2136.00
BOREEN (FR)	28	95	5	9	22	39873.27
BOYNE VALLEY	12	54	1	1	14	8267.81
BREWERY BOY (AUS)	2	7	1	1	1	4649.49
BREZZO (FR)	5	17	1	2	4	12541.75
BRILLIANT INVADER (AUS)	1	9	1	3	6	12881.35
BROADSWORD (USA)	32	87	6	10	21	40593.20
BROKEN HEARTED	15	47	2	3	11	14517.10
BRUSH ASIDE (USA)	37	86	6	7	18	24445.89
BUCKLEY	25	77	2	2	17	12388.86
BUCKSKIN (FR)	155	481	26	35	125	220252.20
BULLDOZER	17	63	2	3	17	23694.97
BURSLEM	11	45	2	3	9	8486.93
BUSTINETO	10	54	5	9	22	59330.61
BUSTINO	22	62	8	15	14	64484.37
BUSTOMI	10	24	1	1	8	6775.24
BUZZARDS BAY	9	24	1	1	8	6529.20
CACHE OF GOLD (USA)	1	5	1	1	2	2036.50
CADEAUX GENEREUX	10	36	3	4	7	13175.08
CADOUDAL (FR)	2	6	2	3	3	21564.50
CAERLEON (USA)	21	107	7	15	38	115387.57
CALLERNISH	83	314	25	38	112	296202.32
CAMDEN TOWN	19	74	4	9	19	114293.03
CAP MARTIN (FR)	4	22	1	3	6	11970.25
CAPOTE (USA)	1	5	1	3	1	15871.50
CAPRICORN LINE	8	25	2	2	5	6961.40
CARDINAL FLOWER	26	91	5	6	16	22905.86
CARLINGFORD CASTLE	78	313	23	36	74	150692.74
CARMELITE HOUSE (USA)	12	55	3	5	14	27758.68
CASTLE KEEP	43	131	6	6	24	53850.07
CATALDI	33	128	5	8	39	38936.70
CELESTIAL STORM (USA)	17	55	6	10	16	46736.20
CELIO RUFO	29	112	6	12	33	48062.95
CELTIC CONE	31	133	10	17	26	124947.55

STALLIONS	RNRS	STARTS	WNRS	WINS	PLACES	TOTAL
CHAMBERLIN (FR)	1	6	1	2	2	52335.00
CHARMER	10	31	4	4	3	11407.29
CHEVAL	5	24	2	2	8	17083.30
CHIEF'S CROWN (USA)	6	33	2	2	3	5203.39
CHIEF SINGER	8	27	3	4	5	16150.95
CHURCH PARADE	3	12	1	1	5	6184.80
CISTO (FR)	3	10	1	3	4	9942.55
CLANTIME	4	10	1	4	1	13984.00
CLASSIC SECRET (USA)	17	44	5	7	8	27249.04
CLAUDE MONET (USA)	3	15	1	1	2	4002.50
CLEARLY BUST	5	19	1	3	7	13418.50
COMEDY STAR (USA)	2	10	1	1	6	4378.70
COMMANCHE RUN	28	97	7	12	27	96585.24
COMMON GROUNDS	9	38	2	2	10	9291.06
CONCORDE JR (USA)	1	14	1	1	10	10476.05
CONNAUGHT	4	11	1	1	4	3889.25
CONQUERING HERO (USA)	10	40	3	4	8	17891.79
CONQUISTADOR CIELO (USA)	2	17	1	2	9	10224.55
CONTRACT LAW (USA)	15	42	2	4	9	15606.95
COOL GUY (USA)	2	8	1	1	5	4708.85
COQUELIN (USA)	5	20	1	3	7	16785.40
CORVARO (USA)	18	64	4	4	12	21560.38
COZZENE (USA)	4	9	2	2	4	20426.00
CRASH COURSE	26	123	10	14	45	132537.77
CREATIVE PLAN (USA)	8	40	1	1	10	7715.91
CRESTED LARK	5	19	1	1	5	3416.30
CROFTHALL	7	23	1	2	5	9797.65
CROGHAN HILL	4	21	2	4	10	26012.90
CRUISE MISSILE	21	59	3	3	11	11716.10
CURE THE BLUES (USA)	4	13	1	1	4	4130.63
CUT ABOVE	4	10	1	2	5	6785.90
CUTLASS (USA)	1	9	1	2	2	9415.50
CYBORG (FR)	2	13	2	7	5	49253.65
CYRANO DE BERGERAC	28	82	4	4	20	18305.20
DAHAR (USA)	2	14	1	4	5	26628.25
DAMISTER (USA)	15	56	2	3	10	16151.05
DANCEHALL (USA)	1	6	1	4	0	16110.75
DANCE OF LIFE (USA)	6	20	2	2	4	8028.13
DANCING BRAVE (USA)	11	52	4	13	18	69873.30
DANCING DISSIDENT (USA)	9	42	4	6	8	23647.50
DANCING HIGH	2	4	1	1	0	1486.50
DANCING LIGHTS (USA)	1	4	1	1	3	8134.02
DANEHILL (USA)	10	34	1	1	7	9441.00
DANZIG CONNECTION (USA)	5	23	1	2	6	6268.22
DARA MONARCH	7	23	1	1	7	4676.84
DARING MARCH	14	39	2	4	11	20540.08
DARSHAAN	19	74	2	4	17	21398.37
DASHING BLADE	2	3	1	1	1	2877.36
DECENT FELLOW	16	54	4	8	15	30684.35
DEEP RUN	57	231	15	26	97	273630.55
DELAMAIN (USA)	3	19	1	3	5	8937.35
DENEL (FR)	38	139	10	13	44	53617.61
DEPLOY	7	30	1	1	14	10541.82
DEPUTY MINISTER (CAN)	3	17	2	2	3	8060.21
DEROULEDE	2	6	1	1	4	7427.50
DERRING ROSE	42	178	11	14	48	72064.99
DERRYLIN	27	100	6	8	17	32083.25
DESERT WINE (USA)	1	10	1	3	4	11137.55
DESTROYER	2	23	1	1	4	3224.50
DIAMOND SHOAL	1	11	1	1	4	3087.10
DIESIS	11	46	4	5	18	24837.81

STALLIONS	RNRS	STARTS	WNRS	WINS	PLACES	TOTAL
DIGAMIST (USA)	20	104	7	8	32	38989.74
DISTINCTLY NORTH (USA)	17	56	3	7	11	22784.40
DOCK LEAF	5	13	1	2	4	7336.60
DOC MARTEN	3	23	1	3	12	17271.85
DOMINION	32	137	13	23	37	193474.98
DOMINION ROYALE	12	59	5	10	19	30520.15
DOM PASQUINI (FR)	4	22	3	5	8	19000.90
DOMYNSKY	9	30	3	7	8	38118.60
DON ROBERTO (USA)	2	10	1	2	3	7218.31
DON'T FORGET ME	41	182	6	10	50	61154.65
DOUBLE BED (FR)	1	6	1	2	2	5312.00
DOULAB (USA)	9	41	3	4	13	18034.91
DOWN THE HATCH	2	14	1	1	6	8249.29
DOWSING (USA)	12	46	4	5	17	25665.11
DOYOUN	14	56	5	8	16	66410.45
DRAGON PALACE (USA)	3	8	1	1	0	2276.00
DREAMS TO REALITY (USA)	5	21	2	2	7	6508.35
DROMOD HILL	11	35	1	1	8	5942.46
DRY DOCK	10	35	4	4	3	12198.58
DUBASSOFF (USA)	14	64	6	10	21	52582.20
DUCA DI BUSTED	5	15	1	2	1	6706.25
DUKY	14	60	7	11	13	55826.00
DUNBEATH (USA)	28	103	4	8	29	37601.30
DURGAM (USA)	6	17	1	2	2	7730.18
EASY GOER (USA)	1	6	1	1	2	3782.00
EFISIO	8	46	5	8	18	32385.95
ELA-MANA-MOU	21	86	7	15	30	67099.01
EL CONQUISTADOR	18	54	3	5	12	22142.25
ELECTRIC	51	150	12	17	39	89179.31
ELEGANT AIR	7	13	1	1	2	3923.75
EL GRAN SENOR (USA)	9	34	1	1	11	8405.79
ELMAAMUL (USA)	4	11	1	1	7	7131.48
EMARATI (USA)	4	19	1	2	2	5595.60
ENCHANTMENT	4	21	1	1	6	6817.40
ENRYCO MIEO	1	4	1	1	1	4915.00
ENTITLED	4	6	1	1	0	2442.50
ENTRE NOUS	3	11	1	2	2	4456.40
ERIN'S HOPE	15	43	2	3	10	19934.96
EUPHEMISM	15	60	7	10	27	45860.00
EUROBUS	3	5	2	3	1	7960.06
EVE'S ERROR	6	30	2	5	8	18731.36
EXACTLY SHARP (USA)	4	11	1	1	3	3080.00
EXECUTIVE PERK	73	232	12	21	51	114070.24
EXHIBITIONER	13	42	2	4	10	11859.47
FAIRY KING (USA)	20	53	2	3	13	11323.60
FARHAAN	11	34	1	3	13	14187.79
FAR NORTH (CAN)	2	5	1	1	0	2911.90
FAST TOPAZE (USA)	1	3	1	1	1	3092.30
FAUSTUS (USA)	21	90	10	17	30	77840.88
FEARLESS ACTION (USA)	6	16	1	2	1	7658.87
FEELINGS (FR)	6	36	2	5	13	23042.50
FIDEL	15	57	5	10	18	47383.45
FIGHTING FIT (USA)	3	6	1	1	2	4426.00
FINAL STRAW	6	18	1	1	6	30483.74
FINE BLADE (USA)	4	18	2	2	12	9546.50
FLASH OF STEEL	8	35	2	7	7	26827.55
FLORIDA SON	8	19	2	3	3	31330.16
FLYING PASTER (USA)	1	13	1	2	2	7000.60
FOOLS HOLME (USA)	13	77	7	19	24	114462.24
FORMIDABLE (USA)	11	40	3	5	12	18823.00
FORTIES FIELD (FR)	1	3	1	1	1	5574.50

STALLIONS	RNRS	STARTS	WNRS	WINS	PLACES	TOTAL
FORTY NINER (USA)	2	12	1	1	5	5901.60
FRESH BREEZE (USA)	3	7	1	1	1	3094.07
FULL OF HOPE	6	31	1	3	13	17763.30
FULL ON ACES (AUS)	1	5	1	1	2	5428.05
FUNNY MAN	8	21	2	2	3	8557.00
FURRY GLEN	44	170	13	22	55	169458.70
GALA PERFORMANCE (USA)	2	3	1	1	1	4003.00
GALLIC LEAGUE	3	14	1	6	0	14469.00
GARDE ROYALE	2	10	1	1	3	6578.50
GEIGER COUNTER (USA)	1	7	1	2	1	5387.10
GENERAL IRONSIDE	9	26	1	2	8	11581.60
GENERAL VIEW	7	32	1	2	11	12784.51
GENEROUS (IRE)	7	29	2	2	12	10354.81
GIANCHI	3	11	1	2	5	10015.40
GINGER BOY	2	15	2	4	4	16540.80
GLACIAL STORM (USA)	24	66	1	1	12	9949.30
GLENSTAL (USA)	29	124	8	13	42	65073.10
GLINT OF GOLD	10	49	4	5	15	26836.31
GLOW (USA)	19	78	5	9	18	33885.64
GODS SOLUTION	2	6	1	1	3	4186.50
GOLDEN LAHAB (USA)	3	15	2	3	4	8691.50
GOLDHILL	2	8	1	1	3	4909.00
GONE FISHIN	4	12	1	1	4	4740.86
GOOD THYNE (USA)	77	293	23	34	70	186987.29
GOOD TIMES (ITY)	8	28	2	4	3	9911.40
GORYTUS (USA)	6	26	2	4	10	19741.10
GOVERNOR GENERAL	18	59	3	4	14	16169.50
GREEN DESERT (USA)	18	72	7	11	25	47113.60
GREEN FOREST (USA)	6	22	1	1	3	5709.96
GREEN RUBY (USA)	5	17	1	1	2	3015.70
GREEN SHOON	10	26	4	6	6	36400.55
GREGORIAN (USA)	1	6	1	1	1	5403.50
GREINTON	2	14	1	1	5	4077.45
GREY DESIRE	8	20	1	4	2	17194.05
GREY GHOST	3	11	1	1	3	4581.15
GULCH (USA)	5	16	2	2	3	6121.00
GUNNER B	48	157	14	27	26	87718.39
HADEER	8	31	2	4	10	13262.30
HALLODRI (ATA)	1	3	1	1	1	3997.00
HALO (USA)	2	9	1	2	4	7077.00
HALYUDH (USA)	1	7	1	3	3	7880.50
HANDSOME SAILOR	6	20	2	3	4	8248.60
HARD FOUGHT	4	16	1	1	1	3347.20
HARP ISLET (USA)	1	5	1	1	3	5260.10
HATIM (USA)	11	36	2	2	11	10341.75
HAWAIIAN RETURN (USA)	6	35	4	6	12	31387.40
HAWKSTER (USA)	3	18	2	5	5	49966.55
HAYS	5	15	1	2	5	9420.20
HEAD FOR HEIGHTS	2	8	1	1	5	2626.28
HEALAUGH FOX	1	4	1	1	2	3414.00
HEIGHTS OF GOLD	2	13	1	2	2	6471.20
HENBIT (USA)	87	323	15	21	94	111869.15
HERALDISTE (USA)	3	16	1	2	2	8899.85
HERES	1	2	1	1	0	1929.20
HIGH ADVENTURE	1	4	1	1	0	2486.00
HIGH ESTATE	8	23	3	3	5	10871.74
HIGHEST HONOR (FR)	2	11	1	5	2	9048.50
HIGH KICKER (USA)	10	36	2	4	4	15606.20
HIGH LINE	13	48	4	7	16	52145.87
HIGH SEASON	3	10	1	1	2	3175.50
HIGH TOP	6	30	2	5	18	32920.60

STALLIONS	RNRS	STARTS	WNRS	WINS	PLACES	TOTAL
HOLST (USA)	1	6	1	1	5	5068.30
HOMEBOY	4	21	1	1	6	14295.53
HOMO SAPIEN	22	72	4	6	10	18993.97
HORAGE	12	65	5	5	23	76858.52
HOTFOOT	6	17	2	3	5	12148.55
HUBBLY BUBBLY (USA)	10	29	2	2	3	7864.50
HYMNS ON HIGH	2	13	1	3	5	18626.75
IDIOT'S DELIGHT	78	267	20	27	52	263111.46
ILE DE BOURBON (USA)	5	23	2	2	4	7810.20
ILIUM	6	17	1	1	1	3402.00
IMPECUNIOUS	5	25	1	1	10	9439.65
IMPERIAL FRONTIER (USA)	5	17	1	1	3	3491.33
IMPORT	14	50	1	2	12	24875.80
IMP SOCIETY (USA)	5	14	2	3	2	10204.50
INDIAN KING (USA)	2	10	1	1	7	7456.47
INDIAN RIDGE	11	40	4	13	8	44339.80
INSAN (USA)	4	19	1	3	7	9950.66
INTERREX (CAN)	9	34	1	3	6	12771.50
IN THE WINGS	5	18	1	2	3	7240.50
INVITED (USA)	7	46	3	6	16	27860.20
IRISH RIVER (FR)	8	33	1	3	8	7133.21
IRON DUKE (FR)	1	9	1	1	2	5298.13
ISLE OF MAN (NZ)	1	6	1	4	0	15421.50
ITALIC (FR)	2	6	1	2	2	31031.13
IVORY HUNTER (USA)	4	23	2	4	9	38149.80
JALMOOD (USA)	12	50	3	3	15	14674.93
JAMESMEAD	8	38	3	6	9	14877.71
JAREER (USA)	21	83	4	6	11	21053.54
JESTER	11	33	2	2	6	7449.00
JEU DE PAILLE (FR)	9	41	2	2	9	9759.30
JIMSUN	2	7	1	1	1	2856.00
JOHN FRENCH	9	41	4	5	9	18075.60
JOLLY JAKE (NZ)	15	51	1	1	11	5874.12
JOSHUA	1	7	1	1	1	3559.00
JULIO MARINER	11	38	3	7	9	58405.25
JUPITER ISLAND	22	63	5	6	16	21239.20
KABOUR	9	29	1	2	5	7721.40
KAHYASI	16	83	10	18	29	131893.01
KALAGLOW	19	66	2	5	16	22394.60
KALA SHIKARI	3	15	1	3	1	9908.60
KAMBALDA	51	245	19	30	89	350162.48
KAMEHAMEHA (USA)	2	14	2	4	4	12394.12
KAYTU	4	21	2	6	6	41694.75
K-BATTERY	12	28	1	2	5	34330.50
KEEN	12	37	4	4	13	20613.06
KEFAAH (USA)	16	67	6	11	14	38624.60
KEMAL (FR)	30	126	8	13	41	187736.80
KENDOR (FR)	1	5	1	3	2	70842.50
KENMARE (FR)	1	3	1	2	0	7944.58
KIND OF HUSH	13	64	4	6	16	22941.00
KINGLET	7	28	2	2	8	9495.75
KING LUTHIER	24	114	7	10	29	42923.90
KING OF CLUBS	7	25	3	4	5	14200.17
KING OF SPAIN	5	33	1	4	10	22856.00
KING PERSIAN	16	68	3	3	17	21018.55
KING'S RIDE	90	284	27	47	80	348962.02
KOMAITE (USA)	7	15	1	1	3	3602.50
KRIS	26	113	9	15	36	68532.47
KRISINSKY (USA)	1	3	1	1	1	3205.00
LABUS (FR)	2	8	1	2	1	2675.00
LAFONTAINE (USA)	57	217	10	19	55	120378.42

STALLIONS	RNRS	STARTS	WNRS	WINS	PLACES	TOTAL
LANCASTRIAN	85	302	17	30	90	169666.58
LANFRANCO	5	13	1	1	4	2367.85
LAPIERRE	5	18	2	3	5	9324.59
LASHKARI	4	22	2	3	6	7840.57
LAST TYCOON	18	60	6	6	20	21771.90
LAW SOCIETY (USA)	31	116	6	9	37	107189.11
LEADING MAN	5	22	3	8	7	32314.30
LEADING STAR	3	14	1	1	4	3904.70
LEANDER	2	7	1	1	3	5239.50
LEAP HIGH (USA)	2	3	1	1	0	1695.54
LEAR FAN (USA)	9	50	4	10	12	32918.14
LE BAVARD (FR)	74	270	21	27	78	143403.59
LE COQ D'OR	8	30	2	2	8	10732.88
LEGAL CIRCLES (USA)	3	7	1	1	2	3844.75
LE GLORIEUX	1	13	1	6	4	15828.40
LE MOSS	56	177	13	15	46	69898.32
LE NAIN JAUNE (FR)	2	13	1	1	3	3355.43
LEPANTO (GER)	8	49	3	7	17	58489.52
LE PONTET (FR)	1	8	1	3	4	20510.80
LE RIVERAIN (FR)	2	9	1	1	3	6491.93
LE SOLARET (FR)	7	31	3	5	5	14476.50
LIBRATE	12	59	2	2	13	10927.70
LIDHAME	4	16	1	1	5	3549.52
LIGHTER	35	109	6	6	34	34744.87
LINKAGE (USA)	1	6	1	2	2	5388.00
LIR	9	35	1	1	9	5323.25
LITTLE BIGHORN	6	20	1	1	4	3787.20
LITTLE WOLF	26	74	4	4	14	19855.03
LOCHNAGER	14	52	3	3	5	8244.40
LOMOND (USA)	10	36	2	4	15	34521.26
LORD AMERICO	51	157	8	12	33	47738.36
LORD BUD	19	59	5	8	11	24346.05
LORD CHANCELLOR (USA)	5	9	1	1	0	4987.50
LORD HA HA	11	54	3	6	18	34799.63
LUCKY RING	2	6	1	1	2	2165.00
LUGANA BEACH	5	23	2	2	5	6601.00
LUTE ANTIQUE (FR)	1	6	1	2	2	13007.40
LYCIUS (USA)	2	6	1	1	2	5002.47
LYPHARD (USA)	8	41	4	8	16	34356.15
MAC'S IMP (USA)	4	16	1	1	1	2810.57
MAELSTROM LAKE	8	40	1	5	8	18197.90
MAGICAL STRIKE (USA)	11	56	5	8	22	35138.24
MAGICAL WONDER (USA)	5	33	3	5	10	19766.05
MAGIC MIRROR	2	9	1	1	2	2575.61
MAGNOLIA LAD	2	24	2	4	17	18642.75
MAJESTIC STREAK	3	16	1	1	4	5558.30
MALASPINA	6	25	2	5	10	19465.40
MANASTASH RIDGE (USA)	1	5	1	2	1	5377.50
MANDALUS	125	466	24	40	107	210097.80
MANDRAKE MAJOR	8	28	3	4	7	9293.00
MANILA (USA)	4	16	2	5	7	29962.90
MANSOOJ	4	14	1	1	2	2570.10
MARFA (USA)	1	6	1	3	2	12049.90
MARIS PIPER	2	9	1	1	4	5546.60
MARJU (IRE)	5	16	2	2	2	5157.14
MARKTINGO	4	9	1	1	2	2438.75
MARTINMAS	4	14	1	1	4	3869.50
MASHHOR DANCER (USA)	4	17	3	3	10	12982.27
MASTER WILLIE	9	42	5	10	10	311012.48
MAZAAD	19	69	6	8	18	30761.59
MAZILIER (USA)	5	23	1	1	6	3686.90

STALLIONS	RNRS	STARTS	WNRS	WINS	PLACES	TOTAL
MEADOWBROOK	25	84	6	9	7	27107.05
MENEVAL (USA)	32	108	6	7	35	41951.87
MIDYAN (USA)	13	42	3	4	9	15702.95
MINER'S LAMP	18	46	2	2	17	13383.32
MINSTER SON	16	62	4	6	19	19480.95
THE MINSTREL (CAN)	5	27	1	2	6	7617.60
MINSTREL STAR	1	7	1	3	2	7485.50
MIRAMAR REEF	2	8	1	1	3	3714.03
MIRROR BOY	2	14	1	1	6	8687.20
MISTER LORD (USA)	47	171	12	24	44	112690.80
MISTER MAJESTIC	13	48	3	5	7	18594.84
MLJET	1	11	1	1	3	3385.85
MONKSFIELD	14	50	3	5	15	35661.95
MONSANTO (FR)	3	9	1	1	4	5894.40
MONTEKIN	9	34	1	2	8	11631.83
MONTELIMAR (USA)	47	167	15	18	66	133832.04
MONTEVIDEO	1	10	1	3	4	11877.20
MON TRESOR	4	9	1	1	2	3243.50
MORGANS CHOICE	2	4	1	1	1	2580.70
MOSCOW SOCIETY (USA)	16	70	3	9	26	70938.84
MOSSBERRY	1	11	1	1	2	3593.20
MOUKTAR	2	6	1	1	4	7778.20
MOVE OFF	17	54	2	2	9	10106.20
MR FLUOROCARBON	6	18	1	2	4	7497.27
MTOTO	16	62	4	9	19	49634.88
MULHOLLANDE (USA)	3	14	1	3	5	12803.72
MUSCATITE	5	24	1	1	8	10610.50
MUSIC BOY	8	38	1	3	8	12631.65
MYJINSKI (USA)	3	19	1	1	4	3474.50
NAHEEZ (USA)	3	7	1	2	0	9003.50
NASHWAN (USA)	11	30	2	2	4	8253.19
NATIONAL TRUST	3	7	1	2	3	4506.00
NATIVE BAZAAR	1	1	1	1	0	2878.00
NATROUN (FR)	2	8	2	3	4	61102.50
NEARLY A HAND	45	159	9	13	38	88447.92
NELTINO	23	75	12	19	20	93705.25
NEPOTISM	2	16	1	2	3	7664.16
NESHAD (USA)	2	3	1	1	1	3287.38
NETHERKELLY	5	23	3	4	5	13026.70
NEW EXPRESS	2	4	1	1	1	3786.50
NEW MEMBER	3	17	2	3	4	25372.60
NICHOLAS BILL	32	100	7	14	28	46639.95
NIELS	5	18	1	2	4	8074.36
NIGHT SHIFT (USA)	16	77	7	11	21	73658.48
NIJIN (USA)	1	15	1	4	4	15186.70
NIJINSKY (CAN)	4	17	2	3	7	21696.60
NIKOS	3	16	1	4	4	14131.15
NINISKI (USA)	21	84	8	15	23	65369.90
NISHAPOUR (FR)	18	62	4	5	14	20580.58
NOALTO	23	68	4	5	10	31127.75
THE NOBLE PLAYER (USA)	25	100	4	6	19	58459.14
NOBODY KNOWS	1	7	1	1	3	5225.52
NODOUBLE (USA)	2	3	2	2	0	7529.64
NOMINATION	13	63	4	8	24	33746.48
NORDANCE (USA)	17	81	5	9	32	60818.09
NORDICO (USA)	31	148	10	20	44	86564.60
NORTH BRITON	7	19	2	2	3	4138.00
NORTHERN BABY (CAN)	10	37	5	10	14	80303.95
NORTHERN FLAGSHIP (USA)	1	11	1	3	6	14904.25
NORTHERN GAME	1	2	1	1	1	11837.80
NORTHERN STATE (USA)	17	52	3	8	18	36040.90

STALLIONS	RNRS	STARTS	WNRS	WINS	PLACES	TOTAL
NORTHERN TEMPEST (USA)	3	14	1	1	3	4595.00
NORTHIAM (USA)	3	8	2	2	4	9527.95
NORTHJET	2	5	1	3	0	7061.70
NORWICK (USA)	16	65	3	7	24	28636.95
NUREYEV (USA)	5	15	2	2	3	8772.40
OATS	57	209	16	22	65	157100.88
OLD JOCUS	2	9	1	2	3	8252.00
OLD VIC	9	25	2	2	5	17318.50
ORANGE REEF	13	53	3	3	9	13020.44
ORCHESTRA	149	629	35	62	166	411484.58
ORE	7	18	1	3	1	7286.50
OUT OF HAND	4	16	1	1	8	6235.10
OVAC (ITY)	27	103	5	5	28	32068.86
OVER THE RIVER (FR)	123	440	32	48	113	341729.04
PABLOND	4	9	1	1	1	2520.00
PADDY'S STREAM	6	21	2	2	4	6135.00
PAEAN	7	22	1	1	6	8035.66
PAMPONI (FR)	2	5	1	1	0	3582.50
PARLIAMENT	8	18	1	3	3	12051.25
THE PARSON	97	425	31	59	126	499990.36
PAS DE SEUL	4	23	1	5	4	20253.75
PAUPER	7	33	3	3	15	16800.20
PEACOCK (FR)	9	53	3	4	12	13246.75
PENNINE WALK	28	104	6	7	30	33368.15
PERSIAN BOLD	33	129	13	24	36	165603.28
PERSIAN HEIGHTS	23	103	8	17	25	59127.84
PERSIAN MEWS	11	32	3	3	9	9213.79
PETIT MONTMORENCY (USA)	1	3	1	1	1	4013.00
PETONG	16	62	2	4	7	16784.41
PETORIUS	24	99	5	7	21	31063.68
PETOSKI	24	73	5	5	21	35494.00
PHARDANTE (FR)	225	861	61	100	223	539176.99
PHARLY (FR)	13	47	4	7	14	26968.19
PILGRIM (USA)	1	4	1	1	2	7918.00
PIMPERNELS TUNE	5	19	1	1	8	41377.13
PIPERHILL	1	7	1	1	4	6232.25
PITSKELLY	1	11	1	3	3	10278.95
POLAR FALCON (USA)	5	16	1	1	5	13777.25
POLISH NAVY (USA)	1	4	1	2	1	7808.75
POLISH PATRIOT (USA)	2	5	1	1	2	2994.75
POLISH PRECEDENT (USA)	10	26	3	5	5	13225.80
POLITICO (USA)	19	72	3	6	22	42872.97
POLLERTON	33	112	6	11	30	46740.90
PORT ETIENNE (FR)	2	18	2	4	7	24799.50
POSEN (USA)	16	74	2	3	15	25223.47
POT D'OR (FR)	1	2	1	1	0	3590.50
PRAGMATIC	26	83	5	11	17	55554.47
PRECOCIOUS	14	45	2	2	7	7762.40
PRESIDIUM	18	69	4	6	20	26926.95
PRIMITIVE RISING (USA)	28	103	5	7	25	32169.10
PRIMO DOMINIE	12	53	3	4	12	13624.00
PRINCE RUPERT (FR)	17	56	2	3	14	16807.79
PRINCE SABO	18	67	2	6	17	23732.60
PRINCES GATE	1	2	1	1	1	3927.00
PROJECT MANAGER	10	33	4	6	8	21235.80
PROVERB	3	13	1	1	3	3864.19
PUISSANCE	9	28	1	2	7	8758.20
PUSH ON	3	8	1	1	2	4464.00
QUAYSIDE	13	42	1	1	12	6834.87
RABDAN	4	16	1	1	4	3631.30
RADICAL	11	35	3	3	5	8212.83

STALLIONS	RNRS	STARTS	WNRS	WINS	PLACES	TOTAL
RAGAPAN	5	30	1	2	11	13248.19
RAHY (USA)	3	13	2	2	5	11098.42
RAINBOW QUEST (USA)	20	88	5	10	23	90778.78
RAKAPOSHI KING	58	179	10	13	43	62710.82
RAMBO DANCER (CAN)	31	106	11	17	29	55822.00
RANKSBOROUGH	1	2	1	1	0	2695.60
RA NOVA	14	53	3	4	16	24430.94
RARE ONE	3	22	1	1	9	6551.49
REACH	3	15	1	3	4	13626.00
REASONABLE (FR)	4	27	1	3	4	13165.34
RED MAN	1	2	1	1	0	4162.50
RED SUNSET	16	47	3	3	10	10006.17
REFERENCE POINT	10	38	3	4	7	15059.01
RELKINO	32	101	7	10	29	54184.13
REMAINDER MAN	36	129	10	21	38	247299.54
REPRIMAND	16	61	3	4	10	51562.38
RHOMAN RULE (USA)	10	34	1	2	2	6863.00
RIBERETTO	10	48	3	6	11	32760.39
RICH CHARLIE	4	8	1	1	2	3756.00
RIGHT REGENT	3	9	1	1	0	3090.00
RING THE BELL (NZ)	2	12	1	4	4	225381.05
RIOT HELMET	7	17	1	4	4	78452.09
RISING	22	69	2	2	20	15326.88
RISK ME (FR)	23	87	4	6	17	20953.75
RIVELAGO (FR)	1	7	1	5	1	17786.00
RIVERMAN (USA)	13	58	6	9	17	40380.40
ROBELLINO (USA)	18	87	6	11	37	74873.42
ROBERTO (USA)	2	12	1	1	5	4916.00
ROCK CITY	8	28	2	3	4	10527.75
ROI DANZIG (USA)	15	72	5	9	22	32461.86
ROLFE (USA)	18	56	3	6	8	80234.75
RORY'S JESTER (AUS)	1	3	1	1	0	2176.20
ROSE LAUREL	2	9	1	2	4	45177.38
ROSELIER (FR)	192	782	66	108	224	783215.61
ROUSILLON (USA)	7	25	3	4	6	18414.53
ROYAL ACADEMY (USA)	12	33	3	5	9	17215.93
ROYAL BOXER	2	19	1	2	1	6515.95
ROYAL CHARTER (FR)	1	1	1	1	0	2687.50
ROYAL FOUNTAIN	38	120	5	5	30	34567.00
ROYAL MATCH	8	36	1	1	12	7924.80
ROYAL VULCAN	20	59	3	5	15	56103.48
RUNAWAY GROOM (CAN)	2	14	1	1	6	9942.00
RUNNETT	6	18	1	1	3	4321.77
RUSTICARO (FR)	6	38	3	5	7	16430.60
RUSTINGO	12	58	2	3	12	16394.25
RYMER	22	65	6	7	9	52786.98
SADLER'S WELLS (USA)	21	81	11	20	30	283468.65
SAHER	2	19	1	1	10	7962.26
SAINT ANDREWS (FR)	2	8	1	2	3	14918.50
SALLUCEVA	17	65	2	2	8	7690.96
SALSE (USA)	14	52	4	9	14	60349.44
SALT DOME (USA)	10	62	3	6	20	29463.77
SANDALAY	23	67	3	6	14	29797.29
SATCO (FR)	27	92	5	5	27	23589.29
SAUNTER	1	2	1	1	0	2390.00
SAXON FARM	9	45	1	1	12	9266.29
SAYF EL ARAB (USA)	12	36	1	1	9	6841.85
SAY PRIMULA	8	38	2	8	12	59780.80
SCALLYWAG	44	176	10	22	47	106957.40
SCENIC	15	58	5	6	22	42231.19
SCORPIO (FR)	20	52	3	3	12	19448.74

STALLIONS	RNRS	STARTS	WNRS	WINS	PLACES	TOTAL
SCOTTISH REEL	15	65	8	18	18	56451.70
SEAMANSHIP	5	18	2	3	6	10765.94
SEATTLE DANCER (USA)	5	22	2	3	5	17072.80
SECLUDE (USA)	20	76	2	3	15	15207.09
SECRETO (USA)	2	6	1	1	2	2828.50
SENANG HATI	1	5	1	1	2	3239.30
SEXTON BLAKE	16	98	6	10	31	58976.76
SEYMOUR HICKS (FR)	25	82	7	7	12	41434.68
SHAAB	10	42	2	2	9	13269.83
SHAADI (USA)	9	20	3	4	6	12424.14
SHADEED (USA)	8	47	4	5	15	24047.60
SHAFOUN (FR)	1	3	1	2	1	55613.75
SHAHRASTANI (USA)	15	66	8	11	17	61970.15
SHARDARI	23	114	9	11	43	57736.36
SHAREEF DANCER (USA)	22	102	8	15	34	188848.31
SHARP CHARTER	3	10	1	1	0	1213.50
SHARPEN UP	2	13	2	3	8	11552.83
SHARPO	11	46	3	5	8	23923.10
SHARP VICTOR (USA)	5	18	1	2	4	7039.58
SHARROOD (USA)	12	51	4	7	20	28093.75
SHEER GRIT	28	118	6	15	40	88153.22
SHERNAZAR	23	95	9	11	34	67928.02
SHIRLEY HEIGHTS	17	69	8	15	16	57374.22
SHOW KING (AUS)	1	4	1	2	1	5686.35
SHY GROOM (USA)	14	69	5	9	22	80892.30
SIBERIAN EXPRESS (USA)	11	60	6	9	19	32072.74
SILLY PRICES	20	64	4	4	15	44199.55
SILVER HAWK (USA)	7	19	2	6	4	27271.43
SIMPLY GREAT (FR)	19	60	4	9	13	63997.51
SIR IVOR	6	33	1	2	12	13494.51
SIZZLING MELODY	11	29	1	1	1	2391.00
SKYLINER	12	45	1	1	5	4768.75
SKYWALKER (USA)	1	10	1	1	1	3529.00
SLEW O' GOLD (USA)	3	9	1	4	3	31107.76
SLIP ANCHOR	16	77	8	14	20	47702.20
SOLFORD (USA)	2	19	2	2	10	10997.65
SON OF SHAKA	1	7	1	2	2	6141.00
SON OF SILVER	1	2	1	1	0	2759.00
SOUGHAAN (USA)	11	39	3	3	8	14335.62
SOUND REASON (CAN)	1	1	1	1	0	1287.00
SOUSA	5	22	1	1	3	2757.00
SOVEREIGN WATER (FR)	1	7	1	2	2	7336.56
SOVIET LAD (USA)	9	40	4	5	15	24236.22
SOVIET STAR (USA)	13	53	3	6	20	53533.20
SPANISH PLACE (USA)	7	26	1	1	7	9453.07
SPEND A BUCK (USA)	3	12	1	1	1	2729.40
SPIN OF A COIN	7	22	2	2	5	6793.59
SQUILL (USA)	3	21	1	1	8	4875.90
STALKER	6	22	1	3	6	12340.78
STANDAAN (FR)	6	14	1	1	3	5925.31
STANFORD	4	11	1	1	3	4147.75
STANSTED	1	8	1	1	3	4365.99
STAR DE NASKRA (USA)	2	14	1	1	2	4372.00
START FAST (FR)	2	9	2	3	5	27864.59
ST COLUMBUS	12	36	2	4	8	11719.35
STEP TOGETHER (USA)	14	47	2	3	12	15689.81
STETCHWORTH (USA)	2	12	1	3	1	7839.11
STORM BIRD (CAN)	8	44	2	5	14	26542.10
STORM CAT (USA)	3	8	1	2	2	5831.00
STRAWBERRY ROAD (AUS)	1	3	1	1	0	2762.00
STRONG GALE	358	1433	105	203	417	1478800.91

STALLIONS	RNRS	STARTS	WNRS	WINS	PLACES	TOTAL
STRONG STATEMENT (USA)	24	110	7	11	46	75406.24
SULAAFAH (USA)	14	69	2	3	20	15127.30
SULA BULA	24	104	4	8	30	49247.60
SUNNY'S HALO (CAN)	2	15	2	2	5	8822.63
SUNSHINE FOREVER (USA)	5	20	4	7	6	38963.80
SUNYBOY	18	66	5	8	26	34098.10
SUPERLATIVE	7	22	3	3	5	10452.55
SUPERPOWER	5	18	1	1	1	2511.00
SUPREME LEADER	160	529	37	53	138	251888.72
SURE BLADE (USA)	11	39	1	1	7	6266.25
SWAN'S ROCK	3	21	1	4	10	20000.41
SYLVAN EXPRESS	4	7	1	2	1	4865.50
TACHYPOUS	1	3	1	1	1	3105.00
TALE QUALE	11	35	2	5	13	24964.49
TANFIRION	5	36	1	3	15	25727.78
TATE GALLERY (USA)	10	53	6	8	19	33142.44
TAUFAN (USA)	25	72	4	7	16	22842.60
TEAMWORK	4	18	2	3	9	16718.95
TEENOSO (USA)	28	73	6	6	14	20927.76
TEJANO (USA)	2	15	1	1	4	5923.50
TENDER KING	8	46	1	2	14	17135.56
TEXT (USA)	1	5	1	1	0	2710.80
THATCHING	17	80	6	14	19	41600.54
THEATRICAL	6	16	2	2	6	12195.39
THETHINGABOUTITIS (USA)	3	12	1	1	1	2886.00
THOWRA (FR)	6	17	1	1	1	1759.20
TICKLED PINK	2	6	1	1	0	6684.00
TIDARO (USA)	9	27	1	3	3	10380.65
TI KING (FR)	3	13	1	1	4	4738.84
TIME FOR A CHANGE (USA)	1	3	1	1	0	2824.74
TIMELESS NATIVE (USA)	1	8	1	1	1	2740.50
TINA'S PET	14	49	2	3	10	11768.20
TINOCO	4	19	2	5	4	22581.71
TIP MOSS (FR)	4	19	2	4	9	20326.80
TIROL	12	48	4	4	8	15634.85
TOM'S SHU (USA)	3	12	2	2	3	10039.38
TOPSIDER (USA)	7	30	4	6	13	27540.26
TOP VILLE	10	51	4	12	19	53867.30
TORUS	87	319	18	28	68	275280.44
TOUCHING WOOD (USA)	8	38	2	4	11	19948.32
TOWN AND COUNTRY	48	187	11	16	43	81465.69
TRAGIC ROLE (USA)	13	43	2	7	7	77675.50
TREASURE HUNTER	10	35	3	4	11	21088.69
TREASURE KAY	13	51	2	4	10	16482.65
TREBROOK (FR)	1	2	1	1	1	5028.00
TREMBLANT	40	130	7	8	33	35786.99
TREMPOLINO (USA)	4	28	2	6	9	28739.58
TRIMMINGHAM	4	36	2	4	12	17926.46
TRISTRAM'S EDITION (NZ)	1	4	1	1	2	2656.00
TROJAN FORT	2	7	1	1	1	2933.30
TRUE SONG	26	108	5	7	36	64494.40
TRY MY BEST (USA)	13	53	4	5	20	20782.10
TURKOMAN (USA)	3	14	1	4	7	15546.60
UNCLE POKEY	20	80	3	6	24	58866.65
UN DESPERADO (FR)	6	22	2	3	5	23247.61
UNDULATE (USA)	1	10	1	1	5	4837.00
UNFUWAIN (USA)	9	39	3	5	15	27840.07
USEFUL (FR)	2	10	2	5	3	42490.50
VAGUELY NOBLE	3	19	1	2	4	6164.20
VAIGLY GREAT	5	20	1	2	3	5056.60
VALIYAR	9	35	4	5	6	17669.75

STALLIONS	RNRS	STARTS	WNRS	WINS	PLACES	TOTAL
VALUTA	2	12	1	2	6	8510.25
VELOSO (NZ)	6	29	3	7	8	22186.40
VIDEO ROCK (FR)	3	9	1	1	4	2348.50
VIKING (USA)	8	33	2	4	11	63581.55
VIN ST BENET	4	17	1	1	3	3238.50
VISION (USA)	19	73	6	9	26	34677.86
VITAL SEASON	6	20	2	3	7	15596.70
WAAJIB	31	116	5	11	24	41013.72
WAR HAWK	1	6	1	3	0	15910.00
WAR HERO	3	10	1	1	1	5197.50
WARNING	10	31	2	3	10	16987.62
WARPATH	5	12	1	1	2	2295.00
WARRSHAN (USA)	7	40	3	10	17	42106.51
WASSL	7	31	1	1	12	7367.05
WASSL MERBAYEH (USA)	1	8	1	1	6	10910.41
WELD	11	27	1	2	7	5904.50
WELDNAAS (USA)	14	60	6	7	11	25288.45
WELSH CAPTAIN	10	35	1	1	8	4817.70
WELSH TERM	21	56	4	6	6	20451.70
WHISTLING DEER	4	28	3	5	13	30523.20
WHITEHALL BRIDGE	2	6	1	1	2	3783.51
WINDJAMMER (USA)	4	18	3	4	4	11198.15
WOLVER HEIGHTS	1	9	1	2	5	9205.60
WOLVERLIFE	7	36	3	4	12	12752.26
WONDERFUL SURPRISE	4	11	1	1	2	3880.00
WOOD CHANTER	9	38	2	3	17	19720.67
WOODMAN (USA)	10	36	2	3	12	14445.30
WORLINGWORTH	1	5	1	2	2	5963.00
YASHGAN	17	74	4	4	16	17821.46
YOUNG MAN (FR)	4	12	1	2	2	6454.80
ZAFFARAN (USA)	17	56	5	5	10	17077.15
ZALAZL (USA)	7	28	1	2	7	7667.80
ZAMAZAAN (FR)	1	5	1	1	3	2753.30
ZAMBRANO	9	32	1	2	3	3713.50
ZIGGY'S BOY (USA)	2	11	1	1	3	2885.04
ZILZAL (USA)	3	16	1	5	4	17851.10

STATISTICS BY KIND PERMISSION OF WEATHERBYS

If an entry is incorrect or has been omitted, please notify the editor by January 8th, 1999. This will ensure it appears correctly in the 1999 edition.